Periodic Table of the Elements

Key

6
C
Carbon
12.01

Atomic number → Symbol
Name → Average atomic mass

An element

Transitional metals

Main group

Period number	Group number																	
	1A 1																	8A 18
1	1 **H** Hydrogen 1.008	2A 2											3A 13	4A 14	5A 15	6A 16	7A 17	2 **He** Helium 4.003
2	3 **Li** Lithium 6.941	4 **Be** Beryllium 9.012											5 **B** Boron 10.81	6 **C** Carbon 12.01	7 **N** Nitrogen 14.01	8 **O** Oxygen 16.00	9 **F** Fluorine 19.00	10 **Ne** Neon 20.18
3	11 **Na** Sodium 22.99	12 **Mg** Magnesium 24.31	3B 3	4B 4	5B 5	6B 6	7B 7	8B 8	8B 9	8B 10	1B 11	2B 12	13 **Al** Aluminum 26.98	14 **Si** Silicon 28.09	15 **P** Phosphorus 30.97	16 **S** Sulfur 32.07	17 **Cl** Chlorine 35.45	18 **Ar** Argon 39.95
4	19 **K** Potassium 39.10	20 **Ca** Calcium 40.08	21 **Sc** Scandium 44.96	22 **Ti** Titanium 47.87	23 **V** Vanadium 50.94	24 **Cr** Chromium 52.00	25 **Mn** Manganese 54.94	26 **Fe** Iron 55.85	27 **Co** Cobalt 58.93	28 **Ni** Nickel 58.69	29 **Cu** Copper 63.55	30 **Zn** Zinc 65.41	31 **Ga** Gallium 69.72	32 **Ge** Germanium 72.64	33 **As** Arsenic 74.92	34 **Se** Selenium 78.96	35 **Br** Bromine 79.90	36 **Kr** Krypton 83.80
5	37 **Rb** Rubidium 85.47	38 **Sr** Strontium 87.62	39 **Y** Yttrium 88.91	40 **Zr** Zirconium 91.22	41 **Nb** Niobium 92.91	42 **Mo** Molybdenum 95.94	43 **Tc** Technetium (98)	44 **Ru** Ruthenium 101.1	45 **Rh** Rhodium 102.9	46 **Pd** Palladium 106.4	47 **Ag** Silver 107.9	48 **Cd** Cadmium 112.4	49 **In** Indium 114.8	50 **Sn** Tin 118.7	51 **Sb** Antimony 121.8	52 **Te** Tellurium 127.6	53 **I** Iodine 126.9	54 **Xe** Xenon 131.3
6	55 **Cs** Cesium 132.9	56 **Ba** Barium 137.3	57 **La** Lanthanum 138.9	72 **Hf** Hafnium 178.5	73 **Ta** Tantalum 180.9	74 **W** Tungsten 183.8	75 **Re** Rhenium 186.2	76 **Os** Osmium 190.2	77 **Ir** Iridium 192.2	78 **Pt** Platinum 195.1	79 **Au** Gold 197.0	80 **Hg** Mercury 200.6	81 **Tl** Thallium 204.4	82 **Pb** Lead 207.2	83 **Bi** Bismuth 209.0	84 **Po** Polonium (209)	85 **At** Astatine (210)	86 **Rn** Radon (222)
7	87 **Fr** Francium (223)	88 **Ra** Radium (226)	89 **Ac** Actinium (227)	104 **Rf** Rutherfordium (267)	105 **Db** Dubnium (268)	106 **Sg** Seaborgium (271)	107 **Bh** Bohrium (272)	108 **Hs** Hassium (270)	109 **Mt** Meitnerium (276)	110 **Ds** Darmstadtium (281)	111 **Rg** Roentgenium (280)	112 **Cn** (285)	113 — (284)	114 — (289)	115 — (288)	116 — (293)	117 — (285)	118 — (294)

Lanthanides 6	58 **Ce** Cerium 140.1	59 **Pr** Praseodymium 140.9	60 **Nd** Neodymium 144.2	61 **Pm** Promethium (145)	62 **Sm** Samarium 150.4	63 **Eu** Europium 152.0	64 **Gd** Gadolium 157.3	65 **Tb** Terbium 158.9	66 **Dy** Dysprosium 162.5	67 **Ho** Holmium 164.9	68 **Er** Erbium 167.3	69 **Tm** Thulium 168.9	70 **Yb** Ytterbium 173.0	71 **Lu** Lutetium 175.0
Actinides 7	90 **Th** Thorium 232.0	91 **Pa** Protactinium 231.0	92 **U** Uranium 238.0	93 **Np** Neptunium (237)	94 **Pu** Plutonium (244)	95 **Am** Americium (243)	96 **Cm** Curium (247)	97 **Bk** Berkelium (247)	98 **Cf** Californium (251)	99 **Es** Einsteinium (252)	100 **Fm** Fermium (257)	101 **Md** Mendelevium (258)	102 **No** Nobelium (259)	103 **Lr** Lawrencium (262)

Metals

Nonmetals

Metalloids

List of the Elements with Their Symbols and Atomic Masses*

Element	Symbol	Atomic Number	Atomic Mass†	Element	Symbol	Atomic Number	Atomic Mass†
Actinium	Ac	89	(227)	Meitnerium	Mt	109	(276)
Aluminum	Al	13	026.9815386	Mendelevium	Md	101	(258)
Americium	Am	95	(243)	Mercury	Hg	80	200.59
Antimony	Sb	51	121.760	Molybdenum	Mo	42	95.94
Argon	Ar	18	39.948	Neodymium	Nd	60	144.242
Arsenic	As	33	74.92160	Neon	Ne	10	20.1797
Astatine	At	85	(210)	Neptunium	Np	93	(237)
Barium	Ba	56	137.327	Nickel	Ni	28	58.6934
Berkelium	Bk	97	(247)	Niobium	Nb	41	92.90638
Beryllium	Be	4	9.012182	Nitrogen	N	7	14.0067
Bismuth	Bi	83	208.98040	Nobelium	No	102	(259)
Bohrium	Bh	107	(272)	Osmium	Os	76	190.23
Boron	B	5	10.811	Oxygen	O	8	15.9994
Bromine	Br	35	79.904	Palladium	Pd	46	106.42
Cadmium	Cd	48	112.411	Phosphorus	P	15	30.973762
Calcium	Ca	20	40.078	Platinum	Pt	78	195.084
Californium	Cf	98	(251)	Plutonium	Pu	94	(244)
Carbon	C	6	12.0107	Polonium	Po	84	(209)
Cerium	Cc	58	140.116	Potassium	K	19	39.0983
Cesium	Cs	55	132.9054519	Praseodymium	Pr	59	140.90765
Chlorine	Cl	17	35.453	Promethium	Pm	61	(145)
Chromium	Cr	24	51.9961	Protactinium	Pa	91	231.03588
Cobalt	Co	27	58.933195	Radium	Ra	88	(226)
Copernicium	Cn	112	(285)	Radon	Rn	86	(222)
Copper	Cu	29	63.546	Rhenium	Re	75	186.207
Curium	Cm	96	(247)	Rhodium	Rh	45	102.90550
Darmstadtium	Ds	110	(281)	Roentgenium	Rg	111	(280)
Dubnium	Db	105	(268)	Rubidium	Rb	37	85.4678
Dysprosium	Dy	66	162.500	Ruthenium	Ru	44	101.07
Einsteinium	Es	99	(252)	Rutherfordium	Rf	104	(267)
Erbium	Er	68	167.259	Samarium	Sm	62	150.36
Europium	Eu	63	151.964	Scandium	Sc	21	44.955912
Fermium	Fm	100	(257)	Seaborgium	Sg	106	(271)
Fluorine	F	9	18.9984032	Selenium	Se	34	78.96
Francium	Fr	87	(223)	Silicon	Si	14	28.0855
Gadolinium	Gd	64	157.25	Silver	Ag	47	107.8682
Gallium	Ga	31	69.723	Sodium	Na	11	22.98976928
Germanium	Ge	32	72.64	Strontium	Sr	38	87.62
Gold	Au	79	196.966569	Sulfur	S	16	32.065
Hafnium	Hf	72	178.49	Tantalum	Ta	73	180.94788
Hassium	Hs	108	(270)	Technetium	Tc	43	(98)
Helium	He	2	4.002602	Tellurium	Te	52	127.60
Holmium	Ho	67	164.93032	Terbium	Tb	65	158.92535
Hydrogen	H	1	1.00794	Thallium	Tl	81	204.3833
Indium	In	49	114.818	Thorium	Th	90	232.03806
Iodine	I	53	126.90447	Thulium	Tm	69	168.93421
Iridium	Ir	77	192.217	Tin	Sn	50	118.710
Iron	Fe	26	55.845	Titanium	Ti	22	47.867
Krypton	Kr	36	83.798	Tungsten	W	74	183.84
Lanthanum	La	57	138.90547	Uranium	U	92	238.02891
Lawrencium	Lr	103	(262)	Vanadium	V	23	50.9415
Lead	Pb	82	207.2	Xenon	Xe	54	131.293
Lithium	Li	3	6.941	Ytterbium	Yb	70	173.04
Lutetium	Lu	71	174.967	Yttrium	Y	39	88.90585
Magnesium	Mg	12	24.3050	Zinc	Zn	30	65.409
Manganese	Mn	25	54.938045	Zirconium	Zr	40	91.224

*These atomic masses show as many significant figures as are known for each element. The atomic masses in the periodic table are shown to four significant figures, which is sufficient for solving the problems in this book.

†Approximate values of atomic masses for radioactive elements are given in parentheses.

McGraw-Hill LearnSmart Student Quick Tips and FAQs

Use this *McGraw-Hill LearnSmart Student Quick Tips and FAQs* to get more out of this learning tool. Remember, LearnSmart is an adaptive learning system designed to help students learn faster, study more efficiently, and retain more knowledge for greater success.

Responding to a LearnSmart Assignment

TIP: Make an honest attempt to assess your confidence level on each probe. Doing so allows LearnSmart to more accurately direct you to the materials you need to study.

1) Click LearnSmart Assignment Title denoted by 🧠 icon.

2) Click on a chapter module.

3) Read the probe & click your level of confidence in knowing the correct answer.

Help Yourself Succeed

TIP: We recommend completing all passive learning activities before you work on LearnSmart – such as reading the chapter, watching animations and videos available in Connect, etc.

Self-Assess

TIP: Before answering each question, click on the most appropriate confidence level to ensure you receive the most efficient learning experience.

Take a Break!

TIP: Use Time-Out! readings to review topics you are struggling to learn.

Refresh Your Memory

TIP: Return to your completed assignments to rework material and refresh your memory before quizzes and tests. Don't be alarmed if you have forgotten some things – it's natural when learning a new subject!

Share Your Feedback

TIP: Click the Challenge Answer button if you feel the content is incorrect or unclear.

Answers to Frequently Asked Questions (FAQs)

How is the percentage for each module calculated?

The percentage indicates the number of correctly answered questions within the module. In other words, the percentage indicates how much of the module you have learned so far. To learn more about your progress and overall status, click the 'Debriefing' button at the top of the screen.

How is my High Score calculated?

The amount of points you earn depends on how you assess your ability to answer a question. For instance, if you click 'Easy' and answer the question correctly, you will get the greatest amount of points. If you answer correctly after selecting one of the other buttons – 'Think I've got it,' 'Unsure,' and 'No idea' – you will also earn points. However, you will receive fewer points for the items you do not believe you know as well. If you select 'Unsure' and get the answer correct, you will get fewer points than if you selected 'Easy' or 'Think I've got it.'

The same applies if you get an answer incorrect. If you do not know the answer after clicking 'Easy,' points will be deducted from your score. Fewer points are deducted if you select 'Think I've got it' or 'Unsure,' and get the answer incorrect. If you click 'Unsure,' points will not be deducted even if you get the question wrong.

Spelling errors, nearly correct answers or partially correct answers also affect your score.

Of course, you can increase your score by going through the same module multiple times, rating your answers as honestly as possible. In essence, the more you learn, the better the score.

Why does the system repeat questions I have already answered?

If you answer a question incorrectly, it will be repeated later in the same session to give you a chance to learn. It might not be the exact same question, but rather a variant that represents the same learning objective. The system will adjust the difficulty of the questions according to your performance. In addition to this, the system will present the same questions the next day to help you remember the material over time. (For more information, see 'Why does it make me start all over on the module when I come back?')

The first day, you might see a 'multiple-choice question about a concept,' and the next day, a 'fill-in-the-blank' for the same concept to make it more difficult. This will assess whether you really know the subject. It closely monitors the exact questions you have been exposed to before, and will vary this in an attempt to match and improve your knowledge level.

Why am I only working on part of a module each day?

Instead of asking you to go through, say, 300 questions in one session, LearnSmart distributes the items and the review of these items over a period of time. Spreading the learning events over multiple sessions increases the likelihood of memory retention. If you are pressed for time, though, you can work ahead and do more questions one day, and LearnSmart will automatically adapt.

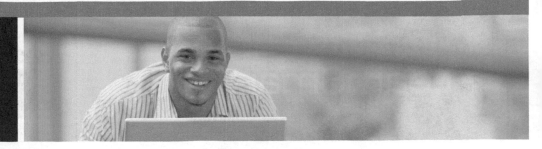

Why does it make me start the module again when I come back?

Research tells us frequency increases memory recall. The module seems to start over when logging in the next day in order to frequently assess your mastery of the material. So if you complete 100 flashcards the first day, you can expect about 25 of those to be repeated each of the next four days. If you answer all of these correctly, around 7 will be repeated each session for the next 14 days, and so on. The program automatically calculates the appropriate repetition interval for each student based on your individual 'forget curve' that is tracked in detail. The 'Learning Plan' feature in the LearnSmart Debriefing screen provides a daily estimate of how much you need to do on each module. This plan also adjusts if you skip a day or two or work ahead.

Why is it so strict about spelling?

If you make a small spelling error, the program will accept your answer. If you make a larger mistake, you will be prompted about the same topic again with a chance to improve your score (and your spelling). You might not see the exact same question, but the program allows another opportunity to demonstrate your knowledge.

'Fill-in-the-blank' questions are often the most difficult questions because they rely on active recall, rather than recognition. Once you master the 'fill-in-the-blank' questions, you are really learning!

Why do I need to click the Confidence buttons?

The 'Confidence' buttons are the self-assessment buttons that affect the high score as described above. In addition, rating your confidence also affects the schedule of questions. Simply put, this information is used to determine your awareness of your own knowledge level. It is applied to adjust your learning path. You can use the Metacognitive Skills report in the LearnSmart Debriefing to learn more about this. Click 'Debriefing' at the top of the screen to get access to this information.

Why are there so many questions?

This program is not just a testing system, but a *learning system*. The modules assess most of the material in the book. As you progress through the modules, you will learn most of the material assigned by your instructor for this course. LearnSmart presents the core or most critical material first. If you do not have time to complete the entire module, just work until you are out of time, and you can be assured your have tackled the most important items.

When you return, the system will recall the material for which you have demonstrated mastery and provide opportunities to practice material that still requires review. Again, LearnSmart presents the most important items first, which may include revisiting previous items or new material.

When the deadline has passed, why do I still have to work on the module?

The program prompts you to keep reviewing the same module to ensure recall and true mastery. Use the Learning Plan feature in the LearnSmart Debriefing screen to see the estimated time required for you to retain the information before the deadline approaches. You can also use the 'Status' feature in the 'Debriefing' screen for an estimate of when you are likely to forget what you have learned. If you follow the schedule proposed by the system, the workload for review will be minimal.

How can I change my name in the High Score list?

Just click your name within the list. You can change your name (to an alias) or become anonymous.

Should I continue to practice after my exam?

If you want to commit your new knowledge to long-term memory, we recommend that you keep working the modules even after the deadline. You have the option of setting a new deadline for your own purposes (e.g. 6 months in the future) as a target. The system will continuously monitor what you know and what you tend to forget. It will not prompt you to work on things you most likely remember, minimizing your workload. This will be the optimal way to learn the content and remember it.

What happens when I provide feedback?

We greatly appreciate your feedback. We do read it and use it to improve LearnSmart so that it better serves students like you. In cases where you have questions about the system, we will try to answer them. If you contest an answer or report incorrect markings, we will investigate and update the modules accordingly.

Need More Help with LearnSmart Assignments?

CONTACT US ONLINE:

Visit us at:

www.mhhe.com/learnsmart/support.html

Browse our most up-to-date support materials including tutorial videos and searchable knowledge base. If you cannot find an answer to your question, click on Contact Us to send us an email.

GIVE US A CALL

Call us at:

1-800-331-5094

Our live support is available:
Mon-Thurs: 8 am – 11 pm CT
Friday: 8 am – 6 pm CT
Sunday: 6 pm – 11 pm CT

General Chemistry for Engineers

CHEM 0960/0970

University of Pittsburgh

CHEMISTRY
Atoms First

Julia Burdge
University of Idaho

Jason Overby
College of Charleston

McGraw Hill **Learning Solutions**

Boston Burr Ridge, IL Dubuque, IA New York San Francisco St. Louis
Bangkok Bogotá Caracas Lisbon London Madrid
Mexico City Milan New Delhi Seoul Singapore Sydney Taipei Toronto

General Chemistry For Engineers
CHEM 0960/0970
University of Pittsburgh

This book is a McGraw-Hill Learning Solutions textbook and contains select material from *Chemistry: Atoms First* by Julia Burdge and Jason Overby. Copyright © 2012 by The McGraw-Hill Companies, Inc. Reprinted with permission of the publisher. Many custom published texts are modified versions or adaptations of our best-selling textbooks. Some adaptations are printed in black and white to keep prices at a minimum, while others are in color.

3 4 5 6 7 8 9 0 KNG KNG 15 14 13

ISBN-13: 978-0-07-776001-4
ISBN-10: 0-07-776001-8
Part of:
ISBN-13: 978-0-07-776002-1
ISBN-10: 0-07-776002-6

Learning Solutions Consultant: Robert Scanlon
Production Editor: Kylie Weitz
Printer/Binder: King Printing
Cover Photo Credits: © 2012 JupiterImages Corporation

To the people who will always matter the most: Katie, Beau, and Sam.
Julia Burdge

To my wonderful wife, Robin, and daughters, Emma and Sarah.
Jason Overby

About the Authors

Julia Burdge received her Ph.D. (1994) from the University of Idaho in Moscow, Idaho. Her research and dissertation focused on instrument development for analysis of trace sulfur compounds in air and the statistical evaluation of data near the detection limit.

In 1994 she accepted a position at The University of Akron in Akron, Ohio, as an assistant professor and director of the Introductory Chemistry program. In the year 2000, she was tenured and promoted to associate professor at The University of Akron on the merits of her teaching, service, and research in chemistry education. In addition to directing the general chemistry program and supervising the teaching activities of graduate students, she helped establish a future-faculty development program and served as a mentor for graduate students and post-doctoral associates. Julia has recently relocated back to the northwest to be near family. She and her children live in Pullman, Washington, home of Washington State University; and she holds an affiliate faculty position in the Chemistry Department at the University of Idaho. She also continues to work with students in Ohio and Florida via an online tutoring program.

Julia and her children are animal lovers and moved three horses, three cats, and a dog with them to the northwest. They are enjoying the changes of seasons, long horseback rides on the Palouse, and frequent visits with family.

Jason Overby received his B.S. degree in chemistry and political science from the University of Tennessee at Martin. He then received his Ph.D. in inorganic chemistry from Vanderbilt University (1997) studying main group and transition metal metallocenes and related compounds. Afterwards, Jason conducted postdoctoral research in transition metal organometallic chemistry at Dartmouth College.

Jason began his academic career at the College of Charleston in 1999 as an assistant professor. Currently, he is an associate professor with teaching interests in general and inorganic chemistry. He is also interested in the integration of technology into the classroom, including the use of online homework. Additionally, he conducts research with undergraduates in inorganic and organic synthetic chemistry as well as computational organometallic chemistry.

In his free time, he enjoys exercising and cooking, and in particular learning and experimenting with new cuisines. He lives in South Carolina with his wife Robin and two daughters, Emma and Sarah.

Brief Contents

1   Chemistry: The Science of Change   2

2   Atoms and the Periodic Table   32

3   Quantum Theory and the Electronic Structure of Atoms   56

4   Periodic Trends of the Elements   106

5   Ionic and Covalent Compounds   140

6   Representing Molecules   182

7   Molecular Geometry and Bonding Theories   214

8   Chemical Reactions   266

9   Chemical Reactions in Aqueous Solutions   306

10   Energy Changes in Chemical Reactions   362

11   Gases   412

12   Intermolecular Forces and the Physical Properties of Liquids and Solids   464

13   Physical Properties of Solutions   510

14   Chemical Kinetics   550

15   Chemical Equilibrium   608

16   Acids and Bases   656

17   Acid-Base Equilibria and Solubility Equilibria   712

18   Entropy, Free Energy, and Equilibrium   762

19   Electrochemistry   804

20   Nuclear Chemistry   850

21   Metallurgy and the Chemistry of Metals   884

22   Coordination Chemistry   906

23   Nonmetallic Elements and Their Compounds   930

24   Organic Chemistry   960

25   Modern Materials   1012

Appendix 1   Mathematical Operations   A-1

Appendix 2   Thermodynamic Data at 1 ATM and 25°C   A-6

Appendix 3   Ionization Constants of Weak Acids and Bases at 25°C   A-13

Appendix 4   Solubility Product Constants at 25°C   A-15

List of Applications

Thinking Outside the Box

Tips for Success in Chemistry Class   19
Measuring Atomic Mass   42
Everyday Occurrences of the Photoelectric Effect   65
Mistaking Strontium for Calcium   126
Functional Groups   159
Species with Unpaired Electrons   200
Intermolecular Forces   226
Phases   247
Molecular Orbitals in Heteronuclear Diatomic Species   251
Atom Economy   287
Visible Spectrophotometry   338
Heat Capacity of Calorimeters   379
Decompression Injury   441
X-ray Diffraction   480
Intravenous Fluids   530
Fluoride Poisoning   531
Surface Area   580
Biological Equilibria   640
Acid Rain   678
Equilibrium and Tooth Decay   743
Thermodynamics and Living Systems   778
Amalgam Fillings and Dental Pain   822
Nuclear Medicine   874
Copper   891
Chelation Therapy   913
Arsenic   948
Thalidomide Analogues   984
Electrically Conducting Polymers   1021

Key Skills

Dimensional Analysis   30
Inter-conversion Among Mass, Moles, and Numbers of Atoms   54
Determining Ground-State Valence Electron Configurations Using the Periodic Table   104
Periodic Trends in Atomic Radius, Ionization Energy, and Electron Affinity   138
Ionic Compounds: Nomenclature and Molar Mass Determination   180
Drawing Lewis Structures   212
Molecular Shape and Polarity   264
Limiting Reactant   304
Net Ionic Equations   360
Enthalpy of Reaction   410
Mole Fractions   462
Intermolecular Forces   508
Entropy as a Driving Force   548
First-Order Kinetics   606
Equilibrium Problems   654
Salt Hydrolysis   710
Buffers   760
Free Energy and Equilibrium   802
Electrolysis of Metals   848

Preface

In recent years, a growing number of educators have begun to develop and implement an *atoms-first* approach to teaching general chemistry. One of the challenges for authors trying to provide a text suitable for the approach is establishing a new table of contents that will result in the logical flow and coherent story that are the essential goals of the atoms-first community. In our vision of atoms first, we have established what we believe is the best order of topics to support the goals of this emerging philosophy. In what follows, we explain in some detail the parts of our table of contents that differ from a standard general chemistry text, and provide our rationale for the contents and organization—and how we believe our presentation and order of topics are beneficial to students.

Chapter 1—Chemistry: The Science of Change

We begin with a chapter very similar to those in most standard general chemistry books, however, there are a few noteworthy differences.

- We do not introduce *compounds* in Chapter 1. We believe that the concept of a chemical compound (as distinguished from simply a *substance*) is neither necessary nor appropriate until a foundation has been established for comprehension of the combination of elements to *form* compounds. Thus, we delay introduction of the term until early in Chapter 5.
- We do introduce the *atomic mass unit*; but rather than present it in the context of its historical definition, we simply supply it along with *angstrom*, as another commonly used, non-SI, magnitude-appropriate unit of measure. We do provide the definition of amu when appropriate, in a later chapter.

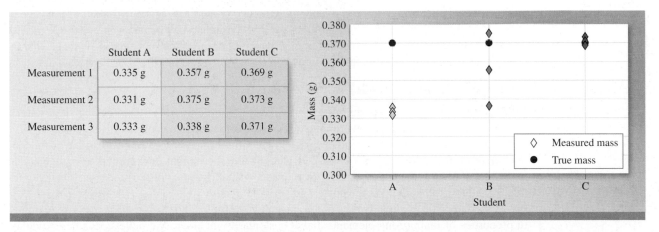

	Student A	Student B	Student C
Measurement 1	0.335 g	0.357 g	0.369 g
Measurement 2	0.331 g	0.375 g	0.373 g
Measurement 3	0.333 g	0.338 g	0.371 g

Figure 1.11 Graphing the students' data illustrates the difference between precision and accuracy. Student A's results are precise (values are close to one another) but not accurate because the average value is far from the true value. Student B's results are neither precise nor accurate. Student C's results are both precise and accurate.

Chapter 2—Atoms and the Periodic Table

Chapter 2 is also similar to many of the traditional texts in that it introduces subatomic particles, atomic number, and mass number. While an argument can be made that introduction of the periodic table should be delayed until after coverage of electron configurations, we think it is best introduced in the same chapter as atomic number. This enables us to provide a context appropriate introduction of *average atomic mass*, the *mole*, and *molar mass* as it applies to atoms.

One of the benefits of our early introduction of the mole is to facilitate discussion of quantum and periodic properties, where we speak in terms of *moles of photons* and where energy changes

Figure 2.11 Bulk nails are sold by the pound. How many nails there are in a pound depends on the size and type of nail.

Type of nail	Size (in)	Nails/lb
3d box	1.5	635
6d box	2	236
10d box	3	94
4d casing	1.5	473
8d casing	2.5	145
2d common	1	876
4d common	1.5	316
6d common	2	181
8d common	2.5	106

associated with chemical process are expressed in kJ/mol. Another benefit is to compel students to become proficient with calculations involving moles prior to their encountering stoichiometry. Although these related topics traditionally are introduced in the same chapter, too many students struggle inordinately trying to master all of the necessary calculations simultaneously. We believe that early practice with simple moles-mass-atoms exercises will better prepare students for a tightly-focused stoichiometry chapter, and mitigate some of this difficulty.

3.1.3   Arrange the following pairs of charged particles in order of increasing magnitude of electrostatic attraction (E_{el}).

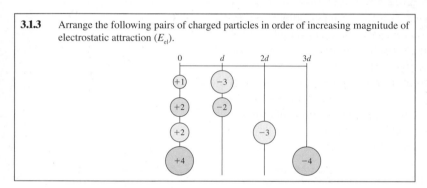

Chapter 3—Quantum Theory and the Electronic Structure of Atoms

Early coverage of quantum theory and electronic structure is one of the hallmarks of the atoms-first approach. Although much of this chapter is very similar to traditional coverage, placing this material before thermochemistry requires that the concepts of energy and energy changes be introduced at the outset.

Staying away from such concepts as *chemical bonds* and *enthalpy*, we begin the chapter with the different types of energy, and the units in which energy is expressed. We pay particular attention to electrostatic energy, which plays an important role in students' understanding of the electronic structure of atoms.

Chapter 4—Periodic Trends of the Elements

While this chapter contains traditional discussions of periodic trends of the elements, it also contains the first appearance of ions (anions and cations) as a logical outgrowth of the discussion of the periodic trends of ionization energy and electron affinity. Thus, rather than have students memorize common atomic ions early and without any theoretical background to explain their existence, our atoms-first approach is to introduce ions in the context of the processes that generate them—and to explain them in the context of periodic trends.

A second distinguishing feature of this chapter is the removal of the descriptive periodic trends in properties of main group elements that is customarily included. We believe it is best to delay this descriptive material until after chemical reactivity has been covered and students have had the opportunity to assimilate the quantum mechanical theory that explains and predicts it.

Figure 4.7 Atomic radius decreases from left to right across a period because of the increased electrostatic attraction between the effective nuclear charge and the charge on the valence shell. The white circle shows the atomic size in each case. The comparison of attractive forces between the nuclei and valence shells is done using Coulomb's law [▸▸ page 121].

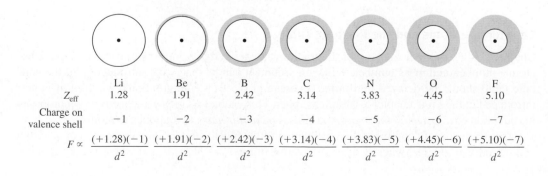

	Li	Be	B	C	N	O	F
Z_{eff}	1.28	1.91	2.42	3.14	3.83	4.45	5.10
Charge on valence shell	−1	−2	−3	−4	−5	−6	−7

$$F \propto \frac{(+1.28)(-1)}{d^2} \quad \frac{(+1.91)(-2)}{d^2} \quad \frac{(+2.42)(-3)}{d^2} \quad \frac{(+3.14)(-4)}{d^2} \quad \frac{(+3.83)(-5)}{d^2} \quad \frac{(+4.45)(-6)}{d^2} \quad \frac{(+5.10)(-7)}{d^2}$$

Chapter 5—Ionic and Covalent Compounds

From the properties of atoms and ions, we progress to an introduction to compounds, beginning with ionic compounds. Starting with Lewis dot symbols provides a basis for understanding the principles of reactivity and bonding—and helps students understand why ions combine in specific ratios. Because enthalpy has not yet been introduced, this chapter does not go into the quantitative aspects of lattice energy. The *concept* of lattice energy is introduced, however, and students learn how to evaluate *relative* lattice energies based on ionic charges and radii. The nomenclature of binary ionic compounds is covered to complete the section.

Covalent compounds are then introduced along with the introductory principles of covalent bonding. Included in this section of the chapter are the necessary discussions of empirical formulas, molecular formulas, and nomenclature. These topics traditionally are introduced in an earlier chapter along with atomic structure in regular general chemistry texts. Nomenclature of simple organic species is also presented although this material can be skipped without any loss of continuity if an instructor wishes to delay introducing organic compounds.

Often nomenclature is grouped together and presented as simply a collection of facts. In our treatment, we strictly enforce teaching nomenclature in the context of the two major bonding modes (ionic and covalent) in separate sections. Also, unique to this text, coverage of polyatomic ions is treated in a separate, dedicated section as a combination of ionic and covalent bonding. This introduces an idea that covalent and ionic bonding are not mutually exclusive and that many ionic species contain units that are themselves held together by covalent bonds.

Another feature of this chapter is the coverage of molecular and formula masses, and molar mass as it applies to compounds. There are several compelling reasons to introduce the quantitative aspect of compounds in this chapter. First, this begins the transition from the more conceptual aspects of quantum chemistry to the quantitative foundations necessary for stoichiometry. Second, introduction to these types of calculations at this point can benefit laboratory programs. Third, the timely return to the concept of molar mass, now in the context of compounds, allows calculations of this type to be incorporated into questions and problems in the following chapters on Lewis structures, molecular geometry and bonding theories. Finally, the separation of molar mass calculations from the traditional stoichiometry chapter allows students and instructors to focus on the qualitative and quantitative aspects of chemical reactions, without the simultaneous introduction of the concepts of the mole and molar mass—a combination that can overwhelm students who are new to chemistry.

Student Annotation: Some oxoanions occur in series of ions that contain the same central atom and have the same charge, but contain different numbers of oxygen atoms.

perchlorate	ClO_4^-
chlorate	ClO_3^-
chlorite	ClO_2^-
hypochlorite	ClO^-
nitrate	NO_3^-
nitrite	NO_2^-
phosphate	PO_4^{3-}
phosphite	PO_3^{3-}
sulfate	SO_4^{2-}
sulfite	SO_3^{2-}

Chapter 6—Representing Molecules

This chapter is devoted entirely to Lewis structures—an especially important topic that tends to be inordinately difficult. A dedicated chapter enables us to provide students with the necessary information and to practice with more tightly focused coverage.

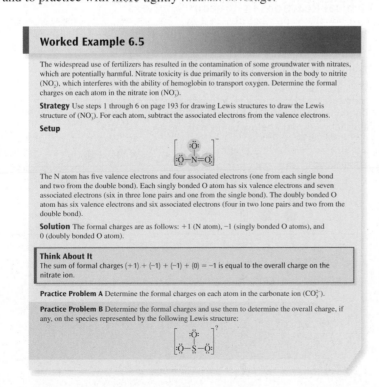

Worked Example 6.5

The widespread use of fertilizers has resulted in the contamination of some groundwater with nitrates, which are potentially harmful. Nitrate toxicity is due primarily to its conversion in the body to nitrite (NO_2^-), which interferes with the ability of hemoglobin to transport oxygen. Determine the formal charges on each atom in the nitrate ion (NO_3^-).

Strategy Use steps 1 through 6 on page 193 for drawing Lewis structures to draw the Lewis structure of (NO_3^-). For each atom, subtract the associated electrons from the valence electrons.

Setup

The N atom has five valence electrons and four associated electrons (one from each single bond and two from the double bond). Each singly bonded O atom has six valence electrons and seven associated electrons (six in three lone pairs and one from the single bond). The doubly bonded O atom has six valence electrons and six associated electrons (four in two lone pairs and two from the double bond).

Solution The formal charges are as follows: +1 (N atom), −1 (singly bonded O atoms), and 0 (doubly bonded O atom).

Think About It
The sum of formal charges (+1) + (−1) + (−1) + (0) = −1 is equal to the overall charge on the nitrate ion.

Practice Problem A Determine the formal charges on each atom in the carbonate ion (CO_3^{2-}).

Practice Problem B Determine the formal charges and use them to determine the overall charge, if any, on the species represented by the following Lewis structure:

Chapter 7—Molecular Geometry and Bonding Theories

Chapter 7 is essentially a traditional chapter on VSEPR geometries and the appropriate bonding theories. One additional feature that we highlight in this chapter is the role of the structure-function relationship of geometry and polarity. Often, polarity is included as an afterthought with coverage of molecular geometry. We prefer to give it somewhat higher billing, illustrating for students the profound effect molecular *polarity* has on molecular *function*.

Although a detailed, quantitative explanation of intermolecular forces is not a part of this chapter, an instructor who wishes to do so can easily incorporate more quantitative information.

Chapter 8—Chemical Reactions

An argument given many times in favor of the atoms-first approach is that it allows students to delay the math normally encountered early in the semester. This chapter is essentially a revised version of the standard stoichiometry chapter. But as noted earlier in Chapter 5, this chapter is focused exclusively on chemical reactions. Since all topics concerning mass and moles have already been covered, students will have had the opportunity to become proficient at the necessary calculations. We believe that this will better prepare them to focus on the principles of stoichiometry and the qualitative and quantitative aspects of chemical reactions.

Another feature of this chapter is the presentation of the periodic trends in chemical properties of elements. Although it is traditionally covered in conjunction with the introduction of the periodic table, we use this heavily descriptive material to build a bridge between the quantum mechanics/atomic/molecular levels and the macroscopic, empirical aspects of chemistry. In some ways, a traditional approach treats first semester general chemistry as two disparate courses: one on stoichiometry and reactivity, and one on quantum mechanics and the nature of compounds. We hope to illustrate to students that even though chemical reactions are being discussed, the role of electron configurations and periodic properties are still very much involved and that chemistry is a continuum from the atomic level to the empirical, observational stage.

Chapter 9—Chemical Reactions in Aqueous Solutions

Chapter 9 is the introduction to chemical reactions and stoichiometry in aqueous solution. Again, we invoke the importance of periodic properties and molecular structure to the various types of reactions covered in this chapter.

9.2.5   Write the balanced net ionic equation for the combination represented below. (Note that the reaction represented below is not balanced.)

Chapter 10—Energy Changes in Chemical Reactions

This chapter is an introduction to thermochemistry. A significant addition to Chapter 10 is coverage of the energetics of ionic and covalent bonding. This material provides the appropriate context to fully develop and discuss the role of energy in the stability and reactivity of ionic and covalent compounds. The process of starting with the atom and building up to chemical reactions and understanding much of what provides a driving force for reactivity is now complete.

Chapter 11—Gases

Much of what is presented in a traditional chapter on gases focuses on the empirical development of the gas laws and ultimately to the ideal gas equation. Only at the end of most such chapters are the atomic, molecular, and energetic aspects of gases included with the introduction of the kinetic molecular theory. Our organization of this chapter takes a true atoms-first approach by beginning with the kinetic molecular theory. This provides an important foundation for students to understand the empirical gas laws in terms of atomic/molecular behavior. Then, logically, the empirical gas laws lead to the ideal gas equation. To further emphasize the molecular nature of gases, real gases are presented immediately after ideal gases, which is then followed by gas mixtures and Dalton's law of partial pressures. For instructors who do not wish to teach the section on real gases, it can be skipped without loss of continuity.

Although many texts employ the ideal gas equation as a means to work stoichiometry problems, we believe that as important as such problems are, they may distract from the development of the atomic/molecular nature of gases. Thus, problems involving reactions with gaseous reactants and/or products are covered after gas mixtures. This arrangement of topics allows instructors to skip the last section of the chapter if they do not wish to have their students review stoichiometry in the context of gases.

For instructors who prefer to cover gases before thermochemistry, our gases chapter is designed to be portable and can be moved earlier in the sequence without loss of continuity or flow of topics.

Figure 10.7 (a) Melting 1 mole of ice at 0°C, an endothermic process, results in an enthalpy increase of 6.01 kJ ($\Delta H = +6.01$ kJ/mol). (b) The burning of 1 mole of methane in oxygen gas, an exothermic process, results in an enthalpy decrease in the system of 890.4 kJ ($\Delta H = -890.4$ kJ/mol). The enthalpy diagrams of these two processes are not shown to the same scale.

(a)

(b)

Figure 11.4 (a) The distribution of speeds for nitrogen gas at three different temperatures. At higher temperatures, more molecules are moving faster. (b) The distribution of speeds for three different gases at the same temperature. On average, lighter molecules move faster than heavier molecules.

Chapter 13—Physical Properties of Solutions

These chapters are the logical accompaniment to gases because the remaining important phases of matter are covered together in the context of intermolecular forces. The structure-function relationship is stressed again so that students appreciate the importance of atomic and molecular structure in the determination of observable macroscopic properties.

This is, of course, just one of the possible ordering of topics. Some instructors may feel that these chapters, along with the one on gases, fit better earlier—before chemical reactivity. As such, it is possible to cover these chapters earlier than their placement in this text with only minor adjustments.

Chapter 14—Chemical Kinetics

Standard presentations of rates of chemical reactions usually begin with observable phenomena of reactants disappearing and products appearing with respect to time. We believe that an atoms-first approach to kinetics should begin by answering the question: "How do chemical reactions occur?" Further, we believe that understanding the phenomena that influence chemical reactions ultimately leads to better understanding of the concept of reaction rate. Therefore, Chapter 14 introduces the idea of kinetics on the molecular level beginning with collision theory and develops the empirical aspects from there.

Chapter 16—Acids and Bases

In this chapter, we depart from tradition by introducing the molecular basis of acids and bases at the beginning of the chapter. Often, presentation of these topics relegates the correlation of molecular structure and acid strength to the end of the chapter where it can seem like an afterthought to the quantitative aspects of acid-base chemistry. From a structure-function perspective, it is necessary to understand why certain compounds are Brønsted acids and why such compounds can be strong or weak. We believe this is yet another opportunity to remind students that energy is a pervasive idea in all of chemistry. After establishing the structure-function relationship, we move on to the customary, computational aspects of acids and bases.

Hypochlorous acid (+1)

Chlorous acid (+3)

Chloric acid (+5)

Perchloric acid (+7)

Figure 16.2 Lewis structures of the oxoacids of chlorine. The oxidation number of the Cl atom is shown in parentheses. Note that although hypochlorous acid is written as HClO, the H atom is bonded to the O atom.

The remaining chapters more closely resemble the order of topics found in most general chemistry texts. However, we return to the atomic properties-macroscopic properties relationship wherever possible— for example, in the context of coordination compounds, organic compounds, and modern materials. Although most instructors do not include these later chapters in a regular two-semester sequence, the chapters do contain material that can be important in a comprehensive approach to teaching chemistry and understanding how the nature of atoms gives rise to all that we observe.

The Construction of a Learning System

Writing a textbook and its supporting learning tools is a multifaceted process. McGraw-Hill's 360° Development Process is an ongoing, market-oriented approach to building accurate and innovative learning systems. It is dedicated to continual large scale and incremental improvement, driven by multiple customer feedback loops and checkpoints.

This is initiated during the early planning stages of new products and intensifies during the development and production stages. The 360° Development Process then begins again upon publication, in anticipation of the next version of each print and digital product. This process is designed to provide a broad, comprehensive spectrum of feedback for refinement and innovation of learning tools for both student and instructor. The 360° Development Process includes market research, content reviews, faculty and student focus groups, course- and product-specific symposia, accuracy checks, and art reviews, all guided by carefully selected Content Advisors.

The Learning System Used in *Chemistry: Atoms First*

Building Problem-Solving Skills. The entirety of the text emphasizes the importance of problem solving as a crucial element in the study of chemistry. Beginning with Chapter 1, a basic guide fosters a consistent approach to solving problems throughout the text. Each **Worked Example** is divided into four consistently applied steps: *Strategy* lays the basic framework for the problem; *Setup* gathers the necessary information for solving the problem; *Solution* takes us through the steps and calculations; *Think About It* makes us consider the feasibility of the answer or information illustrating the relevance of the problem.

After working through this problem-solving approach in the Worked Examples, there are two Practice Problems for students to solve. *Practice Problem A* is always very similar to the Worked Example and can be solved using the same strategy and approach.

Worked Example 3.3

The wavelength of a laser commonly used in the treatment of vascular skin lesions has a wavelength of 532 nm. What is the frequency of this radiation?

Strategy We must convert the wavelength to meters and solve for frequency using Equation 3.3 ($c = \lambda v$).

Setup Rearranging Equation 3.3 to solve for frequency gives $v = \dfrac{c}{\lambda}$. The speed of light, c, is 3.00×10^8 m/s. λ (in meters) = 532 nm $\times \dfrac{1 \times 10^{-9} \text{ m}}{1 \text{ nm}} = 5.32 \times 10^{-7}$ m.

Solution

$$v = \frac{3.00 \times 10^8 \text{ m/s}}{5.32 \times 10^{-7} \text{ m}} = 5.64 \times 10^{14} \text{ s}^{-1}$$

Think About It
Make sure your units cancel properly. A common error in this type of problem is neglecting to convert wavelength to meters.

Practice Problem A What is the wavelength (in meters) of an electromagnetic wave whose frequency is 1.61×10^{12} s^{-1}?

Practice Problem B What is the frequency (in reciprocal seconds) of electromagnetic radiation with a wavelength of 1.03 cm?

Although *Practice Problem B* probes comprehension of the same concept as Practice Problem A, it generally is sufficiently different in that it cannot be solved using the exact approach used in the Worked Example. Practice Problem B takes problem solving to another level by requiring students to develop a strategy independently. The regular use of the Worked Example and Practice Problems in this text will help students develop a robust and versatile set of problem-solving skills.

Section Review. Every section of the book that contains Worked Examples and Practice Problems ends with a Section Review. The Section Review enables the student to evaluate whether they understand the concepts presented in the section.

Key Skills. Located between chapters, Key Skills are easy to find review modules where students can return to refresh and hone specific skills that the authors know are vital to success in later chapters. The answers to the Key Skills can be found in the Answer Appendix in the back of the book.

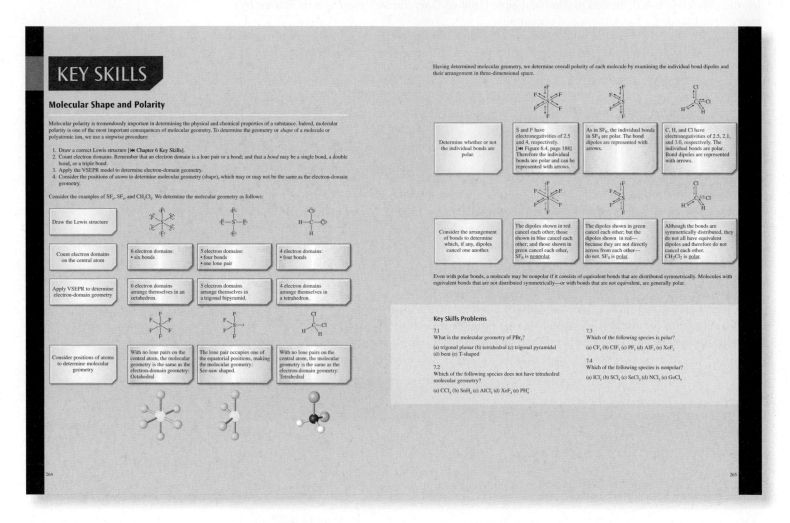

Applications. Each chapter offers a variety of tools designed to help facilitate learning. *Student Annotations* provide helpful hints and simple suggestions to the student.

Empirical Formulas

In addition to the methods we have learned so far, molecular substances can also be represented using **empirical formulas**. The word *empirical* means "from experience" or, in the context of chemical formulas, "from experiment." The empirical formula tells what elements are present in a molecule and in what whole-number ratio they are combined. For example, the molecular formula of hydrogen peroxide is H_2O_2, but its empirical formula is simply HO. Hydrazine, which has been used as a rocket fuel, has the molecular formula N_2H_4, so its empirical formula is NH_2. Although the ratio of nitrogen to hydrogen is 1:2 in

Thinking Outside the Box is an application providing a more in-depth look into a specific topic. *Learning Outcomes* provide a brief overview of the concepts the student should understand after reading the chapter. It's an opportunity to review areas that the student does not feel confident about upon reflection.

Thinking Outside the Box

Functional Groups

Many organic compounds are derivatives of alkanes in which one of the H atoms has been replaced by a group of atoms known as a **functional group.** The functional group determines many of the chemical properties of a compound because it typically is where a chemical reaction *occurs*. Table 5.9 lists the names and provides ball-and-stick models of several important functional groups.

Ethanol, for example, the alcohol in alcoholic beverages, is ethane (C_2H_6) with one of the hydrogen atoms replaced by an alcohol (—OH) group. Its name is derived from that of *ethane*, indicating that it contains *two* carbon atoms.

Ethanol

The molecular formula of ethanol can also be written C_2H_6O, but C_2H_5OH conveys more information about the structure of the molecule. Organic compounds and several functional groups are discussed in greater detail in Chapter 24.

TABLE 5.9	Organic Functional Groups	
Name	**Functional group**	**Molecular model**
Alcohol	—OH	
Aldehyde	—CHO	
Carboxylic acid	—COOH	
Amine	—NH₂	

Visualization. This text seeks to enhance student understanding through a variety of both unique and conventional visual techniques. A truly unique element in this text is the inclusion of a distinctive feature entitled **Visualizing Chemistry.** These two-page spreads appear as needed to emphasize fundamental, vitally important principles of chemistry. Setting them apart visually makes them easier to find and revisit as needed throughout the course term. Each Visualizing Chemistry feature concludes with a "What's the Point?" box that emphasizes the correct take-away message.

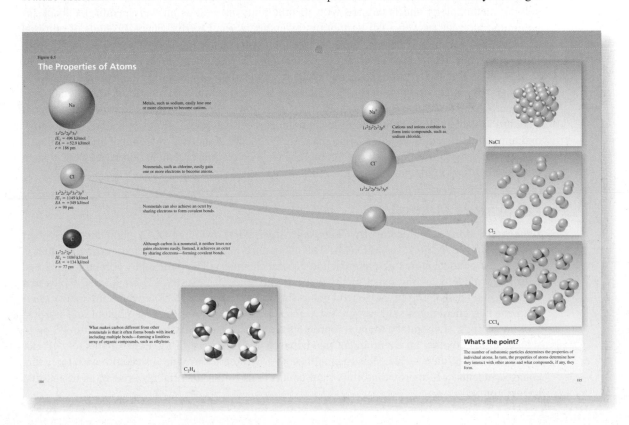

Figure 6.1
The Properties of Atoms

There is a series of conceptual end-of-chapter problems for each Visualizing Chemistry piece. These problems have been incorporated into the online homework and allow students to assess their understanding of the principles in each piece.

Flow Charts and a variety of inter-textual materials such as *Rewind* and *Fast Forward Buttons* and *Section Review* are meant to enhance student understanding and comprehension by reinforcing current concepts and connecting new concepts to those covered in other parts of the text.

Media. Many Visualizing Chemistry pieces have been made into captivating and pedagogically-effective *animations* for additional reinforcement of subject matter first encountered in the textbook. Each Visualizing Chemistry animation is noted by an icon.

Multi 7.8
Formation of pi bonds in ethylene and acetylene

Integration of Electronic Homework. You will find the *electronic homework* integrated into the text in numerous places. All Practice Problem B's are available in our electronic homework program for practice or assignments. A large number of the end-of-chapter problems and animations are in the electronic homework system ready to assign to students.

For us, this text will always remain a work in progress. We encourage you to contact us with any comments or questions.

Julia Burdge
juliaburdge@hotmail.com

Jason Overby
overbyj@cofc.edu

Creation of the Connect Chemistry™

McGraw-Hill has initiated a rigorous process to ensure high quality electronic homework. Our Connect Chemistry has undergone a transition to facilitate adding specific feedback and hints for typical student responses. Each question has been accuracy checked by two or more chemistry professors.

Through careful observation of real students and active instructors we have been able to evolve the online homework tool to an online learning and engagement tool. The goal of Connect is to usher in a new era of meaningful online learning that balances the conceptual and calculated aspect of this most vital discipline.

McGraw-Hill is offering students and instructors an enhanced digital homework experience using **Connect Chemistry**. Each problem within Connect Chemistry carries the text problem-solving methodology and is tailored with specific hints, as well as answer-specific feedback for common incorrect answers—all written by the author, Jason Overby. Several rounds of editorial and chemical accuracy checking, in addition to numerous instructor and student tests of all problems, ensure the accuracy of all content.

In addition to the specific hints and feedback provided for all questions, many questions allow students a chemical drawing experience that can be assessed directly inside of their homework. Connect Chemistry utilizes CambridgeSoft's ChemDraw, which is widely considered the "gold standard" of scientific drawing programs and the cornerstone application for scientists who draw and annotate molecules, reactions, and pathways. This collaboration of Connect and ChemDraw features an easy-to-use, intuitive, and comprehensive course-management and homework system with professional-grade drawing capabilities.

Laboratory Manual

Laboratory Manual to Accompany Chemistry: Atoms First by Gregg Dieckmann and John Sibert from the University of Texas at Dallas. This laboratory manual presents a lab curriculum that is organized around an atoms-first approach to general chemistry. The philosophy behind this manual is to (1) provide engaging experiments that tap into student curiosity, (2) emphasize topics that students find challenging in the general chemistry lecture course, and (3) create a laboratory environment that encourages students to "solve puzzles" or "play" with course content and not just "follow recipes." Laboratory Manual represents a terrific opportunity to get students turned on to science while creating an environment that connects the relevance of the experiments to a greater understanding of their world. This manual has been written to provide instructors with tools that engage students, while providing important connections to the material covered in an atoms-first lecture course.

Conversion from ARIS

↓

Authoring by Professors
Hints—Feedback—Pedagogy

↓

Quality Assurance

↓

Modifications

↓

Editorial Review

↓

Accept

↓

Class Testing with Instructors and Students

↓

Quality Assurance

↓

Modifications

↓

Editorial Review

↓

Accept

↓

Live Product

PROCEDURE

I. Construct Spectroscope

1. fold 8 in x 8 in x 3.5 in (203 mm x 203 mm x 89 mm) box
2. use a strip of black tape on the inside of the box to secure the bottom fold and prevent light from leaking through
3. on the bottom face of the box, use your ruler to draw a line that splits the box bottom in half, this is the long leg of a right triangle (connects points A and B in diagram below)
4. to generate the correct angle (15 °) between the slit and the diffraction grating, the short leg of the triangle (line B-C in diagram below) will measure 53 mm long. NOTE: the length of leg B-C will be different if you use a box that has a length (leg A-B) different than 8 inches; to calculate, use the equation

$$\tan(\theta) = \frac{(B-C)}{(A-B)}$$

where θ = angle C-A-B = 15 °, and A-B and B-C are the lengths of the two legs of the triangle.

Important features of this laboratory manual:

- early experiments focus on topics introduced early in an atoms-first course—properties of light and the use of light to study nanomaterials, line spectra and the structure of atoms, periodic trends, etc.
- prelab or *foundation* exercises encourage students to understand the important concepts/calculations/procedures in the experiment through working together
- postlab or *reflection* exercises put the lab content in the context of a larger chemistry/science picture
- instructor's resources provided with each experiment outline variations that can be incorporated to enrich the student experience or tailor the lab to the resources/equipment available at the institution

Enhanced Support for Faculty and Students

McGraw-Hill offers various tools and technology products in support of *Chemistry: Atoms First* to both faculty and students alike. Instructors can obtain teaching aides by calling the McGraw-Hill Customer Service Department at 1-800-338-3987, visiting our online catalog at www.mhhe.com, or by contacting their local McGraw-Hill sales representative.

To the Instructor

Connect Chemistry

Connect Chemistry **www.mcgrawhillconnect.com/chemistry** McGraw-Hill Connect is a web-based, interactive assignment and assessment platform that incorporates cognitive science to customize the learning process. The chemical drawing tool found within Connect Chemistry is Cambridge-Soft's ChemDraw, which is widely considered the "gold standard" of scientific drawing programs and the cornerstone application for scientists who draw and annotate molecules, reactions, and pathways. This collaboration of Connect and ChemDraw features an easy-to-use, intuitive, and comprehensive course-management and homework system with professional-grade drawing capabilities.

End-of-chapter problems from this textbook are served up in Connect for instructors to build assignments that are automatically graded and tracked through reports that export easily to Excel. Within Connect, instructors can also create and share materials with colleagues. Ask your McGraw-Hill representative for more information, and then check it out at www.mcgraw-hillconnect.com/chemistry.

ConnectPlus

If you or your students are ready for an alternative version of the traditional textbook, McGraw-Hill has your solution. eBooks from McGraw-Hill are smart, interactive, searchable, and portable. Included is a powerful suite of built-in tools that allow detailed searching, highlighting, note taking, and student-to-student or instructor-to-student note sharing. In addition, the media-rich eBook for *Chemistry: Atoms First* integrates relevant animations and videos into the textbook content for a true multimedia learning experience.

McGraw-Hill Higher Education and Blackboard have teamed up.

Blackboard®, the web-based course-management system, has partnered with McGraw-Hill to better allow students and faculty to use online materials and activities to complement face-to-face teaching. Blackboard features exciting social learning and teaching tools that foster more logical, visually impactful and active learning opportunities for students. You'll transform your closed-door classrooms into communities where students remain connected to their educational experience twenty-four hours a day.

This partnership allows you and your students access to McGraw-Hill's Connect™ and Create™ right from within your Blackboard course—all with one single sign-on.

Not only do you get single sign-on with Connect and Create, you also get deep integration of McGraw-Hill content and content engines right in Blackboard. Whether you're choosing a book for your course or building Connect assignments, all the tools you need are right where you want them—inside of Blackboard.

Gradebooks are now seamless. When a student completes an integrated Connect assignment, the grade for that assignment automatically (and instantly) feeds your Blackboard grade center.

McGraw-Hill and Blackboard can now offer you easy access to industry leading technology and content, whether your campus hosts it, or we do. Be sure to ask your local McGraw-Hill representative for details.

McGraw-Hill Tegrity Campus

McGraw-Hill Tegrity Campus is a service that makes class time available all the time by automatically capturing every lecture in a searchable format for students to review when they study and complete assignments. With a simple one-click start and stop process, you capture all computer screens and corresponding audio. Tegrity indexes as it records your slideshow presentations and anything shown on your computer, so students can use keywords to find exactly what they want to study.

Customizable Textbooks: Create

Create what you've only imagined. Introducing McGraw-Hill Create—a new, self-service website that allows you to create custom course materials—print and eBooks—by drawing upon McGraw-Hill's comprehensive, cross-disciplinary content. Add your own content quickly and easily. Tap into other rights-secured third party sources as well. Then, arrange the content in a way that makes the most sense for your course. Even personalize your book with your course name and information. Choose the best format for your course: color print, black and white print, or eBook. The eBook is now viewable on an iPad! And when you are finished customizing, you will receive a free PDF review copy in just minutes! Visit McGraw-Hill Create—www.mcgrawhillcreate.com—today and begin building your perfect book.

Presentation Center

The **Presentation Center** is a complete set of electronic book images and assets for instructors. You can build instructional materials wherever, whenever, and however you want! Accessed from your textbook's Connect website, the Presentation Center is an online digital library containing photos, artwork, animations, and other media types that can be used to create customized lectures, visually enhanced tests and quizzes, compelling course websites, or attractive printed support materials. All assets are copyrighted by McGraw-Hill Higher Education, but can be used by instructors for classroom purposes. The visual resources in this collection include:

- **Art** Full-color digital files of all illustrations in the book.
- **Photos** The photos collection contains digital files of photographs from the text.
- **Tables** Every table that appears in the text is available electronically.
- **Animations** Numerous full-color animations illustrating important processes are also provided.
- **PowerPoint® Lecture Outlines** Ready-made presentations for each chapter of the text.
- **PowerPoint Slides** All illustrations, photos, and tables are pre-inserted by chapter into blank PowerPoint slides.

The instructor side of your textbook's Connect website gives you access to all McGraw-Hill textbooks; and the Presentation Center's dynamic search engine allows you to explore by discipline, course, textbook chapter, asset type, or keyword.

Computerized Test Bank Online

A comprehensive bank of test questions is provided within a computerized test bank, enabling professors to prepare and access tests or quizzes anywhere, at any time. Instructors can create or edit questions, or drag-and-drop questions to prepare tests quickly and easily. Tests may be published to their online course or printed for paper-based assignments.

Instructor's Manual

The instructor's manual provides tips on teaching atoms first, literature citations, integration of media, and end-of-chapter problem difficulty levels and categories.

To the Student

Students can order supplemental study materials by contacting their campus bookstore, calling 1-800-262-4729, or online at www.shopmcgraw-hill.com.

Designed to help students maximize their learning experience in chemistry, we offer the following options to students:

Connect

With Connect Chemistry, students can practice solving assigned homework problems using the same problem-solving methodology they've learned from their textbook. Algorithmic problems serve up multiple versions of similar problems for mastery of content, and hints and feedback for common incorrect answers help students stay on track. Where appropriate, students will learn accurate, professional-grade chemical drawing through the use of CambridgeSoft's ChemDraw tool, which is implemented directly into their homework problems.

Animations and Media Player/MPEG Content

A number of animations are available for download to your MP3 player/iPod through the textbook's Connect site. Also, audio summaries of each chapter will be available for MP3 player/iPod download.

Connect is an electronic study system that offers students a digital portal of knowledge.

Workbook and Student Solutions Manual

The Workbook includes the student solutions manual for a one-stop shop for student use. The Workbook was written by Dawn Richardson and Amina El-Ashmawy from Collin College. The Workbook offers students the opportunity to practice the basic skills and test their understanding of the content knowledge within the chapter. Types of problems and how to solve them are presented along with any key notes on the concepts to facilitate understanding. Key Concepts, Study Questions, Practice Questions, and a Practice Quiz are provided within each chapter.

The student will find detailed solutions and explanations for the odd-numbered problems in this text in the solutions manual by AccuMedia Publishing Services, Julia Burdge, and Jason Overby.

Acknowledgments

We wish to thank the many people who have contributed to the development of this new text.

Focus Group

David L. Boatright *University of West Georgia*	Jon H. Hardesty *Collin College*
Mary J. Bojan *Pennsylvania State University*	David M. Jenkins *University of Tennessee–Knoxville*
Jon P. Camden *University of Tennessee–Knoxville*	Jimmy Reeves *University of North Carolina–Wilmington*
Gregg R. Dieckmann *University of Texas at Dallas*	Alan Van Orden *Colorado State University*

Board of Advisors

Mary J. Bojan *Pennsylvania State University*	Dawn Richardson *Collin College*
Gregg R. Dieckmann *University of Texas at Dallas*	Ed Tisko *University of Nebraska–Omaha*
Peter Hierl *University of Kansas*	Lori Van Der Sluys *Pennsylvania State University*
Richard Nafshun *Oregon State University*	Alan Van Orden *Colorado State University*

List of Reviewers

DeeDee Allen   *Wake Technical Community College*
Kathryn Asala   *University of North Carolina at Charlotte*
David Bailey   *Emporia State University*
Krishna Bapatla   *Brookhaven College*
Edward Barnes   *Fayetteville Technical Community College*
Marna B. Barnett   *Troy University*
Sharmistha Basu-Dutt   *University of West Georgia*
Erin Battin   *West Virginia University*
Shay Bean   *Chattanooga State Community College*
David L. Boatright   *University of West Georgia*
Mary Jo Bojan   *Pennsylvania State University*
Michelle Boucher   *Utica College*
Jon P. Camden   *University of Tennessee*
Peter Campbell   *Arcadia University*
Scott Carr   *Anderson University*
David Cedeno   *Illinois State University*
Tabitha Ruvarashe Chigwada   *West Virginia University*
Jing-Yi Chin   *Suffolk County Community College*
Allen Clabo   *Francis Marion University*
Mapi Cuevas   *Santa Fe College*
Amy Deveau   *University of New England*
Jane DeWitt   *San Francisco State University*
Gregg R. Dieckmann   *University of Texas at Dallas*
Amina K. El-Ashmawy   *Collin College*
Jennifer Firestine-Scar   *Lindenwood University*
Mark Freilich   *University of Memphis*
Al Gotch   *University of Mount Union*
Steven Gravelle   *Saint Vincent College*
Elizabeth Guldan   *Allegheny College*
Stephen C. Haefner   *Bridgewater State College*
Janet Haff   *Suffolk County Community College*
Jon P. Hardesty   *Colin County Community College*
James Horn   *Northern Illinois University*
Alan Jircitano   *Penn State Erie, The Behrend College*
Jason Jones   *Francis Marion University*
Robert Keil   *Moorpark College*
Christine Kelly   *University of Colorado*
Scott Kennedy   *Anderson University*
Farooq A. Khan   *University of West Georgia*
W. Cary Kilner   *University of New Hampshire*
Angela G. King   *Wake Forest University*

Jeffrey Kovac   *University of Tennessee*
John Krenos   *Rutgers University*
Peter Kroll   *The University of Texas at Arlington*
Elisabeth Krupa   *Lone Star College–North Harris*
Rosemary Loza   *The Ohio State University*
Rita T. Maher   *Richland College*
Mark Matthews   *Durham Technical Community College*
Vanessa McCaffrey   *Albion College*
Craig C. McLauchlan   *Illinois State University*
Alison Moore   *Belmont University*
Pamela S. Mork   *Concordia College*
Chifuru Noda   *Bridgewater State College*
Robert Pike   *College of William & Mary*
Jeffrey Rahn   *Eastern Washington University*
Jimmy Reeves   *University of North Carolina–Wilmington*
Dawn Rickey   *Colorado State University*
Tom Ridgway   *University of Cincinnati*
Melinda Ripper   *Butler County Community College*
Victor Ryzhov   *Northern Illinois University*
Sharadha Sambasivan   *Suffolk County Community College, Ammerman Campus*
Sarah Schmidtke   *The College of Wooster*
Jeffery A. Schneider   *SUNY Oswego*
Mark W. Schraf   *West Virginia University*
Ali O. Sezer   *California University of Pennsylvania*
John W. Sibert   *University of Texas at Dallas*
Michael Sierk   *Saint Vincent College*
Joseph Simard   *University of New England*
Sheila Smith   *University of Michigan–Dearborn*
Pamela St. John   *SUNY New Platz*
Lothar Stahl   *University of North Dakota*
Douglas Stuart   *University of West Georgia*
John Stubbs   *The University of New England*
Omar Torres   *Moorpark College*
Marcy Towns   *Purdue University*
Jason K. Vohs   *Saint Vincent College*
Kenneth B. Williams   *Francis Marion University*
Kim Woodrum   *University of Kentucky*
Kimberly Woznack   *California University of Pennsylvania*
Mingming Xu   *West Virginia University*

Raymond Chang's contributions have been invaluable. His unfaltering diligence and legendary attention to detail have added immeasurably to the quality of this book.

Members of our Board of Advisors—Mary Jo Bojan, Gregg Dieckmann, Peter Hierl, Richard Nafshun, Dawn Richardson, Ed Tisko, Lori Van Der Sluys, and Alan Van Orden—have graciously contributed their time, their energy, and their insights to guide the development of this text.

Alan Jircitano checked the manuscript and solved the Practice and Section Review Problems.

A talented group of people at Precision Graphics worked with us closely on the art program and paging.

We both thank and acknowledge our families for their continued and devoted support.

Finally, we must acknowledge our McGraw-Hill family for their inspiration, excitement, and support of this project: Publisher Ryan Blankenship, Executive Editor Jeff Huettman, Senior Development Editor Shirley Oberbroeckling, Lead Project Manager Sheila Frank, Senior Designer David Hash, and Executive Marketing Manager Tami Hodge.

Contents

List of Applications vi

Preface vii

1 CHEMISTRY: THE SCIENCE OF CHANGE 2

1.1 The Study of Chemistry 3
• Chemistry You May Already Know 3 • The Scientific Method 3

1.2 Classification of Matter 5
• States of Matter 5 • Mixtures 5

1.3 The Properties of Matter 7
• Physical Properties 7 • Chemical Properties 7 • Extensive and Intensive Properties 7

1.4 Scientific Measurement 8
• SI Base Units 9 • Mass 9 • Temperature 10 • Derived Units: Volume and Density 11

1.5 Uncertainty in Measurement 13
• Significant Figures 14 • Calculations with Measured Numbers 15 • Accuracy and Precision 17 • Thinking Outside the Box: Tips for Success in Chemistry Class 19

1.6 Using Units and Solving Problems 20
• Conversion Factors 20 • Dimensional Analysis—Tracking Units 20

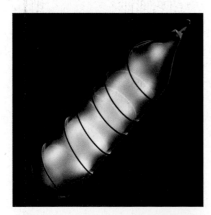

2 ATOMS AND THE PERIODIC TABLE 32

2.1 Atoms First 33

2.2 Subatomic Particles and Atomic Structure 34
• Discovery of the Electron 34 • Radioactivity 36 • The Proton and the Nuclear Model of the Atom 37 • The Neutron 38

2.3 Atomic Number, Mass Number, and Isotopes 39

2.4 Average Atomic Mass 41
• Thinking Outside the Box: Measuring Atomic Mass 42

2.5 The Periodic Table 43

2.6 The Mole and Molar Mass 44
• The Mole 45 • Molar Mass 45 • Interconverting Mass, Moles, and Numbers of Atoms 47

3 QUANTUM THEORY AND THE ELECTRONIC STRUCTURE OF ATOMS 56

3.1 Energy and Energy Changes 57
• Forms of Energy 57 • Units of Energy 58

3.2 The Nature of Light 60
• Properties of Waves 60 • The Electromagnetic Spectrum 61 • The Double-Slit Experiment 61

3.3 Quantum Theory 63
• Quantization of Energy 63 • Photons and the Photoelectric Effect 64 • Thinking Outside the Box: Everyday Occurrences of the Photoelectric Effect 65

3.4   Bohr's Theory of the Hydrogen Atom 67
• Atomic Line Spectra 67 • The Line Spectrum of Hydrogen 68

3.5   Wave Properties of Matter 74
• The de Broglie Hypothesis 74 • Diffraction of Electrons 76

3.6   Quantum Mechanics 76
• The Uncertainty Principle 77 • The Schrödinger Equation 78 • The Quantum Mechanical Description of the Hydrogen Atom 78

3.7   Quantum Numbers 79
• Principal Quantum Number (n) 79 • Angular Momentum Quantum Number (ℓ) 79 • Magnetic Quantum Number (m_ℓ) 79 • Electron Spin Quantum Number (m_s) 81

3.8   Atomic Orbitals 82
• s Orbitals 82 • p Orbitals 82 • d Orbitals and Other Higher-Energy Orbitals 84 • Energies of Orbitals 84

3.9   Electron Configurations 85
• Energies of Atomic Orbitals in Many-Electron Systems 85 • The Pauli Exclusion Principle 86 • The Aufbau Principle 87 • Hund's Rule 87 • General Rules for Writing Electron Configurations 89

3.10   Electron Configurations and the Periodic Table 90

4   PERIODIC TRENDS OF THE ELEMENTS 106

4.1   Development of the Periodic Table 107

4.2   The Modern Periodic Table 109
• Classification of Elements 109

4.3   Effective Nuclear Charge 112

4.4   Periodic Trends in Properties of Elements 113
• Atomic Radius 113 • Ionization Energy 115 • Electron Affinity 118 • Metallic Character 120

4.5   Electron Configuration of Ions 122
• Ions of Main Group Elements 122 • Ions of d-Block Elements 124

4.6   Ionic Radius 125
• Comparing Ionic Radius with Atomic Radius 125 • Thinking Outside the Box: Mistaking Strontium for Calcium 126 • Isoelectronic Series 126

5   IONIC AND COVALENT COMPOUNDS 140

5.1   Compounds 141

5.2   Lewis Dot Symbols 141

5.3   Ionic Compounds and Bonding 143

5.4   Naming Ions and Ionic Compounds 146
• Formulas of Ionic Compounds 147 • Naming Ionic Compounds 148

5.5   Covalent Bonding and Molecules 149
• Molecules 149 • Molecular Formulas 151 • Empirical Formulas 152

5.6   Naming Molecular Compounds 155
• Specifying Numbers of Atoms 155 • Compounds Containing Hydrogen 157 • Organic Compounds 158 • Thinking Outside the Box: Functional Groups 159

5.7   Covalent Bonding in Ionic Species 160
• Polyatomic Ions 160 • Oxoacids 162 • Hydrates 163 • Familiar Inorganic Compounds 164

5.8   Molecular and Formula Masses 165

5.9   Percent Composition of Compounds 166

5.10   Molar Mass 168

• Interconverting Mass, Moles, and Numbers of Particles 168 • Determination of Empirical Formula and Molecular Formula from Percent Composition 170

6   REPRESENTING MOLECULES 182

6.1   The Octet Rule 183

• Lewis Structures 183 • Multiple Bonds 186

6.2   Electronegativity and Polarity 187

• Electronegativity 187 • Dipole Moment, Partial Charges, and Percent Ionic Character 189

6.3   Drawing Lewis Structures 193

6.4   Lewis Structures and Formal Charge 194

6.5   Resonance 197

6.6   Exceptions to the Octet Rule 199

• Incomplete Octets 199 • Thinking Outside the Box: Species with Unpaired Electrons 200 • Odd Numbers of Electrons 200 • Expanded Octets 201

7   MOLECULAR GEOMETRY AND BONDING THEORIES 214

7.1   Molecular Geometry 215

• The VSEPR Model 216 • Electron-Domain Geometry and Molecular Geometry 216 • Deviation from Ideal Bond Angles 219 • Geometry of Molecules with More than One Central Atom 221

7.2   Molecular Geometry and Polarity 223

• Thinking Outside the Box: Intermolecular Forces 226

7.3   Valence Bond Theory 227

7.4   Hybridization of Atomic Orbitals 230

• Hybridization of s and p Orbitals 231 • Hybridization of s, p, and d Orbitals 233

7.5   Hybridization in Molecules Containing Multiple Bonds 238

7.6   Molecular Orbital Theory 245

• Bonding and Antibonding Molecular Orbitals 245 • σ Molecular Orbitals 246 • Thinking Outside the Box: Phases 247 • Bond Order 247 • π Molecular Orbitals 248 • Molecular Orbital Diagrams 250 • Thinking Outside the Box: Molecular Orbitals in Heteronuclear Diatomic Species 251

7.7   Bonding Theories and Descriptions of Molecules with Delocalized Bonding 252

8   CHEMICAL REACTIONS 266

8.1   Chemical Equations 267

• Interpreting and Writing Chemical Equations 267 • Balancing Chemical Equations 269 • Patterns of Chemical Reactivity 273

8.2   Combustion Analysis 275

• Determination of Empirical Formula 275

8.3   Calculations with Balanced Chemical Equations 277

• Moles of Reactants and Products 277 • Mass of Reactants and Products 279

8.4   Limiting Reactants 280
• Determining the Limiting Reactant 281 • Reaction Yield 285

8.5   Periodic Trends in Reactivity of the Main Group Elements 286
• Thinking Outside the Box: Atom Economy 287 • General Trends in Reactivity 288
• Reactions of the Active Metals 289 • Reactions of Other Main Group Elements 290
• Comparison of Group 1A and Group 1B Elements 293

9   CHEMICAL REACTIONS IN AQUEOUS SOLUTIONS 306

9.1   General Properties of Aqueous Solutions 307
• Electrolytes and Nonelectrolytes 307 • Strong Electrolytes and Weak Electrolytes 308

9.2   Precipitation Reactions 312
• Solubility Guidelines for Ionic Compounds in Water 312 • Molecular Equations 314
• Ionic Equations 315 • Net Ionic Equations 315

9.3   Acid-Base Reactions 317
• Strong Acids and Bases 317 • Brønsted Acids and Bases 317 • Acid-Base Neutralization 319

9.4   Oxidation-Reduction Reactions 321
• Oxidation Numbers 323 • Oxidation of Metals in Aqueous Solutions 325 • Balancing
Simple Redox Equations 327 • Other Types of Redox Reactions 329

9.5   Concentration of Solutions 331
• Molarity 331 • Dilution 333 • Serial Dilution 337 • Thinking Outside the Box: Visible
Spectrophotometry 338 • Solution Stoichiometry 339

9.6   Aqueous Reactions and Chemical Analysis 341
• Gravimetric Analysis 341 • Acid-Base Titrations 343

10   ENERGY CHANGES IN CHEMICAL REACTIONS 362

10.1   Energy and Energy Changes 363

10.2   Introduction to Thermodynamics 365
• States and State Functions 365 • The First Law of Thermodynamics 366 • Work and
Heat 367

10.3   Enthalpy 368
• Reactions Carried Out at Constant Volume or at Constant Pressure 368 • Enthalpy and
Enthalpy Changes 370 • Thermochemical Equations 371

10.4   Calorimetry 373
• Specific Heat and Heat Capacity 374 • Constant-Pressure Calorimetry 374 • Constant-
Volume Calorimetry 378 • Thinking Outside the Box: Heat Capacity of Calorimeters 379

10.5   Hess's Law 383

10.6   Standard Enthalpies of Formation 385

10.7   Bond Enthalpy and the Stability of Covalent Molecules 388

10.8   Lattice Energy and the Stability of Ionic Solids 392
• The Born-Haber Cycle 392 • Comparison of Ionic and Covalent Compounds 393

11   GASES 412

11.1   Properties of Gases 413

11.2   The Kinetic Molecular Theory of Gases 415
• Molecular Speed 416 • Diffusion and Effusion 417

11.3 Gas Pressure 418
• Definition and Units of Pressure 419 • Calculation of Pressure 419 • Measurement of Pressure 420

11.4 The Gas Laws 422
• Boyle's Law: The Pressure-Volume Relationship 422 • Charles's and Gay-Lussac's Law: The Temperature-Volume Relationship 424 • Avogadro's Law: The Amount-Volume Relationship 426 • The Gas Laws and Kinetic Molecular Theory 428 • The Combined Gas Law: The Pressure-Temperature-Amount-Volume Relationship 429

11.5 The Ideal Gas Equation 431
• Applications of the Ideal Gas Equation 432

11.6 Real Gases 434
• Factors That Cause Deviation from Ideal Behavior 435 • The van der Waals Equation 435 • van der Waals Constants 437

11.7 Gas Mixtures 438
• Dalton's Law of Partial Pressures 439 • Mole Fractions 440 • Thinking Outside the Box: Decompression Injury 441

11.8 Reactions with Gaseous Reactants and Products 443
• Calculating the Required Volume of a Gaseous Reactant 443 • Determining the Amount of Reactant Consumed Using Change in Pressure 444 • Using Partial Pressures to Solve Problems 445

12 INTERMOLECULAR FORCES AND THE PHYSICAL PROPERTIES OF LIQUIDS AND SOLIDS 464

12.1 Intermolecular Forces 465
• Dipole-Dipole Interactions 466 • Hydrogen Bonding 466 • Dispersion Forces 467 • Ion-Dipole Interactions 469

12.2 Properties of Liquids 470
• Surface Tension 470 • Viscosity 470 • Vapor Pressure 471

12.3 Crystal Structure 475
• Unit Cells 475 • Packing Spheres 476 • Closest Packing 478 • Thinking Outside the Box: X-ray Diffraction 480

12.4 Types of Crystals 482
• Ionic Crystals 482 • Covalent Crystals 485 • Molecular Crystals 486 • Metallic Crystals 486

12.5 Amorphous Solids 487

12.6 Phase Changes 488
• Liquid-Vapor Phase Transition 488 • Solid-Liquid Phase Transition 490 • Solid-Vapor Phase Transition 491

12.7 Phase Diagrams 494

13 PHYSICAL PROPERTIES OF SOLUTIONS 510

13.1 Types of Solutions 511

13.2 A Molecular View of the Solution Process 512
• The Importance of Intermolecular Forces 512 • Energy and Entropy in Solution Formation 513

13.3 Concentration Units 516
• Molality 516 • Percent by Mass 516 • Comparison of Concentration Units 517

13.4 Factors That Affect Solubility 519
• Temperature 519 • Pressure 520

13.5 Colligative Properties 521
• Vapor-Pressure Lowering 522 • Boiling-Point Elevation 524 • Freezing-Point Depression 525 • Osmotic Pressure 527 • Electrolyte Solutions 527 • Thinking Outside the Box: Intravenous Fluids 530 • Thinking Outside the Box: Fluoride Poisoning 531

13.6 Calculations Using Colligative Properties 532

13.7 Colloids 534

14 CHEMICAL KINETICS 550

14.1 Reaction Rates 551

14.2 Collision Theory of Chemical Reactions 551

14.3 Measuring Reaction Progress and Expressing Reaction Rate 553
• Average Reaction Rate 553 • Instantaneous Rate 557 • Stoichiometry and Reaction Rate 560

14.4 Dependence of Reaction Rate on Reactant Concentration 562
• The Rate Law 563 • Experimental Determination of the Rate Law 563

14.5 Dependence of Reactant Concentration on Time 568
• First-Order Reactions 568 • Second-Order Reactions 573

14.6 Dependence of Reaction Rate on Temperature 576
• The Arrhenius Equation 576 • Thinking Outside the Box: Surface Area 580

14.7 Reaction Mechanisms 581
• Elementary Reactions 581 • Rate-Determining Step 582 • Mechanisms with a Fast First Step 586 • Experimental Support for Reaction Mechanisms 587

14.8 Catalysis 589
• Heterogeneous Catalysis 590 • Homogeneous Catalysis 590 • Enzymes: Biological Catalysts 591

15 CHEMICAL EQUILIBRIUM 608

15.1 The Concept of Equilibrium 609

15.2 The Equilibrium Constant 611
• Calculating Equilibrium Constants 612 • Magnitude of the Equilibrium Constant 615

15.3 Equilibrium Expressions 616
• Heterogeneous Equilibria 616 • Manipulating Equilibrium Expressions 617 • Gaseous Equilibria 621

15.4 Using Equilibrium Expressions to Solve Problems 623
• Predicting the Direction of a Reaction 624 • Calculating Equilibrium Concentrations 625

15.5 Factors That Affect Chemical Equilibrium 630
• Addition or Removal of a Substance 630 • Changes in Volume and Pressure 633 • Changes in Temperature 634 • Catalysis 635 • Thinking Outside the Box: Biological Equilibria 640

16 ACIDS AND BASES 656

16.1 Brønsted Acids and Bases 657

16.2 Molecular Structure and Acid Strength 659
• Hydrohalic Acids 659 • Oxoacids 659 • Carboxylic Acids 661

16.3 The Acid-Base Properties of Water 661

16.4 The pH Scale 663

16.5 Strong Acids and Bases 668
• Strong Acids 668 • Strong Bases 669

16.6 Weak Acids and Acid Ionization Constants 672
• The Ionization Constant, K_a 672 • Calculating pH from K_a 673 • Thinking Outside the Box: Acid Rain 678 • Percent Ionization 678 • Using pH to Determine K_a 680

16.7 Weak Bases and Base Ionization Constants 681
• The Ionization Constant K_b 682 • Calculating pH from K_b 682 • Using pH to Determine K_b 683

16.8 Conjugate Acid-Base Pairs 684
• The Strength of a Conjugate Acid or Base 684
• The Relationship Between K_a and K_b of a Conjugate Acid-Base Pair 685

16.9 Diprotic and Polyprotic Acids 688

16.10 Acid-Base Properties of Salt Solutions 690
• Basic Salt Solutions 691 • Acidic Salt Solutions 692 • Neutral Salt Solutions 694
• Salts in Which Both the Cation and the Anion Hydrolyze 695

16.11 Acid-Base Properties of Oxides and Hydroxides 696
• Oxides of Metals and of Nonmetals 696 • Basic and Amphoteric Hydroxides 697

16.12 Lewis Acids and Bases 697

17 ACID-BASE EQUILIBRIA AND SOLUBILITY EQUILIBRIA 712

17.1 The Common Ion Effect 713

17.2 Buffer Solutions 715
• Calculating the pH of a Buffer 715 • Preparing a Buffer Solution with a Specific pH 720

17.3 Acid-Base Titrations 721
• Strong Acid–Strong Base Titrations 721 • Weak Acid–Strong Base Titrations 723 • Strong Acid–Weak Base Titrations 727 • Acid-Base Indicators 729

17.4 Solubility Equilibria 731
• Solubility Product Expression and K_{sp} 732 • Calculations Involving K_{sp} and Solubility 732
• Predicting Precipitation Reactions 735

17.5 Factors Affecting Solubility 737
• The Common Ion Effect 737 • pH 740 • Complex Ion Formation 742 • Thinking Outside the Box: Equilibrium and Tooth Decay 743

17.6 Separation of Ions Using Differences in Solubility 747
• Fractional Precipitation 747 • Qualitative Analysis of Metal Ions in Solution 748

18 ENTROPY, FREE ENERGY, AND EQUILIBRIUM 762

18.1 Spontaneous Processes 763

18.2 Entropy 764
• A Qualitative Description of Entropy 764 • A Quantitative Definition of Entropy 764

18.3 Entropy Changes in a System 766
• Calculating ΔS_{sys} 766 • Standard Entropy, $S°$ 767 • Qualitatively Predicting the Sign of $\Delta S°_{sys}$ 770

18.4 Entropy Changes in the Universe 774
• Calculating ΔS_{surr} 775 • The Second Law of Thermodynamics 775 • Thinking Outside the Box: Thermodynamics and Living Systems 778 • The Third Law of Thermodynamics 778

18.5 Predicting Spontaneity 780
• Gibbs Free-Energy Change, ΔG 780 • Standard Free-Energy Changes, $\Delta G°$ 782 • Using ΔG and $\Delta G°$ to Solve Problems 783

18.6 Free Energy and Chemical Equilibrium 786
• Relationship Between ΔG and $\Delta G°$ 786 • Relationship Between $\Delta G°$ and K 787

18.7 Thermodynamics in Living Systems 790

19 ELECTROCHEMISTRY 804

19.1 Balancing Redox Reactions 805

19.2 Galvanic Cells 809

19.3 Standard Reduction Potentials 812

19.4 Spontaneity of Redox Reactions Under Standard-State Conditions 819
• Thinking Outside the Box: Amalgam Fillings and Dental Pain 822

19.5 Spontaneity of Redox Reactions Under Conditions Other Than Standard State 822
• The Nernst Equation 823 • Concentration Cells 824

19.6 Batteries 827
• Dry Cells and Alkaline Batteries 827 • Lead Storage Batteries 828 • Lithium-Ion Batteries 828 • Fuel Cells 829

19.7 Electrolysis 830
• Electrolysis of Molten Sodium Chloride 830 • Electrolysis of Water 831 • Electrolysis of an Aqueous Sodium Chloride Solution 832 • Quantitative Applications of Electrolysis 833

19.8 Corrosion 835

20 NUCLEAR CHEMISTRY 850

20.1 Nuclei and Nuclear Reactions 851

20.2 Nuclear Stability 853
• Patterns of Nuclear Stability 853 • Nuclear Binding Energy 855

20.3 Natural Radioactivity 858
• Kinetics of Radioactive Decay 858 • Dating Based on Radioactive Decay 859

20.4 Nuclear Transmutation 862

20.5 Nuclear Fission 865

20.6 Nuclear Fusion 871

20.7 Uses of Isotopes 873
• Chemical Analysis 873 • Isotopes in Medicine 873 • Thinking Outside the Box: Nuclear Medicine 874

20.8 Biological Effects of Radiation 875

21 METALLURGY AND THE CHEMISTRY OF METALS 884

21.1 Occurrence of Metals 885

21.2 Metallurgical Processes 886
• Preparation of the Ore 886 • Production of Metals 886 • The Metallurgy of Iron 887 • Steelmaking 888 • Purification of Metals 890 • Thinking Outside the Box: Copper 891

21.3 Band Theory of Conductivity 892
• Conductors 892 • Semiconductors 892

21.4 **Periodic Trends in Metallic Properties 894**
21.5 **The Alkali Metals 894**
21.6 **The Alkaline Earth Metals 897**
       • Magnesium 897 • Calcium 898
21.7 **Aluminum 898**

22 COORDINATION CHEMISTRY 906

22.1 **Coordination Compounds 907**
       • Properties of Transition Metals 907 • Ligands 909 • Nomenclature of Coordination
       Compounds 911 • Thinking Outside the Box: Chelation Therapy 913
22.2 **Structure of Coordination Compounds 914**
22.3 **Bonding in Coordination Compounds: Crystal Field Theory 916**
       • Crystal Field Splitting in Octahedral Complexes 917 • Color 918 • Magnetic
       Properties 919 • Tetrahedral and Square-Planar Complexes 921
22.4 **Reactions of Coordination Compounds 922**
22.5 **Applications of Coordination Compounds 922**

23 NONMETALLIC ELEMENTS AND THEIR COMPOUNDS 930

23.1 **General Properties of Nonmetals 931**
23.2 **Hydrogen 932**
       • Binary Hydrides 933 • Isotopes of Hydrogen 934 • Hydrogenation 934
       • The Hydrogen Economy 935
23.3 **Carbon 935**
23.4 **Nitrogen and Phosphorus 937**
       • Nitrogen 937 • Phosphorus 939
23.5 **Oxygen and Sulfur 942**
       • Oxygen 942 • Sulfur 944 • Thinking Outside the Box: Arsenic 948
23.6 **The Halogens 948**
       • Preparation and General Properties of the Halogens 949 • Compounds of the
       Halogens 951 • Uses of the Halogens 953

24 ORGANIC CHEMISTRY 960

24.1 **Why Carbon Is Different 961**
24.2 **Classes of Organic Compounds 963**
       • Basic Nomenclature 967 • Molecules with Multiple Substituents 970 • Molecules with
       Specific Functional Groups 970
24.3 **Representing Organic Molecules 973**
       • Condensed Structural Formulas 974 • Kekulé Structures 974 • Skeletal Structures 974
       • Resonance 976
24.4 **Isomerism 980**
       • Constitutional Isomerism 980 • Stereoisomerism 980 • Thinking Outside the Box:
       Thalidomide 984

24.5 Organic Reactions 984
• Addition Reactions 985 • Substitution Reactions 987 • Other Types of Organic Reactions 993

24.6 Organic Polymers 994
• Addition Polymers 995 • Condensation Polymers 995 • Biological Polymers 997

25 MODERN MATERIALS 1012

25.1 Polymers 1013
• Addition Polymers 1013 • Condensation Polymers 1018 • Thinking Outside the Box: Electrically Conducting Polymers 1021

25.2 Ceramics and Composite Materials 1021
• Ceramics 1021 • Composite Materials 1023

25.3 Liquid Crystals 1023

25.4 Biomedical Materials 1026
• Dental Implants 1026 • Soft Tissue Materials 1027 • Artificial Joints 1028

25.5 Nanotechnology 1028
• Graphite, Buckyballs, and Nanotubes 1029

25.6 Semiconductors 1030

25.7 Superconductors 1033

Appendixes
1 Mathematical Operations   A-1
2 Thermodynamic Data at 1 ATM and 25°C   A-6
3 Ionization Constants of Weak Acids and Bases at 25°C   A-13
4 Solubility Product Constants at 25°C   A-15

Glossary   G-1

Answers to Odd-Numbered Problems   AP-1

Credits   C-1

Index   I-1

CHAPTER 1

Chemistry: The Science of Change

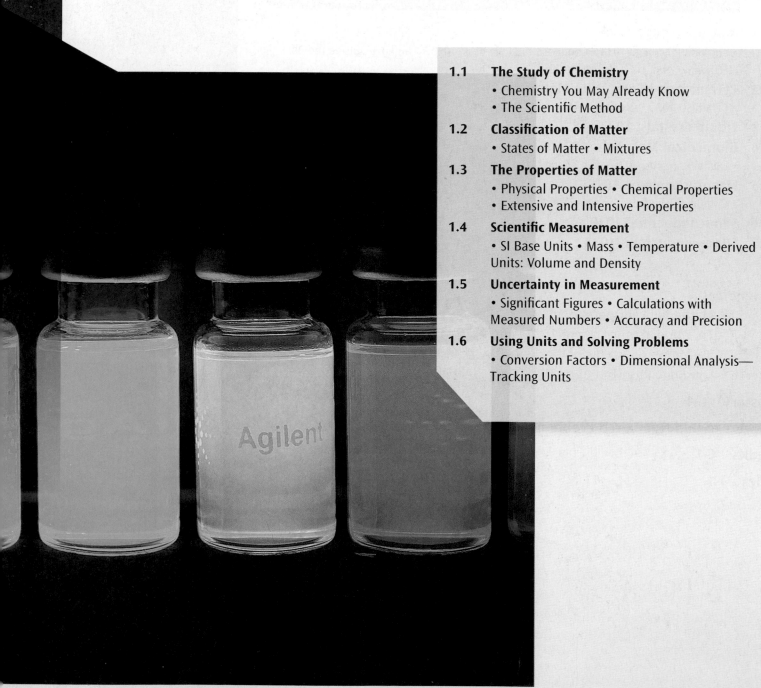

1.1 **The Study of Chemistry**
• Chemistry You May Already Know
• The Scientific Method

1.2 **Classification of Matter**
• States of Matter • Mixtures

1.3 **The Properties of Matter**
• Physical Properties • Chemical Properties
• Extensive and Intensive Properties

1.4 **Scientific Measurement**
• SI Base Units • Mass • Temperature • Derived Units: Volume and Density

1.5 **Uncertainty in Measurement**
• Significant Figures • Calculations with Measured Numbers • Accuracy and Precision

1.6 **Using Units and Solving Problems**
• Conversion Factors • Dimensional Analysis—Tracking Units

With nanotechnology, chemists now have the ability to manipulate matter on the nanometer scale and develop new materials with interesting and unique chemical and physical properties. One such new nanoscale material is quantum dots, semiconductors that range from 2–10 nanometers in size. With precise control of the physical size of the quantum dots, researchers can *tune* quantum dots to emit different colors of light. Such "tunability" makes it possible to incorporate quantum dots into lasers, light-emitting diodes, camera sensors, and solar cells—and to use them for imaging at the cellular level.

1.1 THE STUDY OF CHEMISTRY

Chemistry often is called the *central science* because knowledge of the principles of chemistry can facilitate understanding of other sciences, including physics, biology, geology, astronomy, oceanography, engineering, and medicine. **Chemistry** is the study of *matter* and the *changes* that matter undergoes. Matter is what makes up our bodies, our belongings, our physical environment, and in fact our entire universe. **Matter** is anything that has mass and occupies space.

Chemistry You May Already Know

You may already be familiar with some of the terms used in chemistry. Even if this is your first chemistry course, you may have heard of *molecules* and know them to be tiny pieces of a substance—much too tiny to see. Further, you may know that molecules are made up of *atoms,* even smaller pieces of matter. And even if you don't know what a *chemical formula* is, you probably know that H_2O is water. You may have used, or at least heard, the term *chemical reaction;* and you are undoubtedly familiar with a variety of common processes that are chemical reactions, such as those shown in Figure 1.1. Don't worry if you are not familiar with these terms; they will be defined in the early chapters of this book.

The processes in Figure 1.1 are all things that you can observe at the *macroscopic level.* In other words, these processes and their results are visible to the human eye. In studying chemistry, you will learn to visualize and understand these same processes at the *submicroscopic* or *molecular level.*

The Scientific Method

Advances in our understanding of chemistry (and other sciences) are the result of scientific experiments. Although scientists do not all take the same approach to experimentation, they must follow a set of guidelines known as the **scientific method** in order to have their results added to the larger body of knowledge within a given field. The flowchart in Figure 1.2 illustrates this basic process. The method begins with the gathering of data via observations and experiments. Scientists study these data and try to identify *patterns* or *trends.* When they find a pattern or trend, they may summarize their findings with a **law,** a concise verbal or mathematical statement of a reliable relationship between phenomena. Scientists may then formulate a **hypothesis,** a tentative explanation for their observations. Further experiments are designed to test the hypothesis. If experiments indicate that the hypothesis is incorrect, the scientists go back to the drawing board, try to come up with a different interpretation of their data, and formulate a new hypothesis. The new hypothesis will then be tested by experiment. When a hypothesis stands the test of extensive experimentation, it may evolve into a theory. A **theory** is a unifying principle that explains a body of experimental observations and the laws that are based on them. Theories can also be used to predict related phenomena, so theories are constantly being tested. If a theory is disproved by experiment, then it must be discarded or modified so that it becomes consistent with experimental observations.

A fascinating example of the use of the scientific method is the story of how smallpox was eradicated. Late in the eighteenth century, an English doctor named Edward Jenner observed that even during outbreaks of smallpox in Europe, milkmaids seldom contracted the disease. He reasoned that when people who had frequent contact with cows contracted *cowpox,* a similar but far

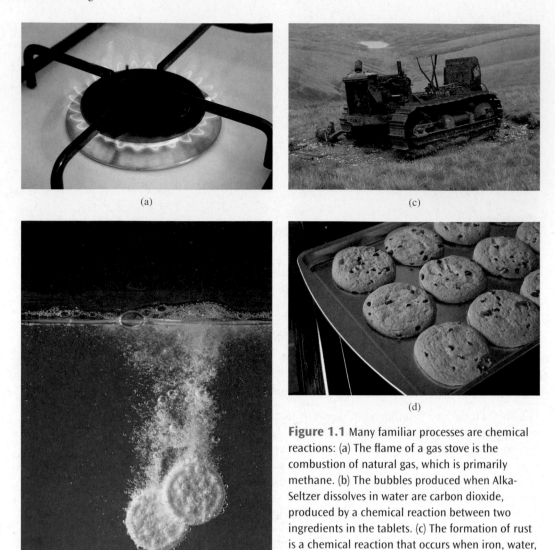

Figure 1.1 Many familiar processes are chemical reactions: (a) The flame of a gas stove is the combustion of natural gas, which is primarily methane. (b) The bubbles produced when Alka-Seltzer dissolves in water are carbon dioxide, produced by a chemical reaction between two ingredients in the tablets. (c) The formation of rust is a chemical reaction that occurs when iron, water, and oxygen are all present. (d) Many baked goods "rise" as the result of a chemical reaction that produces carbon dioxide.

Figure 1.2 Flowchart of the scientific method.

less harmful disease, they developed a natural immunity to smallpox. He predicted that intentional exposure to the cowpox virus would produce the same immunity. In 1796, Jenner exposed an 8-year-old boy to the cowpox virus using pus from the cowpox lesions of an infected milkmaid. Six weeks later, he exposed the boy to the *smallpox* virus and, as Jenner had predicted, the boy did *not* contract the disease. Subsequent experiments using the same technique (later dubbed *vaccination* from the Latin *vacca* meaning *cow*) confirmed that immunity to smallpox could be induced.

A superbly coordinated international effort on the part of healthcare workers was successful in eliminating smallpox worldwide. In 1980, the World Health Organization declared smallpox officially eradicated. This historic triumph over a dreadful disease, one of the greatest medical advances of the twentieth century, began with Jenner's astute observations, inductive reasoning, and careful experimentation—the essential elements of the *scientific method*.

Until recently, almost everyone had a smallpox vaccine scar—usually on the upper arm.

1.2   CLASSIFICATION OF MATTER

Chemists classify matter as either a *substance* or a *mixture* of substances. A **substance** is a form of matter that has a definite (constant) composition and distinct properties, such as color, smell, and taste. Familiar examples include salt (sodium chloride), iron, water, mercury, carbon dioxide, and oxygen. They differ from one another in composition and we can tell them apart because they have different properties. For example, salt can be dissolved in water; iron cannot. Mercury is a liquid with a silvery appearance; carbon dioxide is a colorless gas. Carbon dioxide can be used to extinguish a flame; oxygen most *definitely* cannot.

States of Matter

All substances can, in principle, exist as a solid, a liquid, and a gas, the three physical states depicted in Figure 1.3. In a solid, particles are held close together in an orderly fashion with little freedom of motion. As a result, a solid does not conform to the shape of its container. Particles in a liquid are close together but are not held rigidly in position; they are free to move past one another. Thus, a liquid conforms to the shape of the part of the container it fills. In a gas, the particles are separated by distances that are very large compared to the size of the particles. A sample of gas assumes both the shape and the volume of its container.

We can convert a substance from one state to another without changing the identity of the substance. For example, if solid water (ice) is heated, it will melt to form liquid water. If the liquid water is heated further, it will vaporize to form a gas (water vapor). Conversely, cooling water vapor will cause it to condense into liquid water. When the liquid water is cooled further, it will freeze into ice. Figure 1.4 shows the three physical states of water.

Multi 1.1
Matter—
three states of matter

Mixtures

A **mixture** is a combination of two or more substances in which each substance retains its distinct identity. Like pure substances, mixtures can be solids, liquids, or gases. Some familiar examples are trail mix, sterling silver, apple juice, seawater, and air. Mixtures do not have a universal constant composition. Therefore, samples of air collected in different locations will differ in composition because of differences in altitude, pollution, and other factors. Various brands of apple juice may differ in composition because of the use of different varieties of apples, or there may be differences in processing, packaging, and so on.

Mixtures are either *homogeneous* or *heterogeneous*. When we dissolve a teaspoon of sugar in a glass of water, we get a **homogeneous mixture** because the composition of the mixture is uniform throughout. If we mix sand with iron filings, however, the sand and the iron filings remain distinct and discernible from each other (Figure 1.5). This type of mixture is called a **heterogeneous mixture** because the composition is *not* uniform.

A mixture, whether homogeneous or heterogeneous, can be separated into the substances it contains without changing the identities of the individual substances. Thus, sugar can be recovered from sugar-water by evaporating the mixture to dryness. The solid sugar will be left behind, and the water component can be recovered by condensing the water vapor that evaporates. To separate the sand-iron mixture, we can use a magnet to remove the iron filings from the sand, because sand

Student Annotation: The last naturally occurring case occurred in 1977 in Somalia.

Student Annotation: Some books refer to *substances* as *pure substances*. These two terms generally mean the same thing, although the adjective pure is unnecessary in this context because a substance is, by definition, pure.

Student Annotation: Solids and liquids sometimes are referred to collectively as the *condensed phases*. Liquids and gases sometimes are referred to collectively as *fluids*.

Student Annotation: Homogeneous mixtures are also known as *solutions*. [▶▶ Chapter 9]

Student Annotation: Condensation refers to the change from gas to liquid.

Solid   Liquid   Gas

Figure 1.3 Molecular-level illustrations of a solid, liquid, and gas.

Figure 1.4 Water as a solid (ice), liquid, and gas. (We can't actually see water vapor, any more than we can see the nitrogen and oxygen that make up most of the air we breathe. When we see steam or clouds, what we are actually seeing is water vapor that has condensed upon encountering cold air.)

(a)

(b)

Figure 1.5 (a) A heterogeneous mixture contains iron filings and sand. (b) A magnet is used to separate the iron filings from the mixture.

is not attracted to the magnet [see Figure 1.5(b)]. After separation, the components of the mixture will have the same composition and properties as they did prior to being mixed.

The processes used to separate mixtures are called physical processes. A ***physical process*** is one that does not change the identity of any substance. For example, melting ice causes a change in the physical state of water (solid to liquid), but it does not change the identity of the substance (water). Examples of physical processes that can be used to separate mixtures are shown in Figure 1.6.

(a) (b) (c)

Figure 1.6 (a) Filtration can be used to separate a heterogeneous mixture of a liquid and a solid, such as coffee and coffee grounds. The filter, in this case a coffee filter, allows only the liquid coffee to pass through. (b) Distillation can be used to separate components with different boiling points. The component with the lowest boiling point is vaporized first, leaving behind components with higher boiling points—including dissolved solids. The vapor can be condensed and recovered by cooling. (c) A variety of chromatographic techniques, including paper chromatography, can be used to separate mixtures. Here, paper chromatography is used to separate the dye in candy coatings into its components.

1.3 THE PROPERTIES OF MATTER

Substances are identified by their properties as well as by their composition. Properties of a substance may be *quantitative* (measured and expressed with a number) or *qualitative* (not requiring explicit measurement).

Physical Properties

Color, melting point, boiling point, and physical state are all physical properties. A ***physical property*** is one that can be observed and measured without changing the *identity* of a substance. For example, we can determine the melting point of ice by heating a block of ice and measuring the temperature at which the ice is converted to water. Liquid water differs from ice in appearance but not in composition. Melting is a ***physical change***—one in which the state of matter changes, but the identity of the matter does not change. We can recover the original ice by cooling the water until it freezes. Therefore, the melting point of a substance is a *physical* property. Similarly, when we say that oil is less dense than water, we are referring to the physical property of density.

Chemical Properties

The statement "iron rusts when it is exposed to water and air" describes a ***chemical property*** of iron, because for us to observe this property, a ***chemical change*** or ***chemical process*** must occur. In this case, the chemical change is *corrosion* or *oxidation* of iron. After a chemical change, the original substance (iron metal, in this case) no longer exists. What remains is a different substance (*rust,* in this case). There is no *physical* process by which we can recover the iron from the rust.

Every time we bake cookies, we bring about a chemical change. When heated, the leavening agent (typically baking soda) in cookie dough undergoes a chemical change that produces a gas. The gas forms numerous little bubbles in the dough during the baking process, causing the cookies to "rise." Once the cookies are baked, we cannot recover the baking soda by cooling the cookies, or by *any* physical process. When we eat the cookies, we initiate further chemical changes that occur during digestion and metabolism.

Extensive and Intensive Properties

All properties of matter are either *extensive* or *intensive*. The measured value of an ***extensive property*** depends on the amount of matter. *Mass* is an extensive property. More matter means more mass. Values of the same extensive property can be added together. For example, two copper coins will have a combined mass that is the sum of the individual masses of each coin, and the volume of two cardboard boxes is the sum of their individual volumes.

The value of an ***intensive property*** does *not* depend on the amount of matter. *Density* and *temperature* are intensive properties. Suppose that we have two beakers of water at the same temperature and we combine them to make a single quantity of water in a larger beaker. The density and the temperature of the water in the larger combined quantity will be the same as they were in the two separate beakers. Unlike mass and length, which are additive, temperature, density, and other *intensive* properties are not additive.

1.4   SCIENTIFIC MEASUREMENT

Scientists use a variety of devices to measure the properties of matter. A meterstick is used to measure length; a burette, pipette, graduated cylinder, and volumetric flask are used to measure volume (Figure 1.7); a balance is used to measure mass; and a thermometer is used to measure temperature. Properties that can be measured are called *quantitative* properties because they are expressed using numbers. When we express a measured quantity with a number, though, we must always include the appropriate unit; otherwise, the measurement is meaningless. For example, to say that the depth of a swimming pool is 3 is insufficient to distinguish between one that is 3 *feet* (0.9 meters) and one that is 3 *meters* (9.8 feet) deep. Units are essential to reporting measurements correctly.

The two systems of units with which you are probably most familiar are the *English system* (foot, gallon, pound, etc.) and the *metric system* (meter, liter, kilogram, etc.). Although there has been an increase in the use of metric units in the United States in recent years, English units still are used commonly. For many years, scientists recorded measurements in metric units, but in 1960, the General Conference on Weights and Measures, the international authority on units, proposed a revised metric system for universal use by scientists. We will use both metric and revised metric (SI) units in this book.

Student Annotation: According to the U.S. Metric Association (USMA), the United States is "the only significant holdout" with regard to adoption of the metric system. The other countries that continue to use traditional units are Myanmar (formerly Burma) and Liberia.

Figure 1.7 (a) A burette is used to measure the volume of a liquid that has been added to a container. A reading is taken before and after the liquid is delivered, and the volume delivered is determined by subtracting the first reading from the second. (b) A volumetric pipette is used to deliver a precise amount of liquid. (c) A graduated cylinder is used to measure a volume of liquid. It is less precise than the volumetric flask. (d) A volumetric flask is used to prepare a precise volume of a solution for use in the laboratory.

Burette
(a)

Pipette
(b)

Graduated cylinder
(c)

Volumetric flask
(d)

SI Base Units

The revised metric system is called the ***International System of Units*** (abbreviated SI, from the French *Système Internationale d'Unités*). Table 1.1 lists the seven SI base units. All other units of measurement can be derived from these base units. The ***SI unit*** for *volume,* for instance, is derived by cubing (raising to the power 3) the SI base unit for *length.* The prefixes listed in Table 1.2 are used to denote decimal fractions and decimal multiples of SI units. The use of these prefixes enables scientists to tailor the magnitude of a unit to a particular application. For example, the meter (m) is appropriate for describing the dimensions of a classroom, but the kilometer (km), 1000 m, is more appropriate for describing the distance between two cities. Units that you will encounter frequently in the study of chemistry include those for mass, temperature, volume, and density.

Mass

Although the terms *mass* and *weight* often are used interchangeably, they do not mean the same thing. Strictly speaking, weight is the force exerted by an object or sample due to gravity. ***Mass*** is a measure of the amount of matter in an object or sample. Because gravity varies from location to location (gravity on the moon is only about one-sixth that on Earth), the weight of an object varies depending on where it is measured. The mass of an object remains the same regardless of where it is measured. The SI base unit of mass is the kilogram (kg), but in chemistry the smaller gram (g) often is more convenient and is more commonly used:

$$1 \text{ kg} = 1000 \text{ g} = 1 \times 10^3 \text{ g}$$

TABLE 1.1	Base SI Units	
Base quantity	**Name of unit**	**Symbol**
Length	meter	m
Mass	kilogram	kg
Time	second	s
Electric current	ampere	A
Temperature	kelvin	K
Amount of substance	mole	mol
Luminous intensity	candela	cd

TABLE 1.2		Prefixes Used with SI Units	
Prefix	**Symbol**	**Meaning**	**Example**
Tera-	T	1×10^{12} (1,000,000,000,000)	1 teragram (Tg) = 1×10^{12} g
Giga-	G	1×10^9 (1,000,000,000)	1 gigawatt (GW) = 1×10^9
Mega-	M	1×10^6 (1,000,000)	1 megahertz (MHz) = 1×10^6
Kilo-	k	1×10^3 (1,000)	1 kilometer (km) = 1×10^3 m
Deci-	d	1×10^{-1} (0.1)	1 deciliter (dL) = 1×10^{-1} L
Centi-	c	1×10^{-2} (0.01)	1 centimeter (cm) = 1×10^{-2} m
Milli-	m	1×10^{-3} (0.001)	1 millimeter (mm) = 1×10^{-3} m
Micro-	μ	1×10^{-6} (0.000001)	1 microliter (μL) = 1×10^{-6} L
Nano-	n	1×10^{-9} (0.000000001)	1 nanosecond (ns) = 1×10^{-9} s
Pico-	p	1×10^{-12} (0.000000000001)	1 picogram (pg) = 1×10^{-12} g

Occasionally, the most convenient and/or commonly used unit for a particular application is not an SI unit. One such example is the atomic mass unit. The **atomic mass unit (amu),** as the name suggests, is used to express the masses of atoms—and other objects of similar size. In terms of SI units, the amu is equal to $1.6605378 \times 10^{-24}$ g or $1.6605378 \times 10^{-27}$ kg. Another example is the **angstrom (Å),** a measure of length that is equal to 1×10^{-10} m.

Temperature

> **Student Annotation:** There is no such thing as a negative temperature on the Kelvin scale.

> **Student Annotation:** The theoretical basis of the Kelvin scale has to do with the behavior of gases. [▶▶ Chapter 11]

> **Student Annotation:** Depending on the precision required, the conversion from degrees Celsius to kelvins often is done simply by adding 273, rather than 273.15.

There are two temperature scales used in chemistry: the *Celsius* scale, and the *absolute* or *Kelvin* scale. Their units are the *degree Celsius* (°C) and the *kelvin* (K), respectively. The **Celsius** scale [named after Swedish physicist Ander Celsius (1701–1744)] was originally defined using the freezing point (0°C) and the boiling point (100°C) of pure water at sea level. As Table 1.1 shows, the SI base unit of temperature is the **kelvin.** Kelvin is also known as the *absolute* temperature scale because the lowest temperature theoretically possible is 0 K, a temperature referred to as "absolute zero." No *degree* sign (°) is used to represent a temperature on the Kelvin scale.

Units of the Celsius and Kelvin scales are equal in magnitude, so *a degree Celsius is equivalent to a kelvin.* Thus, if the temperature of an object increases by 5°C, it also increases by 5 K. Absolute zero on the Kelvin scale is equivalent to −273.15°C on the Celsius scale. We use the following equation to convert a temperature from units of degrees Celsius to kelvins:

Equation 1.1 $K = {}^\circ C + 273.15$

Worked Example 1.1 illustrates conversions between these two temperature scales.

Worked Example 1.1

Normal human body temperature can range over the course of the day from about 36°C in the early morning to about 37°C in the afternoon. Express these two temperatures and the range that they span using the Kelvin scale.

Strategy Use Equation 1.1 to convert temperatures from the Celsius scale to the Kelvin scale. Then convert the range of temperatures from degrees Celsius to kelvins, keeping in mind that 1°C is equivalent to 1 K.

Setup Equation 1.1 is already set up to convert the two temperatures from degrees Celsius to kelvins. No further manipulation of the equation is needed. The range in kelvins will be the same as the range in degrees Celsius.

Solution 36°C + 273 = 309 K, 37°C + 273 = 310 K, and the range of 1°C is equal to a range of 1 K.

> **Think About It**
> Check your math and remember that converting a temperature from degrees Celsius to kelvins is different from converting a *difference* in temperature from degrees Celsius to kelvins.

Practice Problem A Express the freezing point of water (0°C), the boiling point of water (100°C), and the range spanned by the two temperatures using the Kelvin scale.

Practice Problem B According to the website of the National Aeronautics and Space Administration (NASA), the average temperature of the universe is 2.7 K. Convert this temperature to degrees Celsius.

Outside of scientific circles, the Fahrenheit temperature scale is the one most used in the United States. Before the work of Daniel Gabriel Fahrenheit (German physicist, 1686–1736), there were numerous different, arbitrarily defined temperature scales, none of which gave consistent measurements. Accounts of exactly how Fahrenheit devised his temperature scale vary from source to source. In one account, in 1724, Fahrenheit labeled as 0° the lowest artificially attainable temperature at the time (the temperature of a mixture of ice, water, and a substance called *ammonium chloride*). Using a traditional scale consisting of 12 degrees, he labeled the temperature of a healthy human body as the twelfth degree. On this scale, the freezing point of water occurred at the fourth degree. For better resolution, each degree was further divided into eight smaller degrees. This convention makes the freezing point of water 32°F and normal body temperature 96°F. (Today we consider normal body temperature to be somewhat higher than 96°F.)

The boiling point of water on the Fahrenheit scale is 212°, meaning that there are 180 degrees (212°F–32°F) between the freezing and boiling points. This separation is considerably more degrees than the 100 between the freezing point and boiling point of water on the Celsius scale. Thus, the size of a degree on the Fahrenheit scale is only 100/180 or five-ninths of a degree on the Celsius scale. Equation 1.2 gives the relationship between temperatures on the Fahrenheit and Celsius scales.

$$\text{temperature in °F} = \frac{9°F}{5°C} \times (\text{temperature in °C}) + 32°F \qquad \textbf{Equation 1.2}$$

Worked Example 1.2 lets you practice converting from Celsius to Fahrenheit.

Worked Example 1.2

A body temperature above 39°C constitutes a high fever. Convert this temperature to the Fahrenheit scale.

Strategy We are given a temperature in degrees Celsius and are asked to convert it to degrees Fahrenheit.

Setup We use Equation 1.2:

$$\text{temperature in Fahrenheit} = \frac{9°F}{5°C} \times (\text{temperature in degrees Celsius}) + 32°F$$

Solution

$$\text{temperature in Fahrenheit} = \frac{9°F}{5°C} \times (39°C) + 32°F = 102°F$$

> **Think About It**
> Knowing that "normal" body temperature on the Fahrenheit scale is approximately 99°F (98.6°F is the number most often cited), 102°F seems like a reasonable answer.

Practice Problem A The average temperature at the summit of Mt. Everest ranges from −36°C during the coldest month (January) and −19°C during the warmest month (July). Convert these temperatures and the range they span to Fahrenheit.

Practice Problem B The average surface temperatures of planets in our solar system range from 867°F on Venus to −330°F on Neptune. Convert these temperatures and the range they span to Celsius.

Student Annotation: The average surface temperature of Pluto is −375°F, but Pluto is no longer classified as a planet.

Derived Units: Volume and Density

There are many quantities, such as volume and density, that require units not included in the base SI units. In these cases, we must combine base units to *derive* appropriate units.

The derived SI unit for volume, the meter cubed (m³), is a much larger volume than is usually convenient. The more commonly used metric unit, the *liter* (L), is derived by cubing the *decimeter* (one-tenth of a meter) and is therefore also referred to as the cubic decimeter (dm³). Another commonly used metric unit of volume is the *milliliter* (mL), which is derived by cubing the centimeter (1/100 of a meter). The milliliter is also referred to as the cubic centimeter (cm³). Figure 1.8 illustrates the relationship between the liter (or dm³) and the milliliter (or cm³).

Density is the ratio of mass to volume. A familiar demonstration of density is the attempt to mix water and oil. Oil floats on water because, in addition to not *mixing* with water, oil has a lower *density* than water. That is, given *equal volumes* of the two liquids, the oil will have a *smaller mass* than the water. Density is calculated using the following equation:

$$d = \frac{m}{V} \qquad \textbf{Equation 1.3}$$

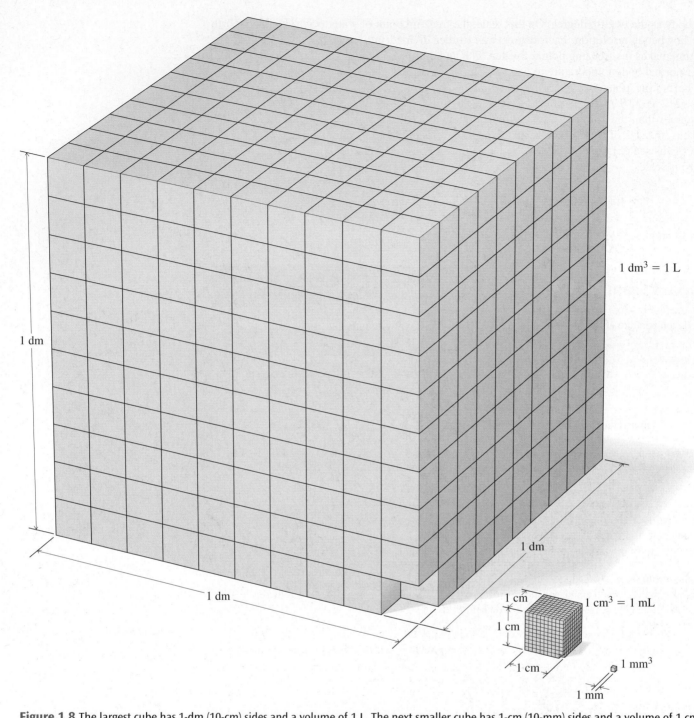

$1 \, dm^3 = 1 \, L$

$1 \, cm^3 = 1 \, mL$

$1 \, mm^3$

Figure 1.8 The largest cube has 1-dm (10-cm) sides and a volume of 1 L. The next smaller cube has 1-cm (10-mm) sides and a volume of 1 cm³ or 1 mL. The smallest cube has 1-mm sides and a volume of 1 mm³. Note that although there are 10 cm in a decimeter, there are 1000 cm³ in a cubic decimeter.

where *d, m,* and *V* denote density, mass, and volume, respectively. The SI-derived unit for density is the kilogram per cubic meter (kg/m³). This unit is too large for most common uses, however, so grams per cubic centimeter (g/cm³) and its equivalent, grams per milliliter (g/mL), are used to express the densities of most solids and liquids. Water, for example, has a density of 1.00 g/cm³ at 4°C. Because gas densities generally are very low, we typically express them in units of grams per liter (g/L):

$$1 \, g/cm^3 = 1 \, g/mL = 1000 \, kg/m^3$$

$$1 \, g/L = 0.001 \, g/mL$$

Worked Example 1.3 shows how to calculate density, and how to use density in the calculation of volume.

Worked Example 1.3

Ice cubes float in a glass of water because solid water is less dense than liquid water. (a) Calculate the density of ice given that, at 0°C, a cube that is 2.0 cm on each side has a mass of 7.36 g, and (b) determine the volume occupied by 23 g of ice at 0°C.

Strategy (a) Determine density by dividing mass by volume (Equation 1.3), and (b) use the calculated density to determine the volume occupied by the given mass.

Setup (a) We are given the mass of the ice cube, but we must calculate its volume from the dimensions given. The volume of the ice cube is $(2.0 \text{ cm})^3$, or 8.0 cm^3. (b) Rearranging Equation 1.3 to solve for volume gives $V = m/d$.

Solution

(a) $d = \dfrac{7.36 \text{ g}}{8.0 \text{ cm}^3} = 0.92 \text{ g/cm}^3$ or 0.92 g/mL

(b) $V = \dfrac{23 \text{ g}}{0.92 \text{ g/cm}^3} = 25 \text{ cm}^3$ or 25 mL

> **Think About It**
> For a sample with a density *less* than 1 g/cm³, the number of cubic centimeters should be *greater* than the number of grams. In this case, 25 (cm³) > 23 (g).

Practice Problem A Given that 20.0 mL of mercury has a mass of 272 g, calculate (a) the density of mercury and (b) the volume of 748 g of mercury.

Practice Problem B Calculate (a) the density of a solid substance if a cube measuring 2.33 cm on one side has a mass of 117 g and (b) the mass of a cube of the same substance measuring 7.41 cm on one side.

SECTION 1.4 REVIEW

Scientific Measurement

1.4.1 The coldest temperature ever recorded on Earth was −128.6°F (recorded at Vostok Station, Antarctica, on July 21, 1983). Express this temperature in degrees Celsius and in kelvins.

1.4.2 What is the density of an object that has a volume of 34.2 cm³ and a mass of 39.6 g?

1.4.3 A sample of liquid is heated from room temperature to just below the boiling point. The overall change in temperature is 75°C. Express this temperature change in kelvins.

1.4.4 Given that the density of gold is 19.3 g/cm³, calculate the volume (in cm³) of a gold nugget with a mass of 5.98 g.

1.5 UNCERTAINTY IN MEASUREMENT

Science makes use of two types of numbers: exact and inexact. *Exact* numbers include numbers with defined values, such as 2.54 in the definition 1 inch (in) = 2.54 cm, 1000 in the definition 1 kg = 1000 g, and 12 in the definition 1 dozen = 12 objects. (The number 1 in each of these definitions is also an exact number.) Exact numbers also include those that are obtained by counting. Numbers measured by any method other than counting are *inexact*.

Measured numbers are inexact because of the measuring devices that are used, the individuals who use them, or both. For example, a ruler that is poorly calibrated will result in measurements that are in error—no matter how carefully it is used. Another ruler may be calibrated properly but have insufficient resolution for the necessary measurement. Finally, whether or not an instrument is properly calibrated or has sufficient resolution, there are unavoidable differences in how different people see and interpret measurements.

Figure 1.9 The width we report for the memory card depends on which ruler we use to measure it.

Student Annotation: It is important not to imply greater certainty in a measured number than is realistic. For example, it would be inappropriate to report the width of the memory card in Figure 1.9 as 2.4500 cm, because this would imply an uncertainty of ±0.0001 cm.

Student Annotation: Appendix 1 reviews scientific notation.

Significant Figures

An inexact number must be reported in such a way as to indicate the uncertainty in its value. This is done using significant figures. **Significant figures** are the *meaningful digits* in a reported number. Consider the measurement of the memory card in Figure 1.9 using the ruler above it. The card's width is between 2 and 3 cm. We may record the width as 2.5 cm, but because there are no gradations between 2 and 3 cm on this ruler, we are *estimating* the second digit. Although we are certain about the 2 in 2.5, we are *not* certain about the 5. The last digit in a measured number is referred to as the *uncertain digit;* and the uncertainty associated with a measured number is generally considered to be ± 1 in the place of the last digit. Thus, when we report the width of the memory card to be 2.5 cm, we are implying that its width is 2.5 ± 0.1 cm—and that its actual width may be as low as 2.4 cm, or as high as 2.6 cm. Each of the digits in a measured number, including the uncertain digit, is a significant figure. The reported width of the memory card, 2.5 cm, contains *two* significant figures.

A ruler with millimeter gradations would enable us to be certain about the second digit in this measurement and to estimate a third digit. Now consider the measurement of the memory card using the ruler below it. We may record the width as 2.45 cm. Again, we estimate one digit beyond those we can read. The reported width of 2.45 cm contains three significant figures. Reporting the width as 2.45 cm implies that the width is 2.45 ± 0.01 cm.

The number of significant figures in any number can be determined using the following guidelines:

1. Any digit that is not zero is significant (112.1 has four significant figures).
2. Zeros located between nonzero digits are significant (305 has three significant figures, and 50.08 has four significant figures).
3. Zeros to the left of the first nonzero digit are not significant (0.0023 has two significant figures, and 0.000001 has one significant figure).
4. Zeros to the right of the last nonzero digit are significant if the number contains a decimal point (1.200 has four significant figures).
5. Zeros to the right of the last nonzero digit in a number that does not contain a decimal point may or may not be significant (100 may have one, two, or three significant figures—it is impossible to tell without additional information). To avoid ambiguity in such cases, it is best to express such numbers using scientific notation. If the intended number of significant figures is one, the number is written as 1×10^2; if the intended number of significant figures is two, the number is written as 1.0×10^2; and if the intended number of significant figures is three, the number is written as 1.00×10^2.

Worked Example 1.4 lets you practice determining the number of significant figures in a number.

Worked Example 1.4

Determine the number of significant figures in the following measurements: (a) 443 cm, (b) 15.03 g, (c) 0.0356 kg, (d) 3.000×10^{-7} L, (e) 50 mL, (f) 0.9550 m.

Strategy All nonzero digits are significant, so the goal will be to determine which of the zeros is significant.

Setup Zeros are significant if they appear between nonzero digits or if they appear after a nonzero digit in a number that contains a decimal point. Zeros may or may not be significant if they appear to the right of the last nonzero digit in a number that does not contain a decimal point.

Solution (a) 3; (b) 4; (c) 3; (d) 4; (e) 1 or 2, an ambiguous case; (f) 4.

> **Think About It**
> Be sure that you have identified zeros correctly as either significant or not significant. They are significant in (b) and (d); they are not significant in (c); it is not possible to tell in (e); and the number in (f) contains one zero that is significant, and one that is not.

Practice Problem A Determine the number of significant figures in the following measurements: (a) 1129 m, (b) 0.0003 kg, (c) 1.094 cm, (d) 3.5×10^{12} atoms, (e) 150 mL, (f) 9.550 km.

Practice Problem B Using scientific notation, express the number *one million* to (a) two significant figures, (b) four significant figures, (c) seven significant figures; and using decimal notation, express the number *one tenth* to (d) three significant figures, (e) five significant figures, and (f) one significant figure.

Calculations with Measured Numbers

Because we often use one or more measured numbers to calculate a desired result, a second set of guidelines specifies how to handle significant figures in calculations.

1. In addition and subtraction, the answer cannot have more digits to the right of the decimal point than any of the original numbers. For example:

$$
\begin{array}{rl}
102.50 & \longleftarrow \text{two digits after the decimal point} \\
\underline{+\ 0.231} & \longleftarrow \text{three digits after the decimal point} \\
102.731 & \longleftarrow \text{round to } 102.73
\end{array}
$$

$$
\begin{array}{rl}
143.29 & \longleftarrow \text{two digits after the decimal point} \\
\underline{-20.1} & \longleftarrow \text{one digit after the decimal point} \\
123.19 & \longleftarrow \text{round to } 123.2
\end{array}
$$

The rounding procedure works as follows. Suppose we want to round 102.13 and 54.86 each to one digit to the right of the decimal point. To begin, we look at the digit(s) that will be dropped. If the leftmost digit to be dropped is less than 5, as in 102.13, we *round down* (to 102.1), meaning that we simply drop the digit(s). If the leftmost digit to be dropped is equal to or greater than 5, as in 54.86, we *round up* (to 54.9), meaning that we add 1 to the preceding digit.

2. In multiplication and division, the number of significant figures in the final product or quotient is determined by the original number that has the smallest number of significant figures. The following examples illustrate this rule:

$1.4 \times 8.011 = 11.2154$ $\longleftarrow$ round to 11
(limited by 1.4 to *two* significant figures)

$11.57/305.88 = 0.037825290964$ $\longleftarrow$ round to 0.03783
(limited by 11.57 to *four* significant figures)

3. *Exact numbers* can be considered to have an infinite number of significant figures and do not limit the number of significant figures in a calculated result. For example, a penny minted after 1982 has a mass of 2.5 g. If we have three such pennies, the total mass is

$$3 \times 2.5 \text{ g} = 7.5 \text{ g}$$

Student Annotation: Note that it is the number of pennies (3), not the mass, that is an exact number.

The answer should *not* be rounded to one significant figure because 3 is an exact number.

4. In calculations with multiple steps, rounding the result of each step can result in "rounding error." Consider the following two-step calculation:

First step: $A \times B = C$

Second step: $C \times D = E$

Suppose that $A = 3.66$, $B = 8.45$, and $D = 2.11$. The value of E depends on whether we round off C prior to using it in the second step of the calculation.

Method 1	Method 2
$C = 3.66 \times 8.45 = 30.9$	$C = 3.66 \times 8.45 = 30.93$
$E = 30.9 \times 2.11 = 65.2$	$E = 30.93 \times 2.11 = 65.3$

In general, it is best to retain at least one extra digit until the end of a multistep calculation, as shown by method 2, to minimize rounding error.

Worked Examples 1.5 and 1.6 show how significant figures are handled in arithmetic operations.

Worked Example 1.5

Perform the following arithmetic operations and report the result to the proper number of significant figures: (a) 317.5 mL + 0.675 mL, (b) 47.80 L − 2.075 L, (c) 13.5 g ÷ 45.18 L, (d) 6.25 cm × 1.175 cm, (e) 5.46×10^2 g + 4.991×10^3 g.

Strategy Apply the rules for significant figures in calculations, and round each answer to the appropriate number of digits.

Setup (a) The answer will contain one digit to the right of the decimal point to match 317.5, which has the fewest digits to the right of the decimal point. (b) The answer will contain two digits to the right of the decimal point to match 47.80. (c) The answer will contain three significant figures to match 13.5, which has the fewest number of significant figures in the calculation. (d) The answer will contain three significant figures to match 6.25. (e) To add numbers expressed in scientific notation, first write both numbers to the same power of 10. That is, $4.991 \times 10^3 = 49.91 \times 10^2$, so the answer will contain two digits to the right of the decimal point (when multiplied by 10^2) to match both 5.46 and 49.91.

Solution

(a) 317.5 mL
$\underline{+\ 0.675\ \text{mL}}$
318.175 mL   ⟵——— round to 318.2 mL

(b) 47.80 L
$\underline{-\ 2.075\ \text{L}}$
45.725 L   ⟵——— round to 45.73 L

(c) $\dfrac{13.5\ \text{g}}{45.18\ \text{L}}$ = 0.298804781 g/L   ⟵——— round to 0.299 g/L

(d) 6.25 cm × 1.175 cm = 7.34375 cm² ⟵——— round to 7.34 cm²

(e) 5.46×10^2 g
$\underline{+\ 49.91 \times 10^2\ \text{g}}$
55.37×10^2 g = 5.537×10^3 g

Think About It
It may look as though the rule of addition has been violated in part (e) because the final answer (5.537×10^3 g) has three places past the decimal point, not two. However, the rule was applied to get the answer 55.37×10^2 g, which has *four* significant figures. Changing the answer to correct scientific notation doesn't change the number of significant figures, but in this case it changes the number of places past the decimal point.

Practice Problem A Perform the following arithmetic operations, and report the result to the proper number of significant figures: (a) 105.5 L + 10.65 L, (b) 81.058 m − 0.35 m, (c) 3.801×10^{21} atoms + 1.228×10^{19} atoms, (d) 1.255 dm × 25 dm, (e) 139 g ÷ 275.55 mL.

Practice Problem B Perform the following arithmetic operations, and report the result to the proper number of significant figures: (a) 1.0267 cm × 2.508 cm × 12.599 cm, (b) 15.0 kg ÷ 0.036 m³, (c) 1.113×10^{10} kg − 1.050×10^9 kg, (d) 25.75 mL + 15.00 mL, (e) 46 cm³ + 180.5 cm³.

Worked Example 1.6

An empty container with a volume of 9.850×10^2 cm³ is weighed and found to have a mass of 124.6 g. The container is filled with a gas and reweighed. The mass of the container and the gas is 126.5 g. Determine the density of the gas to the appropriate number of significant figures.

Strategy This problem requires two steps: subtraction to determine the mass of the gas, and division to determine its density. Apply the corresponding rule regarding significant figures to each step.

Setup In the subtraction of the container mass from the combined mass of the container and the gas, the result can have only one place past the decimal point: 126.5 g – 124.6 g = 1.9 g. Thus, in the division of the mass of the gas by the volume of the container, the result can have only two significant figures.

Solution

$$\text{mass of gas} = \begin{array}{r} 126.5 \text{ g} \\ -124.6 \text{ g} \\ \hline 1.9 \text{ g} \end{array} \quad \longleftarrow \text{one place past the decimal point (two significant figures)}$$

$$\text{density} = \frac{1.9 \text{ g}}{9.850 \times 10^2 \text{ cm}^3} = 0.00193 \text{ g/cm}^3 \quad \longleftarrow \text{round to } 0.0019 \text{ g/cm}^3$$

The density of the gas is 1.9×10^{-3} g/cm³.

> **Think About It**
> In this case, although each of the three numbers we started with has *four* significant figures, the solution has only *two* significant figures.

Practice Problem A An empty container with a volume of 150.0 cm³ is weighed and found to have a mass of 72.5 g. The container is filled with a liquid and reweighed. The mass of the container and the liquid is 194.3 g. Determine the density of the liquid to the appropriate number of significant figures.

Practice Problem B Another empty container with an unknown volume is weighed and found to have a mass of 81.2 g. The container is then filled with a liquid with a density of 1.015 g/cm³ and reweighed. The mass of the container and the liquid is 177.9 g. Determine the volume of the container to the appropriate number of significant figures.

(a)

(b)

(c)

Figure 1.10 The distribution of papers shows the difference between accuracy and precision. (a) Good accuracy and good precision. (b) Poor accuracy but good precision. (c) Poor accuracy and poor precision.

Accuracy and Precision

Accuracy and precision are two ways to gauge the quality of a set of measured numbers. Although the difference between the two terms may be subtle, it is important. *Accuracy* tells us how close a measurement is to the *true* value. *Precision* tells us how close a series of replicate measurements (measurements of the same thing) are to one another (Figure 1.10).

Suppose that three students are asked to determine the mass of an aspirin tablet. Each student weighs the aspirin tablet three times. The results (in grams) are tabulated here.

	Student A	Student B	Student C
	0.335	0.357	0.369
	0.331	0.375	0.373
	0.333	0.338	0.371
Average value	0.333	0.357	0.371

The true mass of the tablet is 0.370 g. Student A's results are more precise than those of student B, but neither set of results is very accurate. Student C's results are both precise (very small deviation of individual masses from the average mass) and accurate (average value very close to the true value). Figure 1.11 shows all three students' results in relation to the true mass of the tablet. Highly accurate measurements are usually precise, as well, although highly precise measurements do not necessarily guarantee accurate results. For example, an improperly calibrated meterstick or a faulty balance may give precise readings that are significantly different from the correct value.

Student Annotation: Even properly calibrated measuring devices can give varied results. Replicate measurements, such as those represented in the table, are used to determine the variability in the value of a measured quantity.

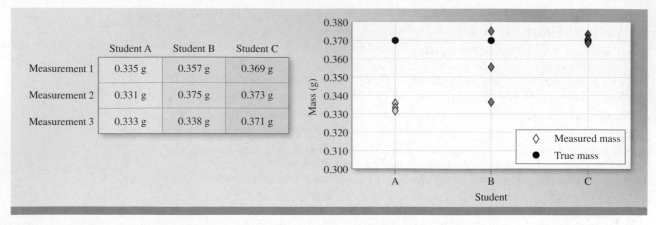

	Student A	Student B	Student C
Measurement 1	0.335 g	0.357 g	0.369 g
Measurement 2	0.331 g	0.375 g	0.373 g
Measurement 3	0.333 g	0.338 g	0.371 g

Figure 1.11 Graphing the students' data illustrates the difference between precision and accuracy. Student A's results are precise (values are close to one another) but not accurate because the average value is far from the true value. Student B's results are neither precise nor accurate. Student C's results are both precise and accurate.

SECTION 1.5 REVIEW

Uncertainty in Measurement

1.5.1   To the proper number of significant figures, what volume of water does the graduated cylinder contain? Note: The volume of water in a graduated cylinder should be read at the *bottom* of the meniscus (the curved surface at the top).

1.5.2   The true dependence of *y* on *x* is represented by the line. Three students measured *y* as a function of *x* and plotted their data on the graph. Which set of data (red, green, or purple) has the best accuracy? Which has the best precision?

1.5.3   Specify the number of significant figures in each of the following numbers and determine the result of the following calculation to the correct number of significant figures.

$$63.102 \times 10.18 =$$

1.5.4   Specify the number of significant figures in each of the following numbers and determine the result of the following calculation to the correct number of significant figures.

$$3.115 + 0.2281 + 712.5 + 45 =$$

1.5.5   What is the result of the following calculation to the correct number of significant figures?

$$153.1 \div 5.3 =$$

1.5.6   What is the result of the following calculation to the correct number of significant figures?

$$(6.266 - 6.261) \div 522.0 =$$

Thinking Outside the Box

Tips for Success in Chemistry Class

Success in a chemistry class depends largely on problem-solving ability. The Worked Examples throughout the text are designed to help you develop problem-solving skills. Each is divided into four steps: Strategy, Setup, Solution, and Think About It.

Strategy: Read the problem carefully and determine what is being asked and what information is provided. The Strategy step is where you should think about what skills are required and lay out a plan for solving the problem. Give some thought to what you expect the result to be. If you are asked to determine the number of atoms in a sample of matter, for example, you should expect the answer to be a whole number. Determine what, if any, units should be associated with the result. When possible, make a ballpark estimate of the magnitude of the correct result, and make a note of your estimate.

Setup: Next, gather the information necessary to solve the problem. Some of the information will have been given in the problem itself. Other information, such as equations, constants, and tabulated data (including atomic masses) should also be brought together in this step. Write down and label clearly all of the information you will use to solve the problem. Be sure to write appropriate units with each piece of information.

Solution: Using the necessary equations, constants, and other information, calculate the answer to the problem. Pay particular attention to the units associated with each number, tracking and canceling units carefully throughout the calculation. In the event that multiple calculations are required, label any intermediate results, but don't round to the necessary number of significant figures until the final calculation. Always carry at least one extra significant figure in intermediate calculations. Make sure that the final answer has the correct number of significant figures.

Think About It: Consider your calculated result and ask yourself whether or not it makes sense. Compare the units and the magnitude of your result with your ballpark estimate from the Strategy step. If your result does not have the appropriate units, or if its magnitude or sign is not reasonable, check your solution for possible errors. A very important part of problem solving is being able to judge whether the answer is reasonable. It is relatively easy to spot a wrong sign or incorrect units, but you should also develop a sense of *magnitude* and be able to tell when an answer is either way too big or way too small. For example, if a problem asks you to determine the length of a sheet of paper in millimeters and you calculate a number that is less than 1, you should know that it cannot be correct.

Each Worked Example is followed by two Practice Problems. Practice Problem A typically is very similar to the Worked Example and can be solved using the same strategy. Practice Problem B generally tests the same skills, but requires an approach slightly different from the one used to solve the preceding Worked Example and Practice Problem A.

Regular use of the Worked Examples and Practice Problems in this text can help you develop an effective set of problem-solving skills. They can also help you assess whether you are ready to move on to the next new concepts. If you struggle with the Practice Problems, then you probably need to review the corresponding Worked Example and the concepts that led up to it.

A final note: Practice Problems B are designed to provide you with opportunities to formulate problem-solving strategies on your own. This is an important step in building the skills and the confidence necessary to solve unfamiliar problems, such as you may encounter on quizzes or tests. To ensure that your performance in this course is the best it can be, you should solve all of the Practice Problems, both A and B, in each chapter that you study.

1.6   USING UNITS AND SOLVING PROBLEMS

Solving problems correctly in chemistry requires careful manipulation of both numbers and units. Paying attention to the units will benefit you greatly as you proceed through this, or any other, chemistry course.

Conversion Factors

A *conversion factor* is a fraction in which the same quantity is expressed one way in the numerator and another way in the denominator. By definition, for example, 1 in = 2.54 cm. We can derive a conversion factor from this equality by writing it as the following fraction:

$$\frac{1 \text{ in}}{2.54 \text{ cm}}$$

Because the numerator and denominator express the same length, this fraction is equal to 1; as a result, we can equally well write the conversion factor as

$$\frac{2.54 \text{ cm}}{1 \text{ in}}$$

Because both forms of this conversion factor are equal to 1, we can multiply a quantity by either form without changing the value of that quantity. This is useful for changing the units in which a given quantity is expressed—something you will do often throughout this text. For instance, if we need to convert a length from inches to centimeters, we multiply the length in inches by the appropriate conversion factor.

$$12.00 \text{ in} \times \frac{2.54 \text{ cm}}{1 \text{ in}} = 30.48 \text{ cm}$$

We chose the form of the conversion factor that cancels the unit inches and produces the desired unit, centimeters. The result contains four significant figures because exact numbers, such as those obtained from definitions, do not limit the number of significant figures in the result of a calculation. Thus, the number of significant figures in the answer to this calculation is based on the number 12.00, not the number 2.54.

Dimensional Analysis—Tracking Units

The use of conversion factors in problem solving is called *dimensional analysis* or the *factor-label method*. Many problems require the use of more than one conversion factor. The conversion of 12.00 in to meters, for example, takes two steps: one to convert inches to centimeters, which we have already demonstrated; and one to convert centimeters to meters. The additional conversion factor required is derived from the equality

$$1 \text{ m} = 100 \text{ cm}$$

and is expressed as either

$$\frac{100 \text{ cm}}{1 \text{ m}} \quad \text{or} \quad \frac{1 \text{ m}}{100 \text{ cm}}$$

We choose the conversion factor that will introduce the unit meter and cancel the unit centimeter (i.e., the one on the right). We can set up a problem of this type as the following series of unit conversions so that it is unnecessary to calculate an intermediate answer at each step:

$$12.00 \text{ in} \times \frac{2.54 \text{ cm}}{1 \text{ in}} \times \frac{1 \text{ m}}{100 \text{ cm}} = 0.3048 \text{ m}$$

Student Annotation: If we had accidentally used the reciprocal of the conversion from centimeters to meters, the result would have been 3048 cm²/m, which would make no sense—both because the units are nonsensical and because the numerical result is not reasonable. You know that 12 inches is a foot and that a foot is not equal to *thousands* of meters!

Careful tracking of units and their cancellation can be a valuable tool in checking your work. If we had accidentally used the *reciprocal* of one of the conversion factors, the resulting units would have been something other than meters. Unexpected or nonsensical units can reveal an error in your problem-solving strategy.

Worked Example 1.7 shows how to derive conversion factors and use them to do unit conversions.

Worked Example 1.7

The Food and Drug Administration (FDA) recommends that dietary sodium intake be no more than 2400 mg per day. What is this mass in pounds (lb), if 1 lb = 453.6 g?

Strategy This problem requires a two-step dimensional analysis, because we must convert milligrams to grams and then grams to pounds. Assume the number 2400 has four significant figures.

Setup The necessary conversion factors are derived from the equalities 1 g = 1000 mg and 1 lb = 453.6 g.

$$\frac{1 \text{ g}}{1000 \text{ mg}} \quad \text{or} \quad \frac{1000 \text{ mg}}{1 \text{ g}} \quad \text{and} \quad \frac{1 \text{ lb}}{453.6 \text{ g}} \quad \text{or} \quad \frac{453.6 \text{ g}}{1 \text{ lb}}$$

From each pair of conversion factors, we select the one that will result in the proper unit cancellation.

Solution

$$2400 \text{ mg} \times \frac{1 \text{ g}}{1000 \text{ mg}} \times \frac{1 \text{ lb}}{453.6 \text{ g}} = 0.005291 \text{ lb}$$

Think About It
Make sure that the magnitude of the result is reasonable and that the units have canceled properly. If we had mistakenly multiplied by 1000 and 453.6 instead of dividing by them, the result (2400 mg × 1000 mg/g × 453.6 g/lb = 1.089×10^9 mg^2/lb) would be unreasonably large—and the units would not have canceled properly.

Student Annotation: Because pounds are much larger than milligrams, a given mass will be a much smaller number of pounds than of milligrams.

Practice Problem A The American Heart Association recommends that healthy adults limit dietary cholesterol to no more than 300 mg per day. Convert this mass of cholesterol to ounces (1 oz = 28.3459 g). Assume 300 mg has just one significant figure.

Practice Problem B A gold nugget has a mass of 0.9347 oz. What is its mass in milligrams?

Worked Example 1.8 shows how to handle problems in which conversion factors are squared or cubed in dimensional analysis.

Worked Example 1.8

An average adult has 5.2 L of blood. What is the volume of blood in cubic meters?

Strategy There are several ways to solve a problem such as this. One way is to convert liters to cubic centimeters and then cubic centimeters to cubic meters.

Setup 1 L = 1000 cm^3 and 1 cm = 1×10^{-2} m. When a unit is raised to a power, the corresponding conversion factor must also be raised to that power in order for the units to cancel appropriately.

Solution

$$5.2 \text{ L} \times \frac{1000 \text{ cm}^3}{1 \text{ L}} \times \left(\frac{1 \times 10^{-2} \text{ m}}{1 \text{ cm}}\right)^3 = 5.2 \times 10^{-3} \text{ m}^3$$

Think About It
Based on the preceding conversion factors, 1 L = 1×10^{-3} m^3. Therefore, 5 L of blood would be equal to 5×10^{-3} m^3, which is close to the calculated answer.

Practice Problem A The density of silver is 10.5 g/cm^3. What is its density in kg/m^3?

Practice Problem B The density of mercury is 13.6 g/cm^3. What is its density in pounds per cubic foot (lb/ft^3)? (1 lb = 453.6 g, 1 in = 2.54 cm)

SECTION 1.6 REVIEW

Using Units and Solving Problems

1.6.1   Convert 43.1 cm^3 to liters.

1.6.2   What is the volume of a 5.75-g object that has a density of 3.97 g/cm^3?

1.6.3   The density of lithium metal is 535 kg/m^3. What is this density in g/cm^3?

1.6.4   How many cubic centimeters are there in a cubic meter?

Learning Outcomes

- Identify the key components of the scientific method.
- Differentiate between states of matter.
- Determine whether a mixture is heterogeneous or homogeneous.
- Categorize properties of matter as being quantitative or qualitative; physical or chemical; extensive or intensive.
- Recall the common base SI units of measurement and their associated symbols.
- Utilize SI unit prefixes.

- Perform conversions between different temperature scales.
- Apply derived units, such as volume and density, to perform calculations.
- Apply significant figure rules in calculations.
- Distinguish between accuracy and precision.
- Utilize conversion factors to conduct unit conversions.
- Apply dimensional analysis toward solving problems with multiple steps or conversions.

Chapter Summary

SECTION 1.1

- *Chemistry* is the study of *matter* and the changes matter undergoes.
- Chemists do research using a set of guidelines and practices known as the *scientific method,* in which observations give rise to *laws,* data give rise to *hypotheses,* hypotheses are tested with experiments, and successful hypotheses give rise to *theories,* which are further tested by experiment.

SECTION 1.2

- All matter exists either as a *substance* or as a mixture of substances. A *mixture* may be *homogeneous* (uniform composition throughout) or *heterogeneous.* Mixtures may be separated using *physical processes.*

SECTION 1.3

- Substances are identified by their *quantitative* (involving numbers) and *qualitative* (not involving numbers) properties.

- *Physical properties* are those that can be determined without changing the identity of the matter in question. A *physical change* is one in which the identity of the matter involved does not change.
- *Chemical properties* are determined only as the result of a *chemical change* or *chemical process,* in which the original substance is converted to a different substance. Physical and chemical properties may be *extensive* (dependent on the amount of matter) or *intensive* (independent of the amount of matter).

SECTION 1.4

- Scientists use a system of units referred to as the *International System of Units,* or *SI units.*
- There are seven *base* SI units including the kilogram (for *mass*) and the *kelvin* (for temperature). SI units for such quantities as volume and *density* are derived from the base units. Some commonly used units are not SI units, such as the degree *Celsius,* the *atomic mass unit (amu)* and the *angstrom (Å).*

SECTION 1.5

- Measured numbers are *inexact*. Numbers that are obtained by counting or that are part of a definition are *exact* numbers.
- *Significant figures* are used to specify the uncertainty in a measured number or in a number calculated using measured numbers. Significant figures must be carried through calculations so that the implied uncertainty in the final answer is reasonable.
- *Accuracy* refers to how close measured numbers are to a *true* value. *Precision* refers to how close measured numbers are to one another.

SECTION 1.6

- A *conversion factor* is a fraction in which the numerator and denominator are the same quantity expressed in different units. Multiplying by a conversion factor is *unit conversion*.
- *Dimensional analysis* is a series of unit conversions used in the solution of a multistep problem.

Key Words

Accuracy, 17
Angstrom (Å), 10
Atomic mass unit (amu), 10
Celsius, 10
Chemical change, 7
Chemical process, 7
Chemical property, 7
Chemistry, 3
Conversion factor, 20

Density, 11
Dimensional analysis, 20
Extensive property, 7
Heterogeneous mixture, 5
Homogeneous mixture, 5
Hypothesis, 3
Intensive property, 8
International System of
    Units, 9

Kelvin, 10
Law, 3
Mass, 9
Matter, 3
Mixture, 5
Physical change, 7
Physical process, 6
Physical property, 7
Precision, 17

Qualitative, 7
Quantitative, 7
Scientific method, 3
SI unit, 9
Significant figures, 14
Substance, 5
Theory, 3

Key Equations

1.1 $K = °C + 273.15$

1.2   temperature in $°F = \dfrac{9°F}{5°C} \times$ (temperature in $°C$) $+ 32°F$

1.3 $d = \dfrac{m}{V}$

Questions and Problems

SECTION 1.1:   THE STUDY OF CHEMISTRY

Review Questions

1.1   Define the terms *chemistry* and *matter*.
1.2   Explain what is meant by the scientific method.
1.3   What is the difference between a hypothesis and a theory?

Problems

1.4   Classify each of the following statements as a hypothesis, law, or theory. (a) Beethoven's contribution to music would have been much greater if he had married. (b) An autumn leaf gravitates toward the ground because there is an attractive force between the leaf and Earth. (c) All matter is composed of very small particles.

1.5   Classify each of the following statements as a hypothesis, law, or theory. (a) The force acting on an object is equal to its mass times its acceleration. (b) The universe as we know it started with a big bang. (c) There are many civilizations more advanced than ours on other planets.

SECTION 1.2:   CLASSIFICATION OF MATTER

Review Questions

1.6   Give an example for each of the following terms: (a) matter, (b) substance, (c) mixture.
1.7   Give an example of a homogeneous mixture and an example of a heterogeneous mixture.

Problems

1.8   Identify each of the diagrams shown here as a solid, liquid, gas, or mixture of two substances.

(a)   (b)   (c)   (d)

1.9   Classify each of the following as a pure substance, a homogeneous mixture, or a heterogeneous mixture: (a) seawater, (b) helium gas, (c) salt, (d) diet cola, (e) a milkshake, (f) bottled water, (g) concrete, (h) 24K gold, (i) liquid nitrogen.

SECTION 1.3:   THE PROPERTIES OF MATTER

Review Questions

1.10   What is the difference between a qualitative property and a quantitative property?

1.11   Using examples, explain the difference between a physical property and a chemical property.

1.12   How does an intensive property differ from an extensive property?

1.13   Determine which of the following properties are intensive and which are extensive: (a) length, (b) volume, (c) temperature, (d) mass.

Problems

1.14   Determine whether the following statements describe chemical or physical properties: (a) Oxygen gas supports combustion. (b) Ingredients in antacids reduce acid reflux. (c) Water boils above 100°C in a pressure cooker. (d) Carbon dioxide is denser than air. (e) Uranium combines with fluorine to form a gas.

1.15   Classify the following as qualitative or quantitative statements, giving your reasons. (a) The sun is approximately 93 million miles from Earth. (b) Leonardo da Vinci was a better painter than Michelangelo. (c) Ice is less dense than water. (d) Butter tastes better than margarine. (e) A stitch in time saves nine.

1.16   Determine whether each of the following describes a physical change or a chemical change: (a) A soda loses its fizz and goes flat. (b) A bruise develops on a football player's arm and gradually changes color. (c) A pile of leaves is burned. (d) Frost forms on a windshield after a cold night. (e) Wet clothes are hung out to dry in the sun.

1.17   Determine whether each of the following describes a physical change or a chemical change: (a) The helium gas inside a balloon tends to leak out after a few hours. (b) A flashlight beam slowly gets dimmer and finally goes out. (c) Frozen orange juice is reconstituted by adding water to it. (d) The growth of plants depends on the sun's energy in a process called photosynthesis. (e) A spoonful of sugar dissolves in a cup of coffee.

SECTION 1.4:   SCIENTIFIC MEASUREMENT

Review Questions

1.18   Name the SI base units that are important in chemistry, and give the SI units for expressing the following: (a) length, (b) volume, (c) mass, (d) time, (e) temperature.

1.19   Write the numbers represented by the following prefixes: (a) mega-, (b) kilo-, (c) deci-, (d) centi-, (e) milli-, (f) micro-, (g) nano-, (h) pico-.

1.20   What units do chemists normally use for the density of liquids and solids? For the density of gas? Explain the differences.

1.21   What is the difference between mass and weight? If a person weighs 168 lb on Earth, about how much would the person weigh on the moon?

1.22   Describe the three temperature scales used in everyday life and in the laboratory: the Fahrenheit, Celsius, and Kelvin scales.

Problems

1.23   Bromine is a reddish-brown liquid. Calculate its density (in g/mL) if 586 g of the substance occupies 188 mL.

1.24   The density of ethanol, a colorless liquid that is commonly known as grain alcohol, is 0.798 g/mL. Calculate the mass of 17.4 mL of the liquid.

1.25   Convert the following temperatures to degrees Celsius or Fahrenheit: (a) 95°F, the temperature on a hot summer day; (b) 12°F, the temperature on a cold winter day; (c) a 103°F fever; (d) a furnace operating at 1852°F; (e) −273.15°C (theoretically the lowest attainable temperature).

1.26   (a) Normally the human body can endure a temperature of 105°F for only short periods of time without permanent damage to the brain and other vital organs. What is this temperature in degrees Celsius? (b) Ethylene glycol is a liquid that is used as an antifreeze in car radiators. It freezes at −11.5°C. Calculate its freezing temperature in degrees Fahrenheit. (c) The temperature on the surface of the sun is about 6300°C. What is this temperature in degrees Fahrenheit?

1.27   The density of water at 40°C is 0.992 g/mL. What is the volume of 2.50 g of water at this temperature?

1.28   The density of platinum is 21.5 g/cm^3 at 25°C. What is the volume of 87.6 g of Pt at this temperature?

1.29   Convert the following temperatures to kelvins: (a) 113°C, the melting point of sulfur; (b) 37°C, the normal body temperature; (c) 357°C, the boiling point of mercury.

1.30   Convert the following temperatures to degrees Celsius: (a) 77 K, the boiling point of liquid nitrogen; (b) 4.2 K, the boiling point of liquid helium; (c) 601 K, the melting point of lead.

1.31 A 37.2-g sample of lead pellets at 20°C is mixed with a 62.7-g sample of lead pellets at the same temperature. What are the final mass, temperature, and density of the combined sample? (The density of lead at 20°C is 11.35 g/cm³.)

1.32 A student pours 44.3 g of water at 10°C into a beaker containing 115.2 g of water at 10°C. What are the final mass, temperature, and density of the combined water? (The density of water at 10°C is 1.00 g/mL.)

SECTION 1.5:   UNCERTAINTY IN MEASUREMENT

Review Questions

1.33 Indicate which of the following numbers is an exact number: (a) 50,247 tickets were sold at a sporting event; (b) 750 mL of water was used to make a birthday cake; (c) 10 eggs were used to make a breakfast; (d) 0.41 g of oxygen was inhaled in each breath; (e) Earth orbits the sun every 365.24 days.

1.34 Define *significant figure*. Discuss the importance of using the proper number of significant figures in measurements and calculations.

1.35 Distinguish between the terms *accuracy* and *precision*. In general, explain why a precise measurement does not always guarantee an accurate result.

Problems

1.36 Express the following numbers in scientific notation: (a) 0.000000027, (b) 356, (c) 47,764, (d) 0.096.

1.37 Express the following numbers as decimals: (a) 1.52×10^{-2}, (b) 7.78×10^{-8}, (c) 3.29×10^{-6}, (d) 8.41×10^{-1}.

1.38 Express the answers to the following calculations in scientific notation:
(a) $145.75 + (2.3 \times 10^{-1})$
(b) $79,500 \div (2.5 \times 10^{2})$
(c) $(7.0 \times 10^{-3}) - (8.0 \times 10^{-4})$
(d) $(1.0 \times 10^{4}) \times (9.9 \times 10^{6})$

1.39 Express the answers to the following calculations in scientific notation:
(a) $0.0095 + (8.5 \times 10^{-3})$
(b) $653 \div (5.75 \times 10^{-8})$
(c) $850,000 - (9.0 \times 10^{5})$
(d) $(3.6 \times 10^{-4}) \times (3.6 \times 10^{6})$

1.40 Report the quantity being measured to the appropriate number of significant figures.

(a) Volume of liquid   (b) Length of box

1.41 Report each temperature to the appropriate number of significant figures.

1.42 Determine the number of significant figures in each of the following measurements: (a) 4867 mi, (b) 56 mL, (c) 60,104 tons, (d) 2900 g, (e) 40.2 g/cm³, (f) 0.0000003 cm, (g) 0.7 min, (h) 46 amu.

1.43 Determine the number of significant figures in each of the following measurements: (a) 0.006 L, (b) 0.0605 dm, (c) 60.5 mg, (d) 605.5 cm², (e) 9.60×10^{3} g, (f) 6 kg, (g) 60 m, (h) 1.42 Å.

1.44 Carry out the following operations as if they were calculations of experimental results, and express each answer in the correct units with the correct number of significant figures:
(a) 5.6792 m + 0.6 m + 4.33 m
(b) 3.70 g − 2.9133 g
(c) 4.51 cm × 3.6666 cm

1.45 Carry out the following operations as if they were calculations of experimental results, and express each answer in the correct units with the correct number of significant figures:
(a) 7.310 km ÷ 5.70 km
(b) $(3.26 \times 10^{-3}$ mg$) - (7.88 \times 10^{-5}$ mg$)$
(c) $(4.02 \times 10^{6}$ dm$) + (7.74 \times 10^{7}$ dm$)$

1.46 Three students (A, B, and C) are asked to determine the volume of a sample of water. Each student measures the volume three times with a graduated cylinder. The results in milliliters are: A (87.1, 88.2, 87.6); B (86.9, 87.1, 87.2); C (87.6, 87.8, 87.9). The true volume is 87.0 mL. Comment on the precision and the accuracy of each student's results.

1.47 Three apprentice carpenters (X, Y, and Z) are assigned the task of measuring the width of a doorway. Each one makes three measurements. The results in inches are X (31.5, 31.6, 31.4); Y (32.8, 32.3, 32.7); Z (31.9, 32.2, 32.1). The true width is 32.0 in. Comment on the precision and the accuracy of each carpenter's measurements.

1.48   The density of the metal bar shown is 7.89 g/cm³. Determine its mass to the appropriate number of significant figures.

1.49   The following shows an experiment used to determine the density of a gas. The evacuated bulb has a volume of 111.5 mL. It was weighed, filled with the gas, and weighed again. Determine the density of the gas to the appropriate number of significant figures.

SECTION 1.6:   USING UNITS AND SOLVING PROBLEMS

Problems

1.50   Carry out the following conversions: (a) 22.6 m to decimeters, (b) 25.4 mg to kilograms, (c) 556 mL to liters, (d) 10.6 kg/m³ to g/cm³.

1.51   Carry out the following conversions: (a) 242 lb to milligrams, (b) 68.3 cm³ to cubic meters, (c) 7.2 m³ to liters, (d) 28.3 µg to pounds.

1.52   Carry out the following conversions: (a) 242 amu to grams, (b) 87 amu to kilograms, (c) 2.21 Å to meters, (d) 1.73 Å to nanometers. [See page 10 for conversion factors for atomic mass units (amu) and angstroms (Å).]

1.53   Carry out the following conversions: (a) 1.1×10^{-22} g to atomic mass units, (b) 1.08×10^{-29} kg to atomic mass units, (c) 8.3×10^{-9} m to angstroms, (d) 132 pm to angstroms. [See page 10 for conversion factors for atomic mass units (amu) and angstroms (Å).]

1.54   The average speed of helium at 25°C is 1255 m/s. Convert this speed to miles per hour (mph).

1.55   How many seconds are there in a solar year (365.24 days)?

1.56   How many minutes does it take light from the sun to reach Earth? (The distance from the sun to Earth is 93 million mi; the speed of light is 3.00×10^8 m/s.)

1.57   A slow jogger runs a mile in 13 min. Calculate the speed in (a) in/s, (b) m/min, (c) km/h (1 mi = 1609 m; 1 in = 2.54 cm).

1.58   A 6.0-ft person weighs 168 lb. Express this person's height in meters and weight in kilograms (1 lb = 453.6 g; 1 m = 3.28 ft).

1.59   The current speed limit on some highways in the United States is 65 mph. What is the speed limit in kilometers per hour (1 mi = 1609 m)?

1.60   For a fighter jet to take off from the deck of an aircraft carrier, it must reach a speed of 62 m/s. Calculate the speed in miles per hour.

1.61   The "normal" lead content in human blood is about 0.40 part per million (that is, 0.40 g of lead per million grams of blood). A value of 0.80 part per million (ppm) is considered to be dangerous. How many grams of lead are contained in 6.0×10^3 g of blood (the amount in an average adult) if the lead content is 0.62 ppm?

1.62   Carry out the following conversions: (a) 1.42 km to miles, (b) 32.4 yd to centimeters, (c) 3.0×10^{10} cm/s to ft/s.

1.63   Carry out the following conversions: (a) 185 nm to meters, (b) 4.5 billion years (roughly the age of Earth) to seconds (assume exactly 365 days in a year), (c) 71.2 cm³ to cubic meters, (d) 88.6 m³ to liters.

1.64   Aluminum is a lightweight metal (density = 2.70 g/cm³) used in aircraft construction, high-voltage transmission lines, beverage cans, and foils. What is its density in kg/m³?

1.65   The density of ammonia gas under certain conditions is 0.625 g/L. Calculate its density in g/cm³.

1.66   A human brain weighs about 1 kg and contains about 10^{11} cells. Assuming that each cell is completely filled with water (density = 1 g/mL), calculate the length of one side of such a cell if it were a cube. If the cells are spread out into a thin layer that is a single cell thick, what is the surface area in square meters?

ADDITIONAL PROBLEMS

1.67   Using the appropriate number of significant figures, report the length of the blue rectangle (a) using the ruler shown above the rectangle and (b) using the ruler shown below the rectangle.

1.68   A piece of metal with a mass of 13.2 g was dropped into a graduated cylinder containing 17.00 mL of water. The graduated cylinder after the addition of the metal is shown. Determine the density of the metal to the appropriate number of significant figures. [Note: The volume of water in a graduated cylinder should be read at the *bottom* of the meniscus (the curved surface at the top).]

1.69 Which of the following statements describe physical properties and which describe chemical properties? (a) Iron has a tendency to rust. (b) Rainwater in industrialized regions tends to be acidic. (c) Hemoglobin molecules are red. (d) When a glass of water is left out in the sun, the water gradually disappears. (e) Carbon dioxide in air is consumed by plants during photosynthesis.

1.70 Give one qualitative and one quantitative statement about each of the following: (a) water, (b) carbon, (c) iron, (d) hydrogen gas, (e) sucrose (cane sugar), (f) table salt, (g) mercury, (h) gold, (i) air.

1.71 In 2004, about 95.0 billion lb of sulfuric acid were produced in the United States. Convert this quantity to tons.

1.72 In determining the density of a rectangular metal bar, a student made the following measurements: length, 8.53 cm; width, 2.4 cm; height, 1.0 cm; mass, 52.7064 g. Calculate the density of the metal to the correct number of significant figures.

1.73 Calculate the mass of each of the following: (a) a sphere of gold with a radius of 10.0 cm (volume of a sphere with a radius r is $V = \frac{4}{3}\pi r^3$; density of gold = 19.3 g/cm^3); (b) a cube of platinum of edge length 0.040 mm (density = 21.4 g/cm^3); (c) 50.0 mL of ethanol (density = 0.798 g/mL).

1.74 A cylindrical glass tube 12.7 cm in length is filled with mercury (density = 13.6 g/mL). The mass of mercury needed to fill the tube is 105.5 g. Calculate the inner diameter of the tube (volume of a cylinder of radius r and length h is $V = \pi r^2 h$).

1.75 The following procedure was used to determine the volume of a flask. The flask was weighed dry and then filled with water. If the masses of the empty flask and filled flask were 56.12 g and 87.39 g, respectively, and the density of water is 0.9976 g/cm^3, calculate the volume of the flask in cubic centimeters.

1.76 The speed of sound in air at room temperature is about 343 m/s. Calculate this speed in miles per hour (1 mi = 1609 m).

1.77 A piece of silver metal weighing 194.3 g is placed in a graduated cylinder containing 242.0 mL of water. The volume of water now reads 260.5 mL. From these data, calculate the density of silver.

1.78 The experiment described in Problem 1.77 is a crude but convenient way to determine the density of some solids. Describe a similar experiment that would enable you to measure the density of ice. Specifically, what would be the requirements for the liquid used in your experiment?

1.79 A lead sphere has a mass of 1.20×10^4 g, and its volume is 1.05×10^3 cm^3. Calculate the density of lead.

1.80 Lithium has a very low density (density = 0.53 g/cm^3). What is the volume occupied by 1.20×10^3 g of lithium?

1.81 The medicinal thermometer commonly used in homes can be read to $\pm 0.1°$F, whereas those in the doctor's office may be accurate to $\pm 0.1°$C. Percent error is often expressed as the absolute value of the difference between the true value and the experimental value, divided by the true value:

$$\text{percent error} = \frac{|\text{true value} - \text{experimental value}|}{\text{true value}} \times 100\%$$

The vertical lines indicate absolute value. In degrees Celsius, express the percent error expected from each of these thermometers in measuring a person's body temperature of 38.9°C.

1.82 Vanillin (used to flavor vanilla ice cream and other foods) is the substance whose aroma the human nose detects in the smallest amount. The threshold limit is 2.0×10^{-11} g per liter of air. If the current price of 50 g of vanillin is $112, determine the cost to supply enough vanillin so that the aroma could be detected in a large aircraft hangar with a volume of 5.0×10^7 ft^3.

1.83 Suppose that a new temperature scale has been devised on which the melting point of ethanol ($-117.3°$C) and the boiling point of ethanol (78.3°C) are taken as 0°S and 100°S, respectively, where S is the symbol for the new temperature scale. Derive an equation relating a reading on this scale to a reading on the Celsius scale. What would this thermometer read at 25°C?

1.84 At what temperature does the numerical value on the Celsius scale equal that on the temperature scale described in Problem 1.83?

1.85 A resting adult requires about 240 mL of pure oxygen per minute and breathes about 12 times every minute. If inhaled air contains 20 percent oxygen by volume and exhaled air 16 percent, what is the volume of air per breath? (Assume that the volume of inhaled air is equal to that of exhaled air.)

1.86 (a) Referring to Problem 1.85, calculate the total volume (in liters) of air an adult breathes in a day. (b) In a city with heavy traffic, the air contains 2.1×10^{-6} L of carbon monoxide (a poisonous gas) per liter. Calculate the average daily intake of carbon monoxide in liters by a person.

1.87 The total volume of seawater is 1.5×10^{21} L. Assume that seawater contains 3.1 percent sodium chloride by mass and that its density is 1.03 g/mL. Calculate the total mass of sodium chloride in kilograms and in tons (1 ton = 2000 lb; 1 lb = 453.6 g).

1.88 Magnesium is used in alloys, in batteries, and in the manufacture of chemicals. It is obtained mostly from seawater, which contains about 1.3 g of magnesium for every kilogram of seawater. Referring to Problem 1.87, calculate the volume of seawater (in liters) needed to extract 8.0×10^4 tons of magnesium, which is roughly the annual production in the United States.

1.89 The unit "troy ounce" is often used for precious metals such as gold and platinum (1 troy ounce = 31.103 g). (a) A gold coin weighs 2.41 troy ounces. Calculate its mass in grams. (b) Is a troy ounce heavier or lighter than an ounce (1 lb = 16 oz; 1 lb = 453.6 g)?

1.90 The surface area and average depth of the Pacific Ocean are 1.8×10^8 km^2 and 3.9×10^3 m, respectively. Calculate the volume of water in the ocean in liters.

1.91   Calculate the percent error for the following measurements: (a) The density of alcohol (ethanol) is found to be 0.802 g/mL (true value = 0.798 g/mL). (b) The mass of gold in an earring is analyzed to be 0.837 g (true value = 0.864 g).

1.92   Venus, the second closest planet to the sun, has a surface temperature of 7.3×10^2 K. Convert this temperature to degrees Celsius and degrees Fahrenheit.

1.93   Chalcopyrite contains 34.63 percent copper by mass. How many grams of copper can be obtained from 5.11×10^3 kg of chalcopyrite?

1.94   It has been estimated that 8.0×10^4 tons of gold have been mined. Assume gold costs $1100 per ounce. What is the total value of this quantity of gold?

1.95   One gallon of gasoline in an automobile's engine produces on the average 9.5 kg of carbon dioxide, which is a greenhouse gas; that is, it promotes the warming of Earth's atmosphere. Calculate the annual production of carbon dioxide in kilograms if there are 40 million cars in the United States and each car covers a distance of 5000 mi at an average consumption rate of 20 miles per gallon.

1.96   A sheet of aluminum foil has a total area of 1.000 ft^2 and a mass of 3.636 g. What is the thickness of the foil in millimeters (density of aluminum = 2.699 g/cm^3)?

1.97   The world's total petroleum reserve is estimated at 2.0×10^{22} joules [a joule (J) is the unit of energy where $1 \text{ J} = 1 \text{ kg} \cdot \text{m}^2/\text{s}^2$]. At the present rate of consumption, 1.8×10^{20} joules per year (J/yr), how long would it take to exhaust the supply?

1.98   A sample of DNA, the genetic material of life, was estimated to have a mass of 308,859 amu. What is this mass in grams? The average width of a DNA double strand is approximately 22 Å to 26 Å. Express this range of widths in meters.

1.99   Pheromones are substances secreted by females of many insect species to attract mates. Typically, 1.0×10^{-8} g of a pheromone is sufficient to reach all targeted males within a radius of 0.50 mi. Calculate the density of the pheromone (in grams per liter) in a cylindrical air space having a radius of 0.50 mi and a height of 40 ft. (Volume of a cylinder of radius r and height h is $\pi r^2 h$.)

1.100   Chlorine is used to disinfect swimming pools. The recommended concentration for this purpose is 1 ppm chlorine, or 1 g of chlorine per million grams of water. Calculate the volume of a chlorine solution (in milliliters) a homeowner should add to her swimming pool if the solution contains 6.0 percent chlorine by mass and there are 2.0×10^4 gallons (gal) of water in the pool (1 gal = 3.79 L; assume the density of both the water and the chlorine solution to be = 1.0 g/mL).

1.101   A graduated cylinder is filled to the 40.00-mL mark with a mineral oil. The masses of the cylinder before and after the addition of the mineral oil are 124.966 g and 159.446 g, respectively. In a separate experiment, a metal ball bearing of mass 18.713 g is placed in the cylinder and the cylinder is again filled to the 40.00-mL mark with the mineral oil. The combined mass of the ball bearing and mineral oil is 50.952 g.

Calculate the density and radius of the ball bearing (volume of a sphere of radius r is $\frac{4}{3}\pi r^3$).

1.102   In water conservation, chemists spread a thin film of a certain inert material over the surface of water to cut down on the rate of evaporation of water in reservoirs. This technique was pioneered by Benjamin Franklin three centuries ago. Franklin found that 0.10 mL of oil could spread over the surface of water about 40 m^2 in area. Assuming that the oil forms a *monolayer,* that is, a layer that is only one molecule thick, estimate the length of each oil molecule in nanometers (1 nm = 1×10^{-9} m).

1.103   A chemist in the nineteenth century collected a sample of unknown matter. In general, do you think it would be more difficult to prove that it is a pure substance or a mixture? Explain.

1.104   A gas company in Massachusetts charges $1.30 for 15.0 ft^3 of natural gas. (a) Convert this rate to dollars per liter of gas. (b) If it takes 0.304 ft^3 of gas to boil a liter of water, starting at room temperature (25°C), how much would it cost to boil a 2.1-L kettle of water?

1.105   You are given a liquid. Briefly describe the steps you would take to show whether it is a pure substance or a homogeneous mixture.

1.106   A bank teller is asked to assemble $1 sets of coins for his clients. Each set is made up of three quarters, one nickel, and two dimes. The masses of the coins are quarter, 5.645 g; nickel, 4.967 g; and dime, 2.316 g. What is the maximum number of complete sets that can be assembled from 33.871 kg of quarters, 10.432 kg of nickels, and 7.990 kg of dimes? What is the total mass (in grams) of the assembled sets of coins?

1.107   A 250-mL glass bottle was filled with 242 mL of water at 20°C and tightly capped. It was then left outdoors overnight, where the average temperature was −5°C. Predict what would happen. The density of water at 20°C is 0.998 g/cm^3 and that of ice at −5°C is 0.916 g/cm^3.

1.108   Bronze is an alloy made of copper and tin. Calculate the mass of a bronze cylinder of radius 6.44 cm and length 44.37 cm. The composition of the bronze is 79.42 percent copper and 20.58 percent tin and the densities of copper and tin are 8.94 g/cm^3 and 7.31 g/cm^3, respectively. What assumption should you make in this calculation?

1.109   Lead poisoning affects nearly every system in the body and can occur with no symptoms, potentially causing it to go undiagnosed. The primary source of lead exposure is the deteriorating lead-based paint in older homes, where young children are particularly vulnerable to exposure because of their tendency to put things in their mouths. In addition to the prevention of exposure, the Centers for Disease Control (CDC) guidelines recommend that public health actions be initiated when lead levels exceed 10 micrograms of lead per deciliter of blood. Determine whether or not the following lead levels would exceed the CDC's threshold level: (a) 3.0×10^{-4} grams per liter of blood, (b) 2.0×10^{-5} milligrams per milliliter of blood, (c) 6.5×10^{-8} grams per cubic centimeter.

1.110 A chemist mixes two liquids A and B to form a homogeneous mixture. The densities of the liquids are 2.0514 g/mL for A and 2.6678 g/mL for B. When she drops a small object into the mixture, she finds that the object becomes suspended in the liquid; that is, it neither sinks nor floats. If the mixture is made of 41.37 percent A and 58.63 percent B by volume, what is the density of the object? Can this procedure be used in general to determine the densities of solids? What assumptions must be made in applying this method?

1.111 In January of 2009, the National Aeronautics and Space Administration (NASA) reported that a planet in our galaxy, known as HD 80606b, underwent a temperature change from 980°F to 2240°F over the course of six hours. (a) Convert these temperatures and the range they span to degrees Celsius, and to kelvins. (b) Determine the rate of temperature change per second in degrees Fahrenheit, degrees Celsius, and kelvins.

1.112 TUMS is a popular remedy for acid indigestion. A typical TUMS tablet contains calcium carbonate plus some inert substances. When ingested, it combines with the gastric juice (hydrochloric acid) in the stomach to give off carbon dioxide gas. When a 1.328-g tablet reacted with 40.00 mL of hydrochloric acid (density = 1.140 g/mL), carbon dioxide gas was given off and the resulting solution weighed 46.699 g. Calculate the number of liters of carbon dioxide gas released if its density is 1.81 g/L.

1.113 Determine (a) the temperature at which the Celsius and Fahrenheit values are numerically equal, and (b) the temperature at which the Kelvin and Fahrenheit values are numerically equal. (c) Is there a temperature at which the Celsius and Kelvin values are numerically equal? Explain.

1.114 The hottest temperature ever recorded on Earth was 136°F (recorded at Al 'Aziziyah, Libya on September 13, 1922). Express this temperature in degrees Celsius and in kelvins.

1.115 The drug *cidofovir* is approved by the Federal Drug Administration (FDA) for the treatment of certain viral infections of the eye in patients with compromised immune systems. It is distributed in vials containing 375 mg of the drug dissolved in 5 mL of water. The manufacturer specifies that the drug should be kept at room temperature (68°F–77°F). The vial contents are first diluted with saline and then administered intravenously with a recommended dosage of 5 mg cidofovir per kilogram of body weight. (a) Convert cidofovir's recommended storage-temperature range to the Celsius scale. (b) If the fluid in a single vial of cidofovir has a volume of 5.00 mL and a mass of 5.89 g, what is the density of the fluid, in g/mL, to the appropriate number of significant figures? (c) Convert the density in part (b) to g/L and to kg/m^3. (d) What mass of cidofovir should be administered to a 185-lb man?

1.116 The composition of pennies has changed over the years, depending on a number of factors, including the availability of various metals. A penny minted in 1825 was pure copper; a penny minted in 1860 was 88 percent copper and 12 percent nickel; a penny minted in 1965 was 95 percent copper and 5 percent zinc; and a penny minted today is 97.5 percent zinc and 2.5 percent copper. Given that the densities of copper, nickel, and zinc are 8.92 g/cm^3, 8.91 g/cm^3, and 7.14 g/cm^3, respectively, determine the density of each penny.

Answers to In-Chapter Materials

PRACTICE PROBLEMS

1.1A 273 K and 373 K, range = 100 K. **1.1B** −270.5°C. **1.2A** −33°F, −2.2°F, range 32°F. **1.2B** 464°C, −201°C, range 665°C. **1.3A** (a) 13.6 g/mL, (b) 55 mL. **1.3B** (a) 9.25 g/cm^3, (b) 3.76 × 10^3 g. **1.4A** (a) 4, (b) 1, (c) 4, (d) 2, (e) 2 or 3, (f) 4. **1.4B** (a) 1.0 × 10^6, (b) 1.000 × 10^6, (c) 1.000000 × 10^6, (d) 0.100, (e) 0.10000, (f) 0.1. **1.5A** (a) 116.2 L, (b) 80.71 m, (c) 3.813 × 10^{21} atoms, (d) 31 dm^2, (e) 0.504 g/mL. **1.5B** (a) 32.44 cm^3, (b) 4.2 × 10^2 kg/m^3, (c) 1.008 × 10^{10} kg, (d) 40.75 mL, (e) 227 cm^3. **1.6A** 0.8120 g/cm^3. **1.6B** 95.3 cm^3. **1.7A** 0.01 oz. **1.7B** 2.649 × 10^4 mg. **1.8A** 1.05 × 10^4 kg/m^3. **1.8B** 849 lb/ft^3.

SECTION REVIEW

1.4.1 −89.2°C, 183.9 K. **1.4.2** 1.16 g/cm^3. **1.4.3** 75 K. **1.4.4** 0.310 cm^3. **1.5.1** 32.5 mL. **1.5.2** Green. Purple. **1.5.3** 642.4. **1.5.4** 761. **1.5.5** 29. **1.5.6** 1 × 10^{-5}. **1.6.1** 0.0431 L. **1.6.2** 1.45 cm^3. **1.6.3** 0.535 g/cm^3. **1.6.4** 1 × 10^6.

KEY SKILLS

Dimensional Analysis

Solving problems in chemistry often involves mathematical combinations of measured values and constants. A conversion factor is a fraction (equal to one) derived from an equality. For example, 1 inch is, by definition, equal to 2.54 centimeters:

$$1 \text{ in} = 2.54 \text{ cm}$$

We can derive two different conversion factors from this equality:

$$\frac{1 \text{ in}}{2.54 \text{ cm}} \quad \text{or} \quad \frac{2.54 \text{ cm}}{1 \text{ in}}$$

Which fraction we use depends on what units we start with, and what units we expect our result to have. If we are converting a distance given in centimeters to inches, we multiply by the first fraction.

$$37.6 \text{ cm} \times \frac{1 \text{ in}}{2.54 \text{ cm}} = 14.8 \text{ in}$$

If we are converting a distance given in inches to centimeters, we multiply by the second fraction.

$$5.23 \text{ in} \times \frac{2.54 \text{ cm}}{1 \text{ in}} = 13.3 \text{ cm}$$

In each case, the units cancel to give the desired units in the result.

When a unit is raised to a power to express, for example, an area (cm^2) or a volume (cm^3), the conversion factor must be raised to the same power. For example, converting an area expressed in square centimeters to square inches requires that we square the conversion factor; converting a volume expressed in cubic centimeters to cubic meters requires that we cube the conversion factor. The following individual flowcharts converting an area in cm^2 to m^2 show why this is so:

$$48.5 \text{ cm}^2 = 48.5 \text{ cm} \times \text{cm} \qquad \left(\frac{1 \text{ in}}{2.54 \text{ cm}}\right)^2 = \frac{1 \text{ in}}{2.54 \text{ cm}} \times \frac{1 \text{ in}}{2.54 \text{ cm}}$$

$$48.5 \text{ cm} \times \text{cm} \times \frac{1 \text{ in}}{2.54 \text{ cm}} \times \frac{1 \text{ in}}{2.54 \text{ cm}} = 7.52 \text{ in}^2$$

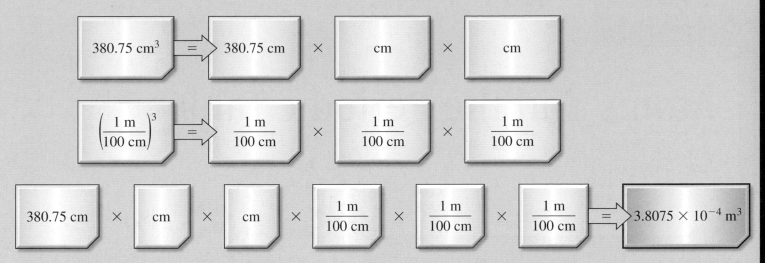

Failure to raise the conversion factor to the appropriate power would result in units not canceling properly.

Often the solution to a problem requires several different conversions, which can be combined on a single line. For example: If we know that a 157-lb athlete running at 7.09 miles per hour consumes 55.8 cm³ of oxygen per kilogram of body weight for every minute spent running, we can calculate how many liters of oxygen this athlete consumes by running 10.5 miles (1 kg = 2.2046 lb, 1 L = 1 dm³).

Key Skills Problems

1.1
Given that the density of gold is 19.3 g/cm³, calculate the volume (in cm³) of a gold nugget with a mass of 5.98 g.

(a) 3.23 cm³ (b) 5.98 cm³ (c) 115 cm³ (d) 0.310 cm³ (e) 13.3 cm³

1.2
The SI unit for energy is the joule (J), which is equal to the kinetic energy possessed by a 2.00-kg mass moving at 1.00 m/s. Convert this velocity to mph (1 mi = 1.609 km).

(a) 4.47×10^{-7} mph (b) 5.79×10^{6} mph (c) 5.79 mph
(d) 0.0373 mph (e) 2.24 mph

1.3
Determine the density of the following object in g/cm³. A cube with edge length = 0.750 m and mass = 14.56 kg.

(a) 0.0345 g/cm³ (b) 1.74 g/cm³ (c) 670 g/cm³ (d) 53.8 g/cm³
(e) 14.6 g/cm³

1.4
A 28-kg child can consume a maximum of 23 children's acetaminophen tablets in an 8-h period without exceeding the safety-limit maximum allowable dose. Given that each children's tablet contains 80 mg of acetaminophen, determine the maximum allowable dose in mg per pound of body weight for one day.

(a) 80 mg/lb (b) 90 mg/lb (c) 430 mg/lb (d) 720 mg/lb (e) 3.7 mg/lb

CHAPTER 2

Atoms and the Periodic Table

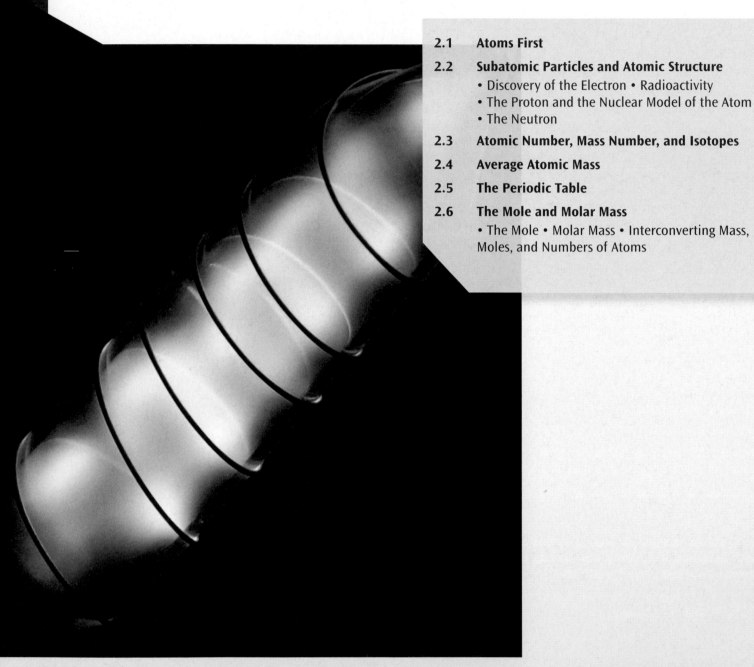

2.1   Atoms First

2.2   Subatomic Particles and Atomic Structure
• Discovery of the Electron • Radioactivity
• The Proton and the Nuclear Model of the Atom
• The Neutron

2.3   Atomic Number, Mass Number, and Isotopes

2.4   Average Atomic Mass

2.5   The Periodic Table

2.6   The Mole and Molar Mass
• The Mole • Molar Mass • Interconverting Mass,
Moles, and Numbers of Atoms

Of matter that exists as isolated atoms, helium is probably the most familiar. Sightings of helium-filled balloons are fairly common. Helium is the product of radioactive decay of the elements uranium (U) and thorium (Th) and is found in and around natural gas deposits. In 1925, the U.S. government officially recognized the strategic value of helium and began an initiative to stockpile it. Estimates vary as to how long Earth's supply of helium will last. Some scientists believe that the shortage could become critical in less than a decade. Because our supply is finite and nonrenewable, efforts by chemical engineers to capture and recycle helium are vitally important as demand increases. In addition to being used to fill balloons, helium is used as a coolant for nuclear reactors and superconducting magnets, to pressurize liquid fuel rockets, and for a host of other applications.

2.1 ATOMS FIRST

Even if you have never studied chemistry before, you probably know already that atoms are extraordinarily small building blocks of matter. Specifically, an *atom* is the smallest quantity of matter that still retains the properties of matter. Further, an *element* is a substance that cannot be broken down into two or more simpler substances by any means. Familiar examples of elements include gold, oxygen, and helium. Consider the example of helium. If we were to divide the helium in a balloon in half, and then divide one of the halves in half, and so on, we would eventually (after a large number of these hypothetical divisions) be left with a sample of helium consisting of just one helium atom. This atom could not be further divided to give two smaller samples of helium. If this is difficult to imagine, think of a collection of DVDs. You could separate the collection into smaller and smaller numbers of DVDs. But when you were down to a single DVD, although you could break it into smaller pieces, none of the pieces would be a DVD. Similarly, an *atom* is the smallest quantity of helium. If we were, somehow, to break this quantity apart, the resulting pieces would not be helium. Figure 2.1 illustrates this concept.

Student Annotation: Atoms are almost unimaginably small. If we could arrange helium atoms end-to-end, it would take over 30 million of them to make a line just one *millimeter* long.

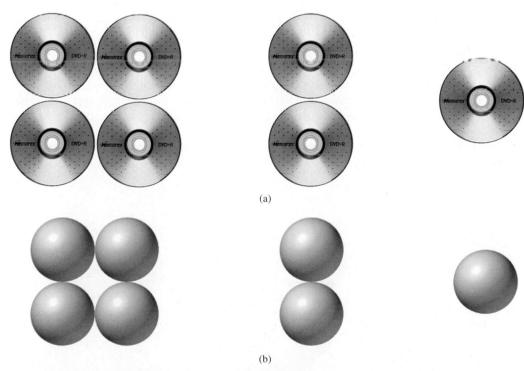

(a)

(b)

Figure 2.1 (a) A collection of DVDs can be separated into smaller and smaller numbers of DVDs; but a single DVD cannot be separated into smaller pieces that are still DVDs. (b) A collection of atoms can be separated into smaller and smaller numbers of atoms; but if we were to separate an atom into smaller pieces, none of the pieces would be an atom.

Student Annotation: Dalton's atomic theory actually consists of three hypotheses. The first, introduced here, is that matter is composed of tiny, indivisible particles; and that in a given *element*, all of the tiny particles are identical. The second and third hypotheses will be introduced in Chapters 5 and 8, respectively.

Student Annotation: The word atom comes from the Greek word *atomos,* which means "uncuttable."

The concept of the atom was first proposed by the philosopher Democritus in the fifth century B.C. Although the notion of matter consisting of atoms endured for many centuries, it was first formalized by the English scientist and school teacher John Dalton.[1] Dalton said that atoms, of which all matter consists, are tiny, indivisible particles. We now know that, in fact, although atoms are tiny, they are not indivisible. Rather, they are made up of still smaller *sub*atomic particles. The nature, number, and arrangement of subatomic particles determine the properties of atoms, which in turn determine the properties of all things material.

Our goal in this book will be to understand how the nature of atoms gives rise to the properties of all matter. To accomplish this, we will take a somewhat untraditional approach. Rather than beginning with observations on the macroscopic scale and working our way backward to the atomic nature of matter to explain these observations, we start by examining the structure of atoms and the tiny subatomic particles that atoms contain.

Multi 2.1
Cathode ray tube experiment

2.2 SUBATOMIC PARTICLES AND ATOMIC STRUCTURE

Contrary to Dalton's description of the atom as *indivisible,* a series of investigations beginning in the middle of the nineteenth century indicated that atoms are made up of even smaller things. These investigations led to the discovery of electrons, protons, and neutrons, and contributed to our understanding of the structure of atoms.

Discovery of the Electron

In the late 1800s, many scientists were doing research involving **radiation,** the emission and transmission of energy in the form of waves. One device that was commonly used to investigate this phenomenon was the cathode ray tube. A ***cathode ray tube*** consists of two metal plates sealed inside a glass tube from which most of the air has been evacuated (Figure 2.2). When the metal plates are connected to a high-voltage source, the negatively charged plate, called the *cathode,* emits radiation known as *cathode rays.* A cathode ray moves toward the positively charged plate, called the *anode,* where it passes through a hole and continues traveling to the other end of the tube. Although a cathode ray itself is invisible, its path is revealed when the ray strikes a phosphor-coated surface, producing a bright light. Most striking about the cathode ray tube experiments was that the results did not depend on the material from which the cathode was made. Cathode rays appeared to be a component even more *fundamental* than atoms themselves, and common to *all* matter.

Student Annotation: Cathode ray tubes were the forerunners of the tubes used in old televisions and computer monitors.

Figure 2.2 A cathode ray tube with an electric field perpendicular to the direction of the cathode rays and an external magnetic field. The symbols N and S denote the north and south poles of the magnet. The cathode rays will strike the end of the tube at point A in the presence of a magnetic field, and at point B in the presence of an electric field. (In the absence of any external field—or when the effects of the electric field and magnetic field cancel each other—the cathode rays will not be deflected but will travel in a straight line and strike the middle of the circular screen.

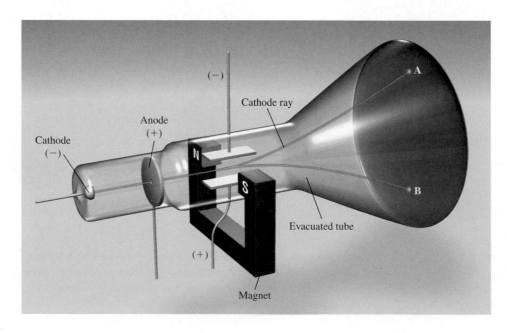

[1]John Dalton (1766–1844). English chemist, mathematician, and philosopher. In addition to his atomic theory, Dalton also formulated several laws governing the behavior of gases, and gave the first detailed description of a particular type of color blindness, from which he suffered.

(a)   (b)

Figure 2.3 (a) When the same poles of two magnets are brought together, the magnets repel each other. When opposite poles are brought together, the magnets attract each other. (b) Like charges, either both positive or both negative, repel each other. Opposite charges attract each other.

One of the things researchers used to interpret their results was the fact that *like* charges *repel* one another, and *opposite* charges *attract* one another. This is, in essence, *Coulomb's law* and is similar to a phenomenon you may have experienced while playing with magnets as a child. When two magnets are brought close together with the same poles facing each other, there is a repulsive force between them. When opposite poles are brought together, there is an attractive force between the magnets. Figure 2.3 summarizes the repulsive and attractive forces between magnets, and between electrical charges.

Student Annotation: Coulomb's law is extraordinarily important in the understanding of chemistry. We will examine it in more detail in the next few chapters.

In addition to originating at the negatively charged cathode and traveling toward the positively charged anode, cathode rays can be deflected by electric or magnetic fields (Figure 2.4). The rays are repelled by a plate bearing a negative charge, and attracted to a plate bearing a positive charge. This prompted English physicist J. J. Thomson (1856–1940) to propose that the "rays" are actually a stream of negatively charged *particles*. Thomson performed a series of experiments in which he applied a variable electric field and measured the degree of deflection of cathode rays. This enabled him to determine the charge-to-mass *ratio* of the tiny, negatively charged particles that we now know as **electrons.** The charge-to-mass ratio he calculated was 1.76×10^8 C/g, where C stands for *coulomb,* the derived SI unit of electric charge.

Early in the twentieth century, American physicist R. A. Millikan (1868–1953) determined the charge on an electron by examining the motion of tiny oil drops in an ingenious experiment (Figure 2.5). The oil drops picked up static charge from particles in the air and were suspended in an electric field. The magnitude of electric field necessary to keep a drop suspended depended on the amount of charge the drop had acquired. Millikan found that the charge on any particular drop was always a multiple of -1.6022×10^{-19} C, which he deduced was the charge on a *single* electron. He then used the charge he had determined, and the charge-to-mass ratio that Thomson had determined, to calculate the *mass* of an electron:

Multi 2.2
Millikan oil-drop experiment

$$\text{mass of an electron} = \frac{\text{charge}}{\text{charge/mass}} = \frac{-1.6022 \times 10^{-19} \text{ C}}{-1.76 \times 10^8 \text{ C/g}} = 9.10 \times 10^{-28} \text{ g}$$

(a)   (b)   (c)

Figure 2.4 (a) A cathode ray produced in a discharge tube. The ray itself is invisible, but a fluorescent coating on the glass causes it to appear green. (b) The cathode ray bends toward one pole of a magnet and (c) bends away from the opposite pole.

Figure 2.5 Schematic diagram of Millikan's oil-drop experiment.

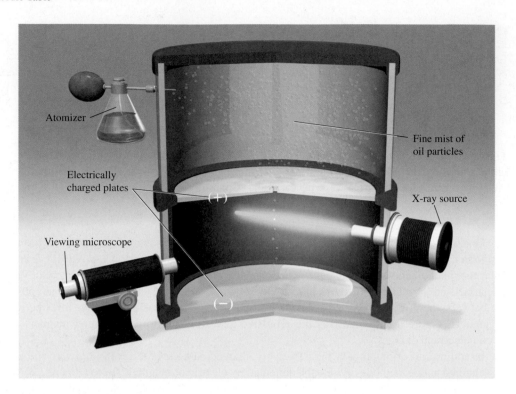

Radioactivity

Another scientist who worked with cathode ray tubes was German physicist Wilhelm Röntgen (1845–1923). Röntgen noticed that pointing cathode rays at glass or metal caused the emission of another type of ray, which he called *X rays*. X rays were sufficiently energetic to penetrate matter and caused a variety of materials to *fluoresce* (give off light). Unlike cathode rays, X rays were not deflected by magnetic or electric fields, which indicated they could not consist of charged particles.

Soon after Röntgen's discovery of X rays, a French physicist Antoine Becquerel (1852–1908), while investigating fluorescence, discovered that uranium caused the darkening of photographic plates that had been wrapped carefully to prevent their exposure to light. Like X rays, the radiation from the uranium was highly energetic and could not be deflected by magnetic or electric fields. Unlike X rays, these rays were emitted spontaneously, and not as the result of exposure to cathode rays. This spontaneous emission of radiation is known as *radioactivity*. Radioactive substances such as uranium can produce three types of radiation. Two of the types are deflected by charged plates, as shown in Figure 2.6. *Alpha* (α) *rays* consist of positively charged particles, called *α particles*, that are deflected *away* from a positively charged plate. *Beta* (β) *rays*, or *β particles*, are *electrons,* so they are deflected away from the *negatively* charged plate. The third type of radioactive emission consists of high-energy *gamma* (γ) *rays*. Like X rays, γ rays have no charge and are unaffected by external electric or magnetic fields.

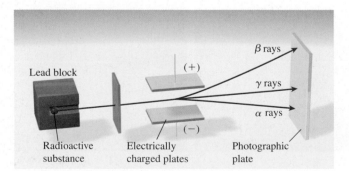

Figure 2.6 Three types of rays emitted by radioactive elements. So-called β rays actually consist of negatively charged particles (electrons) and are therefore attracted by the positively charged plate. The opposite is true for so-called α rays—they are actually positively charged particles and are drawn to the negatively charged plate. Because γ rays are not particles and have no charge, their path is unaffected by an external electric field.

The Proton and the Nuclear Model of the Atom

By the early 1900s, scientists knew that atoms contained negatively charged electrons and that atoms themselves were electrically neutral. In order to be neutral, an atom must therefore contain something positively charged. Thomson proposed that an atom could be thought of as a sphere of positively charged matter in which negatively charged electrons were embedded uniformly, like the raisins in a scoop of rum raisin ice cream. This so-called plum-pudding model was the accepted theory for a number of years—until it was challenged by the work of Ernest Rutherford (New Zealand physicist, 1871–1937), one of Thomson's own students.

Rutherford and his associates, Hans Geiger and Ernest Marsden, carried out a series of experiments in which they directed α particles from a radioactive source at very thin foils of gold and other metals. They observed that, as expected, the majority of particles penetrated the foil either completely undeflected or with only a small angle of deflection. Every now and then, however, an α particle was scattered (or deflected) at a large angle. In some instances, the α particle actually bounced back in the direction of the radioactive source. This was an extraordinarily surprising finding. In Thomson's model, the positive charge of the atom was so diffuse that the relatively massive, positively charged α particles should all have passed through the foil with little or no deflection. To quote Rutherford's initial reaction to these results: "It was as incredible as if you had fired a 15-in shell at a piece of tissue paper and it came back and hit you." Figure 2.7 illustrates the *expected* and *actual* results of the α-scattering experiment.

According to Rutherford, the results of the α-scattering experiment meant that most of the atom must be empty space. This would explain why the majority of α particles passed through the gold foil with little or no deflection. The atom's positive charges, Rutherford proposed, were all concentrated in an extremely dense central *core* within the atom, which he called the **nucleus.** Whenever an α particle came close to a nucleus in the scattering experiment, it experienced a large repulsive force and therefore a large deflection. Moreover, an α particle traveling directly toward a nucleus would be completely repelled and its direction would be reversed.

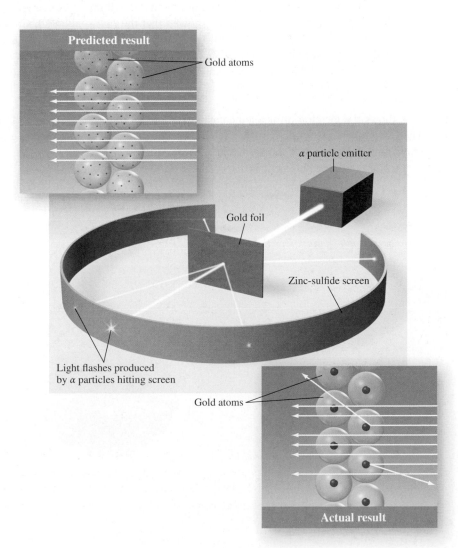

Figure 2.7 Rutherford's experimental design for measuring the scattering of α particles by a piece of gold foil. The plum-pudding model predicted that the α particles would all pass through the gold foil undeflected. The actual result: Most of the α particles do pass through the gold foil with little or no deflection, but a few are deflected at large angles. Occasionally, an α particle bounces off the foil back toward the source. The nuclear model explains the results of Rutherford's experiments.

The positively charged particles in the nucleus are called *protons.* In separate experiments, it was found that each proton carried the same *magnitude* of charge as an electron (just opposite in sign) but had a mass of 1.67262×10^{-24} g. Although this is an extremely small mass, it is nearly 2000 times the mass of an electron.

Based on these data, the atom was believed to consist of a nucleus that accounted for most of the mass of the atom, but which occupied only a tiny fraction of its volume. We express atomic (and molecular) dimensions using the SI unit *picometer* (*pm*), where

$$1 \text{ pm} = 1 \times 10^{-12} \text{ m}$$

A typical atomic radius is on the order of about 100 pm, whereas the radius of an atomic nucleus is only about 5×10^{-3} pm. You can appreciate the relative sizes of an atom and its nucleus by imagining that if an atom were the size of the New Orleans Superdome, the volume of its nucleus would be comparable to that of a marble. While the protons are confined to the nucleus of the atom, the electrons are distributed *around* the nucleus at relatively large distances from it.

The Neutron

Although Rutherford's nuclear model of the atoms was a marked improvement over Thomson's plum-pudding model, protons and electrons alone could not account for all of the mass that most atoms were known to possess. It was known that hydrogen, the simplest atom, contained only one proton and that the helium atom contained two protons. Therefore, the ratio of the mass of a helium atom to that of a hydrogen atom should be 2:1. (Because electrons are much lighter than protons, their contribution to atomic mass can be ignored in an analysis such as this.) In reality, however, the mass ratio is 4:1. Rutherford and others postulated that there must be another type of subatomic particle in the atomic nucleus, the proof of which was provided in 1932 by the English physicist James Chadwick (1891–1974). When Chadwick bombarded a thin sheet of beryllium with α particles, a very high-energy radiation was emitted by the metal that was not deflected by either electric or magnetic fields. Later experiments showed that the rays—although similar to γ rays—actually consisted of a third type of subatomic *particle,* which Chadwick named *neutrons* because they were electrically neutral particles having a mass slightly greater than that of protons. The mystery of the mass ratio could now be explained. A typical helium nucleus consists of two protons and two neutrons, whereas a typical hydrogen nucleus contains only a proton; the mass ratio, therefore, is 4:1.

Figure 2.8 shows the location of the elementary particles (protons, neutrons, and electrons) in an atom. There are other subatomic particles, but the electron, the proton, and the neutron are the three fundamental components of the atom that are important in chemistry. Table 2.1 lists the masses and charges of these three elementary particles.

Figure 2.8 The protons and neutrons in an atom are contained in the tiny volume of the nucleus. Electrons are distributed within the sphere surrounding the nucleus.

TABLE 2.1	Masses and Charges of Subatomic Particles			
Particle	**Mass (g)**	**Mass (amu)**	**Charge (C)**	**Charge unit**
Electron*	9.10938×10^{-28}	5.534×10^{-4}	-1.6022×10^{-19}	-1
Proton	1.67262×10^{-24}	1.0073	$+1.6022 \times 10^{-19}$	$+1$
Neutron	1.67493×10^{-24}	1.0086	0	0

*More refined measurements have resulted in a small change to Millikan's original value.

2.3 ATOMIC NUMBER, MASS NUMBER, AND ISOTOPES

All atoms can be identified by the number of protons and neutrons they contain. The **atomic number (Z)** is the number of protons in the nucleus of each atom of an element. It also indicates the number of *electrons* in the atom—because for an atom to be *neutral*, it must contain the same number of protons and electrons. The elemental identity of an atom can be determined solely from its atomic number. For example, the atomic number of nitrogen is 7. Thus, each atom of the element nitrogen atom has seven protons. Or, viewed another way, any atom that contains seven protons is a nitrogen atom.

The **mass number (A)** is the total number of neutrons *and* protons, collectively referred to as **nucleons**, present in the nucleus of an atom of an element. Except for the most common form of hydrogen, which has one proton and no neutrons, all atomic nuclei contain both protons and neutrons. In general, the mass number is given by

mass number (A) = number of protons (Z) + number of neutrons

The number of neutrons in an atom equals the difference between the mass number and the atomic number, or $(A - Z)$. For example, the mass number of fluorine is 19 and the atomic number is 9 (indicating 9 protons in the nucleus). Thus, the number of neutrons in an atom of fluorine is $19 - 9 = 10$. The atomic number, number of neutrons, and mass number are all positive integers (whole numbers).

The accepted way to denote the atomic number and mass number of an atom of an element (X) is as follows:

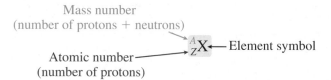

Mass number
(number of protons + neutrons)

Atomic number
(number of protons)

$^{A}_{Z}X$ — Element symbol

Once again, contrary to Dalton's atomic theory, atoms of a given element are *not* all identical. Instead, most elements have two or more **isotopes**, atoms that have the same atomic number (Z) but different mass numbers (A). For example, there are three isotopes of hydrogen, called *hydrogen* (or *protium*), *deuterium,* and *tritium.* Hydrogen has one proton and no neutrons in its nucleus, deuterium has one proton and *one* neutron, and tritium has one proton and *two* neutrons. Thus, to represent the isotopes of hydrogen, we write

$^{1}_{1}H$
protium

$^{2}_{1}H$
deuterium

$^{3}_{1}H$
tritium

Similarly, the two common isotopes of uranium $(Z = 92)$, which have mass numbers of 235 and 238, respectively, can be represented as follows:

$$^{235}_{92}U \qquad ^{238}_{92}U$$

The first isotope, with $235 - 92 = 143$ neutrons in its nucleus, is used in nuclear reactors and atomic bombs, whereas the second isotope, with 146 neutrons, lacks the properties necessary for these applications. With the exception of hydrogen, which has different names for each of its isotopes, the isotopes of other elements are identified by their mass numbers. The two isotopes of uranium are called uranium-235 (pronounced "uranium two thirty-five") and uranium-238 (pronounced "uranium two thirty-eight"). Because the atomic number subscript can be deduced from the elemental symbol, it may be omitted from these representations without the loss of any information. The symbols ^3H and ^{235}U are sufficient to specify the isotopes tritium and uranium-235, respectively.

The chemical properties of an element are determined primarily by the number of protons and electrons in its atoms; not by the number of neutrons. Therefore, isotopes of the same element typically exhibit very similar chemical properties.

Worked Example 2.1 shows how to calculate the number of protons, neutrons, and electrons using atomic numbers and mass numbers

Worked Example 2.1

Determine the numbers of protons, neutrons, and electrons in each of the following species:

(a) $^{35}_{17}Cl$, (b) ^{37}Cl, (c) ^{41}K, and (d) carbon-14.

Strategy Recall that the superscript denotes the mass number, (A), and the subscript denotes the atomic number, (Z). In cases where no subscript is shown, as in parts (b), (c), and (d), the atomic number can be deduced from the elemental symbol or name. For the purpose of determining the number of electrons, remember that atoms are neutral, so the number of electrons is equal to the number of protons.

Setup Number of protons = Z, number of neutrons = $A - Z$, and number of electrons = number of protons. Recall that the 14 in carbon-14 is the *mass number*.

Solution

(a) The atomic number is 17, so there are 17 protons. The mass number is 35, so the number of neutrons is $35 - 17 = 18$. The number of electrons equals the number of protons, so there are 17 electrons.

(b) Because the element is again Cl (chlorine), the atomic number is again 17, so there are 17 protons. The mass number is 37, so the number of neutrons is $37 - 17 = 20$. The number of electrons equals the number of protons, so there are 17 electrons, too.

(c) The atomic number of K (potassium) is 19, so there are 19 protons. The mass number is 41, so there are $41 - 19 = 22$ neutrons. There are 19 electrons.

(d) Carbon-14 can also be represented as ^{14}C. The atomic number of carbon is 6, so there are 6 protons and 6 electrons. There are $14 - 6 = 8$ neutrons.

> **Think About It**
> Verify that the number of protons and the number of neutrons for each example sum to the mass number that is given. In part (a), for example, there are 17 protons and 18 neutrons, which sum to give a mass number of 35, the value given in the problem. In part (b), 17 protons + 20 neutrons = 37. In part (c), 19 protons + 22 neutrons = 41. In part (d), 6 protons + 8 neutrons = 14.

Practice Problem A How many protons, neutrons, and electrons are there in an atom of (a) $^{10}_5B$, (b) ^{36}Ar, (c) $^{85}_{38}Sr$, and (d) carbon-11?

Practice Problem B Give the correct symbols to identify an atom that contains (a) 4 protons, 4 electrons, and 5 neutrons; (b) 23 protons, 23 electrons, and 28 neutrons; (c) 54 protons, 54 electrons, and 70 neutrons; and (d) 31 protons, 31 electrons, and 38 neutrons.

SECTION 2.3 REVIEW

Atomic Number, Mass Number, and Isotopes

2.3.1   How many neutrons are there in an atom of ^{60}Ni?

2.3.2   An atom with a mass number of 114 has 66 neutrons in its nucleus. What element is it?

2.4 AVERAGE ATOMIC MASS

Atomic mass is the mass of an atom in atomic mass units. Recall that an atomic mass unit is equal to $1.6605378 \times 10^{-24}$ g [◄◄ Section 1.4]. In fact, the amu is defined as one-twelfth the mass of a carbon-12 atom. However, when you look up the atomic mass of carbon in a table such as the one on the inside front cover of this book, you will find that its value is 12.01 amu, not 12.00 amu. The difference arises because most naturally occurring elements (including carbon) have more than one isotope. This means that generally, when we determine the atomic mass of an element, what we are actually measuring is the ***average atomic mass*** of the naturally occurring *mixture* of isotopes. For example, the natural abundances of carbon-12 and carbon-13 are 98.93 percent and 1.07 percent, respectively. The atomic mass of carbon-13 has been determined to be 13.003355 amu. Thus, the average atomic mass of natural carbon can be calculated as follows:

> **Student Annotation:** Average atomic mass is also referred to as *atomic weight*.

$$(0.9893)(12.00000 \text{ amu}) + (0.0107)(13.003355 \text{ amu}) = 12.01 \text{ amu}$$

In calculations involving percentages, we need to convert each percent abundance to a fractional abundance. For example, 98.93 percent becomes 98.93/100, or 0.9893. Because there are many more carbon-12 atoms than carbon-13 atoms in naturally occurring carbon, the average atomic mass is much closer to the mass of carbon-12 than to that of carbon-13.

When we say that the atomic mass of carbon is 12.01 amu, we are referring to the average value. If we could examine an individual atom of naturally occurring carbon, we would find either an atom of atomic mass of exactly 12 amu or one of 13.003355 amu, but never one of 12.01 amu.

Worked Example 2.2 shows how to calculate the average atomic mass of oxygen.

Worked Example 2.2

Oxygen is the most abundant element in both Earth's crust and the human body. The atomic masses of its three stable isotopes, $^{16}_{8}O$ (99.757 percent), $^{17}_{8}O$ (0.038 percent), $^{18}_{8}O$ (0.205 percent), are 15.9949, 16.9991, and 17.9992 amu, respectively. Calculate the average atomic mass of oxygen using the relative abundances given in parentheses.

Strategy Each isotope contributes to the average atomic mass based on its relative abundance. Multiplying the mass of each isotope by its fractional abundance (percent value divided by 100) will give its contribution to the average atomic mass.

Setup Each percent abundance must be converted to a fractional abundance: 99.757 percent to 99.757/100 or 0.99757, 0.038 percent to 0.038/100 or 0.00038, and 0.205 percent to 0.205/100 or 0.00205. Once we find the contribution to the average atomic mass for each isotope, we can then add the contributions together to obtain the average atomic mass.

Solution

$$(0.99757)(15.9949 \text{ amu}) + (0.00038)(16.9991 \text{ amu}) + (0.00205)(17.9992) = 15.9994 \text{ amu}$$

Think About It
The average atomic mass should be closest to the atomic mass of the most abundant isotope (in this case, oxygen-16) and, to four significant figures, should be the same number that appears in the periodic table on the inside front cover of this book (in this case, 16.00 amu).

Practice Problem A The atomic masses of the two stable isotopes of copper, $^{63}_{29}Cu$ (69.17 percent) and $^{65}_{29}Cu$ (30.83 percent), are 62.929599 and 64.927793 amu, respectively. Calculate the average atomic mass of copper.

Practice Problem B The average atomic mass of nitrogen is 14.0067. The atomic masses of the two stable isotopes of nitrogen, ^{14}N and ^{15}N, are 14.003074002 and 15.000108898 amu, respectively. Use this information to determine the percent abundance of each nitrogen isotope.

The atomic masses of many isotopes have been accurately determined to five or six significant figures. For most purposes, though, we will use average atomic masses, which are generally given to four significant figures (see the table of atomic masses on the inside front cover). For simplicity, we will usually omit the word *average* when we discuss the atomic masses of the elements.

Thinking Outside the Box

Measuring Atomic Mass

The most direct and most accurate method for determining atomic and molecular masses is mass spectrometry. In a *mass spectrometer,* such as that depicted, a gaseous sample is bombarded by a stream of high-energy electrons. Collisions between the electrons and the gaseous atoms (or molecules) produce positively charged species, called *ions,* by dislodging an electron from the atoms or molecules. These positive ions (of mass m and charge e) are accelerated as they pass through two oppositely charged plates. The emerging ions are deflected into a circular path by a magnet. The radius of the path depends on the charge-to-mass ratio (i.e., e/m). Ions with a small e/m ratio trace a wider arc than those having a larger e/m ratio, so ions with equal charges but different masses are separated from one another. The mass of each ion (and hence its parent atom or molecule) is determined from the magnitude of its deflection. Eventually, the ions arrive at the detector, which registers a current for each type of ion. The amount of current generated is directly proportional to the number of ions, so it enables us to determine the relative abundance of isotopes.

Schematic diagram of one type of mass spectrometer.

The first mass spectrometer, developed in the 1920s by the English physicist F. W. Aston, was crude by today's standards. Nevertheless, it provided indisputable evidence of the existence of isotopes, such as neon-20 (natural abundance 90.48 percent) and neon-22 (natural abundance 9.25 percent). When more sophisticated and sensitive mass spectrometers became available, scientists were surprised to discover that neon has a *third* stable isotope (neon-21) with natural abundance 0.27 percent. This example illustrates how very important experimental accuracy is to a quantitative science like chemistry. Early experiments failed to detect neon-21 because its natural abundance was so small. Only 27 in 10,000 Ne atoms are neon-21.

Mass spectrum of neon.

Average Atomic Mass

2.4.1   Boron has two naturally occurring isotopes, ^{10}B and ^{11}B, which have masses 10.0129 and 11.0093 amu, respectively. Given the average atomic mass of boron (10.81 amu), determine the percent abundance of each isotope.

2.4.2   The two naturally occurring isotopes of antimony, ^{121}Sb (57.21 percent) and ^{123}Sb (42.79 percent), have masses of 120.904 and 122.904 amu, respectively. What is the average atomic mass of Sb?

2.5   THE PERIODIC TABLE

The *periodic table* (Figure 2.9) consists of 118 *elements*. According to Dalton's atomic theory, the atoms of a particular element are all identical; and the atoms of one element are different from the atoms of any other element. Thus, according to Dalton, what makes the elements helium and gold different is that they consist of different kinds of atoms. Further, what makes helium *helium* is that it consists entirely of *identical* helium *atoms*.

The modern periodic table showing atomic number, symbol, name, and average atomic mass labels for Helium (2, He, 1.0079).

1A 1																	8A 18
1 **H** Hydrogen	2A 2											3A 13	4A 14	5A 15	6A 16	7A 17	2 **He** Helium
3 **Li** Lithium	4 **Be** Beryllium											5 **B** Boron	6 **C** Carbon	7 **N** Nitrogen	8 **O** Oxygen	9 **F** Fluorine	10 **Ne** Neon
11 **Na** Sodium	12 **Mg** Magnesium	3B 3	4B 4	5B 5	6B 6	7B 7	8B 8	9	10	1B 11	2B 12	13 **Al** Aluminum	14 **Si** Silicon	15 **P** Phosphorus	16 **S** Sulfur	17 **Cl** Chlorine	18 **Ar** Argon
19 **K** Potassium	20 **Ca** Calcium	21 **Sc** Scandium	22 **Ti** Titanium	23 **V** Vanadium	24 **Cr** Chromium	25 **Mn** Manganese	26 **Fe** Iron	27 **Co** Cobalt	28 **Ni** Nickel	29 **Cu** Copper	30 **Zn** Zinc	31 **Ga** Gallium	32 **Ge** Germanium	33 **As** Arsenic	34 **Se** Selenium	35 **Br** Bromine	36 **Kr** Krypton
37 **Rb** Rubidium	38 **Sr** Strontium	39 **Y** Yttrium	40 **Zr** Zirconium	41 **Nb** Niobium	42 **Mo** Molybdenum	43 **Tc** Technetium	44 **Ru** Ruthenium	45 **Rh** Rhodium	46 **Pd** Palladium	47 **Ag** Silver	48 **Cd** Cadmium	49 **In** Indium	50 **Sn** Tin	51 **Sb** Antimony	52 **Te** Tellurium	53 **I** Iodine	54 **Xe** Xenon
55 **Cs** Cesium	56 **Ba** Barium	57 **La** Lanthanum	72 **Hf** Hafnium	73 **Ta** Tantalum	74 **W** Tungsten	75 **Re** Rhenium	76 **Os** Osmium	77 **Ir** Iridium	78 **Pt** Platinum	79 **Au** Gold	80 **Hg** Mercury	81 **Tl** Thallium	82 **Pb** Lead	83 **Bi** Bismuth	84 **Po** Polonium	85 **At** Astatine	86 **Rn** Radon
87 **Fr** Francium	88 **Ra** Radium	89 **Ac** Actinium	104 **Rf** Rutherfordium	105 **Db** Dubnium	106 **Sg** Seaborgium	107 **Bh** Bohrium	108 **Hs** Hassium	109 **Mt** Meitnerium	110 **Ds** Darmstadtium	111 **Rg** Roentgenium	112 **Cn** Copernicium	113 –	114 –	115 –	116 –	117 –	118 –

58 **Ce** Cerium	59 **Pr** Praseodymium	60 **Nd** Neodymium	61 **Pm** Promethium	62 **Sm** Samarium	63 **Eu** Europium	64 **Gd** Gadolium	65 **Tb** Terbium	66 **Dy** Dysprosium	67 **Ho** Holmium	68 **Er** Erbium	69 **Tm** Thulium	70 **Yb** Ytterbium	71 **Lu** Lutetium
90 **Th** Thorium	91 **Pa** Protactinium	92 **U** Uranium	93 **Np** Neptunium	94 **Pu** Plutonium	95 **Am** Americium	96 **Cm** Curium	97 **Bk** Berkelium	98 **Cf** Californium	99 **Es** Einsteinium	100 **Fm** Fermium	101 **Md** Mendelevium	102 **No** Nobelium	103 **Lr** Lawrencium

Figure 2.9 The modern periodic table. The elements are arranged according to atomic number [◀◀ Section 2.3], which is shown above each element's symbol. With the exception of hydrogen (H), nonmetals appear at the far right of the table. The two rows of metals beneath the main body of the table are set apart to keep the table from being too wide. Actually, cerium (58) should follow lanthanum (57), and thorium (90) should follow actinium (89). The 1–18 group designation has been recommended by the International Union of Pure and Applied Chemistry (IUPAC) but is not yet in wide use. In this text, we generally use the standard U.S. notation for group numbers (1A–8A and 1B–8B). No names have yet been assigned to elements 113–118.

More than half of the elements known today were discovered in the nineteenth century. During this time, some elements were found to share similar physical and chemical properties. These similarities prompted chemists to arrange the known elements in vertical columns called "groups" or "families," which ultimately led to the development of the periodic table. Placing the elements in groups according to their properties enabled chemists to organize a growing body of scientific information.

Each element in the periodic table is represented by a tile containing the element's name; the chemical symbol consisting of one or more commonly *two* letters; the atomic number, an integer; and the average atomic mass, commonly given to four significant figures. The elements are arranged in *periods*, horizontal rows, in order of increasing atomic number. The first period contains just two elements, hydrogen (H) and helium (He). The second and third periods each contain eight elements: lithium (Li) through neon (Ne), and sodium (Na) through argon (Ar), respectively. The fourth and fifth periods each contain 18 elements: potassium (K) through krypton (Kr), and rubidium (Rb) through xenon (Xe), respectively.

Most elements can be categorized as metals or nonmetals. One of the properties used to distinguish metals from nonmetals is their ability to conduct heat and/or electricity. A *metal* is a good conductor of heat and electricity, whereas a *nonmetal* is usually a poor conductor of heat and electricity. A *metalloid* is an element with properties that are intermediate between those of metals and nonmetals. Figure 2.9 shows that the majority of known elements are metals; only 17 elements are nonmetals, and fewer than 10 elements are metalloids. Although most sources, including this text, designate the elements B, Si, Ge, As, Sb, and Te as metalloids, sources vary for the elements Po and At. In this text, we classify both Po and At as metalloids. From left to right across any period, the physical and chemical properties of the elements change gradually from metallic to nonmetallic.

A vertical column of elements in the periodic table is known as a *group*. Groups of elements sometimes are referred to collectively by their group number (Group 1A, Group 2A, and so on). For convenience, however, some element groups have been given special names. The Group 1A elements (Li, Na, K, Rb, Cs, and Fr), are called the *alkali metals*, and the Group 2A elements (Be, Mg, Ca, Sr, Ba, and Ra) are called the *alkaline earth metals*. Elements in Group 6A (O, S, Se, Te, and Po) are sometimes referred to as the *chalcogens*. Elements in Group 7A (F, Cl, Br, I, and At) are known as the *halogens*, and elements in Group 8A (He, Ne, Ar, Kr, Xe, and Rn) are called the *noble gases*. The elements in Group 1B and Groups 3B–8B collectively are called the *transition elements* or the *transition metals*.

The periodic table is a remarkably useful tool that correlates the properties of elements in a systematic way and helps us to predict an element's behavior. We will look at the periodic table and its development in more detail in Chapter 4.

SECTION 2.5 REVIEW

The Periodic Table

2.5.1   Give the numbers of three groups in the periodic table that each contain at least one metal, at least one nonmetal, and at least one metalloid.

2.5.2   Give the number of a group in the periodic table that contains at least two metals, at least two nonmetals, and at least two metalloids.

2.6   THE MOLE AND MOLAR MASS

Atoms are so tiny that even the *smallest* macroscopic quantity of matter contains an *enormous* number of them. It is important, however, for chemists to know how many atoms there are in a sample. Clearly, it would not be convenient to express the quantities used in the laboratory in terms of the numbers of atoms involved. Instead, chemists use a unit of measurement called the *mole*.

The Mole

If you're buying bagels for yourself, you probably buy them individually, but if you're buying them for everyone in your chemistry class, you will probably want to buy them by the dozen. One dozen bagels contains exactly 12 bagels. In fact, a dozen of anything contains exactly 12 of that thing. Pencils typically come 12 to a box, and 12 such boxes may be shipped to the campus bookstore in a bigger box. The bigger box contains one gross of pencils (144). Whether a dozen or a gross, each is a convenient quantity that contains a reasonable, specific, exact number of items.

Chemists, too, have adopted such a number to make it easy to express the number of atoms in a typical macroscopic sample of matter. Atoms are *so* much smaller than bagels or pencils, though, that the number used by chemists is *significantly* bigger than a dozen or a gross. The quantity used by chemists is the **mole** (mol), which is defined as the amount of a substance that contains as many elementary entities (atoms, for example) as there are atoms in exactly 0.012 kg (12 g) of carbon-12. The number of atoms in exactly 12 g of carbon-12, which is determined experimentally, is known as **Avogadro's number (N_A)**, in honor of Italian scientist Amedeo Avogadro (1776–1856). The currently accepted value of Avogadro's number is 6.0221418×10^{23}, although we usually round it to 6.022×10^{23}. Thus, a dozen doughnuts contains 12 doughnuts; a gross of pencils contains 144 pencils; and a mole of helium gas, an amount that at room temperature and ordinary pressure would fill slightly more than half of a 10-gal fish tank, contains 6.022×10^{23} He atoms. Figure 2.10 shows samples containing one mole each of several familiar elements. Note that Avogadro's number has no units. When we convert between moles and numbers of atoms, what we actually use is Avogadro's *constant*, which has units of reciprocal moles: 6.0221418×10^{23} mol^{-1}.

Worked Example 2.3 shows how to convert between moles and atoms.

Figure 2.10 One mole each of several elements: (left to right) aluminum, copper, water, salt, and sugar; and (in balloon) helium.

Worked Example 2.3

Calcium is the most abundant metal in the human body. A typical human body contains roughly 30 moles of calcium. Determine (a) the number of Ca atoms in 30.00 moles of calcium and (b) the number of moles of calcium in a sample containing 1.00×10^{20} Ca atoms.

Strategy Use Avogadro's constant to convert from moles to atoms and from atoms to moles.

Setup When the number of moles is known, we multiply by Avogadro's constant to convert to atoms. When the number of atoms is known, we divide by Avogadro's constant to convert to moles.

Solution

(a) $30.00 \text{ mol Ca} \times \dfrac{6.022 \times 10^{23} \text{ Ca atoms}}{1 \text{ mol Ca}} = 1.807 \times 10^{25} \text{ Ca atoms}$

(b) $1.00 \times 10^{20} \text{ Ca atoms} \times \dfrac{1 \text{ mol Ca}}{6.022 \times 10^{23} \text{ Ca atoms}} = 1.66 \times 10^{-4} \text{ mol Ca}$

> **Think About It**
> Make sure that units cancel properly in each solution and that the result makes sense. In part (a), for example, the number of moles (30) is greater than one, so the number of atoms is greater than Avogadro's number. In part (b), the number of atoms (1×10^{20}) is less than Avogadro's number, so there is less than a mole of substance.

Practice Problem A Potassium is the second most abundant metal in the human body. Calculate (a) the number of atoms in 7.31 moles of potassium and (b) the number of moles of potassium that contains 8.91×10^{25} atoms.

Practice Problem B Calculate (a) the number of atoms in 1.05×10^{-6} mole of helium and (b) the number of moles of helium that contains 2.33×10^{21} atoms.

Molar Mass

Like the dozen and the gross, which are used to quantify specific, convenient numbers of bagels and pencils, respectively, the mole is used to quantify a specific, convenient number of atoms. Unlike the dozen and the gross, which are arrived at by *counting* the objects they quantify, the mole is not a number that can be arrived at by counting. The number of atoms in a macroscopic sample

Type of nail	Size (in)	Nails/lb
3d box	1.5	635
6d box	2	236
10d box	3	94
4d casing	1.5	473
8d casing	2.5	145
2d common	1	876
4d common	1.5	316
6d common	2	181
8d common	2.5	106

Figure 2.11 Bulk nails are sold by the pound. How many nails there are in a pound depends on the size and type of nail.

of matter is simply too big to be counted. Instead, the number of atoms in a quantity of substance is determined by weighing—like nails in a hardware store (Figure 2.11). The number of nails needed to build a fence or a house is fairly large. Therefore, when nails are purchased for such a project, they are not *counted*; but rather, they are *weighed* to determine their number. How many nails there are to a pound depends on the size and type of nail.

For example, if we want to buy 1000 1.5-in 4d common nails, we would not count out a thousand nails. Instead, we would weigh out an amount just over three pounds. Using data from the table in Figure 2.11:

$$1000 \text{ 4d common nails} \times \frac{1 \text{ lb}}{316 \text{ 4d common nails}} = 3.16 \text{ lb}$$

If we were to weigh out something *other* than the calculated amount, we could determine the number of nails using the same conversion factor:

$$5.00 \text{ lb} \times \frac{316 \text{ 4d common nails}}{1 \text{ lb}} = 1580 \text{ 4d common nails}$$

Note that the same mass of a different type of nail would contain a different number of nails. For example, we might weigh out 5.00 lb of 3-in 10d box nails:

$$5.00 \text{ lb} \times \frac{94 \text{ 10d box nails}}{1 \text{ lb}} = 470 \text{ 10d box nails}$$

The number of nails in each case is determined by weighing a sample of nails, and the number of nails in a given mass depends on the type of nail. Numbers of atoms, too, are determined by *weighing* a sample; and the number of atoms per unit mass also depends on the *type* of atom in the sample.

The ***molar mass*** ($\mathcal{M}$) of a substance is the mass in grams of one mole of the substance. By definition, the mass of a mole of carbon-12 is exactly 12 g. Note that the molar mass of carbon-12 is numerically equal to its atomic mass.

Mass of 1 carbon-12 atom: exactly 12 amu

Mass of 1 mole of carbon-12: exactly 12 g

The molar mass of *naturally occurring* carbon, which contains a small amount of carbon-13, is numerically equal to the *average* atomic mass of carbon: 12.01 g. Likewise, the average atomic mass of helium is 4.003 amu and its molar mass is 4.003 g; the average atomic mass of calcium is 40.08 amu and its molar mass is 40.08 g. In fact, any element's molar mass in *grams* is numerically equal to its average atomic mass in *atomic mass units*.

Although the term *molar mass* specifies the mass of one mole of a substance, making the appropriate units simply grams (g), we usually express molar masses in units of grams per mole (g/mol) to facilitate cancellation of units in calculations.

Worked Example 2.4 shows how to use molar mass to convert between mass and moles.

Worked Example 2.4

Determine (a) the number of moles of C in 25.00 g of carbon, (b) the number of moles of He in 10.50 g of helium, and (c) the number of moles of Na in 15.75 g of sodium.

Strategy Molar mass of an element is numerically equal to its average atomic mass. Use the molar mass for each element to convert from mass to moles.

Setup (a) The molar mass of carbon is 12.01 g/mol. (b) The molar mass of helium is 4.003 g/mol. (c) The molar mass of sodium is 22.99 g/mol.

Solution

(a) $25.00 \text{ g C} \times \dfrac{1 \text{ mol C}}{12.01 \text{ g C}} = 2.082 \text{ mol C}$

(b) $10.50 \text{ g He} \times \dfrac{1 \text{ mol He}}{4.003 \text{ g He}} = 2.623 \text{ mol He}$

(c) $15.75 \text{ g Na} \times \dfrac{1 \text{ mol Na}}{22.99 \text{ g Na}} = 0.6851 \text{ mol Na}$

Think About It
Always double-check unit cancellations in problems such as these—errors are common when molar mass is used as a conversion factor. Also make sure that the results make sense. For example, in the case of part (c), a mass smaller than the molar mass corresponds to *less* than a mole.

Practice Problem A Determine the number of moles in (a) 12.25 g of argon (Ar), (b) 0.338 g of gold (Au), and (c) 59.8 g of mercury (Hg).

Practice Problem B Determine the mass in grams of (a) 2.75 moles of calcium, (b) 0.075 mole of helium, and (c) 1.055×10^{-4} mole of potassium.

Interconverting Mass, Moles, and Numbers of Atoms

Molar mass is the conversion factor that we use to convert from mass (m) to moles (n), and vice versa. We use Avogadro's constant to convert from number of moles (n) to number of atoms (N), and vice versa. The flowchart in Figure 2.12 summarizes the operations involved in these conversions.

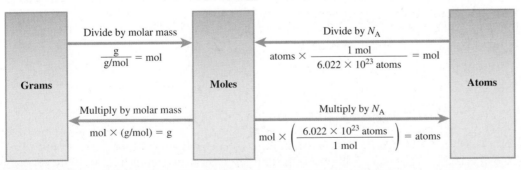

Figure 2.12 Flowchart for conversions among mass, moles, and number of atoms.

Worked Example 2.5 lets you practice these conversions.

Worked Example 2.5

Determine (a) the number of C atoms in 0.515 g of carbon, and (b) the mass of helium that contains 6.89×10^{18} He atoms.

Strategy Use the conversions depicted in Figure 2.12 to convert (a) from grams to moles to atoms, and (b) from atoms to moles to grams.

Setup (a) The molar mass of carbon is 12.01 g/mol. (b) The molar mass of helium is 4.003 g/mol. $N_A = 6.022 \times 10^{23}$.

Solution

(a) $0.515 \text{ g C} \times \dfrac{1 \text{ mol C}}{12.01 \text{ g C}} \times \dfrac{6.022 \times 10^{23} \text{ C atoms}}{1 \text{ mol C}} = 2.58 \times 10^{22}$ C atoms

(b) $6.89 \times 10^{18} \text{ He atoms} \times \dfrac{1 \text{ mol He}}{6.022 \times 10^{23} \text{ He atoms}} \times \dfrac{4.003 \text{ g He}}{1 \text{ mol He}} = 4.58 \times 10^{-5}$ g He

Think About It
A ballpark estimate of your result can help you prevent common errors. For example, the mass in part (a) is smaller than the molar mass of carbon. Therefore, you should expect a number of atoms *smaller* than Avogadro's number. Likewise, the number of atoms in part (b) is smaller than Avogadro's number. Therefore, you should expect a mass of helium *smaller* than the molar mass of helium.

Practice Problem A Determine (a) the number of atoms in 105.5 g of gold, and (b) the mass of calcium that contains 8.075×10^{12} Ca atoms.

Practice Problem B Determine the mass of calcium that contains the same number of atoms as 81.06 g of helium, and (b) the number of gold atoms that has the same mass as 7.095×10^{31} argon atoms.

SECTION 2.6 REVIEW

The Mole and Molar Mass

2.6.1   How many moles of arsenic are there in 6.50 g of arsenic?

2.6.2   How many atoms are there in 3.559×10^{-6} mol of krypton?

2.6.3   How many atoms are there in 30.1 g of magnesium?

2.6.4   What mass of mercury contains the same number of atoms as 90.15 g of helium?

Learning Outcomes

- Understand the concept of the atom and the nature of an element.
- Recognize the importance of experiments conducted by Thomson, Millikan, Röntgen, and Rutherford in regard to understanding the nature and structure of atoms.
- Understand the different types of radiation that radioactive substances can produce.
- Identify the location and physical properties of electrons, protons, and neutrons in atoms.
- Understand the nature and importance of isotopes.
- Calculate the mass number of an isotope.

- Utilize the mass number of an isotope to determine the number of electrons, protons, or neutrons, given other relevant information.
- Understand the nature of the atomic mass scale.
- Calculate the average atomic mass of an element given the atomic mass and relative abundance of each of its naturally occurring isotopes.
- Understand the concept of the mole.
- Use the relationships between Avogadro's number, moles, molar mass, and grams to conduct calculations.
- Interconvert between mass, moles, and number of atoms.

Chapter Summary

SECTION 2.1

- *Atoms* are the tiny building blocks of all matter. *Elements* are substances that cannot be broken down into simpler substances.

SECTION 2.2

- Studies with *radiation* and *cathode ray tubes* indicated that atoms contained subatomic particles, one of which was the *electron.*
- Experiments with *radioactivity* have shown that some atoms give off different types of radiation, called *α rays, β rays,* and *γ rays.* Alpha rays are composed of *α particles.* Beta rays are composed of *β particles,* which are actually electrons. Gamma rays are high-energy radiation.
- Most of the mass of an atom resides in a tiny, dense region known as the *nucleus.* The nucleus contains positively charged particles called *protons* and electrically neutral particles called *neutrons.*

SECTION 2.3

- The *atomic number, Z,* is the number of protons in the nucleus of an atom. Atomic number determines the identity of the atom.
- The *mass number, A,* is the sum of the protons and neutrons in the nucleus. Protons and neutrons are referred to collectively as *nucleons.*
- Atoms with the same atomic number but different mass numbers are called *isotopes.*

SECTION 2.4

- *Atomic mass* is the mass of an atom in atomic mass units. The periodic table contains the *average atomic mass* (sometimes called the *atomic weight*) of each element.

SECTION 2.5

- The *periodic table* arranges the elements in rows (*periods*) and columns (*groups*). Elements in the same group exhibit similar properties.
- *Metals* are good conductors of electricity; *nonmetals* are not good conductors of electricity. *Metalloids* have properties intermediate between those of metals and nonmetals.
- Some of the groups have special names including *alkali metals* (Group 1A, except hydrogen), *alkaline earth metals* (Group 2A), *chalcogens* (Group 6A), *halogens* (Group 7A), *noble gases* (Group 8A), and *transition metals* (Group 1B and Groups 3B–8B).

SECTION 2.6

- A *mole* is the amount of a substance that contains 6.0221418 $\times 10^{23}$ [*Avogadro's number* (N_A)] of elementary particles (such as atoms). Avogadro's constant, with units of reciprocal moles, is used to convert between moles and numbers of atoms.
- *Molar mass* ($\mathcal{M}$) is the mass of one mole of a substance, usually expressed in *grams*. The molar mass of an element in grams is numerically equal to the *atomic* mass of the element in *amu*.
- Molar mass and Avogadro's constant can be used to interconvert among *mass, moles,* and *number of atoms.*

Key Words

Alkali metal, 44
Alkaline earth metal, 44
Alpha particle (α), 36
Alpha rays (α), 36
Atom, 33
Atomic mass, 41
Atomic number (Z), 39
Average atomic mass, 41
Avogadro's number (N_A), 45
Beta particle (β), 36

Beta rays (β), 36
Cathode ray tube, 34
Chalcogens, 44
Electron, 35
Element, 33
Gamma rays (γ), 36
Group, 44
Halogens, 44
Isotope, 39
Mass number (A), 39

Metal, 44
Metalloid, 44
Molar mass ($\mathcal{M}$), 46
Mole, 45
Neutron, 38
Noble gases, 44
Nonmetal, 44
Nucleons, 39
Nucleus, 37
Period, 44

Periodic table, 43
Proton, 38
Radiation, 34
Radioactivity, 36
Transition elements, 44
Transition metal, 44
X rays, 36

Questions and Problems

SECTION 2.1:   ATOMS FIRST

Review Questions

2.1   Define the terms *atom* and *element*.

2.2   Use a familiar macroscopic example as an analogy to describe Dalton's atomic theory. Explain why a substance such as clay or oil is not useful for an analogy of this type.

SECTION 2.2:   SUBATOMIC PARTICLES AND ATOMIC STRUCTURE

Review Questions

2.3   Define the following terms: (a) α particle, (b) β particle, (c) γ ray, (d) X ray.

2.4   Name the types of radiation known to be emitted by radioactive elements.

2.5   Compare the properties of the following: α particles, cathode rays, protons, neutrons, and electrons.

2.6   Describe the contributions of the following scientists to our knowledge of atomic structure: J. J. Thomson, R. A. Millikan, Ernest Rutherford, and James Chadwick.

2.7   Describe the experimental basis for believing that the nucleus occupies a very small fraction of the volume of the atom.

Problems

2.8   The diameter of an argon atom is about 2×10^2 pm. If we could line up argon atoms side by side in contact with one another, how many atoms would it take to span a distance of 1 cm?

2.9   The radius of an atom is on the order of 10,000 times as large as its nucleus. If the atom were enlarged such that the radius of its nucleus were 1.0 cm, what would be the radius of the atom in meters, and in miles (1 mi = 1609 m)?

SECTION 2.3:   ATOMIC NUMBER, MASS NUMBER, AND ISOTOPES

Review Questions

2.10   Use the argon-40 isotope to define atomic number and mass number. Why does knowledge of the atomic number enable us to deduce the number of electrons present in an atom?

2.11   Why do all atoms of an element have the same atomic number, although they may have different mass numbers?

2.12   What do we call atoms of the same elements with different mass numbers?

2.13   Explain the meaning of each term in the symbol $_Z^A X$.

Problems

2.14   What is the mass number of an iron atom that has 31 neutrons?

2.15   Calculate the number of neutrons of ^{243}Pu.

2.16   For each of the following species, determine the number of protons and the number of neutrons in the nucleus: $_3^6$Li, $_{13}^{28}$Al, $_{13}^{29}$Al, $_{23}^{50}$V, $_{34}^{77}$Se, $_{77}^{193}$Ir.

2.17   Indicate the number of protons, neutrons, and electrons in each of the following species: $_8^{17}$O, $_{14}^{29}$Si, $_{28}^{58}$Ni, $_{39}^{89}$Y, $_{73}^{180}$Ta, $_{81}^{203}$Tl.

2.18   Write the appropriate symbol for each of the following isotopes: (a) $Z = 11$, $A = 23$; (b) $Z = 28$, $A = 64$; (c) $Z = 50$, $A = 115$; (d) $Z = 20$, $A = 42$.

2.19   Write the appropriate symbol for each of the following isotopes: (a) $Z = 75$, $A = 187$; (b) $Z = 83$, $A = 209$; (c) $Z = 33$, $A = 75$; (d) $Z = 93$, $A = 236$.

2.20   Determine the mass number of (a) a beryllium atom with 5 neutrons, (b) a sodium atom with 12 neutrons, (c) a selenium atom with 44 neutrons, and (d) a gold atom with 118 neutrons.

2.21   Determine the mass number of (a) a chlorine atom with 18 neutrons, (b) a phosphorus atom with 17 neutrons, (c) an antimony atom with 70 neutrons, and (d) a palladium atom with 59 neutrons.

2.22   The following radioactive isotopes are used in medicine for things such as imaging organs, studying blood circulation, and treating cancer. Give the number of neutrons present in each isotope: ^{198}Au, ^{47}Ca, ^{60}Co, ^{18}F, ^{125}I, ^{131}I, ^{42}K, ^{43}K, ^{24}Na, ^{32}P, ^{85}Sr, ^{99}Tc.

SECTION 2.4: AVERAGE ATOMIC MASS

Review Questions

2.23 What is the mass (in amu) of a carbon-12 atom? Why is the atomic mass of carbon listed as 12.01 amu in the table on the inside front cover of this book?

2.24 Explain clearly what is meant by the statement "The atomic mass of gold is 197.0 amu."

2.25 What information would you need to calculate the average atomic mass of an element?

Problems

2.26 The atomic masses of $^{35}_{17}Cl$ (75.78 percent) and $^{37}_{17}Cl$ (24.22 percent) are 34.969 and 36.966 amu, respectively. Calculate the average atomic mass of chlorine. The percentages in parentheses denote the relative abundances.

2.27 The atomic masses of ^{204}Pb (1.4 percent), ^{206}Pb (24.1 percent), ^{207}Pb (22.1 percent), and ^{208}Pb (52.4 percent) are 203.973020, 205.974440, 206.975872, and 207.976627 amu, respectively. Calculate the average atomic mass of lead. The percentages in parentheses denote the relative abundances.

2.28 The atomic masses of ^{203}Tl and ^{205}Tl are 202.972320 and 204.974401 amu, respectively. Calculate the natural abundances of these two isotopes. To seven significant figures, the average atomic mass of thallium is 204.3833 amu.

2.29 The atomic masses of ^6Li and ^7Li are 6.0151 amu and 7.0160 amu, respectively. Calculate the natural abundances of these two isotopes. The average atomic mass of Li is 6.941 amu.

2.30 The element rubidium has two naturally occurring isotopes. The atomic mass of ^{85}Rb (72.17 percent abundant) is 84.911794 amu. Determine the atomic mass of ^{87}Rb (27.83 percent abundant). The average atomic mass of Rb is 85.4678 amu.

2.31 There are three naturally occurring isotopes of the element magnesium. The atomic masses of ^{25}Mg (10.00 percent abundant) and ^{26}Mg (11.01 percent abundant) are 24.9858374 and 25.9825937 amu, respectively. What is the atomic mass of ^{24}Mg (78.99 percent abundant) given the average atomic mass of Mg is 24.3050 amu?

SECTION 2.5: THE PERIODIC TABLE

Review Questions

2.32 What is the periodic table, and what is its significance in the study of chemistry?

2.33 Write the names and symbols for four elements in each of the following categories: (a) nonmetal, (b) metal, (c) metalloid.

2.34 Give two examples of each of the following: (a) alkali metals, (b) alkaline earth metals, (c) halogens, (d) noble gases, (e) chalcogens, (f) transition metals.

2.35 The explosion of an atomic bomb in the atmosphere releases many radioactive isotopes into the environment. One of the isotopes is ^{90}Sr. Via a relatively short food chain, it can enter the human body. Considering the position of strontium in the periodic table, explain why it is particularly harmful to humans.

Problems

2.36 Elements whose names end with *-ium* are usually metals; sodium is one example. Identify a nonmetal whose name also ends with *-ium*.

2.37 Describe the changes in properties (from metals to nonmetals or from nonmetals to metals) as we move (a) down a periodic group and (b) across the periodic table from left to right.

2.38 Consult the WebElements Periodic Table of the Elements (http://www.webelements.com) to find (a) two metals less dense than water, (b) two metals more dense than mercury, (c) the densest known solid metallic element, and (d) the densest known solid nonmetallic element.

2.39 Group the following elements in pairs that you would expect to show similar properties: K, F, P, Na, Cl, and N.

2.40 Group the following elements in pairs that you would expect to show similar chemical properties: I, Ba, O, Br, S, and Ca.

2.41 Write the symbol for each of the following biologically important elements in the given periodic table: iron (present in hemoglobin for transporting oxygen), iodine (present in the thyroid gland), sodium (present in intracellular and extracellular fluids), phosphorus (present in bones and teeth), sulfur (present in proteins), and magnesium (present in chlorophyll).

SECTION 2.6: THE MOLE AND MOLAR MASS

Review Questions

2.42 Define the term *mole*. What is the unit for mole in calculations? What does the mole have in common with the dozen and the gross? What does Avogadro's number represent?

2.43 What is the molar mass of an element? What units are commonly used for molar mass?

Problems

2.44 Earth's population is about 6.8 billion. Suppose that every person on Earth participates in a process of counting identical particles at the rate of two particles per second. How many years would it take to count 6.0×10^{23} particles? Assume that there are 365 days in a year.

2.45 The diameter of a human hair is 25.4 μm. If atoms with a diameter of 121 pm were aligned side by side across the hair, how many atoms would be required?

2.46 How many atoms are there in 1.60 moles of selenium (Se)?

2.47 How many moles of nickel (Ni) atoms are there in 5.00×10^9 (5 billion) Ni atoms?

2.48 How many moles of strontium (Sr) atoms are in 93.7 g of Sr?

2.49 How many grams of platinum (Pt) are there in 26.4 moles of Pt?

2.50 What is the mass in grams of a single atom of each of the following elements: (a) Os, (b) Kr?

2.51 What is the mass in grams of a single atom of each of the following elements: (a) Sb, (b) Pd?

2.52 What is the mass in grams of 2.00×10^{12} tin (Sn) atoms?

2.53 How many atoms are present in 4.09 g of scandium (Sc)?

2.54 Which of the following has more atoms: 4.56 g of helium atoms or 2.36 g of manganese atoms?

2.55 Which of the following has a greater mass: 173 atoms of gold or 7.5×10^{-22} mole of silver?

ADDITIONAL PROBLEMS

2.56 A sample of uranium is found to be losing mass gradually. Explain what is happening to the sample.

2.57 The element francium (Fr) was the last element of the periodic table discovered in nature. Because of its high radioactivity, it is estimated that no more than 30 g of francium exists at any given time throughout the Earth's crust. Assuming a molar mass of 223 g/mol for francium, what is the approximate number of francium atoms in the Earth's crust?

2.58 One isotope of a metallic element has 35 neutrons in the nucleus. The neutral atom has 30 electrons. Write the symbol for this atom.

2.59 An isotope of a nonmetallic element has mass number 131. An atom of this isotope contains 54 electrons. Write the symbol for this atom.

2.60 Using the information provided in the table, write a symbol for each atom. If there is not enough information, state what additional information is needed to write a correct symbol for that atom.

	Atom of element			
	A	**B**	**C**	**D**
Number of electrons	6	11	29	
Number of protons	6		29	36
Number of neutrons	6	7		47

2.61 Using the information provided in the table, write a symbol for each atom. If there is not enough information, state what additional information is needed to write a correct symbol for that atom.

	Atom of element			
	A	**B**	**C**	**D**
Number of electrons	10		21	50
Number of protons		75	21	50
Number of neutrons	12	110	21	

2.62 Which of the following symbols provides more information about the atom: ^{23}Na or $_{11}$Na? Explain.

2.63 Discuss the significance of assigning an atomic mass of exactly 12 amu to the carbon-12 isotope.

2.64 List the elements that exist as gases at room temperature. (*Hint:* Most of these elements can be found in Groups 5A, 6A, 7A, and 8A.)

2.65 For the noble gases (the Group 8A elements) $^4_2$He, $^{20}_{10}$Ne, $^{40}_{18}$Ar, $^{84}_{36}$Kr, $^{132}_{54}$Xe (a) determine the number of protons and neutrons in the nucleus of each atom, and (b) determine the ratio of neutrons to protons in the nucleus of each atom. Describe any general trend you discover in the way this ratio changes with increasing atomic number.

2.66 The carat is the unit of mass used by jewelers. One carat is exactly 200 mg. How many carbon atoms are present in a 2.5-carat diamond?

2.67 In the geologic record of Earth, the disappearance of the dinosaurs roughly 65 million years ago is marked by a thin line known as the K-T boundary. Because the K-T boundary contains an unusually high concentration of the element *iridium*, which is ordinarily quite rare in Earth's crust, geologists have deduced that the mass extinction was caused by the catastrophic impact of an asteroid. The two naturally occurring isotopes of iridium are ^{191}Ir and ^{193}Ir, with atomic masses of 190.960584 and 192.962917 amu, respectively; and abundances of 37.3 percent and 62.7 percent, respectively. Determine the average atomic mass of iridium and compare your result with the atomic mass given in the periodic table.

2.68 One atom of a particular element with only one naturally occurring isotope has a mass of 3.002×10^{-22} g. What element is this?

2.69 Identify each of the following elements: (a) a halogen containing 53 electrons, (b) a radioactive noble gas with 86 protons, (c) a Group 6A element with 34 electrons, (d) an alkali metal that contains 11 electrons, (e) a Group 4A element that contains 82 electrons.

2.70 Show the locations of (a) alkali metals, (b) alkaline earth metals, (c) the halogens, and (d) the noble gases in the given outline of a periodic table. Also draw dividing lines between metals and metalloids and between metalloids and nonmetals.

2.71 While most isotopes of light elements such as oxygen and phosphorus contain relatively equal amounts of protons and neutrons in the nucleus, recent results indicate that a new class of isotopes called neutron-rich isotopes can be prepared. These neutron-rich isotopes push the limits of nuclear stability as the large numbers of neutrons approach the "neutron drip line." Neutron-rich isotopes may play a critical role in the nuclear processes of stars. Determine the number of neutrons in the following neutron-rich isotopes: (a) ^{40}Mg, (b) ^{44}Si, (c) ^{48}Ca, (d) ^{43}Al.

2.72 Fill in the blanks in the table:

Symbol		$^{121}_{51}$Ge	
Protons	14		
Neutrons	15		117
Electrons			79

2.73 Fill in the blanks in the table:

Symbol	^{101}Ru		
Protons			62
Neutrons		108	88
Electrons		73	

2.74 (a) Describe Rutherford's experiment and how the results revealed the nuclear structure of the atom. (b) Consider the ^{23}Na atom. Given that the radius and mass of the nucleus are 3.04×10^{-15} m and 3.82×10^{-23} g, respectively, calculate the density of the nucleus in g/cm^3. The radius of a ^{23}Na atom is 186 pm. Calculate the density of the space occupied by the electrons outside the nucleus in the sodium atom. Do your results support Rutherford's model of an atom? (The volume of a sphere of radius r is $\frac{4}{3}\pi r^3$.)

2.75 A cube made of platinum (Pt) has an edge length of 1.0 cm. (a) Calculate the number of Pt atoms in the cube. (b) Atoms are spherical in shape. Therefore, the Pt atoms in the cube cannot fill all the available space. If only 74 percent of the space inside the cube is taken up by Pt atoms, calculate the radius in picometers of a Pt atom. The density of Pt is 21.45 g/cm^3, and the mass of a single Pt atom is 3.240×10^{-22} g. (The volume of a sphere of radius r is $\frac{4}{3}\pi r^3$.)

2.76 In the facing page of the periodic table at the front of this book is an alphabetical list of elements with atomic masses given to the number of known significant figures. Compare the number of significant figures given for aluminum, bismuth, lead, and molybdenum. Look these elements up on webelements.com and explain why their atomic masses are reported to such different numbers of significant figures.

Answers to In-Chapter Materials

PRACTICE PROBLEMS

2.1A (a) p = 5, n = 5, e = 5. (b) p = 18, n = 18, e = 18. (c) p = 38, n = 47, e = 38. (d) p = 6, n = 5, e = 6. **2.1B** (a) $^9_4$Be, (b) $^{51}_{23}$V, (c) $^{124}_{54}$Xe, (d) $^{69}_{31}$Ga. **2.2A** 63.55 amu. **2.2B** 99.64% ^{14}N, 0.36% ^{15}N. **2.3A** (a) 4.40 $\times 10^{24}$ atoms K, (b) 1.48 $\times 10^2$ mol K. **2.3B** (a) 6.32 $\times 10^{17}$ atoms He, (b) 3.87 $\times 10^{-3}$ mol He. **2.4A** (a) 0.3066 mol Ar, (b) 1.72 $\times 10^{-3}$ mol Au, (c) 0.298 mol Hg. **2.4B** (a) 1.10 $\times 10^2$ g Ca, (b) 0.30 g He, (c) 4.125 $\times 10^{-3}$ g K. **2.5A** (a) 3.225 $\times 10^{23}$ atoms Au, (b) 5.374 $\times 10^{-10}$ g Ca. **2.5B** (a) 811.6 g Ca, (b) 1.439 $\times 10^{31}$ atoms Au.

SECTION REVIEW

2.3.1 32. **2.3.2** Cadmium. **2.4.1** 20% ^{10}B, 80% ^{11}B. **2.4.2** 121.76 amu. **2.5.1** 4A, 5A, 6A. **2.5.2** 5A. **2.6.1** 8.68 $\times 10^{-2}$ mol As. **2.6.2** 2.143 $\times 10^{18}$ atoms Kr. **2.6.3** 7.46 $\times 10^{23}$ atoms Mg. **2.6.4** 4.518 $\times 10^3$ g Hg.

KEY SKILLS

Interconversion Among Mass, Moles, and Numbers of Atoms

Many problems require you to convert a mass to a number of *moles* or to a number of *atoms*. Conversely, you may need to convert from a number of moles or a number of atoms to a *mass*. The conversion factors necessary for these operations are molar mass (in grams per mole) and Avogadro's constant, N_A (in number of atoms per mole). It's easy to make the mistake of multiplying when you should divide, or vice versa. Track your units carefully to make sure that you have not made this common error. Individual flowcharts for each operation are shown in the examples below.

One of the most common tasks you will encounter is the conversion of mass to moles:

How many moles of helium does a 71.3-g sample of helium contain?

$$\text{mass (g)} \quad \times \quad \frac{1}{\text{molar mass}}\left(\frac{\text{mol}}{\text{g}}\right) \quad = \quad \text{moles}$$

From the periodic table, we get the molar mass of helium: 4.003 g/mol.

$$71.3 \text{ g} \quad \times \quad \left(\frac{1 \text{ mol}}{4.003 \text{ g}}\right) \quad = \quad 17.8 \text{ mol}$$

You may also be asked to convert from the mass of a sample to the number of atoms it contains.

How many helium atoms does a 197-g sample of helium contain?

$$\text{mass (g)} \quad \times \quad \frac{1}{\text{molar mass}}\left(\frac{\text{mol}}{\text{g}}\right) \quad \times \quad \text{moles} \quad \times \quad N_A\left(\frac{\text{atoms}}{\text{mol}}\right) \quad = \quad \text{atoms}$$

Again, we use the molar mass of helium, 4.003 g/amu. Avogadro's constant is 6.0221418×10^{23} atoms/mol. (Because the original mass has only three significant figures, we can use 6.022×10^{23} atoms/mol in this calculation.)

$$197 \text{ g} \quad \times \quad \left(\frac{1 \text{ mol}}{4.003 \text{ g}}\right) \quad = \quad 49.2 \text{ mol} \quad \times \quad \left(\frac{6.022 \times 10^{23} \text{ atoms}}{\text{mol}}\right) \quad = \quad 2.96 \times 10^{25} \text{ atoms}$$

What number of moles of helium contains 8.80×10^{27} helium atoms?

$$\boxed{\text{atoms}} \quad \times \quad \boxed{\frac{1}{N_A}\left(\frac{\text{mol}}{\text{atoms}}\right)} \quad = \quad \boxed{\text{moles}}$$

In this case also, with only three significant figures in the number of atoms, we can use 6.022×10^{23} atoms/mol for Avogadro's number.

$$\boxed{8.80 \times 10^{27} \text{ atoms}} \quad \times \quad \boxed{\frac{1 \text{ mol}}{6.022 \times 10^{23} \text{ atoms}}} \quad = \quad \boxed{1.46 \times 10^4 \text{ mol}}$$

What is the mass of 8.80×10^{27} helium atoms?

$$\boxed{\text{moles}} \quad \times \quad \boxed{\text{molar mass}\left(\frac{\text{g}}{\text{mol}}\right)} \quad = \quad \boxed{\text{mass (g)}}$$

Again, we use the molar mass of helium.

$$\boxed{1.46 \times 10^4 \text{ mol}} \quad \times \quad \boxed{\frac{4.003 \text{ g}}{1 \text{ mol}}} \quad = \quad \boxed{5.85 \times 10^4 \text{ g}}$$

Key Skills Problems

2.1
Convert 0.189 g Cu to moles.

(a) 12.0 mol (b) 0.19 mol (c) 2.97×10^{-3} mol (d) 1.14×10^{-25} mol
(e) 1.14×10^{23} mol

2.2
How many Zn atoms are in 545 g Zn?

(a) 8.33 atoms (b) 8 atoms (c) 1.38×10^{-23} atoms (d) 5.02×10^{24} atoms (e) 3.28×10^{26} atoms

2.3
One container holds a mixture of metals containing 72.09 g of sodium and 6.99 g of strontium. Another container holds 47.87 g of titanium. What mass of calcium would have to be added to the second container for it to hold the same number of atoms as the first container?

(a) 40.08 g (b) 113.6 g (c) 2.834 g (d) 3.215 g (e) 88.80 g

2.4
Arrange the following in order of increasing mass:

1.85×10^{24} Fe atoms	7.68×10^{23} Ba atoms
i	ii
9.68×10^{23} Pd atoms	1.22×10^{24} Kr atoms
iii	iv

(a) i < iii < iv < ii
(b) ii < i < iv < ii
(c) i < iv < iii < ii
(d) iv < iii < i < ii
(e) ii < iv < iii < i

CHAPTER 3

Quantum Theory and the Electronic Structure of Atoms

3.1 Energy and Energy Changes
• Forms of Energy • Units of Energy

3.2 The Nature of Light
• Properties of Waves • The Electromagnetic Spectrum • The Double-Slit Experiment

3.3 Quantum Theory
• Quantization of Energy • Photons and the Photoelectric Effect

3.4 Bohr's Theory of the Hydrogen Atom
• Atomic Line Spectra • The Line Spectrum of Hydrogen

3.5 Wave Properties of Matter
• The de Broglie Hypothesis • Diffraction of Electrons

3.6 Quantum Mechanics
• The Uncertainty Principle • The Schrödinger Equation • The Quantum Mechanical Description of the Hydrogen Atom

3.7 Quantum Numbers
• Principal Quantum Number (n) • Angular Momentum Quantum Number (ℓ) • Magnetic Quantum Number (m_ℓ) • Electron Spin Quantum Number (m_s)

3.8 Atomic Orbitals
• s Orbitals • p Orbitals • d Orbitals and Other Higher-Energy Orbitals • Energies of Orbitals

3.9 Electron Configurations
• Energies of Atomic Orbitals in Many-Electron Systems • The Pauli Exclusion Principle • The Aufbau Principle • Hund's Rule • General Rules for Writing Electron Configurations

3.10 Electron Configurations and the Periodic Table

The very principles of quantum mechanics make visualizing atoms a difficult and daunting task. However, scientists have now harnessed the unique behavior of electrons in atoms to develop such advanced imaging techniques as *atomic force microscopy* and *scanning electron microscopy.* Shown here is an atomic image of a tungsten needle tip, considered to be the "sharpest man-made object ever." The round objects are actually individual tungsten atoms. Due to rapid atomic motion, not all of the atoms can be resolved simultaneously—causing some of the atoms to appear smeared. The ability to image at the atomic level allows scientists to investigate chemical phenomena on *very* small scales.

3.1 ENERGY AND ENERGY CHANGES

Before beginning any description of the electronic structure of the atom, it is necessary to define and discuss energy. **Energy** is the capacity to do work or transfer heat.

Forms of Energy

All forms of energy are either kinetic or potential. **Kinetic energy** is the energy that results from *motion*. It is calculated with the equation

$$E_k = \frac{1}{2}mu^2 \qquad \textbf{Equation 3.1}$$

where m is the mass of the object and u is its velocity. One form of kinetic energy of particular interest to chemists is **thermal energy**, which is the energy associated with the random motion of atoms and molecules. We can monitor changes in thermal energy by measuring temperature changes.

Student Annotation: Some textbooks use the letter v to denote velocity.

  Potential energy is the energy possessed by an object by virtue of its position. The two forms of potential energy of greatest interest to chemists are chemical energy and electrostatic energy. **Chemical energy** is energy stored within the structural units of chemical substances. The amount of chemical energy in a sample of matter depends on the types and arrangements of atoms in the structural units that make up the sample.

Student Annotation: "Structural units" may be *ions* [▶▶ Section 5.2] or *molecules* [▶▶ Section 5.4].

  Electrostatic energy is potential energy that results from the interaction of charged particles. Oppositely charged particles *attract* each other, and particles of like charges *repel* each other. The magnitude of the resulting electrostatic potential energy is proportional to the product of the two charges (Q_1 and Q_2) divided by the distance between them (d).

$$E_{el} \propto \frac{Q_1Q_2}{d} \qquad \textbf{Equation 3.2}$$

Student Annotation: The symbol $\propto$ can be read as "is proportional to." Equation 3.2 can also be written as an equality with a proportionality constant, c:
$$E_{el} = c\frac{Q_1Q_2}{d}$$

If the charges Q_1 and Q_2 are *opposite* (i.e., one positive and one negative), the result is a *negative* value for E_{el}, which indicates *attraction*. Like charges (i.e., both positive or both negative) result in a *positive* value for E_{el}, indicating *repulsion*.

  Kinetic and potential energy are interconvertible—that is, one form can be converted to the other. For example, dropping an object and allowing it to fall converts potential energy to kinetic energy. Although energy can assume many different forms that are interconvertible, the total amount of energy in the universe is constant; that is, energy can be neither created nor destroyed. When energy of one form disappears, the same amount of energy must appear in another form or forms. This principle is known as the **law of conservation of energy**.

Units of Energy

The SI unit of energy is the *joule (J)*, named for the English physicist James Joule.[1] The joule is a fairly small quantity of energy. It is the amount of kinetic energy possessed by a 2-kg mass moving at a speed of 1 m/s.

$$E_k = \frac{1}{2}mu^2 = \frac{1}{2}(2 \text{ kg})(1 \text{ m/s})^2 = 1 \text{ kg} \cdot \text{m}^2/\text{s}^2 = 1 \text{ J}$$

The joule can also be defined as the amount of energy exerted when a force of 1 newton (N) is applied over a distance of 1 meter.

$$1 \text{ J} = 1 \text{ N} \cdot \text{m}$$

where

$$1 \text{ N} = 1 \text{ kg} \cdot \text{m/s}^2$$

Because the magnitude of a joule is so small, we very often express large amounts of energy using the unit kilojoule (kJ).

$$1 \text{ kJ} = 1000 \text{ J}$$

Worked Examples 3.1 and 3.2 show how to calculate kinetic energy, and how to compare electrostatic energies between charged particles.

Worked Example 3.1

Calculate the kinetic energy of a helium atom moving at a speed of 125 m/s.

Strategy Use Equation 3.1 $\left(E_k = \frac{1}{2}mu^2\right)$ to calculate the kinetic energy of an atom. Note that for units to cancel properly, giving E_k in *joules*, the mass of the atom must be expressed in *kilograms*.

Setup The mass of a helium atom is 4.003 amu. The factor for conversion of amu to g is 1.661×10^{-24} g/1 amu [◀◀ Section 1.4]. Therefore, the mass of a helium atom in kilograms is

$$4.003 \text{ amu} \times \frac{1.661 \times 10^{-24} \text{ g}}{1 \text{ amu}} \times \frac{1 \text{ kg}}{1 \times 10^3 \text{ g}} = 6.649 \times 10^{-27} \text{ kg}$$

Solution

$$E_k = \frac{1}{2}mu^2$$

$$= \frac{1}{2}(6.649 \times 10^{-27} \text{ kg})(125 \text{ m/s})^2$$

$$= (5.19 \times 10^{-23} \text{ kg} \cdot \text{m}^2/\text{s}^2 = 5.19 \times 10^{-23} \text{ J}$$

Student Annotation: Remember that the base units of the joule are kg · m²/s².

> **Think About It**
> We expect the energy of a single atom, even a fast-moving one, to be extremely small.

Practice Problem A Calculate the energy in joules of a 5.25-g object moving at a speed of 655 m/s.

Practice Problem B Calculate the velocity (in m/s) of a 0.345-g object that has $E_k = 23.5$ J.

---

[1]James Prescott Joule (1818–1889). As a young man, Joule was tutored by John Dalton. He is most famous for determining the mechanical equivalent of heat, the conversion between mechanical energy and thermal energy.

Worked Example 3.2

How much greater is the attraction between charges of $+2$ and -2 than the attraction between charges of $+1$ and -1 if the opposite charges in each case are separated by the same distance?

Strategy Use Equation 3.2 $\left(E_{el} \propto \dfrac{Q_1 Q_2}{d} \right)$ to compare the magnitudes of the two E_{el} values.

Because the distance between charges is the same in both cases, we can solve for the ratio of E_{el} values without actually knowing the distance. Both the distance and the proportionality constant cancel in the solution.

Setup

$$E_{el(+2,-2)} = c\frac{Q_1 Q_2}{d}, Q_1 = +2 \text{ and } Q_2 = -2.$$

$$E_{el(+1,-1)} = c\frac{Q_1 Q_2}{d}, Q_1 = +1 \text{ and } Q_2 = -1.$$

Solution

$$\frac{c \times \left(\dfrac{2 \times (-2)}{d} \right)}{c \times \left(\dfrac{1 \times (-1)}{d} \right)} = 4$$

The attraction between charges of $+2$ and -2 is four times as large as the attraction between charges of $+1$ and -1.

> **Think About It**
> Doubling both charges causes a *four*-fold increase in the magnitude of the electrostatic energy between charged particles.

Practice Problem A How much greater is the attraction between charges of $+3$ and -2 than the attraction between charges of $+2$ and -2 if the opposite charges in each case are separated by the same distance?

Practice Problem B What must the separation between charges of $+2$ and -2 be for the attraction between them to be the same as the attraction between charges of $+2$ and -3 separated by a distance of 1.00 mm?

SECTION 3.1 REVIEW

Energy and Energy Changes

3.1.1 Calculate the kinetic energy of a 5.0-kg mass moving at 26 m/s.

3.1.2 Calculate the velocity (in m/s) of a 2.34-g object that has $E_k = 46.2$ J.

3.1.3 Arrange the following pairs of charged particles in order of increasing magnitude of electrostatic attraction (E_{el}).

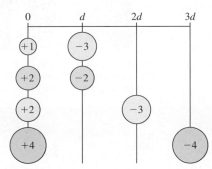

3.2 THE NATURE OF LIGHT

The term *light,* usually refers to *visible* light, which is the light we can detect with our eyes. Visible light, however, is only a small part of the continuum of radiation known as the ***electromagnetic spectrum***. In addition to visible light, the electromagnetic spectrum includes radio waves, microwave radiation, infrared and ultraviolet radiation, X rays, and gamma rays, as shown in Figure 3.1. You are probably familiar with some of these terms. Ultraviolet radiation, for instance, can cause sunburn; microwave radiation is commonly used to cook and/or reheat food; X rays are used for certain medical diagnoses and during routine dental checkups; and you may recall from Chapter 2 that gamma rays are emitted from some radioactive materials. Although these phenomena may seem very different from visible light—and different from one another—they all constitute the transmission of energy in the form of *waves.*

Properties of Waves

The fundamental properties of waves are illustrated in Figure 3.2. Waves are characterized by their wavelength, frequency, and amplitude. ***Wavelength*** λ (lambda) is the distance between identical points on successive waves (e.g., successive peaks or successive troughs). The ***frequency*** v (nu) is the *number* of waves that pass through a particular point in 1 second. ***Amplitude*** is the vertical distance from the midline of a wave to the top of the peak or the bottom of the trough.

The speed of a wave depends on the type of wave and the nature of the medium through which the wave is traveling (e.g., air, water, or a vacuum). The speed of light through a vacuum, c, is 2.99792458×10^8 m/s. The speed, wavelength, and frequency of a wave are related by the equation

> **Student Annotation:** The speed of light is defined to be 2.99792458×10^8 m/s. Therefore, it is an *exact* number and usually does not limit the number of significant figures in a calculated result. In most calculations, however, the speed of light can be rounded to three significant figures: $c = 3.00 \times 10^8$ m/s.

Equation 3.3	$c = \lambda v$

where λ and v are expressed in meters (m) and reciprocal seconds (s^{-1}), respectively. While wavelength in meters is convenient for this equation, the units customarily used to express the wavelength of electromagnetic radiation depend on the type of radiation and the magnitude of the corresponding wavelength. Visible wavelengths are usually expressed in nanometers (nm, or 10^{-9} m). Microwave and X-ray wavelengths are usually expressed in centimeters (cm, or 10^{-2} m) and angstroms (Å, or 10^{-10} m), respectively.

> **Student Annotation:** Frequency is expressed as cycles per second, or simply *reciprocal seconds* (s^{-1}), which is also known as *hertz* (Hz).

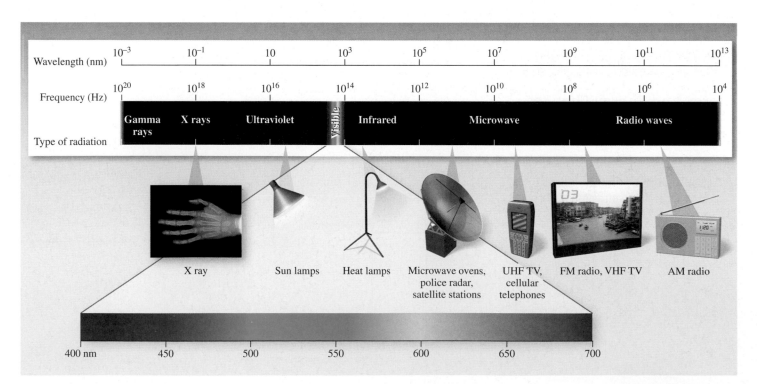

Figure 3.1 Electromagnetic spectrum. Each type of radiation is spread over a specific range of wavelengths (and frequencies). Visible light ranges from 400 nm (violet) to 700 nm (red).

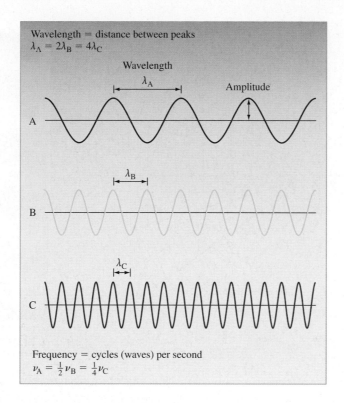

Wavelength = distance between peaks
$\lambda_A = 2\lambda_B = 4\lambda_C$

Wavelength

λ_A

Amplitude

A

λ_B

B

λ_C

C

Frequency = cycles (waves) per second
$\nu_A = \frac{1}{2}\nu_B = \frac{1}{4}\nu_C$

Figure 3.2 Characteristics of waves: wavelength, amplitude, and frequency.

The Electromagnetic Spectrum

In 1873 James Clerk Maxwell,[2] a Scottish physicist and mathematician, proposed that visible light consisted of electromagnetic waves. According to Maxwell's theory, an **electromagnetic wave** has an electric field component and a magnetic field component. These two components have the same wavelength and frequency, and hence the same speed, but they travel in mutually perpendicular planes (Figure 3.3). Maxwell's theory provides a mathematical description of the general behavior of light; and describes accurately how energy in the form of radiation can be propagated through space as oscillating electric and magnetic fields.

The Double-Slit Experiment

A simple yet convincing demonstration of the wave nature of light is the phenomenon of *interference.* When a light source passes through a narrow opening called a *slit,* a bright line is generated in the path of the light through the slit. When the same light source passes through two closely spaced slits, however, as shown in Figure 3.4, the result is not two bright lines, one in the path of each slit, but rather a series of light and dark lines known as an *interference pattern.* When the light

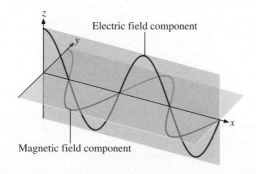

Electric field component

Magnetic field component

Figure 3.3 Electric field and magnetic field components of an electromagnetic wave. These two components have the same wavelength, frequency, and amplitude, but they vibrate in two mutually perpendicular planes.

---

[2]James Clerk Maxwell (1831–1879). Maxwell is considered by many to be one of the most influential physicists in history. His demonstration that electricity, magnetism, and light are all manifestations of the electromagnetic field is referred to as "the second great unification of physics."

Figure 3.4 Double-slit experiment. (a) Red lines correspond to the maximum intensity resulting from constructive interference. Dashed blue lines correspond to the minimum intensity resulting from destructive interference. (b) Interference pattern with alternating bright and dark lines.

First screen

Second screen

— • — Maximum
- - • - - Minimum

(a)   (b)

sources recombine after passing through the slits, they do so *constructively* where the two waves are *in phase* (giving rise to the light lines) and *destructively* where the waves are *out of phase* (giving rise to the dark lines). Constructive interference and destructive interference are properties of waves.

The various types of electromagnetic radiation in Figure 3.1 differ from one another in wavelength and frequency. Radio waves, which have long wavelengths and low frequencies, are emitted by large antennas, such as those used by broadcasting stations. The shorter, visible light waves are produced by the motions of electrons within atoms. The shortest waves, which also have the highest frequency, are γ (gamma) rays, which result from nuclear processes [◄◄ Section 2.2]. As we will see shortly, the higher the frequency, the more energetic the radiation. Thus, ultraviolet radiation, X rays, and γ rays are high-energy radiation, whereas infrared radiation, microwave radiation, and radio waves are low-energy radiation.

Worked Example 3.3 illustrates the conversion between wavelength and frequency.

Worked Example 3.3

The wavelength of a laser commonly used in the treatment of vascular skin lesions has a wavelength of 532 nm. What is the frequency of this radiation?

Strategy We must convert the wavelength to meters and solve for frequency using Equation 3.3 ($c = \lambda v$).

Setup Rearranging Equation 3.3 to solve for frequency gives $v = \dfrac{c}{\lambda}$. The speed of light, c, is 3.00×10^8 m/s. λ (in meters) = 532 nm $\times \dfrac{1 \times 10^{-9}\ \text{m}}{1\ \text{nm}} = 5.32 \times 10^{-7}$ m.

Solution

$$v = \frac{3.00 \times 10^8\ \text{m/s}}{5.32 \times 10^{-7}\ \text{m}} = 5.64 \times 10^{14}\ \text{s}^{-1}$$

Think About It
Make sure your units cancel properly. A common error in this type of problem is neglecting to convert wavelength to meters.

Practice Problem A What is the wavelength (in meters) of an electromagnetic wave whose frequency is 1.61×10^{12} s^{-1}?

Practice Problem B What is the frequency (in reciprocal seconds) of electromagnetic radiation with a wavelength of 1.03 cm?

SECTION 3.2 REVIEW

The Nature of Light

3.2.1 Calculate the wavelength (in nm) of light with frequency 3.45×10^{14} s^{-1}.

3.2.2 Calculate the frequency of light with wavelength 126 nm.

3.2.3 Of the waves pictured below, which has the greatest frequency, which has the greatest wavelength, and which has the greatest amplitude?

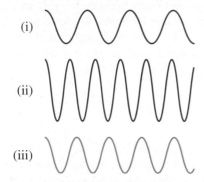

3.2.4 When traveling through a translucent medium, such as glass, light moves more slowly than it does when traveling through a vacuum. Red light with a wavelength of 684 nm travels through Pyrex glass with a frequency of 2.92×10^{14} s^{-1}. Calculate the speed of this light.

3.3 QUANTUM THEORY

Early attempts by nineteenth-century physicists to figure out the structure of the atom met with only limited success. This was largely because they were attempting to understand the inner workings of atoms using the laws of classical physics, which describe the behavior of *macroscopic* objects. It took a long time to realize—and an even longer time to accept—that the behavior of subatomic particles is *not* governed by the same physical laws as larger objects.

Quantization of Energy

When a solid is heated, it emits electromagnetic radiation, known as **blackbody radiation**, over a wide range of wavelengths. The red glow of the element of an electric stove and the bright white light of a tungsten lightbulb are examples of blackbody radiation. Measurements taken in the latter part of the nineteenth century showed that the amount of energy given off by an object at a certain temperature depends on the wavelength of the emitted radiation. Attempts to account for this dependence in terms of established wave theory and thermodynamic laws were only partially successful. One theory was able to explain short-wavelength dependence but failed to account for the longer wavelengths. Another theory accounted for the longer wavelengths but failed for short wavelengths. With no *one* theory that could explain both observations, it seemed that something fundamental was missing from the laws of classical physics.

In 1900, German physicist Max Planck[3] provided the solution and launched a new era in physics with an idea that departed drastically from accepted concepts. Classical physics assumed that radiant energy was continuous; that is, it could be emitted or absorbed in any amount. Based on data from blackbody radiation experiments, Planck proposed that radiant energy could be emitted or absorbed only in discrete quantities, like small packages or bundles. Planck gave the name *quantum* to the smallest quantity of energy that can be emitted (or absorbed) in the form of electromagnetic radiation. The energy E of a single quantum of energy is given by

$$E = h\nu$$

Equation 3.4

---

[3]Max Karl Ernst Ludwig Planck (1858–1947). Planck received the Nobel Prize in Physics in 1918 for his quantum theory. He also made significant contributions in thermodynamics and other areas of physics.

Student Annotation: The National Institute of Standards and Technology (NIST) gives a value of $6.6260693 \times 10^{-34}$ J · s for Planck's constant. Typically, three significant figures are sufficient for solving problems.

where h is called *Planck's constant* and v is the *frequency* of the radiation. The value of Planck's constant is 6.63×10^{-34} J · s.

According to quantum theory, energy is always emitted in whole-number multiples of hv. At the time Planck presented his theory, he could not explain why energies should be fixed or quantized in this manner. Starting with this hypothesis, however, he had no difficulty correlating the experimental data for the emission by solids over the entire range of wavelengths; the experimental data supported his new *quantum theory*.

The idea that energy is *quantized* rather than *continuous* may seem strange, but the concept of quantization has many everyday analogies. For example, as you walk up a staircase, you can stop only at elevations corresponding to the steps—not at an elevation *between* steps. On a piano, you can play only the notes for which there are keys—not notes between keys. Even processes in living systems involve quantized phenomena. The eggs laid by hens are quanta (hens lay only whole eggs). Similarly, when a dog gives birth to a litter, the number of puppies is always an integer. Each puppy is a "quantum" of that animal. Planck's quantum theory revolutionized physics; and the flurry of research that ensued altered our concept of nature forever.

Photons and the Photoelectric Effect

In 1905, only five years after Planck presented his quantum theory, Albert Einstein[4] used the theory to explain another well-known but mysterious physical phenomenon, the ***photoelectric effect***. In the photoelectric effect, electrons are ejected from the surface of a metal exposed to light. However, the light must be of a certain minimum frequency, called the ***threshold frequency*** (Figure 3.5). The *number* of electrons ejected was proportional to the intensity (or brightness) of the light, but the *energies* of the ejected electrons were not. Below the threshold frequency no electrons were ejected no matter how intense the light.

The photoelectric effect could not be explained by the wave theory of light, which associated the energy of light with its intensity. Einstein, however, made an extraordinary assumption. He suggested that a beam of light is really a stream of *particles*. These "particles" of light are now called ***photons***. Using Planck's quantum theory of radiation as a starting point, Einstein deduced that each photon must possess energy E given by the equation

Student Annotation: Note that this is simply Equation 3.4 in which the "quantum" has been specified as a *photon of light*.

$$E_{photon} = hv$$

where h is Planck's constant and v is the frequency of the light. Electrons are held in a metal by attractive forces, and so removing them from the metal requires light of a sufficiently high frequency (which corresponds to a sufficiently high *energy*) to break them free. Shining a beam of light onto a metal surface can be thought of as shooting a beam of particles—*photons*—at the metal atoms. If the frequency of the photons is such that hv exactly equals the energy that binds the electrons in the metal, then the light will have just enough energy to knock the electrons loose. If we use light of a *higher* frequency, then not only will the electrons be knocked loose, but they will also acquire some kinetic energy. This situation is summarized by the equation

Incident light

Metal

Meter

Voltage source

Figure 3.5 Apparatus for studying the photoelectric effect. Light of a certain frequency falls on a clean metal surface. Ejected electrons are attracted toward the positive electrode. The flow of electrons is registered by a detecting meter.

Equation 3.5	$hv = KE + W$

where KE is the kinetic energy of the ejected electron and W is the binding energy of the electron in the metal. Rewriting Equation 3.5 as

$$KE = hv - W$$

shows that the more energetic the photon (i.e., the higher its frequency), the greater the kinetic energy of the ejected electron. If the frequency of light is below the threshold frequency, the photon will simply bounce off the surface and no electrons will be ejected. If the frequency is equal to the threshold frequency, it will dislodge the most loosely held electron. Above the threshold frequency, it will not only dislodge the electron, but also impart certain kinetic energy to the ejected electron.

Now consider two beams of light having the same frequency (greater than the threshold frequency) but different intensities. The more intense beam of light consists of a larger number of

[4]Albert Einstein (1879–1955). A German-born American physicist, Einstein is regarded by many as one of the two greatest physicists the world has known (the other being Newton). The three papers (on special relativity, Brownian motion, and the photoelectric effect) that he published in 1905 while employed as a technical assistant in the Swiss patent office in Berne have profoundly influenced the development of physics. He received the Nobel Prize in Physics in 1921 for his explanation of the photoelectric effect.

Thinking Outside the Box

Everyday Occurrences of the Photoelectric Effect

Chances are good that you encounter the photoelectric effect regularly. Some everyday applications include the type of device that prevents a garage door from closing when something is in the door's path and motion-detection systems used in museums and other high-security environments. These sorts of devices work simply by responding to an interruption in a beam of light. In each case, a beam of light normally shines on a *photocathode,* a surface that emits photoelectrons, and the photoelectrons, accelerated toward an anode by high voltage, constitute a current. When the beam of light is interrupted, the flow of electrons stops and the current is cut off. In the case of the garage-door safety device, when the current stops, the movement of the door stops. In the case of the motion-detection systems, when the current stops, an alarm may sound or a light may turn on.

One of the more exotic uses of the photoelectric effect is night-vision goggles. Although you may never have looked through night-vision goggles, you have probably seen night-vision images on the news or in a suspense-filled movie such as *Silence of the Lambs.* Typically, the night-vision images we see are from what are known as third-generation night-vision devices. These devices use a photocathode material that emits photoelectrons when struck by photons in the *infrared* region of the electromagnetic spectrum. (First- and second-generation devices used different photocathode materials and relied more on the amplification of low-level visible light.) The photoelectrons emitted by the photocathode enter a microchannel plate (MCP), an array of tiny parallel tubes, where each strikes the internal surface of a tube causing many more electrons to be ejected—a process called *secondary emission.* This effectively amplifies the current generated by each photoelectron. The amplified current is then accelerated by high voltage toward a phosphorus screen, where incident electrons cause the emission of visible light, generating the familiar green glow of night vision.

(a)

(b)

(a) Night-vision goggles schematic. 1. Photocathode (gallium arsenide).
2. Microchannel plate (MCP). 3. High-voltage source. 4. Phosphorus screen.
(b) The green glow of night vision.

photons, so it ejects more electrons from the metal's surface than the less-intense beam of light. Thus, the more intense the light, the greater the number of electrons emitted by the target metal; the higher the frequency of the light, the greater the kinetic energy of the ejected electrons.

Worked Example 3.4 shows how to determine the energy of a single photon of light of a given wavelength, and how to determine the kinetic energy of an electron ejected from a metal via the photoelectric effect.

Worked Example 3.4

Calculate the energy (in joules) of (a) a photon with a wavelength of 5.00×10^4 nm (infrared region) and (b) a photon with a wavelength of 52 nm (ultraviolet region). (c) Calculate the maximum kinetic energy of an electron ejected by the photon in part (b) from a metal with a binding energy of 3.7 eV.

Strategy In parts (a) and (b), we are given the wavelength of light. Use Equation 3.3 ($c = \lambda v$) to convert wavelength to frequency, then use Equation 3.4 ($E = hv$) to determine the energy of the photon for each wavelength. In part (c), we are asked to determine the kinetic energy of an ejected electron. For this we use Equation 3.5 ($hv = KE + W$). The binding energy, given in electron volts, must be converted to joules in order for units to cancel.

Setup The wavelengths must be converted from nanometers to meters:

(a) $5.00 \times 10^4 \text{ nm} \times \dfrac{1 \times 10^{-9} \text{ m}}{1 \text{ nm}} = 5.00 \times 10^{-5}$ m

(b) $52 \text{ nm} \times \dfrac{1 \times 10^{-9} \text{ m}}{1 \text{ nm}} = 5.2 \times 10^{-8}$ m

Planck's constant, h, is 6.63×10^{-34} J · s.

(c) $W = 3.7 \text{ eV} \times \dfrac{1.602 \times 10^{-19} \text{ J}}{1 \text{ eV}} = 5.9 \times 10^{-19}$ J

Solution

(a) $v = \dfrac{c}{\lambda} = \dfrac{3.00 \times 10^8 \text{ m/s}}{5.00 \times 10^{-5} \text{ m}} = 6.00 \times 10^{12} \text{ s}^{-1}$ and

$$E = hv = (6.63 \times 10^{-34} \text{ J · s})(6.00 \times 10^{12} \text{ s}^{-1}) = 3.98 \times 10^{-21} \text{ J}$$

This is the energy of a single photon with wavelength 5.00×10^4 nm.

(b) Following the same procedure as in part (a), the energy of a photon of wavelength 52 nm is 3.8×10^{-18} J.

(c) $KE = hv - W = 3.8 \times 10^{-18} \text{ J} - 5.9 \times 10^{-19} \text{ J} = 3.2 \times 10^{-18}$ J.

Think About It

Remember that frequency and wavelength are *inversely* proportional (Equation 3.3). Thus, as wavelength *decreases*, frequency and energy *increase*. Note that in part (c), subtracting the binding energy made a relatively small change to the energy of the incident photon. If the incident photon had been in the X-ray region of the spectrum, the difference between its energy and the kinetic energy of the ejected electron would have been negligible.

Practice Problem A Calculate the energy (in J) of (a) a photon with wavelength 2.11×10^2 nm, and (b) a photon with wavelength 1.69×10^3 mm. (c) Calculate the maximum kinetic energy of an electron ejected by the photon in part (a) from a metal with a binding energy of 4.66 eV.

Practice Problem B (a) Calculate the wavelength (in nm) of light with energy 1.89×10^{-20} J per photon. (b) For light of wavelength 410 nm, calculate the number of photons per joule. (c) Determine the binding energy (in eV) of a metal if the maximum kinetic energy possessed by an electron ejected from it [using one of the photons in part (b)] is 2.93×10^{-19} J.

Einstein's theory of light posed a dilemma for scientists. On the one hand, it explains the photoelectric effect. On the other hand, the particle theory of light is inconsistent with the known wavelike properties of light. The only way to resolve the dilemma is to accept the idea that light possesses properties characteristic of both particles *and* waves. Depending on the experiment, light behaves either as a wave or as a stream of particles. This concept was totally alien to the way physicists had thought about matter and radiation, and it took a long time for them to accept it. We will see in Section 3.5 that possessing properties of both particles and waves is not unique to light but ultimately is characteristic of all matter, including electrons.

Quantum Theory

3.3.1 Calculate the energy per photon of light with wavelength 650 nm.

3.3.2 Calculate the wavelength (in cm) of light that has energy 1.32×10^{-23} J/photon.

3.3.3 Calculate the maximum kinetic energy of an electron ejected by a photon of the light in 3.3.1 from a metal with a binding energy of 1.56 eV.

3.3.4 A clean metal surface is irradiated with light of three different wavelengths: λ_1, λ_2, and λ_3. The kinetic energies of the ejected electrons are as follows: λ_1: 2.9×10^{-20} J; λ_2: approximately zero; λ_3: 4.2×10^{-19} J. Arrange the light in order of increasing wavelength.

3.4 BOHR'S THEORY OF THE HYDROGEN ATOM

In addition to explaining the photoelectric effect, Planck's quantum theory and Einstein's ideas made it possible for scientists to unravel another nineteenth-century mystery in physics: atomic line spectra.

In the seventeenth century, Newton had shown that sunlight is composed of various color components that can be recombined to produce white light. Since that time, chemists and physicists have studied the characteristics of such *emission spectra*. The emission spectrum of a substance can be seen by energizing a sample of material with either thermal energy or some other form of energy (such as a high-voltage electrical discharge if the substance is a gas). A "red-hot" or "white-hot" iron bar freshly removed from a fire produces a characteristic glow. The glow is the visible portion of its emission spectrum. The heat given off by the same iron bar is another portion of its emission spectrum—the infrared region. A feature common to the emission spectrum of the sun and that of a heated solid is that both are continuous; that is, all wavelengths of visible light are present in each spectrum (Figure 3.6).

Student Annotation: If you have ever seen a rainbow, you are familiar with this phenomenon. The rainbow is the visible portion of the sun's emission spectrum.

Atomic Line Spectra

Unlike those of the sun or a white-hot iron bar, the emission spectra of atoms in the gas phase do not show a continuous spread of wavelengths from red to violet; rather, the atoms produce bright lines in distinct parts of the visible spectrum. These *line spectra* are the emission of light only at

(a)

(b)

Figure 3.6 The visible white light emitted by (a) the sun and (b) a white-hot iron bar. In each case, the white light is the combination of all visible wavelengths (see Figure 3.1).

Figure 3.7 (a) Experimental arrangement for studying the emission spectra of atoms and molecules. The gas being studied is in a discharge tube containing two electrodes. As electrons flow from the negative electrode to the positive electrode, they collide with the gas particles. The collisions lead to the emission of light by the atoms (or molecules). The emitted light is separated into its components by a prism. (b) Visible line emission spectrum of hydrogen.

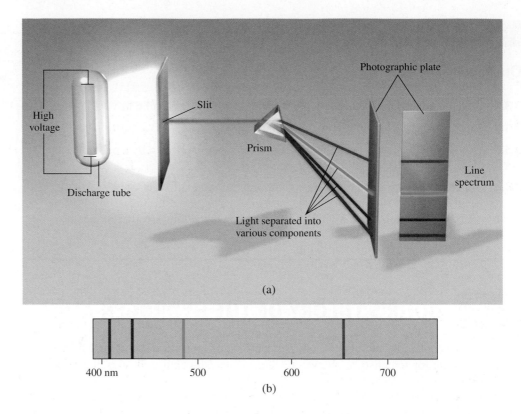

(a)

(b)

specific wavelengths. Figure 3.7 is a schematic diagram of a discharge tube that is used to study emission spectra.

Every element has a unique emission spectrum, so the characteristic lines in atomic spectra can be used in chemical analysis to identify elements, much as fingerprints are used to identify people. When the lines of the emission spectrum of a known element exactly match the lines of the emission spectrum of an unknown sample, the identity of the element in the sample is established. Although the procedure of identifying elements by their line spectra had been used for many years in chemical analysis, the origin of the spectral lines was not understood until early in the twentieth century. Figure 3.8 shows the emission spectra of several elements.

In 1885, Johann Balmer[5] developed a simple equation that could be used to calculate the wavelengths of the four visible lines in the emission spectrum of hydrogen. Johannes Rydberg[6] developed Balmer's equation further, yielding an equation that could calculate not only the *visible* wavelengths, but those of *all* hydrogen's spectral lines:

Equation 3.6
$$\frac{1}{\lambda} = R_\infty \left(\frac{1}{n_1^2} - \frac{1}{n_2^2} \right)$$

Student Annotation: The Rydberg equation is a mathematical relationship that was derived from experimental data. Although it predates quantum theory by decades, it agrees remarkably well with it for one-electron systems such as the hydrogen atom.

In Equation 3.6, now known as the *Rydberg equation*, λ is the wavelength of a line in the spectrum; R_∞ is the Rydberg constant ($1.09737316 \times 10^7 \, \text{m}^{-1}$); and n_1 and n_2 are positive integers, where $n_2 > n_1$.

The Line Spectrum of Hydrogen

In 1913, not long after Planck's and Einstein's discoveries, a theoretical explanation of the emission spectrum of the hydrogen atom was presented by the Danish physicist Niels Bohr.[7] Bohr's treatment is very complex and is no longer considered to be correct in all its details. We will concentrate only on his important assumptions and final results, which account for the observed spectral lines and which provide an important step toward the understanding of quantum theory.

---

[5]Johann Jakob Balmer (1825–1898). From 1859 until his death in 1898, Balmer, a Swiss mathematician, taught math at a secondary school for girls in Basel, Switzerland. Although physicists did not understand why his equation worked until long after his death, the visible series of lines in the spectrum of hydrogen is named for him.

[6]Johannes Robert Rydberg (1854–1919). A Swedish mathematician and physicist, Rydberg analyzed many atomic spectra in an effort to understand the periodic properties of elements. Although he was nominated twice for the Nobel Prize in Physics, he never received it.

[7]Niels Henrik David Bohr (1885–1962). One of the founders of modern physics, he received the Nobel Prize in Physics in 1922 for his theory explaining the line spectrum of hydrogen.

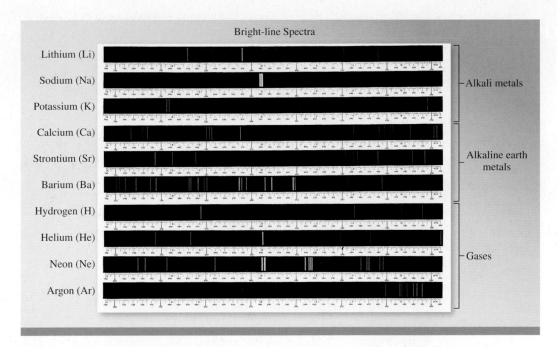

Figure 3.8 Emission spectra of several elements.

When Bohr first approached this problem, physicists already knew that the atom contains electrons and protons. They thought of an atom as an entity in which electrons whirled around the nucleus in circular orbits at high velocities. This was an appealing description because it resembled the familiar model of planetary motion around the sun. However, according to the laws of classical physics, an electron moving in an orbit of a hydrogen atom would experience an acceleration toward the nucleus by radiating away energy in the form of electromagnetic waves. Thus, such an electron would quickly spiral into the nucleus and annihilate itself with the proton. To explain why this does not happen, Bohr postulated that the electron is allowed to occupy only certain orbits of specific energies. In other words, the energies of the electron are quantized. An electron in any of the allowed orbits will not radiate energy and therefore will not spiral into the nucleus.

Bohr attributed the emission of radiation by an energized hydrogen atom to the electron dropping from a higher-energy orbit to a lower one and giving up a quantum of energy (a photon) in the form of light (Figure 3.9). Using arguments based on electrostatic interaction and Newton's laws of motion, Bohr showed that the energies that the electron in the hydrogen atom can possess are given by

$$E_n = -2.18 \times 10^{-18} \text{ J}\left(\frac{1}{n^2}\right)$$

Equation 3.7

where n is an integer with values $n = 1, 2, 3$, and so on. The negative sign in Equation 3.7 is an arbitrary convention, signifying that the energy of the electron in the atom is *lower* than the energy of a *free electron,* which is an electron that is infinitely far from the nucleus. The energy of a free electron is arbitrarily assigned a value of zero. Mathematically, this corresponds to setting n equal to infinity in Equation 3.7:

$$E_n = -2.18 \times 10^{-18} \text{ J}\left(\frac{1}{\infty^2}\right) = 0$$

As the electron gets closer to the nucleus (as n decreases), E_n becomes larger in absolute value, but also more negative. The most negative value, then, is reached when $n = 1$, which corresponds to the most stable energy state. We call this the ***ground state,*** the lowest energy state of an atom. The stability of the electron diminishes as n increases. Each energy state in which $n > 1$ is called an ***excited state***. Each excited state is higher in energy than the ground state. In the hydrogen atom, an electron for which n is greater than 1 is said to be in an excited state.

The radius of each circular orbit in Bohr's model depends on n^2. Thus, as n increases from 1 to 2 to 3, the orbit radius increases very rapidly. The higher the excited state, the farther away the electron is from the nucleus (and the less tightly held it is by the nucleus).

Bohr's theory enables us to explain the line spectrum of the hydrogen atom. Radiant energy absorbed by the atom causes the electron to move from the ground state ($n = 1$) to an excited state ($n > 1$). Conversely, radiant energy (in the form of a photon) is *emitted* when the electron moves from a higher-energy excited state to a lower-energy excited state or the ground state.

Multi 3.1
Emission spectrum of hydrogen

Student Annotation: It is important to recognize that the electron in a hydrogen atom can move from a higher-energy state to *any* lower-energy state. It does not necessarily move from a higher-energy state to the ground state.

Figure 3.9

Emission Spectrum of Hydrogen

Hydrogen atoms in the ground state are excited by the addition of energy. Electrons that have been promoted to higher energy levels ($n > 1$) return to lower energy levels and emit the excess energy as electromagnetic radiation.

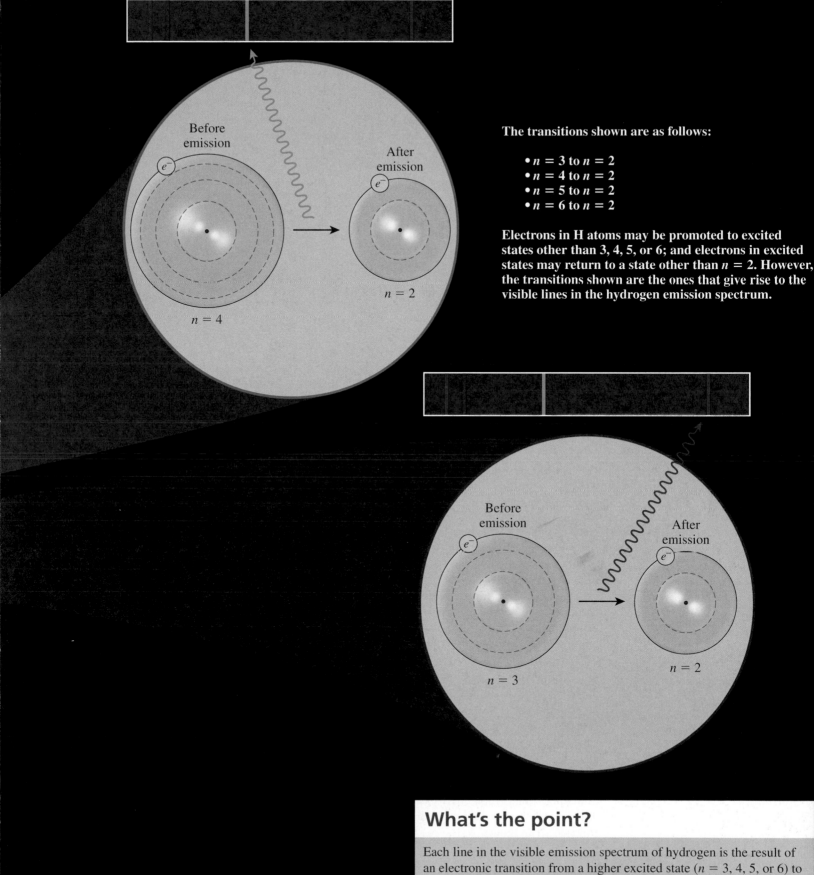

The transitions shown are as follows:

- $n = 3$ to $n = 2$
- $n = 4$ to $n = 2$
- $n = 5$ to $n = 2$
- $n = 6$ to $n = 2$

Electrons in H atoms may be promoted to excited states other than 3, 4, 5, or 6; and electrons in excited states may return to a state other than $n = 2$. However, the transitions shown are the ones that give rise to the visible lines in the hydrogen emission spectrum.

What's the point?

Each line in the visible emission spectrum of hydrogen is the result of an electronic transition from a higher excited state ($n = 3$, 4, 5, or 6) to a lower excited state ($n = 2$). The energy gap between the initial and final states determines the wavelength of the light emitted.

Figure 3.10 Mechanical analogy for the emission processes. The ball can rest on any step but not between steps.

Student Annotation: The symbol delta Δ is commonly used to denote *final* minus *initial*.

Student Annotation: When $n_i > n_f$, ΔE is *negative* indicating energy is *emitted*. When $n_f > n_i$, ΔE is *positive* indicating energy is *absorbed*.

Student Annotation: Because 2.18×10^{-18} J/hc = 1.096×10^7 m^{-1}, which to three significant figures is equal to R_∞, this equation is essentially the same as the Rydberg equation (Equation 3.6).

The quantized movement of the electron from one energy state to another is analogous to the movement of a tennis ball either up or down a set of stairs (Figure 3.10). The ball can be on any of several steps but never between steps. The journey from a lower step to a higher one is an energy-requiring process, whereas movement from a higher step to a lower step is an energy-releasing process. The quantity of energy involved in either type of change is determined by the distance between the beginning and ending steps. Similarly, the amount of energy needed to move an electron in the Bohr atom depends on the difference in energy levels between the initial and final states.

To apply Equation 3.7 to the emission process in a hydrogen atom, let us suppose that the electron is initially in an excited state characterized by n_i. During emission, the electron drops to a lower energy state characterized by n_f (the subscripts i and f denote the *initial* and *final* states, respectively). This lower energy state may be the ground state, but it can be any state lower than the initial excited state. The difference between the energies of the initial and final states is

$$\Delta E = E_f - E_i$$

From Equation 3.7,

$$E_n = -2.18 \times 10^{-18} \text{ J} \left(\frac{1}{n_f^2}\right)$$

and

$$E_n = -2.18 \times 10^{-18} \text{ J} \left(\frac{1}{n_i^2}\right)$$

Therefore,

$$\Delta E = \left(\frac{-2.18 \times 10^{-18} \text{ J}}{n_f^2}\right) - \left(\frac{-2.18 \times 10^{-18} \text{ J}}{n_i^2}\right)$$

$$= -2.18 \times 10^{-18} \text{ J} \left(\frac{1}{n_f^2} - \frac{1}{n_i^2}\right)$$

Because this transition results in the emission of a photon of frequency v and energy hv, we can write

Equation 3.8 $$\Delta E = hv = -2.18 \times 10^{-18} \text{ J} \left(\frac{1}{n_f^2} - \frac{1}{n_i^2}\right)$$

A photon is emitted when $n_i > n_f$. Consequently, the term in parentheses is *positive*, making ΔE *negative* (energy is lost to the surroundings). A photon is absorbed when $n_f > n_i$, making the term in parentheses *negative*, so ΔE is *positive*. Each spectral line in the emission spectrum of hydrogen corresponds to a particular transition in a hydrogen atom. When we study a large number of hydrogen atoms, we observe all possible transitions and hence the corresponding spectral lines. The brightness of a spectral line depends on how many photons of the same wavelength are emitted.

To calculate the wavelength of an emission line, we substitute c/λ for v and then divide both sides of Equation 3.8 by hc. In addition, because wavelength can have only positive values, we take the absolute value of the right side of the equation. (In this case, we do so simply by eliminating the negative sign.)

Equation 3.9 $$\frac{1}{\lambda} = \frac{2.18 \times 10^{-18} \text{ J}}{hc} \left(\frac{1}{n_f^2} - \frac{1}{n_i^2}\right)$$

The emission spectrum of hydrogen includes a wide range of wavelengths from the infrared to the ultraviolet. Table 3.1 lists the series of transitions in the hydrogen spectrum, each with a different value of n_f. The series are named after their discoverers (Lyman, Balmer, Paschen, and Brackett). The Balmer series was the first to be studied because some of its lines occur in the visible region.

Figure 3.11 shows transitions associated with spectral lines in each of the emission series. Each horizontal line represents one of the allowed energy levels for the electron in a hydrogen atom. The energy levels are labeled with their n values.

Worked Example 3.5 illustrates the use of Equation 3.9.

TABLE 3.1	Emission Series in the Hydrogen Spectrum		
Series	n_f	n_i	**Spectrum region**
Lyman	1	2, 3, 4, . . .	Ultraviolet
Balmer	2	3, 4, 5, . . .	Visible and ultraviolet
Paschen	3	4, 5, 6, . . .	Infrared
Brackett	4	5, 6, 7, . . .	Infrared

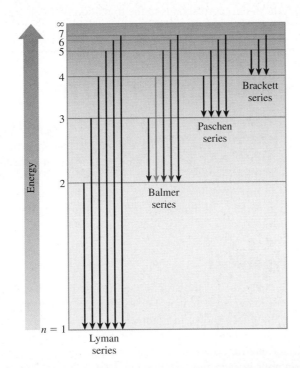

Figure 3.11 Energy levels in the hydrogen atom and the various emission series. Each series terminates at a different value of *n*.

Worked Example 3.5

Calculate the wavelength (in nm) of the photon emitted when an electron transitions from the $n = 4$ state to the $n = 2$ state in a hydrogen atom.

Strategy Use Equation 3.9 to calculate λ.

Setup According to the problem, the transition is from $n = 4$ to $n = 2$, so $n_i = 4$ and $n_f = 2$. The required constants are $h = 6.63 \times 10^{-34}$ J · s and $c = 3.00 \times 10^8$ m/s.

Solution

$$\frac{1}{\lambda} = \frac{2.18 \times 10^{-18}\ \text{J}}{hc}\left(\frac{1}{n_f^2} - \frac{1}{n_i^2}\right)$$

$$= \frac{2.18 \times 10^{-18}\ \text{J}}{(6.63 \times 10^{-34}\ \text{J} \cdot \text{s})(3.00 \times 10^8\ \text{m/s})}\left(\frac{1}{2^2} - \frac{1}{4^2}\right)$$

$$= 2.055 \times 10^6\ \text{m}^{-1}$$

Student Annotation: Remember to keep at least one extra digit in intermediate answers to avoid rounding error in the final result [◄◄ Section 1.5].

Therefore,

$$\lambda = 4.87 \times 10^{-7}\ \text{m} = 487\ \text{nm}$$

Think About It
Look again at the line spectrum of hydrogen in Figure 3.7 and make sure that your result matches one of them. Note that for an emission, n_i is always greater than n_f, and Equation 3.9 gives a positive result.

Practice Problem A What is the wavelength (in nm) of a photon emitted during a transition from the $n = 3$ state to the $n = 1$ state in the H atom?

Practice Problem B What is the value of n_i for an electron that emits a photon of wavelength 93.14 nm when it returns to the ground state in the H atom?

SECTION 3.4 REVIEW

Bohr's Theory of the Hydrogen Atom

3.4.1   Calculate the energy of an electron in the $n = 3$ state in a hydrogen atom.

3.4.2   Calculate ΔE of an electron that goes from $n = 1$ to $n = 5$.

3.4.3   What is the wavelength (in m) of light emitted when an electron in a hydrogen atom goes from $n = 5$ to $n = 3$?

3.4.4   What wavelength (in nm) corresponds to the transition of an electron in a hydrogen atom from $n = 2$ to $n = 1$?

3.5   WAVE PROPERTIES OF MATTER

Bohr's theory was both fascinating and puzzling. It fit the experimental data, but physicists did not understand the underlying principle. Why, for example, was an electron restricted to orbiting the nucleus at certain fixed distances? For a decade, no one, not even Bohr himself, could offer a logical explanation. In 1924, French physicist Louis de Broglie[8] provided a solution to this puzzle. De Broglie reasoned that if energy (light) can, under certain circumstances, behave like a stream of particles (photons), then perhaps particles such as electrons can, under certain circumstances, exhibit wavelike properties.

The de Broglie Hypothesis

In developing his revolutionary theory, de Broglie incorporated his observations of macroscopic phenomena that exhibited quantized behavior. For example, a guitar string has certain discrete frequencies of vibration, like those shown in Figure 3.12(a). The waves generated by plucking a guitar string are *standing* or *stationary waves* because they do not travel along the string. Some points on the string, called **nodes**, do not move at all; that is, the amplitude of the wave at these points is *zero*. There is a node at each end, and there may be one or more nodes between the ends. The greater the frequency of vibration, the shorter the wavelength of the standing wave and the greater the number of nodes. According to de Broglie, an electron in an atom behaves like a *standing wave*. However, as Figure 3.12 shows, only certain wavelengths are possible or *allowed*.

De Broglie argued that if an electron does behave like a standing wave in the hydrogen atom, the wavelength must fit the circumference of the orbit exactly; that is, the circumference of the orbit must be an integral multiple of the wavelength, as shown in Figure 3.12(b). Otherwise, the wave would partially cancel itself by destructive interference on each successive orbit, quickly reducing its amplitude to zero.

The relationship between the circumference of an allowed orbit ($2\pi r$) and the wavelength (λ) of the electron is given by

Equation 3.10	$2\pi r = n\lambda$

where r is the radius of the orbit, λ is the wavelength of the electron wave, and n is a positive integer (1, 2, 3, ...). Because n is an integer, r can have only certain values (integral multiples of λ) as n increases from 1 to 2 to 3 and so on. And, because the energy of the electron depends on the size of the orbit (or the value of r), the energy can have only certain values, too. Thus, the energy of the electron in a hydrogen atom, if it behaves like a standing wave, must be quantized.

De Broglie's reasoning led to the conclusion that waves can behave like particles and particles can exhibit wavelike properties. De Broglie deduced that the particle and wave properties are related by the following expression:

Equation 3.11	$\lambda = \dfrac{h}{mu}$

---

[8]Louis Victor Pierre Raymond Duc de Broglie (1892–1977). A member of an old and noble family in France, he held the title of a prince. In his doctoral dissertation, he proposed that matter and radiation have the properties of both wave and particle. For this work, de Broglie was awarded the Nobel Prize in Physics in 1929.

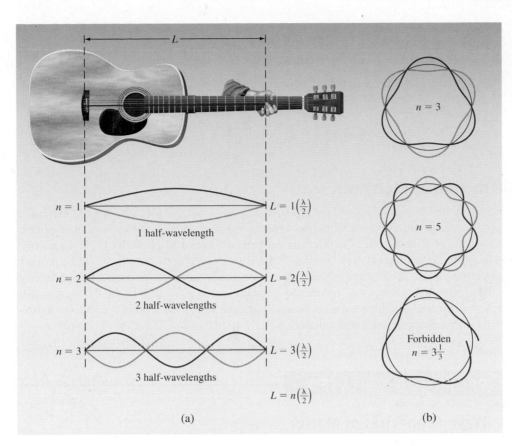

Figure 3.12 Standing waves of a vibrating guitar string. The length of the string must be equal to a whole number times one-half the wavelength ($\lambda/2$). (b) In a circular orbit, only whole number multiples of wavelengths are allowed. Any fractional number of wavelengths would result in cancellation of the wave due to destructive interference.

where λ, m, and u are the wavelength associated with a moving particle, its mass, and its velocity, respectively. Equation 3.11 implies that a particle in motion can be treated as a wave, and a wave can exhibit the properties of a particle. To help you remember this important point, notice that the left side of Equation 3.11 involves the wavelike property of wavelength, whereas the right side involves mass, a property of particles. A wavelength calculated using Equation 3.11 is usually referred to specifically as a ***de Broglie wavelength***.

Worked Example 3.6 illustrates how de Broglie's theory and Equation 3.11 can be applied.

Worked Example 3.6

Calculate the de Broglie wavelength of the "particle" in the following two cases: (a) a 25-g bullet traveling at 612 m/s and (b) an electron ($m = 9.109 \times 10^{-31}$ kg) moving at 63.0 m/s.

Strategy Use Equation 3.11 $\left(\lambda = \dfrac{h}{mu}\right)$ to calculate the de Broglie wavelengths. Remember that the mass in Equation 3.11 must be expressed in kilograms in order for the units to cancel properly.

Setup Planck's constant, h, is 6.63×10^{-34} J · s or, for the purpose of making the unit cancellation obvious, 6.63×10^{-34} kg · m²/s.

Student Annotation: 1 J = 1 kg · m²/s².

Solution

(a) $25 \text{ g} \times \dfrac{1 \text{ kg}}{1000 \text{ g}} = 0.025 \text{ kg}$

$$\lambda = \frac{h}{mu} = \frac{6.63 \times 10^{-34} \text{ kg} \cdot \text{m}^2/\text{s}}{(0.025 \text{ kg})(612 \text{ m/s})} = 4.3 \times 10^{-35} \text{ m}$$

(b) $\lambda = \dfrac{h}{mu} = \dfrac{6.63 \times 10^{-34} \text{ kg} \cdot \text{m}^2/\text{s}}{(9.109 \times 10^{-31} \text{ kg})(612 \text{ m/s})} = 1.16 \times 10^{-5} \text{ m}$

Think About It
While you are new at solving these problems, always write out the units of Planck's constant (J · s) as kg · m²/s. This will enable you to check your unit cancellations and detect common errors such as expressing mass in grams rather than kilograms. Note that the calculated wavelength of a macroscopic object, even one as small as a bullet, is extremely small. An object must be at least as small as a subatomic particle in order for its wavelength to be large enough for us to observe.

(Continued on next page)

Practice Problem A Calculate the de Broglie wavelength (in nm) of a hydrogen atom ($m = 1.674 \times 10^{-27}$ kg) moving at 1500 cm/s.

Practice Problem B Use Equation 3.11 to calculate the *momentum, p* (defined as mass times velocity, $m \times u$) associated with a photon of radiation of wavelength 810 nm. The velocity of a photon is the speed of light, *c*.

Student Annotation: Momentum has units of kg · m/s or N · s, where N is the *newton*, the SI unit of *force*. The newton is a derived SI unit: 1 N = 1 kg · m/s^2.

(a)

(b)

Figure 3.13 (a) X-ray diffraction pattern of aluminum foil. (b) Electron diffraction of aluminum foil. The similarity of these two patterns shows that electrons can behave like X rays and display wave properties.

Diffraction of Electrons

Shortly after de Broglie introduced his equation and predicted that electrons should exhibit wave properties, successful electron diffraction experiments were carried out by American physicists Clinton Davisson[9] and Lester Germer[10] in the United States and physicist G. P. Thomson[11] in England. These experiments demonstrated that electrons do indeed possess wavelike properties. By directing a beam of electrons (which are most definitely particles) through a thin piece of gold foil, Thomson obtained a set of concentric rings on a screen, similar to the diffraction pattern observed when X rays (which are most definitely waves) were used. Figure 3.13 shows X-ray and electron diffraction patterns for aluminum.

SECTION 3.5 REVIEW

Wave Properties of Matter

3.5.1   Calculate the de Broglie wavelength associated with a helium-4 atom (4.00 amu) moving at 3.0×10^6 m/s.

3.5.2   At what speed must a helium-4 atom be traveling to exhibit a de Broglie wavelength of 1.50 Å?

3.5.3   Determine the minimum speed required for a hydrogen atom to have a de Broglie wavelength in the ultraviolet region (10–400 nm) of the electromagnetic spectrum.

3.6   QUANTUM MECHANICS

The discovery that waves could have matterlike properties and that matter could have wavelike properties was revolutionary. Although scientists had long believed that energy and matter were distinct entities, the distinction between them, at least at the atomic level, was no longer clear. Bohr's theory was tremendously successful in explaining the line spectrum of hydrogen, but it failed to explain the spectra of atoms with more than one electron. The electron appeared to behave as a particle in some circumstances and as a wave in others. Neither description could completely explain the behavior of electrons in atoms. This left scientists frustrated in their quest to understand exactly where the electrons in an atom are.

[9]Clinton Joseph Davisson (1881–1958). He and G. P. Thomson shared the Nobel Prize in Physics in 1937 for demonstrating the wave properties of electrons.

[10]Lester Halbert Germer (1896–1972). Discoverer (with Davisson) of the wave properties of electrons.

[11]George Paget Thomson (1892–1975). Son of J. J. Thomson, he received the Nobel Prize in Physics in 1937, along with Clinton Davisson, for demonstrating the wave properties of electrons.

The Uncertainty Principle

To describe the problem of trying to locate a subatomic particle that behaves like a wave, Werner Heisenberg[12] formulated what is now known as the **Heisenberg uncertainty principle**: It is impossible to know simultaneously both the *momentum p* (defined as mass times velocity, $m \times u$) and the *position x* of a particle with certainty. Stated mathematically,

$$\Delta x \cdot \Delta p \geq \frac{h}{4\pi} \qquad \textbf{Equation 3.12}$$

For a particle of mass *m*,

$$\Delta x \cdot m\Delta u \geq \frac{h}{4\pi} \qquad \textbf{Equation 3.13}$$

Student Annotation: Like the de Broglie wavelength equation, Equation 3.12 requires that mass be expressed in kilograms. Unit cancellation will be more obvious if you express Planck's constant in $kg \cdot m^2/s$ rather than $J \cdot s$.

where Δx and Δu are the uncertainties in measuring the position and velocity of the particle, respectively. The $\geq$ signs have the following meaning: If the measured uncertainties of position and velocity are large (say, in a crude experiment), their product can be substantially greater than $h/4\pi$ (hence the $>$ sign). The significance of Equation 3.13 is that even in the most favorable conditions for measuring position and velocity, the product of the uncertainties can never be less than $h/4\pi >$ (hence the $=$ sign). Thus, making measurement of the velocity of a particle *more* precise (i.e., making Δu a *small* quantity) means that the position must become correspondingly *less* precise (i.e., Δx will become *larger*). Similarly, if the position of the particle is known more precisely, its velocity measurement must become less precise.

If the Heisenberg uncertainty principle is applied to the hydrogen atom, we find that the electron cannot orbit the nucleus in a well-defined path, as Bohr thought. If it did, we could determine precisely both the position of the electron (from the radius of the orbit) and its speed (from its kinetic energy) at the same time. This would violate the uncertainty principle.

Worked Example 3.7 shows how to use the Heisenberg uncertainty principle.

Worked Example 3.7

An electron in a hydrogen atom is known to have a velocity of 5×10^6 m/s $\pm$ 1 percent. Using the uncertainty principle, calculate the minimum uncertainty in the position of the electron and, given that the diameter of the hydrogen atom is less than 1 angstrom (Å), comment on the magnitude of this uncertainty compared to the size of the atom.

Strategy The uncertainty in the velocity, 1 percent of 5×10^6 m/s, is Δu. Using Equation 3.13, $\left(\Delta x \cdot m\Delta u \geq \frac{h}{4\pi} \right)$ calculate Δx and compare it with the diameter of the hydrogen atom.

Setup The mass of an electron (from Table 2.1, rounded to three significant figures and converted to kilograms) is 9.11×10^{-31} kg. Planck's constant, *h*, is 6.63×10^{-34} kg $\cdot$ m²/s.

Solution

$$\Delta u = 0.01 \times 5 \times 10^6 \text{ m/s} = 5 \times 10^4 \text{ m/s}$$

$$\Delta x = \frac{h}{4\pi \cdot m\Delta u}$$

Therefore,

$$\Delta x = \frac{6.63 \times 10^{-34} \text{ kg} \cdot \text{m}^2/\text{s}}{4\pi(9.11 \times 10^{-31} \text{ kg})(5 \times 10^4 \text{ m/s})} \geq 1 \times 10^{-9} \text{ m}$$

Think About It
A common error is expressing the mass of the particle in grams instead of kilograms, but you should discover this inconsistency if you check your unit cancellation carefully. Remember that if one uncertainty is small, the other must be large. The uncertainty principle applies in a practical way only to submicroscopic particles. In the case of a macroscopic object, where the mass is much larger than that of an electron, small uncertainties, relative to the size of the object, are possible for both position and velocity.

(Continued on next page)

[12]Werner Karl Heisenberg (1901–1976). One of the founders of modern quantum theory, Heisenberg, a German physicist, received the Nobel Prize in Physics in 1932.

The *minimum* uncertainty in the position x is 1×10^{-9} m $= 10$ Å. The uncertainty in the electron's position is 10 times larger than the atom!

Practice Problem A Calculate the minimum uncertainty in the position of the 25-g bullet from Worked Example 3.6 given that the uncertainty in its velocity is $\pm$ 1 percent.

Practice Problem B (a) Calculate the minimum uncertainty in the momentum of an object for which the uncertainty in position is 3 Å. (b) To what minimum uncertainty in velocity does this correspond if the particle is a neutron (mass = 1.0087 amu)? (c) To what minimum uncertainty in velocity does it correspond if the particle is an electron (mass = 5.486×10^{-4} amu)?

The Schrödinger Equation

Bohr made a significant contribution to our understanding of atoms, and his suggestion that the energy of an electron in an atom is quantized remains unchallenged, but his theory did not provide a complete description of the behavior of electrons in atoms. In 1926 the Austrian physicist Erwin Schrödinger,[13] using a complicated mathematical technique, formulated an equation that describes the behavior and energies of submicroscopic particles in general, an equation analogous to Newton's laws of motion for macroscopic objects. The *Schrödinger equation* requires advanced calculus to solve, and we will not discuss it here. The equation, however, incorporates both particle behavior, in terms of mass *m,* and wave behavior, in terms of a *wave function* ψ (psi), which depends on the location in space of the system (such as an electron in an atom).

The wave function itself has no direct physical meaning. However, the probability of finding the electron in a certain region in space is proportional to the square of the wave function, ψ^2. The idea of relating ψ^2 to probability stemmed from a wave theory analogy. According to wave theory, the intensity of light is proportional to the square of the amplitude of the wave, or ψ^2. The most likely place to find a photon is where the intensity is greatest—that is, where the value of ψ^2 is greatest. A similar argument associates ψ^2 with the likelihood of finding an electron in regions surrounding the nucleus.

Schrödinger's equation launched an entirely new field called *quantum mechanics* (or *wave mechanics*), and began a new era in physics and chemistry. We now refer to the developments in quantum theory from 1913—when Bohr presented his model of the hydrogen atom—to 1926 as "old quantum theory."

The Quantum Mechanical Description of the Hydrogen Atom

The Schrödinger equation specifies the possible energy states the electron can occupy in a hydrogen atom and identifies the corresponding wave functions (ψ). These energy states and wave functions are characterized by a set of *quantum numbers* (to be discussed shortly) with which we can construct a comprehensive model of the hydrogen atom.

Although quantum mechanics does not allow us to specify the exact location of an electron in an atom, it does define the region where the electron is most likely to be at a given time. The concept of **electron density** gives the probability that an electron will be found in a particular region of an atom. The square of the wave function, ψ^2, defines the distribution of electron density in three-dimensional space around the nucleus. Regions of high electron density represent a high probability of locating the electron (Figure 3.14).

To distinguish the quantum mechanical description of an atom from Bohr's model, we speak of an atomic *orbital,* rather than an orbit. An **atomic orbital** can be thought of as the wave function of an electron in an atom. When we say that an electron is in a certain orbital, we mean that the distribution of the electron density or the probability of locating the electron in space is described by the square of the wave function associated with that orbital. An atomic orbital, therefore, has a characteristic energy, as well as a characteristic distribution of electron density.

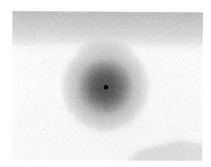

Figure 3.14 Representation of the electron density distribution surrounding the nucleus in the hydrogen atom. It shows a higher probability of finding the electron closer to the nucleus.

---

[13]Erwin Schrödinger (1887–1961). Schrödinger formulated wave mechanics, which laid the foundation for modern quantum theory. He received the Nobel Prize in Physics in 1933.

SECTION 3.6 REVIEW

Quantum Mechanics

3.6.1   What is the minimum uncertainty in the position of an electron moving at a speed of 4×10^6 m/s $\pm$ 1 percent? (The mass of an electron is 9.11×10^{-31} kg.)

3.6.2   What is the minimum uncertainty in the position of a proton moving at a speed of 4×10^6 m/s $\pm$ 1 percent? (The mass of a proton is 1.67×10^{-27} kg.)

3.7 QUANTUM NUMBERS

In Bohr's model of the hydrogen atom, only one number, n, was necessary to describe the location of the electron. In quantum mechanics, three **quantum numbers** are required to describe the *distribution of electron density* in an atom. These numbers are derived from the mathematical solution of Schrödinger's equation for the hydrogen atom. They are called the *principal* quantum number, the *angular momentum* quantum number, and the *magnetic* quantum number. Each atomic orbital in an atom is characterized by a unique set of these three quantum numbers.

Student Annotation: The three quantum numbers n, ℓ, and m_ℓ specify the *size*, *shape*, and *orientation* of an orbital, respectively.

Principal Quantum Number (*n*)

The **principal quantum number (*n*)** designates the *size* of the orbital. The larger n is, the greater the average distance of an electron in the orbital from the nucleus and therefore the larger the orbital. The principal quantum number can have integral values of 1, 2, 3, and so forth, and it corresponds to the quantum number in Bohr's model of the hydrogen atom. Recall from Equation 3.7 that in a hydrogen atom, the value of n determines the energy of an orbital. (As we will see shortly, this is *not* the case for an atom that contains more than one electron.)

Angular Momentum Quantum Number (ℓ)

The **angular momentum quantum number** (ℓ) describes the *shape* of the atomic orbital [▶▶ Section 3.8]. The values of ℓ are integers that depend on the value of the principal quantum number, n. For a given value of n, the possible values of ℓ range from 0 to $n - 1$. If $n = 1$, there is only one possible value of ℓ; that is, 0 ($n - 1$ where $n = 1$). If $n = 2$, there are two values of ℓ: 0 and 1. If $n = 3$, there are three values of ℓ: 0, 1, and 2. The value of ℓ is designated by the letters s, p, d, and f as follows:[14]

ℓ	0	1	2	3
Orbital designation	s	p	d	f

Thus, if $\ell = 0$, we have an s orbital; if $\ell = 1$, we have a p orbital; and so on.

A collection of orbitals with the same value of n is frequently called a *shell*. One or more orbitals with the same n and ℓ values are referred to as a *subshell*. For example, the shell designated by $n = 2$ is composed of two subshells: $\ell = 0$ and $\ell = 1$ (the allowed ℓ values for $n = 2$). These subshells are called the 2s and 2p subshells where 2 denotes the value of n, and s and p denote the values of ℓ.

Magnetic Quantum Number (*m*ℓ)

The **magnetic quantum number (m_ℓ)** describes the orientation of the orbital in space [▶▶ Section 3.8]. Within a subshell, the value of m_ℓ depends on the value of ℓ. For a certain value of ℓ, there are ($2\ell + 1$) integral values of m_ℓ as follows:

$$-\ell, \dots 0, \dots + \ell$$

[14]The unusual sequence of letters (s, p, d, and f) has an historical origin. Physicists who studied atomic emission spectra tried to correlate their observations of spectral lines with the energy states involved in the transitions. They described the emission lines as *sharp*, *principal*, *diffuse*, and *fundamental*.

TABLE 3.2	Allowed Values of the Quantum Numbers n, ℓ, and m_ℓ		
When n is	**ℓ can be**	**When ℓ is**	**m_ℓ can be**
1	only 0	0	only 0
2	0 or 1	0	only 0
		1	$-1, 0,$ or $+1$
3	0, 1, or 2	0	only 0
		1	$-1, 0,$ or $+1$
		2	$-2, -1, 0, +1,$ or $+2$
4	0, 1, 2, or 3	0	only 0
		1	$-1, 0,$ or $+1$
		2	$-2, -1, 0, +1,$ or $+2$
		3	$-3, -2, -1, 0, +1, +2,$ or $+3$
.	.	.	.
.	.	.	.
.	.	.	.

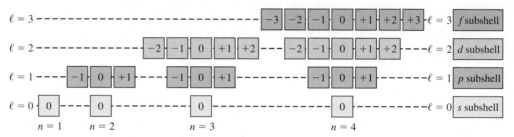

Figure 3.15 Illustration of how quantum numbers designate shells, subshells, and orbitals.

If $\ell = 0$, there is only one possible value of m_ℓ: 0. If $\ell = 1$, then there are *three* values of m_ℓ: -1, 0, and $+1$. If $\ell = 2$, there are *five* values of m_ℓ, namely, -2, -1, 0, $+1$, and $+2$, and so on. The number of m_ℓ values indicates the number of *orbitals* in a subshell with a particular ℓ value; that is, each m_ℓ value refers to a different orbital.

Table 3.2 summarizes the allowed values of the three quantum numbers, n, ℓ, and m_ℓ, and Figure 3.15 illustrates schematically how the allowed values of quantum numbers give rise to the number of subshells and orbitals in each shell of an atom. The number of subshells in a shell is equal to n, and the number of orbitals in a shell is equal to n^2.

Worked Example 3.8 gives you some practice with the allowed values of quantum numbers.

Worked Example 3.8

What are the possible values for the magnetic quantum number (m_ℓ) when the principal quantum number (n) is 3 and the angular momentum quantum number (ℓ) is 1?

Strategy Use the rules governing the allowed values of m_ℓ. Recall that the possible values of m_ℓ depend on the value of ℓ, not on the value of n.

Setup The possible values of m_ℓ are $-\ell,..., 0,..., +\ell$.

Solution The possible values of m_ℓ are $-1, 0,$ and $+1$.

> **Think About It**
> Consult Table 3.2 to make sure your answer is correct. Table 3.2 confirms that it is the value of ℓ, not the value of n, that determines the possible values of m_ℓ.

Practice Problem A What are the possible values for m_ℓ when the principal quantum number (n) is 2 and the angular momentum quantum number (ℓ) is 0?

Practice Problem B What are the possible values for m_ℓ when the principal quantum number (n) is 3 and the angular momentum quantum number (ℓ) is 2?

Electron Spin Quantum Number (m_s)

Whereas three quantum numbers are sufficient to describe an atomic orbital, an additional quantum number becomes necessary to describe an *electron* that *occupies* the orbital.

Experiments on the emission spectra of hydrogen and sodium atoms indicated that each line in the emission spectra could be split into two lines by the application of an external magnetic field. The only way physicists could explain these results was to assume that electrons act like tiny magnets. If electrons are thought of as spinning on their own axes, as Earth does, their magnetic properties can be accounted for. According to electromagnetic theory, a spinning charge generates a magnetic field, and it is this motion that causes an electron to behave like a magnet. Figure 3.16 shows the two possible "spins" of an electron. To specify the electron's spin, we use the ***electron spin quantum number (m_s)***. Because there are two possible directions of spin, opposite each other, m_s has two possible values: $+\frac{1}{2}$ and $-\frac{1}{2}$.

Conclusive proof of electron spin was established by German physicists Otto Stern[15] and Walther Gerlach[16] in 1924. Figure 3.17 shows the basic experimental arrangement. A beam of gaseous atoms generated in a hot furnace passes through a nonuniform magnetic field. The interaction between an electron and the magnetic field causes the atom to be deflected from its straight-line path. Because the direction of spin is random, the electrons in *half* of the atoms will be spinning in one direction. Those atoms will be deflected in one way. The electrons in the other half of the atoms will be spinning in the *opposite* direction. Those atoms will be deflected in the other direction. Thus, two spots of equal intensity are observed on the detecting screen.

To summarize, we can designate an *orbital* in an atom with a set of *three* quantum numbers. These three quantum numbers indicate the size (n), shape (ℓ), and orientation (m_ℓ) of the orbital. A fourth quantum number (m_s) is necessary to designate the spin of an electron in the orbital.

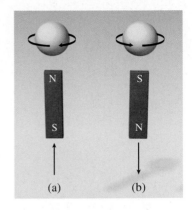

Figure 3.16 (a) Clockwise and (b) counterclockwise spins of an electron. The magnetic fields generated by these two spinning motions are analogous to those from the two magnets. The upward and downward arrows are used to denote the direction of spin.

Student Annotation: Two electrons in the same orbital with opposite spins are referred to as "*paired.*"

Figure 3.17 Experimental arrangement for demonstrating electron spin. A beam of atoms is directed through a magnetic field. When a hydrogen atom, with a single electron, passes through the field, it is deflected in one direction or the other, depending on the direction of the electron's spin. In a stream consisting of many atoms, there will be equal distributions of the two kinds of spins, so two spots of equal intensity are detected on the screen.

SECTION 3.7 REVIEW

Quantum Numbers

3.7.1 How many orbitals are there in a subshell designated by the quantum numbers $n = 3$, $\ell = 2$?

3.7.2 How many subshells are there in the shell designated by $n = 3$?

3.7.3 What is the total number of orbitals in the shell designated by $n = 4$?

3.7.4 What is the minimum value of the principal quantum number for an orbital in which $m_\ell = +2$?

---

[15]Otto Stern (1888–1969). He made important contributions to the study of the magnetic properties of atoms and the kinetic theory of gases. Stern was awarded the Nobel Prize in Physics in 1943.

[16]Walther Gerlach (1889–1979). Gerlach's main area of research was in quantum theory.

3.8   ATOMIC ORBITALS

Strictly speaking, an atomic orbital does not have a well-defined shape because the wave function characterizing the orbital extends from the nucleus to infinity. In that sense, it is difficult to say what an orbital looks like. On the other hand, it is certainly useful to think of orbitals as having specific shapes. Being able to visualize atomic orbitals is essential to understanding the formation of chemical bonds and molecular geometry, which are discussed in Chapters 5 and 7. In this section, we will look at each type of orbital separately.

s Orbitals

For any value of the principal quantum number (n), the value 0 is possible for the angular momentum quantum number (ℓ), corresponding to an s subshell. Furthermore, when $\ell = 0$, the magnetic quantum number (m_ℓ) has only one possible value, 0, corresponding to an s orbital. Therefore, there is an s subshell in every shell, and each s subshell contains just one orbital, an **s orbital.**

Student Annotation: The radial probability distribution can be thought of as a map of "where the electron spends most of its time."

Figure 3.18 illustrates three ways to represent the distribution of electrons: the probability density, the spherical distribution of electron density, and the radial probability distribution (the probability of finding the electron as a function of distance from the nucleus) for the 1s, 2s, and 3s orbitals of hydrogen. The boundary surface (the outermost surface of the spherical representation) is a common way to represent atomic orbitals, incorporating the volume in which there is about a 90 percent probability of finding the electron at any given time.

All s orbitals are spherical in shape but differ in size, which increases as the principal quantum number increases. The radial probability distribution for the 1s orbital exhibits a maximum at 52.9 pm (0.529 Å) from the nucleus. Interestingly, this distance is equal to the radius of the $n = 1$ orbit in the Bohr model of the hydrogen atom. The radial probability distribution plots for the 2s and 3s orbitals exhibit two and three maxima, respectively, with the greatest probability occurring at a greater distance from the nucleus as n increases. Between the two maxima for the 2s orbital, there is a point on the plot where the probability drops to zero. This corresponds to a *node* in the electron density, where the standing wave has zero amplitude. There are two such nodes in the radial probability distribution plot of the 3s orbital.

Although the details of electron density variation within each boundary surface are lost, the most important features of atomic orbitals are their overall shapes and relative sizes, which are adequately represented by boundary surface diagrams.

p Orbitals

When the principal quantum number (n) is 2 or greater, the value 1 is possible for the angular momentum quantum number (ℓ), corresponding to a p subshell. And, when $\ell = 1$, the magnetic quantum number (m_ℓ) has three possible values: −1, 0, and +1, each corresponding to a different **p orbital.** Therefore, there is a p subshell in every shell for which $n \geq 2$, and each p subshell contains three p orbitals. These three p orbitals are labeled p_x, p_y, and p_z (Figure 3.19), with the subscripted letters indicating the axis along which each orbital is oriented. These three p orbitals are identical in size, shape, and energy; they differ from one another only in orientation. Note, however, that there is no simple relation between the values of m_ℓ and the x, y, and z directions. For our purpose, you need only remember that because there are three possible values of m_ℓ, there are three p orbitals with different orientations.

The boundary surface diagrams of p orbitals in Figure 3.19 show that each p orbital can be thought of as two lobes on opposite sides of the nucleus. Like s orbitals, p orbitals increase in size from 2p to 3p to 4p orbital and so on.

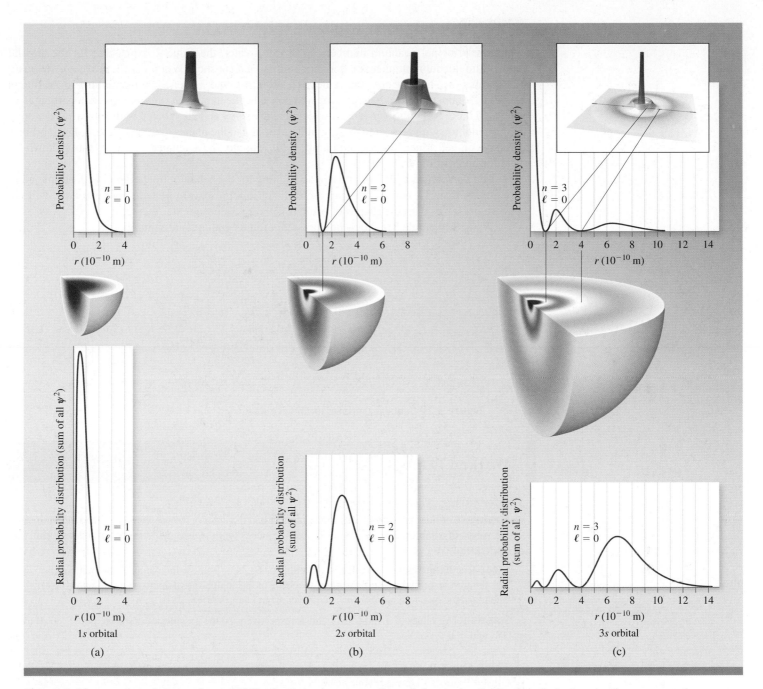

Figure 3.18 From top to bottom, the *probability density* and corresponding relief map, the distribution of electron density represented spherically with shading corresponding to the relief map above, and the *radial probability distribution* for (a) the 1s, (b) the 2s, and (c) the 3s orbitals of hydrogen.

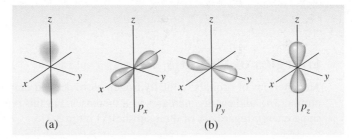

Figure 3.19 (a) Electron distribution in a *p* orbital. (b) Boundary surfaces for the p_x, p_y, and p_z orbitals.

d Orbitals and Other Higher-Energy Orbitals

When the principal quantum number (n) is 3 or greater, the value 2 is possible for the angular momentum quantum number (ℓ), corresponding to a *d* subshell. When $\ell = 2$, the magnetic quantum number (m_ℓ) has *five* possible values, $-2, -1, 0, +1$, and $+2$, each corresponding to a different **d orbital**. Again, there is no direct correspondence between a given orientation and a particular m_ℓ value. All the 3*d* orbitals in an atom are identical in energy and are labeled with subscripts denoting their orientation with respect to the *x, y,* and *z* axes and to the planes defined by them. The *d* orbitals that have higher principal quantum numbers (4*d*, 5*d*, etc.) have shapes similar to those shown for the 3*d* orbitals in Figure 3.20.

The **f orbitals** are important when accounting for the behavior of elements with atomic numbers greater than 57, but their shapes are difficult to represent. In general chemistry, we will not concern ourselves with the shapes of orbitals having ℓ values greater than 2.

Worked Example 3.9 shows how to label orbitals with quantum numbers.

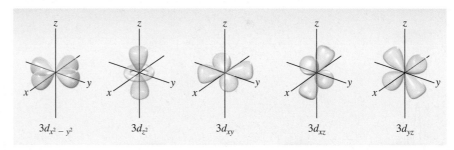

Figure 3.20 Boundary surfaces for the *d* orbitals.

Worked Example 3.9

List the values of n, ℓ, and m_ℓ for each of the orbitals in a 4*d* subshell.

Strategy Consider the significance of the number and the letter in the 4*d* designation and determine the values of n and ℓ. There are multiple possible values for m_ℓ, which will have to be deduced from the value of ℓ.

Setup The integer at the beginning of an orbital designation is the principal quantum number (n). The letter in an orbital designation gives the value of the angular momentum quantum number (ℓ). The magnetic quantum number (m_ℓ) can have integral values of $-\ell$, ..., 0, ..., $+\ell$.

Solution The values of n and ℓ are 4 and 2, respectively, so the possible values of m_ℓ are $-2, -1, 0, +1$, and $+2$.

Think About It
Consult Figure 3.15 to verify your answers.

Practice Problem A Give the values of n, ℓ, and m_ℓ for the orbitals in a 3*d* subshell.

Practice Problem B Using the rules governing the allowed values of quantum numbers, explain why there is no 2*d* subshell.

Energies of Orbitals

The energies of orbitals in the hydrogen atom depend only on the value of the principal quantum number (n), and energy increases as n increases. For this reason, orbitals in the same shell have the same energy regardless of their subshell (Figure 3.21).

$$1s < 2s = 2p < 3s = 3p = 3d < 4s = 4p = 4d = 4f$$

Thus, all four orbitals (one 2*s* and three 2*p*) in the second shell have the same energy; all nine orbitals (one 3*s*, three 3*p*, and five 3*d*) in the third shell have the same energy; and all sixteen orbitals (one 4*s*, three 4*p*, five 4*d*, and seven 4*f*) in the fourth shell have the same energy. The energy picture is more complex for many-electron atoms than it is for hydrogen, as is discussed in Section 3.9.

Figure 3.21 Orbital energy levels in the hydrogen atom. Each box represents one orbital. Orbitals with the same principal quantum number (*n*) all have the same energy.

SECTION 3.8 REVIEW

Atomic Orbitals

3.8.1 How many orbitals are there in the 5*f* subshell?

3.8.2 The energy of an orbital in the hydrogen atom depends on which quantum number?

3.8.3 List all the orbitals in a hydrogen atom that have energies lower than the 3*p* orbital.

3.8.4 Explain what, if anything, is wrong with each of the following sets of quantum numbers (n, ℓ, m_ℓ, m_s): (a) 2, 1, −2, $+\frac{1}{2}$, (b) 2, 2, 0, $+\frac{1}{2}$, (c) 2, 1, −1, $-\frac{1}{2}$, (d) 0, 0, 0, $+\frac{1}{2}$.

3.9 ELECTRON CONFIGURATIONS

The hydrogen atom is a particularly simple system because it contains only one electron. The electron may reside in the 1*s* orbital (the *ground state*), or it may be found in some higher-energy orbital (an *excited state*). With many-electron systems, we need to know the ground-state ***electron configuration***—that is, how the electrons are distributed in the various atomic orbitals. To do this, we need to know the relative energies of atomic orbitals in a many-electron system, which differ from those in a one-electron system such as hydrogen.

Energies of Atomic Orbitals in Many-Electron Systems

Consider the two emission spectra shown in Figure 3.22. The spectrum of helium contains more lines than that of hydrogen. This indicates that there are more possible transitions, corresponding to emission in the visible range, in a helium atom than in a hydrogen atom. This is due to the *splitting* of energy levels caused by electrostatic interactions between helium's two electrons.

Student Annotation: "*Splitting*" of energy levels refers to the splitting of a shell into subshells of different energies, as shown in Figure 3.23.

Figure 3.22 Comparison of the emission spectra of H and He.

Figure 3.23 Orbital energy levels in many-electron atoms. For a given value of n, orbital energy increases with the value of ℓ.

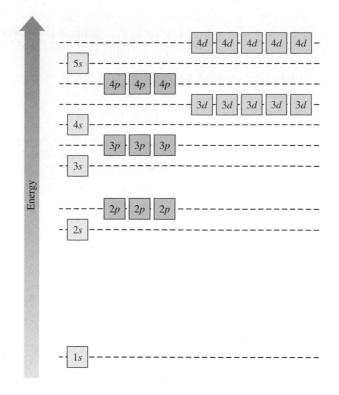

Figure 3.23 shows the general order of orbital energies in a many-electron atom. In contrast to the hydrogen atom, in which the energy of an orbital depends only on the value of n (Figure 3.21), the energy of an orbital in a many-electron system depends on both the value of n and the value of ℓ. For example, $3p$ orbitals all have the same energy, but they are higher in energy than the $3s$ orbital and lower in energy than the $3d$ orbitals. In a many-electron atom, for a given value of n, the energy of an orbital increases with increasing value of ℓ. One important consequence of the splitting of energy levels is the relative energies of d orbitals in one shell and the s orbital in the next higher shell. As Figure 3.23 shows, the $4s$ orbital is lower in energy than the $3d$ orbitals. Likewise, the $5s$ orbital is lower in energy than the $4d$ orbital, and so on. This fact becomes important when we determine the order in which electrons in an atom populate the atomic orbitals.

The Pauli Exclusion Principle

According to the ***Pauli exclusion principle***, no two electrons in an atom can have the same four quantum numbers.[17] If two electrons in an atom have the same n, ℓ, and m_ℓ values (meaning that they occupy the same *orbital*), then they must have different values of m_s; that is, one must have $m_s = +\frac{1}{2}$ and the other must have $m_s = -\frac{1}{2}$. Because there are only two possible values for m_s, and no two electrons in the same orbital may have the same value for m_s, a maximum of *two* electrons may occupy an atomic orbital, and these two electrons must have opposite spins.

We can indicate the arrangement of electrons in atomic orbitals with labels that identify each orbital (or subshell) and the number of electrons in it. Thus, we could describe a hydrogen atom in the ground state using $1s^1$.

Student Annotation: $1s^1$ is read as "one s one."

Denotes the principal quantum number n —→ $1s^1$ ←— Denotes the number of electrons in the orbital or subshell
Denotes the angular momentum quantum number ℓ

We can also represent the arrangement of electrons in an atom using *orbital diagrams* in which each orbital is represented by a labeled box. The orbital diagram for a hydrogen atom in the ground state is

H   [↑]
     $1s^1$

---

[17]Wolfgang Pauli (1900–1958). One of the founders of quantum mechanics, Austrian physicist Pauli was awarded the Nobel Prize in Physics in 1945.

The upward arrow denotes one of the two possible spins (one of the two possible m_s values) of the electron in the hydrogen atom (the other possible spin is indicated with a downward arrow). Under certain circumstances, as we will see shortly, it is useful to indicate the explicit locations of electrons.

The orbital diagram for a helium atom in the ground state is

$$\text{He} \quad \boxed{\uparrow\downarrow}$$
$$1s^2$$

The label $1s^2$ indicates there are *two* electrons in the $1s$ orbital. Note also that the arrows in the box point in opposite directions, representing opposite electron spins. Generally, when an orbital diagram includes an orbital with a single electron, we represent it with an upward arrow—although we could represent it equally well with a downward arrow. The choice is arbitrary and has no effect on the energy of the electron.

> **Student Annotation:** The *ground state* for a many-electron atom is the one in which all the electrons occupy orbitals of the lowest possible energy.

> **Student Annotation:** $1s^2$ is read as "one s two," *not* as "one s squared."

The Aufbau Principle

We can continue the process of writing electron configurations for elements based on the order of orbital energies and the Pauli exclusion principle. This process is based on the ***Aufbau principle***, which makes it possible to "build" the periodic table of the elements and determine their electron configurations by steps. Each step involves adding one proton to the nucleus and one electron to the appropriate atomic orbital. Through this process we gain a detailed knowledge of the electron configurations of the elements. As we will see in later chapters, knowledge of electron configurations helps us understand and predict the properties of the elements. It also explains why the elements fit into the periodic table the way they do.

After helium, the next element in the periodic table is lithium, which has three electrons. Because of the restrictions imposed by the Pauli exclusion principle, an orbital can accommodate no more than two electrons. Thus, the third electron cannot reside in the $1s$ orbital. Instead, it must reside in the next available orbital with the lowest possible energy. According to Figure 3.23, this is the $2s$ orbital. Therefore, the electron configuration of lithium is $1s^2 2s^1$, and the orbital diagram is

$$\text{Li} \quad \boxed{\uparrow\downarrow} \quad \boxed{\uparrow}$$
$$1s^2 \qquad 2s^1$$

Similarly, we can write the electron configuration of beryllium as $1s^2 2s^2$ and represent it with the orbital diagram

$$\text{Be} \quad \boxed{\uparrow\downarrow} \quad \boxed{\uparrow\downarrow}$$
$$1s^2 \qquad 2s^2$$

With both the $1s$ and the $2s$ orbitals filled to capacity, the next electron, which is needed for the electron configuration of boron, must reside in the $2p$ subshell. Because all three $2p$ orbitals are of equal energy, or ***degenerate***, the electron can occupy any one of them. By convention, we usually show the first electron to occupy the p subshell in the first empty box in the orbital diagram.

$$\text{B} \quad \boxed{\uparrow\downarrow} \quad \boxed{\uparrow\downarrow} \quad \boxed{\uparrow\;|\;\;|\;\;}$$
$$1s^2 \qquad 2s^2 \qquad 2p^1$$

Hund's Rule

Will the sixth electron, which is needed to represent the electron configuration of carbon, reside in the $2p$ orbital that is already half occupied, or will it reside in one of the other, empty $2p$ orbitals? According to ***Hund's rule***, the most stable arrangement of electrons in orbitals of equal energy is the one in which the number of electrons with the same spin is maximized.[18] As we have seen, no two electrons in any orbital may have the same spin, so maximizing the number of electrons with the same spin requires putting the electrons in separate orbitals. Accordingly, in any subshell, an electron will occupy an empty orbital rather than one that already contains an electron.

---

[18]Frederick Hund (1896–1997). A German physicist, Hund worked mainly in quantum mechanics. He also helped to develop the molecular orbital theory of chemical bonding.

The electron configuration of carbon is, therefore, $1s^2 2s^2 2p^2$, and its orbital diagram is

C $\boxed{\uparrow\downarrow}$ $\boxed{\uparrow\downarrow}$ $\boxed{\uparrow\,|\,\uparrow\,|\,}$
      $1s^2$ $2s^2$ $2p^2$

Similarly, the electron configuration of nitrogen is $1s^2 2s^2 2p^3$, and its orbital diagram is

N $\boxed{\uparrow\downarrow}$ $\boxed{\uparrow\downarrow}$ $\boxed{\uparrow\,|\,\uparrow\,|\,\uparrow}$
      $1s^2$ $2s^2$ $2p^3$

Once all the $2p$ orbitals are singly occupied, additional electrons will have to pair with those already in the orbitals. Thus, the electron configurations and orbital diagrams for O, F, and Ne are

O $1s^2 2s^2 2p^4$ $\boxed{\uparrow\downarrow}$ $\boxed{\uparrow\downarrow}$ $\boxed{\uparrow\downarrow\,|\,\uparrow\,|\,\uparrow}$
                          $1s^2$ $2s^2$ $2p^4$

F $1s^2 2s^2 2p^5$ $\boxed{\uparrow\downarrow}$ $\boxed{\uparrow\downarrow}$ $\boxed{\uparrow\downarrow\,|\,\uparrow\downarrow\,|\,\uparrow}$
                          $1s^2$ $2s^2$ $2p^5$

Ne $1s^2 2s^2 2p^6$ $\boxed{\uparrow\downarrow}$ $\boxed{\uparrow\downarrow}$ $\boxed{\uparrow\downarrow\,|\,\uparrow\downarrow\,|\,\uparrow\downarrow}$
                          $1s^2$ $2s^2$ $2p^6$

By examining the ground-state electron configurations of O, F, and Ne, we can see that some atoms have configurations in which all of the electrons are paired (Ne), and some have configuration in which one or more electrons are unpaired (O and F). These two conditions give rise to different magnetic properties of atoms. Those with all paired electrons are called ***diamagnetic***; and those with one or more unpaired electrons are called ***paramagnetic***. Diamagnetic substances are repelled by a magnetic field. For example, neon atoms, with electron configuration $1s^2 2s^2 2p^6$ (no unpaired electrons), are weakly repelled by a magnet. Paramagnetic substances are attracted to a magnetic field. Oxygen atoms, with electron configuration $1s^2 2s^2 2p^4$ (two unpaired electrons), are weakly attracted to a magnet. One way that the magnetic behavior of a substance can be determined is using a magnetic balance like the one shown in Figure 3.24.

The mass of a substance suspended in an electromagnet is determined with the magnet off, and again with the magnet on. If the substance is diamagnetic, it will be repelled by the magnetic field and will have a lower apparent mass with the magnet on. If a substance is paramagnetic, it will be attracted by the magnetic field and will have a greater apparent mass with the magnet on. The magnetic behavior of a substance can provide information about the arrangement of its electrons.

Figure 3.24 The sample is suspended in an electromagnet and is weighed twice: once with the electromagnet off and once with it on. For a diamagnetic sample (a), the apparent mass will be slightly lower when the magnet is on. For a paramagnetic sample (b), the apparent mass will be greater when the magnet is on because the sample is attracted by the magnetic field. This technique is of particular use for species containing transition metals while other methods are typically employed for other elements on the periodic table.

General Rules for Writing Electron Configurations

Based on the preceding examples, we can formulate the following general rules for determining the electron configuration of an element in the ground state:

1. Electrons will reside in the available orbitals of the lowest possible energy.
2. Each orbital can accommodate a maximum of two electrons.
3. Electrons will not pair in degenerate orbitals if an empty orbital is available.
4. Orbitals will fill in the order indicated in Figure 3.23. Figure 3.25 provides a simple way for you to remember the proper order.

> **Student Annotation:** Remember that in this context, *degenerate* means "of equal energy." Orbitals in the same subshell are degenerate.

Worked Example 3.10 illustrates the procedure for determining the ground-state electron configuration of an atom.

Worked Example 3.10

Write the electron configuration and give the orbital diagram of a calcium (Ca) atom ($Z = 20$).

Strategy Use the general rules given and the Aufbau principle to "build" the electron configuration of a calcium atom and represent it with an orbital diagram.

Setup Because $Z = 20$, we know that a Ca atom has 20 electrons. They will fill orbitals in the order designated in Figure 3.23, obeying the Pauli exclusion principle and Hund's rule. Orbitals will fill in the following order: $1s$, $2s$, $2p$, $3s$, $3p$, $4s$. Each s subshell can contain a maximum of two electrons, whereas each p subshell can contain a maximum of six electrons.

Solution

Ca $\quad 1s^2 2s^2 2p^6 3s^2 3p^6 4s^2$

$$\underset{1s^2}{\boxed{\uparrow\downarrow}} \quad \underset{2s^2}{\boxed{\uparrow\downarrow}} \quad \underset{2p^6}{\boxed{\uparrow\downarrow}\boxed{\uparrow\downarrow}\boxed{\uparrow\downarrow}} \quad \underset{3s^2}{\boxed{\uparrow\downarrow}} \quad \underset{3p^6}{\boxed{\uparrow\downarrow}\boxed{\uparrow\downarrow}\boxed{\uparrow\downarrow}} \quad \underset{4s^2}{\boxed{\uparrow\downarrow}}$$

> **Think About It**
> Look at Figure 3.23 again to make sure you have filled the orbitals in the right order and that the sum of electrons is 20. Remember that the $4s$ orbital fills before the $3d$ orbitals.

Practice Problem A Write the electron configuration and give the orbital diagram of a rubidium (Rb) atom ($Z = 37$).

Practice Problem B Write the electron configuration and give the orbital diagram of a bromine (Br) atom ($Z = 35$).

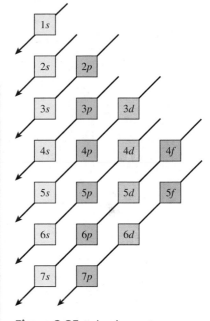

Figure 3.25 A simple way to remember the order in which orbitals fill with electrons.

Multi 3.2
Atomic structure—electron configuration

SECTION 3.9 REVIEW

Electron Configurations

3.9.1 Write the electron configuration of Ti.

3.9.2 What element is represented by the following electron configuration?

$$1s^2 2s^2 2p^6 3s^2 3p^6 4s^2 3d^{10} 4p^4$$

3.9.3 Draw the orbital diagram for the ground state of an S atom.

3.10 ELECTRON CONFIGURATIONS AND THE PERIODIC TABLE

The electron configurations of all elements except hydrogen and helium can be represented using a **_noble gas core_**, which shows in brackets the completed-shell electron configuration of the noble gas element that most recently precedes the element in question, followed by the electron configuration in the outermost occupied subshells. Figure 3.26 gives the ground-state electron configurations of elements from H ($Z = 1$) through element 118. Notice the similar pattern of electron configurations in the elements lithium ($Z = 3$) through neon ($Z = 10$) and those of sodium ($Z = 11$) through argon ($Z = 18$). Both Li and Na, for example, have the configuration ns^1 in their outermost occupied subshells. For Li, $n = 2$; for Na, $n = 3$. Both F and Cl have electron configuration ns^2np^5, where $n = 2$ for F and $n = 3$ for Cl, and so on.

As mentioned in Section 3.9, the $4s$ subshell is filled before the $3d$ subshell in a many-electron atom (see Figure 3.23). Thus, the electron configuration of potassium ($Z = 19$) is $1s^22s^22p^63s^23p^64s^1$.

Figure 3.26 Outermost ground-state electron configurations for the known elements.

Because $1s^2 2s^2 2p^6 3s^2 3p^6$ is the electron configuration of argon, we can simplify the electron configuration of potassium by writing $[Ar]4s^1$, where $[Ar]$ denotes the "argon core."

$$K \qquad 1s^2 2s^2 2p^6 3s^2 3p^6 4s^1$$

$$\underbrace{\qquad\qquad\qquad\qquad}_{[Ar]} \qquad \longrightarrow \quad [Ar]4s^1$$

The placement of the outermost electron in the $4s$ orbital (rather than in the $3d$ orbital) of potassium is strongly supported by experimental evidence. The physical and chemical properties of potassium are very similar to those of lithium and sodium, the first two alkali metals. In both lithium and sodium, the outermost electron is in an s orbital (there is no doubt that their outermost electrons occupy s orbitals because there is no $1d$ or $2d$ subshell). Based on its similarities to the other alkali metals, we expect potassium to have an analogous electron configuration; that is, we expect the last electron in potassium to occupy the $4s$ rather than the $3d$ orbital.

The elements from Group 3B through Group 1B are *transition metals* [◀◀ Section 2.5]. Transition metals either have incompletely filled d subshells or readily give rise to cations that have incompletely filled d subshells. In the first transition metal series, from scandium ($Z = 21$) through copper ($Z = 29$), additional electrons are placed in the $3d$ orbitals according to Hund's rule. However, there are two anomalies. The electron configuration of chromium ($Z = 24$) is $[Ar]4s^1 3d^5$ and not $[Ar]4s^2 3d^4$, as we might expect. A similar break in the pattern is observed for copper, whose electron configuration is $[Ar]4s^1 3d^{10}$ rather than $[Ar]4s^2 3d^9$. The reason for these anomalies is that a slightly greater stability is associated with d subshells that are either half filled ($3d^5$) or completely filled ($3d^{10}$).

For elements Zn ($Z = 30$) through Kr ($Z = 36$), the $3d$, $4s$, and $4p$ subshells fill in a straightforward manner. With rubidium ($Z = 37$), electrons begin to enter the $n = 5$ energy level.

Some of the electron configurations in the second transition metal series [yttrium ($Z = 39$) through silver ($Z = 47$)] are also irregular, but the details of many of these irregularities are beyond the scope of this text and we will not be concerned with them.

The sixth period of the periodic table begins with cesium ($Z = 55$), barium ($Z = 56$), and lanthanum ($Z = 57$), whose electron configurations are $[Xe]6s^1$, $[Xe]6s^2$, and $[Xe]6s^2 5d^1$, respectively. Following lanthanum, there is a gap in the periodic table where the **lanthanide (rare earth) series** belongs. The lanthanides are a series of 14 elements that have incompletely filled $4f$ subshells or that readily give rise to *cations* that have incompletely filled $4f$ subshells. The lanthanides (and the actinides, to be discussed next) are shown at the bottom of the periodic table to keep the table from being too wide.

The last row of elements begins with francium ($Z = 87$; electron configuration $[Rn]7s^1$), radium ($Z = 88$; electron configuration $[Rn]7s^2$), and actinium ($Z = 89$; $[Rn]7s^2 6d^1$), and then continues with the **actinide series**, which starts at thorium ($Z = 90$) and ends with element 112. The actinide series has partially filled $5f$ and/or $6d$ subshells.

With few exceptions, you should be able to write the electron configuration of any element, using Figure 3.23 (or Figure 3.25) as a guide. Elements that require particular care are the transition metals, the lanthanides, and the actinides. You may notice from looking at the electron configurations of gadolinium ($Z = 64$) and curium ($Z = 96$) that half-filled f subshells also appear to exhibit slightly enhanced stability. As we noted earlier, at larger values of the principal quantum number n, the order of subshell filling may be irregular due to the closeness of the energy levels.

Figure 3.27 groups the elements according to the type of subshell in which the outermost electrons are placed. Elements whose outermost electrons are in an s subshell are referred to as s-block elements, those whose outermost electrons are in a p subshell are referred to as p-block elements, and so on.

Student Annotation: Although zinc and the other elements in Group 2B sometimes are included under the heading "transition metals," they neither have nor readily acquire partially filled d subshells. Strictly speaking, they are *not* transition metals.

Student Annotation: Electron configurations such as these may also be written with the d subshell first. For example, $[Ar]4s^1 3d^{10}$ can also be written as $[Ar]3d^{10}4s^1$. Either way is acceptable.

Student Annotation: When $n = 4$, ℓ can equal 3, corresponding to an f subshell. There are seven possible values for m_ℓ when $\ell = 3$: $-3, -2, -1, 0, +1, +2,$ and $+3$. Therefore, there are seven f orbitals.

Student Annotation: In theory, the lanthanides arise from the filling of the seven degenerate $4f$ orbitals. In reality, however, the energies of the $5d$ and $4f$ orbitals are very close and the electron configurations of these elements sometimes involve $5d$ electrons.

Student Annotation: Most of these elements are not found in nature but have been synthesized in nuclear reactions, which are the subject of Chapter 20.

1s				
2s				2p
3s				3p
4s		3d		4p
5s		4d		5p
6s	4f	5d		6p
7s	5f	6d		7p

Figure 3.27 Classification of groups of elements in the periodic table according to the type of subshell being filled with electrons.

Worked Example 3.11 shows how to write electron configurations.

Worked Example 3.11

Without referring to Figure 3.26, write the electron configuration for an arsenic atom ($Z = 33$) in the ground state.

Strategy Use Figure 3.23 or Figure 3.25 to determine the order in which the subshells will fill, and then assign electrons to the appropriate subshells.

Setup The noble gas core for As is [Ar], where $Z = 18$ for Ar. The order of filling beyond the noble gas core is $4s$, $3d$, and $4p$. Fifteen electrons must go into these subshells because there are $33 - 18 = 15$ electrons in As beyond its noble gas core.

Solution

$$[Ar]4s^23d^{10}4p^3$$

Think About It
Arsenic is a p-block element; therefore, we should expect its outermost electrons to reside in a p subshell.

Practice Problem A Without referring to Figure 3.26, write the electron configuration for a radium atom ($Z = 88$) in the ground state.

Practice Problem B Without referring to Figure 3.26, determine the identity of the element with the following electron configuration:

$$[Xe]6s^24f^{14}5d^{10}6p^5$$

SECTION 3.10 REVIEW

Electron Configurations and the Periodic Table

3.10.1   Write the electron configuration of an Ag atom.

3.10.2   What element is represented by the following electron configuration: $[Kr]5s^24d^{10}5p^5$?

3.10.3   How many d-block elements are there?

3.10.4   How many p-block elements are there?

Learning Outcomes

- Identify energy as being kinetic or potential and, if potential, as being chemical or electrostatic.
- Understand the law of conservation of energy.
- Describe properties of waves including wavelength, frequency, and amplitude.
- Calculate the wavelength or frequency of light given one of these values.
- Cite examples of the electromagnetic spectrum in regard to wavelength and type of radiation.
- Understand the basis of quantum theory and its relationship to the frequency of radiation.
- Describe the basis of the photoelectric effect in terms of photon energy and frequency of radiation.
- Identify the relevance of the de Broglie hypothesis in regard to how electrons may behave as waves as opposed to particles.
- Give in your own words the relevance of the Heisenberg uncertainty principle to the theoretical structure of atomic orbitals.

- Understand how electron density helps to define the shape of atomic orbitals.
- Provide the meaning of each type of quantum number (principal, angular momentum, magnetic, and electron spin).
- Apply quantum number rules to determine allowable values for each type of quantum number.
- Understand the basis of atomic orbitals.
- Arrange atomic orbitals based upon energy levels.
- Understand the meaning of the Pauli exclusion principle and how it relates to electron configurations.
- Apply Hund's rule in drawing electron orbital diagrams.
- Determine the electron configuration of an atom using the Aufbau principle.
- Use the periodic table to determine the electron configuration of an atom.

Chapter Summary

SECTION 3.1

- *Energy* is the capacity to do work or transfer heat. Energy may be *kinetic energy* (the energy associated with *motion*) or *potential energy* (energy possessed by virtue of *position*). *Thermal energy* is a form of kinetic energy. *Chemical energy* and *electrostatic energy* are forms of potential energy.
- The *law of conservation of energy* states that energy can neither be created nor destroyed. The SI unit of energy is the *joule (J)*.

SECTION 3.2

- What we commonly refer to as "light" is actually the visible portion of the *electromagnetic spectrum.* All light has certain common characteristics including wavelength, frequency, and amplitude.
- *Wavelength (λ)* is the distance between two crests or two troughs of a wave. *Frequency (v)* is the number of waves that pass a point per unit time. *Amplitude* is the distance between the midpoint and crest or trough of a wave.
- *Electromagnetic waves* have both electric and magnetic components that are both mutually perpendicular and in phase.

SECTION 3.3

- *Blackbody radiation* is the electromagnetic radiation given off by a solid when it is heated.
- Max Planck proposed that energy, like matter, was composed of tiny, indivisible "packages" called *quanta. Quanta* is the plural of *quantum.*
- Albert Einstein used Planck's revolutionary quantum theory to explain the *photoelectric effect,* in which electrons are emitted when light of a certain minimum frequency, the *threshold frequency,* shines on a metal surface.
- A *quantum* of light is referred to as a *photon*.

SECTION 3.4

- An *emission spectrum* is the light given off by an object when it is excited thermally. An emission spectrum may be *continuous,* including all the wavelengths within a particular range, or it may be a *line spectrum,* consisting only of certain discrete wavelengths.
- The *ground state* is the lowest possible energy state for an atom. An *excited state* is any energy level higher than the ground state.

SECTION 3.5

- A *node* is a point at which a standing wave has zero amplitude.
- Having observed that light could exhibit particle-like behavior, de Broglie proposed that matter might also exhibit wavelike behavior. The *de Broglie wavelength* is the wavelength associated with a particle of very small mass. Soon after de Broglie's proposal, experiments showed that electrons could exhibit diffraction—a property of waves.

SECTION 3.6

- According to the *Heisenberg uncertainty principle,* the product of the uncertainty of the *location* and the uncertainty of the *momentum* of a very small particle must have a certain minimum value. It is thus impossible to know simultaneously both the location and momentum of an electron.
- The *electron density* gives the probability of finding an electron in a particular region in an atom. An *atomic orbital* is the region of three-dimensional space, defined by ψ^2 (the square of the wave function, ψ), where the probability of finding an electron is high. An atomic orbital can accommodate a maximum of *two* electrons.

SECTION 3.7

- An atomic orbital is defined by three *quantum numbers:* the *principal quantum number (n),* the *angular momentum quantum number (ℓ),* and the *magnetic quantum number (m_ℓ).*
- The principal quantum number (n) indicates distance from the nucleus. Possible values of n are (1, 2, 3, ...). The angular momentum quantum number (ℓ) indicates the shape of the orbital. Possible values of ℓ are (0, 1, ..., $n-1$). The magnetic quantum number (m_ℓ) indicates the orbital's orientation in space. Possible values of m_ℓ are ($-\ell$, ..., 0, ..., $+\ell$).
- Two electrons that occupy the same atomic orbital in the ground state must have different *electron spin quantum numbers (m_s),* either $+\frac{1}{2}$ or $-\frac{1}{2}$.

SECTION 3.8

- The value of the angular momentum quantum number (ℓ) determines the type of the atomic orbital: $\ell = 0$ corresponds to an *s orbital,* $\ell = 1$ corresponds to a *p orbital,* $\ell = 2$ corresponds to a *d orbital,* and $\ell = 3$ corresponds to an *f orbital.*

SECTION 3.9

- The *electron configuration* specifies the arrangement of electrons in the atomic orbitals of an atom.
- According to the *Pauli exclusion principle,* no two electrons in an atom in the ground state can have the same four quantum numbers, n, ℓ, m_ℓ, and m_s.
- The *Aufbau principle* describes the theoretical, sequential building up of the elements in the periodic table by the stepwise addition of protons and electrons.
- Atomic orbitals that have the same energy are called *degenerate.* According to *Hund's rule,* degenerate orbitals must all contain one electron before any can contain two electrons.
- Atoms with electron configurations in which there are one or more unpaired electrons are *paramagnetic* and are weakly attracted to a magnetic field. Atoms with electron configurations in which there are no unpaired electrons are *diamagnetic* and are weakly repelled by a magnetic field.

SECTION 3.10

- The *noble gas core* makes it possible to abbreviate the writing of electron configurations.
- The *lanthanide (rare earth) series* and *actinide series* appear at the bottom of the periodic table. They represent the filling of *f* orbitals.

Key Words

Actinide series, 91

Amplitude, 60

Angular momentum quantum number (ℓ), 79

Atomic orbital, 78

Aufbau principle, 87

Blackbody radiation, 63

Chemical energy, 57

d orbital, 84

de Broglie wavelength, 75

Degenerate, 87

Diamagnetic, 88

Electromagnetic spectrum, 60

Electromagnetic wave, 61

Electron configuration, 85

Electron density, 78

Electron spin quantum number (m_s), 81

Electrostatic energy, 57

Emission spectrum, 67

Energy, 57

Excited state, 69

f orbital, 84

Frequency (ν), 60

Ground state, 69

Heisenberg uncertainty principle, 77

Hund's rule, 87

Joule (J), 58

Kinetic energy, 57

Lanthanide (rare earth) series, 91

Law of conservation of energy, 57

Line spectrum, 67

Magnetic quantum number (m_ℓ), 79

Noble gas core, 90

Node, 74

p orbital, 82

Paramagnetic, 88

Pauli exclusion principle, 86

Photoelectric effect, 64

Photon, 64

Potential energy, 57

Principal quantum number (n), 79

Quantum, 63

Quantum numbers, 79

s orbital, 82

Thermal energy, 57

Threshold frequency, 64

Wavelength (λ), 60

Key Equations

3.1 $\quad E_k = \frac{1}{2}mu^2$

3.2 $\quad E_{el} \propto \dfrac{Q_1 Q_2}{d}$

3.3 $\quad c = \lambda v$

3.4 $\quad E = hv$

3.5 $\quad hv = KE + W$

3.6 $\quad \dfrac{1}{\lambda} = R_\infty \left(\dfrac{1}{n_1^2} - \dfrac{1}{n_2^2} \right)$

3.7 $\quad E_n = 2.18 \times 10^{-18} \text{ J} \left(\dfrac{1}{n^2} \right)$

3.8 $\quad \Delta E = hv = -2.18 \times 10^{-18} \text{ J} \left(\dfrac{1}{n_f^2} - \dfrac{1}{n_i^2} \right)$

3.9 $\quad \dfrac{1}{\lambda} = \dfrac{2.18 \times 10^{-18} \text{ J}}{hc} \left(\dfrac{1}{n_f^2} - \dfrac{1}{n_i^2} \right)$

3.10 $\quad 2\pi r = n\lambda$

3.11 $\quad \lambda = \dfrac{h}{mu}$

3.12 $\quad \Delta x \cdot \Delta p \geq \dfrac{h}{4\pi}$

3.13 $\quad \Delta x \cdot m\Delta u \geq \dfrac{h}{4\pi}$

Questions and Problems

SECTION 3.1: ENERGY AND ENERGY CHANGES

Review Questions

3.1 Define these terms: *potential energy, kinetic energy, law of conservation of energy.*

3.2 What are the units for energy commonly employed in chemistry?

3.3 A truck initially traveling at 60 km/h is brought to a complete stop at a traffic light. Does this change violate the law of conservation of energy? Explain.

3.4 Describe the interconversions of forms of energy occurring in these processes: (a) You throw a softball up into the air and catch it. (b) You switch on a flashlight. (c) You ride the ski lift to the top of the hill and then ski down. (d) You strike a match and let it burn completely.

Problems

3.5 Determine the kinetic energy of (a) a 7.5-kg mass moving at 7.9 m/s, (b) a car weighing 3250 lb moving at 55 mph, (c) an electron moving at 315 m/s, (d) a helium atom moving at 275 m/s.

3.6 Determine the kinetic energy of (a) a 25-kg mass moving at 61.3 m/s, (b) a tennis ball weighing 58.1 g moving at 66.2 mph, (c) a beryllium atom moving at 275 m/s, (d) a neutron moving at 2.000×10^3 m/s.

3.7 Determine (a) the velocity of a Ne atom that has $E_k = 1.12 \times 10^{-20}$ J, (b) the velocity of a Kr atom that has $E_k = 1.12 \times 10^{-20}$ J, (c) the mass and identity of an atom moving at 315 m/s that has $E_k = 3.704 \times 10^{-21}$ J.

3.8 Determine (a) the velocity of an electron that has $E_k = 3.41 \times 10^{-21}$ J, (b) the velocity of a neutron that has $E_k = 3.41 \times 10^{-21}$ J, (c) the mass and identity of a subatomic particle moving at 1.566×10^3 m/s that has $E_k = 2.0509 \times 10^{-21}$ J.

3.9 (a) How much greater is the electrostatic energy between charges of +3 and −3 than charges of +2 and −3 if the charges in each case are separated by the same distance? (b) By what distance would charges of +2 and −3 have to be separated for the electrostatic energy between them to be the same as that between charges of +3 and −3 separated by a distance of d?

3.10 (a) How much greater is the electrostatic energy between charges of +4 and −3 than charges of +2 and −3 if the charges in each case are separated by the same distance? (b) By what distance would charges of +4 and −3 have to be separated for the electrostatic energy between them to be the same as that between charges of +2 and −3 separated by a distance of d?

SECTION 3.2: THE NATURE OF LIGHT

Review Questions

3.11   What is a wave? Using a diagram, define the following terms associated with waves: wavelength, frequency, amplitude.

3.12   What are the units for wavelength and frequency of electromagnetic waves? What is the speed of light in meters per second and miles per hour?

3.13   List the types of electromagnetic radiation, starting with the radiation having the longest wavelength and ending with the radiation having the shortest wavelength.

3.14   Give the high and low wavelength values that define the visible region of the electromagnetic spectrum.

Problems

3.15   (a) What is the wavelength (in nm) of light having a frequency of 8.6×10^{13} Hz? (b) What is the frequency (in Hz) of light having a wavelength of 566 nm?

3.16   (a) What is the frequency of light having a wavelength of 456 nm? (b) What is the wavelength (in nm) of radiation having a frequency of 2.45×10^9 Hz? (This is the type of radiation used in microwave ovens.)

3.17   The average distance between Mars and Earth is about 1.3×10^8 mi. How long would it take TV pictures transmitted from the Mars rover robot geologist on Mars' surface to reach Earth (1 mi = 1.61 km)?

3.18   How many minutes would it take a radio wave to travel from the planet Venus to Earth? (The average distance from Venus to Earth = 28 million mi.)

3.19   The SI unit of time is the second, which is defined as 9,192,631,770 cycles of radiation associated with a certain emission process in the cesium atom. Calculate the wavelength of this radiation (to three significant figures). In which region of the electromagnetic spectrum is this wavelength found?

3.20   The SI unit of length is the meter, which is defined as the length equal to 1,650,763.73 wavelengths of the light emitted by a particular energy transition in krypton atoms. Calculate the frequency of the light to three significant figures.

SECTION 3.3: QUANTUM THEORY

Review Questions

3.21   Briefly explain Planck's quantum theory and explain what a quantum is. What are the units for Planck's constant?

3.22   Give two everyday examples that illustrate the concept of quantization.

3.23   Explain what is meant by the photoelectric effect.

3.24   What is a photon? What role did Einstein's explanation of the photoelectric effect play in the development of the particle-wave interpretation of the nature of electromagnetic radiation?

Problems

3.25   A photon has a wavelength of 705 nm. Calculate the energy of the photon in joules.

3.26   The blue color of the sky results from the scattering of sunlight by one of the components of air. The blue light has a frequency of about 7.5×10^{14} Hz. (a) Calculate the wavelength (in nm) associated with this radiation, and (b) calculate the energy (in joules) of a single photon associated with this frequency.

3.27   A photon has a frequency of 6.5×10^9 Hz. (a) Convert this frequency into wavelength (nm). Does this frequency fall in the visible region? (b) Calculate the energy (in joules) of this photon. (c) Calculate the energy (in joules) of 1 mole of photons all with this frequency.

3.28   What is the wavelength (in nm) of radiation that has an energy content of 2.13×10^3 kJ/mol? In which region of the electromagnetic spectrum is this radiation found?

3.29   Calculate the difference in energy (in joules) between a photon with $\lambda = 680$ nm (red) and a photon with $\lambda = 442$ nm (blue).

3.30   How much more energy per photon is there in green light of wavelength 532 nm than in red light of wavelength 635 nm?

3.31   When copper is bombarded with high-energy electrons, X rays are emitted. Calculate the energy (in joules) associated with the photons if the wavelength of the X rays is 0.154 nm.

3.32   A particular form of electromagnetic radiation has a frequency of 9.87×10^{15} Hz. (a) What is its wavelength in nanometers? In meters? (b) To what region of the electromagnetic spectrum would you assign it? (c) What is the energy (in joules) of one quantum of this radiation?

3.33   Photosynthesis makes use of visible light to bring about chemical changes. Explain why heat energy in the form of infrared radiation is ineffective for photosynthesis.

3.34   The retina of a human eye can detect light when radiant energy incident on it is at least 4.0×10^{-17} J. For light of 585-nm wavelength, how many photons does this energy correspond to?

3.35   The radioactive ^{60}Co isotope is used in nuclear medicine to treat certain types of cancer. Calculate the wavelength and frequency of an emitted gamma photon having the energy of 1.29×10^{11} J/mol.

3.36   The binding energy of magnesium metal is 5.86×10^{-19} J. Calculate the minimum frequency of light required to release electrons from the metal.

3.37   What is the kinetic energy of the ejected electron if light of frequency 2.00×10^{15} s^{-1} is used to irradiate the magnesium metal in Problem 3.36?

SECTION 3.4: BOHR'S THEORY OF THE HYDROGEN ATOM

Review Questions

3.38   What are emission spectra? How do line spectra differ from continuous spectra?

3.39   What is an energy level? Explain the difference between ground state and excited state.

3.40   Briefly describe Bohr's theory of the hydrogen atom and how it explains the appearance of an emission spectrum. How does Bohr's theory differ from concepts of classical physics?

3.41   Explain the meaning of the negative sign in Equation 3.7.

Problems

3.42 Explain why elements produce their own characteristic colors when they emit photons.

3.43 Some copper-containing substances emit green light when they are heated in a flame. How would you determine whether the light is of one wavelength or a mixture of two or more wavelengths?

3.44 Is it possible for a fluorescent material (one that absorbs and then reemits light) to emit radiation in the ultraviolet region after absorbing visible light? Explain your answer.

3.45 Explain how astronomers are able to tell which elements are present in distant stars by analyzing the electromagnetic radiation emitted by the stars.

3.46 Consider the following energy levels of a hypothetical atom:

E_4: -1.0×10^{-19} J
E_3: -5.0×10^{-19} J
E_2: -10×10^{-19} J
E_1: -15×10^{-19} J

(a) What is the wavelength of the photon needed to excite an electron from E_1 to E_4? (b) What is the energy (in joules) a photon must have in order to excite an electron from E_2 to E_3? (c) When an electron drops from the E_3 level to the E_1 level, the atom is said to undergo emission. Calculate the wavelength of the photon emitted in this process.

3.47 The first line of the Balmer series occurs at a wavelength of 656.3 nm. What is the energy difference between the two energy levels involved in the emission that results in this spectral line?

3.48 Calculate the wavelength (in nm) of a photon emitted by a hydrogen atom when its electron drops from the $n = 5$ state to the $n = 2$ state.

3.49 Calculate the frequency (Hz) and wavelength (nm) of the emitted photon when an electron drops from the $n = 4$ to the $n = 3$ level in a hydrogen atom.

3.50 What wavelength of light is needed to excite the electron in the hydrogen atom from the ground state to $n = 10$? In what region of the electromagnetic spectrum does a photon of this wavelength lie?

3.51 An electron in the hydrogen atom makes a transition from an energy state of principal quantum number n_i to the $n = 2$ state. If the photon emitted has a wavelength of 434 nm, what is the value of n_i?

SECTION 3.5: WAVE PROPERTIES OF MATTER

Review Questions

3.52 How does de Broglie's hypothesis account for the fact that the energies of the electron in a hydrogen atom are quantized?

3.53 Why is Equation 3.11 meaningful only for submicroscopic particles, such as electrons and atoms, and not for macroscopic objects?

3.54 Explain why we cannot observe the wave behavior of a macroscopic moving object such as a baseball.

Problem

3.55 Thermal neutrons are neutrons that move at speeds comparable to those of particles in air at room temperature. These neutrons are most effective in initiating a nuclear chain reaction among ^{235}U isotopes. Calculate the wavelength (in nm) associated with a beam of neutrons moving at 7.00×10^2 m/s (mass of a neutron = 1.675×10^{-27} kg).

3.56 Protons can be accelerated to speeds near that of light in particle accelerators. Estimate the wavelength (in nm) of such a proton moving at 2.90×10^8 m/s (mass of a proton = 1.673×10^{-27} kg).

3.57 What is the de Broglie wavelength (in cm) of a 8.45-g honeybee flying at 6.28 mph (1 mi = 1.61 km)?

3.58 What is the de Broglie wavelength (in nm) associated with a 2.5-g Ping-Pong ball traveling at 15 mph?

3.59 How fast must a neutron be traveling to have a de Broglie wavelength of 10.5 Å?

3.60 What is the minimum speed an electron must be traveling to have a *visible* de Broglie wavelength? (Assume the range of visible wavelengths is 400–700 nm.)

SECTION 3.6: QUANTUM MECHANICS

Review Questions

3.61 What are the inadequacies of Bohr's theory?

3.62 What is the Heisenberg uncertainty principle? What is the Schrödinger equation?

3.63 What is the physical significance of the wave function?

3.64 How is the concept of electron density used to describe the position of an electron in the quantum mechanical treatment of an atom?

3.65 What is an atomic orbital? How does an atomic orbital differ from an orbit?

Problems

3.66 The speed of a thermal neutron (see Problem 3.55) is known to within 2.0 km/s. What is the minimum uncertainty in the position of the thermal neutron?

3.67 Suppose that photons of red light (675 nm) are used to locate the position of a 2.80-g Ping-Pong ball in flight and that the uncertainty in the position is equal to one wavelength. What is the minimum uncertainty in the speed of the Ping-Pong ball? Comment on the magnitude of your result.

SECTION 3.7: QUANTUM NUMBERS

Review Questions

3.68 Describe the four quantum numbers used to characterize an electron in an atom.

3.69 Which quantum number defines a shell? Which quantum numbers define a subshell?

3.70 Which of the four quantum numbers (n, ℓ, m_ℓ, m_s) determine (a) the energy of an electron in a hydrogen atom and in a many-electron atom, (b) the size of an orbital, (c) the shape of an orbital, (d) the orientation of an orbital in space?

Problems

3.71 An electron in a certain atom is in the $n = 2$ quantum level. List the possible values of ℓ and m_ℓ that it can have.

3.72 An electron in an atom is in the $n = 3$ quantum level. List the possible values of ℓ and m_ℓ that it can have.

3.73 List all the possible subshells and orbitals associated with the principal quantum number n, if $n = 4$.

3.74 List all the possible subshells and orbitals associated with the principal quantum number n, if $n = 5$.

SECTION 3.8: ATOMIC ORBITALS

Review Questions

3.75 Describe the shapes of s, p, and d orbitals. How are these orbitals related to the quantum numbers n, ℓ, and m_ℓ?

3.76 List the hydrogen orbitals in increasing order of energy.

3.77 Describe the characteristics of an s orbital, p orbital, and d orbital. Which of the following orbitals do not exist: $1p$, $2s$, $2d$, $3p$, $3d$, $3f$, $4g$?

3.78 Why is a boundary surface diagram useful in representing an atomic orbital?

Problems

3.79 Give the values of the quantum numbers associated with the following orbitals: (a) $2p$, (b) $3s$, (c) $5d$.

3.80 Give the values of the four quantum numbers of an electron in the following orbitals: (a) $3s$, (b) $4p$, (c) $3d$.

3.81 Describe how a $1s$ orbital and a $2s$ orbital are similar. Describe how they are different.

3.82 What is the difference between a $2p_x$ and a $2p_y$ orbital?

3.83 Why do the $3s$, $3p$, and $3d$ orbitals have the same energy in a hydrogen atom but different energies in a many-electron atom?

3.84 Make a chart of all allowable orbitals in the first four principal energy levels of the hydrogen atom. Designate each by type (for example, s, p), and indicate how many orbitals of each type there are.

3.85 For each of the following pairs of hydrogen orbitals, indicate which is higher in energy: (a) $1s$, $2s$; (b) $2p$, $3p$; (c) $3d_{xy}$, $3d_{yz}$; (d) $3s$, $3d$; (e) $4f$, $5s$.

3.86 Which orbital in each of the following pairs is lower in energy in a many-electron atom: (a) $2s$, $2p$; (b) $3p$, $3d$; (c) $3s$, $4s$; (d) $4d$, $5f$?

SECTION 3.9: ELECTRON CONFIGURATIONS

Review Questions

3.87 What is electron configuration? Describe the roles that the Pauli exclusion principle and Hund's rule play in writing the electron configuration of elements.

3.88 Explain the meaning of the symbol $4d^6$.

3.89 State the Aufbau principle, and explain the role it plays in classifying the elements in the periodic table.

3.90 Define the terms *diamagnetic* and *paramagnetic*.

3.91 Explain how it is possible for an atom with an *even* number of electrons to have one or more *unpaired* electrons.

Problems

3.92 Calculate the total number of electrons that can occupy (a) one s orbital, (b) three p orbitals, (c) five d orbitals, (d) seven f orbitals.

3.93 Determine the total number of electrons that can be held in all orbitals having the same principal quantum number n when (a) $n = 1$, (b) $n = 2$, (c) $n = 3$, and (d) $n = 4$.

3.94 Determine the maximum number of electrons that can be found in each of the following subshells: $3s$, $3d$, $4p$, $4f$, $5f$.

3.95 Indicate the total number of (a) p electrons in N ($Z = 7$); (b) s electrons in Si ($Z = 14$); and (c) $3d$ electrons in S ($Z = 16$).

3.96 Indicate which of the following sets of quantum numbers in an atom are unacceptable and explain why: (a) $(1, 1, +\frac{1}{2}, -\frac{1}{2})$; (b) $(3, 0, -1, +\frac{1}{2})$; (c) $(2, 0, +1, +\frac{1}{2})$; (d) $(4, 3, -2, +\frac{1}{2})$; (e) $(3, 2, +1, 1)$.

3.97 The ground-state electron configurations listed here are incorrect. Explain what mistakes have been made in each and write the correct electron configurations.

Al: $1s^2 2s^2 2p^4 3s^2 3p^3$
B: $1s^2 2s^2 2p^5$
F: $1s^2 2s^2 2p^6$

3.98 The electron configuration of an atom in the ground state is $1s^2 2s^2 2p^6 3s^2$. Write a complete set of quantum numbers for each of the electrons. Name the element.

3.99 List the following atoms in order of increasing number of unpaired electrons: B, C, N, O, F.

3.100 Determine the number of unpaired electrons in each atom: K, Ca, Sc, Ti, V, Cr, Mn.

3.101 Determine the number of unpaired electrons in each of the following atoms in the ground state and identify each as diamagnetic or paramagnetic: (a) Rb, (b) As, (c) I, (d) Cr, (e) Zn.

3.102 Determine the number of unpaired electrons in each of the following atoms in the ground state and identify each as diamagnetic or paramagnetic: (a) C, (b) S, (c) Cu, (d) Pb, (e) Ti.

SECTION 3.10: ELECTRON CONFIGURATIONS AND THE PERIODIC TABLE

Review Questions

3.103 Describe the characteristics of transition metals.

3.104 What is the noble gas core? How does it simplify the writing of electron configurations?

3.105 What are the group and period of the element tantalum?

3.106 Define the following terms and give an example of each: *lanthanides, actinides*.

3.107 Explain why the ground-state electron configurations of Cr and Cu are different from what we might expect.

3.108 Write the electron configuration of a xenon core.

3.109 Comment on the correctness of the following statement: The probability of finding two electrons with the same four quantum numbers in an atom is zero.

Problems

3.110 Use the Aufbau principle to obtain the ground-state electron configuration of tellurium.

3.111 Use the Aufbau principle to obtain the ground-state electron configuration of iridium.

3.112 Write the ground-state electron configurations for the following elements: B, V, C, As, I, Au.

3.113 Write the ground-state electron configurations for the following elements: Ge, Fe, Zn, Ni, W, Tl.

3.114 What is the symbol of the element with the following ground-state electron configurations? (a) $[Ar]4s^23d^8$; (b) $[Ne]3s^23p^2$; (c) $[Kr]5s^24d^{10}5p^4$; (d) $[Ar]4s^23d^{10}4p^3$.

3.115 What is the symbol of the element with the following ground-state electron configurations? (a) $[Ar]4s^23d^{10}4p^1$; (b) $[Kr]5s^24d^1$; (c) $[Ar]4s^13d^5$; (d) $[Rn]7s^26d^1$.

ADDITIONAL PROBLEMS

3.116 When a substance containing cesium is heated in a Bunsen burner flame, photons with an energy of 4.30×10^{-19} J are emitted. What color is the cesium flame?

3.117 Discuss the current view of the correctness of the following statements. (a) The electron in the hydrogen atom is in an orbit that never brings it closer than 100 pm to the nucleus. (b) Atomic absorption spectra result from transitions of electrons from lower to higher energy levels. (c) A many-electron atom behaves somewhat like a solar system that has a number of planets.

3.118 Distinguish carefully between the following terms: (a) *wavelength* and *frequency*, (b) *wave properties* and *particle properties*, (c) *quantization of energy* and *continuous variation in energy.*

3.119 What is the maximum number of electrons in an atom that can have the following quantum numbers? Specify the orbitals in which the electrons would be found. (a) $n = 2, m_s = +\frac{1}{2}$; (b) $n = 4, m_\ell = +1$; (c) $n = 3, \ell = 2$; (d) $n = 2, \ell = 0, m_s = -\frac{1}{2}$; (e) $n = 4, \ell = 3; m_\ell = -2$.

3.120 Identify the following individuals and their contributions to the development of quantum theory: Bohr, de Broglie, Einstein, Planck, Heisenberg, Schrödinger.

3.121 A red light was shined onto a metal sample and the result shown in (i) was observed. When the light source was changed to a blue light, the result shown in (ii) was observed. Explain how these results can be interpreted with respect to the photoelectric effect.

Describe the result you would expect for each of the following: (a) The intensity of red light is increased. (b) The intensity of blue light is increased. (c) Violet light is used.

3.122 A baseball pitcher's fastballs have been clocked at 101 mph. (a) Calculate the wavelength of a 0.141-kg baseball (in nm) at this speed. (b) What is the wavelength of a hydrogen atom at the same speed (1 mi = 1609 m)?

3.123 A ruby laser produces radiation of wavelength 633 nm in pulses with a duration of 1.00×10^{-9} s. (a) If the laser produces 0.376 J of energy per pulse, how many photons are produced in each pulse? (b) Calculate the power (in watts) delivered by the laser per pulse (1 W = 1 J/s).

3.124 Four atomic energy levels of an atom are shown here. When an electron in an excited atom moves from (d) ⟶ (c), (c) ⟶ (b), and (b) ⟶ (a), a photon of light is emitted each time. The wavelengths of the various photons are 575 nm, 162 nm, and 131 nm. Determine the energies of each photon emitted and match each emission to the appropriate wavelength knowing the energy levels are drawn to scale.

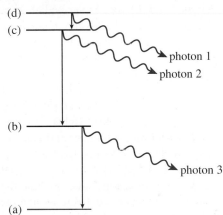

3.125 A single atom of an unknown element travels at 15 percent of the speed of light. The de Broglie wavelength of this atom is 1.06×10^{-16} m. What element is this?

3.126 Spectral lines of the Lyman and Balmer series do not overlap. Verify this statement by calculating the longest wavelength associated with the Lyman series and the shortest wavelength associated with the Balmer series (in nm).

3.127 Only a fraction of the electric energy supplied to a tungsten lightbulb is converted to visible light. The rest of the energy shows up as infrared radiation (that is, heat). A 75-W lightbulb converts 15.0 percent of the energy supplied to it into visible light (assume the wavelength to be 550 nm). How many photons are emitted by the lightbulb per second (1 W = 1 J/s)?

3.128 A 3s orbital is illustrated here. Using this as a reference to show the relative size of the other four orbitals, answer the following questions.

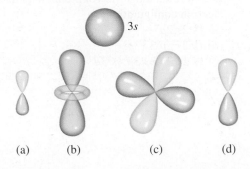

(a) Which orbital has the greatest value of n? (b) How many orbitals have a value of $\ell = 1$? (c) How many other orbitals with the same value of n would have the same general shape as orbital (b)?

3.129   When one of helium's electrons is removed, the resulting species is the helium ion, He^+. The He^+ ion contains only one electron and is therefore a "hydrogen-like ion." Calculate the wavelengths, in increasing order, of the first four transitions in the Balmer series of the He^+ ion. Compare these wavelengths with the same transitions in an H atom. Comment on the differences. (The Rydberg constant for He is 4.39×10^7 m^{-1}.)

3.130   The retina of a human eye can detect light when radiant energy incident on it is at least 4.0×10^{-17} J. For light of 575-nm wavelength, how many photons does this correspond to?

3.131   An electron in an excited state in a hydrogen atom can return to the ground state in two different ways: (a) via a direct transition in which a photon of wavelength λ_1 is emitted and (b) via an intermediate excited state reached by the emission of a photon of wavelength λ_2. This intermediate excited state then decays to the ground state by emitting another photon of wavelength λ_3. Derive an equation that relates λ_1 to λ_2 and λ_3.

3.132   A photoelectric experiment was performed by separately shining a laser at 450 nm (blue light) and a laser at 560 nm (yellow light) on a clean metal surface and measuring the number and kinetic energy of the ejected electrons. Which light would generate more electrons? Which light would eject electrons with greater kinetic energy? Assume that the same total amount of energy is delivered to the metal surface by each laser and that the frequencies of the laser lights exceed the threshold frequency.

3.133   The electron configurations described in this chapter all refer to gaseous atoms in their ground states. An atom may absorb a quantum of energy and promote one of its electrons to a higher-energy orbital. When this happens, we say that the atom is in an excited state. The electron configurations of some excited atoms are given. Identify these atoms and write their ground-state configurations:
(a) $1s^1 2s^1$
(b) $1s^1 2s^2 2p^2 3d^1$
(c) $1s^2 2s^2 2p^6 4s^1$
(d) $[Ar]4s^1 3d^{10} 4p^4$
(e) $[Ne]3s^2 3p^4 3d^1$

3.134   Draw the shapes (boundary surfaces) of the following orbitals: (a) $2p_y$, (b) $3d_{z^2}$, (c) $3d_{x^2-y^2}$. (Show coordinate axes in your sketches.)

3.135   Draw orbital diagrams for atoms with the following electron configurations:
(a) $1s^2 2s^2 2p^5$
(b) $1s^2 2s^2 2p^6 3s^2 3p^3$
(c) $1s^2 2s^2 2p^6 3s^2 3p^6 4s^2 3d^7$

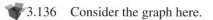 3.136   Consider the graph here.

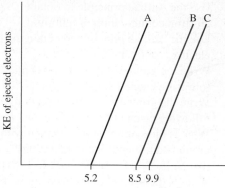

(a) Calculate the binding energy (W) of each metal. Which metal has the highest binding energy? (b) A photon with a wavelength of 333 nm is fired at the three metals. Which, if any, of the metals will eject an electron?

3.137   Scientists have found interstellar hydrogen atoms with quantum number n in the hundreds. Calculate the wavelength of light emitted when a hydrogen atom undergoes a transition from $n = 236$ to $n = 235$. In what region of the electromagnetic spectrum does this wavelength fall?

3.138   Ionization energy is the minimum energy required to remove an electron from an atom. It is usually expressed in units of kJ/mol, that is, the energy in kilojoules required to remove one mole of electrons from one mole of atoms. (a) Calculate the ionization energy for the hydrogen atom. (b) Repeat the calculation, assuming in this second case that the electrons are removed from the $n = 2$ state instead of from the ground state.

3.139   An electron in a hydrogen atom is excited from the ground state to the $n = 4$ state. Comment on the correctness of the following statements (true or false).
(a) $n = 4$ is the first excited state.
(b) It takes more energy to ionize (remove) the electron from $n = 4$ than from the ground state.
(c) The electron is farther from the nucleus (on average) in $n = 4$ than in the ground state.
(d) The wavelength of light emitted when the electron drops from $n = 4$ to $n = 1$ is longer than that from $n = 4$ to $n = 2$.
(e) The wavelength the atom absorbs in going from $n = 1$ to $n = 4$ is the same as that emitted as it goes from $n = 4$ to $n = 1$.

3.140   The ionization energy of a certain element is 412 kJ/mol (see Problem 3.138). However, when the atoms of this element are in the first excited state, the ionization energy is only 126 kJ/mol. Based on this information, calculate the wavelength of light emitted in a transition from the first excited state to the ground state.

3.141 The cone cells of the human eye are sensitive to three wavelength ranges, which the eye interprets as blue (419 nm), green (531 nm), and red (558 nm). If the optic nerve in the eye requires 2.0×10^{-17} J of energy to initiate the sight impulses to the brain, how many photons of blue light (419 nm), green light (531 nm), and red light (558 nm) are needed to see these colors?

3.142 Portions of orbital diagrams representing the ground-state electron configurations of certain elements are shown here. Which of them violate the Pauli exclusion principle? Which violate Hund's rule?

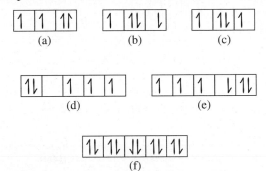

3.143 The UV light that is responsible for tanning the skin falls in the 320-nm to 400-nm region. Calculate the total energy (in joules) absorbed by a person exposed to this radiation for 2.5 h, given that there are 2.0×10^{16} photons hitting Earth's surface per square centimeter per second over a 80-nm (320 to 400 nm) range and that the exposed body area is 0.45 m². Assume that only half of the radiation is absorbed and the other half is reflected by the body. (*Hint:* Use an average wavelength of 360 nm in calculating the energy of a photon.)

3.144 The sun is surrounded by a white circle of gaseous material called the corona, which becomes visible during a total eclipse of the sun. The temperature of the corona is in the millions of degrees Celsius, which is high enough to remove some or all of the electrons from atoms. One way astronomers have been able to estimate the temperature of the corona is by studying the emission lines of ions of certain elements. For example, the emission spectrum of Fe^{14+} ions (iron atoms from which 14 electrons have been removed) has been recorded and analyzed. Knowing that it takes 3.5×10^4 kJ/mol to convert Fe^{13+} to Fe^{14+}, estimate the temperature of the sun's corona. (*Hint:* The average kinetic energy of one mole of a gas is $\frac{3}{2}RT$.)

3.145 When an electron makes a transition between energy levels of a hydrogen atom, there are no restrictions on the initial and final values of the principal quantum number n. However, there is a quantum mechanical rule that restricts the initial and final values of the orbital angular momentum ℓ. This is the *selection rule,* which states that $\Delta\ell = \pm 1$; that is, in a transition, the value of ℓ can increase or decrease by only 1. According to this rule, which of the following transitions are allowed:
(a) $1s \longrightarrow 2s$, (b) $2p \longrightarrow 1s$, (c) $1s \longrightarrow 3d$,
(d) $3d \longrightarrow 4f$, (e) $4d \longrightarrow 3s$?

3.146 In 1996, physicists created an anti-atom of hydrogen. In such an atom, which is the antimatter equivalent of an ordinary atom, the electric charges of all the component particles are reversed. Thus, the nucleus of an anti-atom is made of an antiproton, which has the same mass as a proton but bears a negative charge, and the electron is replaced by an anti-electron (also called a positron) with the same mass as an electron but bearing a positive charge. Would you expect the energy levels, emission spectra, and atomic orbitals of an antihydrogen atom to be different from those of a hydrogen atom? What would happen if an anti-atom of hydrogen collided with a hydrogen atom?

3.147 In an electron microscope, electrons are accelerated by passing them through a voltage difference. The kinetic energy thus acquired by the electrons is equal to the voltage times the charge on the electron. Thus, a voltage difference of 1 volt imparts a kinetic energy of 1.602×10^{-19} volt-coulomb or 1.602×10^{-19} J. Calculate the wavelength associated with electrons accelerated by 5.00×10^3 volts.

3.148 The figure below illustrates a series of transitions that occur in a hydrogen atom.

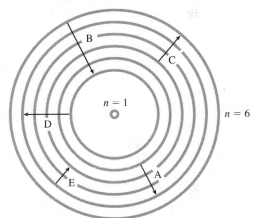

(a) Which transitions are absorptions and which are emissions?
(b) Rank the emissions in order of increasing energy.
(c) Rank the emissions in order of increasing wavelength of light emitted.

3.149 Calculate the wavelength and frequency of an emitted photon of gamma radiation that has energy of 3.14×10^{11} J/mol.

3.150 (a) An electron in the ground state of the hydrogen atom moves at an average speed of 5×10^6 m/s. If the speed is known to an uncertainty of 20 percent, what is the minimum uncertainty in its position? Given that the radius of the hydrogen atom in the ground state is 5.29×10^{-11} m, comment on your result. The mass of an electron is 9.1094×10^{-31} kg. (b) A 0.15-kg baseball thrown at 99 mph has a momentum of 6.7 kg · m/s. If the uncertainty in measuring the momentum is 1.0×10^{-7} of the momentum, calculate the uncertainty in the baseball's position.

3.151   The mathematical equation for studying the photoelectric effect is

$$h\nu = W + \frac{1}{2}m_e u^2$$

where ν is the frequency of light shining on the metal; W is the energy needed to remove an electron from the metal; and m_e and u are the mass and speed of the ejected electron, respectively. In an experiment, a student found that a maximum wavelength of 351 nm is needed to just dislodge electrons from a zinc metal surface. Calculate the velocity (in m/s) of an ejected electron when the student employed light with a wavelength of 313 nm.

3.152   According to Einstein's special theory of relativity, the mass of a moving particle, m_{moving}, is related to its mass at rest, m_{rest}, by the following equation

$$m_{moving} = \frac{m_{rest}}{\sqrt{1 - (u/c)^2}}$$

where u and c are the speeds of the particle and light, respectively. (a) In particle accelerators, protons, electrons, and other charged particles are often accelerated to speeds close to the speed of light. Calculate the wavelength (in nm) of a proton moving at 50.0 percent the speed of light. The mass of a proton is 1.67×10^{-27} kg. (b) Calculate the mass of a 6.0×10^{-2}-kg tennis ball moving at 63 m/s. Comment on your results.

3.153   Blackbody radiation is the term used to describe the dependence of the radiation energy emitted by an object on wavelength at a certain temperature. Planck proposed the quantum theory to account for the dependence. Shown in the figure is a plot of the radiation energy emitted by our sun versus wavelength. This curve is characteristic of objects at about 6000 K, which is the temperature at the surface of the sun. At a higher temperature, the curve has a similar shape but the maximum will shift to a shorter wavelength. (a) What does this curve reveal about two consequences of great biological significance on Earth? (b) How are astronomers able to determine the temperature at the surface of stars in general?

3.154   In the beginning of the twentieth century, some scientists thought that a nucleus may contain both electrons and protons. Use the Heisenberg uncertainty principle to show that an electron cannot be confined within a nucleus. Repeat the calculation for a proton. Comment on your results. Assume the radius of a nucleus to be 1.0×10^{-15} m. The masses of an electron and a proton are 9.109×10^{-31} kg and 1.673×10^{-27} kg, respectively. (*Hint:* Treat the radius of the nucleus as the uncertainty in position.)

Answers to In-Chapter Materials

PRACTICE PROBLEMS

3.1A 1.13×10^3 J. **3.1B** 3.70×10^2 m/s. **3.2A** 1.5 times greater. **3.2B** 0.667 mm. **3.3A** 1.86×10^{-4} m. **3.3B** 2.91×10^{10} s^{-1}. **3.4A** (a) 9.43×10^{-19} J, (b) 1.18×10^{-25} J, (c) 1.96×10^{-19} J. **3.4B** (a) 1.05×10^4 nm, (b) 2.1×10^{18}, (c) 1.2 eV. **3.5A** 103 nm. **3.5B** 7. **3.6A** 26 nm. **3.6B** 8.2×10^{-28} kg · m/s. **3.7A** (a) 3×10^{-34} m. **3.7B** (a) $\pm 2 \times 10^{-25}$ kg · m/s, (b) $\pm 1 \times 10^2$ m/s, (c) $\pm 2 \times 10^5$ m/s. **3.8A** Only 0. **3.8B** $-2, -1, 0, +1, +2$. **3.9A** $n = 3$, $\ell = 2$, $m_\ell = -2, -1, 0, +1, +2$. **3.9B** For a d orbital, $\ell = 2$, but when $n = 2$, ℓ cannot be 2. **3.10A** $1s^2 2s^2 2p^6 3s^2 3p^6 4s^2 3d^{10} 4p^6 5s^1$. **3.10B** $1s^2 2s^2 2p^6 3s^2 3p^6 4s^2 3d^{10} 4p^5$. **3.11A** [Rn]$7s^2$. **3.11B** At.

SECTION REVIEW

3.1.1 1.7×10^3 J. **3.1.2** 199 m/s. **3.1.3** yellow = green < blue < purple. **3.2.1** 8.70×10^2 nm. **3.2.2** 2.38×10^{15} s^{-1}. **3.2.3** ii, i, ii. **3.2.4** 2.00×10^8 m/s. **3.3.1** 3.06×10^{-19} J. **3.3.2** 1.51 cm. **3.3.3** 5.61×10^{-20} J. **3.3.4** $\lambda_3 < \lambda_1 < \lambda_2$. **3.4.1** -2.42×10^{-19} J. **3.4.2** 2.09×10^{-18} J. **3.4.3** 1.28×10^{-6} m. **3.4.4** 122 nm. **3.5.1** 3.3×10^{-14} m. **3.5.2** 665 m/s. **3.5.3** 0.990 m/s. **3.6.1** 1×10^{-9} m. **3.6.2** 8×10^{-13} m. **3.7.1** 5. **3.7.2** 3. **3.7.3** 16. **3.7.4** $n = 3$. **3.8.1** 7. **3.8.2** n. **3.8.3** $1s, 2s, 2p$. **3.8.4** (a) m_ℓ cannot be -2 when $\ell = 1$, (b) ℓ cannot be 2 when $n = 2$, (c) this is an acceptable set of quantum numbers, (d) n cannot be 0. **3.9.1** $1s^2 2s^2 2p^6 3s^2 3p^6 4s^2 3d^2$. **3.9.2** Se.

3.9.3

$\uparrow\downarrow$	$\uparrow\downarrow$	$\uparrow\downarrow$	$\uparrow\downarrow$	$\uparrow\downarrow$	$\uparrow\downarrow$	$\uparrow\downarrow$	$\uparrow$	$\uparrow$
$1s^2$	$2s^2$		$2p^6$			$3s^2$		$3p^4$

3.10.1 [Kr]$5s^1 4d^{10}$. **3.10.2** I. **3.10.3** 40. **3.10.4** 36.

KEY SKILLS

Determining Ground-State Valence Electron Configurations Using the Periodic Table

An easy way to determine the electron configuration of an element is by using the periodic table. Although the table is arranged by atomic number, it is also divided into blocks that indicate the type of orbital occupied by an element's outermost electrons. Outermost valence electrons of elements in the *s*-block (shown below in yellow), reside in *s* orbitals; those of elements in the *p*-block (blue) reside in *p* orbitals; and so on.

1 $1s_1$																	2 $1s_2$
3 / 4 ←$2s$→ ₁ ₂												5 6 7 8 9 10 ←$2p$→ ₁ ₂ 3 4 5 6					
11 / 12 ←$3s$→ ₁ ₂												13 14 15 16 17 18 ←$3p$→ ₁ ₂ 3 4 5 6					
19 20 ←$4s$→ ₁ ₂		21 22 23 24 25 26 27 28 29 30 ←$3d$→ ₁ ₂ 3 4 5 6 7 8 9 10										31 32 33 34 35 36 ←$4p$→ ₁ ₂ 3 4 5 6					
21 22 ←$5s$→ ₁ ₂		39 40 41 42 43 44 45 46 47 48 ←$4d$→ ₁ ₂ 3 4 5 6 7 8 9 10										49 50 51 52 53 54 ←$5p$→ ₁ ₂ 3 4 5 6					
55 56 57 ←$6s$→ ₁ ₂		72 73 74 75 76 77 78 79 66 ←$5d$→ ₁ ₂ 3 4 5 6 7 8 9 10										81 83 84 85 86 ←$6p$→ ₁ ₂ 3 4 5 6					
87 88 89 ←$7s$→ ₁ ₂		104 105 106 107 108 109 110 111 112 ←$6d$→ ₁ ₂ 3 4 5 6 7 8 9 10										113 114 115 116 117 118 ←$7p$→ ₁ ₂ 3 4 5 6					

21	22	23	24	25	26	27	28	29	30	31	32	33	34
←$4f$→ 1 2		3	4	5	6	7	8	9	10	11	12	13	14
39	40	41	42	43	44	45	46	47	48	49	50	51	52
←$5f$→ 1 2		3	4	5	6	7	8	9	10	11	12	13	14

To determine the ground-state electron configuration of any element, we start with the most recently completed noble gas core, and count across the following period to determine the valence electron configuration. Consider the example of Cl, which has atomic number 17. The noble gas that precedes Cl is Ne, with atomic number 10. Therefore, we begin by writing [Ne]. The noble gas symbol in square brackets represents the core electrons—with a completed p subshell. To complete the electron configuration, we count from the left of period 3 as shown by the red arrow, adding the last (rightmost) configuration label from each block the arrow touches:

[Ne]	$3s^2$	$3p^5$

There are seven electrons in addition to the noble gas core. Two of them reside in an s subshell, and five of them reside in a p subshell. By simply counting across the third period, we can determine the specific subshells that contain the valence electrons, and arrive at the correct ground-state electron configuration: $[Ne]3s^23p^5$.

For Ga, with atomic number 31, the preceding noble gas is Ar, with atomic number 18. Counting across the fourth period (green arrow) gives the ground-state electron configuration: $[Ar]4s^23d^{10}4p^1$.

There are a few elements for which this method will not give the correct configuration. For example, there is no element with a ground-state valence electron configuration ending in $3d^4$ or $3d^9$. Instead, Cr and Cu are $[Ar]4s^13d^5$ and $[Ar]4s^13d^{10}$, respectively. Remember that this is the result of the unusual stability of either a *half-filled* or a *filled d* subshell [◄◄ Section 3.10].

We can also use the periodic table to determine the identity of an element, given its ground-state electron configuration. For example, given the configuration $[Ne]3s^23p^4$, we focus on the last entry in the configuration: $3p^4$. This tells us that the element is in the *third* period (3), in the p-block (p), and that it has *four* electrons in its p subshell (superscript 4). This corresponds to atomic number 16, which is the element sulfur (S).

Key Skills Problems

3.1
What is the noble gas core for Mo?

(a) Ar (b) Kr (c) Xe (d) Ne (e) Rn

3.2
Which of the following electron configurations correctly represents the V atom?

(a) $[Ar]3d^5$ (b) $[Ar]4s^23d^2$ (c) $[Ar]4s^23d^4$ (d) $[Ar]4s^23d^3$
(e) $[Kr]4s^23d^3$

3.3
What element is represented by the electron configuration $[Kr]5s^24d^{10}5p^1$?

(a) Sn (b) Ga (c) In (d) Tl (e) Zr

3.4
What is the electron configuration of the Lu atom?

(a) $[Xe]6s^24f^{14}$ (b) $[Xe]6s^25d^1$ (c) $[Xe]6s^24f^{13}$ (d) $[Xe]6s^24f^{14}5d^1$
(e) $[Xe]4f^{14}$

CHAPTER 4

Periodic Trends of the Elements

117

Uus

Ununseptium

(294)

2
8
18
32
32
18
7

4.1   **Development of the Periodic Table**

4.2   **The Modern Periodic Table**
- Classification of Elements

4.3   **Effective Nuclear Charge**

4.4   **Periodic Trends in Properties of Elements**
- Atomic Radius • Ionization Energy • Electron Affinity • Metallic Character

4.5   **Electron Configuration of Ions**
- Ions of Main Group Elements • Ions of *d*-Block Elements

4.6   **Ionic Radius**
- Comparing Ionic Radius with Atomic Radius
- Isoelectronic Series

The periodic recurrence of the properties of the elements—a phenomenon known as *periodicity*—provides the foundation of the modern periodic table. Based on the work of Dmitri Mendeleev and Lothar Meyer, this careful tabulation of the elements allowed chemists to predict the existence and properties of elements that had not yet been discovered. Mendeleev himself predicted the eventual discovery of an element similar to aluminum, which he dubbed eka-aluminum. Indeed, when the element *gallium* was subsequently discovered, it had the very properties that Mendeleev had predicted for eka-aluminum. Since that time, chemists and physicists have succeeded in completing the current periodic table by producing elements that are not found in nature. Element 117, the last element produced—and whose properties are predicted to be similar to other Group 7A elements, was reported in 2010.

- Electrostatic energy [◄◄ Section 3.1]
- Electron configurations and the periodic table [◄◄ Section 3.10]

4.1   DEVELOPMENT OF THE PERIODIC TABLE

Although chemists in the nineteenth century generally agreed that matter consisted of atoms, they knew nothing of the *structure* of atoms. Nevertheless, the need to organize a growing body of scientific information about the known elements inspired a number of attempts to arrange the elements in a table. Because accurate measurements of the atomic masses of many elements had already been made, one seemingly logical approach was to organize the elements in order of increasing atomic mass.

In 1864, the English chemist John Newlands[1] noticed that when the elements were arranged in order of increasing atomic mass, every eighth element had similar properties. Newlands referred to this peculiar relationship as the *law of octaves*. However, this "law" turned out to be inadequate for elements beyond calcium, and Newlands's work was not accepted by the scientific community.

In 1869, the Russian chemist Dmitri Mendeleev[2] and the German chemist Lothar Meyer[3] independently proposed a much more extensive tabulation of the elements based on the regular, periodic recurrence of properties—a phenomenon known as *periodicity*.

Mendeleev's classification system was a great improvement over Newlands's for two reasons. First, it grouped the elements together more accurately, according to their properties. Second, and equally important, it made it possible to predict the properties of several elements that had not yet been discovered. For example, Mendeleev proposed the existence of an unknown element that he called eka-aluminum and predicted a number of its properties. (*Eka* is a Sanskrit word meaning "first"; thus, eka-aluminum would be the first element under aluminum in the same group.) When gallium was discovered 4 years later, its properties matched the predicted properties of eka-aluminum remarkably well:

	Eka-Aluminum (Ea)	Gallium (Ga)
Atomic mass	68 amu	69.9 amu
Melting point	Low	30.15°C
Density	5.9 g/cm^3	5.94 g/cm^3
Formula of oxide	Ea_2O_3	Ga_2O_3

Mendeleev's periodic table included 66 known elements. By 1900, 30 more had been added to the list, filling in some of the empty spaces. Figure 4.1 gives the time period during which each element was discovered.

---

[1]John Alexander Reina Newlands (1838–1898). Newlands's work was a step in the right direction in the classification of the elements. Unfortunately, because of its shortcomings, he was subjected to much criticism and even ridicule. At one meeting he was asked if he had ever examined the elements according to the order of their initial letters! Nevertheless, in 1887 Newlands was honored by the Royal Society of London for his contribution.

[2]Dmitri Ivanovich Mendeleev (1836–1907). His work on the periodic classification of elements is regarded by many as the most significant achievement in chemistry in the nineteenth century.

[3]Julius Lothar Meyer (1830–1895). In addition to his contribution to the periodic table, Meyer also discovered the chemical affinity of hemoglobin for oxygen.

Figure 4.1 Periodic table of elements classified by dates of discovery.

Although this periodic table was remarkably successful, the early versions had some inconsistencies that were impossible to overlook. For example, the atomic mass of argon (39.95 amu) is greater than that of potassium (39.10 amu), but argon comes before potassium in the periodic table. If elements were arranged solely according to increasing atomic mass, argon would appear in the position occupied by potassium in our modern periodic table (see the inside front cover). It simply would not make sense to put sodium (a metal) in a group where every other member is a gas—or to put argon (a gas) in a group where every other member is a metal. This and other discrepancies suggested that some fundamental property other than atomic mass must be the basis of periodicity. The fundamental property turned out to be the number of protons in an atom's nucleus, something that could not have been known by Mendeleev and his contemporaries.

In 1913 a young English physicist, Henry Moseley,[4] discovered a correlation between what he called *atomic number* and the frequency of X rays generated by bombarding an element with high-energy electrons. Moseley noticed that, in general, the frequencies of X rays emitted from the elements increased with increasing atomic mass. Among the few exceptions he found were argon and potassium. Although argon has a greater atomic mass than potassium, the X-ray emission from potassium indicated that it has the greater atomic number. Ordering the periodic table using atomic number enabled scientists to make sense out of the discrepancies that had puzzled them earlier. Moseley concluded that the atomic number was equal to the number of protons in the nucleus and to the number of electrons in an atom.

Entries in modern periodic tables usually include an element's atomic number along with its symbol. Electron configurations of elements help to explain the periodic recurrence of physical and chemical properties. The importance and usefulness of the periodic table lie in the fact that we can use our understanding of the general properties and trends within a group or a period to predict with considerable accuracy the properties of any element, even though that element may be unfamiliar to us.

Worked Example 4.1 shows how the periodic table can be used to predict similarities in the properties of elements.

---

[4]Henry Gwyn-Jeffreys Moseley (1887–1915). Moseley discovered the relationship between X-ray spectra and atomic number. A lieutenant in the Royal Engineers, he was killed in action at the age of 28 during the British campaign in Gallipoli, Turkey.

Worked Example 4.1

What elements would you expect to exhibit properties most similar to those of chlorine?

Strategy Because elements in the same group tend to have similar properties, you should identify elements in the same group as chlorine.

Setup Chlorine is a member of Group 7A.

Solution Fluorine, bromine, and iodine, the other nonmetals in Group 7A, should have properties most similar to those of chlorine.

Think About It
Astatine (At) is also in Group 7A. Astatine, though, is classified as a metalloid, and we have to be careful comparing nonmetals to *metalloids* (or to *metals*). As a metalloid, the properties of astatine should be less similar to those of chlorine than the other members of Group 7A.

Student Annotation: Actually, astatine is radioactive and very little is known about its properties.

Practice Problem A (a) What element(s) would you expect to exhibit properties most similar to those of silicon (Si)? (b) Which of the elements in Group 5A would you expect to exhibit properties *least* similar to those of nitrogen?

Practice Problem B Arrange the following Group 5A elements in order of increasing similarity of properties to N: As, Bi, and P.

SECTION 4.1 REVIEW

Development of the Periodic Table

4.1.1 Would you expect Se, Si, Te, or Sb to have chemical properties most similar to those of S?

4.1.2 Name two elements that you would expect to have chemical properties most similar to those of Sr.

4.1.3 The first-ever production of element 117 was recently reported by scientists in the United States and Russia. However, only a very small number of atoms have been produced. Based on its position in the periodic table, (a) to which of the known elements would you expect its properties to be most similar; and (b) would you expect it to be a metal, a nonmetal, or a metalloid?

4.2 THE MODERN PERIODIC TABLE

Figure 4.2 shows the modern periodic table together with the outermost ground-state electron configurations of the elements. (The electron configurations of the elements are also given in Figure 3.27.) Starting with hydrogen, the electronic subshells are filled in the order shown in Figure 3.25 [◄◄ Section 3.9].

Classification of Elements

Based on the type of subshell containing the outermost electrons, the elements can be divided into categories—the main group elements, the noble gases, the transition elements (or transition metals), the lanthanides, and the actinides. The ***main group elements*** (also called the *representative elements*) are the elements in Groups 1A through 7A. With the exception of helium, each of

Student Annotation: In this context, outermost electrons refers to those that are placed in orbitals last using the Aufbau principle [◄◄ Section 3.9].

Figure 4.2 Valence-electron configurations of the elements. For simplicity, the filled *f* subshells are not shown in elements 72 through 86, 104 through 118.

Group 1A (1): H 1 $1s^1$ · Li 3 $2s^1$ · Na 11 $3s^1$ · K 19 $4s^1$ · Rb 37 $5s^1$ · Cs 55 $6s^1$ · Fr 87 $7s^1$

Group 2A (2): Be 4 $2s^2$ · Mg 12 $3s^2$ · Ca 20 $4s^2$ · Sr 38 $5s^2$ · Ba 56 $6s^2$ · Ra 88 $7s^2$

Group 3B (3): Sc 21 $4s^23d^1$ · Y 39 $5s^24d^1$ · La 57 $6s^25d^1$ · Ac 89 $7s^26d^1$

Group 4B (4): Ti 22 $4s^23d^2$ · Zr 40 $5s^24d^2$ · Hf 72 $6s^25d^2$ · Rf 104 $7s^26d^2$

Group 5B (5): V 23 $4s^23d^3$ · Nb 41 $5s^14d^4$ · Ta 73 $6s^25d^3$ · Db 105 $7s^26d^3$

Group 6B (6): Cr 24 $4s^13d^5$ · Mo 42 $5s^14d^5$ · W 74 $6s^25d^4$ · Sg 106 $7s^26d^4$

Group 7B (7): Mn 25 $4s^23d^5$ · Tc 43 $5s^24d^5$ · Re 75 $6s^25d^5$ · Bh 107 $7s^26d^5$

Group 8B (8): Fe 26 $4s^23d^6$ · Ru 44 $5s^14d^7$ · Os 76 $6s^25d^6$ · Hs 108 $7s^26d^6$

Group 8B (9): Co 27 $4s^23d^7$ · Rh 45 $5s^14d^8$ · Ir 77 $6s^25d^7$ · Mt 109 $7s^26d^7$

Group 8B (10): Ni 28 $4s^23d^8$ · Pd 46 $4d^{10}$ · Pt 78 $6s^15d^9$ · Ds 110 $7s^26d^8$

Group 1B (11): Cu 29 $4s^13d^{10}$ · Ag 47 $5s^14d^{10}$ · Au 79 $6s^15d^{10}$ · Rg 111 $7s^26d^9$

Group 2B (12): Zn 30 $4s^23d^{10}$ · Cd 48 $5s^24d^{10}$ · Hg 80 $6s^25d^{10}$ · Cn 112 $7s^26d^{10}$

Group 3A (13): B 5 $2s^22p^1$ · Al 13 $3s^23p^1$ · Ga 31 $4s^24p^1$ · In 49 $5s^25p^1$ · Tl 81 $6s^26p^1$ · 113 — $7s^27p^1$

Group 4A (14): C 6 $2s^22p^2$ · Si 14 $3s^23p^2$ · Ge 32 $4s^24p^2$ · Sn 50 $5s^25p^2$ · Pb 82 $6s^26p^2$ · 114 — $7s^27p^2$

Group 5A (15): N 7 $2s^22p^3$ · P 15 $3s^23p^3$ · As 33 $4s^24p^3$ · Sb 51 $5s^25p^3$ · Bi 83 $6s^26p^3$ · 115 — $7s^27p^3$

Group 6A (16): O 8 $2s^22p^4$ · S 16 $3s^23p^4$ · Se 34 $4s^24p^4$ · Te 52 $5s^25p^4$ · Po 84 $6s^26p^4$ · 116 — $7s^27p^4$

Group 7A (17): F 9 $2s^22p^5$ · Cl 17 $3s^23p^5$ · Br 35 $4s^24p^5$ · I 53 $5s^25p^5$ · At 85 $6s^26p^5$ · 117 — $7s^27p^5$

Group 8A (18): He 2 $1s^2$ · Ne 10 $2s^22p^6$ · Ar 18 $3s^23p^6$ · Kr 36 $4s^24p^6$ · Xe 54 $5s^25p^6$ · Rn 86 $6s^26p^6$ · 118 — $7s^27p^6$

Lanthanides: Ce 58 $6s^24f^15d^1$ · Pr 59 $6s^24f^3$ · Nd 60 $6s^24f^4$ · Pm 61 $6s^24f^5$ · Sm 62 $6s^24f^6$ · Eu 63 $6s^24f^7$ · Gd 64 $6s^24f^75d^1$ · Tb 65 $6s^24f^9$ · Dy 66 $6s^24f^{10}$ · Ho 67 $6s^24f^{11}$ · Er 68 $6s^24f^{12}$ · Tm 69 $6s^24f^{13}$ · Yb 70 $6s^24f^{14}$ · Lu 71 $6s^24f^{14}5d^1$

Actinides: Th 90 $7s^26d^2$ · Pa 91 $7s^25f^26d^1$ · U 92 $7s^25f^36d^1$ · Np 93 $7s^25f^46d^1$ · Pu 94 $7s^25f^6$ · Am 95 $7s^25f^7$ · Cm 96 $7s^25f^76d^1$ · Bk 97 $7s^25f^9$ · Cf 98 $7s^25f^{10}$ · Es 99 $7s^25f^{11}$ · Fm 100 $7s^25f^{12}$ · Md 101 $7s^25f^{13}$ · No 102 $7s^25f^{14}$ · Lr 103 $7s^25f^{14}6d^1$

> **Student Annotation:** Even when an atom from Group 2B loses one or two electrons, as is common, its electron configuration includes a completed *d* subshell [◄◄ Section 3.9]. Thus, strictly speaking, Zn, Cd, and Hg are *not* transition metals.

the *noble gases* (the Group 8A elements) has a completely filled *p* subshell. The valence-electron configurations are $1s^2$ for helium and ns^2np^6 for the other noble gases, where *n* is the principal quantum number for the outermost shell.

The transition metals are the elements in Groups 1B and 3B through 8B. Transition metals either have incompletely filled *d* subshells or readily lose electrons to *achieve* incompletely filled *d* subshells. According to this definition, the elements of Group 2B (Zn, Cd, and Hg) are *not* transition metals as their electron configurations always include a completed *d* subshell. They are *d*-block elements, though, so they generally are included in the discussion of transition metals.

The lanthanides and actinides are sometimes called *f*-block transition elements because they have incompletely filled *f* subshells. Figure 4.3 distinguishes the groups of elements discussed here.

There is a distinct pattern to the electron configurations of the elements in a particular group. See, for example, the electron configurations of Groups 1A and 2A in Table 4.1. Each member of Group 1A has a noble gas core plus one additional electron, giving each alkali metal the general electron configuration of [noble gas]ns^1. Similarly, the Group 2A alkaline earth metals have a noble gas core and an outer electron configuration of ns^2.

Figure 4.3 Periodic table with color-coding of main group elements (grey), noble gases (yellow), transition metals (blue), group 2B metals (light green), lanthanides (dark green), and actinides (pink).

TABLE 4.1		Electron Configurations of Group 1A and Group 2A Elements	
Group 1A		**Group 2A**	
Li	$[He]2s^1$	Be	$[He]2s^2$
Na	$[Ne]3s^1$	Mg	$[Ne]3s^2$
K	$[Ar]4s^1$	Ca	$[Ar]4s^2$
Rb	$[Kr]5s^1$	Sr	$[Kr]5s^2$
Cs	$[Xe]6s^1$	Ba	$[Xe]6s^2$
Fr	$[Rn]7s^1$	Ra	$[Rn]7s^2$

The outermost electrons of an atom are called ***valence electrons.*** Valence electrons determine how atoms interact with one another. Having the same valence-electron configuration is what causes the elements in the same group, such as those in Group 2A, to exhibit similar chemical properties. This observation holds true for the other main group elements as well. For example, the halogens (Group 7A) all have valence-electron configurations of ns^2np^5, and they exhibit similar properties.

In predicting properties for Groups 3A through 7A, we must take into account that each of these groups contains both *metals* and *non*metals. For example, the elements in Group 4A all have the same outer electron configuration, ns^2np^2, but there is considerable variation in chemical properties among these elements because carbon is a *nonmetal,* silicon and germanium are *metalloids,* and tin and lead are *metals.*

As a group, the noble gases behave very similarly. The noble gases are chemically inert because they all have completely filled outer ns and np subshells, a condition that imparts unusual stability. With the exception of the heavier members of the group, krypton and xenon, they do not generally interact with other elements.

Although the outer electron configuration of the transition metals is not always the same within a group and there is often no regular pattern in the way the electron configuration changes from one metal to the next in the same period, all transition metals share many characteristics, such as magnetic properties, that set them apart from other elements. These properties are similar because all these metals have incompletely filled d subshells. Likewise, the lanthanide and actinide elements resemble one another because they have incompletely filled f subshells.

Worked Example 4.2 shows how to determine the electron configuration from the number of electrons in an atom.

Worked Example 4.2

Without using a periodic table, give the ground-state electron configuration and block designation (s-, p-, d-, or f-block) of an atom with (a) 17 electrons, (b) 37 electrons, and (c) 22 electrons. Classify each atom as a main group element or transition metal.

Strategy Use the Aufbau principle discussed in Section 3.9. Start writing each electron configuration with principal quantum number $n = 1$, and then continue to assign electrons to orbitals in the order presented in Figure 3.25 until all the electrons have been accounted for.

Setup According to Figure 3.25, orbitals fill in the following order: $1s$, $2s$, $2p$, $3s$, $3p$, $4s$, $3d$, $4p$, $5s$, $4d$, $5p$, $6s$, and so on. Recall that an s subshell contains one orbital, a p subshell contains three orbitals, and a d subshell contains five orbitals. Remember, too, that each orbital can accommodate a maximum of two electrons. The block designation of an element corresponds to the type of subshell occupied by the last electrons added to the configuration according to the Aufbau principle.

Solution

(a) $1s^2 2s^2 2p^6 3s^2 3p^5$, p-block, main group

(b) $1s^2 2s^2 2p^6 3s^2 3p^6 4s^2 3d^{10} 4p^6 5s^1$, s-block, main group

(c) $1s^2 2s^2 2p^6 3s^2 3p^6 4s^2 3d^2$, d-block, transition metal

> **Think About It**
> Consult Figure 3.26 to confirm your answers.

Practice Problem A Without using a periodic table, give the ground-state electron configuration and block designation (s-, p-, d-, or f-block) of an atom with (a) 15 electrons, (b) 20 electrons, and (c) 35 electrons.

Practice Problem B Identify the elements represented by (a) $1s^2 2s^2 2p^6 3s^2 3p^1$, (b) $1s^2 2s^2 2p^6 3s^2 3p^6 4s^2 3d^{10}$, and (c) $1s^2 2s^2 2p^6 3s^2 3p^6 4s^2 3d^{10} 4p^6 5s^2$.

SECTION 4.2 REVIEW

The Modern Periodic Table

4.2.1   What is the correct electron configuration for a germanium (Ge) atom in the ground state?

4.2.2   What element is represented by the ground-state electron configuration $1s^2 2s^2 2p^6 3s^2 3p^6 4s^2 3d^{10} 4p^6 5s^2 4d^{10} 5p^2$?

4.3   EFFECTIVE NUCLEAR CHARGE

As we have seen, the electron configurations of the elements show a periodic variation with increasing atomic number. In this and the next few sections, we will examine how electron configuration explains the periodic variation of physical and chemical properties of the elements. We begin by introducing the concept of *effective nuclear charge*.

Nuclear charge (Z) is simply the number of protons in the nucleus of an atom. **Effective nuclear charge (Z_{eff})** is the actual magnitude of positive charge that is "experienced" by an electron in the atom. The only atom in which the nuclear charge and effective nuclear charge are the same is hydrogen, which has only one electron. In all other atoms, the electrons are simultaneously attracted to the nucleus and repelled by one another. This results in a phenomenon known as *shielding*. An electron in a many-electron atom is partially shielded from the positive charge of the nucleus by the other electrons in the atom.

Student Annotation: *Shielding* is also known as *screening*.

One way to illustrate how electrons in an atom shield one another is to consider the amounts of energy required to remove the two electrons from a helium atom, shown in Figure 4.4. Experiments show that it takes 3.94×10^{-18} J to remove the first electron but 8.72×10^{-18} J to remove the second one. There is no shielding once the first electron is removed, so the second electron feels the full effect of the $+2$ nuclear charge and is more difficult to remove.

Although all the electrons in an atom shield one another to some extent, those that are most effective at shielding are the *core* electrons. As a result, the value of Z_{eff} increases steadily from left to right across a period of the periodic table because the number of core electrons remains the same (only the number of protons, Z, and the number of *valence* electrons increases).

As we move to the right across period 2, the nuclear charge increases by 1 with each new element, but the *effective* nuclear charge increases only by an average of 0.64. (If the valence electrons did *not* shield one another, the effective nuclear charge would also increase by 1 each time a proton was added to the nucleus.)

> **Student Annotation:** Core electrons are those in the completed inner shells.

	Li	Be	B	C	N	O	F
Z	3	4	5	6	7	8	9
Z_{eff} (felt by valence electrons)	1.28	1.91	2.42	3.14	3.83	4.45	5.10

In general, the effective nuclear charge is given by

$$Z_{eff} = Z - \sigma \qquad \textbf{Equation 4.1}$$

where σ is the shielding constant. The shielding constant is greater than zero but smaller than Z.

The change in Z_{eff} as we move from the top of a group to the bottom is generally less significant than the change as we move across a period. Although each step down a group represents a large increase in the nuclear charge, there is also an additional shell of core electrons to shield the valence electrons from the nucleus. Consequently, the *effective* nuclear charge changes less than the nuclear charge as we move down a column of the periodic table.

4.4 PERIODIC TRENDS IN PROPERTIES OF ELEMENTS

Several physical and chemical properties of the elements depend on effective nuclear charge. To understand the trends in these properties, it is helpful to visualize the electrons of an atom in *shells*. Recall that the value of the principal quantum number (n) increases as the distance from the nucleus increases [◄◄ Section 3.8]. If we take this statement literally, and picture all the electrons in a shell at the same distance from the nucleus, the result is a sphere of uniformly distributed negative charge, with its distance from the nucleus depending on the value of n. With this as a starting point, we will examine the periodic trends in atomic radius, ionization energy, electron affinity, and metallic character.

Atomic Radius

Intuitively, we think of the **atomic radius** as the distance between the nucleus of an atom and its valence shell (i.e., the outermost shell that is occupied by one or more electrons), because we usually envision atoms as spheres with discrete boundaries. According to the quantum mechanical model of the atom, though, there is no specific distance from the nucleus beyond which an electron may not be found [◄◄ Section 3.8]. Therefore, the atomic radius requires a specific definition.

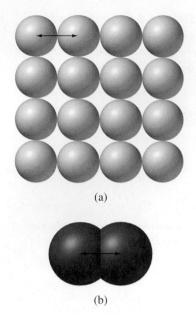

(a)

(b)

Figure 4.5 (a) Atomic radius in metals is defined as half the distance between adjacent metal atoms. (b) Atomic radius in nonmetals is defined as half the distance between bonded identical atoms in a molecule.

Student Annotation: Although the overall trend in atomic size for transition elements is also to decrease from left to right and increase from top to bottom, the observed radii do not vary in as regular a way as do those of the main group elements.

Multi 4.1
Periodic table—atomic radius

There are two ways in which the atomic radius is commonly defined. One is the ***metallic radius,*** which is half the distance between the nuclei of two adjacent, identical metal atoms [Figure 4.5(a)]. The other is the ***covalent radius,*** which is half the distance between adjacent, identical nuclei that are connected by a *chemical bond* [▶▶ Chapter 5] [Figure 4.5(b)].

Figure 4.6 shows the atomic radii of the main group elements according to their positions in the periodic table. There are two distinct trends. The atomic radius *decreases* as we move from left to right across a period and *increases* from top to bottom as we move down within a group.

The increase down a group is fairly easily explained. As we step down a column, the outermost occupied shell has an ever-increasing value of *n*, so it lies farther from the nucleus, making the radius bigger.

Now let's try to understand the decrease in radius from left to right across a period. Although this trend may at first seem counterintuitive, given that the number of valence electrons is increasing with each new element, consider the shell model in which all the electrons in a shell form a uniform sphere of negative charge around the nucleus at a distance specified by the value of *n*. As we move from left to right across a period, the effective nuclear charge increases and each step to the right adds another electron to the valence shell. Coulomb's law [▶▶ page 121] dictates that there will be a more powerful attraction between the nucleus and the valence shell when the magnitudes of both charges increase. The result is that as we step across a period, the valence shell is drawn closer to the nucleus making the atomic radius smaller. Figure 4.7 shows how the effective nuclear charge, charge on the valence shell, and atomic radius vary across period 2. We can picture the valence shells in all the atoms as being initially at the same distance (determined by *n*) from the nuclei, but being pulled closer by a larger attractive force resulting from increases in both Z_{eff} and the number of valence electrons.

Worked Example 4.3 shows how to use these trends to compare the atomic radii of different elements.

Increasing atomic radius →

Increasing atomic radius ↓

1A	2A	3A	4A	5A	6A	7A	8A
H 37							He 31
Li 152	Be 112	B 85	C 77	N 75	O 73	F 72	Ne 70
Na 186	Mg 160	Al 143	Si 118	P 110	S 103	Cl 99	Ar 98
K 227	Ca 197	Ga 135	Ge 123	As 120	Se 117	Br 114	Kr 112
Rb 248	Sr 215	In 166	Sn 140	Sb 141	Te 143	I 133	Xe 131
Cs 265	Ba 222	Ti 171	Pb 175	Bi 155	Po 164	At 142	Rn 140

Figure 4.6 Atomic radii of the elements (in picometers).

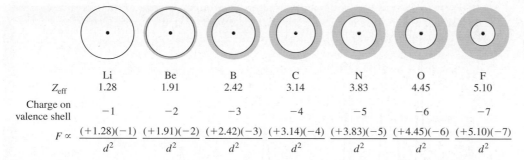

	Li	Be	B	C	N	O	F
Z_{eff}	1.28	1.91	2.42	3.14	3.83	4.45	5.10
Charge on valence shell	−1	−2	−3	−4	−5	−6	−7

$$F \propto \frac{(+1.28)(-1)}{d^2} \quad \frac{(+1.91)(-2)}{d^2} \quad \frac{(+2.42)(-3)}{d^2} \quad \frac{(+3.14)(-4)}{d^2} \quad \frac{(+3.83)(-5)}{d^2} \quad \frac{(+4.45)(-6)}{d^2} \quad \frac{(+5.10)(-7)}{d^2}$$

Figure 4.7 Atomic radius decreases from left to right across a period because of the increased electrostatic attraction between the effective nuclear charge and the charge on the valence shell. The white circle shows the atomic size in each case. The comparison of attractive forces between the nuclei and valence shells is done using Coulomb's law [▶▶ page 121].

Worked Example 4.3

Referring only to a periodic table, arrange the elements P, S, and O in order of increasing atomic radius.

Strategy Use the left-to-right (decreasing) and top-to-bottom (increasing) trends to compare the atomic radii of two of the three elements at a time.

Setup Sulfur is to the right of phosphorus in the third row, so sulfur should be smaller than phosphorus. Oxygen is above sulfur in Group 6A, so oxygen should be smaller than sulfur.

Solution

O < S < P.

> **Think About It**
> Consult Figure 4.6 to confirm the order. Note that there are circumstances under which the trends alone will be insufficient to compare the radii of two elements. Using only a periodic table, for example, it would not be possible to determine that bromine (r = 114 pm) has a smaller radius than silicon (r = 118 pm).

Practice Problem A Referring only to a periodic table, arrange the elements Ge, Se, and F in order of increasing atomic radius.

Practice Problem B For which of the following pairs of elements can the atomic radii *not* be compared using the periodic table alone: Si and Se, Se and Cl, or P and O?

Ionization Energy

Ionization energy (IE) is the minimum energy required to remove an electron from an atom in the gas phase. The result is an *ion,* a chemical species with a net charge. We will represent this by writing the initial state, a sodium atom in the gas phase, on the left; and the final state, a sodium ion (also in the gas phase) and the electron that has been removed, on the right. The initial and final states are separated by an arrow, pointing to the right, which represents the ionization process.

$$Na(g) \longrightarrow Na^+(g) + e^-$$

Typically, we express ionization energy in kJ/mol, the number of kilojoules required to remove a mole of electrons from a mole of gaseous atoms. Sodium, for example, has an ionization energy of 495.8 kJ/mol, meaning that the energy input required to remove one mole of electrons from one mole of gaseous sodium atoms is 495.8 kJ. Specifically, 495.8 kJ/mol is the *first* ionization energy of sodium, IE_1(Na), which corresponds to the removal of the most loosely held electron from each sodium atom. Figure 4.8(a) shows the first ionization energies of the main group elements according to their positions in the periodic table. Figure 4.8(b) shows a graph of IE_1 as a function of atomic number.

Student Annotation: This sort of representation is known as a *chemical equation.* We will discuss chemical equations in more detail in Chapter 8. Note that we can indicate the physical state of a substance with an italicized letter in parentheses: (s), (l), or (g).

Student Annotation: As with atomic radius, ionization energy changes in a similar but somewhat less regular way among the transition elements.

IE_1 values for main group elements (kJ/mol)

(a)

(b)

Figure 4.8 (a) First ionization energies (in kJ/mol) of the main group elements. (b) First ionization energy as a function of atomic number.

The *loss* of one or more electrons from an atom yields a ***cation,*** an ion with a net *positive* charge. For example, a sodium atom (Na) can readily lose an electron to become a sodium cation, which is represented by Na⁺:

Na Atom	Na⁺ Ion
11 protons	11 protons
11 electrons	10 electrons

In general, as effective nuclear charge increases, ionization energy also increases. Thus, IE_1 increases from left to right across a period. Despite this trend, the graph in Figure 4.8(b) shows that IE_1 for a Group 3A element is smaller than that for the corresponding Group 2A element. Likewise, IE_1 for a Group 6A element is smaller than that for the corresponding Group 5A element. Both of these *interruptions* of the upward trend in IE_1 can be explained by using electron configuration.

Recall that the energy of an electron in a many-electron system depends not only on the principal quantum number (n), but also on the angular momentum quantum number (l) [◄◄ Section 3.9, Figure 3.23]. Within a given shell, electrons with the higher value of l have a higher energy (are less tightly held by the nucleus) and are therefore *easier* to remove. Figure 4.9(a) shows the relative energies of an s subshell ($l = 0$) and a p subshell ($l = 1$). Ionization of an element in Group 2A requires the removal of an electron from an s orbital, whereas ionization of an element in Group 3A requires the removal of an electron from a p orbital; therefore, the element in Group 3A has a lower ionization energy than the element in Group 2A.

As for the decrease in ionization energy in elements of Group 6A compared to those in Group 5A, both ionizations involve the removal of a p electron, but the ionization of an atom in Group 6A involves the removal of a *paired* electron. The repulsive force between two electrons in the same orbital makes it easier to remove one of them, making the ionization energy for the Group 6A element actually lower than that for the Group 5A element. [See Figure 4.9(b).]

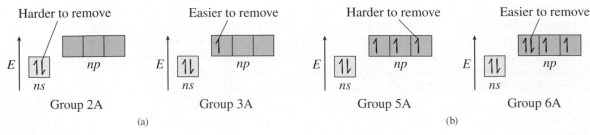

Figure 4.9 (a) It is harder to remove an electron from an s orbital than it is to remove an electron from a p orbital with the same principal quantum number. (b) Within a p subshell, it is easier to remove an electron from a doubly occupied orbital than from a singly occupied orbital.

The first ionization energy IE_1 decreases as we move from top to bottom within a group due to the increasing atomic radius. Although the effective nuclear charge does not change significantly as we step down a group, the atomic radius increases because the value of n for the valence shell increases. According to Coulomb's law, the attractive force between a valence electron and the effective nuclear charge gets *weaker* as the distance between them increases. This makes it easier to remove an electron, and so IE_1 decreases.

It is possible to remove additional electrons in subsequent ionizations, giving IE_2, IE_3, and so on. The second and third ionizations of sodium, for example, can be represented, respectively, as

$$\text{Na}^+(g) \longrightarrow \text{Na}^{2+}(g) + e^- \quad \text{and} \quad \text{Na}^{2+}(g) \longrightarrow \text{Na}^{3+}(g) + e^-$$

However, the removal of successive electrons requires ever-increasing amounts of energy because it is harder to remove an electron from a cation than from an atom (and it gets even harder as the charge on the cation increases). Table 4.2 lists the ionization energies of the elements in period 2 and of sodium. These data show that it takes much more energy to remove core electrons than to remove valence electrons. There are two reasons for this. First, core electrons are closer to the nucleus, and second, core electrons experience a greater effective nuclear charge because there are fewer filled shells shielding them from the nucleus. Both of these factors contribute to a greater attractive force between the electrons and the nucleus, which must be overcome in order to remove the electrons.

Ionization energy is an example of a *chemical property* [◄◄ Section 1.3] and the process of ionization is a **chemical process**, one in which the identity of the matter involved *changes*.

Worked Example 4.4 shows how to use these trends to compare first ionization energies, and subsequent ionization energies, of specific atoms.

Student Annotation: Although the symbols Na and Na⁺ are nearly identical, the sodium *atom* and the sodium *ion* are chemically distinct and have very different properties.

TABLE 4.2	Ionization Energies (in kJ/mol) for Elements 3 through 11*									
	Z	IE_1	IE_2	IE_3	IE_4	IE_5	IE_6	IE_7	IE_8	IE_9	IE_{10}
Li	3	520	7,298	11,815							
Be	4	899	1,757	14,848	21,007						
B	5	800	2,427	3,660	25,026	32,827					
C	6	1,086	2,353	4,621	6,223	37,831	47,277				
N	7	1,402	2,856	4,578	7,475	9,445	53,267	64,360			
O	8	1,314	3,388	5,301	7,469	10,990	13,327	71,330	84,078		
F	9	1,681	3,374	6,050	8,408	11,023	15,164	17,868	92,038	106,434	
Ne	10	2,080	3,952	6,122	9,371	12,177	15,238	19,999	23,069	115,380	131,432
Na	11	496	4,562	6,910	9,543	13,354	16,613	20,117	25,496	28,932	141,362

*Cells shaded with blue represent the removal of core electrons.

Worked Example 4.4

Would you expect Na or Mg to have the greater first ionization energy (IE_1)? Which should have the greater second ionization energy (IE_2)?

Strategy Consider effective nuclear charge and electron configuration to compare the ionization energies. Effective nuclear charge increases from left to right in a period (thus increasing IE), and it is more difficult to remove a paired core electron than an unpaired valence electron.

Setup Na is in Group 1A, and Mg is beside it in Group 2A. Na has one valence electron, and Mg has two valence electrons.

Solution

$IE_1(\text{Mg}) > IE_1(\text{Na})$ because Mg is to the right of Na in the periodic table (i.e., Mg has the greater effective nuclear charge, so it is more difficult to remove its electron). $IE_2(\text{Na}) > IE_2(\text{Mg})$ because the second ionization of Mg removes a valence electron, whereas the second ionization of Na removes a core electron.

(Continued on next page)

Electron Affinity

Student Annotation: Some books define electron affinity as the energy absorbed, rather than the energy released. The numeric values are the same, only the sign is different.

Electron affinity (EA) is the energy released when an atom in the gas phase accepts an electron. Consider the process in which a gaseous chlorine atom accepts an electron:

$$Cl(g) + e^- \longrightarrow Cl^-(g)$$

When a mole of gaseous chlorine atoms accepts a mole of electrons, 349.0 kJ/mol of energy are released (the definition of electron affinity). A positive electron affinity indicates a process that is energetically favorable. In general, the larger and more positive the *EA* value, the more favorable the process and the more apt it is to occur. Figure 4.10 shows electron affinities for the main group elements.

The species formed by the addition of an electron to a neutral atom is an anion. An *anion* is an ion whose net charge is *negative* due to an *increase* in the number of electrons. The Cl atom, for example, gains an electron to become the Cl⁻ anion:

Cl Atom	Cl⁻ Ion
17 protons	17 protons
17 electrons	18 electrons

Student Annotation: Although *IE* and *EA* both increase from left to right across a period, an increase in *IE* means that it is *less* likely that an electron will be *removed* from an atom. An increase in *EA*, on the other hand, means that it is *more* likely that an electron will be *accepted* by an atom.

Like ionization energy, electron affinity increases from left to right across a period. This trend in *EA* is due to the increase in effective nuclear charge from left to right (i.e., it becomes progressively easier to add a negatively charged electron as the positive charge of the element's nucleus increases). There are also periodic interruptions of the upward trend of *EA* from left to right, similar to those observed for IE_1, although they do *not* occur for the same elements. For example, the *EA* of a Group 2A element is lower than that for the corresponding Group 1A element, and the *EA* of a Group 5A element is lower than that for the corresponding Group 4A element. These exceptions to the trend are due to the electron configurations of the elements involved.

It is harder to add an electron to a Group 2A element (ns^2) than to the Group 1A element (ns^1) in the same period because the electron added to the Group 2A element is placed in an orbital of higher energy (a *p* orbital versus an *s* orbital). Likewise, it is harder to add an electron to a Group 5A element (ns^2np^3) than to the corresponding Group 4A element (ns^2np^2) because the electron added to the Group 5A element must be placed in an orbital that already contains an electron. Figure 4.11 illustrates these points.

Student Annotation: There is a much less significant and less regular variation in electron affinities from top to bottom within a group. See Figure 4.11(a).

Just as more than one electron can be removed from an atom, more than one electron can also be added to an atom. While many first electron affinities are positive, subsequent electron affinities are always negative. Considerable energy is required to overcome the repulsive forces between the electron and the negatively charged ion. The addition of two electrons to a gaseous oxygen atom can be represented as:

Process	Electron affinity
$O(g) + e^- \longrightarrow O^-(g)$	$EA_1 = 141$ kJ/mol
$O^-(g) + e^- \longrightarrow O^{2-}(g)$	$EA_2 = -744$ kJ/mol

The term *second electron affinity* may seem like something of a misnomer, because an anion in the gas phase has no real "affinity" for an electron. A process that must absorb a significant amount of energy such as the addition of an electron to a gaseous O⁻ ion happens only in concert with one or more processes that more than compensate for the required energy input.

1A 1								8A 18
H +72.8	2A 2	3A 13	4A 14	5A 15	6A 16	7A 17		**He** (0.0)
Li +59.6	**Be** ≤0	**B** +26.7	**C** +122	**N** −7	**O** +141	**F** +328		**Ne** (−29)
Na +52.9	**Mg** ≤0	**Al** +42.5	**Si** +134	**P** +72.0	**S** +200	**Cl** +349		**Ar** (−35)
K +48.4	**Ca** +2.37	**Ga** +28.9	**Ge** +119	**As** +78.2	**Se** +195	**Br** +325		**Kr** (−39)
Rb +46.9	**Sr** +5.03	**In** +28.9	**Sn** +107	**Sb** +103	**Te** +190	**I** +295		**Xe** (−41)
Cs +45.5	**Ba** +13.95	**Tl** +19.3	**Pb** +35.1	**Bi** +91.3	**Po** +183	**At** +270		**Rn** (−41)

(a)

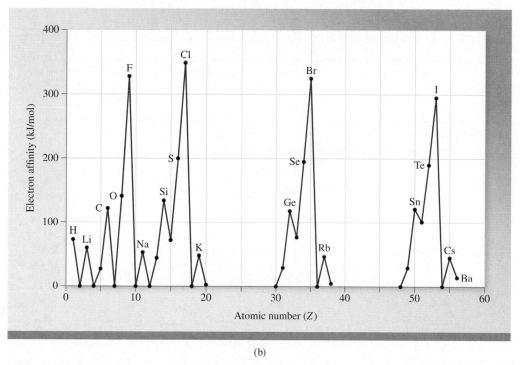

(b)

Figure 4.10 (a) Electron affinities (kJ/mol) of the main group elements. (b) Electron affinity as a function of atomic number.

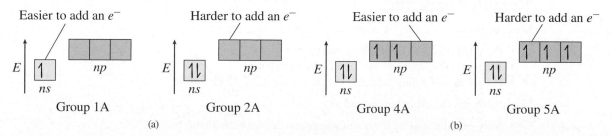

Easier to add an e^- Harder to add an e^- Easier to add an e^- Harder to add an e^-

Group 1A Group 2A Group 4A Group 5A

(a) (b)

Figure 4.11 (a) It is easier to add an electron to an *s* orbital than to add one to a *p* orbital with the same principal quantum number. (b) Within a *p* subshell, it is easier to add an electron to an empty orbital than to add one to an orbital that already contains an electron.

Worked Example 4.5 lets you practice using the periodic table to compare the electron affinities of elements.

Worked Example 4.5

For each pair of elements, indicate which one you would expect to have the greater first electron affinity, EA_1: (a) Al or Si, (b) Si or P.

Strategy Consider the effective nuclear charge and electron configuration to compare the electron affinities. The effective nuclear charge increases from left to right in a period (thus generally increasing EA), and it is more difficult to add an electron to a partially occupied orbital than to an empty one. Writing out orbital diagrams for the valence electrons is helpful for this type of problem.

Setup

(a) Al is in Group 3A and Si is beside it in Group 4A. Al has three valence electrons ($[Ne]3s^23p^1$), and Si has four valence electrons ($[Ne]3s^23p^2$).

(b) P is in Group 5A (to the right of Si), so it has five valence electrons ($[Ne]3s^23p^3$).

Solution

(a) $EA_1(Si) > EA_1(Al)$ because Si is to the right of Al and therefore has a greater effective nuclear charge.

(b) $EA_1(Si) > EA_1(P)$ because although P is to the right of Si in the third period of the periodic table (giving P the larger Z_{eff}), adding an electron to a P atom requires placing it in a $3p$ orbital that is partially occupied. The energy cost of *pairing* electrons outweighs the energy advantage of adding an electron to an atom with a larger effective nuclear charge.

Think About It
The first electron affinities of Al, Si, and P are 42.5, 134, and 72.0 kJ/mol, respectively.

$$3s^2 \quad 3p^1$$
Valence orbital diagram for Al

$$3s^2 \quad 3p^2$$
Valence orbital diagram for Si

$$3s^2 \quad 3p^3$$
Valence orbital diagram for P

Practice Problem A Would you expect Mg or Al to have the greater EA_1?

Practice Problem B Explain why the EA_1 for Ge is greater than the EA_1 for As.

Metallic Character

Student Annotation: *Malleability* is the property that allows metals to be pounded into thin sheets. *Ductility* is the capacity to be drawn out into wires.

Metals tend to

- Be shiny, lustrous, malleable, and ductile
- Be good conductors of both heat and electricity
- Have low ionization energies (so they commonly form *cations*)

Nonmetals, on the other hand, tend to

- Vary in color and lack the shiny appearance associated with metals
- Be brittle, rather than malleable
- Be poor conductors of both heat and electricity
- Have high electron affinities (so they commonly form *anions*)

Student Annotation: Metallic character is actually defined using a combination of physical and chemical properties. Apart from ionization energy and electron affinity, the chemical properties of metals and nonmetals will be discussed in Chapter 8.

Metallic character increases from top to bottom in a group and decreases from left to right within a period.

Metalloids are elements with properties intermediate between those of metals and nonmetals. Because the definition of metallic character depends on a combination of properties, there may be some variation in the elements identified as metalloids in different sources. Astatine (At), for example, is listed as a metalloid in some sources and a nonmetal in others.

Many of the periodic trends in properties of the elements can be explained using Coulomb's law, which states that the force (F) between two charged objects (Q_1 and Q_2) is directly proportional to the product of the two charges and *inversely* proportional to the distance (d) between the objects squared. Recall that the *energy* between two oppositely charged particles, E_{el}, is inversely proportional to d [◄◄ Section 3.1, Equation 3.2]. The SI unit of force is the newton (1 N = 1 kg · m/s^2) and the SI unit of energy is the joule (1 J = 1 kg · m^2/s^2).

$$F \propto \frac{Q_1 \times Q_2}{d^2}$$

Equation 4.2

When the charges have opposite signs, F is negative—indicating an *attractive* force between the objects. When the charges have the same sign, F is positive—indicating a *repulsive* force. Table 4.3 shows how the magnitude of the attractive force between two oppositely charged objects at a fixed distance from each other varies with changes in the magnitudes of the charges.

Worked Example 4.6 illustrates how Coulomb's law can be used to compare the magnitudes of attractive forces between charged objects.

TABLE 4.3	Attractive Force Between Oppositely Charged Objects at a Fixed Distance ($d = 1$) from Each Other	
Q_1	**Q_2**	**Attractive force is proportional to**
+1	−1	1
+2	−2	4
+3	−3	9

Worked Example 4.6

For carbon and nitrogen, use the effective nuclear charges given in Figure 4.7 and the atomic radii given in Figure 4.6 to compare the attractive force between the nucleus in each atom and the valence electron that would be removed by the first ionization.

Strategy Use Coulomb's law to calculate a number to which the attractive force will be proportional in each case.

Setup From Figure 4.7, the effective nuclear charges of C and N are 3.14 and 3.83, respectively; and the radii of C and N are 77 pm and 75 pm, respectively. The first ionization energies are 1086 kJ/mol (C) and 1402 kJ/mol (N). The charge on the valence electron in each case is −1.

Solution

For C: $F \propto \dfrac{(3.14) \times (-1)}{(77 \text{ pm})^2} = -5.3 \times 10^{-4}$

For N: $F \propto \dfrac{(3.83) \times (-1)}{(75 \text{ pm})^2} = -6.8 \times 10^{-4}$

Note that in this type of comparison, it doesn't matter what units we use for the distance between the charges. We are not trying to calculate a particular attractive force, only to compare the magnitudes of these two attractive forces.

Think About It
Remember that the negative sign indicates simply that the force is attractive rather than repulsive. The calculated number for nitrogen is about 28 percent larger than that for carbon.

Practice Problem A Between which two charges is the attractive force larger: +3.26 and −1.15 separated by a distance of 1.5 pm or +2.84 and −3.63 separated by a distance of 2.5 pm?

Practice Problem B What must the distance be between charges of +2.25 and −1.86 in order for the attractive force between them to be the same as that between charges of +4.06 and −2.11 separated by a distance of 2.16 pm?

Diagonal relationships

The product of a positive number and a negative number is a negative number. When we are simply comparing the magnitudes of attractive forces, however, it is unnecessary to include the sign. Worked Example 4.6 illustrates the use of Coulomb's law to compare the attractive forces between pairs of opposite charges.

Another trend in the chemical behavior of main group elements is the diagonal relationship. A *diagonal relationship* refers to similarities between pairs of elements in different groups and periods of the periodic table. Specifically, the first three members of the second period (Li, Be, and B) exhibit many similarities to the elements located diagonally below them in the periodic table (Mg, Al, and Si). The reason for this phenomenon is the similarity of charge densities of their cations. (Charge density is the charge on an ion divided by its volume.) Cations with comparable charge densities behave similarly and therefore exhibit some of the same chemical properties. Thus, the chemical properties of lithium resemble those of magnesium in some ways; the same holds for beryllium and aluminum and for boron and silicon. Each of these pairs is said to exhibit a diagonal relationship.

SECTION 4.4 REVIEW

Periodic Trends in Properties of Atoms

4.4.1   Arrange the elements Ca, Sr, and Ba in order of increasing IE_1.

4.4.2   Arrange the elements Li, Be, and B in order of increasing IE_2.

4.4.3   For each of the following pairs of elements, indicate which will have the greater EA_1: Rb or Sr, C or N, O or F.

4.4.4   Which element, K or Ca, will have the greater IE_1, which will have the greater IE_2, and which will have the greater EA_1?

4.4.5   Between which pair of opposite charges is the attractive force greater: $+2$ and -2 separated by 1.5 pm or $+3$ and -3 separated by 2.5 pm?

4.4.6   What must the separation between charges of $+2$ and -3 be for the attractive force between them to be the same as that between charges of $+3$ and -3 that are separated by a distance of 1.5 pm?

4.5   ELECTRON CONFIGURATION OF IONS

Student Annotation: "Monatomic" ions are those consisting of a single atom that has either gained (anion) or lost (cation) one or more electrons. We will encounter *polyatomic* ions in Chapter 5.

Because many substances are made up of monatomic anions and cations, it is helpful to know how to write the electron configurations of these ionic species. Just as for atoms, we use the Pauli exclusion principle and Hund's rule to write the ground-state electron configurations of cations and anions.

We can use the periodic table to predict the charges on many of the ions formed by main group elements. With very few exceptions, metals tend to form cations and nonmetals form anions. Elements in Groups 1A and 2A, for example, form ions with charges of $+1$ and $+2$, respectively. Most of the anions that form from elements of Groups 4A through 7A have charges equal to the corresponding group number minus 8. Elements in Groups 6A and 7A form ions with charges of -2 and -1, respectively. For example, the monatomic anion formed by oxygen (Group 6A) has a charge of $6 - 8 = -2$. Knowing something about electron configurations enables us to explain these charges.

Ions of Main Group Elements

In Section 4.4, we learned about the tendencies of atoms to lose or gain electrons. In every period of the periodic table, the element with the highest IE_1 is the Group 8A element, the noble gas. [See Figure 4.8(b).] Also, Group 8A is the only group in which none of the members has *any* tendency

Figure 4.12 Common monatomic ions arranged by their positions in the periodic table. Note that mercury(I), Hg_2^{2+}, is actually a *poly*atomic ion.

to accept an electron; that is, they all have negative *EA* values. [See Figure 4.10(b).] The $1s^2$ configuration of He and the ns^2np^6 ($n \geq 2$) valence-electron configurations of the other noble gases are extraordinarily stable. In fact, other main group elements tend to either lose or gain the number of electrons needed to achieve the same number of electrons as the nearest noble gas. Species with identical electron configurations, such as a Group 7A atom that has gained one electron and the noble gas immediately to its right in the periodic table, are called ***isoelectronic.*** Figure 4.12 shows the charges on the most common monatomic ions.

To write the electron configuration of an ion formed by a main group element, we first write the configuration for the atom and either add or remove the appropriate number of electrons. Electron configurations for the sodium and chloride ions are

$$\text{Na: } 1s^22s^22p^63s^1 \longrightarrow \text{Na}^+\text{: } 1s^22s^22p^6 \text{ (10 electrons total, isoelectronic with Ne)}$$

$$\text{Cl: } 1s^22s^22p^63s^23p^5 \longrightarrow \text{Cl}^-\text{: } 1s^22s^22p^63s^23p^6 \text{ (18 electrons total, isoelectronic with Ar)}$$

We can also write electron configurations for ions using the noble gas core.

$$\text{Na: } [\text{Ne}]3s^1 \longrightarrow \text{Na}^+\text{: } [\text{Ne}]$$

$$\text{Cl: } [\text{Ne}]3s^23p^5 \longrightarrow \text{Cl}^-\text{: } [\text{Ne}]3s^23p^6 \text{ or } [\text{Ar}]$$

Worked Example 4.7 gives you some practice writing electron configurations for the ions of main group elements.

> **Student Annotation:** It is a common error to mistake species with the same valence-electron configuration for isoelectronic species. For example, F^- and Ne are isoelectronic. F^- and Cl^- are not.

Worked Example 4.7

Write electron configurations for the following ions of main group elements: (a) N^{3-}, (b) Ba^{2+}, and (c) Be^{2+}.

Strategy First write electron configurations for the atoms. Then add electrons (for anions) or remove electrons (for cations) to account for the charge.

Setup

(a) N^{3-} forms when N ($1s^22s^22p^3$ or $[\text{He}]2s^22p^3$), a main group nonmetal, gains three electrons.

(b) Ba^{2+} forms when Ba ($1s^22s^22p^63s^23p^64s^23d^{10}4p^65s^24d^{10}5p^66s^2$ or $[\text{Xe}]6s^2$) loses two electrons.

(c) Be^{2+} forms when Be ($1s^22s^2$ or $[\text{He}]2s^2$) loses two electrons.

Solution

(a) $[\text{He}]2s^22p^6$ or $[\text{Ne}]$

(b) $[\text{Kr}]5s^24d^{10}5p^6$ or $[\text{Xe}]$

(c) $1s^2$ or $[\text{He}]$

(Continued on next page)

> **Think About It**
> Be sure to add electrons to form an anion, and remove electrons to form a cation.

Practice Problem A Write electron configurations for (a) O^{2-}, (b) Ca^{2+}, and (c) Se^{2-}.

Practice Problem B List all the species (atoms and/or ions) that are likely to have the following electron configuration: $1s^2 2s^2 2p^6$.

Ions of *d*-Block Elements

Recall from Section 3.9 that the $4s$ orbital fills before the $3d$ orbitals for the elements in the first row of the *d*-block (Sc to Zn) [◄◄ Section 3.9]. Following the pattern for writing electron configurations for main group ions, then, we might expect the two electrons lost in the formation of the Fe^{2+} ion to come from the $3d$ subshell. It turns out, though, that an atom always loses electrons first from the shell with the *highest* value of n. In the case of Fe, that would be the $4s$ subshell.

> **Student Annotation:** This explains, in part, why many of the transition metals can form ions with a +2 charge.

$$Fe: [Ar]4s^2 3d^6 \longrightarrow Fe^{2+}: [Ar]3d^6$$

Iron can also form the Fe^{3+} ion, in which case the third electron is removed from the $3d$ subshell.

$$Fe: [Ar]4s^2 3d^6 \longrightarrow Fe^{3+}: [Ar]3d^5$$

In general, when a *d*-block element becomes an ion, it loses electrons first from the ns subshell and then from the $(n-1)d$ subshell.

Worked Example 4.8 gives you some practice writing electron configurations for the ions of *d*-block elements.

Worked Example 4.8

Write electron configurations for the following ions of *d*-block elements: (a) Zn^{2+}, (b) Mn^{2+}, and (c) Cr^{3+}.

Strategy First write electron configurations for the atoms. Then add electrons (for anions) or remove electrons (for cations) to account for the charge. The electrons removed from a *d*-block element must come first from the outermost *s* subshell, not the partially filled *d* subshell.

Setup

(a) Zn^{2+} forms when Zn ($1s^2 2s^2 2p^6 3s^2 3p^6 4s^2 3d^{10}$ or $[Ar]4s^2 3d^{10}$) loses two electrons.

(b) Mn^{2+} forms when Mn ($1s^2 2s^2 2p^6 3s^2 3p^6 4s^2 3d^5$ or $[Ar]4s^2 3d^5$) loses two electrons.

(c) Cr^{3+} forms when Cr ($1s^2 2s^2 2p^6 3s^2 3p^6 4s^1 3d^5$ or $[Ar]4s^1 3d^5$) loses three electrons—one from the $4s$ subshell and two from the $3d$ subshell.

> **Student Annotation:** Remember that the electron configuration of Cr is anomalous in that it has only one 4s electron, making its *d* subshell half filled [◄◄ Section 3.10].

Solution

(a) $[Ar]3d^{10}$

(b) $[Ar]3d^5$

(c) $[Ar]3d^3$

> **Think About It**
> Be sure to *add* electrons to form an anion and *remove* electrons to form a cation. Also, double-check to make sure that electrons removed from a *d*-block element come first from the *ns* subshell and then, if necessary, from the $(n-1)d$ subshell.

Practice Problem A Write electron configurations for (a) Co^{3+}, (b) Cu^{2+}, and (c) Ag^+.

Practice Problem B What common *d*-block ion (see Figure 4.12) is isoelectronic with Zn^{2+}?

Electron Configuration of Ions

4.5.1   What is the charge on a titantium ion that is isoelectronic with argon?

4.5.2   What ions of As and Sr are isoelectronic with krypton?

4.5.3   Write the correct ground-state electron configuration for Ti^{2+}.

4.5.4   Write the correct ground-state electron configuration for S^{2-}.

4.5.5   Identify each of the following ions as diamagnetic or paramagnetic: Co^{2+}, Co^{3+}, Ni^{2+}, Cu^+, Cu^{2+}, Zn^{2+}.

4.6   IONIC RADIUS

When an atom gains or loses one or more electrons to become an ion, its radius changes. The *ionic radius,* the radius of a cation or an anion, affects the physical and chemical properties of the substance of which it is a part. The three-dimensional structure of such a substance, for example, depends on the relative sizes of its cations and anions.

Comparing Ionic Radius with Atomic Radius

When an atom loses an electron and becomes a cation, its radius decreases due in part to a reduction in electron-electron repulsions (and consequently a reduction in shielding) in the valence shell. A significant decrease in radius occurs when *all* of an atom's valence electrons are removed. This is the case with ions of most main group elements, which are isoelectronic with the noble gases preceding them. Consider Na, which loses its $3s$ electron to become Na^+.

Multi 4.2
Periodic table—atomic and ionic radii

Na: $1s^2 2s^2 2p^6 3s^1$ $\longrightarrow$ Na^+: $1s^2 2s^2 2p^6$

   The valence electron of Na has a principal quantum number of $n = 3$. When it has been removed, the resulting Na^+ ion no longer has any electrons in the $n = 3$ shell. The outermost electrons of the Na^+ ion have a principal quantum number of $n = 2$. Because the value of n determines the distance from the nucleus, this corresponds to a smaller radius.

   When an atom gains one or more electrons and becomes an anion, its radius increases due to increased electron-electron repulsions. Adding an electron causes the rest of the electrons in the valence shell to spread out and take up more space in order to maximize the distance between them.

   Figure 4.13 [▶▶ page 127] shows the ionic radii for those ions of main group elements that are isoelectronic with noble gases and compares them to the radii of the parent atoms. Note that the ionic radius, like the atomic radius, increases from top to bottom in a group.

Thinking Outside the Box

Mistaking Strontium for Calcium

One of the consequences of two chemical species having similar properties is that human physiology sometimes mistakes one species for another. Healthy bones require constant replenishment of calcium. Our dietary calcium comes primarily from dairy products but can also be found in some vegetables—especially dark, leafy greens such as spinach and kale. Strontium-90, a radioactive isotope, is found in the fallout of atomic bomb explosions and is a component in the waste generated by nuclear power facilities. Strontium-90 released into the atmosphere will eventually settle on land and water, and it can reach our bodies through ingestion—especially of vegetation—and through the inhalation of airborne particles. Because calcium and strontium are chemically similar, Sr^{2+} ions are mistaken by the body for Ca^{2+} ions and are incorporated into the bones. Constant exposure to the radiation emitted by strontium-90 affects not only the bone and surrounding soft tissue, but also the bone marrow, damaging and destroying stem cells vital to the immune system. Such long-term exposure leads to an increased risk of leukemia and other cancers.

X-ray image of a human skeleton

Ca and Sr, being in the same group, have similar chemical properties.

Isoelectronic Series

An *isoelectronic series* is a series of two or more species that have identical electron configurations, but different nuclear charges. For example, O^{2-}, F^-, and Ne constitute an isoelectronic series. Although these three species have identical electron configurations, they have different radii. In an isoelectronic series, the species with the smallest nuclear charge (i.e., the smallest atomic number, Z) will have the largest radius. The species with the largest nuclear charge (i.e., the largest Z) will have the smallest radius.

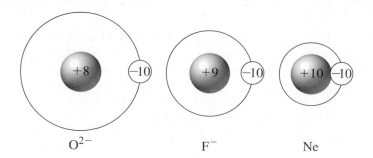

O^{2-} F^- Ne

Worked Example 4.9 shows how to identify members of an isoelectronic series and how to arrange them according to radius.

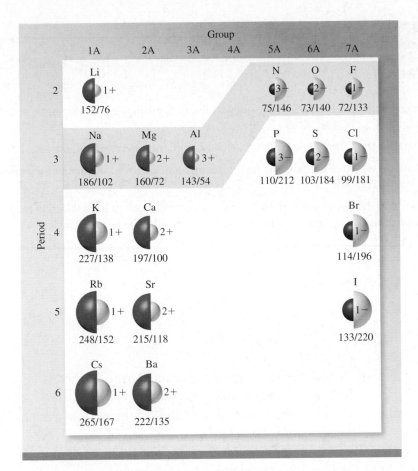

Figure 4.13 A comparison of atomic and ionic radii (in picometers) for main group elements and their common ions (those that are isoelectronic with noble gases).

Worked Example 4.9

Identify the isoelectronic series in the following group of species, and arrange them in order of increasing radius: K^+, Ne, Ar, Kr, P^{3-}, S^{2-}, and Cl^-.

Strategy Isoelectronic series are species with identical electron configurations but different nuclear charges. Determine the number of electrons in each species. The radii of isoelectronic series members decreases with increasing nuclear charge.

Setup The number of electrons in each species is as follows: 18 (K^+), 10 (Ne), 18 (Ar), 36 (Kr), 18 (P^{3-}), 18 (S^{2-}), and 18 (Cl^-). The nuclear charges of the species with 18 electrons are $+19$ (K^+), $+18$ (Ar), $+15$ (P^{3-}), $+16$ (S^{2-}), and $+17$ (Cl^-).

Solution

The isoelectronic series includes K^+, Ar, P^{3-}, S^{2-}, and Cl^-. In order of increasing radius:
$K^+ < Ar < Cl^- < S^{2-} < P^{3-}$.

Think About It
Consult Figure 4.13 to check your result. With identical electron configurations, the attractive force between the valence electrons and the nucleus will be strongest for the largest nuclear charge. Thus, the larger the nuclear charge, the closer in the valence electrons will be pulled and the smaller the radius will be.

Practice Problem A Arrange the following isoelectronic series in order of increasing radius: Se^{2-}, Br^-, Kr, and Rb^+.

Practice Problem B List all the common ions that are isoelectronic with Ne.

SECTION 4.6 REVIEW

Ionic Radius

4.6.1   Identify the largest ion and the smallest ion in the following isoelectronic series: Mg^{2+}, N^{3-}, O^{2-}, Na^+, C^{4-}.

4.6.2   Arrange the following species in the correct order of increasing radius: Ar, K^+, Cl^-, Ca^{2+}.

4.6.3   Explain why it is not possible for an isoelectronic series to include two members of Group 7A.

4.6.4   Is it possible for two members of an isoelectronic series to have different magnetic properties (i.e., can one be *diamagnetic* and the other be *paramagnetic*)?

Learning Outcomes

- Explain how elements are arranged in the periodic table.
- Use the location of an element in the periodic table to predict some of its characteristics.
- Utilize the periodic table to determine the electron configuration of an element.
- Describe the importance of valence electrons to chemical characteristics.
- Define effective nuclear charge, atomic radius, ionization energy, and electron affinity.
- Predict differences in effective nuclear charge, atomic radius, ionization energy, and electron affinity between elements using periodic trends.

- Provide some of the characteristics of metals, nonmetals, and metalloids.
- Predict the charge of an ion formed from a main group element.
- Determine the electron configurations of ions of main group and *d*-block elements.
- Predict the sizes of ions relative to atoms of the same element.
- Define isoelectronic species and arrange a series of isoelectronic species according to ionic/atomic radius.

Chapter Summary

SECTION 4.1

- The modern periodic table was devised independently by Dmitri Mendeleev and Lothar Meyer in the nineteenth century. The elements that were known at the time were grouped based on their physical and chemical properties. Using his arrangements of the elements, Mendeleev successfully predicted the existence of elements that had not yet been discovered.
- Early in the twentieth century, Henry Moseley refined the periodic table with the concept of the *atomic number,* thus resolving a few inconsistencies in the tables proposed by Mendeleev and Meyer.
- Elements in the same group of the periodic table tend to have similar physical and chemical properties.

SECTION 4.2

- The periodic table can be divided into the ***main group elements*** (also known as the *representative elements*) and the *transition metals.* It is further divided into smaller groups or *columns* of elements that all have the same configuration of ***valence electrons.***
- The 18 columns of the periodic table are labeled 1A through 8A (*s*- and *p*-block elements) and 1B through 8B (*d*-block elements), or by the numbers 1 through 18.

SECTION 4.3

- ***Effective nuclear charge*** (Z_{eff}) is the nuclear charge that is "felt" by the valence electrons. It is usually lower than the nuclear charge due to ***shielding*** by the core electrons.

SECTION 4.4

- ***Atomic radius*** is the distance between an atom's nucleus and its valence shell. The atomic radius of a metal atom is defined as the ***metallic radius,*** which is one-half the distance between adjacent, identical nuclei in a metal solid. The atomic radius of a nonmetal is defined as the ***covalent radius,*** which is one-half the distance between adjacent, identical nuclei in a substance. In general, atomic radii *decrease* from left to right across a *period* of the periodic table and *increase* from top to bottom down a *group.*
- ***Ionization energy (IE)*** is the energy required to remove an electron from an atom. The first ionization energy (IE_1) is smaller than subsequent ionization energies [e.g., second (IE_2), third (IE_3), and so on]. The first ionization of any atom removes a valence electron. An ***ion*** with a net positive charge is a ***cation.*** Ionization energies increase dramatically when core electrons are being removed. Ionization energy is a chemical property, and ionization is a ***chemical process.***

- First ionization energies (IE_1 values) tend to increase across a period and decrease down a group. Exceptions to this trend can be explained based upon the electron configuration of the element.
- ***Electron affinity (EA)*** is the energy released when an atom in the gas phase accepts an electron [$A(g) + e^- \longrightarrow A^-(g)$]. An ion with a net negative charge is an ***anion.***
- Electron affinities tend to increase across a period. As with first ionization energies, exceptions to the trend can be explained based on the electron configuration of the element. Electron affinity is also a chemical property.
- Metals tend to be shiny, lustrous, malleable, ductile, and conducting (for both heat and electricity). Metals typically lose electrons to form cations.
- Nonmetals vary in color, tend to be brittle, and are generally not good conductors (for either heat or electricity). They can gain electrons to form anions.
- In general, metallic character decreases across a period and increases down a group of the periodic table. ***Metalloids*** are elements with properties intermediate between metals and nonmetals.
- A ***diagonal relationship*** refers to the similar properties shared by elements in different groups and periods in the periodic table.

SECTION 4.5

- Ions of main group elements are ***isoelectronic*** with noble gases. When a *d*-block element loses one or more electrons, it loses them first from the shell with the highest principal quantum number (e.g., electrons in the 4*s* subshell are lost before electrons in the 3*d* subshell).

SECTION 4.6

- ***Ionic radius*** is the distance between the nucleus and valence shell of a cation or an anion. A cation is smaller than its parent atom. An anion is larger than its parent atom.
- An ***isoelectronic series*** consists of one or more ions and a noble gas, all of which have identical electron configurations. Within an isoelectronic series, the greater the nuclear charge, the smaller the radius.

Key Words

Anion, 118
Atomic radius, 113
Cation, 116
Chemical process, 117
Covalent radius, 114

Diagonal relationship, 122
Effective nuclear charge
   (Z_{eff}), 112
Electron affinity (EA), 118
Ion, 115

Ionic radius, 125
Ionization energy (IE), 115
Isoelectronic, 123
Isoelectronic series, 126
Main group elements, 109

Metallic radius, 114
Metalloid, 121
Shielding, 112
Valence electrons, 111

Key Equations

4.1 $Z_{eff} = Z - \sigma$

4.2 $F \propto \dfrac{Q_1 \times Q_2}{d^2}$

Questions and Problems

SECTION 4.1:   DEVELOPMENT OF THE PERIODIC TABLE

Review Questions

4.1   Briefly describe the significance of Mendeleev's periodic table.

4.2   What is Moseley's contribution to the modern periodic table?

4.3   Describe the general layout of a modern periodic table.

4.4   What is the most important relationship among elements in the same group in the periodic table?

SECTION 4.2:   THE MODERN PERIODIC TABLE

Review Questions

4.5   Classify each of the following elements as a metal, a nonmetal, or a metalloid: Sb, Kr, Co, Na, Al, F, Sr, As, Br, Ge.

4.6   List the properties of metals.

4.7   List the properties of nonmetals.

4.8   What is a main group element? Give names and symbols of six main group elements: two metals, two nonmetals, and two metalloids.

4.9   Without referring to a periodic table, write the name and give the symbol for one element in each of the following groups: 1A, 2A, 3A, 4A, 5A, 6A, 7A, 8A, transition metals.

4.10   What are valence electrons? For atoms of main group elements, the number of valence electrons is equal to the group number. Write electron configurations to show that this is true for the following elements: Na, Ca, Li, I, N, Se, Si.

4.11   Write the outer electron configurations for the (a) alkali metals, (b) alkaline earth metals, (c) halogens, (d) noble gases.

4.12   Use the first-row transition metals (Sc to Cu) as an example to illustrate the characteristics of the electron configurations of transition metals.

4.13   For centuries, arsenic has been the poison of choice for murders and murder mysteries alike. Based on its position in the periodic table, suggest a possible reason for its toxicity.

Problems

4.14   In the periodic table, the element hydrogen is sometimes grouped with the alkali metals and sometimes with the halogens. Explain how hydrogen can resemble the Group 1A *and* the Group 7A elements.

4.15   An atom of a certain element has 16 electrons. Consulting only the periodic table, identify the element and write its ground-state electron configuration.

4.16   Group the following electron configurations in pairs that would represent elements with similar properties:
(a) $1s^2 2s^2 2p^6 3s^2$
(b) $1s^2 2s^2 2p^3$
(c) $1s^2 2s^2 2p^6 3s^2 3p^6 4s^2 3d^{10} 4p^6$
(d) $1s^2 2s^2$
(e) $1s^2 2s^2 2p^6$
(f) $1s^2 2s^2 2p^6 3s^2 3p^3$

4.17 Group the following electron configurations in pairs that would represent elements with similar properties:
(a) $1s^2 2s^2 2p^5$
(b) $1s^2 2s^1$
(c) $1s^2 2s^2 2p^6$
(d) $1s^2 2s^2 2p^6 3s^2 3p^5$
(e) $1s^2 2s^2 2p^6 3s^2 3p^6 4s^1$
(f) $1s^2 2s^2 2p^6 3s^2 3p^6 4s^2 3d^{10} 4p^6$

4.18 Without referring to a periodic table, write the electron configuration of elements with the following atomic numbers: (a) 10, (b) 22, (c) 28, (d) 35.

4.19 Specify the group on the periodic table in which each of the following elements is found: (a) $[Ar]4s^1$; (b) $[Ar]4s^2 3d^{10} 4p^3$; (c) $[Ne]3s^2 3p^3$; (d) $[Ar]4s^2 3d^6$.

4.20 For each of the following ground-state electron configurations, determine the corresponding group number on the periodic table: (a) $ns^2(n-1)d^8$; (b) $ns^2(n-1)d^{10}np^3$; (c) $ns^2(n-1)d^3$.

4.21 Determine what element is designated by each of the following: (a) fifth period, $ns^2(n-1)d^{10}np^2$; (b) fourth period, $ns^2(n-1)d^3$; (c) third period, ns^2np^5; (d) sixth period, ns^2.

SECTION 4.3: EFFECTIVE NUCLEAR CHARGE

Review Questions

4.22 Explain the term *effective nuclear charge*.

4.23 Explain why there is a greater increase in effective nuclear charge from left to right across a period than there is from top to bottom in a group.

Problems

4.24 The electron configuration of B is $1s^2 2s^2 2p^1$. (a) If each core electron (that is, the $1s$ electrons) were totally effective in shielding the valence electrons (that is, the $2s$ and $2p$ electrons) from the nucleus and the valence electrons did not shield one another, what would be the shielding constant (σ) and the effective nuclear charge (Z_{eff}) for the $2s$ and $2p$ electrons? (b) In reality, the shielding constants for the $2s$ and $2p$ electrons in B are slightly different. They are 2.42 and 2.58, respectively. Calculate Z_{eff} for these electrons, and explain the differences from the values you determined in part (a).

4.25 The electron configuration of C is $1s^2 2s^2 2p^2$. (a) If each core electron (that is, the $1s$ electrons) were totally effective in screening the valence electrons (that is, the $2s$ and $2p$ electrons) from the nucleus and the valence electrons did not shield one another, what would be the shielding constant (σ) and the effective nuclear charge (Z_{eff}) for the $2s$ and $2p$ electrons? (b) In reality, the shielding constants for the $2s$ and $2p$ electrons in C are slightly different. They are 2.78 and 2.86, respectively. Calculate Z_{eff} for these electrons, and explain the differences from the values you determined in part (a).

SECTION 4.4: PERIODIC TRENDS IN PROPERTIES OF ELEMENTS

Review Questions

4.26 Define *atomic radius* and explain why such a definition is necessary.

4.27 How does atomic radius change (a) from left to right across a period and (b) from top to bottom in a group?

4.28 Equation 4.2 is used to calculate the force between charged particles. Explain the significance of the sign of the result.

4.29 Use the second period of the periodic table as an example to show that the size of atoms decreases as we move from left to right. Explain the trend.

4.30 Why is the radius of the lithium atom considerably larger than the radius of the hydrogen atom?

4.31 Explain why the atomic radius of S is larger than that of O, but smaller than that of P.

4.32 Define *ionization energy*. Explain why ionization energy measurements are usually made when atoms are in the gaseous state. Why is the second ionization energy always greater than the first ionization energy for any element? What types of elements have the highest ionization energies and what types have the lowest ionization energies?

4.33 Define the terms *cation* and *anion*.

4.34 (a) Define the term *electron affinity*. (b) Explain why electron affinity measurements are made with gaseous atoms. (c) Ionization energy is always a positive quantity, whereas electron affinity may be either positive or negative. Explain.

4.35 Explain the trend in electron affinity from aluminum to chlorine (see Figure 4.10).

4.36 Define *diagonal relationship* and explain what causes it.

4.37 According to the information on page 122, there are two alkaline earth metals (Group 2A) that exhibit diagonal relationships with other elements. Identify the alkaline earth metals and the element with which each has a diagonal relationship.

Problems

4.38 Consider two ions with opposite charges separated by a distance d. What effect does each of the following changes have on the force between the ions? (a) The positive charge is doubled. (b) The positive charge is doubled and the negative charge is halved. (c) The distance is doubled. (d) The distance is halved. (e) Both charges and the distance are doubled.

4.39 Consider two ions with opposite charges separated by a distance d. What effect does each of the following changes have on the force between the ions? (a) Both charges are doubled. (b) The positive charge is doubled and the negative charge is tripled. (c) The negative charge and the distance are doubled. (d) The positive charge is doubled and the distance is halved. (e) Both charges and the distance are halved.

4.40   Arrange the following pairs of charged particles in order of increasing magnitude of attractive force.

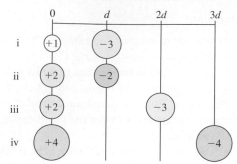

4.41   Arrange the following pairs of charged particles in order of increasing magnitude of attractive force.

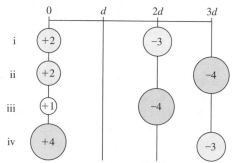

4.42   On the basis of their positions in the periodic table, select the atom with the larger atomic radius in each of the following pairs:
(a) Mg, P; (b) Sr, Be; (c) As, Br; (d) Cl, I; (e) Xe, Kr.

4.43   Arrange the following atoms in order of increasing atomic radius: Si, Mg, Cl, P, Al.

4.44   Which is the largest atom in the third period of the periodic table?

4.45   Which is the smallest atom in Group 6A?

4.46   Based on size, identify the spheres shown as Na, Mg, O, and S.

4.47   Based on size, identify the spheres shown as K, Ca, S, and Se.

4.48   Arrange the following in order of increasing first ionization energy: Na, Cl, Al, S, and Cs.

4.49   Arrange the following in order of increasing first ionization energy: F, K, P, Ca, and Ne.

4.50   Use the third period of the periodic table as an example to illustrate the change in first ionization energies of the elements as we move from left to right. Explain the trend.

4.51   In general, the first ionization energy increases from left to right across a given period. Aluminum, however, has a lower first ionization energy than magnesium. Explain.

4.52   The first and second ionization energies of K are 419 and 3052 kJ/mol, and those of Ca are 590 and 1145 kJ/mol, respectively. Compare their values and comment on the differences.

4.53   Two atoms have the electron configurations $1s^2 2s^2 2p^6$ and $1s^2 2s^2 2p^6 3s^1$. The first ionization energy of one is 2080 kJ/mol, and that of the other is 496 kJ/mol. Match each ionization energy with one of the given electron configurations. Justify your choice.

4.54   The graph shows IE_1, IE_2, IE_3, and IE_4 for three main group elements: A, B, and C. Using information from the graph, determine the group number for each element.

4.55   The graph shows IE_1, IE_2, IE_3, and IE_4 for three main group elements: A, B, and C. Using information from the graph, determine the group number for each element.

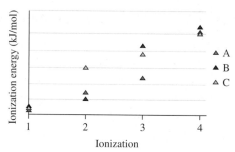

4.56   A hydrogen-like ion is an ion containing only one electron. The energies of the electron in a hydrogen-like ion are given by

$$E_n = -(2.18 \times 10^{-18} \text{ J})Z^2\left(\frac{1}{n^2}\right)$$

where n is the principal quantum number and Z is the atomic number of the element. Calculate the ionization energy (in kJ/mol) of the He^+ ion.

4.57   Plasma is a state of matter consisting of positive gaseous ions and electrons. In the plasma state, a mercury atom could be stripped of its 80 electrons and therefore would exist as Hg^{80+}. Use the equation in Problem 4.56 to calculate the energy required for the last ionization step, that is,

$$Hg^{79+}(g) \longrightarrow Hg^{80+}(g) + e^-$$

4.58   Arrange the elements in each of the following groups in order of increasing electron affinity: (a) Li, Na, K; (b) F, Cl, Br, I.

4.59   Specify which of the following elements you would expect to have the greatest electron affinity: He, K, Co, S, Cl.

4.60   Considering their electron affinities, do you think it is possible for the alkali metals to form an anion like M⁻, where M represents an alkali metal?

4.61 Explain why alkali metals have a greater affinity for electrons than alkaline earth metals.

4.62 The effective nuclear charges for oxygen and sulfur are 4.45 and 5.48, respectively. Use this information and the atomic radii given in Figure 4.6 to compare the attractive force between the nucleus in each atom and the valence electron that would be removed by the first ionization.

4.63 The effective nuclear charges for sodium and magnesium are 2.51 and 3.31, respectively. Use this information and the atomic radii given in Figure 4.6 to compare the attractive force between the nucleus in each atom and the valence electron that would be removed by the first ionization.

SECTION 4.5: ELECTRON CONFIGURATION OF IONS

Review Questions

4.64 How does the electron configuration of ions derived from main group elements give them stability?

4.65 What do we mean when we say that two ions or an atom and an ion are *isoelectronic?*

4.66 Is it possible for the atoms of one element to be isoelectronic with the atoms of another element? Explain.

4.67 Explain why an isoelectronic series cannot include more than one member of the same group.

Problems

4.68 Write the ground-state electron configurations of the following ions: (a) Li^+, (b) H^-, (c) N^{3-}, (d) F^-, (e) S^{2-}, (f) Al^{3+}, (g) Se^{2-}, (h) Br^-.

4.69 Write the ground-state electron configurations of the following ions: (a) Rb^+, (b) Sr^{2+}, (c) Sn^{2+}, (d) Te^{2-}, (e) Ba^{2+}, (f) In^{3+}, (g) Tl^+, (h) Tl^{3+}.

4.70 Write the ground-state electron configurations of the following ions, which play important roles in biochemical processes in our bodies: (a) Na^+, (b) Mg^{2+}, (c) Cl^-, (d) Ca^{2+}.

4.71 Write the ground-state electron configurations of the following ions, which play important roles in various biological processes: (a) Fe^{2+}, (b) Cu^{2+}, (c) Co^{2+}, (d) Mn^{2+}.

4.72 Write the ground-state electron configurations of the following metal ions: (a) Sc^{3+}, (b) Ti^{4+}, (c) V^{5+}, (d) Cr^{3+}, (e) Mn^{3+}.

4.73 Write the ground-state electron configurations of the following metal ions: (a) Ni^{2+}, (b) Cu^+, (c) Ag^+, (d) Au^+, (e) Au^{3+}.

4.74 Identify the ions, each with a net charge of +1, that have the following electron configurations: (a) [Ar], (b) $[Ar]3d^{10}$, (c) $[Kr]5s^24d^{10}$, (d) [Xe].

4.75 Identify the ions, each with a net charge of +3, that have the following electron configurations: (a) $[Ar]3d^3$, (b) [Ar], (c) $[Kr]4d^6$, (d) $[Xe]4f^{14}5d^6$.

4.76 Which of the following species are isoelectronic with each other: C, Cl^-, Mn^{2+}, B^-, Ar, Zn, Fe^{3+}, Ge^{2+}?

4.77 Group the species that are isoelectronic: Be^{2+}, F^-, Fe^{2+}, N^{3-}, He, S^{2-}, Co^{3+}, Ar.

4.78 For each pair of ions, determine which will have the greater number of unpaired electrons: (a) Fe^{2+}, Fe^{3+}; (b) P^{3+}, P^{5+}; (c) Cr^{2+}, Cr^{3+}.

4.79 Rank the following ions in order of increasing number of unpaired electrons: Ti^{3+}, Fe^{2+}, V^{3+}, Cu^+, Mn^{4+}.

4.80 A cation with a net +3 charge is shown to have a total of ten electrons. Identify the element from which the cation is derived.

4.81 An anion with a net −2 charge has a total of 36 electrons. Identify the element from which the anion is derived.

4.82 A M^{2+} ion derived from a metal in the first transition metal series has four electrons in the $3d$ subshell. What element might M be?

4.83 A metal ion with a net +3 charge has five electrons in the $3d$ subshell. Identify the metal.

4.84 Identify the atomic ground-state electron configurations that do not exist. For those that do exist, identify the element.

(a) [Ar] ⇅ ↑ ↑ ↑ __ __
(b) [Ne] ⇅ ⇅ __ __
(c) [Kr] ⇅ ↑ ↑ ↑
(d) [Ne] ⇅ ↑ ↑ ↑
(e) [Ar] ⇅ ↑ ↑ ↑ ↑ __
(f) [Kr] ↑ ⇅ ⇅ ⇅ ⇅ ⇅

4.85 Each of the following ground-state electron configurations represents one or more of the transition metal ions in Figure 4.12. Identify the ion or ions represented by each.

(a) [Ar] __ ⇅ ↑ ↑ ↑ ↑
(b) [Kr] __ ⇅ ⇅ ⇅ ⇅ ⇅
(c) [Ar] __ ⇅ ⇅ ⇅ ⇅ ↑
(d) [Ar] __ ⇅ ⇅ ⇅ ⇅ ⇅
(e) [Ar] __ ↑ ↑ ↑ __ __
(f) [Ar] __ ⇅ ⇅ ↑ ↑ ↑

SECTION 4.6: IONIC RADIUS

Review Questions

4.86 Define *ionic radius*. How does the size of an atom change when it becomes (a) an anion and (b) a cation?

4.87 Explain why, for a cation and an anion that are isoelectronic, the anion is larger than the cation.

Problems

4.88 List the following ions in order of increasing ionic radius: N^{3-}, Na^+, F^-, Mg^{2+}, O^{2-}.

4.89 Indicate which one of the two species in each of the following pairs is smaller: (a) Cl or Cl^-; (b) Na or Na^+; (c) O^{2-} or S^{2-}; (d) Mg^{2+} or Al^{3+}; (e) Au or Au^{3+}.

4.90 Explain which of the following anions is larger and why: Se^{2-} or Te^{2-}.

4.91 Explain which of the following cations is larger and why: Cu^+ or Cu^{2+}.

4.92 Which of the following is the most realistic representation of an atom from Group 1A becoming an ion?

(a) ◯ + e^- ⟶ ⊕

(b) ◯ ⟶ ⊕ + e^-

(c) ◯ + e^- ⟶ ⊖

(d) ◯ ⟶ ⊕ + e^-

(e) ◯ + e^- ⟶ ⊖

4.93 Which of the following is the most realistic representation of an atom from Group 6A becoming an ion?

(a) ◯ + e^- + e^- ⟶ ②⁺

(b) ◯ ⟶ ②⁺ + e^- + e^-

(c) ◯ + e^- + e^- ⟶ ②⁻

(d) ◯ ⟶ ②⁺ + e^- + e^-

(e) ◯ + e^- + e^- ⟶ ②⁻

4.94 Although sodium and potassium occur in similar amounts in the Earth's crust, living cells accumulate potassium ions almost exclusively. K^+ cannot be replaced by Na^+ in cells, but it is possible for other ions to replace K^+. Based on the similarity of their chemical properties, which of the following ions might be suitable replacements for K^+ in cells: Rb^+, Al^{3+}, Ga^+, Cs^+, Fe^{2+}?

4.95 Ga^{3+} ions are commonly used in a variety of solid state devices that emit light. Assuming ions with sufficiently similar properties could successfully be used in place of Ga^{3+} in such a device, which one of the following ions would be most suitable: Fe^{3+}, Ca^{2+}, Ti^{3+}, In^{3+}, Tl^+?

4.96 State whether each of the following properties of the main group elements generally increases or decreases (a) from left to right across a period and (b) from top to bottom within a group: metallic character, atomic size, ionization energy, acidity of oxides.

4.97 Referring to the periodic table, name (a) the halogen in the fourth period, (b) an element similar to phosphorus in chemical properties, (c) the metal in the fifth period with the lowest ionization energy, (d) an element that has an atomic number smaller than 20 and is similar to strontium.

ADDITIONAL PROBLEMS

4.98 Write equations representing the following processes:
(a) the electron affinity of S^-
(b) the third ionization energy of titanium
(c) the electron affinity of Mg^{2+}
(d) the ionization energy of O^{2-}

4.99 Arrange the following isoelectronic species in order of increasing ionization energy: O^{2-}, F^-, Na^+, Mg^{2+}.

4.100 The following table gives numbers of electrons and protons in ions of several elements. (a) Which species are cations? (b) Which species are anions? (c) Write the symbols for all of the species.

	Ion of element					
	A	**B**	**C**	**D**	**E**	**F**
Number of electrons	10	18	46	54	46	36
Number of protons	7	20	48	52	49	41

4.101 Arrange the following species in isoelectronic pairs: O^+, Ar, S^{2-}, Ne, Zn, Cs^+, N^{3-}, As^{3+}, N, Xe.

4.102 In which of the following are the species written in decreasing order by size of radius: (a) Be, Mg, Ba; (b) N^{3-}, O^{2-}, F^-; (c) Tl^{3+}, Tl^{2+}, Tl^+?

4.103 Which of the following properties show a clear periodic variation: (a) first ionization energy, (b) molar mass of the elements, (c) number of isotopes of an element, (d) atomic radius?

4.104 Rb and Br atoms are shown here.

Rb   Br

What isoelectronic ions are formed by Rb and Br? Which scene most accurately reflects the relative sizes of the ions once a pair of isoelectronic ions is formed by Rb and Br?

(a)   (b)   (c)   (d)

4.105 Both Mg^{2+} and Ca^{2+} are important biological ions. One of their functions is to bind to the phosphate group of ATP molecules or amino acids of proteins. For Group 2A metals in general, the tendency for binding to the anions increases in the order $Ba^{2+} < Sr^{2+} < Ca^{2+} < Mg^{2+}$. Explain this trend.

4.106 For each pair of elements listed, give three properties that show their chemical similarity: (a) sodium and potassium and (b) chlorine and bromine.

4.107 Given the following valence orbital diagrams, rank these elements in order of increasing (a) atomic size and (b) ionization energy.

4.108   Fill in the blanks in the table:

Symbol		$^{54}_{26}Fe^{3+}$	
Protons	5		46
Neutrons	6	16	59
Electrons	2	18	44
Net charge			−3

4.109   Contrary to the generalized trend that atomic radius increases down a group, the atomic radius of Zr (159 pm) is actually larger than that of Hf (156 pm) even though the number of electrons increases from 40 (Zr) to 72 (Hf). Suggest a reason for this anomaly. (*Hint:* Many elements of the sixth period after Hf exhibit this same phenomenon in which their atomic radius is not significantly larger or is even smaller than that of the fifth period element above it.)

4.110   Explain why the first electron affinity of sulfur is 200 kJ/mol but the second electron affinity is −649 kJ/mol.

4.111   The H⁻ ion and the He atom each have two $1s$ electrons. Which of the two species is larger? Explain.

4.112   Given the following electron configurations, rank these elements in order of increasing atomic radius: $[Kr]5s^2$, $[Ne]3s^23p^3$, $[Ar]4s^23d^{10}4p^3$, $[Kr]5s^1$, $[Kr]5s^24d^{10}5p^4$.

4.113   The formula for calculating the energies of an electron in a hydrogen-like ion is given in Problem 4.56. This equation can be applied only to one-electron atoms or ions. One way to modify it for more complex species is to replace Z with $Z − \sigma$ or Z_{eff}. Calculate the value of σ if the first ionization energy of helium is 3.94×10^{18} J per atom. (Disregard the minus sign in the given equation in your calculation.)

4.114   Why do noble gases have negative electron affinity values?

4.115   The effective nuclear charge felt by the $3p$ valence electron in aluminum is 4.07. Explain how the analogous effective nuclear charge felt by the $4p$ valence electron in gallium can be 6.22, despite the presence of 18 additional electrons in gallium.

4.116   What is the percent change in the force of attraction when two equal but oppositely charged ions are moved from a distance of 125 pm to a distance of 145 pm?

4.117   The atomic radius of K is 227 pm and that of K⁺ is 138 pm. Calculate the percent decrease in volume that occurs when K(g) is converted to K⁺(g). (The volume of a sphere is $\frac{4}{3}\pi r^3$, where r is the radius of the sphere.)

4.118   The atomic radius of F is 72 pm and that of F⁻ is 133 pm. Calculate the percent increase in volume that occurs when F(g) is converted to F⁻(g). (See Problem 4.117 for the volume of a sphere.)

4.119   A technique called photoelectron spectroscopy is used to measure the ionization energy of atoms. A gaseous sample is irradiated with UV light, and electrons are ejected from the valence shell. The kinetic energies of the ejected electrons are measured. Because the energy of the UV photon and the kinetic energy of the ejected electron are known, we can write

$$hv = IE + \frac{1}{2}mu^2$$

where h is Planck's constant, v is the frequency of the UV light, and m and u are the mass and velocity of the electron, respectively. In one experiment, the kinetic energy of the ejected electron from potassium is found to be 5.34×10^{-19} J using a UV source of wavelength 162 nm. Calculate the ionization energy of potassium. How can you be sure that this ionization energy corresponds to the electron in the valence shell (that is, the most loosely held electron)?

4.120   The energy needed for the following process is 1.96×10^4 kJ/mol:

$$Li(g) \longrightarrow Li^{3+}(g) + 3e^-$$

If the first ionization energy of lithium is 520 kJ/mol, calculate the second ionization energy of lithium, that is, the energy required for the process

$$Li^+(g) \longrightarrow Li^{2+}(g) + e^-$$

(*Hint:* You need the equation in Problem 4.56.)

4.121   Using your knowledge of the periodic trends with size, identify the spheres below based on their relative sizes as Rb, Rb⁺, Mg, F⁻, and F.

A   B   C   D   E

4.122   What is the electron affinity of the Na⁺ ion?

4.123   The ionization energies of sodium (in kJ/mol), starting with the first and ending with the eleventh, are 496, 4562, 6910, 9543, 13,354, 16,613, 20,117, 25,496, 28,932, 141,362, 159,075. Plot the log of ionization energy (y axis) versus the number of ionization (x axis); for example, log 496 is plotted versus 1 (labeled IE_1, the first ionization energy), log 4562 is plotted versus 2 (labeled IE_2, the second ionization energy), and so on. (a) Label IE_1 through IE_{11} with the electrons in orbitals such as $1s$, $2s$, $2p$, and $3s$. (b) What can you deduce about electron shells from the breaks in the curve?

4.124   Experimentally, the electron affinity of an element can be determined by using a laser light to ionize the anion of the element in the gas phase:

$$X^-(g) + hv \longrightarrow X(g) + e^-$$

Referring to Figure 4.10, calculate the photon wavelength (in nm) corresponding to the electron affinity for chlorine. In what region of the electromagnetic spectrum does this wavelength fall?

4.125   Explain, in terms of their electron configurations, why Fe²⁺ is more easily converted to Fe³⁺ than Mn²⁺ is converted to Mn³⁺.

4.126   Explain why, in general, atomic radius and ionization energy have opposite periodic trends.

4.127   Explain why the electron affinity of nitrogen is approximately zero, while the elements on either side, carbon and oxygen, have substantial positive electron affinities.

4.128   The graph below charts the first six ionization energies of an unknown gaseous atom.

(a)   If this element is in the third period, what is its electron configuration?

(b)   If this element is in the first row of transition metals, what is its electron configuration?

(c)   For each of the elements in parts (a) and (b), explain why there is such a large gap between IE_4 and IE_5.

4.129   Although it is possible to determine the second, third, and higher ionization energies of an element, the same cannot usually be done with the electron affinities of an element. Explain.

4.130   Calculate the maximum wavelength of light (in nm) required to ionize a single lithium atom.

4.131   As discussed in the chapter, the atomic mass of argon is greater than that of potassium. This observation created a problem in the early development of the periodic table because it meant that argon should be placed after potassium. (a) How was this difficulty resolved? (b) From the following data, calculate the average atomic masses of argon and potassium: Ar-36 (35.9675 amu, 0.337 percent), Ar-38 (37.9627 amu, 0.063 percent), Ar-40 (39.9624 amu, 99.60 percent), K-39 (38.9637 amu, 93.258 percent), K-40 (39.9640 amu, 0.0117 percent), K-41 (40.9618 amu, 6.730 percent).

4.132   Why do elements that have high ionization energies also have more positive electron affinities? Which group of elements would be an exception to this generalization?

4.133   Predict the atomic number and ground-state electron configuration of the next member of the alkali metals after francium.

4.134   Thallium (Tl) is a neurotoxin and mostly forms only the Tl^+ ion. Aluminum (Al), which causes anemia and dementia, normally only forms the Al^{3+} ion. The first, second, and third ionization energies of Tl are 589, 1971, and 2878 kJ/mol, respectively. The first, second, and third ionization energies of Al are 577.5, 1817, and 2745 kJ/mol, respectively. Plot the ionization energies of Al and Tl versus atomic number and explain the trends.

4.135   The first four ionization energies of an element are approximately 738, 1450, 7.7×10^3, and 1.1×10^4 kJ/mol. To which periodic group does this element belong? Explain your answer.

4.136   What must the charges be on the following elements for them to be isoelectronic with a noble gas? (a) Zr, (b) Cr, (c) Nb, (d) Y.

4.137   The first six ionizations of a gaseous atom can be achieved with light of the following wavelengths, respectively: 218 nm, 113 nm, 29 nm, 22 nm, 17 nm, and 14 nm. To what group of the periodic table does the atom belong?

4.138   A monatomic ion has a charge of +2. The nucleus of the parent atom has a mass number of 55 and the number of neutrons in the nucleus is 1.2 times that of the number of protons. Give the name and symbol of the element.

4.139   An enzyme that requires a metal ion to exhibit biological activity is called a *metalloenzyme*. For a metalloenzyme that requires Zn^{2+} to function, which of the following ions might successfully replace Zn^{2+} while maintaining the activity of the metalloenzyme: Cu^{2+}, Sn^{4+}, Sc^{3+}, Pb^{2+}, Co^{2+}?

Answers to In-Chapter Materials

PRACTICE PROBLEMS

4.1A (a) Ge, (b) Bi. **4.1B** Bi < As < P. **4.2A** (a) $1s^2 2s^2 2p^6 3s^2 3p^3$, p-block, (b) $1s^2 2s^2 2p^6 3s^2 3p^6 4s^2$, s-block, (c) $1s^2 2s^2 2p^6 3s^2 3p^6 4s^2 3d^{10} 4p^5$, p-block. **4.2B** (a) Al, (b) Zn, (c) Sr. **4.3A** F < Se < Ge. **4.3B** Si and Se. **4.4A** Mg, Mg. **4.4B** Rb has a smaller Z_{eff} but IE_2 for Rb corresponds to removal of a core electron. **4.5A** Al. **4.5B** Adding an electron to As involves pairing. **4.6A** The attractive force is slightly larger between +3.26 and −1.15 separated by 1.5 pm. **4.6B** 1.51 pm. **4.7A** (a) [Ne], (b) [Ar], (c) [Kr]. **4.7B** N^{3-}, O^{2-}, F^-, Ne, Na^+, Mg^{2+}, Al^{3+}. **4.8A** (a) $[Ar]3d^6$, (b) $[Ar]3d^9$, (c) $[Kr]4d^{10}$. **4.8B** Cu^+. **4.9A** Rb^+ < Kr < Br^- < Se^{2-}. **4.9B** F^-, O^{2-}, N^{3-}, Na^+, Mg^{2+}, Al^{3+}.

SECTION REVIEW

4.1.1 Se. **4.1.2** Ca, Ba. **4.1.3** (a) At, (b) metalloid. **4.2.1** $1s^2 2s^2 2p^6 3s^2 3p^6 4s^2 3d^{10} 4p^2$. **4.2.2** Sn. **4.4.1** Ba < Sr < Ca. **4.4.2** Be < B < Li. **4.4.3** Rb, C, F. **4.4.4** Ca, K, K. **4.4.5** The attractive force is larger between +2 and −2 separated by 1.5 pm. **4.4.6** 1.2 pm. **4.5.1** 4+. **4.5.2** As^{3-} and Sr^{2+}. **4.5.3** $[Ar]3d^2$. **4.5.4** $[Ne]3s^2 3p^6$ or [Ar]. **4.5.5** Paramagnetic, paramagnetic, paramagnetic, diamagnetic, paramagnetic, diamagnetic. **4.6.1** Largest, C^{4-}; smallest, Mg^{2+}. **4.6.2** Ca^{2+} < K^+ < Ar < Cl^-. **4.6.3** Each element in Group 7A contains valence electrons with different values of n. **4.6.4** It is not possible. Isoelectronic species all have the same configuration.

KEY SKILLS

Periodic Trends in Atomic Radius, Ionization Energy, and Electron Affinity

The properties of an element are determined in large part by the *size* (radius) and the valence-shell *electron configuration* of its atoms and ions. Together, principal quantum number (n), effective nuclear charge (Z_{eff}), and charge on the valence shell (number of valence electrons) determine atomic radius.

Atomic radius decreases

Atomic radius increases

From left to right across a period, Z_{eff} and charge on the valence shell both *increase*. Each step to the right involves the addition of a proton, which increases Z, and the addition of an electron. Each additional electron resides in the same shell. Remember that electrons in the same shell do not shield one another well. The result is that Z_{eff} increases by nearly as much as Z. As the magnitude of opposite charges increases, coulombic attraction between them increases, and they are drawn closer together, thus reducing the atomic radius.

From top to bottom within a group, valence electrons reside in shells with increasingly larger values of n, putting them farther away from the nucleus—thereby increasing the atomic radius. Valence-shell electron configuration and, to a large extent, Z_{eff} remain the same from top to bottom in a group. Variations in atomic radii of the *d*-block elements vary less regularly than the main group elements.

From left to right across a period, Z_{eff} *increases* and radius *decreases*. Both factors contribute to stronger coulombic attraction between the positively charged nucleus and the valence electrons—making it harder to remove an electron; therefore, ionization energy (IE_1) *increases*. From top to bottom within a group, although Z_{eff} remains fairly constant, radius increases. The increased distance between the nucleus and the valence electrons corresponds to weaker coulombic attraction, making it easier to remove an electron; therefore, IE_1 *decreases*.

Because Z_{eff} *increases* and radius *decreases* from left to right across a period, the coulombic attraction between the positively charged nucleus and an added electron gets stronger, making it easier to add an electron; therefore, electron affinity (EA) *increases*. And because Z_{eff} remains fairly constant and radius *increases* from top to bottom within a group, there is a smaller coulombic attraction between the nucleus and an added electron—making it harder to add an electron; therefore, *EA decreases*.

Specific anomalies in the general trends of IE_1 and EA are determined by valence-electron configuration.

Ionization energy (IE_1) increases → IE_1 decreases ↓

1							2
1312							2372

3	4	5	6	7	8	9	10
520	899	800	1086	1402	1314	1681	2080
11 496	**12** 738	**13** 577	**14** 786	**15** 1012	**16** 999	**17** 1256	**18** 1520
19 419	**20** 590	**31** 579	**32** 761	**33** 947	**34** 941	**35** 1143	**36** 1351
21 403	**22** 549	**49** 558	**50** 708	**51** 834	**52** 869	**53** 1009	**54** 1170
55 376	**56** 503	**81** 589	**82** 715	**83** 703	**84** 813	**85** (926)	**86** 1037

Electron affinity (EA) increases → Electron affinity (EA) decreases ↓

1							2
+72.8							(0.0)

3	4	5	6	7	8	9	10
+59.6	≤0	+26.7	+122	−7	+141	+328	(−29)
11 +52.9	**12** ≤0	**13** +42.5	**14** +134	**15** +72.0	**16** +200	**17** +349	**18** (−35)
19 +48.4	**20** +2.37	**31** +28.9	**32** +119	**33** +78.2	**34** +195	**35** +325	**36** (−39)
21 +46.9	**22** +5.03	**49** +28.9	**50** +107	**51** +103	**52** +190	**53** +295	**54** (−41)
55 +45.5	**56** +13.95	**81** +19.3	**82** +35.1	**83** +91.3	**84** +183	**85** +270	**86** (−41)

For example, although the trend is an increase in IE_1 from left to right, IE_1 for Group 3A is lower than IE_1 for Group 2A—within a period. This is because the electron removed by ionization comes from the p subshell, which is higher in energy than the s subshell [◄◄ Figure 4.9(a)]. Likewise, IE_1 for Group 6A is lower than IE_1 for Group 5A. In this case, the electron removed by ionization is one of a pair of electrons in a p orbital. Because paired electrons in a single orbital repel one another, removing one of them is relatively easy [◄◄ Figure 4.9(b)].

Similarly, despite the general trend, EA for Group 2A is lower than EA for Group 1A. In this case, the electron added by electron affinity goes into the p subshell, which is higher in energy than the s subshell [◄◄ Figure 4.11(a)]. And EA for Group 5A is lower than that for Group 4A because the added electron must go into an already occupied p orbital [◄◄ Figure 4.11(b)].

Each of these periodic properties can be explained and understood using Coulomb's law: $F \propto \dfrac{Q_1 \times Q_2}{d^2}$.

Key Skills Problems

4.1
Group 8A exhibits the highest first ionization energy. Which group do you expect to exhibit the highest *second* ionization energy (EA_2)?

(a) 7A   (b) 6A   (c) 5A   (d) 2A   (e) 1A

4.2
Which of the following best describes why Z_{eff} does not change significantly from top to bottom within a group?

(a) There are fewer completed electron shells.
(b) There are fewer valence electrons.
(c) There are more valence electrons.
(d) There are more completed electron shells.
(e) The number of protons in the nucleus does not change significantly.

4.3
Imagine an arrangement of atomic orbitals in an alternate universe, in which the s subshell contains *two* orbitals instead of one, and the p subshell contains *four* orbitals rather than three. Under these circumstances, in which groups would you expect the anomalously low first ionization energies to occur?

(a) 3 and 6
(b) 5 and 9
(c) 2 and 5
(d) 4 and 8
(e) 3 and 7

4.4
In the same arrangement described in 4.3, in which groups would you expect the anomalously low electron affinities to occur?

(a) 3 and 6
(b) 5 and 9
(c) 2 and 5
(d) 4 and 8
(e) 3 and 7

CHAPTER 5

Ionic and Covalent Compounds

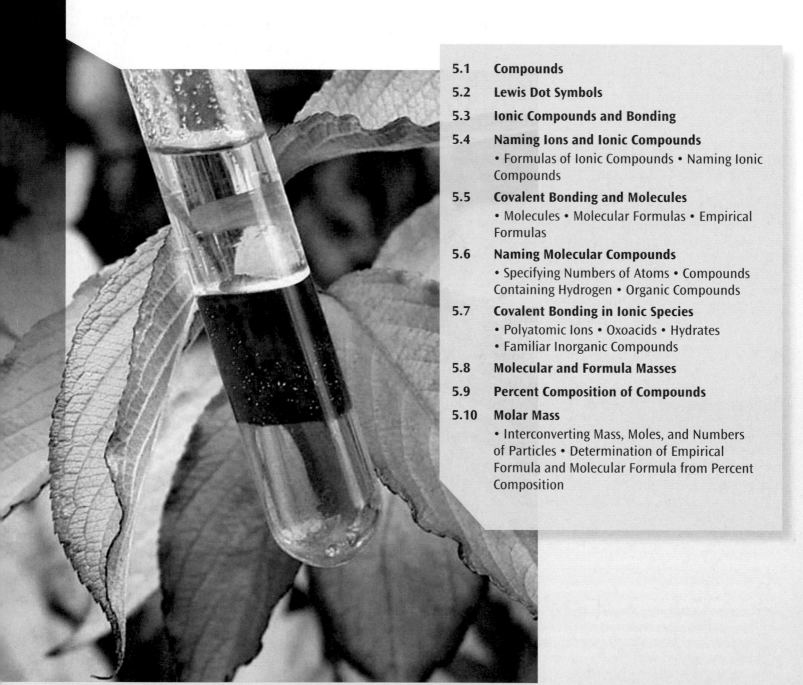

5.1 **Compounds**

5.2 **Lewis Dot Symbols**

5.3 **Ionic Compounds and Bonding**

5.4 **Naming Ions and Ionic Compounds**
• Formulas of Ionic Compounds • Naming Ionic Compounds

5.5 **Covalent Bonding and Molecules**
• Molecules • Molecular Formulas • Empirical Formulas

5.6 **Naming Molecular Compounds**
• Specifying Numbers of Atoms • Compounds Containing Hydrogen • Organic Compounds

5.7 **Covalent Bonding in Ionic Species**
• Polyatomic Ions • Oxoacids • Hydrates • Familiar Inorganic Compounds

5.8 **Molecular and Formula Masses**

5.9 **Percent Composition of Compounds**

5.10 **Molar Mass**
• Interconverting Mass, Moles, and Numbers of Particles • Determination of Empirical Formula and Molecular Formula from Percent Composition

Many compounds exhibit predominantly either *ionic* or *covalent* bonding. Recently, though, chemists have succeeded in preparing a new class of compounds called *ionic liquids*. These unusual compounds demonstrate significant concurrent covalent and ionic bonding. Many of these substances possess unusual and useful properties, including being *liquid* at room temperature—a property not normally associated with ionic

compounds. Shown here is a three-part heterogeneous mixture comprising the hydrocarbon nonane (top), water colored with blue dye (middle), and an ionic liquid (bottom). The unusual properties of ionic liquids allow chemists to use them for cellulose processing, storage media for solar-thermal energy systems, waste recycling, and as solvents for green chemistry applications.

COMPOUNDS

Most of the substances we encounter every day are not elements. Rather, they are *compounds*. A ***compound*** is a substance composed of two or more elements combined in a specific ratio and held together by *chemical bonds* [▶▶ Sections 5.3 and 5.5]. Unlike a mixture [◄◄ Section 1.2], a compound cannot be separated into simpler substances by a physical process. Familiar examples of compounds include water, which is a combination of the elements oxygen and hydrogen; and salt, which is a combination of the elements sodium and chlorine. The discovery of the correlation between electron configuration and periodic properties of the elements [◄◄ Section 4.2] gave chemists a way to explain both the *existence* and the *formation* of compounds.

 LEWIS DOT SYMBOLS

Early in the twentieth century, American chemist Gilbert Lewis[1] suggested that atoms combine in order to achieve a more stable electron configuration. In fact, we have already seen that common monatomic ions result when atoms of main group elements either gain or lose enough electrons to become isoelectronic with noble gases—thereby achieving maximum stability.

When atoms interact to form compounds, it is their *valence electrons* that actually interact. Therefore, it is helpful to have a method for depicting the valence electrons of the atoms involved. This is done using Lewis dot symbols. A ***Lewis dot symbol*** consists of the element's symbol surrounded by dots, where each dot represents a valence electron. For the main group elements, the number of dots in the Lewis dot symbol is the same as the group number, as shown in Figure 5.1. (Because they have incompletely filled inner shells, transition metals typically are not represented with Lewis dot symbols.)

Figure 5.1 shows that dots are placed above and below as well as to the left and right of the symbol. The exact order in which the dots are placed around the element symbol is not important, but the number of dots is. Thus, any of the following would be correct for the Lewis dot symbol for boron:

$$\cdot\dot{B}\cdot \qquad \dot{\ddot{B}} \qquad \cdot\dot{B} \qquad \dot{\ddot{B}}$$

When writing Lewis dot symbols, although each side can have a maximum of two dots, we do not "pair" dots until absolutely necessary. Thus, we would *not* represent boron with a pair of dots on one side and a single dot on another.

For main group metals such as Na or Mg, the number of dots in the Lewis dot symbol for the atom is equal to the number of electrons lost when the atom forms a cation that is isoelectronic with the preceding noble gas. For nonmetals of the second period (B through F), the number of unpaired dots is the number of bonds the atom can form.

In addition to atoms, we can also represent atomic *ions* with Lewis dot symbols. To do so, we simply add (for anions) or subtract (for cations) the appropriate number of dots from the Lewis dot symbol of the *atom* and include the ion's charge.

Student Annotation: Remember that for two species to be *isoelectronic*, they must have exactly the same electron configuration [◄◄ Section 4.5].

Student Annotation: As we will see shortly [▶▶ Section 6.6], a larger nonmetal atom (one in the third period or beyond) can actually form as many bonds as the total number of dots in its Lewis dot symbol.

---

[1]Gilbert Newton Lewis (1875–1946). Lewis made many important contributions in the areas of chemical bonding, thermodynamics, acids and bases, and spectroscopy. Despite the significance of Lewis's work, he was never awarded a Nobel Prize.

Figure 5.1 Lewis dot symbols of the main group elements.

1A 1																	8A 18
·H	2A 2											3A 13	4A 14	5A 15	6A 16	7A 17	He:
·Li	·Be·											·B·	·C·	·N·	·O·	·F·	:Ne:
·Na	·Mg·	3B 3	4B 4	5B 5	6B 6	7B 7	—8B— 8	9	10	1B 11	2B 12	·Al·	·Si·	·P·	·S·	:Cl·	:Ar:
·K	·Ca·											·Ga·	·Ge·	·As·	·Se·	:Br·	:Kr:
·Rb	·Sr·											·In·	·Sn·	·Sb·	·Te·	·I·	:Xe:
·Cs	·Ba·											·Tl·	·Pb·	·Bi·	·Po·	:At·	:Rn:
·Fr	·Ra·																

Worked Example 5.1 shows how to use Lewis dot symbols to represent atomic ions.

Worked Example 5.1

Write Lewis dot symbols for (a) fluoride ion (F^-), (b) potassium ion (K^+), and (c) sulfide ion (S^{2-}).

Strategy Starting with the Lewis dot symbol for each element, add dots (for anions) or remove dots (for cations) as needed to achieve the correct charge on each ion. Don't forget to include the appropriate charge on the Lewis dot symbol.

Setup The Lewis dot symbols for F, K, and S are :F·, ·K, and ·S·, respectively.

Solution

(a) $\left[:\ddot{F}:\right]^-$

(b) K^+

(c) $\left[:\ddot{S}:\right]^{2-}$

> **Think About It**
> For ions that are isoelectronic with noble gases, cations should have no dots remaining around the element symbol, whereas anions should have eight dots around the element symbol. Note, too, that for anions, we put square brackets around the Lewis dot symbol and place the negative charge outside the brackets. Because the symbol for a common cation such as the potassium ion has no remaining dots, square brackets are not necessary.

Practice Problem A Write Lewis dot symbols for (a) Ca^{2+}, (b) N^{3-}, and (c) I^-.

Practice Problem B Indicate the charge on each of the ions represented by the following Lewis dot symbols: (a) $\left[:\ddot{O}:\right]^?$, (b) $H^?$, and (c) $\left[:\ddot{P}:\right]^?$.

SECTION 5.2 REVIEW

Lewis Dot Symbols

5.2.1   Using only a periodic table, determine the correct Lewis dot symbol for a silicon (Si) atom.

5.2.2   Using only a periodic table, determine the correct Lewis dot symbol for the bromide ion (Br^-).

5.2.3   To what group of the periodic table does element X belong if its Lewis dot symbol is ·X·?

5.2.4   Is it possible to determine the group number of a main group atom by looking at the Lewis dot symbol of its common ion? Explain.

5.3 IONIC COMPOUNDS AND BONDING

Recall from Chapter 4 that atoms of elements with low ionization energies, typically *metals,* tend to form *cations*; and those with high positive electron affinities, typically *non*metals, tend to form *anions.* When cations and anions are brought together, they can combine to form a compound.

When a compound consists of cations and anions, it is known as an ***ionic compound.*** Typically, ionic compounds consist of metal cations and nonmetal anions, held together by ***ionic bonding,*** which simply refers to the electrostatic attraction between oppositely charged particles. As an example, let us consider the ionic compound sodium chloride, known commonly as *salt.*

The electron configuration of sodium is $[Ne]3s^1$ and that of chlorine is $[Ne]3s^23p^5$. When sodium and chlorine atoms come into contact with each other, the valence electron of sodium is transferred to the chlorine atom. We can imagine these processes taking place separately and represent each process using Lewis dot symbols.

$$Na\cdot \longrightarrow Na^+ + e^-$$

$$:\ddot{C}l\cdot + e^- \longrightarrow \left[:\ddot{C}l:\right]^-$$

The sum of these two equations is

$$Na\cdot \; | \; :\ddot{C}l\cdot \longrightarrow Na^+ \; | \; \left[:\ddot{C}l:\right]^-$$

The electrostatic attraction, or *ionic bonding,* between the resulting cation (Na^+) and anion (Cl^-) draws them together to form the electrically neutral compound, sodium chloride, which we represent with the chemical formula NaCl. The ***chemical formula,*** or simply ***formula,*** of an ionic compound denotes the constituent elements of the compound and the ratio in which they combine. Sodium chloride, for example, consists of equal numbers of sodium ions and chloride ions. Note that although an ionic compound consists of oppositely charged ions, we do not show the charges on the ions in the chemical formula.

The structure of an ionic compound consists of a vast array of interspersed cations and anions called a ***lattice.*** For example, solid sodium chloride is a three-dimensional network of alternating cations and anions (Figure 5.2). As Figure 5.2 shows, no Na^+ ion in NaCl is associated with just one particular Cl^- ion. In fact, each Na^+ ion is surrounded by six Cl^- ions and vice versa. In other ionic compounds, the actual structure may be different, but the arrangement of cations and anions is such that the compounds are all electrically neutral.

The net energy change associated with the formation of Na^+ and Cl^- ions indicates that energy must be supplied in order for the overall transfer of an electron from Na to Cl to take place. The ionization of sodium requires the input of 496 kJ/mol, and the electron affinity of chlorine is 349 kJ/mol [◄◄ Section 4.4]. If the transfer of electrons *from* sodium and *to* chlorine were the only steps in the formation of NaCl, an input of $[496 + (-349)] = 147$ kJ of energy would be required

Student Annotation: Because the electron produced by ionization of the sodium atom is immediately added to the chlorine atom, it does not appear in the overall equation.

Student Annotation: A compound in which the ratio of combination is something other than 1:1 would indicate the ratio of combination with subscript numbers, as we will see shortly.

Student Annotation: Remember that the electron affinity, *EA*, is the energy *released* when a gaseous atom accepts an electron. A *positive EA* corresponds to a process that is energetically favorable. [◄◄ Section 4.4].

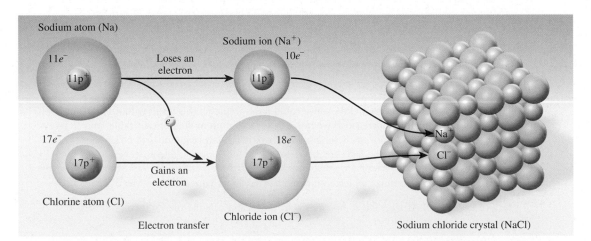

Figure 5.2 An electron is transferred from the sodium atom to the chlorine atom, giving a sodium ion and a chloride ion. The oppositely charged ions are attracted to each other and form a solid lattice.

Multi 5.1
Electron transfer between sodium
and chlorine

for the formation of one mole of NaCl. In reality, the formation of ionic compounds typically gives *off* energy—in many cases, a great deal of energy. In fact, the formation of ionic bonds *releases* a large amount of energy that more than compensates for the energy input required to transfer electrons from metal atoms to nonmetal atoms. We can quantify the energy change associated with the formation of ionic bonds with *lattice energy.*

Lattice energy is the amount of energy required to convert a mole of ionic solid to its constituent ions in the gas phase. For example, the lattice energy of sodium chloride is 788 kJ/mol. Thus, it takes 788 kJ of energy to convert one mole of NaCl(s) to one mole each of Na$^+$(g) and Cl$^-$(g). The magnitude of lattice energy is a measure of an ionic compound's stability. The greater the lattice energy, the more stable the compound. Table 5.1 lists the lattice energies for some ionic compounds.

Lattice energy depends on the magnitudes of the charges and on the distance between them. For example, LiI, NaI, and KI all have the same anion (I$^-$) and all have cations with the same charge (+1). The trend in their lattice energies (LiI > NaI > KI) can be explained on the basis of ionic radius. The radii of alkali metal ions increase as we move down a group in the periodic table ($r_{Li^+} < r_{Na^+} < r_{K^+}$) [◄◄ Section 4.6]. Knowing the radius of each ion, we can use Coulomb's law to compare the attractive forces between the ions in these three compounds as shown in Figure 5.3(a).

LiI, with the smallest distance between ions, has the strongest attractive forces. It should therefore have the largest lattice energy. KI, with the largest distance between ions, has the weakest attractive forces, and should have the smallest lattice energy. NaI has an intermediate distance between ions and should have an intermediate lattice energy. Thus, Coulomb's law correctly predicts the relative magnitudes of the lattice energies of LiI, NaI, and KI.

Now consider the compounds LiF, MgO, and ScN, shown in Figure 5.3(b). With similar distances between ions (0.76 + 1.33 = 2.09 Å for LiF; 0.72 + 1.40 = 2.12 Å for MgO; and 0.88 + 1.46 = 2.34 Å for ScN), we can see that the charges play a major role in determining the magnitude of lattice energy.

Worked Example 5.2 shows how to use ionic radii and Coulomb's law to compare lattice energies for ionic compounds.

Worked Example 5.2

Arrange MgO, CaO, and SrO in order of increasing lattice energy.

Strategy Consider the charges on the ions and the distances between them. Apply Coulomb's law to determine the relative lattice energies.

Setup MgO, CaO, and SrO all contain the same anion (O^{2-}) and all contain cations with the same charge (+2). In this case, then, the distance between ions will determine the relative lattice energies. Recall that lattice energy increases as the distance between ions decreases (because the force between oppositely charged particles increases as the distance between them decreases). Because all three compounds contain the same anion, we need only consider the radii of the cations when determining the distance between ions. From Figure 4.13, the ionic radii are 0.72 Å (Mg^{2+}), 1.00 Å (Ca^{2+}), and 1.18 Å (Sr^{2+}).

Solution MgO has the smallest distance between ions, whereas SrO has the largest distance between ions. Therefore, in order of increasing lattice energy: SrO < CaO < MgO.

Think About It
Mg, Ca, and Sr are all Group 2A metals, so we could have predicted this result without knowing their radii. Recall that ionic radii increase as we move down a column in the periodic table, and charges that are farther apart are more easily separated (meaning the lattice energy will be smaller). The lattice energies of SrO, CaO, and MgO are 3217, 3414, and 3890 kJ/mol, respectively.

Practice Problem A Determine which compound has the larger lattice energy: MgCl$_2$ or SrCl$_2$.

Practice Problem B Arrange the compounds NaF, MgO, and AlN in order of increasing lattice energy.

Compound	Lattice energy (kJ/mol)	Melting point (°C)
LiF	1017	845
LiCl	860	610
LiBr	787	550
LiI	732	450
NaCl	787	801
NaBr	736	750
NaI	686	662
KCl	699	772
KBr	689	735
KI	632	680
$MgCl_2$	2527	714
Na_2O	2570	Sub*
MgO	3890	2800
ScN	7547	> 3000

*Na_2O sublimes at 1275°C.

(a)

(b)

Figure 5.3 (a) As the distance between two oppositely charged ions increases, the attractive force between them is diminished and the lattice energy of the compound *decreases*. (b) As the magnitudes of charges increase, the attractive force between oppositely charged ions gets larger and lattice energy *increases*. Note that the effect of charge magnitude is more dramatic than that of distance between ions.

SECTION 5.3 REVIEW

Ionic Compounds and Bonding

5.3.1   How does the lattice energy of KF compare to that of LiF, KCl, and KI?

5.3.2   Lattice energies are graphed for three series of compounds in which the ion charges are $+2, -2; +2, -1$, and $+1, -1$. The ions in each series of compounds are separated by different distances. Identify the series.

5.4   NAMING IONS AND IONIC COMPOUNDS

When chemistry was a relatively new science, it was possible for practitioners to memorize the names of the relatively small number of known compounds. Often a compound's name was derived from its physical appearance, properties, origin, or application—for example, milk of magnesia, laughing gas, formic acid (*formica* is the Latin word for ant, and *formic acid* is the compound responsible for the sting of an ant bite), and baking soda.

Today there are many millions of known compounds, and many more being made every year, so it would be impossible to memorize all their names. Fortunately, it is unnecessary, because over the years chemists have devised a system for naming chemical substances. The rules are the same worldwide, facilitating communication among scientists and providing a useful way of labeling an overwhelming variety of substances. Mastering these rules now will benefit you tremendously as you progress through your chemistry course. You must be able to name a compound, given its chemical formula, and you must be able to write the chemical formula of a compound, given its name.

We begin our discussion of chemical *nomenclature* with monatomic ions [◄◄ Section 4.4]. What charges are possible for the monatomic ions of elements in Groups 1A through 7A? The cations that form from elements of Groups 1A, 2A, and 3A have charges equal to their respective group numbers. Most of the anions that form from elements of Groups 4A through 7A have charges equal to the corresponding group number minus 8. For example, the monatomic anion formed by oxygen (Group 6A) has a charge of $6 - 8 = -2$. You should be able to determine the charges on ions of elements in Groups 1A through 7A (for any element that forms only one common ion) using only a periodic table. Figure 4.12 (page 123) shows the charges of many of the monatomic ions from across the periodic table.

A monatomic cation is named simply by adding the word *ion* to the name of the element. Thus, the ion of potassium, K^+, is known as potassium ion. Similarly, the cations formed by the elements magnesium and aluminum (Mg^{2+} and Al^{3+}) are called magnesium ion and aluminum ion, respectively. It is not necessary for the name to specify the charge on these ions because their charges are equal to their group numbers

Certain metals, especially the *transition metals,* can form cations of more than one possible charge. Iron, for example, can form Fe^{2+} and Fe^{3+}. An older nomenclature system that is still in limited use assigns the ending *–ous* to the cation with the *smaller* positive charge and the ending *–ic* to the cation with the *greater* positive charge:

$$Fe^{2+}: \text{ferrous ion}$$

$$Fe^{3+}: \text{ferric ion}$$

This method of naming ions has some distinct limitations. First, the *–ous* and *–ic* suffixes indicate the *relative* charges of the two cations involved, not the *actual* charges. Thus, Fe^{3+} is the ferric ion, but Cu^{2+} is the cupric ion. In addition, the *–ous* and *–ic* endings make it possible to name only two cations with different charges. Some metals, such as manganese (Mn), can form cations with three or more different charges.

Therefore, it has become increasingly common to designate different cations with Roman numerals, using the Stock system.[2] In this system, the Roman numeral I indicates a positive charge of one, II means a positive charge of two, and so on, as shown for manganese:

$$Mn^{2+}: \text{manganese(II) ion}$$

$$Mn^{3+}: \text{manganese(III) ion}$$

$$Mn^{4+}: \text{manganese(IV) ion}$$

These names are pronounced "manganese-two ion," "manganese-three ion," and "manganese-four ion," respectively. Using the Stock system, the ferrous and ferric ions are iron(II) and iron(III), respectively. To avoid confusion, and in keeping with modern practice, we will use the Stock system to name compounds in this textbook.

A monatomic anion is named by changing the ending of the element's name to *–ide,* and adding the word *ion.* Thus, the anion of chlorine, Cl^-, is called *chloride ion.* The anions of carbon, nitrogen, and oxygen (C^{4-}, N^{3-}, and O^{2-}) are called *carbide, nitride,* and *oxide.* Because there is only one possible charge for an ion formed from a nonmetal, it is unnecessary for the ion's name to specify its charge. The common anions formed by nonmetal elements are shown in Figure 4.12. Table 5.2 lists alphabetically a number of common monatomic ions.

Formulas of Ionic Compounds

As we have seen, the formulas of ionic compounds give the ratio of combination of ions—generally in the smallest possible whole numbers. In order for ionic compounds to be electrically neutral, the sum of the charges on the cation and anion in the formula must be zero. When the charges on the cation and anion are numerically equal, it is easy to see that they will combine in a 1:1 ratio, as in the case of sodium chloride (NaCl). If the charges on the cations and anions are numerically different, you can apply the following guideline to make the formula electrically neutral (and thus obtain the simplest formula): Write a subscript for the cation that is numerically equal to the charge on the anion and a subscript for the anion that is numerically equal to the charge on the cation. Let's consider some examples.

Potassium Bromide The potassium ion (K^+) and the bromide ion (Br^-) combine to form the ionic compound *potassium bromide.* The sum of the charges is $1 + (-1) = 0$, so no subscripts are necessary. The formula is KBr.

Zinc Iodide The zinc ion (Zn^{2+}) and the iodide ion (I^-) combine to form *zinc iodide.* The sum of the charges of one Zn^{2+} ion and one I^- ion is $+2 + (-1) = +1$. To make the charges add up to zero, we multiply the -1 charge of the anion by 2 and add the subscript "2" to the symbol for iodine. Thus, the formula for zinc iodide is ZnI_2.

Aluminum Oxide The cation is Al^{3+} and the anion is O^{2-}. The following diagram can be used to determine the subscripts for this compound:

The sum of the charges for aluminum oxide is $2(+3) + 3(-2) = 0$. Thus, the formula is Al_2O_3.

TABLE 5.2	Names and Formulas of Some Common Monatomic Ions

Name	Formula
Cations	
aluminum	Al^{3+}
barium	Ba^{2+}
cadmium	Cd^{2+}
calcium	Ca^{2+}
cesium	Cs^+
chromium(III)	Cr^{3+}
cobalt(II)	Co^{2+}
copper(I)	Cu^+
copper(II)	Cu^{2+}
hydrogen	H^+
iron(II)	Fe^{2+}
iron(III)	Fe^{3+}
lead(II)	Pb^{2+}
lithium	Li^+
magnesium	Mg^{2+}
manganese(II)	Mn^{2+}
mercury(II)	Hg^{2+}
potassium	K^+
silver	Ag^+
sodium	Na^+
strontium	Sr^{2+}
tin(II)	Sn^{2+}
zinc	Zn^{2+}
Anions	
bromide	Br^-
chloride	Cl^-
fluoride	F^-
hydride	H^-
iodide	I^-
nitride	N^{3-}
oxide	O^{2-}
sulfide	S^{2-}

[2]Alfred E. Stock (1876–1946). German chemist, Stock did most of his research in the synthesis and characterization of boron, beryllium, and silicon compounds. He was a pioneer in the study of mercury poisoning.

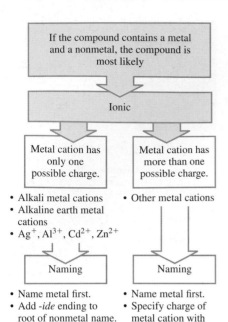

Figure 5.4 Flowchart for naming binary ionic compounds.

Naming Ionic Compounds

Most ionic compounds are **binary** ionic compounds, substances that consist of just two different ions derived from two different elements—one *metal* and one *nonmetal*. An ionic compound is named using the name of the cation followed by the name of the anion, eliminating the word *ion* from each. Several examples were given in the Formulas of Ionic Compounds section. Other examples are sodium bromide (NaBr), calcium fluoride (CaF_2), lithium nitride (Li_3N), and sodium sulfide (Na_2S).

In cases where a metal cation may have more than one possible charge, recall that the charge is indicated in the name of the ion with a Roman numeral in parentheses. Thus, the compounds $FeCl_2$ and $FeCl_3$ are named *iron(II) chloride* and *iron(III) chloride,* respectively. (These are pronounced "iron-two chloride" and "iron-three chloride.") Figure 5.4 summarizes the steps for identifying and naming ionic compounds.

Worked Examples 5.3 and 5.4 illustrate how to name ionic compounds and write formulas for ionic compounds based on the information given in Figure 5.4 and Table 5.2.

Worked Example 5.3

Name the following ionic compounds: (a) CaO, (b) Mg_3N_2, and (c) Fe_2S_3.

Strategy Begin by identifying the cation and the anion in each compound, and then combine the names for each, eliminating the word *ion*.

Setup CaO contains Ca^{2+} and O^{2-}, the calcium ion and the oxide ion; Mg_3N_2 contains Mg^{2+} and N^{3-}, the magnesium ion and the nitride ion; and $FeCl_2$ contains Fe^{2+} and Cl^-, the barium ion and the chloride ion. We know that the iron in Fe_2S_3 is Fe^{3+} because it combines with the S^{2-} ion in a 2:3 ratio to give a neutral formula.

Solution (a) Combining the cation and anion names, and eliminating the word *ion* from each of the individual ions' names, we get *calcium oxide* as the name of CaO; (b) Mg_3N_2 is *magnesium nitride;* and (c) Fe_2S_3 is *iron(III) sulfide.*

> **Think About It**
> Be careful not to confuse the subscript in a formula with the charge on the metal ion. In part (c), for example, the subscript on Fe is 2, but this is an iron(III) compound.

Practice Problem A Name the following ionic compounds: (a) BaS, (b) Cu_2S, (c) $CrCl_3$.

Practice Problem B Name the following ionic compounds: (a) $AlBr_3$, (b) Rb_2Se, (c) Cu_3N_2.

Worked Example 5.4

Deduce the formulas of the following ionic compounds: (a) mercury(II) chloride, (b) lead(II) bromide, and (c) potassium nitride.

Strategy Identify the ions in each compound, and determine their ratios of combination using the charges on the cation and anion in each.

Setup (a) Mercury(II) chloride is a combination of Hg^{2+} and Cl^-. In order to produce a neutral compound, these two ions must combine in a 1:2 ratio. (b) Lead(II) bromide is a combination of Pb^{2+} and Br^-. These ions also combine in a 1:2 ratio. (c) Potassium nitride is a combination of K^+ and N^{3-}. These ions combine in a 3:1 ratio.

Solution The formulas are (a) $HgCl_2$, (b) $PbBr_2$, and (c) K_3N.

> **Think About It**
> Make sure that the charges sum to zero in each compound formula. In part (a), for example, $Hg^{2+} + 2Cl^- = (+2) + 2(-1) = 0$; in part (b), $(+2) + 2(-1) = 0$; and in part (c), $3(+1) + (-3) = 0$.

Practice Problem A Deduce the formulas of the following ionic compounds: (a) lead(II) chloride, (b) cobalt(III) oxide, and (c) sodium selenide.

Practice Problem B Deduce the formulas of the following ionic compounds: (a) iron(III) sulfide, (b) mercury(II) iodide, and (c) potassium sulfide.

SECTION 5.4 REVIEW

Naming Ions and Ionic Compounds

5.4.1   What is the correct name of the compound PbS?

5.4.2   What is the correct formula for the compound iron(III) nitride?

5.4.3   What is the correct formula for sodium nitride?

5.4.4   What is the correct name for the compound $ZnBr_2$?

5.5   COVALENT BONDING AND MOLECULES

We learned in Section 5.4 that ionic compounds tend to form between metals and nonmetals when electrons are transferred from an element with a low ionization energy (the metal) to one with a high electron affinity (the nonmetal). When compounds form between elements with more similar properties, electrons are not transferred from one element to another but instead are *shared* in order to give each atom a noble gas electron configuration. It was Gilbert Lewis who first suggested that a chemical bond involves atoms sharing electrons, and this approach is known as the ***Lewis theory of bonding.***

Lewis theory depicts the formation of the bond in H_2 as

$$H\cdot \ + \cdot H \ \longrightarrow \ H{:}H$$

In essence, two H atoms move close enough to each other to *share* the electron pair. Although there are still two atoms and just two electrons, this arrangement allows each H atom to "count" both electrons as its own and to "feel" as though it has the noble gas electron configuration of helium. This type of arrangement, where two atoms share a pair of electrons, is known as ***covalent bonding,*** and the shared pair of electrons constitutes the ***covalent bond.*** In a covalent bond, each electron in a shared pair is attracted to the nuclei of both atoms. It is this attraction that holds the two atoms together.

> **Student Annotation:** For the sake of simplicity, the shared pair of electrons can be represented by a dash, rather than by two dots: H—H.

Molecules

The formation of a covalent bond between two H atoms produces a species known as a *molecule.* A ***molecule*** is a neutral combination of at least two atoms in a specific arrangement held together by chemical forces (also called *chemical bonds*). A molecule may contain two or more atoms of a single element, or it may contain atoms of two or more elements joined in a fixed ratio.

Thus, a molecule can be of an *element* or it can be of a *compound,* which, by definition, is made up of two or more elements. This definition stems from Dalton's atomic theory, which we first encountered in Chapter 2. Dalton's theory actually consisted of three hypotheses, the first of which was that matter is composed of atoms [◄◄ Section 2.1]. The second hypothesis was that *compounds* are composed of atoms of more than one element; and in any given compound, the same types of atoms are always present in the same relative numbers. Hydrogen gas, for example, is an element, but it consists of molecules, each of which is made up of two H atoms. Water, on the other hand, is a *compound* that consists of molecules, each of which always contains two H atoms and one O atom. We will revisit Dalton's theory and learn about his third hypothesis when we discuss chemical reactions [►► Chapter 8].

Dalton's second hypothesis suggests that, in order to form a certain compound, we need not only atoms of the right *kinds* of elements, but specific *numbers* of these atoms as well. This idea is an extension of a law published in 1799 by Joseph Proust, a French chemist. According to Proust's ***law of definite proportions,*** different samples of a given compound always contain the same elements in the same mass *ratio*. Thus, if we were to analyze samples of carbon dioxide gas obtained from different sources, such as the exhaust from a car in Mexico City or the air above a pine forest in northern Maine, each sample would contain the same ratio by mass of oxygen to

$$\frac{\text{O to C ratio in CO}_2}{\text{O to C ratio in CO}}$$

Figure 5.5 An illustration of the law of multiple proportions.

carbon. Consider the following results of the analysis of three samples of carbon dioxide, each from a different source:

Sample	Mass of O (g)	Mass of C (g)	Ratio (g O : g C)
123 g carbon dioxide	89.4	33.6	2.66:1
50.5 g carbon dioxide	36.7	13.8	2.66:1
88.6 g carbon dioxide	64.4	24.2	2.66:1

In any sample of pure carbon dioxide, there are 2.66 g of oxygen for every gram of carbon present. This constant mass ratio can be explained by assuming that the elements exist in tiny particles of fixed mass (atoms), and that compounds are formed by the combination of fixed numbers of each type of particle.

Dalton's second hypothesis also supports the ***law of multiple proportions.*** According to this law, if two elements can combine with each other to form two or more *different* compounds, the ratio of masses of one element that combine with a fixed mass of the other element can be expressed in small whole numbers. For example, carbon combines with oxygen to form two different compounds: carbon dioxide and carbon monoxide. In any sample of pure carbon monoxide, there are 1.33 g oxygen for every gram of carbon.

Sample	Mass of O (g)	Mass of C (g)	Ratio (g O : g C)
16.3 g carbon monoxide	9.31	6.99	1.33:1
25.9 g carbon monoxide	14.8	11.1	1.33:1
88.4 g carbon monoxide	50.5	37.9	1.33:1

Thus, the mass ratio of oxygen to carbon in carbon *di*oxide is 2.66; and the ratio of oxygen to carbon in carbon *mon*oxide is 1.33. According to the law of multiple proportions, the *ratio* of two such *mass ratios* can be expressed as small whole numbers.

$$\frac{\text{mass ratio of O to C in carbon dioxide}}{\text{mass ratio of O to C in carbon monoxide}} = \frac{2.66}{1.33} = 2{:}1$$

Homonuclear diatomic

Heteronuclear diatomic

Polyatomic

For samples containing equal masses of carbon, the mass ratio of oxygen in carbon dioxide to oxygen in carbon monoxide is 2:1. Modern measurement techniques indicate that one atom of carbon combines with two atoms of oxygen in carbon dioxide and with one atom of oxygen in carbon monoxide. This result is consistent with the law of multiple proportions (Figure 5.5).

The hydrogen molecule, symbolized as H_2, is called a ***diatomic molecule*** because it contains *two* atoms. Other elements that normally exist as diatomic molecules are nitrogen (N_2), oxygen (O_2), and the Group 7A elements—fluorine (F_2), chlorine (Cl_2), bromine (Br_2), and iodine (I_2). These are known as ***homonuclear*** diatomic molecules because both atoms in each molecule are of the same element. A diatomic molecule can also contain atoms of different elements. Examples of these ***heteronuclear*** diatomic molecules include hydrogen chloride (HCl) and carbon monoxide (CO).

Most molecules contain more than two atoms. They can all be atoms of the same element, as in ozone (O_3) and white phosphorus (P_4), or they can be combinations of two or more different elements, as in water (H_2O) and methane (CH_4). Molecules containing more than two atoms are called ***polyatomic molecules.***

TABLE 5.3	Colors of Elements Commonly Used in Molecular Art

Hydrogen	○	Sodium	●
Boron	○	Phosphorus	●
Carbon	●	Sulfur	○
Nitrogen	●	Chlorine	●
Oxygen	●	Bromine	●
Fluorine	○	Iodine	●

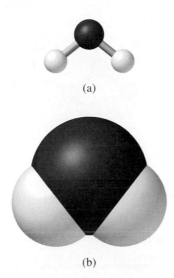

(a)

(b)

Figure 5.6 Water represented with a (a) ball-and-stick model, and (b) space-filling model.

Molecules are far too small for us to observe them directly. An effective means of visualizing them is by the use of molecular models. Throughout this book, we will represent matter at the molecular level using *molecular art,* the two-dimensional equivalent of molecular models. In these pictures, atoms are represented as spheres, and atoms of particular elements are represented using specific colors. Table 5.3 lists some of the elements that you will encounter most often and the colors used to represent them in this book. Molecular art can be of *ball-and-stick* models, in which the bonds connecting atoms appear as sticks [Figure 5.6(a)], or of *space-filling* models, in which the atoms appear to overlap one another [Figure 5.6(b)]. Ball-and-stick and space-filling models illustrate the specific, three-dimensional arrangement of the atoms. The ball-and-stick models generally do a good job of illustrating the arrangement of atoms, but they exaggerate the distances between atoms, relative to their sizes. By contrast, the space-filling models give a more accurate picture of the interatomic distances but can sometimes obscure the details of the three-dimensional arrangement.

Molecular Formulas

A *chemical formula* [◄◄ Section 5.3] can be used to denote the composition of any substance—ionic or molecular. A ***molecular formula*** shows the exact number of atoms of each element in a *molecule*. In our discussion of molecules, each example was given with its molecular formula in parentheses. Thus, H_2 is the molecular formula for hydrogen, O_2 is that for oxygen, O_3 is that for ozone, and H_2O is that of water. The subscript number indicates the number of atoms of an element present in the molecule. There is no subscript for O in H_2O because there is only one oxygen atom in a molecule of water. The number "one" is never used as a subscript in a chemical formula. Oxygen (O_2) and ozone (O_3) are allotropes of oxygen. An ***allotrope*** is one of two or more distinct forms of an element. Two of the allotropic forms of the element carbon—diamond and graphite—have dramatically different properties (and *prices*).

We can also represent molecules with *structural formulas*. The ***structural formula*** shows not only the elemental composition, but also the general arrangement of atoms within the molecule. In the case of water, each of the hydrogen atoms is connected to the oxygen atom. Thus, water can be represented with the structural formula HOH.

In Chapter 6, you will learn how to use the molecular formula to deduce the structural formula and the three-dimensional arrangement of atoms in a molecule. We will use all of these methods for representing molecules throughout the book, so you should be familiar with each method and with the information it provides. Worked Example 5.5 shows how to write a molecular formula from the corresponding molecular model.

Worked Example 5.5

Write the molecular formula of ethanol based on its ball-and-stick model, shown here.

Ethanol

Strategy Refer to the labels on the atoms (or see Table 5.3).

Setup There are *two* carbon atoms, *six* hydrogen atoms, and *one* oxygen atom, so the subscript on C will be 2 and the subscript on H will be 6, and there will be no subscript on O.

Solution C_2H_6O

Think About It
Often the molecular formula for a compound such as ethanol (consisting of carbon, hydrogen, and oxygen) is written so that the formula more closely resembles the actual arrangement of atoms in the molecule. Thus, the molecular formula for ethanol is commonly written as C_2H_5OH.

Practice Problem A Chloroform was used as an anesthetic for childbirth and surgery during the nineteenth century. Write the molecular formulas for (a) chloroform, and (b) acetone based on the molecular model shown below.

Chloroform   Acetone

Practice Problem B Draw (a) a space-filling molecular model of carbon disulfide (CS_2), and (b) a ball-and-stick molecular model for xenon tetrafluoride (XeF_4).

Student Annotation: Note that acetone contains a double bond between the oxygen atom and one of the carbon atoms. Multiple bonds between atoms will be discussed in Chapter 6.

Empirical Formulas

Student Annotation: The formulas of ionic compounds are usually *empirical* formulas.

In addition to the methods we have learned so far, molecular substances can also be represented using ***empirical formulas.*** The word *empirical* means "from experience" or, in the context of chemical formulas, "from experiment." The empirical formula tells what elements are present in a molecule and in what whole-number ratio they are combined. For example, the molecular formula of hydrogen peroxide is H_2O_2, but its empirical formula is simply HO. Hydrazine, which has been used as a rocket fuel, has the molecular formula N_2H_4, so its empirical formula is NH_2. Although the ratio of nitrogen to hydrogen is 1:2 in

TABLE 5.4	Molecular and Empirical Formulas			
Compound	**Molecular formula**	**Model**	**Empirical formula**	**Molecular model**
Water	H_2O		H_2O	
Hydrogen peroxide	H_2O_2		HO	
Ethane	C_2H_6		CH_3	
Propane	C_3H_8		C_3H_8	
Acetylene	C_2H_2		CH	
Benzene	C_6H_6		CH	

both the molecular formula (N_2H_4) and the empirical formula (NH_2), only the molecular formula tells us the actual number of N atoms (two) and H atoms (four) present in a hydrazine molecule

In many cases, the empirical and molecular formulas are identical. In the case of water, for example, there is no combination of smaller whole numbers that can convey the ratio of two H atoms for every one O atom, so the empirical formula is the same as the molecular formula: H_2O. Table 5.4 lists the molecular and empirical formulas for several compounds and shows molecular models for each.

Empirical formulas are the *simplest* chemical formulas; they are written by reducing the subscripts in molecular formulas to the smallest possible whole numbers (without altering the relative numbers of atoms). Molecular formulas are the *true* formulas of molecules. As we will see in Chapter 8, when chemists analyze an unknown compound, the first step is usually the determination of the compound's empirical formula. Worked Example 5.6 lets you practice determining empirical formulas from molecular formulas

Worked Example 5.6

Write the empirical formulas for the following molecules: (a) glucose ($C_6H_{12}O_6$), a substance known as blood sugar; (b) adenine ($C_5H_5N_5$), also known as vitamin B_4; and (c) nitrous oxide (N_2O), a gas that is used as an anesthetic ("laughing gas") and as an aerosol propellant for whipped cream.

Strategy To write the empirical formula, the subscripts in the molecular formula must be reduced to the smallest possible whole numbers (without altering the relative numbers of atoms).

(Continued on next page)

Setup The molecular formulas in parts (a) and (b) each contain subscripts that are divisible by common numbers. Therefore, we will be able to express the formulas with smaller whole numbers than those in the molecular formulas. In part (c), the molecule has only one O atom, so it is impossible to simplify this formula further.

Solution

(a) Dividing each of the subscripts in the molecular formula for glucose by 6, we obtain the empirical formula CH_2O. If we had divided the subscripts by 2 or 3, we would have obtained the formulas $C_3H_6O_3$ and $C_2H_4O_2$, respectively. Although the ratio of carbon to hydrogen to oxygen atoms in each of these formulas is correct (1:2:1), neither is the simplest formula because the subscripts are not in the smallest possible whole-number ratio.

(b) Dividing each subscript in the molecular formula of adenine by 5, we get the empirical formula CHN.

(c) Because the subscripts in the formula for nitrous oxide are already the smallest possible whole numbers, its empirical formula is the same as its molecular formula N_2O.

> **Think About It**
> Make sure that the *ratio* in each empirical formula is the same as that in the corresponding molecular formula and that the subscripts are the smallest possible whole numbers. In part (a), for example, the ratio of C:H:O in the molecular formula is 6:12:6, which is equal to 1:2:1, the ratio expressed in the empirical formula.

Practice Problem A Write empirical formulas for the following molecules: (a) caffeine ($C_8H_{10}N_4O_2$), a stimulant found in tea and coffee; (b) butane (C_4H_{10}), used in cigarette lighters; and (c) glycine ($C_2H_5NO_2$), an amino acid.

Caffeine   Butane   Glycine

Practice Problem B For which of the following molecular formulas is the formula shown in parentheses the correct empirical formula? (a) $C_{12}H_{22}O_{12}$ ($C_6H_{11}O_6$), (b) $C_8H_{12}O_4$ ($C_4H_6O_2$), (c) Na_2O_2 (Na_2O).

SECTION 5.5 REVIEW

Covalent Bonding and Molecules

5.5.1   What is the correct formula for the compound carbon tetrachloride?

5.5.2   Give the correct molecular formula and the correct empirical formula for the compound shown.

5.6   NAMING MOLECULAR COMPOUNDS

The nomenclature of molecular compounds follows in a similar manner to that of ionic compounds. Most molecular compounds are composed of two nonmetals (see Figure 2.9, page 49). In order to name such a compound, we first name the element that appears first in the formula. For HCl that would be hydrogen. We then name the second element, changing the ending of its name to −*ide*. For HCl, the second element is chlorine, so we would change chlorine to chloride. Thus, the systematic name of HCl is *hydrogen chloride*. Similarly, HI is hydrogen iodide (iod*ine* ⟶ iod*ide*) and SiC is silicon carbide (carb*on* ⟶ carb*ide*).

> **Student Annotation:** Recall that compounds composed of two elements are called *binary* compounds.

Specifying Numbers of Atoms

It is quite common for one pair of elements to form several different binary molecular compounds. In these cases, confusion in naming the compounds is avoided by the use of Greek prefixes to denote the number of atoms of each element present. Some of the Greek prefixes are listed in Table 5.5, and several compounds named using prefixes are listed in Table 5.6.

TABLE 5.5	Greek Prefixes		
Prefix	**Meaning**	**Prefix**	**Meaning**
Mono–	1	Hexa–	6
Di–	2	Hepta–	7
Tri–	3	Octa–	8
Tetra–	4	Nona–	9
Penta–	5	Deca–	10

TABLE 5.6	Some Compounds Named Using Greek Prefixes		
Compound	**Name**	**Compound**	**Name**
CO	Carbon monoxide	SO_3	Sulfur trioxide
CO_2	Carbon dioxide	NO_2	Nitrogen dioxide
SO_2	Sulfur dioxide	N_2O_5	Dinitrogen pentoxide

The prefix *mono–* is generally omitted for the first element. SO_2, for example, is named *sulfur dioxide,* not *monosulfur dioxide.* Thus, the absence of a prefix for the first element usually means there is only one atom of that element present in the molecule. In addition, for ease of pronunciation, we usually eliminate the last letter of a prefix that ends in "o" or "a" when naming an oxide. Thus, N_2O_5 is *dinitrogen pentoxide,* rather than *dinitrogen pentaoxide.* Worked Example 5.7 gives you some practice naming binary molecular compounds from their formulas.

Worked Example 5.7

Name the following binary molecular compounds: (a) NF_3 and (b) N_2O_4.

Strategy Each compound will be named using the systematic nomenclature including, where necessary, appropriate Greek prefixes.

(Continued on next page)

Setup With binary compounds, we start with the name of the element that appears *first* in the formula, and we change the ending of the *second* element's name to *–ide*. We use prefixes, where appropriate, to indicate the number of atoms of each element. In part (a), the molecule contains one nitrogen atom and three fluorine atoms. We will omit the prefix *mono–* for nitrogen because it is the first element listed in the formula, and we will use the prefix *tri–* to denote the number of fluorine atoms. In part (b), the molecule contains two nitrogen atoms and four oxygen atoms, so we will use the prefixes *di–* and *tetra–* in naming the compound. Recall that in naming an oxide, we omit the last letter of a prefix that ends in "a" or "o."

Solution (a) nitrogen trifluoride and (b) dinitrogen tetroxide

> **Think About It**
> Make sure that the prefixes match the subscripts in the molecular formulas and that the word *oxide* is not preceded immediately by an "a" or an "o."

Practice Problem A Name the following binary molecular compounds: (a) Cl_2O and (b) $SiCl_4$.

Practice Problem B Name the following binary molecular compounds:

Writing the formula for a molecular compound, given its systematic name, is usually straightforward. For instance, the name *phosphorus pentachloride* indicates the presence of one phosphorus atom (no prefix) and five chlorine atoms (penta–), so the corresponding molecular formula is PCl_5. Note once again that the order of the elements is the same in both the name and the formula. Worked Example 5.8 gives you some practice determining the formulas of binary molecular compounds from their names.

Worked Example 5.8

Write the chemical formulas for the following binary molecular compounds: (a) sulfur tetrafluoride and (b) tetraphosphorus decasulfide.

Strategy The formula for each compound will be deduced using the systematic nomenclature guidelines.

Setup In part (a), there is no prefix for sulfur, so there is only one sulfur atom in a molecule of the compound. Therefore, we will use no prefix for the S in the formula. The prefix *tetra–* means that there are four fluorine atoms. In part (b), the prefixes *tetra–* and *deca–* denote four and ten, respectively.

Solution (a) SF_4 and (b) P_4S_{10}

> **Think About It**
> Double-check that the subscripts in the formulas match the prefixes in the compound names:
> (a) 4 = tetra and (b) 4 = tetra and 10 = deca.

Practice Problem A Give the molecular formula for each of the following compounds: (a) carbon disulfide and (b) dinitrogen trioxide.

Practice Problem B Give the molecular formula for each of the following compounds: (a) sulfur trioxide and (b) disulfur decafluoride.

There is another group of substances for which we can use Greek prefixes to denote numbers of atoms. It includes such compounds as $SnCl_4$ and $PbCl_4$, which each consist of a metal and a nonmetal—but in which the apparent charge on the metal is unusually high. For example, knowing that Cl forms the chloride ion (Cl^-), we would deduce a charge of +4 on Sn in $SnCl_4$. Given that a great deal of energy would be required to remove four electrons from a tin atom [◄◄ Section 4.4], it seems unlikely that a compound containing a metal with such a high "apparent charge" is actually ionic. In fact, the bonding in $SnCl_4$ is covalent, rather than ionic. Part of the evidence of covalent bonding is that $SnCl_4$ is a liquid at room temperature. (Ionic compounds typically are solids at room temperature.) Although such compounds consist of a metal and a nonmetal but are not truly ionic in nature, we can use either the ionic or the molecular system of nomenclature for binary compounds. Thus, $SnCl_4$ can be named either tin(IV) chloride or tin tetrachloride.

Student Annotation: The concept of "apparent charge" or *oxidation state* [►► Section 9.4] will be discussed in detail in Chapter 9.

Compounds Containing Hydrogen

The names of molecular compounds containing hydrogen do not usually conform to the systematic nomenclature guidelines. Traditionally, many of these compounds are called either by their common, nonsystematic names or by names that do not indicate explicitly the number of H atoms present:

B_2H_6	Diborane	PH_3	Phosphine
SiH_4	Silane	H_2O	Water
NH_3	Ammonia	H_2S	Hydrogen sulfide

Student Annotation: Binary compounds containing carbon and hydrogen are *organic* compounds and do not follow the same naming conventions as other molecular compounds. Organic compounds and their nomenclature are discussed in detail in Chapter 24.

Even the order in which the elements are written in these hydrogen-containing compounds is irregular. In water and hydrogen sulfide, H is written first, whereas it is written last in the other compounds.

Acids make up another important class of molecular compounds that contain hydrogen. One definition of an **acid** is a substance that produces hydrogen ions (H^+) when dissolved in water. Several binary molecular compounds produce hydrogen ions when dissolved in water and are, therefore, acids. In these cases, two different names can be assigned to the same chemical formula. For example, HCl, *hydrogen chloride,* is a gaseous compound. When it is dissolved in water, however, we call it *hydrochloric acid.* The rules for naming binary acids such as these are as follows: remove the *–gen* ending from hydrogen (leaving *hydro–*), change the *–ide* ending on the second element to *–ic,* combine the two words, and add the word *acid.*

Student Annotation: In Chapter 16 we will explore acids and bases in greater detail; and we will see that there are other ways to define the terms *acid* and *base.*

hydrogen (− *gen*) becomes hydro

+

chloride (− *ide*, + *ic*) becomes chloric

+

acid ⟶ hydrochloric acid

Likewise, hydrogen fluoride (HF) becomes *hydrofluoric acid.* Table 5.7 lists these and other examples.

In order for a compound to produce hydrogen ions upon dissolving, it must contain at least one **ionizable hydrogen atom.** An ionizable hydrogen atom is one that separates from the molecule upon dissolving and becomes a hydrogen ion, H^+.

TABLE 5.7	Some Simple Acids	
Formula	**Binary compound name**	**Acid name**
HF	Hydrogen fluoride	Hydrofluoric acid
HCl	Hydrogen chloride	Hydrochloric acid
HBr	Hydrogen bromide	Hydrobromic acid
HI	Hydrogen iodide	Hydroiodic acid
HCN*	Hydrogen cyanide	Hydrocyanic acid

*Although HCN is not a *binary* compound, it is included in this table because it is similar chemically to HF, HCl, HBr, and HI.

Organic Compounds

So far our discussion of nomenclature has focused on *inorganic compounds,* which are generally defined as compounds that do not contain carbon. Another important class of molecular substances is *organic* compounds, which have their own system of nomenclature. *Organic compounds* contain carbon and hydrogen, sometimes in combination with other elements such as oxygen, nitrogen, sulfur, and the halogens. The simplest organic compounds are those that contain only carbon and hydrogen and are known as *hydrocarbons.* Among hydrocarbons, the simplest examples are compounds known as *alkanes.* The name of an alkane depends on the number of carbon atoms in the molecule. Table 5.8 gives the molecular formulas, systematic names of some of the simplest alkanes, and ball-and-stick models.

TABLE 5.8	Formulas, Names, and Models of Some Simple Alkanes	
Formula	**Name**	**Molecular model**
CH_4	Methane	
C_2H_6	Ethane	
C_3H_8	Propane	
C_4H_{10}	Butane	
C_5H_{12}	Pentane	
C_6H_{14}	Hexane	
C_7H_{16}	Heptane	
C_8H_{18}	Octane	
C_9H_{20}	Nonane	
$C_{10}H_{22}$	Decane	

Thinking Outside the Box

Functional Groups

Many organic compounds are derivatives of alkanes in which one of the H atoms has been replaced by a group of atoms known as a **functional group.** The functional group determines many of the chemical properties of a compound because it typically is where a chemical reaction *occurs.* Table 5.9 lists the names and provides ball-and-stick models of several important functional groups.

Ethanol, for example, the alcohol in alcoholic beverages, is ethane (C_2H_6) with one of the hydrogen atoms replaced by an alcohol (—OH) group. Its name is derived from that of *ethane,* indicating that it contains *two* carbon atoms.

Ethanol

The molecular formula of ethanol can also be written C_2H_6O, but C_2H_5OH conveys more information about the structure of the molecule. Organic compounds and several functional groups are discussed in greater detail in Chapter 24.

TABLE 5.9	Organic Functional Groups	
Name	**Functional group**	**Molecular model**
Alcohol	—OH	
Aldehyde	—CHO	
Carboxylic acid	—COOH	
Amine	—NH$_2$	

SECTION 5.6 REVIEW

Naming Molecular Compounds

5.6.1   What is the correct systematic name of SF$_6$?

5.6.2   What is the correct systematic name of P$_2$I$_4$?

5.6.3   What is the correct systematic name of BrO_2?

5.6.4   What is the name of the compound shown?

5.7   COVALENT BONDING IN IONIC SPECIES

So far, the compounds we have encountered have been either *ionic,* held together by ionic bonding; or *molecular,* held together by covalent bonding; and the ions we have encountered have all been *monatomic* ions. However, many common ionic substances contain *poly*atomic ions, which are held together by covalent bonding. Moreover, some ionic substances, known as *hydrates,* actually contain water molecules within their formulas. In this section, we examine the chemical species that are held together by a combination of ionic and covalent bonding.

Polyatomic Ions

Ions that consist of a combination of two or more atoms are called ***polyatomic ions.*** Because these ions are commonly encountered in general chemistry, you must know the names, formulas, and charges of the polyatomic ions listed in Table 5.10. Although most of the common polyatomic ions are anions, a few are cations. For compounds containing polyatomic ions, formulas are determined following the same rule as for ionic compounds containing only monatomic ions: ions must be combined in a ratio that gives a neutral formula overall. The following examples illustrate how this is done.

> **Ammonium Chloride** The cation is NH_4^+ and the anion is Cl^-. The sum of the charges is $1 + (-1) = 0$, so the ions combine in a 1:1 ratio and the resulting formula is NH_4Cl.
> **Calcium Phosphate** The cation is Ca^{2+} and the anion is PO_4^{3-}. The following diagram can be used to determine the subscripts:

The sum of the charges is $3(+2) + 2(-3) = 0$. Thus, the formula for calcium phosphate is $Ca_3(PO_4)_2$. When we add a subscript to a polyatomic ion, we must first put parentheses around the ion's formula to indicate that the subscript applies to *all* the atoms in the polyatomic ion. Other examples are sodium cyanide (NaCN), potassium permanganate ($KMnO_4$), and ammonium sulfate [$(NH_4)_2SO_4$].

Unlike the naming of *molecular* compounds, the naming of ionic compounds does not require the use of Greek prefixes. For example, Li_2CO_3 is lithium carbonate, not dilithium carbonate, even though there are two lithium ions for every one carbonate ion. Prefixes are unnecessary because each of the ions has a specific, *known* charge. Lithium ion always has a charge of $+1$, and carbonate ion always has a charge of -2. The only ratio in which they *can* combine to form a neutral compound is two Li^+ ions for every one CO_3^{2-} ion. Therefore, the name *lithium carbonate* is sufficient to convey the compound's empirical formula.

Worked Example 5.9 lets you practice naming compounds that contain polyatomic ions.

TABLE 5.10	Common Polyatomic Ions

Name	Formula/Charge
Cations	
ammonium	NH_4^+
hydronium	H_3O^+
mercury(I)	Hg_2^{2+}
Anions	
acetate	$C_2H_3O_2^-$
azide	N_3^-
carbonate	CO_3^{2-}
chlorate	ClO_3^-
chlorite	ClO_2^-
chromate	CrO_4^{2-}
cyanide	CN^-
dichromate	$Cr_2O_7^{2-}$
dihydrogen phosphate	$H_2PO_4^-$
hydrogen carbonate or bicarbonate	HCO_3^-
hydrogen phosphate	HPO_4^{2-}
hydrogen sulfate or bisulfate	HSO_4^-
hydroxide	OH^-
hypochlorite	ClO^-
nitrate	NO_3^-
nitrite	NO_2^-
oxalate	$C_2O_4^{2-}$
perchlorate	ClO_4^-
permanganate	MnO_4^-
peroxide	O_2^{2-}
phosphate	PO_4^{3-}
phosphite	PO_3^{3-}
sulfate	SO_4^{2-}
sulfite	SO_3^{2-}
thiocyanate	SCN^-

Student Annotation: Some oxoanions occur in series of ions that contain the same central atom and have the same charge, but contain different numbers of oxygen atoms.

perchlorate	ClO_4^-
chlorate	ClO_3^-
chlorite	ClO_2^-
hypochlorite	ClO^-
nitrate	NO_3^-
nitrite	NO_2^-
phosphate	PO_4^{3-}
phosphite	PO_3^{3-}
sulfate	SO_4^{2-}
sulfite	SO_3^{2-}

Worked Example 5.9

Name the following ionic compounds: (a) $Fe_2(SO_4)_3$, (b) $Al(OH)_3$, and (c) Hg_2O.

Strategy Begin by identifying the cation and the anion in each compound, and then combine the names for each, eliminating the word *ion*.

Setup $Fe_2(SO_4)_3$ contains Fe^{3+} and SO_4^{2-}, the iron(III) ion, and the sulfate ion. We know that the iron in $Fe_2(SO_4)_3$ is iron(III), Fe^{3+}, because it is combined with the sulfate ion in a 2:3 ratio; $Al(OH)_3$ contains Al^{3+} and OH^-, the aluminum ion and the hydroxide ion; and Hg_2O contains Hg_2^{2+} and O^{2-}, the mercury(I) ion and the oxide ion.

Solution (a) Combining the cation and anion names, and eliminating the word *ion* from each of the individual ions' names, we get *iron(III) sulfate* as the name of $Fe_2(SO_4)_3$; (b) $Al(OH)_3$ is *aluminum hydroxide*; and (c) Hg_2O is *mercury(I) oxide*.

(Continued on next page)

> **Think About It**
> Be careful not to confuse the subscript in a formula with the charge on the metal ion. In part (a), for example, the subscript on Fe is 2, but this is an iron(III) compound.
>
> **Practice Problem A** Name the following ionic compounds: (a) Na_2SO_4, (b) $Cu(NO_3)_2$, (c) $Fe_2(CO_3)_3$.
>
> **Practice Problem B** Write formulas for the following ionic compounds: (a) potassium dichromate, (b) lithium oxalate, (c) copper(II) nitrate.

Student Annotation: Note that most of the polyatomic ions in Table 5.10 are oxoanions.

Oxoanions are polyatomic anions that contain one or more oxygen atoms and one atom (the "central atom") of another element. Examples include the chlorate (ClO_3^-), nitrate (NO_3^-), and sulfate (SO_4^{2-}) ions. Often, oxoanions occur in series of two or more ions that have the same central atom but different numbers of O atoms (e.g., NO_3^- and NO_2^-). Starting with the oxoanions whose names end in *−ate* (see Table 5.10), we can name these ions as follows:

1. The ion with one *more* O atom than the *−ate* ion is called the *per . . . ate* ion. Thus, ClO_3^- is the chlorate ion, so ClO_4^- is the *perchlorate ion.*
2. The ion with one *less* O atom than the *−ate* anion is called the *−ite* ion. Thus, ClO_2^- is the *chlorite ion.*
3. The ion with *two* fewer O atoms than the *−ate* ion is called the *hypo . . . ite* ion. Thus, ClO^- is the *hypochlorite ion.*

At a minimum, you must commit to memory the formulas and charges of the oxoanions whose names end in *−ate* so that you can apply these guidelines when necessary.

Oxoacids

Student Annotation: Although oxoacids themselves are not ionic compounds, they do *produce* ionic species when dissolved in water.

In addition to the binary acids discussed in Section 5.6, there is another important class of acids known as *oxoacids* which, when dissolved in water, produce hydrogen ions and the corresponding oxoanions. The formula of an oxoacid can be determined by adding enough H^+ ions to the corresponding oxoanion to yield a formula with no net charge. For example, the formulas of oxoacids based on the nitrate (NO_3^-) and sulfate (SO_4^{2-}) ions are HNO_3 and H_2SO_4, respectively. The names of oxoacids are derived from the names of the corresponding oxoanions using the following guidelines:

1. An acid based on an *−ate* ion is called . . . *ic* acid. Thus, $HClO_3$ is called *chloric acid.*
2. An acid based on an *−ite* ion is called . . . *ous* acid. Thus, $HClO_2$ is called *chlorous acid.*
3. Prefixes in oxoanion names are retained in the names of the corresponding oxoacids. Thus, $HClO_4$ and $HClO$ are called *perchloric acid* and *hypochlorous acid,* respectively.

Most of the acids that we have encountered thus far have been *monoprotic*; that is, they each have just *one* ionizable hydrogen atom. Many oxoacids, such as H_2SO_4 and H_3PO_4, are *polyprotic*—meaning that they have *more* than one ionizable hydrogen atom. In these cases, the names of anions in which one or more (but not all) of the hydrogen ions have been removed must indicate the number of H ions that remain, as shown for the anions derived from phosphoric acid:

H_3PO_4	Phosphoric acid
$H_2PO_4^-$	Dihydrogen phosphate ion
HPO_4^{2-}	Hydrogen phosphate ion
PO_4^{3-}	Phosphate ion

Worked Examples 5.10 and 5.11 let you practice naming oxoacids and oxoanions.

Worked Example 5.10

Name the following species: (a) BrO_4^-, (b) HCO_3^-, and (c) H_2CO_3.

Strategy Each species is either an oxoanion or an oxoacid. Identify the "reference oxoanion" (the one with the −*ate* ending) for each, and apply the rules to determine appropriate names.

Setup (a) Chlorine, bromine, and iodine (members of Group 7A) all form analogous series of oxoanions with one to four oxygen atoms. Thus, the reference oxoanion is bromate (BrO_3^-), which is analogous to chlorate (ClO_3^-). In parts (b) and (c), HCO_3^- and H_2CO_3 have one and two more hydrogens, respectively, than the carbonate ion (CO_3^{2-}).

Solution (a) BrO_4^- has one more O atom than the bromate ion (BrO_3^-), so BrO_4^- is the *perbromate* ion. (b) CO_3^{2-} is the carbonate ion. Because HCO_3^- has one ionizable hydrogen atom, it is called the *hydrogen carbonate ion*. (c) With two ionizable hydrogen atoms and no charge on the compound, H_2CO_3 is *carbonic acid*.

> **Think About It**
> Remembering all these names and formulas is greatly facilitated by memorizing the common ions that end in −*ate*
>
> | | | | |
> |---|---|---|---|
> | chlorate | ClO_3^- | nitrate | NO_3^- |
> | iodate | IO_3^- | carbonate | CO_3^{2-} |
> | bromate | BrO_3^- | oxalate | $C_2O_4^{2-}$ |
> | sulfate | SO_4^{2-} | chromate | CrO_4^{2-} |
> | phosphate | PO_4^{3-} | permanganate | MnO_4^- |

Practice Problem A Name the following species: (a) HBrO, (b) HSO_4^-, and (c) $H_2C_2O_4$.

Practice Problem B Name the following species: (a) HIO_3, (b) $HCrO_4^-$, and (c) $HC_2O_4^-$.

Worked Example 5.11

Determine the formula of sulfurous acid.

Strategy The −*ous* ending in the name of an acid indicates that the acid is derived from an oxoanion ending in −*ite*. Determine the formula and charge of the oxoanion, and add enough hydrogens to make a neutral formula.

Setup The sulfite ion is SO_3^{2-}.

Solution The formula of sulfurous acid is H_2SO_3.

> **Think About It**
> Remembering all these names and formulas is greatly facilitated by memorizing the common ions that end in −*ate*. (See Think About It box in Worked Example 5.10.)

Practice Problem A Determine the formula of perbromic acid. (Refer to the information in Worked Example 5.10.)

Practice Problem B Determine the formula of chromic acid.

Hydrates

A *hydrate* is a compound that has a specific number of water molecules within its solid structure. In its normal state, for example, each unit of copper(II) sulfate has five water molecules associated with it. The systematic name for this compound is copper(II) sulfate pentahydrate, and its formula is written as $CuSO_4 \cdot 5H_2O$. The water molecules can be driven off by heating. When this occurs, the resulting compound is $CuSO_4$, which is sometimes called anhydrous copper(II) sulfate; *anhydrous* means that the compound no longer has water molecules associated with it. Hydrates and the corresponding anhydrous compounds often have distinctly different physical and chemical properties (Figure 5.7).

Figure 5.7 $CuSO_4$ is white. The pentahydrate, $CuSO_4 \cdot 5H_2O$, is blue.

Some other hydrates are

$BaCl_2 \cdot 2H_2O$	Barium chloride dihydrate
$LiCl \cdot H_2O$	Lithium chloride monohydrate
$MgSO_4 \cdot 7H_2O$	Magnesium sulfate heptahydrate
$Sr(NO_3)_2 \cdot 4H_2O$	Strontium nitrate tetrahydrate

Familiar Inorganic Compounds

Some compounds are better known by their common names than by their systematic chemical names. Familiar examples are listed in Table 5.11.

TABLE 5.11	Common and Systematic Names of Some Familiar Inorganic Compounds	
Formula	**Common name**	**Systematic name**
H_2O	Water	Dihydrogen monoxide
NH_3	Ammonia	Trihydrogen nitride
CO_2	Dry ice	Solid carbon dioxide
$NaCl$	Salt	Sodium chloride
N_2O	Nitrous oxide, laughing gas	Dinitrogen monoxide
$CaCO_3$	Marble, chalk, limestone	Calcium carbonate
$NaHCO_3$	Baking soda	Sodium hydrogen carbonate
$MgSO_4 \cdot 7H_2O$	Epsom salt	Magnesium sulfate heptahydrate
$Mg(OH)_2$	Milk of magnesia	Magnesium hydroxide

SECTION 5.7 REVIEW

Covalent Bonding in Ionic Species

5.7.1   What is the correct formula for nitrous acid?

5.7.2   What is the formula of nickel(II) nitrate hexahydrate?

5.7.3   What is the correct name of the compound Hg_2CrO_4?

5.7.4   What is the formula of the compound iron(III) carbonate?

5.8 MOLECULAR AND FORMULA MASSES

Using a compound's molecular formula and atomic masses from the periodic table, we can determine the mass (in amu [◄◄ Section 1.4]) of an individual molecule—a quantity known as the ***molecular mass.*** The molecular mass is simply the sum of the atomic masses of the atoms that make up the molecule. We multiply the atomic mass of each element by the number of atoms of that element in the molecule and then sum the masses for each element present. For example,

molecular mass of H_2O = 2(atomic mass of H) + atomic mass of O

= 2(1.008 amu) + 16.00 amu = 18.02 amu

Because the atomic masses on the periodic table are *average* atomic masses, the result of such a determination is an *average* molecular mass, sometimes referred to as the ***molecular weight.***

Although an ionic compound does not have a *molecular* mass, we can use its empirical formula to determine its ***formula mass*** (the mass of a "formula unit"), sometimes called the ***formula weight.*** Worked Example 5.12 illustrates how to determine molecular mass and formula mass.

Worked Example 5.12

Calculate the molecular mass or the formula mass, as appropriate, for each of the following compounds: (a) propane, C_3H_8, (b) lithium hydroxide, LiOH, and (c) barium acetate, $Ba(C_2H_3O_2)_2$.

Strategy Determine the molecular mass (for each molecular compound) or formula mass (for each ionic compound) by summing all the atomic masses.

Setup Using the formula for each compound, determine the number of atoms of each element present. A molecule of propane contains three C atoms and eight H atoms. The compounds in parts (b) and (c) are ionic and will therefore have formula masses rather than molecular masses. A formula unit of lithium hydroxide contains one Li atom, one O atom, and one H atom. A formula unit of barium acetate contains one Ba atom, four C atoms, six H atoms, and four O atoms. (Remember that the subscript after the parentheses means that there are two acetate ions, each of which contains two C atoms, three H atoms, and two O atoms.)

Solution For each compound, multiply the number of atoms by the atomic mass of each element and then sum the calculated values.

(a) The molecular mass of propane is 3(12.01 amu) + 8(1.008 amu) = 44.09 amu.

(b) The formula mass of lithium hydroxide is 6.941 amu + 16.00 amu + 1.008 amu = 23.95 amu.

(c) The formula mass of barium acetate is 137.3 amu + 4(12.01 amu) + 6(1.008 amu) + 4(16.00 amu) = 255.4 amu.

> **Think About It**
> Double-check that you have counted the number of atoms correctly for each compound and that you have used the proper atomic masses from the periodic table.

Practice Problem A Calculate the molecular or formula mass of each of the following compounds: (a) magnesium chloride ($MgCl_2$), (b) sulfuric acid (H_2SO_4), and (c) ibuprofen ($C_{13}H_{18}O_2$).

Practice Problem B Calculate the molecular or formula mass of each of the following compounds: (a) calcium carbonate ($CaCO_3$), (b) nitrous acid (HNO_2), and (c) caffeine ($C_8H_{10}N_4O_2$).

Caffeine

Molecular and Formula Masses

5.8.1   Determine the molecular mass of citric acid ($H_3C_6H_5O_7$).

Citric acid

5.8.2   Determine the formula mass of calcium citrate [$Ca_3(C_6H_5O_7)_2$].

5.8.3   Determine the molecular mass of perchloric acid.

5.8.4   Determine the formula mass of iron(III) chromate.

5.8.5   Explain what's wrong with the following statement: "The molecular mass of sodium chloride is 58.44 amu."

5.8.6   Determine the formula mass of manganese(II) chloride tetrahydrate.

5.9   PERCENT COMPOSITION OF COMPOUNDS

Student Annotation: Often the terms *percent composition by mass* and *percent composition* are used interchangeably. In this book, unless otherwise specified, *percent composition* means percent composition *by mass.*

The formula of a compound indicates the number of atoms of each element in a unit of the compound. From a molecular or empirical formula, we can calculate what percentage of the total mass is contributed by each element in a compound. A list of the percent by mass of each element in a compound is known as the compound's ***percent composition by mass.*** Percent composition is calculated by dividing the mass of each element in a unit of the compound by the molecular or formula mass of the compound and then multiplying by 100 percent. Mathematically, the percent composition of an element in a compound is expressed as

Equation 5.1 $\text{percent by mass of an element} = \dfrac{n \times \text{atomic mass of element}}{\text{molecular or formula mass of compound}} \times 100\%$

where n is the number of atoms of the element in a molecule or formula unit of the compound. For example, in a molecule of hydrogen peroxide (H_2O_2), there are two H atoms and two O atoms. The atomic masses of H and O are 1.008 and 16.00 amu, respectively, so the molecular mass of H_2O_2 is 34.02 amu. Therefore, the percent composition of H_2O_2 is calculated as follows:

$$\%H = \frac{2 \times 1.008 \text{ amu H}}{34.02 \text{ amu } H_2O_2} \times 100\% = 5.926\%$$

$$\%O = \frac{2 \times 16.00 \text{ amu O}}{34.02 \text{ amu } H_2O_2} \times 100\% = 94.06\%$$

The sum of percentages is 5.926% + 94.06% = 99.99%. The small discrepancy from 100 percent is due to rounding of the atomic masses of the elements. We could equally well have used the *empirical* formula of hydrogen peroxide (HO) for the calculation. In this case, we would have used the ***empirical formula mass,*** the mass in amu of one empirical formula, in place of the molecular mass. The empirical formula mass of H_2O_2 (the mass of HO) is 17.01 amu.

$$\%H = \frac{1.008 \text{ amu H}}{17.01 \text{ amu } H_2O_2} \times 100\% = 5.926\%$$

$$\%O = \frac{16.00 \text{ amu O}}{17.01 \text{ amu } H_2O_2} \times 100\% = 94.06\%$$

Because both the molecular formula and the empirical formula tell us the composition of the compound, they both give the same percent composition by mass. Worked Example 5.13 shows how to calculate percent composition by mass.

Worked Example 5.13

Lithium carbonate, Li_2CO_3, was the first "mood-stabilizing" drug approved by the FDA for the treatment of mania and manic-depressive illness, also known as bipolar disorder. Calculate the percent composition by mass of lithium carbonate.

Strategy Use Equation 5.1 to determine the percent by mass contributed by each element in the compound.

Setup Lithium carbonate is an ionic compound that contains Li, C, and O. In a formula unit, there are two Li atoms, one C atom, and three O atoms with atomic masses 6.941, 12.01, and 16.00 amu, respectively. The formula mass of Li_2CO_3 is 2(6.941 amu) + 12.01 amu + 3(16.00 amu) = 73.89 amu.

Solution For each element, multiply the number of atoms by the atomic mass, divide by the formula mass, and multiply by 100 percent.

$$\%Li = \frac{2 \times 6.941 \text{ amu Li}}{73.89 \text{ amu Li}_2\text{CO}_3} \times 100\% = 18.79\%$$

$$\%C = \frac{12.01 \text{ amu C}}{73.89 \text{ amu Li}_2\text{CO}_3} \times 100\% = 16.25\%$$

$$\%O = \frac{3 \times 16.00 \text{ amu O}}{73.89 \text{ amu Li}_2\text{CO}_3} \times 100\% = 64.96\%$$

Think About It
Make sure that the percent composition results for a compound sum to approximately 100. (In this case, the results sum to exactly 100 percent—18.79% + 16.25% + 64.96% = 100.00%—but remember that because of rounding, the percentages may sum to very slightly more or very slightly less.)

Practice Problem A Determine the percent composition by mass of acetaminophen ($C_8H_9NO_2$), the active ingredient in over-the-counter pain relievers such as Tylenol.

Practice Problem B Determine the percent composition by mass of the artificial sweetener aspartame ($C_{14}H_{18}N_2O_5$).

SECTION 5.9 REVIEW

Percent Composition of Compounds

5.9.1 What is the percent composition by mass of aspirin ($C_9H_8O_4$)?

Aspirin

5.9.2 What is the percent composition by mass of sodium bicarbonate ($NaHCO_3$)?

5.10   MOLAR MASS

Although chemists often wish to combine substances in specific mole ratios, there is no direct way to measure the number of moles in a sample of matter. Instead, chemists determine how many moles there are of a substance by measuring its mass (usually in grams). The molar mass of the substance is then used to convert from grams to moles.

The ***molar mass (M)*** of a substance is the mass in grams of one mole of the substance. By definition, the mass of a mole of carbon-12 is exactly 12 g. Note that the molar mass of carbon is numerically equal to its atomic mass. Likewise, the atomic mass of calcium is 40.08 amu and its molar mass is 40.08 g, the atomic mass of sodium is 22.99 amu and its molar mass is 22.99 g, and so on. In general, an element's molar mass in grams is numerically equal to its atomic mass in atomic mass units. The molar mass (in grams) of any compound is numerically equal to its molecular or formula mass (in amu). The molar mass of water, for example, is 18.02 g, and the molar mass of sodium chloride ($NaCl$) is 58.44 g.

Recall from Section 1.4 that

$$1 \text{ amu} = 1.661 \times 10^{-24} \text{ g}$$

This is the reciprocal of Avogadro's number. Expressed another way:

$$1 \text{ g} = 6.022 \times 10^{23} \text{ amu}$$

In effect, there is one mole of atomic mass units in a gram.

When it comes to expressing the molar mass of elements such as oxygen and hydrogen, we have to be careful to specify what form of the element we mean. For instance, the element oxygen exists predominantly as diatomic molecules (O_2). Thus, if we say one mole of oxygen and by *oxygen* we mean O_2, the molecular mass is 32.00 amu and the molar mass is 32.00 g. If, on the other hand, we mean a mole of atomic oxygen (O), then the molar mass is only 16.00 g, which is numerically equal to the atomic mass of O (16.00 amu). You should be able to tell from the context which form of an element is intended, as the following examples illustrate:

Context	*Oxygen* means	Molar mass
How many moles of oxygen react with 2 moles of hydrogen to produce water?	O_2	32.00 g
How many moles of oxygen are there in 1 mole of water?	O	16.00 g
Air is approximately 21 percent oxygen.	O_2	32.00 g
Many organic compounds contain oxygen.	O	16.00 g

Although the term *molar mass* specifies the mass of one mole of a substance, making the appropriate units simply grams (g), we usually express molar masses in units of grams per mole (g/mol) to facilitate calculations involving moles.

Interconverting Mass, Moles, and Numbers of Particles

Molar mass is the conversion factor that we use to convert from mass (*m*) to moles (*n*), and vice versa. We use Avogadro's number to convert from number of moles to number of particles (*N*), and vice versa. *Particles* in this context may refer to atoms, molecules, ions, or formula units. Figure 5.8 summarizes the operations involved in these conversions.

Figure 5.8 Flowchart for conversions among mass, moles, and number of particles.

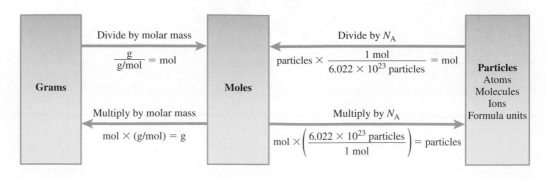

Worked Examples 5.14 and 5.15 illustrate how the conversions are done.

Worked Example 5.14

Determine (a) the number of moles of CO_2 in 10.00 g of carbon dioxide and (b) the mass of 0.905 mole of sodium chloride.

Strategy Use molar mass to convert from mass to moles and to convert from moles to mass.

Setup The molar mass of carbon dioxide is 44.01 g/mol. The molar mass of a compound is numerically equal to its formula mass. The molar mass of sodium chloride (NaCl) is 58.44 g/mol.

Solution

(a) $10.00 \text{ g } CO_2 \times \dfrac{1 \text{ mol } CO_2}{44.01 \text{ g } CO_2} = 0.2272 \text{ mol } CO_2$

(b) $0.905 \text{ mol NaCl} \times \dfrac{58.44 \text{ g NaCl}}{1 \text{ mol NaCl}} = 52.9 \text{ g NaCl}$

> **Think About It**
> Always double-check unit cancellations in problems such as these—errors are common when molar mass is used as a conversion factor. Also make sure that the results make sense. In both cases, a mass smaller than the molar mass corresponds to less than a mole of substance.

Practice Problem A Determine the mass in grams of 2.75 moles of glucose ($C_6H_{12}O_6$).

Practice Problem B Determine the number of moles in 59.8 g of sodium nitrate ($NaNO_3$).

Worked Example 5.15

(a) Determine the number of water molecules and the numbers of H and O atoms in 3.26 g of water.

(b) Determine the mass of 7.92×10^{19} carbon dioxide molecules.

Strategy Use molar mass and Avogadro's number to convert from mass to molecules, and vice versa. Use the molecular formula of water to determine the numbers of H and O atoms.

Setup (a) Starting with mass (3.26 g of water), we use molar mass (18.02 g/mol) to convert to moles of water. From moles, we use Avogadro's number to convert to number of water molecules. In part (b), we reverse the process in part (a) to go from number of molecules to mass of carbon dioxide.

Solution

(a) $3.26 \text{ g } H_2O \times \dfrac{1 \text{ mol } H_2O}{18.02 \text{ g } H_2O} \times \dfrac{6.022 \times 10^{23} \text{ } H_2O \text{ molecules}}{1 \text{ mol } H_2O} = 1.09 \times 10^{23} \text{ } H_2O \text{ molecules}$

Using the molecular formula, we can determine the number of H and O atoms in 3.26 g of H_2O as follows:

$1.09 \times 10^{23} \text{ } H_2O \text{ molecules} \times \dfrac{2 \text{ H atoms}}{1 \text{ } H_2O \text{ molecule}} = 2.18 \times 10^{23} \text{ H atoms}$

$1.09 \times 10^{23} \text{ } H_2O \text{ molecules} \times \dfrac{1 \text{ O atom}}{1 \text{ } H_2O \text{ molecule}} = 1.09 \times 10^{23} \text{ O atoms}$

(b) $7.92 \times 10^{19} \text{ } CO_2 \text{ molecules} \times \dfrac{1 \text{ mol } CO_2}{6.022 \times 10^{23} \text{ } CO_2 \text{ molecules}} \times \dfrac{44.01 \text{ g } CO_2}{1 \text{ mol } CO_2} = 5.79 \times 10^{-3} \text{ g } CO_2$

> **Think About It**
> Again, check the cancellation of units carefully and make sure that the magnitudes of your results are reasonable.

Practice Problem A Calculate the number of oxygen molecules in 35.5 g of O_2.

Practice Problem B Calculate the mass of 12.3 moles of SO_3 molecules.

Determination of Empirical Formula and Molecular Formula from Percent Composition

Student Annotation: Comparison of calculated and experimentally determined percent composition can be used to verify the purity of a compound. We will explore one of the experimental methods used to determine percent composition in Chapter 8.

In Section 5.9, we learned how to use the chemical formula (either molecular or empirical) to determine the percent composition by mass. With the concepts of the mole and molar mass, we can now use percent composition that has been determined experimentally to determine the empirical formula and/or the molecular formula of a compound.

The empirical formula gives only the ratio of combination of the atoms in a molecule, so there may be numerous compounds with the same empirical formula. If we know the approximate molar mass of the compound, though, we can determine the molecular formula from the empirical formula. For instance, the molar mass of glucose is about 180 g. The *empirical formula mass* of CH_2O is about 30 g [12.01 g + 2(1.008 g) + 16.00 g]. To determine the molecular formula, we first divide the molar mass by the empirical formula mass: 180 g/30 g = 6. This tells us that there are six empirical-formula units per molecule in glucose. Multiplying each subscript by 6 (recall that when none is shown, the subscript is understood to be a 1) gives the molecular formula, $C_6H_{12}O_6$.

Worked Example 5.16 shows how to determine the empirical formula and molecular formula of a compound from its percent composition and approximate molar mass.

Worked Example 5.16

Determine the empirical formula of a compound that is 30.45 percent nitrogen and 69.55 percent oxygen by mass. Given that the molar mass of the compound is approximately 92 g/mol, determine the molecular formula of the compound.

Strategy Assume a 100-g sample so that the mass percentages of nitrogen and oxygen given in the problem statement correspond to the masses of N and O in the compound. Then, using the appropriate molar masses, convert the grams of each element to moles. Use the resulting numbers as subscripts in the empirical formula, reducing them to the lowest possible whole numbers for the final answer. To calculate the molecular formula, first divide the molar mass given in the problem statement by the empirical formula mass. Then, multiply the subscripts in the empirical formula by the resulting number to obtain the subscripts in the molecular formula.

Setup The empirical formula of a compound consisting of N and O is N_xO_y. The molar masses of N and O are 14.01 and 16.00 g/mol, respectively. One hundred grams of a compound that is 30.45 percent nitrogen and 69.55 percent oxygen by mass contains 30.45 g N and 69.55 g O.

Solution

$$30.45 \text{ g N} \times \frac{1 \text{ mol N}}{14.01 \text{ g N}} = 2.173 \text{ mol N}$$

$$69.55 \text{ g O} \times \frac{1 \text{ mol O}}{16.00 \text{ g O}} = 4.347 \text{ mol O}$$

This gives a formula of $N_{2.173}O_{4.347}$. Dividing both subscripts by the smaller of the two to get the smallest possible whole numbers (2.173/2.173 = 1, 4.347/2.173 ≈ 2) gives an empirical formula of NO_2.

Finally, dividing the approximate molar mass (92 g/mol) by the empirical formula mass [14.01 g/mol + 2(16.00 g/mol) = 46.01 g/mol] gives 92/46.01 ≈ 2. Then, multiplying both subscripts in the empirical formula by 2 gives the molecular formula, N_2O_4.

Think About It
Use the method described in Worked Example 5.13 to calculate the percent composition of the molecular formula N_2O_4 and verify that it is the same as that given in this problem.

Practice Problem A Determine the empirical formula of a compound that is 53.3 percent C, 11.2 percent H, and 35.5 percent O by mass. What is the molecular formula if the molar mass is approximately 90 g/mol?

Practice Problem B Determine the empirical formula of a compound that is 89.9 percent C and 10.1 percent H by mass. What is the molecular formula if the molar mass is approximately 120 g/mol?

SECTION 5.10 REVIEW

Molar Mass

5.10.1 How many molecules are in 30.1 g of sulfur dioxide (SO_2)?

5.10.2 How many moles of hydrogen are there in 6.50 g of ammonia (NH_3)?

5.10.3 Determine the empirical formula of a compound that has the following composition: 92.3 percent C and 7.7 percent H.

5.10.4 Determine the molecular formula of a compound that has the following composition: 48.6 percent C, 8.2 percent H, and 43.2 percent O, and the molar mass is approximately 148 g/mol.

Learning Outcomes

- Understand the term *compound* and be able to distinguish compounds, elements, and mixtures.
- Prepare Lewis dot symbols of elements and ions.
- Define ionic bonding and provide examples of compounds that contain ionic bonds.
- Use Coulomb's law and distance between ions to rank lattice energies of ionic compounds.
- Describe the Lewis theory of bonding.
- Utilize rules of nomenclature to name the different types of compounds including: ionic compounds, covalent compounds, oxoacids, hydrates, and simple alkanes.
- Recognize covalent bonding in ionic species.
- Name polyatomic ions and know their formulas and charges.

- Calculate the percent composition by mass and molecular/formula/molar mass of a compound.
- Use the relationships between Avogadro's number, moles, molar mass, and grams to perform calculations involving compounds.
- Interconvert between mass, moles, and number of particles.
- Determine the empirical formula of a compound from percent composition or from combustion analysis data.
- Utilize the empirical formula and molar mass to determine the molecular formula of a compound.
- Compare properties of ionic and covalent compounds.

Chapter Summary

SECTION 5.1

- A *compound* is a substance made up of two or more elements.

SECTION 5.2

- A *Lewis dot symbol* depicts an atom or an atomic ion of a main group element with dots (representing the valence electrons) arranged around the element's symbol. Main group atoms lose or gain one or more electrons to become isoelectronic with noble gases.

SECTION 5.3

- An *ionic compound* is one that consists of cations and anions in an electrically neutral combination that is held together by electrostatic attraction known as *ionic bonding.*

- A *chemical formula* (or simply *formula*) denotes the composition of a substance.
- A three-dimensional array of alternating cations and anions is called a *lattice. Lattice energy* is the energy required to separate a mole of an ionic compound into its constituent ions in the gas phase.

SECTION 5.4

- Cations are named using the name of the element from which they are derived. When a cation's charge is known unambiguously, it is not specified in the name. When an element can form cations of different charges, the charge is specified with a roman numeral in parentheses. Anions are named similarly, but the element's ending is changed to *-ide*. Ionic compounds are named systematically using the rules of nomenclature.

- *Binary* compounds consist of two elements. Ionic compounds typically are binary and consist of a metal and a nonmetal.

SECTION 5.5

- According to the *Lewis theory of bonding, covalent bonding* results when atoms *share* valence electrons. The atoms in molecules and those in polyatomic ions are held together by *covalent bonds.*
- A *molecule* is an electrically neutral group of two or more atoms.
- According to the *law of definite proportions,* any sample of a given compound will always contain the same elements in the same mass ratio. The *law of multiple proportions* states that if two elements can form more than one compound with one another, the mass ratio of one will be related to the mass ratio of the other by a small whole number.
- Molecules consisting of just two atoms are called *diatomic.* Diatomic molecules may be *homonuclear* (just one kind of atom) or *heteronuclear* (two kinds of atoms). In general, molecules containing more than two atoms are called *polyatomic.*
- A *molecular formula* specifies the exact numbers of atoms in a molecule of a compound. A *structural formula* shows the arrangement of atoms in a substance. Molecules are depicted using molecular art that may be ball-and-stick models or space-filling models.
- An *allotrope* is one of two or more different forms of an element.
- An *empirical formula* expresses, in the smallest possible whole numbers, the ratio of the combination of atoms of the elements in a compound. The empirical and molecular formulas of a compound may or may not be identical

SECTION 5.6

- Molecular compounds are usually composed of two or more nonmetals. The nomenclature of molecular compounds is similar to that of ionic compounds, but because there are often multiple possible combinations, Greek prefixes are used to specify the number of each kind of atom in the molecule.
- An *acid* is a substance that generates hydrogen ions when it dissolves in water. An *ionizable hydrogen atom* is one that can be removed in water to become a hydrogen ion, H^+.

- *Inorganic compounds* are generally those that do not contain carbon. *Organic compounds* contain carbon and hydrogen, sometimes in combination with other elements. *Hydrocarbons* contain only carbon and hydrogen. The simplest hydrocarbons are the *alkanes.* A *functional group* is a group of atoms that determines the chemical properties of an organic compound.

SECTION 5.7

- Many chemical species contain both *ionic* and *covalent* bonds. *Polyatomic ions* are those that contain more than one atom held together by covalent bonding. *Oxoanions* are polyatomic ions that contain one or more oxygen atoms.
- *Oxoacids* are acids based on oxoanions. Acids with one ionizable hydrogen atom are called *monoprotic.* Acids with more than one ionizable hydrogen atom are called *polyprotic.*
- *Hydrates* are compounds whose formulas include a specific number of water molecules. Some familiar compounds are known by common or nonsystematic names.

SECTION 5.8

- *Molecular mass* is calculated by summing the masses of all atoms in a molecule. *Molecular weight* is another term for molecular mass.
- For ionic compounds, we use the analogous terms *formula mass* and *formula weight.*
- Molecular masses, molecular weights, formula masses, and formula weights are expressed in atomic mass units (amu).

SECTION 5.9

- Molecular mass, formula mass, or *empirical formula mass* can be used to determine *percent composition by mass* of a compound. Empirical formula mass is expressed in atomic mass units (amu).

SECTION 5.10

- *Molar mass (M)* is the mass of one mole of a substance, usually expressed in grams. The molar mass of a substance in grams is numerically equal to the *atomic, molecular,* or *formula* mass of the substance in amu.
- Molar mass and Avogadro's number can be used to interconvert among *mass, moles,* and *number of particles* (atoms, molecules, ions, formula units, etc.).

Key Words

Acid, 157	Formula mass, 165	Lattice energy, 144	Monoprotic, 162
Alkane, 158	Formula weight, 165	Law of definite proportions,	Organic compound, 158
Allotrope, 152	Functional group, 159	149	Oxoacids, 162
Binary, 148	Heteronuclear, 150	Law of multiple proportions,	Oxoanions, 162
Chemical formula, 143	Homonuclear, 150	150	Percent composition by mass,
Compound, 141	Hydrate, 163	Lewis dot symbol, 141	166
Covalent bond, 149	Hydrocarbon, 158	Lewis theory of bonding, 149	Polyatomic ion, 160
Covalent bonding, 149	Inorganic compound, 158	Molar mass (M), 168	Polyatomic molecule, 150
Diatomic molecule, 150	Ionic bonding, 143	Molecular formula, 151	Polyprotic, 162
Empirical formula, 152	Ionic compound, 143	Molecular mass, 165	Structural formula, 152
Empirical formula mass, 166	Ionizable hydrogen atom, 157	Molecular weight, 165	
Formula, 143	Lattice, 143	Molecule, 149	

Key Equation

5.1   percent by mass of an element $= \dfrac{n \times \text{atomic mass of element}}{\text{molecular or formula mass of compound}} \times 100\%$

Questions and Problems

SECTION 5.1: COMPOUNDS

Review Questions

5.1   Define the term *compound* and explain how a compound differs from a mixture.

5.2   Classify each of the following as an element, a compound, or a mixture: (a) helium, (b) sugar, (c) gold, (d) hydrogen peroxide, (e) air, (f) seawater.

SECTION 5.2: LEWIS DOT SYMBOLS

Review Questions

5.3   What is a Lewis dot symbol? What information does a Lewis dot symbol provide?

5.4   Which elements do we generally represent with Lewis symbols? Explain why we can't use Lewis symbols to represent every element.

5.5   Use the second member of each group from Group 1A to Group 7A to show that the number of valence electrons on an atom of the element is the same as its group number.

Problems

5.6   Without referring to Figure 5.1, write Lewis dot symbols for the following atoms/ions: (a) Be, (b) K, (c) Ca, (d) Ga, (e) O, (f) Li^+, (g) Cl^-, (h) S^{2-}, (i) Sr^{2+}, (j) N^{3-}.

5.7   Without referring to Figure 5.1, write Lewis dot symbols for the following atoms/ions: (a) Br, (b) N, (c) I, (d) As, (e) F, (f) P^{3-}, (g) Na^+, (h) Mg^{2+}, (i) As^{3+}, (j) Pb^{2+}.

5.8   Indicate the charge on each of the ions represented by the following Lewis dot symbols: (a) $\left[:\overset{\cdot\cdot}{\underset{\cdot\cdot}{Se}}: \right]^{?}$, (b) $K^{?}$, and (c) $\left[:\overset{\cdot\cdot}{\underset{\cdot}{As}}: \right]^{?}$.

5.9   To what group of the periodic table does element X belong if its Lewis dot symbol is (a) $\cdot \dot{X} \cdot$, (b) $: \dot{X} :$, (c) $\left[: \overset{\cdot\cdot}{\underset{\cdot\cdot}{X}} : \right]^{-}$?

SECTION 5.3: IONIC COMPOUNDS AND BONDING

Review Questions

5.10   Explain what *ionic bonding* is.

5.11   Explain how ionization energy and electron affinity determine whether atoms of elements will combine to form ionic compounds.

5.12   Explain why ions with charges greater than ± 3 are seldom found in ionic compounds.

5.13   What is *lattice energy* and what does it indicate about the stability of an ionic compound?

Problems

5.14   An ionic bond is formed between a cation A^+ and an anion B^-. Based on Coulomb's law

$$E \propto \frac{Q_1 \times Q_2}{d}$$

how would the energy of the ionic bond be affected by the following changes: (a) tripling the radius of A^+, (b) doubling the charge on A^+, (c) tripling the charges on A^+ and B^-, (d) doubling the radii of A^+ and B^-?

5.15   An ionic bond is formed between a cation A^+ and an anion B^-. Based on Coulomb's law

$$E \propto \frac{Q_1 \times Q_2}{d}$$

how would the energy of the ionic bond be affected by the following changes: (a) doubling the radius of A^+, (b) tripling the charge on A^+, (c) doubling the charges on A^+ and B^-, and (d) decreasing the radii of A^+ and B^- to half their original values?

5.16   Use Lewis dot symbols to show the transfer of electrons between the following atoms to form cations and anions: (a) Na and F, (b) K and I.

5.17   Use Lewis dot symbols to show the transfer of electrons between the following atoms to form cations and anions: (a) Ba and O, (b) Al and N.

SECTION 5.4: NAMING IONS AND IONIC COMPOUNDS

Review Questions

5.18   Give an example of each of the following: (a) a monatomic cation, (b) a monatomic anion.

5.19   What is an ionic compound? How is electrical neutrality maintained in an ionic compound?

5.20   Explain why the chemical formulas of ionic compounds are usually the same as their empirical formulas.

5.21   What is the Stock system? What are its advantages over the older system of naming cations?

Problems

5.22   Give the formulas and names of the compounds formed from the following pairs of ions: (a) Rb^+ and I^-, (b) Cs^+ and Se^{2-}, (c) Sr^{2+} and N^{3-}, (d) Al^{3+} and S^{2-}.

5.23   Give the formulas and names of the compounds formed from the following pairs of ions: (a) K^+ and F^-, (b) Rb^+ and O^{2-}, (c) Ba^{2+} and P^{3-}, (d) Ga^{3+} and Se^{2-}.

5.24 Write the formulas for the following ionic compounds:
(a) copper bromide (containing the Cu^+ ion),
(b) manganese oxide (containing the Mn^{3+} ion),
(c) mercury iodide (containing the Hg_2^{2+} ion),
(d) magnesium phosphide.

5.25 Write the formulas for the following ionic compounds:
(a) sodium oxide, (b) iron sulfide (containing the
Fe^{2+} ion), (c) cobalt telluride (containing the Co^{3+}
and Te^{2-} ions), (d) barium fluoride.

5.26 Name the following compounds: (a) CdI_2, (b) FeO,
(c) Fe_2O_3, (d) $TiCl_4$.

5.27 Name the following compounds: (a) NaH, (b) Li_3N,
(c) Na_2O, (d) Na_2O_2.

5.28 In the diagrams shown here, match each of the
drawings with the following ionic compounds:
Al_2O_3, LiH, Na_2S, $MgCl_2$. (Green spheres represent
cations and red spheres represent anions.)

| (a) | (b) | (c) | (d) |

5.29 Given the formulas for the ionic compounds, draw
the correct ratio of cations to anions as shown in
Problem 5.28: (a) BaS, (b) CaF_2, (c) Mg_3N_2, (d) K_2O.

SECTION 5.5: COVALENT BONDING AND MOLECULES

Review Questions

5.30 Describe Lewis's contribution to our understanding of
the covalent bond.

5.31 State the laws of definite proportions and multiple
proportions. Illustrate each with an example.

5.32 The elements nitrogen and oxygen can form a variety
of different compounds. Two such compounds, NO and
N_2O_4, were decomposed into their constituent elements.
One produced 0.8756 g N for every gram of O; the
other produced 0.4378 g N for every gram of O. Show
that these results are consistent with the law of multiple
proportions.

5.33 Two different compounds, each containing only
phosphorus and chlorine, were decomposed into their
constituent elements. One produced 0.2912 g P for
every gram of Cl; the other produced 0.1747 g P for
every gram of Cl. Show that these results are consistent
with the law of multiple proportions.

5.34 Sulfur reacts with fluorine to produce three different
compounds. The mass ratio of fluorine to sulfur for
each compound is given in the following table:

Compound	Mass F: Mass S
S_2F_{10}	2.962
SF_4	2.370
SF_6	3.555

Show that these data are consistent with the law of
multiple proportions.

5.35 Both FeO and Fe_2O_3 contain only iron and oxygen.
The mass ratio of oxygen to iron for each compound is
given in the following table:

Compound	Mass O: Mass Fe
FeO	0.2865
Fe_2O_3	0.4297

Show that these data are consistent with the law of
multiple proportions.

5.36 Describe the two commonly used molecular models.

5.37 What does a chemical formula represent? Determine
the ratio of the atoms in the following molecular
formulas: (a) NO, (b) NCl_3, (c) N_2O_4, (d) P_4O_6.

5.38 Define molecular formula and empirical formula.
What are the similarities and differences between
the empirical formula and molecular formula of a
compound?

5.39 Give an example of a case in which two molecules
have different molecular formulas but the same
empirical formula.

Problems

5.40 For each of the following diagrams, determine whether
it represents molecules of a compound or molecules of
an element.

| (a) | (b) | (c) |

5.41 For each of the following diagrams, determine whether
it represents molecules of a compound or molecules of
an element.

| (a) | (b) | (c) |

5.42 Identify the following as elements or compounds:
P_4, PH_3, N_2O, C_6H_6, Hg, Cl_2, N_2, PCl_5.

5.43 Identify the following as elements or compounds:
NH_3, N_2, S_8, NO, CO, CO_2, H_2, SO_2.

5.44 For the two compounds pictured, evaluate the
following ratio:

$$\frac{\text{g green: 1.00 g yellow (right)}}{\text{g green: 1.00 g yellow (left)}}$$

5.45 For the two compounds pictured, evaluate the following ratio:

$$\frac{\text{g blue: } 1.00 \text{ g red (right)}}{\text{g blue: } 1.00 \text{ g red (left)}}$$

5.46 Write the empirical formulas of the following compounds: (a) Al_2Br_6, (b) $Na_2S_2O_4$, (c) N_2O_5, (d) $K_2Cr_2O_7$.

5.47 Write the empirical formulas of the following compounds: (a) C_2N_2, (b) C_6H_6, (c) C_9H_{20}, (d) P_4O_{10}, (e) B_2H_6.

5.48 Write the molecular formula of ethanol from the model shown.

5.49 Write the molecular formula of alanine, an amino acid used in protein synthesis, from the model shown.

SECTION 5.6: NAMING MOLECULAR COMPOUNDS

Review Questions

5.50 Describe how the naming of *molecular* binary compounds is different from the naming of *ionic* binary compounds. Explain why the two approaches are different.

5.51 Define the term *acid*.

5.52 Describe the difference between naming HF when it is in the gas phase and HF when it is dissolved in water. Give another example of a compound that has one name when in the gas phase and another name when dissolved in water.

5.53 What is the difference between an *inorganic* compound and an *organic* compound?

Problems

5.54 Write chemical formulas for the following molecular compounds: (a) phosphorus tribromide, (b) dinitrogen tetrafluoride, (c) xenon tetroxide, (d) selenium trioxide.

5.55 Name the following binary molecular compounds: (a) NCl_3, (b) IF_7, (c) P_4O_6, (d) S_2Cl_2.

5.56 Write the molecular formulas and names of the following compounds.

(a)   (b)   (c)

5.57 Write the molecular formulas and names of the following compounds.

(a)   (b)   (c)

5.58 The GABA molecule, shown here, is a naturally produced inhibitory neurotransmitter in mammals. GABA is also marketed as a supplement that is said, among other things, to decrease anxiety, promote REM sleep, and improve mental clarity. Identify the functional group(s) in the GABA molecule.

5.59 The molecule shown here is one of the intermediates in a particular metabolic pathway in some prokaryotes. It is also a precursor to one of the compounds responsible for the characteristic flavor of strawberries. Identify the functional group(s) in this molecule.

SECTION 5.7: COVALENT BONDING IN IONIC SPECIES

Problems

5.60 Name the following compounds: (a) K_3PO_4, (b) CoC_2O_4, (c) Li_2CO_3, (d) $K_2Cr_2O_7$, (e) NH_4NO_2, (f) HIO_3, (g) $SrSO_4$, (h) $Al(OH)_3$.

5.61 Name the following compounds: (a) $KClO$, (b) Ag_2CO_3, (c) HNO_2, (d) $KMnO_4$, (e) $CsClO_3$, (f) KNH_4SO_4, (g) $Fe(BrO_4)_2$, (h) K_2HPO_4.

5.62 Write the formulas for the following compounds: (a) rubidium nitrite, (b) potassium sulfate, (c) sodium hydrogen sulfide, (d) magnesium phosphate, (e) calcium hydrogen phosphate, (f) potassium dihydrogen phosphate, (g) ammonium sulfate, (h) silver perchlorate.

5.63 Write the formulas for the following compounds: (a) copper(I) cyanide, (b) strontium chlorite, (c) perbromic acid, (d) hydroiodic acid, (e) disodium ammonium phosphate, (f) lead(II) carbonate, (g) tin(II) sulfite, (h) cadmium thiocyanate.

SECTION 5.8: MOLECULAR AND FORMULA MASSES

Review Questions

5.64   What is meant by the term *molecular mass,* and why is the molecular mass that we calculate generally an *average* molecular mass?

5.65   Explain the difference between the terms *molecular mass* and *formula mass.* To what type of compound does each term refer?

Problems

5.66   Calculate the molecular mass (in amu) of each of the following substances: (a) C_6H_6O, (b) H_2SO_4, (c) C_6H_6, (d) $C_6H_{12}O_6$, (e) BCl_3, (f) N_2O_5, (g) H_3PO_4.

5.67   Calculate the molecular mass (in amu) of each of the following substances: (a) CH_3Cl, (b) N_2O_4, (c) SO_2, (d) C_6H_{12}, (e) H_2O_2, (f) $C_{12}H_{22}O_{11}$, (g) NH_3.

5.68   Calculate the molecular mass or formula mass (in amu) of each of the following substances: (a) Li_2CO_3, (b) C_2H_6, (c) NF_2, (d) Al_2O_3, (e) $Fe(NO_3)_3$, (f) PCl_5, (g) Mg_3N.

5.69   Calculate the molecular mass or formula mass (in amu) of each of the following substances: (a) CH_4, (b) NO_2, (c) SO_3, (d) C_6H_6, (e) NaI, (f) K_2SO_4, (g) $Ca_3(PO_4)_2$.

5.70   Calculate the molecular mass (in amu) of each of the following substances.

(a)   (b)   (c)

5.71   Calculate the formula mass (in amu) of each of the following substances.

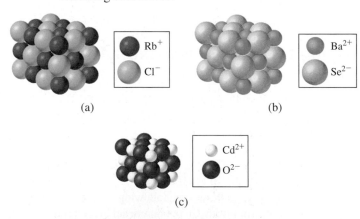

(a)   (b)

(c)

SECTION 5.9: PERCENT COMPOSITION OF COMPOUNDS

Review Questions

5.72   Use dinitrogen monoxide (N_2O) to explain what is meant by the percent composition by mass of a compound.

5.73   Describe how the knowledge of the percent composition by mass of an unknown compound can help us identify the compound.

Problems

5.74   For many years chloroform ($CHCl_3$) was used as an inhalation anesthetic in spite of the fact that it is also a toxic substance that may cause severe liver, kidney, and heart damage. Calculate the percent composition by mass of this compound.

5.75   Tin (Sn) exists in Earth's crust as SnO_2. Calculate the percent composition by mass of Sn and O in SnO_2.

5.76   The anticaking agent added to Morton salt is calcium silicate ($CaSiO_3$). This compound can absorb up to 2.5 times its mass of water and still remain a free-flowing powder. Calculate the percent composition of $CaSiO_3$.

5.77   Tooth enamel is $Ca_5(PO_4)_3(OH)$. Calculate the percent composition of the elements present.

5.78   Interhalogens are compounds that contain two different halogens. Which of these interhalogen compounds contains the smallest percentage of fluorine by mass? (a) ClF_3 (b) BrF_5 (c) IF_5 (d) ClF_5

5.79   All the substances listed here are fertilizers that contribute nitrogen to the soil. Based on mass percentage, which of these is the richest source of nitrogen?
  (a)   Urea [$(NH_2)_2CO$]
  (b)   Ammonium nitrate (NH_4NO_3)
  (c)   Guanidine [$HNC(NH_2)_2$]
  (d)   Ammonia (NH_3)

SECTION 5.10: MOLAR MASS

Review Questions

5.80   What is the molar mass of a compound? What are the commonly used units for molar mass?

5.81   *Molar* mass is numerically equivalent to *molecular mass* for a covalent compound, although the units are different. What is the advantage of using the term *molar mass* when discussing ionic compounds?

Problems

5.82   Calculate the molar mass of the following substances: (a) Li_2CO_3, (b) CS_2, (c) $CHCl_3$ (chloroform), (d) $C_6H_8O_6$ (ascorbic acid, or vitamin C), (e) KNO_3, (f) Mg_3N_2.

5.83   Calculate the molar mass of a compound if 0.372 mole of it has a mass of 152 g.

5.84   How many molecules of ethane (C_2H_6) are present in 0.334 g of C_2H_6?

5.85   Calculate the number of C, H, and O atoms in 1.50 g of glucose ($C_6H_{12}O_6$), a sugar.

5.86   Urea [$(NH_2)_2CO$] is used for fertilizer and many other things. Calculate the number of N, C, O, and H atoms in 1.68×10^4 g of urea.

5.87   Pheromones are a special type of compound secreted by the females of many insect species to attract the males for mating. One pheromone has the molecular formula $C_{19}H_{38}O$. Normally, the amount of this pheromone secreted by a female insect is about 1.0×10^{-12} g. How many molecules does this quantity contain?

5.88   The density of water is 1.00 g/mL at 4°C. How many water molecules are present in 5.81 mL of water at this temperature?

5.89 Cinnamic alcohol is used to add a pleasant scent to soaps, perfumes, and some cosmetics. Its molecular formula is $C_9H_{10}O$. (a) Calculate the percent composition by mass of C, H, and O in cinnamic alcohol. (b) How many molecules of cinnamic alcohol are contained in a sample of mass 1.028 g?

5.90 The chemical formula for rust can be represented by Fe_2O_3. How many moles of Fe are present in 1.00 kg of the compound?

5.91 Tin(II) fluoride (SnF_2) is added to some toothpastes to aid in the prevention of tooth decay. What mass of F (in grams) does 7.10 g of the compound contain?

5.92 In pharmacology, the term *bioavailability* refers to the fraction of an administered dose of drug that reaches the "site of action" via the circulatory system. A particular drug with the chemical formula $C_{16}H_{16}ClNO_2S$ has a bioavailability of 55 percent. How many molecules of this drug reach the site of action in the patient's body if a 75.0 mg dose is administered?

5.93 Toxicologists use the term LD_{50} to describe the number of grams of a substance per kilogram of body weight that constitutes a lethal dose for 50 percent of test animals. Calculate the number of arsenic(III) oxide formula units corresponding to an LD_{50} value of 0.018 for a 212-lb man, assuming that the test animals and humans have the same LD_{50}.

5.94 The organic compound squaric acid, shown here, is useful for preparing a variety of dyes. Determine the number of moles of squaric acid in 143.8 g.

5.95 The arsenic-containing compound cacodylic acid, shown here, is one of the components of the herbicide "Agent Blue." Determine the mass (in grams) of 3.57 moles of cacodylic acid?

5.96 The amino acid cysteine plays an important role in the three-dimensional structure of proteins by forming "disulfide bridges." The percent composition of cysteine is 29.74 percent C, 5.82 percent H, 26.41 percent O, 11.56 percent N, and 26.47 percent S. What is its molecular formula if its molar mass is approximately 121 g/mol?

5.97 Equilin is an estrogen isolated from the urine of pregnant mares. The percent composition of equilin is 80.56 percent C, 7.51 percent H, and 11.92 percent O. What is its molecular formula if its molar mass is approximately 268 g/mol?

ADDITIONAL PROBLEMS

5.98 Predict the formula and name of a binary compound formed from the following elements: (a) Na and H, (b) B and O, (c) Na and S, (d) Al and F, (e) F and O, (f) Sr and Cl.

5.99 The formula for calcium oxide is CaO. What are the formulas for sodium oxide and strontium oxide?

5.100 What is wrong with the name (given in parentheses or brackets) for each of the following compounds: (a) $BaCl_2$ (barium dichloride), (b) Fe_2O_3 [iron(II) oxide], (c) $CsNO_2$ (cesium nitrate), (d) $Mg(HCO_3)_2$ [magnesium(II) bicarbonate]?

5.101 What is wrong with or ambiguous about the phrase "four molecules of NaCl"?

5.102 Rank the following oxohalide compounds in order of increasing percentage of oxygen by mass: $KBrO_3$, $KClO_3$, KIO_3.

5.103 Which of the following are elements, which are molecules but not compounds, which are compounds but not molecules, and which are both compounds and molecules? (a) SO_2, (b) S_8, (c) Cs, (d) N_2O_5, (e) O, (f) O_2, (g) O_3, (h) CH_4, (i) KBr, (j) S, (k) P_4, (l) LiF.

5.104 The following phosphorus sulfides are known: P_4S_3, P_4S_7, and P_4S_{10}. Do these compounds obey the law of multiple proportions? Explain.

5.105 Ethane and acetylene are two gaseous hydrocarbons. Chemical analyses show that in one sample of ethane, 2.65 g of carbon are combined with 0.665 g of hydrogen, and in one sample of acetylene, 4.56 g of carbon are combined with 0.383 g of hydrogen. (a) Are these results consistent with the law of multiple proportions? Explain. (b) Write reasonable molecular formulas for these compounds.

5.106 Which of the following compounds are likely to be ionic? Which are likely to be molecular? CH_4, NaBr, BaF_2, CCl_4, ICl, CsCl, NF_3.

5.107 Which of the following compounds are likely to be ionic? Which are likely to be molecular? $SiCl_4$, LiF, $BaCl_2$, B_2H_6, KCl, C_2H_4.

5.108 The mineral *tschermigite* is essentially pure $NH_4Al(SO_4)_2 \cdot 12H_2O$. Determine the percent oxygen by mass in the mineral.

5.109 The formulas for the fluorides of the third-period elements are NaF, MgF_2, AlF_3, SiF_4, PF_5, SF_6, and ClF_3. Classify each of these compounds as covalent or ionic.

5.110 Complete the table by filling in the blanks with appropriate information.

Cation	Anion	Formula	Name
Co^{2+}	PO_4^{3-}		
Hg_2^{2+}	I^-		
		Cu_2CO_3	
			Lithium nitride
Al^{3+}	S^{2-}		

5.111   Complete the table by filling in the blanks with appropriate information.

Cation	Anion	Formula	Name
			Magnesium bicarbonate
		$SrCl_2$	
Fe^{3+}	NO_2^-		
			Manganese(II) chlorate
		$SnBr_4$	

5.112   Determine the molecular and empirical formulas of the compounds shown here. (Black spheres are carbon, and white spheres are hydrogen.)

(a)   (b)   (c)   (d)

5.113   Rank the four compounds shown in Problem 5.112 according to increasing percent carbon by mass.

5.114   For each of the following pairs of elements, state whether the binary compound they form is likely to be ionic or covalent. Write the empirical formula and name of the compound: (a) I and Cl, (b) Mg and F.

5.115   For each of the following pairs of elements, state whether the binary compound they form is likely to be ionic or covalent. Write the empirical formula and name of the compound: (a) B and F, (b) K and Br.

5.116   Cysteine, shown here, is one of the 20 amino acids found in proteins in humans. Write the molecular formula of cysteine, and calculate its molar mass. What is the mass of 0.153 mole of cysteine?

5.117   Isoflurane, shown here, is a common inhalation anesthetic. Write its molecular formula, and calculate its molar mass. How many moles of isoflurane are in 3.82 g?

5.118   The atomic mass of element X is 33.42 amu. A 27.22-g sample of X combines with 84.10 g of another element Y to form a compound XY. Calculate the atomic mass of Y.

5.119   How many moles of O are needed to combine with 0.212 mole of C to form (a) CO and (b) CO_2?

5.120   A sample of ammonium dichromate contains 1.81×10^{24} hydrogen atoms. How many grams of nitrogen does the sample contain?

5.121   Which of the following are ionic compounds and which are covalent compounds: $RbCl$, PF_5, BrF_3, KO_2, CI_4?

5.122   Classify the following substances as ionic compounds or covalent compounds containing discrete molecules: CH_4, KF, CO, $SiCl_4$, $BaCl_2$.

5.123   The formula of aluminum molybdate is $Al_2(MoO_4)_3$. What is the formula of magnesium molybdate?

5.124   Determine what is wrong with the chemical formula and write the correct chemical formula for each of the following compounds: (a) $(NH_3)_2CO_3$ (ammonium carbonate), (b) $CaOH$ (calcium hydroxide), (c) $CdSO_3$ (cadmium sulfide), (d) $ZnCrO_4$ (zinc dichromate).

5.125   Which of the following has the greater mass: 0.72 g of O_2 or 0.0011 mole of chlorophyll ($C_{55}H_{72}MgN_4O_5$)?

5.126   Chemical analysis shows that the oxygen-carrying protein hemoglobin is 0.34 percent Fe by mass. What is the minimum possible molar mass of hemoglobin? The actual molar mass of hemoglobin is about 65,000 g. How would you account for the discrepancy between your minimum value and the experimental value?

5.127   One mole of a particular compound is shown to contain 6.02×10^{23} atoms of hydrogen, 35.45 g of chlorine, and 64.0 g of oxygen. Determine the formula of this compound.

5.128   The compound 2,3-dimercaptopropanol ($HSCH_2CHSHCH_2OH$), commonly known as British Anti-Lewisite (BAL), was developed during World War I as an antidote to arsenic-containing poison gas. (a) If each BAL molecule binds one arsenic (As) atom, how many As atoms can be removed by 1.0 g of BAL? (b) BAL can also be used to remove poisonous heavy metals like mercury (Hg) and lead (Pb). If each BAL binds one Hg atom, calculate the mass percent of Hg in a BAL-Hg complex. (An H atom is removed when a BAL molecule binds an Hg atom.)

5.129   Mustard gas ($C_4H_8Cl_2S$) is a poisonous gas that was used in World War I and banned afterward. It causes general destruction of body tissues, resulting in the formation of large water blisters. There is no effective antidote. Calculate the percent composition by mass of the elements in mustard gas.

5.130   Myoglobin stores oxygen for metabolic processes in muscle. Chemical analysis shows that it contains 0.34 percent Fe by mass. What is the molar mass of myoglobin? (There is one Fe atom per molecule.)

5.131   Hemoglobin ($C_{2952}H_{4664}N_{812}O_{832}S_8Fe_4$) is the oxygen carrier in blood. (a) Calculate its molar mass. (b) An average adult has about 5.0 L of blood. Every milliliter of blood has approximately 5.0×10^9 erythrocytes, or red blood cells, and every red blood cell has about 2.8×10^8 hemoglobin molecules. Calculate the mass of hemoglobin molecules in grams in an average adult.

5.132 A mixture of NaBr and Na_2SO_4 contains 29.96 percent Na by mass. Calculate the percent by mass of each compound in the mixture.

5.133 Calculate the number of cations and anions in each of the following compounds: (a) 8.38 g of KBr, (b) 5.40 g of Na_2SO_4, (c) 7.45 g of $Ca_3(PO_4)_2$.

5.134 Calculate the percent composition by mass of all the elements in calcium phosphate $[Ca_3(PO_4)_2]$, a major component of bone.

5.135 Which of the following substances contains the greatest mass of chlorine: (a) 5.0 g Cl_2, (b) 60.0 g $NaClO_3$, (c) 0.10 mol KCl, (d) 30.0 g $MgCl_2$, (e) 0.50 mol Cl_2?

5.136 The natural abundances of the two stable isotopes of hydrogen (hydrogen and deuterium) are 99.99 percent ^1_1H and 0.01 percent ^2_1H. Assume that water exists as either H_2O or D_2O. Calculate the number of D_2O molecules in exactly 400 mL of water (density 1.00 g/mL).

5.137 Air is a mixture of many gases and as such, it does not have a molar mass. However, we can calculate an *effective molar mass* as a weighted average of the individual components. To do so, we only need to consider the three major components: nitrogen, oxygen, and argon. Given that one mole of air at sea level is made up of 78.08 percent nitrogen, 20.95 percent oxygen, and 0.97 percent argon, what is the effective molar mass of air?

5.138 Serine, shown here, is a biologically important molecule involved in the function of RNA and DNA, fat and fatty acid metabolism, muscle formation, and the maintenance of a healthy immune system. Identify the functional group(s) in the serine molecule.

Answers to In-Chapter Materials

PRACTICE PROBLEMS

5.1A (a) Ca^{2+}, (b) $\left[:\ddot{N}:\right]^{3-}$, (c) $\left[:\ddot{I}:\right]^-$. **5.1B** (a) 2−, (b) +, (c) 3−. **5.2A** $MgCl_2$. **5.2B** NaF < MgO < AlN. **5.3A** (a) barium sulfide, (b) copper(I) sulfide, (c) chromium(III) chloride. **5.3B** (a) aluminum bromide, (b) rubidium selenide, (c) copper(II) nitride. **5.4A** (a) $PbCl_2$, (b) Co_2O_3, (c) Na_2Se. **5.4B** (a) Fe_2S_3, (b) HgI_2, (c) K_2S. **5.5A** (a) $CHCl_3$, (b) C_3H_6O. **5.5B** (a) ,

(b) **5.6A** (a) $C_4H_5N_2O$, (b) C_2H_5, (c) $C_2H_5NO_2$.

5.6B (a) and (b). **5.7A** (a) dichlorine monoxide, (b) silicon tetrachloride. **5.7B** (a) carbon tetrachloride, (b) dinitrogen monoxide. **5.8A** (a) CS_2, (b) N_2O_3. **5.8B** (a) SO_3, (b) S_2F_{10}. **5.9A** (a) sodium sulfate, (b) copper(II) nitrate, (c) iron(III) carbonate. **5.9B** (a) $K_2Cr_2O_7$, (b) $Li_2C_2O_4$, (c) $Cu(NO_3)_2$. **5.10A** (a) hypobromous acid, (b) hydrogen sulfate ion, (c) oxalic acid. **5.10B** (a) iodic acid, (b) hydrogen chromate ion, (c) hydrogen oxalate ion. **5.11A** $HBrO_4$. **5.11B** H_2CrO_4. **5.12A** (a) 95.21 amu, (b) 98.09 amu, (c) 206.27 amu. **5.12B** (a) 100.09 amu, (b) 47.02 amu, (c) 194.20 amu. **5.13A** 63.56% C, 6.002% H, 9.268% N, 21.17% O. **5.13B** 57.13% C, 6.165% H, 9.521% N, 27.18% O. **5.14A** 495 g. **5.14B** 0.704 mol. **5.15A** 6.68×10^{23} O_2 molecules. **5.15B** 985 g. **5.16A** C_2H_5O; $C_4H_{10}O_2$. **5.16B** C_3H_4; C_9H_{12}.

SECTION REVIEW

5.2.1 $\cdot\ddot{Si}\cdot$. **5.2.2** $\left[:\ddot{Br}:\right]^-$. **5.2.3** 5A. **5.2.4** Yes, if the charge is known. If the charge is not known, the group number cannot be determined from the Lewis symbol alone. **5.3.1** Smaller, larger, and larger. **5.3.2** Red +2, −2; blue +2, −1; green +1, −1. **5.4.1** Lead(II) sulfide. **5.4.2** FeN. **5.4.3** Na_3N. **5.4.4** Zinc bromide. **5.5.1** CCl_4. **5.5.2** C_6H_6, CH. **5.6.1** Sulfur hexafluoride. **5.6.2** Diphosphorus tetraiodide. **5.6.3** Bromine dioxide. **5.6.4** Methanol. **5.7.1** HNO_2. **5.7.2** $Ni(NO_3)_2 \cdot 6H_2O$. **5.7.3** Mercury(I) chromate. **5.7.4** $Fe_2(CO_3)_3$. **5.8.1** 192.12 amu. **5.8.2** 498.44 amu. **5.8.3** 100.46 amu. **5.8.4** 459.67 amu. **5.8.5** Sodium chloride is an ionic compound and therefore does exist as discrete molecules. The correct term to use is "formula mass." **5.8.6** 197.90 amu. **5.9.1** 60.00% C, 4.47% H, 35.53% O. **5.9.2** 27.37% Na, 1.20% H, 14.30% C, 57.14% O. **5.10.1** 2.83×10^{23} molecules. **5.10.2** 1.14 mol. **5.10.3** CH. **5.10.4** $C_6H_{12}O_4$.

KEY SKILLS

Ionic Compounds: Nomenclature and Molar Mass Determination

The process of naming binary ionic compounds follows the simple procedure outlined on page 148. Naming compounds that contain polyatomic ions follows essentially the same procedure; but it does require you to recognize the common polyatomic ions [◄◄ Table 5.10]. Because many ionic compounds contain polyatomic ions, it is important that you know their names, formulas, and charges—well enough that you can identify them readily.

In ionic compounds with ratios of combination other than 1:1, subscript numbers are used to denote the number of each ion in the formula.

Examples: $CaBr_2$, Na_2S, $AlCl_3$, Al_2O_3, FeO, Fe_2O_3

Recall that because the common ions of main group elements have predictable charges, it is unnecessary to use prefixes to denote their numbers when naming compounds that contain them. Thus, the names of the first four examples above are calcium bromide, sodium sulfide, aluminum chloride, and aluminum oxide. The last two contain transition metal ions, many of which have more than one possible charge. In these cases, in order to avoid ambiguity, the charge on the metal ion is designated with a roman numeral in parentheses. The names of these two compounds are iron(II) oxide and iron(III) oxide, respectively.

When a subscript number is required for a polyatomic ion, the ion's formula must first be enclosed in parentheses.

Examples: $Ca(NO_3)_2$, $(NH_4)_2S$, $Ba(C_2H_3O_2)_2$, $(NH_4)_3(SO_4)_2$, $Fe_3(PO_4)_2$, $Co_2(CO_3)_3$

Names: calcium nitrate, ammonium sulfide, barium acetate, ammonium sulfate, iron(II) phosphate, cobalt(III) carbonate

The process of naming ionic compounds given their formulas can be summarized with the following flowchart:

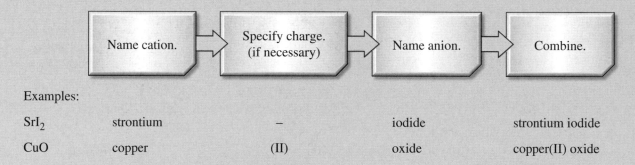

Examples:

SrI_2	strontium	–	iodide	strontium iodide
CuO	copper	(II)	oxide	copper(II) oxide

It is equally important that you be able to write the formula of an ionic compound given its name. Again, knowledge of the common polyatomic ions is critical. The process of writing a compound's formula given its name is summarized as follows:

Examples:

Cesium sulfide $\qquad$ Cs^+ $\qquad$ S^{2-} $\qquad$ $2Cs^+ + 1S^{2-}$ $\qquad$ Cs_2S

Ammonium phosphate $\qquad$ NH_4^+ $\qquad$ PO_4^{3-} $\qquad$ $3NH_4^+ + 1PO_4^{3-}$ $\qquad$ $(NH_4)_3PO_4$

Knowing the formula of an ionic compound, or any compound, enables us to determine the compound's molar mass. To do this, it is important to count atoms carefully—especially in compounds with polyatomic ions enclosed in parentheses. For example, the formula $Ba(C_2H_3O_2)_2$ contains *one* barium, *four* carbons, *six* hydrogens, and *four* oxygens. Its molar mass is calculated as:

Key Skills Problems

5.1
What is the correct name for $CaSO_4$?

(a) calcium sulfoxide (b) calcium sulfite (c) calcium sulfur oxide
(d) calcium sulfate (e) calcium sulfide tetroxide

5.2
What is the correct formula for nickel(II) perchlorate?

(a) $NiClO_4$ (b) Ni_2ClO_4 (c) $Ni(ClO_4)_2$ (d) $NiClO_3$ (e) $Ni(ClO_3)_2$

5.3
Determine the molar mass of $Co(NO_2)_2$.

(a) 151.0 g/mol (b) 209.9 g/mol (c) 163.9 g/mol (d) 119.0 g/mol
(e) 104.0 g/mol

5.4
Determine the molar mass of iron(III) sulfate.

(a) 151.9 g/mol (b) 344.1 g/mol (c) 399.9 g/mol (d) 271.9 g/mol
(e) 359.7 g/mol

CHAPTER 6

Representing Molecules

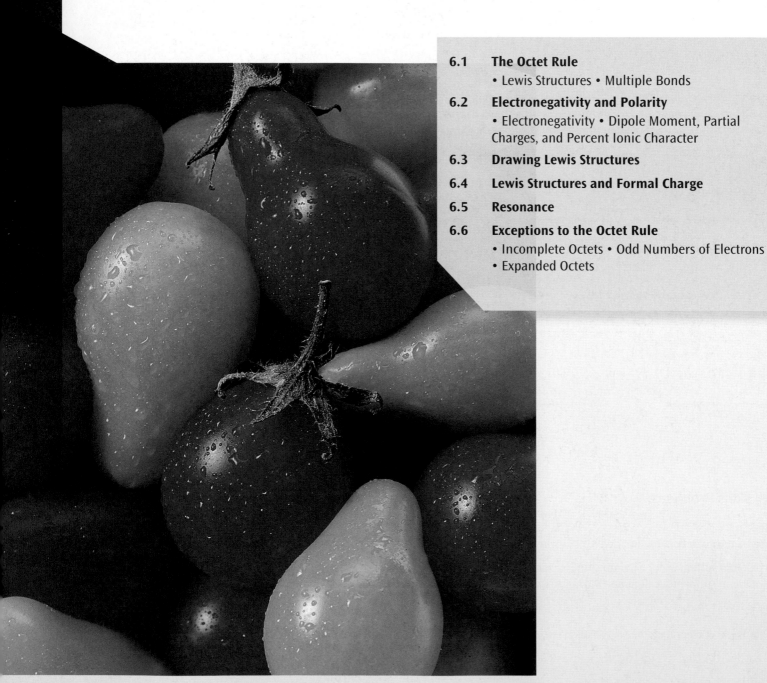

6.1 The Octet Rule
• Lewis Structures • Multiple Bonds

6.2 Electronegativity and Polarity
• Electronegativity • Dipole Moment, Partial Charges, and Percent Ionic Character

6.3 Drawing Lewis Structures

6.4 Lewis Structures and Formal Charge

6.5 Resonance

6.6 Exceptions to the Octet Rule
• Incomplete Octets • Odd Numbers of Electrons • Expanded Octets

In most chemical species, all of the electrons are paired. One class of molecules, known as *radicals* or *free* radicals, have one or more *unpaired* electrons. Free radicals are important in the preparation of polymers, and in many necessary biological processes. However, free radicals also are responsible for some undesirable processes that cause cell damage. The body does have mechanisms to minimize radical damage and biochemists have identified molecules known as *antioxidants* that can prevent or slow radical damage. Fruits and vegetables (including tomatoes, shown here) are good sources of important antioxidants such as vitamin C, vitamin E, and the phytochemical *lycopene*.

6.1 THE OCTET RULE

Lewis summarized much of his theory of chemical bonding with the octet rule. According to the *octet rule,* atoms will lose, gain, or share electrons in order to achieve a noble gas electron configuration. This rule enables us to predict many of the formulas for compounds consisting of specific elements. The octet rule holds for nearly all the compounds made up of second period elements and is therefore especially important in the study of organic compounds, which contain mostly C, N, and O atoms. Whether a particular atom achieves an octet by losing, gaining, or sharing electrons depends on the properties of the atom—which are determined by the number of subatomic particles within the atom. Figure 6.1 (pages 184–185) summarizes how atomic properties determine what sort of bonds an atom will form.

As with ionic bonding, covalent bonding of many-electron atoms involves only the valence electrons. Consider the fluorine molecule (F_2). The electron configuration of F is $1s^2 2s^2 2p^5$. The $1s$ electrons are low in energy and stay near the nucleus most of the time, so they do not participate in bond formation. Thus, each F atom has seven valence electrons (two $2s$ electrons and five $2p$ electrons). The Lewis symbol of fluorine indicates that only one of its valence electrons is unpaired [◄◄ Figure 5.1, page 142], so the formation of the F_2 molecule can be represented as follows:

$$:\ddot{\text{F}}\cdot \ + \ \cdot\ddot{\text{F}}: \ \longrightarrow \ :\ddot{\text{F}}\!:\!\ddot{\text{F}}: \quad \text{or} \quad :\ddot{\text{F}}\!-\!\ddot{\text{F}}:$$

Only two valence electrons participate in the formation of the F_2 bond. The other, nonbonding, electrons are called *lone pairs*—pairs of valence electrons that are not involved in covalent bond formation. Thus, each F in F_2 has three lone pairs of electrons.

$$\longrightarrow :\ddot{\text{F}}\!-\!\ddot{\text{F}}: \longleftarrow\text{lone pair}$$

Lewis Structures

The structures used to represent molecules held together by covalent bonds, such as H_2 and F_2, are called *Lewis structures.* A *Lewis structure* is a representation of covalent bonding in which shared electron pairs are shown either as dashes or as pairs of dots between two atoms, and lone pairs are shown as pairs of dots on individual atoms. Only valence electrons are shown in a Lewis structure.

To draw the Lewis structure of the water molecule, recall that the Lewis dot symbol for oxygen has two unpaired dots [◄◄ Figure 5.1, page 142], meaning that it has two unpaired electrons and can form two bonds. Because hydrogen has only one electron, it can form only one covalent bond. Thus, the Lewis structure for water is

$$\text{H}\!:\!\ddot{\text{O}}\!:\!\text{H} \quad \text{or} \quad \text{H}\!-\!\ddot{\text{O}}\!-\!\text{H}$$

In this case, the O atom has two lone pairs. The hydrogen atom has no lone pairs because its only valence electron is used to form a covalent bond.

In the F_2 and H_2O molecules, the F, H, and O atoms each achieve a stable noble gas configuration by sharing electrons, thus illustrating the octet rule:

$$\text{F with } 8 \ e^- \ \frown \ \overparen{(\text{F}\!:\!\text{F})} \ \frown \ \text{F with } 8 \ e^-$$

$$\text{H with } 2 \ e^- \ \frown \ \overparen{(\text{H}\!:\!\text{O}\!:\!\text{H})} \ \frown \ \text{H with } 2 \ e^-$$

$$\text{O with } 8 \ e^-$$

Student Annotation: For nearly all elements, achieving a noble gas electron configuration results in eight valence electrons around each atom—hence the name *octet* rule.

Student Annotation: Recall that a pair of shared electrons can be represented either with two dots or with a dash. [◄◄ Section 5.5]

Student Annotation: Lewis structures are also referred to as Lewis dot structures. In this book, we will use the term *Lewis structure* to avoid confusion with the term *Lewis dot symbol.*

Student Annotation: For H, the octet rule dictates that it have two electrons, giving it the electron configuration of the noble gas He.

Figure 6.1

The Properties of Atoms

Metals, such as sodium, easily lose one
or more electrons to become cations.

$1s^2 2s^2 2p^6 3s^1$
$IE_1 = 496$ kJ/mol
$EA = +52.9$ kJ/mol
$r = 186$ pm

Nonmetals, such as chlorine, easily gain
one or more electrons to become anions.

$1s^2 2s^2 2p^6 3s^2 3p^5$
$IE_1 = 1256$ kJ/mol
$EA = +349$ kJ/mol
$r = 99$ pm

Nonmetals can also achieve an octet by
sharing electrons to form covalent bonds.

Although carbon is a nonmetal, it neither loses nor
gains electrons easily. Instead, it achieves an octet
by sharing electrons—forming covalent bonds.

$1s^2 2s^2 2p^2$
$IE_1 = 1086$ kJ/mol
$EA = +122$ kJ/mol
$r = 77$ pm

What makes carbon different from other
nonmetals is that it often forms bonds with itself,
including multiple bonds—forming a limitless
array of organic compounds, such as ethylene.

C_2H_4

Na$^+$

$1s^22s^22s^22p^6$

Cations and anions combine to form ionic compounds, such as sodium chloride.

Cl$^-$

$1s^22s^22p^63s^23p^6$

NaCl

Cl$_2$

CCl$_4$

What's the point?

The number of subatomic particles determines the properties of individual atoms. In turn, the properties of atoms determine how they interact with other atoms and what compounds, if any, they form.

The octet rule works best for elements in the second period of the periodic table. These elements have only 2*s* and 2*p* valence subshells, which can hold a total of eight electrons. When an atom of one of these elements forms a covalent compound, it can attain the noble gas electron configuration [Ne] by sharing electrons with other atoms in the same compound. In Section 6.6, we will discuss some important exceptions to the octet rule.

Multiple Bonds

When the bond between two atoms consists of one shared pair of electrons, the bond is said to be a *single bond*. *Multiple bonds* form, on the other hand, when two atoms share two or more pairs of electrons. A multiple bond in which the atoms share two pairs of electrons is called a *double bond*. Double bonds are found in molecules such as carbon dioxide (CO_2) and ethylene (C_2H_4):

Each O has 8 e^- O꞉꞉C꞉꞉O   or   :O=C=O:

C has 8 e^-

Student Annotation: Note that each shared pair of electrons can be represented with a dash.

Each H has 2 e^- H꞉C꞉꞉C꞉H (H H top)   or   (structure with H H / C=C / H H)

Each C has 8 e^-

A *triple bond* arises when two atoms share three pairs of electrons, as in molecules such as nitrogen (N_2) and acetylene (C_2H_2):

Each N has 8 e^- :N꞉꞉꞉N: or   :N≡N:

Each H has 2 e^- H꞉C꞉꞉꞉C꞉H   or   H—C≡C—H

Each C has 8 e^-

Student Annotation: An important exception to this is carbon monoxide, CO:

:C≡O:

In ethylene and acetylene, all the valence electrons are used in bonding; there are no lone pairs on the carbon atoms. In fact, most stable molecules containing carbon do not have lone pairs on the carbon atoms.

Multiple bonds are shorter than single bonds. *Bond length* is defined as the distance between the nuclei of two covalently bonded atoms in a molecule (Figure 6.2). Table 6.1 shows some experimentally determined bond lengths. For a given pair of atoms, such as carbon and nitrogen, triple bonds are shorter than double bonds, and double bonds are shorter than single bonds.

N₂
Bond length 1.10 Å

CO
Bond length 1.13 Å

Figure 6.2 Bond length is the distance between the nuclei of two bonded atoms.

TABLE 6.1	Average Bond Lengths of Some Common Single, Double, and Triple Bonds		
Bond type	**Bond length (pm)**	**Bond type**	**Bond length (pm)**
C—H	107	C=N	138
O—H	96	C≡N	116
C—O	143	N—N	147
C=O	121	N=N	124
C≡O	113	N≡N	110
C—C	154	N—O	136
C=C	133	N=O	122
C≡C	120	O—O	148
C—N	143	O=O	121

The shorter multiple bonds are also stronger than single bonds. We can quantify the strength of a bond by measuring the quantity of energy required to break it. Specifically, we measure the energy change associated with breaking one mole of bonds of a particular type. For example, the bond energy of the diatomic hydrogen molecule is

$$H_2(g) \longrightarrow H(g) + H(g) \qquad \text{Bond energy} = 436.4 \text{ kJ/mol}$$

> **Student Annotation:** This quantity is actually a bond *enthalpy*. Enthalpy [▶▶ Chapter 10] is a thermodynamic quantity that is closely related to energy.

According to this equation, breaking all the covalent bonds in one mole of gaseous H_2 molecules (one mole of H—H bonds) requires 436.4 kJ of energy. Because multiple bonds involve the sharing of multiple pairs of electrons, the bond energies of double and triple bonds between two atoms are higher than a single bond between the same atoms. We will examine the energy changes associated with breaking chemical bonds in more detail in Chapter 10.

6.2   ELECTRONEGATIVITY AND POLARITY

So far, we have described chemical bonds as either *ionic,* when they occur between a metal and a nonmetal, or *covalent,* when they occur between nonmetals. In fact, ionic and covalent bonds are simply the extremes in a spectrum of bonding. Bonds that fall between these two extremes are *polar,* meaning that electrons are shared but are not shared equally. Such bonds are referred to as *polar covalent bonds.* The following shows a comparison of the different types of bonds, where M and X represent two atoms:

M:X	$M^{\delta+}X^{\delta-}$	M^+X^-
Pure covalent bond	**Polar covalent bond**	**Ionic bond**
Neutral atoms held together by *equally* shared electrons	Partially charged atoms held together by *unequally* shared electrons	Oppositely charged ions held together by electrostatic attraction

To illustrate the spectrum of bonding, let's consider three substances: H_2, HF, and NaF. In the H_2 molecule, where the two bonding atoms are identical, the electrons are shared equally. That is, the electrons in the covalent bond spend roughly the same amount of time in the vicinity of each H atom. In the HF molecule, on the other hand, where the two bonding atoms are different, the electrons are *not* shared equally. They spend more time in the vicinity of the F atom than in the vicinity of the H atom. (The δ symbol is used to denote partial charges on the atoms.) In NaF, the electrons are not shared at all but rather are transferred from sodium to fluorine.

> **Student Annotation:** In fact, the transfer of electrons in NaF is *nearly* complete. Even in an ionic bond, the electrons in question spend a small amount of time near the cation.

One way to visualize the distribution of electrons in species such as H_2, HF, and NaF is to use electrostatic potential models (Figure 6.3). These models show regions where electrons spend a lot of time in red, and regions where electrons spend very little time in blue. (Regions where electrons spend a moderate amount of time appear green.)

Electronegativity

Electronegativity is the ability of an atom to draw shared electrons (the electrons in a covalent bond) toward itself. It determines how the electron density [◀◀ Section 3.6] in a molecule or a polyatomic ion is distributed; what we have previously referred to as *where the electrons spend most of their time.* An element with a high electronegativity has a greater tendency to attract electron density than does an element with low electronegativity. We can make a qualitative prediction of an atom's electronegativity based on its electron affinity (*EA*) and its first ionization energy (IE_1)

> **Student Annotation:** Electrons spend *more* time around atoms with *high* electronegativities, and *less* time around atoms with *low* electronegativities.

H_2 HF   NaF

Figure 6.3 Electron density maps show the distribution of charge in a covalent species (H_2), a polar covalent species (HF), and an ionic species (NaF). The most electron-rich regions are red; the most electron-poor regions are blue.

Multi 6.1
Periodic table—electronegativity

Student Annotation: The trend in electronegativities can also be related to atomic radius. The smaller an atom, the closer the shared electrons will be to its nucleus; therefore, the more powerfully they will be attracted to it.

[◄◄ Section 4.4]. An atom such as fluorine, which has a high electron affinity (tends to *accept* electrons) and a high ionization energy (has little or no tendency to *lose* electrons), has a *high* electronegativity. Sodium, on the other hand, has a low electron affinity, a low ionization energy, and therefore a *low* electronegativity.

Electronegativity is a relative concept, meaning that an element's electronegativity can be measured only in relation to the electronegativity of other elements. Linus Pauling[1] devised one method for calculating the relative electronegativities of most elements. These values are shown in Figure 6.4. In general, electronegativity increases from left to right across a period in the periodic table, as the metallic character of the elements decreases. Within each group, electronegativity decreases with increasing atomic number and increasing metallic character. The trend in transition metals is less regular. The most electronegative elements (the halogens, oxygen, nitrogen, and sulfur) are found in the upper right-hand corner of the periodic table, and the least electronegative elements (the alkali and alkaline earth metals) are clustered near the lower left-hand corner. These trends are readily apparent in the graph in Figure 6.5.

Figure 6.4 Electronegativities of common elements.

Figure 6.5 Variation of electronegativity with atomic number.

---

[1]Linus Carl Pauling (1901–1994). This American chemist is regarded by many as the most influential chemist of the twentieth century. Pauling received the Nobel Prize in Chemistry in 1954 for his work on protein structure, and the Nobel Peace Prize in 1962 for his tireless campaign against the testing and proliferation of nuclear arms. He is the only person ever to have received two unshared Nobel Prizes.

Electronegativity and electron affinity are related but distinct concepts. Both indicate the tendency of an atom to attract electrons. Electron affinity, however, refers to an isolated atom's ability to attract an additional electron in the gas phase, whereas electronegativity refers to the ability of an atom in a chemical bond (with another atom) to attract the *shared* electrons. Electron affinity, moreover, is an experimentally measurable quantity, whereas electronegativity is an estimated number that cannot be measured directly.

Atoms of elements with widely different electronegativities tend to form ionic compounds with each other because the atom of the less electronegative element gives up its electrons to the atom of the more electronegative element. Atoms of elements with comparable electronegativities tend to form polar covalent bonds, or simply polar bonds, with each other because the shift in electron density from one atom to the other is usually small. Only atoms of the same element, which have the same electronegativity, can be joined by a *pure* covalent bond.

There is no sharp distinction between *nonpolar covalent* and *polar covalent* or between *polar covalent* and *ionic,* but the following guidelines can help distinguish among them:

- A bond between atoms whose electronegativities differ by less than 0.5 is generally considered purely covalent or ***nonpolar.***
- A bond between atoms whose electronegativities differ by the range of 0.5 to 2.0 is generally considered *polar covalent.*
- A bond between atoms whose electronegativities differ by 2.0 or more is generally considered *ionic.*

Multi 6.2
Chemical bonding—ionic covalent and polar covalent bonds

Sometimes chemists describe bonds using the term *percent ionic character.* A purely ionic bond would have 100 percent ionic character (although no such bond is known). A purely covalent, nonpolar bond has 0 percent ionic character.

Worked Example 6.1 shows how to use electronegativities to determine whether a chemical bond is nonpolar, polar, or ionic.

Worked Example 6.1

Classify the following bonds as nonpolar, polar, or ionic: (a) the bond in ClF, (b) the bond in CsBr, and (c) the carbon-carbon double bond in C_2H_4.

Strategy Using the information in Figure 6.4, determine which bonds have identical, similar, and widely different electronegativities.

Setup Electronegativity values from Figure 6.4 are: Cl (3.0), F (4.0), Cs (0.7), Br (2.8), C (2.5).

Solution

(a) The difference between the electronegativities of F and Cl is $4.0 - 3.0 = 1.0$, making the bond in ClF polar.

(b) In CsBr, the difference is $2.8 - 0.7 = 2.1$, making the bond ionic.

(c) In C_2H_4, the two atoms are identical. (Not only are they the same element, but each C atom is bonded to two H atoms.) The carbon-carbon double bond in C_2H_4 is nonpolar.

> **Think About It**
> By convention, the difference in electronegativity is always calculated by subtracting the smaller number from the larger one, so the result is always positive.

Practice Problem A Classify the following bonds as nonpolar, polar, or ionic: (a) the bonds in H_2S, (b) the H—O bonds in H_2O_2, and (c) the O—O bond in H_2O_2.

Practice Problem B Using data from Figure 6.4, list all the main group elements that can form ionic compounds with N.

Dipole Moment, Partial Charges, and Percent Ionic Character

The shift of electron density in a polar bond is symbolized by placing a crossed arrow (a dipole arrow) above the Lewis structure to indicate the direction of the shift. For example,

$$\overset{\longmapsto}{H} - \ddot{\ddot{F}}:$$

The consequent charge separation can be represented as

$$\overset{\delta+}{H}\!-\!\overset{\delta-}{\ddot{\underset{\cdot\cdot}{F}}}\!:$$

Student Annotation: The distance, r, between partial charges in a polar diatomic molecule is the bond length expressed in meters. Bond lengths are usually given in angstroms (Å), or picometers (pm), so it is generally necessary to convert to meters.

where the deltas denote partial positive and negative charges. A quantitative measure of the polarity of a bond is its **dipole moment (μ)**, which is calculated as the product of the charge (Q) and the distance (r) between the charges:

Equation 6.1 $\qquad\qquad\qquad\qquad \mu = Q \times r$

In order for a diatomic molecule containing a polar bond to be electrically neutral, the partial positive and partial negative charges must have the same magnitude. Therefore, the Q term in Equation 6.1 refers to the magnitude of the partial charges and the calculated value of μ is always positive. Dipole moments are usually expressed in debye units (D), named for Peter Debye.[2] In terms of more familiar SI units,

Student Annotation: We usually express the charge on an electron as -1. This refers to *units of electronic charge*. However, remember that the charge on an electron can also be expressed in *coulombs* [◄◄ Section 2.2]. The conversion factor between the two is necessary to calculate dipole moments: $1\,e^- = 1.6022 \times 10^{-19}$ C.

$$1\ D = 3.336 \times 10^{-30}\ C \cdot m$$

where C is coulombs and m is meters. Table 6.2 lists several polar diatomic molecules, their bond lengths, and their experimentally measured dipole moments.

Worked Example 6.2 shows how to use bond lengths and dipole moments to determine the magnitude of the partial charges in a polar diatomic molecule.

TABLE 6.2	Bond Lengths and Dipole Moments of the Hydrogen Halides	
Molecule	**Bond length (Å)**	**Dipole moment (D)**
HF	0.92	1.82
HCl	1.27	1.08
HBr	1.41	0.82
HI	1.61	0.44

Student Annotation: Hydrofluoric acid has several important industrial applications, including the etching of glass and the manufacture of electronic components.

Worked Example 6.2

Burns caused by hydrofluoric acid [HF(aq)] are unlike any other acid burns and present unique medical complications. HF solutions typically penetrate the skin and damage internal tissues, including bone, often with minimal surface damage. Less concentrated solutions actually can cause greater injury than more concentrated ones by penetrating more deeply before causing injury, thus delaying the onset of symptoms and preventing timely treatment. Determine the magnitude of the partial positive and partial negative charges in the HF molecule.

Strategy Rearrange Equation 6.1 to solve for Q. Convert the resulting charge in coulombs to charge in units of electronic charge.

Setup According to Table 6.2, $\mu = 1.82$ D and $r = 0.92$ Å for HF. The dipole moment must be converted from debye to C · m and the distance between the ions must be converted to meters.

$$\mu = 1.82\ D \times \frac{3.336 \times 10^{-30}\ C \cdot m}{1\ D} = 6.07 \times 10^{-30}\ C \cdot m$$

$$r = 0.92\ \mathring{A} \times \frac{1 \times 10^{-10}\ m}{1\ \mathring{A}} = 9.2 \times 10^{-11}\ m$$

---

[2]Peter Joseph William Debye (1884–1966). An American chemist and physicist of Dutch origin, Debye made many significant contributions to the study of molecular structure, polymer chemistry, X-ray analysis, and electrolyte solutions. He was awarded the Nobel Prize in Chemistry in 1936.

Solution In coulombs:

$$Q = \frac{\mu}{r} = \frac{6.07 \times 10^{-30}\ \text{C} \cdot \text{m}}{9.2 \times 10^{-11}\ \text{m}} = 6.598 \times 10^{-20}\ \text{C}$$

In units of electronic charge:

$$6.598 \times 10^{-20}\ \text{C} \times \frac{1\ e^-}{1.6022 \times 10^{-19}\ \text{C}} = 0.41\ e^-$$

Therefore, the partial charges in HF are +0.41 and −0.41 on H and F, respectively.

$$^{+0.41}\text{H}—\ddot{\underset{..}{\text{F}}}:^{-0.41}$$

> **Think About It**
> Calculated partial charges should always be less than 1. If a "partial" charge were 1 or greater, it would indicate that at least one electron had been transferred from one atom to the other. Remember that polar bonds involve unequal *sharing* of electrons, not a complete transfer of electrons.

Practice Problem A Using data from Table 6.2, determine the magnitude of the partial charges in HBr.

Practice Problem B Given that the partial charges on C and O in carbon monoxide are +0.020 and −0.020, respectively, calculate the dipole moment of CO. (The distance between the partial charges, *r*, is 113 pm.)

Although the designations "covalent," "polar covalent," and "ionic" can be useful, sometimes chemists wish to describe and compare chemical bonds with more precision. For this purpose, we can use Equation 6.1 to calculate the dipole moment we would *expect* if the charges on the atoms were discrete instead of partial; that is, if an electron had actually been transferred from one atom to the other. Comparing this calculated dipole moment with the measured value gives us a quantitative way to describe the nature of a bond using the term *percent ionic character*. **Percent ionic character** is defined as the ratio of observed μ to calculated μ, multiplied by 100.

$$\text{percent ionic character} = \frac{\mu\ (\text{observed})}{\mu\ (\text{calculated assuming discrete charges})} \times 100\% \qquad \textbf{Equation 6.2}$$

Figure 6.6 illustrates the relationship between percent ionic character and the electronegativity difference in a heteronuclear diatomic molecule.

Figure 6.6 Relationship between percent ionic character and electronegativity difference.

Worked Example 6.3 shows how to calculate percent ionic character using Equation 6.2.

Worked Example 6.3

Using data from Table 6.2, calculate the percent ionic character of the bond in HI.

Strategy Use Equation 6.1 to calculate the dipole moment in HI assuming that the charges on H and I are +1 and −1, respectively; and use Equation 6.2 to calculate percent ionic character. The magnitude of the charges must be expressed as coulombs (1 e^- = 1.6022 × 10^{-19} C); the bond length (r) must be expressed as meters (1 Å = 1 × 10^{-10} m); and the calculated dipole moment should be expressed as debyes (1 D = 3.336 × 10^{-30} C · m).

Setup From Table 6.2, the bond length in HI is 1.61 Å (1.61 × 10^{-10} m) and the measured dipole moment of HI is 0.44 D.

Solution The dipole we would expect if the magnitude of charges were 1.6022 × 10^{-19} C is

$$\mu = Q \times r = (1.6022 \times 10^{-19}\ \text{C}) \times (1.61 \times 10^{-10}\ \text{m}) = 2.58 \times 10^{-29}\ \text{C} \cdot \text{m}$$

Converting to debyes gives

$$2.58 \times 10^{-29}\ \cancel{\text{C} \cdot \text{m}} \times \frac{1\ \text{D}}{3.336 \times 10^{-30}\ \cancel{\text{C} \cdot \text{m}}} = 7.73\ \text{D}$$

The percent ionic character of the H—I bond is $\dfrac{0.44\ \text{D}}{7.73\ \text{D}} \times 100\% = 5.7\%$.

Think About It
A purely covalent bond (in a homonuclear diatomic molecule such as H$_2$) would have 0 percent ionic character. In theory, a purely ionic bond would be expected to have 100 percent ionic character, although no such bond is known.

Practice Problem A Using data from Table 6.2, calculate the percent ionic character of the bond in HF.

Practice Problem B Using information from Figure 4.13 (page 127), and given that the NaI bond has 59.7 percent ionic character, determine the measured dipole moment of NaI.

SECTION 6.2 REVIEW

Electronegativity and Polarity

6.2.1   In which of the following molecules are the bonds most polar? H$_2$O, BCl$_3$, PCl$_5$

6.2.2   Arrange molecules A through E in order of increasing percent ionic character.

6.2.3   Using data from Table 6.2, calculate the magnitude of the partial charges in HI.

6.2.4   Using data from Table 6.2, calculate the percent ionic character of HCl.

6.3 DRAWING LEWIS STRUCTURES

Although the octet rule and Lewis structures alone do not present a complete picture of covalent bonding, they do help us account for some of the properties of molecules and polyatomic ions. In addition, Lewis structures provide a starting point for the bonding theories that we will examine in Chapter 7. It is crucial, therefore, that you learn a system for drawing correct Lewis structures for molecules and polyatomic ions. The basic steps are as follows:

1. From the molecular formula, draw the skeletal structure of the compound, using chemical symbols and placing bonded atoms next to one another. For simple compounds, this step is fairly easy. Often there will be a unique central atom surrounded by a group of other identical atoms. In general, the *least* electronegative atom will be the central atom. Draw a single covalent bond (dash) between the central atom and each of the surrounding atoms. (For more complex compounds whose structures might not be obvious, you may need to be given information in addition to the molecular formula.)

2. Count the total number of valence electrons present. Remember that an element's *group number* (1A–8A) gives the number of valence electrons it contributes to the total number. For polyatomic ions, add electrons to the total number to account for negative charges; subtract electrons from the total number to account for positive charges.

3. For each bond (dash) in the skeletal structure, subtract two electrons from the total valence electrons (determined in step 2) to determine the number of remaining electrons.

4. Use the remaining electrons to complete the octets of the terminal atoms (those bonded to the central atom) by placing pairs of electrons on each atom. (Remember that an H atom only requires two electrons to complete its valence shell.) If there is more than one type of terminal atom, complete the octets of the most electronegative atoms first.

5. If any electrons remain after step 4, place them in pairs on the central atom.

6. If the central atom has fewer than eight electrons after completing steps 1 to 5, move one or more pairs from the terminal atoms to form multiple bonds between the central atom and the terminal atoms.

Student Annotation: H cannot be a central atom because it only forms *one* covalent bond.

Steps for Drawing Lewis Structures

Step	CH₄	CCl₄	H₂O	O₂	CN⁻
1	H—C—H (with H top and bottom)	Cl—C—Cl (with Cl top and bottom)	H—O—H	O—O	C—N
2	8	32	8	12	10
3	$8 - 8 = 0$	$32 - 8 = 24$	$8 - 4 = 4$	$12 - 2 = 10$	$10 - 2 = 8$
4	H—C—H (with H top and bottom)	:Cl̈—C—Cl̈: (with :Cl̈: top and bottom)	H—O—H	:Ö—Ö:	:C—N̈:
5	—	—	H—Ö—H	—	—
6	—	—	—	:O=O:	[:C≡N:]⁻

Student Annotation: To summarize the process of drawing Lewis structures:

1. Draw the skeletal structure.
2. Count the valence electrons.
3. Subtract two electrons for each bond.
4. Complete the octets of as many terminal atoms as possible.
5. Place any remaining electrons on the central atom.
6. Use multiple bonds if necessary to complete the octets of all atoms.

Student Annotation: Like Lewis dot symbols for atomic anions, Lewis structures for polyatomic anions are enclosed by square brackets.

Worked Example 6.4 shows how to draw a Lewis structure.

Worked Example 6.4

Draw the Lewis structure for carbon disulfide (CS_2).

Strategy Use the procedure described in steps 1 through 6 on page 193 for drawing Lewis structures.

Setup

Step 1: C and S have identical electronegativities. We will draw the skeletal structure with the unique atom, C, at the center.

$$S-C-S$$

Step 2: The total number of valence electrons is 16: 6 from each S atom and 4 from the C atom $[2(6) + 4 = 16]$.

Step 3: Subtract 4 electrons to account for the bonds in the skeletal structure, leaving us 12 electrons to distribute.

Step 4: Distribute the 12 remaining electrons as 3 lone pairs on each S atom.

$$:\ddot{S}-C-\ddot{S}:$$

Step 5: There are no electrons remaining after step 4, so step 5 does not apply.

Step 6: To complete carbon's octet, use one lone pair from each S atom to make a double bond to the C atom.

Solution

$$:\ddot{S}=C=\ddot{S}:$$

> **Think About It**
> Counting the total number of valence electrons should be relatively simple to do, but it is often done hastily and is therefore a potential source of error in this type of problem. Remember that the number of valence electrons for each element is equal to the group number of that element.

Practice Problem A Draw the Lewis structure for NF_3.

Practice Problem B Draw the Lewis structure for ClO_3^-.

SECTION 6.3 REVIEW

Drawing Lewis Structures

6.3.1   Draw the correct Lewis structure for formic acid (HCOOH).

6.3.2   Draw the correct Lewis structure for hydrogen peroxide (H_2O_2).

6.4   LEWIS STRUCTURES AND FORMAL CHARGE

So far you have learned one method of electron "bookkeeping." In Section 6.2, you learned how to calculate partial charges. There is one additional commonly used method of electron bookkeeping—namely, *formal charge,* which can be used to determine the most plausible Lewis structures when more than one possibility exists for a compound. Formal charge is determined by comparing the number of electrons associated with an atom in a Lewis structure with the number of electrons that would be associated with the isolated atom. In an isolated atom, the number of electrons associated with the atom is simply the number of valence electrons. (As usual, we need not be concerned with the core electrons.)

Multi 6.3
Chemical bonding—formal charge calculations

To determine the number of electrons associated with an atom in a Lewis structure, keep in mind the following:

- All the atom's nonbonding electrons are associated with the atom.
- Half of the atom's bonding electrons are associated with the atom.

An atom's formal charge is calculated as follows:

$$\text{formal charge} = \text{valence electrons} - \text{associated electrons} \qquad \textbf{Equation 6.3}$$

We can illustrate the concept of formal charge using the ozone molecule (O_3). Use the step-by-step method for drawing Lewis structures to draw the Lewis structure for ozone, and then determine the formal charge on each O atom by subtracting the number of associated electrons from the number of valence electrons.

$$2 \text{ unshared} + \frac{6 \text{ shared}}{2} = 5\, e^-$$

$$4 \text{ unshared} + \frac{4 \text{ shared}}{2} = 6\, e^- \qquad\qquad 6 \text{ unshared} + \frac{2 \text{ shared}}{2} = 7\, e^-$$

Valence e^-	6	6	6
$-$ Associated e^-	6	5	7
Difference (formal charge)	0	$+1$	-1

:Ö=Ö—Ö:

Student Annotation: While you are new at determining formal charges, it may be helpful to draw Lewis structures with all dots, rather than dashes. This can make it easier to see how many electrons are associated with each atom.

Remember that for the purpose of counting associated electrons, those shared by two atoms are evenly split between them.

The sum of the formal charges must equal the overall charge on the species. Because O_3 is a molecule, its formal charges must sum to zero. For ions, the formal charges must sum to the overall charge on the ion.

Formal charges do *not* represent actual charges on atoms in a molecule. In the O_3 molecule, for example, there is no evidence that the central atom bears a net $+1$ charge or that one of the terminal atoms bears a -1 charge. Assigning formal charges to the atoms in the Lewis structure merely helps us keep track of the electrons involved in bonding in the molecule.

Worked Example 6.5 lets you practice determining formal charges.

Worked Example 6.5

The widespread use of fertilizers has resulted in the contamination of some groundwater with nitrates, which are potentially harmful. Nitrate toxicity is due primarily to its conversion in the body to nitrite (NO_2^-), which interferes with the ability of hemoglobin to transport oxygen. Determine the formal charges on each atom in the nitrate ion (NO_3^-).

Strategy Use steps 1 through 6 on page 193 for drawing Lewis structures to draw the Lewis structure of (NO_3^-). For each atom, subtract the associated electrons from the valence electrons.

Setup

$$\left[\begin{array}{c} \ddot{\text{O}}\text{:} \\ | \\ \text{:}\ddot{\text{O}}\text{—N}=\ddot{\text{O}}\text{:} \end{array} \right]^-$$

The N atom has five valence electrons and four associated electrons (one from each single bond and two from the double bond). Each singly bonded O atom has six valence electrons and seven associated electrons (six in three lone pairs and one from the single bond). The doubly bonded O atom has six valence electrons and six associated electrons (four in two lone pairs and two from the double bond).

Solution The formal charges are as follows: $+1$ (N atom), -1 (singly bonded O atoms), and 0 (doubly bonded O atom).

(Continued on next page)

Think About It
The sum of formal charges $(+1) + (-1) + (-1) + (0) = -1$ is equal to the overall charge on the nitrate ion.

Practice Problem A Determine the formal charges on each atom in the carbonate ion (CO_3^{2-}).

Practice Problem B Determine the formal charges and use them to determine the overall charge, if any, on the species represented by the following Lewis structure:

$$\begin{bmatrix} :\ddot{O}: \\ | \\ :\ddot{O}-\underset{..}{\overset{..}{S}}-\ddot{O}: \end{bmatrix}^{?}$$

Sometimes, there is more than one possible skeletal arrangement of atoms for the Lewis structure for a given species. In such cases, we often can select the best skeletal arrangement by using formal charges and the following guidelines:

- For molecules, a Lewis structure in which all formal charges are zero is preferred to one in which there are nonzero formal charges.
- Lewis structures with small formal charges (0 and ±1) are preferred to those with large formal charges (±2, ±3, and so on).
- The best skeletal arrangement of atoms will give rise to Lewis structures in which the formal charges are consistent with electronegativities. For example, the more electronegative atoms should have the more negative formal charges.

Worked Example 6.6 shows how formal charge can be used to determine the best skeletal arrangement of atoms for the Lewis structure of a molecule or polyatomic ion.

Worked Example 6.6

Formaldehyde (CH_2O), which can be used to preserve biological specimens, is commonly sold as a 37 percent aqueous solution. Use formal charges to determine which skeletal arrangement of atoms shown here is the best choice for the Lewis structure of CH_2O.

$$H-C-O-H \qquad \overset{\overset{O}{|}}{H-C-H}$$

Strategy Complete the Lewis structures for each of the CH_2O skeletons shown and determine the formal charges on the atoms in each one.

Setup The completed Lewis structures for the skeletons shown are:

$$H-\ddot{C}=\ddot{O}-H \qquad \overset{\overset{\cdot\ddot{O}\cdot}{\|}}{H-C-H}$$

In the structure on the left, the formal charges are as follows:

Both H atoms: 1 valence e^- − 1 associated e^- (from single bond) = 0

C atom: 4 valence e^- − 5 associated e^- (two in the lone pair, one from the single bond, and two from the double bond) = −1

O atom: 6 valence e^- − 5 associated e^- (two from the lone pair, one from the single bond, and two from the double bond) = +1

$$H-\ddot{C}=\ddot{O}-H$$
$$\text{Formal charges} \quad 0 \quad -1 \ +1 \ \ 0$$

In the structure on the right, the formal charges are as follows:

Both H atoms: 1 valence e^- − 1 associated e^- (from single bond) = 0

C atom: 4 valence e^- − 4 associated e^- (one from each single bond, and two from the double bond) = 0

O atom: 6 valence e^- − 6 associated e^- (four from the two lone pairs and two from the double bond) = 0

$$\overset{\displaystyle \overset{\cdot\cdot}{\underset{\cdot\cdot}{O}}}{\underset{\displaystyle H-C-H}{\|}}$$

Formal charges all zero

Solution Of the two possible arrangements, the structure on the left has an O atom with a positive formal charge, which is inconsistent with oxygen's high electronegativity. Therefore, the structure on the right, in which both H atoms are attached directly to the C atom and all atoms have a formal charge of zero, is the better choice for the Lewis structure of CH_2O.

> **Think About It**
> For a molecule, formal charges of zero are preferred. When there are nonzero formal charges, they should be consistent with the electronegativities of the atoms in the molecule. A positive formal charge on oxygen, for example, is inconsistent with oxygen's high electronegativity.

Practice Problem A Two possible arrangements are shown for the Lewis structure of a carboxyl group, —COOH. Use formal charges to determine which of the two arrangements is better.

$$\overset{\displaystyle \overset{\cdot\cdot}{O}}{\underset{\displaystyle -\overset{}{C}-\overset{\cdot\cdot}{\underset{\cdot\cdot}{O}}-H}{\|}} \qquad -\overset{\cdot}{C}-\overset{\cdot\cdot}{O}=\overset{\cdot\cdot}{O}-H$$

Practice Problem B Use Lewis structures and formal charges to determine the best skeletal arrangement of atoms in (NCl_2^-).

SECTION 6.4 REVIEW

Lewis Structures and Formal Charge

6.4.1 Determine the formal charges on H, C, and N, respectively, in HCN.

6.4.2 Draw three different valid Lewis structures for NCO^- and determine using formal charges which is most likely the preferred structure.

6.5 RESONANCE

Our drawing of the Lewis structure for ozone (O_3) satisfied the octet rule for the central O atom because we placed a double bond between it and one of the two terminal O atoms. In fact, we can put the double bond at either end of the molecule, as shown by the following two equivalent Lewis structures:

$$\overset{\cdot\cdot}{O}=\overset{\cdot\cdot}{O}-\overset{\cdot\cdot}{\underset{\cdot\cdot}{O}}: \quad \longleftrightarrow \quad :\overset{\cdot\cdot}{\underset{\cdot\cdot}{O}}-\overset{\cdot\cdot}{O}=\overset{\cdot\cdot}{O}:$$

A single bond between O atoms should be longer than a double bond between O atoms, but experimental evidence indicates that both of the bonds in O_3 are equal in length (128 pm). Because neither one of these two Lewis structures accounts for the known bond lengths in O_3, we use both Lewis structures to represent the ozone molecule.

Each of the Lewis structures is called a resonance structure. A ***resonance structure*** is one of two or more equally valid Lewis structures for a single species that cannot be represented accurately by a single Lewis structure. The double-headed arrow (⟷) indicates that the structures shown are resonance structures. Like the medieval European traveler to Africa who described a rhinoceros as a cross between a griffin and a unicorn (two familiar but imaginary animals), we describe ozone, a real molecule, in terms of two familiar but nonexistent structures.

A common misconception about resonance is that a molecule such as ozone somehow shifts quickly back and forth from one resonance structure to the other. In fact, neither resonance structure adequately represents the actual molecule, which has its own unique, stable structure. "Resonance" is a human invention, designed to address the limitations of a simple bonding model. To extend the animal analogy, a rhinoceros is a distinct, real creature, not some oscillation between the mythical griffin and unicorn!

The carbonate ion provides another example of resonance:

$$
\left[\begin{array}{c} :\ddot{O}: \\ | \\ \ddot{O}=C-\ddot{O}: \end{array}\right]^{2-} \longleftrightarrow \left[\begin{array}{c} \cdot\ddot{O}\cdot \\ || \\ :\ddot{O}-C-\ddot{O}: \end{array}\right]^{2-} \longleftrightarrow \left[\begin{array}{c} :\ddot{O}: \\ | \\ :\ddot{O}-C=\ddot{O} \end{array}\right]^{2-}
$$

According to experimental evidence, all three carbon-oxygen bonds in CO_3^{2-} are equivalent. Therefore, the properties of the carbonate ion are best explained by considering its resonance structures together.

The concept of resonance applies equally well to organic systems. A good example is the benzene molecule (C_6H_6):

If one of these resonance structures corresponded to the actual structure of benzene, there would be two different bond lengths between adjacent C atoms, one with the properties of a single bond and the other with the properties of a double bond. In fact, the distance between all adjacent C atoms in benzene is 140 pm, which is shorter than a C—C bond (154 pm) and longer than a C=C bond (133 pm).

A simpler way of drawing the structure of the benzene molecule and other compounds containing the benzene ring is to show only the skeleton and not the carbon and hydrogen atoms. By this convention, the resonance structures are represented by

Student Annotation: The representation of organic compounds is discussed in more detail in Chapter 24.

Note that the C atoms at the corners of the hexagon and the H atoms are not shown, although they are understood to be there. Only the bonds between the C atoms are shown.

Resonance structures differ only in the positions of their *electrons*—not in the positions of their atoms. Thus, $:\ddot{N}=N=\ddot{O}:$ and $:N\equiv N-\ddot{O}:$ are resonance structures of each other, whereas $:\ddot{N}=N=\ddot{O}:$ and $:\ddot{N}=O=\ddot{N}:$ are not.

Worked Example 6.7 shows how to draw resonance structures.

Worked Example 6.7

High oil and gasoline prices have renewed interest in alternative methods of producing energy, including the "clean" burning of coal. Part of what makes "dirty" coal *dirty* is its high sulfur content. Burning dirty coal produces sulfur dioxide (SO_2), among other pollutants. Sulfur dioxide is oxidized in the atmosphere to form sulfur trioxide (SO_3), which subsequently combines with water to produce sulfuric acid—a major component of acid rain. Draw all possible resonance structures of sulfur trioxide.

Strategy Draw two or more Lewis structures for SO_3 in which the atoms are arranged the same way but the electrons are arranged differently.

Setup Following the steps for drawing Lewis structures, we determine that a correct Lewis structure for SO_3 contains two sulfur-oxygen single bonds and one sulfur-oxygen double bond.

$$
\begin{array}{c} :\ddot{O}: \\ | \\ :\ddot{O}=S-\ddot{O}: \end{array}
$$

But the double bond can be put in any one of three positions in the molecule.

Solution

$$:\ddot{O}: \quad\quad \ddot{O} \quad\quad :\ddot{O}:$$
$$\ddot{O}=\overset{\mid}{S}-\ddot{O}: \quad\longleftrightarrow\quad :\ddot{O}-\overset{\parallel}{S}-\ddot{O}: \quad\longleftrightarrow\quad :\ddot{O}-\overset{\mid}{S}=\ddot{O}:$$

> **Think About It**
> Always make sure that resonance structures differ only in the positions of the electrons, *not* in the positions of the atoms.

Practice Problem A Draw all possible resonance structures for the nitrate ion (NO_3^-).

Practice Problem B Draw three resonance structures for the thiocyanate ion (NCS^-), and determine the formal charges in each resonance structure.

SECTION 6.5 REVIEW

Resonance

6.5.1 How many resonance structures can be drawn for the nitrite ion (NO_2^-)? (N and O must obey the octet rule.)

6.5.2 Draw all resonance structures of SO_2. (S and O must obey the octet rule.)

6.6 EXCEPTIONS TO THE OCTET RULE

The octet rule almost always holds for second-period elements. Exceptions to the octet rule fall into three categories:

1. The central atom has fewer than eight electrons due to a shortage of electrons.
2. The central atom has fewer than eight electrons due to an odd number of electrons.
3. The central atom has more than eight electrons.

Incomplete Octets

In some compounds, the number of electrons surrounding the central atom in a stable molecule is fewer than eight. Beryllium, for example, which is the Group 2A element in the second period, has the electron configuration $[He]2s^2$. Thus, it has two valence electrons in the $2s$ orbital. In the gas phase, beryllium hydride (BeH_2) exists as discrete molecules. The Lewis structure of BeH_2 is

$$H{-}Be{-}H$$

Only four electrons surround the Be atom, so there is no way to satisfy the octet rule for beryllium in this molecule.

Elements in Group 3A also tend to form compounds in which they are surrounded by fewer than eight electrons. Boron, for example, has the electron configuration $[He]2s^22p^1$, so it has only three valence electrons. Boron reacts with the halogens to form a class of compounds having the general formula BX_3, where X is a halogen atom. Thus, there are only six electrons around the boron atom in boron trifluoride:

$$:\ddot{F}:$$
$$:\ddot{F}-\overset{\mid}{B}-\ddot{F}:$$

Thinking Outside the Box

Species with Unpaired Electrons

Beginning about a week after the September 11, 2001, attacks, letters containing anthrax bacteria were mailed to several news media offices and to two U.S. Senators. Of the 22 people who subsequently contracted anthrax, 5 died. Anthrax is a spore-forming bacterium (*Bacillus anthracis*) and, like smallpox, is classified by the CDC as a *Category A bioterrorism agent*. Spore-forming bacteria are notoriously difficult to kill, making the cleanup of the buildings contaminated by anthrax costly and time-consuming. The American Media Inc. (AMI) building in Boca Raton, Florida, was not deemed safe to enter until July of 2004, after it had been treated with chlorine dioxide (ClO_2), the only structural fumigant approved by the Environmental Protection Agency (EPA) for anthrax decontamination. The effectiveness of ClO_2 in killing anthrax and other hardy biological agents stems in part from its being a *radical,* meaning that it contains an odd number of electrons.

While ClO_2 is normally produced at a required site using a chlorine dioxide generator, radicals occur naturally in a number of places ranging from interstellar space to the human body. The hydroxyl radical ($OH\cdot$) was first detected in interstellar space in 1963 but is also found in the atmosphere and mammalian cells. In the troposphere, hydroxyl radical interacts with various air pollutants; in cells, this same species attacks macromolecules such as carbohydrates, amino acids, and DNA—potentially leading to cancer. The superoxide radical (O_2^-) is generated in humans as part of the immune response but excess amounts are harmful. Fortunately, the enzyme *superoxide dismutase* can provide some protection by "scavenging" this biologically toxic radical. Finally, nitric oxide (NO) is an important radical species involved in a number of signaling roles in cells.

The American Media Inc. building in Boca Raton, Florida.

We actually *can* satisfy the octet rule for boron in BF_3 by using a lone pair on one of the F atoms to form a double bond between the F atom and boron. This gives rise to three additional resonance structures:

$$:\!\ddot{F}\!: \qquad\qquad \dot{\ddot{F}} \qquad\qquad :\!\ddot{F}\!:$$
$$:\!\ddot{F}\!\!=\!\!B\!\!-\!\!\ddot{F}\!: \quad\longleftrightarrow\quad :\!\ddot{F}\!\!-\!\!B\!\!-\!\!\ddot{F}\!: \quad\longleftrightarrow\quad :\!\ddot{F}\!\!-\!\!B\!\!=\!\!\ddot{F}\!:$$

Although these resonance structures result in boron carrying a negative formal charge while fluorine carries a positive formal charge, a situation that is inconsistent with the electronegativities of the atoms involved, the experimentally determined bond length in BF_3 (130.9 pm) is shorter than a single bond (137.3 pm). The shorter bond length would appear to support the idea behind the three resonance structures.

On the other hand, boron trifluoride combines with ammonia to give a species in which boron's octet is complete. This is easier to picture starting with the resonance structure in which boron has only six valence electrons around it:

$$:\!\ddot{F}\!: \qquad\qquad H \qquad\qquad\qquad\qquad :\!\ddot{F}\!:\ \ H$$
$$:\!\ddot{F}\!\!-\!\!B \quad+\quad :\!N\!\!-\!\!H \quad\longrightarrow\quad :\!\ddot{F}\!\!-\!\!B\!\!-\!\!N\!\!-\!\!H$$
$$:\!\ddot{F}\!: \qquad\qquad H \qquad\qquad\qquad\qquad :\!\ddot{F}\!:\ \ H$$

No *one* of the three resonance structures is sufficient to describe the bonding in BF_3. Rather, *all* of them are necessary to account for the physical and chemical properties that we observe.

The B—N bond in F_3B—NH_3 is different from the covalent bonds discussed so far in the sense that both electrons are contributed by the N atom. This type of bond is called a ***coordinate covalent bond*** (also referred to as a ***dative bond***), which is defined as a covalent bond in which one of the atoms donates both electrons. Although the properties of a coordinate covalent bond do not differ from those of a normal covalent bond (i.e., the electrons are shared in both cases), the distinction is useful for keeping track of valence electrons and assigning formal charges.

> **Student Annotation:** When experimental evidence supports the "correctness" of a resonance structure, we say that the resonance structure is "important." If the experimental evidence supports a particular resonance structure more strongly than the others, we call that resonance structure "more important."

Odd Numbers of Electrons

Some molecules, such as nitrogen dioxide (NO_2), contain an odd number of electrons.

$$:\!\ddot{O}\!\!=\!\!\dot{N}\!\!-\!\!\ddot{O}\!:$$

Because we need an even number of electrons for every atom in a molecule to have a complete octet, the octet rule cannot be obeyed for all the atoms in these molecules. Molecules with an odd number of electrons are sometimes referred to as *free radicals* (or just *radicals*). Many radicals are highly reactive, because there is a tendency for the unpaired electron to form a covalent bond with an unpaired electron on another molecule. When two nitrogen dioxide molecules collide, for example, they form dinitrogen tetroxide, a molecule in which the octet rule *is* satisfied for both the N and O atoms.

Worked Example 6.8 lets you practice drawing Lewis structures for a species with an odd number of electrons.

Worked Example 6.8

Draw the Lewis structure of chlorine dioxide (ClO_2).

Strategy The skeletal structure is

$$O-Cl-O$$

This puts the unique atom, Cl, in the center and puts the more electronegative O atoms in terminal positions.

Setup There are a total of 19 valence electrons (7 from the Cl and 6 from each of the two O atoms). We subtract 4 electrons to account for the two bonds in the skeleton, leaving us with 15 electrons to distribute as follows: three lone pairs on each O atom, one lone pair on the Cl atom, and the last remaining electron also on the Cl atom.

Solution

$$:\ddot{O}-\ddot{Cl}-\ddot{O}:$$

> **Think About It**
> ClO_2 is used primarily to bleach wood pulp in the manufacture of paper, but it is also used to bleach flour, disinfect drinking water, and deodorize certain industrial facilities. Recently, it has been used to eradicate the toxic mold in homes in New Orleans that were damaged by the devastating floodwaters of Hurricane Katrina in 2005.

Practice Problem A Draw the Lewis structure for the OH species.

Practice Problem B Draw the Lewis structure for the NS_2 molecule.

Severe flooding in New Orleans after Hurricane Katrina in 2005.

> **Student Annotation:** The OH species is a *radical*, not to be confused with the hydroxide *ion* (OH^-).

Expanded Octets

Atoms of the second-period elements cannot have more than eight valence electrons around them, but atoms of elements in and beyond the third period of the periodic table can. In addition to the $3s$ and $3p$ orbitals, elements in the third period also have $3d$ orbitals that can be used in bonding. These orbitals enable an atom to form an *expanded octet*. One compound in which there is an expanded octet is sulfur hexafluoride, a very stable compound. The electron configuration of sulfur is $[Ne]3s^2 3p^4$. In SF_6, each of sulfur's 6 valence electrons forms a covalent bond with a fluorine atom, so there are 12 electrons around the central sulfur atom:

In Chapter 7, we will see that these 12 electrons, or six bonding pairs, are accommodated in six orbitals that originate from the one $3s$, the three $3p$, and two of the five $3d$ orbitals. Sulfur also forms many compounds in which it does obey the octet rule. In sulfur dichloride, for instance, S is surrounded by only 8 electrons:

Worked Examples 6.9 and 6.10 involve compounds that do not obey the octet rule.

Worked Example 6.9

Draw the Lewis structure of boron triiodide (BI_3).

Strategy Follow the step-by-step procedure for drawing Lewis structures. The skeletal structure is

$$\begin{array}{c} I \\ | \\ I-B-I \end{array}$$

Setup There are a total of 24 valence electrons in BI_3 (3 from the B and 7 from each of the three I atoms). We subtract 6 electrons to account for the three bonds in the skeleton, leaving 18 electrons to distribute as three lone pairs on each I atom.

Solution

$$\begin{array}{c} :\ddot{I}: \\ | \\ :\ddot{I}-B-\ddot{I}: \end{array}$$

> **Think About It**
> Boron is one of the elements that does not always follow the octet rule. Like BF_3, however, BI_3 can be drawn with a double bond in order to satisfy the octet of boron. This gives rise to a total of four resonance structures:
>
> $$\begin{array}{c} :\ddot{I}: \\ | \\ :\ddot{I}-B-\ddot{I}: \end{array} \longleftrightarrow \begin{array}{c} :\ddot{I}: \\ | \\ \cdot\ddot{I}=B-\ddot{I}: \end{array} \longleftrightarrow \begin{array}{c} \cdot\dot{I}\cdot \\ || \\ :\ddot{I}-B-\ddot{I}: \end{array} \longleftrightarrow \begin{array}{c} :\ddot{I}\cdot \\ | \\ :\ddot{I}-B=\ddot{I}\cdot \end{array}$$

Practice Problem A Draw the Lewis structure of beryllium fluoride (BeF_2).

Practice Problem B Draw the Lewis structure of boron trichloride (BCl_3).

Worked Example 6.10

Draw the Lewis structure of arsenic pentafluoride (AsF_5).

Strategy Follow the steps for drawing Lewis structures. The skeletal structure already has more than an octet around the As atom.

$$\begin{array}{c} F \\ F\diagdown\,| \\ \quad As-F \\ F\diagup\,| \\ F \end{array}$$

Setup There are 40 total valence electrons [5 from As (Group 5A) and 7 from each of the five F atoms (Group 7A)]. We subtract 10 electrons to account for the five bonds in the skeleton, leaving 30 to be distributed. Next, we place three lone pairs on each F atom, thereby completing all their octets and using up all the electrons.

Solution

$$\begin{array}{c} :\ddot{F}: \\ :\ddot{F}\diagdown\,| \\ \quad As-\ddot{F}: \\ :\ddot{F}\diagup\,| \\ :\ddot{F}: \end{array}$$

> **Think About It**
> Always make sure that the number of electrons represented in your final Lewis structure matches the total number of valence electrons you are supposed to have.

Practice Problem A Draw the Lewis structure of phosphorus pentachloride (PCl_5).

Practice Problem B Draw the Lewis structure of antimony pentafluoride (SbF_5).

In some cases, a species can be represented by a Lewis structure in which the octet rule is obeyed, or by one in which the central atom has an expanded octet. The sulfate ion (SO_4^{2-}), for example, can be represented by a Structure I, which obeys the octet rule, or by Structure II, which does not.

$$
\begin{bmatrix} :\overset{-1}{\overset{\displaystyle\ddot{O}:}{\underset{\displaystyle:\overset{..}{\underset{..}{O}}:}{\underset{-1}{|}}} \\ {}^{-1}:\overset{..}{\underset{..}{O}} - \overset{+2}{S} - \overset{..}{\underset{..}{O}}:^{-1} \end{bmatrix}^{2-}
\qquad
\begin{bmatrix} :\overset{-1}{\overset{\displaystyle\ddot{O}:}{}} \\ :O = S = O: \\ :\overset{..}{\underset{..}{O}}:_{-1} \end{bmatrix}^{2-}
$$

Structure I   Structure II

In Structure I, although the octet rule is obeyed for the central atom, there are nonzero formal charges (shown in blue) on all of the atoms. In Structure II, by relocating a lone pair from each of two oxygen atoms and creating two double bonds, we change three of the formal charges to zero. Although some chemists have a strong preference for one or the other (structures in which the octet rule is obeyed or structures in which formal charges are minimized), both are valid Lewis structures.

Worked Example 6.11 gives you some practice drawing resonance structures for species that can obey the octet rule, but that also can be drawn with expanded octets to minimize formal charges.

Worked Example 6.11

Draw two resonance structures for sulfurous acid (H_2SO_3): one that obeys the octet rule for the central atom, and one that minimizes the formal charges. Determine the formal charge on each atom in both structures.

Strategy Begin by drawing the skeletal structure and counting the total number of valence electrons. Use the steps outlined in Section 6.4 to draw the first structure and reposition one or more lone pairs to adjust the formal charges for the second structure.

Setup The skeletal structure is

$$
\begin{array}{c} O \\ | \\ H-O-S-O-H \end{array}
$$

Note that each hydrogen in an oxoacid is attached to an oxygen atom, and *not* directly to the central atom. The total number of valence electrons is 26 (6 from S, 6 from each O, and 1 from each H).

Solution Following the steps outlined on page 193, we get the first structure:

$$
\begin{array}{c} :\overset{-1}{\ddot{O}:} \\ | \\ H-\ddot{O}-\overset{+1}{S}-\ddot{O}-H \end{array}
$$

From the top O atom, which has three lone pairs, we reposition one lone pair to create a double bond between O and S to get the second structure:

$$
\begin{array}{c} \ddot{O} \\ || \\ H-\ddot{O}-S-\ddot{O}-H \end{array}
$$

Incorporating the double bond results in every atom having a formal charge of zero.

> **Think About It**
> In some species, such as the sulfate ion, it is possible to incorporate too many double bonds. Structures with *three* and *four* double bonds to sulfur would give formal charges on S and O that are inconsistent with the electronegativities of these elements. In general, if you are trying to minimize formal charges by expanding the central atom's octet, only add enough double bonds to make the formal charge on the central atom zero.

Practice Problem A Draw three resonance structures for the hydrogen sulfite ion (HSO_3^-), one that obeys the octet rule for the central atom, and two that expand the octet of the central atom. Calculate the formal charges on all atoms in each structure and determine which, if any, of the resonance structures has formal charges that are inconsistent with the elements' electronegativities.

Practice Problem B Draw two resonance structures for each species—one that obeys the octet rule, and one in which the formal charge on the central atom is zero: PO_4^{3-}, $HClO_3$, SO_3, SO_2.

When drawing Lewis structures of compounds containing a central atom from the third period and beyond, occasionally you may find that the octet rule is satisfied for all the atoms before all the valence electrons have been distributed. When this happens, the extra electrons should be placed as lone pairs on the central atom. Worked Example 6.12 illustrates this approach.

Worked Example 6.12

Draw the Lewis structure of xenon tetrafluoride (XeF_4).

Strategy Follow the steps for drawing Lewis structures. The skeletal structure is

$$
\begin{array}{c}
\text{F} \\
| \\
\text{F}-\text{Xe}-\text{F} \\
| \\
\text{F}
\end{array}
$$

Setup There are 36 total valence electrons (8 from Xe and 7 from each of the four F atoms). We subtract 8 electrons to account for the bonds in the skeleton, leaving 28 to distribute. We first complete the octets of all four F atoms. When this is done, 4 electrons remain, so we place two lone pairs on the Xe atom.

Solution

$$
\begin{array}{c}
:\ddot{\text{F}}: \\
| \\
:\ddot{\text{F}}-\ddot{\text{Xe}}-\ddot{\text{F}}: \\
| \\
:\ddot{\text{F}}:
\end{array}
$$

> **Think About It**
> Atoms beyond the second period can accommodate more than an octet of electrons, whether those electrons are used in bonds or reside on the atom as lone pairs.

Practice Problem A Draw the Lewis structure of the iodine tetrachloride ion (ICl_4^-).

Practice Problem B Draw the Lewis structure of krypton difluoride (KrF_2).

SECTION 6.6 REVIEW

Exceptions to the Octet Rule

6.6.1   How many electrons are around the central atom in BrO_3^-?

6.6.2   Why can N not have an expanded octet?

6.6.3   How many electrons are around the central atom in BBr_3?

6.6.4   How many lone pairs are there on the central atom in the Lewis structure of ICl_2^-?

Learning Outcomes

- Define the octet rule as it relates to Lewis structures of compounds.
- Apply rules for drawing Lewis structures toward determining the Lewis structures of compounds.
- Determine the polarity of a bond using differences in electronegativity.
- Define electronegativity, dipole moment, partial charge, and percent ionic character.
- Determine the formal charge on the atoms in a Lewis structure.
- Use formal charges to identify the most likely structure of a compound when more than one Lewis structure can be drawn.

- Define resonance and determine the resonance structures of a species.
- Determine Lewis structures of species that do not follow the octet rule, including radicals.
- Explain why period 1 and period 2 atoms cannot exceed the octet rule.
- Explain why period 3 atoms and beyond can exceed the octet rule.
- Draw Lewis structures with expanded octets and without expanded octets for species where both are possible.

Chapter Summary

SECTION 6.1

- According to the *octet rule,* atoms will lose, gain, or share electrons in order to achieve a noble gas configuration. Pairs of valence electrons that are *not* involved in the covalent bonding in a molecule or polyatomic ion (i.e., valence electrons that are not shared) are called *lone pairs.*
- *Lewis structures* are drawn to represent molecules and polyatomic ions, showing the arrangement of atoms and the positions of all valence electrons. Lewis structures represent the shared pairs of valence electrons either as two dots, ··, or as a single dash, —. Any *unshared* electrons are represented as dots.
- One shared pair of electrons between atoms constitutes a *single bond. Multiple bonds* form between atoms that share more than one pair of electrons. Two shared pairs constitute a *double bond,* and three shared pairs constitute a *triple bond.*

SECTION 6.2

- Bonds in which electrons are not shared equally are *polar* and are referred to as *polar covalent bonds.*
- *Electronegativity* is an atom's ability to draw shared electrons toward itself. Bonds between elements of widely different electronegativities ($\Delta \geq 2.0$) are *ionic.* Covalent bonds between atoms with significantly different electronegativities ($0.5 \leq \Delta < 2.0$) are *polar.* Bonds between atoms with very similar electronegativities ($\Delta < 0.5$) are *nonpolar.*
- *Percent ionic character* quantifies the polarity of a bond, and is determined by comparing the measured dipole moment to the one predicted by assuming that the bonded atoms have discrete charges.
- The *dipole moment (μ)* is a quantitative measure of the polarity of a bond.

SECTION 6.3

- Lewis structures of molecules or polyatomic ions can be drawn using the following step-by-step procedure:
    1. Use the molecular formula to draw the skeletal structure.
    2. Count the total number of valence electrons, adding electrons to account for a negative charge and subtracting electrons to account for a positive charge.
    3. Subtract two electrons for each bond in the skeletal structure.
    4. Distribute the remaining valence electrons to complete octets, completing the octets of the more electronegative atoms first.
    5. Place any remaining electrons on the central atom.
    6. Include double or triple bonds, if necessary, to complete the octets of all atoms.

SECTION 6.4

- *Formal charge* is a way of keeping track of the valence electrons in a species. Formal charges should be consistent with electronegativities and can be used to determine the best arrangement of atoms and electrons for a Lewis structure.

SECTION 6.5

- *Resonance structures* are two or more equally correct Lewis structures that differ in the positions of the electrons but *not* in the positions of the atoms. Different resonance structures of a compound can be separated by a resonance arrow, ←——→.

SECTION 6.6

- In an ordinary covalent bond, each atom contributes one electron to the shared pair of electrons. In cases where just one of the atoms contributes *both* of the electrons, the bond is called a *coordinate covalent bond* or a *dative bond.*
- A species that contains an odd number of electrons is called a *free radical.*

Key Words

Coordinate covalent bond, 200
Dative bond, 200
Dipole moment (μ), 190
Double bond, 186
Electronegativity, 187

Formal charge, 194
Free radical, 201
Lewis structure, 183
Lone pair, 183
Multiple bond, 186

Nonpolar, 189
Octet rule, 183
Percent ionic character, 191
Polar, 187
Polar covalent bond, 187

Resonance structure, 197
Single bond, 186
Triple bond, 186

Key Equations

6.1 $\mu = Q \times r$

6.2   percent ionic character $= \dfrac{\mu \text{ (observed)}}{\mu \text{ (calculated assuming discrete charges)}} \times 100\%$

6.3   formal charge $=$ valence electrons $-$ associated electrons

Questions and Problems

SECTION 6.1:   THE OCTET RULE

Review Questions

6.1   Explain Lewis's contribution to our understanding of the covalent bond.
6.2   Explain the difference between a *Lewis symbol* and a *Lewis structure*.
6.3   Use examples to illustrate each of the following terms: *lone pair, Lewis structure, octet rule, bond length.*
6.4   Explain the octet rule and why it applies mainly to second period elements.
6.5   Explain how the octet rule applies to hydrogen.
6.6   Compare single, double, and triple bonds in a molecule, and give an example of each. For the same bonding atoms, how does the bond length change from single bond to double bond to triple bond?
6.7   For a given pair of bonded atoms, explain how bond *length* relates to bond *strength*.

Problems

6.8   For each of the following pairs of elements, state whether the binary compound they form is likely to be ionic or covalent. Write the empirical formula and name of the compound: (a) I and Cl, (b) Mg and F.
6.9   For each of the following pairs of elements, state whether the binary compound they form is likely to be ionic or covalent. Write the empirical formula and name of the compound: (a) B and F, (b) K and Br.

SECTION 6.2:   ELECTRONEGATIVITY AND POLARITY

Review Questions

6.10   Define *electronegativity* and explain the difference between electronegativity and electron affinity. Describe in general how the electronegativities of the elements change according to their position in the periodic table.
6.11   What is a *polar covalent bond?* Name two compounds that contain one or more polar covalent bonds.

Problems

6.12   List the following bonds in order of increasing ionic character: the lithium-to-fluorine bond in LiF, the potassium-to-oxygen bond in K_2O, the nitrogen-to-nitrogen bond in N_2, the sulfur-to-oxygen bond in SO_2, the chlorine-to-fluorine bond in ClF_3.
6.13   Arrange the following bonds in order of increasing ionic character: carbon to hydrogen, fluorine to hydrogen, bromine to hydrogen, sodium to chlorine, potassium to fluorine, lithium to chlorine.
6.14   Four different atoms are represented by colored spheres: , , , and .
Their electronegativities are as follows: $= 3.8$, $= 3.3$, $= 2.8$, and $= 1.3$.
If the atoms of these elements form the molecules , , , and , how would you arrange these molecules in order of increasing covalent bond character?

6.15 List the following bonds in order of increasing ionic character: cesium to fluorine, chlorine to chlorine, bromine to chlorine, silicon to carbon.

6.16 Classify the following bonds as ionic, polar covalent, or nonpolar covalent, and explain: (a) the CC bond in H_3CCH_3, (b) the KI bond in KI, (c) the NB bond in H_3NBCl_3, (d) the CF bond in CF_4.

6.17 Classify the following bonds as ionic, polar covalent, or nonpolar covalent, and explain: (a) the SiSi bond in $Cl_3SiSiCl_3$, (b) the SiCl bond in $Cl_3SiSiCl_3$, (c) the CaF bond in CaF_2, (d) the NH bond in NH_3.

6.18 The radical species ClO has a dipole moment of 1.24 D and the Cl—O bond distance is 1.57 Å. Determine the magnitude of the partial charges in ClO.

6.19 Given that the partial charges on Al and F in aluminum monofluoride are +0.019 and −0.019, respectively, calculate the dipole moment of AlF. (The distance between the partial charges, r, is 165 pm.)

6.20 The measured dipole moment of bromine monofluoride, BrF, is 1.42 D and the Br—F bond distance is 1.76 Å. Determine the percent ionic character of the bond in BrF.

6.21 Given that the BaO bond has 85.3 percent ionic character and the Ba—O bond length is 194 pm, determine the measured dipole moment of BaO.

SECTION 6.3:   DRAWING LEWIS STRUCTURES

Problems

6.22 Draw Lewis structures for the following molecules and ions: (a) NCl_3, (b) OCS, (c) H_2O_2, (d) CH_3COO^-, (e) CN^-, (f) $CH_3CH_2NH_3^+$.

6.23 Draw Lewis structures for the following molecules and ions: (a) OF_2, (b) N_2F_2, (c) Si_2H_6, (d) OH^-, (e) CH_2ClCOO^-, (f) $CH_3NH_3^+$.

6.24 Draw Lewis structures for the following molecules: (a) ICl, (b) PH_3, (c) P_4 (each P is bonded to three other P atoms), (d) H_2S, (e) N_2H_4, (f) $HClO_3$, (g) $COBr_2$ (C is bonded to O and Br atoms).

6.25 Draw Lewis structures for the following molecules: (a) ClF_3, (b) H_2Se, (c) NH_2OH, (d) $POCl_3$ (P is bonded to O and Cl atoms), (e) CH_3CH_2Br, (f) NCl_3, (g) CH_3NH_2.

SECTION 6.4:   LEWIS STRUCTURES AND FORMAL CHARGE

Review Questions

6.26 Explain the concept of *formal charge*.

6.27 Do formal charges represent an actual separation of charges?

Problems

6.28 Draw Lewis structures for the following ions: (a) O_2^{2-}, (b) C_2^{2-}, (c) NO^+, (d) NH_4^+.

6.29 Draw Lewis structures for the following ions: (a) NO_2^+, (b) SCN^-, (c) S_2^{2-}, (d) ClF_2^+. Show formal charges.

6.30 The following Lewis structures are incorrect. Explain what is wrong with each one, and give a correct Lewis structure for the molecule. (Relative positions of atoms are shown correctly.)

(a) $H—\ddot{C}=\ddot{N}$ (d) structure   (g) structure

(b) $H=C=C=H$ (e) $H—\ddot{O}=\ddot{F}$:

(c) $\ddot{O}—Sn—\ddot{O}$ (f) structure

6.31 The skeletal structure of acetic acid shown here is correct but some of the bonds are wrong. (a) Identify the incorrect bonds and explain what is wrong with them. (b) Draw the correct Lewis structure for acetic acid.

structure

SECTION 6.5:   RESONANCE

Review Questions

6.32 What are *resonance structures*? Is it possible to isolate one resonance structure of a compound for analysis? Explain.

6.33 What are the rules for drawing resonance structures?

Problems

6.34 Draw three resonance structures for the chlorate ion (ClO_3^-). Show formal charges.

6.35 Draw all of the resonance structures for the following species and show formal charges: (a) HCO_2^-, (b) $CH_2NO_2^-$. The relative positions of the atoms are as follows:

```
        O            H    O
    H  C              C    N
        O            H    O
```

6.36 Draw two resonance structures for diazomethane (CH_2N_2). Show formal charges. The skeletal structure of the molecule is

```
    H
      C  N  N
    H
```

6.37 Draw three resonance structures for hydrazoic acid (HN_3). The atomic arrangement is HNNN. Show formal charges.

6.38 Draw three resonance structures for the molecule N_2O in which the atoms are arranged in the order NNO. Indicate formal charges.

6.39 Draw three reasonable resonance structures for the OCN^- ion. Show formal charges.

6.40   Indicate which of the following are resonance structures of :C̈l—Be—C̈l:. For the others, explain why they are *not* resonance structures of :C̈l—Be—C̈l:.
(a) :C̈l=Be=C̈l:
(b) :Cl≡Be—C̈l:
(c) :Be≡Cl—C̈l:
(d) :C̈l—Be≡Cl:
(e) :Be=Cl=C̈l:

6.41   Indicate which of the following are resonance

structures of
:O:
‖
C
:C̈l   C̈l:
(select all that apply).

(a)
:O:
‖
C
C̈l   C̈l

(b)
:Ö:
|
C
C̈l   C̈l:

(c)
:O:
‖
C
C̈l   C̈l:

(d)
:Ö:
|
C
:C̈l   Cl

(e)
:Ö:
|
C
:C̈l   C̈l

6.42   Draw one additional resonance structure of the adenine molecule shown here, which is part of the DNA structure.

6.43   Draw a resonance structure of the guanine molecule shown here, which is part of the DNA structure.

SECTION 6.6:   EXCEPTIONS TO THE OCTET RULE

Review Questions

6.44   Why does the octet rule not hold for many compounds containing elements in the third period of the periodic table and beyond?

6.45   Give three examples of compounds that do not satisfy the octet rule. Draw a Lewis structure for each.

6.46   Because fluorine has seven valence electrons $(2s^2 2p^5)$, in principle, seven covalent bonds could form around the atom as in FH_7 or FCl_7. Explain why these compounds have never been prepared.

6.47   What is a *coordinate covalent bond*? How is it different from an ordinary covalent bond? How is it the same?

Problems

6.48   The AlI_3 molecule has an incomplete octet around Al. Draw three resonance structures of the molecule in which the octet rule is satisfied for both the Al and the I atoms. Show formal charges.

6.49   In the vapor phase, beryllium chloride consists of discrete $BeCl_2$ molecules. Is the octet rule satisfied for Be in this compound? If not, can you form an octet around Be by drawing another resonance structure? Is this structure plausible? Explain.

6.50   Until the early 1960s, the noble gases were not known to form any compounds. Since then, a few compounds of Kr, Xe, and Rn—and one compound of Ar—have been made in laboratories. Draw Lewis structures for the following molecules: (a) XeF_2, (b) XeF_4, (c) XeF_6, (d) $XeOF_4$, (e) XeO_2F_2. In each case Xe is the central atom.

6.51   Draw a Lewis structure for the tetrachloraluminate ion, $AlCl_4^-$. This ion can be considered as a combination of $AlCl_3$ and Cl^-. What kind of bond joins $AlCl_3$ and Cl^- in $AlCl_4^-$?

6.52   Draw Lewis structures for SeF_4 and SeF_6. Is the octet rule satisfied for Se?

6.53   Draw a Lewis structure for $SbCl_5$. Does this molecule obey the octet rule?

6.54   Draw Lewis structures for the radical species ClF_2 and BrO_2.

6.55   Draw Lewis structures for the radical species HO_2 and ClO.

6.56   Draw two resonance structures for the bromate ion (BrO_3^-), one that obeys the octet rule and one in which the formal charge on the central atom is zero.

6.57   Draw two resonance structures for the sulfite ion (SO_3^{2-}), one that obeys the octet rule and one in which the formal charge on the central atom is zero.

ADDITIONAL PROBLEMS

6.58   Draw Lewis structures for BrF_3, ClF_5, and IF_7. Identify those in which the octet rule is not obeyed.

6.59   Draw three reasonable resonance structures for the azide ion N_3^- in which the atoms are arranged as NNN. Show formal charges.

6.60   The amide group plays an important role in determining the structure of proteins:

Draw another resonance structure for this group. Show formal charges.

6.61 Give an example of an ion or molecule containing Al that (a) obeys the octet rule, (b) has an expanded octet, and (c) has an incomplete octet.

6.62 Draw four reasonable resonance structures for the PO_3F^{2-} ion. The central P atom is bonded to the three O atoms and to the F atom. Show formal charges.

6.63 Attempts to prepare the compounds CF_2, LiO_2, $CsCl_2$, and PI_5 as stable species under atmospheric conditions have failed. Suggest possible reasons for the failure.

6.64 Draw reasonable resonance structures for the following ions: (a) HSO_4^-, (b) PO_4^{3-}, (c) HSO_3^-, (d) SO_3^{2-}.

6.65 Are the following statements true or false? (a) Formal charges represent an actual separation of charges. (b) All second-period elements obey the octet rule in their compounds. (c) The resonance structures of a molecule can be separated from one another in the laboratory.

6.66 A rule for drawing plausible Lewis structures is that the central atom is generally less electronegative than the surrounding atoms. Explain why this is so.

6.67 Which of the following molecules has the shortest nitrogen-to-nitrogen bond: N_2H_4, N_2O, N_2, N_2O_4? Explain.

6.68 Most organic acids can be represented as RCOOH, where COOH is the carboxyl group and R is the rest of the molecule. [For example, R is CH_3 in acetic acid (CH_3COOH).] (a) Draw a Lewis structure for the carboxyl group. (b) Upon ionization, the carboxyl group is converted to the carboxylate group (COO^-). Draw resonance structures for the carboxylate group.

6.69 Which of the following species are isoelectronic: NH_4^+, C_6H_6, CO, CH_4, N_2, $B_3N_3H_6$? (The term *isoelectronic* means the same thing in the context of molecules and polyatomic ions as it does with regard to atoms and monatomic ions: isoelectronic species have the same number and arrangement of electrons.)

6.70 The following is a simplified (skeletal) structure of the amino acid histidine. Draw a complete Lewis structure of the molecule.

6.71 The following is a simplified (skeletal) structure of the amino acid tryptophan. Draw a complete Lewis structure of the molecule.

6.72 The following species have been detected in interstellar space: (a) CH, (b) OH, (c) C_2, (d) HNC, (e) HCO. Draw Lewis structures for these species.

6.73 The sulfur oxides SO_2 and SO_3 are significant pollutants in the air and contributors to the formation of acid rain. It is thought that these compounds can be converted into radical anions inside of cells. Draw plausible Lewis structures of the radical anions SO_2^- and SO_3^-.

6.74 Draw Lewis structures for the following organic molecules: (a) tetrafluoroethylene (C_2F_4), (b) propane (C_3H_8), (c) butadiene ($CH_2CHCHCH_2$), (d) propyne (CH_3CCH), (e) benzoic acid (C_6H_5COOH). (To draw C_6H_5COOH, replace an H atom in benzene with a COOH group.)

6.75 The triiodide ion (I_3^-) in which the I atoms are arranged in a straight line is stable, but the corresponding F_3^- ion does not exist. Explain.

6.76 Draw Lewis structures for the following organic molecules: C_2H_3F, C_3H_6, C_4H_8. In each there is one C=C bond, and the rest of the carbon atoms are joined by C—C bonds.

6.77 Methyl isocyanate (CH_3NCO) is used to make certain pesticides. In December 1984, water leaked into a tank containing this substance at a chemical plant, producing a toxic cloud that killed thousands of people in Bhopal, India. Draw Lewis structures for CH_3NCO, showing formal charges.

6.78 The chlorine nitrate ($ClONO_2$) molecule is believed to be involved in the destruction of ozone in the Antarctic stratosphere. Draw a plausible Lewis structure for this molecule.

6.79 Several resonance structures for the molecule CO_2 are shown here. Which of these species is/are most important in describing the bonding in this molecule? Explain why the others are less important.

(a) $\ddot{O}=C=\ddot{O}$

(b) $:O\equiv C-\ddot{O}:$

(c) $:O\equiv\ddot{C}-\ddot{O}:$

(d) $:\ddot{O}-C-\ddot{O}:$

6.80 For each of the following organic molecules draw a Lewis structure in which the carbon atoms are bonded to each other by single bonds: (a) C_2H_6, (b) C_4H_{10}, (c) C_5H_{12}. For parts (b) and (c) show only structures in which each C atom is bonded to no more than two other C atoms.

6.81 Draw Lewis structures for the following chlorofluorocarbons (CFCs), which are partly responsible for the depletion of ozone in the stratosphere: (a) $CFCl_3$, (b) CF_2Cl_2, (c) CHF_2Cl, (d) CF_3CHF_2.

6.82 Draw Lewis structures for the following organic molecules: (a) methanol (CH_3OH); (b) ethanol (CH_3CH_2OH); (c) tetraethyl lead [$Pb(CH_2CH_3)_4$], which is used in "leaded gasoline"; (d) methylamine (CH_3NH_2), which is used in tanning; (e) mustard gas ($ClCH_2CH_2SCH_2CH_2Cl$), a poisonous gas used in World War I; (f) urea [$(NH_2)_2CO$], a fertilizer; and (g) glycine (NH_2CH_2COOH), an amino acid.

6.83 Draw Lewis structures for the following four isoelectronic species: (a) CO, (b) NO^+, (c) CN^-, (d) N_2. Show formal charges. (See Problem 6.69)

6.84 Oxygen forms three types of ionic compounds in which the anions are oxide (O^{2-}), peroxide (O_2^{2-}), and superoxide (O_2^-). Draw Lewis structures of these ions.

6.85 Is there a group of elements that always violates the octet rule? Explain.

6.86 Draw three resonance structures for (a) the cyanate ion (NCO^-) and (b) the isocyanate ion (CNO^-). In each case, rank the resonance structures in order of increasing importance.

6.87 The $N-O$ bond distance in nitric oxide is 115 pm, which is intermediate between a triple bond (106 pm) and a double bond (120 pm). (a) Draw two resonance structures for NO, and comment on their relative importance. (b) Is it possible to draw a resonance structure having a triple bond between the atoms?

6.88 Within the comet Hale-Bopp, a number of sulfur-containing diatomic molecules have been detected including sulfur mononitride (SN) and sulfur monoxide (SO). (a) Determine the partial charges in SN given the dipole moment (1.81 D) and S$-$N bond distance (149 pm). (b) If the partial charges on S and O in sulfur monoxide are $+0.022$ and -0.022, respectively, calculate the dipole moment of SO. (The distance between the partial charges, r, is 1.48 Å.)

6.89 In the gas phase, aluminum chloride exists as a dimer (a unit of two) with the formula Al_2Cl_6. Its skeletal structure is given by

$$
\begin{array}{ccccc}
Cl & & Cl & & Cl \\
\diagdown & & \diagdown & & \diagup \\
& Al & & Al & \\
\diagup & & \diagdown & & \diagdown \\
Cl & & Cl & & Cl
\end{array}
$$

Complete the Lewis structure and identify the coordinate covalent bonds in the molecules. Would you expect this molecule to be polar? Explain.

6.90 Draw a Lewis structure for nitrogen pentoxide (N_2O_5) in which each N is bonded to three O atoms.

6.91 Determine the percent ionic character of RbF and of RbI. The dipole moments of RbF and RbI are 8.55 D and 11.48 D, respectively. [Use information from Figure 4.13 (page 127) to calculate the bond distances in each ionic compound.] Comment on the difference between your two answers.

6.92 Nitrogen dioxide (NO_2) is a stable compound. Explain why there is a tendency for two such molecules to combine to form dinitrogen tetroxide (N_2O_4). Draw four resonance structures of N_2O_4, showing formal charges.

6.93 Electrostatic potential maps for three compounds A, B, and C are shown below.

Using the data in the following table, determine which compound corresponds to which electrostatic potential map and determine the dipole moment of each compound. Fill in the missing data in the table.

Compound	Partial charges	Distance between charges (pm)	Dipole moment
	±0.19	213	
	±0.051	214	
	±0.68	315	

6.94 Vinyl chloride (C_2H_3Cl) differs from ethylene (C_2H_4) in that one of the H atoms is replaced with a Cl atom. Vinyl chloride is used to prepare poly(vinyl chloride), which is an important polymer used in pipes. (a) Draw the Lewis structure of vinyl chloride. (b) The repeating unit in poly(vinyl chloride) is $-CH_2-CHCl-$. Draw a portion of the molecule showing three such repeating units.

6.95 Pyridine has a structure similar to that of benzene, but one of the carbon atoms (and the hydrogen bonded to it) are replaced by a nitrogen atom. Draw the two resonance structures of pyridine and using information from Table 6.1, estimate the length of the C$-$N bonds.

6.96 Among the common inhaled anesthetics are:
Halothane ($CF_3CHClBr$)
Isoflurane ($CF_3CHClOCHF_2$)
Enflurane ($CHFClCF_2OCHF_2$)
Methoxyflurane ($CHCl_2CF_2OCH_3$)
Draw Lewis structures of these molecules.

6.97 In 1999 an unusual cation containing only nitrogen (N_5^+) was prepared. Draw three resonance structures of the ion, showing formal charges. (*Hint:* The N atoms are joined in a linear fashion.)

6.98 In each of the following Lewis structures, Z and X represent different third-period main group elements.

$$
\left[\begin{array}{c} \ddot{O}: \\ | \\ H-\ddot{O}-Z-\ddot{O}: \\ | \\ :O: \end{array} \right]^- \qquad \begin{array}{c} :\ddot{F}: \\ | \\ :\ddot{X}-\ddot{F}: \\ | \\ :\ddot{F}: \end{array}
$$

Draw the Lewis structure for the compound ZX_3.

6.99 The American chemist Robert S. Mulliken suggested a different definition for the electronegativity (EN) of an element, given by

$$EN = \frac{IE_1 + EA}{2}$$

where IE_1 is the first ionization energy and EA is the electron affinity of the element. Calculate the electronegativities of O, F, and Cl using the preceding equation and data from the Chapter 4 Key Skills (pages 138–139). Compare the electronegativities of these elements on the Mulliken and Pauling scales. (To convert to the Pauling scale, divide each EN value by 230 kJ/mol.)

6.100 Electrostatic potential maps for three compounds A, B, and C are shown below.

A B C

Using the data in the following table, determine which compound corresponds to which electrostatic potential map and fill in the missing data in the table.

Compound	Partial charges	Distance between charges (pm)	Dipole moment
	±0.16	157	
	±0.43		3.10
		258	8.89

Answers to In-Chapter Materials

PRACTICE PROBLEMS

6.1A (a) polar, (b) polar, (c) nonpolar. **6.1B** Li through Fr in Group 1A, and Ca through Ra in Group 2A. **6.2A** 0.12. **6.2B** 0.11 D. **6.3A** 41%. **6.3B** 9.23 D.

6.4A :F̈—N̈—F̈: **6.4B** [:Ö—Cl̈—Ö:]⁻ **6.5A** C atom = 0, double-bonded O atom = 0, single-bonded O atoms = −1. **6.5B** S atom = +1, O atoms = −1, overall charge = −2. **6.6A** —C̈—Ö—H. **6.6B** Cl—N—Cl.

6.7A [:Ö=N—Ö:]⁻ ⟷ [:Ö—N—Ö:]⁻ ⟷ [:Ö—N=Ö:]⁻

6.7B [:N̈—C≡S:]⁻ ⟷ [:N̈=C=S̈:]⁻ ⟷ [:N≡C—S̈:]⁻
(with formal charges −2 0 +1 ; −1 0 0 ; 0 0 −1)

6.8A ·Ö—H **6.8B** :S̈=N̈—S̈: **6.9A** :F̈—Be—F̈: **6.9B** :Cl̈—B—Cl̈:

6.10A (Cl)₃P—Cl structure **6.10B** (F)₄Sb—F structure

6.11A
[H—Ö—S—Ö:]⁻ series of phosphate/sulfate structures

6.11B
:Ö—S—Ö: ⟷ :Ö=S=O: ⟷ :Ö=S—Ö: ⟷ :O=S=O:

6.12A [:Cl̈—I—Cl̈:]⁻ (with Cl above and below) **6.12B** :F̈—Kr—F̈:

SECTION REVIEW

6.2.1 H_2O. **6.2.2** A < B < C < D = E. **6.2.3** 0.057. **6.2.4** 17.7%.

6.3.1 H—C(=O)—Ö—H **6.3.2** H—Ö—Ö—H **6.4.1** 0, 0, and 0.

6.4.2 [:N=C=Ö:]⁻ , [:N̈—C≡O:]⁻ , [:N≡C—Ö:]⁻ , best structure [:N≡C—Ö:]⁻ **6.5.1** 2. **6.5.2** Ö=S̈—Ö: ⟷ :Ö—S̈=Ö **6.6.1** 8 if the octet rule is obeyed; 12 if two Br—O double bonds are used to optimize the formal charges. **6.6.2** There are no *d* orbitals in the *n* = 2 shell. **6.6.3** 6. **6.6.4** 3.

KEY SKILLS

Drawing Lewis Structures

The first step in solving many problems is drawing a correct Lewis structure. The process of drawing a Lewis structure was first described on page 193. The steps, which are summarized in the flowchart below, are:

1. Count the total valence electrons. Recall that each atom contributes a number equal to its group number; and remember to add or subtract valence electrons to account for charge on a polyatomic ion.

2. Use the chemical formula to draw a skeletal structure. Usually, the central atom is less electronegative than the terminal atoms; although hydrogen cannot be a central atom because it can form only one bond.

3. For each bond in the skeletal formula, subtract two from the total number of valence electrons.

4. Distribute the remaining electrons, satisfying first the octets of the more electronegative (usually terminal) atoms.

5. If all terminal atoms have complete octets, and there are valence electrons still to be distributed, place them on the central atom as lone pairs.

6. If the valence electrons run out before all octets are satisfied, use multiple bonds to complete the octets of all atoms.

7. For a charged species, enclose the Lewis structure in square brackets and add a superscript charge.

There are exceptions to the octet rule.

- Be and B, small atoms with low electronegativity, need not obey the octet rule.
- Elements in the third period and beyond need not obey the octet rule.
- Species with an odd number of valence electrons cannot obey the octet rule.
- A larger central atom (from the third period or beyond) can accommodate more than eight electrons and can have an "expanded" octet.

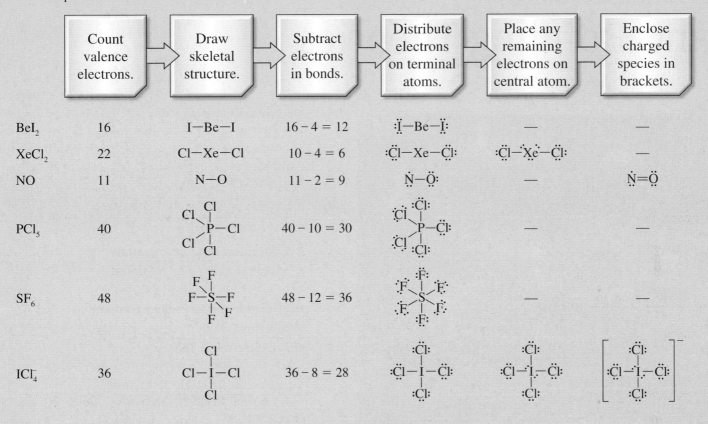

Key Skills Problems

6.1

Which of the following atoms must always obey the octet rule? (Select all that apply.)

(a) C (b) N (c) S (d) Br (e) Xe

6.2

Which of the following species has an odd number of electrons? (Select all that apply.)

(a) N_2O (b) NO_2 (c) NO_2^- (d) NO_3^- (e) NS

6.3

How many lone pairs are on the central atom in $XeOF_2$?

(a) 0 (b) 1 (c) 2 (d) 3 (e) 4

6.4

How many lone pairs are on the central atom in the perchlorate ion?

(a) 0 (b) 1 (c) 2 (d) 3 (e) 4

CHAPTER 7

Molecular Geometry and Bonding Theories

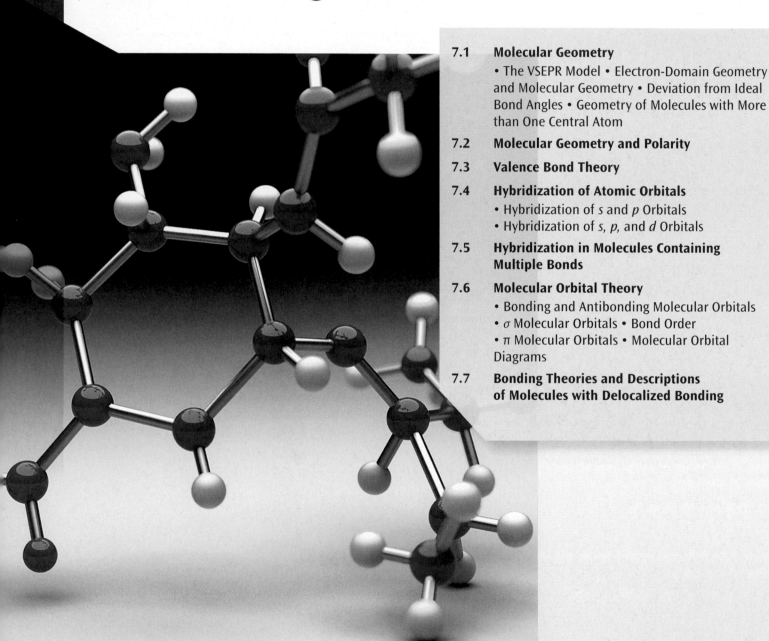

7.1 **Molecular Geometry**
• The VSEPR Model • Electron-Domain Geometry and Molecular Geometry • Deviation from Ideal Bond Angles • Geometry of Molecules with More than One Central Atom

7.2 **Molecular Geometry and Polarity**

7.3 **Valence Bond Theory**

7.4 **Hybridization of Atomic Orbitals**
• Hybridization of *s* and *p* Orbitals
• Hybridization of *s*, *p*, and *d* Orbitals

7.5 **Hybridization in Molecules Containing Multiple Bonds**

7.6 **Molecular Orbital Theory**
• Bonding and Antibonding Molecular Orbitals
• σ Molecular Orbitals • Bond Order
• π Molecular Orbitals • Molecular Orbital Diagrams

7.7 **Bonding Theories and Descriptions of Molecules with Delocalized Bonding**

Molecular structure profoundly affects the properties of a substance and determines how it interacts with other chemical species. By paying particular attention to the structure and shape of molecules, medicinal chemists can design drugs to inhibit the action of specific pathogenic viruses and bacteria. One example of this is the antiviral drug Tamiflu®, a model of which is shown here. Tamiflu prevents reproductive budding of the influenza virus by binding effectively in the active site of an important enzyme. By understanding the importance of molecular structure, synthetic chemists can now design better and more effective drugs for a multitude of diseases and illnesses.

Before You Begin, Review These Skills

- Shapes of atomic orbitals [◄◄ Section 3.8]
- Electron configurations of atoms [◄◄ Section 3.9]
- Drawing Lewis structures [◄◄ Section 6.3]

7.1 MOLECULAR GEOMETRY

Many familiar chemical and biochemical processes depend heavily on the three-dimensional shapes of the molecules and/or ions involved. Our sense of smell is one example; the effectiveness of a particular drug is another. Although the shape of a molecule or polyatomic ion must be determined experimentally, we can predict their shapes reasonably well using Lewis structures [◄◄ Section 6.3] and the *valence-shell electron-pair repulsion (VSEPR)* model. In this section, we will focus primarily on determining the shapes of molecules of the general type AB_x, where A is a central atom surrounded by x B atoms and x can have integer values of 2 to 6. For example, NH_3 is an AB_3 molecule in which A is nitrogen, B is hydrogen, and $x = 3$. The Lewis structure of NH_3 is shown here.

> **Student Annotation:** Any atom that is bonded to two or more other atoms can be considered a "central" atom.

$$H—\overset{..}{N}—H$$
$$|$$
$$H$$

Lewis structure of NH_3

Table 7.1 lists examples of each type of AB_x molecule and polyatomic ion that we will consider. Throughout this chapter, we will discuss concepts that apply both to molecules and to polyatomic ions, but we will usually refer to them collectively as "molecules."

Having the molecular formula alone is insufficient to predict the shape of a molecule. For instance, AB_2 molecules may be linear or bent:

Linear   Bent

Moreover, AB_3 molecules may be planar, pyramidal, or T-shaped:

Trigonal planar   Trigonal pyramidal   T-shaped

In order to determine shape, we must start with a correct Lewis structure and apply the VSEPR model.

Multi 7.1
Chemical bonding—valence-shell electron-pair repulsion theory

TABLE 7.1	Examples of AB_x Molecules and Polyatomic Ions
AB_2	$BeCl_2$, SO_2, H_2O, NO_2^-
AB_3	BF_3, NH_3, ClF_3, SO_3^{2-}
AB_4	CCl_4, NH_4^+, SF_4, XeF_4, ClO_4^-
AB_5	PCl_5, IF_5, SbF_5, BrF_5
AB_6	SF_6, UF_6, $TiCl_6^{3-}$

The VSEPR Model

The basis of the VSEPR model is that electron pairs in the valence shell of an atom *repel* one another. As we learned in Chapter 6, there are two types of electron pairs: bonding pairs and nonbonding pairs (also known as lone pairs). Furthermore, bonding pairs may be found in single bonds or in multiple bonds. For clarity, we will refer to electron *domains* instead of electron pairs when we use the VSEPR model. An ***electron domain*** in this context is a lone pair or a bond, regardless of whether the bond is single, double, or triple. Consider the following examples:

	CO_2	O_3	NH_3	PCl_5	XeF_4
	$\ddot{O}=C=\ddot{O}$	$\ddot{O}=\ddot{O}-\ddot{O}$	H—Ṅ—H │ H	(Lewis structure)	(Lewis structure)
	2 double bonds	1 single bond 1 double bond + 1 lone pair	3 single bonds + 1 lone pair	5 single bonds	4 single bonds + 2 lone pairs
Total number of electron domains on central atom	2 electron domains	3 electron domains	4 electron domains	5 electron domains	6 electron domains

Note the number of electron domains on the central atom in each molecule. The VSEPR model predicts that because these electron domains repel one another, they will arrange themselves to be as far apart as possible, thus minimizing the repulsive interactions between them.

We can visualize the arrangement of electron domains using balloons, as shown in Figure 7.1. Like the B atoms in our AB_x molecules, the balloons are all connected to a central, fixed point, which represents the central atom (A). When they are as far apart as possible, they adopt the five geometries shown in the figure. When there are only two balloons, they orient themselves to point in opposite directions [Figure 7.1(a)]. With three balloons, the arrangement is a trigonal plane [Figure 7.1(b)]. With four balloons, the arrangement adopted is a tetrahedron [Figure 7.1(c)]. With five balloons, three of them adopt positions in a trigonal plane whereas the other two point opposite to each other, forming an axis that is perpendicular to the trigonal plane [Figure 7.1(d)]. This geometry is called a trigonal bipyramid. Finally, with six balloons, the arrangement is an octahedron, which is essentially a square bipyramid [Figure 7.1(e)]. Each of the AB_x molecules we consider will have one of these five electron-domain geometries: linear, trigonal planar, tetrahedral, trigonal bipyramidal, or octahedral.

Electron-Domain Geometry and Molecular Geometry

It is important to distinguish between the ***electron-domain geometry,*** which is the arrangement of electron domains (bonds and lone pairs) around the central atom, and the ***molecular geometry,*** which is the arrangement of bonded *atoms*. Figure 7.2 illustrates the molecular geometries of AB_x molecules in which all the electron domains are bonds—that is, there are no lone pairs on any of the central atoms. In these cases, the molecular geometry is the same as the electron-domain geometry.

In an AB_x molecule, a ***bond angle*** is the angle between two adjacent A—B bonds. In an AB_2 molecule, there are only two bonds and therefore only one bond angle, and, provided that there are no lone pairs on the central atom, the bond angle is 180°. AB_3 and AB_4 molecules have three and four bonds, respectively. However, in each case there is only one bond angle possible between any two A—B bonds. In an AB_3 molecule, the bond angle is 120°, and in an AB_4 molecule, the bond angle is 109.5°—again, provided that there are no lone pairs on the central atoms. Similarly, in an AB_6 molecule, the bond angles between adjacent bonds are all 90°. (The angle between any two A—B bonds that point in opposite directions is 180°.)

AB_5 molecules contain two different bond angles between adjacent bonds. The reason for this is that, unlike those in the other AB_x molecules, the positions occupied by bonds in a trigonal bipyramid are not all equivalent. The three bonds that are arranged in a trigonal plane are referred

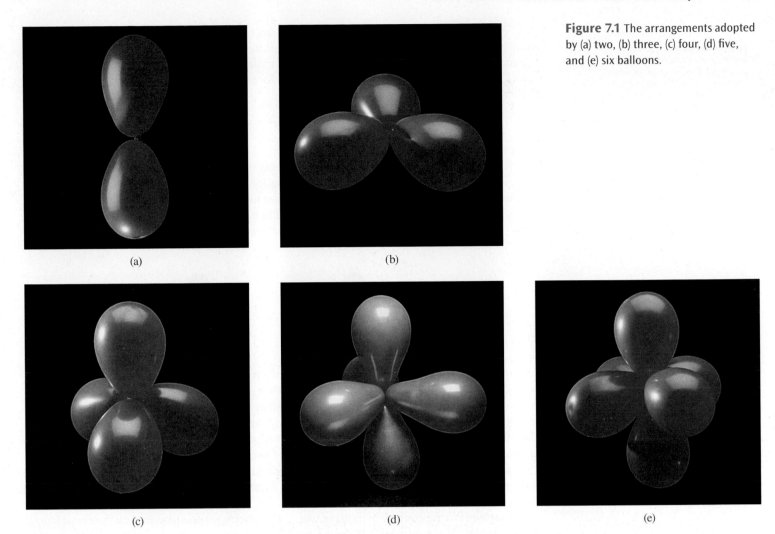

Figure 7.1 The arrangements adopted by (a) two, (b) three, (c) four, (d) five, and (e) six balloons.

(a)

(b)

(c)

(d)

(e)

Figure 7.1 The arrangements adopted by (a) two, (b) three, (c) four, (d) five, and (e) six balloons.

to as *equatorial.* The bond angle between any two of the three equatorial bonds is 120°. The two bonds that form an axis perpendicular to the trigonal plane are referred to as *axial.* The bond angle between either of the axial bonds and any one of the equatorial bonds is 90°. (As in the case of the AB_6 molecule, the angle between any two A—B bonds that point in opposite directions is 180°.) Figure 7.2 illustrates all these bond angles. The angles shown in the figure are the bond angles that are observed when all the electron domains on the central atom are identical. As we will see later in this section, the bond angles in many molecules will differ slightly from these *ideal* values.

Multi 7.2
Chemical bonding—VSEPR and molecular geometry (interactive)

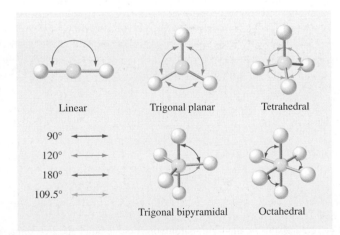

Figure 7.2 Five geometries of AB_x molecules in which all the electron domains are bonds.

When the central atom in an AB_x molecule bears one or more lone pairs, the electron-domain geometry and the molecular geometry are no longer the same. However, we still use the electron-domain geometry as a first step in determining the molecular geometry. The first step in determining the molecular geometry of O_3 (or any species), for example, is to draw its Lewis structure. Two different resonance structures can be drawn for O_3:

$$:\ddot{O}=\ddot{O}-\ddot{O}: \quad \longleftrightarrow \quad :\ddot{O}-\ddot{O}=\ddot{O}:$$

Either one can be used to determine its geometry.

The next step is to count the electron domains on the central atom. In this case, there are three: one single bond, one double bond, and one lone pair. Using the VSEPR model, we first determine the electron-domain geometry. According to the information in Figure 7.2, three electron domains on the central atom will be arranged in a trigonal plane. Molecular geometry, however, is dictated by the arrangement of *atoms*. If we consider only the positions of the three atoms in this molecule, the molecular geometry (the molecule's shape) is *bent*.

Electron-domain geometry: Molecular geometry:
trigonal planar   bent

In addition to the five basic geometries depicted in Figure 7.2, you must be familiar with how molecular geometry can differ from electron-domain geometry. Table 7.2 (page 220) shows the common molecular geometries where there are one or more lone pairs on the central atom. Note the positions occupied by the lone pairs in the trigonal bipyramidal electron-domain geometry. When there are lone pairs on the central atom in a trigonal bipyramid, the lone pairs preferentially occupy equatorial positions because repulsion is greater when the angle between electron domains is 90° or less. Placing a lone pair in an *axial* position would put it at 90° to three other electron domains. Placing it in an *equatorial* position puts it at 90° to only two other domains, thus minimizing the number of strong repulsive interactions.

All positions are equivalent in the octahedral geometry, so one lone pair on the central atom can occupy any of the positions. If there is a second lone pair in this geometry, though, it must occupy the position opposite the first. This arrangement minimizes the repulsive forces between the two lone pairs (they are 180° apart instead of 90° apart).

In summary, the steps to determine the electron-domain and molecular geometries are as follows:

1. Draw the Lewis structure of the molecule or polyatomic ion.
2. Count the number of electron domains on the central atom.
3. Determine the electron-domain geometry by applying the VSEPR model.
4. Determine the molecular geometry by considering the positions of the atoms only.

Worked Example 7.1 shows how to determine the shape of a molecule or polyatomic ion.

Worked Example 7.1

Determine the shapes of (a) SO_3 and (b) ICl_4^-.

Strategy Use Lewis structures and the VSEPR model to determine first the electron-domain geometry and then the molecular geometry (shape).

Setup (a) The Lewis structure of SO_3 is:

$$:\ddot{O}:$$
$$|$$
$$:\ddot{O}=S-\ddot{O}:$$

There are three electron domains on the central atom: one double bond and two single bonds.

(b) The Lewis structure of ICl_4^- is:

$$\left[\begin{array}{c} :\ddot{C}l: \\ | \\ :\ddot{C}l-\ddot{I}-\ddot{C}l: \\ | \\ :\ddot{C}l: \end{array} \right]^{-}$$

There are six electron domains on the central atom in ICl_4^-: four single bonds and two lone pairs.

Solution

(a) According to the VSEPR model, three electron domains will be arranged in a trigonal plane. Since there are no lone pairs on the central atom in SO_3, the molecular geometry is the same as the electron-domain geometry. Therefore, the shape of SO_3 is trigonal planar.

Electron-domain geometry: trigonal planar ⟶ Molecular geometry: trigonal planar

(b) Six electron domains will be arranged in an octahedron. Two lone pairs on an octahedron will be located on opposite sides of the central atom, making the shape of ICl_4^- square planar.

Electron-domain geometry: octahedral ⟶ Molecular geometry: square planar

---

Think About It

Compare these results with the information in Figure 7.2 and Table 7.2. Make sure that you can draw Lewis structures correctly. Without a correct Lewis structure, you will be unable to determine the shape of a molecule.

Practice Problem A Determine the shapes of (a) CO_2 and (b) SCl_2.

Practice Problem B (a) From what group must the terminal atoms come in an AB_x molecule where the central atom is from Group 6A, for the electron-domain geometry and the molecular geometry both to be trigonal planar? (b) From what group must the terminal atoms come in an AB_x molecule where the central atom is from Group 7A, for the electron-domain geometry to be octahedral and the molecular geometry to be square pyramidal?

Deviation from Ideal Bond Angles

Some electron domains are better than others at repelling neighboring domains. As a result, the bond angles may be slightly different from those shown in Figure 7.2. For example, the electron-domain geometry of ammonia (NH_3) is tetrahedral, so we might predict the H—N—H bond angles to be $109.5°$. In fact, the bond angles are about $107°$, slightly smaller than predicted. The lone pair on the nitrogen atom repels the N—H bonds more strongly than the bonds repel one another. It therefore "squeezes" them closer together than the ideal tetrahedral angle of $109.5°$.

In effect, a lone pair takes up more *space* than the bonding pairs. This can be understood by considering the attractive forces involved in determining the location of the electron pairs. A lone pair on a central atom is attracted only to the nucleus of that atom. A bonding pair of electrons, on the other hand, is simultaneously attracted by the nuclei of both of the bonding atoms. As a result, the lone pair has more freedom to spread out and greater capacity to repel other electron domains.

TABLE 7.2		Electron-Domain and Molecular Geometries of Molecules with Lone Pairs on the Central Atom				
Total number of electron domains	**Number of lone pairs**	**Type of molecule**	**Electron-domain geometry**	**Placement of lone pairs**	**Molecular geometry**	**Example**
3	1	AB_2	Trigonal planar		Bent	SO_2
4	1	AB_3	Tetrahedral		Trigonal pyramidal	NH_3
4	2	AB_2	Tetrahedral		Bent	H_2O
5	1	AB_4	Trigonal bipyramidal		Seesaw-shaped	SF_4
5	2	AB_3	Trigonal bipyramidal		T-shaped	ClF_3
5	3	AB_2	Trigonal bipyramidal		Linear	IF_2^-
6	1	AB_5	Octahedral		Square pyramidal	BrF_5
6	2	AB_4	Octahedral		Square planar	XeF_4

Also, because they contain more electron density, multiple bonds repel more strongly than single bonds. Consider the bond angles in each of the following examples:

| NH$_3$ | CH$_2$O | SF$_4$ | BrF$_5$ |

Geometry of Molecules with More Than One Central Atom

Thus far we have considered the geometries of molecules having only one central atom. We can determine the overall geometry of more complex molecules by treating them as though they have multiple central atoms. Methanol (CH$_3$OH), for example, has a central C atom and a central O atom, as shown in the following Lewis structure:

Both the C and the O atoms are surrounded by four electron domains. In the case of C, they are three C—H bonds and one C—O bond. In the case of O, they are one O—C bond, one O—H bond, and two lone pairs. In each case, the electron-domain geometry is tetrahedral. However, the molecular geometry of the C part of the molecule is *tetrahedral,* whereas the molecular geometry of the O part of the molecule is *bent.* Note that although the Lewis structure makes it appear as though there is a 180° angle between the O—C and O—H bonds, the angle is actually approximately 109.5°, the angle in a tetrahedral arrangement of electron domains.

Worked Example 7.2 shows how to determine when bond angles differ from ideal values.

Student Annotation: When we specify the geometry of a particular portion of a molecule, we refer to it as the geometry "about" a particular atom. In methanol, for example, we say that the geometry is *tetrahedral about the C atom* and *bent about the O atom.*

Worked Example 7.2

Acetic acid, the substance that gives vinegar its characteristic smell and sour taste, is sometimes used in combination with corticosteroids to treat certain types of ear infections. Its Lewis structure is

Determine the molecular geometry about each of the central atoms, and determine the approximate value of each of the bond angles in the molecule. Which if any of the bond angles would you expect to be smaller than the ideal values?

Strategy Identify the central atoms and count the number of electron domains around each of them. Use the VSEPR model to determine each electron-domain geometry, and the information in Table 7.2 to determine the molecular geometry about each central atom.

Setup The leftmost C atom is surrounded by four electron domains: one C—C bond and three C—H bonds. The middle C atom is surrounded by three electron domains: one C—C bond, one C—O bond, and one C=O (double) bond. The O atom is surrounded by four electron domains: one O—C bond, one O—H bond, and two lone pairs.

Solution The electron-domain geometry of the leftmost C is tetrahedral. Because all four electron domains are bonds, the molecular geometry of this part of the molecule is also tetrahedral. The electron-domain geometry of the middle C is trigonal planar. Again, because all the domains are bonds, the molecular geometry is also trigonal planar. The electron-domain geometry of the O atom is tetrahedral. Because two of the domains are lone pairs, the molecular geometry about the O atom is bent.

(Continued on next page)

Bond angles are determined using electron-domain geometry. Therefore, the approximate bond angles about the leftmost C are 109.5°, those about the middle C are 120°, and those about the O are 109.5°. The angle between the two single bonds on the middle carbon will be *less* than 120° because the double bond repels the single bonds more strongly than they repel each other. Likewise, the bond angle between the two bonds on the O will be less than 109.5° because the lone pairs on O repel the single bonds more strongly than they repel each other and push the two bonding pairs closer together. The angles are labeled as follows:

Think About It
Compare these answers with the information in Figure 7.2 and Table 7.2.

Practice Problem A Ethanolamine ($HOCH_2CH_2NH_2$) has a smell similar to ammonia and is commonly found in biological tissues. Its Lewis structure is

Determine the molecular geometry about each central atom and label all the bond angles. Cite any expected deviations from ideal bond angles.

Practice Problem B The bond angle in NH_3 is significantly smaller than the ideal bond angle of 109.5° because of the lone pair on the central atom. Explain why the bond angle in SO_2 is very close to 120° despite there being a lone pair on the central atom.

SECTION 7.1 REVIEW

Molecular Geometry

7.1.1 What are the electron-domain geometry and molecular geometry of CO_3^{2-}?

7.1.2 What are the electron-domain geometry and molecular geometry of ClO_3^-?

7.1.3 What is the approximate value of the bond angle indicated?

7.1.4 What is the approximate value of the bond angle indicated?

7.2 MOLECULAR GEOMETRY AND POLARITY

Multi 7.3
Chemical bonding—molecular
geometry and polarity (interactive)

Molecular geometry is tremendously important in understanding the physical and chemical behavior of a substance. *Molecular polarity,* for example, is one of the most important consequences of molecular geometry, because molecular polarity influences physical, chemical, and biological properties. Recall from Section 6.2 that a bond between two atoms of different electronegativities is polar and that a diatomic molecule containing a polar bond is a *polar molecule.* Whether a molecule made up of three or more atoms is polar depends not only on the polarity of the individual bonds, but also on its molecular geometry.

Each of the CO_2 and H_2O molecules contains two identical atoms bonded to a central atom and two polar bonds. However, only one of these molecules is polar. To understand why, think of each individual bond dipole as a vector. The overall dipole moment of the molecule is determined by vector addition of the individual bond dipoles.

In the case of CO_2, we have two identical vectors pointing in opposite directions. When the vectors are placed on a Cartesian coordinate system, they have no y component and their x components are equal in magnitude but opposite in sign. The sum of these two vectors is zero in both the x and y directions. Thus, although the *bonds* in CO_2 are polar, the *molecule* is nonpolar.

Student Annotation: Recall that we can represent an individual bond dipole using a crossed arrow that points towards the more electronegative atom [◄◄ Section 6.2].

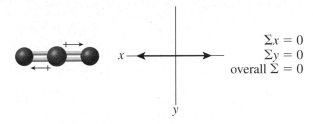

The vectors representing the bond dipoles in water, although equal in magnitude and opposite in the x direction, are not opposite in the y direction. Therefore, although their x components sum to zero, their y components do not. This means that there is a net resultant dipole and H_2O is *polar.*

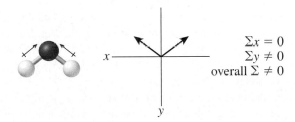

In AB_x molecules where $x \geq 3$, it may be less obvious whether the individual bond dipoles cancel one another. Consider the molecule BF_3, for example, which has a trigonal planar geometry:

We will simplify the math in this analysis by assigning the vectors representing the three identical B—F bonds an arbitrary magnitude of 1.00. The x, y coordinates for the end of arrow 1 are (0, 1.00). Determining the coordinate for the ends of arrows 2 and 3 requires the use of trigonometric functions. You may have learned the mnemonic SOH CAH TOA, where the letters stand for

Sin = Opposite over Hypotenuse
Cos = Adjacent over Hypotenuse
Tan = Opposite over Adjacent

The x coordinate for the end of arrow 2 corresponds to the length of the line opposite the 60° angle. The hypotenuse of the triangle has a length of 1.00 (the arbitrarily assigned value). Therefore, using SOH,

$$\sin 60° = 0.866 = \frac{\text{opposite}}{\text{hypotenuse}} = \frac{\text{opposite}}{1}$$

so the x coordinate for the end of arrow 2 is 0.866.

The magnitude of the y coordinate corresponds to the length of the line adjacent to the 60° angle. Using TOA,

$$\tan 60° = 1.73 = \frac{\text{opposite}}{\text{adjacent}} = \frac{0.866}{\text{adjacent}}$$

$$\text{adjacent} = \frac{0.866}{1.73} = 0.500$$

so the y coordinate for the end of arrow 2 is −0.500. (The trigonometric formula gives us the length of the side. We know from the diagram that the sign of this y component is negative.)

Arrow 3 is similar to arrow 2. Its x component is equal in magnitude but opposite in sign, and its y component is the same magnitude and sign as that for arrow 2. Therefore, the x and y coordinates for all three vectors are

	x	y
Arrow 1	0	1
Arrow 2	0.866	−0.500
Arrow 3	−0.866	−0.500
Sum =	0	0

Because the individual bond dipoles (represented here as the vectors) sum to zero, the molecule is nonpolar overall.

Although it is somewhat more complicated, a similar analysis can be done to show that all x, y, and z coordinates sum to zero when there are four identical polar bonds arranged in a tetrahedron about a central atom. In fact, any time there are identical bonds symmetrically distributed around a central atom, with no lone pairs on the central atom, the molecule will be nonpolar overall, even if the bonds themselves are polar.

In cases where *non*-identical bonds are distributed symmetrically around the central atom, the nature of the atoms surrounding the central atom determines whether the molecule is polar overall. For example, CCl_4 and $CHCl_3$ have the same molecular geometry (tetrahedral), but CCl_4 is nonpolar because the bond dipoles cancel one another. In $CHCl_3$, however, the bonds are not all identical, and therefore the bond dipoles do not sum to zero. The $CHCl_3$ molecule is polar.

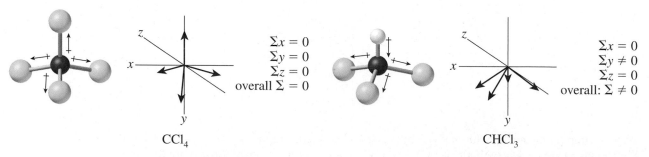

CCl_4 $CHCl_3$

Worked Example 7.3 shows you how to determine whether a molecule is polar.

Worked Example 7.3

Determine whether (a) PCl_5 and (b) H_2CO (C double bonded to O) are polar.

Strategy For each molecule, draw the Lewis structure, use the VSEPR model to determine its molecular geometry, and then determine whether the individual bond dipoles cancel.

Setup

(a) The Lewis structure of PCl_5 is

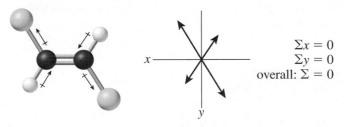

With five identical electron domains around the central atom, the electron-domain and molecular geometries are trigonal bipyramidal. The equatorial bond dipoles will cancel one another, just as in the case of BF_3, and the axial bond dipoles will also cancel each other.

(b) The Lewis structure of H_2CO is

The bond dipoles, although symmetrically distributed around the C atom, are not identical and therefore will not sum to zero.

Solution

(a) PCl_5 is nonpolar.

(b) H_2CO is polar.

Think About It

Make sure that your Lewis structures are correct and that you count electron domains on the central atom carefully. This will give you the correct electron-domain and molecular geometries. Molecular polarity depends both on individual bond dipoles and molecular geometry.

Practice Problem A Determine whether (a) CH_2Cl_2 and (b) XeF_4 are polar.

Practice Problem B For each of the following hypothetical molecules, draw one structure that is polar and one structure that is nonpolar: (a) H_2SF_4 and (b) H_2PCl_3.

Dipole moments can be used to distinguish between molecules that have the same chemical formula but different arrangements of atoms. Such compounds are called **structural isomers**. For example, there are two structural isomers of dichloroethylene ($C_2H_2Cl_2$). Because the individual bond dipoles sum to zero in *trans*-dichloroethylene, the *trans* isomer is nonpolar:

$$\Sigma x = 0$$
$$\Sigma y = 0$$
overall: $\Sigma = 0$

Thinking Outside the Box

Intermolecular Forces

Attractive coulombic interactions between molecules in a substance are referred to as *intermolecular forces*. We have already seen one example of coulombic attraction in the form of ionic bonding [◀◀ Section 5.3], although those attractive forces were between oppositely charged *ions*. Neutral molecules with only *partial* charges [◀◀ Section 6.2] can also exhibit attractive forces, which are partly responsible for the properties associated with a particular substance.

The attractive force between two polar molecules of a substance is known as a *dipole-dipole attraction*. Consider a diatomic molecule with elements of significantly different electronegativities, such as HF. In this molecule, the shared electrons are not shared equally. The molecule, therefore, has a partial positive charge (δ+) on the H atom; and a partial negative charge (δ–) on the F atom. The positive end of one HF molecule is attracted to the negative end of an adjacent HF molecule.

The strength of intermolecular forces determines the physical state of a substance under a given set of conditions. HF, for example, is a gas at room temperature and ordinary pressures. Under conditions in which the HF molecules are less energetic (lower temperature) and/or closer together (higher pressure), however, the intermolecular attractions will draw and hold the molecules together—causing the gas to condense to a liquid. As we will see in Chapter 12, the strength of intermolecular forces also depends on molar mass. But for molecules of comparable molar mass, the magnitude of intermolecular attractions generally increases with increasing polarity.

The partial negative charge on one HF molecule is attracted to the partial negative charge on another.

The bond dipoles in the *cis* isomer do not cancel one another, so *cis*-dichloroethylene is polar:

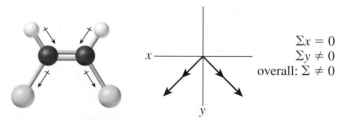

$$\Sigma x = 0$$
$$\Sigma y \neq 0$$
$$\text{overall: } \Sigma \neq 0$$

Because of the difference in polarity, these two isomers can be distinguished experimentally by measuring the dipole moment.

SECTION 7.2 REVIEW

Molecular Geometry and Polarity

7.2.1   Identify the polar molecules in the following group: HBr, CH_4, CS_2.

7.2.2   Identify the nonpolar molecules in the following group: SO_2, NH_3, XeF_2.

7.3 VALENCE BOND THEORY

The Lewis theory of chemical bonding provides a relatively simple way for us to visualize the arrangement of electrons in molecules. It is insufficient, however, to explain the differences between the covalent bonds in molecules such as H_2, F_2, and HF. Although Lewis theory describes the bonds in these three molecules in exactly the same way, they really are quite different from one another, as evidenced by their bond lengths and bond energies listed in Table 7.3. Understanding these differences and why covalent bonds form in the first place requires a bonding model that combines Lewis's notion of atoms sharing electron pairs and the quantum mechanical descriptions of atomic orbitals.

According to ***valence bond theory,*** atoms share electrons when an atomic orbital on one atom overlaps with an atomic orbital on the other. Each of the overlapping atomic orbitals must contain a single, unpaired electron. Furthermore, the two electrons shared by the bonded atoms must have opposite spins [◄◄ Section 3.7]. The nuclei of both atoms are attracted to the shared pair of electrons. It is this mutual attraction for the shared electrons that holds the atoms together.

The quantum mechanical model of the atom treats electrons in atoms as waves, rather than particles. Therefore, rather than use arrows to denote the locations, the convention used here shows a singly occupied atomic *s* orbital as light yellow and a doubly occupied orbital as a darker version of yellow. The H—H bond in H_2 forms when the singly occupied 1*s* orbitals of the two H atoms overlap:

Student Annotation: Recall that *bond energy* is the amount of energy required to break a mole of identical bonds [◄◄ Section 6.1].

H—H

:F̈—F̈:

H—F̈:

Lewis dot structures of H_2, F_2, and HF

Note that in this case, although there are still just two electrons, each H atom "thinks" it owns them both. So when the two singly occupied orbitals overlap, *both* orbitals end up doubly occupied.

Similarly, the F—F bond in F_2 forms when the singly occupied 2*p* orbitals of the two F atoms overlap:

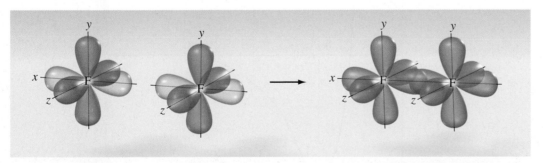

TABLE 7.3	Bond Lengths and Bond Energies of H_2, F_2, and HF	
	Bond length (Å)	**Bond energy (kJ/mol)**
H_2	0.74	436.4
F_2	1.42	150.6
HF	0.92	568.2

$2s^2$ $2p^5$

Orbital diagram for F

Following the convention introduced earlier, atomic p orbitals will be represented as light blue if singly occupied and darker blue if doubly occupied. Empty p orbitals will appear white. Recall that the ground-state electron configuration of the F atom is $[He]2s^22p^5$ [◄◄ Section 3.9]. (The ground-state orbital diagram of F is shown in the margin.)

We can also use the valence bond model to depict the formation of an H—F bond. In this case, the singly occupied $1s$ orbital of the H atom overlaps with the singly occupied $2p$ orbital of the F atom:

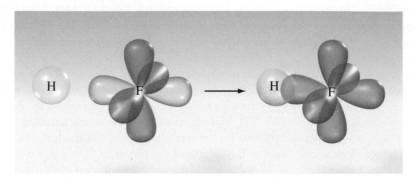

According to the quantum mechanical model, the sizes, shapes, and energies of the $1s$ orbital of H and the $2p$ orbital of F are different. Therefore, it is not surprising that the bonds in H_2, F_2, and HF vary in strength and length.

One of the advantages of valence bond theory over Lewis theory is that it explains *why* covalent bonds form. According to valence bond theory, a covalent bond will form between two atoms if the potential energy of the resulting molecule is lower than the combined potential energies of the isolated atoms. Simply put, this means that the formation of covalent bonds gives off energy. While this may not seem intuitively obvious, you know that energy must be *supplied* to a molecule to *break* covalent bonds. It should make sense then, that the reverse process—the *formation* of bonds—must give *off* energy. Figure 7.3 illustrates how the total potential energy of two hydrogen atoms varies with distance between the nuclei.

Valence bond theory also introduces the concept of *directionality* to chemical bonds. For example, we expect the bond formed by the overlap of a p orbital to coincide with the axis along which the p orbital lies. Consider the molecule H_2S. Unlike the other molecules that we have encountered, H_2S does not have the bond angle that Lewis theory and the VSEPR model would lead us to predict. (With four electron domains on the central atom, we would expect the bond angle to be on the order of 109.5°.) In fact, the H—S—H bond angle is 92°. Looking at this in terms

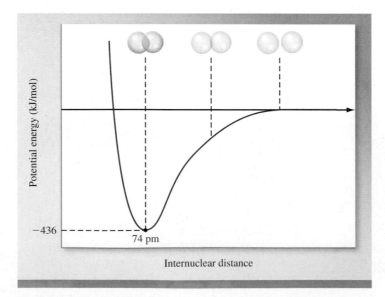

Figure 7.3 The change in potential energy of two hydrogen atoms as a function of internuclear distance. The minimum potential energy (–436 kJ/mol) occurs when the distance between the nuclei is 74 pm. The yellow spheres represent the $1s$ orbitals of hydrogen.

of valence bond theory, the central atom (S) has two unpaired electrons, each of which resides in a $3p$ orbital. The orbital diagram for the ground-state electron configuration of the S atom is

Student Annotation: In order for you to understand the material in this section and Section 7.4, you must be able to draw orbital diagrams for ground-state electron configurations [◀◀ Section 3.9].

$$\text{S} \quad [\text{Ne}] \quad \boxed{\uparrow\downarrow} \qquad \boxed{\uparrow\downarrow}\boxed{\uparrow}\boxed{\uparrow}$$
$$\phantom{\text{S} \quad [\text{Ne}] \quad} 3s^2 \qquad\quad 3p^4$$

Remember that p orbitals are mutually perpendicular, lying along the x, y, and z axes [◀◀ Section 3.8]. We can rationalize the observed bond angle by envisioning the overlap of each of the singly occupied $3p$ orbitals with the $1s$ orbital of a hydrogen atom:

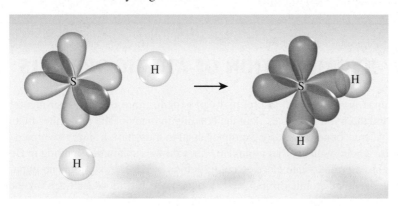

In summary, the important features of valence bond theory are as follows:

- A bond forms when singly occupied atomic orbitals on two atoms overlap.
- The two electrons shared in the region of orbital overlap must be of opposite spin.
- Formation of a bond results in a lower potential energy for the system.

Worked Example 7.4 shows how to use valence bond theory to explain the bonding in a molecule.

Worked Example 7.4

Hydrogen selenide (H_2Se) is a foul-smelling gas that can cause eye and respiratory tract inflammation. The H—Se—H bond angle in H_2Se is approximately 92°. Use valence bond theory to describe the bonding in this molecule.

Strategy Consider the central atom's ground-state electron configuration and determine what orbitals are available for bond formation.

Setup The ground-state electron configuration of Se is $[\text{Ar}]4s^2 3d^{10} 4p^4$. Its orbital diagram (showing only the $4p$ orbitals) is

$$4p^4$$

Solution Two of the $4p$ orbitals are singly occupied and therefore available for bonding. The bonds in H_2Se form as the result of the overlap of a hydrogen $1s$ orbital with each of these orbitals on the Se atom.

Think About It
Because the $4p$ orbitals on the Se atom are all mutually perpendicular, we should expect the angles between bonds formed by their overlap to be approximately 90°.

Practice Problem A Use valence bond theory to describe the bonding in phosphine (PH_3), which has H—P—H bond angles of approximately 94°.

Practice Problem B For which molecule(s) can we not use valence bond theory to explain the bonding: SO_2 (O—S—O bond angle ~120°), CH_4 (H—C—H bond angles = 109.5°), AsH_3 (H—As—H bond angles = 92°)? Explain.

SECTION 7.3 REVIEW

Valence Bond Theory

7.3.1   For each element in the second period of the periodic table (Li–Ne), determine the number of unpaired electrons in the ground-state electron configuration.

7.3.2   According to valence bond theory, how many bonds would you expect a nitrogen atom (in its ground state) to form?

7.4 HYBRIDIZATION OF ATOMIC ORBITALS

Although valence bond theory is useful and can explain more of our experimental observations than Lewis bond theory, it fails to explain the bonding in many of the molecules that we encounter. According to valence bond theory, for example, an atom must have a singly occupied atomic orbital in order to form a bond with another atom. How then do we explain the bonding in $BeCl_2$? The central atom, Be, has a ground-state electron configuration of $[He]2s^2$, so it has no unpaired electrons. With no singly occupied atomic orbitals in its ground state, how does Be form two bonds?

Furthermore, in cases where the ground-state electron configuration of the central atom *does* have the required number of unpaired electrons, how do we explain the observed bond angles? Carbon, like sulfur, has two unpaired electrons in its ground state. Using valence bond theory as our guide, we might envision the formation of two covalent bonds with oxygen, as in CO_2. If the two unpaired electrons on C (each residing in a $2p$ orbital) were to form bonds, however, the O–C–O bond angle should be on the order of 90°, like the bond angle in H_2S. In fact, the bond angle in CO_2 is 180°:

180°

Actual bond angle is 180°.

Bond angle should be 90°.

In order to explain these and other observations, we need to extend our discussion of orbital overlap to include the concept of ***hybridization*** or *mixing* of atomic orbitals.

The idea of hybridization of atomic orbitals begins with the molecular geometry and works backward to explain the bonds and the observed bond angles in a molecule. To extend our discussion of orbital overlap and introduce the concept of hybridization of atomic orbitals, we first consider beryllium chloride ($BeCl_2$), which has two electron domains on the central atom. Using its Lewis structure (shown in the margin) and the VSEPR model, we predict that $BeCl_2$ will have a Cl–Be–Cl bond angle of 180°. If this is true, though, how does Be form two bonds with no unpaired electrons, and why is the angle between the two bonds 180°?

To answer the first part of the question, we envision the *promotion* of one of the electrons in the $2s$ orbital to an empty $2p$ orbital. Recall that electrons can be promoted from a lower atomic orbital to a higher one [◄◄ Section 3.4]. The ground-state electron configuration is the one in which all the electrons occupy orbitals of the lowest possible energy. A configuration in which one or more electrons occupy a *higher* energy orbital is called an *excited* state. An excited state generally is denoted with a star (e.g., Be* for an excited-state Be atom). Showing only the valence orbitals, we can represent the promotion of one of the valence electrons of beryllium as

With one of its valence electrons promoted to the $2p$ subshell, the Be atom now has two unpaired electrons and therefore can form two bonds. However, the orbitals in which the two unpaired electrons reside are different from each other, so we would expect bonds formed as a result of the overlap of these two orbitals (each with a $3p$ orbital on a Cl atom) to be different:

Orbital diagram for Cl

Experimentally, though, the bonds in BeCl$_2$ are identical in length and strength.

Hybridization of *s* and *p* Orbitals

To explain how beryllium forms two identical bonds, we must mix the orbitals in which the unpaired electrons reside, thus yielding two equivalent orbitals. The mixing of beryllium's $2s$ orbital with one of its $2p$ orbitals, a process known as *hybridization,* yields two **hybrid orbitals** that are neither *s* nor *p,* but have some character of each. The hybrid orbitals are designated $2sp$ or simply *sp.*

> **Student Annotation:** Hybrid orbitals are another type of *electron domain.*

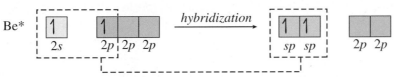

Mixing of one *s* orbital and one *p* orbital to yield two *sp* orbitals

The mathematical combination of the quantum mechanical wave functions for an *s* orbital and a *p* orbital gives rise to two new, equivalent wave functions. As shown in Figure 7.4(a), each *sp* hybrid orbital has one small lobe and one large lobe and, like any two electron domains on an atom, they are oriented in opposite directions with a 180° angle between them. The figure shows the atomic and hybrid orbitals separately for clarity. Note that the hybrid orbitals are shown in two ways: the first is a more realistic shape, whereas the second is a simplified shape that we use to keep the figures clear and make the visualization of orbitals easier. Note also that the representations of hybrid orbitals are green. Figure 7.4(b) and (c) show the locations of the atomic orbitals and the hybrid orbitals, respectively, relative to the beryllium nucleus.

> **Student Annotation:** In picturing the shapes of the resulting hybrid orbitals, it may help to remember that orbitals, like waves, can combine constructively or destructively. We can think of the large lobe of each *sp* hybrid orbital as the result of a *constructive* combination and the small lobe of each as the result of a *destructive* combination.

With two *sp* hybrid orbitals, each containing a single unpaired electron, we can see how the Be atom is able to form two identical bonds with two Cl atoms [Figure 7.4(c)]. Each of the singly occupied *sp* hybrid orbitals on the Be atom overlaps with the singly occupied $3p$ atomic orbital on a Cl atom.

We can do a similar analysis of the bonds and the trigonal-planar geometry of boron trifluoride (BF$_3$). The ground-state electron configuration of the B atom is [He]$2s^2 2p^1$, containing just one unpaired electron. Promotion of one of the $2s$ electrons to an empty $2p$ orbital gives the three unpaired electrons needed to explain the formation of *three* bonds. The ground-state and excited-state electron configurations can be represented by

> **Student Annotation:** The energy required to promote an electron in an atom is more than compensated for by the energy given off when a bond forms.

Because the three bonds in BF$_3$ are identical, we must hybridize the three singly occupied atomic orbitals (the one *s* and two *p* orbitals) to give three singly occupied hybrid orbitals:

Mixing of one *s* orbital and two
p orbitals to yield three sp^2 orbitals

Figure 7.5 (page 233) illustrates the hybridization and bond formation in BF$_3$.

Figure 7.4 (a) An atomic *s* orbital (yellow) and one atomic *p* orbital (blue) combine to form two *sp* hybrid orbitals (green). The realistic hybrid orbital shapes are shown first. The thinner representations are used to keep diagrams clear. (b) The 2*s* orbital and one of the 2*p* orbitals on Be combine to form two *sp* hybrid orbitals. Unoccupied orbitals are shown in white. Like any two electron domains, the hybrid orbitals on Be are 180° apart. (c) The hybrid orbitals on Be each overlap with a singly occupied 3*p* orbital on a Cl atom.

(a)

(b)

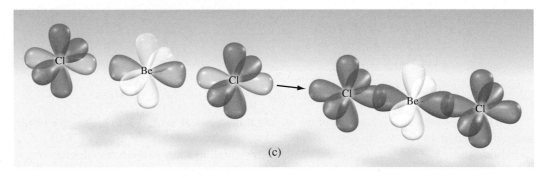
(c)

Student Annotation: Empty unhybridized *p* orbitals are important in certain types of bond formation, as we will see in Chapters 16 and 24.

CH$_4$

In both cases (i.e., for BeCl$_2$ and BF$_3$), some but not *all* of the *p* orbitals are hybridized. When the remaining unhybridized atomic *p* orbitals do not contain electrons, as in the case of BF$_3$, they will not be part of the discussion of bonding in this chapter. As we will see in Section 7.5, though, unhybridized atomic orbitals that *do* contain electrons are important in our description of the bonding in a molecule.

We can now apply the same kind of analysis to the methane molecule (CH$_4$). The Lewis structure of CH$_4$ has four electron domains around the central carbon atom. This means that we need four hybrid orbitals, which in turn means that four atomic orbitals must be hybridized. The ground-state electron configuration of the C atom contains two unpaired electrons. Promotion of one electron from the 2*s* orbital to the empty 2*p* orbital yields the four unpaired electrons needed for the formation of four bonds:

Hybridization of the *s* orbital and the three *p* orbitals yields four hybrid orbitals designated *sp*^{3}. We can then place the electrons that were originally in the *s* and *p* atomic orbitals into the *sp*^{3} hybrid orbitals.

Mixing of one *s* orbital and
three *p* orbitals to yield four *sp*^{3} orbitals

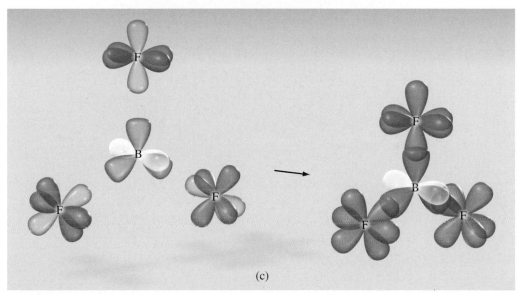

Figure 7.5 (a) An s atomic orbital and two p atomic orbitals combine to form three sp^2 hybrid orbitals. (b) The three sp^2 hybrid orbitals on B are arranged in a trigonal plane. (Empty atomic orbitals are shown in white.) (c) Hybrid orbitals on B overlap with $2p$ orbitals on F.

The set of four sp^3 hybrid orbitals on carbon, like any four electron domains on a central atom, assumes a tetrahedral arrangement. Figure 7.6 illustrates how the hybridization of the C atom results in the formation of the four bonds and the 109.5° bond angles observed in CH_4.

Hybridization of *s*, *p*, and *d* Orbitals

Recall that elements in the third period of the periodic table and beyond do not necessarily obey the octet rule because they have d orbitals that can hold additional electrons [◄◄ Section 6.6]. In order to explain the bonding and geometry of molecules in which there are more than four electron domains on the central atom, we must include d orbitals in our hybridization scheme. PCl_5, for example, has five electron domains around the P atom. In order to explain the five bonds in this molecule, we will need five singly occupied hybrid orbitals. The ground-state electron configuration of the P atom is $[Ne]3s^2 3p^3$, which contains three unpaired electrons. In this case, though, because all three of the p orbitals are occupied, promotion of an electron from the $3s$ orbital to a $3p$

PCl_5

Figure 7.6 (a) An *s* atomic orbital and three *p* atomic orbitals combine to form four *sp*³ hybrid orbitals. (b) The four *sp*³ hybrid orbitals on C are arranged in a tetrahedron. (c) Hybrid orbitals on C overlap with 1*s* orbitals on H. For clarity, the small lobes of the hybrid orbitals are not shown.

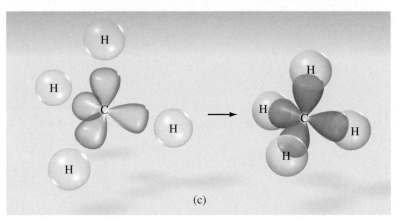

orbital would *not* result in additional unpaired electrons. However, we can envision the promotion of an electron from the 3*s* orbital to an empty 3*d* orbital resulting in the five unpaired electrons needed:

Hybridization of the *s* orbital, the three *p* orbitals, and one of the *d* orbitals yields hybrid orbitals that are designated *sp*³*d*. After placing the five electrons in the five hybrid orbitals, we can rationalize the formation of five bonds in the molecule:

Student Annotation: Note that the superscript numbers in hybrid orbital notation are used to designate the number of atomic orbitals that have undergone hybridization. When the superscript is 1, it is not shown (analogous to the subscripts in chemical formulas).

Mixing of one *s* orbital, three *p* orbitals,
and one *d* orbital to yield five *sp*³*d* orbitals

The *sp*³*d* orbitals have shapes similar to those we have seen for the *sp*, *sp*², and *sp*³ hybrid orbitals, that is, one large lobe and one small lobe. In addition, the five hybrid orbitals adopt a trigonal bipyramidal arrangement, enabling us to explain the geometry and bond angles in PCl₅:

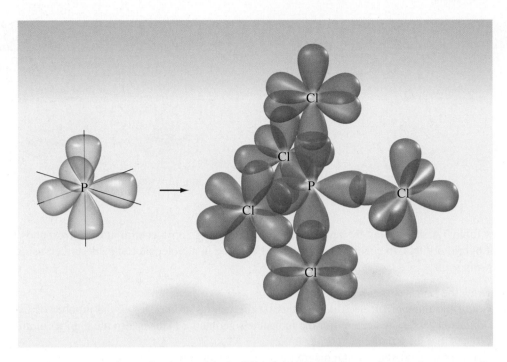

A similar analysis can be done with the SF_6 molecule. The ground-state electron configuration of the S atom is $[Ne]3s^2 3p^4$, giving it only two unpaired electrons. In order to obtain the six unpaired electrons needed to form six S−F bonds, we must promote *two* electrons to empty d orbitals: one from the $3s$ orbital and one from the doubly occupied $3p$ orbital. The resulting hybrid orbitals are designated $sp^3 d^2$.

Mixing of one *s* orbital, three *p* orbitals,
and two *d* orbitals to yield six $sp^3 d^2$ orbitals

The six bonds in SF_6 form, therefore, when each $sp^3 d^2$ hybrid orbital on the S atom overlaps with a singly occupied $2p$ orbital on an F atom:

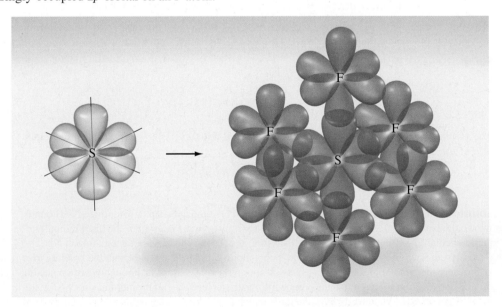

Student Annotation: There is some controversy surrounding the use of *d* orbitals to describe the hybridization of atoms with expanded octets [◀◀ Section 6.6]. The relatively high energies of *d* orbitals would seem to prohibit their participation in the formation of hybrid orbitals. Although it is beyond the scope of this text, it is possible to explain the bonding in these species using molecular orbital theory [▶▶ Section 7.6]. Nevertheless, including *d* orbitals in our picture of hybridization is a convenient way to describe the bonding in molecules such as PCl_5 and SF_6.

TABLE 7.4	Number of Electron Domains and Hybrid Orbitals on Central Atom				
Number of electron domains on central atom	2	3	4	5	6
Hybrid orbitals	sp	sp^2	sp^3	sp^3d	sp^3d^2
Geometry	Linear	Trigonal planar	Tetrahedral	Trigonal bipyramidal	Octahedral

Table 7.4 shows how the number of electron domains on a central atom corresponds to a set of hybrid orbitals. In general, the hybridized bonding in a molecule can be described using the following steps:

1. Draw the Lewis structure.
2. Count the number of electron domains on the central atom. This is the number of hybrid orbitals necessary to account for the molecule's geometry. (This is also the number of *atomic* orbitals that must undergo hybridization.)
3. Draw the ground-state orbital diagram for the central atom.
4. Maximize the number of unpaired valence electrons by promotion.
5. Combine the necessary number of atomic orbitals to generate the required number of hybrid orbitals.
6. Place electrons in the hybrid orbitals, putting one electron in each orbital before pairing any electrons.

Student Annotation: The electrons that you place in hybrid orbitals are those that originally resided in the atomic orbitals that have undergone hybridization.

It is important to recognize that we do not use hybrid orbitals to *predict* molecular geometries, but rather to *explain* geometries that are already known. As we saw in Section 7.3, the bonding in many molecules can be explained without the use of hybrid orbitals. Hydrogen sulfide (H_2S), for example, has a bond angle of 92°. This bond angle is best explained without the use of hybrid orbitals.

Worked Example 7.5 shows how to use hybridization to explain the bonding and geometry in a molecule.

Worked Example 7.5

Ammonia (NH_3) is a trigonal pyramidal molecule with H—N—H bond angles of about 107°. Describe the formation of three equivalent N—H bonds, and explain the angles between them.

Strategy Starting with a Lewis structure, determine the number and type of hybrid orbitals necessary to rationalize the bonding in NH_3.

Setup The Lewis structure of NH_3 is

$$H-\ddot{N}-H \atop \underset{H}{|} \,107°$$

The ground-state electron configuration of the N atom is $[He]2s^22p^3$. Its valence orbital diagram is

N [↑↓] [↑][↑][↑]
   $2s^2$ $2p^3$

Solution Although the N atom has the three unpaired electrons needed to form three N—H bonds, we would expect bond angles of ~90° (not 107°) to form from the overlap of the three mutually perpendicular 2p orbitals. Hybridization, therefore, is necessary to explain the bonding in NH_3. (Recall from Section 7.3 that valence bond theory alone could be used to explain the bonding in H_2S, where the bond angles are ~90°—hybridization was unnecessary.) Although we often need to promote an electron to maximize the number of unpaired electrons, no promotion is necessary for the nitrogen in NH_3. We already have the three unpaired electrons necessary, and the promotion of an electron from the 2s orbital to one of the 2p orbitals would not result in any additional unpaired electrons. Furthermore, there are no empty *d* orbitals in the second shell. According to the Lewis structure, there are four electron domains on the central atom (three bonds and a lone pair of electrons). Four electron domains on the central atom require four hybrid orbitals, and four hybrid orbitals require the hybridization of four atomic orbitals: one *s* and three *p*. This corresponds to sp^3 hybridization. Because the atomic orbitals involved in the hybridization contain a total of five electrons, we place five electrons in the resulting hybrid orbitals. This means that one of the hybrid orbitals will contain a lone pair of electrons:

Each N—H bond is formed by the overlap between an sp^3 hybrid orbital on the N atom and the 1*s* atomic orbital on an H atom. Because there are four electron domains on the central atom, we expect them to be arranged in a tetrahedron. In addition, because one of the electron domains is a lone pair, we expect the H—N—H bond angles to be slightly smaller than the ideal tetrahedral bond angle of 109.5°:

Think About It
This analysis agrees with the experimentally observed geometry and bond angles of 107° in NH_3.

Practice Problem A Use hybrid orbital theory to describe the bonding and explain the bond angles in bromine pentafluoride (BrF_5).

Practice Problem B Use hybrid orbital theory to describe the bonding and explain the bond angles in BeF_2:

180°

F — Be — F

SECTION 7.4 REVIEW

Hybridization of Atomic Orbitals

7.4.1   How many orbitals does a set of sp^2 hybrid orbitals contain?

7.4.2   How many *p* atomic orbitals are required to generate a set of sp^3 hybrid orbitals?

7.5 HYBRIDIZATION IN MOLECULES CONTAINING MULTIPLE BONDS

The concept of valence bond theory and hybridization can also be used to describe the bonding in molecules containing double and triple bonds, such as ethylene (C_2H_4) and acetylene (C_2H_2). The Lewis structure of ethylene is

$$
\begin{array}{c}
H \qquad\qquad H \\
\diagdown \qquad \diagup \\
C = C \\
\diagup \qquad \diagdown \\
H \qquad\qquad H
\end{array}
$$

Each carbon atom is surrounded by three electron domains (two single bonds and one double bond). Thus, we expect the hybridization about each C atom to be sp^2, just like the B atom in BF_3. Applying the procedure described in Section 7.4, we first maximize the number of unpaired electrons by promoting an electron from the $2s$ orbital to the empty $2p$ orbital:

$$
C \;\; \boxed{\uparrow\downarrow} \quad \boxed{\uparrow\,|\,\uparrow\,|\,\;} \xrightarrow{\;\;promotion\;\;} C^* \;\; \boxed{\uparrow} \quad \boxed{\uparrow\,|\,\uparrow\,|\,\uparrow}
$$
$$
\;\;\;\;2s^2 \qquad 2p^2 \qquad\qquad\qquad\quad 2s^1 \qquad 2p^3
$$

We then hybridize the required number of atomic orbitals, which in this case is three (one for each electron domain on the C atom):

$$
C^* \;\; \boxed{\uparrow} \quad \boxed{\uparrow\,|\,\uparrow\,|\,\uparrow} \xrightarrow{\;\;hybridization\;\;} \boxed{\uparrow\,|\,\uparrow\,|\,\uparrow} \quad \boxed{\uparrow}
$$
$$
\;\;\;\;2s \quad\;\; 2p\;\;2p\;\,2p \qquad\qquad\qquad sp^2\;sp^2\;sp^2 \qquad 2p
$$

The three equivalent sp^2 hybrid orbitals, arranged in a trigonal plane, enable us to explain the three bonds about each C atom. In this case, however, each C atom is left with a singly occupied, *unhybridized* atomic orbital. As we will see, it is the singly occupied p orbitals *not* involved in hybridization that give rise to multiple bonds in molecules.

In the bonding schemes that we have described thus far, the overlap of atomic orbitals or hybrid orbitals occurs directly between the two nuclei involved in bonding. Such bonds, in which the shared electron density is concentrated directly along the internuclear axis, are called ***sigma (σ) bonds***. The ethylene molecule (also known as *ethene*) contains five sigma bonds: one between the two C atoms (the result of the overlap of one of the sp^2 hybrid orbitals on each C atom) and four between the C and H atoms (each the result of the overlap of an sp^2 hybrid orbital on a C atom and the $1s$ orbital on an H atom). The leftover unhybridized p orbital is perpendicular to the plane in which the atoms of the molecule lie. Figure 7.7(a) illustrates the formation and the overlap of sp^2 hybrid orbitals and shows the positions of the remaining p orbital on each C atom.

Remember that the shapes used to represent the atomic and hybrid orbitals are simplified to make visualization of the molecules easier. The actual shapes of both atomic and hybrid orbitals are such that when the sp^2 hybrid orbitals overlap to form a sigma bond between the two C atoms, the remaining unhybridized p orbitals also overlap, although to a smaller extent. Figure 7.7(b) shows the overlap of the unhybridized p orbitals on the two C atoms in ethylene. The resulting regions of electron density are concentrated above and below the plane of the molecule, in contrast to a sigma bond in which the electron density is concentrated directly along the internuclear axis. Bonds that form from the sideways overlap of p orbitals are called ***pi (π) bonds***. The two regions of overlap shown in Figure 7.7(b) together make up one pi bond. It is the formation of the pi bond that makes the ethylene molecule planar.

A sigma bond and a pi bond together constitute a *double* bond. Because the sideways overlap of p orbitals is not as effective as the overlap of hybrid orbitals that point directly toward each other, the contribution of the pi bond to the overall strength of the bond is less than that of the sigma bond. The bond energy of a carbon-carbon double bond (620 kJ/mol) is greater than that of a carbon-carbon single bond (347 kJ/mol), but it is not twice as large.

Multi 7.6
Chemical bonding—sigma-pi bonding

Multi 7.7
Chemical bonding—sigma and pi bonding in benzene

Student Annotation: Bond energy was introduced in Chapter 6 [◄◄ Section 6.1].

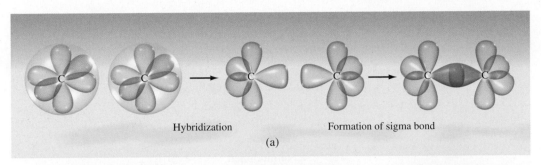

Hybridization   Formation of sigma bond

(a)

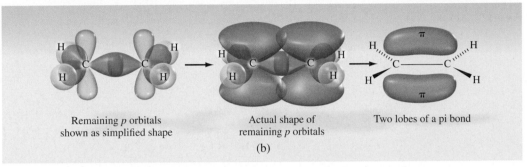

Remaining *p* orbitals   Actual shape of   Two lobes of a pi bond
shown as simplified shape   remaining *p* orbitals

(b)

Worked Example 7.6 shows how to use a Lewis structure to determine the number of sigma and pi bonds in a molecule.

Worked Example 7.6

Thalidomide ($C_{13}H_{10}N_2O_4$) is a sedative and antiemetic that was widely prescribed during the 1950s, although not in the United States, for pregnant women suffering from morning sickness. Its use was largely discontinued when it was determined to be responsible for thousands of devastating birth defects. Determine the number of carbon-carbon sigma bonds and the total number of pi bonds in thalidomide.

Thalidomide

Strategy Use the Lewis structure to determine the number of single and double bonds. Then, to convert the number of single and double bonds to the number of sigma and pi bonds, remember that a single bond is composed of a sigma bond, whereas a double bond is usually composed of one sigma bond and one pi bond.

Setup There are nine carbon-carbon single bonds and three carbon-carbon double bonds. Overall there are seven double bonds in the molecule (three C=C and four C=O).

Solution Thalidomide contains 12 carbon-carbon sigma bonds and a total of seven pi bonds (three in carbon-carbon double bonds and four in carbon-oxygen double bonds).

Think About It
The Lewis structure given for thalidomide is one of two possible resonance structures. Draw the other resonance structure, and count sigma and pi bonds again. Make sure you get the same answer.

(Continued on next page)

Practice Problem A The active ingredient in Tylenol and a host of other over-the-counter pain relievers is acetaminophen ($C_8H_9NO_2$). Determine the total number of sigma and pi bonds in the acetaminophen molecule.

Acetaminophen

Practice Problem B Determine the total number of sigma and pi bonds in a molecule of aspirin ($C_9H_8O_4$).

Aspirin

Because the *p* orbitals that form pi bonds must be parallel to each other, pi bonds restrict the rotation of a molecule in a way that sigma bonds do not. For example, the molecule 1,2-dichloroethane exists as a single isomer. Although we can draw the molecule in several different ways, including the two shown in Figure 7.8(a), all of them are equivalent because the molecule can rotate freely about the sigma bond between the two carbon atoms.

On the other hand, 1,2-dichloroethylene exists as two distinct isomers—*cis* and *trans*—as shown in Figure 7.8(b). The double bond between the carbon atoms consists of one sigma bond and one pi bond. The pi bond restricts rotation about the sigma bond, making the molecules rigid, planar, and not interchangeable. To change one isomer into the other, the pi bond would have to be broken and rotation would have to occur about the sigma bond and the pi bond. This process would require a significant input of energy.

H—C≡C—H

C_2H_2

The acetylene molecule (C_2H_2) is linear. Because each carbon atom has two electron domains around it in the Lewis structure, the carbon atoms are *sp* hybridized. As before, promotion of an electron first maximizes the number of unpaired electrons:

The 2*s* orbital and one of the 2*p* orbitals then mix to form two *sp* hybrid orbitals:

This leaves two unhybridized *p* orbitals (each containing an electron) on each C atom. Figure 7.9 shows the sigma and pi bonds in the acetylene molecule (also known as *ethyne*). Just as one sigma bond and one pi bond make up a *double* bond, one sigma bond and two pi bonds make up a *triple* bond. Figure 7.10 (p. 242) summarizes the formation of bonds in ethane, ethylene, and acetylene.

Multi 7.8
Formation of pi bonds in ethylene and acetylene

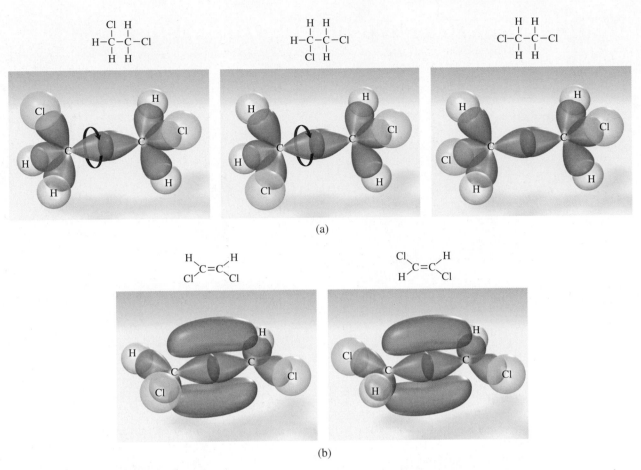

(a)

(b)

Figure 7.8 (a) In 1,2-dichloroethane, there is free rotation about the C—C single bond. All three Lewis structures represent the same molecule. (b) In 1,2-dichloroethylene, there is no rotation about the C=C double bond. The two Lewis structures represent two different molecules.

(a)

(b)

Figure 7.9 (a) Formation of the sigma bond in acetylene. (b) Formation of the pi bonds in acetylene.

Figure 7.10

Formation of Pi Bonds in Ethylene and Acetylene

2s and 2p atomic orbitals on two C atoms

In ethane (C_2H_6) the C atoms are sp^3-hybridized.

In ethylene (C_2H_4) the C atoms are sp^2-hybridized.

Overlap of sp^2 hybrid orbitals forms a sigma bond between the two C atoms.

In acetylene (C_2H_2) the C atoms are sp-hybridized.

Overlap of sp hybrid orbitals forms a sigma bond between the two C atoms.

Overlap of sp^3 hybrid orbitals forms a sigma bond between the two C atoms.

Each C atom forms three sigma bonds with H atoms.

Each C atom forms two sigma bonds with H atoms. Each C atom has one leftover unhybridized p orbital.

Using the more realistic shape shows how p orbitals overlap.

The parallel, unhybridized p orbitals overlap to form a pi bond with two lobes.

Each C atom forms one sigma bond with an H atom. Each C atom has two leftover unhybridized p orbitals.

Each pair of parallel, unhybridized p orbitals overlaps to form a pi bond with two lobes.

What's the point?

When carbon is sp^2- or sp-hybridized, parallel, unhybridized p orbitals interact to form pi bonds. Each pi bond consists of two lobes as a result of the overlap.

Worked Example 7.7 shows how hybrid orbitals and pi bonds can be used to explain the bonding in formaldehyde, a molecule with a carbon-oxygen double bond.

Worked Example 7.7

In addition to its use in aqueous solution as a preservative for laboratory specimens, formaldehyde gas is used as an antibacterial fumigant. Use hybridization to explain the bonding in formaldehyde (CH_2O).

Strategy Draw the Lewis structure of formaldehyde, determine the hybridization of the C and O atoms, and describe the formation of the sigma and pi bonds in the molecule.

Setup The Lewis structure of formaldehyde is

$$\ddot{\underset{\|}{O}}$$
$$H-C-H$$

The C and O atoms each have three electron domains around them. [Carbon has two single bonds (C—H) and a double bond (C=O); oxygen has a double bond (O=C) and two lone pairs.]

Solution Three electron domains correspond to sp^2 hybridization. For carbon, promotion of an electron from the $2s$ orbital to the empty $2p$ orbital is necessary to maximize the number of unpaired electrons. For oxygen, no promotion is necessary. Each undergoes hybridization to produce sp^2 hybrid orbitals; and each is left with a singly occupied, unhybridized p orbital:

A sigma bond is formed between the C and O atoms by the overlap of one of the sp^2 hybrid orbitals from each of them. Two more sigma bonds form between the C atom and the H atoms by the overlap of carbon's remaining sp^2 hybrid orbitals with the $1s$ orbital on each H atom. Finally, the remaining p orbitals on C and O overlap to form a pi bond:

Think About It
Our analysis describes the formation of both a sigma bond and a pi bond between the C and O atoms. This corresponds correctly to the double bond predicted by the Lewis structure.

Practice Problem A Use valence bond theory and hybrid orbitals to explain the bonding in hydrogen cyanide (HCN).

Practice Problem B Use valence bond theory and hybrid orbitals to explain the bonding in diatomic nitrogen (N_2).

SECTION 7.5 REVIEW

Hybridization in Molecules Containing Multiple Bonds

7.5.1   How many pi bonds are present in CO_2?

7.5.2   From left to right, give the hybridization of each carbon atom in the allene molecule ($H_2C{=}C{=}CH_2$).

7.5.3   Can $1s$ and $2p_x$ orbitals on adjacent nuclei overlap to form a sigma bond? Explain. (Assume that the x axis is the internuclear axis.)

7.5.4   Can $3p_y$ and $3p_z$ orbitals on adjacent nuclei overlap to form a pi bond? Explain. (Assume that the x axis is the internuclear axis.)

7.6   MOLECULAR ORBITAL THEORY

Although the bonding theories we have seen thus far provide simple and effective ways for us to visualize molecules and to predict their shapes and bond angles, Lewis structures and valence bond theory do not enable us to describe or predict some important properties of molecules. Diatomic oxygen, for example, exhibits *paramagnetism.* Recall that paramagnetic species have one or more unpaired electrons [◄◄ Section 3.9], and that they are attracted by magnetic fields; whereas *diamagnetic* species, with no unpaired electrons, are weakly repelled by magnetic fields.

Because O_2 exhibits paramagnetism, it must contain unpaired electrons. According to the Lewis structure of O_2 (shown in the margin) and the valence bond theory description of O_2, however, all the electrons in O_2 are paired. In order to account for the paramagnetism of O_2, we need a new bonding theory. The theory that correctly describes this and other important molecular properties is *molecular orbital theory.*

According to **molecular orbital theory,** the atomic orbitals involved in bonding actually combine to form new orbitals that are the "property" of the entire molecule, rather than of the individual atoms forming the bonds. These new orbitals are called **molecular orbitals**. In molecular orbital theory, electrons shared by atoms in a molecule reside in the molecular orbitals.

Molecular orbitals are like atomic orbitals in several ways: they have specific shapes and specific energies, and they can each accommodate a maximum of two electrons. As was the case with atomic orbitals, two electrons residing in the same molecular orbital must have opposite spins, as required by the Pauli exclusion principle. And, like hybrid orbitals, the number of molecular orbitals we get is equal to the number of atomic orbitals we combine.

Our treatment of molecular orbital theory in this book will be limited to descriptions of bonding in diatomic molecules consisting of elements from the first two periods of the periodic table (H through Ne).

Bonding and Antibonding Molecular Orbitals

To begin our discussion, we consider H_2, the simplest homonuclear diatomic molecule. According to *valence* bond theory, an H_2 molecule forms when two H atoms are close enough for their $1s$ atomic orbitals to overlap. According to *molecular* orbital theory, two H atoms come together to form H_2 when their $1s$ atomic orbitals combine to give molecular orbitals. Figure 7.11 shows the $1s$ atomic orbitals of the isolated H atoms and the molecular orbitals that result from their constructive and destructive combinations. The *constructive* combination of the two $1s$ orbitals gives rise to a molecular orbital [Figure 7.11(b)] that lies along the internuclear axis directly between the two H nuclei. Just as electron density shared between two nuclei in overlapping atomic orbitals drew the nuclei together, electron density in a molecular orbital that lies between two nuclei will draw them together, too. Thus, this molecular orbital is referred to as a **bonding molecular orbital**.

The *destructive* combination of the $1s$ atomic orbitals also gives rise to a molecular orbital that lies along the internuclear axis, but, as Figure 7.11(c) shows, this molecular orbital, which consists of two lobes, does not lie between the two nuclei. Electron density in this molecular orbital would actually pull the two nuclei in opposite directions, rather than toward each other. This is referred to as an **antibonding molecular orbital**.

Liquid oxygen is attracted to the poles of a magnet because O_2 is paramagnetic.

Liquid nitrogen is not attracted to the poles of a magnet because N_2 is diamagnetic.

$$:\ddot{O}{=}\ddot{O}:$$
$$O_2$$

Multi 7.9
Chemical bonding—paramagnetic liquid oxygen

Student Annotation: Recall that a homonuclear diatomic molecule is one in which both atoms are the same element [◄◄ Section 5.5].

Student Annotation: Remember that the quantum mechanical approach treats atomic orbitals as *wave functions* [◄◄ Section 3.6], and that one of the properties of waves is their capacity for both constructive combination and destructive combination [◄◄ Section 3.2].

Multi 7.10
Chemical bonding—formation molecular orbitals

Figure 7.11 (a) Two *s* atomic orbitals combine to give two sigma molecular orbitals. (b) One of the molecular orbitals is lower in energy than the original atomic orbitals (darker), and (c) one is higher in energy (lighter). The two light yellow lobes make up one molecular orbital. (d) Atomic and molecular orbitals shown relative to the H nuclei.

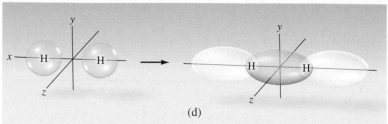

σ Molecular Orbitals

Molecular orbitals that lie along the internuclear axis (such as the bonding and antibonding molecular orbitals in H_2) are referred to as *σ molecular orbitals*. Specifically, the *bonding* molecular orbital formed by the combination of two 1*s* atomic orbitals is designated σ_{1s} and the *antibonding* orbital is designated σ_{1s}^*, where the asterisk distinguishes an antibonding orbital from a bonding orbital. Figure 7.11(d) summarizes the combination of two 1*s* atomic orbitals to yield two molecular orbitals: one bonding and one antibonding.

Student Annotation: The designations σ and π are used in molecular orbital theory just as they are in valence bond theory: σ refers to electron density along the internuclear axis, and π refers to electron density that influences both nuclei but that does not lie directly along the internuclear axis.

Like atomic orbitals, molecular orbitals have specific energies. The combination of two atomic orbitals of equal energy, such as two 1*s* orbitals on two H atoms, yields one molecular orbital that is lower in energy (bonding) and one molecular orbital that is higher in energy (antibonding) than the original atomic orbitals. The bonding molecular orbital in H_2 is concentrated between the nuclei, along the internuclear axis. Electron density in this molecular orbital both attracts the nuclei and shields them from each other, stabilizing the molecule. Thus, the bonding molecular orbital is lower in energy than the isolated atomic orbitals. In contrast, the antibonding molecular orbital has most of its electron density outside the internuclear region. Electron density in this orbital does not shield one nucleus from the other, which increases the nuclear repulsions and makes the antibonding molecular orbital *higher* in energy than the isolated atomic orbitals.

Showing all the molecular orbitals in a molecule can make for a very complicated picture. Rather than represent molecules with pictures of their molecular orbitals, we generally use diagrams in which molecular orbitals are represented with boxes placed at the appropriate relative energy levels. Figure 7.12 shows the energies of the σ_{1s} and σ_{1s}^* molecular orbitals in H_2, relative to the energy of the original 1*s* orbitals on two isolated H atoms. Like atomic orbitals, molecular orbitals fill in order of increasing energy. Note that the electrons that originally resided in the atomic orbitals both occupy the lowest-energy molecular orbital, σ_{1s}, with opposite spins.

Student Annotation: The molecular orbital diagram shows the two H atoms having electrons with paired spins (↑ and ↓). H atoms whose electrons have parallel spin (↑ and ↑, or ↓ and ↓) actually repel one another and will not bond to form H_2.

We can construct a similar molecular orbital diagram for the hypothetical molecule He_2. Like the H atom, the He atom has a 1*s* orbital (unlike H, though, the 1*s* orbital on He has two electrons, not one). The combination of 1*s* orbitals to form molecular orbitals in He_2 is essentially the same as what we have described for H_2. The placement of electrons is shown in Figure 7.13.

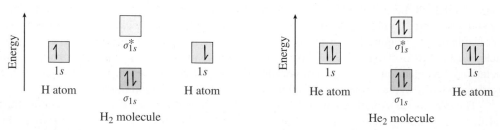

Figure 7.12 Relative energies of atomic orbitals in H and molecular orbitals in H_2.

Figure 7.13 Relative energies of atomic orbitals in He and molecular orbitals in He_2.

Thinking Outside the Box

Phases

In the double-slit experiment [◄◄ Section 3.2, Figure 3.4], bright lines result from constructive interference of light waves and dark lines result from destructive interference of light waves. To picture how interference works, imagine combining two sets of one-dimensional waves shown here. Note that the amplitude of each wave can be positive, zero, or negative. The sign of a wave's amplitude, positive or negative, is referred to as its **phase.** On the left, the waves are *in phase*—meaning that their peaks and troughs coincide exactly. In this case, addition yields a wave in which the amplitude is twice that of the individual waves. On the right, the waves are *out of phase*. Addition causes the amplitudes to cancel one another at each point along the *x* axis, resulting in a flat line.

Recall that according to the quantum mechanical model of the atom, it is the *square* of the wave function (Ψ^2) that defines the distribution of electron density in three-dimensional space around a nucleus. Because it is obtained by squaring the wave function, Ψ^2 can be greater than or equal to zero—it cannot have *negative* values. However, the wave function itself (Ψ) can have values that are positive, zero, or negative. Thus, like one-dimensional waves, wave functions can have positive or negative *phase*. Because they can have both positive and negative phases, atomic orbitals can add *con*structively (constructive interference) or *de*structively (destructive interference).

The different phases of wave functions can be represented by the use of different colors in our depictions of atomic orbitals. For example, rather than representing a *p* orbital with two blue lobes, we can represent it with one blue lobe (positive phase) and one red lobe (negative) as shown here. Although pictures of atomic orbitals without phases are adequate for showing the regions of electron density in an atom, the phases help us account for the formation of bonding and antibonding molecular orbitals. Constructive interference of atomic orbitals produces *bonding* molecular orbitals. Destructive interference produces *antibonding* molecular orbitals.

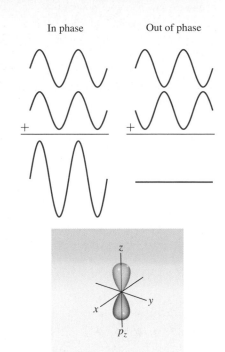

Bond Order

With molecular orbital diagrams such as those for H_2 and He_2, we can begin to see the power of molecular orbital theory. For a diatomic molecule described using molecular orbital theory, we can calculate the **bond order.** The value of the bond order indicates, qualitatively, how *stable* a molecule is. The higher the bond order, the more stable the molecule. Bond order is calculated in the following way:

$$\text{bond order} = \frac{\text{\# of electrons in bonding molecular orbitals} - \text{\# of electrons in antibonding molecular orbitals}}{2}$$

Equation 7.1

In the case of H_2, where both electrons reside in the σ_{1s} orbital, the bond order is $[(2 - 0)/2] = 1$. In the case of He_2, where the two additional electrons reside in the σ_{1s}^* orbital, the bond order is $[(2 - 2)/2] = 0$. Molecular orbital theory predicts that a molecule with a bond order of zero will not exist and He_2, in fact, does *not* exist.

We can do similar analyses of the molecules Li_2 and Be_2. (The Li and Be atoms have ground-state electron configurations of [He]$2s^1$ and [He]$2s^2$, respectively.) The $2s$ atomic orbitals also combine to form the corresponding σ and σ^* molecular orbitals. Figure 7.14 shows the molecular orbital diagrams and bond orders for Li_2 and Be_2.

As predicted by molecular orbital theory, Li_2, with a bond order of 1, is a stable molecule, whereas Be_2, with a bond order of 0, does not exist.

Student Annotation: When we draw molecular orbital diagrams, we need only show the valence orbitals and electrons.

Figure 7.14 Bond order determination for Li_2 and Be_2.

π Molecular Orbitals

To consider diatomic molecules beyond Be$_2$, we must also consider the combination of p atomic orbitals. Like s orbitals, p orbitals combine both constructively, to give bonding molecular orbitals that are lower in energy than the original atomic orbitals, and destructively, to give antibonding molecular orbitals that are higher in energy than the original atomic orbitals. However, the orientations of p_x, p_y, and p_z orbitals give rise to two different types of molecular orbitals: σ molecular orbitals, in which the regions of electron density in the bonding and antibonding molecular orbitals lie along the internuclear axis; and π molecular orbitals, in which the regions of electron density affect both nuclei but do *not* lie along the internuclear axis.

Orbitals that lie along the internuclear axis, as the $2p_x$ orbitals do in Figure 7.15(a), point directly toward each other and combine to form σ molecular orbitals. Figure 7.15(b) shows the combination of two $2p_x$ atomic orbitals to give two molecular orbitals designated σ_{2p_x} and $\sigma^*_{2p_x}$. Figure 7.15(c) shows the relative energies of these molecular orbitals.

Orbitals that are aligned parallel to each other, like the $2p_y$ and $2p_z$ orbitals shown in Figure 7.15(a), combine to form π molecular orbitals. These bonding molecular orbitals are designated π_{2p_y} and π_{2p_z}; the corresponding antibonding molecular orbitals are designated $\pi^*_{2p_y}$ and $\pi^*_{2p_z}$. Often we refer to the molecular orbitals collectively using the designations $\pi_{2p_{y,z}}$ and $\pi^*_{2p_{y,z}}$. Figure 7.16(a) shows the constructive and destructive combination of parallel p orbitals. Figure 7.16(b) shows the locations of the molecular orbitals resulting from the combination of p_y and p_z orbitals relative to the two atomic nuclei. Again, electron density in the resulting *bonding* molecular orbitals serves to hold the nuclei together, whereas electron density in the *antibonding* molecular orbitals does not.

Just as the p atomic orbitals within a particular shell are higher in energy than the s orbital in the same shell, all the molecular orbitals resulting from the combination of p atomic orbitals are higher in energy than the molecular orbitals resulting from the combination of s atomic orbitals. To understand better the relative energy levels of the molecular orbitals resulting from p orbital combinations, consider the fluorine molecule (F$_2$).

Figure 7.15 (a) Two sets of 2p orbitals. (b) The p atomic orbitals that point toward each other (p_x) combine to give bonding and antibonding σ molecular orbitals. (c) The antibonding σ molecular orbital is higher in energy than the corresponding bonding σ molecular orbital.

(a)

(b)

(c)

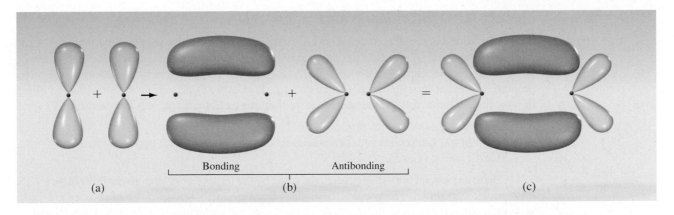

Bonding   Antibonding

(a)   (b)   (c)

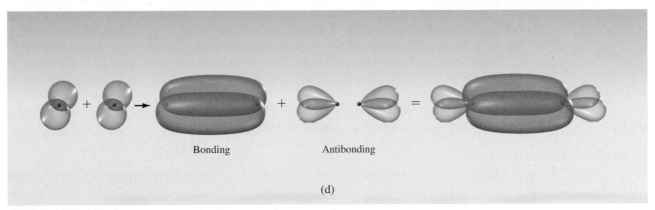

Bonding   Antibonding

(d)

Figure 7.16 Formation of molecular orbitals from the interaction of parallel *p* orbitals on adjacent atoms (a). Bonding and antibonding molecular orbitals shown separately (b), and together relative to the two nuclei (c). (d) Formation of molecular orbitals from interaction of *p* orbitals perpendicular to those shown in part (a).

In general, molecular orbital theory predicts that the more effective the interaction or overlap of the atomic orbitals, the lower in energy the resulting bonding molecular orbital will be and the higher in energy the resulting antibonding molecular orbital will be. Thus, the relative energy levels of molecular orbitals in F_2 can be represented by the diagram in Figure 7.17(a). The p_x orbitals, which lie along the internuclear axis, overlap most effectively, giving the lowest-energy bonding molecular orbital and the highest-energy antibonding molecular orbital.

The order of orbital energies shown in Figure 7.17(a) assumes that *p* orbitals interact only with other *p* orbitals and *s* orbitals interact only with other *s* orbitals—that there is no significant interaction between *s* and *p* orbitals. In fact, the relatively smaller nuclear charges of boron, carbon, and nitrogen atoms cause their atomic orbitals to be held less tightly than those of atoms with larger nuclear charges, and some *s-p* interaction does take place. This results in a change in the relative energies of the σ_{2p_x} and $\pi_{2p_{y,z}}$ molecular orbitals. Although energies of several of the resulting molecular orbitals change, the most important of these changes is the energy of the σ_{2p} orbital, making it higher than the $\pi_{2p_{y,z}}$ orbitals. The relative energy levels of molecular orbitals in the Li_2, B_2, C_2, and N_2 molecules can be represented by the diagram in Figure 7.17(b).

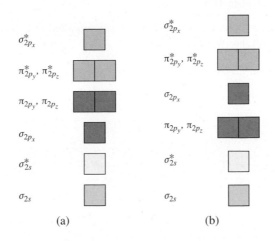

$\sigma^*_{2p_x}$

$\pi^*_{2p_y}, \pi^*_{2p_z}$

π_{2p_y}, π_{2p_z}

σ_{2p_x}

σ^*_{2s}

σ_{2s}

(a)

$\sigma^*_{2p_x}$

$\pi^*_{2p_y}, \pi^*_{2p_z}$

σ_{2p_x}

π_{2p_y}, π_{2p_z}

σ^*_{2s}

σ_{2s}

(b)

Figure 7.17 (a) Ordering of molecular orbital energies for O_2 and F_2. (b) Ordering of molecular orbital energies for Li_2, B_2, C_2, and N_2. Bonding orbitals are darker; antibonding orbitals are lighter.

Molecular Orbital Diagrams

Beginning with oxygen, the nuclear charge is sufficiently large to prevent the interaction of s and p orbitals. Thus, for O_2 and Ne_2, the order of molecular orbital energies is the same as that for F_2, which is shown in Figure 7.17(a). Figure 7.18 gives the molecular orbital diagrams, magnetic properties, bond orders, and bond energies for Li_2, B_2, C_2, N_2, O_2, F_2, and Ne_2. Note that the filling of molecular orbitals follows the same rules as the filling of atomic orbitals [◄◄ Section 3.9]:

- Lower energy orbitals fill first.
- Each orbital can accommodate a maximum of two electrons with opposite spins.
- Hund's rule is obeyed.

There are several important predictions made by the molecular orbital diagrams in Figure 7.18. First, molecular orbital theory correctly predicts that Ne_2, with a bond order of 0, does not exist. Second, it correctly predicts the magnetic properties of the molecules that do exist. Both B_2 and O_2 are known to be paramagnetic. Third, although bond order is only a qualitative measure of bond strength, the calculated bond orders of the molecules correlate well with the measured bond energies. The N_2 molecule, with a bond order of 3, has the largest bond energy of the five molecules. The B_2 and F_2 molecules, each with a bond order of 1, have the smallest bond enthalpies. Its ability to predict correctly the properties of molecules makes molecular orbital theory a powerful tool in the study of chemical bonding.

Worked Example 7.8 shows how to use molecular orbital diagrams to determine the magnetic properties and bond order of a molecule or polyatomic ion.

Molecular orbital diagram for O_2^-

Worked Example 7.8

The superoxide ion (O_2^-) has been implicated in a number of degenerative conditions, including aging and Alzheimer's disease. Using molecular orbital theory, determine whether (O_2^-) is paramagnetic or diamagnetic, and then calculate its bond order.

Strategy Start with the molecular orbital diagram for O_2, add an electron, and then use the resulting diagram to determine the magnetic properties and bond order.

Setup The molecular orbital diagram for O_2 is shown in Figure 7.18. The additional electron must be added to the lowest-energy molecular orbital available.

Solution In this case, either of the two singly occupied π_{2p}^* orbitals can accommodate an additional electron. This gives a molecular orbital diagram in which there is one unpaired electron, making (O_2^-) paramagnetic. The new diagram has six electrons in bonding molecular orbitals and three in antibonding molecular orbitals. We can ignore the electrons in the σ_{2s} and σ_{2s}^* orbitals because their contributions to the bond order cancel each other. The bond order is $(6 - 3)/2 = 1.5$.

> **Think About It**
> Experiments confirm that the superoxide ion is paramagnetic. Also, any time we add one or more electrons to an antibonding molecular orbital, as we did in this problem, we should expect the bond order to decrease. Electrons in antibonding orbitals cause a bond to be less stable.

Practice Problem A Use molecular orbital theory to determine whether N_2^{2-} is paramagnetic or diamagnetic, and then calculate its bond order.

Practice Problem B Use molecular orbital theory to determine whether F_2^{2+} is paramagnetic or diamagnetic, and then calculate its bond order.

Thinking Outside the Box

Molecular Orbitals in Heteronuclear Diatomic Species

Our description of molecular orbital theory can also be applied to heteronuclear diatomic species, in which the two atoms are different, such as NO. In a case such as this, our description of the molecular orbitals involved in bonding must be modified slightly.

The atomic orbitals of a more electronegative atom are lower in energy than the corresponding atomic orbitals of a less electronegative atom. The 2s and 2p atomic orbitals are lower in energy for oxygen, which is more electronegative than nitrogen. (See Figure 6.4 on page 188.) When atomic orbitals of different energies interact to form molecular orbitals, the lower-energy atomic orbital contributes more to the *bonding* molecular orbital; and the higher-energy atomic orbital contributes more to the *antibonding* molecular orbital. The result is that the bonding molecular orbital more closely resembles the atomic orbital of the *more* electronegative atom, and the antibonding molecular orbital more closely resembles the atomic orbital of the *less* electronegative atom. The result of this is that electron density in the resulting bonding molecular orbital is *greater* in the vicinity of the *more* electronegative atom.

Recall that the order of energies of molecular orbitals in second-period homonuclear diatomic molecules is different for B_2, C_2, and N_2, than it is for O_2, F_2, and Ne_2 (Figure 7.18). For second-period heteronuclear diatomic species containing one atom from each group, such as NO and CO, there is no simple rule that can tell us which order the molecular orbitals follow. Note that the molecular orbitals in NO follow the same order as those in O_2.

Often the bond order determined from a molecular orbital diagram corresponds to the number of bonds in the Lewis structure of the molecule. In the case of NO, though, the Lewis structure contains a double bond whereas the molecular orbital approach gives a bond order of 2.5. In fact, the molecular orbital approach gives a bond order that is more consistent with experimental data. The experimentally determined strength of the bond in NO (631 kJ/mol) is greater than that of the average nitrogen-oxygen double bond (607 kJ/mol) [▶ Section 10.7].

Molecular orbital diagram for NO

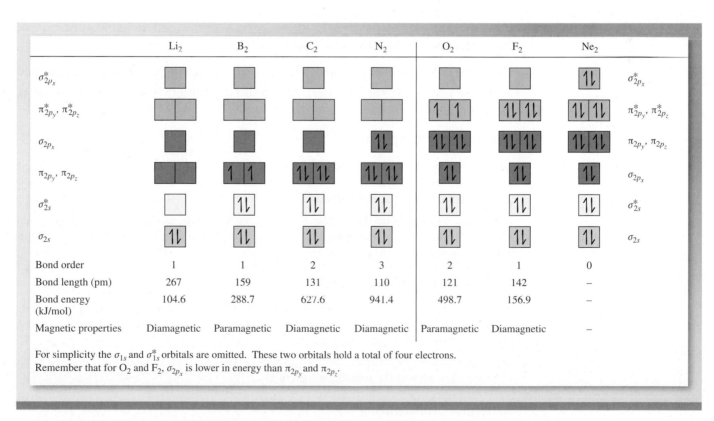

Figure 7.18 Molecular orbital diagrams for second-period homonuclear diatomic molecules.

SECTION 7.6 REVIEW

Molecular Orbital Theory

7.6.1   Calculate the bond order of N_2^{2+}, and determine whether it is paramagnetic or diamagnetic.

7.6.2   Determine if C_2^{2+} is paramagnetic or diamagnetic.

7.6.3   Calculate the bond order of He_2^+.

7.6.4   What is the negative charge on the $F_2^{?-}$ species if it has a bond order of 0?

7.7   BONDING THEORIES AND DESCRIPTIONS OF MOLECULES WITH DELOCALIZED BONDING

The progression of bonding theories in this chapter illustrates the importance of model development. Scientists use models to understand experimental results and to predict future observations. A model is useful as long as it agrees with observation. When it fails to do so, it must be replaced with a new model. What follows is a synopsis of the strengths and weaknesses of the bonding theories presented in Chapters 6 and 7.

Lewis Theory

Strength: The Lewis theory of bonding enables us to make qualitative predictions about bond strengths and bond lengths. Lewis structures are easy to draw and are widely used by chemists.

Weakness: Lewis structures are two-dimensional, whereas molecules are three-dimensional. In addition, Lewis theory fails to account for the differences between bonds in compounds such as H_2, F_2, and HF. It also fails to explain *why* bonds form.

The Valence-Shell Electron-Pair Repulsion Model

Strength: The VSEPR model enables us to predict the shapes of many molecules and polyatomic ions.

Weakness: Because the VSEPR model is based on the Lewis theory of bonding, it also fails to explain why bonds form.

Valence Bond Theory

Strength: Valence bond theory describes the formation of covalent bonds as the overlap of atomic orbitals. It further explains that bonds form because the resulting molecule has a lower potential energy than the original, isolated atoms.

Weakness: Valence bond theory alone fails to explain the bonding in many molecules such as $BeCl_2$, BF_3, and CH_4, in which the central atom in its ground state does not have enough unpaired electrons to form the observed number of bonds.

Hybridization of Atomic Orbitals

Strength: The hybridization of atomic orbitals is not a separate bonding theory; rather, it is an *extension* of valence bond theory. Using hybrid orbitals, we can understand the bonding and geometry of more molecules, including $BeCl_2$, BF_3, and CH_4.

Weakness: Valence bond theory and hybrid orbitals fail to predict some of the important properties of molecules, such as the paramagnetism of O_2.

Molecular Orbital Theory

Strength: Molecular orbital theory enables us to predict accurately the magnetic and other properties of molecules and ions.

Weakness: Pictures of molecular orbitals can be very complex.

Although molecular orbital theory is in many ways the most powerful of the bonding models, it is also the most complex, so we continue to use the other models when they do an adequate job of explaining or predicting the properties of a molecule. For example, if you need to predict the three-dimensional shape of an AB_x molecule on an exam, you should draw its Lewis structure and apply the VSEPR model. On the other hand, if you need to determine the bond order of a diatomic molecule or ion, you should draw a molecular orbital diagram. In general chemistry, it is best to use the *simplest* theory that can answer a particular question.

Because they remain useful, we don't discard the old models when we develop new ones. In fact, the bonding in some molecules, such as benzene (C_6H_6), is best described using a combination of models. Benzene can be represented with two resonance structures [◄◄ Section 6.5].

According to its Lewis structure and valence bond theory, the benzene molecule contains 12 σ bonds (6 carbon-carbon, and 6 carbon-hydrogen) and 3 π bonds. From experimental evidence, however, we know that benzene does not have 3 single bonds and 3 double bonds between carbon atoms. Rather, there are 6 equivalent carbon-carbon bonds. This is precisely the reason that two different Lewis structures are necessary to represent the molecule. Neither one alone accurately depicts the nature of the carbon-carbon bonds. In fact, the π bonds in benzene are **delocalized**, meaning that they are spread out over the entire molecule, rather than confined between two specific atoms. (Bonds that are confined between two specific atoms are called **localized** bonds.) Valence bond theory does a good job of describing the localized σ bonds in benzene, but molecular orbital theory does a better job of using delocalized π bonds to describe the bonding scheme in benzene.

To describe the σ bonds in benzene, begin with a Lewis structure and count the electron domains on the carbon atoms. (Either resonance structure will give the same result.) Each C atom has three electron domains around it (two single bonds and one double bond). Recall from Table 7.4 that an atom that has three electron domains is sp^2 hybridized. To obtain the three unpaired electrons necessary on each C atom, one electron from each C atom must be promoted from the doubly occupied 2s orbital to an empty 2p orbital:

This actually creates four unpaired electrons. Next, the orbitals are sp^2 hybridized, leaving one singly occupied, unhybridized 2p orbital on each C atom:

The sp^2 hybrid orbitals adopt a trigonal planar arrangement and overlap with one another (and with 1s orbitals on H atoms) to form the σ bonds in the molecule.

The remaining unhybridized $2p$ orbitals (one on each C atom) combine to form molecular orbitals. Because the p orbitals are all parallel to one another, only π_{2p} and π_{2p}^* molecular orbitals form. The combination of these six $2p$ atomic orbitals forms six molecular orbitals: three bonding and three antibonding. These molecular orbitals are delocalized over the entire benzene molecule:

σ bonds in benzene

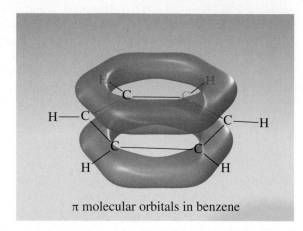

π molecular orbitals in benzene

In the ground state, the lower-energy bonding molecular orbitals contain all six electrons. The electron density in the delocalized π molecular orbitals lies above and below the plane that contains all the atoms and the σ bonds in the molecule.

Worked Example 7.9 lets you practice using multiple bonding theories to describe the bonding in a species with delocalized π bonds.

Worked Example 7.9

It takes three resonance structures to represent the carbonate ion CO_3^{2-}:

$$\left[\begin{array}{c} :\ddot{O}: \\ \ddot{O}{-}C{-}\ddot{O}: \end{array} \right]^{2-} \longleftrightarrow \left[\begin{array}{c} \ddot{O} \\ \ddot{O}{-}C{-}\ddot{O}: \end{array} \right]^{2-} \longleftrightarrow \left[\begin{array}{c} :\ddot{O}: \\ \ddot{O}{-}C{-}\ddot{O} \end{array} \right]^{2-}$$

Student Annotation: Double bonds that appear in different places in different resonance structures represent delocalized π bonds.

None of the three, though, is a completely accurate depiction. As with benzene, the bonds that are shown in the Lewis structure as one double and two single are actually three equivalent bonds. Use a combination of valence bond theory and molecular orbital theory to explain the bonding in CO_3^{2-}.

Strategy Starting with the Lewis structure, use valence bond theory and hybrid orbitals to describe the σ bonds. Then use molecular orbital theory to describe the delocalized π bonding.

Setup The Lewis structure of the carbonate ion shows three electron domains around the central C atom, so the carbon must be sp^2 hybridized.

Solution Each of the sp^2 hybrid orbitals on the C atom overlaps with a singly occupied p orbital on an O atom, forming the three σ bonds. Each O atom has an additional, singly occupied p orbital perpendicular to the one involved in σ bonding. The unhybridized p orbital on C overlaps with the p orbitals on O to form π bonds, which have electron densities above and below the plane of the molecule. Because the species can be represented with resonance structures, we know that the π bonds are delocalized.

> **Think About It**
> Although the Lewis structure of CO_3^{2-} shows three electron domains on one of the O atoms, we generally do not treat *terminal* atoms (those with single bonds to only one other atom) as though they are hybridized because it is unnecessary to do so.

Practice Problem A Use a combination of valence bond theory and molecular orbital theory to describe the bonding in ozone (O_3).

Practice Problem B Use a combination of valence bond theory and molecular orbital theory to describe the bonding in the nitrite ion (NO_2^-).

Bonding Theories and Descriptions of Molecules with Delocalized Bonding

7.7.1 How many delocalized π bonds does NO_2^- contain?

7.7.2 Which of the atoms in BCl_3 need hybrid orbitals to describe the bonding in the molecule?

7.7.3 Can hybrid orbitals be used to explain how a central atom can form more bonds than the number of unpaired electrons in its ground-state configuration?

7.7.4 Which theory enables us to explain the paramagnetism of O_2?

Learning Outcomes

- Use the valence-shell electron-pair repulsion (VSEPR) model to determine the shape of a molecule.
- Define electron domain.
- Describe the difference between electron-domain geometry and molecular geometry.
- Recognize the difference between axial and equatorial positions in AB_5 molecules.
- Understand why deviations from ideal bond angles occur.
- Determine when molecules will be polar or nonpolar.
- Identify structural isomers of compounds.
- Use valence bond theory to describe the bonding in molecules.

- Predict the hybridization of molecules to explain bonding in molecules.
- Describe the bonding in molecules containing double and triple bonds.
- Understand how atomic orbitals combine to form molecular orbitals according to molecular orbital theory.
- Identify bonding and antibonding molecular orbitals.
- Calculate the bond order of diatomic species.
- Describe localized and delocalized bonds in molecules.

Chapter Summary

SECTION 7.1

- According to the ***valence-shell electron-pair repulsion (VSEPR)*** model, electron pairs in the valence shell of an atom repel one another. An ***electron domain*** is a lone pair or a bond. Any bond (single, double, or triple) constitutes one electron domain.
- The arrangement of electron domains about a central atom, determined using the VSEPR model, is called the ***electron-domain geometry.*** The arrangement of *atoms* in a molecule is called the ***molecular geometry.*** The basic molecular geometries are linear, bent, trigonal planar, tetrahedral, trigonal pyramidal, trigonal bipyramidal, seesaw-shaped, T-shaped, octahedral, square pyramidal, and square planar.
- The ***bond angle*** is the angle between two adjacent bonds in a molecule or polyatomic ion. A trigonal bipyramid contains two types of bonds: ***axial*** and ***equatorial.***

SECTION 7.2

- The polarity of a molecule depends on the polarity of its individual bonds and on its molecular geometry. Even a molecule containing polar bonds may be nonpolar overall if the bonds are distributed symmetrically.
- ***Structural isomers*** are molecules with the same chemical formula, but different structural arrangements.

SECTION 7.3

- According to ***valence bond theory,*** bonds form between atoms when atomic orbitals overlap, thus allowing the atoms to share valence electrons. A bond forms when the resulting molecule is lower in energy than the original, isolated atoms.

SECTION 7.4

- To explain the bonding in some molecules, we need to employ the concept of *hybridization,* in which atomic orbitals mix to form *hybrid orbitals.*
- In order to use hybrid-orbital analysis, we must already know the molecular geometry and bond angles in a molecule. Hybrid orbitals are not used to predict molecular geometries.

SECTION 7.5

- *Sigma (σ) bonds* form when the region of orbital overlap lies directly between the two atoms. *Pi (π) bonds* form when parallel, unhybridized *p* orbitals interact. Usually, a *double* bond consists of one sigma bond and one pi bond; and a *triple* bond consists of one sigma bond and two pi bonds.

SECTION 7.6

- A paramagnetic species is one that contains unpaired electrons. A diamagnetic species is one in which there are no unpaired electrons. Paramagnetic species are weakly attracted by a magnetic field, whereas diamagnetic species are weakly repelled by a magnetic field.
- According to *molecular orbital theory,* atomic orbitals combine to form new *molecular orbitals* that are associated with the molecule rather than with individual atoms. Molecular orbitals may be *sigma,* if the orbital lies directly along the internuclear axis, or *pi,* if the orbital does not lie directly along the internuclear axis.

- Molecular orbitals may be *bonding* or *antibonding.* A **bonding molecular orbital** is lower in energy than the isolated atomic orbitals that combined to form it. The corresponding **antibonding molecular orbital** is higher in energy than the isolated atomic orbitals.
- Bonding molecular orbitals result from the interaction of atomic orbitals that are *in phase*; antibonding molecular orbitals result from the interaction of atomic orbitals that are out *of phase.* Electrons in bonding molecular orbitals contribute to the strength of a bond. Electrons in antibonding molecular orbitals detract from the strength of a bond. **Bond order** is a measure of the *strength* of a bond and can be determined using a molecular orbital diagram.

SECTION 7.7

- It is generally best to use the bonding theory that most easily describes the bonding in a particular molecule or polyatomic ion. In species that can be represented by two or more resonance structures, the pi bonds are **delocalized,** meaning that they are spread out over the molecule and not constrained to just two atoms. *Localized* bonds are those constrained to two atoms. Many species are best described using a combination of valence bond theory and molecular orbital theory.

Key Words

Antibonding molecular orbital, 245

Axial, 217

Bond angle, 216

Bonding molecular orbital, 245

Bond order, 247

Delocalized, 253

Electron domain, 216

Electron-domain geometry, 216

Equatorial, 217

Hybridization, 230

Hybrid orbital, 231

Localized, 253

Molecular geometry, 216

Molecular orbital, 245

Molecular orbital theory, 245

Phase, 247

Pi (π) bond, 238

Sigma (σ) bond, 238

Structural isomer, 225

Valence bond theory, 227

Valence-shell electron-pair repulsion (VSEPR), 215

Key Equation

7.1 $$\text{bond order} = \frac{\text{\# of electrons in bonding molecular orbitals} - \text{\# of electrons in antibonding molecular orbitals}}{2}$$

Questions and Problems

SECTION 7.1: MOLECULAR GEOMETRY

Review Questions

7.1 How is the geometry of a molecule defined, and why is the study of molecular geometry important?

7.2 Sketch the shape of a linear triatomic molecule, a trigonal planar molecule containing four atoms, a tetrahedral molecule, a trigonal bipyramidal molecule, and an octahedral molecule. Give the bond angles in each case.

7.3 How many atoms are directly bonded to the central atom in a tetrahedral molecule, a trigonal bipyramidal molecule, and an octahedral molecule?

7.4 Discuss the basic features of the VSEPR model. Explain why the magnitude of repulsion decreases in the following order: lone pair–lone pair > lone pair–bonding pair > bonding pair–bonding pair.

7.5 In the trigonal bipyramidal arrangement, why does a lone pair occupy an equatorial position rather than an axial position?

Problems

7.6 Predict the geometry of the following molecules and ion using the VSEPR model: (a) CH_3I, (b) ClF_3, (c) H_2S, (d) SO_3, (e) SO_4^{2-}.

7.7 Predict the geometry of the following molecules and ion using the VSEPR model: (a) CBr_4, (b) BCl_3, (c) NF_3, (d) H_2Se, (e) NO_2^-.

7.8 Predict the geometries of the following species: (a) $AlCl_3$, (b) $AlCl_4^-$, (c) $ZnCl_2$, (d) $ZnCl_4^{2-}$.

7.9 Predict the geometries of the following species using the VSEPR method: (a) PCl_3, (b) $CHCl_3$, (c) SiH_4, (d) $TeCl_4$.

7.10 Predict the geometries of the following ions: (a) NH_4^+, (b) NH_2^-, (c) CO_3^{2-}, (d) ICl_2^-, (e) ICl_4^-, (f) AlH_4^-, (g) $SnCl_5^-$, (h) H_3O^+, (i) BeF_4^{2-}.

7.11 Predict the geometry of the following molecules using the VSEPR method: (a) $HgBr_2$, (b) N_2O (arrangement of atoms is NNO), (c) SCN^- (arrangement of atoms is SCN).

7.12 Which of the following species are tetrahedral: $SiCl_4$, SeF_4, XeF_4, CI_4, $CdCl_4^{2-}$?

7.13 Describe the geometry around each of the three central atoms in the CH_3COOH molecule.

7.14 Describe the geometry about each of the central atoms in ethanolamine, shown here.

7.15 Which of the following shows a deviation from ideal bond angles that is not possible for an AB_x molecule? Explain.

T-shaped	Seesaw-shaped	Trigonal pyramidal	Square pyramidal
(i)	(ii)	(iii)	(iv)

SECTION 7.2: MOLECULAR GEOMETRY AND POLARITY

Review Questions

7.16 Explain why an atom cannot have a permanent dipole moment.

7.17 The bonds in beryllium hydride (BeH_2) molecules are polar, and yet the dipole moment of the molecule is zero. Explain.

Problems

7.18 Determine whether (a) NBr_3, (b) OCS, and (c) XeF_4 are polar.

7.19 Determine whether (a) BrF_5, (b) ClF_3, and (c) BCl_3 are polar.

7.20 Which of the molecules shown is polar?

(a)	(b)	(c)	(d)

7.21 Which of the molecules shown is polar?

(a)	(b)	(c)	(d)

7.22 Determine which molecule will condense to a liquid at the higher temperature and explain why: NH_3 or CH_4.

7.23 Determine which molecule will condense to a liquid at the higher temperature and explain why: SiH_4 or PH_3.

SECTION 7.3: VALENCE BOND THEORY

Review Questions

7.24 What is valence bond theory? How does it differ from the Lewis concept of chemical bonding?

7.25 Use valence bond theory to explain the bonding in Cl_2 and HCl. Show how the atomic orbitals overlap when a bond is formed.

7.26 According to valence bond theory, how many bonds would you expect each of the following atoms (in the ground state) to form: Be, C?

7.27 According to valence bond theory, how many bonds would you expect each of the following atoms (in the ground state) to form: P, S?

Problems

7.28 For which molecule(s) can we *not* use valence bond theory to explain the bonding: $BeCl_2$ (Cl—Be—Cl bond angle = 180°), Br_2, SF_6 (F—S—F bond angles = 90° and 180°)? Explain.

7.29 For which molecule(s) can we *not* use valence bond theory to explain the bonding: N_2, BF_3 (F—B—F bond angles = 120°), HI? Explain.

SECTION 7.4: HYBRIDIZATION OF ATOMIC ORBITALS

Review Questions

7.30 What is the hybridization of atomic orbitals? Why do we never refer to isolated atoms as hybridized?

7.31 Is it possible for two $2p$ orbitals on an atom to combine to give two hybrid orbitals? Explain.

7.32 Determine the hybridization of the central atom in a molecule with the following molecular geometries: (a) tetrahedral, (b) trigonal planar, (c) trigonal bipyramidal, (d) linear, (e) octahedral.

7.33 What is the angle between any two of the following two hybrid orbitals on an atom: (a) sp, (b) sp^2, (c) sp^3? Explain why the answer to this question would be more complicated for sp^3d and sp^3d^2 hybrid orbitals.

Problems

7.34   Describe the bonding scheme of the AsH_3 molecule in terms of hybridization.

7.35   What is the hybridization of Si in SiH_4 and in $H_3Si-SiH_3$?

7.36   What is the hybridization of the nitrogen atoms in the following species: (a) NH_3, (b) H_2N-NH_2, (c) NO_3^-?

7.37   Describe the hybridization of phosphorus in PF_5.

7.38   Describe the change in hybridization (if any) of the Al atom when aluminum trichloride, $AlCl_3$, interacts with a chloride ion to form the tetrachloroaluminate ion, $AlCl_4^-$. (*Hint:* Start by drawing Lewis structures.)

7.39   Describe the changes in hybridization (if any) of the B and N atoms as a result of the formation of F_3B-NH_3 from BF_3 and NH_3. (*Hint:* Start by drawing Lewis structures.)

SECTION 7.5:   HYBRIDIZATION IN MOLECULES CONTAINING MULTIPLE BONDS

Visualizing Chemistry
Figure 7.10

VC 7.1   How is a sigma bond different from a pi bond?
(a) A sigma bond is a bonding molecular orbital; a pi bond is an antibonding molecular orbital.
(b) A sigma bond is a single bond, whereas a pi bond is a double bond.
(c) The electron density in a sigma bond lies along the internuclear axis; that of a pi bond does not.

VC 7.2   Pi bonds form when _____ atomic orbitals on _____ atom(s) overlap.
(a) perpendicular, adjacent
(b) parallel, adjacent
(c) parallel, the same

VC 7.3   Formation of two pi bonds requires the combination of _____ atomic orbitals.
(a) two
(b) four
(c) six

VC 7.4   Why are there no pi bonds in ethane (C_2H_6)?
(a) The remaining unhybridized p orbitals do not contain any electrons.
(b) There are no unhybridized p orbitals remaining on either C atom.
(c) The remaining unhybridized p orbitals are not parallel to each other.

Review Questions

7.40   Describe the difference between a sigma bond and a pi bond.

7.41   Which of the following pairs of atomic orbitals of adjacent nuclei can overlap to form a sigma bond? Which overlap to form a pi bond? Which cannot overlap (no bond)? Consider the x axis to be the internuclear axis,

that is, the line joining the nuclei of the two atoms. (a) $1s$ and $1s$, (b) $1s$ and $2p_x$, (c) $2p_x$ and $2p_y$, (d) $3p_y$ and $3p_y$, (e) $2p_x$ and $2p_x$, (f) $1s$ and $2s$.

Problems

7.42   Determine the hybridization of each carbon atom in the following molecules:
(a) H_3C-CH_3
(b) $H_3C-CH=CH_2$
(c) $CH_3-C{\equiv}C-CH_2OH$
(d) $CH_3CH=O$
(e) CH_3COOH

7.43   Determine the hybridization of the carbon atoms in the following species: (a) CO, (b) CO_2, (c) CN^-.

7.44   The allene molecule ($H_2C=C=CH_2$) is linear (the three C atoms lie on a straight line). Determine the hybridization of each carbon atom. Draw diagrams to show the formation of sigma bonds and pi bonds in allene.

7.45   What is the hybridization of the central N atom in the azide ion (N_3^-)? (The arrangement of atoms is NNN.)

7.46   How many sigma bonds and pi bonds are there in each of the following molecules?

$$
\begin{array}{ccc}
\underset{\displaystyle H}{\overset{\displaystyle H}{Cl-\underset{|}{\overset{|}{C}}-Cl}} & \underset{\displaystyle \underset{H}{\diagup}\,\,\underset{H}{\diagdown}}{\overset{\displaystyle \overset{H}{\diagdown}\,\,\overset{Cl}{\diagup}}{C=C}} & H_3C-\underset{\underset{H}{|}}{\overset{\overset{H}{|}}{C}}=\overset{}{C}-C{\equiv}C-H \\
(a) & (b) & (c)
\end{array}
$$

7.47   How many pi bonds and sigma bonds are there in the tetracyanoethylene molecule?

$$
\begin{array}{cc}
N{\equiv}C & C{\equiv}N \\
\diagdown & \diagup \\
C & =C \\
\diagup & \diagdown \\
N{\equiv}C & C{\equiv}N
\end{array}
$$

7.48   Tryptophan is one of the 20 amino acids in the human body. Describe the hybridization of the C atoms and the N atoms, and determine the number of sigma and pi bonds in the molecule.

$$
CH_2-\underset{\underset{H}{|}}{\overset{\overset{NH_2}{|}}{C}}-\underset{\underset{O}{||}}{C}-OH
$$

7.49   Benzo[a]pyrene is a potent carcinogen found in coal and cigarette smoke. Determine the number of sigma and pi bonds in the molecule.

SECTION 7.6: MOLECULAR ORBITAL THEORY

Review Questions

7.50 What is molecular orbital theory? How does it differ from valence bond theory?

7.51 Define the following terms: bonding molecular orbital, antibonding molecular orbital, pi molecular orbital, sigma molecular orbital.

7.52 Sketch the shapes of the following molecular orbitals: σ_{1s}, σ_{1s}^*, π_{2p}, π_{2p}^*. How do their energies compare?

7.53 Explain the significance of bond order. How can bond order be used for quantitative comparisons of the strengths of chemical bonds?

Problems

7.54 Using molecular orbital theory, explain the changes that occur in the H—H internuclear distance as the molecule H_2 is ionized first to H_2^+ and then to H_2^{2+}.

7.55 The formation of H_2 from two H atoms is an energetically favorable process. Yet, statistically there is less than a 100 percent chance that any two H atoms will undergo the reaction. Apart from energy considerations, how would you account for this observation based on the electron spins in the two H atoms?

7.56 Draw a molecular orbital energy level diagram for each of the following species: He_2, HHe, He_2^+. Compare their relative stabilities in terms of bond orders. (Treat HHe as a diatomic molecule with three electrons.)

7.57 Arrange the following species in order of increasing stability: Li_2, Li_2^+, Li_2^-. Justify your choice with a molecular orbital energy level diagram.

7.58 It has long been predicted that Be_2 could not exist because the molecule would not be stable. However, in 2009, the existence of Be_2 was confirmed by spectroscopy. Use molecular orbital theory to explain why the Be_2 molecule was predicted not to exist.

7.59 Which of these species has a longer bond, B_2 or B_2^+? Explain in terms of molecular orbital theory.

7.60 Acetylene (C_2H_2) has a tendency to lose two protons (H^+) and form the carbide ion (C_2^{2-}), which is present in a number of ionic compounds, such as CaC_2 and MgC_2. Describe the bonding in the C_2^{2-} ion in terms of molecular orbital theory. Compare the bond order in C_2^{2-} with that in C_2.

7.61 Compare the Lewis and molecular orbital treatments of the oxygen molecule.

7.62 Explain why the bond order of N_2 is greater than that of N_2^+, but the bond order of O_2 is less than that of O_2^+.

7.63 Compare the relative bond orders of the following species and indicate their magnetic properties (that is, diamagnetic or paramagnetic): O_2, O_2^+, O_2^- (superoxide ion), O_2^{2-} (peroxide ion).

7.64 Use molecular orbital theory to compare the relative stabilities of F_2 and F_2^+.

7.65 A single bond is almost always a sigma bond, and a double bond is almost always made up of a sigma bond and a pi bond. There are very few exceptions to this rule. Show that the B_2 and C_2 molecules are examples of the exceptions.

 7.66 Draw the molecular orbital diagram for the cyanide ion (CN^-). (Assume the ordering of molecular orbitals to be like that in N_2.) Write the electron configuration of the cyanide ion (CN^-).

 7.67 Given that BeO is diamagnetic, use a molecular orbital diagram to determine whether the orbitals are ordered like those of Be_2 or those of O_2.

SECTION 7.7: BONDING THEORIES AND DESCRIPTIONS OF MOLECULES WITH DELOCALIZED BONDING

Review Questions

7.68 How does a delocalized molecular orbital differ from a molecular orbital such as that found in H_2 or C_2H_4? What do you think are the minimum conditions (for example, number of atoms and types of orbitals) for forming a delocalized molecular orbital?

7.69 In Chapter 6 we saw that the resonance concept is useful for dealing with species such as the benzene molecule and the carbonate ion. How does molecular orbital theory deal with these species?

Problems

7.70 Both ethylene (C_2H_4) and benzene (C_6H_6) contain the C=C bond, yet benzene is more stable in that it does not combine readily with other molecules—whereas ethylene *does*. Explain this difference in the chemical properties of these two species.

7.71 Chemists often represent benzene with the structure shown on the left. Explain why the structure on the left is a better representation of the benzene molecule than the one on the right.

7.72 Determine which of these molecules has a more delocalized orbital, and justify your choice. (*Hint:* Both molecules contain two benzene rings. In naphthalene, the two rings are fused together. In biphenyl, the two rings are joined by a single bond around which the two rings can rotate.)

Biphenyl   Naphthalene

7.73 Nitryl fluoride (FNO_2) is used in rocket propellants. The fluorine and oxygen atoms are bonded to the nitrogen atom. (a) Draw a Lewis structure for FNO_2.

(b) Indicate the hybridization of the nitrogen atom.
(c) Describe the bonding in terms of molecular orbital theory. Where would you expect delocalized molecular orbitals to form?

7.74   Describe the bonding in the nitrate ion NO_3^- in terms of delocalized molecular orbitals.

7.75   What is the hybridization of the central O atom in O_3? Describe the bonding in O_3 in terms of delocalized molecular orbitals.

ADDITIONAL PROBLEMS

7.76   Which of the following species is not likely to have a tetrahedral shape: (a) $SiBr_4$, (b) NF_4^+, (c) SF_4, (d) $BeCl_4^{2-}$, (e) BF_4^-, (f) $AlCl_4^-$?

7.77   Draw the Lewis structure of mercury(II) bromide. Is this molecule linear or bent? How would you establish its geometry?

7.78   Although both carbon and silicon are in Group 4A, very few Si=Si bonds are known. Account for the instability of silicon-to-silicon double bonds in general. (*Hint:* Compare the atomic radii of C and Si in Figure 4.6. What effect would the larger size have on pi bond formation?)

7.79   Predict the geometry of sulfur dichloride (SCl_2) and the hybridization of the sulfur atom.

7.80   Antimony pentafluoride (SbF_5) combines with XeF_4 and XeF_6 to form ionic compounds, $XeF_3^+SbF_6^-$ and $XeF_5^+SbF_6^-$. Describe the geometries of the cations and anion in these two compounds.

7.81   The molecular model of vitamin C is shown here.
(a) Write the molecular formula of the compound.
(b) What is the hybridization of each C and O atom?
(c) Describe the geometry about each C and O atom.

7.82   The molecular model of nicotine (a stimulant) is shown here. (a) Write the molecular formula of the compound.
(b) What is the hybridization of each C and N atom?
(c) Describe the geometry about each C and N atom.

7.83   Predict the bond angles for the following molecules:
(a) $BeCl_2$, (b) BCl_3, (c) CCl_4, (d) CH_3Cl, (e) Hg_2Cl_2 (arrangement of atoms: ClHgHgCl), (f) $SnCl_2$, (g) H_2O_2, (h) SnH_4.

7.84   The germanium pentafluoride anion (GeF_5^-) has been observed as part of an ionic compound with cesium at low temperatures. The anion is formed by the interaction of GeF_4 with F^-. Which figure best illustrates the change in molecular geometry around Ge in the transformation from GeF_4 to GeF_5^-?

(a)   (c)

(b)   (d)

7.85   Draw Lewis structures and give the other information requested for the following molecules: (a) BF_3. Shape: planar or nonplanar? (b) ClO_3^-. Shape: planar or nonplanar? (c) HCN. Polar or nonpolar? (d) OF_2. Polar or nonpolar? (e) NO_2. Estimate the ONO bond angle.

7.86   Which figure best illustrates the hybridization of arsenic in (a) arsenic pentafluoride (AsF_5) and (b) arsenic trifluoride (AsF_3)?

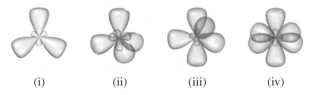

(i)   (ii)   (iii)   (iv)

7.87   The disulfide bond, $-S-S-$, plays an important role in determining the three-dimensional structure of proteins. Describe the nature of the bond and the hybridization of the S atoms.

7.88   Draw Lewis structures and give the other information requested for the following: (a) SO_3. Polar or nonpolar molecule? (b) PF_3. Polar or nonpolar? (c) F_3SiH. Polar or nonpolar? (d) SiH_3^-. Shape: planar or pyramidal? (e) Br_2CH_2. Polar or nonpolar molecule?

7.89   Which of the following molecules are linear: ICl_2^-, IF_2^+, OF_2, SnI_2, $CdBr_2$?

7.90   Semiconducting materials such as indium phosphide (InP) can be prepared from a single-source precursor like $(CH_3)_3In-P(CH_3)_3$. Which pair of figures best illustrates the hybridization of In and P, respectively, in $(CH_3)_3In-P(CH_3)_3$?

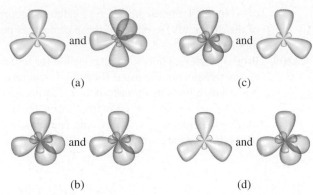

(a)　　　　　　　(c)

(b)　　　　　　　(d)

7.91 The N_2F_2 molecule can exist in either of the following two forms:

(a) What is the hybridization of N in each case?
(b) Identify each structure as polar or nonpolar.

7.92 Cyclopropane (C_3H_6) has the shape of a triangle in which a C atom is bonded to two H atoms and two other C atoms at each corner. Cubane (C_8H_8) has the shape of a cube in which a C atom is bonded to one H atom and three other C atoms at each corner. (a) Draw Lewis structures of these molecules. (b) Compare the CCC angles in these molecules with those predicted for an sp^3-hybridized C atom. (c) Would you expect these molecules to be easy to make? Explain.

7.93 The compound 1,2-dichloroethane ($C_2H_4Cl_2$) is nonpolar, while *cis*-dichloroethylene ($C_2H_2Cl_2$) has a dipole moment. The reason for the difference is that groups connected by a single bond can rotate with respect to each other, but no rotation occurs when a double bond connects the groups. On the basis of bonding considerations, explain why rotation occurs in 1,2-dichloroethane but not in *cis*-dichloroethylene.

1,2-dichloroethane　　*cis*-dichloroethylene

7.94 Does the following molecule have a dipole moment? Explain.

7.95 So-called greenhouse gases, which contribute to global warming, have a dipole moment or can be bent or distorted during molecular vibration into shapes that have a *temporary* dipole moment. Based on this, which of the following gases are greenhouse gases: N_2, O_2, O_3, CO, CO_2, NO_2, N_2O, CH_4, $CFCl_3$?

7.96 Carbon suboxide (C_3O_2) is a colorless pungent-smelling gas. Does this molecule possess a dipole moment? Explain.

7.97 The compound 3′-azido-3′-deoxythymidine, commonly known as AZT, is one of the drugs used to treat AIDS. What are the hybridization states of the C and N atoms in this molecule?

7.98 The following molecules (AX_4Y_2) all have an octahedral geometry. Group the molecules that are equivalent to each other.

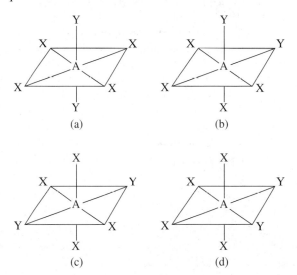

(a)　　　　　　　(b)

(c)　　　　　　　(d)

7.99 The amino acid selenocysteine is one of the components of selenoproteins, more than 20 of which have been identified so far in human cells.

In the structure of this interesting amino acid, how many of each type of hybrid orbital illustrated here are present?

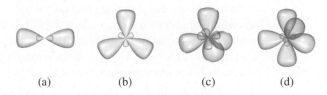

(a)　　　　(b)　　　　(c)　　　　(d)

7.100 Write the ground-state electron configuration for B_2. Is the molecule diamagnetic or paramagnetic?

7.101 What is the hybridization of C and of N in this molecule?

7.102 The stable allotropic form of phosphorus is P_4, in which each P atom is bonded to three other P atoms. Draw a Lewis structure of this molecule and describe its geometry. At high temperatures, P_4 dissociates to form P_2 molecules containing a P=P bond. Explain why P_4 is more stable than P_2.

7.103 The BO^+ ion is paramagnetic. Determine (a) whether the order of molecular-orbital energies is like that in B_2 or in O_2; (b) the bond order; and (c) the number of unpaired electrons in the ion.

7.104 Use molecular orbital theory to explain the bonding in the azide ion (N_3^-). (See Problem 7.45.)

7.105 Which best illustrates the change in geometry about the central S atom when SO_3 gains two electrons to become the SO_3^{2-} ion?

(a)   (c)

(b)   (d)

7.106 Draw three Lewis structures for compounds with the formula $C_2H_2F_2$. Indicate which of the compounds is/are polar.

7.107 Consider three of the vibrational modes of carbon dioxide

where the arrows indicate the movement of the atoms. (During a complete cycle of vibration, the atoms move toward one extreme position and then reverse their direction to the other extreme position.) Which of the preceding vibrations are responsible for CO_2 behaving as a greenhouse gas? (See Problem 7.95.)

7.108 Aluminum trichloride ($AlCl_3$) is an electron-deficient molecule. It has a tendency to form a dimer (a molecule made up of two $AlCl_3$ units), Al_2Cl_6. (a) Draw a Lewis structure for the dimer. (b) Describe the hybridization of Al in $AlCl_3$ and in Al_2Cl_6. (c) Sketch the geometry of the dimer. (d) Do either of these molecules possess a dipole moment?

7.109 Progesterone is a hormone responsible for female sex characteristics. In the usual shorthand structure, each point where lines meet represents a C atom, and most H atoms are not shown. Draw the complete structure of the molecule, showing all C and H atoms. Indicate which C atoms are sp^2- and sp^3-hybridized.

7.110 The molecule benzyne (C_6H_4) resembles benzene in that it has a six-membered ring of carbon atoms, but it is far less stable. Draw a Lewis structure of the molecule and account for the molecule's lack of stability.

7.111 Assume that the third-period element phosphorus forms a diatomic molecule, P_2, in an analogous way as nitrogen does to form N_2. (a) Write the electronic configuration for P_2. Use $[Ne_2]$ to represent the electron configuration for the first two periods. (b) Calculate its bond order. (c) What are its magnetic properties (diamagnetic or paramagnetic)?

7.112 Consider an N_2 molecule in its first excited electronic state, that is, when an electron in the highest occupied molecular orbital is promoted to the lowest empty molecular orbital. (a) Identify the molecular orbitals involved, and sketch a diagram to show the transition. (b) Compare the bond order and bond length of N_2^* with N_2, where the asterisk denotes the excited molecule. (c) Is N_2^* diamagnetic or paramagnetic? (d) When N_2^* loses its excess energy and converts to the ground state N_2, it emits a photon of wavelength 470 nm, which makes up part of the auroras' lights. Calculate the energy difference between these levels.

7.113 The Lewis structure for O_2 is

$$\ddot{O}{=}\ddot{O}$$

Use molecular orbital theory to show that the structure actually corresponds to an excited state of the oxygen molecule.

7.114 Draw the Lewis structure of ketene (C_2H_2O) and describe the hybridization of the C atoms. (The molecule does not contain O—H bonds.) On separate diagrams, sketch the formation of the sigma and pi bonds.

7.115 The compound TCDD, or 2,3,7,8-tetrachlorodibenzo-p-dioxin, is highly toxic:

It gained considerable notoriety in 2004 when it was implicated in the attempted murder of a Ukrainian politician. (a) Describe its geometry, and state whether the molecule has a dipole moment. (b) How many pi bonds and sigma bonds are there in the molecule?

7.116 Liquid bromine (Br_2) and the interhalogen compound ICl have nearly identical molecular masses, yet their boiling points differ by 38°C. Which one has the higher boiling point and why?

7.117 Carbon monoxide (CO) is a poisonous compound due to its ability to bind strongly to Fe^{2+} in the hemoglobin molecule. The molecular orbitals of CO have the same energy order as those of the N_2 molecule. (a) Draw a Lewis structure of CO and assign formal charges. Explain why CO has a rather small dipole moment of 0.12 D. (b) Compare the bond order of CO with that from molecular orbital theory. (c) Which of the atoms (C or O) is more likely to form bonds with the Fe^{2+} ion in hemoglobin?

7.118 Which of the following ions possess a dipole moment: (a) ClF_2^+, (b) ClF_2^-, (c) IF_4^+, (d) IF_4^-?

7.119 Which of the following geometries has a greater stability for tin(IV) hydride (SnH_4)?

7.120 Carbon dioxide has a linear geometry and is nonpolar. Yet we know that the molecule exhibits bending and stretching motions that create a dipole moment. How would you reconcile these seemingly conflicting descriptions of CO_2?

7.121 The bond length of the transient diatomic molecule CF is 129.1 pm and that of the molecular ion CF^+ is 117.3 pm. Using molecular orbital theory, explain why the CF bond shortens with the loss of an electron.

Answers to In-Chapter Materials

PRACTICE PROBLEMS

7.1A (a) linear, (b) bent. **7.1B** (a) Group 6A, (b) Group 7A. **7.2A** Bent about O, tetrahedral about each C, trigonal pyramidal about N. All bond angles are ~109.5°. Angles labeled in blue are <109.5°.

$$H-\overset{\frown}{\underset{}{\ddot{O}}}-\underset{\underset{H}{|}}{\overset{\overset{H}{|}}{C}}-\underset{\underset{H}{|}}{\overset{\overset{H}{|}}{C}}-\underset{\underset{H}{|}}{\overset{\overset{H}{}}{\ddot{N}}}-H$$

7.2B SO_2 contains double bonds, which are not pushed together by the central atom's lone pair as easily as the single bonds in NH_3. **7.3A** (a) polar, (b) nonpolar.

7.3B (a) polar   nonpolar , (b) polar   nonpolar
7.4A Singly occupied $3p$ orbitals from the P atom overlap with s orbitals from H atoms. **7.4B** We cannot use valence bond theory to explain the bonding in SO_2 or CH_4. In the case of SO_2, although the central atom has two unpaired electrons and can form two bonds, the unpaired electrons on S are in $3p$ orbitals. Formation of two bonds by the overlap of two $3p$ orbitals on S would be expected to result in a bond angle of approximately 90°. In the case of CH_4, the central atom does not have enough unpaired electrons to form four bonds. **7.5A** Two of the $4p$ electrons in Br are promoted to empty d orbitals. The s orbital, all three p orbitals, and two of the d orbitals hybridize to form six sp^3d^2 hybrid orbitals. One of the hybrid orbitals contains the lone pair. Each of the remaining hybrid orbitals contains one electron and overlaps with a singly occupied $2p$ orbital on an F atom. The arrangement of hybrid orbitals is octahedral and the bond angles are ~90°. **7.5B** One of the $2s$ electrons in Be is promoted to an empty p orbital. The s orbital and one p orbital hybridize to form two sp hybrid orbitals. Each hybrid orbital

contains one electron and overlaps with a singly occupied $2p$ orbital on an F atom. The arrangement is linear with a bond angle of ~180°. **7.6A** 16 σ bonds and 4 π bonds. **7.6B** 17 σ bonds and 5 π bonds. **7.7A** C and N atoms are sp-hybridized. The triple bond between C and N is composed of one sigma bond (from overlap of hybrid orbitals) and two pi bonds (from interaction of remaining p orbitals). The single bond between H and C is the result of an sp orbital from C overlapping with an s orbital from H. **7.7B** Each N atom is sp-hybridized. One sp orbital on each is singly occupied and one contains a lone pair. The singly occupied sp orbitals overlap to form a sigma bond between the N atoms. The remaining unhybridized p orbitals interact to form two pi bonds. **7.8A** Paramagnetic; bond order = 2. **7.8B** Paramagnetic; bond order = 2. **7.9A** Two different resonance structures are possible; therefore we consider all three atoms to be sp^2-hybridized. One of the hybrid orbitals on the central O atom contains the lone pair, the other two form sigma bonds to the terminal O atoms. Each atom has one remaining unhybridized p orbital. The p orbitals combine to form π molecular orbitals. **7.9B** Two different resonance structures are possible; therefore we consider all three atoms to be sp^2-hybridized. One of the hybrid orbitals on the central N atom contains the lone pair, the other two form sigma bonds to the terminal O atoms. Each atom has one remaining unhybridized p orbital. The p orbitals combine to form π molecular orbitals.

SECTION REVIEW

7.1.1 Trigonal planar, trigonal planar. **7.1.2** Tetrahedral, trigonal pyramidal. **7.1.3** 120°. **7.1.4** 109.5°. **7.2.1** HBr. **7.2.2** XeF_2. **7.3.1** Li l, Be 0, B 1, C 2, N 3, O 2, F 1, Ne 0. **7.3.2** 3. **7.4.1** 3. **7.4.2** 3. **7.5.1** 2. **7.5.2** sp^2, sp, sp^2. **7.5.3** Yes. These two orbitals may overlap in a linear fashion along the internuclear axis to form a sigma bond. **7.5.4** No. The $3p_y$ and $3p_z$ orbitals are mutually perpendicular and cannot align properly to overlap to form a pi bond. **7.6.1** 2, diamagnetic. **7.6.2** Paramagnetic. **7.6.3** 0.5. **7.6.4** 2−. **7.7.1** 1. **7.7.2** Only the B atom. **7.7.3** Yes. **7.7.4** Molecular orbital theory.

KEY SKILLS

Molecular Shape and Polarity

Molecular polarity is tremendously important in determining the physical and chemical properties of a substance. Indeed, molecular polarity is one of the most important consequences of molecular geometry. To determine the geometry or *shape* of a molecule or polyatomic ion, we use a stepwise procedure:

1. Draw a correct Lewis structure [◀◀ Chapter 6 Key Skills].
2. Count electron domains. Remember that an electron domain is a lone pair or a bond; and that a *bond* may be a single bond, a double bond, or a triple bond.
3. Apply the VSEPR model to determine electron-domain geometry.
4. Consider the positions of *atoms* to determine molecular geometry (shape), which may or may not be the same as the electron-domain geometry.

Consider the examples of SF_6, SF_4, and CH_2Cl_2. We determine the molecular geometry as follows:

Draw the Lewis structure			

Count electron domains on the central atom	6 electron domains: • six bonds	5 electron domains: • four bonds • one lone pair	4 electron domains: • four bonds
Apply VSEPR to determine electron-domain geometry	6 electron domains arrange themselves in an octahedron.	5 electron domains arrange themselves in a trigonal bipyramid.	4 electron domains arrange themselves in a tetrahedron.
Consider positions of atoms to determine molecular geometry	With no lone pairs on the central atom, the molecular geometry is the same as the electron-domain geometry: Octahedral	The lone pair occupies one of the equatorial positions, making the molecular geometry: See-saw shaped.	With no lone pairs on the central atom, the molecular geometry is the same as the electron-domain geometry: Tetrahedral

Having determined molecular geometry, we determine overall polarity of each molecule by examining the individual bond dipoles and their arrangement in three-dimensional space.

| Determine whether or not the individual bonds are polar. | S and F have electronegativities of 2.5 and 4, respectively. [◄◄ Figure 6.4, page 188] Therefore the individual bonds are polar and can be represented with arrows. | As in SF₆, the individual bonds in SF₄ are polar. The bond dipoles are represented with arrows. | C, H, and Cl have electronegativities of 2.5, 2.1, and 3.0, respectively. The individual bonds are polar. Bond dipoles are represented with arrows. |

| Consider the arrangement of bonds to determine which, if any, dipoles cancel one another. | The dipoles shown in red cancel each other; those shown in blue cancel each other; and those shown in green cancel each other, SF₆ is <u>nonpolar</u>. | The dipoles shown in green cancel each other; but the dipoles shown in red— because they are not directly across from each other— do not. SF₄ is <u>polar</u>. | Although the bonds are symmetrically distributed, they do not all have equivalent dipoles and therefore do not cancel each other. CH₂Cl₂ is <u>polar</u>. |

Even with polar bonds, a molecule may be nonpolar if it consists of equivalent bonds that are distributed symmetrically. Molecules with equivalent bonds that are not distributed symmetrically—or with bonds that are not equivalent, are generally polar.

Key Skills Problems

7.1
What is the molecular geometry of PBr_3?

(a) trigonal planar (b) tetrahedral (c) trigonal pyramidal (d) bent (e) T-shaped

7.2
Which of the following species does not have tetrahedral molecular geometry?

(a) CCl_4 (b) SnH_4 (c) $AlCl_4^-$ (d) XeF_4 (e) PH_4^+

7.3
Which of the following species is polar?

(a) CF_4 (b) ClF_3 (c) PF_5 (d) AlF_3 (e) XeF_2

7.4
Which of the following species is nonpolar?

(a) ICl_2^- (b) SCl_4 (c) $SeCl_2$ (d) NCl_3 (e) $GeCl_4$

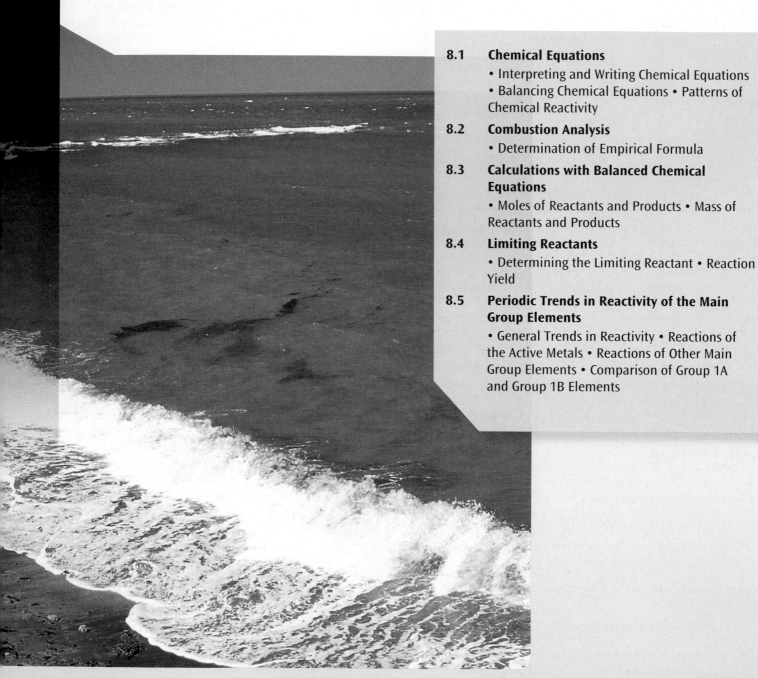

CHAPTER 8

Chemical Reactions

8.1 Chemical Equations
• Interpreting and Writing Chemical Equations
• Balancing Chemical Equations • Patterns of
Chemical Reactivity

8.2 Combustion Analysis
• Determination of Empirical Formula

**8.3 Calculations with Balanced Chemical
Equations**
• Moles of Reactants and Products • Mass of
Reactants and Products

8.4 Limiting Reactants
• Determining the Limiting Reactant • Reaction
Yield

**8.5 Periodic Trends in Reactivity of the Main
Group Elements**
• General Trends in Reactivity • Reactions of
the Active Metals • Reactions of Other Main
Group Elements • Comparison of Group 1A
and Group 1B Elements

In marine coastal environments, harmful algal blooms known as "red tides" (shown here) result when microscopic algal species grow uncontrolled. These events can potentially imperil populations of fish, seabirds, and marine mammals. In addition, because these algae produce potent neurotoxins, consumption of contaminated seafood can pose a serious risk to human health. To facilitate study of the chemistry and biochemistry of red tides, chemists have synthesized brevetoxin-2, one of the toxins produced by algae responsible for red tides. The synthesis requires a sequence of 123 individual chemical reactions. Although the average percent yield for the individual reactions is relatively high (91%), the final amount of product recovered is on the order of 1×10^{-5} g—a very small amount by conventional measures but enough for further study in laboratory settings.

Before You Begin, Review These Skills

- The mole and molar masses of elements [◄◄ Section 2.6]
- Formulas of ionic compounds [◄◄ Section 5.4]
- Formulas of molecular compounds [◄◄ Section 5.5]
- The mole and molar masses of compounds [◄◄ Section 5.10]

CHEMICAL EQUATIONS

Thus far, we have examined the structure of atoms and how the number and arrangement of sub-atomic particles give rise to the properties of atoms. The *properties* of atoms determine how they interact with one another to become the matter that we encounter every day. In this chapter, we investigate the chemical changes that matter can undergo, how we represent these changes with *chemical equations*, and how we can *use* chemical equations to solve quantitative problems.

The third hypothesis of John Dalton's atomic theory described a ***chemical reaction*** as a process that neither creates nor destroys atoms, but that rearranges atoms in chemical compounds. Examples of chemical reactions include the rusting of iron and the explosive combination of hydrogen and oxygen gases to produce water. Like the other chemical processes that we have encountered (electron transitions, ionization, electron affinity, and formation of chemical bonds), chemical reactions involve changes in energy.

A ***chemical equation*** uses chemical symbols to denote what occurs in a chemical reaction. We have seen how chemists represent elements and compounds using chemical symbols. Now we will look at how chemists represent chemical reactions using chemical equations.

Student Annotation: Recall that chemical changes can also be referred to as *chemical processes* [◄◄ Section 1.3]. The terms *chemical change, chemical process,* and *chemical reaction* are all roughly equivalent.

Student Annotation: The three hypotheses that make up Dalton's atomic theory are:

1. Matter is composed of tiny, indivisible particles called atoms; and all atoms of a given element are identical. [◄◄ Section 2.1]
2. *Compounds* are made up of specific combinations of atoms of two or more different elements. [◄◄ Section 5.5]
3. Chemical reactions cause the *rearrangement* of atoms, but do not cause either the creation or the destruction of atoms.

Interpreting and Writing Chemical Equations

A chemical equation represents a *chemical statement*. When you encounter a chemical equation, you may find it useful to read it as though it were a sentence. Read

$$NH_3 + HCl \longrightarrow NH_4Cl$$

as "Ammonia and hydrogen chloride react to produce ammonium chloride." Read

$$CaCO_3 \longrightarrow CaO + CO_2$$

as "Calcium carbonate reacts to produce calcium oxide and carbon dioxide." Thus, the plus signs can be interpreted simply as the word *and,* and the arrows can be interpreted as the phrase "react(s) to produce."

In addition to interpreting chemical equations, you must also be able to write chemical equations to represent reactions. For example, the equation for the process by which sulfur and oxygen react to produce sulfur dioxide is written as

$$S + O_2 \longrightarrow SO_2$$

Likewise, we write the equation for the reaction of sulfur trioxide and water to produce sulfuric acid as

$$SO_3 + H_2O \longrightarrow H_2SO_4$$

Each chemical species that appears to the left of the arrow is called a ***reactant.*** Reactants are those substances that are *consumed* in the course of a chemical reaction. Each species that appears to the right of the arrow is called a ***product.*** Products are the substances that *form* during the course of a chemical reaction.

Chemists usually indicate the physical states of reactants and products with italicized letters in parentheses following each species in the equation. Gases, liquids, and solids are labeled with (g), (l), and (s), respectively. Chemical species that are dissolved in water are said to be *aqueous* and are labeled (aq). The equation examples given previously can be written as follows:

$$NH_3(g) + HCl(g) \longrightarrow NH_4Cl(s) \qquad\qquad S(s) + O_2(g) \longrightarrow SO_2(g)$$

$$CaCO_3(s) \longrightarrow CaO(s) + CO_2(g) \qquad\qquad SO_3(g) + H_2O(l) \longrightarrow H_2SO_4(l)$$

At this point, it is useful to discuss how substances are represented in chemical equations. Compounds, whether they are ionic or molecular, are represented with their chemical formulas. However, because *free* elements (those that are *uncombined*) exist in a variety of forms, and because some elements can exist as different allotropes [◀◀ Section 5.5], there are two different ways to represent them.

Metals

Because metals usually do not exist in discrete molecular units but rather in complex, three-dimensional networks of atoms [▶▶ Chapter 12], we always use their empirical formulas in chemical equations. The empirical formulas are the same as the symbols that represent the elements. For example, the empirical formula for iron is Fe, the same as the symbol for the element.

Nonmetals

There is no single rule regarding the representation of nonmetals in chemical equations. Carbon, for example, exists in several allotropic forms. Regardless of the allotrope, we use its empirical formula C to represent elemental carbon in chemical equations. Often the symbol C will be followed by the specific allotrope in parentheses. Thus, we represent two of carbon's allotropic forms as C(graphite) and C(diamond).

For nonmetals that exist as polyatomic molecules, we generally use the molecular formula in equations: H_2, N_2, O_2, F_2, Cl_2, Br_2, I_2, and P_4, for example. In the case of sulfur, however, we usually use the empirical formula S rather than the molecular formula S_8—although the molecular formula S_8 is equally correct and is used sometimes.

Noble Gases

All the noble gases exist as isolated atoms, so we use their symbols: He, Ne, Ar, Kr, Xe, and Rn.

Metalloids

The metalloids, like the metals, generally have complex three-dimensional networks, so we also represent them with their empirical formulas—that is, their symbols: B, Si, Ge, and so on.

Chemical equations are also used to represent *physical* processes. Sucrose ($C_{12}H_{22}O_{11}$) dissolving in water, for example, is a physical process [◀◀ Section 1.2] that can be represented with the following chemical equation:

$$C_{12}H_{22}O_{11}(s) \xrightarrow{H_2O} C_{12}H_{22}O_{11}(aq)$$

The H_2O over the arrow in the equation denotes the process of dissolving a substance in water. Although formulas or symbols are sometimes omitted for simplicity, they can be written over an arrow in a chemical equation to indicate the conditions under which the reaction takes place. For example, in the chemical equation

$$2KClO_3(s) \xrightarrow{\Delta} 2KCl(s) + 3O_2(g)$$

the symbol Δ indicates that the addition of heat energy is necessary to make $KClO_3$ react to form KCl and O_2.

Balancing Chemical Equations

Based on what you have learned so far, the chemical equation for the explosive reaction of hydrogen gas with oxygen gas to form liquid water would be

$$H_2(g) \quad + \quad O_2(g) \quad \longrightarrow \quad H_2O(l)$$

This equation as it is written, however, violates the *law of conservation of mass* because four atoms (two H and two O) react to produce only three atoms (two H and one O). The law of conservation of mass is another way of stating Dalton's third hypothesis, which is that atoms can be neither created nor destroyed.

The equation must be *balanced* so that the same number of each kind of atom appears on both sides of the reaction arrow. Balancing is achieved by writing appropriate *stoichiometric coefficients* (often referred to simply as *coefficients*) to the left of the chemical formulas. In this case, we write a coefficient of 2 to the left of both the $H_2(g)$ and the $H_2O(l)$:

$$2H_2(g) \quad + \quad O_2(g) \quad \longrightarrow \quad 2H_2O(l)$$

There are now four H atoms and two O atoms on each side of the arrow. When balancing a chemical equation, we can change only the coefficients that precede the chemical formulas, *not* the subscripts within the chemical formulas. Changing the subscripts would change the formulas for the species involved in the reaction. For example, changing the product from H_2O to H_2O_2 would result in equal numbers of each kind of atom on both sides of the equation, but the equation we set out to balance represented the combination of hydrogen gas and oxygen gas to form water (H_2O), not hydrogen peroxide (H_2O_2). Additionally, we cannot add reactants or products to the chemical equation for the purpose of balancing it. To do so would result in an equation that represents the wrong reaction. The chemical equation must be made quantitatively correct without changing its qualitative chemical statement.

Balancing a chemical equation requires something of a trial-and-error approach. You may find that you change the coefficient for a particular reactant or product, only to have to change it again later in the process. In general, it will facilitate the balancing process if you do the following:

1. Change the coefficients of compounds (e.g., CO_2) before changing the coefficients of elements (e.g., O_2).
2. Treat polyatomic ions that appear on both sides of the equation (e.g., CO_3^{2-}) as units, rather than counting their constituent atoms individually.
3. Count atoms and/or polyatomic ions carefully, and track their numbers each time you change a coefficient.

To balance the chemical equation for the combustion of butane, we first take an inventory of the numbers of each type of atom on each side of the arrow.

$$C_4H_{10}(g) + O_2(g) \longrightarrow CO_2(g) + H_2O(l)$$

$$4 - C - 1$$

$$10 - H - 2$$

$$2 - O - 3$$

> **Student Annotation:** When we study electrochemistry in detail, we will learn a method for balancing certain equations that *does* allow addition of H_2O, H^+, and OH^- [▶▶ Section 19.1].

> **Student Annotation:** *Combustion* refers to burning in the presence of oxygen. Combustion of a hydrocarbon such as butane produces carbon dioxide and water.

Initially, there are 4 C atoms on the left and 1 on the right; 10 H atoms on the left and 2 on the right; and 2 O atoms on the left with 3 on the right. As a first step, we will place a coefficient of 4 in front of $CO_2(g)$ on the product side.

$$C_4H_{10}(g) + O_2(g) \longrightarrow 4CO_2(g) + H_2O(l)$$

$$4 - C - 4$$

$$10 - H - 2$$

$$2 - O - 9$$

This changes the tally of atoms as shown. Thus, the equation is balanced for carbon, but not for hydrogen or oxygen. Next, we place a coefficient of 5 in front of $H_2O(l)$ on the product side and tally the atoms on both sides again.

$$C_4H_{10}(g) + O_2(g) \longrightarrow 4CO_2(g) + 5H_2O(l)$$

$$4 - C - 4$$

$$10 - H - 10$$

$$2 - O - 13$$

Now the equation is balanced for carbon and hydrogen. Only oxygen remains to be balanced. There are 13 O atoms on the product side of the equation (8 in CO_2 molecules and another 5 in H_2O molecules), so we need 13 O atoms on the reactant side. Because each oxygen molecule contains 2 O atoms, we will have to place a coefficient of $\frac{13}{2}$ in front of $O_2(g)$:

$$C_4H_{10}(g) + \frac{13}{2}O_2(g) \longrightarrow 4CO_2(g) + 5H_2O(l)$$

$$4 - C - 4$$

$$10 - H - 10$$

$$13 - O - 13$$

Student Annotation: A balanced equation is, in a sense, a mathematical equality. We can multiply or divide through by any number, and the equality will still be valid.

With equal numbers of each kind of atom on both sides of the equation, this equation is now balanced. For now, however, you should practice balancing equations with the smallest possible *whole* number coefficients. Multiplying each coefficient by 2 gives all whole numbers and a final balanced equation:

$$2C_4H_{10}(g) + 13O_2(g) \longrightarrow 8CO_2(g) + 10H_2O(l)$$

$$8 - C - 8$$

$$20 - H - 20$$

$$26 - O - 26$$

Worked Examples 8.1 and 8.2 let you practice writing and balancing chemical equations.

Worked Example 8.1

Write and balance the chemical equation for the aqueous reaction of barium hydroxide and perchloric acid to produce aqueous barium perchlorate and water.

Strategy Determine the formulas and physical states of all reactants and products, and use them to write a chemical equation that makes the correct chemical statement. Finally, adjust coefficients in the resulting chemical equation to ensure that there are identical numbers of each type of atom on both sides of the reaction arrow.

Student Annotation: You may wish to review how to deduce a compound's formula from its name [◀◀ Sections 5.4 and 5.6].

Setup The reactants are $Ba(OH)_2$ and $HClO_4$, and the products are $Ba(ClO_4)_2$ and H_2O. Because the reaction is aqueous, all species except H_2O will be labeled (aq) in the equation. Being a liquid, H_2O will be labeled (l).

Solution The chemical statement "barium hydroxide and perchloric acid react to produce barium perchlorate and water" can be represented with the following unbalanced equation:

$$Ba(OH)_2(aq) + HClO_4(aq) \longrightarrow Ba(ClO_4)_2(aq) + H_2O(l)$$

Perchlorate ions (ClO_4^-) appear on both sides of the equation, so count them as units, rather than count the individual atoms they contain. Thus, the tally of atoms and polyatomic ions is

$$1 \text{ --- Ba --- } 1$$

$$2 \text{ --- O --- } 1 \text{ (not including O atoms in } ClO_4^- \text{ ions)}$$

$$3 \text{ --- H --- } 2$$

$$1 \text{ --- } ClO_4^- \text{ --- } 2$$

The barium atoms are already balanced, and placing a coefficient of 2 in front of $HClO_4(aq)$ balances the number of perchlorate ions.

$$Ba(OH)_2(aq) + 2HClO_4(aq) \longrightarrow Ba(ClO_4)_2(aq) + H_2O(l)$$

$$1 \text{ --- Ba --- } 1$$

$$2 \text{ --- O --- } 1 \text{ (not including O atoms in } ClO_4^- \text{ ions)}$$

$$4 \text{ --- H --- } 2$$

$$2 \text{ --- } ClO_4^- \text{ --- } 2$$

Placing a coefficient of 2 in front of $H_2O(l)$ balances both the O and H atoms, giving us the final balanced equation:

$$Ba(OH)_2(aq) + 2HClO_4(aq) \longrightarrow Ba(ClO_4)_2(aq) + 2H_2O(l)$$

$$1 \text{ --- Ba --- } 1$$

$$2 \text{ --- O --- } 2 \text{ (not including O atoms in } ClO_4^- \text{ ions)}$$

$$4 \text{ --- H --- } 4$$

$$2 \text{ --- } ClO_4^- \text{ --- } 2$$

Think About It

Check to be sure the equation is balanced by counting all the atoms individually.

$$1 \text{ --- Ba --- } 1$$

$$10 \text{ --- O --- } 10$$

$$4 \text{ --- H --- } 4$$

$$2 \text{ --- Cl --- } 2$$

Practice Problem A Write and balance the chemical equation that represents the combustion of propane (i.e., the reaction of propane gas with oxygen gas to produce carbon dioxide gas and liquid water).

Practice Problem B Write and balance the chemical equation that represents the reaction of sulfuric acid with sodium hydroxide to form water and sodium sulfate.

Worked Example 8.2

Butyric acid (also known as butanoic acid, $C_4H_8O_2$) is one of many compounds found in milk fat. First isolated from rancid butter in 1869, butyric acid has received a great deal of attention in recent years as a potential anticancer agent. Write a balanced equation for the metabolism of butyric acid. Assume that the overall process of metabolism and combustion are the same (i.e., reaction with oxygen to produce carbon dioxide and water).

(Continued on next page)

Strategy Begin by writing an unbalanced equation to represent the combination of reactants and formation of products as stated in the problem, and then balance the equation.

Butyric acid

Setup Metabolism in this context refers to the combination of $C_4H_8O_2$ with O_2 to produce CO_2 and H_2O.

Solution

$$C_4H_8O_2(aq) + O_2(g) \longrightarrow CO_2(g) + H_2O(l)$$

Balance the number of C atoms by changing the coefficient for CO_2 from 1 to 4.

$$C_4H_8O_2(aq) + O_2(g) \longrightarrow 4CO_2(g) + H_2O(l)$$

Balance the number of H atoms by changing the coefficient for H_2O from 1 to 4.

$$C_4H_8O_2(aq) + O_2(g) \longrightarrow 4CO_2(g) + 4H_2O(l)$$

Finally, balance the number of O atoms by changing the coefficient for O_2 from 1 to 5.

$$C_4H_8O_2(aq) + 5O_2(g) \longrightarrow 4CO_2(g) + 4H_2O(l)$$

Think About It

Count the number of each type of atom on each side of the reaction arrow to verify that the equation is properly balanced. There are 4 C, 8 H, and 12 O in the reactants and in the products, so the equation is balanced.

Practice Problem A Another compound found in milk fat that appears to have anticancer and anti-obesity properties is conjugated linoleic acid (CLA; $C_{18}H_{32}O_2$). Assuming again that the only products are CO_2 and H_2O, write a balanced equation for the metabolism of CLA.

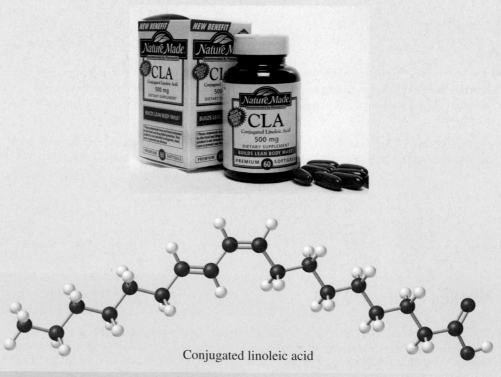

Conjugated linoleic acid

Practice Problem B Write a balanced equation for the combination of ammonia gas with solid copper(II) oxide to form copper metal, nitrogen gas, and liquid water.

Patterns of Chemical Reactivity

As you continue to study chemistry, you will encounter a wide variety of chemical reactions. The sheer number of different reactions can seem daunting at times, but most of them fall into a relatively small number of categories. Becoming familiar with several reaction types and learning to recognize *patterns* of reactivity will help you make sense out of the reactions in this book. Three of the most commonly encountered reaction types are *combination, decomposition,* and *combustion.*

Combination. A reaction in which two or more reactants combine to form a single product is known as a ***combination reaction.*** Examples include the reaction of ammonia and hydrogen chloride to form ammonium chloride,

$$NH_3(g) + HCl(g) \longrightarrow NH_4Cl(s)$$

and the reaction of nitrogen and hydrogen gases to form ammonia,

$$N_2(g) + 3H_2(g) \longrightarrow 2NH_3(g)$$

Decomposition. A reaction in which two or more products form from a single reactant is known as a ***decomposition reaction.*** A decomposition reaction is essentially the opposite of a combination reaction. Examples of this type of reaction include the decomposition of calcium carbonate to produce calcium oxide and carbon dioxide gas,

$$CaCO_3(s) \xrightarrow{\Delta} CaO(s) + CO_2(g)$$

and the decomposition of hydrogen peroxide to produce water and oxygen gas,

$$2H_2O_2(aq) \longrightarrow 2H_2O(l) + O_2(g)$$

Combustion. A ***combustion reaction*** is one in which a substance burns in the presence of oxygen. Combustion of a compound that contains C and H (or C, H, and O) produces carbon dioxide gas and water. By convention, we will consider the water produced in a combustion reaction to be *liquid* water. Examples of this type of combustion are the combustion of formaldehyde,

$$CH_2O(l) + O_2(g) \longrightarrow CO_2(g) + H_2O(l)$$

and the combustion of methane,

$$CH_4(g) + 2O_2(g) \longrightarrow CO_2(g) + 2H_2O(l)$$

Although these combustion reactions are shown here as balanced equations, oxygen is generally supplied in excess in such processes to ensure complete combustion. Worked Example 8.3 lets you practice classifying reactions.

Worked Example 8.3

Determine whether each of the following equations represents a combination reaction, a decomposition reaction, or a combustion reaction: (a) $H_2(g) + Br_2(g) \longrightarrow 2HBr(g)$, (b) $2HCO_2H(l) + O_2(g) \longrightarrow 2CO_2(g) + 2H_2O(l)$, (c) $2KClO_3(s) \longrightarrow 2KCl(s) + 3O_2(g)$.

Strategy Look at the reactants and products in each balanced equation to see if two or more reactants combine into one product (a combination reaction), if one reactant splits into two or more products (a decomposition reaction), or if the main products formed are carbon dioxide gas and water (a combustion reaction).

Setup The equation in part (a) depicts *two reactants* and *one product*. The equation in part (b) represents a combination of a compound containing C, H, and O—with O_2—to produce CO_2 and H_2O. The equation in part (c) represents *two products* being formed from a *single reactant*.

Solution These equations represent (a) a combination reaction, (b) a combustion reaction, and (c) a decomposition reaction.

Think About It
Make sure that a reaction identified as a combination has only one product [as in part (a)], a reaction identified as a combustion consumes O_2 and produces CO_2 and H_2O [as in part (b)], and a reaction identified as a decomposition has only one reactant [as in part (c)].

Practice Problem A Identify each of the following as a combination, decomposition, or combustion reaction: (a) $C_2H_4O_2(l) + 2O_2(g) \longrightarrow 2CO_2(g) + 2H_2O(l)$, (b) $2Na(s) + Cl_2(g) \longrightarrow 2NaCl(s)$, (c) $2NaH(s) \longrightarrow 2Na(s) + H_2(g)$.

Practice Problem B Using the chemical species A_2, B, and AB, write a balanced equation for a combination reaction.

SECTION 8.1 REVIEW

Chemical Equations

8.1.1 Balance the following equation:

$$CH_4(g) + H_2O(g) \longrightarrow H_2(g) + CO_2(g)$$

8.1.2 Balance the following equation:

$$S(s) + O_3(g) \longrightarrow SO_2(g)$$

8.1.3 Write a balanced chemical equation for the reaction represented here.

8.1.4 Write a balanced chemical equation for the reaction represented here.

8.1.5 Identify the reaction shown as a combination, decomposition, or combustion.

8.2 COMBUSTION ANALYSIS

As we saw in Section 5.5, knowing the mass of each element contained in a sample of a substance enables us to determine the empirical formula of the substance. One common, practical use of this ability is the experimental determination of empirical formula by *combustion analysis.*

Combustion analysis of organic compounds (containing carbon, hydrogen, and sometimes oxygen) is carried out using an apparatus like the one shown in Figure 8.1. A sample of known mass is placed in the furnace and heated in the presence of oxygen. The carbon dioxide and water produced from carbon and hydrogen, respectively, in the combustion reaction are collected in "traps," which are weighed before and after the combustion. The difference in mass of each trap before and after the reaction is the mass of the collected product. Knowing the mass of each product, we can determine the percent composition of the compound. And, from percent composition, we can determine the empirical formula.

Determination of Empirical Formula

When a compound such as glucose is burned in a combustion analysis apparatus, carbon dioxide (CO_2) and water (H_2O) are produced. Because only oxygen gas is added to the reaction, the carbon and hydrogen present in the products must have come from the glucose. The oxygen in the products may have come from the glucose, but it may also have come from the added oxygen. Suppose that in one such experiment the combustion of 18.8 g of glucose produced 27.6 g of CO_2 and 11.3 g of H_2O. We can calculate the mass of carbon and hydrogen in the original 18.8-g sample of glucose as follows:

$$\text{mass of C} = 27.6 \text{ g } CO_2 \times \frac{1 \text{ mol } CO_2}{44.01 \text{ g } CO_2} \times \frac{1 \text{ mol C}}{1 \text{ mol } CO_2} \times \frac{12.01 \text{ g C}}{1 \text{ mol C}} = 7.53 \text{ g C}$$

$$\text{mass of H} = 11.3 \text{ g } H_2O \times \frac{1 \text{ mol } H_2O}{18.02 \text{ g } H_2O} \times \frac{2 \text{ mol H}}{1 \text{ mol } H_2O} \times \frac{1.008 \text{ g H}}{1 \text{ mol H}} = 1.26 \text{ g H}$$

Thus, 18.8 g of glucose contains 7.53 g of carbon and 1.26 g of hydrogen. The remaining mass [18.8 g − (7.53 g + 1.26 g) = 10.0 g] is oxygen.

The number of moles of each element present in 18.8 g of glucose is

$$\text{moles of C} = 7.53 \text{ g C} \times \frac{1 \text{ mol C}}{12.01 \text{ g C}} = 0.627 \text{ mol C}$$

$$\text{moles of H} = 1.26 \text{ g H} \times \frac{1 \text{ mol H}}{1.008 \text{ g H}} = 1.25 \text{ mol H}$$

$$\text{moles of O} = 10.0 \text{ g O} \times \frac{1 \text{ mol O}}{16.00 \text{ g O}} = 0.626 \text{ mol O}$$

Figure 8.1 Schematic of a combustion analysis apparatus. CO_2 and H_2O produced in combustion are trapped and weighed. The amounts of these products are used to determine how much carbon and hydrogen the combusted sample contained. (CuO is used to ensure complete combustion of all carbon to CO_2.)

The empirical formula of glucose can therefore be written $C_{0.627}H_{1.25}O_{0.626}$. Because the numbers in an empirical formula must be integers, we divide each of the subscripts by the smallest subscript, 0.626. Thus, we have $0.627/0.626 \approx 1$, $1.25/0.626 \approx 2$, and $0.626/0.626 = 1$; and we obtain CH_2O for the empirical formula. Using the method discussed in Chapter 5 [◄◄ Section 5.10], we can determine the molecular formula of this compound if we know the molar mass.

Worked Example 8.4 shows how to determine the molecular formula of a compound from its combustion data and molar mass.

Worked Example 8.4

Combustion of a 5.50-g sample of benzene produces 18.59 g CO_2 and 3.81 g H_2O. Determine the empirical formula and the molecular formula of benzene, given that its molar mass is approximately 78 g/mol.

Strategy From the product masses, determine the mass of C and the mass of H in the 5.50-g sample of benzene. Sum the masses of C and H; the difference between this sum and the original sample mass is the mass of O in the sample (if O is in fact present in benzene). Convert the mass of each element to moles, and use the results as subscripts in a chemical formula. Convert the subscripts to whole numbers by dividing each by the smallest subscript. This gives the empirical formula. To calculate the molecular formula, first divide the molar mass given in the problem statement by the empirical formula mass. Then, multiply the subscripts in the empirical formula by the resulting number to obtain the subscripts in the molecular formula.

Setup The necessary molar masses are CO_2, 44.01 g/mol; H_2O, 18.02 g/mol; C, 12.01 g/mol; H, 1.008 g/mol; and O, 16.00 g/mol.

Solution We calculate the mass of carbon and the mass of hydrogen in the products (and therefore in the original 5.50-g sample) as follows:

$$\text{mass of C} = 18.59 \text{ g } CO_2 \times \frac{1 \text{ mol } CO_2}{44.01 \text{ g } CO_2} \times \frac{1 \text{ mol C}}{1 \text{ mol } CO_2} \times \frac{12.01 \text{ g C}}{1 \text{ mol C}} = 5.073 \text{ g C}$$

$$\text{mass of H} = 3.81 \text{ g } H_2O \times \frac{1 \text{ mol } H_2O}{18.02 \text{ g } H_2O} \times \frac{2 \text{ mol H}}{1 \text{ mol } H_2O} \times \frac{1.008 \text{ g H}}{1 \text{ mol H}} = 0.426 \text{ g H}$$

The total mass of products is 5.073 g + 0.426 g = 5.499 g. Because the combined masses of C and H account for the entire mass of the original sample (5.499 g $\approx$ 5.50 g), this compound must not contain O.

Converting mass to moles for each element present in the compound,

$$\text{moles of C} = 5.073 \text{ g C} \times \frac{1 \text{ mol C}}{12.01 \text{ g C}} = 0.4224 \text{ mol C}$$

$$\text{moles of H} = 0.426 \text{ g H} \times \frac{1 \text{ mol H}}{1.008 \text{ g H}} = 0.423 \text{ mol H}$$

gives the formula $C_{0.4224}H_{0.423}$. Converting the subscripts to whole numbers ($0.4224/0.4224 = 1$; $0.423/0.4224 \approx 1$) gives the empirical formula CH.

Finally, dividing the approximate molar mass (78 g/mol) by the empirical formula mass (12.01 g/mol + 1.008 g/mol = 13.02 g/mol) gives $78/13.02 \approx 6$. Then, multiplying both subscripts in the empirical formula by 6 gives the molecular formula C_6H_6.

Think About It
Use the molecular formula to determine the molar mass and make sure that the result agrees with the molar mass given in the problem. For C_6H_6, the molar mass is 6(12.01 g/mol) + 6(1.008 g/mol) = 78.11 g/mol, which agrees with the 78 g/mol given in the problem statement.

Practice Problem A The combustion of a 28.1-g sample of ascorbic acid (vitamin C) produces 42.1 g CO_2 and 11.5 g H_2O. Determine the empirical and molecular formulas of ascorbic acid. The molar mass of ascorbic acid is approximately 176 g/mol.

Practice Problem B Determine the masses of products in the combustion of 11.85 g of a compound with empirical formula $C_4H_{10}O$.

Combustion Analysis

8.2.1 Determine the mass of products formed by the combustion of 7.600 g of a compound with empirical formula C_7H_{12}.

8.2.2 What is the empirical formula of a compound containing C, H, and O if combustion of 1.23 g of the compound yields 1.8 g CO_2 and 0.74 g H_2O?

8.2.3 What are the empirical and molecular formulas of a hydrocarbon if combustion of 2.10 g of the compound yields 6.59 g CO_2 and 2.70 g H_2O and its molar mass is about 84 g/mol?

8.3 CALCULATIONS WITH BALANCED CHEMICAL EQUATIONS

Often we would like to predict how much of a particular product will form from a given amount of a reactant. Other times, we perform an experiment, measure the amount of product formed, and use this information to deduce the quantity or composition of a reactant. Balanced chemical equations can be powerful tools for this type of problem solving.

Multi 8.1
Matter—stoichiometry

Moles of Reactants and Products

Based on the equation for the reaction of carbon monoxide with oxygen to produce carbon dioxide,

$$2CO(g) + O_2(g) \longrightarrow 2CO_2(g)$$

2 moles of CO combine with 1 mole of O_2 to produce 2 moles of CO_2. In stoichiometric calculations, we say that 2 moles of CO are *equivalent* to 2 moles of CO_2, which can be represented as

$$2 \text{ mol CO} \simeq 2 \text{ mol CO}_2$$

> **Student Annotation:** When reactants are combined in exactly the mole ratio specified by the balanced chemical equation, they are said to be combined *in stoichiometric amounts.*

where the symbol $\simeq$ means "is stoichiometrically equivalent to" or simply "is equivalent to." The ratio of moles of CO consumed to moles of CO_2 produced is 2:2 or 1:1. Regardless of the number of moles of CO consumed in the reaction, the same number of moles of CO_2 will be produced. We can use this constant ratio as a conversion factor that can be written as

$$\frac{2 \text{ mol CO}}{2 \text{ mol CO}_2} \quad \text{or} \quad \frac{1 \text{ mol CO}}{1 \text{ mol CO}_2}$$

The ratio can also be written as the reciprocal,

$$\frac{2 \text{ mol CO}_2}{2 \text{ mol CO}} \quad \text{or} \quad \frac{1 \text{ mol CO}_2}{1 \text{ mol CO}}$$

These conversion factors enable us to determine how many moles of CO_2 will be produced upon reaction of a given amount of CO, or how much CO is necessary to produce a specific amount of CO_2. Consider the complete reaction of 3.82 moles of CO to form CO_2. In order to calculate the number of moles of CO_2 produced, we use the conversion factor with moles of CO_2 in the numerator and moles of CO in the denominator.

$$\text{moles CO}_2 \text{ produced} = 3.82 \text{ mol CO} \times \frac{1 \text{ mol CO}_2}{1 \text{ mol CO}} = 3.82 \text{ mol CO}_2$$

Similarly, we can use other ratios represented in the balanced equation as conversion factors. For example, we have 1 mol $O_2 \,\hat{=}\, 2$ mol CO_2 and 2 mol $CO \,\hat{=}\, 1$ mol O_2. The corresponding conversion factors allow us to calculate the amount of CO_2 produced upon reaction of a given amount of O_2, and the amount of one reactant necessary to react completely with a given amount of the other. Using the preceding example, we can determine the ***stoichiometric amount*** of O_2 (the exact number of moles of O_2 needed to react with 3.82 moles of CO)

$$\text{moles } O_2 \text{ needed} = 3.82 \; \cancel{\text{mol CO}} \times \frac{1 \text{ mol } O_2}{2 \; \cancel{\text{mol CO}}} = 1.91 \text{ mol } CO_2$$

Worked Example 8.5 illustrates how to determine reactant and product amounts using a balanced chemical equation.

Worked Example 8.5

Urea [$(NH_2)_2CO$] is a by-product of protein metabolism. This waste product is formed in the liver and then filtered from the blood and excreted in the urine by the kidneys. Urea can be synthesized in the laboratory by the combination of ammonia and carbon dioxide according to the equation

$$2NH_3(g) + CO_2(g) \longrightarrow (NH_2)_2CO(aq) + H_2O(l)$$

(a) Calculate the amount of urea that will be produced by the complete reaction of 5.25 moles of ammonia. (b) Determine the stoichiometric amount of carbon dioxide required to react with 5.25 moles of ammonia.

Strategy Use the balanced chemical equation to determine the correct stoichiometric conversion factors, and then multiply by the number of moles of ammonia given.

Setup According to the balanced chemical equation, the conversion factor for ammonia and urea is either

$$\frac{2 \text{ mol } NH_3}{1 \text{ mol } (NH_2)_2CO} \quad \text{or} \quad \frac{1 \text{ mol } (NH_2)_2CO}{2 \text{ mol } NH_3}$$

In order to multiply by moles of NH_3 and have the units cancel properly, we use the conversion factor with moles of NH_3 in the denominator.

Similarly, the conversion factor for ammonia and carbon dioxide can be written as

$$\frac{2 \text{ mol } NH_3}{1 \text{ mol } CO_2} \quad \text{or} \quad \frac{1 \text{ mol } CO_2}{2 \text{ mol } NH_3}$$

Again, we select the conversion factor with ammonia in the denominator so that moles of NH_3 will cancel in the calculation.

Solution

(a) moles $(NH_2)_2CO$ produced $= 5.25 \; \cancel{\text{mol } NH_3} \times \dfrac{1 \text{ mol } (NH_2)_2CO}{2 \; \cancel{\text{mol } NH_3}} = 2.63$ mol $(NH_2)_2CO$

(b) moles CO_2 produced $= 5.25 \; \cancel{\text{mol } NH_3} \times \dfrac{1 \text{ mol } CO_2}{2 \; \cancel{\text{mol } NH_3}} = 2.63$ mol CO_2

Think About It
As always, check to be sure that units cancel properly in the calculation. Also, the balanced equation indicates that there will be *fewer* moles of urea produced than ammonia consumed. Therefore, your calculated number of moles of urea (2.63) should be *smaller* than the number of moles given in the problem (5.25). Similarly, the stoichiometric coefficients in the balanced equation are the same for carbon dioxide and urea, so your answers to this problem should also be the same for both species.

Practice Problem A Nitrogen and hydrogen react to form ammonia according to the following balanced equation: $N_2(g) + 3H_2(g) \longrightarrow 2NH_3(g)$. Calculate the number of moles of hydrogen required to react with 0.0880 mole of nitrogen, and the number of moles of ammonia that will form.

Practice Problem B Tetraphosphorus decoxide (P_4O_{10}) reacts with water to produce phosphoric acid. Write a balanced equation for this reaction and determine the number of moles of each reactant required to produce 5.80 moles of phosphoric acid.

Mass of Reactants and Products

Balanced chemical equations give us the relative amounts of reactants and products in terms of moles. However, because we measure reactants and products in the laboratory by weighing them, most often such calculations start with mass rather than the number of moles.

Worked Example 8.6 illustrates how to determine amounts of reactants and products in terms of grams.

Worked Example 8.6

Dinitrogen monoxide (N_2O), also known as *nitrous oxide* or "laughing gas," is used as an anesthetic in dentistry. It is manufactured by heating ammonium nitrate. The balanced equation is

$$NH_4NO_3(s) \xrightarrow{\Delta} N_2O(g) + 2H_2O(l)$$

(a) Calculate the mass of ammonium nitrate that must be heated in order to produce 10.0 g of nitrous oxide. (b) Determine the corresponding mass of water produced in the reaction.

Strategy For part (a), use the molar mass of nitrous oxide to convert the given mass of nitrous oxide to moles, use the appropriate stoichiometric conversion factor to convert to moles of ammonium nitrate, and then use the molar mass of ammonium nitrate to convert to grams of ammonium nitrate. For part (b), use the molar mass of nitrous oxide to convert the given mass of nitrous oxide to moles, use the stoichiometric conversion factor to convert from moles of nitrous oxide to moles of water, and then use the molar mass of water to convert to grams of water.

Setup The molar masses are as follows: 80.05 g/mol for NH_4NO_3, 44.02 g/mol for N_2O, and 18.02 g/mol for H_2O. The conversion factors from nitrous oxide to ammonium nitrate and from nitrous oxide to water are, respectively:

$$\frac{1 \text{ mol } NH_4NO_3}{1 \text{ mol } N_2O} \quad \text{and} \quad \frac{2 \text{ mol } H_2O}{1 \text{ mol } N_2O}$$

Solution

(a) $\qquad 10.0 \text{ g } N_2O \times \dfrac{1 \text{ mol } N_2O}{44.02 \text{ g } N_2O} = 0.227 \text{ mol } N_2O$

$\qquad 0.227 \text{ mol } N_2O \times \dfrac{1 \text{ mol } NH_4NO_3}{1 \text{ mol } N_2O} = 0.227 \text{ mol } NH_4NO_3$

$0.227 \text{ mol } NH_4NO_3 \times \dfrac{80.05 \text{ g } NH_4NO_3}{1 \text{ mol } NH_4NO_3} = 18.2 \text{ g } NH_4NO_3$

Thus, 18.2 g of ammonium nitrate must be heated in order to produce 10.0 g of nitrous oxide.

(b) Starting with the number of moles of nitrous oxide determined in the first step of part (a),

$$0.227 \text{ mol } N_2O \times \frac{2 \text{ mol } H_2O}{1 \text{ mol } N_2O} = 0.454 \text{ mol } H_2O$$

$$0.454 \text{ mol } H_2O \times \frac{18.02 \text{ g } H_2O}{1 \text{ mol } H_2O} = 8.18 \text{ g } H_2O$$

Therefore, 8.18 g of water will also be produced in the reaction.

Think About It
Use the law of conservation of mass to check your answers. Make sure that the combined mass of both products is equal to the mass of reactant you determined in part (a). In this case (rounded to the appropriate number of significant figures), 10.0 g + 8.18 g = 18.2 g. Remember that small differences may arise as the result of rounding.

Practice Problem A Calculate the mass of water produced by the metabolism of 56.8 g of glucose ($C_6H_{12}O_6$). (Remember that the chemical equation for metabolism is the same as the equation for combustion.)

Practice Problem B What mass of glucose must be metabolized in order to produce 175 g of water?

SECTION 8.3 REVIEW

Calculations with Balanced Chemical Equations

8.3.1 How many moles of LiOH will be produced if 0.550 mol Li reacts according to the following equation?

$$2Li(s) + 2H_2O(l) \longrightarrow 2LiOH(aq) + H_2(g)$$

8.3.2 What mass of lithium nitride is produced when 75.0 g of lithium metal react with nitrogen according to the following equation?

$$6Li(s) + N_2(g) \longrightarrow 2Li_3N(s)$$

8.3.3 What mass of iron(III) oxide must react with carbon monoxide to produce 124.5 kg iron metal according to the following equation?

$$Fe_2O_3(s) + 3CO(g) \longrightarrow 2Fe(s) + 3CO_2(g)$$

8.3.4 Determine the stoichiometric amount (in grams) of O_2 necessary to react with 5.71 g Al according to the following equation:

$$4Al(s) + 3O_2(g) \longrightarrow 2Al_2O_3(s)$$

8.4 LIMITING REACTANTS

When a chemist carries out a reaction, the reactants usually are not present in stoichiometric amounts. Because the goal of a reaction is usually to produce the maximum quantity of a useful compound from the starting materials, an excess of one reactant is commonly supplied to ensure that the more expensive or more important reactant is converted completely to the desired product. Consequently, some of the reactant supplied in excess will be left over at the end of the reaction. The reactant used up first in a reaction is called the ***limiting reactant,*** because the amount of this reactant *limits* the amount of product that can form. When all the limiting reactant has been consumed, no more product can be formed. ***Excess reactants*** are those present in quantities *greater* than necessary to react with the quantity of the limiting reactant.

The concept of a limiting reactant applies to everyday tasks, too, such as making beef and mushroom kabobs. Suppose you want to make the maximum number of kabobs possible, each of which will consist of 1 skewer, 4 mushrooms, and 3 pieces of beef. If you have 4 skewers, 12 mushrooms, and 15 pieces of beef, how many kabobs can you make? The answer, as Figure 8.2 illustrates, is 3. After making 3 kabobs, your supply of mushrooms will be exhausted. Although you will still have 1 skewer and 6 pieces of beef remaining, you will not have the necessary ingredients to make any more kabobs according to the recipe. In this example, because the mushrooms will run out first, mushrooms are the limiting "reactant." The total amount of product, in this case the total number of kabobs, is limited by the amount of one ingredient.

Student Annotation: Limiting reactants and excess reactants are also referred to as *limiting reagents* and *excess reagents*.

Multi 8.2
Limiting reactant in reaction of NO and O_2

4 skewers, 12 mushrooms, 15 pieces of beef
(a)

3 assembled kabobs, 1 skewer, and 6 pieces of beef
(b)

Figure 8.2 Part (a) 4 skewers, 12 mushrooms, 15 pieces of beef, (b) 3 assembled kabobs, 1 skewer, and 6 pieces of beef. The number of mushrooms limits the number of kabobs that can be assembled according to the recipe.

Determining the Limiting Reactant

In problems involving limiting reactants, the first step is to determine which is the limiting reactant. After the limiting reactant has been identified, the rest of the problem can be solved using the approach outlined in Section 8.3. Consider the formation of methanol (CH_3OH) from carbon monoxide and hydrogen:

$$CO(g) + 2H_2(g) \longrightarrow CH_3OH(l)$$

Suppose that initially we have 5 moles of CO and 8 moles of H_2, the ratio shown in Figure 8.3(a). We can use the stoichiometric conversion factors to determine how many moles of H_2 are necessary in order for all the CO to react. From the balanced equation, we have 1 mol CO $\approx$ 2 mol H_2. Therefore, the amount of H_2 necessary to react with 5 mol CO is

$$\text{moles of } H_2 = 5 \text{ mol CO} \times \frac{2 \text{ mol } H_2}{1 \text{ mol CO}} = 10 \text{ mol } H_2$$

Because there are only 8 moles of H_2 available, there is insufficient H_2 to react with all the CO. Therefore, H_2 is the limiting reactant and CO is the excess reactant. H_2 will be used up first, and when it is gone, the formation of methanol will cease and there will be some CO left over, as shown in Figure 8.3(b). To determine how much CO will be left over when the reaction is complete, we must first calculate the amount of CO that will react with all 8 moles of H_2:

$$\text{moles of CO} = 8 \text{ mol } H_2 \times \frac{1 \text{ mol CO}}{2 \text{ mol } H_2} = 4 \text{ mol CO}$$

Thus, there will be 4 moles of CO consumed and 1 mole (5 mol − 4 mol) left over.

Worked Example 8.7 illustrates how to combine the concept of a limiting reactant with the conversion between mass and moles. Figure 8.4 (pp. 282–283) illustrates the steps for this type of calculation.

(a)   (b)

Figure 8.3 The reaction of (a) H_2 and CO to form (b) CH_3OH. Each molecule represents 1 mole of substance. In this case, H_2 is the limiting reactant and there is 1 mole of CO remaining when the reaction is complete.

Worked Example 8.7

Alka-Seltzer tablets contain aspirin, sodium bicarbonate, and citric acid. When they come into contact with water, the sodium bicarbonate ($NaHCO_3$) and citric acid ($H_3C_6H_5O_7$) react to form carbon dioxide gas, among other products.

$$3NaHCO_3(aq) + H_3C_6H_5O_7(aq) \longrightarrow 3CO_2(g) + 3H_2O(l) + Na_3C_6H_5O_7(aq)$$

The formation of CO_2 causes the trademark fizzing when the tablets are dropped into a glass of water. An Alka-Seltzer tablet contains 1.700 g of sodium bicarbonate and 1.000 g of citric acid. Determine, for a single tablet dissolved in water, (a) which ingredient is the limiting reactant, (b) what mass of the excess reactant is left over when the reaction is complete, and (c) what mass of CO_2 forms.

Strategy Convert each of the reactant masses to moles. Use the balanced equation to write the necessary stoichiometric conversion factor and determine which reactant is limiting. Again, using the balanced equation, write the stoichiometric conversion factors to determine the number of moles of excess reactant remaining and the number of moles of CO_2 produced. Finally, use the appropriate molar masses to convert moles of excess reactant and moles of CO_2 to grams.

(Continued on page 284)

Figure 8.4

Limiting Reactant Problems

START

Determine what mass of NH_3 forms when 84.06 g N_2 and 22.18 g H_2 react according to the equation:

$$N_2 \ + \ 3H_2 \ \longrightarrow \ 2NH_3$$

Convert to moles.

$$\frac{84.06 \text{ g } N_2}{28.02 \text{ g/mol}} = 3.000 \text{ mol } N_2$$

$$\frac{22.18 \text{ g } H_2}{2.016 \text{ g/mol}} = 11.00 \text{ mol } H_2$$

Determine moles NH_3.

Total mass before reaction:

$$84.06 \text{ g } N_2 \ + \ 22.18 \text{ g } H_2 \ = \ 106.24 \text{ g}$$

Compare the total mass *after* the reaction with the total mass *before* the reaction. The small difference between the masses before and after is due to rounding.

$$\sum \text{ after reaction } = \ 102.2 \text{ g } NH_3 \ + \ 4.03 \text{ g } H_2 \ = \ 106.2 \text{ g}$$

Add the mass of the product and the mass of leftover excess reactant to get the total mass after reaction.

Use coefficients as conversion factors.

Method 1

$$3.000 \; \text{mol N}_2 \times \frac{2 \; \text{mol NH}_3}{1 \; \text{mol N}_2} = 6.000 \; \text{mol NH}_3$$

$$11.00 \; \text{mol H}_2 \times \frac{2 \; \text{mol NH}_3}{3 \; \text{mol H}_2} = 7.333 \; \text{mol NH}_3$$

Either way, the *smaller* amount of product is correct.

or

Method 2

Rewrite the balanced equation using actual amounts. According to the balanced equation, 3.667 mol N$_2$ are required to react with 11.00 mol H$_2$.

$$3.000 \; \text{N}_2 + 9.000 \; \text{H}_2 \longrightarrow 6.000 \; \text{NH}_3$$

$$3.667 \; \text{N}_2 + 11.00 \; \text{H}_2 \longrightarrow 7.333 \; \text{NH}_3$$

6.000 mol NH$_3$

Convert to grams.

$$6.000 \; \text{mol NH}_3 \times \frac{17.03 \; \text{g NH}_3}{1 \; \text{mol NH}_3} = 102.2 \; \text{g NH}_3$$

CHECK

N$_2$ was the limiting reactant. Calculate how much H$_2$ is left over.

$$2.00 \; \text{mol H}_2 \times \frac{2.016 \; \text{g H}_2}{1 \; \text{mol H}_2} = 4.03 \; \text{g H}_2$$

Convert to grams.

```
  11.00 mol initially
−  9.00 mol consumed
   2.00 mol H₂ remaining
```

What's the point?

There is more than one correct method for solving many types of problems. This limiting reactant problem shows two different routes to the correct answer, and shows how the result can be compared to the information given in the problem to determine whether or not it is reasonable and correct.

Setup The required molar masses are 84.01 g/mol for $NaHCO_3$, 192.12 g/mol for $H_3C_6H_5O_7$, and 44.01 g/mol for CO_2. From the balanced equation we have 3 mol $NaHCO_3 \simeq$ 1 mol $H_3C_6H_5O_7$, 3 mol $NaHCO_3 \simeq$ 3 mol CO_2, and 1 mol $H_3C_6H_5O_7 \simeq$ 3 mol CO_2. The necessary stoichiometric conversion factors are therefore:

$$\frac{3 \text{ mol } NaHCO_3}{1 \text{ mol } H_3C_6H_5O_7} \quad \frac{1 \text{ mol } H_3C_6H_5O_7}{3 \text{ mol } NaHCO_3} \quad \frac{3 \text{ mol } CO_2}{3 \text{ mol } NaHCO_3} \quad \frac{3 \text{ mol } CO_2}{1 \text{ mol } NaHCO_3}$$

Solution

$$1.700 \text{ g } NaHCO_3 \times \frac{1 \text{ mol } NaHCO_3}{84.01 \text{ g } NaHCO_3} = 0.02024 \text{ mol } NaHCO_3$$

$$1.000 \text{ g } H_3C_6H_5O_7 \times \frac{1 \text{ mol } H_3C_6H_5O_7}{192.12 \text{ g } H_3C_6H_5O_7} = 0.005205 \text{ mol } H_3C_6H_5O_7$$

(a) To determine which reactant is limiting, calculate the amount of citric acid necessary to react completely with 0.02024 mol sodium bicarbonate.

$$0.02024 \text{ mol } NaHCO_3 \times \frac{1 \text{ mol } H_3C_6H_5O_7}{3 \text{ mol } NaHCO_3} = 0.006745 \text{ mol } H_3C_6H_5O_7$$

The amount of $H_3C_6H_5O_7$ required to react with 0.02024 mol of $NaHCO_3$ is more than a tablet contains. Therefore, citric acid is the limiting reactant and sodium bicarbonate is the excess reactant.

(b) To determine the mass of excess reactant ($NaHCO_3$) left over, first calculate the amount of $NaHCO_3$ that will react:

$$0.005205 \text{ mol } H_3C_6H_5O_7 \times \frac{3 \text{ mol } NaHCO_3}{1 \text{ mol } H_3C_6H_5O_7} = 0.01562 \text{ mol } NaHCO_3$$

Thus, 0.01562 mole of $NaHCO_3$ will be consumed, leaving 0.00462 mole unreacted. Convert the unreacted amount to grams as follows:

$$0.00462 \text{ mol } NaHCO_3 \times \frac{84.01 \text{ g } NaHCO_3}{1 \text{ mol } NaHCO_3} = 0.388 \text{ g } NaHCO_3$$

(c) To determine the mass of CO_2 produced, first calculate the number of moles of CO_2 produced from the number of moles of limiting reactant ($H_3C_6H_5O_7$) consumed:

$$0.005205 \text{ mol } H_3C_6H_5O_7 \times \frac{3 \text{ mol } CO_2}{1 \text{ mol } H_3C_6H_5O_7} = 0.01562 \text{ mol } CO_2$$

Convert this amount to grams as follows:

$$0.01562 \text{ mol } CO_2 \times \frac{44.01 \text{ g } CO_2}{1 \text{ mol } CO_2} = 0.6874 \text{ g } CO_2$$

To summarize the results: (a) citric acid is the limiting reactant, (b) 0.388 g sodium bicarbonate remains unreacted, and (c) 0.6874 g carbon dioxide is produced.

Think About It

In a problem such as this, it is a good idea to check your work by calculating the amounts of the other products in the reaction. According to the law of conservation of mass, the combined starting mass of the two reactants (1.700 g + 1.000 g = 2.700 g) should equal the sum of the masses of products and leftover excess reactant. In this case, the masses of H_2O and $Na_3C_6H_5O_7$ produced are 0.2815 g and 1.343 g, respectively. The mass of CO_2 produced is 0.6874 g [from part (c)] and the amount of excess $NaHCO_3$ is 0.388 g [from part (b)]. The total, 0.2815 g + 1.343 g + 0.6874 g + 0.388 g, is 2.700 g, identical to the total mass of the reactants.

Practice Problem A Ammonia is produced by the reaction of nitrogen and hydrogen according to the equation $N_2(g) + 3H_2(g) \longrightarrow 2NH_3(g)$. Calculate the mass of ammonia produced when 35.0 g of nitrogen react with 12.5 g of hydrogen. Which is the excess reactant and how much of it will be left over when the reaction is complete?

Practice Problem B Potassium hydroxide and phosphoric acid react to form potassium phosphate and water according to the equation $3KOH(aq) + H_3PO_4(aq) \longrightarrow K_3PO_4(aq) + 3H_2O(l)$. Determine the starting mass of each reactant if 55.7 g K_3PO_4 are produced and 89.8 g H_3PO_4 remain unreacted.

Reaction Yield

When you use stoichiometry to calculate the amount of product formed in a reaction, you are calculating the ***theoretical yield*** of the reaction. The theoretical yield is the amount of product that forms when *all* the limiting reactant reacts to form the desired product. It is the *maximum* obtainable yield, predicted by the balanced equation. In practice, the ***actual yield***—the amount of product actually obtained from a reaction—is almost always less than the theoretical yield. There are many reasons for the difference between the actual and theoretical yields. For instance, some of the reactants may not react to form the desired product. They may react to form different products, in something known as *side reactions,* or they may simply remain unreacted. In addition, it may be difficult to isolate and recover all the product at the end of the reaction. Chemists often determine the efficiency of a chemical reaction by calculating its ***percent yield,*** which tells *what percentage the actual yield is of the theoretical yield.* It is calculated as follows:

$$\% \text{ yield} = \frac{\text{actual yield}}{\text{theoretical yield}} \times 100\%$$
                                                                                          Equation 8.1

Percent yields may range from a tiny fraction to 100 percent. (They cannot exceed 100 percent.) Chemists try to maximize percent yield in a variety of ways. Factors that can affect percent yield, including temperature and pressure, are discussed in Chapter 15.

    Worked Example 8.8 shows how to calculate the percent yield of a pharmaceutical manufacturing process.

Worked Example 8.8

Aspirin, acetylsalicylic acid ($C_9H_8O_4$), is the most commonly used pain reliever in the world. It is produced by the reaction of salicylic acid ($C_7H_6O_3$) and acetic anhydride ($C_4H_6O_3$) according to the following equation:

$$C_7H_6O_3 \quad + \quad C_4H_6O_3 \quad \longrightarrow \quad C_9H_8O_4 \quad + \quad HC_2H_3O_2$$
salicylic acid   acetic anhydride   acetylsalicylic acid   acetic acid

In a certain aspirin synthesis, 104.8 g of salicylic acid and 110.9 g of acetic anhydride are combined. Calculate the percent yield of the reaction if 105.6 g of aspirin are produced.

Strategy Convert reactant grams to moles, and determine which is the limiting reactant. Use the balanced equation to determine the number of moles of aspirin that can be produced, and convert this number of moles to grams for the theoretical yield. Use the actual yield (given in the problem) and the calculated theoretical yield to calculate the percent yield.

Setup The necessary molar masses are 138.12 g/mol for salicylic acid, 102.09 g/mol for acetic anhydride, and 180.15 g/mol for aspirin.

Solution

$$104.8 \text{ g } C_7H_6O_3 \times \frac{1 \text{ mol } C_7H_6O_3}{138.12 \text{ g } C_7H_6O_3} = 0.7588 \text{ mol } C_7H_6O_3$$

$$110.9 \text{ g } C_4H_6O_3 \times \frac{1 \text{ mol } C_4H_6O_3}{102.09 \text{ g } C_4H_6O_3} = 1.086 \text{ mol } C_4H_6O_3$$

Because the two reactants combine in a 1:1 mole ratio, the reactant present in the smallest number of moles (in this case, salicylic acid) is the limiting reactant. According to the balanced equation, one mole of aspirin is produced for every mole of salicylic acid consumed.

$$1 \text{ mol salicylic acid } (C_7H_6O_3) \approx 1 \text{ mol aspirin } (C_9H_8O_4)$$

Therefore, the theoretical yield of aspirin is 0.7588 mol. We convert this to grams using the molar mass of aspirin:

$$0.7588 \text{ mol } C_9H_8O_4 \times \frac{180.15 \text{ g } C_9H_8O_4}{1 \text{ mol } C_9H_8O_4} = 136.7 \text{ g } C_9H_8O_4$$

(Continued on next page)

Thus, the theoretical yield is 136.7 g. If the actual yield is 105.6 g, the percent yield is

$$\% \text{ yield} = \frac{105.6 \text{ g}}{136.7 \text{ g}} \times 100\% = 77.25\% \text{ yield}$$

Think About It
Make sure you have used the proper molar masses and remember that percent yield can never exceed 100 percent.

Practice Problem A Diethyl ether is produced from ethanol according to the following equation:

$$2CH_3CH_2OH(l) \longrightarrow CH_3CH_2OCH_2CH_3(l) + H_2O(l)$$

Calculate the percent yield if 68.6 g of ethanol react to produce 16.1 g of ether.

Practice Problem B What mass of ether will be produced if 207 g of ethanol react with a 73.2 percent yield?

SECTION 8.4 REVIEW

Limiting Reactants

8.4.1 How many moles of NH_3 can be produced by the combination of 3.0 mol N_2 and 1.5 mol H_2?

8.4.2 What mass of $CaSO_4$ is produced according to the given equation when 5.00 g of each reactant are combined?

$$CaF_2(s) + H_2SO_4(aq) \longrightarrow CaSO_4(s) + 2HF(g)$$

8.4.3 What is the percent yield for a process in which 10.4 g CH_3OH react and 10.1 g CO_2 form according to the following equation?

$$2CH_3OH(l) + 3O_2(g) \longrightarrow 2CO_2(g) + 4H_2O(l)$$

8.4.4 What mass of water is produced by the reaction of 50.0 g CH_3OH with an excess of O_2 when the yield is 53.2 percent?

$$2CH_3OH(l) + 3O_2(g) \longrightarrow 2CO_2(g) + 4H_2O(l)$$

8.4.5 Reactants A (red) and B (blue) combine to form a single product C according to the equation $2A + B \longrightarrow C$. What is the limiting reactant in the reaction vessel shown?

8.5 PERIODIC TRENDS IN REACTIVITY OF THE MAIN GROUP ELEMENTS

Student Annotation: Recall that ionization energy and electron affinity refer specifically to atoms and ions in the *gas phase* [◄◄ Section 4.4].

Ionization energy and electron affinity [◄◄ Section 4.4] enable us to understand the types of reactions that elements undergo and the types of compounds they are likely to form. These two parameters actually measure similar things. Ionization energy is a measure of how powerfully an atom attracts its own electrons, while electron affinity is a measure of how powerfully an atom can attract electrons from another source. As a very simple example of how this helps us to understand

Thinking Outside the Box

Atom Economy

Many of the reactions carried out by chemists produce multiple products—not all of which are useful. The consequence is that even a reaction that proceeds quantitatively and without side reactions can generate a significant amount of chemical waste. Often the processes necessary to dispose of such waste add significantly to the cost of production. Although percent yield is an excellent measure of the overall efficiency of a chemical reaction, it does not indicate how efficiently the reactants are converted into *useful* products.

In the 1990s, as a part of the focus on green chemistry, the concept of *atom economy* was developed by Barry Trost, a professor of chemistry at Stanford University. Atom economy is a measure of how much of the starting mass of reactants ends up in the final mass of desired products in a chemical reaction. The atom economy of a reaction can be determined according to the equation

Student Annotation: A reaction is said to *proceed quantitatively* if its percent yield is very close to 100 percent.

Student Annotation: In green chemistry, also called *sustainable* chemistry, chemical processes are designed to minimize the use and production of hazardous substances. [http://www.epa.gov/greenchemistry/]

$$\text{Atom economy} = \frac{\text{Mass of atoms in desired product(s)}}{\text{Mass of atoms in all reactants}} \times 100\% \quad \textbf{Equation 8.2}$$

Note how this approach is different from a percent yield analysis. In fact, according to this formula, the atom economy of a reaction can be low even if the percent yield is very high. Consider the following example. Historically, phenol (C_6H_5OH) has been manufactured by combining benzene (C_6H_6) with sulfuric acid (H_2SO_4) and sodium hydroxide (NaOH).

The atom economy of this process is

$$\frac{\text{Mass of } C_6H_5OH}{\text{Mass of } C_6H_6, H_2SO_4, \text{ and NaOH}} \times 100\% = \frac{94.11 \text{ g}}{216.19 \text{ g}} \times 100\% = 43.53\%$$

Today, the manufacture of phenol is done by combining benzene with propene (C_3H_6) and oxygen.

In terms of phenol production alone, the atom economy of this process is

$$\frac{\text{Mass of } C_6H_5OH}{\text{Mass of } C_6H_6, C_3H_6, \text{ and } O_2} \times 100\% = \frac{94.11 \text{ g}}{152.19 \text{ g}} \times 100\% = 61.84\%$$

But when we consider that the other product of the reaction, acetone, is a substance with commercial value and is easily recovered from this process, the atom economy rises to 100 percent. Atom economy encourages chemists to find better, less expensive, and more sustainable methods of synthesizing important compounds.

Another striking example is the nonsteroidal anti-inflammatory drug ibuprofen. Beginning in the 1960s, ibuprofen was manufactured using a six-step industrial process that generated a considerable amount of chemical waste and had an atom economy of just over 40 percent. By the 1990s, one manufacturer, Hoechst Celanese, had developed a more efficient synthesis of ibuprofen. The new method, known as the BHC method, costs less, has only three steps, produces far less waste, and has an atom economy of over 77 percent. Moreover, if we consider that one of the other products in the BHC method, acetic acid, can be recovered and ultimately used in other industrial processes, the atom economy is over 99 percent.

Figure 8.5 Formation of NaCl from its constituent elements. Note that although the charges are not all shown, the solid consists of a three-dimensional array of alternating oppositely-charged ions.

$$2Na + Cl_2 \longrightarrow 2Na^+ + 2Cl^- \longrightarrow 2NaCl$$

Multi 8.3
Periodic table—properties of alkali and alkaline earth metals

a chemical reaction, consider the combination of a sodium atom and a chlorine atom, shown in Figure 8.5.

Sodium, with its low ionization energy, has a relatively weak attraction for its one valence electron. Chlorine, with its energetically favorable electron affinity, has the ability to attract electrons from another source. In this case, the electron that is loosely held by the Na atom, and powerfully attracted by the Cl atom, is transferred from Na to Cl, thus producing a sodium ion (Na^+) and a chloride ion (Cl^-). According to Coulomb's law, oppositely charged objects attract each other. The positively charged sodium ion and the negatively charged chloride ion are drawn together by electrostatic attraction, and the result is the formation of the solid ionic compound sodium chloride (NaCl).

General Trends in Reactivity

Before we examine the reactivity of elements in individual groups, let's identify some overall trends. We have said that elements in the same group resemble one another in chemical behavior because they have similar valence electron configurations. This statement, although correct in the general sense, must be applied with caution. Chemists have long known that the properties of the first member of each group (Li, Be, B, C, N, O, and F) are different from those of the rest of the members of the same group. Lithium, for example, exhibits many, but not all, of the properties characteristic of the Group 1A (alkali) metals. For example, unlike the other Group 1A elements, Li reacts with the O_2 and N_2 in air to form a simple oxide (Li_2O) and nitride (Li_3N), respectively. Similarly, beryllium is a somewhat atypical member of Group 2A (alkaline earth metals) in that it forms covalent compounds, and so on. The differences can be attributed to the unusually small size of the first element in each group [◄◄ Figure 4.6].

Another trend in the chemical reactivity of main group elements is the *diagonal relationship*. Diagonal relationships refer to similarities between pairs of elements in different groups and periods of the periodic table [◄◄ Section 4.4]. Not only do the first three members of the second period (Li, Be, and B) exhibit chemical properties similar to those of the elements located diagonally below them in the periodic table (Mg, Al, and Si), they also show similar patterns in reactivity. For example, as noted in Section Review Question 8.3.2 (page 280), lithium reacts with N_2 to form lithium nitride (Li_3N). Magnesium reacts in an analogous way to form magnesium nitride (Mg_3N_2):

$$6Li(s) + N_2(g) \longrightarrow 2Li_3N(s)$$

$$3Mg(s) + N_2(g) \xrightarrow{\Delta} Mg_3N_2(s)$$

The reaction of magnesium with nitrogen is shown in Figure 8.6. Lithium is the only member of Group 1A to exhibit this reactivity toward nitrogen.

A comparison of the properties of elements in the same group is most valid if the elements in question have a similar metallic (or nonmetallic) character. The elements in Groups 1A and 2A, for example, are all metals, whereas those in Groups 7A and 8A are all nonmetals. We have to be more careful when comparing the elements of Groups 3A through 6A, though, because a single group may contain metals, metalloids, and nonmetals. In these groups, we should expect a greater variation in chemical properties even though all group members have similar valence electron configurations.

Figure 8.6 Magnesium burning in pure nitrogen.

Hydrogen ($1s^1$)

Although it is the simplest and most abundant element in the universe, there is no completely suitable position for hydrogen in the periodic table (it really belongs in a group by itself). Traditionally hydrogen is shown at the top of Group 1A, because, like the alkali metals, it has a single *s* valence electron and forms a cation with a charge of $+1$ (H^+). On the other hand, hydrogen also forms the *hydride* ion (H^-) in ionic compounds such as NaH and CaH_2. In this respect, hydrogen resembles the members of Group 7A (halogens), all of which form -1 anions (F^-, Cl^-, Br^-, and I^-) in ionic compounds. Ionic hydrides react with water to produce hydrogen gas and the corresponding metal hydroxides:

$$2NaH(s) + 2H_2O(l) \longrightarrow 2NaOH(aq) + 2H_2(g)$$

$$CaH_2(s) + 2H_2O(l) \longrightarrow Ca(OH)_2(aq) + 2H_2(g)$$

Arguably, the most important compound of hydrogen is water, which forms when hydrogen burns in air:

$$2H_2(g) + O_2(g) \longrightarrow 2H_2O(l)$$

Reactions of the Active Metals

Group 1A Elements (ns^1, $n \geq 2$)

These elements all have low ionization energies, making it easy for them to become M^+ ions. In fact, these metals are so reactive that they are never found in nature in the pure elemental state. They react with water to produce hydrogen gas and the corresponding metal hydroxide (Figure 8.7):

$$2M(s) + 2H_2O(l) \longrightarrow 2MOH(aq) + H_2(g)$$

where M denotes an alkali metal. When exposed to air, they gradually lose their shiny appearance as they react with oxygen to form metal oxides. Lithium forms lithium oxide (containing the oxide ion, O^{2-}):

$$4Li(s) + O_2(g) \longrightarrow 2Li_2O(s)$$

The other alkali metals all form oxides or *peroxides* (containing the peroxide O_2^{2-}):

$$2Na(s) + O_2(g) \longrightarrow Na_2O_2(s)$$

Potassium, rubidium, and cesium also form *superoxides* (containing the superoxide ion, O_2^-):

$$K(s) + O_2(g) \longrightarrow KO_2(s)$$

(a) (b) (c)

Figure 8.7 Alkali metals reacting with water: (a) sodium, (b) potassium, and (c) cesium. The reaction becomes increasingly violent as ionization energy of the metal decreases down the group.

The type of oxide that forms when an alkali metal reacts with oxygen has to do with the stability of the various oxides. Because these oxides are all ionic compounds, their stability depends on how strongly the cations and anions attract one another. Lithium tends to form predominantly the oxide because lithium oxide is more stable than lithium peroxide.

> **Student Annotation:** Because they have less metallic character than the other Group 2A elements, beryllium and magnesium form some molecular compounds such as BeH_2 and MgH_2.

Group 2A Elements (ns^2, $n \geq 2$)

As a group, the alkaline earth metals are somewhat less reactive than the alkali metals. Both the first and the second ionization energies decrease (and metallic character increases) from beryllium to barium. Group 2A elements tend to form M^{2+} ions, where M denotes an alkaline earth metal atom.

The reactions of alkaline earth metals with water vary considerably. Beryllium does not react with water; magnesium reacts slowly with steam; and calcium, strontium, and barium react vigorously with cold water (Figure 8.8).

$$Ca(s) + 2H_2O(l) \longrightarrow Ca(OH)_2(aq) + H_2(g)$$

$$Sr(s) + 2H_2O(l) \longrightarrow Sr(OH)_2(aq) + H_2(g)$$

$$Ba(s) + 2H_2O(l) \longrightarrow Ba(OH)_2(aq) + H_2(g)$$

The reactivity of the alkaline earth metals toward oxygen also increases from Be to Ba. Beryllium and magnesium form oxides (BeO and MgO) only at elevated temperatures, whereas CaO, SrO, and BaO form at room temperature.

Magnesium reacts with aqueous acid [represented by $H^+(aq)$] to produce hydrogen gas:

$$Mg(s) + 2H^+(aq) \longrightarrow Mg^{2+}(aq) + H_2(g)$$

Calcium, strontium, and barium also react with aqueous acid solutions to produce hydrogen gas. However, because the metals also react with water, the two different reactions (with H^+ and with H_2O) occur simultaneously.

Figure 8.8 Barium reacting with water.

Reactions of Other Main Group Elements

Group 3A Elements (ns^2np^1, $n \geq 2$)

Boron, the first member of the group, is a metalloid; the others (Al, Ga, In, and Tl) are metals. Boron does not form binary ionic compounds and is unreactive toward both oxygen and water. Aluminum, the next element in the group, readily forms aluminum oxide when exposed to air:

$$4Al(s) + 3O_2(g) \longrightarrow 2Al_2O_3(s)$$

The aluminum oxide forms a protective coating, preventing the underlying metal from reacting further (Figure 8.9). This fact makes it possible to use aluminum for structural materials, such as aluminum siding and the shells of airplanes. Without the protective coating, layer after layer of Al atoms would become oxidized, and the structure would eventually crumble.

Aluminum forms the Al^{3+} ion. It reacts with acid according to the equation:

$$2Al(s) + 6H^+(aq) \longrightarrow 2Al^{3+}(aq) + 3H_2(g)$$

The other Group 3A metals (Ga, In, and Tl) can form both M^+ and M^{3+} ions. As we move down the group, the M^+ ion becomes the more stable of the two.

The metallic elements in Group 3A also form many molecular compounds. For example, aluminum reacts with hydrogen to form AlH_3, which has properties similar to those of BeH_2. The progression of properties across the second row of the periodic table illustrates the gradual shift from metallic to nonmetallic character in the main group elements.

(a)

(b)

Figure 8.9 (a) Finely-divided aluminum metal being sprinkled into a flame to form aluminum oxide (Al_2O_3). (b) A thin layer of aluminum oxide prevents the underlying metal from further oxidation.

Group 4A Elements (ns^2np^2, $n \geq 2$)

Carbon, the first member of the group, is a nonmetal, whereas silicon and germanium, the next two members, are metalloids. Tin and lead, the last two members of the group, are metals. They do not react with water, but they do react with aqueous acid to produce hydrogen gas:

$$Sn(s) + 2H^+(aq) \longrightarrow Sn^{2+}(aq) + H_2(g)$$

$$Pb(s) + 2H^+(aq) \longrightarrow Pb^{2+}(aq) + H_2(g)$$

The Group 4A elements form compounds containing both +2 and +4 cations. For carbon and silicon, the +4 ion is the more stable one. For example, CO_2 is more stable than CO—although the C in CO_2 is not really a C^{4+} ion. Similarly, SiO_2 is a stable compound, but SiO does not exist under ordinary conditions. As we move down the group, however, the relative stability of the two ions is reversed. In tin compounds, the +4 ion is only slightly more stable than the +2 ion. In lead compounds, the +2 ion is the more stable one. The outer electron configuration of lead is $6s^2 6p^2$, and lead tends to lose only the $6p$ electrons to form Pb^{2+} rather than both the $6p$ and $6s$ electrons to form Pb^{4+}.

> **Student Annotation:** Often in cases where the apparent charge on a cation is especially high (≥ 4), the "ion" is not really an *ion*; that is, it has achieved a stable electron configuration by *sharing* rather than by *losing* electrons [◄◄ Section 5.5]. In Chapter 9, we will learn a method for keeping track of the electrons in covalent species.

Group 5A Elements ($ns^2 np^3$, $n \geq 2$)

Nitrogen and phosphorus are *nonmetals*, arsenic and antimony are *metalloids*, and bismuth is a *metal*. Like Group 4A, Group 5A contains elements in all three categories. Thus, we expect significant variation in chemical properties among the group members.

Elemental nitrogen is a diatomic gas (N_2). It forms a variety of oxides (NO, N_2O, NO_2, N_2O_4, and N_2O_5), all of which are gases except for N_2O_5, which is a solid at room temperature. Nitrogen has a tendency to accept three electrons to form the nitride ion (N^{3-}). Most metal nitrides, such as Li_3N and Mg_3N_2, are ionic compounds. Phosphorus exists as individual P_4 molecules (white phosphorus) or chains of P_4 molecules (red phosphorus). It forms two solid oxides with the formulas P_4O_6 and P_4O_{10}. The industrially important oxoacids—nitric acid and phosphoric acid—form when N_2O_5 and P_4O_{10}, respectively, react with water (Figure 8.10):

$$N_2O_5(s) + H_2O(l) \longrightarrow 2HNO_3(aq)$$

$$P_4O_{10}(s) + 6H_2O(l) \longrightarrow 4H_3PO_4(aq)$$

Arsenic, antimony, and bismuth have extensive three-dimensional structures. Bismuth is far less reactive than metals in the preceding groups.

Group 6A Elements ($ns^2 np^4$, $n \geq 2$)

The first three members of the group (oxygen, sulfur, and selenium) are nonmetals, whereas the last two (tellurium and polonium) are metalloids. Oxygen is a colorless, odorless, diatomic gas; elemental sulfur and selenium exist as the molecules S_8 and Se_8, respectively; and tellurium and polonium have more extensive three-dimensional structures. (Polonium is a radioactive element that is difficult to study in the laboratory.) Oxygen has a tendency to accept two electrons to form the oxide ion (O^{2-}) in many compounds. Sulfur, selenium, and tellurium also form ions by accepting two electrons: S^{2-}, Se^{2-}, and Te^{2-}. The elements in Group 6A (especially oxygen) form a large number of molecular compounds with nonmetals. Some of the important compounds of sulfur are SO_2, SO_3, and H_2S. Sulfuric acid, an oxoacid, forms when sulfur trioxide reacts with water (Figure 8.11):

$$SO_3(g) + H_2O(l) \longrightarrow H_2SO_4(aq)$$

(a)   (b)

Figure 8.10 Addition of nonmetal oxides to water containing an acid-base indicator. In each case, the color change indicates that an acid is produced by the reaction. (a) $N_2O_5(s) + H_2O(l) \longrightarrow 2HNO_3(aq)$, (b) $P_4O_{10}(s) + 6H_2O(l) \longrightarrow 4H_3PO_4(aq)$.

Figure 8.11 A forest damaged by acid rain.

Group 7A Elements (ns^2np^5, $n \geq 2$)

All the halogens are nonmetals with the general formula X_2, where X denotes a halogen element. Like the Group 1A metals, the Group 7A nonmetals are too reactive to be found in nature in the elemental form. (Astatine, the last member of Group 7A, is radioactive. Very little is known about its properties.)

The halogens have high ionization energies and large, energetically favorable electron affinities. Anions derived from the halogens (F^-, Cl^-, Br^-, and I^-) are called *halides*. The vast majority of alkali metal halides are ionic compounds. The halogens also form many molecular compounds among themselves, such as ICl and BrF_3, and with nonmetals in other groups, such as NF_3, PCl_5, and SF_6. The halogens react with hydrogen to form hydrogen halides (Figure 8.12):

$$H_2(g) + X_2(g) \longrightarrow 2HX(g)$$

This reaction is explosive when it involves fluorine, but it becomes less and less violent as we substitute chlorine, bromine, and iodine. The hydrogen halides dissolve in water to form hydrohalic acids.

Figure 8.12 Colorless H_2 gas reacts with purple I_2 to form colorless HI gas.

$$H_2(g) \qquad + \qquad I_2(g) \qquad \longrightarrow \qquad 2HI(g)$$

Group 8A Elements (ns^2np^6, $n \geq 2$)

All the noble gases exist as monatomic species. With the exception of helium, which has the electron configuration $1s^2$, their atoms have completely filled outer ns and np subshells. Their electron configurations give the noble gases their great stability. The Group 8A ionization energies are among the highest of all the elements; their electron affinities are all less than zero, so they have no tendency to accept extra electrons [◄◄ Chapter 4 Key Skills, pages 138 and 139].

For years, the noble gases were called *inert gases* because they were not known to react with anything. Beginning in 1963, however, compounds were prepared from xenon and krypton by exposing them to very strong oxidizing agents such as fluorine and oxygen. In 2000, the first successful preparation of an argon compound, HArF, was reported—although it is stable only at temperatures below $-256°C$. Some of the more stable compounds that have been prepared are XeF_4, XeO_3, $XeOF_4$, and KrF_2 (Figure 8.13). Although the chemistry of the noble gases is interesting, the compounds of noble gases are not involved in any natural biological processes or major commercial applications.

Comparison of Group 1A and Group 1B Elements

Although the outer electron configurations of Groups 1A and 1B are similar (members of both groups have a single valence electron in an s orbital), their chemical properties are very different.

The first ionization energies of Cu, Ag, and Au are 745, 731 and 890 kJ/mol, respectively. Because these values are considerably larger than those of the alkali metals, the Group 1B elements are much less reactive. The higher ionization energies of the Group 1B elements result from incomplete shielding of the nucleus by the inner d electrons (compared with the more effective shielding by the completely filled noble gas cores). Consequently, the outer s electrons of the Group 1B elements are more strongly attracted by the nucleus. In fact, copper, silver, and gold are so unreactive that they are usually found in the uncombined state in nature. The inertness, rarity, and attractive appearance of these metals make them valuable in the manufacture of coins and jewelry. For this reason, these metals are also known as "coinage metals." Similar reasoning can be used to explain the differences in the chemistry of the elements in Group 2A from that of the elements in Group 2B.

Student Annotation: Note that the common ions formed by the other main group elements are those that make them isoelectronic with a noble gas. In Group 1A elements, for example, each atom *loses* one electron to become isoelectronic with the noble gas that immediately precedes it; in Group 7A elements, each atom *gains* one electron to become isoelectronic with the noble gas that immediately follows it; and so on.

Student Annotation: Because of the trend in ionization energy within a group [◄◄ Section 4.4], you might expect radon to react with fluorine more readily than krypton or xenon and, in fact, it *does*. However, primarily because of radon's radioactivity, very little is known about the compound that forms.

Figure 8.13 Xenon tetrafluoride (XeF_4) crystals.

Learning Outcomes

- Define chemical reaction, chemical equation, reactant, and product.
- Recognize physical states of reactants and products in a chemical equation.
- Balance chemical equations by changing stoichiometric coefficients.
- Describe the three commonly encountered reaction types (combustion, combination, and decomposition).
- Use combustion analysis to determine the empirical formula of a compound.

- Determine amounts of reactant required or product formed using stoichiometry.
- Identify the limiting reactant in a reaction.
- Define theoretical yield, actual yield, and percent yield.
- Predict the theoretical yield of a reaction.
- Find the percent yield of a reaction.
- Use the periodic table to predict general trends in reactivity of main group metals.

Chapter Summary

SECTION 8.1

- A *chemical equation* is a written representation of a *chemical reaction* or a physical process. Chemical species on the left side of the equation are called *reactants,* and those on the right side of the equation are called *products.*
- The physical state of each reactant and product is specified in parentheses as (*s*), (*l*), (*g*), or (*aq*) for *solid, liquid, gas,* and *aqueous* (dissolved in water), respectively.
- Chemical equations are balanced only by changing the *stoichiometric coefficients* or simply *coefficients* of the reactants and/or products, and never by changing the formulas of the reactants and/or products (i.e., by changing their subscript numbers).
- Three commonly encountered reaction types are *combustion* (in which a substance burns in the presence of oxygen), *combination* (in which two or more reactants combine to form a single product), and *decomposition* (in which a reactant splits apart to form two or more products).

SECTION 8.2

- *Combustion analysis* is used to determine the empirical formula of a compound. The *empirical formula* can be used to calculate percent composition.

SECTION 8.3

- A balanced chemical equation can be used to determine how much product will form from given amounts of reactants, how much of one reactant is necessary to react with a given amount of another, or how much reactant is required to produce a specified amount of product. Reactants that are combined in exactly the ratio specified by the balanced equation are said to be "combined in *stoichiometric amounts.*"

SECTION 8.4

- The *limiting reactant* is the reactant that is consumed completely in a chemical reaction. An *excess reactant* is the reactant that is not consumed completely. The maximum amount of product that can form depends on the amount of limiting reactant.
- The *theoretical yield* of a reaction is the amount of product that will form if all the limiting reactant is consumed by the desired reaction. The *actual yield* is the amount of product actually recovered. *Percent yield* [(actual/theoretical) × 100%] is a measure of the efficiency of a chemical reaction.

SECTION 8.5

- Although members of a group in the periodic table exhibit similar chemical and physical properties, the first member of each group tends to be significantly different from the other members. Hydrogen is essentially a group unto itself.
- The alkali metals (Group 1A) tend to be highly reactive toward oxygen, water, and acid. Group 2A metals are less reactive than Group 1A metals, but the heavier members all react with water to produce metal hydroxides and hydrogen gas. Groups that contain both metals and nonmetals (e.g., Groups 4A, 5A, and 6A) tend to show greater variability in their physical and chemical properties.

Key Words

Actual yield, 285
Aqueous, 268
Chemical equation, 267
Chemical reaction, 267
Coefficient, 269

Combination reaction, 273
Combustion analysis, 275
Combustion reaction, 273
Decomposition reaction, 273
Excess reactant, 280

Law of conservation
    of mass, 269
Limiting reactant, 280
Percent yield, 285
Product, 267

Reactant, 267
Stoichiometric amount, 278
Stoichiometric coefficients,
    269
Theoretical yield, 285

Key Equations

8.1 $\quad \% \text{ yield} = \dfrac{\text{actual yield}}{\text{theoretical yield}} \times 100\%$

8.2 $\quad \text{Atom economy} = \dfrac{\text{Mass of atoms in desired product(s)}}{\text{Mass of atoms in all reactants}} \times 100\%$

Questions and Problems

SECTION 8.1: CHEMICAL EQUATIONS

Review Questions

8.1 Use the formation of water from hydrogen and oxygen to explain the following terms: *chemical reaction, reactant,* and *product.*

8.2 What is the difference between a chemical reaction and a chemical equation?

8.3 Why must a chemical equation be balanced? What law is not obeyed by an unbalanced chemical equation?

Problems

8.4 Write an unbalanced equation to represent each of the following reactions: (a) nitrogen and oxygen react to form nitrogen dioxide, (b) dinitrogen pentoxide reacts to form dinitrogen tetroxide and oxygen, (c) ozone reacts to form oxygen, (d) chlorine and sodium iodide react to form iodine and sodium chloride, and (e) magnesium and oxygen react to form magnesium oxide.

8.5 Write an unbalanced equation to represent each of the following reactions: (a) potassium hydroxide and phosphoric acid react to form potassium phosphate and water; (b) zinc and silver chloride react to form zinc chloride and silver; (c) sodium hydrogen carbonate reacts to form sodium carbonate, water, and carbon dioxide; (d) ammonium nitrite reacts to form nitrogen and water; and (e) carbon dioxide and potassium hydroxide react to form potassium carbonate and water.

8.6 For each of the following unbalanced chemical equations, write the corresponding chemical statement.
(a) $S_8 + O_2 \longrightarrow SO_2$
(b) $CH_4 + O_2 \longrightarrow CO_2 + H_2O$
(c) $N_2 + H_2 \longrightarrow NH_3$
(d) $P_4O_{10} + H_2O \longrightarrow H_3PO_4$
(e) $S + HNO_3 \longrightarrow H_2SO_4 + NO_2 + H_2O$

8.7 For each of the following unbalanced chemical equations, write the corresponding chemical statement.
(a) $K + H_2O \longrightarrow KOH + H_2$
(b) $Ba(OH)_2 + HCl \longrightarrow BaCl_2 + H_2O$
(c) $Cu + HNO_3 \longrightarrow Cu(NO_3)_2 + NO + H_2O$
(d) $Al + H_2SO_4 \longrightarrow Al_2(SO_4)_3 + H_2$
(e) $HI \longrightarrow H_2 + I_2$

8.8 Balance the following equations using the method outlined in Section 8.1.
(a) $C + O_2 \longrightarrow CO$
(b) $CO + O_2 \longrightarrow CO_2$
(c) $H_2 + Br_2 \longrightarrow HBr$
(d) $Rb + H_2O \longrightarrow RbOH + H_2$
(e) $Mg + O_2 \longrightarrow MgO$
(f) $O_3 \longrightarrow O_2$
(g) $H_2O_2 \longrightarrow H_2O + O_2$
(h) $N_2 + H_2 \longrightarrow NH_3$
(i) $Zn + AgCl \longrightarrow ZnCl_2 + Ag$
(j) $S_8 + O_2 \longrightarrow SO_2$
(k) $NaOH + H_2SO_4 \longrightarrow Na_2SO_4 + H_2O$
(l) $Cl_2 + NaI \longrightarrow NaCl + I_2$
(m) $KOH + H_3PO_4 \longrightarrow K_3PO_4 + H_2O$
(n) $CH_4 + Br_2 \longrightarrow CBr_4 + HBr$

8.9 Balance the following equations using the method outlined in Section 8.1.
(a) $N_2O_5 \longrightarrow N_2O_4 + O_2$
(b) $KNO_3 \longrightarrow KNO_2 + O_2$
(c) $NH_4NO_3 \longrightarrow N_2O + H_2O$
(d) $NH_4NO_2 \longrightarrow N_2 + H_2O$
(e) $NaHCO_3 \longrightarrow Na_2CO_3 + H_2O + CO_2$
(f) $P_4O_{10} + H_2O \longrightarrow H_3PO_4$
(g) $HCl + CaCO_3 \longrightarrow CaCl_2 + H_2O + CO_2$
(h) $Al + H_2SO_4 \longrightarrow Al_2(SO_4)_3 + H_2$
(i) $CO_2 + KOH \longrightarrow K_2CO_3 + H_2O$

(j) $CH_4 + O_2 \longrightarrow CO_2 + H_2O$

(k) $Be_2C + H_2O \longrightarrow Be(OH)_2 + CH_4$

(l) $Cu + HNO_3 \longrightarrow Cu(NO_3)_2 + NO + H_2O$

(m) $S + HNO_3 \longrightarrow H_2SO_4 + NO_2 + H_2O$

(n) $NH_3 + CuO \longrightarrow Cu + N_2 + H_2O$

8.10 Which of the following equations best represents the reaction shown in the diagram?

(a) $8A + 4B \longrightarrow C + D$

(b) $4A + 8B \longrightarrow 4C + 4D$

(c) $2A + B \longrightarrow C + D$

(d) $4A + 2B \longrightarrow 4C + 4D$

(e) $2A + 4B \longrightarrow C + D$

8.11 Which of the following equations best represents the reaction shown in the diagram?

(a) $A + B \longrightarrow C + D$

(b) $6A + 4B \longrightarrow C + D$

(c) $A + 2B \longrightarrow 2C + D$

(d) $3A + 2B \longrightarrow 2C + D$

(e) $3A + 2B \longrightarrow 4C + 2D$

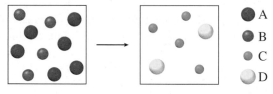

8.12 Determine whether each of the following equations represents a combination reaction, a decomposition reaction, or a combustion reaction:

(a) $2NaHCO_3 \longrightarrow Na_2CO_3 + CO_2 + H_2O$

(b) $NH_3 + HCl \longrightarrow NH_4Cl$

(c) $2CH_3OH + 3O_2 \longrightarrow 2CO_2 + 4H_2O$

8.13 Determine whether each of the following equations represents a combination reaction, a decomposition reaction, or a combustion reaction:

(a) $C_3H_8 + 5O_2 \longrightarrow 3CO_2 + 4H_2O$

(b) $2NF_2 \longrightarrow N_2F_4$

(c) $CuSO_4 \cdot 5H_2O \longrightarrow CuSO_4 + 5H_2O$

SECTION 8.2: COMBUSTION ANALYSIS

Review Questions

8.14 Explain how the combined mass of CO_2 and H_2O produced in combustion analysis can be greater than the mass of the sample being analyzed.

8.15 Explain why, in combustion analysis, we cannot determine the amount of oxygen in the sample directly from the amount of oxygen in the products H_2O and CO_2.

Problems

8.16 Determine the empirical formula of an organic compound containing only C and H given that combustion of a 1.50-g sample of the compound produces 4.71 g CO_2 and 1.93 g H_2O.

8.17 Menthol is a flavoring agent extracted from peppermint oil. It contains C, H, and O. In one analysis, combustion of 10.00 mg of the substance yields 11.53 mg H_2O and 28.16 mg CO_2. What is the empirical formula of menthol?

8.18 Perchloroethylene, also known as "perc," is the solvent used in most dry cleaning. It consists of C and Cl. Determine the empirical formula of perchloroethylene given that a 2.58-g sample yields 1.37 g CO_2 in a combustion analysis experiment.

8.19 Lactic acid, which consists of C, H, and O, has long been thought to be responsible for muscle soreness following strenuous exercise. Determine the empirical formula of lactic acid given that combustion of a 10.0-g sample produces 14.7 g CO_2 and 6.00 g H_2O.

8.20 Ascorbic acid (vitamin C) contains C, H, and O. In one analysis, combustion of 5.24 g of ascorbic acid yields 7.86 g CO_2 and 2.14 g H_2O. Calculate the empirical formula and molecular formula of ascorbic acid given that its molar mass is about 176 g.

8.21 Paradichlorobenzene, a common ingredient in solid air fresheners, contains only C, H, and Cl and has a molar mass of about 147 g. Given that combustion of 1.68 g of this compound produces 3.02 g CO_2 and 0.412 g H_2O, determine its empirical and molecular formulas.

SECTION 8.3: CALCULATIONS WITH BALANCED CHEMICAL EQUATIONS

Review Questions

8.22 On what law is stoichiometry based? Why is it essential to use balanced equations in solving stoichiometric problems?

8.23 Describe the steps involved in balancing a chemical equation.

Problems

8.24 Consider the combustion of carbon monoxide (CO) in oxygen gas:

$$2CO(g) + O_2(g) \longrightarrow 2CO_2(g)$$

Starting with 3.60 moles of CO, calculate the number of moles of CO_2 produced if there is enough oxygen gas to react with all the CO.

8.25 Silicon tetrachloride ($SiCl_4$) can be prepared by heating Si in chlorine gas:

$$Si(s) + 2Cl_2(g) \longrightarrow SiCl_4(l)$$

In one reaction, 0.507 mole of $SiCl_4$ is produced. How many moles of molecular chlorine were used in the reaction?

8.26 Ammonia is a colorless gas with a pungent, characteristic odor. It is prepared by the reaction between hydrogen and nitrogen:

$$3H_2(g) + N_2(g) \longrightarrow 2NH_3(g)$$

In a particular reaction, 6.0 moles of NH_3 were produced. How many moles of H_2 and how many moles of N_2 were consumed to produce this amount of NH_3?

8.27 Consider the combustion of butane (C_4H_{10}):

$$2C_4H_{10}(g) + 13O_2(g) \longrightarrow 8CO_2(g) + 10H_2O(l)$$

In a particular reaction, 5.0 moles of C_4H_{10} react with an excess of O_2. Calculate the number of moles of CO_2 formed.

8.28 The annual production of sulfur dioxide from burning coal and fossil fuels, auto exhaust, and other sources is about 26 million tons. The equation for the reaction is

$$S(s) + O_2(g) \longrightarrow SO_2(g)$$

How many tons of sulfur would it take to produce that quantity of SO_2?

8.29 When baking soda (sodium bicarbonate or sodium hydrogen carbonate, $NaHCO_3$) is heated, it releases carbon dioxide gas, which is responsible for the rising of cookies, cakes, and other baked goods. (a) Write a balanced equation for the decomposition of the compound (one of the products is Na_2CO_3). (b) Calculate the mass of $NaHCO_3$ required to produce 20.5 g of CO_2.

8.30 Potassium cyanide (KCN) reacts with acids to form a deadly poisonous gas, hydrogen cyanide (HCN). The reaction is represented by the equation:

$$KCN(aq) + HCl(aq) \longrightarrow KCl(aq) + HCN(g)$$

If a sample of 0.140 g of KCN is treated with an excess of HCl, calculate the amount of HCN produced, in grams.

8.31 Part of wine making is fermentation, a complex chemical process that converts glucose to ethanol and carbon dioxide:

$$\underset{\text{glucose}}{C_6H_{12}O_6} \longrightarrow \underset{\text{ethanol}}{2C_2H_5OH} + 2CO_2$$

What is the maximum quantity of ethanol (in grams and in liters) that can be produced from 500.4 g of glucose? (density of ethanol = 0.789 g/mL)

8.32 When copper(II) sulfate pentahydrate ($CuSO_4 \cdot 5H_2O$) is heated in air above 100°C, it loses the water molecules and its blue color:

$$CuSO_4 \cdot 5H_2O \longrightarrow CuSO_4 + 5H_2O$$

If 9.60 g of $CuSO_4$ are left after heating 15.01 g of the blue compound, calculate the number of moles of H_2O originally present in the compound.

8.33 For many years, the extraction of gold from other materials involved the use of potassium cyanide:

$$4Au + 8KCN + O_2 + 2H_2O \longrightarrow 4KAu(CN)_2 + 4KOH$$

What is the minimum mass of KCN needed to extract 29.0 g (about an ounce) of gold?

8.34 Limestone ($CaCO_3$) is decomposed to quicklime (CaO) and carbon dioxide by heating. Calculate how many grams of quicklime can be produced from 1.0 kg of limestone.

8.35 Nitrous oxide (N_2O) is also called "laughing gas." It can be prepared by the thermal decomposition of ammonium nitrate (NH_4NO_3). The other product is

H_2O. (a) Write a balanced equation for this reaction. (b) How many grams of N_2O are formed if 0.46 mole of NH_4NO_3 is used in the reaction?

8.36 The fertilizer ammonium sulfate [$(NH_4)_2SO_4$] is prepared by the reaction between ammonia (NH_3) and sulfuric acid:

$$2NH_3(g) + H_2SO_4(aq) \longrightarrow (NH_4)_2SO_4(aq)$$

How many kilograms of NH_3 are needed to produce 1.00×10^5 kg of $(NH_4)_2SO_4$?

8.37 A common laboratory preparation of oxygen gas is the thermal decomposition of potassium chlorate ($KClO_3$). Assuming complete decomposition, calculate the number of grams of O_2 gas that can be obtained from 46.0 g of $KClO_3$. (The products are KCl and O_2.)

SECTION 8.4: LIMITING REACTANTS

Review Questions

8.38 Define *limiting reactant* and *excess reactant*. What is the significance of the limiting reactant in predicting the amount of the product obtained in a reaction? Can there be a limiting reactant if only one reactant is present? Explain.

8.39 Give an everyday example that illustrates the limiting reactant concept.

8.40 Why is the theoretical yield of a reaction determined only by the amount of the limiting reactant?

8.41 Why is the actual yield of a reaction almost always smaller than the theoretical yield?

Problems

8.42 Consider the reaction

$$2A + B \longrightarrow C$$

(a) In the diagram here that represents the reaction, which reactant, A or B, is the limiting reactant? (b) Assuming a complete reaction, draw a molecular-model representation of the amounts of reactants and products left after the reaction. The atomic arrangement in C is ABA.

8.43 Consider the reaction

$$N_2 + 3H_2 \longrightarrow 2NH_3$$

Assuming each model represents one mole of the substance, show the number of moles of the product and the excess reactant left after the complete reaction.

8.44   Reactants A (red) and B (blue) combine in the reaction vessel shown to form a single product C (purple) according to the equation 2A + B ⟶ C.

Which of the following scenes represents the contents of the reaction vessel after the reaction is complete?

(a)

(b)

(c)

(d)

(e)

8.45   Consider the reaction pictured, where each red sphere represents an oxygen atom and each blue sphere represents a nitrogen atom. Write the balanced equation and identify the limiting reactant.

8.46   Nitric oxide (NO) reacts with oxygen gas to form nitrogen dioxide (NO_2), a dark-brown gas:

$$2NO(g) + O_2(g) \longrightarrow 2NO_2(g)$$

In one experiment, 0.886 mole of NO is mixed with 0.503 mole of O_2. Determine which of the two reactants is the limiting reactant. Calculate also the number of moles of NO_2 produced.

8.47   The depletion of ozone (O_3) in the stratosphere has been a matter of great concern among scientists in recent years. It is believed that ozone can react with nitric oxide (NO) that is discharged from high-altitude jet planes. The reaction is

$$O_3 + NO \longrightarrow O_2 + NO_2$$

If 0.740 g of O_3 reacts with 0.670 g of NO, how many grams of NO_2 will be produced? Which compound is the limiting reactant? Calculate the number of moles of the excess reactant remaining at the end of the reaction.

8.48   Propane (C_3H_8) is a minor component of natural gas and is used in domestic cooking and heating. (a) Balance the following equation representing the combustion of propane in air:

$$C_3H_8 + O_2 \longrightarrow CO_2 + H_2O$$

(b) How many grams of carbon dioxide can be produced by burning 3.65 moles of propane? Assume that oxygen is the excess reactant in this reaction.

8.49   Consider the reaction

$$MnO_2 + 4HCl \longrightarrow MnCl_2 + Cl_2 + 2H_2O$$

If 0.86 mole of MnO_2 and 48.2 g of HCl react, which reactant will be used up first? How many grams of Cl_2 will be produced?

8.50   Hydrogen fluoride is used in the manufacture of Freons (which destroy ozone in the stratosphere) and in the production of aluminum metal. It is prepared by the reaction

$$CaF_2 + H_2SO_4 \longrightarrow CaSO_4 + 2HF$$

In one process, 6.00 kg of CaF_2 are treated with an excess of H_2SO_4 to yield 2.86 kg of HF. Calculate the percent yield of HF.

8.51   Nitroglycerin ($C_3H_5N_3O_9$) is a powerful explosive. Its decomposition may be represented by

$$4C_3H_5N_3O_9 \longrightarrow 6N_2 + 12CO_2 + 10H_2O + O_2$$

This reaction generates a large amount of heat and gaseous products. It is the sudden formation of these gases, together with their rapid expansion, that produces the explosion. (a) What is the maximum amount of O_2 in grams that can be obtained from 2.00×10^2 g of nitroglycerin? (b) Calculate the percent yield in this reaction if the amount of O_2 generated is found to be 6.55 g.

8.52 Titanium(IV) oxide (TiO_2) is a white substance produced by the action of sulfuric acid on the mineral ilmenite ($FeTiO_3$):

$$FeTiO_3 + H_2SO_4 \longrightarrow TiO_2 + FeSO_4 + H_2O$$

Its opaque and nontoxic properties make it suitable as a pigment in plastics and paints. In one process, 8.00×10^3 kg of $FeTiO_3$ yielded 3.67×10^3 kg of TiO_2. What is the percent yield of the reaction?

8.53 Ethylene (C_2H_4), an important industrial organic chemical, can be prepared by heating hexane (C_6H_{14}) at 800°C:

$$C_6H_{14} \longrightarrow C_2H_4 + \text{other products}$$

If the yield of ethylene production is 42.5 percent, what mass of hexane must be used to produce 481 g of ethylene?

8.54 When heated, lithium reacts with nitrogen to form lithium nitride:

$$6Li(s) + N_2(g) \longrightarrow 2Li_3N(s)$$

What is the theoretical yield of Li_3N in grams when 12.3 g of Li are heated with 33.6 g of N_2? If the actual yield of Li_3N is 5.89 g, what is the percent yield of the reaction?

8.55 Disulfur dichloride (S_2Cl_2) is used in the vulcanization of rubber, a process that prevents the slippage of rubber molecules past one another when stretched. It is prepared by heating sulfur in an atmosphere of chlorine:

$$S_8(l) + 4Cl_2(g) \longrightarrow 4S_2Cl_2(l)$$

What is the theoretical yield of S_2Cl_2 in grams when 4.06 g of S_8 are heated with 6.24 g of Cl_2? If the actual yield of S_2Cl_2 is 6.55 g, what is the percent yield?

8.56 Maleic anhydride ($C_4H_2O_3$) is an important industrial intermediate chemical prepared from benzene according to the reaction below.

$$4C_6H_6 + 15O_2 \longrightarrow 4C_4H_2O_3 + 8CO_2 + 6H_2O$$

What is the atom economy of this reaction?

8.57 The Cativa process is used industrially to prepare acetic acid by carbonylation of methanol according to the following equation:

$$CH_3OH + CO \longrightarrow CH_3CO_2H$$

What is the atom economy of this process?

SECTION 8.5: PERIODIC TRENDS IN REACTIVITY OF THE MAIN GROUP ELEMENTS

Review Questions

8.58 Why do members of a group exhibit similar chemical properties?

8.59 Why are Group 1B elements more stable than Group 1A elements even though they seem to have the same outer electron configuration, ns^1, where n is the principal quantum number of the outermost shell?

Problems

8.60 Use the alkali metals and alkaline earth metals as examples to show how we can predict the chemical properties of elements simply from their electron configurations.

8.61 Explain why the noble gases as a group are very stable chemically.

ADDITIONAL PROBLEMS

8.62 The diagram represents the products (CO_2 and H_2O) formed by the combustion of a hydrocarbon (a compound containing only C and H atoms). Write an equation for the reaction. (*Hint:* The molar mass of the hydrocarbon is about 30 g.)

8.63 Consider the reaction of hydrogen gas with oxygen gas:

$$2H_2(g) + O_2(g) \longrightarrow 2H_2O(g)$$

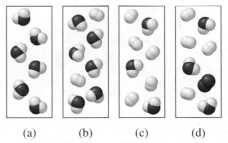

Assuming a complete reaction, which of the diagrams (a–d) shown here represents the amounts of reactants and products left after the reaction?

(a)   (b)   (c)   (d)

8.64 Industrially, nitric acid is produced by the Ostwald process represented by the following equations:

$$4NH_3(g) + 5O_2(g) \longrightarrow 4NO(g) + 6H_2O(l)$$
$$2NO(g) + O_2(g) \longrightarrow 2NO_2(g)$$
$$2NO_2(g) + H_2O(l) \longrightarrow HNO_3(aq) + HNO_2(aq)$$

What mass of NH_3 (in grams) must be used to produce 1.00 ton of HNO_3 by the Ostwald process, assuming an 80 percent yield in each step (1 ton = 2000 lb; 1 lb = 453.6 g)?

8.65 A sample of a compound of Cl and O reacts with an excess of H_2 to give 0.233 g of HCl and 0.403 g of H_2O. Determine the empirical formula of the compound.

8.66 What is the maximum mass of P_2I_4 that can be prepared from 7.25 g of P_4O_6 and 12.00 g of iodine according to the reaction

$$5P_4O_6 + 8I_2 \longrightarrow 4P_2I_4 + 3P_4O_{10}$$

8.67 How many moles of O are needed to combine with 0.212 mole of C to form (a) CO and (b) CO_2?

8.68 A mixture of 8.00 moles of H_2 and 6.00 moles of O_2 is ignited, forming water. What is the composition of the mixture by mass after the reaction is completed?

8.69 The explosive nitroglycerin ($C_3H_5N_3O_9$) has also been used as a drug to treat heart patients to relieve pain (angina pectoris). We now know that nitroglycerin produces nitric oxide (NO), which causes muscles to relax and allows the arteries to dilate. If each nitroglycerin molecule releases one NO per atom of N, calculate the mass percent of NO in nitroglycerin.

8.70 Carbon monoxide reacts with oxygen to produce carbon dioxide according to the following balanced equation:

$$2CO(g) + O_2(g) \longrightarrow 2CO_2(g)$$

A reaction vessel containing the reactants is pictured.

Which of the following represents the contents of the reaction vessel when the reaction is complete?

(a)

(b)

(c)

(d)

8.71 An iron bar weighed 664 g. After the bar had been standing in moist air for a month, exactly one-eighth of the iron turned to rust (Fe_2O_3). Calculate the final mass of the iron bar and rust.

8.72 One of the reactions that occurs in a blast furnace, where iron ore is converted to cast iron, is

$$Fe_2O_3 + 3CO \longrightarrow 2Fe + 3CO_2$$

Suppose that 1.64×10^3 kg of Fe are obtained from a 2.62×10^3-kg sample of Fe_2O_3. Assuming that the reaction goes to completion, what is the percent purity of Fe_2O_3 in the original sample?

8.73 An impure sample of zinc (Zn) is treated with an excess of sulfuric acid (H_2SO_4) to form zinc sulfate ($ZnSO_4$) and molecular hydrogen (H_2). (a) Write a balanced equation for the reaction. (b) If 0.0764 g of H_2 is obtained from 3.86 g of the sample, calculate the percent purity of the sample. (c) What assumptions must you make in part (b)?

8.74 A mixture of methane (CH_4) and ethane (C_2H_6) of mass 13.43 g is completely burned in oxygen. If the total mass of CO_2 and H_2O produced is 64.84 g, calculate the fraction of CH_4 in the mixture.

8.75 Aspirin or acetyl salicylic acid is synthesized by combining salicylic acid with acetic anhydride:

$$\underset{\substack{\text{Salicylic}\\\text{acid}}}{C_7H_6O_3} + \underset{\substack{\text{acetic}\\\text{anhydride}}}{C_4H_6O_3} \longrightarrow \underset{\text{aspirin}}{C_9H_8O_4} + \underset{\text{acetic acid}}{HC_2H_3O_2}$$

(a) How much salicylic acid is required to produce 0.400 g of aspirin (about the content in a tablet), assuming acetic anhydride is present in excess?
(b) Calculate the amount of salicylic acid needed if only 74.9 percent of salicylic is converted to aspirin.
(c) In one experiment, 9.26 g of salicylic acid react with 8.54 g of acetic anhydride. Calculate the theoretical yield of aspirin and the percent yield if only 10.9 g of aspirin are produced.

8.76 A certain sample of coal contains 1.6 percent sulfur by mass. When the coal is burned, the sulfur is converted to sulfur dioxide. To prevent air pollution, this sulfur dioxide is treated with calcium oxide (CaO) to form calcium sulfite ($CaSO_3$). Calculate the daily mass (in kilograms) of CaO needed by a power plant that uses 6.60×10^6 kg of coal per day.

8.77 A certain metal oxide has the formula MO where M denotes the metal. A 39.46-g sample of the compound is strongly heated in an atmosphere of hydrogen to remove oxygen as water molecules. At the end, 31.70 g of the metal are left over. If O has an atomic mass of 16.00 amu, calculate the atomic mass of M and identify the element.

8.78 The combustion of a 5.50-g sample of oxalic acid produces 5.38 g CO_2 and 1.10 g H_2O. Determine the empirical and molecular formulas of oxalic acid. The molar mass of oxalic acid is approximately 90 g/mol.

8.79 When 0.273 g of Mg is heated strongly in a nitrogen (N_2) atmosphere, a chemical reaction occurs. The product of the reaction weighs 0.378 g. Calculate the empirical formula of the compound containing Mg and N. Name the compound.

8.80 Octane (C_8H_{18}) is a component of gasoline. Complete combustion of octane yields H_2O and CO_2. Incomplete combustion produces H_2O and CO, which not only reduces the efficiency of the engine using the fuel but is also toxic. In a certain test run, 1.000 gallon (gal) of octane is burned in an engine. The total mass of CO, CO_2, and H_2O produced is 11.53 kg. Calculate the efficiency of the process; that is, calculate the fraction of octane converted to CO_2. The density of octane is 2.650 kg/gal.

8.81 Leaded gasoline contains an additive to prevent engine "knocking." On analysis, the additive compound is found to contain carbon, hydrogen, and lead (Pb) (hence, "leaded gasoline"). When 51.36 g of this compound are burned in an apparatus such as that shown in Figure 8.1, 55.90 g of CO_2 and 28.61 g of H_2O are produced. Determine the empirical formula of the gasoline additive.

8.82 Because of its detrimental effect on the environment, the lead compound described in Problem 8.81 has been replaced in recent years by methyl *tert*-butyl ether (a compound of C, H, and O) to enhance the performance of gasoline. (As of 1999, this compound is also being phased out because of its contamination of drinking water.) When a 12.1-g sample of the compound is burned in an apparatus like the one shown in Figure 8.1, 30.2 g of CO_2 and 14.8 g of H_2O are formed. What is the empirical formula of the compound?

8.83 Industrially, hydrogen gas can be prepared by combining propane gas (C_3H_8) with steam at about 400°C. The products are carbon monoxide (CO) and hydrogen gas (H_2). (a) Write a balanced equation for the reaction. (b) How many kilograms of H_2 can be obtained from 2.84×10^3 kg of propane?

8.84 A reaction having a 90 percent yield may be considered a successful experiment. However, in the synthesis of complex molecules such as chlorophyll and many anticancer drugs, a chemist often has to carry out a multiple-step synthesis. What is the overall percent yield for such a synthesis, assuming it is a 30-step reaction with a 90 percent yield at each step?

8.85 Potash is any potassium mineral that is used for its potassium content. Most of the potash produced in the United States goes into fertilizer. The major sources of potash are potassium chloride (KCl) and potassium sulfate (K_2SO_4). Potash production is often reported as the potassium oxide (K_2O) equivalent or the amount of K_2O that could be made from a given mineral. (a) If KCl costs $0.55 per kg, for what price (dollar per kg) must K_2SO_4 be sold in order to supply the same amount of potassium on a per dollar basis? (b) What mass (in kg) of K_2O contains the same number of moles of K atoms as 1.00 kg of KCl?

8.86 A 21.496-g sample of magnesium is burned in air to form magnesium oxide and magnesium nitride. When the products are treated with water, 2.813 g of gaseous ammonia is generated. Calculate the amounts of magnesium nitride and magnesium oxide formed.

8.87 What is wrong or ambiguous with each of the following statements? (a) NH_4NO_2 is the limiting reactant in the reaction

$$NH_4NO_2(s) \longrightarrow N_2(g) + 2H_2O(l)$$

(b) The limiting reactants for the reaction shown here are NH_3 and NaCl.

$$NH_3(aq) + NaCl(aq) + H_2CO_3(aq)$$
$$\longrightarrow NaHCO_3(aq) + NH_4Cl(aq)$$

8.88 A sample of iron weighing 15.0 g was heated with potassium chlorate ($KClO_3$) in an evacuated container. The oxygen generated from the decomposition of $KClO_3$ converted some of the Fe to Fe_2O_3. If the combined mass of Fe and Fe_2O_3 was 17.9 g, calculate the mass of Fe_2O_3 formed and the mass of $KClO_3$ decomposed.

8.89 What mass of water is produced by the combustion of the oxygen in 30.0 g of air (20.0 percent oxygen by mass) with C_4H_{10}?

8.90 A sample of 10.0 g of sodium reacts with oxygen to form 13.87 g of sodium oxide (Na_2O) and sodium peroxide (Na_2O_2). Calculate the percent composition of the product mixture.

8.91 Write a balanced equation for the reaction shown here.

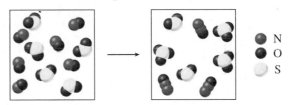

8.92 Write a balanced equation for the reaction shown here.

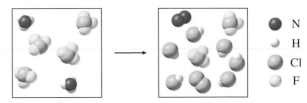

8.93 The compound $NH_4V_3O_8$ can be prepared according to the following sequence of reactions:

$$N_2 + 3H_2 \longrightarrow 2NH_3$$
$$2NH_3 + V_2O_5 + H_2O \longrightarrow 2NH_4VO_3$$
$$3NH_4VO_3 + 2HCl \longrightarrow NH_4V_3O_8 + 2NH_4Cl + H_2O$$

What is the maximum number of moles of $NH_4V_3O_8$ that can be prepared starting from 2.5 moles each of N_2 and H_2. Assume all other reactants are not limiting reagents.

8.94 The interhalogen compound ClF_3 reacts with NH_3 to produce three products according to the figure shown here:

If 30.0 g of NH_3 and 175 g of ClF_3 are allowed to react, what masses of each product would be recovered assuming complete reaction?

8.95 The organic chemical ethylene oxide $H_2C\overset{O}{\overset{\triangle}{-}}CH_2$ is commonly used to sterilize the majority of medical supplies such as bandages, sutures, and surgical implements. It has traditionally been prepared according to the following reaction:

$$H_2C{=}CH_2 + Cl_2 + Ca(OH)_2$$
$$\longrightarrow H_2C\overset{O}{\overset{\triangle}{-}}CH_2 + CaCl_2 + H_2O$$

A more recent synthesis for ethylene oxide is shown here:

$$H_2C{=}CH_2 + \tfrac{1}{2}O_2 \longrightarrow H_2C\overset{O}{\overset{\triangle}{-}}CH_2$$

Compare the atom economies of these two methods for preparing ethylene oxide.

8.96 Heating 2.40 g of the oxide of metal X (molar mass of X = 55.9 g/mol) in carbon monoxide (CO) yields the pure metal and carbon dioxide. The mass of the metal product is 1.68 g. From the data given, show that the simplest formula of the oxide is X_2O_3 and write a balanced equation for the reaction.

8.97 A compound X contains 63.3 percent manganese (Mn) and 36.7 percent O by mass. When X is heated, oxygen gas is evolved and a new compound Y containing 72.0 percent Mn and 28.0 percent O is formed. (a) Determine the empirical formulas of X and Y. (b) Write a balanced equation for the conversion of X to Y.

Answers to In-Chapter Materials

PRACTICE PROBLEMS

8.1A $C_3H_8(g) + 5O_2(g) \longrightarrow 3CO_2(g) + 4H_2O(l)$. **8.1B** $H_2SO_4(aq) +$
$2NaOH(aq) \longrightarrow Na_2SO_4(aq) + 2H_2O(l)$. **8.2A** $C_{18}H_{32}O_2(aq) +$
$25O_2(g) \longrightarrow 18CO_2(g) + 16H_2O(l)$. **8.2B** $2NH_3(g) + 3CuO(s)$
$\longrightarrow 3Cu(s) + N_2(g) + 3H_2O(l)$. **8.3A** (a) combustion, (b) combination,
(c) decomposition. **8.3B** $A_2 + 2B \longrightarrow 2AB$. **8.4A** $C_3H_4O_3$ and $C_6H_8O_6$.
8.4B 28.14 g CO_2, 14.40 H_2O. **8.5A** 0.264 mol H_2 and 0.176 mol NH_3.
8.5B $P_4O_{10} + 6H_2O \longrightarrow 4H_3PO_4$; 1.45 mol P_4O_{10}, 8.70 mol H_2O.
8.6A 34.1 g. **8.6B** 292 g. **8.7A** 42.6 g ammonia; nitrogen is the limiting
reactant, 4.95 g hydrogen left over. **8.7B** 44.2 g KOH, 115.5 g H_3PO_4.
8.8A 29.2%. **8.8B** 122 g.

SECTION REVIEW

8.1.1 $CH_4(g) + 2H_2O(g) \longrightarrow 4H_2(g) + CO_2(g)$.
8.1.2 $3S(s) + 2O_3(g) \longrightarrow 3SO_2(g)$. **8.1.3** $2N_2O_5 \longrightarrow 2N_2 + 5O_2$.
8.1.4 $N_2 + 3H_2 \longrightarrow 2NH_3$. **8.1.5** decomposition. **8.2.1** 24.35 g CO_2,
8.543 g H_2O. **8.2.2** CH_2O. **8.2.3** CH_2, C_6H_{12}. **8.3.1** 0.550 mol.
8.3.2 125 g. **8.3.3** 178.0 kg. **8.3.4** 5.08 g. **8.4.1** 1.0 mol. **8.4.2** 6.94 g.
8.4.3 70.7%. **8.4.4** 29.9 g. **8.4.5** A.

KEY SKILLS

Limiting Reactant

The amount of product that can be produced in a chemical reaction typically is limited by the amount of *one* of the reactants—known as the *limiting* reactant. The practice of identifying the limiting reactant, calculating the maximum possible amount of product, and determining the percent yield and remaining amount of an excess reactant requires several skills:

- Balancing chemical equations [◄◄ Section 8.1]
- Determining molar mass [◄◄ Key Skills Chapter 5]
- Converting mass to moles [◄◄ Section 5.10]
- Using stoichiometric conversion factors [◄◄ Section 8.3]
- Converting moles to mass [◄◄ Section 5.10]

Consider the following example. Hydrazine (N_2H_4) reacts with dinitrogen tetroxide (N_2O_4) to form nitrogen monoxide (NO) and water. Determine the mass of NO that can be produced when 10.45 g of N_2H_4 and 53.68 g of N_2O_4 are combined. The unbalanced equation is

$$N_2H_4 + N_2O_4 \longrightarrow NO + H_2O$$

We first balance the equation.

$$N_2H_4 + 2N_2O_4 \longrightarrow 6\,NO + 2H_2O$$

Next, we determine the necessary molar masses.

$$N_2H_4: 2(14.01) + 4(1.008) = \boxed{\dfrac{32.05\ \text{g}}{\text{mol}}} \qquad N_2O_4: 2(14.01) + 4(16.00) = \boxed{\dfrac{92.02\ \text{g}}{\text{mol}}} \qquad NO: 14.01 + 16.00 = \boxed{\dfrac{30.01\ \text{g}}{\text{mol}}}$$

We convert the reactant masses given in the problem to moles. Then we determine the mole amount of NO that could be produced from the mole amount of each reactant by multiplying each of the *reactant* mole amounts by the appropriate stoichiometric conversion factor, which we derive from the balanced equation. According to the balanced equation:

$$1\ \text{mol}\ N_2H_4 \simeq 6\ \text{mol}\ NO \qquad \text{and} \qquad 2\ \text{mol}\ N_2O_4 \simeq 6\ \text{mol}\ NO$$

$$\dfrac{10.45\ \text{g}\ N_2H_4}{32.05\ \text{g/mol}} = \Rightarrow 0.32605\ \text{mol}\ N_2H_4 \qquad 0.32605\ \text{mol}\ N_2H_4 \times \dfrac{6\ \text{mol}\ NO}{1\ \text{mol}\ N_2H_4} = \Rightarrow 1.9563\ \text{mol}\ NO$$

$$\dfrac{53.68\ \text{g}\ N_2O_4}{92.02\ \text{g/mol}} = \Rightarrow 0.58335\ \text{mol}\ N_2O_4 \qquad 0.58335\ \text{mol}\ N_2O_4 \times \dfrac{6\ \text{mol}\ NO}{2\ \text{mol}\ N_2O_4} = \Rightarrow 1.7501\ \text{mol}\ NO$$

The reactant that produces the smaller amount of product is the limiting reactant; in this case, N_2O_4.

We continue the problem using the mole amount of NO produced by reaction of the given amount of N_2O_4. To convert from moles to mass (grams), we multiply the number of moles NO by the molar mass of NO:

Thus, 52.52 g NO can be produced by the reaction. Note that we retained an extra significant figure until the end of the calculation.

To determine the mass of remaining excess reactant, we must first determine what amount was consumed in the reaction. To do this, we multiply the mole amount of limiting reactant (N_2O_4) by the appropriate stoichiometric conversion factor. According to the balanced equation:

$$1 \text{ mol } N_2H_4 \simeq 2 \text{ mol } N_2O_4$$

This is the amount of N_2H_4 consumed. The amount remaining is the difference between this and the original amount. We convert the remaining mole amount to grams using the molar mass of N_2H_4.

Thus, 1.102 g N_2H_4 remain when the reaction is complete.

We can check our work in a problem such as this by also calculating the mass of the other product, in this case water. The mass of all products plus the mass of any remaining reactant must equal the sum of starting reactant masses.

Key Skills Problems

8.1
Calculate the mass of water produced in the example above.

(a) 21.02 g (b) 10.51 g (c) 11.61 g (d) 11.75 g (e) 5.400 g

Use the following information to answer questions 8.2, 8.3, and 8.4.

Calcium phosphide (Ca_3P_2) and water react to form calcium hydroxide and phosphine (PH_3). In a particular experiment, 225.0 g Ca_3P_2 and 125.0 g water are combined.

$$Ca_3P_2(s) + H_2O(l) \longrightarrow Ca(OH)_2(aq) + PH_3(g)$$

(Don't forget to balance the equation.)

8.2
How much PH_3 can be produced?

(a) 350.0 g (b) 235.0 g (c) 78.59 g (d) 83.96 g (e) 41.98 g

8.3
How much $Ca(OH)_2$ can be produced?

(a) 91.51 g (b) 274.5 g (c) 513.8 g (d) 85.63 g (e) 257.0 g

8.4
How much of the excess reactant remains when the reaction is complete?

(a) 14.37 g (b) 235.0 g (c) 78.56 g (d) 83.96 g (e) 41.98 g

CHAPTER 9

Chemical Reactions in Aqueous Solutions

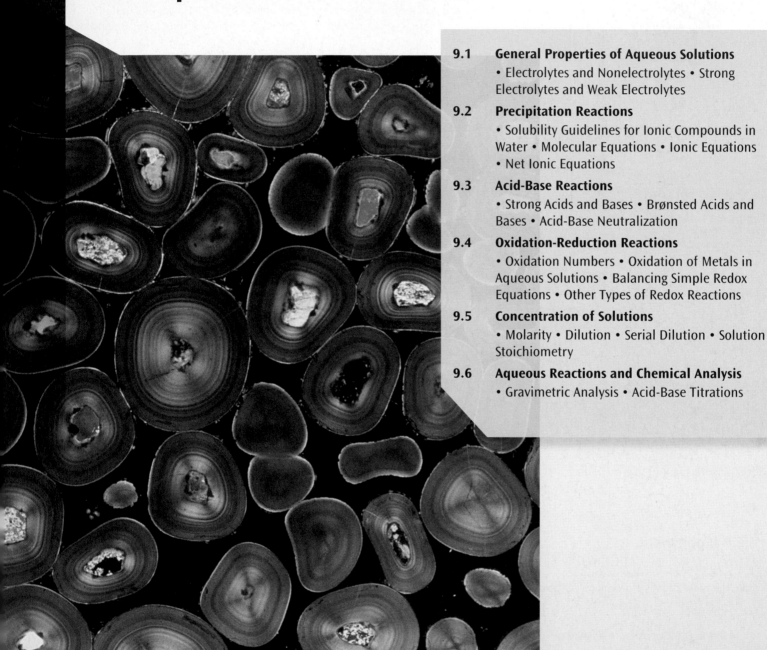

9.1 **General Properties of Aqueous Solutions**
• Electrolytes and Nonelectrolytes • Strong Electrolytes and Weak Electrolytes

9.2 **Precipitation Reactions**
• Solubility Guidelines for Ionic Compounds in Water • Molecular Equations • Ionic Equations • Net Ionic Equations

9.3 **Acid-Base Reactions**
• Strong Acids and Bases • Brønsted Acids and Bases • Acid-Base Neutralization

9.4 **Oxidation-Reduction Reactions**
• Oxidation Numbers • Oxidation of Metals in Aqueous Solutions • Balancing Simple Redox Equations • Other Types of Redox Reactions

9.5 **Concentration of Solutions**
• Molarity • Dilution • Serial Dilution • Solution Stoichiometry

9.6 **Aqueous Reactions and Chemical Analysis**
• Gravimetric Analysis • Acid-Base Titrations

"Hard water" is the result of dissolved metal ions such as Ca^{2+} and Mg^{2+}. The presence of these dissolved ions can prevent soap from lathering properly; and can result in the formation of hard-water deposits, such as bathtub rings. Dissolved ions also contribute to the corrosion of metals that are exposed to the water. To combat these problems, chemists have devised "water-softening" methods to selectively replace or remove aqueous ions from solution. Typically this is achieved by passing hard water over water pellets (shown here) where insoluble salts such as calcium carbonate ($CaCO_3$) form around the pellets— thereby removing calcium ions from the water. These methods are also useful in the removal of other more harmful metal ions such as lead and arsenic.

Before You Begin, Review These Skills

- Identifying compounds as either molecular or ionic
  [◄◄ Sections 5.3 and 5.5]
- Names, formulas, and charges of the common polyatomic ions
  [◄◄ Table 5.9]
- Stoichiometric calculations [◄◄ Section 8.3]

9.1 GENERAL PROPERTIES OF AQUEOUS SOLUTIONS

A *solution* is a homogeneous mixture [◄◄ Section 1.2] of two or more substances. Solutions may be gaseous (such as air), solid (such as brass), or liquid (such as saltwater). Usually, the substance present in the largest amount is referred to as the *solvent* and any substance present in a smaller amount is called a *solute.* For example, if we dissolve a teaspoon of sugar in a glass of water, water is the solvent and sugar is the solute. In this chapter, we will focus on the properties of aqueous solutions—those in which water is the solvent. Throughout the remainder of this chapter, unless otherwise noted, *solution* will refer specifically to an *aqueous* solution.

Multi 9.1
Solutions—strong, weak, and nonelectrolytes

Electrolytes and Nonelectrolytes

You have probably heard of electrolytes in the context of sports drinks such as Gatorade. Electrolytes in body fluids are necessary for the transmission of electrical impulses, which are critical to physiological processes such as nerve impulses and muscle contractions. In general, an *electrolyte* is a substance that dissolves in water to yield a solution that conducts electricity. By contrast, a *nonelectrolyte* is a substance that dissolves in water to yield a solution that does *not* conduct electricity. Every water-soluble substance fits into one of these two categories.

Student Annotation: A substance that *dissolves* in a particular solvent is said to be "soluble" in that solvent. In this chapter, we will use the word *soluble* to mean "water-soluble."

The difference between an aqueous solution that conducts electricity and one that does not is the presence or absence of *ions*. As an illustration, consider solutions of sugar and salt. The physical processes of sugar (sucrose, $C_{12}H_{22}O_{11}$) dissolving in water and salt (sodium chloride, NaCl) dissolving in water can be represented with the following chemical equations:

$$C_{12}H_{22}O_{11}(s) \xrightarrow{H_2O} C_{12}H_{22}O_{11}(aq) \quad \text{and} \quad NaCl(s) \xrightarrow{H_2O} Na^+(aq) + Cl^-(aq)$$

Note that while the sucrose molecules remain intact upon dissolving, becoming aqueous sucrose molecules, the sodium chloride dissociates, producing aqueous sodium ions and aqueous chloride ions. *Dissociation* is the process by which an ionic compound, upon dissolution, breaks apart into its constituent ions. It is the presence of ions that allows the solution of sodium chloride to conduct electricity. Thus, sodium chloride is an *electrolyte* and sucrose is a *nonelectrolyte*.

Like sucrose, which is a molecular compound [◄◄ Section 5.5], many water-soluble molecular compounds are nonelectrolytes. Some molecular compounds are electrolytes, however, because they ionize on dissolution. *Ionization* is the process by which a molecular compound forms ions when it dissolves. Recall from Chapter 5 that acids are compounds that dissolve in water to produce hydrogen ions (H⁺) [◄◄ Section 5.6]. HCl, for example, ionizes to produce H⁺ ions and Cl⁻ ions.

$$HCl(g) \xrightarrow{H_2O} H^+(aq) + Cl^-(aq)$$

Acids constitute one of two important classes of molecular compounds that are electrolytes. Molecular bases constitute the other one. A *base* is a compound that dissolves in water to produce hydroxide ions (OH⁻). Ammonia (NH_3), for example, ionizes in water to produce ammonium (NH_4^+) and hydroxide (OH⁻) ions.

Student Annotation: Bases may be *molecular*, like ammonia (NH_3), or *ionic*, like sodium hydroxide (NaOH).

$$NH_3(g) + H_2O(l) \rightleftharpoons NH_4^+(aq) + OH^-(aq)$$

Strong Electrolytes and Weak Electrolytes

In a solution of sodium chloride, all of the dissolved compound exists in the form of ions. Thus, NaCl, which is an ionic compound [◄◄ Section 5.3], is said to have *dissociated completely*. An electrolyte that dissociates completely is known as a ***strong electrolyte.*** All water-soluble ionic compounds dissociate completely upon dissolving, so all water-soluble ionic compounds are strong electrolytes.

The list of molecular compounds that are strong electrolytes is fairly short. It comprises the seven strong acids, which are listed in Table 9.1. A strong acid ionizes completely, resulting in a solution that contains hydrogen ions and the corresponding anions but essentially no acid molecules.

Most of the molecular compounds that are electrolytes are weak electrolytes. A ***weak electrolyte*** is a compound that produces ions upon dissolving but exists in solution *predominantly* as molecules that are *not* ionized. Most acids (except those listed in Table 9.1) are weak electrolytes. Acetic acid ($HC_2H_3O_2$) is not one of the strong acids listed in Table 9.1, so it is a weak acid. Its ionization in water is represented by the following chemical equation:

$$HC_2H_3O_2(l) \rightleftharpoons H^+(aq) + C_2H_3O_2^-(aq)$$

Note the use of the double arrow, $\rightleftharpoons$, in this equation and in two earlier equations, including one in Table 9.1. This denotes a reaction that occurs in both directions and does not result in *all* the reactant(s) (e.g., acetic acid) being converted permanently to product(s) (e.g., hydrogen ions and acetate ions). Instead, forward and reverse reactions both occur, and a state of *dynamic chemical equilibrium* is established.

Although acetic acid molecules ionize, the resulting ions have a strong tendency to recombine to form acetic acid molecules again. Eventually, the ions produced by the ionization will be recombining at the same rate at which they are produced, and there will be no further change in the numbers of acetic acid molecules, hydrogen ions, or acetate ions. Because there is a stronger tendency for the ions to recombine than for the molecules to *ionize,* at any given point in time, most of the dissolved acetic acid exists as molecules that are not ionized (reactant). Only a very small percentage exists in the form of hydrogen ions and acetate ions (products).

The ionization of a weak base, while similar in many ways to the ionization of a weak acid, requires some additional explanation. Ammonia (NH_3) is a common weak base. The ionization of ammonia in water is represented by the equation

$$NH_3(g) + H_2O(l) \rightleftharpoons NH_4^+(aq) + OH^-(aq)$$

Note that the ammonia molecule does not ionize by breaking apart into ions. Rather, it does so by ionizing a *water* molecule. The H^+ ion from a water molecule attaches to an ammonia molecule, producing an ammonium ion (NH_4^+) and leaving what remains of the water molecule, the OH^- ion, in solution.

Student Annotation: In a state of *dynamic chemical equilibrium,* or simply *equilibrium,* both forward and reverse reactions continue to occur. However, because they are occurring at the same *rate,* no net change is observed over time in the amounts of reactants or products. Chemical equilibrium is the subject of Chapters 15 to 17.

TABLE 9.1	The Strong Acids
Acid	**Ionization equation**
Hydrochloric acid	$HCl(aq) \longrightarrow H^+(aq) + Cl^-(aq)$
Hydrobromic acid	$HBr(aq) \longrightarrow H^+(aq) + Br^-(aq)$
Hydroiodic acid	$HI(aq) \longrightarrow H^+(aq) + I^-(aq)$
Nitric acid	$HNO_3(aq) \longrightarrow H^+(aq) + NO_3^-(aq)$
Chloric acid	$HClO_3(aq) \longrightarrow H^+(aq) + ClO_3^-(aq)$
Perchloric acid	$HClO_4(aq) \longrightarrow H^+(aq) + ClO_4^-(aq)$
Sulfuric acid*	$H_2SO_4(aq) \longrightarrow H^+(aq) + HSO_4^-(aq)$
	$HSO_4^-(aq) \rightleftharpoons H^+(aq) + SO_4^{2-}(aq)$

*Note that although each sulfuric acid molecule has two ionizable hydrogen atoms, it only undergoes the first ionization completely, effectively producing one H^+ ion and one HSO_4^- ion per H_2SO_4 molecule. The second ionization happens only to a very small extent.

$$NH_3(g) \quad + \quad H_2O(l) \quad \rightleftharpoons \quad NH_4^+(aq) \quad + \quad OH^-(aq)$$

As with the ionization of a weak acid, the reverse process predominates and at any given point in time, there will be far more NH_3 molecules present than there will be NH_4^+ and OH^- ions.

We can distinguish between electrolytes and nonelectrolytes experimentally using an apparatus like the one pictured in Figure 9.1. A lightbulb is connected to a battery using a circuit that includes the contents of the beaker. For the bulb to light, electric current must flow from one electrode to the other. Pure water is a very poor conductor of electricity because H_2O ionizes to only an extremely small extent. There are virtually no ions in pure water to conduct the current, so H_2O is considered a nonelectrolyte. If we add a small amount of salt (sodium chloride), however, the lightbulb will begin to glow as soon as the salt dissolves in the water. Sodium chloride dissociates completely in water to give Na^+ and Cl^- ions. Because the NaCl solution conducts electricity, we say that NaCl is an electrolyte.

If the solution contains a nonelectrolyte, as it does in Figure 9.1(a), the bulb will not light. If the solution contains an electrolyte, as it does in Figure 9.1(b) and (c), the bulb will light. The cations in solution are attracted to the negative electrode, and the anions are attracted to the positive electrode. This movement sets up an electric current that is equivalent to the flow of electrons along a metal wire. How brightly the bulb burns depends upon the number of ions in solution. In

Figure 9.1 An apparatus for distinguishing between electrolytes and nonelectrolytes and between weak electrolytes and strong electrolytes. A solution's ability to conduct electricity depends on the number of ions it contains. (a) Pure water contains almost no ions and does not conduct electricity; therefore the lightbulb is not lit. (b) A weak electrolyte solution such as HF(*aq*) contains a small number of ions, and the lightbulb is dimly lit. (c) A strong electrolyte solution such as NaCl(*aq*) contains a large number of ions, and the lightbulb is brightly lit. The molar amounts of dissolved substances in the beakers in (b) and (c) are equal.

Figure 9.1(b), the solution contains a *weak* electrolyte and therefore a relatively small number of ions, so the bulb lights only weakly. The solution in Figure 9.1(c) contains a *strong* electrolyte, which produces a relatively large number of ions, so the bulb lights brightly.

Although the experimental method illustrated in Figure 9.1 can be useful, often you will have to characterize a compound as a nonelectrolyte, a weak electrolyte, or a strong electrolyte just by looking at its formula. A good first step is to determine whether the compound is *ionic* or *molecular*.

An ionic compound contains a *cation* (which is either a metal ion or the ammonium ion) and an *anion* (which may be atomic or polyatomic). A binary compound that contains a metal and a nonmetal is almost always ionic. This is a good time to review the polyatomic anions in Table 5.10 [◄◄ Section 5.7]. You will need to be able to recognize them in the formulas of compounds. Any ionic compound that dissolves in water is a strong electrolyte.

If a compound does not contain a metal cation or the ammonium cation, it is molecular. In this case, you will need to determine whether or not the compound is an acid. Acids generally can be recognized by the way their formulas are written, with the ionizable hydrogens written first. $HC_2H_3O_2$, H_2CO_3, and H_3PO_4 are acetic acid, carbonic acid, and phosphoric acid, respectively. Formulas of carboxylic acids, such as acetic acid, often are written with their ionizable hydrogen atoms *last* in order to keep the atoms of the functional group together in the formula. Thus, either $HC_2H_3O_2$ or CH_3COOH is correct for acetic acid. To make it easier to identify compounds as acids, in this chapter we will write all acid formulas with the ionizable H atom(s) first. If a compound is an acid, it is an electrolyte. If it is one of the acids listed in Table 9.1, it is a *strong* acid and therefore a *strong* electrolyte. Any acid not listed in Table 9.1 is a *weak* acid and therefore a *weak* electrolyte.

If a molecular compound is not an acid, you must then consider whether or not it is a weak base. Many weak bases are related to ammonia in that they consist of a nitrogen atom bonded to hydrogen and/or carbon atoms. Examples include methylamine (CH_3NH_2), pyridine (C_5H_5N), and hydroxylamine (NH_2OH). *Weak* bases are *weak* electrolytes.

If a molecular compound is neither an acid nor a weak base, it is a nonelectrolyte. The flowchart in Figure 9.2 can be useful for classification of water-soluble compounds.

Student Annotation: For "insoluble" ionic compounds, which are actually very *slightly* soluble, the small amount that dissolves does dissociate completely—making them strong electrolytes.

Figure 9.2 Flowchart for determining if a compound is a strong electrolyte, a weak electrolyte, or a nonelectrolyte.

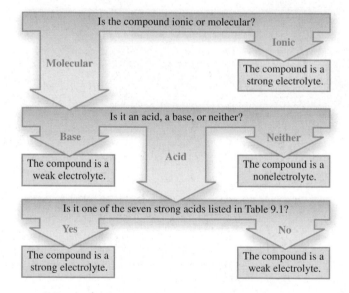

Worked Example 9.1 shows how to classify compounds as nonelectrolytes, weak electrolytes, and strong electrolytes.

Worked Example 9.1

Sports drinks typically contain sucrose ($C_{12}H_{22}O_{11}$), fructose ($C_6H_{12}O_6$), sodium citrate ($Na_3C_6H_5O_7$), potassium citrate ($K_3C_6H_5O_7$), and ascorbic acid ($H_2C_6H_6O_6$), among other ingredients. Classify each of these ingredients as a nonelectrolyte, a weak electrolyte, or a strong electrolyte.

Strategy Identify each compound as ionic or molecular; identify each molecular compound as acid, base, or neither; and identify each acid as strong or weak.

Setup Sucrose and fructose contain no cations and are therefore molecular compounds—neither is an acid or a base. Sodium citrate and potassium citrate contain metal cations and are therefore ionic compounds. Ascorbic acid is an acid that does not appear on the list of strong acids in Table 9.1, so ascorbic acid is a weak acid.

Solution Sucrose and fructose are nonelectrolytes. Sodium citrate and potassium citrate are strong electrolytes. Ascorbic acid is a weak electrolyte.

Think About It
Remember that any soluble ionic compound is a strong electrolyte, whereas most molecular compounds are nonelectrolytes or weak electrolytes. The only molecular compounds that are strong electrolytes are the strong acids listed in Table 9.1.

Practice Problem A A so-called "enhanced water" contains citric acid ($H_3C_6H_5O_7$), magnesium lactate [$Mg(C_3H_5O_3)_2$], calcium lactate [$Ca(C_3H_5O_3)_2$], and potassium phosphate (K_3PO_4). Classify each of these compounds as a nonelectrolyte, a weak electrolyte, or a strong electrolyte.

Practice Problem B For each of the following solutions, classify the solute as a nonelectrolyte, a weak electrolyte, or a strong electrolyte.

SECTION 9.1 REVIEW

General Properties of Aqueous Solutions

9.1.1 Classify each of the following compounds as a nonelectrolyte, a weak electrolyte, or a strong electrolyte: (a) LiCl, (b) $(C_2H_5)_2NH$, (c) KNO_3, (d) NaI, (e) HNO_2.

9.1.2 For each of the following substances, determine if an aqueous solution of the substance, used to complete the circuit in the apparatus shown in Figure 9.1, would result in the lightbulb lighting brightly, lighting dimly, or not lighting at all: (a) HF, (b) H_2CO_3, (c) NaF, (d) NH_3, (e) H_2O_2.

9.1.3 Each of the following figures represents an aqueous solution. For each solute, write the molecular formula and classify it as a nonelectrolyte, a weak electrolyte, or a strong electrolyte.

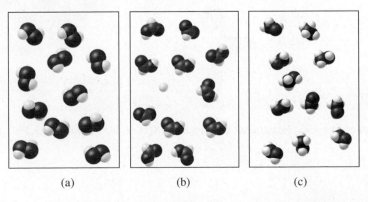

(a)　　　　(b)　　　　(c)

9.2   PRECIPITATION REACTIONS

When an aqueous solution of lead(II) nitrate [$Pb(NO_3)_2$] is added to an aqueous solution of sodium iodide (NaI), a yellow insoluble solid—lead(II) iodide (PbI_2)—forms. Sodium nitrate ($NaNO_3$), the other reaction product, remains in solution. Figure 9.3 shows this reaction in progress. An insoluble solid product that separates from a solution is called a *precipitate,* and a chemical reaction in which a precipitate forms is called a *precipitation reaction.*

Precipitation reactions usually involve ionic compounds, but only certain combinations of electrolyte solutions result in the formation of a precipitate. Whether or not a precipitate forms when two solutions are mixed depends on the solubility of the products.

Multi 9.2
Precipitation of $BaSO_4$

Solubility Guidelines for Ionic Compounds in Water

When an ionic substance such as sodium chloride dissolves in water, the water molecules remove individual ions from the three-dimensional solid structure and surround them. This process, called *hydration,* is shown in Figure 9.4. Water is an excellent solvent for ionic compounds because H_2O is a *polar* molecule [◀◀ Section 6.2]. There is a partial negative charge on the oxygen atom, denoted by the $\delta-$ symbol, and partial positive charges, denoted by the $\delta+$ symbol, on each of the hydrogen atoms. The oxygen atoms in the surrounding water molecules are attracted to the cations, while the hydrogen atoms are attracted to the anions. These attractions explain the orientation of water molecules around each of the ions in solution. The surrounding water molecules prevent the cations and anions from recombining.

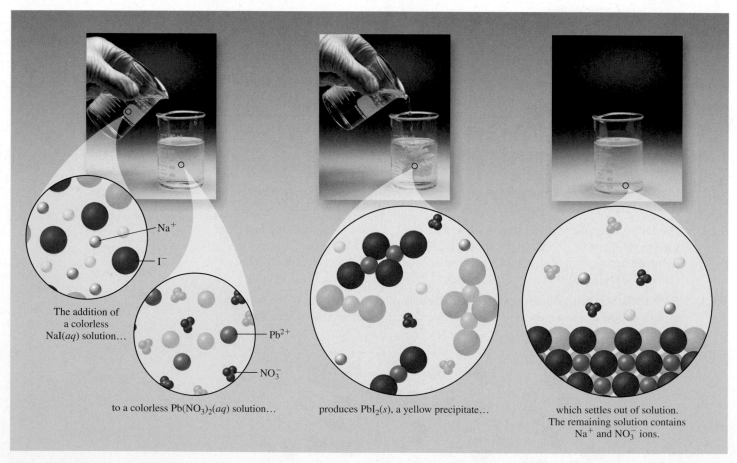

The addition of a colorless NaI(*aq*) solution...   to a colorless $Pb(NO_3)_2(aq)$ solution...   produces $PbI_2(s)$, a yellow precipitate...   which settles out of solution. The remaining solution contains Na^+ and NO_3^- ions.

Figure 9.3 A colorless aqueous solution of NaI is added to a colorless aqueous solution of $Pb(NO_3)_2$. A yellow precipitate, PbI_2, forms. Na^+ and NO_3^- ions remain in solution.

Figure 9.4 Hydration of anions and cations of a soluble ionic compound. Water molecules surround each anion with their partial positive charges (H atoms) oriented toward the negatively charged anion; and they surround each cation with their partial negative charges (O atoms) oriented toward the positively charged cation.

Multi 9.3
Chemical reactions—predicting precipitation reactions (interactive)

Solubility is defined as the maximum amount of solute that will dissolve in a given quantity of solvent at a specific temperature. Not all ionic compounds dissolve in water. Whether or not an ionic compound is water soluble depends on the relative magnitudes of the water molecules' attraction to the ions, and the ions' attraction for each other. We learned about the magnitudes of attractive forces in ionic compounds in Chapter 5; now it is useful to learn some guidelines that enable us to predict the solubility of ionic compounds. Table 9.2 lists groups of compounds that are *soluble* and shows the *insoluble* exceptions. Table 9.3 lists groups of compounds that are *insoluble* and shows the *soluble* exceptions.

Student Annotation: Essentially, if the water molecules' attraction for the ions exceeds the ions' attraction to one another, then the ionic compound will dissolve. If the ions' attraction to each other exceeds the water molecules' attraction to the ions, then the compound won't dissolve.

TABLE 9.2	Solubility Guidelines: Soluble Compounds	
Water-soluble compounds	**Insoluble exceptions**
Compounds containing an alkali metal cation (Li^+, Na^+, K^+, Rb^+, Cs^+) or the ammonium ion (NH_4^+)	
Compounds containing the nitrate ion (NO_3^-), acetate ion ($C_2H_3O_2^-$), or chlorate ion (ClO_3^-)	
Compounds containing the chloride ion (Cl^-), bromide ion (Br^-), or iodide ion (I^-)	Compounds containing Ag^+, Hg_2^{2+}, or Pb^{2+}
Compounds containing the sulfate ion (SO_4^{2-})	Compounds containing Ag^+, Hg_2^{2+}, Pb^{2+}, Ca^{2+}, Sr^{2+}, or Ba^{2+}

Student Annotation: Some books list fewer exceptions to these solubility rules. In fact, ionic compounds listed here as "insoluble" are actually *very slightly* soluble. It is *how* soluble a compound must be to be called "soluble" that may vary from book to book.

Student Annotation: Ionic compounds often are classified according to the anions they contain. Compounds that contain the chloride ion are called *chlorides*, compounds containing the nitrate ion are called *nitrates*, and so on.

TABLE 9.3	Solubility Guidelines: Insoluble Compounds	
Water-insoluble compounds	**Soluble exceptions**
Compounds containing the carbonate ion (CO_3^{2-}), phosphate ion (PO_4^{3-}), chromate ion (CrO_4^{2-}), or sulfide ion (S^{2-})	Compounds containing Li^+, Na^+, K^+, Rb^+, Cs^+, or NH_4^+
Compounds containing the hydroxide ion (OH^-)	Compounds containing Li^+, Na^+, K^+, Rb^+, Cs^+, or Ba^{2+}

Student Annotation: Note the reoccurrence of the same three groups of ions in the exceptions columns in Tables 9.2 and 9.3: Group 1A or the ammonium cation; Ag^+, Hg_2^{2+}, or Pb^{2+}; and the heavier Group 2A cations.

Worked Example 9.2 gives you some practice applying the solubility guidelines.

Worked Example 9.2

Classify each of the following compounds as soluble or insoluble in water: (a) $AgNO_3$, (b) $CaSO_4$, (c) K_2CO_3.

Strategy Use the guidelines in Tables 9.2 and 9.3 to determine whether or not each compound is expected to be water soluble.

Setup

(a) $AgNO_3$ contains the nitrate ion (NO_3^-). According to Table 9.2, *all* compounds containing the nitrate ion are soluble.

(b) $CaSO_4$ contains the sulfate ion (SO_4^{2-}). According to Table 9.2, compounds containing the sulfate ion are soluble unless the cation is Ag^+, Hg_2^{2+}, Pb^{2+}, Ca^{2+}, Sr^{2+}, or Ba^{2+}. Thus, the Ca^{2+} ion is one of the insoluble exceptions.

(c) K_2CO_3 contains an alkali metal cation (K^+) for which, according to Table 9.2, there are no insoluble exceptions. Alternatively, Table 9.3 shows that most compounds containing the carbonate ion (CO_3^{2-}) are insoluble—but compounds containing a Group 1A cation such as K^+ are soluble exceptions.

Solution (a) Soluble, (b) Insoluble, (c) Soluble.

> **Think About It**
> Check the ions in each compound against the information in Tables 9.2 and 9.3 to confirm that you have drawn the right conclusions.

Practice Problem A Classify each of the following compounds as soluble or insoluble in water: (a) $PbCl_2$, (b) $(NH_4)_3PO_4$, (c) $Fe(OH)_3$.

Practice Problem B Classify each of the following compounds as soluble or insoluble in water: (a) $MgBr_2$, (b) $Ca_3(PO_4)_2$, (c) $KClO_3$.

Molecular Equations

The reaction shown in Figure 9.3 can be represented with the chemical equation

$$Pb(NO_3)_2(aq) + 2NaI(aq) \longrightarrow 2NaNO_3(aq) + PbI_2(s)$$

Based on this chemical equation, the metal cations seem to exchange anions. That is, the Pb^{2+} ion, originally paired with NO_3^- ions, ends up paired with I^- ions; similarly, each Na^+ ion, originally paired with an I^- ion, ends up paired with an NO_3^- ion. This equation, as written, is called a *molecular equation,* which is a chemical equation written with all compounds represented by their chemical formulas, making it look as though they exist in solution as molecules or formula units.

You now know enough chemistry to predict the products of this type of chemical reaction! Simply write the formulas for the reactants, and then write formulas for the compounds that would form if the cations in the reactants were to trade anions. For example, if you want to write the equation for the reaction that occurs when solutions of sodium sulfate and barium hydroxide are combined, you would first write the formulas of the reactants [◄◄ Chapter 5]:

$$Na_2SO_4(aq) + Ba(OH)_2(aq) \longrightarrow$$

Student Annotation: It is important to know the formulas and charges of the common polyatomic ions [◄◄ Section 5.7, Table 5.10]. If you are unable to identify the ions that make up an ionic compound, you won't be able to deduce the products of these reactions.

Then you would write the formula for one product by combining the cation from the first reactant (Na^+), with the anion from the second reactant (OH^-); and write the formula for the other product by combining the cation from the second reactant (Ba^{2+}) with the anion from the first (SO_4^{2-}). Thus, the equation is

$$Na_2SO_4(aq) + Ba(OH)_2(aq) \longrightarrow 2NaOH + BaSO_4$$

Although we have balanced the equation [◄◄ Section 8.1], we have not yet put phases in parentheses for the products.

The final step in predicting the outcome of such a reaction is to determine which of the products, if any, will precipitate from solution. We do this using the solubility guidelines for ionic compounds (Tables 9.2 and 9.3). The first product (NaOH) contains a Group 1A cation (Na^+) and will therefore be soluble. We indicate its phase as (aq). The second product ($BaSO_4$) contains the sulfate ion (SO_4^{2-}). Sulfate compounds are soluble unless the cation is Ag^+, Hg_2^{2+}, Pb^{2+}, Ca^{2+}, Sr^{2+}, or Ba^{2+}. $BaSO_4$ is therefore insoluble and will precipitate. We indicate its phase as (s):

$$Na_2SO_4(aq) + Ba(OH)_2(aq) \longrightarrow 2NaOH(aq) + BaSO_4(s)$$

Reactions in which compounds exchange ions are sometimes called *metathesis* or *double replacement* reactions.

Ionic Equations

Although molecular equations are useful, especially from the standpoint of knowing which solutions to combine in the laboratory, they are in a sense unrealistic. As we saw in Section 9.1, soluble ionic compounds are *strong electrolytes*. As such, they exist in solution as hydrated *ions*, rather than as formula units. Thus, it would be more realistic to represent the aqueous species in the reaction of $Na_2SO_4(aq)$ with $Ba(OH)_2(aq)$ as follows:

$$Na_2SO_4(aq) \longrightarrow 2Na^+(aq) + SO_4^{2-}(aq)$$

$$Ba(OH)_2(aq) \longrightarrow Ba^{2+}(aq) + 2OH^-(aq)$$

$$NaOH(aq) \longrightarrow Na^+(aq) + OH^-(aq)$$

If we were to rewrite the equation, representing the dissolved compounds as hydrated ions, it would be

$$2Na^+(aq) + SO_4^{2-}(aq) + Ba^+(aq) + 2OH^-(aq) \longrightarrow 2Na^+(aq) + 2OH^-(aq) + BaSO_4(s)$$

This version of the equation is called an *ionic equation*, a chemical equation in which any compound that exists completely or predominantly as *ions* in solution is represented as those ions. Species that are *insoluble* or that exist in solution completely or predominantly as *molecules* are represented with their chemical formulas, as they were in the molecular equation.

Net Ionic Equations

$Na^+(aq)$ and $OH^-(aq)$ both appear as reactants and products in the ionic equation for the reaction of $Na_2SO_4(aq)$ with $Ba(OH)_2(aq)$. Ions that appear on both sides of the equation arrow are called *spectator ions* because they do not participate in the reaction. Spectator ions cancel one another, just as identical terms on both sides of an algebraic equation cancel one another, so we need not show spectator ions in chemical equations.

Eliminating the spectator ions yields the following equation:

$$Ba^{2+}(aq) + SO_4^{2-}(aq) \longrightarrow BaSO_4(s)$$

This version of the equation is called a *net ionic equation*, which is a chemical equation that includes only the species that are actually involved in the reaction. The net ionic equation, in effect, tells us what actually happens when we combine solutions of sodium sulfate and barium hydroxide.

The steps necessary to determine the molecular, ionic, and net ionic equations for a precipitation reaction are as follows:

1. Write and balance the molecular equation, predicting the products by assuming that the cations trade anions.
2. Write the ionic equation by separating strong electrolytes into their constituent ions.
3. Write the net ionic equation by identifying and canceling spectator ions on both sides of the equation.

Student Annotation: Although the reactants may be written in either order in the net ionic equation, it is common for the cation to be shown first and the anion second.

If both products of a reaction are strong electrolytes, all the ions in solution are spectator ions. In this case, there is no net ionic equation and no reaction takes place.

Worked Example 9.3 illustrates the stepwise determination of molecular, ionic, and net ionic equations.

Worked Example 9.3

Write the molecular, ionic, and net ionic equations for the reaction that occurs when aqueous solutions of lead acetate [$Pb(C_2H_3O_2)_2$], and calcium chloride ($CaCl_2$), are combined.

Strategy Predict the products by exchanging ions and balance the equation. Determine which product will precipitate based on the solubility guidelines in Tables 9.2 and 9.3. Rewrite the equation showing strong electrolytes as ions. Identify and cancel spectator ions.

Solution

Molecular equation:

$$Pb(C_2H_3O_2)_2(aq) + CaCl_2(aq) \longrightarrow PbCl_2(s) + Ca(C_2H_3O_2)_2(aq)$$

Ionic equation:

$$Pb^{2+}(aq) + 2C_2H_3O_2^-(aq) + Ca^+(aq) + 2Cl^-(aq) \longrightarrow PbCl_2(s) + Ca^{2+}(aq) + 2C_2H_3O_2^-(aq)$$

Net ionic equation:

$$Pb^{2+}(aq) + 2Cl^-(aq) \longrightarrow PbCl_2(s)$$

> **Think About It**
> Remember that the charges on ions in a compound must sum to zero. Make sure that you have written correct formulas for the products and that each of the equations you have written is balanced. If you find that you are having trouble balancing an equation, check to make sure you have correct formulas for the products.

Practice Problem A Write the molecular, ionic, and net ionic equations for the combination of $Sr(NO_3)_2(aq)$ and $Li_2SO_4(aq)$.

Practice Problem B Determine the reactants and write the balanced molecular, ionic, and net ionic equations for the combination that results in the formation of $NH_4NO_3(aq)$ and $BaCO_3(s)$.

SECTION 9.2 REVIEW

Precipitation Reactions

9.2.1   Classify each of the following as soluble or insoluble in water: (a) $Ba(C_2H_3O_2)_2$, (b) Na_2S, (c) $CaCO_3$, (d) $CuBr_2$, (e) Hg_2Cl_2.

9.2.2   Classify each of the following as soluble or insoluble in water: (a) Ag_2CrO_4, (b) Li_2CO_3, (c) $Ca_3(PO_4)_2$, (d) $BaSO_4$, (e) $ZnCl_2$.

9.2.3   What are the spectator ions in the ionic equation for the combination of $Li_2CO_3(aq)$ and $Ba(OH)_2(aq)$?

9.2.4   Write the balanced net ionic equation for the combination of $Fe(NO_3)_2(aq)$ and $Na_2CO_3(aq)$.

9.2.5   Write the balanced net ionic equation for the combination represented below. (Note that the reaction represented below is not balanced.)

A = ●   B = ●   C = ○   D = ●

9.3   ACID-BASE REACTIONS

Another type of reaction occurs when two solutions, one containing an acid and one containing a base, are combined. We frequently encounter acids and bases in everyday life (Figure 9.5). Ascorbic acid, for instance, is also known as vitamin C, acetic acid is the component responsible for the sour taste and characteristic smell of vinegar, and hydrochloric acid is the acid in muriatic acid and is also the principal ingredient in gastric juice (stomach acid). Ammonia, found in many cleaning products, and sodium hydroxide, found in drain cleaner, are common bases. Acid-base chemistry is extremely important to biological processes. Let's look again at the properties of acids and bases, and then look at acid-base reactions.

Strong Acids and Bases

As we saw in Section 9.1, the seven strong acids ionize completely in solution. (See Table 9.1 on page 308.) All other acids are weak acids. The strong bases are the hydroxides of Group 1A and heavy Group 2A metals. These are soluble ionic compounds, which dissociate completely and exist entirely as ions in solution. Thus, both strong acids and strong bases are strong electrolytes. Table 9.4 lists the strong acids and strong bases. It is important that you know these compounds.

Multi 9.4
Acids and bases—dissociation of strong and weak acids

Brønsted Acids and Bases

In Section 5.6 we defined an acid as a substance that ionizes in water to produce H^+ ions, and a base as a substance that ionizes (or dissociates, in the case of an ionic base) in water to produce OH^- ions. These definitions are attributed to the Swedish chemist Svante Arrhenius.[1] Although the

Figure 9.5 Some common acids and bases. From left to right: Sodium hydroxide (NaOH), ascorbic acid ($C_6H_8O_6$ or, with its ionizable hydrogens written first, $H_2C_6H_6O_6$), hydrochloric acid (HCl), acetic acid ($HC_2H_3O_2$), and ammonia (NH_3). HCl and NaOH are both strong electrolytes and exist in solution entirely as ions. Water molecules are not shown.

---

[1]Svante August Arrhenius (1859–1927) made important contributions to the study of chemical kinetics and electrolyte solutions. (He also speculated that life had come to Earth from other planets.) Arrhenius was awarded the Nobel Prize in Chemistry in 1903.

TABLE 9.4	Strong Acids and Strong Bases	
Strong acids		**Strong bases**
HCl		LiOH
HBr		NaOH
HI		KOH
HNO_3		RbOH
$HClO_3$		CsOH
$HClO_4$		$Ca(OH)_2$
H_2SO_4		$Sr(OH)_2$
		$Ba(OH)_2$

Student Annotation: Although three of the Group 2A hydroxides [$Ca(OH)_2$, $Sr(OH)_2$, and $Ba(OH)_2$] are typically classified as strong bases, only $Ba(OH)_2$ is sufficiently soluble to be used commonly in the laboratory. For any ionic compound, what does dissolve—even if it is only a tiny amount—dissociates completely.

Student Annotation: The H atom consists of a proton and an electron. When the electron is lost, all that remains is the proton—hence the use of the term *proton* in this context.

Arrhenius acid and *Arrhenius base* definitions are useful, they are restricted to the behavior of compounds in aqueous solution. More inclusive definitions were proposed by the Danish chemist Johannes Brønsted[2] in 1932. A *Brønsted acid* is a proton *donor*, and a *Brønsted base* is a proton *acceptor*. In this context, the word *proton* refers to a hydrogen atom that has lost its electron—also known as a *hydrogen ion* (H^+). Consider the ionization of the weak base ammonia (NH_3).

This equation shows that NH_3 is a base in the Arrhenius sense; that is, it produces OH^- in solution. It is also a base in the Brønsted sense because it accepts a proton (H^+) from the water molecule to become the ammonium ion (NH_4^+).

$$NH_3(aq) + H_2O(l) \rightleftharpoons NH_4^+(aq) + OH^-(aq)$$

Now consider the ionization of hydrofluoric acid (HF), a weak acid.

$$HF(aq) \rightleftharpoons H^+(aq) + F^-(aq)$$

HF is an acid in the Arrhenius sense because it produces H^+ in solution. It is also an acid in the Brønsted sense because it donates a proton to water.

$$HF(aq) + H_2O(l) \rightleftharpoons H_3O^+(aq) + F^-(aq)$$

Student Annotation: In reality, aqueous protons are surrounded by water molecules, just as other ions are. We use H_3O^+ in chemical equations, showing just one of the water molecules involved, to emphasize that the proton is hydrated in solution.

These two chemical equations mean essentially the same thing, but it is important to recognize that an aqueous proton (H^+) does not exist as an isolated species in solution. Rather, it is hydrated just as other aqueous ions are. (See Figure 9.4.) The proton, being positively charged, is strongly attracted to the partial negative charge on the oxygen atom in a water molecule. Thus, it is convenient and more *realistic* for us to represent the ionization of HF with the equation

$$HF(aq) + H_2O(l) \rightleftharpoons H_3O^+(aq) + F^-(aq)$$

Student Annotation: The terms and symbols *hydrogen ion, proton, hydronium ion*, H^+, and H_3O^+ all refer to the same aqueous species and are used interchangeably.

where we include the water molecule to which the proton becomes attached, both before and after the ionization. (We could show H_3O^+ as $H_2O \cdot H^+$ to emphasize that it is a water molecule attached to a proton.) With the equation written this way, we show that HF donates a proton to H_2O, thus converting the H_2O molecule to the *hydronium ion* (H_3O^+).

$$HF(aq) + H_2O(l) \rightleftharpoons H_3O^+(aq) + F^-(aq)$$

---

[2]Johannes Nicolaus Brønsted (1879–1947). In addition to his theory of acids and bases, Brønsted worked on thermodynamics and the separation of mercury into its isotopes. In some books, Brønsted acids and bases are called Brønsted-Lowry acids and bases. Brønsted and Thomas Martin Lowry (1874–1936) developed essentially the same acid-base theory independently in 1923.

Both H^+ and H_3O^+ will be used in chemical equations throughout the text. You should be aware that they refer to the same aqueous species.

The Brønsted definitions of acids and bases are not restricted to species in aqueous solution. In fact, Brønsted acid-base reactions sometimes take place in the gas phase. For example, in the reaction between HCl and NH_3 gases, HCl acts as the Brønsted acid, donating its proton to NH_3, which, by accepting the proton, acts as a Brønsted base. The products of this proton transfer are the chloride ion (Cl^-) and the ammonium ion (NH_4^+), which subsequently combine to form the ionic solid ammonium chloride.

$$HCl(g) + NH_3(g) \longrightarrow NH_4Cl(s)$$

Most of the strong acids are **monoprotic,** meaning that each acid molecule has one proton to donate. One of the strong acids, H_2SO_4, is a **diprotic acid,** meaning that each acid molecule has two protons that it can donate. Other diprotic acids include oxalic acid ($H_2C_2O_4$) and carbonic acid (H_2CO_3). There are also **triprotic acids,** those with three protons, although they are relatively less common than mono- or diprotic acids. Examples include phosphoric acid (H_3PO_4) and citric acid ($H_3C_6H_5O_7$).

In general, acids with more than one proton are called **polyprotic.** Of the polyprotic acids, only sulfuric acid (H_2SO_4) is a strong acid—although it is strong only in its *first* ionization in water. H_2SO_4 ionizes completely to yield H^+ and HSO_4^-, the subsequent ionization of the hydrogen sulfate ion (HSO_4^-) happens only to a very small extent. (See Table 9.1.) Note the single and double arrows in the following two equations.

$$H_2SO_4(aq) \longrightarrow H^+(aq) + HSO_4^-(aq)$$

$$HSO_4^-(aq) \rightleftharpoons H^+(aq) + SO_4^{2-}(aq)$$

For all other polyprotic acids, each ionization is incomplete and is represented by an equation with a double arrow. The first, second, and third ionizations of phosphoric acid are represented as

$$H_3PO_4(aq) \rightleftharpoons H^+(aq) + H_2PO_4^-(aq)$$

$$H_2PO_4^-(aq) \rightleftharpoons H^+(aq) + HPO_4^{2-}(aq)$$

$$HPO_4^{2-}(aq) \rightleftharpoons H^+(aq) + PO_4^{3-}(aq)$$

Some of each of the species shown is present in a solution of phosphoric acid. Because each successive ionization happens to a smaller and smaller extent, the relative concentrations of species in solution are as follows:

$$[H_3PO_4] > [H^+] \approx [H_2PO_4^-] > [HPO_4^{2-}] > [PO_4^{3-}]$$

> **Student Annotation:** These relative concentrations are true only in an aqueous solution of phosphoric acid that contains no other dissolved compounds. We will look in detail at how to determine concentrations in aqueous solutions of polyprotic acids in Chapter 16.

Just as some acids produce more than one H^+ ion, some strong bases produce more than one OH^- ion. Barium hydroxide, for example, dissociates to produce 2 moles of hydroxide ion for every mole of $Ba(OH)_2$ dissolved.

$$Ba(OH)_2(s) \xrightarrow{H_2O} Ba^{2+}(aq) + 2OH^-(aq)$$

Compounds such as this are referred to as **dibasic** bases, indicating that they produce 2 moles of hydroxide per mole of compound. Those that produce only 1 mole of hydroxide per mole of compound, such as NaOH, are called **monobasic** bases.

Acid-Base Neutralization

A **neutralization reaction** is a reaction between an acid and a base. In general, an aqueous acid-base reaction produces water and a **salt,** which is an ionic compound made up of the cation from a base and the anion from an acid. The substance we know as table salt, NaCl, is a familiar example. It is a product of the following acid-base reaction:

> **Student Annotation:** A compound in which the anion is oxide (O^{2-}) or hydroxide (OH^-) is not considered a salt.

$$HCl(aq) + NaOH(aq) \longrightarrow H_2O(l) + NaCl(aq)$$

However, because the acid, base, and salt are all strong electrolytes, they exist entirely as ions in solution. The ionic equation is

Multi 9.5
Acids and bases—neutralization reaction of NaOH and HCl

$$H^+(aq) + Cl^-(aq) + Na^+(aq) + OH^-(aq) \longrightarrow H_2O(l) + Na^+(aq) + Cl^-(aq)$$

The net ionic equation is

$$H^+(aq) + OH^-(aq) \longrightarrow H_2O(l)$$

Both Na^+ and Cl^- are spectator ions. If we were to carry out the preceding reaction using stoichiometric amounts [◀◀ Section 8.3] of HCl and NaOH, the result would be neutral saltwater with no leftover acid or base.

The following are also examples of acid-base neutralization reactions, represented by molecular equations:

Student Annotation: Acid-base neutralization reactions, like precipitation reactions [◀◀ Section 9.2], are *metathesis* reactions, where two species exchange ions.

$$HNO_3(aq) + KOH(aq) \longrightarrow H_2O(l) + KNO_3(aq)$$

$$H_2SO_4(aq) + 2NaOH(aq) \longrightarrow 2H_2O(l) + Na_2SO_4(aq)$$

$$2HC_2H_3O_2(aq) + Ba(OH)_2(aq) \longrightarrow 2H_2O(l) + Ba(C_2H_3O_2)_2(aq)$$

$$HCl(aq) + NH_3(aq) \longrightarrow NH_4Cl(aq)$$

The last equation looks different because it does not show water as a product. Recall, however, that $NH_3(aq)$ ionizes to give $NH_4^+(aq)$ and $OH^-(aq)$. If we include these two species as reactants in place of $NH_3(aq)$, the equation becomes

$$HCl(aq) + NH_4^+(aq) + OH^-(aq) \longrightarrow H_2O(l) + NH_4Cl(aq)$$

Worked Example 9.4 involves an acid-base neutralization reaction.

Worked Example 9.4

Student Annotation: Most suspended solids will settle to the bottom of the bottle, making it necessary to "shake well before using." Shaking redistributes the solid throughout the liquid.

Milk of magnesia, an over-the-counter laxative, is a mixture of magnesium hydroxide [$Mg(OH)_2$] and water. Because $Mg(OH)_2$ is insoluble in water (see Table 9.3), milk of magnesia is a *suspension* rather than a solution. The undissolved solid is responsible for the milky appearance of the product. When acid such as HCl is added to milk of magnesia, the suspended $Mg(OH)_2$ dissolves, and the result is a clear, colorless solution. Write balanced molecular, ionic, and net ionic equations for this reaction.

(a) Milk of magnesia   (b) Addition of HCl   (c) Resulting clear, colorless solution

Strategy Determine the products of the reaction; then write and balance the equation. Remember that one of the reactants, $Mg(OH)_2$, is a solid. Identify any strong electrolytes and rewrite the equation showing strong electrolytes as ions. Identify and cancel the spectator ions.

Setup Because this is an acid-base neutralization reaction, one of the products is water. The other product is a salt comprising the cation from the base, Mg^{2+}, and the anion from the acid, Cl^-. In order for the formula to be neutral, these ions combine in a 1:2 ratio, giving $MgCl_2$ as the formula of the salt.

Solution

$$Mg(OH)_2(s) + 2HCl(aq) \longrightarrow 2H_2O(l) + MgCl_2(aq)$$

Of the species in the molecular equation, only HCl and $MgCl_2$ are strong electrolytes. Therefore, the ionic equation is

$$Mg(OH)_2(s) + 2H^+(aq) + 2Cl^-(aq) \longrightarrow 2H_2O(l) + Mg^{2+}(aq) + 2Cl^-(aq)$$

Cl^- is the only spectator ion. The net ionic equation is

$$Mg(OH)_2(s) + 2H^+(aq) \longrightarrow 2H_2O(l) + Mg^{2+}(aq)$$

Think About It
Make sure your equation is balanced and that you only show strong electrolytes as ions. $Mg(OH)_2$ is *not* shown as aqueous ions because it is insoluble.

Practice Problem A Write balanced molecular, ionic, and net ionic equations for the neutralization reaction between $Ba(OH)_2(aq)$ and $HF(aq)$.

Practice Problem B Write balanced molecular, ionic, and net ionic equations for the neutralization reaction between $NH_3(aq)$ and $H_2SO_4(aq)$.

SECTION 9.3 REVIEW

Acid-Base Reactions

9.3.1 Identify the Brønsted acid in the following equation:

$$H_2SO_4(aq) + NH_3(aq) \longrightarrow (NH_4)_2SO_4(aq)$$

9.3.2 Identify the Brønsted base in the following equation:

$$HCl(aq) + NO_2^-(aq) \longrightarrow HNO_2(aq) + Cl^-(aq)$$

9.3.3 Write the balanced net ionic equation for the reaction of H_2SO_4 and KOH.

9.3.4 Write the balanced net ionic equation for the reaction of HF and LiOH.

9.4 OXIDATION-REDUCTION REACTIONS

In Sections 9.2 and 9.3, we encountered two types of chemical reactions that can occur when two electrolyte solutions are combined: *precipitation,* in which ionic compounds exchange ions, and *acid-base neutralization,* in which a proton is transferred from an acid to a base. In this section, we will learn about **oxidation-reduction reactions,** commonly called *redox* reactions. A **redox reaction** is a chemical reaction in which *electrons* are transferred from one reactant to another. For example, if we place a piece of zinc metal into a solution that contains copper ions, the following reaction will occur:

$$Zn(s) + Cu^{2+}(aq) \longrightarrow Zn^{2+}(aq) + Cu(s)$$

This reaction is shown in Figure 9.6. In this process, zinc atoms are *oxidized* (they lose electrons) and copper ions are *reduced* (they gain electrons). Each zinc atom loses two electrons to become a zinc ion, and each copper ion gains two electrons to become a copper atom.

$$Zn(s) \longrightarrow Zn^{2+}(aq) + 2e^-$$

$$Cu^{2+}(aq) + 2e^- \longrightarrow Cu(s)$$

These two equations show electrons as a product in the zinc reaction and as a reactant in the copper reaction. Each of these two equations represents a **half-reaction,** the oxidation or the reduction

Figure 9.6 Oxidation of zinc in a solution of copper(II) sulfate.

(a)
Zinc atoms enter the solution as zinc ions (Zn^{2+}).
Copper ions are reduced to copper atoms
on the surface of the metal.

(b)
Cu atoms have replaced Zn atoms in the solid, and
Zn^{2+} ions have replaced Cu^{2+} ions in solution.

reaction in a redox reaction. The sum of the two half-reaction equations is the overall equation for the redox reaction:

$$Zn(s) \longrightarrow Zn^{2+}(aq) + 2e^-$$

$$Cu^{2+}(aq) + 2e^- \longrightarrow Cu(s)$$

$$\overline{Zn(s) + Cu^{2+}(aq) + 2e^- \longrightarrow Zn^{2+}(aq) + Cu(s) + 2e^-}$$

Although these two processes can be represented by separate equations, they cannot occur separately. In order for one species to gain electrons, another must lose them, and vice versa.

Student Annotation: Oxidation originally was used by chemists to mean "reaction with oxygen." Like definitions of acids and bases, though, it has been redefined to be more inclusive. The term *oxidation* now refers to any reaction in which electrons are lost.

Oxidation is the *loss* of electrons. The opposite process, the *gain* of electrons, is called *reduction.* In the reaction of Zn with Cu^{2+}, Zn is called the ***reducing agent*** because it donates electrons, causing Cu^{2+} to be reduced. Cu^{2+} is called the ***oxidizing agent,*** on the other hand, because it accepts electrons, causing Zn to be oxidized.

Another example of a redox reaction is the formation of calcium oxide (CaO) from its constituent elements.

$$2Ca(s) + O_2(g) \longrightarrow 2CaO(s)$$

In this reaction, each calcium atom loses two electrons (is oxidized) and each oxygen atom gains two electrons (is reduced). The corresponding half-reactions are

$$2Ca \longrightarrow 2Ca^{2+} + 4e^-$$

$$O_2(g) + 4e^- \longrightarrow 2O^{2-}$$

Multi 9.6
Chemical reactions—formation of Ag_2S
by oxidation reduction

The resulting Ca^{2+} and O^{2-} ions combine to form CaO.

Redox reactions take place because atoms of different elements have different tendencies to gain electrons. Oxygen, for instance, has a much greater tendency to gain electrons than does calcium. Calcium, being a metal, has a significant tendency to lose electrons. Compounds that form between elements with significantly different tendencies to gain electrons generally are ionic. By knowing the charges on the monatomic ions in such compounds, we can keep track of the electrons that have been lost and gained.

Oxidation Numbers

When elements of similar abilities to gain electrons combine, they tend to form molecular compounds, as in the formation of HF and NH_3 from their respective elements:

$$H_2(g) + F_2(g) \longrightarrow 2HF(g)$$

$$N_2(g) + 3H_2(g) \longrightarrow 2NH_3(g)$$

In the formation of hydrogen fluoride (HF), therefore, fluorine does not gain an electron per se—and hydrogen does not lose one. Experimental evidence shows, however, that there is a partial transfer of electrons from H to F. Oxidation numbers provide us with a way to "balance the books" with regard to electrons in a chemical equation. The ***oxidation number,*** also called the ***oxidation state,*** is the charge an atom would have *if* electrons were transferred completely. For example, we can rewrite the preceding equations for the formation of HF and NH_3 as follows:

Student Annotation: The number in a circle under each element's symbol contains the oxidation state of the element. The number in a square contains the total contribution to charge by that element.

The numbers in circles below each element are the oxidation numbers, and the numbers in the boxes are each atom's contribution to overall charge. In both of the reactions shown, the reactants are all homonuclear diatomic molecules. Thus, we would expect *no* transfer of electrons from one atom to the other and the oxidation number of each is zero. For the product molecules, however, for the sake of determining oxidation numbers, we assume that complete electron transfer has taken place and that each atom has either gained or lost one or more electrons. The oxidation numbers reflect the number of electrons assumed to have been transferred.

Oxidation numbers enable us to identify elements that are oxidized and reduced at a glance. The elements that show an *increase* in oxidation number—hydrogen in the preceding examples—are oxidized, whereas the elements that show a *decrease* in oxidation number—fluorine and nitrogen—are reduced.

The following guidelines will help you assign oxidation numbers. There are essentially two rules:

1. The oxidation number of any element, in its elemental form, is zero.
2. The oxidation numbers in any chemical species must sum to the overall charge on the species. That is, oxidation numbers must sum to zero for any molecule and must sum to the charge on any polyatomic ion. The oxidation number of a monatomic ion is equal to the charge on the ion.

In addition to these two rules, it is necessary to know the elements that always, or nearly always, have the same oxidation number. Table 9.5 lists elements whose oxidation numbers are "reliable," in order of decreasing reliability.

To determine oxidation numbers in a compound or a polyatomic ion, you must use a stepwise, systematic approach. Draw a circle under each element's symbol in the chemical formula. Then draw a square under each circle. In the circle, write the oxidation number of the element; in the square, write the total contribution to charge by that element. Start with the oxidation numbers you know, and use them to figure out the ones you don't know. Here is an example:

$$KMnO_4$$

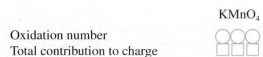

Oxidation number
Total contribution to charge

Fill in the oxidation number first for the element that appears highest on the list in Table 9.5. Potassium (K) is a Group 1A metal. In its compounds, it always has the oxidation number +1. We write +1 in the circle beneath the K. Because there is only one K atom in this formula, the total contribution to charge is also +1, so we also write +1 in the square beneath the K.

TABLE 9.5	Elements with Reliable Oxidation Numbers in Compounds or Polyatomic Ions	
Element	**Oxidation number**	**Exceptions**
Fluorine	-1	
Group 1A or 2A metal	$+1$ or $+2$, respectively	
Hydrogen	$+1$	Any combination with a Group 1A or 2A metal to form a metal hydride. Examples: LiH and CaH_2—the oxidation number of H is -1 in both examples.
Oxygen	-2	Any combination with something higher on the list that necessitates its having a different oxidation number (see rule 2 for assigning oxidation numbers). Examples: H_2O_2 and KO_2—the oxidation number of O for H_2O_2 is -1 and for KO_2 is $-\frac{1}{2}$.
Group 7A (other than fluorine)	-1	Any combination with something higher on the list that necessitates its having a different oxidation number (see rule 2 for assigning oxidation numbers). Examples: ClF, BrO_4^-, and IO_3^-—the oxidation numbers of Cl, Br, and I are $+1$, $+7$, and $+5$, respectively. Remember that these exceptions do not apply to fluorine, which *always* has an oxidation state of -1 when it is part of a compound.

$KMnO_4$

Oxidation number
Total contribution to charge

Next on the list is oxygen (O). In compounds, O usually has the oxidation number -2, so we assign it -2. Because there are four O atoms in the formula, the total contribution to charge by O atoms is $4(-2) = -8$.

$KMnO_4$

Oxidation number
Total contribution to charge

The numbers in the squares, all the contributions to overall charge, must sum to zero. This requires putting $+7$ in the box beneath the Mn atom. Because there is just one Mn atom in this formula, the contribution to charge is the same as the oxidation number. Thus, $(+1) + (+7) + (-8) = 0$.

$KMnO_4$

Oxidation number
Total contribution to charge

Worked Example 9.5 lets you determine oxidation numbers in three more compounds and a polyatomic ion.

Worked Example 9.5

Determine the oxidation number of each atom in the following compounds and ion: (a) SO_2, (b) NaH, (c) CO_3^{2-}, (d) N_2O_5.

Strategy For each compound, assign an oxidation number first to the element that appears higher in Table 9.5. Then use rule 2 to determine the oxidation number of the other element.

Setup

(a) O appears in Table 9.5 but S does not, so we assign oxidation number -2 to O. Because there are two O atoms in the molecule, the total contribution to charge by O is $2(-2) = -4$. The lone S atom must therefore contribute $+4$ to the overall charge.

(b) Both Na and H appear in Table 9.5, but Na appears higher in the table, so we assign the oxidation number $+1$ to Na. This means that H must contribute -1 to the overall charge.

(c) We assign the oxidation number -2 to O. Because there are three O atoms in the carbonate ion, the total contribution to charge by O is -6. To have the contributions to charge sum to the charge on the ion (-2), the C atom must contribute $+4$.

Student Annotation: H^- is the hydride ion.

(d) We assign the oxidation number −2 to O. Because there are five O atoms in the N_2O_5 molecule, the total contribution to charge by O is −10. To have the contributions to charge sum to zero, the contribution by N must be +10, and because there are two N atoms, each one must contribute +5. Therefore, the oxidation number of N is +5.

Solution

(a) In SO_2, the oxidation numbers of S and O are +4 and −2, respectively.

$$SO_2$$

$$\boxed{\text{(+4)(−2)}}$$
$$\boxed{\text{+4 | −4}}$$

(b) In NaH, the oxidation numbers of Na and H are +1 and −1, respectively.

$$NaH$$

$$\text{(+1)(−1)}$$
$$\boxed{\text{+1 | −1}}$$

(c) In CO_3^{2-}, the oxidation numbers of C and O are +4 and −2, respectively.

$$CO_3^{2-}$$

$$\text{(+4)(−2)}$$
$$\boxed{\text{+4 | −6}}$$

(d) In N_2O_5, the oxidation numbers of N and O are +5 and −2, respectively.

$$N_2O_5$$

$$\text{(+5)(−2)}$$
$$\boxed{\text{+10 | −10}}$$

> **Think About It**
> Use the circle and square system to verify that the oxidation numbers you have assigned do indeed sum to the overall charge on each species.

Practice Problem A Assign oxidation numbers to each atom in the following compounds and ion: H_2O_2, ClO_3^-, H_2SO_4.

Practice Problem B Assign oxidation numbers to each atom in the following species: O_2^{2-}, ClO_3^-, MnO_2.

As with formal charges [◄◄ Section 6.4], each atom's oxidation number makes a contribution to the overall charge on the species. Note that the oxidation numbers in both HF [(+1) + (−1) = 0] and NH_3 [(−3) + 3(+1) = 0] sum to zero. Because compounds are electrically neutral, the oxidation numbers in any compound will sum to zero. For a polyatomic ion, oxidation numbers must sum to the charge on the ion. (The oxidation number of a monatomic ion is equal to its charge.)

Oxidation of Metals in Aqueous Solutions

Recall from the beginning of this section that zinc metal reacts with aqueous copper ions to form aqueous zinc ions and copper metal. One way that this reaction might be carried out is for zinc metal to be immersed in a solution of copper(II) chloride ($CuCl_2$), as depicted in Figure 9.6. The molecular equation for this reaction is

$$\text{Zn}(s) \; + \; \text{CuCl}_2(aq) \; \longrightarrow \; \text{ZnCl}_2(aq) \; + \; \text{Cu}(s)$$

This is an example of a ***displacement reaction.*** Zinc *displaces,* or *replaces,* copper in the dissolved salt by being oxidized from Zn to Zn^{2+}. Copper is displaced from the salt (and removed from solution) by being reduced from Cu^{2+} to Cu. Chloride (Cl^-), which is neither oxidized nor reduced, is a spectator ion in this reaction.

What would happen, then, if we placed copper metal into a solution containing zinc chloride ($ZnCl_2$)? Would $Cu(s)$ be oxidized to $Cu^{2+}(aq)$ by $Zn^{2+}(aq)$ the way $Zn(s)$ is oxidized to $Zn^{2+}(aq)$ by $Cu^{2+}(aq)$? The answer is no. In fact, no reaction would occur if we were to immerse copper metal into an aqueous solution of $ZnCl_2$.

$$Cu(s) + ZnCl_2(aq) \longrightarrow \text{no reaction}$$

No reaction occurs between $Cu(s)$ and $Zn^{2+}(aq)$, whereas a reaction does occur between $Zn(s)$ and $Cu^{2+}(aq)$ because zinc is more easily oxidized than copper.

The **activity series** (Table 9.6) is a list of metals (and hydrogen) arranged from top to bottom in order of decreasing ease of oxidation. The second column shows the oxidation half-reaction corresponding to each element in the first column. Note the positions of zinc and copper in the table. Zinc appears higher in the table and is therefore oxidized more easily. In fact, an element in the series will be oxidized by the ions of any element that appears below it. According to Table 9.6, therefore, zinc metal will be oxidized by a solution containing any of the following ions: Cr^{3+}, Fe^{2+}, Cd^{2+}, Co^{2+}, Ni^{2+}, Sn^{2+}, H^+, Cu^{2+}, Ag^+, Hg^{2+}, Pt^{2+}, or Au^{2+}. On the other hand, zinc will not be oxidized by a solution containing Mn^{2+}, Al^{2+}, Mg^{2+}, Na^+, Ca^{2+}, Ba^{2+}, K^+ or Li^+ ions.

Metals listed at the top of the activity series are called the *active metals*. These include the alkali and alkaline earth metals. These metals are so reactive that they are not found in nature in their elemental forms. Metals at the bottom of the series, such as copper, silver, platinum, and gold, are called the *noble metals* because they have very little tendency to react. These are the metals most often used for jewelry and coins.

Student Annotation: In this context, *activity* and *ease of oxidation* mean the same thing.

Student Annotation: When a metal is *oxidized* by an aqueous solution, it becomes an aqueous ion.

Multi 9.8
Sodium, lithium, and potassium reaction series

TABLE 9.6	Activity Series
Element	**Oxidation half-reaction**
Lithium	$Li \longrightarrow Li^+ + e^-$
Potassium	$K \longrightarrow K^+ + e^-$
Barium	$Ba \longrightarrow Ba^{2+} + 2e^-$
Calcium	$Ca \longrightarrow Ca^{2+} + 2e^-$
Sodium	$Na \longrightarrow Na^+ + e^-$
Magnesium	$Mg \longrightarrow Mg^{2+} + 2e^-$
Aluminum	$Al \longrightarrow Al^{3+} + 3e^-$
Manganese	$Mn \longrightarrow Mn^{2+} + 2e^-$
Zinc	$Zn \longrightarrow Zn^{2+} + 2e^-$
Chromium	$Cr \longrightarrow Cr^{3+} + 3e^-$
Iron	$Fe \longrightarrow Fe^{2+} + 2e^-$
Cadmium	$Cd \longrightarrow Cd^{2+} + 2e^-$
Cobalt	$Co \longrightarrow Co^{2+} + 2e^-$
Nickel	$Ni \longrightarrow Ni^{2+} + 2e^-$
Tin	$Sn \longrightarrow Sn^{2+} + 2e^-$
Lead	$Pb \longrightarrow Pb^{2+} + 2e^-$
Hydrogen	$H_2 \longrightarrow 2H^+ + 2e^-$
Copper	$Cu \longrightarrow Cu^{2+} + 2e^-$
Silver	$Ag \longrightarrow Ag^+ + e^-$
Mercury	$Hg \longrightarrow Hg^{2+} + 2e^-$
Platinum	$Pt \longrightarrow Pt^{2+} + 2e^-$
Gold	$Au \longrightarrow Au^{3+} + 3e^-$

Increasing ease of oxidation

Balancing Simple Redox Equations

To learn how to balance redox equations, let's revisit the practice of balancing equations. In Chapter 8, you learned to balance equations by counting the number of each kind of atom on each side of the equation arrow. For the purpose of balancing redox equations, it is also necessary to count electrons. For example, consider the net ionic equation for the reaction of chromium metal with nickel ion:

$$Cr(s) + Ni^{2+}(aq) \longrightarrow Cr^{3+}(aq) + Ni(s)$$

Although this equation has equal numbers of each type of atom on both sides, it is not balanced because there is a charge of $+2$ on the reactant side and a charge of $+3$ on the product side. In order to balance it, we can separate it into its half-reactions.

$$Cr(s) \longrightarrow Cr^{3+}(aq) + 3e^-$$

$$Ni^{2+}(aq) + 2e^- \longrightarrow Ni(s)$$

When we add half-reactions to get the overall reaction, the electrons must cancel. Because any electrons lost by one species must be gained by the other, electrons may *not* appear in an overall chemical equation. Therefore, prior to adding these two half-reactions, we must multiply the chromium half-reaction by 2

$$2[Cr(s) \longrightarrow Cr^{3+}(aq) + 3e^-]$$

and the nickel half-reaction by 3.

$$3[Ni^{2+}(aq) + 2e^- \longrightarrow Ni(s)]$$

Then when we add the half-reactions, the electrons cancel and we get the balanced overall equation.

$$2Cr(s) \longrightarrow 2Cr^{3+}(aq) + 6e^-$$
$$+ \; 3Ni^{2+}(aq) + 6e^- \longrightarrow 3Ni(s)$$
$$\overline{2Cr(s) + 3Ni^{2+}(aq) \longrightarrow 2Cr^{3+}(aq) + 3Ni(s)}$$

This is known as the ***half-reaction method*** of balancing redox equations. We will use this method extensively when we examine more complex redox reactions in Chapter 19.

The activity series enables us to predict whether or not a metal will be oxidized by a solution containing a particular salt or by an acid. Worked Examples 9.6 and 9.7 give you more practice making such predictions and balancing redox equations.

Worked Example 9.6

Using the activity series, predict which of the following reactions will occur, and for those that will occur, write the net ionic equation and indicate which element is oxidized and which is reduced:
(a) $Fe(s) + PtCl_2(aq) \longrightarrow$? (b) $Cr(s) + AuCl_3(aq) \longrightarrow$? (c) $Pb(s) + Zn(NO_3)_2(aq) \longrightarrow$?

Strategy Recognize that the salt in each equation (the compound on the reactant side) is a strong electrolyte. What is important is the identity of the metal cation *in* the salt. For each equation, compare the positions in Table 9.6 of the solid metal and the metal cation from the salt to determine whether or not the solid metal will be oxidized. If the cation appears lower in the table, the solid metal will be oxidized (i.e., the reaction will occur). If the cation appears higher in the table, the solid metal will not be oxidized (i.e., no reaction will occur).

Setup

(a) The cation in $PtCl_2$ is Pt^{2+}. Platinum appears lower in Table 9.6 than iron, so $Pt^{2+}(aq)$ will oxidize $Fe(s)$.

(b) The cation in $AuCl_3$ is Au^{3+}. Gold appears lower in Table 9.6 than chromium, so $Au^{3+}(aq)$ will oxidize $Cr(s)$.

(c) The cation in $Zn(NO_3)_2$ is Zn^{2+}. Zinc appears higher in Table 9.6 than lead, so $Zn^{2+}(aq)$ will not oxidize $Pb(s)$.

(Continued on next page)

Solution

(a) $Fe(s) + Pt^{2+}(aq) \longrightarrow Fe^{2+}(aq) + Pt(s)$; iron is oxidized (0 to +2) and platinum is reduced (+2 to 0).

(b) $Cr(s) + Au^{3+}(aq) \longrightarrow Cr^{3+}(aq) + Au(s)$; chromium is oxidized (0 to +3) and gold is reduced (+3 to 0).

(c) No reaction.

Think About It

Check your conclusions by working each problem backward. For part (b), for example, write the net ionic equation in reverse, using the products as the reactants: $Au(s) + Cr^{3+}(aq) \longrightarrow$? Now compare the positions of gold and chromium in Table 9.6 again. Chromium is higher, so chromium(III) ions cannot oxidize gold. This confirms your conclusion that the forward reaction (the oxidation of chromium by gold ions) will occur.

Practice Problem A Using the activity series, predict which of the following reactions will occur, and for those that will occur, write the net ionic equation and indicate which element is oxidized and which is reduced: (a) $Co(s) + BaI_2(aq) \longrightarrow$? (b) $Sn(s) + CuBr_2(aq) \longrightarrow$? (c) $Ag(s) + NaCl(aq) \longrightarrow$?

Practice Problem B Using the activity series, predict which of the following reactions will occur, and for those that will occur, write the net ionic equation and indicate which element is oxidized and which is reduced: (a) $Ni(s) + Cu(NO_3)_2(aq) \longrightarrow$? (b) $Ag(s) + KCl(aq) \longrightarrow$? (c) $Al(s) + AuCl_3(aq) \longrightarrow$?

Worked Example 9.7

Predict which of the following reactions will occur, and for those that will occur, balance the equation and indicate which element is oxidized and which is reduced: (a) $Al(s) + CaCl_2(aq) \longrightarrow$? (b) $Cr(s) + Pb(C_2H_3O_2)_2(aq) \longrightarrow$? (c) $Sn(s) + HI(aq) \longrightarrow$?

Strategy As in Worked Example 9.6, identify the cation in the aqueous species and for each equation, compare the positions in Table 9.6 of the solid metal and the cation to determine whether or not the solid metal will be oxidized. If the cation appears lower in the table, the reaction will occur.

Setup

(a) The cation in $CaCl_2$ is Ca^{2+}. Calcium appears higher in Table 9.6 than aluminum, so $Ca^{2+}(aq)$ will not oxidize $Al(s)$.

(b) The cation in $Pb(C_2H_3O_2)_2$ is Pb^{2+}. Lead appears lower in Table 9.6 than chromium, so $Pb^{2+}(aq)$ will oxidize $Cr(s)$.

(c) The cation in HI is H^+. Hydrogen appears lower in Table 9.6 than tin, so $H^+(aq)$ will oxidize $Sn(s)$.

Solution

(a) No reaction.

(b) The two half-reactions are represented by the following:

$$\text{Oxidation: } Cr(s) \longrightarrow Cr^{3+}(aq) + 3e^-$$

$$\text{Reduction: } Pb^{2+}(aq) + 2e^- \longrightarrow Pb(s)$$

In order to balance the charges, we must multiply the oxidation half-reaction by 2 and the reduction half-reaction by 3:

$$2 \times [Cr(s) \longrightarrow Cr^{3+}(aq) + 3e^-] = 2Cr(s) \longrightarrow 2Cr^{3+}(aq) + 6e^-$$

$$3 \times [Pb^{2+}(aq) + 2e^- \longrightarrow Pb(s)] = 3Pb^{2+}(aq) + 6e^- \longrightarrow 3Pb(s)$$

We can then add the two half-reactions, canceling the electrons on both sides to get

$$2Cr(s) + 3Pb^{2+}(aq) \longrightarrow 2Cr^{3+}(aq) + 3Pb(s)$$

The overall, balanced molecular equation is

$$2Cr(s) + 3Pb(C_2H_3O_2)_2(aq) \longrightarrow 2Cr(C_2H_3O_2)_3(aq) + 3Pb(s)$$

Chromium is oxidized (0 to +3) and lead is reduced (+2 to 0).

(c) The two half-reactions are as follows:

$$\text{Oxidation: } Sn(s) \longrightarrow SnI^2(aq) + 2e^-$$

$$\text{Reduction: } 2H^+(aq) + 2e^- \longrightarrow H_2(g)$$

Adding the two half-reactions and canceling the electrons on both sides yields

$$Sn(s) + 2H^+(aq) \longrightarrow SnI^2(aq) + H_2(g)$$

The overall, balanced molecular equation is

$$Sn(s) + 2HI(aq) \longrightarrow SnI^2(aq) + H_2(g)$$

Tin is oxidized (0 to +2) and hydrogen is reduced (+1 to 0). Reactions in which hydrogen ion is reduced to hydrogen gas are known as *hydrogen displacement* reactions.

> **Think About It**
> Check your conclusions by working each problem backward. Write each equation in reverse and compare the positions of the elements in the activity series.

Practice Problem A Predict which of the following reactions will occur, and for those that will occur, give the overall, balanced molecular equation and indicate which element is oxidized and which is reduced. (a) $Mg(s) + Cr(C_2H_3O_2)_3(aq) \longrightarrow$? (b) $Cu(s) + HBr(aq) \longrightarrow$? (c) $Cd(s) + AgNO_3(aq) \longrightarrow$?

Practice Problem B Predict which of the following reactions will occur, and for those that will occur, indicate which element is oxidized and which is reduced. (a) $Pt(s) + Cu(NO_3)_2(aq) \longrightarrow$? (b) $Ag(s) + AuCl_3(aq) \longrightarrow$? (c) $Sn(s) + HNO_3(aq) \longrightarrow$?

Other Types of Redox Reactions

Several of the reaction types that you have already encountered are also redox reactions.

Combination Reactions

Combination reactions such as the formation of ammonia from its constituent elements can involve oxidation and reduction.

$$N_2(g) \quad + \quad 3H_2(g) \quad \longrightarrow \quad 2NH_3(g)$$

In this reaction, nitrogen is reduced from 0 to −3, while hydrogen is oxidized from 0 to +1. Other examples of combination reactions include those shown in Figure 9.7.

Decomposition

Decomposition can also be a redox reaction, as illustrated by the following examples:

$$2NaH(s) \longrightarrow 2Na(s) + H_2(g)$$

$$2KClO_3(s) \longrightarrow 2KCl(s) + 3O_2(g)$$

$$2H_2O_2(aq) \longrightarrow 2H_2O(l) + O_2(g)$$

Figure 9.7 (a) Reaction between sodium and chlorine to form sodium chloride, and (b) reaction between hydrogen and oxygen to form water. For each element, the oxidation number appears in the circle and the total contribution to charge appears in the square below it. Remember that ionic compounds such as NaCl do not exist as discrete formula units but rather as three-dimensional networks or *lattices* [◄◄ Section 5.3] of alternating oppositely charged ions.

$$2Na \quad + \quad Cl_2 \quad \longrightarrow \quad 2NaCl$$

(a)

$$2H_2 \quad + \quad O_2 \quad \longrightarrow \quad 2H_2O$$

(b)

The decomposition of hydrogen peroxide, shown in the preceding equation, is an example of a *disproportionation reaction,* in which one element undergoes both oxidation and reduction. In the case of H_2O_2, the oxidation number of O is initially -1. In the products of the decomposition, O has an oxidation number of -2 in H_2O and of 0 in O_2.

$$2H_2O_2(aq) \quad \longrightarrow \quad 2H_2O(l) \quad + \quad O_2(g)$$

Combustion

Finally, *combustion* [◄◄ Section 8.1] is a redox process.

$$CH_4(g) \quad + \quad 2O_2(g) \quad \longrightarrow \quad CO_2(g) \quad + \quad 2H_2O(l)$$

Figure 9.8 shows the known oxidation numbers of elements in compounds—arranged according to their positions in the periodic table.

SECTION 9.4 REVIEW

Oxidation-Reduction Reactions

9.4.1   Determine the oxidation number of sulfur in each of the following species: H_2S, HSO_3^-, SCl_2, and S_8.

9.4.2   What species is the reducing agent in the following equation?
$$Mg(s) + 2HCl(aq) \longrightarrow MgCl_2(aq) + H_2(g)$$

9.4.3   Does the following equation represent a redox reaction?
$$2Mg(s) + O_2(g) \longrightarrow 2MgO(s)$$

9.4.4   According to the activity series, does the following redox reaction occur?
$$Fe(s) + NiBr_2(aq) \longrightarrow FeBr_2(aq) + Ni(s)$$

1 1A																	18 8A
1 **H** +1 −1	2 2A											13 3A	14 4A	15 5A	16 6A	17 7A	**2** **He**
3 **Li** +1	**4** **Be** +2											**5** **B** +3	**6** **C** +4 +2 −4	**7** **N** +5 +4 +3 +2 +1 −3	**8** **O** +2 −½ −1 −2	**9** **F** −1	**10** **Ne**
11 **Na** +1	**12** **Mg** +2	3 3B	4 4B	5 5B	6 6B	7 7B	8	9 8B	10	11 1B	12 2B	**13** **Al** +3	**14** **Si** +4 −4	**15** **P** +5 +3 −3	**16** **S** +6 +4 +2 −2	**17** **Cl** +7 +6 +5 +4 +3 +1 −1	**18** **Ar**
19 **K** +1	**20** **Ca** +2	**21** **Sc** +3	**22** **Ti** +4 +3 +2	**23** **V** +5 +4 +3 +2	**24** **Cr** +6 +5 +4 +3 +2	**25** **Mn** +7 +6 +4 +3 +2	**26** **Fe** +3 +2	**27** **Co** +3 +2	**28** **Ni** +2	**29** **Cu** +2 +1	**30** **Zn** +2	**31** **Ga** +3	**32** **Ge** +4 −4	**33** **As** +5 +3 −3	**34** **Se** +6 +4 −2	**35** **Br** +5 +3 +1 −1	**36** **Kr** +4 +2
37 **Rb** +1	**38** **Sr** +2	**39** **Y** +3	**40** **Zr** +4	**41** **Nb** +5 +4	**42** **Mo** +6 +4 +3	**43** **Tc** +7 +6 +4	**44** **Ru** +8 +6 +4 +3	**45** **Rh** +4 +3 +2	**46** **Pd** +4 +2	**47** **Ag** +1	**48** **Cd** +2	**49** **In** +3	**50** **Sn** +4 +2	**51** **Sb** +5 +3 −3	**52** **Te** +6 +4 −2	**53** **I** +7 +5 +1 −1	**54** **Xe** +6 +4 +2
55 **Cs** +1	**56** **Ba** +2	**57** **La** +3	**72** **Hf** +4	**73** **Ta** +5	**74** **W** +6 +4	**75** **Re** +7 +6 +4	**76** **Os** +8 +4	**77** **Ir** +4 +3	**78** **Pt** +4 +2	**79** **Au** +3 +1	**80** **Hg** +2 +1	**81** **Tl** +3 +1	**82** **Pb** +4 +2	**83** **Bi** +5 +3	**84** **Po** +2	**85** **At** −1	**86** **Rn**

Figure 9.8 Periodic table showing oxidation numbers for each element. The most common oxidation numbers are shown in red.

9.5 CONCENTRATION OF SOLUTIONS

One of the factors that can influence reactions in aqueous solution is concentration. The *concentration* of a solution is the amount of solute dissolved in a given quantity of solvent or solution. Consider the two solutions of iodine pictured in Figure 9.9. The solution on the left is more concentrated than the one on the right—that is, it contains a higher ratio of solute to solvent. By contrast, the solution on the right is more dilute. The color is more intense in the more concentrated solution. Often the concentrations of reactants determine how fast a chemical reaction occurs. For example, the reaction of magnesium metal and acid [◀◀ Section 9.4] happens faster if the concentration of acid is greater. As we will see in Chapter 13, there are several different ways to express the concentration of a solution. In this chapter, we introduce only molarity, which is one of the most commonly used units of concentration.

Multi 9.9
Solutions—preparation of solutions

Student Annotation: The qualitative terms *concentrated* and *dilute* are relative terms, like *expensive* and *cheap*.

Molarity

Molarity, or *molar concentration,* symbolized *M*, is defined as the number of moles of solute per liter of solution. Thus, 1 L of a 1.5 molar solution of glucose ($C_6H_{12}O_6$), written as 1.5 *M* $C_6H_{12}O_6$, contains 1.5 moles of dissolved glucose. Half a liter of the same solution would contain 0.75 mole

Student Annotation: Molarity can equally well be defined as millimoles per milliliter (mmol/mL), which can simplify some calculations.

Figure 9.9 Two solutions of iodine in benzene. The solution on the left is more concentrated. The solution on the right is more dilute.

Concentrated solution:
More solute particles per unit volume

Dilute solution:
Fewer solute particles per unit volume

of dissolved glucose, a milliliter of the solution would contain 1.5×10^{-3} mole of dissolved glucose, and so on.

Equation 9.1	$$\text{molarity} = \frac{\text{moles solute}}{\text{liters solution}}$$

In order to calculate the molarity of a solution, we divide the number of moles of solute by the volume of the solution in liters.

Equation 9.1 can be rearranged in three ways to solve for any of the three variables: molarity (*M*), moles of solute (mol), or volume of solution in liters (L).

Student Annotation: Students sometimes have difficulty seeing how units cancel in these equations. It may help to write *M* as mol/L until you become completely comfortable with these equations.

$$(1)\ M = \frac{\text{mol}}{\text{L}} \qquad (2)\ L = \frac{\text{mol}}{M} \qquad (3)\ \text{mol} = M \times L$$

Worked Example 9.8 illustrates how to use these equations to solve for molarity, volume of solution, and moles of solute.

Worked Example 9.8

For an aqueous solution of glucose ($C_6H_{12}O_6$), determine (a) the molarity of 2.00 L of a solution that contains 50.0 g of glucose, (b) the volume of this solution that would contain 0.250 mole of glucose, and (c) the number of moles of glucose in 0.500 L of this solution.

Strategy Convert the mass of glucose given to moles, and use the equations for interconversions of *M*, liters, and moles to calculate the answers.

Setup The molar mass of glucose is 180.2 g.

$$\text{moles of glucose} = \frac{50.0\ \text{g}}{180.2\ \text{g/mol}} = 0.277\ \text{mol}$$

Solution

Student Annotation: A common way to state the concentration of this solution is to say, "This solution is 0.139 *M* in glucose."

(a) $\text{molarity} = \dfrac{0.277\ \text{mol}\ C_6H_{12}O_6}{2.00\ \text{L solution}} = 0.139\ M$

(b) $\text{volume} = \dfrac{0.250\ \text{mol}\ C_6H_{12}O_6}{0.139\ M\ \text{solution}} = 1.80\ \text{L}$

(c) moles of $C_6H_{12}O_6$ in 0.500 L = 0.500 L $\times$ 0.139 M = 0.0695 mol

Think About It

Check to see that the magnitudes of your answers are logical. For example, the mass given in the problem corresponds to 0.277 mole of solute. If you are asked, as in part (b), for the volume that contains a number of moles smaller than 0.277, make sure your answer is smaller than the original volume.

Practice Problem A For an aqueous solution of sucrose ($C_{12}H_{22}O_{11}$), determine (a) the molarity of 5.00 L of a solution that contains 235 g of sucrose, (b) the volume of this solution that would contain 1.26 mole of sucrose, and (c) the number of moles of sucrose in 1.89 L of this solution.

Practice Problem B For an aqueous solution of sodium chloride (NaCl), determine (a) the molarity of 3.75 L of a solution that contains 155 g of sodium chloride, (b) the volume of this solution that would contain 4.58 moles of sodium chloride, and (c) the number of moles of sodium chloride in 22.75 L of this solution.

The procedure for preparing a solution of known molarity is shown in Figure 9.10 (pp. 334–335). First, the solute is weighed accurately and transferred, often with a funnel, to a volumetric flask of the desired volume. Next, water is added to the flask, which is then swirled to dissolve the solid. After all the solid has dissolved, more water is added slowly to bring the level of solution exactly to the volume mark. Knowing the volume of the solution in the flask and the quantity of compound dissolved, we can determine the molarity of the solution using Equation 9.1. Note that this procedure does not require that we know the exact amount of water added. Because of the way molarity is defined, it is important only that we know the final volume of the *solution*.

Multi 9.10
Figure 9.10 Preparing a solution from a solid

Student Annotation: It is important to remember that molarity is defined in terms of the volume of solution, not the volume of solvent. In many cases, these two are not the same.

Dilution

Concentrated "stock" solutions of commonly used substances typically are kept in the laboratory stockroom. Often we need to dilute these stock solutions before using them. *Dilution* is the process of preparing a less concentrated solution from a more concentrated one. Suppose that we want to prepare 1.00 L of a 0.400 M $KMnO_4$ solution from a solution of 1.00 M $KMnO_4$. For this purpose we need 0.400 mole of $KMnO_4$. Because there is 1.00 mole of $KMnO_4$ in 1.00 L of a 1.00 M $KMnO_4$ solution, there is 0.400 mole of $KMnO_4$ in 0.400 L of the same solution:

Multi 9.11
Solution—dilution

$$\frac{1.00 \text{ mol } KMnO_4}{1.00 \text{ L of solution}} = \frac{0.400 \text{ mol } KMnO_4}{0.400 \text{ L of solution}}$$

Therefore, we must withdraw 400 mL from the 1.00 M $KMnO_4$ solution and dilute it to 1.00 L by adding water (in a 1.00-L volumetric flask). This method gives us 1.00 L of the desired 0.400 M $KMnO_4$.

In carrying out a dilution process, it is useful to remember that adding more solvent to a given amount of the stock solution changes (decreases) the concentration of the solution without changing the number of moles of solute present in the solution (Figure 9.11, p. 336).

moles of solute before dilution = moles of solute after dilution   **Equation 9.2**

Using arrangement (3) of Equation 9.1, we can calculate the number of moles of solute:

$$\text{moles of solute} = \frac{\text{moles of solute}}{\text{liters of solution}} \times \text{liters of solution}$$

Because the number of moles of solute before the dilution is the same as that after dilution, we can write

$$M_c \times L_c = M_d \times L_d \qquad \qquad \textbf{Equation 9.3}$$

where the subscripts c and d stand for *concentrated* and *dilute*, respectively. Thus, by knowing the molarity of the concentrated stock solution (M_c) and the desired final molarity (M_d) and volume (L_d) of the dilute solution, we can calculate the volume of stock solution required for the dilution (L_c).

Figure 9.10

Preparing a Solution from a Solid

Weigh out the solid KMnO$_4$.
(The tare function on a digital
balance automatically subtracts
the mass of the weighing paper.)

The mass likely will not be
exactly the calculated number.

Transfer the weighed KMnO$_4$
to the volumetric flask.

Calculate the mass of KMnO$_4$ necessary
for the target concentration of 0.1 M.

$$\frac{0.1 \text{ mol}}{\text{L}} \times 0.2500 \text{ L} = 0.02500 \text{ mol}$$

$$0.02500 \text{ mol} \times \frac{158.04 \text{ g}}{\text{mol}} = 3.951 \text{ g KMnO}_4$$

Add water sufficient to dissolve the KMnO₄.

Swirl the flask to dissolve the solid.

Add more water.

Fill exactly to the calibration mark using a wash bottle or eye dropper.

After capping and inverting the flask to ensure complete mixing, we calculate the actual concentration of the prepared solution.

$$3.896 \text{ g KMnO}_4 \times \frac{1 \text{ mol}}{158.04 \text{ g}} = 0.024652 \text{ mol}$$

$$\frac{0.024652 \text{ mol}}{0.2500 \text{ L}} = 0.09861 \ M$$

What's the point?

The goal is to prepare a solution of precisely known concentration, with that concentration being very close to the target concentration of 0.1 M. Note that because 0.1 is a *specified* number, it does not limit the number of significant figures in our calculations.

Figure 9.11 Dilution changes the concentration of a solution; it does not change the number of moles of solute in the solution.

Add solvent

Before dilution:
More solute particles per unit volume

After dilution:
Fewer solute particles per unit volume

Because most volumes measured in the laboratory are in milliliters rather than liters, it is worth pointing out that Equation 9.3 can be written with volumes of the concentrated and dilute solutions in milliliters.

Student Annotation: Students sometimes resist using the unit *millimole*. However, using the $M_c \times mL_c = M_d \times mL_d$ form of Equation 9.4 often reduces the number of steps in a problem thereby reducing the number of opportunities to make calculation errors.

Equation 9.4	$M_c \times mL_c = M_d \times mL_d$

In this form of the equation, the product of each side is in millimoles (mmol) rather than moles. We apply Equation 9.4 in Worked Example 9.9.

Worked Example 9.9

What volume of 12.0 *M* HCl, a common laboratory stock solution, must be used to prepare 250.0 mL of 0.125 *M* HCl?

Strategy Because the desired final volume is given in milliliters, we use Equation 9.4 to determine the volume of 12.0 *M* HCl required for the dilution.

Setup $M_c = 12.0\ M$, $M_d = 0.125\ M$, $mL_d = 250.0\ mL$.

Solution

$$12.0\ M \times mL_c = 0.125\ M \times 250.0\ mL$$

$$mL_c = \frac{0.125\ M \times 250.0\ mL}{12.0\ M} = 2.60\ mL$$

Student Annotation: It is very important to note that, for safety, when diluting a concentrated acid, the acid must be added to the water, and *not* the other way around.

Think About It
Plug the answer into Equation 9.4, and make sure that the product of concentration and volume on both sides of the equation give the same result.

Practice Problem A What volume of 6.0 *M* H_2SO_4 is needed to prepare 500.0 mL of a solution that is 0.25 *M* in H_2SO_4?

Practice Problem B What volume of 0.20 *M* H_2SO_4 can be prepared by diluting 125 mL of 6.0 *M* H_2SO_4?

Serial Dilution

A series of dilutions may be used in the laboratory to prepare a number of increasingly dilute solutions from a stock solution. The method involves preparing a solution as described on pages 334 and 335 and diluting a portion of the prepared solution to make a *more* dilute solution. For example, we could use a 0.400 *M* $KMnO_4$ solution to prepare a series of five increasingly dilute solutions, with the concentration decreasing by a factor of 10 at each stage. Using a volumetric pipette, we withdraw 10.00 mL of the 0.400 *M* solution and deliver it into a 100.00-mL volumetric flask as shown in Figure 9.12(a). We then dilute to the volumetric mark and cap and invert the flask to ensure complete mixing. The concentration of the newly prepared solution is determined using Equation 9.4, where M_c is 0.400 *M*, and mL_c and mL_d are 10.00 mL and 100.00 mL, respectively.

$$0.400 \ M \times 10.00 \ mL = M_d \times 100.00 \ mL$$

$$M_d = 0.0400 \ M \text{ or } 4.00 \times 10^{-2} \ M$$

Repeating this process four more times, each time using the most recently prepared solution as the "concentrated" solution and diluting 10.00 mL to 100.00 mL, we get five $KMnO_4$ solutions with concentrations $4.00 \times 10^{-2} \ M$, $4.00 \times 10^{-3} \ M$, $4.00 \times 10^{-4} \ M$, $4.00 \times 10^{-5} \ M$, and $4.00 \times 10^{-6} \ M$ [Figure 9.12(b)]. This type of serial dilution is commonly used to prepare "standard" solutions with precisely known concentrations, for quantitative analysis.

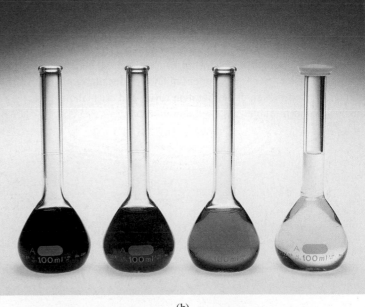

(a)   (b)

Figure 9.12 Serial dilution. (a) A solution of precisely known concentration is prepared in a volumetric flask. A precise volume of the solution is transferred to a second volumetric flask and subsequently diluted. (b) A precise volume of the second solution is transferred to a third volumetric flask and diluted. The process is repeated several times, each time producing more dilute solution. In this example, the concentration is reduced by a factor of 10 at each stage.

Thinking Outside the Box

Visible Spectrophotometry

As we saw in Chapter 3, white light is composed of all the colors of the rainbow. In fact, a rainbow results from the separation of white light by water droplets into the wavelengths that make up the visible spectrum [◄◄ Section 3.2]. Selective absorption of visible light is what makes some solutions appear colored; and, for a solution that is colored, the intensity of color is related to the solution's concentration (see Figure 9.9). This effect gives rise to a type of analysis known as *visible spectrophotometry*. A visible spectrophotometer compares the intensity of light that enters a sample (called the incident light) I_0, with the intensity of the light that is transmitted through the sample, I. *Transmittance* (T) is the ratio of I to I_0.

$$T = \frac{I}{I_0}$$

Absorbance (A) measures how much light is absorbed by the solution and is defined as the negative logarithm of transmittance.

Student Annotation: Both transmittance and absorbance are *unitless* quantities.

$$A = -\log T = -\log \frac{I}{I_0}$$

Plotting absorbance as a function of wavelength gives an absorption spectrum. The absorption spectrum, that is, the characteristic absorption over a range of wavelengths, can serve as a sort of fingerprint for the identification of a compound in solution.

The quantitative relationship between absorbance and a solution's concentration is called the Beer-Lambert law and is expressed as

$$A = \varepsilon bc$$

where ε = proportionality constant called the molar absorptivity

b = path length of solution (in cm) through which light travels

c = molar concentration of solution

The *molar absorptivity* is specific to a chemical species and is a measure of how strongly the species absorbs light a particular wavelength. The diagram above at right shows how absorbance depends on path length and concentration. Quantitative analysis using visible spectrophotometry generally requires selection of the appropriate wavelength for analysis (usually the wavelength at which absorbance is highest), determination of absorbance for a series of solutions of known concentration (the standards), construction of a calibration curve, and calculation of an unknown concentration using the calibration curve.

(a) A colored solution absorbs some of the incident visible light, diminishing the light's intensity from I_0 to I. (b) The intensity is reduced more when the light travels through a longer path length of the same solution or (c) when the light travels through the same path length of a more concentrated solution.

A calibration curve with absorbance (A) on the y axis and molar concentration on the x axis. Linear regression is done using a spreadsheet or graphing calculator to generate the line that best fits all the calibration data. An unknown concentration can be determined by drawing a dashed line from the point on the calibration line corresponding to the measured absorbance to the x axis, as shown. In this case, a measured absorbance of 0.83 corresponds to a concentration of 1.1 M.

Worked Example 9.10 illustrates the method of serial dilution to prepare a series of standard HCl solutions.

Worked Example 9.10

Starting with a 2.0 M stock solution of hydrochloric acid, four standard solutions (1 to 4) are prepared by sequential diluting 10.00 mL of each solution to 250.00 mL. Determine (a) the concentrations of all four standard solutions and (b) the number of moles of HCl in each solution.

Strategy In part (a), because the volumes are all given in milliliters, we will use Equation 9.4, rearranged to solve for M_d, to determine the molar concentration of each standard solution. In part (b), Equation 9.1, rearranged to solve for moles, can be used to calculate the number of moles in each. We must remember to convert each solution's volume to liters so that units will cancel properly.

Setup (a) $M_d = \dfrac{M_c \times mL_c}{mL_d}$; (b) mol = $M \times$ L, 250.00 mL = 2.500×10^{-1} L

Solution (a) $M_{d1} = \dfrac{2.00\ M \times 10.00\ mL}{250.00\ mL} = 8.00 \times 10^{-2}\ M$

$M_{d2} = \dfrac{8.00 \times 10^{-2}\ M \times 10.00\ mL}{250.00\ mL} = 3.20 \times 10^{-3}\ M$

$M_{d3} = \dfrac{3.20 \times 10^{-3}\ M \times 10.00\ mL}{250.00\ mL} = 1.28 \times 10^{-4}\ M$

$M_{d4} = \dfrac{1.28 \times 10^{-4}\ M \times 10.00\ mL}{250.00\ mL} = 5.12 \times 10^{-6}\ M$

(b) $mol_1 = 8.00 \times 10^{-2}\ M \times 2.500 \times 10^{-1}\ L = 2.00 \times 10^{-2}\ mol$
$mol_2 = 3.20 \times 10^{-3}\ M \times 2.500 \times 10^{-1}\ L = 8.00 \times 10^{-4}\ mol$
$mol_3 = 1.28 \times 10^{-4}\ M \times 2.500 \times 10^{-1}\ L = 3.20 \times 10^{-5}\ mol$
$mol_4 = 5.12 \times 10^{-6}\ M \times 2.500 \times 10^{-1}\ L = 1.28 \times 10^{-6}\ mol$

Think About It
Serial dilution is one of the fundamental practices of homeopathy. Some remedies undergo so many serial dilutions that very few (if any) molecules of the original substance still exist in the final preparation.

Practice Problem A Starting with a 6.552 M stock solution of HNO_3, five standard solutions are prepared via serial dilution. At each stage, 25.00 mL of solution is diluted to 100.00 mL. Determine (a) the concentration of and (b) the number of moles of HNO_3 in each standard solution.

Practice Problem B Five standard solutions of HBr are prepared by serial dilution in which, at each stage, 10.00 mL is diluted to 150.00 mL. Given that the concentration of the most dilute solution is $3.22 \times 10^{-6}\ M$, determine the concentration of the original HBr stock solution.

Solution Stoichiometry

Soluble ionic compounds such as $KMnO_4$ are strong electrolytes, so they undergo complete dissociation upon dissolution and exist in solution entirely as ions. $KMnO_4$ dissociates, for example, to give 1 mole of potassium ion and 1 mole of permanganate ion for every mole of potassium permanganate. Thus, a 0.400 M solution of $KMnO_4$ will be 0.400 M in K^+ and 0.400 M in MnO_4^-.

In the case of a soluble ionic compound with other than a 1:1 combination of constituent ions, we must use the subscripts in the chemical formula to determine the concentration of each ion in solution. Sodium sulfate (Na_2SO_4) dissociates, for example, to give twice as many sodium ions as sulfate ions.

$$Na_2SO_4(s) \xrightarrow{H_2O} 2Na^+(aq) + SO_4^{2-}(aq)$$

Therefore, a solution that is 0.35 M in Na_2SO_4 is actually 0.70 M in Na^+ and 0.35 M in SO_4^{2-}. Frequently, molar concentrations of dissolved species are expressed using square brackets. Thus, the concentrations of species in a 0.35 M solution of Na_2SO_4 can be expressed as follows: $[Na^+] = 0.70\ M$ and $[SO_4^{2-}] = 0.35\ M$. Worked Example 9.11 lets you practice relating concentrations of compounds and concentrations of individual ions using solution stoichiometry.

Worked Example 9.11

Using square-bracket notation, express the concentration of (a) chloride ion in a solution that is 1.02 M in $AlCl_3$, (b) nitrate ion in a solution that is 0.451 M in $Ca(NO_3)_2$, and (c) Na_2CO_3 in a solution in which $[Na^+] = 0.124\ M$.

Strategy Use the concentration given in each case and the stoichiometry indicated in the corresponding chemical formula to determine the concentration of the specified ion or compound.

Setup

(a) There are 3 moles of Cl^- ion for every 1 mole of $AlCl_3$,

$$AlCl_3(s) \xrightarrow{H_2O} Al^{3+}(aq) + 3Cl^-(aq)$$

so the concentration of Cl^- will be three times the concentration of $AlCl_3$.

(b) There are 2 moles of nitrate ion for every 1 mole of $Ca(NO_3)_2$,

$$Ca(NO_3)_2(s) \xrightarrow{H_2O} Ca^{2+}(aq) + 2NO_3^-(aq)$$

so $[NO_3^-]$ will be twice $[Ca(NO_3)_2]$.

(c) There is 1 mole of Na_2CO_3 for every 2 moles of sodium ion,

$$Na_2CO_3(s) \xrightarrow{H_2O} 2Na^+(aq) + CO_3^{2-}(aq)$$

so $[Na_2CO_3]$ will be half of $[Na^+]$. (Assume that Na_2CO_3 is the only source of Na^+ ions in this solution.)

Solution

(a) $[Cl^-] = [AlCl_3] \times \dfrac{3\ mol\ Cl^-}{1\ mol\ AlCl_3}$

$\quad = \dfrac{1.02\ mol\ AlCl_3}{L} \times \dfrac{3\ mol\ Cl^-}{1\ mol\ AlCl_3}$

$\quad = \dfrac{3.06\ mol\ Cl^-}{L}$

$\quad = 3.06\ M$

(b) $[NO_3^-] = [Ca(NO_3)_2] \times \dfrac{2\ mol\ NO_3^-}{1\ mol\ Ca(NO_3)_2}$

$\quad = \dfrac{0.451\ mol\ Ca(NO_3)_2}{L} \times \dfrac{2\ mol\ NO_3^-}{1\ mol\ Ca(NO_3)_2}$

$\quad = \dfrac{0.902\ mol\ NO_3^-}{L}$

$\quad = 0.902\ M$

(c) $[Na_2CO_3] = \dfrac{[Na^+] \times 1\ mol\ Na_2CO_3}{2\ mol\ Na^+}$

$\quad = \dfrac{0.124\ mol\ Na^+}{L} \times \dfrac{1\ mol\ Na_2CO_3}{2\ mol\ Na^+}$

$\quad = \dfrac{0.0620\ mol\ Na_2CO_3}{L}$

$\quad = 0.0620\ M$

Think About It
Make sure that units cancel properly. Remember that the concentration of an ion can never be less than the concentration of its dissolved parent compound. It will always be the concentration of the parent compound times its stoichiometric subscript in the chemical formula.

Practice Problem A Using the square-bracket notation, express the concentrations of ions in a solution that is 0.750 M in aluminum sulfate [$Al_2(SO_4)_3$].

Practice Problem B Determine the concentration of the compound for a solution in which [SO_4^{2-}] = 0.36 M, if the compound is (a) Na_2SO_4, (b) $MgSO_4$, and (c) $Al_2(SO_4)_3$.

SECTION 9.5 REVIEW

Concentration of Solutions

9.5.1 Calculate the molar concentration of a solution prepared by dissolving 58.5 g NaOH in enough water to yield 1.25 L of solution.

9.5.2 What mass of glucose ($C_6H_{12}O_6$) in grams must be used in order to prepare 500 mL of a solution that is 2.50 M in glucose?

9.5.3 What volume in mL of a 1.20 M HCl solution must be diluted in order to prepare 1.00 L of 0.0150 M HCl?

9.5.4 For a solution that is 0.18 M in Na_2CO_3, express the concentration in terms of each of the individual ions.

9.6 AQUEOUS REACTIONS AND CHEMICAL ANALYSIS

Certain aqueous reactions are useful for determining how much of a particular substance is present in a sample. For example, if we want to know the concentration of lead in a sample of water, or if we need to know the concentration of an acid, knowledge of precipitation reactions, acid-base reactions, and solution stoichiometry will be useful. Two common types of such quantitative analyses are *gravimetric analysis* and *acid-base titration*.

Student Annotation: Experiments that measure the amount of a substance present are called *quantitative analysis*.

Gravimetric Analysis

Gravimetric analysis is an analytical technique based on the measurement of mass. One type of gravimetric analysis experiment involves the formation and isolation of a precipitate, such as AgCl(s):

Student Annotation: According to the information in Table 9.2, AgCl is an insoluble exception to the chlorides, which typically are soluble.

$$AgNO_3(aq) + NaCl(aq) \longrightarrow NaNO_3(aq) + AgCl(s)$$

This reaction is often used in gravimetric analysis because the reactants can be obtained in pure form. The net ionic equation is

$$Ag^+(aq) + Cl^-(aq) \longrightarrow AgCl(s)$$

Suppose, for example, that we wanted to test the purity of a sample of NaCl by determining the percent by mass of Cl. First, we would accurately weigh out some NaCl and dissolve it in water.

To this mixture, we would add enough $AgNO_3$ solution to cause the precipitation of all the Cl^- ions present in solution as AgCl. (In this procedure, NaCl is the limiting reagent and $AgNO_3$ is the excess reagent.) We would then separate, dry, and weigh the AgCl precipitate. From the measured mass of AgCl, we would be able to calculate the mass of Cl using the percent by mass of Cl in AgCl. Because all the Cl in the precipitate came from the dissolved NaCl, the amount of Cl that we calculate is the amount that was present in the original NaCl sample. We could then calculate the percent by mass of Cl in the NaCl and compare it to the known composition of NaCl to determine its purity.

Gravimetric analysis is a highly accurate technique, because the mass of a sample can be measured accurately. However, this procedure is applicable only to reactions that go to completion or have nearly 100 percent yield. In addition, if AgCl were soluble to any significant degree, it would not be possible to remove all the Cl^- ions from the original solution, and the subsequent calculation would be in error. Worked Example 9.12 shows the calculations involved in a gravimetric experiment.

Worked Example 9.12

A 0.8633-g sample of an ionic compound containing chloride ions and an unknown metal cation is dissolved in water and treated with an excess of $AgNO_3$. If 1.5615 g of AgCl precipitate forms, what is the percent by mass of Cl in the original compound?

Strategy Using the mass of AgCl precipitate and the percent composition of AgCl, determine what mass of chloride the precipitate contains. The chloride in the precipitate was originally in the unknown compound. Using the mass of chloride and the mass of the original sample, determine the percent Cl in the compound.

Setup To determine the percent Cl in AgCl, divide the molar mass of Cl by the molar mass of AgCl:

$$\frac{34.45 \text{ g}}{(34.45 \text{ g} + 107.9 \text{ g})} \times 100\% = 24.72\%$$

The mass of Cl in the precipitate is $0.2472 \times 1.5615 \text{ g} = 0.3860 \text{ g}$.

Solution The percent Cl in the unknown compound is the mass of Cl in the precipitate divided by the mass of the original sample:

$$\frac{0.3860 \text{ g}}{0.8633 \text{ g}} \times 100\% = 44.71\%$$

Think About It
Pay close attention to which numbers correspond to which quantities. It is easy in this type of problem to lose track of which mass is the precipitate and which is the original sample. Dividing by the wrong mass at the end will result in an incorrect answer.

Practice Problem A A 0.5620-g sample of an ionic compound containing the bromide ion (Br^-) is dissolved in water and treated with an excess of $AgNO_3$. If the mass of the AgBr precipitate that forms is 0.8868 g, what is the percent by mass of Br in the original compound?

Practice Problem B A sample that is 63.9 percent chloride by mass is dissolved in water and treated with an excess of $AgNO_3$. If the mass of the AgCl precipitate that forms is 1.085 g, what was the mass of the original sample?

Gravimetric analysis is a quantitative method, not a qualitative one, so it does not establish the identity of the unknown substance. Thus, the results in Worked Example 9.12 do *not* identify the cation. However, knowing the percent by mass of Cl greatly helps us narrow the possibilities. Because no two compounds containing the same anion (or cation) have the same percent composition by mass, comparison of the percent by mass obtained from gravimetric analysis with that calculated from a series of known compounds could reveal the identity of the unknown compounds.

Acid-Base Titrations

Quantitative studies of acid-base neutralization reactions are most conveniently carried out using a technique known as titration. In **titration**, a solution of accurately known concentration, called a **standard solution**, is added gradually to another solution of unknown concentration, until the chemical reaction between the two solutions is complete, as shown in Figure 9.13. If we know the volumes of the standard and unknown solutions used in the titration, along with the concentration of the standard solution, we can calculate the concentration of the unknown solution.

A solution of the strong base sodium hydroxide can be used as the standard solution in a titration, but it must first be *standardized,* because sodium hydroxide in solution reacts with carbon dioxide in the air, making its concentration unstable over time. We can standardize the sodium hydroxide solution by titrating it against an acid solution of accurately known concentration. The acid often chosen for this task is a monoprotic acid called potassium hydrogen phthalate (KHP), for which the molecular formula is $KHC_8H_4O_4$. KHP is a white, soluble solid that is commercially available in highly pure form. The reaction between KHP and sodium hydroxide is

$$KHC_8H_4O_4(aq) + NaOH(aq) \longrightarrow KNaC_8H_4O_4(aq) + H_2O(l)$$

$$HC_8H_4O_4^-$$

Multi 9.12
Chemical reactions—titrations

Student Annotation: *Standardization* in this context is the meticulous determination of concentration.

Student Annotation: Note that KHP is a *monoprotic* acid, so it reacts in a 1:1 ratio with hydroxide ion.

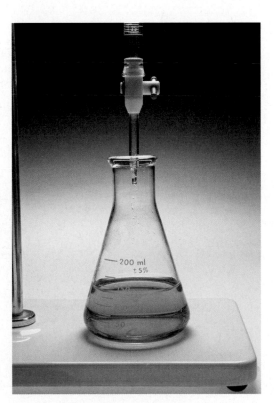

Figure 9.13 Apparatus for titration.

and the net ionic equation is

$$HC_8H_4O_4^-(aq) + OH^-(aq) \longrightarrow C_8H_4O_4^{2-}(aq) + H_2O(l)$$

To standardize a solution of NaOH with KHP, a known amount of KHP is transferred to an Erlenmeyer flask and some distilled water is added to make up a solution. Next, NaOH solution is carefully added to the KHP solution from a buret until all the acid has reacted with base. This point in the titration, where the acid has been completely neutralized, is called the *equivalence point.* It is usually signaled by the *endpoint,* where an indicator causes a sharp change in the color of the solution. In acid-base titrations, *indicators* are substances that have distinctly different colors in acidic and basic media. One commonly used indicator is phenolphthalein, which is colorless in acidic and neutral solutions but reddish pink in basic solutions. At the equivalence point, all the KHP present has been neutralized by the added NaOH and the solution is still colorless. However, if we add just one more drop of NaOH solution from the buret, the solution will be basic and will immediately turn pink. Worked Example 9.13 illustrates just such a titration.

Student Annotation: The endpoint in a titration is used to approximate the equivalence point. A careful choice of indicators, which we will discuss in Chapter 16, helps make this approximation reasonable. Phenolphthalein, although very common, is not appropriate for every acid-base titration.

Worked Example 9.13

In a titration experiment, a student finds that 25.49 mL of an NaOH solution is needed to neutralize 0.7137 g of KHP. What is the concentration (in M) of the NaOH solution?

Strategy Using the mass given and the molar mass of KHP, determine the number of moles of KHP. Recognize that the number of moles of NaOH in the volume given is equal to the number of moles of KHP. Divide moles of NaOH by volume (in liters) to get molarity.

Setup The molar mass of KHP ($KHC_8H_4O_4$) = [39.1 g + 5(1.008 g) + 8(12.01 g) + 4(16.00 g)] = 204.2 g/mol.

Solution

$$\text{moles of KHP} = \frac{0.7137 \text{ g}}{204.2 \text{ g/mol}} = 0.003495 \text{ mol}$$

Because moles of KHP = moles of NaOH, then moles of NaOH = 0.003495 mol.

$$\text{molarity of NaOH} = \frac{0.003495 \text{ mol}}{0.02549 \text{ L}} = 0.1371 \text{ } M$$

Think About It
Remember that molarity can also be defined as mmol/mL. Try solving the problem again using millimoles and make sure you get the same answer.

$$0.003495 \text{ mol} = 3.495 \times 10^{-3} \text{ mol}$$

$$= 3.495 \text{ mmol}$$

and

$$\frac{3.495 \text{ mmol}}{25.49 \text{ mL}} = 0.1371 \text{ } M$$

Practice Problem A How many grams of KHP are needed to neutralize 22.36 mL of a 0.1205 M NaOH solution?

Practice Problem B What volume (in mL) of a 0.2550 M NaOH solution can be neutralized by 10.75 g of KHP?

The reaction between NaOH and KHP is a relatively simple acid-base neutralization. Suppose, though, that instead of KHP, we wanted to use a diprotic acid such as H_2SO_4 for the titration. The reaction is represented by

$$2NaOH(aq) + H_2SO_4(aq) \longrightarrow Na_2SO_4(aq) + 2H_2O(l)$$

Because 2 mol NaOH $\simeq$ 1 mol H_2SO_4, we need twice as much NaOH to react completely with an H_2SO_4 solution of the *same* molar concentration and volume as a monoprotic acid such as HCl. On the other hand, we would need twice the amount of HCl to neutralize a $Ba(OH)_2$ solution compared to an NaOH solution having the same concentration and volume because 1 mole of $Ba(OH)_2$ yields 2 moles of OH^- ions:

$$2HCl(aq) + Ba(OH)_2(aq) \longrightarrow BaCl_2(aq) + 2H_2O(l)$$

In any acid-base titration, regardless of what acid and base are reacting, the total number of moles of H^+ ions that have reacted at the equivalence point must be equal to the total number of moles of OH^- ions that have reacted. Worked Example 9.14 explores the titration of an NaOH solution with a diprotic acid.

Worked Example 9.14

What volume (in mL) of a 0.203 *M* NaOH solution is needed to neutralize 25.0 mL of a 0.188 *M* H_2SO_4 solution?

Strategy First, write and balance the chemical equation that corresponds to the neutralization reaction:

$$2NaOH(aq) + H_2SO_4(aq) \longrightarrow Na_2SO_4(aq) + 2H_2O(l)$$

The base and the diprotic acid combine in a 2:1 ratio: 2NaOH $\simeq$ H_2SO_4. Use the molarity and the volume given to determine the number of millimoles of H_2SO_4. Use the number of millimoles of H_2SO_4 to determine the number of millimoles of NaOH. Using millimoles of NaOH and the concentration given, determine the volume of NaOH that will contain the correct number of millimoles.

Setup The necessary conversion factors are:

From the balanced equation: $\dfrac{2 \text{ mmol NaOH}}{1 \text{ mmol } H_2SO_4}$

From the molarity of the NaOH given: $\dfrac{1 \text{ mL NaOH}}{0.203 \text{ mmol NaOH}}$

Solution

$$\text{millimoles of } H_2SO_4 = 0.188 \text{ } M \times 25.0 \text{ mL} = 4.70 \text{ mmol}$$

$$\text{millimoles of NaOH required} = 4.70 \text{ mmol } H_2SO_4 \times \frac{2 \text{ mmol NaOH}}{1 \text{ mmol } H_2SO_4} = 9.40 \text{ mmol NaOH}$$

$$\text{volume of 0.203 } M \text{ NaOH} = 9.40 \text{ mmol NaOH} \times \frac{1 \text{ mL NaOH}}{0.203 \text{ mmol NaOH}} = 46.3 \text{ mL}$$

> **Student Annotation:** Remember: molarity × mL = millimoles. This saves steps in titration problems.

Think About It
Notice that the two concentrations 0.203 *M* and 0.188 *M* are similar. Both round to the same value (~0.20 *M*) to two significant figures. Therefore, the titration of a diprotic acid with a monobasic base of roughly equal concentration should require roughly twice as much base as the beginning volume of acid: 2 × 25.0 mL ≈ 46.3 mL.

Practice Problem A How many milliliters of a 1.42 *M* H_2SO_4 solution are needed to neutralize 95.5 mL of a 0.336 *M* KOH solution?

Practice Problem B How many milliliters of a 0.211 *M* HCl solution are needed to neutralize 275 mL of a 0.0350 *M* $Ba(OH)_2$ solution?

Worked Example 9.15 shows how titration with a standard base can be used to determine the molar mass of an unknown acid.

Worked Example 9.15

A 0.1216-g sample of a monoprotic acid is dissolved in 25 mL water, and the resulting solution is titrated with 0.1104 *M* NaOH solution. A 12.5-mL volume of the base is required to neutralize the acid. Calculate the molar mass of the acid.

Strategy Using the concentration and volume of the base, we can determine the number of moles of base required to neutralize the acid. We then determine the number of moles of acid and divide the mass of the acid by the number of moles to get molar mass.

Setup Because the acid is monoprotic, it will react in a 1:1 ratio with the base; therefore, the number of moles of acid will be equal to the number of moles of base. The volume of base in liters is 0.0125 L.

Solution

$$\text{moles of base} = \frac{0.0125\ \text{L}}{0.1104\ \text{mol/L}} = 0.00138\ \text{mol}$$

Because moles of base = moles of acid, the moles of acid = 0.00138 mol. Therefore,

$$\text{molar mass of the acid} = \frac{0.1216\ \text{g}}{0.00138\ \text{mol}} = 88.1\ \text{g/mol}$$

> **Think About It**
> In order for this technique to work, we must know whether the acid is monoprotic, diprotic, or polyprotic. A diprotic acid, for example, would combine in a 1:2 ratio with the base, and the result would have been a molar mass twice as large.

Practice Problem A What is the molar mass of a monoprotic acid if 28.1 mL of 0.0788 *M* NaOH is required to neutralize a 0.205-g sample?

Practice Problem B What is the molar mass of a diprotic acid if 30.5 mL of 0.1112 *M* NaOH is required to neutralize a 0.1365-g sample?

SECTION 9.6 REVIEW

Aqueous Reactions and Chemical Analysis

9.6.1   What mass of AgCl will be recovered if a solution containing 5.00 g of NaCl is treated with enough $AgNO_3$ to precipitate all the chloride ion?

9.6.2   A 10.0-g sample of an unknown ionic compound is dissolved, and the solution is treated with enough $AgNO_3$ to precipitate all the chloride ion and 30.1 g of AgCl are recovered. Is the unknown ionic compound NaCl, KCl, $MgCl_2$, or $BaCl_2$?

9.6.3   If 25.0 mL of an H_2SO_4 solution requires 39.9 mL of 0.228 *M* NaOH to neutralize, what is the concentration of the H_2SO_4 solution?

9.6.4   What volume of 0.144 *M* H_2SO_4 is required to neutralize 25.0 mL of 0.0415 *M* $Ba(OH)_2$?

Learning Outcomes

- Categorize compounds as nonelectrolytes, weak electrolytes, or strong electrolytes.
- Identify weak and strong acids and bases.
- Apply solubility rules toward determining whether a reaction will produce a precipitate.
- Produce the molecular, ionic, and net ionic equations for a reaction.
- Identify the spectator ions in a reaction.
- Identify the driving force for a reaction in aqueous solution.
- Understand the definition of Arrhenius and Brønsted acids and bases.
- Identify an acid as monoprotic, diprotic, or triprotic.
- Predict the neutralization reaction between an acid and a base.
- Identify the various components of an oxidation-reduction reaction including reducing/oxidizing agents and half-reactions.

- Apply oxidation number rules toward determining the oxidation number of each element in a compound or polyatomic ion.
- Utilize the activity series to determine whether a reaction occurs between a metal and ions of another metal.
- Predict the balanced equation for an oxidation-reduction reaction.
- Identify the different types of reactions that may be oxidation-reduction reactions including: combustion, decomposition, and disproportionation.
- Calculate the molarity of a solution.
- Determine the concentration of a solution that has been diluted in addition to applying dilution principles toward serial dilutions.
- Apply concepts of stoichiometry toward reactions in solution and their associated problems including gravimetric analysis and titrations.

Chapter Summary

SECTION 9.1

- A *solution* is a homogeneous mixture consisting of a *solvent* and one or more dissolved species called *solutes.*
- An *electrolyte* is a compound that dissolves in water to give an electrically conducting solution. *Nonelectrolytes* dissolve to give nonconducting solutions. Acids and *bases* are electrolytes.
- Electrolytes may be ionic or molecular. Ionic electrolytes undergo *dissociation* in solution; molecular electrolytes undergo *ionization.* *Strong electrolytes* dissociate (or ionize) completely. *Weak electrolytes* ionize only partially.

SECTION 9.2

- A *precipitation reaction* results in the formation of an insoluble product called a *precipitate.* From general guidelines about solubilities of ionic compounds, we can predict whether a precipitate will form in a reaction.
- *Hydration* is the process in which water molecules surround solute particles.
- *Solubility* is the amount of solute that will dissolve in a specified amount of a given solvent at a specified temperature.
- A *molecular equation* represents a reaction as though none of the reactants or products has dissociated or ionized.
- An *ionic equation* represents the strong electrolytes in a reaction as ions.

- A *spectator ion* is one that is *not* involved in the reaction. Spectator ions appear on both sides of the ionic equation. A *net ionic equation* is an ionic equation from which spectator ions have been eliminated. Reactions in which cations in two ionic compounds exchange anions are called *metathesis* or *double replacement reactions*.

SECTION 9.3

- The hydrogen ion in solution is more realistically represented as the *hydronium ion* (H_3O^+). The terms *hydrogen ion, hydronium ion,* and *proton* are used interchangeably in the context of acid-base reactions.
- *Arrhenius acids* ionize in water to give H^+ ions, whereas *Arrhenius bases* ionize (or *dissociate*) in water to give OH^- ions. *Brønsted acids* donate protons (H^+ ions), whereas *Brønsted bases* accept protons.
- Brønsted acids may be *monoprotic, diprotic,* or *triprotic,* depending on the number of protons they have to donate (the number of ionizable hydrogen atoms they have). In general, an acid with more than one ionizable hydrogen atom is called *polyprotic.* Bases may be *monobasic* or *dibasic.*
- The reaction of an acid and a base is a *neutralization reaction.* The products of a neutralization reaction are water and a *salt.*

SECTION 9.4

- *Oxidation-reduction,* or *redox, reactions* are those in which *electrons* are exchanged. Oxidation and reduction always occur *simultaneously.* You cannot have one without the other.
- *Oxidation* is the loss of electrons; *reduction* is the gain of electrons. In a redox reaction, the *oxidizing agent* is the reactant that gets reduced and the *reducing agent* is the reactant that gets oxidized.
- *Oxidation numbers* or *oxidation states* help us keep track of charge distribution and are assigned to all atoms in a compound or ion according to specific rules.
- Many redox reactions can be further classified as *combination, decomposition, displacement, hydrogen displacement, combustion,* or *disproportionation* reactions. The *activity series* can be used to determine whether or not a displacement reaction will occur.
- A *half-reaction* is a chemical equation representing only the oxidation or only the reduction of an oxidation-reduction reaction. Redox equations, which must be balanced for both mass and charge, can be balanced using the *half-reaction method.*

SECTION 9.5

- The *concentration* of a solution is the amount of solute dissolved in a given amount of solution. *Molarity* (M) or *molar concentration* expresses concentration as the number of moles of solute in 1 L of solution.
- Adding a solvent to a solution, a process known as *dilution,* decreases the concentration (molarity) of the solution without changing the total number of moles of solute present in the solution.

SECTION 9.6

- *Gravimetric analysis* often involves a precipitation reaction.
- Acid-base *titration* involves an acid-base reaction. Typically, a solution of known concentration (a *standard solution*) is added gradually to a solution of unknown concentration with the goal of determining the unknown concentration.
- The point at which the reaction in the titration is complete is called the *equivalence point.* An *indicator* is a substance that changes color at or near the equivalence point of a titration. The point at which the indicator changes color is called the *endpoint* of the titration.

Key Words

Activity series, 326	Electrolyte, 307	Molecular equation, 314	Redox reaction, 321
Arrhenius acid, 318	Endpoint, 344	Monobasic, 319	Reducing agent, 322
Arrhenius base, 318	Equivalence point, 344	Monoprotic, 319	Reduction, 322
Base, 307	Gravimetric analysis, 341	Net ionic equation, 315	Salt, 319
Brønsted acid, 318	Half-reaction, 321	Neutralization reaction, 319	Solubility, 313
Brønsted base, 318	Half-reaction method, 327	Nonelectrolyte, 307	Solute, 307
Concentration, 331	Hydration, 312	Oxidation, 322	Solution, 307
Dibasic, 319	Hydrogen displacement, 329	Oxidation number, 323	Solvent, 307
Dilution, 333	Hydronium ion, 318	Oxidation state, 323	Spectator ion, 315
Diprotic acid, 319	Indicator, 344	Oxidation-reduction reaction, 321	Standard solution, 343
Displacement reaction, 325	Ionic equation, 315		Strong electrolyte, 308
Disproportionation reaction, 330	Ionization, 307	Oxidizing agent, 322	Titration, 343
	Metathesis, 315	Polyprotic, 319	Triprotic acid, 319
Dissociation, 307	Molar concentration, 331	Precipitate, 312	Weak electrolyte, 308
Double replacement, 315	Molarity, 331	Precipitation reaction, 312	

Key Equations

9.1 $$\text{molarity} = \frac{\text{moles solute}}{\text{liters solution}}$$

9.2   moles of solute before dilution = moles of solute after dilution

9.3 $M_c \times L_c = M_d \times L_d$

9.4 $M_c \times mL_c = M_d \times mL_d$

Questions and Problems

SECTION 9.1: GENERAL PROPERTIES OF AQUEOUS SOLUTIONS

Review Questions

9.1 Define *solute, solvent,* and *solution* by describing the process of dissolving a solid in a liquid.

9.2 What is the difference between a nonelectrolyte and an electrolyte? Between a weak electrolyte and a strong electrolyte?

9.3 What is the difference between the symbols $\longrightarrow$ and $\rightleftharpoons$ in chemical equations?

9.4 Although water is classified as a nonelectrolyte, in reality it is an *extremely weak* electrolyte and therefore cannot conduct electricity. Nevertheless, it can be dangerous to operate electrical appliances with wet hands. Explain.

9.5 Identify the species present in aqueous solutions of the following strong electrolytes: (a) LiF, (b) NH_4NO_3, (c) $CaBr_2$, (d) Na_2CO_3.

9.6 The passage of electricity through an electrolyte solution is caused by the movement of (a) electrons only, (b) cations only, (c) anions only, (d) both cations and anions.

9.7 You are given a water-soluble compound X. Describe how you would determine whether it is an electrolyte or a nonelectrolyte. If it is an electrolyte, how would you determine whether it is strong or weak?

Problems

9.8 These diagrams show aqueous solutions of three different compounds: (a) AB, (b) AC, and (c) AD. Arrange the compounds in order of increasing electrolyte strength.

(a)   (b)   (c)

9.9 These diagrams show aqueous solutions of three different compounds: (a) A_2E, (b) A_2F, and (c) A_2G. Arrange the compounds in order of increasing electrolyte strength.

(a)   (b)   (c)

9.10 The aqueous solutions of three compounds are shown in the diagram. Identify each compound as a nonelectrolyte, a weak electrolyte, or a strong electrolyte.

(a)   (b)   (c)

9.11 Which of the following diagrams best represents the hydration of NaCl when dissolved in water? The Cl^- ion is larger in size than the Na^+ ion.

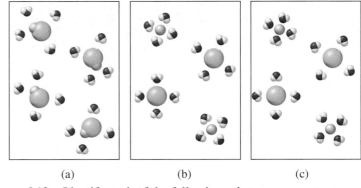

(a)   (b)   (c)

9.12 Identify each of the following substances as a strong electrolyte, weak electrolyte, or nonelectrolyte: (a) H_2O, (b) KCl, (c) HNO_3, (d) $HC_2H_3O_2$, (e) $C_{12}H_{22}O_{11}$.

9.13 Identify each of the following substances as a strong electrolyte, weak electrolyte, or nonelectrolyte: (a) $Ba(NO_3)_2$, (b) Ne, (c) NH_3, (d) NaOH, (e) HF.

SECTION 9.2: PRECIPITATION REACTIONS

Review Questions

9.14 Describe hydration. What properties of water enable its molecules to interact with ions in solution?

9.15 What is the difference between a *molecular equation* and an *ionic equation*? Between an *ionic equation* and a *net ionic equation*? What is the advantage of writing net ionic equations?

Problems

9.16 Two aqueous solutions of KOH and $MgCl_2$ are mixed. Which of the following diagrams best represents the resulting combination?

$K^+ = $ ● $OH^- = $ ● $Mg^{2+} = $ ● $Cl^- = $ ●

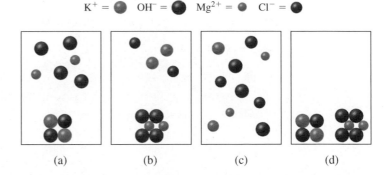

(a)   (b)   (c)   (d)

9.17 Two aqueous solutions of $AgNO_3$ and NaCl are mixed. Which of the following diagrams best represents the mixture?

$Ag^+ = $ ● $Cl^- = $ ● $Na^+ = $ ● $NO_3^- = $ ●

(a)   (b)   (c)   (d)

9.18 Which reaction is represented by the net ionic equation for the combination of aqueous solutions of $LiNO_3$ and $NaC_2H_3O_2$?

$Li^+ = $ ○ $NO_3^- = $ ● $Na^+ = $ ● $C_2H_3O_2^- = $ ●

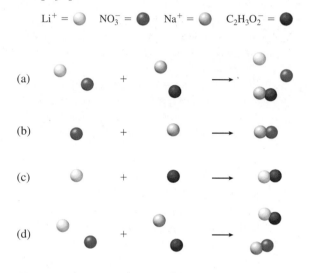

(a)

(b)

(c)

(d)

(e) There is no net ionic equation. No reaction occurs.

9.19 Which reaction is represented by the net ionic equation for the combination of aqueous solutions of LiOH and $Cu(NO_3)_2$?

$Li^+ = $ ○ $OH^- = $ ● $Cu^{2+} = $ ● $NO_3^- = $ ●

(a)

(b)

(c)

(d)

(e) There is no net ionic equation. No reaction occurs.

9.20 Characterize the following compounds as soluble or insoluble in water: (a) $CaCO_3$, (b) $ZnSO_4$, (c) $Hg(NO_3)_2$, (d) $HgSO_4$, (e) NH_4ClO_4.

9.21 Characterize the following compounds as soluble or insoluble in water: (a) $Ca_3(PO_4)_2$, (b) $Mn(OH)_2$, (c) $AgClO_3$, (d) K_2S, (e) $Pb_3(PO_4)_2$.

9.22 Write ionic and net ionic equations for the following reactions:
(a) $Na_2S(aq) + ZnCl_2(aq) \longrightarrow$
(b) $K_3PO_4(aq) + 3Sr(NO_3)_2(aq) \longrightarrow$
(c) $Mg(NO_3)_2(aq) + 2NaOH(aq) \longrightarrow$

9.23 Write ionic and net ionic equations for the following reactions:
(a) $AgNO_3(aq) + Na_2SO_4(aq) \longrightarrow$
(b) $BaCl_2(aq) + ZnSO_4(aq) \longrightarrow$
(c) $(NH_4)_2CO_3(aq) + CaCl_2(aq) \longrightarrow$

9.24 Which of the following processes will likely result in a precipitation reaction? (a) Mixing a $FeCl_3$ solution with a LiOH solution; (b) mixing a KNO_3 solution with a $CaCl_2$ solution; (c) mixing a $(NH_4)_2CO_3$ solution with a Na_2CO_3 solution; (d) mixing a $Sr(NO_3)_2$ solution with a $Ca(OH)_2$ solution. For mixtures that result in precipitation, write the formula of the precipitate.

9.25 Which of the following processes will likely result in a precipitation reaction? (a) Mixing a $NaNO_3$ solution with a $CuSO_4$ solution; (b) mixing a $BaCl_2$ solution with a K_2SO_4 solution; (c) mixing a $AgNO_3$ solution with a $LiC_2H_3O_2$ solution. Write a net ionic equation for each combination.

SECTION 9.3: ACID-BASE REACTIONS

Review Questions

9.26 List the general properties of acids and bases.

9.27 Give Arrhenius's and Brønsted's definitions of an acid and a base. Why are Brønsted's definitions more useful in describing acid-base properties?

9.28 Give an example of a monoprotic acid, a diprotic acid, and a triprotic acid.

9.29 What are the products of an acid-base neutralization reaction?

9.30 What factors qualify a compound as a salt? Specify which of the following compounds are salts: CH_4, NaF, NaOH, CaO, $BaSO_4$, HNO_3, NH_3, KBr.

9.31 Identify the following as a weak or strong acid or base: (a) NH_3, (b) H_3PO_4, (c) LiOH, (d) HCOOH (formic acid), (e) H_2SO_4, (f) HF, (g) $Ba(OH)_2$.

Problems

9.32 Identify each of the following species as a Brønsted acid, base, or both: (a) HI, (b) $C_2H_3O_2^-$ (c) $H_2PO_4^-$, (d) HSO_4^-.

9.33 Identify each of the following species as a Brønsted acid, base, or both: (a) PO_4^{3-} (b) ClO_2^- (c) NH_4^+ (d) HCO_3^-.

9.34 Balance the following equations and write the corresponding ionic and net ionic equations (if appropriate):
(a) $HBr(aq) + NH_3(aq) \longrightarrow$
(b) $Ba(OH)_2(aq) + H_3PO_4(aq) \longrightarrow$
(c) $HClO_4(aq) + Mg(OH)_2(s) \longrightarrow$

9.35 Balance the following equations and write the corresponding ionic and net ionic equations (if appropriate):
(a) $HC_2H_3O_2(aq) + KOH(aq) \longrightarrow$
(b) $H_2CO_3(aq) + NaOH(aq) \longrightarrow$
(c) $HNO_3(aq) + Ba(OH)_2(aq) \longrightarrow$

SECTION 9.4: OXIDATION-REDUCTION REACTIONS

Review Questions

9.36 Give an example of a redox reaction that is (a) a combination reaction, (b) a decomposition reaction, (c) a displacement reaction, and (d) a disproportionation reaction.

9.37 What is an oxidation number? How is it used to identify redox reactions?

9.38 Explain how oxidation number is different from *charge* or *partial charge*. Explain under what circumstances it is the same.

9.39 Describe how the activity series is organized, and how it is used to make predictions about redox reactions.

9.40 Use the following reaction to define the terms *redox reaction*, *half-reaction*, *oxidizing agent*, and *reducing agent*:

$$4Na(s) + O_2(g) \longrightarrow 2Na_2O(s)$$

9.41 Is it possible to have a reaction in which oxidation occurs and reduction does not? Explain.

Problems

9.42 For the complete redox reactions represented here, write the half-reactions and identify the oxidizing and reducing agents:
(a) $4Fe + 3O_2 \longrightarrow 2Fe_2O_3$
(b) $Cl_2 + 2NaBr \longrightarrow 2NaCl + Br_2$
(c) $Si + 2F_2 \longrightarrow SiF_4$
(d) $H_2 + Cl_2 \longrightarrow 2HCl$

9.43 For the complete redox reactions represented here, break down each reaction into its half-reactions, identify the oxidizing agent, and identify the reducing agent.
(a) $2Sr + O_2 \longrightarrow 2SrO$
(b) $2Li + H_2 \longrightarrow 2LiH$
(c) $2Cs + Br_2 \longrightarrow 2CsBr$
(d) $3Mg + N_2 \longrightarrow Mg_3N_2$

9.44 Phosphorus forms a variety of oxoacids. Indicate the oxidation number of phosphorus in each of the following acids: (a) HPO_3, (b) H_3PO_2, (c) H_3PO_3, (d) H_3PO_4, (e) $H_4P_2O_7$, (f) $H_5P_3O_{10}$.

9.45 Arrange the following species in order of increasing oxidation number of the sulfur atom: (a) H_2S, (b) S_8, (c) H_2SO_4, (d) S^{2-}, (e) HS^-, (f) SO_2, (g) SO_3.

9.46 Give the oxidation number for the following species: H_2, Se_8, P_4, O, U, As_4, B_{12}.

9.47 Give the oxidation numbers for the underlined atoms in the following molecules and ions: (a) $\underline{Cl}F$, (b) $\underline{I}F_7$, (c) $\underline{C}H_4$, (d) $\underline{C}_2H_2$, (e) $\underline{C}_2H_4$, (f) $K_2\underline{Cr}O_4$, (g) $K_2\underline{Cr}_2O_7$, (h) $K\underline{Mn}O_4$, (i) $NaH\underline{C}O_3$, (j) $\underline{Li}_2$, (k) $Na\underline{I}O_3$, (l) $K\underline{O}_2$, (m) $P\underline{F}_6^-$, (n) $K\underline{Au}Cl_4$.

9.48 Give the oxidation numbers for the underlined atoms in the following molecules and ions: (a) $Mg_3\underline{N}_2$, (b) $Cs\underline{O}_2$, (c) $Ca\underline{C}_2$, (d) $\underline{C}O_3^{2-}$, (e) $\underline{C}_2O_4^{2-}$, (f) $Zn\underline{O}_2^{2-}$, (g) $Na\underline{B}H_4$, (h) $\underline{W}O_4^{2-}$.

9.49 Give the oxidation numbers for the underlined atoms in the following molecules and ions: (a) $\underline{Cs}_2O$, (b) $Ca\underline{I}_2$, (c) $\underline{Al}_2O_3$, (d) $H_3\underline{As}O_3$, (e) $\underline{Ti}O_2$, (f), $\underline{Mo}O_4^{2-}$, (g) $\underline{Pt}Cl_4^{2-}$, (h) $\underline{Pt}Cl_6^{2-}$ (i) $\underline{Sn}F_2$, (j) $\underline{Cl}F_3$, (k) $\underline{Sb}F_6^-$.

9.50 Determine which of the following metals can react with water: (a) Au, (b) Li, (c) Hg, (d) Ca, (e) Pt.

9.51 Nitric acid is a strong oxidizing agent. State which of the following species is *least* likely to be produced when nitric acid reacts with a strong reducing agent such as zinc metal, and explain why: N_2O, NO, NO_2, N_2O_4, N_2O_5, NH_4^+.

9.52 Predict the outcome of the reactions represented by the following equations by using the activity series, and balance the equations.
(a) $Cu(s) + HCl(aq) \longrightarrow$
(b) $Au(s) + NaBr(aq) \longrightarrow$
(c) $Mg(s) + CuSO_4(aq) \longrightarrow$
(d) $Zn(s) + KBr(aq) \longrightarrow$

9.53 One of the following oxides does not react with molecular oxygen: NO, N_2O, SO_2, SO_3, P_4O_6. Based on oxidation numbers, which one is it? Explain.

9.54 Classify the following redox reactions as *combination*, *decomposition*, *displacement*, and/or *disproportionation*:
(a) $P_4 + 10Cl_2 \longrightarrow 4PCl_5$
(b) $2NO \longrightarrow N_2 + O_2$
(c) $Cl_2 + 2KI \longrightarrow 2KCl + I_2$
(d) $3HNO_2 \longrightarrow HNO_3 + H_2O + 2NO$

9.55 Classify the following redox reactions as *combination, decomposition, displacement*, and/or *disproportionation*:
(a) $2H_2O_2 \longrightarrow 2H_2O + O_2$
(b) $Mg + 2AgNO_3 \longrightarrow Mg(NO_3)_2 + 2Ag$
(c) $NH_4NO_2 \longrightarrow N_2 + 2H_2O$
(d) $H_2 + Br_2 \longrightarrow 2HBr$

SECTION 9.5: CONCENTRATION OF SOLUTIONS

Visualizing Chemistry
Figure 9.10 Preparing a Solution from a Solid

VC 9.1 Which of the following would result in the actual concentration of the prepared solution being higher than the final, calculated value?
(a) Loss of some of the solid during transfer to the volumetric flask.
(b) Neglecting to add the last bit of water with the wash bottle to fill to the volumetric mark.
(c) Neglecting to tare the balance with the weigh paper on the pan.

VC 9.2 Why can't we prepare the solution by first filling the volumetric flask to the mark and then adding the solid?
(a) The solid would not all dissolve.
(b) The solid would not all fit into the flask.
(c) The final volume would not be correct.

VC 9.3 What causes the concentration of the prepared solution not to be exactly 0.1 M?
(a) Rounding error in the calculations.
(b) The volume of the flask is not exactly 250 mL.
(c) The amount of solid weighed out is not exactly the calculated mass.

VC 9.4 The volumetric flask used to prepare a solution from a solid is shown before and after the last of the water has been added.

(i)   (ii)

Which of the following statements is true?
(a) The concentration of solute is greater in (i) than in (ii).
(b) The concentration of solute is smaller in (i) than in (ii).
(c) The concentration of solute in (i) is equal to the concentration of solute in (ii).

Review Questions

9.56 Write the equation for calculating molarity. Why is molarity a convenient concentration unit in chemistry?

9.57 Describe the steps involved in preparing a solution of known molar concentration using a volumetric flask.

9.58 Describe the basic steps involved in diluting a solution of known concentration.

9.59 Write the equation that enables us to calculate the concentration of a diluted solution. Give units for all the terms.

Problems

9.60 Describe how you would prepare 250 mL of a 0.707 M NaNO$_3$ solution.

9.61 Calculate the mass of KI in grams required to prepare 5.00×10^2 mL of a 2.80 M solution.

9.62 How many grams of KOH are present in 35.0 mL of a 5.50 M KOH solution?

9.63 How many moles of MgCl$_2$ are present in 60.0 mL of a 0.100 M MgCl$_2$ solution?

9.64 Calculate the molarity of each of the following solutions: (a) 6.57 g of methanol (CH$_3$OH) in 1.50×10^2 mL of solution, (b) 10.4 g of calcium chloride (CaCl$_2$) in 2.20×10^2 mL of solution, (c) 7.82 g of naphthalene (C$_{10}$H$_8$) in 85.2 mL of benzene solution.

9.65 Calculate the molarity of each of the following solutions: (a) 29.0 g of ethanol (C$_2$H$_5$OH) in 545 mL of solution, (b) 15.4 g of sucrose (C$_{12}$H$_{22}$O$_{11}$) in 74.0 mL of solution, (c) 9.00 g of sodium chloride (NaCl) in 86.4 mL of solution.

9.66 Determine how many grams of each of the following solutes would be needed to make 2.50×10^2 mL of a 0.100-M solution: (a) cesium iodide (CsI), (b) sulfuric acid (H$_2$SO$_4$), (c) sodium carbonate (Na$_2$CO$_3$), (d) potassium dichromate (K$_2$Cr$_2$O$_7$), (e) potassium permanganate (KMnO$_4$).

9.67 Calculate the volume in milliliters of a solution required to provide the following: (a) 2.14 g of sodium chloride from a 0.270-M solution, (b) 4.30 g of ethanol from a 1.50-M solution, (c) 0.85 g of acetic acid (HC$_2$H$_3$O$_2$) from a 0.30-M solution.

9.68 Which best represents the before-and-after molecular-level view of the dilution of a concentrated stock solution?

Before   After
(a)

Before   After
(c)

Before   After
(b)

Before   After
(d)

9.69 Which best represents an aqueous solution of sodium sulfate?

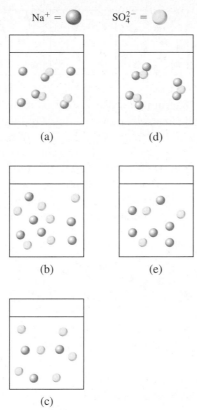

$Na^+ =$ ⬤ $SO_4^{2-} =$ ⬤

(a)   (d)

(b)   (e)

(c)

9.70 Water is added to 25.0 mL of a 0.866 M KNO_3 solution until the volume of the solution is exactly 500 mL. What is the concentration of the final solution?

9.71 Describe how to prepare 1.00 L of a 0.646 M HCl solution, starting with a 2.00 M HCl solution.

9.72 You have 505 mL of a 0.125 M HCl solution and you want to dilute it to exactly 0.100 M. How much water should you add?

9.73 How would you prepare 60.0 mL of 0.200 M HNO_3 from a stock solution of 4.00 M HNO_3?

9.74 A volume of 46.2 mL of a 0.568 M calcium nitrate $[Ca(NO_3)_2]$ solution is mixed with 80.5 mL of a 1.396 M calcium nitrate solution. Calculate the concentration of the final solution.

9.75 A volume of 35.2 mL of a 1.66 M $KMnO_4$ solution is mixed with 16.7 mL of a 0.892 M $KMnO_4$ solution. Calculate the concentration of the final solution.

9.76 The maximum level of fluoride that the EPA allows in U.S. drinking water is 4 mg/L. Convert this concentration to molarity.

9.77 According to the website labtestsonline.org, a fasting blood sugar (glucose, $C_6H_{12}O_6$) level of at least 126 milligrams per deciliter (mg/dL) can indicate Type 2 diabetes. Convert this concentration to molarity.

9.78 (a) What is the Na^+ concentration in each of the following solutions: 3.25 M sodium sulfate, 1.78 M sodium carbonate, 0.585 M sodium bicarbonate? (b) What is the concentration of a lithium carbonate solution that is 0.595 M in Li^+?

9.79 (a) Determine the chloride ion concentration in each of the following solutions: 0.150 M $BaCl_2$, 0.566 M NaCl, 1.202 M $AlCl_3$. (b) What is the concentration of a $Sr(NO_3)_2$ solution that is 2.55 M in nitrate ion?

9.80 What volume of 0.112 M ammonium sulfate contains 5.75 g of ammonium ion?

9.81 Determine the resulting nitrate ion concentration when 95.0 mL of 0.992 M potassium nitrate and 155.5 mL of 1.570 M calcium nitrate are combined.

9.82 Absorbance values for five standard solutions of a colored solute were determined at 410 nm with a 1.00-cm path length, giving the following table of data:

Solute concentration (M)	A
0.250	0.165
0.500	0.317
0.750	0.510
1.000	0.650
1.250	0.837

The absorbance of a solution of unknown concentration containing the same solute was 0.400. What is the concentration of the unknown solution? (See page 338.)

9.83 Referring to Problem 9.82, (a) determine the absorbance values you would expect for solutions with the following concentrations: 0.4 M, 0.6 M, 0.8 M, 1.1 M. (b) Using data in the table in Problem 9.82, calculate the average molar absorptivity of the compound and determine the units of molar absorptivity. (See page 338.)

SECTION 9.6:   AQUEOUS REACTIONS AND CHEMICAL ANALYSIS

Review Questions

9.84 Describe the basic steps involved in gravimetric analysis. How does this procedure help us determine the identity of a compound or the purity of a compound if its formula is known?

9.85 Explain why distilled water must be used in the gravimetric analysis of chlorides.

9.86 Describe the basic steps involved in an acid-base titration. Why is this technique of great practical value?

9.87 How does an acid-base indicator work?

9.88 A student carried out two titrations using an NaOH solution of unknown concentration in the burette. In one titration she weighed out 0.2458 g of KHP (see page 343) and transferred it to an Erlenmeyer flask. She then added 20.00 mL of distilled water to dissolve the acid. In the other titration she weighed out 0.2507 g of KHP but added 40.00 mL of distilled water to dissolve the acid. Assuming no experimental error, would she obtain the same result for the concentration of the NaOH solution?

9.89 Would the volume of a 0.10 M NaOH solution needed to titrate 25.0 mL of a 0.10 M HNO_2 (a weak acid) solution be different from that needed to titrate 25.0 mL of a 0.10 M HCl (a strong acid) solution?

Problems

9.90   Which of the following best represents the contents of a beaker in which equal volumes of 0.10 M $BaCl_2$ and 0.10 M $AgNO_3$ were combined?

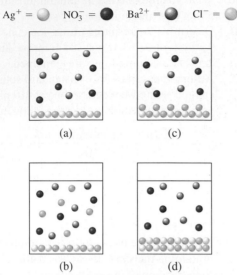

$Ag^+ = $ ○ $NO_3^- = $ ● $Ba^{2+} = $ ● $Cl^- = $ ○

(a)   (c)

(b)   (d)

9.91   Which of the following best represents the contents of a beaker in which equal volumes of 0.10 M NaCl and 0.10 M $Pb(NO_3)_2$ were combined?

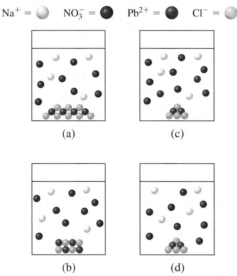

$Na^+ = $ ○ $NO_3^- = $ ● $Pb^{2+} = $ ● $Cl^- = $ ○

(a)   (c)

(b)   (d)

9.92   A sample of 0.6760 g of an unknown compound containing barium ions (Ba^{2+}) is dissolved in water and treated with an excess of Na_2SO_4. If the mass of the $BaSO_4$ precipitate formed is 0.4105 g, what is the percent by mass of Ba in the original unknown compound?

9.93   If 30.0 mL of 0.150 M $CaCl_2$ is added to 15.0 mL of 0.100 M $AgNO_3$, what is the mass in grams of AgCl precipitate?

9.94   Diagram (a) shows a solution of a base and an acid before the neutralization reaction. Each of the after-reaction diagrams, (b)–(d), shows the products of reaction with one of the following acids: HCl, H_2SO_4, H_3PO_4. Determine which diagram corresponds to which acid. Blue spheres = OH^- ions, red spheres = acid molecules, green spheres = anions

of the acids. Assume all the acid-base neutralization reactions go to completion.

(a)   (b)   (c)   (d)

9.95   Diagram (a) shows a solution of HCl and a base before the neutralization reaction. Of diagrams (b)–(d), which represents the products of reaction when the base is sodium hydroxide and which represents the products when the base is barium hydroxide? Blue spheres = base, red spheres = H^+, grey spheres = cations of the bases. Assume all the acid-base neutralization reactions go to completion.

(a)   (b)   (c)   (d)

9.96   The concentration of Cu^{2+} ions in the water (which also contains sulfate ions) discharged from a certain industrial plant is determined by adding excess sodium sulfide (Na_2S) solution to 0.800 L of the water. The molecular equation is

$$Na_2S(aq) + CuSO_4(aq) \longrightarrow Na_2SO_4(aq) + CuS(aq)$$

Write the net ionic equation and calculate the molar concentration of Cu^{2+} in the water sample if 0.0177 g of solid CuS is formed.

9.97   How many grams of NaCl are required to precipitate most of the Ag ions from 2.50×10^2 mL of a 0.0113 M $AgNO_3$ solution? Write the net ionic equation for the reaction.

9.98   Calculate the concentration (in molarity) of an NaOH solution if 25.0 mL of the solution is needed to neutralize 17.4 mL of a 0.312 M HCl solution.

9.99   A quantity of 18.68 mL of a KOH solution is needed to neutralize 0.4218 g of KHP. What is the concentration (in molarity) of the KOH solution?

9.100 Determine the volume of 0.500 M HCl needed to neutralize each of the following:
(a) 10.0 mL of a 0.300 M NaOH solution
(b) 10.0 mL of a 0.200 M $Ba(OH)_2$ solution

9.101 Calculate the volume in milliliters of a 1.420 M NaOH solution required to titrate the following solutions:
(a) 25.00 mL of a 2.430 M HCl solution
(b) 25.00 mL of a 4.500 M H_2SO_4 solution
(c) 25.00 mL of a 1.500 M H_3PO_4 solution

ADDITIONAL PROBLEMS

9.102 Oxygen (O_2) and carbon dioxide (CO_2) are colorless and odorless gases. Suggest two chemical tests that would allow you to distinguish between these two gases.

9.103 Which of the following aqueous solutions would you expect to be the best conductor of electricity at 25°C? Explain your answer.
(a) 0.20 M NaCl
(b) 0.60 M $HC_2H_3O_2$
(c) 0.25 M HCl
(d) 0.20 M $Mg(NO_3)_2$

9.104 A 5.00×10^2 mL sample of 2.00 M HCl solution is treated with 4.47 g of magnesium. Calculate the concentration of the acid solution after all the metal has reacted. Assume that the volume remains unchanged.

9.105 Calculate the volume of a 0.156 M $CuSO_4$ solution that would react with 7.89 g of zinc.

9.106 Sodium carbonate (Na_2CO_3) is available in very pure form and can be used to standardize acid solutions. What is the molarity of an HCl solution if 28.3 mL of the solution is required to react with 0.256 g of Na_2CO_3?

9.107 Identify each of the following compounds as a nonelectrolyte, a weak electrolyte, or a strong electrolyte: (a) ethanolamine ($H_2NC_2H_4OH$), (b) potassium fluoride (KF), (c) ammonium nitrate (NH_4NO_3), (d) isopropanol (C_3H_7OH).

9.108 Identify each of the following compounds as a nonelectrolyte, a weak electrolyte, or a strong electrolyte: (a) lactose ($C_{12}H_{22}O_{11}$), (b) lactic acid ($HC_3H_5O_3$), (c) dimethylamine [$(CH_3)_2NH$], (d) barium hydroxide [$Ba(OH)_2$].

9.109 Determine the predominant species (there may be more than one) in an aqueous solution for each of the compounds in Problem 9.107.

9.110 Determine the predominant species (there may be more than one) in an aqueous solution for each of the compounds in Problem 9.108.

9.111 A 3.664-g sample of a monoprotic acid was dissolved in water. It took 20.27 mL of a 0.1578 M NaOH solution to neutralize the acid. Calculate the molar mass of the acid.

9.112 Acetic acid ($HC_2H_3O_2$) is an important ingredient of vinegar. A sample of 50.0 mL of a commercial vinegar is titrated against a 1.00 M NaOH solution. What is the concentration (in M) of acetic acid present in the vinegar if 5.75 mL of the base is needed for the titration?

9.113 A 15.00-mL solution of potassium nitrate (KNO_3) was diluted to 125.0 mL, and 25.00 mL of this solution was then diluted to 1.000×10^3 mL. The concentration of the final solution is 0.00383 M. Calculate the concentration of the original solution.

9.114 When 2.50 g of a zinc strip was placed in an $AgNO_3$ solution, silver metal formed on the surface of the strip. After some time had passed, the strip was removed from the solution, dried, and weighed. If the mass of the strip was 3.37 g, calculate the mass of Ag and Zn metals present.

9.115 Calculate the mass of the precipitate formed when 2.27 L of 0.0820 M $Ba(OH)_2$ is mixed with 3.06 L of 0.0664 M Na_2SO_4.

9.116 What is the oxidation number of O in HFO?

9.117 Classify the following reactions according to the types discussed in the chapter:
(a) $Cl_2 + 2OH^- \longrightarrow Cl^- + ClO^- + H_2O$
(b) $Ca^{2+} + CO_3^{2-} \longrightarrow CaCO_3$
(c) $NH_3 + H^+ \longrightarrow NH_4^+$
(d) $2CCl_4 + CrO_4^{2-} \longrightarrow 2COCl_2 + CrO_2Cl_2 + 2Cl^-$
(e) $Ca + F_2 \longrightarrow CaF_2$
(f) $2Li + H_2 \longrightarrow 2LiH$
(g) $Ba(NO_3)_2 + Na_2SO_4 \longrightarrow 2NaNO_3 + BaSO_4$
(h) $CuO + H_2 \longrightarrow Cu + H_2O$
(i) $Zn + 2HCl \longrightarrow ZnCl_2 + H_2$
(j) $2FeCl_2 + Cl_2 \longrightarrow 2FeCl_3$

9.118 Calculate the concentration of the acid (or base) remaining in solution when 10.7 mL of 0.211 M HNO_3 is added to 16.3 mL of 0.258 M NaOH.

9.119 (a) Describe a preparation for magnesium hydroxide [$Mg(OH)_2$] and predict its solubility. (b) Milk of magnesia contains mostly $Mg(OH)_2$ and is effective in treating acid (mostly hydrochloric acid) indigestion. Calculate the volume of a 0.035 M HCl solution (a typical acid concentration in an upset stomach) needed to react with two spoonfuls (approximately 10 mL) of milk of magnesia [at 0.080 g $Mg(OH)_2$/mL].

9.120 A quantitative definition of solubility is the number of grams of a solute that will dissolve in a given volume of water at a particular temperature. Describe an experiment that would enable you to determine the solubility of a soluble compound.

9.121 A 60.0-mL 0.513 M glucose ($C_6H_{12}O_6$) solution is mixed with 120.0 mL of a 2.33 M glucose solution. What is the concentration of the final solution? Assume the volumes are additive.

9.122 An ionic compound X is only slightly soluble in water. What test would you employ to show that the compound does indeed dissolve in water to a certain extent?

9.123 You are given a colorless liquid. Describe three chemical tests you would perform on the liquid to show that it is water.

9.124 Using the apparatus shown in Figure 9.1, a student found that a sulfuric acid solution caused the lightbulb to glow brightly. However, after the addition of a certain amount of a barium hydroxide [$Ba(OH)_2$] solution, the light began to dim even though $Ba(OH)_2$ is also a strong electrolyte. Explain.

9.125 Which of the diagrams shown corresponds to the reaction between AgOH(s) and HNO_3(aq)? Write a balanced equation for the reaction. (For simplicity, water molecules are not shown.)

(a)   (b)   (c)

● Ag^+
● NO_3^-

9.126   Which of the diagrams shown corresponds to the reaction between $Ba(OH)_2(aq)$ and $H_2SO_4(aq)$? Write a balanced equation for the reaction. (For simplicity, water molecules are not shown.)

○ Ba^{2+}
● SO_4^{2-}

   (a)   (b)   (c)

9.127   You are given a soluble compound of an unknown molecular formula.
   (a) Describe three tests that would show that the compound is an acid.
   (b) Once you have established that the compound is an acid, describe how you would determine its molar mass using an NaOH solution of known concentration. (Assume the acid is monoprotic.)
   (c) How would you find out whether the acid is weak or strong? You are provided with a sample of NaCl and an apparatus like that shown in Figure 9.1 for comparison.

9.128   You are given two colorless solutions, one containing NaCl and the other sucrose ($C_{12}H_{22}O_{11}$). Suggest a chemical and a physical test that would allow you to distinguish between these two solutions.

9.129   The concentration of lead ions (Pb^{2+}) in a sample of polluted water that also contains nitrate ions (NO_3^-) is determined by adding solid sodium sulfate (Na_2SO_4) to exactly 500 mL of the water. (a) Write the molecular and net ionic equations for the reaction. (b) Calculate the molar concentration of Pb^{2+} if 0.00450 g of Na_2SO_4 was needed for the complete precipitation of Pb^{2+} ions as $PbSO_4$.

9.130   Hydrochloric acid is not an oxidizing agent in the sense that sulfuric acid and nitric acid are. Explain why the chloride ion is not a strong oxidizing agent like SO_4^{2-} and NO_3^-.

9.131   Explain how you would prepare potassium iodide (KI) by means of (a) an acid-base reaction and (b) a reaction between an acid and a carbonate compound.

9.132   Sodium reacts with water to yield hydrogen gas. Why is this reaction not used in the laboratory preparation of hydrogen?

9.133   Describe how you would prepare the following compounds: (a) $Mg(OH)_2$, (b) AgI, (c) $Ba_3(PO_4)_2$.

9.134   Someone spilled concentrated sulfuric acid on the floor of a chemistry laboratory. To neutralize the acid, would it be preferable to pour concentrated sodium hydroxide solution or spray solid sodium bicarbonate over the acid? Explain your choice and the chemical basis for the action.

9.135   Describe in each case how you would separate the cations or anions in the following aqueous solutions:
(a) $NaNO_3$ and $Ba(NO_3)_2$, (b) $Mg(NO_3)_2$ and KNO_3, (c) KBr and KNO_3, (d) K_3PO_4 and KNO_3, (e) Na_2CO_3 and $NaNO_3$.

9.136   The following are common household compounds: salt (NaCl), sugar (sucrose), vinegar (contains acetic acid, $HC_2H_3O_2$), baking soda ($NaHCO_3$), washing soda ($Na_2CO_3 \cdot 10H_2O$), boric acid (H_3BO_3, used in eyewash), Epsom salts ($MgSO_4 \cdot 7H_2O$), sodium hydroxide (used in drain openers), ammonia, milk of magnesia [$Mg(OH)_2$], and calcium carbonate. Based on what you have learned in this chapter, describe tests that would allow you to identify each of these compounds.

9.137   Sulfites (compounds containing the SO_3^{2-} ions) are used as preservatives in dried fruits and vegetables and in wine making. In an experiment to test for the presence of sulfite in fruit, a student first soaked several dried apricots in water overnight and then filtered the solution to remove all solid particles. She then treated the solution with hydrogen peroxide (H_2O_2) to oxidize the sulfite ions to sulfate ions. Finally, the sulfate ions were precipitated by treating the solution with a few drops of a barium chloride ($BaCl_2$) solution. Write a balanced equation for each of the preceding steps.

9.138   A 0.8870-g sample of a mixture of NaCl and KCl is dissolved in water, and the solution is then treated with an excess of $AgNO_3$ to yield 1.913 g of AgCl. Calculate the percent by mass of each compound in the mixture.

9.139   Chlorine forms a number of oxides with the following oxidation numbers: +1, +3, +4, +6, and +7. Write a formula for each of these compounds.

9.140   One of the uses of oxalic ($H_2C_2O_4$) acid is rust removal. It reacts with rust (Fe_2O_3) according to the equation

$$Fe_2O_3(s) + 6H_2C_2O_4(aq) \longrightarrow$$
$$2Fe_2(C_2O_4)_3^{3-}(aq) + 3H_2O(l) + 6H^+(aq)$$

Calculate the number of grams of rust that can be removed by 5.00×10^2 mL of a 0.100 M solution of oxalic acid.

9.141   Acetylsalicylic acid ($HC_9H_7O_4$) is a monoprotic acid commonly known as "aspirin." A typical aspirin tablet, however, contains only a small amount of the acid. In an experiment to determine its composition, an aspirin tablet was crushed and dissolved in water. It took 12.25 mL of 0.1466 M NaOH to neutralize the solution. Calculate the number of grains of aspirin in the tablet (one grain = 0.0648 g).

9.142   A 0.9157-g mixture of $CaBr_2$ and NaBr is dissolved in water, and $AgNO_3$ is added to the solution to form AgBr precipitate. If the mass of the precipitate is 1.6930 g, what is the percent by mass of NaBr in the original mixture?

9.143   Hydrogen halides (HF, HCl, HBr, HI) are highly reactive compounds that have many industrial and laboratory uses. (a) In the laboratory, HF and HCl can be generated by reacting CaF_2 and NaCl with concentrated sulfuric acid. Write appropriate equations for the reactions. (*Hint:* These are not redox reactions.) (b) Why is it that HBr and HI cannot be prepared similarly, that is, by reacting NaBr and NaI with concentrated sulfuric acid? (*Hint:* H_2SO_4 is a stronger oxidizing agent than both Br_2 and I_2.) (c) HBr can be prepared by combining phosphorus tribromide (PBr_3) with water. Write an equation for this reaction.

9.144 A 325-mL sample of solution contains 25.3 g of $CaCl_2$. (a) Calculate the molar concentration of Cl^- in this solution. (b) How many grams of Cl^- are in 0.100 L of this solution?

9.145 Phosphoric acid (H_3PO_4) is an important industrial chemical used in fertilizers, detergents, and the food industry. It is produced by two different methods. In the *electric furnace method,* elemental phosphorus (P_4) is burned in air to form P_4O_{10}, which is then combined with water to give H_3PO_4. In the *wet process,* the mineral phosphate rock [$Ca_5(PO_4)_3F$] is combined with sulfuric acid to give H_3PO_4 (and HF and $CaSO_4$). Write equations for these processes, and classify each step as precipitation, acid-base, or redox reaction.

9.146 Ammonium nitrate (NH_4NO_3) is one of the most important nitrogen-containing fertilizers. Its purity can be analyzed by titrating a solution of NH_4NO_3 with a standard NaOH solution. In one experiment, a 0.2041-g sample of industrially prepared NH_4NO_3 required 24.42 mL of 0.1023 *M* NaOH for neutralization. (a) Write a net ionic equation for the reaction. (b) What is the percent purity of the sample?

9.147 Potassium superoxide (KO_2) is used in some self-containing breathing equipment by firefighters. It reacts with carbon dioxide in respired (exhaled) air to form potassium carbonate and oxygen gas. (a) Write an equation for the reaction. (b) What is the oxidation number of oxygen in the O_2^{2-} ion? (c) How many liters of respired air can react with 7.00 g of KO_2 if each liter of respired air contains 0.063 g of CO_2?

9.148 Barium sulfate ($BaSO_4$) has important medical uses. The dense salt absorbs X rays and acts as an opaque barrier. Thus, X-ray examination of a patient who has swallowed an aqueous suspension of $BaSO_4$ particles allows the radiologist to diagnose an ailment of the patient's digestive tract. Given the following starting compounds, describe how you would prepare $BaSO_4$ by neutralization and by precipitation: $Ba(OH)_2$, $BaCl_2$, $BaCO_3$, H_2SO_4, and K_2SO_4.

9.149 Is the following reaction a redox reaction? Explain.

$$3O_2(g) \longrightarrow 2O_3(g)$$

9.150 Absorbance values for five standard $KMnO_4$ solutions were determined at a wavelength of 528 nm. The data are tabulated here.

Solute concentration (*M*)	A
0.0500	0.172
0.100	0.310
0.150	0.502
0.200	0.680
0.250	0.822

The absorbance of a $KMnO_4$ solution with unknown concentration, analyzed under the same conditions, was 0.550. Determine the concentration of the unknown solution. (See page 338.)

9.151 Draw molecular models to represent the following acid-base reactions:
(a) $OH^- + H_3O^+ \longrightarrow 2H_2O$
(b) $NH_4^+ + NH_2^- \longrightarrow 2NH_3$
Identify the Brønsted acid and base in each case.

9.152 On standing, a concentrated nitric acid gradually turns yellow. Explain. (*Hint:* Nitric acid slowly decomposes. Nitrogen dioxide is a colored gas.)

9.153 When preparing a solution of known concentration, explain why one must first dissolve the solid completely before adding enough solvent to fill the volumetric flask to the mark.

9.154 Can the following decomposition reaction be characterized as an acid-base reaction? Explain.

$$NH_4Cl(s) \longrightarrow NH_3(g) + HCl(g)$$

9.155 Give a chemical explanation for each of the following: (a) When calcium metal is added to a sulfuric acid solution, hydrogen gas is generated. After a few minutes, the reaction slows down and eventually stops even though none of the reactants is used up. Explain. (b) In the activity series, aluminum is above hydrogen, yet the metal appears to be unreactive toward hydrochloric acid. Why? (*Hint:* Al forms an oxide, Al_2O_3, on the surface.) (c) Sodium and potassium lie above copper in the activity series. Explain why Cu^{2+} ions in a $CuSO_4$ solution are not converted to metallic copper upon the addition of these metals. (d) A metal M reacts slowly with steam. There is no visible change when it is placed in a pale green iron(II) sulfate solution. Where should we place M in the activity series? (e) Before aluminum metal was obtained by electrolysis, it was produced by reducing its chloride ($AlCl_3$) with an active metal. What metals would you use to produce aluminum in that way?

9.156 The recommended procedure for preparing a very dilute solution is not to weigh out a very small mass or measure a very small volume of a stock solution. Instead, it is done by serial dilution. A sample of 0.8214 g of $KMnO_4$ was dissolved in water and made up to the volume in a 500-mL volumetric flask. A 2.000-mL sample of this solution was transferred to a 1000-mL volumetric flask and diluted to the mark with water. Next, 10.00 mL of the diluted solution was transferred to a 250-mL flask and diluted to the mark with water. (a) Calculate the concentration (in molarity) of the final solution. (b) Calculate the mass of $KMnO_4$ needed to directly prepare the final solution and comment on why dilute solutions are not typically prepared directly.

9.157 The following "cycle of copper" experiment is performed in some general chemistry laboratories. The series of reactions starts with copper and ends with metallic copper. The steps are as follows: (1) A piece of copper wire of known mass is allowed to react with concentrated nitric acid [the products are copper(II) nitrate, nitrogen dioxide, and water]. (2) The copper(II) nitrate is treated with a sodium hydroxide solution to form copper(II) hydroxide precipitate. (3) On heating, copper(II) hydroxide decomposes to yield copper(II) oxide. (4) The copper(II) oxide is combined with concentrated sulfuric acid to yield copper(II) sulfate. (5) Copper(II) sulfate is treated with an excess of zinc metal to form metallic copper. (6) The remaining zinc metal is removed by treatment with hydrochloric acid, and metallic copper is filtered, dried, and weighed.

(a) Write a balanced equation for each step and classify the reactions. (b) Assuming that a student started with 65.6 g of copper, calculate the theoretical yield at each step. (c) Considering the nature of the steps, comment on why it is possible to recover most of the copper used at the start.

9.158   Use the periodic table framework given here to show the names and positions of two metals that can (a) displace hydrogen from cold water and (b) displace hydrogen from acid. (c) Also show two metals that do not react with either water or acid. Use trends in periodic properties to explain the differences in your answers to parts (a) and (b).

9.159   A 22.02-mL solution containing 1.615 g $Mg(NO_3)_2$ is mixed with a 28.64-mL solution containing 1.073 g NaOH. Calculate the concentrations of the ions remaining in solution after the reaction is complete. Assume volumes are additive.

9.160   Because the acid-base and precipitation reactions discussed in this chapter all involve ionic species, their progress can be monitored by measuring the electrical conductance of the solution. Match each of the following reactions with one of the diagrams shown here. The electrical conductance is shown in arbitrary units. Explain the significance of the point at which the slope changes in each diagram.

(1) A 1.0 M KOH solution is added to 1.0 L of 1.0 M $HC_2H_3O_2$.

(2) A 1.0 M NaOH solution is added to 1.0 L of 1.0 M HCl.

(3) A 1.0 M $BaCl_2$ solution is added to 1.0 L of 1.0 M K_2SO_4.

(4) A 1.0 M NaCl solution is added to 1.0 L of 1.0 M $AgNO_3$.

(5) A 1.0 M $HC_2H_3O_2$ solution is added to 1.0 L of 1.0 M NH_3.

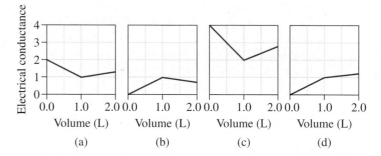

Answers to In-Chapter Materials

PRACTICE PROBLEMS

9.1A Weak electrolyte, strong electrolyte, strong electrolyte, strong electrolyte. **9.1B** Strong electrolyte, strong electrolyte, weak electrolyte. **9.2A** (a) insoluble, (b) soluble, (c) insoluble. **9.2B** (a) soluble, (b) insoluble, (c) soluble. **9.3A** $Sr(NO_3)_2(aq)$ + $Li_2SO_4(aq) \longrightarrow SrSO_4(s) + 2LiNO_3(aq)$; $Sr^{2+}(aq) + 2NO_3^-(aq)$ + $2Li^+(aq) + SO_4^{2-}(aq) \longrightarrow SrSO_4(s) + 2Li^+(aq) + 2NO_3^-(aq)$; $Sr^{2+}(aq) + SO_4^{2-}(aq) \longrightarrow SrSO_4(s)$. **9.3B** $(NH_4)_2CO_3(aq)$ + $Ba(NO_3)_2(aq)$; $(NH_4)_2CO_3(aq) + Ba(NO_3)_2(aq) \longrightarrow BaCO_3(s)$ + $2NH_4NO_3(aq)$; $2NH_4^+(aq) + CO_3^{2-}(aq) + Ba^{2+}(aq) + 2NO_3^-(aq) \longrightarrow$ $BaCO_3(s) + 2NH_4^+(aq) + 2NO_3^-(aq)$; $Ba^{2+}(aq) + CO_3^{2-}(aq) \longrightarrow$ $BaCO_3(s)$. **9.4A** $Ba(OH)_2(aq) + 2HF(aq) \longrightarrow BaF_2(s) + H_2O(l)$; $Ba^{2+}(aq) + 2OH^-(aq) + 2HF(aq) \longrightarrow BaF_2(s) + 2H_2O(l)$; $Ba^{2+}(aq)$ + $2OH^-(aq) + 2HF(aq) \longrightarrow BaF_2(s) + 2H_2O(l)$. **9.4B** $2NH_3(aq)$ + $H_2SO_4(aq) \longrightarrow (NH_4)_2SO_4(aq)$; $2NH_3(aq) + H^+(aq) + HSO_4^-(aq)$ $\longrightarrow 2NH_4^+(aq) + SO_4^{2-}(aq)$; $2NH_3(aq) + H^+(aq) + HSO_4^-(aq) \longrightarrow$ $2NH_4^+(aq) + SO_4^{2-}(aq)$. **9.5A** H = +1, O = −2; Cl = +5, O = −2; H = +1, S = +6, O = −2. **9.5B** O = −1; Cl = +1, O = −2; Mn = +4, O = −2. **9.6A** (a) no reaction, (b) $Sn(s) + Cu^{2+}(aq) \longrightarrow Sn^{2+}(aq)$ + $Cu(s)$, (c) no reaction. **9.6B** (a) $Ni(s) + Cu^{2+}(aq) \longrightarrow Ni^{2+}(aq)$ + $Cu(s)$, (b) no reaction, (c) $Al(s) + Au^{3+}(aq) \longrightarrow Al^{3+}(aq) + Au(s)$. **9.7A** (a) $3Mg(s) + 2Cr(C_2H_3O_2)_3(aq) \longrightarrow 3Mg(C_2H_3O_2)_2(aq)$ + $2Cr(s)$, Mg is oxidized and Cr is reduced; (b) no reaction; (c) $Cd(s)$ + $2AgNO_3(aq) \longrightarrow 2Ag(s) + Cd(NO_3)_2(aq)$, Cd is oxidized and Ag is reduced. **9.7B** (a) no reaction, (b) Au is reduced and Ag is oxidized, (c) H is reduced and Sn is oxidized. **9.8A** (a) 0.137 M, (b) 9.18 L, (c) 0.259 mol. **9.8B** (a) 0.707 M, (b) 6.48 L, (c) 16.1 mol. **9.9A** 21 mL. **9.9B** 3.8 mL. **9.10A** (a) 1.638 M, 0.4095 M, 0.1024 M, 2.559×10^{-2} M, 6.398×10^{-3} M; (b) 0.1638 mol, 4.095×10^{-2} mol, 1.024×10^{-2} mol, 2.559×10^{-3} mol, 6.398×10^{-4} mol. **9.10B** 2.45 M. **9.11A** $[Al^{3+}]$ = 1.50 M, $[SO_4^{2-}]$ = 2.25 M. **9.11B** (a) 0.36 M, (b) 0.36 M, (c) 0.12 M. **9.12A** 67.13%. **9.12B** 0.420 g. **9.13A** 0.5502 g KHP. **9.13B** 206.4 mL. **9.14A** 11.3 mL. **9.14B** 91.2 mL. **9.15A** 92.6 g/mol. **9.15B** 80.5 g/mol.

SECTION REVIEW

9.1.1 (a) strong electrolyte, (b) nonelectrolyte, (c) strong electrolyte, (d) strong electrolyte, (e) weak electrolyte. **9.1.2** (a) lighting dimly, (b) lighting dimly, (c) lighting brightly, (d) not lighting at all, (e) not lighting at all. **9.1.3** (a) nonelectrolyte, (b) weak electrolyte, (c) nonelectrolyte. **9.2.1** (a) soluble, (b) soluble, (c) insoluble, (d) soluble, (e) insoluble. **9.2.2** (a) insoluble, (b) soluble, (c) insoluble, (d) insoluble, (e) soluble. **9.2.3** Li^+ and OH^-. **9.2.4** $Fe^{2+}(aq) + CO_3^{2-}(aq) \longrightarrow$ $FeCO_3(s)$. **9.2.5** 3B + 6C $\longrightarrow$ $3BC_2$. **9.3.1** $H_2SO_4(aq)$. **9.3.2** $NO_2^-(aq)$. **9.3.3** $H^+(aq) + HSO_4^-(aq) + OH^-(aq) \longrightarrow 2H_2O(l) + SO_4^{2-}(aq)$. **9.3.4** $HF(aq) + OH^-(aq) \longrightarrow H_2O(l) + F^-(aq)$. **9.4.1** −2, +4, +2, 0. **9.4.2** Mg(s). **9.4.3** Yes. **9.4.4** Yes. **9.5.1** 1.17 M. **9.5.2** 225 g. **9.5.3** 12.5 mL. **9.5.4** 0.36 M in Na^+, 0.18 M in CO_3^{2-}. **9.6.1** 12.3 g. **9.6.2** $MgCl_2$. **9.6.3** 0.182 M. **9.6.4** 7.20 mL.

KEY SKILLS

Net Ionic Equations

A molecular equation is necessary to do stoichiometric calculations [◄◄ Section 8.3] but molecular equations often misrepresent the species in a solution.

Net ionic equations are preferable in many instances because they indicate more succinctly the species in solution and the actual chemical process that a chemical equation represents. Writing net ionic equations is an important part of solving a variety of problems including those involving precipitation reactions, redox reactions, and acid-base neutralization reactions. To write net ionic equations, you must draw on several skills from earlier chapters:

- Recognition of the common polyatomic ions [◄◄ Section 5.7]
- Balancing chemical equations and labeling species with (s), (l), (g), or (aq) [◄◄ Section 8.1]
- Identification of strong electrolytes, weak electrolytes, and nonelectrolytes [◄◄ Section 9.1]

Writing a net ionic equation begins with writing and balancing the molecular equation. For example, consider the precipitation reaction that occurs when aqueous solutions of sodium iodide and lead(II) nitrate are combined.

$$Pb(NO_3)_2(aq) \quad + \quad NaI(aq) \quad \longrightarrow$$

Exchanging the ions of the two aqueous reactants gives us the formulas of the products. The phases of the products are determined by considering the solubility guidelines [◄◄ Tables 9.2 and 9.3].

$$Pb(NO_3)_2(aq) \quad + \quad NaI(aq) \quad \longrightarrow \quad PbI_2(s) \quad + \quad NaNO_3(aq)$$

We balance the equation and separate the soluble strong electrolytes to get the ionic equation.

$$Pb(NO_3)_2(aq) \quad + \quad 2\ NaI(aq) \quad \longrightarrow \quad PbI_2(s) \quad + \quad 2\ NaNO_3(aq)$$

$$Pb^{2+}(aq) \quad + \quad 2\ NO_3^-(aq) \quad + \quad 2\ Na^+(aq) \quad + \quad 2\ I^-(aq) \quad \longrightarrow \quad PbI_2(s) \quad + \quad 2\ Na^+(aq) \quad + \quad 2\ NO_3^-(aq)$$

We then identify the spectator ions, those that are identical on both sides of the equation, and eliminate them.

$$Pb^{2+}(aq) \quad + \quad 2\ NO_3^-(aq) \quad + \quad 2\ Na^+(aq) \quad + \quad 2\ I^-(aq) \quad \longrightarrow \quad PbI_2(s) \quad + \quad 2\ Na^+(aq) \quad + \quad 2\ NO_3^-(aq)$$

What remains is the net ionic equation.

$$Pb^{2+}(aq) \quad + \quad 2I^-(aq) \quad \longrightarrow \quad PbI_2(s)$$

Consider now the reaction that occurs when aqueous solutions of hydrochloric acid and potassium fluoride are combined.

$$HCl(aq) \quad + \quad KF(aq) \longrightarrow$$

Again, exchanging the ions of the two aqueous reactants gives us the formulas of the products.

$$HCl(aq) \quad + \quad KF(aq) \longrightarrow HF(aq) \quad + \quad KCl(aq)$$

This equation is already balanced. We separate soluble strong electrolytes into their constituent ions. In this case, although the products are both aqueous, only one is a strong electrolyte. The other, HF, is a *weak* electrolyte.

$$H^+(aq) \quad + \quad Cl^-(aq) \quad + \quad K^+(aq) \quad + \quad F^-(aq) \longrightarrow HF(aq) \quad + \quad K^+(aq) \quad + \quad Cl^-(aq)$$

We identify the spectator ions and eliminate them.

$$H^+(aq) \quad + \quad \boxed{Cl^-(aq)} \quad + \quad \boxed{K^+(aq)} \quad + \quad F^-(aq) \longrightarrow HF(aq) \quad + \quad \boxed{K^+(aq)} \quad + \quad \boxed{Cl^-(aq)}$$

What remains is the net ionic equation.

$$H^+(aq) \quad + \quad F^-(aq) \longrightarrow HF(aq)$$

You must be able to identify the species in solution as strong, weak, or nonelectrolytes so that you know which should be separated into ions and which should be left as molecular or formula units.

Key Skills Problems

9.1
What is the balanced net ionic equation for the precipitation of $FeSO_4(s)$ when aqueous solutions of K_2SO_4 and $FeCl_2$ are combined?

(a) $2K^+(aq) + SO_4^{2-}(aq) + Fe^{2+}(aq) + 2Cl^-(aq) \longrightarrow$
$\qquad\qquad\qquad FeSO_4(s) + 2K^+(aq) + 2Cl^-(aq)$
(b) $Fe^{2+}(aq) + SO_4^{2-}(aq) \longrightarrow FeSO_4(s)$
(c) $K_2SO_4(aq) + FeCl_2(aq) \longrightarrow FeSO_4(s) + 2KCl(aq)$
(d) $Fe^{2+}(aq) + 2SO_4^{2-}(aq) \longrightarrow FeSO_4(s)$
(e) $2K^+(aq) + SO_4^{2-}(aq) + Fe^{2+}(aq) + 2Cl^-(aq) \longrightarrow FeSO_4(s)$

9.2
Consider the following net ionic equation: $Cd^{2+}(aq) + 2OH^-(aq)$ $\longrightarrow Cd(OH)_2(s)$. If the spectator ions in the ionic equation are $NO_3^-(aq) + K^+(aq)$, what is the molecular equation for this reaction?

(a) $CdNO_3(aq) + KOH(aq) \longrightarrow Cd(OH)_2(s) + KNO_3(aq)$
(b) $Cd^{2+}(aq) + NO_3^-(aq) + 2K^+(aq) + OH^-(aq) \longrightarrow$
$\qquad\qquad\qquad Cd(OH)_2(s) + 2K^+(aq) + NO_3^-(aq)$
(c) $Cd(NO_3)_2(aq) + 2KOH(aq) \longrightarrow Cd(OH)_2(s) + 2KNO_3(aq)$
(d) $Cd(OH)_2(s) + 2KNO_3(aq) \longrightarrow Cd(NO_3)_2(aq) + 2KOH(aq)$
(e) $Cd^{2+}(aq) + NO_3^-(aq) + K^+(aq) + OH^-(aq) \longrightarrow$
$\qquad\qquad\qquad Cd(OH)_2(s) + K^+(aq) + NO_3^-(aq)$

9.3
The net ionic equation for the neutralization of acetic acid $(HC_2H_3O_2)$ with lithium hydroxide [LiOH(aq)] is

(a) $H^+(aq) + OH^-(aq) \longrightarrow H_2O(l)$
(b) $H^+(aq) + C_2H_3O_2^-(aq) \longrightarrow HC_2H_3O_2(aq)$
(c) $HC_2H_3O_2(aq) + OH^-(aq) \longrightarrow H_2O(l) + C_2H_3O_2^-(aq)$
(d) $HC_2H_3O_2(aq) + Li^+(aq) + OH^-(aq) \longrightarrow$
$\qquad\qquad\qquad H_2O(l) + LiC_2H_3O_2(aq)$
(e) $H^+(aq) + C_2H_3O_2^-(aq) + OH^-(aq) \longrightarrow H_2O(l) + C_2H_3O_2^-(aq)$

9.4
When steel wool [Fe(s)] is placed in a solution of $CuSO_4(aq)$, the steel becomes coated with copper metal and the characteristic blue color of the solution fades. What is the net ionic equation for this reaction?

(a) $Fe(s) + CuSO_4(aq) \longrightarrow FeSO_4(aq) + Cu(s)$
(b) $Fe^{2+}(aq) + Cu(s) \longrightarrow Fe(s) + Cu^{2+}(aq)$
(c) $FeSO_4(aq) + Cu(s) \longrightarrow Fe(s) + CuSO_4(aq)$
(d) $Fe(s) + Cu^{2+}(aq) \longrightarrow Fe^{2+}(aq) + Cu(s)$
(e) $Fe(s) + Cu(aq) \longrightarrow Fe(aq) + Cu(s)$

CHAPTER 10

Energy Changes in Chemical Reactions

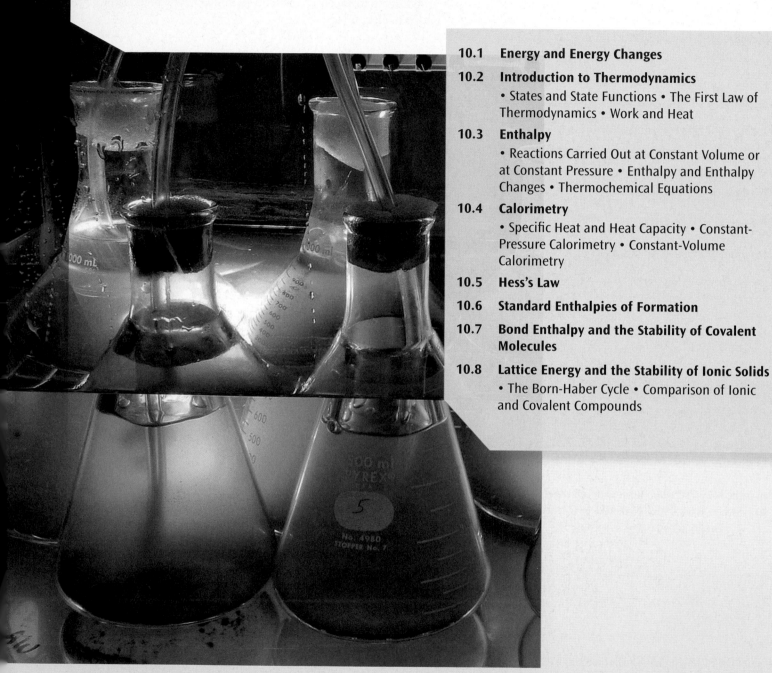

10.1 **Energy and Energy Changes**

10.2 **Introduction to Thermodynamics**
• States and State Functions • The First Law of Thermodynamics • Work and Heat

10.3 **Enthalpy**
• Reactions Carried Out at Constant Volume or at Constant Pressure • Enthalpy and Enthalpy Changes • Thermochemical Equations

10.4 **Calorimetry**
• Specific Heat and Heat Capacity • Constant-Pressure Calorimetry • Constant-Volume Calorimetry

10.5 **Hess's Law**

10.6 **Standard Enthalpies of Formation**

10.7 **Bond Enthalpy and the Stability of Covalent Molecules**

10.8 **Lattice Energy and the Stability of Ionic Solids**
• The Born-Haber Cycle • Comparison of Ionic and Covalent Compounds

Fossil fuels are a nonrenewable source of energy. According to some estimates, the world's supply of petroleum fuels will be exhausted within the next 50 years—prompting chemists to begin the search for alternative fuels. Of particular interest are biofuels—fuels derived from renewable sources such as corn, soybeans, rapeseeds, and even algae (shown here). Biodiesel is one such biofuel that is readily produced from a variety of oils and fats, and that may have potential as an alternative to petroleum for use in automobiles.

Before You Begin, Review These Skills

- Tracking units [◄◄ Section 1.6]
- Balancing chemical equations [◄◄ Section 8.1]
- Drawing Lewis structures [◄◄ Section 6.3]

10.1 ENERGY AND ENERGY CHANGES

You have already learned that matter can undergo physical changes and chemical changes [◄◄ Section 1.3]. The melting of ice, for example, is a physical change that can be represented by the following equation:

$$H_2O(s) \longrightarrow H_2O(l)$$

The formation of water from its constituent elements, represented by the following equation, is an example of a chemical change:

$$2H_2(g) + O_2(g) \longrightarrow 2H_2O(l)$$

In each case, there is energy involved in the change. Energy (in the form of heat) must be *supplied* to melt ice, whereas energy (in the form of heat and light) is *produced* by the explosive combination of hydrogen and oxygen gases. In fact, every change that matter undergoes is accompanied by either the absorption or the release of energy [◄◄ Section 3.1]. In this chapter, we will focus on the energy changes associated with physical and chemical processes.

To analyze energy changes associated with physical processes and chemical reactions, we must first define the *system,* the specific part of the universe that is of interest to us. For chemists, systems usually include the substances involved in physical and chemical changes. In an experiment involving the melting of an ice cube, for example, the system would be the ice, and the surroundings would be the rest of the universe. In an acid-base neutralization experiment, the system may be the reactants HCl and NaOH; and the rest of the universe, including the container itself and the water in which the reactants are dissolved, may constitute the *surroundings.*

Many chemical reactions are carried out for the purpose of exploiting the associated energy change, rather than for the purpose of obtaining the products of the reactions. For example, combustion reactions involving fossil fuels are carried out for the thermal energy they produce, not for their products, which are carbon dioxide and water.

It is important to distinguish between thermal energy and heat. *Heat* is the transfer of thermal energy between two bodies that are at different temperatures. Although the term *heat* by itself implies the transfer of energy, we customarily talk of "heat flow," meaning "energy absorbed" or "energy released," when describing the energy changes that occur during a process. *Thermochemistry* is the study of the heat (the transfer of thermal energy) associated with chemical reactions.

The combustion of hydrogen gas in oxygen is one of many chemical reactions that release considerable quantities of energy (Figure 10.1):

$$2H_2(g) + O_2(g) \longrightarrow 2H_2O(l) + energy$$

In this case, we label the mixture of reactants and product (hydrogen, oxygen, and water molecules) the *system.* Because energy cannot be created or destroyed, any energy released by the system must be gained by the surroundings. Thus, the heat generated by the combustion process is transferred from the system to its surroundings. This reaction is an example of an *exothermic process,* which is any process that gives off heat—that is, transfers thermal energy *from* the system *to* the surroundings. Figure 10.2 shows the energy change for the combustion of hydrogen gas.

Next, consider the decomposition of mercury(II) oxide (HgO) at high temperatures:

$$energy + 2HgO(s) \longrightarrow 2Hg(l) + O_2(g)$$

Figure 10.1 The Hindenburg, a German airship filled with hydrogen gas, was destroyed in a horrific fire as it landed at Lakehurst, New Jersey, in 1937.

Student Annotation: Although "surroundings" includes everything in the universe apart from the system, when chemists refer to the *surroundings* they generally mean the *immediate* surroundings—the part of the universe that is closest to the system.

Student Annotation: Emission of a photon from an atom when an electron falls from an excited state to a lower state [◄◄ Section 3.4] and most first electron affinities [◄◄ Section 4.4] are examples of exothermic processes that we have encountered in previous chapters.

Figure 10.2 (a) An exothermic reaction. Heat is given off by the system. (b) An endothermic reaction. Heat is absorbed by the system.

Multi 10.1
Thermochemistry—heat flow in endothermic and exothermic reactions

> **Student Annotation:** In these examples, all the energy released or absorbed by the system is *thermal* energy, which is commonly referred to as heat. In Section 10.2, we will consider examples in which some of the energy is in the form of *work*.

> **Student Annotation:** The triple equal sign is used to denote a definition. Recall that numbers with defined values are exact numbers, which do not limit the number of significant figures in a calculation [◄◄ Section 1.5].

This reaction is an ***endothermic process*** because heat has to be supplied to the system (i.e., to HgO) by the surroundings [Figure 10.2(b)] in order for the reaction to occur. Thus, thermal energy is transferred *from* the surroundings *to* the system in an endothermic process.

According to Figure 10.2, the energy of the products of an exothermic reaction is lower than the energy of the reactants. The difference in energy between the reactants H_2 and O_2 and the product H_2O is the heat released by the system to the surroundings. In an endothermic reaction, on the other hand, the energy of the products is higher than the energy of the reactants. Here, the difference between the energy of the reactant HgO and the products Hg and O_2 is the heat absorbed by the system from the surroundings.

Recall that the SI unit for energy is the joule, which is the amount of energy possessed by a 1 kg object moving at 1 m/s [◄◄ Section 3.1]. Another unit used to express energy is the calorie (cal), which was originally defined as the amount of energy required to raise the temperature of one gram of water by one degree (°C). Although the calorie is not an SI unit, its use is still quite common. The calorie is now defined in terms of the joule:

$$1 \text{ cal} \equiv 4.184 \text{ J}$$

Because this is a definition, the number 4.184 is an *exact* number, which does not limit the number of significant figures in a calculation [◄◄ Section 1.5]. You may be familiar with the term *calorie* from nutrition labels. In fact, the "calories" listed on food packaging are really *kilocalories*. Often the distinction is made by capitalizing the "C" in "calorie" when it refers to the energy content of food:

$$1 \text{ Cal} \equiv 1000 \text{ cal}$$

and

$$1 \text{ Cal} \equiv 4184 \text{ J}$$

SECTION 10.1 REVIEW

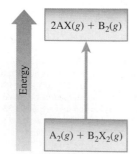

Energy and Energy Changes

10.1.1   Calculate the number of calories in 723.01 J.

10.1.2   The label on packaged food indicates that it contains 215 Cal per serving. Convert this amount of energy to joules.

10.1.3   Use the figure shown here to write (a) a chemical equation representing an exothermic process, and (b) a chemical equation representing an endothermic process.

10.2 INTRODUCTION TO THERMODYNAMICS

Thermochemistry is part of a broader subject called *thermodynamics,* which is the scientific study of the interconversion of heat and other kinds of energy. The laws of thermodynamics provide useful guidelines for understanding the energetics and directions of processes. In this section, we will introduce the first law of thermodynamics, which is particularly relevant to the study of thermochemistry. We will continue our discussion of thermodynamics in Chapter 18.

We have defined a system as the part of the universe we are studying. There are three types of systems. An *open system* can exchange mass and energy with its surroundings. For example, an open system may consist of a quantity of water in an open container, as shown in Figure 10.3(a). If we close the flask, as in Figure 10.3(b), so that no water vapor can escape from or condense into the container, we create a *closed system,* which allows the transfer of *energy* but not *mass.* By placing the water in an insulated container, as shown in Figure 10.3(c), we can construct an *isolated system,* which does not exchange either mass or energy with its surroundings.

> **Student Annotation:** The energy exchanged between open systems or closed systems and their surrounding is usually in the form of heat.

States and State Functions

In thermodynamics, we study changes in the *state of a system,* which is defined by the values of all relevant macroscopic properties, such as composition, energy, temperature, pressure, and volume. Energy, pressure, volume, and temperature are said to be *state functions*—properties that are determined by the state of the system, regardless of how that condition was achieved. In other words, when the state of a system changes, the magnitude of change in any state function depends only on the initial and final states of the system and not on how the change is accomplished.

Consider, for example, your position in a six-story building. Your elevation depends upon which floor you are on. If you change your elevation by taking the stairs from the ground floor up to the fourth floor, the change in your elevation depends only upon your initial state (the ground floor—the floor you started on) and your final state (the fourth floor—the floor you went to). It does not depend on whether you went directly to the fourth floor or up to the sixth and then down to the fourth floor. Your overall change in elevation is the same either way because it depends only on your initial and final elevations. Thus, elevation is a state function.

The amount of effort it takes to get from the ground floor to the fourth floor, on the other hand, depends on how you get there. More effort has to be exerted to go from the ground floor to the sixth floor and back down to the fourth floor than to go from the ground floor to the fourth floor directly. The effort required for this change in elevation is *not* a state function. Furthermore, if you subsequently return to the ground floor, your overall change in elevation will be zero, because your initial and final states are the same, but the amount of effort you exerted going from the ground floor to the fourth floor and back to the ground floor is *not* zero. Even though your initial and final states are the same, you do not get back the effort that went into climbing up and down the stairs.

Figure 10.3 (a) An open system allows exchange of both energy and matter with the surroundings. (b) A closed system allows exchange of energy but not matter. (c) An isolated system does not allow exchange of energy or matter. (This flask is enclosed by an insulating vacuum jacket.)

Figure 10.4 The change in elevation that occurs when a person goes from the ground floor to the fourth floor in a building does not depend on the path taken.

Fourth floor

Change in elevation

Ground floor

Energy is a state function, too. Using potential energy as an example, your net increase in gravitational potential energy is always the same, regardless of how you get from the ground floor to the fourth floor of a building (Figure 10.4).

The First Law of Thermodynamics

The *first law of thermodynamics,* which is based on the law of conservation of energy, states that energy can be converted from one form to another but cannot be created or destroyed. It would be impossible to demonstrate this by measuring the total amount of energy in the universe; in fact, just determining the total energy content of a small sample of matter would be extremely difficult. Fortunately, because energy is a state function, we can demonstrate the first law by measuring the change in the energy of a system between its initial state and its final state in a process. The change in internal energy, ΔU, is given by

$$\Delta U = U_f - U_i$$

Student Annotation: The symbol U is used to denote the internal energy of a *system,* as opposed to the symbol E, which is used to denote the energy possessed by a particle or associated with a particular process.

Student Annotation: Recall that the symbol Δ is commonly used to mean *final* minus *initial.*

where U_i and U_f are the internal energies of the system in the initial and final states, respectively.

The internal energy of a system has two components: kinetic energy and potential energy. The kinetic energy component consists of various types of molecular motion and the movement of electrons within molecules. Potential energy is determined by the attractive interactions between electrons and nuclei and by repulsive interactions between electrons and between nuclei in individual molecules, as well as by interactions between molecules. It is impossible to measure all these contributions accurately, so we cannot calculate the total energy of a system with any certainty. *Changes* in energy, on the other hand, can be determined experimentally.

Consider the reaction between 1 mole of sulfur and 1 mole of oxygen gas to produce 1 mole of sulfur dioxide:

Student Annotation: Elemental sulfur exists as S_8 molecules but we typically represent it simply as S to simplify chemical equations [◄◄ Section 8.1].

$$S(s) + O_2(g) \longrightarrow SO_2(g)$$

In this case our system is composed of the reactant molecules and the product molecules. We do not know the internal energy content of either the reactants or the product, but we can accurately measure the *change* in energy content ΔU given by

$$\Delta U = U(\text{products}) - U(\text{reactants})$$

$$= \text{energy content of 1 mol } SO_2(g) - \text{energy content of 1 mol } S(s) \text{ and 1 mol } O_2(g)$$

Student Annotation: Later in this chapter, we will learn about the experimental techniques used to measure energy changes [►► Section 10.4].

This reaction gives off heat: 296.4 kJ, to be exact. Therefore, the energy of the product is less than that of the reactants, and ΔU is negative (−296.4 kJ/mol).

The release of heat that accompanies this reaction indicates that some of the chemical energy contained in the system has been converted to thermal energy. Furthermore, the thermal energy released by the system is absorbed by the surroundings. The transfer of energy from the system to the surroundings does not change the total energy of the universe. That is, the sum of the energy changes is zero:

$$\Delta U_{sys} + \Delta U_{surr} = 0$$

where the subscripts "sys" and "surr" denote system and surroundings, respectively. Thus, if a system undergoes an energy change ΔU_{sys}, the rest of the universe, or the surroundings, must undergo a change in energy that is equal in magnitude but opposite in sign:

$$\Delta U_{sys} = -\Delta U_{surr}$$

Energy released in one place must be gained somewhere else. Furthermore, because energy can be changed from one form to another, the energy lost by one system can be gained by another system in a different form. For example, the energy released by burning coal in a power plant may ultimately turn up in our homes as electric energy, heat, light, and so on.

Work and Heat

Recall from Section 3.1 that energy is defined as the capacity to do work or transfer heat. When a system releases or absorbs heat, its internal energy changes. Likewise, when a system does work on its surroundings, or when the surroundings do work on the system, the system's internal energy also changes. The overall change in the system's internal energy is given by

$$\Delta U = q + w \qquad \textbf{Equation 10.1}$$

where q is heat (released or absorbed by the system) and w is work (done *on* the system or done *by* the system). Note that it is possible for the heat and work components to cancel each other out and for there to be no change in the system's internal energy.

In chemistry, we are normally interested in the energy changes associated with the system rather than the surroundings. Therefore, unless otherwise indicated, ΔU will refer specifically to ΔU_{sys}. The sign conventions for q and w are as follows: q is positive for an endothermic process and negative for an exothermic process, and w is positive for work done on the system by the surroundings and negative for work done by the system on the surroundings. Table 10.1 summarizes the sign conventions for q and w.

The drawings in Figure 10.5 illustrate the logic behind the sign conventions for q and w. If a system releases heat to the surroundings or does work on the surroundings [Figure 10.5(a)], we would expect its internal energy to decrease because they are energy-depleting processes. For this

Student Annotation: The units for heat and work are the same as those for energy: joules, kilojoules, or calories.

Student Annotation: Interestingly, although neither q nor w is a state function (each depends on the path between the initial and final states of the system), their sum, ΔU, does *not* depend on the path between initial and final states because U is a state function.

TABLE 10.1	Sign Conventions for Heat (q) and Work (w)
Process	**Sign**
Heat absorbed by the system (endothermic process)	q is positive
Heat released by the system (exothermic process)	q is negative
Work done on the system by the surroundings (for example, a volume decrease)	w is positive
Work done by the system on the surroundings (for example, a volume increase)	w is negative

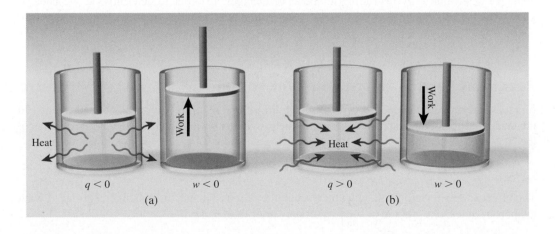

$q < 0 \qquad w < 0 \qquad q > 0 \qquad w > 0$

(a) \qquad (b)

Figure 10.5 (a) When heat is released by the system (to the surroundings), q is negative. When work is done by the system (on the surroundings), w is negative. (b) When heat is absorbed by the system (from the surroundings), q is positive. When work is done on the system (by the surroundings), w is positive.

reason, both q and w are negative. Conversely, if heat is added to the system or if work is done on the system [Figure 10.5(b)] then the internal energy of the system increases. In this case, both q and w are positive.

Worked Example 10.1 shows how to determine the overall change in the internal energy of a system.

Worked Example 10.1

Calculate the overall change in internal energy, ΔU, (in joules) for a system that absorbs 188 J of heat and does 141 J of work on its surroundings.

Strategy Combine the two contributions to internal energy using Equation 10.1 and the sign conventions for q and w.

Setup The system absorbs heat, so q is *positive*. The system does work on the surroundings, so w is negative.

Solution

$$\Delta U = q + w = 188 \text{ J} + (-141 \text{ J}) = 47 \text{ J}$$

> **Think About It**
> Consult Table 10.1 to make sure you have used the proper sign conventions for q and w.

Practice Problem A Calculate the change in total internal energy for a system that releases 1.34×10^4 kJ of heat and does 2.98×10^4 kJ of work on the surroundings.

Practice Problem B Calculate the magnitude of q for a system that does 7.05×10^5 kJ of work on its surroundings and for which the change in total internal energy is -9.55×10^3 kJ. Indicate whether heat is absorbed or released by the system.

SECTION 10.2 REVIEW

Introduction to Thermodynamics

10.2.1 Calculate the overall change in internal energy for a system that releases 43 J in heat in a process in which no work is done.

10.2.2 Calculate w, and determine whether work is done by the system or on the system when 928 kJ of heat is released and $\Delta U = -1.47 \times 10^3$ kJ.

10.3 ENTHALPY

To calculate ΔU, we must know the values and signs of both q and w. As we will see in Section 10.4, we determine q by measuring temperature changes. In order to determine w, we need to know whether the reaction occurs under constant-volume conditions, or under constant-pressure conditions.

Reactions Carried Out at Constant Volume or at Constant Pressure

Imagine carrying out the decomposition of sodium azide (NaN$_3$) in two different experiments. In the first experiment, the reactant is placed in a metal cylinder with a fixed volume. When detonated, the NaN$_3$ reacts, generating a large quantity of N_2 gas inside the closed, fixed-volume container.

$$2NaN_3(s) \longrightarrow 2Na(s) + 3N_2(g)$$

The effect of this reaction will be an increase in the pressure inside the container, similar to what happens if you shake a bottle of soda vigorously prior to opening it.

Figure 10.6 (a) The explosive decomposition of NaN_3 at constant volume results in an increase in pressure inside the vessel. (b) The decomposition at constant pressure, in a vessel with a movable piston, results in an increase in volume. The resulting change in volume, ΔV, can be used to calculate the work done by the system.

Now imagine carrying out the same reaction in a metal cylinder with a movable piston. As this explosive decomposition proceeds, the piston in the metal cylinder will move. The gas produced in the reaction pushes the cylinder upward, thereby increasing the volume of the container and preventing any increase in pressure. This is a simple example of mechanical work done by a chemical reaction. Specifically, this type of work is known as *pressure-volume*, or *PV*, work. The amount of work done by such a process is given by

$$w = -P\Delta V \qquad \qquad \textbf{Equation 10.2}$$

where P is the external, opposing pressure and ΔV is the change in the volume of the container as the result of the piston being pushed upward. In keeping with the sign conventions in Table 10.1, an increase in volume results in a negative value for w, whereas a decrease in volume results in a positive value for w. Figure 10.6 illustrates this reaction (a) being carried out at a constant volume, and (b) at a constant pressure.

Worked Example 10.2 shows how to calculate the work associated with a volume change.

> **Student Annotation:** Pressure-volume work and electrical work are two important types of work done by chemical reactions. Electrical work will be discussed in detail in Chapter 19.

> **Student Annotation:** The SI unit of pressure is the *pascal* (Pa), which, in SI base units is 1 kg/(m · s²). Volume, in SI base units is cubic meters (m³). Therefore, multiplying units of *pressure* by units of *volume* gives $[1 \text{ kg/(m} \cdot \text{s}^2)] \times (\text{m}^3) = 1 \text{ (kg} \cdot \text{m}^2)/\text{s}^2$, which is the definition of the *joule* (J). Thus, $P\Delta V$ has units of *energy*.
> Another commonly used unit of pressure is the *atmosphere* (atm) [▶▶ Section 11.3]. Worked Example 10.2 uses atmospheres to express pressure.

Worked Example 10.2

Determine the work done (in joules) when a sample of gas expands from 552 mL to 891 mL at constant temperature (a) against a constant pressure of 1.25 atm, (b) against a constant pressure of 1.00 atm, and (c) against a vacuum (1 L · atm = 101.3 J).

Strategy Determine change in volume (ΔV), identify the external pressure (P), and use Equation 10.2 to calculate w. The result of Equation 10.2 will be in L · atm; use the equality 1 L · atm = 101.3 J to convert to joules.

Setup $\Delta V = (891 - 552)\text{mL} = 339$ mL. (a) $P = 1.25$ atm, (b) $P = 1.00$ atm, (c) $P = 0$ atm.

Solution

(a) $w = -(1.25 \text{ atm})(339 \text{ mL}) \left(\dfrac{1 \text{ L}}{1000 \text{ mL}} \right)\left(\dfrac{101.3 \text{ J}}{1 \text{ L} \cdot \text{atm}} \right) = -42.9$ J

(b) $w = -(1.00 \text{ atm})(339 \text{ mL}) \left(\dfrac{1 \text{ L}}{1000 \text{ mL}} \right)\left(\dfrac{101.3 \text{ J}}{1 \text{ L} \cdot \text{atm}} \right) = -34.3$ J

(c) $w = -(0 \text{ atm})(339 \text{ mL}) \left(\dfrac{1 \text{ L}}{1000 \text{ mL}} \right)\left(\dfrac{101.3 \text{ J}}{1 \text{ L} \cdot \text{atm}} \right) = 0$ J

(Continued on next page)

Think About It
Remember that the negative sign in the answers to parts (a) and (b) indicate that the system does work on the surroundings. When an expansion happens against a vacuum, no work is done. This example illustrates that work is *not* a state function. For an equivalent change in volume, the work varies depending on the external pressure against which the expansion must occur.

Practice Problem A Calculate the work done by or on the system during the following processes: (a) A sample of gas expands from 1.2 L to 3.8 L against an external pressure of 1.01 atm; (b) A sample of gas is compressed from 87.5 mL to 72.9 mL by a pressure of 2.72 atm; (c) The volume of a 2.00-L gas sample increases by a factor of 2 against an external pressure of 0.998 atm.

Practice Problem B (a) Against what external pressure must a gas sample expand from 50.0 mL to 219 mL to do 8.34 J of work? (b) To what volume will a 200.0-mL gas sample be compressed by an external pressure of 7.8 atm if 100.0 J of work are done on the system? (c) To what volume must a 200.0-mL gas sample expand against an external pressure of 7.8 atm to do 100.0 J of work?

When a chemical reaction is carried out at constant volume, then no PV work can be done because $\Delta V = 0$ in Equation 10.2. From Equation 10.1 it follows that

Equation 10.3	$\Delta U = q - P\Delta V$

and, because $P\Delta V = 0$ at constant volume,

Equation 10.4	$q_V = \Delta U$

We add the subscript "V" to indicate that this is a constant-volume process. This equality may seem strange at first. We said earlier that q is *not* a state function. However, for a process carried out under constant-volume conditions, q can have only one specific value, which is equal to ΔU. In other words, although q is *not* a state function, q_V *is* one.

Constant-volume conditions are often inconvenient and sometimes impossible to achieve. Most reactions occur in open containers, under conditions of constant pressure (usually at whatever the atmospheric pressure happens to be where the experiments are conducted). In general, for a constant-pressure process, we write

$$\Delta U = q + w$$

$$= q_P - P\Delta V$$

or

Equation 10.5	$q_P = \Delta U + P\Delta V$

where the subscript "P" denotes constant pressure.

Enthalpy and Enthalpy Changes

There is a thermodynamic function of a system called **enthalpy** (H), which is defined by Equation 10.6:

Equation 10.6	$H = U + PV$

where U is the internal energy of the system and P and V are the pressure and volume of the system, respectively. Because U and PV have energy units, enthalpy also has energy units. Furthermore, U, P, and V are all state functions—that is, the changes in $(U + PV)$ depend only on the initial and final states. It follows, therefore, that the change in H, or ΔH, also depends only on the initial and final states. Thus, H is a state function.

For any process, the *change* in enthalpy is given by

Equation 10.7	$\Delta H = \Delta U + \Delta(PV)$

If the pressure is held constant, then

$$\Delta H = \Delta U + P\Delta V \qquad \textbf{Equation 10.8}$$

If we solve Equation 10.8 for ΔU,

$$\Delta U = \Delta H - P\Delta V$$

Then, substituting the result for ΔU into Equation 10.5, we obtain

$$q_P = (\Delta H - P\Delta V) + P\Delta V$$

The $P\Delta V$ terms cancel, and for a constant-pressure process, the heat exchanged between the system and the surroundings is equal to the enthalpy change:

$$q_P = \Delta H \qquad \textbf{Equation 10.9}$$

Again, q is *not* a state function, but q_P *is* one; that is, the heat change at constant pressure can have only one specific value and is equal to ΔH.

We now have two quantities—ΔU and ΔH—that can be associated with a reaction. If the reaction occurs under constant-volume conditions, then the heat change, q_V, is equal to ΔU. If the reaction is carried out at constant pressure, on the other hand, the heat change, q_P, is equal to ΔH.

Because most laboratory reactions are constant-pressure processes, the heat exchanged between the system and surroundings is equal to the change in enthalpy for the process. For any reaction, we define the change in enthalpy, called the ***enthalpy of reaction*** (ΔH), as the difference between the enthalpies of the products and the enthalpies of the reactants:

$$\Delta H = H(\text{products}) - H(\text{reactants}) \qquad \textbf{Equation 10.10}$$

> **Student Annotation:** The enthalpy of reaction is often symbolized by ΔH_{rxn}. The subscript can be changed to denote a specific type of reaction or physical process: ΔH_{vap} can be used for the enthalpy of *vaporization*, for example.

The enthalpy of reaction can be positive or negative, depending on the process. For an endothermic process (where heat is absorbed by the system from the surroundings), ΔH is positive (i.e., $\Delta H > 0$). For an exothermic process (where heat is released by the system to the surroundings), ΔH is negative (i.e., $\Delta H < 0$).

We will now apply the idea of enthalpy changes to two common processes, the first involving a physical change and the second involving a chemical change.

Thermochemical Equations

Under ordinary atmospheric conditions at sea level, ice melts to form liquid water at temperatures above 0°C. Measurements show that for every mole of ice converted to liquid water under these conditions, 6.01 kJ of heat energy is absorbed by the system (the ice). Because the pressure is constant, the heat change is equal to the enthalpy change, ΔH. This is an *endothermic* process ($\Delta H > 0$), because heat is absorbed by the ice from its surroundings (Figure 10.7a). The equation for this physical change is

> **Student Annotation:** Although, strictly speaking, it is unnecessary to include the sign of a positive number, we will include the sign of all positive ΔH values to emphasize the thermochemical sign convention.

$$H_2O(s) \longrightarrow H_2O(l) \qquad\qquad \Delta H = +6.01 \text{ kJ/mol}$$

Figure 10.7 (a) Melting 1 mole of ice at 0°C, an endothermic process, results in an enthalpy increase of 6.01 kJ ($\Delta H = +6.01$ kJ/mol). (b) The burning of 1 mole of methane in oxygen gas, an exothermic process, results in an enthalpy decrease in the system of 890.4 kJ ($\Delta H = -890.4$ kJ/mol). The enthalpy diagrams of these two processes are not shown to the same scale.

The "per mole" in the unit for ΔH means that this is the enthalpy change *per mole of the reaction (or process) as it is written*—that is, when 1 mole of ice is converted to 1 mole of liquid water. Now consider the combustion of methane (CH_4), the principal component of natural gas:

$$CH_4(g) + 2O_2(g) \longrightarrow CO_2(g) + 2H_2O(l) \qquad \Delta H = -890.4 \text{ kJ/mol}$$

From experience we know that burning natural gas releases heat to the surroundings, so it is an exothermic process. Under constant-pressure conditions, this heat change is equal to the enthalpy change and ΔH must have a negative sign [Figure 10.7(b)]. Again, the "per mole" in the units for ΔH means that when 1 mole of CH_4 reacts with 2 moles of O_2 to yield 1 mole of CO_2 and 2 moles of liquid H_2O, 890.4 kJ of heat is released to the surroundings.

> **Student Annotation:** When you specify that a particular amount of heat is released, it is not necessary to include a negative sign.

It is important to keep in mind that the ΔH value in kJ/mol does not mean *per mole* of a particular reactant or product. It refers to all the species in a reaction in the molar amounts specified by the coefficients in the balanced equation. Thus, for the combustion of methane, the ΔH value of −890.4 kJ/mol can be expressed in any of the following ways:

$$\frac{-890.4 \text{ kJ}}{1 \text{ mol } CH_4} \qquad \frac{-890.4 \text{ kJ}}{2 \text{ mol } O_2} \qquad \frac{-890.4 \text{ kJ}}{1 \text{ mol } CO_2} \qquad \frac{-890.4 \text{ kJ}}{2 \text{ mol } H_2O}$$

Although the importance of expressing ΔH in units of kJ/mol (rather than just kilojoules) will become apparent when we study thermodynamics in greater detail [▶▶ Chapter 18], you should learn and become comfortable with this convention now.

The equations for the melting of ice and the combustion of methane are examples of ***thermochemical equations,*** which are chemical equations that show the enthalpy changes as well as the mass relationships. It is essential to specify a balanced chemical equation when quoting the enthalpy change of a reaction. The following guidelines are helpful in interpreting, writing, and manipulating thermochemical equations:

1. When writing thermochemical equations, we must always specify the physical states of all reactants and products, because they help determine the actual enthalpy changes. In the equation for the combustion of methane, for example, changing the liquid water product to water vapor changes the value of ΔH:

$$CH_4(g) + 2O_2(g) \longrightarrow CO_2(g) + 2H_2O(g) \qquad \Delta H = -802.4 \text{ kJ/mol}$$

The enthalpy change is −802.4 kJ rather than −890.4 kJ (see page 371) because 88.0 kJ are needed to convert 2 moles of liquid water to 2 moles of water vapor; that is,

> **Student Annotation:** Remember that the "per mole" in this context refers to per mole of *reaction*—not, in this case, per mole of water.

$$2H_2O(l) \longrightarrow 2H_2O(g) \qquad \Delta H = +88.0 \text{ kJ/mol}$$

2. If we multiply both sides of a thermochemical equation by a factor n, then ΔH must also be multiplied by the same factor. Thus, for the melting of ice, if $n = 2$, we have

$$2H_2O(s) \longrightarrow 2H_2O(l) \qquad \Delta H = 2(+6.01 \text{ kJ/mol}) = +12.02 \text{ kJ/mol}$$

3. When we reverse a chemical equation, we change the roles of reactants and products. Consequently, the magnitude of ΔH for the equation remains the same, but its sign changes. For example, if a reaction consumes thermal energy from its surroundings (i.e., if it is endothermic), then the reverse reaction must release thermal energy back to its surroundings (i.e., it must be exothermic) and the enthalpy change expression must also change its sign. Thus, reversing the melting of ice and the combustion of methane, the thermochemical equations become

$$H_2O(l) \longrightarrow H_2O(s) \qquad \Delta H = -6.01 \text{ kJ/mol}$$

$$CO_2(g) + 2H_2O(l) \longrightarrow CH_4(g) + 2O_2(g) \qquad \Delta H = +890.4 \text{ kJ/mol}$$

> **Student Annotation:** A convenient way to summarize this concept is:
>
> $$\Delta H_{\text{forward}} = -\Delta H_{\text{reverse}}$$

What was an endothermic process becomes an exothermic process when reversed, and vice versa.

Worked Example 10.3 illustrates the use of a thermochemical equation to relate the mass of a product to the energy consumed in the reaction.

Worked Example 10.3

Given the thermochemical equation for photosynthesis,

$$6H_2O(l) + 6CO_2(g) \longrightarrow C_6H_{12}O_6(s) + 6O_2(g) \qquad \Delta H = +2803 \text{ kJ/mol}$$

calculate the solar energy required to produce 75.0 g of $C_6H_{12}O_6$.

Strategy The thermochemical equation shows that for every mole of $C_6H_{12}O_6$ produced, 2803 kJ is absorbed. We need to find out how much energy is absorbed for the production of 75.0 g of $C_6H_{12}O_6$. We must first find out how many moles there are in 75.0 g of $C_6H_{12}O_6$.

Setup The molar mass of $C_6H_{12}O_6$ is 180.2 g/mol, so 75.0 g of $C_6H_{12}O_6$ is

$$75.0 \text{ g } C_6H_{12}O_6 \times \frac{1 \text{ mol } C_6H_{12}O_6}{180.2 \text{ g } C_6H_{12}O_6} = 0.416 \text{ mol } C_6H_{12}O_6$$

We will multiply the thermochemical equation, including the enthalpy change, by 0.416, in order to write the equation in terms of the appropriate amount of $C_6H_{12}O_6$.

Solution

$$(0.416 \text{ mol})[6H_2O(l) + 6CO_2(g) \longrightarrow C_6H_{12}O_6(s) + 6O_2(g)]$$

and $\qquad (0.416 \text{ mol})(\Delta H) = (0.416 \text{ mol})(2803 \text{ kJ/mol})$ gives

$$2.50H_2O(l) + 2.50CO_2(g) \longrightarrow 0.416C_6H_{12}O_6(s) + 2.50O_2(g) \qquad \Delta H = +1.17 \times 10^3 \text{ kJ}$$

Therefore, 1.17×10^3 kJ of energy in the form of sunlight is consumed in the production of 75.0 g of $C_6H_{12}O_6$. Note that the "per mole" units in ΔH are canceled when we multiply the thermochemical equation by the number of moles of $C_6H_{12}O_6$.

Think About It
The specified amount of $C_6H_{12}O_6$ is less than half a mole. Therefore, we should expect the associated enthalpy change to be less than half that specified in the thermochemical equation for the production of 1 mole of $C_6H_{12}O_6$.

Practice Problem A Calculate the solar energy required to produce 5255 g of $C_6H_{12}O_6$.

Practice Problem B Calculate the mass (in grams) of O_2 that is produced by photosynthesis when 2.49×10^4 kJ of solar energy is consumed.

SECTION 10.3 REVIEW

Enthalpy

10.3.1 Given the thermochemical equation: $H_2(g) + Br_2(l) \longrightarrow 2HBr(g)$, $\Delta H = -72.4$ kJ/mol, calculate the amount of heat released when a kilogram of $Br_2(l)$ is consumed in this reaction.

10.3.2 Given the thermochemical equation: $2Cu_2O(s) \longrightarrow 4Cu(s) + O_2(g)$, $\Delta H = +333.8$ kJ/mol, calculate the mass of copper produced when 1.47×10^4 kJ is consumed in this reaction.

10.4 CALORIMETRY

In the study of thermochemistry, heat changes that accompany physical and chemical processes are measured with a *calorimeter,* a closed container designed specifically for this purpose. We begin our discussion of **calorimetry,** the measurement of heat changes, by defining two important terms: *specific heat* and *heat capacity.*

Specific Heat and Heat Capacity

The **specific heat** (s) of a substance is the amount of heat required to raise the temperature of 1 g of the substance by 1°C. The **heat capacity** (C) is the amount of heat required to raise the temperature of an *object* by 1°C. We can use the specific heat of a substance to determine the heat capacity of a specified quantity of that substance. For example, we can use the specific heat of water, 4.184 J/(g · °C), to determine the heat capacity of a kilogram of water:

$$\text{Heat capacity of 1 kg of water} = \frac{4.184 \text{ J}}{1 \text{ g} \cdot °\text{C}} \times 1000 \text{ g} = 4184 \text{ or } 4.184 \times 10^3 \text{ J/°C}$$

Note that specific heat has the units J/(g · °C) and heat capacity has the units J/°C. Table 10.2 shows the specific heat values of some common substances. If we know the specific heat and the amount of a substance, then the change in the sample's temperature (ΔT) will tell us the amount of heat (q) that has been absorbed or released in a particular process. One equation for calculating the heat associated with a temperature change is given by

Equation 10.11	$q = sm\Delta T$

where s is the specific heat, m is the mass of the substance undergoing the temperature change, and ΔT is the temperature change: $\Delta T = T_{\text{final}} - T_{\text{initial}}$. Another equation for calculating the heat associated with a temperature change is given by

Equation 10.12	$q = C\Delta T$

where C is the heat capacity and ΔT is the temperature change: The sign convention for q is the same as that for an enthalpy change: q is positive for endothermic processes and negative for exothermic processes. Worked Example 10.4 shows how to use the specific heat of a substance to calculate the amount of heat needed to raise the temperature of the substance by a particular amount.

Worked Example 10.4

Calculate the amount of heat (in kJ) required to heat 255 g of water from 25.2°C to 90.5°C.

Strategy Use Equation 10.11 ($q = sm\Delta T$) to calculate q.

Setup $s = 4.184$ J/g · °C, $m = 255$ g, and $\Delta T = 90.5°\text{C} - 25.2°\text{C} = 65.3°\text{C}$.

Solution

$$q = \frac{4.184 \text{ J}}{\text{g} \cdot °\text{C}} \times 255 \text{ g} \times 65.3°\text{C} = 6.97 \times 10^4 \text{ J or } 69.7 \text{ kJ}$$

Think About It
Look carefully at the cancellation of units and make sure that the number of kilojoules is smaller than the number of joules. It is a common error to multiply by 1000 instead of dividing in conversions of this kind.

Practice Problem A Calculate the amount of heat (in kJ) required to heat 1.01 kg of water from 0.05°C to 35.81°C.

Practice Problem B What will be the final temperature of a 514-g sample of water, initially at 10.0°C, after the addition of 90.8 kJ?

Constant-Pressure Calorimetry

A crude constant-pressure calorimeter can be constructed from two Styrofoam coffee cups, as shown in Figure 10.8. This device, called a coffee-cup calorimeter, can be used to measure the heat exchanged between the system and surroundings for a variety of reactions, such as acid-base neutralization, heat of solution, and heat of dilution. Because the pressure is constant, the heat change for the process (q) is equal to the enthalpy change (ΔH). In such experiments, we consider the reactants and products to be the system, and the water in the calorimeter to be the surroundings. We neglect the small heat capacity of the Styrofoam cups in our calculations. In the case of an exothermic reaction, the heat released by the system is absorbed by the water (surroundings), thereby increasing its temperature. Knowing the mass of the water in the calorimeter, the specific heat of water, and the change in temperature, we can calculate q_p of the system using the equation

$$q_{sys} = -sm\Delta T \qquad \textbf{Equation 10.13}$$

Note that the minus sign makes q_{sys} a negative number if ΔT is a positive number (i.e., if the temperature goes up). This is in keeping with the sign conventions listed in Table 10.1. A negative ΔH or a negative q indicates an exothermic process, whereas a positive ΔH or a positive q indicates an endothermic process. Table 10.3 lists some of the reactions that can be studied with a constant-pressure calorimeter. Figure 10.9 (pages 376–377) shows how constant-pressure calorimetry can be used to determine ΔH for a reaction.

Constant-pressure calorimetry can also be used to determine the heat capacity of an object or the specific heat of a substance. Suppose, for example, that we have a lead pellet with a mass of 26.47 g originally at 89.98°C. We drop the pellet into a constant-pressure calorimeter containing 100.0 g of water at 22.50°C. The temperature of the water increases to 23.17°C. In this case, we consider the pellet to be the system and the water to be the surroundings. Because it is the temperature of the surroundings that we measure, and because $q_{sys} = -q_{surr}$, we calculate q_P of the surroundings as

$$q_{surr} = sm\Delta T \qquad \textbf{Equation 10.14}$$

Thus, q_{water} of the water is

$$q = \frac{4.184 \text{ J}}{\text{g} \cdot {}°\text{C}} \times 100.0 \text{ g} \times (23.17°\text{C} - 22.50°\text{C}) = 280 \text{ J}$$

and q_{pellet} is −280 J. The negative sign indicates that heat is *released* by the pellet. Dividing q_{pellet} by the temperature change (ΔT) gives us the heat capacity of the pellet (C_{pellet}).

$$C_{pellet} = \frac{-280 \text{ J}}{23.17°\text{C} - 89.95°\text{C}} = 4.19 \text{ J}/{}°\text{C}$$

TABLE 10.2	Specific Heat Values of Some Common Substances
Substance	**Specific heat (J/g · °C)**
Al(*s*)	0.900
Au(*s*)	0.129
C (graphite)	0.720
C (diamond)	0.502
Cu(*s*)	0.385
Fe(*s*)	0.444
Hg(*l*)	0.139
H$_2$O(*l*)	4.184
C$_2$H$_5$OH(*l*) (ethanol)	2.46

TABLE 10.3	Heats of Some Typical Reactions and Physical Processes Measured at Constant Pressure	
Type of reaction	**Example**	**ΔH (kJ/mol)**
Heat of neutralization	$HCl(aq) + NaOH(aq) \longrightarrow H_2O(l) + NaCl(aq)$	−56.2
Heat of ionization	$H_2O(l) \longrightarrow H^+(aq) + OH^-(aq)$	+56.2
Heat of fusion	$H_2O(s) \longrightarrow H_2O(l)$	+6.01
Heat of vaporization	$H_2O(l) \longrightarrow H_2O(g)$	+44.0*

*Measured at 25°C. At 100°C, the value is +40.79 kJ.

Multi 10.2
Figure 10.9 Determination of $\Delta H°_{rxn}$ by Constant-Pressure Calorimetry

Student Annotation: The temperature of the water stops changing when it and the temperature of the lead pellet are equal. Therefore, the final temperature of the pellet is also 23.17°C.

Thermometer

Stirrer

Styrofoam cups

Reaction mixture

Figure 10.8 A constant-pressure coffee-cup calorimeter made of two Styrofoam cups. The nested cups help to insulate the reaction mixture from the surroundings. Two solutions of known volume containing the reactants at the same temperature are carefully mixed in the calorimeter. The heat produced or absorbed by the reaction can be determined by measuring the temperature change.

Figure 10.9

Determination of ΔH°_{rxn} by Constant-Pressure Calorimetry

We pour the solutions into the calorimeter one at a time.

START

We start with 50.0 mL each of 1.00 *M* HCl and 1.00 *M* NaOH. Both solutions are at room temperature, which in this example is 25.0°C. The net ionic equation that represents the reaction is

$$H^+(aq) + OH^-(aq) \longrightarrow H_2O(l)$$

We have 0.0500 L × 1.00 *M* = 0.0500 mol of each reactant.

When both solutions have been added, we cap the calorimeter to prevent loss of energy to the environment and use the stirrer to ensure that the solutions are mixed thoroughly.

As the reaction proceeds, the temperature of the water increases as it absorbs the energy given off by the reaction. We record the maximum water temperature as 31.7°C.

Assuming the density and specific heat of the solution to be the same as those of water (1 g/mL, 4.184 J/g · °C), we calculate q_{soln} as follows:

q_{soln} = specific heat of water × mass of water × temperature change

$$= \frac{4.184 \text{ J}}{1 \text{ g} \cdot °\text{C}} \times 100.0 \text{ g} \times (31.7 - 25.0)°\text{C} = 2803 \text{ J}$$

Assuming that the heat capacity of the calorimeter is negligible, we know that $q_{soln} = -q_{rxn}$, and we can write

$$q_{rxn} = -2803 \text{ J}$$

This is the heat of reaction when 0.0500 mol H^+ reacts with 0.0500 mol OH^-. To determine ΔH_{rxn}, we divide q_{rxn} by the number of moles. (These reactants are present in stoichiometric amounts. If there were a *limiting* reactant, we would divide by the number of moles of limiting reactant.)

$$\Delta H_{rxn} = \frac{-2803 \text{ J}}{0.0500 \text{ mol}} = -5.61 \times 10^4 \text{ J/mol or } -56.1 \text{ kJ/mol}$$

This result is very close to the number we get using Equation 10.17 [▶▶ Section 10.6] and the data in Appendix 2.

What's the point?

Constant-pressure calorimetry can be used to determine ΔH_{rxn}—the heat of reaction for the reactant quantities specified by the balanced equation. However, when we carry out calorimetry experiments in the laboratory, we typically use much smaller quantities of reactants than those represented in a chemical equation. By measuring the temperature change of the surroundings (a known quantity of water in which the reactants are dissolved), we can determine q_{rxn} for the reactant quantities in the experiment. We can then divide q_{rxn} by the number of moles of reactant to determine ΔH_{rxn}.

Furthermore, because we know the *mass* of the pellet, we can determine the specific heat of lead (s_{Pb}):

$$s_{Pb} = \frac{C_{pellet}}{m_{pellet}} = \frac{4.19 \text{ J/}°\text{C}}{26.47 \text{ g}} = 0.158 \text{ J/g} \cdot °\text{C or } 0.16 \text{ J/g} \cdot °\text{C}$$

Multi 10.3
Figure 10.10 Determination of Specific Heat by Constant-Pressure Calorimetry

Worked Example 10.5 shows how to use constant-pressure calorimetry to calculate the heat capacity (C) of a substance. Figure 10.10 (pages 380–381) illustrates the process of determining the specific heat of a metal using constant-pressure calorimetry.

Worked Example 10.5

A metal pellet with a mass of 100.0 g, originally at 88.4°C, is dropped into 125 g of water originally at 25.1°C. The final temperature of both the pellet and the water is 31.3°C. Calculate the heat capacity C (in J/°C) of the pellet.

Strategy Water constitutes the *surroundings*; the pellet is the *system*. Use Equation 10.14 ($q_{surr} = sm\Delta T$) to determine the heat absorbed by the water; then use Equation 10.12 ($q = C\Delta T$) to determine the heat capacity of the metal pellet.

Setup m_{water} = 125 g, s_{water} = 4.184 J/g · °C, and ΔT_{water} = 31.3°C − 25.1°C = 6.2°C. The heat absorbed by the water must be released by the pellet: $q_{water} = -q_{pellet}$, m_{pellet} = 100.0 g, and ΔT_{pellet} = 31.3°C − 88.4°C = −57.1°C.

Solution From Equation 10.14, we have

$$q_{water} = \frac{4.184 \text{ J}}{\text{g} \cdot °\text{C}} \times 125 \text{ g} \times 6.2°\text{C} = 3242.6 \text{ J}$$

Thus,

$$q_{pellet} = -3242.6 \text{ J}$$

From Equation 10.12, we have

$$-3242.6 \text{ J} = C_{pellet} \times (-57.1°\text{C})$$

Thus,

$$C_{pellet} = 57 \text{ J/}°\text{C}$$

> **Think About It**
> The units cancel properly to give appropriate units for heat capacity. Moreover, ΔT_{pellet} is a negative number because the temperature of the pellet decreases.

Practice Problem A What would the final temperature be if the pellet from Worked Example 10.5, initially at 95°C, were dropped into a 218-g sample of water, initially at 23.8°C?

Practice Problem B What mass of water could be warmed from 23.8°C to 46.3°C by the pellet in Worked Example 10.5 initially at 116°C?

Constant-Volume Calorimetry

The heat of combustion is usually measured using constant-volume calorimetry. Typically, a known mass of the compound to be analyzed is placed in a steel container called a *constant-volume bomb*, or simply a *bomb*, which is pressurized with oxygen. The closed bomb is then immersed in a known amount of water in an insulated container, as shown in Figure 10.11 (page 382). (Together, the steel bomb and the water in which it is submerged constitute the *calorimeter*.) The sample is ignited electrically, and the heat released by the combustion of the sample is absorbed by the bomb and the water and can be determined by measuring the increase in temperature of the water. The special design of this type of calorimeter allows us to assume that no heat (or mass) is lost to the surroundings during the time it takes to carry out the reaction and measure the temperature change. Therefore, we can call the bomb and the water in which it is submerged an *isolated* system. Because no heat enters or leaves the system during the process, the heat change of the system overall (q_{system}) is zero and we can write

$$q_{cal} = -q_{rxn}$$

Thinking Outside the Box

Heat Capacity of Calorimeters

Although we usually assume that no heat is absorbed by the Styrofoam cups we use in the laboratory for constant-pressure calorimetry, in reality, the calorimeter generally does absorb a small portion of the heat produced by a chemical reaction. We can determine the heat capacity of a coffee-cup calorimeter by combining reactant solutions with precisely known concentrations and masses. Once we have determined the heat capacity, we can correct for the heat absorbed by the calorimeter when we carry out other experiments.

Consider an experiment in which we combine 50.0 mL of 0.250 M HCl(aq) with 50.0 mL of 0.250 M NaOH. The calorimeter and both solutions are initially at 23.50°C, and the density and specific heat of the combined solution are the same as that of water (1.000 g/mL and 4.184 J/g · °C, respectively). We can determine the amount of heat the reaction will generate using moles of reactants and the heat of neutralization value from Table 10.3. We have 0.0500 L × 0.250 M = 0.0125 mole of each reactant. According to Table 10.3, the heat of neutralization is −56.2 kJ/mol. Thus, we expect the enthalpy change of the system to be 0.0125 mol × (−56.2 kJ/mol) = −0.703 kJ. Converting this to joules and using Equation 10.13, we calculate the temperature change we expect from the combination of these reactants.

$$q_{sys} = -703 \text{ J} = -\frac{4.184 \text{ J}}{\text{g} \cdot °\text{C}} \times 100.0 \text{ g} \times \Delta T$$

$$\Delta T = \frac{-703 \text{ J}}{-(4.184 \text{ J/g} \cdot °\text{C})(100.0 \text{ g})} = 1.68°\text{C}$$

Thus, we expect the temperature to increase by 1.68°C. However, the measured final temperature is 25.09°C, an increase of only 1.59°C. The water temperature increased by less than expected because the calorimeter absorbed part of the heat produced by the neutralization reaction. We can determine how much heat the calorimeter absorbed using Equation 10.14. This time, we use the measured temperature change to calculate the amount of heat absorbed by the water.

$$q_{surr} = \frac{4.184 \text{ J}}{\text{g} \cdot °\text{C}} \times 100.0 \text{ g} \times 1.59°\text{C} = 665 \text{ J}$$

We know that the reaction produced 703 J but the water absorbed only 665 J. The remaining energy, 703 − 665 = 38 J, is $q_{calorimeter}$, the heat absorbed by the calorimeter itself. We use Equation 10.12 to calculate the heat capacity of the calorimeter.

$$38 \text{ J} = C_{calorimeter} \times 1.59°\text{C}$$

$$C_{calorimeter} = 23.9 \text{ J/°C}$$

Student Annotation: The calorimeter had the same initial temperature and the same final temperature as the solutions.

where q_{cal} and q_{rxn} are the heat changes for the calorimeter and the reaction, respectively. Thus,

$$q_{rxn} = -q_{cal}$$

To calculate q_{cal}, we need to know the heat capacity of the calorimeter (C_{cal}) and the change in temperature, that is,

$$q_{cal} = C_{cal}\Delta T \qquad \textbf{Equation 10.15}$$

And, because $q_{rxn} = -q_{cal}$,

$$q_{rxn} = -C_{cal}\Delta T \qquad \textbf{Equation 10.16}$$

The heat capacity of the calorimeter (C_{cal}) is determined by burning a substance with an accurately known heat of combustion. For example, it is known that the combustion of a 1.000-g sample of benzoic acid (C_6H_5COOH) releases 26.38 kJ of heat. If the measured temperature increase is 4.673°C, then the heat capacity of the calorimeter is given by

$$C_{cal} = \frac{q_{cal}}{\Delta T} = \frac{26.38 \text{ kJ}}{4.673°\text{C}} = 5.645 \text{ kJ/°C}$$

Once C_{cal} has been determined, the calorimeter can be used to measure the heat of combustion of other substances. Because a reaction in a bomb calorimeter occurs under constant-volume rather than constant-pressure conditions, the measured heat change corresponds to the *internal*

Figure 10.10

Determination of Specific Heat by Constant-Pressure Calorimetry

We add metal shot (125.0 g at 100.0°C) to the water, and we cap the calorimeter to prevent loss of energy to the environment.

We place 100.0 mL (100.0 g) of water in the calorimeter. The temperature of this water is 25.0°C.

We place 125.0 g of metal shot in a test tube and immerse it in boiling water long enough to heat all of the metal to the boiling point of water (100.0°C).

As energy is transferred from the metal shot to the water, the temperature of the water increases and the temperature of the metal shot decreases. We use the stirrer to ensure thorough mixing. The thermometer measures the temperature of the water.

When the temperature of the metal shot and the water are equal, the temperature of the water has reached a maximum value. We record this temperature as 34.1°C.

We know that $q_{\text{water}} = -q_{\text{metal}}$.
Substituting in the information given we write:

q_{water} = specific heat of water × mass of water × temperature change

$$= \frac{4.184 \text{ J}}{1 \text{ g} \cdot {}^{\circ}\text{C}} \times 100.0 \text{ g} \times (34.1 - 25.0){}^{\circ}\text{C} = 3807 \text{ J}$$

q_{metal} = specific heat of metal × mass of metal × temperature change

$$= x \times 125.0 \text{ g} \times (34.1 - 100.0){}^{\circ}\text{C} = -8238 \, x \text{ g} \cdot {}^{\circ}\text{C}$$

and

$$3807 \text{ J} = -(-8238 \, x) \text{ g} \cdot {}^{\circ}\text{C}$$

$$x = \frac{3807 \text{ J}}{8238 \text{ g} \cdot {}^{\circ}\text{C}} = 0.46 \text{ J/g} \cdot {}^{\circ}\text{C}$$

The specific heat of the metal is therefore 0.46 J/g · °C.

What's the point?

We can determine the specific heat of a metal by combining a known mass of the metal at a known temperature with a known mass of water at a known temperature. Assuming the calorimeter has a negligible heat capacity, the amount of energy lost by the hotter metal is equal to the amount of energy gained by the cooler water.

Figure 10.11 A constant-volume bomb calorimeter. The calorimeter is filled with oxygen gas at high pressure before it is placed in the bucket. The sample is ignited electrically, and the heat produced by the reaction is determined by measuring the temperature increase in the known amount of water surrounding the bomb.

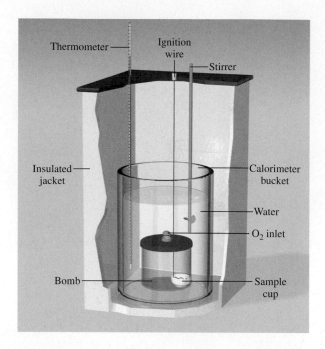

energy change (ΔU) rather than to the *enthalpy* change (ΔH) (see Equations 10.4 and 10.9). It is possible to correct the measured heat changes so that they correspond to ΔH values, but the corrections usually are quite small, so we will not concern ourselves with the details here.

Worked Example 10.6 shows how to use constant-volume calorimetry to determine the energy content per gram of a substance.

Worked Example 10.6

A Famous Amos bite-sized chocolate chip cookie weighing 7.25 g is burned in a bomb calorimeter to determine its energy content. The heat capacity of the calorimeter is 39.97 kJ/°C. During the combustion, the temperature of the water in the calorimeter increases by 3.90°C. Calculate the energy content (in kJ/g) of the cookie.

Strategy Use Equation 10.16 ($q_{rxn} = -C_{cal}\Delta T$) to calculate the heat released by the combustion of the cookie. Divide the heat released by the mass of the cookie to determine its energy content per gram.

Setup C_{cal} = 39.97 kJ/°C and ΔT = 3.90°C.

Solution From Equation 10.16 we have

Student Annotation: The negative sign in the result indicates that heat is released by the combustion.

$$q_{rxn} = -C_{cal}\Delta T = -(39.97 \text{ kJ/°C})(3.90°C) = -1.559 \times 10^2 \text{ kJ}$$

Because energy content is a positive quantity, we write

$$\text{energy content per gram} = \frac{1.559 \times 10^2 \text{ kJ}}{7.25 \text{ g}} = 21.5 \text{ kJ/g}$$

Think About It
According to the label on the cookie package, a serving size is four cookies, or 29 g, and each serving contains 150 Cal. Convert the energy per gram to Calories per serving to verify the result.

$$\frac{21.5 \text{ kJ}}{\text{g}} \times \frac{1 \text{ Cal}}{4.184 \text{ kJ}} \times \frac{29 \text{ g}}{\text{serving}} = 1.5 \times 10^2 \text{ Cal/serving}$$

Practice Problem A A serving of Grape-Nuts cereal (5.80 g) is burned in a bomb calorimeter with a heat capacity of 43.7 kJ/°C. During the combustion, the temperature of the water in the calorimeter increased by 1.92°C. Calculate the energy content (in kJ/g) of Grape-Nuts.

Practice Problem B The energy content of raisin bread is 13.1 kJ/g. Calculate the temperature increase when a slice of raisin bread (32.0 g) is burned in the calorimeter in Worked Example 10.6.

Calorimetry

10.4.1 A 1.000-g sample of benzoic acid is burned in a calorimeter in order to determine its heat capacity, C_{cal}. The reaction gives off 26.42 kJ of heat and the temperature of the water in the calorimeter increases from 23.40°C to 27.20°C. What is the heat capacity of the calorimeter?

10.4.2 In a constant-pressure calorimetry experiment, a reaction gives off 21.8 kJ of heat. The calorimeter contains 150 g of water, initially at 23.4°C. What is the final temperature of the water? The heat capacity of the calorimeter is negligibly small.

10.4.3 A reaction, carried out in a bomb calorimeter with C_{cal} = 5.01 kJ/°C, gives off 318 kJ of heat. The initial temperature of the water is 24.8°C. What is the final temperature of the water in the calorimeter?

10.4.4 Quantities of 50.0 mL of 1.00 *M* HCl and 50.0 mL of 1.00 *M* NaOH are combined in a constant-pressure calorimeter. Both solutions are initially at 24.4°C. Calculate the final temperature of the combined solutions. (Use the data from Table 10.3. Assume that the mass of the combined solutions is 100.0 g and that the solution's specific heat is the same as that for water, 4.184 J/g · °C.) The heat capacity of the calorimeter is negligibly small.

10.5 HESS'S LAW

Because enthalpy is a state function, the change in enthalpy that occurs when reactants are converted to products in a reaction is the same whether the reaction takes place in one step or in a series of steps. This observation is called *Hess's law.*[1] An analogy for Hess's law can be made to the floors in a building. Suppose, for example, that you take the elevator from the first floor to the sixth floor of the building. The net gain in your gravitational potential energy (which is analogous to the enthalpy change for the overall process) is the same whether you go directly there or stop at each floor on your way up (breaking the trip into a series of steps).

Recall from Section 10.3 that the enthalpy change for the combustion of a mole of methane depends on whether the product water is liquid or gas. More heat is given off by the reaction that produces liquid water. We can use this example to illustrate Hess's law by envisioning the first of these reactions happening in two steps. In step 1, methane and oxygen are converted to carbon dioxide and liquid water, releasing heat.

$$CH_4(g) + 2O_2(g) \longrightarrow CO_2(g) + 2H_2O(l) \qquad \Delta H = -890.4 \text{ kJ/mol}$$

In step 2, the liquid water is vaporized, which requires an input of heat.

$$2H_2O(l) \longrightarrow 2H_2O(g) \qquad \Delta H = +88.0 \text{ kJ/mol}$$

We can add balanced chemical equations just as we can add algebraic equalities, canceling identical items on opposite sides of the equation arrow:

$$CH_4(g) + 2O_2(g) \longrightarrow CO_2(g) + 2\cancel{H_2O(l)} \qquad \Delta H = -890.4 \text{ kJ/mol}$$
$$+ 2\cancel{H_2O(l)} \longrightarrow 2H_2O(g) \qquad \Delta H = +88.0 \text{ kJ/mol}$$
$$CH_4(g) + 2O_2(g) \longrightarrow CO_2(g) + 2H_2O(g) \qquad \Delta H = -802.4 \text{ kJ/mol}$$

---

[1] Germain Henri Hess (1802–1850), a Swiss chemist, was born in Switzerland but spent most of his life in Russia. For formulating Hess's law, he is called the father of thermochemistry.

When we add thermochemical equations, we add the ΔH values as well. This gives us the overall enthalpy change for the net reaction. Using this method, we can deduce the enthalpy changes for many reactions, some of which may not be possible to carry out directly. In general, we apply Hess's law by arranging a series of chemical equations (corresponding to a series of steps) in such a way that they sum to the desired overall equation. Often, in applying Hess's law, we must manipulate the equations involved, multiplying by appropriate coefficients, reversing equations, or both. It is important to follow the guidelines [◄◄ Section 10.3] for the manipulation of thermochemical equations and to make the corresponding change to the enthalpy change of each step.

Worked Example 10.7 illustrates the use of this method for determining ΔH.

Worked Example 10.7

Given the following thermochemical equations,

$$NO(g) + O_3(g) \longrightarrow NO_2(g) + O_2(g) \qquad \Delta H = -198.9 \text{ kJ/mol}$$

$$O_3(g) \longrightarrow \tfrac{3}{2}O_2(g) \qquad \Delta H = -142.3 \text{ kJ/mol}$$

$$O_2(g) \longrightarrow 2O(g) \qquad \Delta H = +495 \text{ kJ/mol}$$

determine the enthalpy change for the reaction

$$NO(g) + O(g) \longrightarrow NO_2(g)$$

Strategy Arrange the given thermochemical equations so that they sum to the desired equation. Make the corresponding changes to the enthalpy changes, and add them to get the desired enthalpy change.

Setup The first equation has NO as a reactant with the correct coefficient, so we use it as is.

$$NO(g) + O_3(g) \longrightarrow NO_2(g) + O_2(g) \qquad \Delta H = -198.9 \text{ kJ/mol}$$

The second equation must be reversed so that the O_3 introduced by the first equation will cancel (O_3 is not part of the overall chemical equation). We also must change the sign on the corresponding ΔH value.

$$\tfrac{3}{2}O_2(g) \longrightarrow O_3(g) \qquad \Delta H = +142.3 \text{ kJ/mol}$$

These two steps sum to give the following:

$$NO(g) + \cancel{O_3(g)} \longrightarrow NO_2(g) + \cancel{O_2(g)} \qquad \Delta H = -198.9 \text{ kJ/mol}$$

$$+ \tfrac{1}{2}O_2(g)\ \cancel{\tfrac{3}{2}O_2(g)} \longrightarrow \cancel{O_3(g)} \qquad \Delta H = +142.3 \text{ kJ/mol}$$

$$NO(g) + \tfrac{1}{2}O_2(g) \longrightarrow NO_2(g) \qquad \Delta H = -56.6 \text{ kJ/mol}$$

We then replace the $\tfrac{1}{2}O_2$ on the left with O by incorporating the last equation. To do so, we divide the third equation by 2 and reverse its direction. As a result, we must also divide its ΔH value by 2 and change its sign.

$$O(g) \longrightarrow \tfrac{1}{2}O_2(g) \qquad \Delta H = -247.5 \text{ kJ/mol}$$

Finally, we sum all the steps and add their enthalpy changes.

Solution

$$NO(g) + \cancel{O_3(g)} \longrightarrow NO_2(g) + \cancel{O_2(g)} \qquad \Delta H = -198.9 \text{ kJ/mol}$$

$$\tfrac{3}{2}\cancel{O_2(g)} \longrightarrow \cancel{O_3(g)} \qquad \Delta H = +142.3 \text{ kJ/mol}$$

$$+ O(g) \longrightarrow \tfrac{1}{2}\cancel{O_2(g)} \qquad \Delta H = -247.5 \text{ kJ/mol}$$

$$NO(g) + O(g) \longrightarrow NO_2(g) \qquad \Delta H = -304 \text{ kJ/mol}$$

Think About It
Double-check the cancellation of identical items—especially where fractions are involved.

Practice Problem A Use the thermochemical equations provided in Worked Example 10.7 to determine the enthalpy change for the reaction $2NO(g) + 4O(g) \longrightarrow 2NO_2(g) + O_2(g)$.

Practice Problem B Use the thermochemical equations provided in Worked Example 10.7 to determine the enthalpy change for the reaction $2NO_2(g) \longrightarrow 2NO(g) + O_2(g)$.

Hess's Law

10.5.1 Given the following information, determine ΔH for $3H_2(g) + O_3(g) \longrightarrow 3H_2O(g)$:

$$2H_2(g) + O_2(g) \longrightarrow 2H_2O(g) \qquad \Delta H = -483.6 \text{ kJ/mol}$$

$$3O_2(g) \longrightarrow 2O_3(g) \qquad \Delta H = +284.6 \text{ kJ/mol}$$

10.5.2 Given the following information, determine ΔH_{rxn} for $P_4O_6(s) + 2O_2(g) \longrightarrow P_4O_{10}(s)$:

$$P_4(s) + 3O_2(g) \longrightarrow P_4O_6(s) \qquad \Delta H = -1640.1 \text{ kJ/mol}$$

$$P_4(s) + 5O_2(g) \longrightarrow P_4O_{10}(s) \qquad \Delta H = -2940.1 \text{ kJ/mol}$$

10.6 STANDARD ENTHALPIES OF FORMATION

So far we have learned that we can determine the enthalpy change that accompanies a reaction by measuring the heat absorbed or released (at constant pressure). According to Equation 10.10, ΔH can also be calculated if we know the enthalpies of all reactants and products. However, there is no way to measure the *absolute* value of the enthalpy of a substance. Only values *relative* to an arbitrary reference can be determined. This problem is similar to the one geographers face in expressing the elevations of specific mountains or valleys. Rather than trying to devise some type of "absolute" elevation scale (perhaps based on the distance from the center of Earth), by common agreement all geographical heights and depths are expressed relative to sea level, an arbitrary reference with a defined elevation of "zero" meters or feet. Similarly, chemists have agreed on an arbitrary reference point for enthalpy.

The "sea level" reference point for all enthalpy expressions is called the *standard enthalpy of formation* (ΔH_f°), which is defined as the heat change that results when 1 mole of a compound is formed from its constituent elements in their standard states. The superscript degree sign denotes standard-state conditions, and the subscript f stands for *formation*. The phrase "in their standard states" refers to the most stable form of an element under standard conditions, meaning at ordinary atmospheric pressure. The element oxygen, for example, can exist as atomic oxygen (O), diatomic oxygen (O_2), or ozone (O_3). By far the most stable form at ordinary atmospheric pressure, though, is diatomic oxygen. Thus, the standard state of oxygen is O_2. Although the standard state does not specify a temperature, we will always use (ΔH_f°) values measured at 25°C.

Appendix 2 lists the standard enthalpies of formation for a number of elements and compounds. By convention, the standard enthalpy of formation of any element in its most stable form is zero. Again, using the element oxygen as an example, we can write $\Delta H_f^\circ(O_2) = 0$, but $\Delta H_f^\circ(O_3) \neq 0$ and $\Delta H_f^\circ(O) \neq 0$. Similarly, graphite is a more stable allotropic form of carbon than diamond under standard conditions and 25°C, so we have $\Delta H_f^\circ(\text{graphite}) = 0$ and $\Delta H_f^\circ(\text{diamond}) \neq 0$.

The importance of the standard enthalpies of formation is that once we know their values, we can readily calculate the *standard enthalpy of reaction* (ΔH_{rxn}°), defined as the enthalpy of a reaction carried out under standard conditions. For example, consider the hypothetical reaction

$$a\text{A} + b\text{B} \longrightarrow c\text{C} + d\text{D}$$

where a, b, c, and d are stoichiometric coefficients. For this reaction, ΔH_{rxn}° is given by

$$\Delta H_{rxn}^\circ = [c\Delta H_f^\circ(\text{C}) + d\Delta H_f^\circ(\text{D})] - [a\Delta H_f^\circ(\text{A}) + b\Delta H_f^\circ(\text{B})] \qquad \textbf{Equation 10.17}$$

We can generalize Equation 10.17 as

$$\Delta H_{rxn}^\circ = \sum n\Delta H_f^\circ(\text{products}) - \sum m\Delta H_f^\circ(\text{reactants}) \qquad \textbf{Equation 10.18}$$

where m and n are the stoichiometric coefficients for the reactants and products, respectively, and Σ (sigma) means "the sum of." In these calculations, the stoichiometric coefficients are treated as numbers without units. Thus, the result has units of kJ/mol, where again, "per mole" means per mole of reaction as written. To use Equation 10.18 to calculate ΔH_{rxn}°, we must know the ΔH_f° values of the compounds that take part in the reaction. These values, tabulated in Appendix 2, are determined either by the direct method or the indirect method.

The *direct* method of measuring ΔH_f° works for compounds that can be synthesized from their elements easily and safely. Suppose we want to know the enthalpy of formation of carbon dioxide. We must measure the enthalpy of the reaction when carbon (graphite) and molecular oxygen in their standard states are converted to carbon dioxide in its standard state:

$$C(graphite) + O_2(g) \longrightarrow CO_2(g) \qquad \Delta H_{rxn}^\circ = -393.5 \text{ kJ/mol}$$

We know from experience that this combustion goes to completion. Thus, from Equation 10.18 we can write

$$\Delta H_{rxn}^\circ = \Delta H_f^\circ(CO_2) - [\Delta H_f^\circ(graphite) + \Delta H_f^\circ(O_2)] = -393.5 \text{ kJ/mol}$$

Because graphite and O_2 are the most stable allotropic forms of their respective elements, $\Delta H_f^\circ(graphite)$ and $\Delta H_f^\circ(O_2)$ are both zero. Therefore,

$$\Delta H_{rxn}^\circ = \Delta H_f^\circ(CO_2) = -393.5 \text{ kJ/mol}$$

or

$$\Delta H_f^\circ(CO_2) = -393.5 \text{ kJ/mol}$$

Arbitrarily assigning a value of zero to ΔH_f° for each element in its standard state does *not* affect the outcome of these calculations. Remember, in thermochemistry we are interested only in enthalpy changes because they can be determined experimentally, whereas the absolute enthalpy values cannot. The choice of a zero "reference level" for enthalpy is intended to simplify the calculations. Referring again to the terrestrial altitude analogy, we find that Mt. Everest (the highest peak in the world) is 8708 ft higher than Mt. Denali (the highest peak in North America). This difference in altitude would be the same whether we had chosen sea level or the center of Earth as our reference elevation.

Other compounds that can be studied by the direct method are SF_6, P_4O_{10}, and CS_2. The equations representing their syntheses are

$$S(rhombic) + 3F_2(g) \longrightarrow SF_6(g)$$

$$P_4(white) + 5O_2(g) \longrightarrow P_4O_{10}(s)$$

$$C(graphite) + 2S(rhombic) \longrightarrow CS_2(l)$$

S(rhombic) and P(white) are the most stable allotropes of sulfur and phosphorus, respectively, at 1 atm and 25°C, so their ΔH_f° values are zero.

Worked Example 10.8 shows how ΔH_f° values can be used to determine ΔH_{rxn}°.

Worked Example 10.8

Using data from Appendix 2, calculate ΔH_{rxn}° for $Ag^+(aq) + Cl^-(aq) \longrightarrow AgCl(s)$.

Strategy Use Equation 10.18 [$\Delta H_{rxn}^\circ = \Sigma n\Delta H_f^\circ(products) - \Sigma m\Delta H_f^\circ(reactants)$] and ΔH_f° values from Appendix 2 to calculate ΔH_{rxn}°.

Setup The (ΔH_f°) values for $Ag^+(aq)$, $Cl^-(aq)$, and $AgCl(s)$ are $+105.9$, -167.2, and -127.0 kJ/mol, respectively.

Solution Using Equation 10.18,

$$\Delta H_{rxn}^\circ = \Delta H_f^\circ(AgCl) - [\Delta H_f^\circ(Ag^+) + \Delta H_f^\circ(Cl^-)]$$

$$= -127.0 \text{ kJ/mol} - [(+105.9 \text{ kJ/mol}) + (-167.2 \text{ kJ/mol})]$$

$$= -127.0 \text{ kJ/mol} - (-61.3 \text{ kJ/mol}) = -65.7 \text{ kJ/mol}$$

Think About It
Watch out for misplaced or missing minus signs. This is an easy place to lose track of them.

Practice Problem A Using data from Appendix 2, calculate (ΔH_{rxn}°) for $CaCO_3(s) \longrightarrow$ $CaO(s) + CO_2(g)$.

Practice Problem B Using data from Appendix 2, calculate (ΔH_{rxn}°) for $2SO(g) + \frac{2}{3}O_3(g) \longrightarrow$ $2SO_2(g)$.

Many compounds cannot be synthesized from their elements directly. In some cases, the reaction proceeds too slowly, or side reactions produce substances other than the desired compound. In these cases, ΔH_f° can be determined by an *indirect* approach, using Hess's law. If we know a series of reactions for which ΔH_{rxn}° can be measured, and we can arrange them in such a way as to have them sum to the equation corresponding to the formation of the compound of interest, we can calculate ΔH_f° for the compound.

Worked Example 10.9 shows how to use Hess's law to calculate the ΔH_f° value by the indirect method for a compound that cannot be produced easily from its constituent elements.

Worked Example 10.9

Given the following information, calculate the standard enthalpy of formation of acetylene (C_2H_2) from its constituent elements:

$$C(graphite) + O_2(g) \longrightarrow CO_2(g) \qquad \Delta H_{rxn}^\circ = -393.5 \text{ kJ/mol} \qquad (1)$$

$$H_2(g) + \tfrac{1}{2}O_2(g) \longrightarrow H_2O(l) \qquad \Delta H_{rxn}^\circ = -285.8 \text{ kJ/mol} \qquad (2)$$

$$2C_2H_2(g) + 5O_2(g) \longrightarrow 4CO_2(g) + 2H_2O(l) \qquad \Delta H_{rxn}^\circ = -2598.8 \text{ kJ/mol} \qquad (3)$$

Strategy Arrange the equations that are provided so that they will sum to the desired equation. This may require reversing or multiplying one or more of the equations. For any such change, the corresponding change must also be made to the ΔH_{rxn}° value.

Setup The desired equation, corresponding to the standard enthalpy of formation of acetylene, is

$$2C(graphite) + H_2(g) \longrightarrow C_2H_2(g)$$

We multiply Equation (1) and its ΔH_{rxn}° value by 2:

$$2C(graphite) + 2O_2(g) \longrightarrow 2CO_2(g) \qquad \Delta H_{rxn}^\circ = -787.0 \text{ kJ/mol}$$

We include Equation (2) and its ΔH_{rxn}° value as is:

$$H_2(g) + \tfrac{1}{2}O_2(g) \longrightarrow H_2O(l) \qquad \Delta H_{rxn}^\circ = -285.8 \text{ kJ/mol}$$

We reverse Equation (3) and divide it by 2 (i.e., multiply through by 1/2):

$$2CO_2(g) + H_2O(l) \longrightarrow C_2H_2(g) + \tfrac{5}{2}CO_2(g) \qquad \Delta H_{rxn}^\circ = +1299.4 \text{ kJ/mol}$$

Student Annotation: The original ΔH_{rxn}° value of Equation (3) has its sign reversed and it is divided by 2.

Solution Summing the resulting equations and the corresponding ΔH_{rxn}° values:

$$2C(graphite) + 2O_2(g) \longrightarrow 2CO_2(g) \qquad \Delta H_{rxn}^\circ = -787.0 \text{ kJ/mol}$$

$$H_2(g) + \tfrac{1}{2}O_2(g) \longrightarrow H_2O(l) \qquad \Delta H_{rxn}^\circ = -285.8 \text{ kJ/mol}$$

$$2CO_2(g) + H_2O(l) \longrightarrow C_2H_2(g) + \tfrac{5}{2}CO_2(g) \qquad \Delta H_{rxn}^\circ = +1299.4 \text{ kJ/mol}$$

$$\overline{2C(graphite) + H_2(g) \longrightarrow C_2H_2(g) \qquad \Delta H_f^\circ = +226.6 \text{ kJ/mol}}$$

Think About It
Remember that a ΔH_{rxn}° is only a ΔH_f° when there is just *one product*, just *one mole* is produced, and all the reactants are *elements in their standard states*.

Practice Problem A Use the following data to calculate ΔH_f° for $CS_2(l)$:

$$C(graphite) + O_2(g) \longrightarrow CO_2(g) \qquad \Delta H_{rxn}^\circ = -393.5 \text{ kJ/mol}$$

$$S(rhombic) + O_2(g) \longrightarrow SO_2(g) \qquad \Delta H_{rxn}^\circ = -296.4 \text{ kJ/mol}$$

$$CS_2(l) + 3O_2(g) \longrightarrow CO_2(g) + 2SO_2(g) \qquad \Delta H_{rxn}^\circ = -1073.6 \text{ kJ/mol}$$

Practice Problem B ΔH_f° of hydrogen chloride [$HCl(g)$] is -92.3 kJ/mol. Given the following data, determine the identity of the two missing products and calculate ΔH_{rxn}° for Equation 3. [*Hint:* Start by writing the chemical equation that corresponds to ΔH_f° for $HCl(g)$.]

$$N_2(g) + 4H_2(g) + Cl_2(g) \longrightarrow 2NH_4Cl(s) \qquad \Delta H_{rxn}^\circ = -630.78 \text{ kJ/mol} \qquad (1)$$

$$N_2(g) + 3H_2(g) \longrightarrow 2NH_3(g) \qquad \Delta H_{rxn}^\circ = -92.6 \text{ kJ/mol} \qquad (2)$$

$$NH_4Cl(s) \longrightarrow \qquad (3)$$

SECTION 10.6 REVIEW

Standard Enthalpies of Formation

10.6.1 Using data from Appendix 2, calculate ΔH°_{rxn} for $H_2(g) + F_2(g) \longrightarrow 2HF(g)$.

10.6.2 Using data from Appendix 2, calculate ΔH°_{rxn} for $2NO_2(g) \longrightarrow N_2O_4(g)$.

10.6.3 Using the following data, calculate ΔH°_f for $CO(g)$:

$$C(graphite) + O_2(g) \longrightarrow CO_2(g) \qquad\qquad \Delta H^\circ_{rxn} = -393.5 \text{ kJ/mol}$$

$$CO(g) + \tfrac{1}{2}O_2(g) \longrightarrow CO_2(g) \qquad\qquad \Delta H^\circ_{rxn} = -283.0 \text{ kJ/mol}$$

10.7   BOND ENTHALPY AND THE STABILITY OF COVALENT MOLECULES

Why do covalent bonds form? According to valence bond theory, a covalent bond will form between two atoms if the potential energy of the resulting molecule is lower than that of the isolated atoms. Simply put, this means that the formation of covalent bonds is exothermic. While this fact may not seem intuitively obvious, you know that energy must be supplied to a molecule in order to *break* covalent bonds. Because the formation of a bond is the *reverse* process, we should expect energy to be given off when a bond forms.

One measure of the stability of a molecule is its **bond enthalpy,** which is the enthalpy change associated with breaking a particular bond in 1 mole of gaseous molecules. (Bond enthalpies in solids and liquids are affected by neighboring molecules.) The experimentally determined bond enthalpy of the diatomic hydrogen molecule, for example, is

> **Student Annotation:** Recall that we previously used the term *bond energy* to refer to this property, before the term *enthalpy* had been introduced. [◄◄ Section 6.1]

$$H_2(g) \longrightarrow H(g) + H(g) \qquad\qquad \Delta H^\circ = 436.4 \text{ kJ/mol}$$

According to this equation, breaking the covalent bonds in 1 mole of gaseous H_2 molecules requires 436.4 kJ of energy. For the less stable chlorine molecule,

$$Cl_2(g) \longrightarrow Cl(g) + Cl(g) \qquad\qquad \Delta H^\circ = 242.7 \text{ kJ/mol}$$

Bond enthalpies can also be directly measured for heteronuclear diatomic molecules, such as HCl,

$$HCl(g) \longrightarrow H(g) + Cl(g) \qquad\qquad \Delta H^\circ = 431.9 \text{ kJ/mol}$$

as well as for molecules containing multiple bonds:

$$O_2(g) \longrightarrow O(g) + O(g) \qquad\qquad \Delta H^\circ = 498.7 \text{ kJ/mol}$$

$$N_2(g) \longrightarrow N(g) + N(g) \qquad\qquad \Delta H^\circ = 941.4 \text{ kJ/mol}$$

Measuring the strength of covalent bonds in polyatomic molecules is more complicated. For example, measurements show that the energy needed to break the first O—H bond in H_2O is different from that needed to break the second O—H bond:

$$H_2O(g) \longrightarrow H(g) + OH(g) \qquad\qquad \Delta H^\circ = 502 \text{ kJ/mol}$$

$$OH(g) \longrightarrow H(g) + O(g) \qquad\qquad \Delta H^\circ = 427 \text{ kJ/mol}$$

In each case, an O—H bond is broken, but the first step requires the input of more energy than the second. The difference between the two ΔH° values suggests that the second O—H bond itself undergoes change, because of the changes in its chemical environment.

We can now understand why the bond enthalpy of the same O—H bond in two different molecules, such as methanol (CH_3OH) and water (H_2O), will not be the same: their environments

TABLE 10.4	Bond Enthalpies		
Bond	Bond enthalpy (kJ/mol)	Bond	Bond enthalpy (kJ/mol)
H–H*	436.4	N–N	193
H–N	393	N=N	418
H–O	460	N≡N	941.4
H–S	368	N–O	176
H–P	326	N=O	607
H–F	568.2	N–F	272
H–Cl	431.9	N–Cl	200
H–Br	366.1	N–Br	243
H–I	298.3	N–I	159
C–H	414	O–O	142
C–C	347	O=O	498.7
C=C	620	O–P	502
C≡C	812	O=S	469
C–N	276	O–F	190
C=N	615	O–Cl	203
C≡N	891	O–Br	234
C–O	351	O–I	234
C=O†	745	P–P	197
C≡O	1070	P=P	489
C–P	263	S–S	268
C–S	255	S=S	352
C=S	477	F–F	156.9
C–F	453	Cl–Cl	242.7
C Cl	339	Cl–F	193
C–Br	276	Br–Br	192.5
C–I	216	I–I	151.0

*Bond enthalpies shown in red are for diatomic molecules.

†The C=O bond enthalpy in CO_2 is 799 kJ/mol.

Student Annotation: Bond enthalpies for diatomic molecules have more significant figures than those for polyatomic molecules. Those for polyatomic molecules are *average* values based on the bonds in more than one compound.

are different. For polyatomic molecules, therefore, we speak of the *average* bond enthalpy of a particular bond. For example, we can measure the enthalpy of the O–H bond in 10 different polyatomic molecules and obtain the average O–H bond enthalpy by dividing the sum of the bond enthalpies by 10. Table 10.4 lists the average bond enthalpies of a number of diatomic and polyatomic molecules. As we noted earlier, triple bonds are stronger than double bonds, and double bonds are stronger than single bonds.

A comparison of the thermochemical changes that take place during a number of reactions reveals a strikingly wide variation in the enthalpies of different reactions. For example, the combustion of hydrogen gas in oxygen gas is fairly *exothermic:*

$$H_2(g) + \frac{1}{2}O_2(g) \longrightarrow H_2O(l) \qquad \Delta H° = -285.8 \text{ kJ/mol}$$

The formation of glucose from carbon dioxide and water, on the other hand, best achieved by photosynthesis, is highly *endothermic:*

$$6CO_2(g) + 6H_2O(l) \longrightarrow C_6H_{12}O_6(s) + 6O_2(g) \qquad \Delta H° = 2801 \text{ kJ/mol}$$

We can account for such variations by looking at the stability of individual reactant and product molecules. After all, most chemical reactions involve the making and breaking of bonds. Therefore, knowing the bond enthalpies and hence the stability of molecules reveals something about the thermochemical nature of the reactions that molecules undergo.

In many cases, it is possible to predict the approximate enthalpy of a reaction by using the average bond enthalpies. Because energy is always required to break chemical bonds and chemical bond formation is always accompanied by a release of energy, we can estimate the enthalpy of a reaction by counting the total number of bonds broken and formed in the reaction and recording all the corresponding enthalpy changes. The enthalpy of reaction in the gas phase is given by

Equation 10.19 $\Delta H° = \sum BE \text{ (reactants)} - \sum BE \text{ (products)}$

$= \text{total energy } input - \text{total energy } released$
$\quad\quad (\text{to } break \text{ bonds}) \quad\quad (\text{by bond } formation)$

where BE stands for average bond enthalpy and Σ is the summation sign. As written, Equation 10.19 takes care of the sign convention for $\Delta H°$. Thus, if the total energy input needed to break bonds in the reactants is less than the total energy released when bonds are formed in the products, then $\Delta H°$ is negative and the reaction is exothermic [Figure 10.12(a)]. On the other hand, if less energy is released (bond making) than absorbed (bond breaking), $\Delta H°$ is positive and the reaction is endothermic [Figure 10.12(b)].

If all the reactants and products are diatomic molecules, then the equation for the enthalpy of reaction will yield accurate results because the bond enthalpies of diatomic molecules are accurately known. If some or all of the reactants and products are polyatomic molecules, the equation will yield only approximate results because the bond enthalpies used will be averages.

Worked Example 10.10 shows how to estimate enthalpies of reaction using bond enthalpies.

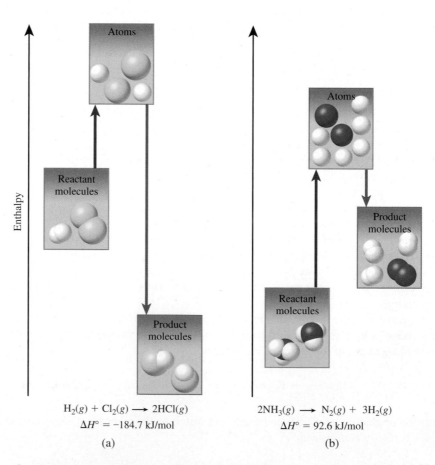

Figure 10.12 Enthalpy changes in (a) an exothermic reaction and (b) an endothermic reaction. The $\Delta H°$ values are calculated using Equation 10.18 and tabulated $\Delta H_f°$ values from Appendix 2.

Worked Example 10.10

Use bond enthalpies from Table 10.4 to estimate the enthalpy of reaction for the combustion of methane:

$$CH_4(g) + 2O_2(g) \longrightarrow CO_2(g) + 2H_2O(l)$$

Strategy Draw Lewis structures to determine what bonds are to be broken and what bonds are to be formed.

Setup

$$
\begin{array}{ccc}
\overset{\displaystyle H}{\underset{\displaystyle H}{H-\overset{|}{\underset{|}{C}}-H}} & + & \ddot{O}=\ddot{O} \\
 & & \ddot{O}=\ddot{O}
\end{array}
\longrightarrow
\ddot{O}=C=\ddot{O}
\quad + \quad
\begin{array}{c}
H-\ddot{O}-H \\
H-\ddot{O}-H
\end{array}
$$

Bonds to break: 4 C—H and 2 O=O.
Bonds to form: 2 C=O and 4 H—O.
Bond enthalpies from Table 10.4: 414 kJ/mol (C—H), 498.7 kJ/mol (O=O), 799 kJ/mol (C=O in CO_2), and 460 kJ/mol (H—O).

Solution
$[4(414 \text{ kJ/mol}) + 2(498.7 \text{ kJ/mol})] - [2(799 \text{ kJ/mol}) + 4(460 \text{ kJ/mol})] = -785 \text{ kJ/mol}.$

> **Think About It**
> Use Equation 10.18 [◄◄ Section 10.6] and data from Appendix 2 to calculate this enthalpy of reaction again; then compare your results using the two approaches. The difference in this case is due to two things: most tabulated bond enthalpies are averages and, by convention, we show the product of combustion as liquid water—but average bond enthalpies apply to species in the gas phase, where there is little or no influence exerted by neighboring molecules.

Practice Problem A Use bond enthalpies from Table 10.4 to estimate the enthalpy of reaction for the combination of carbon monoxide and oxygen to produce carbon dioxide:

$$2CO(g) + O_2(g) \longrightarrow 2CO_2(g)$$

Practice Problem B Using the following chemical equation, data from Table 10.4, and data from Appendix 2, determine the P—Cl bond enthalpy:

$$PH_3(g) + 3HCl(g) \longrightarrow PCl_3(g) + 3H_2(g)$$

Student Annotation: Don't skip the step of drawing Lewis structures [◄◄ Section 6.3]. This is the only way to know for certain what types and numbers of bonds must be broken and formed.

Student Annotation: Remember that heats of reaction are expressed in kJ/mol, where the "per mole" refers to *per mole of reaction as written* [◄◄ Section 10.3].

SECTION 10.7 REVIEW

Bond Enthalpy and the Stability of Covalent Molecules

10.7.1 Use data from Table 10.4 to estimate ΔH_{rxn} for the reaction of ethylene with hydrogen to produce ethane.

$$C_2H_4(g) + H_2(g) \longrightarrow C_2H_6(g)$$

10.7.2 Use data from Table 10.4 to estimate ΔH_{rxn} for the reaction of fluorine and chlorine to produce ClF.

$$F_2(g) + Cl_2(g) \longrightarrow 2ClF(g)$$

10.7.3 Use bond enthalpies to determine ΔH_{rxn} for the reaction shown.

10.7.4 Use bond enthalpies to determine ΔH_{rxn} for the reaction shown

10.8 LATTICE ENERGY AND THE STABILITY OF IONIC SOLIDS

Unlike covalent compounds, ionic compounds consist of vast arrays of interspersed cations and anions, not discrete molecular units. For example, solid sodium chloride (NaCl) consists of equal numbers of Na^+ and Cl^- ions arranged in a three-dimensional network, the lattice, of alternating cations and anions (Figure 5.2, page 143).

We learned in Chapter 5 that the energy change associated with the formation of a lattice is the *lattice energy*. Although lattice energy is a useful measure of an ionic compound's stability, it is *not* a quantity that we can measure directly. Instead, we use various thermodynamic quantities that can be measured, and calculate lattice energy using Hess's law [◀◀ Section 10.5].

> **Student Annotation:** Recall that *lattice energy* is the amount of energy required to convert one mole of ionic solid to its constituent ions in the gas phase [◀◀ Section 5.3]. For NaCl, the equation representing the process is:
>
> $$NaCl(s) \longrightarrow Na^+(g) + Cl^-(g)$$

The Born-Haber Cycle

We have described the formation of an ionic compound as though it happens when gaseous ions coalesce into a solid. In fact, the reactions that produce ionic solids generally do not occur this way. Figure 10.13 illustrates the formation of sodium chloride (NaCl) from its constituent elements.

We can imagine the reaction of Na(s) and $Cl_2(g)$ to form NaCl(s) as taking place in a series of steps for which the energy changes can be measured. This method of determining the lattice energy is known as the **Born-Haber cycle.** Table 10.5 lists the energy changes associated with each step.

The net reaction resulting from the series of steps in Table 10.5 is

$$Na(s) + \frac{1}{2}Cl_2(g) \longrightarrow Na^+(g) + Cl^-(g)$$

The final step in the formation of NaCl(g) would be the coalescence of $Na^+(g) + Cl^-(g)$. This is the step for which we cannot measure the energy change directly. However, we *can* measure the standard heat of formation of NaCl(s). (It is tabulated in Appendix 2 as −410.9 kJ/mol.) Although the formation of NaCl(s) from its constituent elements is not actually a step in our imaginary process, knowing its value enables us to calculate the lattice energy of NaCl. Figure 10.14 (pages 394–395) illustrates how this is done using all of these thermodynamic data and Hess's law. The numbered steps correspond to the steps in Table 10.5. The Born-Haber cycle enables us to calculate the lattice energy, which we cannot measure directly, using the quantities that we can measure.

Multi 10.4
Figure 10.14 Born-Haber Cycle

$$Cl_2 + 2Na \longrightarrow 2NaCl$$

Figure 10.13 Sodium metal and chlorine gas combine to produce sodium chloride in a highly exothermic reaction.

TABLE 10.5	Hypothetical Steps in the Formation of $Na^+(g)$ and $Cl^-(g)$ from $Na(s)$ and $Cl_2(g)$

Chemical equation	Energy change (kJ/mol)
$Na(s) \longrightarrow Na(g)$	107.7*
$\frac{1}{2}Cl_2(g) \longrightarrow Cl(g)$	121.7†
$Na(g) \longrightarrow Na^+(g) + e^-$	495.9‡
$Cl(g) + e^- \longrightarrow Cl^-(g)$	−349§

*Standard heat of formation (ΔH_f°) of $Na(g)$ from Appendix 2.
†Standard heat of formation (ΔH_f°) of $Cl(g)$ from Appendix 2.
‡First ionization energy (IE_1) of Na from Figure 4.8.
§$\Delta H°$ for this process is negative. (Recall that by definition, EA is the amount of energy *released* [◄◄ Section 4.4]. This ΔH is equal to $-EA$.)

Worked Example 10.11 shows how to use the Born-Haber cycle to calculate the lattice energy.

Worked Example 10.11

Using data from Figures 4.8 and 4.10 and Appendix 2, calculate the lattice energy of cesium chloride (CsCl).

Strategy Using Figure 10.14 as a guide, combine the pertinent thermodynamic data and use Hess's law to calculate the lattice energy.

Setup From Figure 4.8, $IE_1(Cs) = 376$ kJ/mol. From Figure 4.10, $EA_1(Cl) = 349.0$ kJ/mol. From Appendix 2, $\Delta H_f^\circ[Cs(g)] = 76.50$ kJ/mol, $\Delta H_f^\circ[Cl(g)] = 121.7$ kJ/mol, $\Delta H_f^\circ[CsCl(s)] = -422.8$ kJ/mol. Because we are interested in magnitudes only, we can use the absolute values of the thermodynamic data. And, because only the standard heat of formation of CsCl(s) is a negative number, it is the only one for which the sign changes.

Solution

$$[\Delta H_f^\circ[Cs(g)] + \Delta H_f^\circ[Cl(g)] + IE_1(Cs) + |\Delta H_f^\circ[CsCl(s)]|] - EA_1(Cl) = \text{lattice energy}$$

$$= (76.50 \text{ kJ/mol} + 121.7 \text{ kJ/mol} + 376 \text{ kJ/mol} + 422.8 \text{ kJ/mol}) - 349.0 \text{ kJ/mol}$$

$$= 648 \text{ kJ/mol}$$

Think About It
Compare this value to that for NaCl in Figure 10.14 (787 kJ/mol). Both compounds contain the same anion (Cl^-) and both have cations with the same charge (+1), so the relative sizes of the cations will determine the relative strengths of their lattice energies. Because Cs^+ is larger than Na^+, the lattice energy of CsCl is smaller than the lattice energy of NaCl.

Practice Problem A Using data from Figures 4.8 and 4.10 and Appendix 2, calculate the lattice energy of rubidium iodide (RbI).

Practice Problem B The lattice energy of MgO is 3890 kJ/mol, and the second ionization energy (IE_2) of Mg is 1450.6 kJ/mol. Using these data, as well as data from Figures 4.8 and 4.10 and Appendix 2, determine the second electron affinity for oxygen, $EA_2(O)$.

Comparison of Ionic and Covalent Compounds

Ionic and covalent compounds differ markedly in their general physical properties because of differences in the nature of their bonds. There are two types of attractive forces in covalent compounds, the *intramolecular* bonding force that holds the atoms together in a molecule, and the *intermolecular* forces between molecules. Bond enthalpy can be used to quantify the intramolecular bonding force. Intermolecular forces are usually quite weak compared to the forces holding atoms together within a molecule, so molecules of a covalent compound are not held together tightly. As a result, covalent compounds are usually gases, liquids, or low-melting solids.

On the other hand, the electrostatic forces [◄◄ Section 5.3] holding ions together in an ionic compound are usually very strong, so ionic compounds are solids at room temperature and have

Figure 10.14

Born-Haber Cycle

$IE_1(\text{Na})$

④

$\Delta H_f^\circ[\text{Cl}(g)]$

③

$\Delta H_f^\circ[\text{Na}(g)]$

②

$\Delta H_f^\circ[\text{NaCl}(s)]$

①

Step 4

The first ionization energy of sodium, $IE_1(\text{Na})$, gives the amount of energy required to convert 1 mole of Na(g) to 1 mole of Na$^+$(g):

$$\text{Na}(g) \longrightarrow \text{Na}^+(g) + e^-$$

Step 3

The tabulated value of ΔH_f° for Cl(g) gives the amount of energy needed to convert $\frac{1}{2}$ mole of $\text{Cl}_2(g)$ to 1 mole of Cl(g):

$$\tfrac{1}{2}\text{Cl}_2(g) \longrightarrow \text{Cl}(g)$$

Step 2

The tabulated value of ΔH_f° for Na(g) gives the amount of energy needed to convert 1 mole of Na(s) to 1 mole of Na(g):

$$\text{Na}(s) \longrightarrow \text{Na}(g)$$

Step 1

The tabulated value of ΔH_f° for NaCl(s) gives us the energy produced when 1 mole of Na and $\frac{1}{2}$ mole of Cl_2 combine to form 1 mole of NaCl:

$$\text{Na}(s) + \tfrac{1}{2}\text{Cl}_2(g) \longrightarrow \text{NaCl}(s)$$

Step 1 in the Born-Haber cycle involves converting 1 mole of NaCl into 1 mole of Na and $\frac{1}{2}$ mole of Cl_2 (the reverse of the ΔH_f° reaction):

$$\text{NaCl}(s) \longrightarrow \text{Na}(s) + \tfrac{1}{2}\text{Cl}_2(g)$$

Therefore, ΔH for step 1 is $-\Delta H_f^\circ[\text{NaCl}(s)]$

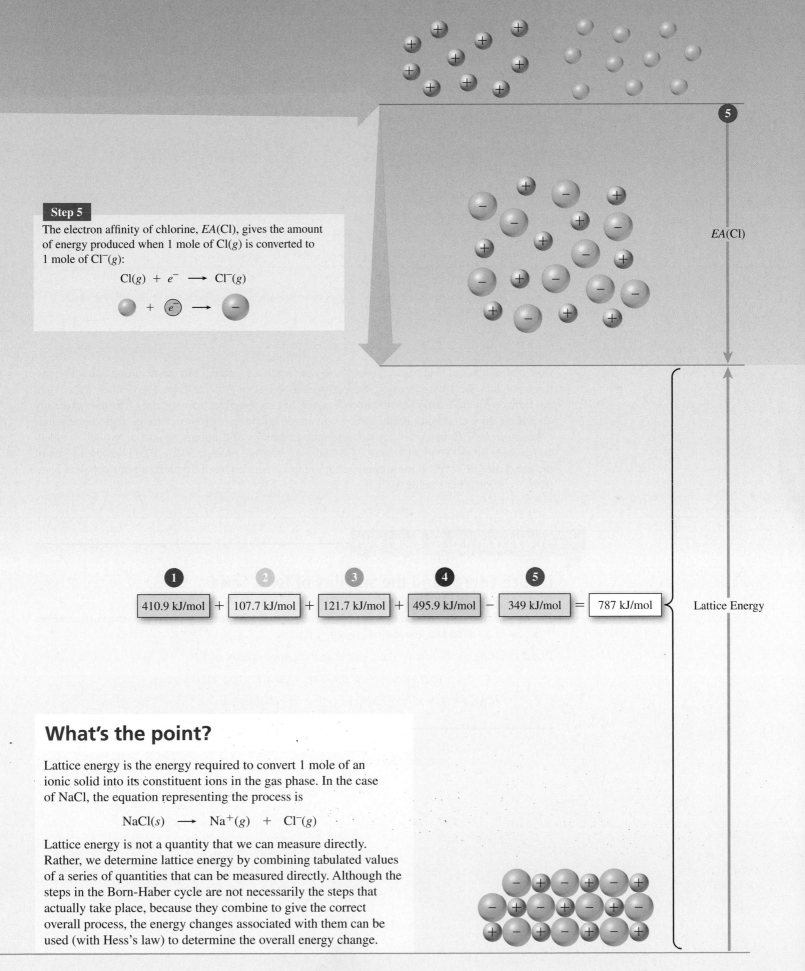

Step 5

The electron affinity of chlorine, EA(Cl), gives the amount of energy produced when 1 mole of Cl(g) is converted to 1 mole of Cl$^-$(g):

$$Cl(g) + e^- \longrightarrow Cl^-(g)$$

EA(Cl)

1		2		3		4		5		
410.9 kJ/mol	+	107.7 kJ/mol	+	121.7 kJ/mol	+	495.9 kJ/mol	−	349 kJ/mol	=	787 kJ/mol

Lattice Energy

What's the point?

Lattice energy is the energy required to convert 1 mole of an ionic solid into its constituent ions in the gas phase. In the case of NaCl, the equation representing the process is

$$NaCl(s) \longrightarrow Na^+(g) + Cl^-(g)$$

Lattice energy is not a quantity that we can measure directly. Rather, we determine lattice energy by combining tabulated values of a series of quantities that can be measured directly. Although the steps in the Born-Haber cycle are not necessarily the steps that actually take place, because they combine to give the correct overall process, the energy changes associated with them can be used (with Hess's law) to determine the overall energy change.

TABLE 10.6	Comparison of Some Properties of an Ionic Compound (NaCl) and a Covalent Compound (CCl_4)	
Property	**NaCl**	**CCl_4**
Appearance	White solid	Colorless liquid
Melting point (°C)	801	−23
Molar heat of fusion* (kJ/mol)	30.2	2.5
Boiling point (°C)	1413	76.5
Molar heat of vaporization* (kJ/mol)	600	30
Density (g/cm³)	2.17	1.59
Solubility in water	High	Very low
Electrical conductivity		
Solid	Poor	Poor
Liquid	Good	Poor
Aqueous	Good	Poor

*The *molar heat of fusion* and *molar heat of vaporization* are the amounts of heat needed to melt 1 mole of the solid and to vaporize 1 mole of the liquid, respectively.

high melting points. Many ionic compounds are soluble in water, and the resulting aqueous solutions conduct electricity because the compounds are strong electrolytes [◄◄ Section 9.1]. Most covalent compounds are insoluble in water, or if they do dissolve, their aqueous solutions generally do not conduct electricity because the compounds are nonelectrolytes. Molten ionic compounds conduct electricity because they contain mobile cations and anions; liquid or molten covalent compounds do *not* conduct electricity because no ions are present. Table 10.6 compares some of the properties of a typical ionic compound, sodium chloride (NaCl), with those of a covalent compound, carbon tetrachloride (CCl_4).

SECTION 10.8 REVIEW

Lattice Energy and the Stability of Ionic Solids

10.8.1 Compare the lattice energy of KF with (a) the lattice energy of LiF, (b) the lattice energy of KCl, and (c) the lattice energy of KI.

10.8.2 Using the following data, calculate the lattice energy of KF:

$$\Delta H_f^\circ[K(g)] = 89.99 \text{ kJ/mol}, \Delta H_f^\circ[F(g)] = 80.0 \text{ kJ/mol},$$

$$IE_1(K) = 419 \text{ kJ/mol}, \Delta H_f^\circ[KF(s)] = -547 \text{ kJ/mol}, \text{ and } EA_1(F) = 328 \text{ kJ/mol}.$$

Learning Outcomes

- Identify the system and surroundings for a given experiment.
- Identify a process as endothermic or exothermic.
- Understand the various units used to measure energy including joules and calories.
- Identify a system as being open, closed, or isolated.
- Understand the concept of state functions and be able to identify state functions and nonstate functions.
- Define work and heat and understand the sign conventions associated with these terms.
- Understand the key differences between internal energy measurements using constant-pressure and constant-volume calorimetry.
- Understand enthalpy and enthalpy changes.

- Calculate the enthalpy change of a reaction and understand how it is dependent upon stoichiometric amounts of products and reactants.
- Perform calorimetric calculations involving specific heat or heat capacity.
- Apply Hess's law in the determination of the heat of reaction of a multistep process.
- Understand the nature of the standard state, particularly as it applies to standard heat of formation.
- Use the standard heats of formation of products and reactants to calculate the enthalpy change of a reaction.
- Use bond enthalpies to calculate an estimate of the enthalpy change of a reaction.
- Calculate the lattice energy of a compound using the Born-Haber cycle.

Chapter Summary

SECTION 10.1

- The *system* is the particular part of the universe that we are interested in studying—such as the reactants and products in a chemical reaction. The term *surroundings* refers to the rest of the universe. System + surroundings = universe.
- *Heat* refers to the flow of thermal energy between two bodies at different temperatures. *Thermochemistry* is the study of the heat associated with chemical reactions and physical processes.
- In an *exothermic process,* heat is released to the surroundings, so the energy of the system decreases. In an *endothermic process,* heat is absorbed from the surroundings, so the energy of the system increases.

SECTION 10.2

- *Thermodynamics* is the study of the conversions among different types of energy. Thermochemistry is a branch of thermodynamics.
- An *open system* is one that can exchange both matter and energy with its surroundings. A *closed system* is one that can exchange energy but not matter with its surroundings. An *isolated system* is one that cannot exchange either energy or matter with its surroundings.
- The *state of a system* is defined by the values of all relevant macroscopic properties, such as temperature, volume, and pressure. A *state function* is one whose value depends only on the

state of the system and not on how that state was achieved. State functions include energy, pressure, volume, and temperature.
- The *first law of thermodynamics* states that energy cannot be created or destroyed, but it can be changed from one form to another. The first law of thermodynamics is based on the law of conservation of energy.

SECTION 10.3

- *Enthalpy* is the heat exchanged between the system and surroundings at constant pressure. It is a state function. *Enthalpy of reaction* (ΔH_{rxn}) is the heat exchanged at constant pressure for a specific reaction.
- A *thermochemical equation* is a balanced chemical equation for which the enthalpy change (ΔH_{rxn}) is given.

SECTION 10.4

- *Calorimetry* is the science of measuring temperature changes to determine heats associated with chemical reactions. Calorimetry may be carried out at constant pressure (in a coffee-cup calorimeter) or at constant volume (in a bomb calorimeter).
- The *specific heat* (s) of a substance is the amount of heat required to increase the temperature of 1 g of the substance by 1°C. The *heat capacity* of an object is the amount of heat required to increase the temperature of the object by 1°C.

SECTION 10.5

- **Hess's law** states that the enthalpy change for a reaction that occurs in a series of steps is equal to the sum of the enthalpy changes of the individual steps. Hess's law is valid because enthalpy is a state function.

SECTION 10.6

- The **standard enthalpy of formation** (ΔH_f°) is the enthalpy change associated with the formation of 1 mole of a substance from its constituent elements, each in its standard state. The **standard enthalpy of reaction** (ΔH_{rxn}°) can be calculated for any reaction using tabulated standard enthalpies of formation (ΔH_f°) of the products and reactants.

SECTION 10.7

- **Bond enthalpy** is the energy required to break 1 mole of a particular type of bond. Bond enthalpies are a measure of the stability of covalent bonds and can be used to estimate the enthalpy change for a reaction.

SECTION 10.8

- Lattice energy is the amount of energy required to convert a mole of ionic solid to its constituent ions in the gas phase. Lattice energy cannot be measured directly, but is determined using the **Born-Haber cycle** and thermodynamic quantities that can be measured directly.

Key Words

Bond enthalpy, 388
Born-Haber cycle, 392
Calorimetry, 373
Closed system, 365
Endothermic process, 364
Enthalpy, 370
Enthalpy of reaction, 371

Exothermic process, 363
First law of thermodynamics, 366
Heat, 363
Heat capacity, 374
Hess's law, 383
Isolated system, 365

Open system, 365
Specific heat, 374
Standard enthalpy of formation, 385
Standard enthalpy of reaction, 385
State function, 365

State of a system, 365
Surroundings, 363
System, 363
Thermochemical equation, 372
Thermochemistry, 363
Thermodynamics, 365

Key Equations

10.1 $\quad \Delta U = q + w$

10.2 $\quad w = -P\Delta V$

10.3 $\quad \Delta U = q - P\Delta V$

10.4 $\quad q_V = \Delta U$

10.5 $\quad q_P = \Delta U + P\Delta V$

10.6 $\quad H = U + PV$

10.7 $\quad \Delta H = \Delta U + \Delta(PV)$

10.8 $\quad \Delta H = \Delta U + P\Delta V$

10.9 $\quad q_P = \Delta H$

10.10 $\quad \Delta H = H(\text{products}) - H(\text{reactants})$

10.11 $\quad q = sm\Delta T$

10.12 $\quad q = C\Delta T$

10.13 $\quad q_{sys} = -sm\Delta T$

10.14 $\quad q_{surr} = sm\Delta T$

10.15 $\quad q_{cal} = C_{cal}\Delta T$

10.16 $\quad q_{rxn} = -C_{cal}\Delta T$

10.17 $\quad \Delta H_{rxn}^\circ = [c\Delta H_f^\circ(C) + d\Delta H_f^\circ(D)] - [a\Delta H_f^\circ(A) + b\Delta H_f^\circ(B)]$

10.18 $\quad \Delta H_{rxn}^\circ = \sum n\Delta H_f^\circ(\text{products}) - \sum m\Delta H_f^\circ(\text{reactants})$

10.19 $\quad \Delta H^\circ = \sum BE \text{ (reactants)} - \sum BE \text{ (products)}$
$\quad\quad\quad = $ total energy *input* (to *break* bonds) $-$ total energy *released* (by bond *formation*)

Questions and Problems

SECTION 10.1:   ENERGY AND ENERGY CHANGES

Review Questions

10.1   Define these terms: *system, surroundings, thermal energy, chemical energy.*

10.2   What is heat? How does heat differ from thermal energy? Under what condition is heat transferred from one system to another?

10.3   These are various forms of energy: chemical, heat, light, mechanical, and electrical. Suggest several ways of converting one form of energy to another.

10.4   Define these terms: *thermochemistry, exothermic process, endothermic process.*

10.5   Stoichiometry is based on the law of conservation of mass. On what law is thermochemistry based?

10.6   Describe two exothermic processes and two endothermic processes.

10.7   Decomposition reactions are usually endothermic, whereas combination reactions are usually exothermic. Give a qualitative explanation for this observation.

SECTION 10.2:   INTRODUCTION TO THERMODYNAMICS

Review Questions

10.8   On what law is the first law of thermodynamics based? Explain the sign conventions in the equation

$$\Delta U = q + w$$

10.9   Explain what is meant by a state function. Give two examples of quantities that are state functions and two that are not state functions.

Problems

10.10   In a gas expansion, 87 J of heat is absorbed from the surroundings and the energy of the system decreases by 128 J. Calculate the work done.

10.11   The work done to compress a gas is 74 J. As a result, 26 J of heat is given off to the surroundings. Calculate the change in energy of the gas.

10.12   Calculate q, and determine whether heat is absorbed or released when a system does work on the surroundings equal to 64 J and $\Delta U = -213$ J.

10.13   Calculate w, and determine whether work is done *by* the system or *on* the system when 67 J of heat is released and $\Delta U = 510$ J.

SECTION 10.3:   ENTHALPY

Review Questions

10.14   Consider these changes.
(a) $Hg(l) \longrightarrow Hg(g)$
(b) $3O_2(g) \longrightarrow 2O_3(g)$
(c) $CuSO_4 \cdot 5H_2O(s) \longrightarrow CuSO_4(s) + 5H_2O(g)$
(d) $H_2(g) + F_2(g) \longrightarrow 2HF(g)$
At constant pressure, in which of the reactions is work done by the system on the surroundings? By the surroundings on the system? In which of them is no work done?

10.15   Define these terms: *enthalpy* and *enthalpy of reaction.* Under what condition is the heat of a reaction equal to the enthalpy change of the same reaction?

10.16   In writing thermochemical equations, why is it important to indicate the physical state (that is, gaseous, liquid, solid, or aqueous) of each substance?

10.17   Explain the meaning of this thermochemical equation:

$$2CH_3OH(g) + 3O_2(g) \longrightarrow 2CO_2(g) + 4H_2O(l)$$

$$\Delta H = -1452.8 \text{ kJ/mol}$$

What is the value of ΔH if (a) the equation is multiplied throughout by 2; (b) the direction of the reaction is reversed so that the products become the reactants, and vice versa; (c) water vapor instead of liquid water is formed as the product?

Problems

10.18   A sample of nitrogen gas expands in volume from 1.6 to 5.4 L at constant temperature. Calculate the work done in joules if the gas expands (a) against a vacuum, (b) against a constant pressure of 0.80 atm, and (c) against a constant pressure of 3.7 atm. (See Equation 10.2.)

10.19   A gas expands in volume from 26.7 to 89.3 mL at constant temperature. Calculate the work done (in joules) if the gas expands (a) against a vacuum, (b) against a constant pressure of 1.5 atm, and (c) against a constant pressure of 2.8 atm. (See Equation 10.2.)

10.20   A gas expands and does *PV* work on the surroundings equal to 325 J. At the same time, it absorbs 127 J of heat from the surroundings. Calculate the change in energy of the gas.

10.21   The first step in the industrial recovery of zinc from the zinc sulfide ore is roasting, that is, the conversion of ZnS to ZnO by heating:

$$2ZnS(s) + 3O_2(g) \longrightarrow 2ZnO(s) + 2SO_2(g)$$

$$\Delta H = -879 \text{ kJ/mol}$$

Calculate the heat evolved (in kJ) per gram of ZnS roasted.

10.22   Determine the amount of heat (in kJ) given off when 1.26×10^4 g of NO_2 are produced according to the equation

$$2NO(g) + O_2(g) \longrightarrow 2NO_2(g)$$

$$\Delta H = -114.6 \text{ kJ/mol}$$

10.23   Consider the reaction

$$2H_2O(g) \longrightarrow 2H_2(g) + O_2(g) \quad \Delta H = +483.6 \text{ kJ/mol}$$

at a certain temperature. If the increase in volume is 32.7 L against an external pressure of 1.00 atm, calculate ΔU for this reaction. (The conversion factor is $1 \text{ L} \cdot \text{atm} = 101.3 \text{ J}$.)

10.24   Consider the reaction

$$H_2(g) + Cl_2(g) \longrightarrow 2HCl(g) \quad \Delta H = -184.6 \text{ kJ/mol}$$

If 3 moles of H_2 react with 3 moles of Cl_2 to form HCl, calculate the work done (in joules) against a pressure of 1.0 atm. What is ΔU for this reaction? Assume the reaction goes to completion and that $\Delta V = 0$. (The conversion factor is $1 \text{ L} \cdot \text{atm} = 101.3 \text{ J}$.)

10.25   For most biological processes, the changes in internal energy are approximately equal to the changes in enthalpy. Explain.

SECTION 10.4:   CALORIMETRY

Visualizing Chemistry
Figure 10.9 and Figure 10.10

VC 10.1   Referring to Figure 10.9, which of the following would result in the calculated value of ΔH_{rxn} being too high?
(a) Spilling some of one of the reactant solutions before adding it to the calorimeter.
(b) Reading the final temperature before it reached its maximum value.
(c) Misreading the thermometer at the beginning of the experiment and recording too low an initial temperature.

VC 10.2   How would the ΔH_{rxn} calculated in Figure 10.9 be affected if the concentration of one of the reactant solutions were twice as high as it was supposed to be?
(a) The calculated ΔH_{rxn} would not be affected.
(b) The calculated ΔH_{rxn} would be too low.
(c) The calculated ΔH_{rxn} would be too high.

VC 10.3   For an exothermic reaction like the one depicted in Figure 10.9, if the heat capacity of the calorimeter is not negligibly small, the heat absorbed by the water will be _____ the heat given off by the reaction.
(a) greater than
(b) less than
(c) equal to

VC 10.4   Referring to Figure 10.9, how would the results of the experiment have been different if the reaction had been endothermic?
(a) The results would have been the same.
(b) There would have been a smaller temperature increase.
(c) There would have been a temperature decrease.

VC 10.5   What would happen to the specific heat calculated in Figure 10.10 if some of the warm metal shot were lost during the transfer to the calorimeter?
(a) It would not affect the calculated value of specific heat.
(b) It would cause the calculated value of specific heat to be too high.
(c) It would cause the calculated value of specific heat to be too low.

VC 10.6   What would happen to the specific heat calculated in Figure 10.10 if the test tube containing the metal shot were left in the boiling water for longer than the recommended time?
(a) It would not affect the calculated value of specific heat.
(b) It would cause the calculated value of specific heat to be too high.
(c) It would cause the calculated value of specific heat to be too low.

VC 10.7   What would happen to the specific heat calculated in Figure 10.10 if some of the water were spilled prior to being added to the calorimeter?
(a) It would not affect the calculated value of specific heat.
(b) It would cause the calculated value of specific heat to be too high.
(c) It would cause the calculated value of specific heat to be too low.

VC 10.8   Referring to the process depicted in Figure 10.10, which of the following must be known precisely for the calculated specific heat to be accurate.
(a) The mass of the boiling water.
(b) The temperature of the metal shot before it is immersed in the boiling water.
(c) The mass of the water that is added to the calorimeter.

Review Questions

10.26   What is the difference between specific heat and heat capacity? What are the units for these two quantities? Which is the *intensive* property and which is the *extensive* property?

10.27   Consider two metals A and B, each having a mass of 100 g and an initial temperature of 20°C. The specific heat of A is larger than that of B. Under the same heating conditions, which metal would take longer to reach a temperature of 21°C?

10.28 Define *calorimetry* and describe two commonly used calorimeters. In a calorimetric measurement, why is it important that we know the heat capacity of the calorimeter? How is this value determined?

10.29 Consider the following data:

Metal	Al	Cu
Mass (g)	10	30
Specific heat [J/(g · °C)]	0.900	0.385
Temperature (°C)	40	60

When these two metals are placed in contact, which of the following will take place?
(a) Heat will flow from Al to Cu because Al has a larger specific heat.
(b) Heat will flow from Cu to Al because Cu has a larger mass.
(c) Heat will flow from Cu to Al because Cu has a larger heat capacity.
(d) Heat will flow from Cu to Al because Cu is at a higher temperature.
(e) No heat will flow in either direction.

Problems

10.30 A piece of silver with a mass 362 g has a heat capacity of 85.7 J/°C. What is the specific heat of silver?

10.31 A 6.22-kg piece of copper metal is heated from 20.5°C to 324.3°C. Calculate the heat absorbed (in kJ) by the metal.

10.32 Calculate the amount of heat liberated (in kJ) from 366 g of mercury when it cools from 77.0°C to 12.0°C.

10.33 A sheet of gold weighing 10.0 g and at a temperature of 18.0°C is placed flat on a sheet of iron weighing 20.0 g and at a temperature of 55.6°C. What is the final temperature of the combined metals? Assume that no heat is lost to the surroundings. (*Hint:* The heat gained by the gold must be equal to the heat lost by the iron. The specific heats of the metals are given in Table 10.2.)

10.34 A 0.1375-g sample of solid magnesium is burned in a constant-volume bomb calorimeter that has a heat capacity of 3024 J/°C. The temperature increases by 1.126°C. Calculate the heat given off by the burning Mg, in kJ/g and in kJ/mol.

10.35 A quantity of 2.00×10^2 mL of 0.862 M HCl is mixed with 2.00×10^2 mL of 0.431 M Ba(OH)$_2$ in a constant-pressure calorimeter of negligible heat capacity. The initial temperature of the HCl and Ba(OH)$_2$ solutions is the same at 20.48°C. For the process

$$H^+(aq) + OH^-(aq) \longrightarrow H_2O(l)$$

the heat of neutralization is −56.2 kJ/mol. What is the final temperature of the mixed solution? Assume the specific heat of the solution is the same as that for pure water.

10.36 The fuel value of hamburger is approximately 3.6 kcal/g. If a man eats 1 lb of hamburger for lunch and if none of the energy is stored in his body, estimate the amount of water that would have to be lost in perspiration to keep his body temperature constant. The heat of vaporization of water may be taken as 2.41 kJ/g (1 lb = 453.6 g).

10.37 Metabolic activity in the human body releases approximately 1.0×10^4 kJ of heat per day. Assuming the body contains 50 kg of water, how fast would the body temperature rise if it were an isolated system? How much water must the body eliminate as perspiration to maintain the normal body temperature (98.6°F)? The heat of vaporization of water may be taken as 2.41 kJ/g. Comment on your results.

10.38 A 50.75-g sample of water at 75.6°C is added to a sample of water at 24.1°C in a constant-pressure calorimeter. If the final temperature of the combined water is 39.4°C and the heat capacity of the calorimeter is 26.3 J/°C, calculate the mass of the water originally in the calorimeter.

10.39 A 25.95-g sample of methanol at 35.6°C is added to a 38.65-g sample of ethanol at 24.7°C in a constant-pressure calorimeter. If the final temperature of the combined liquids is 28.5°C and the heat capacity of the calorimeter is 19.3 J/°C, determine the specific heat of methanol.

SECTION 10.5: HESS'S LAW

Review Questions

10.40 State Hess's law. Explain, with one example, the usefulness of Hess's law in thermochemistry.

10.41 Describe how chemists use Hess's law to determine the ΔH_f° of a compound by measuring its heat (enthalpy) of combustion.

Problems

10.42 From the following data,

$$C(\text{graphite}) + O_2(g) \longrightarrow CO_2(g)$$
$$\Delta H_{rxn}^\circ = -393.5 \text{ kJ/mol}$$

$$H_2(g) + \tfrac{1}{2}O_2(g) \longrightarrow H_2O(l)$$
$$\Delta H_{rxn}^\circ = -285.8 \text{ kJ/mol}$$

$$2C_2H_6(g) + 7O_2(g) \longrightarrow 4CO_2(g) + 6H_2O(l)$$
$$\Delta H_{rxn}^\circ = -3119.6 \text{ kJ/mol}$$

calculate the enthalpy change for the reaction

$$2C(\text{graphite}) + 3H_2(g) \longrightarrow C_2H_6(g)$$

10.43 From these data,

$$S(\text{rhombic}) + O_2(g) \longrightarrow SO_2(g)$$
$$\Delta H_{rxn}^\circ = -296.06 \text{ kJ/mol}$$

$$S(\text{monoclinic}) + O_2(g) \longrightarrow SO_2(g)$$
$$\Delta H_{rxn}^\circ = -296.36 \text{ kJ/mol}$$

calculate the enthalpy change for the transformation

$$S(\text{rhombic}) \longrightarrow S(\text{monoclinic})$$

(Monoclinic and rhombic are different allotropic forms of elemental sulfur.)

10.44   Calculate the standard enthalpy change for the reaction

$$2Al(s) + Fe_2O_3(s) \longrightarrow 2Fe(s) + Al_2O_3(s)$$

given that

$$2Al(s) + \tfrac{3}{2}O_2(g) \longrightarrow Al_2O_3(s) \quad \Delta H^\circ_{rxn} -1601 \text{ kJ/mol}$$

$$2Fe(s) + \tfrac{3}{2}O_2(g) \longrightarrow Fe_2O_3(s) \quad \Delta H^\circ_{rxn} -821 \text{ kJ/mol}$$

10.45   From the following heats of combustion,

$$CH_3OH(l) + \tfrac{3}{2}O_2(g) \longrightarrow CO_2(g) + 2H_2O(l)$$
$$\Delta H^\circ_{rxn} = -726.4 \text{ kJ/mol}$$

$$C(graphite) + O_2(g) \longrightarrow CO_2(g)$$
$$\Delta H^\circ_{rxn} = -393.5 \text{ kJ/mol}$$

$$H_2(g) + \tfrac{1}{2}O_2(g) \longrightarrow H_2O(l) \quad \Delta H^\circ_{rxn} = -285.8 \text{ kJ/mol}$$

calculate the enthalpy of formation of methanol (CH_3OH) from its elements:

$$C(graphite) + 2H_2(g) + \tfrac{1}{2}O_2(g) \longrightarrow CH_3OH(l)$$

SECTION 10.6: STANDARD ENTHALPIES OF FORMATION

Review Questions

10.46   What is meant by the standard-state condition?
10.47   How are the standard enthalpies of an element and of a compound determined?
10.48   What is meant by the standard enthalpy of a reaction?
10.49   Write the equation for calculating the enthalpy of a reaction. Define all the terms.

Problems

10.50   The ΔH°_f values of the two allotropes of oxygen, O_2 and O_3, are 0 kJ/mol and 142.2 kJ/mol, respectively, at 25°C. Which is the more stable form at this temperature?

10.51   Which of the following standard enthalpy of formation values is not zero at 25°C: Na(monoclinic), Ne(g), CH_4(g), S_8(monoclinic), Hg(l), H(g)?

10.52   Predict the value of ΔH°_f (greater than, less than, or equal to zero) for these elements at 25°C: (a) $Br_2(g)$, $Br_2(l)$; (b) $I_2(g)$, $I_2(s)$.

10.53   Which is the more negative quantity at 25°C: ΔH°_f for $H_2O(l)$ or ΔH°_f for $H_2O(g)$?

10.54   Suggest ways (with appropriate equations) that would allow you to measure the ΔH°_f values of $Ag_2O(s)$ and $CaCl_2(s)$ from their elements. No calculations are necessary.

10.55   In general, compounds with negative ΔH°_f values are more stable than those with positive ΔH°_f values. $H_2O_2(l)$ has a negative ΔH°_f (see Appendix 2). Why, then, does $H_2O_2(l)$ have a tendency to decompose to $H_2O(l)$ and $O_2(g)$?

10.56   The standard enthalpies of formation of ions in aqueous solutions are obtained by arbitrarily assigning a value of zero to H^+ ions; that is, $\Delta H^\circ_f = [H^+(aq)] = 0$. (a) For the following reaction

$$HCl(g) \xrightarrow{\text{H}_2\text{O}} H^+(aq) + Cl^-(aq)$$
$$\Delta H^\circ_f = -74.9 \text{ kJ/mol}$$

calculate ΔH°_f for the Cl^- ion. (b) Given that ΔH°_f for OH^- ion is -229.6 kJ/mol, calculate the enthalpy of neutralization when 1 mole of a strong monoprotic acid (such as HCl) is titrated by 1 mole of a strong base (such as KOH) at 25°C.

10.57   Calculate the heat of decomposition for this process at constant pressure and 25°C:

$$CaCO_3(s) \longrightarrow CaO(s) + CO_2(g)$$

(Look up the standard enthalpy of formation of the reactant and products in Appendix 2.)

10.58   Calculate the heats of combustion for the following reactions from the standard enthalpies of formation listed in Appendix 2:
(a) $C_2H_4(g) + 3O_2(g) \longrightarrow 2CO_2(g) + 2H_2O(l)$
(b) $2H_2S(g) + 3O_2(g) \longrightarrow 2H_2O(l) + 2SO_2(g)$

10.59   Calculate the heats of combustion for the following reactions from the standard enthalpies of formation listed in Appendix 2:
(a) $2H_2(g) + O_2(g) \longrightarrow 2H_2O(l)$
(b) $2C_2H_2(g) + 5O_2(g) \longrightarrow 4CO_2(g) + 2H_2O(l)$

10.60   The standard enthalpy change for the following reaction is 436.4 kJ/mol:

$$H_2(g) \longrightarrow H(g) + H(g)$$

Calculate the standard enthalpy of formation of atomic hydrogen (H).

10.61   Methanol, ethanol, and n-propanol are three common alcohols. When 1.00 g of each of these alcohols is burned in air, heat is liberated as follows: (a) methanol (CH_3OH), −22.6 kJ; (b) ethanol (C_2H_5OH), −29.7 kJ; (c) n-propanol (C_3H_7OH), −33.4 kJ. Calculate the heats of combustion of these alcohols in kJ/mol.

10.62   Pentaborane-9 (B_5H_9) is a colorless, highly reactive liquid that will burst into flames when exposed to oxygen. The reaction is

$$2B_5H_9(l) + 12O_2(g) \longrightarrow 5B_2O_3(s) + 9H_2O(l)$$

Calculate the kilojoules of heat released per gram of the compound reacted with oxygen. The standard enthalpy of formation of B_5H_9 is 73.2 kJ/mol.

10.63   From the standard enthalpies of formation, calculate ΔH°_{rxn} for the reaction

$$C_6H_{12}(l) + 9O_2(g) \longrightarrow 6CO_2(g) + 6H_2O(l)$$

For $C_6H_{12}(l)$, $\Delta H^\circ_f = -151.9$ kJ/mol.

10.64   At 850°C, CaCO_3 undergoes substantial decomposition to yield CaO and CO_2. Assuming that the ΔH°_f values of the reactant and products are the same at 850°C as they are at 25°C, calculate the enthalpy change (in kJ) if 66.8 g of CO_2 is produced in one reaction.

10.65 Determine the amount of heat (in kJ) given off when 1.26×10^4 g of ammonia is produced according to the equation

$$N_2(g) + 3H_2(g) \longrightarrow 2NH_3(g) \quad \Delta H_f^\circ = -92.6 \text{ kJ/mol}$$

Assume that the reaction takes place under standard-state conditions at 25°C.

SECTION 10.7: BOND ENTHALPY AND THE STABILITY OF COVALENT MOLECULES

Review Questions

10.66 What is *bond enthalpy*? Bond enthalpies of polyatomic molecules are average values, whereas those of diatomic molecules can be accurately determined. Why?

10.67 Explain why the bond enthalpy of a molecule is usually defined in terms of a gas-phase reaction. Why are bond-breaking processes always endothermic and bond-forming processes always exothermic?

Problems

10.68 From the following data, calculate the average bond enthalpy for the N—H bond:

$$NH_3(g) \longrightarrow NH_2(g) + H(g) \quad \Delta H^\circ = 435 \text{ kJ/mol}$$
$$NH_2(g) \longrightarrow NH(g) + H(g) \quad \Delta H^\circ - 381 \text{ kJ/mol}$$
$$NH(g) \longrightarrow N(g) + H(g) \quad \Delta H^\circ = 360 \text{ kJ/mol}$$

10.69 For the reaction

$$O(g) + O_2(g) \longrightarrow O_3(g) \quad \Delta H^\circ = -107.2 \text{ kJ/mol}$$

Calculate the average bond enthalpy in O_3.

10.70 The bond enthalpy of $F_2(g)$ is 156.9 kJ/mol. Calculate ΔH_f° for F(g).

10.71 For the reaction

$$2C_2H_6(g) + 7O_2(g) \longrightarrow 4CO_2(g) + 6H_2O(g)$$

(a) Predict the enthalpy of reaction from the average bond enthalpies in Table 10.4.

(b) Calculate the enthalpy of reaction from the standard enthalpies of formation (see Appendix 2) of the reactant and product molecules, and compare the result with your answer for part (a).

10.72 Use average bond enthalpies from Table 10.4 to estimate ΔH_{rxn} for the following reaction.

10.73 Use average bond enthalpies from Table 10.4 to estimate ΔH_{rxn} for the following reaction.

SECTION 10.8: LATTICE ENERGY AND THE STABILITY OF IONIC SOLIDS

 Visualizing Chemistry
Figure 10.14

VC 10.9 What additional information would you need to calculate the lattice energy for a compound if the charges on the cation and anion were +2 and −1, respectively, rather than +1 and −1?
(a) No additional information is needed.
(b) IE_2 of the cation.
(c) IE_2 of the cation and EA_2 of the anion.

VC 10.10 What additional information would you need to calculate the lattice energy for a compound if the charges on the cation and anion were +2 and −2, respectively, rather than +1 and −1?
(a) No additional information is needed.
(b) IE_2 of the cation.
(c) IE_2 of the cation and EA_2 of the anion.

VC 10.11 How would the magnitude of the lattice energy calculated using the Born-Haber cycle change if the charges on the cation and anion were +2 and −2, respectively, rather than +1 and −1?
(a) Lattice energy would increase.
(b) Lattice energy would decrease.
(c) Whether lattice energy would increase or decrease depends on the relative magnitudes of IE_2 of the cation and EA_2 of the anion.

VC 10.12 What law enables us to use the Born-Haber cycle to calculate lattice energy?
(a) Coulomb's law
(b) Hess's law
(c) law of multiple proportions

Review Questions

10.74 Explain how the lattice energy of an ionic compound such as KCl can be determined using the Born-Haber cycle. On what law is this procedure based?

10.75 Specify which compound in each of the following pairs of ionic compounds should have the higher lattice energy: (a) KCl or MgO, (b) LiF or LiBr, (c) Mg_3N_2 or NaCl, (d) AlN or CaO, (e) NaF or CsF, (f) $MgCl_2$ or MgF_2. Explain your choice.

Problems

10.76 Calculate the lattice energy of LiCl. Use data from Figures 4.8 and 4.10 and Appendix 2.

10.77 Use the Born-Haber cycle outlined in Section 10.8 for NaCl to calculate the lattice energy of $CaCl_2$. Use data from Figures 4.8 and 4.10 and Appendix 2. (The second ionization energy of Ca, IE_2, is 1145 kJ/mol.)

ADDITIONAL PROBLEMS

10.78 Consider the following two reactions:

$$A \longrightarrow 2B \qquad \Delta H^\circ_{rxn} = \Delta H_1$$

$$A \longrightarrow C \qquad \Delta H^\circ_{rxn} = \Delta H_2$$

Determine the enthalpy change for the process

$$2B \longrightarrow C$$

10.79 Consider the reaction

$$NH_3(g) + 3F_2(g) \longrightarrow NF_3(g) + 3HF(g)$$

$$\Delta H^\circ_{rxn} = -881.2 \text{ kJ/mol}$$

Using data from Appendix 2, determine the standard enthalpy of formation of NF_3.

10.80 Based on changes in enthalpy, which of the following reactions will occur more readily?
(a) $Cl(g) + CH_4(g) \longrightarrow CH_3Cl(g) + H(g)$
(b) $Cl(g) + CH_4(g) \longrightarrow CH_3(g) + HCl(g)$

10.81 The standard enthalpy change ΔH° for the thermal decomposition of silver nitrate according to the following equation is $+78.67$ kJ:

$$AgNO_3(s) \longrightarrow AgNO_2(s) + \tfrac{1}{2}O_2(g)$$

The standard enthalpy of formation of $AgNO_3(s)$ is -123.02 kJ/mol. Calculate the standard enthalpy of formation of $AgNO_2(s)$.

10.82 Hydrazine (N_2H_4) decomposes according to the following reaction:

$$3N_2H_4(l) \longrightarrow 4NH_3(g) + N_2(g)$$

(a) Given that the standard enthalpy of formation of hydrazine is 50.42 kJ/mol, calculate ΔH° for its decomposition. (b) Both hydrazine and ammonia burn in oxygen to produce $H_2O(l)$ and $N_2(g)$. Write balanced equations for each of these processes, and calculate ΔH° for each of them. On a mass basis (per kg), which would be the better fuel: hydrazine or ammonia?

10.83 Consider the reaction

$$N_2(g) + 3H_2(g) \longrightarrow 2NH_3(g) \quad \Delta H^\circ_f = -92.6 \text{ kJ/mol}$$

When 2 moles of N_2 react with 6 moles of H_2 to form 4 moles of NH_3 at 1 atm and a certain temperature, there is a decrease in volume equal to 98 L. Calculate ΔU for this reaction. (The conversion factor is 1 L · atm = 101.3 J.)

10.84 Calculate the heat released when 2.00 L of $Cl_2(g)$ with a density of 1.88 g/L reacts with an excess of sodium metal at 25°C and 1 atm to form sodium chloride.

10.85 Using the following information and the fact that the average C—H bond enthalpy is 414 kJ/mol, estimate the standard enthalpy of formation of methane (CH_4).

$$C(s) \longrightarrow C(g) \qquad \Delta H^\circ_{rxn} = 716 \text{ kJ/mol}$$

$$2H_2(g) \longrightarrow 4H(g) \qquad \Delta H^\circ_{rxn} = 872.8 \text{ kJ/mol}$$

10.86 Compare the bond enthalpy of F_2 with the overall energy change for the following process:

$$F_2(g) \longrightarrow F^+(g) + F^-(g)$$

Which is the preferred dissociation for F_2, energetically speaking? (*Hint:* You will need data from pages 116 and 119.)

10.87 Calculate ΔH° for the reaction

$$H_2(g) + I_2(g) \longrightarrow 2HI(g)$$

(a) using Equation 10.18, given that ΔH°_f for $I_2(g)$ is 61.0 kJ/mol, and (b) using Equation 10.19.

10.88 Consider the reaction

$$2Na(s) + 2H_2O(l) \longrightarrow 2NaOH(aq) + H_2(g)$$

When 2 moles of Na react with water at 25°C and 1 atm, the volume of H_2 formed is 24.5 L. Calculate the work done in joules when 0.34 g of Na reacts with water under the same conditions. (The conversion factor is 1 L · atm = 101.3 J.)

10.89 You are given the following data:

$$H_2(g) \longrightarrow 2H(g) \qquad \Delta H^\circ = 436.4 \text{ kJ/mol}$$

$$Br_2(g) \longrightarrow 2Br(g) \qquad \Delta H^\circ = 192.5 \text{ kJ/mol}$$

$$H_2(g) + Br_2(g) \longrightarrow 2HBr(g) \qquad \Delta H^\circ = -72.4 \text{ kJ/mol}$$

Calculate ΔH° for the reaction

$$H(g) + Br(g) \longrightarrow HBr(g)$$

10.90 Methanol (CH_3OH) is an organic solvent and is also used as a fuel in some automobile engines. From the following data, calculate the standard enthalpy of formation of methanol:

$$2CH_3OH(l) + 3O_2(g) \longrightarrow 2CO_2(g) + 4H_2O(l)$$

$$\Delta H^\circ_{rxn} = -1452.8 \text{ kJ/mol}$$

10.91 A 44.0-g sample of an unknown metal at 99.0°C was placed in a constant-pressure calorimeter containing 80.0 g of water at 24.0°C. The final temperature of the system was found to be 28.4°C. Calculate the specific heat of the metal. (The heat capacity of the calorimeter is 12.4 J/°C.)

10.92 A student mixes 88.6 g of water at 74.3°C with 57.9 g of water at 24.8°C in an insulated flask. What is the final temperature of the combined water?

10.93 Producer gas (carbon monoxide) is prepared by passing air over red-hot coke:

$$C(s) + \tfrac{1}{2}O_2(g) \longrightarrow CO(g)$$

Water gas (a mixture of carbon monoxide and hydrogen) is prepared by passing steam over red-hot coke:

$$C(s) + H_2O(g) \longrightarrow CO(g) + H_2(g)$$

For many years, both producer gas and water gas were used as fuels in industry and for domestic cooking. The large-scale preparation of these gases was carried out alternately, that is, first producer gas, then water gas, and so on. Using thermochemical reasoning, explain why this procedure was chosen.

10.94 Compare the heat produced by the complete combustion of 1 mole of methane (CH_4) with a mole of water gas (0.50 mole H_2 and 0.50 mole CO) under the same conditions. On the basis of your answer, would you prefer methane over water gas as a fuel? Can you suggest two other reasons why methane is preferable to water gas as a fuel?

10.95 The so-called hydrogen economy is based on hydrogen produced from water using solar energy. The gas is then burned as a fuel:

$$2H_2(g) + O_2(g) \longrightarrow 2H_2O(l)$$

A primary advantage of hydrogen as a fuel is that it is nonpolluting. A major disadvantage is that it is a gas and therefore is harder to store than liquids or solids. Calculate the number of moles of H_2 required to produce an amount of energy equivalent to that produced by the combustion of a gallon of octane (C_8H_{18}). The density of octane is 2.66 kg/gal, and its standard enthalpy of formation is −249.9 kJ/mol.

10.96 Ethanol (C_2H_5OH) and gasoline (assumed to be all octane, C_8H_{18}) are both used as automobile fuel. If gasoline is selling for $2.79/gal, what would the price of ethanol have to be in order to provide the same amount of heat per dollar? The density and ΔH_f° of octane are 0.7025 g/mL and −249.9 kJ/mol, respectively, and of ethanol are 0.7894 g/mL and −277.0 kJ/mol, respectively (1 gal = 3.785 L).

10.97 How many moles of ethane (C_2H_6) would have to be burned for the combustion to heat 855 g of water from 25.0°C to 98.0°C?

10.98 Using the data in Appendix 2, calculate the enthalpy change for the gaseous reaction shown here. (*Hint:* First determine the limiting reactant.)

CO NO CO_2 N_2

10.99 The heat of vaporization of a liquid (ΔH_{vap}) is the energy required to vaporize 1.00 g of the liquid at its boiling point. In one experiment, 60.0 g of liquid nitrogen (boiling point = −196°C) is poured into a Styrofoam cup containing 2.00×10^2 g of water at 55.3°C. Calculate the molar heat of vaporization of liquid nitrogen if the final temperature of the water is 41.0°C.

10.100 Explain the cooling effect experienced when ethanol is rubbed on your skin, given that

$$C_2H_5OH(l) \longrightarrow C_2H_5OH(g) \qquad \Delta H^\circ = 42.2 \text{ kJ/mol}$$

10.101 For which of the following reactions does $\Delta H_{rxn}^\circ = \Delta H_f^\circ$?
(a) $H_2(g) + S(\text{rhombic}) \longrightarrow H_2S(g)$
(b) $C(\text{diamond}) + O_2(g) \longrightarrow CO_2(g)$
(c) $H_2(g) + CuO(s) \longrightarrow H_2O(l) + Cu(s)$
(d) $O(g) + O_2(g) \longrightarrow O_3(g)$

10.102 Calculate the work done (in joules) when 1.0 mole of water is frozen at 0°C and 1.0 atm. The volumes of 1 mole of water and ice at 0°C are 0.0180 and 0.0196 L, respectively. (The conversion factor is 1 L · atm = 101.3 J.)

10.103 A certain gas initially at 0.050 L undergoes expansion until its volume is 0.50 L. Calculate the work done (in joules) by the gas if it expands (a) against a vacuum and (b) against a constant pressure of 0.20 atm. (The conversion factor is 1 L · atm = 101.3 J.)

10.104 Calculate the standard enthalpy of formation for diamond, given that

$$C(\text{graphite}) + O_2(g) \longrightarrow CO_2(g)$$
$$\Delta H^\circ = -393.5 \text{ kJ/mol}$$
$$C(\text{diamond}) + O_2(g) \longrightarrow CO_2(g)$$
$$\Delta H^\circ = -393.4 \text{ kJ/mol}$$

10.105 The first step in the industrial recovery of zinc from zinc sulfide ore is known as *roasting*. Roasting is the conversion of ZnS to ZnO by heating according to the following *unbalanced* equation:

$$ZnS(s) + O_2(g) \longrightarrow ZnO(s) + SO_2(g)$$

Determine the amount of heat involved when 1.26×10^4 g of SO_2 are produced in the roasting process.

10.106 Calculate the standard enthalpy change for the fermentation process, in which glucose ($C_6H_{12}O_6$) is converted to ethanol (C_2H_5OH) and carbon dioxide.

10.107 Portable hot packs are available for skiers and people engaged in other outdoor activities in a cold climate. The air-permeable paper packet contains a mixture of powdered iron, sodium chloride, and other components, all moistened by a little water. The exothermic reaction that produces the heat is a very common one—the rusting of iron:

$$4Fe(s) + 3O_2(g) \longrightarrow 2Fe_2O_3(s)$$

When the outside plastic envelope is removed, O_2 molecules penetrate the paper, causing the reaction to begin. A typical packet contains 250 g of iron to warm your hands or feet for up to 4 hours. Using data from Appendix 2, determine how much heat (in kJ) is produced by this reaction.

10.108 The bond enthalpy of the C—N bond in the amide group of proteins (see Problem 6.60) can be treated as an average of C—N and C=N bonds. Calculate the maximum wavelength of light needed to break the bond.

10.109 The total volume of the Pacific Ocean is estimated to be 7.2×10^8 km³. A medium-sized atomic bomb produces 1.0×10^{15} J of energy upon explosion. Calculate the number of atomic bombs needed to release enough energy to raise the temperature of the water in the Pacific Ocean by 1°C.

10.110 A woman expends 95 kJ of energy in walking a kilometer. The energy is supplied by the metabolic breakdown of food intake and has a 35 percent efficiency. How much energy does she save by walking the kilometer instead of driving a car that gets 8.2 km per liter of gasoline (approximately 20 mi/gal)? The density of gasoline is 0.71 g/mL, and its enthalpy of combustion is −49 kJ/g.

10.111 The carbon dioxide exhaled by sailors in a submarine is often removed by reaction with an aqueous lithium hydroxide solution. (a) Write a balanced equation for this process. (*Hint:* The products are water and a soluble salt.) (b) If every sailor consumes 1.2×10^4 kJ of energy every day and assuming that this energy is totally supplied by the metabolism of glucose ($C_6H_{12}O_6$), calculate the amounts of CO_2 produced and LiOH required to purify the air.

10.112 The enthalpy of combustion of benzoic acid (C_6H_5COOH) is commonly used as the standard for calibrating constant-volume bomb calorimeters; its value has been accurately determined to be −3226.7 kJ/mol. When 1.9862 g of benzoic acid are burned in a calorimeter, the temperature rises from 21.84°C to 25.67°C. What is the heat capacity of the bomb? (Assume that the quantity of water surrounding the bomb is exactly 2000 g.)

10.113 Calcium oxide (CaO) is used to remove sulfur dioxide generated by coal-burning power stations:

$$2CaO(s) + 2SO_2(g) + O_2(g) \longrightarrow 2CaSO_4(s)$$

Calculate the enthalpy change if 6.6×10^5 g of SO_2 is removed by this process.

10.114 Glauber's salt, sodium sulfate decahydrate ($Na_2SO_4 \cdot 10H_2O$), undergoes a phase transition (that is, melting or freezing) at a convenient temperature of about 32°C:

$$Na_2SO_4 \cdot 10H_2O(s) \longrightarrow Na_2SO_4 + 10H_2O(l)$$

$$\Delta H° = 74.4 \text{ kJ/mol}$$

As a result, this compound is used to regulate the temperature in homes. It is placed in plastic bags in the ceiling of a room. During the day, the endothermic melting process absorbs heat from the surroundings, cooling the room. At night, it gives off heat as it freezes. Calculate the mass of Glauber's salt in kilograms needed to lower the temperature of air in a room by 8.2°C. The mass of air in the room is 605.4 kg; the specific heat of air is 1.2 J/g · °C.

10.115 An excess of zinc metal is added to 50.0 mL of a 0.100 *M* $AgNO_3$ solution in a constant-pressure calorimeter like the one pictured in Figure 10.8. As a result of the reaction

$$Zn(s) + 2Ag^+(aq) \longrightarrow Zn^{2+}(aq) + 2Ag(s)$$

the temperature rises from 19.25°C to 22.17°C. If the heat capacity of the calorimeter is 98.6 J/°C, calculate the enthalpy change for the given reaction on a molar basis. Assume that the density and specific heat of the solution are the same as those for water, and ignore the specific heats of the metals.

10.116 (a) A person drinks four glasses of cold water (3.0°C) every day. The volume of each glass is 2.5×10^2 mL. How much heat (in kJ) does the body have to supply to raise the temperature of the water to 37°C, the body temperature? (b) How much heat would your body lose if you were to ingest 8.0×10^2 g of snow at 0°C to quench your thirst? (The amount of heat necessary to melt snow is 6.01 kJ/mol.)

10.117 Which of the following $\Delta H°_{rxn}$ values is a $\Delta H°_f$ value? For any that is not a $\Delta H°_f$ value, explain why it is not.

(a) $H_2(g) + Br_2(l) \longrightarrow 2HBr(g)$

$$\Delta H°_{rxn} = -72.4 \text{ kJ/mol}$$

(b) $4Al(s) + 3O_2(g) \longrightarrow 2Al_2O_3(s)$

$$\Delta H°_{rxn} = -3339.6 \text{ kJ/mol}$$

(c) $Ag(s) + \frac{1}{2}Cl_2(g) \longrightarrow AgCl(s)$

$$\Delta H°_{rxn} = -127.0 \text{ kJ/mol}$$

(d) $Cu^{2+}(aq) + SO_4^{2-}(aq) \longrightarrow CuSO_4(s)$

$$\Delta H°_{rxn} = +73.25 \text{ kJ/mol}$$

(e) $\frac{1}{2}H_2(g) + \frac{1}{2}N_2(g) + \frac{3}{2}O_2(g) \longrightarrow HNO_3(l)$

$$\Delta H°_{rxn} = -173.2 \text{ kJ/mol}$$

10.118 At 25°C the standard enthalpy of formation of HF(*aq*) is −320.1 kJ/mol; of OH^-(*aq*), it is −229.6 kJ/mol; of F^-(*aq*), it is −329.1 kJ/mol; and of $H_2O(l)$, it is −285.8 kJ/mol. (a) Calculate the standard enthalpy of neutralization of HF(*aq*):

$$HF(aq) + OH^-(aq) \longrightarrow F^-(aq) + H_2O(l)$$

(b) Using the value of −56.2 kJ as the standard enthalpy change for the reaction

$$H^+(aq) + OH^-(aq) \longrightarrow H_2O(l)$$

calculate the standard enthalpy change for the reaction

$$HF(aq) \longrightarrow H^+(aq) + F^+(aq)$$

10.119 Why are cold, damp air and hot, humid air more uncomfortable than dry air at the same temperatures? [The specific heats of water vapor and air are approximately 1.9 J/(g · °C) and 1.0 J/(g · °C), respectively.]

10.120 Vinyl chloride (C_2H_3Cl) differs from ethylene (C_2H_4) in that one of the H atoms is replaced with a Cl atom. Vinyl chloride is used to prepare poly(vinyl chloride), which is an important polymer used in pipes. Calculate the enthalpy change when 1.0×10^3 kg of vinyl chloride forms poly(vinyl chloride).

10.121 A 46-kg person drinks 500 g of milk, which has a "caloric" value of approximately 3.0 kJ/g. If only 17 percent of the energy in milk is converted to mechanical work, how high (in meters) can the person climb based on this energy intake? [*Hint:* The work done in ascending is given by *mgh*, where *m* is the mass (in kg), *g* is the gravitational acceleration (9.8 m/s²), and *h* is the height (in meters).]

10.122 The height of Niagara Falls on the American side is 51 m. (a) Calculate the potential energy of 1.0 g of water at the top of the falls relative to the ground level. (b) What is the speed of the falling water if all the potential energy is converted to kinetic energy? (c) What would be the increase in temperature of the water if all the kinetic energy were converted to heat? (See Problem 10.121 for information.)

10.123 In the nineteenth century, two scientists named Dulong and Petit noticed that for a solid element, the product of its molar mass and its specific heat is approximately 25 J/°C. This observation, now called Dulong and Petit's law, was used to estimate the specific heat of metals. Verify the law for the metals listed in Table 10.2. The law does not apply to one of the metals. Which one is it? Why?

10.124 Determine the standard enthalpy of formation of ethanol (C_2H_5OH) from its standard enthalpy of combustion (−1367.4 kJ/mol).

10.125 Acetylene (C_2H_2) and benzene (C_6H_6) have the same empirical formula. In fact, benzene can be made from acetylene as follows:

$$3C_2H_2(g) \longrightarrow C_6H_6(l)$$

The enthalpies of combustion for C_2H_2 and C_6H_6 are −1299.4 and −3267.4 kJ/mol, respectively. Calculate the standard enthalpies of formation of C_2H_2 and C_6H_6 and hence the enthalpy change for the formation of C_6H_6 from C_2H_2.

10.126 From the lattice energy of KCl in Table 5.1, and the first ionization energy of K and electron affinity on Cl on pages 116 and 119, calculate the $\Delta H°$ for the reaction

$$K(g) + Cl(g) \longrightarrow KCl(s)$$

10.127 The hydroxyl radical (OH) plays an important role in atmospheric chemistry. It is highly reactive and has a tendency to combine with an H atom from other compounds, causing them to break up. Thus, OH is sometimes called a "detergent" radical because it helps to clean up the atmosphere.
(a) Estimate the enthalpy change for the following reaction:

$$OH(g) + CH_4(g) \longrightarrow CH_3(g) + H_2O(g)$$

(b) The radical is generated when sunlight hits water vapor. Calculate the maximum wavelength (in nm) required to break an O—H bond in H_2O.

10.128 How much metabolic energy must a 5.2-g hummingbird expend to fly to a height of 12 m? (See the hint in Problem 10.121.)

10.129 (a) From the following data, calculate the bond enthalpy of the F_2^- ion.

$$F_2(g) \longrightarrow 2F(g) \qquad \Delta H°_{rxn} = 156.9 \text{ kJ/mol}$$
$$F^-(g) \longrightarrow F(g) + e^- \qquad \Delta H°_{rxn} = 333 \text{ kJ/mol}$$
$$F_2^-(g) \longrightarrow F_2(g) + e^- \qquad \Delta H°_{rxn} = 290 \text{ kJ/mol}$$

(b) Explain the difference between the bond enthalpies of F_2 and F_2^-.

10.130 The average temperature in deserts is high during the day but quite cool at night, whereas that in regions along the coastline is more moderate. Explain.

10.131 Both glucose and fructose are simple sugars with the same molecular formula of $C_6H_{12}O_6$. Sucrose ($C_{12}H_{22}O_{11}$), or table sugar, consists of a glucose molecule bonded to a fructose molecule (a water molecule is eliminated in the formation of sucrose). (a) Calculate the energy released when a 2.0-g glucose tablet is burned in air. (b) To what height can a 65-kg person climb after ingesting such a tablet, assuming only 30 percent of the energy released is available for work. (See the hint for Problem 10.121.) Repeat the calculations for a 2.0-g sucrose tablet.

10.132 About 6.0×10^{13} kg of CO_2 is fixed (converted to more complex organic molecules) by photosynthesis every year. (a) Assuming all the CO_2 ends up as glucose ($C_6H_{12}O_6$), calculate the energy (in kJ) stored by photosynthesis per year. (b) A typical coal-burning electric power station generates about 2.0×10^6 W per year. How many such stations are needed to generate the same amount of energy as that captured by photosynthesis (1 W = 1 J/s)?

10.133 Experiments show that it takes 1656 kJ/mol to break all the bonds in methane (CH_4) and 4006 kJ/mol to break all the bonds in propane (C_3H_8). Based on these data, calculate the average bond enthalpy of the C—C bond.

10.134 From a thermochemical point of view, explain why a carbon dioxide fire extinguisher or water should not be used on a magnesium fire.

10.135 Consider the reaction

$$2H_2(g) + O_2(g) \longrightarrow 2H_2O(l)$$

Under atmospheric conditions (1.00 atm), it was found that the formation of water resulted in a decrease in volume equal to 73.4 L. Calculate ΔU for the process $\Delta H = -571.6$ kJ/mol. (The conversion factor is 1 L · atm = 101.3 J.)

10.136 *Lime* is a term that includes calcium oxide (CaO, also called quicklime) and calcium hydroxide [$Ca(OH)_2$, also called slaked lime]. It is used in the steel industry to remove acidic impurities, in air-pollution control to remove acidic oxides such as SO_2, and in water treatment. Quicklime is made industrially by heating limestone ($CaCO_3$) above 2000°C:

$$CaCO_3(s) \longrightarrow CaO(s) + CO_2(g)$$
$$\Delta H° = 177.8 \text{ kJ/mol}$$

Slaked lime is produced by treating quicklime with water:

$$CaO(s) + H_2O(l) \longrightarrow Ca(OH)_2(s)$$
$$\Delta H° = -62.5 \text{ kJ/mol}$$

The exothermic reaction of quicklime with water and the rather small specific heats of both quicklime [0.946 J/(g · °C)] and slaked lime [1.20 J/(g · °C)] make it hazardous to store and transport lime in vessels made of wood. Wooden sailing ships carrying lime would occasionally catch fire when water leaked into the hold. (a) If a 500.0-g sample of water reacts with an equimolar amount of CaO (both at an initial temperature of 25°C), what is the final temperature of the product, $Ca(OH)_2$? Assume that the product absorbs all the heat released in the reaction. (b) Given that the standard enthalpies of formation of CaO and H_2O are -635.6 and -285.8 kJ/mol, respectively, calculate the standard enthalpy of formation of $Ca(OH)_2$.

10.137   A 4.117-g impure sample of glucose ($C_6H_{12}O_6$) was burned in a constant-volume calorimeter having a heat capacity of 19.65 kJ/°C. If the rise in temperature is 3.134°C, calculate the percent by mass of the glucose in the sample. Assume that the impurities are unaffected by the combustion process and that $\Delta U = \Delta H$. See Appendix 2 for thermodynamic data.

10.138   The combustion of 0.4196 g of a hydrocarbon releases 17.55 kJ of heat. The masses of the products are $CO_2 = 1.419$ g and $H_2O = 0.290$ g. (a) What is the empirical formula of the compound? (b) If the approximate molar mass of the compound is 76 g/mol, calculate its standard enthalpy of formation.

10.139   Photosynthesis produces glucose ($C_6H_{12}O_6$) and oxygen from carbon dioxide and water:

$$6CO_2(g) + 6H_2O(l) \longrightarrow C_6H_{12}O_6(s) + 6O_2(g)$$

(a) How would you determine experimentally the ΔH_f° value for this reaction? (b) Solar radiation produces about 7.0×10^{14} kg of glucose a year on Earth. What is the corresponding ΔH° change?

10.140   Ice at 0°C is placed in a Styrofoam cup containing 361 g of a soft drink at 23°C. The specific heat of the drink is about the same as that of water. Some ice remains after the ice and soft drink reach an equilibrium temperature of 0°C. Determine the mass of ice that has melted. Ignore the heat capacity of the cup. (*Hint:* It takes 334 J to melt 1 g of ice at 0°C.)

10.141   Acetylene (C_2H_2) can be made by combining calcium carbide (CaC_2) with water. (a) Write an equation for the reaction. (b) What is the maximum amount of heat (in joules) that can be obtained from the combustion of acetylene, starting with 74.6 g of CaC_2?

10.142   In 1998, scientists using a special type of electron microscope were able to measure the force needed to break a *single* chemical bond. If 2.0×10^{-9} N was needed to break a C—Si bond, estimate the bond enthalpy in kJ/mol. Assume that the bond has to be stretched by a distance of 2 Å (2×10^{-10} m) before it is broken.

10.143   A driver's manual states that the stopping distance quadruples as the speed doubles; that is, if it takes 30 ft to stop a car moving at 25 mph, then it would take 120 ft to stop a car moving at 50 mph. Justify this statement by using mechanics and the first law of thermodynamics. [Assume that when a car is stopped, its kinetic energy ($\frac{1}{2} mu^2$) is totally converted to heat.]

10.144   From the enthalpy of formation for CO_2 and the following information, calculate the standard enthalpy of formation for carbon monoxide (CO).

$$CO(g) + \frac{1}{2}O_2(g) \longrightarrow CO_2(g)$$
$$\Delta H^\circ = -283.3 \text{ kJ/mol}$$

Why can't we obtain the standard enthalpy of formation directly by measuring the enthalpy of the following reaction?

$$C(graphite) + \frac{1}{2}O_2(g) \longrightarrow CO(g)$$

10.145   The atoms in the H_3^+ ion are arranged in an equilateral triangle. Given the following information

$$2H + H^+ \longrightarrow H_3^+ \qquad \Delta H^\circ = -849 \text{ kJ/mol}$$
$$H_2 \longrightarrow 2H \qquad \Delta H^\circ = 436.4 \text{ kJ/mol}$$

calculate ΔH° for the reaction

$$H^+ + H_2 \longrightarrow H_3^+$$

10.146   A man ate 0.50 lb of cheese (an energy intake of 4×10^3 kJ). Suppose that none of the energy was stored in his body. What mass (in grams) of water would he need to perspire in order to maintain his original temperature? (It takes 44.0 kJ to vaporize 1 mole of water.)

10.147   When 1.034 g of naphthalene ($C_{10}H_8$) is burned in a constant-volume bomb calorimeter at 298 K, 41.56 kJ of heat is evolved. Calculate ΔU and w for the reaction on a molar basis.

10.148   A hemoglobin molecule (molar mass = 65,000 g) can bind up to four oxygen molecules. In a certain experiment, a 0.085-L solution containing 6.0 g of deoxyhemoglobin (hemoglobin without oxygen molecules bound to it) was combined with an excess of oxygen in a constant-pressure calorimeter of negligible heat capacity. Calculate the enthalpy of reaction per mole of oxygen bound if the temperature rose by 0.044°C. Assume the solution is dilute so that the specific heat of the solution is equal to that of water.

10.149   A gas company in Massachusetts charges 27 cents for a mole of natural gas (CH_4). Calculate the cost of heating 200 mL of water (enough to make a cup of coffee or tea) from 20°C to 100°C. Assume that only 50 percent of the heat generated by the combustion is used to heat the water; the rest of the heat is lost to the surroundings.

10.150   A 12.1-g piece of aluminum at 81.7°C is added to a sample of water at 23.4°C in a constant-pressure calorimeter. If the final temperature of the water is 24.9°C, and the heat capacity of the calorimeter is 19.8 J/°C, calculate the mass of the water in the calorimeter.

10.151   Using Table 10.4, compare the following bond enthalpies: C—C in C_2H_6, N—N in N_2H_4, and O—O in H_2O_2. What effect do lone pairs on adjacent atoms appear to have on bond enthalpy? (*Hint:* Start by drawing Lewis structures of each molecule.)

10.152 According to information obtained from www.krispykreme.com, a Krispy Kreme original glazed doughnut weighs 52 g and contains 200 Cal and 12 g of fat. (a) Assuming that the fat in the doughnut is metabolized according to the given equation for tristearin

$$C_{57}H_{110}O_6(s) + 81.5O_2(g) \longrightarrow 57CO_2(g) + 55H_2O(l)$$

$$\Delta H° = -37,760 \text{ kJ/mol}$$

calculate the number of Calories in the reported 12 g of fat in each doughnut. (b) If all the energy contained in a Krispy Kreme doughnut (and just in the fat) were transferred to 6.00 kg of water originally at 25.5°C, what would be the final temperature of the water? (c) When a Krispy Kreme apple fritter weighing 101 g is burned in a bomb calorimeter with $C_{cal} = 95.3$ kJ/°C, the measured temperature increase is 16.7°C. Calculate the number of Calories in a Krispy Kreme apple fritter. (d) What would the $\Delta H°$ value be for the metabolism of 1 mole of the fat tristearin if the water produced by the reaction were gaseous instead of liquid? [*Hint:* Use data from Appendix 2 to determine the $\Delta H°$ value for the reaction $H_2O(l) \longrightarrow H_2O(g)$.]

Answers to In-Chapter Materials

PRACTICE PROBLEMS

10.1A -4.32×10^4 J. **10.1B** 6.95×10^5 kJ, heat is absorbed. **10.2A** (a) -270 J, (b) 4.02 J, (c) -202 J. **10.2B** (a) 0.487 atm, (b) 73.4 mL, (c) 326.6 mL. **10.3A** 8.174×10^4 kJ. **10.3B** 1.71×10^3 g. **10.4A** 151 kJ. **10.4B** 52.2°C. **10.5A** 28°C. **10.5B** 42 g. **10.6A** 14.5 kJ/g. **10.6B** 10.5°C rise. **10.7A** -1103 kJ/mol. **10.7B** 113.2 kJ/mol. **10.8A** 177.8 kJ/mol. **10.8B** -697.6 kJ/mol. **10.9A** 87.3 kJ/mol. **10.9B** $NH_3(g) + HCl(g)$, 176.8 kJ/mol. **10.10A** -557 kJ/mol. (See footnote to Table 10.4 regarding the C=O bond enthalpy in CO_2.) **10.10B** 328 kJ/mol. **10.11A** 629 kJ/mol. **10.11B** -841 kJ/mol. (Remember that we define electron affinity as the energy *given off* [◄◄ Section 4.4]. A negative *EA* value indicates that energy is *absorbed*, as we would expect to be the case with any *second EA*.)

SECTION REVIEW

10.1.1 172.80 cal. **10.1.2** 9.00×10^5 J. **10.1.3** (a) $2AX(g) + B_2(g) \longrightarrow A_2(g) + B_2X_2(g)$, (b) $A_2(g) + B_2X_2(g) \longrightarrow 2AX(g) + B_2(g)$. **10.2.1** -43 J. **10.2.2** $w = -5.4 \times 10^2$ kJ, done by the system. **10.3.1** 453 kJ. **10.3.2** 11.2 kg. **10.4.1** 6.95 kJ/°C. **10.4.2** 58.1°C. **10.4.3** 88.3°C. **10.4.4** 31.1°C. **10.5.1** -867.7 kJ/mol. **10.5.2** -1300.0 kJ/mol. **10.6.1** -543.2 kJ/mol. **10.6.2** -58.04 kJ/mol. **10.6.3** -110.5 kJ/mol. **10.7.1** -119 kJ/mol. **10.7.2** 13.6 kJ/mol. **10.7.3** -114 kJ/mol. **10.7.4** -2.00×10^2 kJ/mol. **10.8.1** (a) KF < LiF, (b) KF > KCl, (c) KF > KI. **10.8.2** 808 kJ/mol.

KEY SKILLS

Enthalpy of Reaction

Using tabulated ΔH_f° values, we can calculate the standard enthalpy of reaction (ΔH_{rxn}°) using Equation 10.18:

$$\Delta H_{rxn}^\circ = \sum n\Delta H_f^\circ \,(\text{products}) - \sum m\Delta H_f^\circ \,(\text{reactants})$$

This method of calculating thermodynamic quantities such as enthalpy of reaction is important not only in this chapter, but also in Chapters 18 and 19. The following examples illustrate the use of Equation 10.18 and data from Appendix 2. Each example provides a specific reminder of one of the important facets of this approach.

Each ΔH_f° value must be multiplied by the corresponding stoichiometric coefficient in the balanced equation.

$$Ba(s) + 2H_2O(l) \longrightarrow Ba(OH)_2(aq) + H_2(g)$$

By definition, the standard enthalpy of formation for an element in its standard state is zero. In addition, many tables of thermodynamic data, including Appendix 2, do not contain values for aqueous strong electrolytes such as barium hydroxide. However, the tables do include values for the individual aqueous ions. Therefore, determination of this enthalpy of reaction is facilitated by rewriting the equation with $Ba(OH)_2$ written as separate ions:

You will find more than one tabulated ΔH_f° value for some substances, such as water. It is important to select the value that corresponds to the phase of matter represented in the chemical equation. In previous examples, water has appeared in the balanced equations as a liquid. It can also appear as a gas.

Key Skills Problems

10.1
Using data from Appendix 2, calculate the standard enthalpy of the following reaction:

$$Mg(OH)_2(s) \longrightarrow MgO(s) + H_2O(l)$$

(a) −608.7 kJ/mol (b) −81.1 kJ/mol (c) −37.1 kJ/mol
(d) +81.1 kJ/mol (e) +37.1 kJ/mol

10.2
Using data from Appendix 2, calculate the standard enthalpy of the following reaction:

$$4HBr(g) + O_2(g) \longrightarrow 2H_2O(l) + 2Br_2(l)$$

(a) −426.8 kJ/mol (b) −338.8 kJ/mol (c) −249.6 kJ/mol
(d) +426.8 kJ/mol (e) +338.8 kJ/mol

10.3
Using data from Appendix 2, calculate the standard enthalpy of the following reaction (you must first balance the equation):

$$P(red) + Cl_2(g) \longrightarrow PCl_3(g)$$

(a) −576.1 kJ/mol (b) −269.7 kJ/mol (c) −539.3 kJ/mol
(d) −602.6 kJ/mol (e) +639.4 kJ/mol

10.4
Using only whole-number coefficients, the combustion of hexane can be represented as:

$$2C_6H_{14}(l) + 19O_2(g) \longrightarrow 12CO_2(g) + 14H_2O(l)$$

$$\Delta H^\circ = -8388.4 \text{ kJ/mol}$$

Using this and data from Appendix 2, determine the standard enthalpy of formation of hexane.

(a) −334.8 kJ/mol (b) −167.4 kJ/mol (c) −669.6 kJ/mol
(d) +334.8 kJ/mol (e) +669.6 kJ/mol

CHAPTER 11

Gases

11.1 Properties of Gases

11.2 The Kinetic Molecular Theory of Gases
• Molecular Speed • Diffusion and Effusion

11.3 Gas Pressure
• Definition and Units of Pressure • Calculation of Pressure • Measurement of Pressure

11.4 The Gas Laws
• Boyle's Law: The Pressure-Volume Relationship • Charles's and Gay-Lussac's Law: The Temperature-Volume Relationship • Avogadro's Law: The Amount-Volume Relationship • The Gas Laws and Kinetic Molecular Theory • The Combined Gas Law: The Pressure-Temperature-Amount-Volume Relationship

11.5 The Ideal Gas Equation
• Applications of the Ideal Gas Equation

11.6 Real Gases
• Factors That Cause Deviation from Ideal Behavior • The van der Waals Equation • van der Waals Constants

11.7 Gas Mixtures
• Dalton's Law of Partial Pressures • Mole Fractions

11.8 Reactions with Gaseous Reactants and Products
• Calculating the Required Volume of a Gaseous Reactant • Determining the Amount of Reactant Consumed Using Change in Pressure • Using Partial Pressures to Solve Problems

Early in the study of gaseous substances, the anesthetic properties of various gases were investigated. The first anesthetics included the compounds *nitrous oxide, diethyl ether,* and *chloroform.* Knowledge of the chemical and physical properties of gases has enabled chemists and physicians to optimize a variety of anesthetic gaseous mixtures for use in medical and veterinary procedures.

• Tracking units [◄◄ Section 1.6]
• Stoichiometry [◄◄ Section 8.3]

Before You Begin, Review These Skills

11.1 PROPERTIES OF GASES

Recall from Chapter 1 that matter exists in one of three states: solid, liquid, or gas. In fact, most substances that are solid or liquid at room temperature (25°C) *can* exist as gases under appropriate conditions. Water, for instance, *evaporates* under the right conditions. Water vapor is a gas. In this chapter, we will explore the nature of gases and how their properties at the molecular level give rise to the macroscopic properties that we observe. Figure 11.1 illustrates the three states of matter at the macroscopic level and at the molecular level.

Relatively few elements exist as gases at room temperature. Those that do are hydrogen, nitrogen, oxygen, fluorine, chlorine, and the noble gases. Of these, the noble gases exist as isolated atoms, whereas the others exist as diatomic molecules [◄◄ Section 5.5]. Figure 11.2 shows where the gaseous elements appear in the periodic table.

Many molecular compounds, most often those with low molar masses, exist as gases at room temperature. Table 11.1 lists some gaseous compounds that may be familiar to you.

Student Annotation: In general, the term vapor is used to refer to the gaseous state of a substance that is a liquid or solid at room temperature.

Student Annotation: Recall that oxygen also exists as the triatomic molecule ozone (O_3) [◄◄ Section 5.5]. Diatomic O_2, however, is the more stable allotrope at room temperature.

Figure 11.1 Solid, liquid, and gaseous states of a substance.

Figure 11.2 Elements that exist as gases at room temperature.

TABLE 11.1	Molecular Compounds That Are Gases at Room Temperature	
Molecular formula	**Compound name**	
HCl	Hydrogen chloride	
NH_3	Ammonia	
CO_2	Carbon dioxide	
N_2O	Dinitrogen monoxide or nitrous oxide	
CH_4	Methane	
HCN	Hydrogen cyanide	

Gases differ from the condensed phases (solids and liquids) in the following important ways:

1. *A sample of gas assumes both the shape and volume of its container.* Like a liquid, a gas consists of particles (molecules or atoms) that do not have fixed positions in the sample [◄◄ Section 1.2]. As a result, both liquids and gases are able to *flow*. (Recall from Chapter 1 that we refer to liquids and gases collectively as *fluids*.) While a sample of liquid will assume the shape of the part of its container that it occupies, a sample of gas will expand to fill the entire *volume* of its container.

2. *Gases are compressible.* Unlike a solid or a liquid, a gas consists of particles with relatively large distances between them; that is, the distance between any two particles in a gas is much larger than the size of a molecule or atom. Because gas particles are far apart, it is possible to move them closer together by confining them to a smaller volume.

3. *The densities of gases are much smaller than those of liquids and solids; and the density of a gaseous substance is highly variable depending on temperature and pressure.* The densities of gases are typically expressed in g/L, whereas those of liquids and solids are typically expressed in g/mL or g/cm³.

   > **Student Annotation:** 1 mL = 1 cm³ [◄◄ Section 1.4].

   When we compress a sample of gas, we decrease its volume. Because its mass remains the same, the ratio of mass to volume (density) increases. Conversely, if we increase the volume to which a sample of gas is confined, we decrease its density.

   If you have ever seen a hot-air balloon aloft, you have seen a demonstration of how the density of a gas varies with temperature. Hot air is less dense than cold air, so hot air "floats" on cold air, much like oil floats on water.

4. *Gases form homogeneous mixtures (solutions) with one another in any proportion.* Some liquids (e.g., oil and water) do not mix with one another. Gases, on the other hand, because their particles are so far apart, do not interact with one another to any significant degree unless a chemical reaction takes place between them. This allows molecules of different gases to mix uniformly. That is, gases that don't react with each other are mutually *miscible*.

Each of these four characteristics is the result of the properties of gases at the molecular level.

11.2 THE KINETIC MOLECULAR THEORY OF GASES

The *kinetic molecular theory,* which was put forth in the nineteenth century by a number of physicists, notably Ludwig Boltzmann[1] and James Maxwell,[2] explains how the molecular nature of gases gives rise to their macroscopic properties. The four basic assumptions of the kinetic molecular theory are as follows:

1. A gas is composed of particles that are separated by relatively large distances. The volume occupied by individual molecules is negligible. Gases are compressible because molecules in the gas phase are separated by large distances and can be moved closer together by decreasing the volume occupied by a sample of gas (Figure 11.3).
2. Gas molecules are constantly in random motion, moving in straight paths, colliding with the walls of their container and with one another in perfectly elastic collisions. (Energy is *transferred* but not *lost* in the collisions.)
3. Gas molecules do not exert attractive or repulsive forces on one another.
4. The average kinetic energy, $\overline{E_k}$ of gas molecules in a sample is proportional to the absolute temperature:

$$\overline{E_k} \propto T$$

Recall that kinetic energy is the energy associated with motion [◀◀ Section 3.1]:

$$E_k = \frac{1}{2} mu^2$$

Thus, the kinetic energy of an individual gas molecule is proportional to its mass and its velocity squared. When we talk about a group of gas molecules, we determine the average kinetic energy using the *mean square speed, $\overline{u^2}$*, which is the average of the speed squared for all the molecules in the sample:

$$\overline{u^2} = \frac{u_1^2 + u_2^2 + u_3^2 + \ldots u_N^2}{N}$$

where N is the number of molecules in the sample.

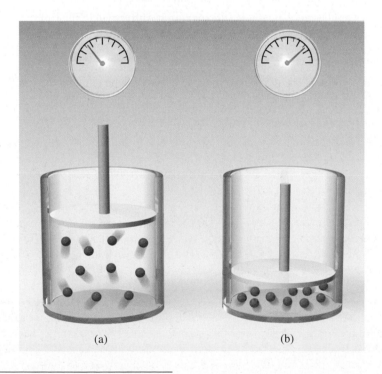

(a) (b)

Figure 11.3 Gases can be compressed by decreasing their volume. (a) Before volume decrease. (b) After volume decrease, the increased frequency of collisions between molecules and the walls of their container constitutes higher pressure.

[1]Ludwig Eduard Boltzmann (1844–1906). Although Boltzmann, an Austrian physicist, was one of the greatest theoretical physicists of all time, his work was not recognized by other scientists in his own lifetime. He suffered from poor health and severe depression and committed suicide in 1906.

[2]James Clerk Maxwell (1831–1879), a Scottish physicist, was one of the great theoretical physicists of the nineteenth century. His work covered many areas in physics, including the kinetic theory of gases, thermodynamics, and electricity and magnetism.

Molecular Speed

One of the important outcomes of the kinetic molecular theory is that the total kinetic energy of a mole of gas (any gas) is equal to $\frac{3}{2}RT$, where R is the **gas constant,** 8.314 J/K · mol. With assumption 4, we saw that the average kinetic energy of one molecule is $\frac{1}{2}m\overline{u^2}$. For 1 mole of the gas, we write

$$N_A\left(\frac{1}{2}m\overline{u^2}\right) = \frac{3}{2}RT$$

where N_A is Avogadro's number. Because $m \times N_A = \mathcal{M}$ we can rearrange the preceding equation as follows:

$$\overline{u^2} = \frac{3RT}{\mathcal{M}}$$

Taking the square root of both sides gives

$$\sqrt{\overline{u^2}} = \sqrt{\frac{3RT}{\mathcal{M}}}$$

Where $\sqrt{\overline{u^2}}$ is the **root-mean-square (rms) speed (u_{rms}).** The result,

Equation 11.1 $u_{rms} = \sqrt{\dfrac{3RT}{\mathcal{M}}}$

gives us the root-mean-square speed, which is the speed of a molecule with the average kinetic energy in a gas sample. Equation 11.1 indicates two important things: (1) The root-mean-square speed is directly proportional to the square root of the absolute temperature, and (2) the root-mean-square speed is inversely proportional to the square root of $\mathcal{M}$. Thus, for any two samples of gas at the same temperature, the gas with the larger molar mass will have the lower root-mean-square speed, u_{rms}.

Keep in mind that most molecules will have speeds either higher or lower than u_{rms}—and that u_{rms} is temperature dependent. James Maxwell studied extensively the behavior of gas molecules at various temperatures. Figure 11.4(a) shows typical Maxwell speed distribution curves for nitrogen gas at three different temperatures. At a given temperature, the distribution curve tells us the number of molecules moving at a certain speed. The maximum of each curve represents the most probable speed—that is, the speed of the largest number of molecules. Note that the most probable speed increases as temperature increases [the maximum shifts toward the right in Figure 11.4(a)]. Furthermore, the curve also begins to flatten out with increasing temperature, indicating that larger numbers of molecules are moving faster.

Figure 11.4(b) shows the speed distributions of three different gases (Cl_2, N_2, and He) at the same temperature (300 K). The difference in these curves can be explained by noting that lighter molecules, on average, move faster than heavier ones.

(a)

(b)

Figure 11.4 (a) The distribution of speeds for nitrogen gas at three different temperatures. At higher temperatures, more molecules are moving faster. (b) The distribution of speeds for three different gases at the same temperature. On average, lighter molecules move faster than heavier molecules.

Although we can use Equation 11.1 to calculate u_{rms} of a molecule in a particular sample, we will generally find it more useful to compare the u_{rms} values of molecules in different gas samples. For example, we can write Equation 11.1 for two different gases:

$$u_{rms}(1) = \sqrt{\frac{3RT}{\mathcal{M}_1}} \quad \text{and} \quad u_{rms}(2) = \sqrt{\frac{3RT}{\mathcal{M}_2}}$$

We can then determine the u_{rms} of a molecule in one gas relative to that in the other gas:

$$\frac{u_{rms}(1)}{u_{rms}(2)} = \frac{\sqrt{\dfrac{3RT}{\mathcal{M}_1}}}{\sqrt{\dfrac{3RT}{\mathcal{M}_2}}}$$

Canceling identical terms, when both gases are at the same temperature, we can write

$$\frac{u_{rms}(1)}{u_{rms}(2)} = \sqrt{\frac{\mathcal{M}_2}{\mathcal{M}_1}} \qquad \textbf{Equation 11.2}$$

Using Equation 11.2 we can compare u_{rms} values of molecules with different molar masses (at a given temperature). Worked Example 11.1 shows how this is done.

> **Student Annotation:** Note that because Equation 11.2 contains the ratio of two molar masses, we can express the molar masses as g/mol or kg/mol. (In Equation 11.1, we had to express molar mass as kg/mol for the units to cancel properly.)

Worked Example 11.1

Determine how much faster a helium atom moves, on average, than a carbon dioxide molecule at the same temperature.

Strategy Use Equation 11.2 and the molar masses of He and CO_2 to determine the ratio of their root-mean-square speeds. When solving a problem such as this, it is generally best to label the lighter of the two molecules as molecule 1 and the heavier molecule as molecule 2. This ensures that the result will be greater than 1, which is relatively easy to interpret.

Setup The molar masses of He and CO_2 are 4.003 and 44.02 g/mol, respectively.

Solution

$$\frac{u_{rms}(He)}{u_{rms}(CO_2)} = \sqrt{\frac{\dfrac{44.02\ g}{mol}}{\dfrac{4.003\ g}{mol}}} = 3.316$$

On average, He atoms move 3.316 times as fast as than CO_2 molecules at the same temperature.

> **Think About It**
> Remember that the relationship between molar mass and molecular speed (Equation 11.2) is reciprocal. A CO_2 molecule has approximately 10 times the mass of an He atom. Therefore, we should expect an He atom, on average, to be moving approximately $\sqrt{10}$ times (~3.2 times) as fast as a CO_2 molecule.

Practice Problem A Determine the relative root-mean-square speeds of O_2 and SF_6 at a given temperature.

Practice Problem B Determine the molar mass of a gas that moves 4.67 times as fast as CO_2.

Diffusion and Effusion

The random motion of gas molecules gives rise to two readily observable phenomena: diffusion and effusion. **Diffusion** is the mixing of gases as the result of random motion and frequent collisions (Figure 11.5), while **effusion** is the escape of gas molecules from a container to a region of vacuum (Figure 11.6). One of the earliest successes of the kinetic molecular theory was its ability to explain diffusion and effusion.

Multi 11.1
Diffusion of gases

(a)

(b)

Figure 11.5 Diffusion is the mixing of gases. (a) Two different gases in separate containers. (b) When the stopcock is opened, the gases mix by diffusion.

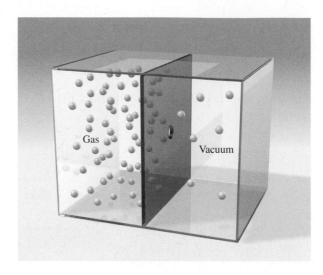

Gas

Vacuum

Figure 11.6 Effusion is the escape of a gas into a vacuum.

Graham's law states that the rate of diffusion or effusion of a gas is inversely proportional to the square root of its molar mass:

$$\text{Rate} \propto \frac{1}{\sqrt{\mathcal{M}}}$$

This is essentially a restatement of Equation 11.1. Thus, lighter gases diffuse and effuse more rapidly than heavier gases.

SECTION 11.2 REVIEW

The Kinetic Molecular Theory of Gases

11.2.1   Methane (CH_4) diffuses 2.433 times as fast as a certain closely related gaseous compound. Determine the molar mass of the unknown gas and suggest what compound it might be.

11.2.2   Which gas effuses faster, He or Ar, and how much faster does it effuse?

Student Annotation: Common pencil-type pressure gauges actually measure the difference between internal and external pressure. Thus, if the tire is completely flat, the reading of 0 psi means that the pressure *inside* the tire is the same as that *outside* the tire.

Pencil-type tire gauge

11.3   GAS PRESSURE

According to kinetic molecular theory, gas molecules in a sample are in constant motion, colliding with one another and with the walls of their container. The collisions of gas molecules with the walls of a container constitute the *pressure* exerted by a sample of gas. For example, the air in the tires of your car exerts pressure by virtue of the molecules in the air colliding with the inside walls of the tires. In fact, gases exert pressure on everything they touch. Thus, while you may add enough air to increase the pressure inside your tire to 32 pounds per square inch (psi), there is also a pressure of approximately 14.7 psi, called *atmospheric pressure,* acting on the outside of the tire—and on everything else, including your body. The reason you don't feel the pressure of the atmosphere pushing on the outside of your body is that an equal pressure exists inside your body so that there is no net pressure on you.

Atmospheric pressure, the pressure exerted by Earth's atmosphere, can be demonstrated using the empty metal container shown in Figure 11.7(a). Because the container is open to the atmosphere, atmospheric pressure acts on both the internal and external walls of the container. When we attach a vacuum pump to the opening of the container and draw air out of it, however, we reduce the pressure inside the container. When the pressure against the interior walls is reduced, atmospheric pressure crushes the container [Figure 11.7(b)].

Definition and Units of Pressure

Pressure is defined as the force applied per unit area:

$$\text{pressure} = \frac{\text{force}}{\text{area}}$$

The SI unit of force is the ***newton (N),*** where

$$1\ \text{N} = 1\ \text{kg} \cdot \text{m/s}^2$$

The SI unit of pressure is the ***pascal (Pa),*** defined as 1 newton per square meter.

$$1\ \text{Pa} = 1\ \text{N/m}^2$$

Although the pascal is the SI unit of pressure, there are other units of pressure that are more commonly used. Table 11.2 lists the units in which pressure is most commonly expressed in chemistry and their definitions in terms of pascals. Which of these units you encounter most often will depend on your specific field of study. Use of *atmospheres* (atm) is common in chemistry, although use of the *bar* is becoming increasingly common. Use of *millimeters mercury* (mmHg) is common in medicine and meteorology. We will use all of these units in this text.

(a)

(b)

Figure 11.7 (a) An empty metal can. (b) When the air is removed by a vacuum pump, atmospheric pressure crushes the can.

Calculation of Pressure

The force experienced by an area exposed to Earth's atmosphere is equal to the weight of the column of air above it. For example, the mass of air above a spot on the ground near sea level, with an area of 1 cm^2, is approximately 1 kg (Figure 11.8).

The weight of an object that is subject to Earth's gravitational pull is equal to its mass times the gravitational constant, 9.80665 m/s^2. Thus, the force exerted by this column of air is

$$1\ \text{kg} \times \frac{9.80665\ \text{m}}{\text{s}^2} \approx 10\ \text{kg} \cdot \text{m/s}^2 = 10\ \text{N}$$

Pressure, though, is force per unit area. Specifically, pressure in *pascals* is equal to force in *newtons* per *square meter.* We must first convert area from cm^2 to m^2,

$$1\ \text{cm}^2 \times \left(\frac{1\ \text{m}}{100\ \text{cm}}\right)^2 = 0.0001\ \text{m}^2$$

and then divide force by area,

$$\frac{10\ \text{N}}{0.0001\ \text{m}^2} = 1 \times 10^5\ \text{Pa}$$

This pressure is roughly equal to 1 atm (~1×10^5 Pa), which we would expect at sea level.

Student Annotation: Remember that when a unit is raised to a power, any conversion factor you use must also be raised to that power [◄◄ Section 1.6].

TABLE 11.2	Units of Pressure Commonly Used in Chemistry	
Unit	**Origin**	**Definition**
standard atmosphere (atm)	Pressure at sea level	1 atm = 101,325 Pa
mmHg	Barometer measurement	1 mmHg = 133.322 Pa
torr	Name given to mmHg in honor of Torricelli, the inventor of the barometer	1 torr = 133.322 Pa
bar	Same order of magnitude as atm, but a decimal multiple of Pa	1 bar = 1×10^5 Pa

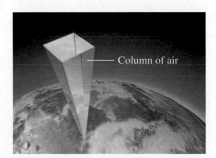

Column of air

Figure 11.8 A column of air 1 cm × 1 cm from Earth's surface to the top of the atmosphere weighs approximately 1 kg.

We can calculate the pressure exerted by a column of any fluid (gas or liquid) in the same way. In fact, this is how atmospheric pressure is commonly measured—by determining the height of a column of mercury it can support.

Measurement of Pressure

A simple *barometer,* an instrument used to measure atmospheric pressure, consists of a long glass tube, closed at one end and filled with mercury. The tube is carefully inverted in a container of mercury so that no air enters the tube. When the tube is inverted, and the open end is submerged in the mercury in the container, some of the mercury in the tube will flow out into the container, creating an empty space at the top (closed end) of the tube (Figure 11.9). The weight of the mercury remaining in the tube is supported by atmospheric pressure pushing down on the surface of the mercury in the container. In other words, the pressure exerted by the column of mercury is *equal* to the pressure exerted by the atmosphere. **Standard atmospheric pressure** (1 atm) was originally defined as the pressure that would support a column of mercury exactly 760 mm high at 0°C at sea level. The mmHg unit is also called the torr, after the Italian scientist Evangelista Torricelli,[3] who invented the barometer. Standard atmospheric pressure is given in all the common units of pressure in the margin.

A *manometer* is a device used to measure pressures other than atmospheric pressure. The principle of operation of a manometer is similar to that of a barometer. There are two types of manometers, both of which are shown in Figure 11.10. The closed-tube manometer [Figure 11.10(a)] is normally used to measure pressures below atmospheric pressure, whereas the open-tube manometer [Figure 11.10(b)] is generally used to measure pressures equal to or greater than atmospheric pressure.

The pressure exerted by a column of fluid, such as that in a barometer (Figure 11.9), is given by Equation 11.3.

Equation 11.3	$P = hdg$

Student Annotation:

1 atm*
101,325 Pa
760 mmHg*
760 torr*
1.01325 bar
14.7 psi
*These are exact numbers.

Figure 11.9 Barometer.

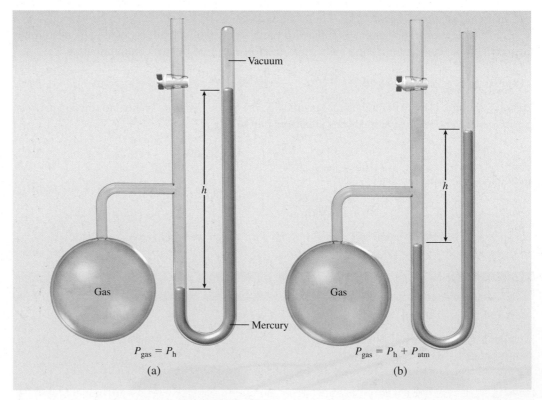

$$P_{gas} = P_h$$

(a)

$$P_{gas} = P_h + P_{atm}$$

(b)

Figure 11.10 (a) Closed-tube manometer. The space labeled "vacuum" actually contains a small amount of mercury vapor. (b) Open-tube manometer.

---

[3]Evangelista Torricelli (1608–1674) was supposedly the first person to recognize the existence of atmospheric pressure.

Where h is the height of the column in meters, d is the density of the fluid in kg/m^3, and g is the gravitational constant equal to 9.80665 m/s^2. This equation explains why barometers historically have been constructed using mercury. The height of a column of fluid supported by a given pressure is inversely proportional to the density of the fluid. (At a given P, as d goes up, h must go down—and vice versa.) Mercury's high density made it possible to construct barometers and manometers of manageable size. For example, a barometer filled with mercury that stands 1 m tall would have to be over 13 m tall if it were filled with water.

Worked Example 11.2 shows how to calculate the pressure exerted by a column of fluid.

Worked Example 11.2

Calculate the pressure exerted by a column of mercury 70.0 cm high. Express the pressure in pascals, in atmospheres, and in bars. The density of mercury is 13.5951 g/cm^3.

Strategy Use Equation 11.3 to calculate pressure. Remember that the height must be expressed in meters and density must be expressed in kg/m^3.

Setup

$$h = 70.0 \text{ cm} \times \frac{1 \text{ m}}{100 \text{ cm}} = 0.700 \text{ m}$$

$$d = \frac{13.5951 \text{ g}}{\text{cm}^3} \times \frac{1 \text{ kg}}{1000 \text{ g}} \times \left(\frac{100 \text{ cm}}{1 \text{ m}}\right)^3 = 1.35951 \times 10^4 \text{ kg/m}^3$$

$$g = 9.80665 \text{ m/s}^2$$

Solution

$$\text{pressure} = 0.700 \text{ m} \times \frac{1.35951 \times 10^4 \text{ kg}}{\text{m}^3} \times \frac{9.80665 \text{ m}}{\text{s}^2} = 9.33 \times 10^4 \text{ kg/m} \cdot \text{s}^2 = 9.33 \times 10^4 \text{ Pa}$$

$$9.33 \times 10^4 \text{ Pa} \times \frac{1 \text{ atm}}{101{,}325 \text{ Pa}} = 0.921 \text{ atm}$$

$$0.921 \text{ atm} \times \frac{1.01325 \text{ bar}}{1 \text{ atm}} = 0.933 \text{ bar}$$

Think About It
Make sure your units cancel properly in this type of problem. Common errors include forgetting to express height in meters and density in kg/m^3. You can avoid these errors by becoming familiar with the value of atmospheric pressure in the various units. A column of mercury slightly less than 760 mm is equivalent to slightly less than 101,325 Pa, slightly less than 1 atm, and slightly less than 1 bar.

Practice Problem A What pressure (in atm) is exerted by a column of mercury exactly 1 m high?

Practice Problem B What would be the height of a column of water supported by the pressure you calculated in Worked Example 11.2? Assume that the density of the water is 1.00 g/cm^3.

SECTION 11.3 REVIEW

Gas Pressure

11.3.1 Express a pressure of 1.15 atm in units of bar.

11.3.2 Express 1748 torr in units of atm.

11.3.3 Calculate the height of a column of ethanol that would be supported by atmospheric pressure (1 atm). The density of ethanol is 0.789 g/cm^3.

11.3.4 What pressure (in atm) is exerted by a column of water 50.0 m high? Assume the density of the water is 1.00 g/cm^3.

11.3.5 Rank the pressures exerted by the columns of water shown in the margin from lowest to highest.

(i) (ii) (iii)

Multi 11.2
Gas laws—interactive gas laws
(interactive)

11.4 THE GAS LAWS

In contrast to the condensed phases, all gases, even those with vastly different chemical compositions, exhibit remarkably similar physical behavior. Numerous experiments carried out in the seventeenth and eighteenth centuries showed that the physical state of a sample of gas can be described completely with just four parameters: temperature (T), pressure (P), volume (V), and number of moles (n). Knowing any three of these parameters enables us to calculate the fourth. The relationships between these parameters are known as the ***gas laws***.

Boyle's Law: The Pressure-Volume Relationship

Imagine that you have a plastic syringe filled with air. If you hold your finger tightly against the tip of the syringe and push the plunger with your other hand, decreasing the volume of the air, you will increase the pressure in the syringe. During the seventeenth century, Robert Boyle[4] conducted systematic studies of the relationship between gas volume and pressure using a simple apparatus like the one shown in Figure 11.11. The J-shaped tube contains a sample of gas confined by a column of mercury. The apparatus functions as an open-end manometer. When the mercury levels on both sides are equal [Figure 11.11(a)], the pressure of the confined gas is equal to atmospheric pressure. When more mercury is added through the open end, the pressure of the confined gas is increased by an amount proportional to the height of the added mercury—and the volume of the gas decreases. If, for example, as shown in Figure 11.11(b), we *double* the pressure on the confined gas by adding enough mercury to make the difference in mercury levels on the left and right 760 mm (the height of a mercury column that exerts a pressure equal to 1 atm), the volume

Figure 11.11 Demonstration of Boyle's law. The volume of a sample of gas is inversely proportional to its pressure. (a) $P = 760$ mmHg, $V = 100$ mL. (b) $P = 1520$ mmHg, $V = 50$ mL. (c) $P = 2280$ mmHg, $V = 33$ mL. Note that the total pressure exerted on the gas is the sum of atmospheric pressure (760 mmHg) and the difference in height of the mercury.

---

[4]Robert Boyle (1627–1691), British chemist and natural philosopher, is best known for the gas law that bears his name. He also made many other significant contributions to the fields of chemistry and physics.

TABLE 11.3	Typical Data from Experiments with the Apparatus of Figure 11.11								
P (mmHg)	760	855	950	1045	1140	1235	1330	1425	1520	2280
V (mL)	100	89	78	72	66	59	55	54	50	33
	Shown in Figure 11.11(a)								Shown in Figure 11.11(b)	Shown in Figure 11.11(c)

of the gas is reduced by *half*. If we triple the original pressure on the confined gas by adding more mercury, the volume of the gas is reduced to one-third of its original volume [Figure 11.11(c)].

Table 11.3 gives a set of data typical of Boyle's experiments. Figure 11.12(a) and (b) shows some of the volume data plotted as a function of pressure and as a function of the inverse of pressure, respectively. These data illustrate **Boyle's law,** which states that the pressure of a fixed amount of gas at a constant temperature is inversely proportional to the volume of the gas. This inverse relationship between pressure and volume can be expressed mathematically as follows:

$$V \propto \frac{1}{P}$$

or

Student Annotation: Remember that the symbol $\propto$ means "is proportional to."

$$V \propto k_1 \frac{1}{P} \text{ (at constant temperature)} \qquad \textbf{Equation 11.4(a)}$$

where k_1 is a *proportionality constant*. We can rearrange Equation 11.4(a) to get

$$PV = k_1 \text{ (at constant temperature)} \qquad \textbf{Equation 11.4(b)}$$

According to this form of Boyle's law, the *product* of the pressure and the volume of a given sample of gas (at constant temperature) is a *constant*.

Although the individual values of pressure and volume can vary greatly for a given sample of gas, the product of P and V is always equal to the same constant as long as the temperature is held constant and the amount of gas does not change. Therefore, for a given sample of gas under two different sets of conditions at constant temperature, we can write

$$P_1 V_1 = k_1 = P_2 V_2$$

$$P_1 V_1 = P_2 V_2 \text{ (at constant temperature)} \qquad \textbf{Equation 11.5}$$

where V_1 is the volume at pressure P_1 and V_2 is the volume at pressure P_2.

(a)

(b)

Figure 11.12 Plots of volume (a) as a function of pressure and (b) as a function of 1/pressure.

Worked Example 11.3 illustrates the use of Boyle's law.

Worked Example 11.3

If a skin diver takes a breath at the surface, filling his lungs with 5.82 L of air, what volume will the air in his lungs occupy when he dives to a depth where the pressure is 1.92 atm? (Assume constant temperature and that the pressure at the surface is exactly 1 atm.)

Strategy Use Equation 11.5 to solve for V_2.

Setup $P_1 = 1.00$ atm, $V_1 = 5.82$ L, and $P_2 = 1.92$ atm.

Solution

$$V_2 = \frac{P_1 \times V_1}{P_2} = \frac{1.00 \text{ atm} \times 5.82 \text{ L}}{1.92 \text{ atm}} = 3.03 \text{ L}$$

Think About It
At higher pressure, the volume should be smaller. Therefore, the answer makes sense.

Practice Problem A Calculate the volume of a sample of gas at 5.75 atm if it occupies 5.14 L at 2.49 atm. (Assume constant temperature.)

Practice Problem B At what pressure would a sample of gas occupy 7.86 L if it occupies 3.44 L at 4.11 atm? (Assume constant temperature.)

Multi 11.3
Gas laws—Charles's law

Charles's and Gay-Lussac's Law: The Temperature-Volume Relationship

If you took a helium-filled Mylar balloon outdoors on a cold day, the balloon would shrink somewhat when it came into contact with the cold air. This would occur because the volume of a sample of gas depends on the temperature. A more dramatic illustration is shown in Figure 11.13, where liquid nitrogen is being poured over a balloon. The large drop in temperature of the air in the balloon (the boiling liquid nitrogen has a temperature of −196°C) results in a significant decrease in its volume, causing the balloon to shrink.

Figure 11.13 (a) Air-filled balloon. (b) Lowering the temperature with liquid nitrogen causes a volume decrease. The pressure inside the balloon, which is roughly equal to the external pressure, remains constant in this process.

(a)   (b)

(a)

(b)

Figure 11.14 (a) Plot of the volume of a sample of gas as a function of temperature. (b) Plot of the volume of a sample of gas as a function of temperature at three different pressures.

The first to study the relationship between gas volume and temperature were French scientists Jacques Charles[5] and Joseph Gay-Lussac.[6] Their studies showed that, at constant pressure, the volume of a gas sample increases when heated and decreases when cooled. Figure 11.14(a) shows a plot of data typical of Charles's and Gay-Lussac's experiments. Note that with pressure held constant, the volume of a sample of gas plotted as a function of temperature yields a straight line. These experiments were carried out at several different pressures [Figure 11.14(b)], each yielding a different straight line. Interestingly, if the lines are extrapolated to zero volume, they all meet at the x axis at the temperature −273.15°C. The implication is that a gas sample occupies zero volume at −273.15°C. This is not observed in practice, however, because all gases condense to form liquids or solids before −273.15°C is reached.

In 1848, Lord Kelvin[7] realized the significance of the extrapolated lines all meeting at −273.15°C. He identified −273.15°C as ***absolute zero,*** theoretically the lowest attainable temperature. Then he set up an ***absolute temperature scale,*** now called the ***Kelvin temperature scale,*** with absolute zero as the lowest point [◄◄ Section 1.4]. On the Kelvin scale, 1 kelvin (K) is equal in magnitude to 1 degree Celsius. The difference is simply an offset of 273.15. We obtain the absolute temperature by adding 273.15 to the temperature expressed in Celsius, although we often use simply 273 instead of 273.15. Several important points on the two scales match up as follows:

Student Annotation: Remember that a kelvin and a degree Celsius have the same magnitude. Thus, while we add 273.15 to the temperature in °C to get the temperature in K, a *change* in temperature in Celsius is *equal* to the change in temperature in K. A temperature of 20°C is the same as 293.15 K. A *change* in temperature of 20°C, however, is the same as a *change* in temperature of 20 K.

	Kelvin scale (K)	Celsius scale (°C)
Absolute zero	0 K	−273.15°C
Freezing point of water	273.15 K	0°C
Boiling point of water	373.15 K	100°C

The dependence of the volume of a sample of gas on temperature is given by

$$V = k_2 T \text{ (at constant pressure)} \qquad \textbf{Equation 11.6(a)}$$

$$V \propto T$$

or

$$\frac{V}{T} = k_2 \text{ (at constant pressure)} \qquad \textbf{Equation 11.6(b)}$$

Student Annotation: Don't forget that volume is proportional to absolute temperature. The volume of a sample of gas at constant pressure doubles if the temperature increases from 100 K to 200 K—but *not* if the temperature increases from 100°C to 200°C!

where k_2 is the proportionality constant. Equations 11.6(a) and (b) are expressions of ***Charles's and Gay-Lussac's law,*** often referred to simply as ***Charles's law,*** which states that the volume

[5]Jacques Alexandre Cesar Charles (1746–1823) was a gifted lecturer, an inventor of scientific apparatus, and the first person to use hydrogen to inflate balloons.

[6]Joseph Louis Gay-Lussac (1778–1850), French chemist and physicist, like Charles, was a balloon enthusiast. Once he ascended to an altitude of 20,000 ft to collect air samples for analysis.

[7]William Thomson, Lord Kelvin (1824–1907), was a Scottish mathematician and physicist. Kelvin did important work in many branches of physics.

of a fixed amount of gas maintained at constant pressure is directly proportional to the absolute temperature of the gas.

Just as we did with the pressure-volume relationship at constant temperature, we can compare two sets of volume-temperature conditions for a given sample of gas at constant pressure. From Equation 11.6, we can write

$$\frac{V_1}{T_1} = k_2 = \frac{V_2}{T_2}$$

or

Equation 11.7 $\dfrac{V_1}{T_1} = \dfrac{V_2}{T_2}$ (at constant pressure)

where V_1 is the volume of the gas at T_1 and V_2 is the volume of the gas at T_2.

Worked Example 11.4 shows how to use Charles's law.

Worked Example 11.4

A sample of argon gas that originally occupied 14.6 L at 25.0°C was heated to 50.0°C at constant pressure. What is its new volume?

Strategy Use Equation 11.7 to solve for V_2. Remember that temperatures must be expressed in kelvin.

Setup T_1 = 298.15 K, V_1 = 14.6 L, and T_2 = 323.15 K.

Solution

$$V_2 = \frac{V_1 \times T_2}{T_1} = \frac{14.6\ \text{L} \times 323.15\ \text{K}}{298.15\ \text{K}} = 15.8\ \text{L}$$

Think About It
When temperature increases at constant pressure, the volume of a gas sample increases.

Practice Problem A A sample of gas originally occupies 29.1 L at 0.0°C. What is its new volume when it is heated to 15.0°C? (Assume constant pressure.)

Practice Problem B At what temperature (in °C) will a sample of gas occupy 82.3 L if it occupies 50.0 L at 75.0°C? (Assume constant pressure.)

Avogadro's Law: The Amount-Volume Relationship

In 1811, the Italian scientist Amedeo Avogadro proposed that equal volumes of different gases contain the same number of particles (molecules or atoms) at the same temperature and pressure. This hypothesis gave rise to *Avogadro's law,* which states that the volume of a sample of gas is directly proportional to the number of moles in the sample at constant temperature and pressure:

$$V \propto n$$

or

Equation 11.8(a) $V = k_3 n$ (at constant temperature and pressure)

Rearranging 11.8(a) gives

Equation 11.8(b) $\dfrac{V}{n} = k_3$

Equations 11.8(a) and (b) are expressions of Avogadro's law.

As with other gas laws, we can compare two sets of conditions using Avogadro's law when n and V both change at constant pressure and temperature and write

$$\frac{V_1}{n_1} = k_3 = \frac{V_2}{n_2}$$

or

$$\frac{V_1}{n_1} = \frac{V_2}{n_2}$$

Equation 11.9

where V_1 is the volume of a sample of gas consisting of n_1 moles and V_2 is the volume of a sample consisting of n_2 moles—under conditions of constant temperature and pressure. Coupled with a balanced chemical equation, Avogadro's law enables us to predict the volumes of gaseous reactants and products. Consider the reaction of H_2 and N_2 to form NH_3:

$$3H_2(g) + N_2(g) \longrightarrow 2NH_3(g)$$

The balanced equation reveals the ratio of combination of reactants in terms of *moles* [◄◄ Section 8.3]. However, because the volume of a gas (at a given temperature and pressure) is directly *proportional* to the number of moles, the balanced equation also reveals the ratio of combination in terms of *volume*. Thus, if we were to combine three volumes (liters, milliliters, etc.) of hydrogen gas with one volume of nitrogen gas, assuming they react completely according to the balanced equation, we would expect two volumes of ammonia gas to be produced (Figure 11.15). The ratio of combination of H_2 and N_2 (and production of NH_3), whether expressed in moles or units of volume, is 3:1:2.

Worked Example 11.5 shows how to apply Avogadro's law.

Worked Example 11.5

If we combine 3.0 L of NO and 1.5 L of O_2, and they react according to the balanced equation $2NO(g) + O_2(g) \longrightarrow 2NO_2(g)$, what volume of NO_2 will be produced? (Assume that the reactants and product are all at the same temperature and pressure.)

Strategy Apply Avogadro's law to determine the volume of a gaseous product.

Setup Because volume is proportional to the number of moles, the balanced equation determines in what volume ratio the reactants combine and the ratio of product volume to reactant volume. The amounts of reactants given are stoichiometric amounts [◄◄ Section 8.3].

Solution According to the balanced equation, the volume of NO_2 formed will be equal to the volume of NO that reacts. Therefore, 3.0 L of NO_2 will form.

Think About It
Remember that the coefficients in balanced chemical equations indicate ratios in molecules or moles. Under conditions of constant temperature and pressure, the volume of a gas is proportional to the number of moles. Therefore, the coefficients in balanced equations containing only gases also indicate ratios in liters, provided the reactions occur at constant temperature and pressure.

Practice Problem A What volume (in liters) of water vapor will be produced when 34 L of H_2 and 17 L of O_2 react according to the equation $2H_2(g) + O_2(g) \longrightarrow 2H_2O(g)$?

Practice Problem B What volumes (in liters) of carbon monoxide and oxygen gas must react according to the equation $2CO(g) + O_2(g) \longrightarrow 2CO_2(g)$ to form 3.16 L of carbon dioxide?

Student Annotation: It is important to recognize that coefficients indicate ratios in liters only in balanced equations in which all of the reactants and products are gases. We cannot apply the same approach to reactions in which there are solid, liquid, or aqueous species.

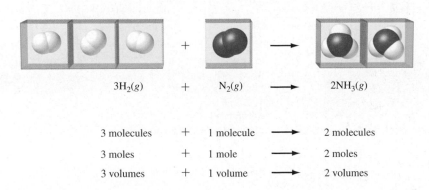

$3H_2(g)$	+	$N_2(g)$	$\longrightarrow$	$2NH_3(g)$
3 molecules	+	1 molecule	$\longrightarrow$	2 molecules
3 moles	+	1 mole	$\longrightarrow$	2 moles
3 volumes	+	1 volume	$\longrightarrow$	2 volumes

Figure 11.15 Illustration of Avogadro's law. The volume of a sample of gas is directly proportional to the number of moles.

The Gas Laws and Kinetic Molecular Theory

Each of the empirical gas laws describes a facet of the behavior of macroscopic samples of gas; and each can be explained and understood at the *molecular* level using the kinetic molecular theory of gases.

Boyle's law: The pressure exerted by a gas is the result of the collisions of gas molecules with the walls of their container (assumption 2). The magnitude of the pressure depends on both the frequency of collision and the speed of molecules when they collide with the walls. Decreasing the volume occupied by a sample of gas increases the frequency of these collisions, thus increasing the pressure (Figure 11.3).

Charles's law: Heating a sample of gas increases its average kinetic energy (assumption 4). Because the masses of the molecules do not change, an increase in average kinetic energy must be accompanied by an increase in the mean square speed of the molecules. In other words, heating a sample of gas makes the gas molecules move faster. Faster-moving molecules collide more frequently and with greater speed at impact, thus increasing the pressure. If the container can expand (as is the case with a balloon or a cylinder with a movable piston), the volume of the gas sample will increase, thereby decreasing the frequency of collisions until the pressure inside the container and the pressure outside are again equal (Figure 11.16).

Figure 11.16 Charles's law. (a) The volume of a sample of gas at constant pressure is proportional to its absolute temperature. (b) The pressure of a sample of gas at constant volume is proportional to its absolute temperature.

Heating or cooling a gas at constant pressure

Lower temperature (Volume decreases) Higher temperature (Volume increases)

At constant P, $V \propto T$.

(a)

Charles's La

Heating or cooling a gas at constant volume

Lower temperature (Pressure decreases) Higher temperature (Pressure increases)

At constant V, $P \propto T$.

(b)

Dependence of volume on amount
of gas at constant temperature and pressure

Gas
cylinder

P

Remove gas
(Volume decreases)

Valve

P

Add
gas molecules
(Volume increases)

P

At constant P and T, $V \propto n$.

Figure 11.17 Avogadro's law. The volume of a gas at constant temperature and pressure is proportional to the number of moles.

Avogadro's law: Because the magnitude of the pressure exerted by a sample of gas depends on the frequency of the collisions with the container wall, the presence of more molecules would cause an increase in pressure. Again, the container will expand if it can. Expansion of the container will decrease the frequency of collisions until the pressures inside and outside the container are once again equal (Figure 11.17).

As we will see, the kinetic molecular theory can also be used to explain the behavior of gas *mixtures* [▶▶ Section 11.7].

The Combined Gas Law: The Pressure-Temperature-Amount-Volume Relationship

Although the gas laws we have discussed so far are useful, each requires that two of the system's parameters be held constant.

Problem type	Relates	Requires constant
Boyle's law	P and V	n and T
Charles's law	T and V	n and P
Avogadro's law	n and V	P and T

Many of the problems we will encounter involve changes to *P, T, and V,* and, in some cases, also to *n.* To solve such problems, we need a gas law that relates all the variables. By combining Equations 11.5, 11.7, and 11.9, we obtain the **combined gas law:**

$$\frac{P_1 V_1}{n_1 T_1} = \frac{P_2 V_2}{n_2 T_2}$$

Equation 11.10(a)

The combined gas law can be used to solve problems where any or all of the variables change. Note that when a problem involves a fixed quantity of gas, Equation 11.10(a) reduces to the more common form of the combined gas law:

$$\frac{P_1 V_1}{T_1} = \frac{P_2 V_2}{T_2}$$

Equation 11.10(b)

Worked Example 11.6 illustrates the use of the combined gas law.

Worked Example 11.6

If a child releases a 6.25-L helium balloon in the parking lot of an amusement park where the temperature is 28.50°C and the air pressure is 757.2 mmHg, what will the volume of the balloon be when it has risen to an altitude where the temperature is −34.35°C and the air pressure is 366.4 mmHg?

Strategy In this case, because there is a fixed amount of gas, we use Equation 11.10(b). The only value we don't know is V_2. Temperatures must be expressed in kelvins. We can use any units of pressure, as long as we are consistent.

Setup $T_1 = 301.65$ K, $T_2 = 238.80$ K. Solving Equation 11.10(b) for V_2 gives

$$V_2 = \frac{P_1 T_2 V_1}{P_2 T_1}$$

Solution

$$V_2 = \frac{757.2 \text{ mmHg} \times 238.80 \text{ K} \times 6.25 \text{ L}}{366.4 \text{ mmHg} \times 301.65 \text{ K}} = 10.2 \text{ L}$$

Think About It

Note that the solution is essentially multiplying the original volume by the ratio of P_1 to P_2, and by the ratio of T_2 to T_1. The effect of decreasing external pressure is to increase the balloon volume. The effect of decreasing *temperature* is to *decrease* the volume. In this case, the effect of decreasing pressure predominates and the balloon volume increases significantly.

Practice Problem A What would be the volume of the balloon in Worked Example 11.6 if, instead of being released to rise in the atmosphere, it were submerged in a swimming pool to a depth where the pressure is 922.3 mmHg and the temperature is 26.35°C?

Practice Problem B The volume of a bubble that starts at the bottom of a lake at 4.55°C increases by a factor of 10 as it rises to the surface where the temperature is 18.45°C and the air pressure is 0.965 atm. Assuming that the density of the lake water is 1.00 g/cm³, determine the depth of the lake. (*Hint:* You will need to use Equation 11.3.)

SECTION 11.4 REVIEW

The Gas Laws

11.4.1   Given $P_1 = 1.50$ atm, $V_1 = 37.3$ mL, and $P_2 = 1.18$ atm, calculate V_2. Assume that n and T are constant.

11.4.2   Given $T_1 = 21.5$°C, $V_1 = 25.0$ mL, and $T_2 = 316$°C, calculate V_2. Assume that n and P are constant.

11.4.3   At what temperature will a gas sample occupy 100.0 L if it originally occupies 76.1 L at 89.5°C? Assume constant P.

11.4.4   What volume of NH_3 will be produced when 180 mL of H_2 reacts with 60.0 mL of N_2 according to the following equation:

$$3H_2(g) + N_2(g) \longrightarrow 2NH_3(g)$$

Assume constant T and P for reactants and products.

11.4.5   Which diagram could represent the result of increasing the temperature and decreasing the external pressure on a fixed amount of gas in a balloon?

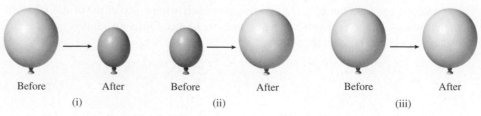

Before	After	Before	After	Before	After
(i)		(ii)		(iii)	

11.4.6   Which diagram in Question 11.4.5 could represent the result of decreasing both the temperature and the pressure?

11.5 THE IDEAL GAS EQUATION

Multi 11.4
Gas laws—ideal gas law (interactive)

Recall that the state of a sample of gas is described completely using the four variables *T*, *P*, *V*, and *n*. Each of the gas laws introduced in Section 11.4 relates one variable of a sample of gas to another while the *other* two variables are held constant. In experiments with gases, however, there are usually changes in more than just two of the variables. Therefore, it is useful for us to combine the equations representing the gas laws into a single equation that will enable us to account for changes in any or all of the four variables.

Summarizing the gas law equations from Section 11.4:

$$\text{Boyle's law: } V \propto \frac{1}{P}$$

$$\text{Charles's law: } V \propto T$$

$$\text{Avogadro's law: } V \propto n$$

We can combine these equations into the following general equation that describes the physical behavior of all gases:

$$V \propto \frac{nT}{P}$$

or

$$V = R\frac{nT}{P}$$

where *R* is the proportionality constant. This equation can be rearranged to give:

$PV = nRT$	**Equation 11.11**

Equation 11.11 is the most commonly used form of the **ideal gas equation,** which describes the relationship among the four variables *P*, *V*, *n*, and *T*. An **ideal gas** is a hypothetical sample of gas whose pressure-volume-temperature behavior is predicted accurately by the ideal gas equation. Although the behavior of *real* gases generally differs slightly from that predicted by Equation 11.11, in most of the cases we will encounter, the differences are usually small enough for us to use the ideal gas equation to make reasonably good predictions about the behavior of gases.

The proportionality constant, *R*, in Equation 11.11 is the gas constant [◄◄ Section 11.2]. The value and units of *R* depend on the units in which *P* and *V* are expressed. (The variables *n* and *T* are always expressed in mol and K, respectively.) Recall from Section 11.3 that pressure is commonly expressed in atmospheres, mmHg (torr), pascals, or bar. Volume is typically expressed in liters or milliliters, but can also be expressed in other units, such as m³. Table 11.4 lists several different expressions of the gas constant, *R*.

Keep in mind that despite having different numerical values, all these expressions of *R* are *equal* to one another; just as 1 yard, 3 feet, and 36 inches are all equal to one another. They are simply expressed in different units.

One of the simplest uses of the ideal gas equation is the calculation of one of the variables when the other three are already known. For example, we can calculate the volume of 1 mole of an ideal gas at 0°C and 1 atm, conditions known as **standard temperature and pressure (STP).** In

Student Annotation: We will discuss the conditions that result in deviation from ideal behavior in Section 11.6.

Student Annotation: When you use *R* in a calculation, use the version that facilitates proper cancellation of units.

Student Annotation: In thermochemistry, we often used 25°C as the "standard" temperature—although temperature is *not* actually part of the definition of the *standard state* [◄◄ Section 10.6]. The standard temperature for gases is defined specifically as 0°C.

TABLE 11.4	Various Equivalent Expressions of the Gas Constant, *R*
Numerical value	**Unit**
0.08206	L · atm/K · mol
62.36	L · torr/K · mol
0.08314	L · bar/K · mol
8.314	m³ · Pa/K · mol
8.314	J/K · mol
1.987	cal/K · mol

Note that the product of volume and pressure gives units of *energy* (i.e., joules and calories).

this case, n, T, and P are given. R is a constant, leaving V as the only unknown. We can rearrange Equation 11.11 to solve for V,

$$V = \frac{nRT}{P}$$

enter the information that is given, and calculate V. Remember that in calculations using the ideal gas equation, temperature must *always* be expressed in kelvins.

Student Annotation: In this problem, because they are specified rather than measured, 0°C, 1 mole, and 1 atm are *exact* numbers and do not affect the number of significant figures in the result [◄◄ Section 1.5].

$$V = \frac{(1 \text{ mol})(0.08206 \text{ L} \cdot \text{atm/K} \cdot \text{mol})(273.15 \text{ K})}{1 \text{ atm}} = 22.41 \text{ L}$$

Thus, the volume occupied by 1 mole of an ideal gas at STP is 22.41 L, a volume slightly less than 6 gal.

Worked Example 11.7 shows how to calculate the molar volume of a gas at a temperature other than 0°C.

Worked Example 11.7

Calculate the volume of a mole of ideal gas at room temperature (25°C) and 1 atm.

Strategy Convert the temperature in °C to temperature in kelvins, and use the ideal gas equation to solve for the unknown volume.

Setup The data given are $n = 1$ mol, $T = 298.15$ K, and $P = 1.00$ atm. Because the pressure is expressed in atmospheres, we use $R = 0.08206$ L · atm/K · mol in order to solve for volume in liters.

Solution

$$V = \frac{(1 \text{ mol})(0.08206 \text{ L} \cdot \text{atm/K} \cdot \text{mol})(298.15 \text{ K})}{1 \text{ atm}} = 24.5 \text{ L}$$

Think About It
With the pressure held constant, we should expect the volume to increase with increased temperature. Room temperature is higher than the standard temperature for gases (0°C), so the molar volume at room temperature (25°C) *should* be higher than the molar volume at 0°C—and it is.

Practice Problem A What is the volume of 5.12 moles of an ideal gas at 32°C and 1.00 atm?

Practice Problem B At what temperature (in °C) would 1 mole of ideal gas occupy 50.0 L ($P = 1.00$ atm)?

Applications of the Ideal Gas Equation

Using some simple algebraic manipulation, we can solve for variables other than those that appear explicitly in the ideal gas equation. For example, if we know the molar mass of a gas (g/mol), we can determine its density at a given temperature and pressure. Recall from Section 11.1 that the density of a gas is generally expressed in units of g/L. We can rearrange the ideal gas equation to solve for mol/L:

$$\frac{n}{V} = \frac{P}{RT}$$

Student Annotation: $n \times \mathcal{M} = m$, where m is mass in grams.

If we then multiply both sides by the molar mass, $\mathcal{M}$, we get

$$\mathcal{M} \times \frac{n}{V} = \frac{P}{RT} \times \mathcal{M}$$

where $\mathcal{M} \times n/V$ gives g/L or density, d. Therefore,

Student Annotation: Another way to arrive at Equation 11.12 is to substitute $m/\mathcal{M}$ for n in the ideal gas equation and rearrange to solve for m/V (density):

$$PV = \frac{m}{\mathcal{M}}RT \quad \text{and} \quad \frac{m}{V} = d = \frac{P\mathcal{M}}{RT}$$

Equation 11.12
$$d = \frac{P\mathcal{M}}{RT}$$

Conversely, if we know the density of a gas, we can determine its molar mass:

Equation 11.13
$$\mathcal{M} = \frac{dRT}{P}$$

Figure 11.18 (a) Evacuated flask. (b) Flask filled with gas. The mass of the gas is the difference between the two masses. The density of the gas is determined by dividing mass by volume.

(a)   (b)

In a typical experiment, in which the molar mass of a gas is determined, a flask of known volume is evacuated and weighed [Figure 11.18(a)]. It is then filled (to a known pressure) with the gas of unknown molar mass and reweighed [Figure 11.18(b)]. The difference in mass is the mass of the gas sample. Dividing by the known volume of the flask gives the density of the gas, and the molar mass can then be determined using Equation 11.13.

Similarly, the molar mass of a volatile liquid can be determined by placing a small volume of it in the bottom of a flask, the mass and volume of which are known. The flask is then immersed in a hot-water bath, causing the volatile liquid to completely evaporate and its vapor to fill the flask. Because the flask is open, some of the excess vapor escapes. When no more vapor escapes, the flask is capped and removed from the water bath. The flask is then weighed to determine the mass of the vapor. (At this point, some or all of the vapor has condensed but the mass remains the same.) The density of the vapor is determined by dividing the mass of the vapor by the volume of the flask. Equation 11.13 is then used to calculate the molar mass of the volatile liquid.

Worked Examples 11.8 and 11.9 illustrate the use of Equations 11.12 and 11.13.

Student Annotation: Because the flask is open to the atmosphere while the volatile liquid vaporizes, we can use atmospheric pressure as P. Also, because the flask is capped at the water bath temperature, we can use the water bath temperature as T.

Worked Example 11.8

Carbon dioxide is effective in fire extinguishers partly because its density is greater than that of air, so CO_2 can smother the flames by depriving them of oxygen. (Air has a density of approximately 1.2 g/L at room temperature and 1 atm.) Calculate the density of CO_2 at room temperature (25°C) and 1.0 atm.

Strategy Use Equation 11.12 to solve for density. Because the pressure is expressed in atm, we should use $R = 0.08206$ L · atm/K · mol. Remember to express temperature in kelvins.

Setup The molar mass of CO_2 is 44.01 g/mol.

Solution

$$d = \frac{P\mathcal{M}}{RT} = \frac{(1 \text{ atm})\left(\dfrac{44.01 \text{ g}}{\text{mol}}\right)}{\left(\dfrac{0.08206 \text{ L} \cdot \text{atm}}{\text{K} \cdot \text{mol}}\right)(298.15 \text{ K})} = 1.8 \text{ g/L}$$

Think About It
The calculated density of CO_2 is greater than that of air under the same conditions (as expected). Although it may seem tedious, it is a good idea to write units for each and every entry in a problem such as this. Unit cancellation is very useful for detecting errors in your reasoning or your solution setup.

Practice Problem A Calculate the density of helium in a helium balloon at 25.0°C. (Assume that the pressure inside the balloon is 1.10 atm.)

Practice Problem B Calculate the density of air at 0°C and 1 atm. (Assume that air is 80 percent N_2 and 20 percent O_2.)

Worked Example 11.9

A company has just patented a new synthetic alcohol for alcoholic beverages. The new product is said to have all the pleasant properties associated with ethanol but none of the undesirable effects such as hangover, impairment of motor skills, and risk of addiction. The chemical formula is proprietary. You analyze a sample of the new product by placing a small volume of it in a round-bottomed flask with a volume of 511.0 mL and an evacuated mass of 131.918 g. You submerge the flask in a water bath at 100.0°C and allow the volatile liquid to vaporize. You then cap the flask and remove it from the water bath. You weigh it and determine the mass of the vapor in the flask to be 0.768 g. What is the molar mass of the volatile liquid, and what does it mean with regard to the new product? (Assume the pressure in the laboratory is 1 atm.)

Strategy Use the measured mass of the vapor and the given volume of the flask to determine the density of the vapor at 1 atm and 100.0°C, and then use Equation 11.13 to determine molar mass.

Setup $P = 1$ atm, $V = 0.5110$ L, $R = 0.08206$ L $\cdot$ atm/K $\cdot$ mol, and $T = 373.15$ K.

Solution

$$d = \frac{0.768 \text{ g}}{0.5110 \text{ L}} = 1.5029 \text{ g/L}$$

$$\mathcal{M} = \frac{\left(\dfrac{1.5029 \text{ g}}{\cancel{L}}\right)\left(\dfrac{0.08206\, \cancel{L} \cdot \text{atm}}{\cancel{K} \cdot \text{mol}}\right)(373.15\, \cancel{K})}{1 \, \cancel{\text{atm}}} = 46.02 \text{ g/mol}$$

The result is a molar mass suspiciously close to that of ethanol!

> **Think About It**
> Because more than one compound can have a particular molar mass, this method is not definitive for identification. However, in this circumstance, further testing of the proprietary formula certainly would be warranted.

Practice Problem A Determine the molar mass of a gas with a density of 1.905 g/L at 80.0°C and 1.00 atm.

Practice Problem B Determine the molar mass of a gas with a density of 5.14 g/L at 73.0°C and 1.00 atm.

SECTION 11.5 REVIEW

The Ideal Gas Equation

11.5.1   Calculate the volume occupied by 8.75 moles of an ideal gas at STP.

11.5.2   Calculate the pressure exerted by 11.2 moles of an ideal gas in a 7.5-L vessel at 150°C.

11.5.3   Determine the density of a gas with $\mathcal{M} = 146.07$ g/mol at 1.00 atm and 100.0°C.

11.5.4   Determine the molar mass of a gas with $d = 1.963$ g/L at 1.00 atm and 100.0°C.

11.6 REAL GASES

The gas laws and the kinetic molecular theory assume that molecules in the gas phase occupy negligible volume (assumption 1) and that they do not exert any force on one another, either attractive or repulsive (assumption 3). Gases that behave as though these assumptions were strictly true are said to exhibit *ideal behavior.* Many gases do exhibit ideal or nearly ideal behavior under ordinary conditions. Figure 11.19 shows the molar volumes of some common gases at STP. All are remarkably close to the ideal value of 22.41 L. Although we generally assume that real gases behave ideally, there are conditions, namely, high pressure and low temperature, under which the behavior of a real gas deviates from ideal.

Figure 11.19 Molar volumes of some common gases at STP.

Factors That Cause Deviation from Ideal Behavior

At high pressures, gas molecules are relatively close together. We can assume that gas molecules occupy no volume only when the distances between molecules are large. When the distances between molecules are reduced, the volume occupied by each individual molecule becomes more significant.

At low temperatures, gas molecules are moving more slowly. We can assume that there are no intermolecular forces between gas molecules, either attractive or repulsive, when the gas molecules are moving very fast and the magnitude of their kinetic energies is much larger than the magnitude of any intermolecular forces. When molecules move more slowly, they have lower kinetic energies and the magnitude of the forces between them becomes more significant.

The van der Waals Equation

Because there are conditions under which use of the ideal gas equation would result in large errors (i.e., high pressure and/or low temperature), we must use a slightly different approach when gases do not behave ideally. Analyses of real gases that took into account nonzero molecular volumes and intermolecular forces were first carried out by J. D. van der Waals[8] in 1873. Van der Waals's treatment provides us with an interpretation of the behavior of real gases at the molecular level.

Consider the approach of a particular molecule toward the wall of its container (Figure 11.20). The intermolecular attractions exerted by neighboring molecules prevent the molecule from hitting the wall as hard as it otherwise would. This results in the pressure exerted by a real gas being lower than that predicted by the ideal gas equation. Van der Waals suggested that the pressure exerted by an ideal gas, P_{ideal}, is related to the experimentally measured pressure, P_{real}, by the equation

$$P_{ideal} = P_{real} + \frac{an^2}{V^2}$$

where a is a constant and n and V are the number of moles and volume of the gas, respectively. The correction term for pressure (an^2/V^2) can be understood as follows. The intermolecular interaction that gives rise to nonideal behavior depends on how frequently any two molecules encounter each other. The number of such encounters increases with the square of the number of molecules per unit volume (n/V), and a is a proportionality constant. The quantity P_{ideal} is the pressure we would measure if there were no intermolecular attractions.

The other correction concerns the volume occupied by the gas molecules. In the ideal gas equation, V represents the volume of the container. However, each molecule actually occupies a very small but nonzero volume. We can correct for the volume occupied by the gas molecules by subtracting a term, nb, from the volume of the container:

$$V_{real} = V_{ideal} - nb$$

where n and b are the number of moles and the proportionality constant, respectively.

Incorporating both corrections into the ideal gas equation gives us the **van der Waals equation,** with which we can analyze gases under conditions where ideal behavior is not expected.

Figure 11.20 The effect of intermolecular attractions on the pressure exerted by a gas.

---

[8]Johannes Diderik van der Waals (1837–1923), a Dutch physicist, received the Nobel Prize in Physics in 1910 for his work on the properties of gases and liquids.

TABLE 11.5		Van der Waals Constants of Some Common Gases			
Gas	$a\left(\dfrac{atm \cdot L^2}{mol^2}\right)$	$b\left(\dfrac{L}{mol}\right)$	Gas	$a\left(\dfrac{atm \cdot L^2}{mol^2}\right)$	$b\left(\dfrac{L}{mol}\right)$
He	0.034	0.0237	O_2	1.36	0.0318
Ne	0.211	0.0171	Cl_2	6.49	0.0562
Ar	1.34	0.0322	CO_2	3.59	0.0427
Kr	2.32	0.0398	CH_4	2.25	0.0428
Xe	4.19	0.0510	CCl_4	20.4	0.138
H_2	0.244	0.0266	NH_3	4.17	0.0371
N_2	1.39	0.0391	H_2O	5.46	0.0305

experimentally measured pressure   container volume

Equation 11.14
$$\left(P + \frac{an^2}{V^2}\right)(V - nb) = nRT$$

corrected   corrected
pressure term   volume term

The van der Waals constants a and b for a number of gases are listed in Table 11.5. The magnitude of a indicates how strongly molecules of a particular type of gas attract one another. The magnitude of b is related to molecular (or atomic) size, although the relationship is not a simple one.

Worked Example 11.10 shows how to use the van der Waals equation.

Worked Example 11.10

A sample of 3.50 moles of NH_3 gas occupies 5.20 L at 47°C. Calculate the pressure of the gas (in atm) using (a) the ideal gas equation and (b) the van der Waals equation.

Strategy (a) Use the ideal gas equation, $PV = nRT$. (b) Use Equation 11.14 and a and b values for NH_3 from Table 11.5.

Setup $T = 320.15$ K, $a = 4.17$ atm $\cdot$ L/mol^2, and $b = 0.0371$ L/mol.

Solution (a) $P = \dfrac{nRT}{V} = \dfrac{(3.50 \text{ mol})\left(\dfrac{0.08206 \text{ L} \cdot \text{atm}}{\text{K} \cdot \text{mol}}\right)(320.15 \text{ K})}{5.20 \text{ L}} = 17.7$ atm

(b) Evaluating the correction terms in the van der Waals equation, we get

$$\frac{an^2}{V^2} = \frac{\left(\dfrac{4.17 \text{ atm} \cdot \text{L}^2}{\text{mol}^2}\right)(3.50 \text{ mol})^2}{(5.20 \text{ L})^2} = 1.89 \text{ atm} \qquad nb = (3.50 \text{ mol})\left(\frac{0.0371 \text{ L}}{\text{mol}}\right) = 0.130 \text{ L}$$

Finally, substituting these results into Equation 11.14, we have

$$(P + 1.89 \text{ atm})(5.20 \text{ L} - 0.130 \text{ L}) = (3.50 \text{ mol})\left(\frac{0.08206 \text{ L} \cdot \text{atm}}{\text{K} \cdot \text{mol}}\right)(320.15 \text{ K})$$
$$P = 16.2 \text{ atm}$$

Think About It
As is often the case, the pressure exerted by the real gas sample is lower than predicted by the ideal gas equation.

Practice Problem A Using data from Table 11.5, calculate the pressure exerted by 11.9 moles of neon gas in a volume of 5.75 L at 25°C using (a) the ideal gas equation and (b) the van der Waals equation (Equation 11.14). Compare your results.

Practice Problem B Calculate the pressure exerted by 0.35 mole of oxygen gas in a volume of 6.50 L at 32°C using (a) the ideal gas equation and (b) the van der Waals equation.

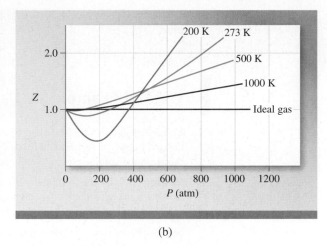

(a)   (b)

Figure 11.21 (a) Compressibility factor (*Z*) as a function of pressure for several gases at 0°C. (b) Compressibility factor as a function of pressure for N$_2$ gas at several different temperatures.

One way to measure a gas's deviation from ideal behavior is to determine its compressibility factor, *Z*, where $Z = PV/RT$. For one mole of an ideal gas, *Z* is equal to 1 at all pressures and temperatures. For real gases, the factors that contribute to nonideal behavior cause the value of *Z* to deviate from 1. Intermolecular forces help to account for the plots in Figure 11.21(a). Molecules exert both attraction and repulsion on one another. At large separations (low pressures), attraction predominates. In this region, the gas is more compressible than an ideal gas and the curve dips below the horizontal line ($Z < 1$). As molecules are brought closer together under pressure, repulsion begins to play an important role. If the pressure continues to increase, a point is reached when the gas becomes less compressible than an ideal gas because the molecules repel one another and the curve rises above the horizontal line ($Z > 1$). Figure 11.21(b) shows the plots of *Z* versus pressure at different temperatures. We see that as the temperature increases, the gas behaves more like an ideal gas (the curves become closer to the horizontal line). The increase in the molecules' kinetic energy makes molecular attraction less important.

van der Waals Constants

The constants used in the van der Waals equation allow us to correct for the nonideal behavior of real gases. For example, contrary to assumption 3 of the kinetic molecular theory of gases, there *are* attractive forces between the molecules in a sample of gas. Evidence of this includes the fact that when a gas is cooled and/or compressed, it condenses to a liquid. Even in the gas phase, the attractive forces between molecules can impact the observed behavior of a substance. As illustrated in Figure 11.20, a molecule that is attracted to other molecules in a sample of gas will not strike the wall of the container with as high velocity as it would if there were no such intermolecular attractions. The pressure term in the van der Waals equation, $P + a(n/V)^2$, is the experimentally determined pressure, *P*, plus a correction for the pressure that we do *not* observe because of attractive forces between the gas molecules. Note that the correction factor depends on the moles-per-unit-volume (*n/V*) squared. The value of the constant *a* is specific to a particular gas.

Also contrary to one of the assumptions of kinetic molecular theory (assumption 1), gas molecules do not actually have negligible volumes. When two gas molecules (assumed to be spherical) approach each other, the distance of closest approach is the sum of the radii (2*r*). The volume around each molecule into which the center of another molecule cannot penetrate is called the *excluded volume*. The effect of the excluded volume is to limit the fraction of the container volume actually available for molecules to move about in a gas sample. Thus, the volume term in the van der Waals equation, $V - nb$, is the container volume *V* minus the correction for the excluded volume, *nb*, where *n* is the number of moles of the gas and *b* is the excluded volume per mole of the gas.

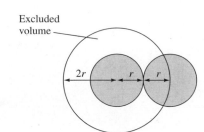

Worked Example 11.11 shows how to use the van der Waals equation to calculate excluded volume.

Worked Example 11.11

Consider a gas sample consisting of molecules with radius r. (a) Determine the excluded volume defined by two molecules and (b) calculate the excluded volume per mole (b) for the gas. Compare the excluded volume per mole with the volume actually occupied by a mole of the molecules.

Strategy (a) Use the formula for volume of a sphere to calculate the volume of a sphere of radius $2r$. This is the excluded volume defined by two molecules. (b) Multiply the excluded volume per molecule by Avogadro's number to determine excluded volume per mole.

Setup The equation for volume of a sphere is $\frac{4}{3}\pi r^3$; $N_A = 6.022 \times 10^{23}$.

Solution (a) Excluded volume defined by two molecules $= \frac{4}{3}\pi(2r)^3 = 8\left(\frac{4}{3}\pi r^3\right)$.

(b) Excluded volume per mole $= \dfrac{8\left(\frac{4}{3}\pi r^3\right)}{2 \text{ molecules}} \times \dfrac{N_A \text{ molecules}}{1 \text{ mole}} = \dfrac{4N_A\left(\frac{4}{3}\pi r^3\right)}{1 \text{ mole}}$.

The volume actually occupied by a mole of molecules with radius r is $N_A\left(\frac{4}{3}\pi r^3\right)$.

> **Think About It**
> The excluded volume per mole is four times the volume actually occupied by a mole of molecules.

Practice Problem A Determine the excluded volume per mole and the total volume of the molecules in a mole for a gas consisting of molecules with radius 165 pm. [Note: To obtain the volume in liters, we must express the radius in decimeters (dm).]

Practice Problem B Because the van der Waals constant b is the excluded volume per mole of a gas, we can use the value of b to estimate the radius of a molecule or atom. Consider a gas that consists of molecules, for which the van der Waals constant b is 0.0315 L/mol. Estimate the molecular radius in picometers (pm). Assume that the molecules are spherical.

SECTION 11.6 REVIEW

Real Gases

11.6.1   Using the van der Waals equation, calculate the pressure exerted by 1.5 moles of carbon dioxide in a 3.75-L vessel at 10°C.

11.6.2   Using the van der Waals equation, calculate the temperature (in °C) of a 3.74-mol sample of methane gas in a 1.00-L vessel when the measured pressure is 1.30 atm.

11.7 GAS MIXTURES

So far our discussion of the physical properties of gases has focused on the behavior of *pure* gaseous substances, even though the gas laws were all developed based on observations of samples of air, which is a *mixture* of gases. In this section, we will consider gas mixtures and their physical behavior. We will restrict our discussion in this section to gases that do not react with one another—that is, ideal gases.

Dalton's Law of Partial Pressures

When two or more gaseous substances are placed in a container, each gas behaves as though it occupies the container alone. For example, if we place 1.00 mole of N_2 gas in a 5.00-L container at 0°C, it exerts a pressure of

$$P = \frac{(1 \text{ mol})(0.08206 \text{ L} \cdot \text{atm/K} \cdot \text{mol})(273.15 \text{ K})}{5.00 \text{ L}} = 4.48 \text{ atm}$$

If we then add a mole of another gas, such as O_2, the pressure exerted by N_2 does not change. It remains at 4.48 atm. The O_2 gas exerts its own pressure, also 4.48 atm. Neither gas is affected by the presence of the other. In a mixture of gases, the pressure exerted by each gas is known as the *partial pressure* (P_i) of the gas. We use subscripts to denote partial pressures:

$$P_{N_2} = \frac{(1 \text{ mol})(0.08206 \text{ L} \cdot \text{atm/K} \cdot \text{mol})(273.15 \text{ K})}{5.00 \text{ L}} = 4.48 \text{ atm}$$

$$P_{O_2} = \frac{(1 \text{ mol})(0.08206 \text{ L} \cdot \text{atm/K} \cdot \text{mol})(273.15 \text{ K})}{5.00 \text{ L}} = 4.48 \text{ atm}$$

and we can solve the ideal gas equation for each component of any gas mixture:

$$P_i = \frac{n_i RT}{V}$$

Dalton's law of partial pressures states that the total pressure exerted by a gas mixture is the sum of the partial pressures exerted by each component of the mixture:

$$P_{total} = \Sigma P_i$$

Thus, the total pressure exerted by a mixture of 1.00 mol N_2 and 1.00 mol O_2 in a 5.00-L vessel at 0°C is

$$P_{total} = P_{N_2} + P_{O_2} = 4.48 \text{ atm} + 4.48 \text{ atm} = 8.96 \text{ atm}$$

Figure 11.22 illustrates Dalton's law of partial pressures.

As with the other gas laws, Dalton's law of partial pressures can be explained using the kinetic molecular theory. Gas molecules do not attract or repel one another (assumption 3), so the pressure exerted by one gas is unaffected by the presence of another gas. Consequently, the total pressure exerted by a mixture of gases is simply the sum of the partial pressures of the individual components in the mixture.

Volume and temperature are constant

P_1 + P_2 Combining the gases → $P_T = P_1 + P_2$

Figure 11.22 Each component of a gas mixture exerts a pressure independent of the other components. The total pressure is the sum of the individual components' partial pressures.

Worked Example 11.12 shows how to apply Dalton's law of partial pressures.

Worked Example 11.12

A 1.00-L vessel contains 0.215 mole of N_2 gas and 0.0118 mole of H_2 gas at 25.5°C. Determine the partial pressure of each component and the total pressure in the vessel.

Strategy Use the ideal gas equation to find the partial pressure of each component of the mixture, and sum the two partial pressures to find the total pressure.

Setup $T = 298.65$ K.

Solution

$$P_{N_2} = \frac{(0.215 \text{ mol})\left(\dfrac{0.08206 \text{ L} \cdot \text{atm}}{\text{K} \cdot \text{mol}}\right)(298.65 \text{ K})}{1.00 \text{ L}} = 5.27 \text{ atm}$$

$$P_{H_2} = \frac{(0.0118 \text{ mol})\left(\dfrac{0.08206 \text{ L} \cdot \text{atm}}{\text{K} \cdot \text{mol}}\right)(298.65 \text{ K})}{1.00 \text{ L}} = 0.289 \text{ atm}$$

$$P_{total} = P_{N_2} + P_{H_2} = 5.27 \text{ atm} + 0.289 \text{ atm} = 5.56 \text{ atm}$$

Think About It
The total pressure in the vessel can also be determined by summing the number of moles of mixture components (0.215 + 0.0118 = 0.227 mol) and solving the ideal gas equation for P_{total}:

$$P_{total} = \frac{(0.227 \text{ mol})\left(\dfrac{0.08206 \text{ L} \cdot \text{atm}}{\text{K} \cdot \text{mol}}\right)(298.65 \text{ K})}{1.00 \text{ L}} = 5.56 \text{ atm}$$

Practice Problem A Determine the partial pressures and the total pressure in a 2.50-L vessel containing the following mixture of gases at 15.8°C: 0.0194 mol He, 0.0411 mol H_2, and 0.169 mol Ne.

Practice Problem B Determine the number of moles of each gas present in a mixture of CH_4 and C_2H_6 in a 2.00-L vessel at 25.0°C and 1.50 atm, given that the partial pressure of CH_4 is 0.39 atm.

Mole Fractions

The relative amounts of the components of a gas mixture can be specified using *mole fractions*. The ***mole fraction*** (χ_i) of a component of a mixture is the number of moles of the component divided by the total number of moles in the mixture:

Student Annotation: Mole fractions do not refer only to gas mixtures. They can be used to specify the concentrations of components of mixtures in any phase. Mole fractions are used extensively in Chapter 13.

Equation 11.15
$$\chi_i = \frac{n_i}{n_{total}}$$

There are three things to remember about mole fractions:

1. The mole fraction of a mixture component is always less than 1.
2. The sum of mole fractions for all components of a mixture is always 1.
3. Mole fraction is dimensionless.

In addition, n and P are proportional $\left[n = P \times \left(\dfrac{V}{RT}\right)\right]$ at a specified T and V, so we can determine mole fraction by dividing the partial pressure of a component by the total pressure:

Equation 11.16
$$\chi_i = \frac{P_i}{P_{total}}$$

Rearranging Equations 11.15 and 11.16 gives

Equation 11.17
$$\chi_i \times n_{total} = n_i$$

and

Equation 11.18
$$\chi_i \times P_{total} = P_i$$

Thinking Outside the Box

Decompression Injury

One of the first lessons taught in SCUBA certification is that divers must never hold their breath during ascent to the surface. Failure to heed this warning can result in serious injury or death. During underwater ascent, the air in a diver's lungs expands. If the air is not expelled, it causes overexpansion and rupture of alveoli—the tiny sacks that normally fill with air on inhalation. This condition, known as "burst lung," can cause air to escape into the chest cavity, where further expansion can collapse the ruptured lung. The potential for these catastrophic injuries is not limited to deep-sea divers, though, as burst lung can occur during a rapid ascent of as little as 3 meters, a depth common in public swimming pools. Furthermore, *spontaneous pneumothorax,* the medical term for this injury, can be caused even without the failure to exhale if there is an air-filled cyst in the diver's lung, or if there is a region of lung tissue blocked by phlegm due to a respiratory tract infection. In addition to the risk of spontaneous pneumothorax, burst lung can result in gas bubbles entering the bloodstream. Expansion of these bubbles during rapid underwater ascent can block circulation, a condition known as *gas embolism,* which can lead to heart attack or stroke.

Because the cause of burst lung in divers is rapid *de*compression, treatment for the resulting conditions, especially gas embolism, usually includes *re*compression in a hyperbaric chamber. Hyperbaric chambers are cylindrical enclosures built to withstand pressures significantly above atmospheric pressure. With the victim of a rapid decompression and, in some cases, medical personnel inside the enclosure, the door is sealed and high-pressure air is pumped in until the interior pressure is high enough to compress the gas bubbles in the victim's system. The victim usually breathes pure oxygen through a mask to help purge the undesirable gases during treatment. The pressure in a typical medical hyperbaric chamber can be increased to as many as six times atmospheric pressure.

Student Annotation: "Monoplace" hyperbaric chambers, which are large enough to accommodate only one person, typically are pressurized with pure oxygen.

Pneumothorax

Monoplace hyperbaric chamber

In 1918, during the Spanish flu epidemic that claimed tens of millions of lives worldwide, physician Orville Cunningham noted that people living at lower elevations appeared to have a greater chance of surviving the flu than those living at higher elevations. Believing this to be the result of increased air pressure, he developed a hyperbaric chamber to treat flu victims. One of Cunningham's earliest and most notable successes was the recovery of a flu-stricken colleague who had been near death. Cunningham subsequently built a hyperbaric chamber large enough to accommodate dozens of patients and treated numerous flu victims, most with success.

Student Annotation: One unfortunate group of patients was undergoing treatment when the power to the chamber was shut off accidentally. All the patients died. At the time, their deaths were attributed to influenza, but they almost certainly died as the result of the unintended rapid decompression.

In the decades following the Spanish flu epidemic, hyperbaric therapy fell out of favor with the medical community and was largely discontinued. Interest in it was revived when the U.S. military ramped up its underwater activities in the 1940s and hyperbaric chambers were constructed to treat military divers suffering from decompression sickness (DCS), also known as "the bends." Significant advancement in hyperbaric methods began in the 1970s when the Undersea Medical Society (renamed the Undersea and Hyperbaric Medical Society in 1976) became involved in the clinical use of hyperbaric chambers. Today, hyperbaric oxygen therapy (HBOT) is used to treat a wide variety of conditions, including carbon monoxide poisoning, anemia caused by critical blood loss, severe burns, and life-threatening bacterial infections. Once considered an "alternative" therapy and viewed with skepticism, HBOT is now covered by most insurance plans.

Worked Example 11.13 lets you practice calculations involving mole fractions, partial pressures, and total pressure.

Worked Example 11.13

In 1999, the FDA approved the use of nitric oxide (NO) to treat and prevent lung disease, which occurs commonly in premature infants. The nitric oxide used in this therapy is supplied to hospitals in the form of a N_2/NO mixture. Calculate the mole fraction of NO in a 10.00-L gas cylinder at room temperature (25°C) that contains 6.022 mol N_2 and in which the total pressure is 14.75 atm.

Strategy Use the ideal gas equation to calculate the total number of moles in the cylinder. Subtract moles of N_2 from the total to determine moles of NO. Divide moles NO by total moles to get mole fraction (Equation 11.15).

Setup The temperature is 298.15 K.

Solution

$$\text{total moles} = \frac{PV}{RT} = \frac{(14.75 \text{ atm})(10.00 \text{ L})}{\left(\dfrac{0.08206 \text{ L} \cdot \text{atm}}{\text{K} \cdot \text{mol}}\right)(298.15 \text{ K})} = 6.029 \text{ mol}$$

$$\text{mol NO} = \text{total moles} - \text{mol } N_2 = 6.029 - 6.022 = 0.007 \text{ mol NO}$$

$$\chi_{NO} = \frac{n_{NO}}{n_{total}} = \frac{0.007 \text{ mol NO}}{6.029 \text{ mol}} = 0.001$$

Think About It

To check your work, determine χ_{N_2} by subtracting χ_{NO} from 1. Using each mole fraction and the total pressure, calculate the partial pressure of each component using Equation 11.16 and verify that they sum to the total pressure.

Practice Problem A Determine the mole fractions and partial pressures of CO_2, CH_4, and He in a sample of gas that contains 0.250 mole of CO_2, 1.29 moles of CH_4, and 3.51 moles of He, and in which the total pressure is 5.78 atm.

Practice Problem B Determine the partial pressure and number of moles of each gas in a 15.75-L vessel at 30.0°C containing a mixture of xenon and neon gases only. The total pressure in the vessel is 6.50 atm, and the mole fraction of xenon is 0.761.

SECTION 11.7 REVIEW

Gas Mixtures

11.7.1   What is the partial pressure of He in a 5.00-L vessel at 25°C that contains 0.0410 mole of He, 0.121 mole of Ne, and 0.0922 mole of Ar?

11.7.2   What is the mole fraction of CO_2 in a mixture of 0.756 mole of N_2, 0.189 mole of O_2, and 0.0132 mole of CO_2?

11.7.3   What is the partial pressure of oxygen in a gas mixture that contains 4.10 moles of oxygen, 2.38 moles of nitrogen, and 0.917 mole of carbon dioxide and that has a total pressure of 2.89 atm?

11.7.4   In the diagram at left, each color represents a different gas molecule. Calculate the mole fraction of each gas.

11.7.5   Calculate the partial pressure of each gas in the diagram in Question 11.7.4 if the total pressure is 8.21 atm.

11.8 REACTIONS WITH GASEOUS REACTANTS AND PRODUCTS

In Chapter 8, we used balanced chemical equations to calculate amounts of reactants and/or products in chemical reactions—expressing those amounts in mass (usually grams). However, in the case of reactants and products that are gases, it is more practical to measure and express amounts in volume (liters or milliliters). This makes the ideal gas equation useful in the stoichiometric analysis of chemical reactions that involve gases.

Calculating the Required Volume of a Gaseous Reactant

According to Avogadro's law, the volume of a gas at a given temperature and pressure is proportional to the number of moles. Moreover, balanced chemical equations give the ratio of combination of gaseous reactants in both moles and volume (Figure 11.15). Therefore, if we know the volume of one reactant in a gaseous reaction, we can determine the required amount of another reactant (at the same temperature and pressure). For example, consider the reaction of carbon monoxide and oxygen to yield carbon dioxide:

$$2CO(g) + O_2(g) \longrightarrow 2CO_2(g)$$

The ratio of combination of CO and O_2 is 2:1, whether we are talking about moles or units of volume. Thus, if we want to determine the stoichiometric amount [◀◀ Section 8.3] of O_2 required to combine with a particular volume of CO, we simply use the conversion factor provided by the balanced equation, which can be expressed as any of the following:

$$\frac{1 \text{ mol } O_2}{2 \text{ mol CO}} \quad \text{or} \quad \frac{1 \text{ L } O_2}{2 \text{ L CO}} \quad \text{or} \quad \frac{1 \text{ mL } O_2}{2 \text{ mL CO}}$$

Let's say we want to determine what volume of O_2 is required to react completely with 65.8 mL of CO at STP. We could use the ideal gas equation to convert the volume of CO to moles, use the stoichiometric conversion factor to convert to moles O_2, and then use the ideal gas equation again to convert moles O_2 to volume. But this method involves several unnecessary steps. We get the same result simply by using the conversion factor expressed in milliliters:

$$65.8 \text{ mL CO} \times \frac{1 \text{ mL } O_2}{2 \text{ mL CO}} = 32.9 \text{ mL } O_2$$

In cases where only one of the reactants is a gas, we *do* need to use the ideal gas equation in our analysis. Recall, for example, the reaction of sodium metal and chlorine gas used to illustrate the Born-Haber cycle [◀◀ Section 10.8]:

$$2Na(s) + Cl_2(g) \longrightarrow 2NaCl(s)$$

Given moles (or more commonly the *mass*) of Na, and information regarding temperature and pressure, we can determine the volume of Cl_2 required to react completely:

$$\times \frac{1 \text{ mol Na}}{22.99 \text{ g Na}} = \qquad \times \frac{1 \text{ mol } Cl_2}{2 \text{ mol Na}} = \qquad \times \frac{RT}{P} =$$

| grams Na | ⟶ | moles Na | ⟶ | moles Cl_2 | ⟶ | liters Cl_2 |

Worked Example 11.14 shows how to use the ideal gas equation in a stoichiometric analysis.

Worked Example 11.14

Sodium peroxide (Na_2O_2) is used to remove carbon dioxide from (and add oxygen to) the air supply in spacecrafts. It works by reacting with CO_2 in the air to produce sodium carbonate (Na_2CO_3) and O_2.

$$2Na_2O(s) + 2CO_2(g) \longrightarrow 2Na_2CO_3(s) + O_2(g)$$

What volume (in liters) of CO_2 (at STP) will react with a kilogram of Na_2O_2?

Strategy Convert the given mass of Na_2O_2 to moles, use the balanced equation to determine the stoichiometric amount of CO_2, and then use the ideal gas equation to convert moles of CO_2 to liters.

Setup The molar mass of Na_2O_2 is 77.98 g/mol (1 kg = 1000 g). (Treat the specified mass of Na_2O_2 as an exact number.)

Solution

$$1000 \text{ g Na}_2\text{O}_2 \times \frac{1 \text{ mol Na}_2\text{O}_2}{77.98 \text{ g Na}_2\text{O}_2} = 12.82 \text{ mol Na}_2\text{O}_2$$

$$12.82 \text{ mol Na}_2\text{O}_2 \times \frac{2 \text{ mol CO}_2}{2 \text{ mol Na}_2\text{O}_2} = 12.82 \text{ mol CO}_2$$

$$V_{CO_2} = \frac{(12.82 \text{ mol CO}_2)(0.08206 \text{ L} \cdot \text{atm/K} \cdot \text{mol})(273.15 \text{ K})}{1 \text{ atm}} = 287.4 \text{ L CO}_2$$

> **Think About It**
> The answer seems like an enormous volume of CO_2. If you check the cancellation of units carefully in ideal gas equation problems, however, with practice you will develop a sense of whether such a calculated volume is reasonable.

Practice Problem A What volume (in liters) of CO_2 can be consumed at STP by 525 g Na_2O_2?

Practice Problem B What mass (in grams) of Na_2O_2 is necessary to consume 1.00 L CO_2 at STP?

Determining the Amount of Reactant Consumed Using Change in Pressure

Although none of the empirical gas laws focuses on the relationship between n and P explicitly, we can rearrange the ideal gas equation to show that n is directly proportional to P at constant V and T:

Equation 11.19(a) $n = P \times \left(\dfrac{V}{RT}\right)$ (at constant V and T)

Therefore, we can use the change in pressure in a reaction vessel to determine how many moles of a gaseous reactant are consumed in a chemical reaction:

Equation 11.19(b) $\Delta n = \Delta P \times \left(\dfrac{V}{RT}\right)$ (at constant V and T)

> **Student Annotation:** This refers to a reaction in which there is only *one* gaseous reactant and in which none of the products is a gas, such as the reaction described in Worked Example 11.15. In reactions involving multiple gaseous species, Δn refers to the *net* change in number of moles of gas—and the analysis gets somewhat more complicated.

where Δn is the number of moles of gas consumed and ΔP is the change in pressure in the reaction vessel. Worked Example 11.15 shows how to use Equation 11.19(b).

Worked Example 11.15

Another air-purification method for enclosed spaces involves the use of "scrubbers" containing aqueous lithium hydroxide, which react with carbon dioxide to produce lithium carbonate and water:

$$2LiOH(aq) + CO_2(g) \longrightarrow Li_2CO_3(s) + H_2O(l)$$

Consider the air supply in a submarine with a total volume of 2.5×10^5 L. The pressure is 0.9970 atm, and the temperature is 25°C. If the pressure in the submarine drops to 0.9891 atm as the result of carbon dioxide being consumed by an aqueous lithium hydroxide scrubber, how many moles of CO_2 are consumed?

Strategy Use Equation 11.19(b) to determine Δn, the number of moles of CO_2 consumed.

Setup $\Delta P = 0.9970$ atm $- 0.9891$ atm $= 7.9 \times 10^{-3}$ atm. According to the problem statement, $V = 2.5 \times 10^5$ L and $T = 298.15$ K. For problems in which P is expressed in atmospheres and V in liters, use $R = 0.08206$ L $\cdot$ atm/K $\cdot$ mol.

Solution

$$\Delta n_{CO_2} = 7.9 \times 10^{-3} \text{ atm} \times \frac{2.5 \times 10^5 \text{ L}}{(0.08206 \text{ L} \cdot \text{atm/K} \cdot \text{mol}) \times (298.15 \text{ K})} = 81 \text{ moles } CO_2 \text{ consumed}$$

Think About It
Careful cancellation of units is *essential*. Note that this amount of CO_2 corresponds to 162 moles or 3.9 kg of LiOH. (It's a good idea to verify this yourself.)

Practice Problem A Using all the same conditions as those described in Worked Example 11.15, calculate the number of moles of CO_2 consumed if the pressure drops by 0.010 atm.

Practice Problem B By how much would the pressure in the submarine drop if 2.55 kg of LiOH were completely consumed by reaction with CO_2? (Assume the same starting P, V, and T as in Worked Example 11.15.)

Using Partial Pressures to Solve Problems

The volume of gas produced by a chemical reaction can be measured using an apparatus like the one shown in Figure 11.23. Dalton's law of partial pressures is useful in the analysis of these kinds of experimental results. For example, the decomposition of potassium chlorate ($KClO_3$), the reaction used to generate emergency oxygen supplies on airplanes, produces potassium chloride and oxygen:

Multi 11.5
Gas laws—collecting a gas over water

$$2KClO_3(s) \longrightarrow 2KCl(s) + 3O_2(g)$$

The oxygen gas is collected over water, as shown in Figure 11.23(a). The volume of water displaced by the gas is equal to the volume of gas produced. (Prior to reading the volume of the gas, the level of the graduated cylinder must be adjusted such that the water levels inside and outside the cylinder are the *same*. This ensures that the *pressure* inside the graduated cylinder is the same as atmospheric pressure [Figure 11.23(b)].) However, because the measured volume contains both the oxygen produced by the reaction *and* water vapor, the pressure exerted inside the graduated cylinder is the sum of the two partial pressures:

$$P_{total} = P_{O_2} + P_{H_2O}$$

By subtracting the partial pressure of water from the total pressure, which is equal to atmospheric pressure, we can determine the partial pressure of oxygen—and thereby determine how many moles are produced by the reaction. We get the partial pressure of water, which depends on temperature, from a table of values. Table 11.6 lists the partial pressure (also known as the *vapor pressure*) of water at various temperatures. Figure 11.24 illustrates an experimental technique that involves collection of a gas over water.

Multi 11.6
Figure 11.24—Molar volume of a gas

(a)   (b)

Figure 11.23 (a) Apparatus for measuring the amount of gas produced in a chemical reaction. (b) When the water levels inside and outside the collection vessel are the same, the pressure inside the vessel is equal to atmospheric pressure.

Figure 11.24

Molar Volume of a Gas

The reaction between zinc and hydrochloric acid produces hydrogen gas. The net ionic equation for the reaction is

$$Zn(s) + 2H^+(aq) \longrightarrow Zn^{2+}(aq) + H_2(g)$$

The H_2 gas evolved in the reaction is collected in the inverted graduated cylinder. Using the balanced equation, we determine how much H_2 will be produced.

$$0.072 \; \text{g Zn} \times \frac{1 \; \text{mol Zn}}{65.41 \; \text{g Zn}} = 0.0011 \; \text{mol Zn}$$

$$0.0011 \; \text{mol Zn} \times \frac{1 \; \text{mol H}_2}{1 \; \text{mol Zn}} = 0.0011 \; \text{mol H}_2$$

The reservoir is inverted and the zinc drops into the 1.0 *M* HCl.

START

A 0.072-g sample of zinc is placed in the reservoir. The vessel contains approximately 5 mL of 1.0 *M* HCl. A graduated cylinder is filled with water and inverted over the tubing to collect the gas produced by the reaction of zinc and acid. The temperature of the water is 25.0°C and the pressure in the room is 748.0 torr.

Zn is the limiting reactant. When all of the zinc has been consumed, the reaction is complete and no more gas is evolved.

We adjust the level of the graduated cylinder to make the water level the same inside and outside of the cylinder. This lets us know that the pressure inside the cylinder is the same as the pressure in the room. When the water levels are the same, we can read the volume of gas collected, which is 26.5 mL.

The pressure inside the cylinder is the sum of two partial pressures: that of the collected H_2, and that of water vapor. To determine the partial pressure of H_2, which is what we want, we must subtract the vapor pressure of water from the total pressure. Table 11.6 gives the vapor pressure of water at 25.0°C as 23.8 torr. Therefore, the pressure of H_2 is 748.0 − 23.8 = 724.2 torr. Using Equation 11.10(b),

$$\frac{P_1 V_1}{T_1} = \frac{P_2 V_2}{T_2}$$

we calculate the volume the H_2 gas would occupy at STP.

$$\frac{(724.2 \text{ torr})(26.5 \text{ mL})}{298.15 \text{ K}} = \frac{(760 \text{ torr})V_2}{273.15 \text{ K}}$$

$$V_2 = \frac{(724.2 \text{ torr})(26.5 \text{ mL})(273.15 \text{ K})}{(760 \text{ torr})(298.15 \text{ K})} = 23.13 \text{ mL}$$

This is the volume of 0.0011 mol H_2. The molar volume is

$$\frac{23.13 \text{ mL}}{0.0011 \text{ mol}} = 2.1 \times 10^4 \text{ mL/mol or 21 L/mol}$$

What's the point?

The gas collected in the graduated cylinder is a mixture of the gas produced by the reaction and water vapor. We determine the pressure of the gas produced by the reaction by subtracting the tabulated partial pressure of water from the total pressure. Knowing the volume, pressure, and temperature of a sample of gas, in this case H_2, we can determine what volume the same sample of gas would occupy at STP. This enables us to determine experimentally the molar volume of H_2 at STP, which turns out to be fairly close to the accepted value of 22.4 L. Several sources of error, including uncertainty in the volume of the collected gas, contribute to the result not being exactly 22.4 L.

TABLE 11.6		Vapor Pressure of Water (P_{H_2O}) as a Function of Temperature			
T(°C)	P(torr)	T(°C)	P(torr)	T(°C)	P(torr)
0	4.6	35	42.2	70	233.7
5	6.5	40	55.3	75	289.1
10	9.2	45	71.9	80	355.1
15	12.8	50	92.5	85	433.6
20	17.5	55	118.0	90	525.8
25	23.8	60	149.4	95	633.9
30	31.8	65	187.5	100	760.0

Worked Example 11.16 shows how to use Dalton's law of partial pressures to determine the amount of gas produced in a chemical reaction and collected over water.

Worked Example 11.16

Calcium metal reacts with water to produce hydrogen gas [◄◄ Section 8.5]:

$$Ca(s) + 2H_2O(l) \longrightarrow Ca(OH)_2(aq) + H_2(g)$$

Determine the mass of H_2 produced at 25°C and 0.967 atm when 525 mL of the gas is collected over water as shown in Figure 11.23.

Strategy Use Dalton's law of partial pressures to determine the partial pressure of H_2, use the ideal gas equation to determine moles of H_2, and then use the molar mass of H_2 to convert to mass. (Pay careful attention to units. Atmospheric pressure is given in atmospheres, whereas the vapor pressure of water is tabulated in torr.)

Setup $V = 0.525$ L and $T = 298.15$ K. The partial pressure of water at 25°C is 23.8 torr (Table 11.6) or 23.8 torr (1 atm/760 torr) = 0.0313 atm. The molar mass of H_2 is 2.016 g/mol.

Solution

$$P_{H_2} = P_{total} - P_{H_2O} = 0.967 \text{ atm} - 0.0313 \text{ atm} = 0.936 \text{ atm}$$

$$\text{moles of } H_2 = \frac{(0.9357 \text{ atm})(0.525 \text{ L})}{\left(\dfrac{0.08206 \text{ L} \cdot \text{atm}}{\text{K} \cdot \text{mol}}\right)(298.15 \text{ K})} = 2.01 \times 10^{-2} \text{ mol}$$

$$\text{moles of } H_2 = (2.008 \times 10^{-2} \text{ mol})(2.016 \text{ g/mol}) = 0.0405 \text{ g } H_2$$

Think About It
Check unit cancellation carefully, and remember that the densities of gases are relatively low. The mass of approximately half a liter of hydrogen at or near room temperature and 1 atm should be a very small number.

Practice Problem A Calculate the mass of O_2 produced by the decomposition of $KClO_3$ when 821 mL of O_2 is collected over water at 30.0°C and 1.015 atm.

Practice Problem B Determine the volume of gas collected over water when 0.501 g O_2 is produced by the decomposition of $KClO_3$ at 35.0°C and 1.08 atm.

SECTION 11.8 REVIEW

Reactions with Gaseous Reactants and Products

11.8.1   Determine the volume of Cl_2 gas at STP that will react with 1.00 mole of Na solid to produce NaCl according to the equation,

$$2Na(s) + Cl_2(g) \longrightarrow 2NaCl(s)$$

11.8.2   Determine the mass of NaN_3 required for an air bag to produce 100.0 L of N_2 gas at 85.0°C and 1.00 atm according to the equation,

$$2NaN_3(s) \longrightarrow 2Na(s) + 3N_2(g)$$

11.8.3   What mass of acetylene (C_2H_2) is produced by the reaction of calcium carbide (CaC_2) and water,

$$CaC_2(s) + 2H_2O(l) \longrightarrow C_2H_2(g) + Ca(OH)_2(aq),$$

if 425 mL of the gas is collected over water at 30°C and a pressure of 0.996 atm?

Learning Outcomes

- List the characteristics of gases that distinguish them from solids and liquids.
- List the basic assumptions of the kinetic molecular theory of gases.
- Define effusion and diffusion.
- Give a definition for pressure and provide examples of some units for pressure.
- Demonstrate the ability to interconvert units of pressure.
- Describe the major characteristics of the various gas laws: Boyle's, Charles's, Avogadro's, and combined.
- Use the combined gas law to interconvert measurements of pressure, volume, or temperature for a given gas.
- Use the ideal gas equation to determine the pressure, volume, moles, or temperature of a gas given all of the other values.

- Identify the values for standard temperature and standard pressure of gases.
- Apply the ideal gas equation to determine characteristics of a gas including density and molecular weight.
- Identify factors that may cause gases to deviate from ideal gas behavior.
- Use the van der Waals equation to determine the pressure of a real gas.
- Define and be able to calculate mole fraction.
- Use Dalton's law of partial pressures to determine the mole fraction or partial pressure of gases in a mixture of gases.
- Use the ideal gas equation in stoichiometric calculations.

Chapter Summary

SECTION 11.1

- A gas assumes the volume and shape of its container and is compressible. Gases generally have low densities (expressed in g/L) and will mix in any proportions to give homogeneous solutions.

SECTION 11.2

- According to the *kinetic molecular theory,* gases are composed of particles with negligible volume that are separated by large distances; the particles are in constant, random motion, and collisions between the particles and between the particles and their container walls are perfectly elastic; there are no attractive or repulsive forces between the particles; and the average kinetic energy of particles in a sample is proportional to the absolute temperature of the sample.

- The **root-mean-square (rms) speed (u_{rms})** of gas molecules in a sample at a given temperature is inversely proportional to the molecular mass.
- According to **Graham's law,** the rates of **diffusion** (mixing of gases) and **effusion** (escape of a gas from a container into a vacuum) are inversely proportional to the square root of the molar mass of the gas.

SECTION 11.3

- Gases exert **pressure,** which is the force per unit area. The SI units of force and pressure are the **newton (N)** and the **pascal (Pa),** respectively. Other commonly used units of pressure are atmosphere (atm), mmHg, torr, and bar.
- Pressure can be measured using a **barometer** or a **manometer.**
- **Standard atmospheric pressure** (1 atm) is the pressure exerted by the atmosphere at sea level.

SECTION 11.4

- The physical state of a sample of gas can be described using four parameters: temperature (T), pressure (P), volume (V), and number of moles (n). Equations relating these parameters are called the **gas laws.**
- **Boyle's law** states that the volume of a sample of gas at constant temperature is inversely proportional to pressure.
- Experiments done by Charles and Gay-Lussac showed that the volume of a gas at constant pressure is directly proportional to temperature. Lord Kelvin used Charles's and Gay-Lussac's data to propose that **absolute zero** is the lowest theoretically attainable temperature. The **absolute temperature scale,** also known as the **Kelvin temperature scale,** is used for all calculations involving gases.
- **Charles's and Gay-Lussac's law,** commonly known as **Charles's law,** states that the volume of a sample of gas at constant pressure is directly proportional to its absolute temperature.
- **Avogadro's law** states that the volume of a sample of gas at constant temperature and pressure is directly proportional to the number of moles.

- The **combined gas law** combines the laws of Boyle, Charles, and Avogadro and relates pressure, volume, temperature, and number of moles without assuming that any of the parameters is constant.

SECTION 11.5

- The **ideal gas equation,** $PV = nRT$, makes it possible to predict the behavior of gases. An **ideal gas** is one that behaves in a way predicted by the ideal gas equation. R is the **gas constant,** which may be expressed in a variety of units. The units used to express R depend on the units used to express P and V.
- **Standard temperature and pressure (STP)** is defined as 0°C and 1 atm.
- The ideal gas equation can be used to calculate the density of a gas and to interconvert between density and molar mass.

SECTION 11.6

- Deviation from ideal behavior is observed at high pressure and/or low temperature. The **van der Waals equation** makes corrections for the nonzero volume of gas molecules and the attractive forces between molecules.

SECTION 11.7

- Each component in a mixture of gases exerts a **partial pressure (P_i)** independent of the other mixture components. **Dalton's law of partial pressures** states that the total pressure exerted by a gas **mixture** is the sum of the partial pressures of the components.
- **Mole fraction (χ_i)** is the unitless quotient of the number of moles of a mixture component and the total number of moles in the mixture, n_i/n_{total}.

SECTION 11.8

- For a reaction occurring at constant temperature and pressure, and involving only gases, the coefficients in the balanced chemical equation apply to units of volume, as well as to numbers of molecules or moles.
- A balanced chemical equation and the ideal gas equation can be used to determine volumes of gaseous reactants and/or products in a reaction.

Key Words

Absolute temperature scale, 425

Absolute zero, 425

Avogadro's law, 426

Barometer, 420

Boyle's law, 423

Charles's and Gay-Lussac's law, 425

Charles's law, 425

Combined gas law, 429

Dalton's law of partial pressures, 439

Diffusion, 417

Effusion, 417

Gas constant (R), 416

Gas laws, 422

Graham's law, 418

Ideal gas equation, 431

Ideal gas, 431

Kelvin temperature scale, 425

Kinetic molecular theory, 415

Manometer, 420

Mole fraction (χ_i), 440

Newton (N), 419

Partial pressure (P_i), 439

Pascal (Pa), 419

Pressure, 419

Root-mean-square (rms) speed (u_{rms}), 416

Standard atmospheric pressure, 420

Standard temperature and pressure (STP), 431

van der Waals equation, 435

Key Equations

11.1 $\quad u_{rms} = \sqrt{\dfrac{3RT}{\mathcal{M}}}$

11.2 $\quad \dfrac{u_{rms}(1)}{u_{rms}(2)} = \sqrt{\dfrac{\mathcal{M}_2}{\mathcal{M}_1}}$

11.3 $\quad P = hdg$

11.4(a) $\quad V \propto k_1 \dfrac{1}{P}$ (at constant temperature)

11.4(b) $\quad PV = k_1$ (at constant temperature)

11.5 $\quad P_1V_1 = P_2V_2$ (at constant temperature)

11.6(a) $\quad V = k_2T$ (at constant pressure)

11.6(b) $\quad \dfrac{V}{T} = k_2$ (at constant pressure)

11.7 $\quad \dfrac{V_1}{T_1} = \dfrac{V_2}{T_2}$ (at constant pressure)

11.8(a) $\quad V = k_3n$ (at constant temperature and pressure)

11.8(b) $\quad \dfrac{V}{n} = k_3$

11.9 $\quad \dfrac{V_1}{n_1} = \dfrac{V_2}{n_2}$

11.10(a) $\quad \dfrac{P_1V_1}{n_1T_1} = \dfrac{P_2V_2}{n_2T_2}$

11.10(b) $\quad \dfrac{P_1V_1}{T_1} = \dfrac{P_2V_2}{T_2}$

11.11 $\quad PV = nRT$

11.12 $\quad d = \dfrac{P\mathcal{M}}{RT}$

11.13 $\quad \mathcal{M} = \dfrac{dRT}{P}$

11.14 $\quad \left(P + \dfrac{an^2}{V^2}\right)(V - nb) = nRT$

11.15 $\quad \chi_i = \dfrac{n_i}{n_{total}}$

11.16 $\quad \chi_i = \dfrac{P_i}{P_{total}}$

11.17 $\quad \chi_i \times n_{total} = n_i$

11.18 $\quad \chi_i \times P_{total} = P_i$

11.19(a) $\quad n = P \times \left(\dfrac{V}{RT}\right)$ (at constant V and T)

11.19(b) $\quad \Delta n = \Delta P \times \left(\dfrac{V}{RT}\right)$ (at constant V and T)

Questions and Problems

SECTION 11.1: PROPERTIES OF GASES

Review Questions

11.1   Name five elements and five compounds that exist as gases at room temperature.

11.2   List the physical characteristics of gases.

SECTION 11.2: THE KINETIC MOLECULAR THEORY OF GASES

Review Questions

11.3   What are the basic assumptions of the kinetic molecular theory of gases?

11.4   What does the Maxwell speed distribution curve tell us? Does Maxwell's theory work for a sample of 200 molecules? Explain.

11.5   Which of the following statements is correct? (a) Heat is produced by the collision of gas molecules against one another. (b) When a gas is heated at constant volume, the molecules collide with one another more often.

11.6   Three fluorine-containing gases are shown here. Which of the three gases will have the highest root-mean-square

speed? Which of the three gases will have the highest average kinetic energy at a given temperature?

11.7   What is the difference between gas diffusion and effusion?

Problems

11.8   Compare the root-mean-square speeds of O_2 and UF_6 at 65°C.

11.9   The average temperature in the stratosphere is −23°C. Calculate the root-mean-square speeds of N_2, O_2, and O_3 molecules in this region.

11.10   The average distance traveled by a molecule between successive collisions is called the *mean free path*.

For a given amount of a gas, how does the mean free path of a gas depend on (a) density, (b) temperature at constant volume, (c) pressure at constant temperature, (d) volume at constant temperature, and (e) size of the atoms?

11.11   At a certain temperature, the speeds of six gaseous molecules in a container are 2.0, 2.2, 2.6, 2.7, 3.3, and 3.5 m/s. Calculate the root-mean-square speed and the average speed of the molecules. These two average values are close to each other, but the root-mean-square value is always the larger of the two. Why?

11.12   The ^{235}U isotope undergoes fission when bombarded with neutrons. However, its natural abundance is only 0.72 percent. To separate it from the more abundant ^{238}U isotope, uranium is first converted to UF_6, which is easily vaporized above room temperature. The mixture of the $^{235}UF_6$ and $^{238}UF_6$ gases is then subjected to many stages of effusion. Calculate how much faster $^{235}UF_6$ effuses than $^{238}UF_6$.

11.13   An unknown gas evolved from the fermentation of glucose is found to effuse through a porous barrier in 15.0 min. Under the same conditions of temperature and pressure, it takes an equal volume of N_2 12.0 min to effuse through the same barrier. Calculate the molar mass of the unknown gas, and suggest what the gas might be.

11.14   Nickel forms a gaseous compound of the formula $Ni(CO)_x$. Given the fact that under the same conditions of temperature and pressure, methane (CH_4) effuses 3.3 times faster than $Ni(CO)_x$, what is the value of x?

SECTION 11.3:   GAS PRESSURE

Review Questions

11.15   Define *pressure* and give the common units for pressure.

11.16   Describe how a barometer and a manometer are used to measure gas pressure.

11.17   Why is mercury a more suitable substance to use in a barometer than water?

11.18   Explain why the height of mercury in a barometer is independent of the cross-sectional area of the tube.

11.19   Is the atmospheric pressure in a mine that is 500 m below sea level greater or less than 1 atm?

11.20   If the maximum distance that water may be brought up a well by a suction pump is 34 ft (10.3 m), how is it possible to obtain water and oil from hundreds of feet below the surface of Earth?

11.21   Why is it that if the barometer reading falls in one part of the world, it must rise somewhere else?

Problems

11.22   The atmospheric pressure at the summit of Mt. McKinley is 581 mmHg on a certain day. What is the pressure in atmospheres, in kilopascals, and in bars?

11.23   Convert 375 mmHg to atmospheres, bars, torr, and pascals.

11.24   Calculate the height of a column of ethylene glycol [$CH_2(OH)CH_2(OH)$] that would be supported by atmospheric pressure (1 atm). The density of ethylene glycol is 1.12 g/cm³.

11.25   Calculate the height of a column of methanol (CH_3OH) that would be supported by atmospheric pressure. The density of methanol is 0.787 g/cm³.

11.26   What pressure (in atm and in bars) is exerted by a column of isopropanol (C_3H_7OH) 264 m high? The density of isopropanol is 0.785 g/cm³.

11.27   What pressure (in atm and in bars) is exerted by a column of toluene (C_7H_8) 87 m high? The density of toluene is 0.867 g/cm³.

SECTION 11.4:   THE GAS LAWS

Review Questions

11.28   State each of the following gas laws in words and also in the form of an equation: Boyle's law, Charles's law, Avogadro's law. In each case, indicate the conditions under which the law is applicable, and give the units for each quantity in the equation.

11.29   Explain why a helium weather balloon expands as it rises in the air. Assume that the temperature remains constant.

Problems

11.30   Consider the following gaseous sample in a cylinder fitted with a movable piston. Initially there are n moles of the gas at temperature T, pressure P, and volume V.

Choose the cylinder that correctly represents the gas after each of the following changes. (1) The pressure on the piston is tripled at constant n and T. (2) The absolute temperature is doubled at constant n and P. (3) n more moles of the gas are added at constant T and P. (4) Absolute temperature is halved at constant P.

11.31   A gaseous sample of a substance is cooled at constant pressure. Which of the following diagrams best represents the situation if the final temperature is (a) above the boiling point of the substance and (b) below the boiling point but above the freezing point of the substance?

(a)   (b)   (c)   (d)

11.32 At 46°C, a sample of ammonia gas exerts a pressure of 5.3 atm. What is the pressure when the volume of the gas is reduced to one-fourth of the original value at the same temperature?

11.33 A gas sample occupying a volume of 25.6 mL at a pressure of 0.970 atm is allowed to expand at constant temperature until its pressure reaches 0.541 atm. What is its final volume?

11.34 A sample of air occupies 3.8 L when the pressure is 1.2 atm. (a) What volume does it occupy at 6.6 atm? (b) What pressure is required in order to compress it to 0.075 L? (The temperature is kept constant.)

11.35 The volume of a gas is 7.15 L, measured at 1.00 atm. What is the pressure of the gas in mmHg if the volume is changed to 9.25 L? (The temperature remains constant.)

11.36 Under constant-pressure conditions, a sample of hydrogen gas initially at 88°C and 9.6 L is cooled until its final volume is 3.4 L. What is its final temperature?

11.37 A 28.4-L volume of methane gas is heated from 35°C to 72°C at constant pressure. What is the final volume of the gas?

11.38 Molecular chlorine and molecular fluorine combine to form a gaseous product. Under the same conditions of temperature and pressure it is found that one volume of Cl_2 reacts with three volumes of F_2 to yield two volumes of the product. What is the formula of the product?

11.39 Ammonia burns in oxygen gas to form nitric oxide (NO) and water vapor. How many volumes of NO are obtained from one volume of ammonia at the same temperature and pressure?

SECTION 11.5: THE IDEAL GAS EQUATION

Review Questions

11.40 What are standard temperature and pressure (STP)? What is the significance of STP in relation to the volume of 1 mole of an ideal gas?

11.41 Why is the density of a gas much lower than that of a liquid or solid under atmospheric conditions? What units are normally used to express the density of gases?

Problems

11.42 A sample of nitrogen gas in a 4.5-L container at a temperature of 27°C exerts a pressure of 4.1 atm. Calculate the number of moles of gas in the sample.

11.43 Given that 6.9 moles of carbon monoxide gas are present in a container of volume 30.4 L, what is the pressure of the gas (in atm) if the temperature is 82°C?

11.44 What volume will 9.8 moles of sulfur hexafluoride (SF_6) gas occupy if the temperature and pressure of the gas are 105°C and 9.4 atm, respectively?

11.45 A certain amount of gas at 25°C and at a pressure of 0.800 atm is contained in a vessel. Suppose that the vessel can withstand a pressure no higher than 5.00 atm. How high can you raise the temperature of the gas without bursting the vessel?

11.46 A gas-filled balloon having a volume of 2.50 L at 1.2 atm and 20°C is allowed to rise to the stratosphere (about 30 km above the surface of Earth), where the temperature and pressure are −23°C and 3.00×10^{-3} atm, respectively. Calculate the final volume of the balloon.

11.47 The temperature of 2.5 L of a gas initially at STP is raised to 210°C at constant volume. Calculate the final pressure of the gas in atmospheres.

11.48 The pressure of 6.0 L of an ideal gas in a flexible container is decreased to one-third of its original pressure, and its absolute temperature is decreased by one-half. What is the final volume of the gas?

11.49 A gas evolved during the fermentation of glucose (wine making) has a volume of 0.67 L at 22.5°C and 1.00 atm. What was the volume of this gas at the fermentation temperature of 36.5°C and 1.00 atm pressure?

11.50 An ideal gas originally at 0.85 atm and 66°C was allowed to expand until its final volume, pressure, and temperature were 94 mL, 0.60 atm, and 45°C, respectively. What was its initial volume?

11.51 Calculate the volume (in liters) of 124.3 g of CO_2 at STP.

11.52 A gas at 572 mmHg and 35.0°C occupies a volume of 6.15 L. Calculate its volume at STP.

11.53 Dry ice is solid carbon dioxide. A 0.050-g sample of dry ice is placed in an evacuated 4.6-L vessel at 30°C. Calculate the pressure inside the vessel after all the dry ice has been converted to CO_2 gas.

11.54 At STP, 0.280 L of a gas weighs 0.400 g. Calculate the molar mass of the gas.

11.55 At 741 torr and 44°C, 7.10 g of a gas occupies a volume of 5.40 L. What is the molar mass of the gas?

11.56 Ozone molecules in the stratosphere absorb much of the harmful radiation from the sun. Typically, the temperature and pressure of ozone in the stratosphere are 250 K and 1.0×10^{-3} atm, respectively. How many ozone molecules are present in 1.0 L of air under these conditions?

11.57 Assuming that air contains 78 percent N_2, 21 percent O_2, and 1.0 percent Ar, all by volume, how many molecules of each type of gas are present in 1.0 L of air at STP?

11.58 A 2.10-L vessel contains 4.65 g of a gas at 1.00 atm and 27.0°C. (a) Calculate the density of the gas in g/L. (b) What is the molar mass of the gas?

11.59 Calculate the density of hydrogen bromide (HBr) gas in g/L at 733 mmHg and 46°C.

11.60 A certain anesthetic contains 64.9 percent C, 13.5 percent H, and 21.6 percent O by mass. At 120°C and 750 mmHg, the mass of 1.00 L of the gaseous compound is 2.30 g. What is the molecular formula of the compound?

11.61 A compound has the empirical formula SF_4. At 20°C, 0.100 g of the gaseous compound occupies a volume of 22.1 mL and exerts a pressure of 1.02 atm. What is the molecular formula of the gas?

SECTION 11.6:   REAL GASES

Review Questions

11.62   Cite two pieces of evidence to show that gases do not behave ideally under all conditions. Under which set of conditions would a gas be expected to behave most ideally: (a) high temperature and low pressure, (b) high temperature and high pressure, (c) low temperature and high pressure, or (d) low temperature and low pressure?

11.63   Figure 11.21(a) shows that at 0°C, with the exception of H_2, each of the gases has a pressure at which its compressibility factor is equal to 1—the point at which the curve crosses the ideal gas line. What is the significance of this point? Does each of these gases have a pressure at which the assumptions of ideal behavior (negligible molecular volume and no intermolecular attractions) are valid? Explain.

11.64   Write the van der Waals equation for a real gas. Explain the corrective terms for pressure and volume.

11.65   (a) A real gas is introduced into a flask of volume V. Is the corrected volume of the gas greater or less than V? (b) Ammonia has a larger a value than neon does (see Table 11.5). What can you conclude about the relative strength of the attractive forces between molecules of ammonia and between atoms of neon?

Problems

11.66   At 27°C, 10.0 moles of a gas in a 1.50-L container exert a pressure of 130 atm. Is this an ideal gas?

11.67   Using the data shown in Table 11.5, calculate the pressure exerted by 2.50 moles of CO_2 confined in a volume of 5.00 L at 450 K. Compare the pressure with that predicted by the ideal gas equation.

SECTION 11.7:   GAS MIXTURES

Review Questions

11.68   State Dalton's law of partial pressures and explain what *mole fraction* is. Does mole fraction have units?

11.69   What are the approximate partial pressures of N_2 and O_2 in air at the top of a mountain where atmospheric pressure is 0.8 atm? (See Problem 11.57.)

Problems

11.70   A mixture of gases contains 0.31 mol CH_4, 0.25 mol C_2H_6, and 0.29 mol C_3H_8. The total pressure is 1.50 atm. Calculate the partial pressures of the gases.

11.71   A 2.5-L flask at 15°C contains a mixture of N_2, He, and Ne at partial pressures of 0.32 atm for N_2, 0.15 atm for He, and 0.42 atm for Ne. (a) Calculate the total pressure of the mixture. (b) Calculate the volume in liters at STP occupied by He and Ne if the N_2 is removed selectively.

11.72   Dry air near sea level, where atmospheric pressure is 1.00 atm, has the following composition by volume: N_2, 78.08 percent; O_2, 20.94 percent; Ar, 0.93 percent; CO_2, 0.05 percent. Calculate (a) the partial pressure of each gas in atmospheres and (b) the concentration

of each gas in mol/L at 0°C. (*Hint:* Because volume is proportional to the number of moles present, mole fractions of gases can be expressed as ratios of volumes at the same temperature and pressure.)

11.73   A mixture of helium and neon gases is collected over water at 28.0°C and 745 mmHg. If the partial pressure of helium is 368 mmHg, what is the partial pressure of neon? (Vapor pressure of water at 28°C = 28.3 mmHg.)

11.74   Helium is mixed with oxygen gas for deep-sea divers. Calculate the percent by volume of oxygen gas in the mixture if the diver has to submerge to a depth where the total pressure is 5.2 atm. The partial pressure of oxygen is maintained at 0.20 atm at this depth.

11.75   A sample of ammonia (NH_3) gas is completely decomposed to nitrogen and hydrogen gases over heated iron wool. If the total pressure is 866 mmHg after the reaction, calculate the partial pressures of N_2 and H_2.

11.76   Consider the three containers shown, all of which have the same volume and are at the same temperature. (a) Which container has the smallest mole fraction of gas A (red)? (b) Which container has the highest partial pressure of gas B (green)? (c) Which container has the highest total pressure?

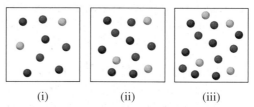

(i)   (ii)   (iii)

11.77   The volume of the box on the right is twice that of the box on the left. The boxes contain helium atoms (red) and hydrogen molecules (green) at the same temperature. (a) Which box has a higher total pressure? (b) Which box has a higher partial pressure of helium?

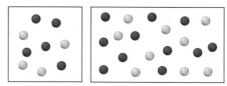

11.78   The Catalina hyperbaric chamber at the University of Southern California's Wrigley Marine Science Center treats mostly victims of diving accidents. In one treatment protocol, the chamber is pressurized to 4.6 atm with compressed air and the patient breathes a mixture of gases that contains oxygen. If the partial pressure of oxygen is 2.8 atm, what is the mole fraction of oxygen?

11.79   Considering the hyperbaric chamber in problem 11.78, what chamber pressure would be required for a patient to receive the therapeutic partial pressure of O_2 (2.8 atm) without breathing a special mixture of gases through a mask? Assume that the air used to pressurize the chamber is 21 percent O_2 by volume.

SECTION 11.8:   REACTIONS WITH GASEOUS REACTANTS AND PRODUCTS

Visualizing Chemistry
Figure 11.24

VC 11.1 The molar volume of hydrogen can be determined using the reaction of zinc metal and acid,

$$Zn(s) + 2H^+(aq) \longrightarrow Zn^{2+}(aq) + H_2(g)$$

as shown in Figure 11.24. When the reaction is complete, what does the space above the water in the graduated cylinder contain?
(a) $H_2(g)$, $Zn^{2+}(aq)$, and $H_2O(g)$
(b) $H_2(g)$ and $H_2O(g)$
(c) $H_2(g)$, $H_2O(g)$, and air

VC 11.2 How would the calculated molar volume be affected if we neglected to subtract the partial pressure of water vapor from the total pressure?
(a) It would be greater.
(b) It would be smaller.
(c) It would not change.

VC 11.3 How would the calculated molar volume be affected if we neglected to adjust the level of the graduated cylinder prior to reading the volume of gas collected? Assume that the level of water inside the graduated cylinder is higher than the level outside.
(a) It would be greater.
(b) It would be smaller.
(c) It would not change.

VC 11.4 How would the calculated molar volume be affected if some of the zinc metal failed to drop into the aqueous acid?
(a) It would be greater.
(b) It would be smaller.
(c) It would not change.

Problems

11.80 Consider the formation of nitrogen dioxide from nitric oxide and oxygen:

$$2NO(g) + O_2(g) \longrightarrow 2NO_2(g)$$

If 9.0 L of NO is combined with excess O_2 at STP, what is the volume in liters of the NO_2 produced?

11.81 Methane, the principal component of natural gas, is used for heating and cooking. The combustion process is

$$CH_4(g) + 2O_2(g) \longrightarrow CO_2(g) + 2H_2O(l)$$

If 15.0 moles of CH_4 react with oxygen, what is the volume of CO_2 (in liters) produced at 23.0°C and 0.985 atm?

11.82 When coal is burned, the sulfur present in coal is converted to sulfur dioxide (SO_2), which is largely responsible for the production of acid rain:

$$S(s) + O_2(g) \longrightarrow SO_2(g)$$

Calculate the volume of SO_2 gas (in mL) formed at 30.5°C and 1.04 atm when 3.15 kg of S reacts with excess oxygen.

11.83 In alcohol fermentation, yeast converts glucose to ethanol and carbon dioxide:

$$C_6H_{12}O_6(s) \longrightarrow 2C_2H_5OH(l) + 2CO_2(g)$$

If 5.97 g of glucose reacts and 1.44 L of CO_2 gas is collected at 293 K and 0.984 atm, what is the percent yield of the reaction?

11.84 A compound of P and F was analyzed as follows: Heating 0.2324 g of the compound in a 378-cm^3 container turned all of it to gas, which had a pressure of 97.3 mmHg at 77°C. Then the gas was mixed with calcium chloride solution, which converted all the F to 0.2631 g of CaF_2. Determine the molecular formula of the compound.

11.85 A quantity of 0.225 g of a metal M (molar mass = 27.0 g/mol) reacted with an excess of hydrochloric acid to produce 0.303 L of molecular hydrogen (measured at 17°C and 741 mmHg). Deduce from these data the corresponding equation, and write formulas for the oxide and the sulfate of the metal M.

11.86 What is the mass of the solid NH_4Cl formed when 73.0 g of NH_3 is mixed with an equal mass of HCl? What is the volume of the gas remaining, measured at 14.0°C and 752 mmHg? What gas is it?

11.87 Dissolving 3.00 g of an impure sample of calcium carbonate in hydrochloric acid produced 0.656 L of carbon dioxide (measured at 20.0°C and 792 mmHg). Calculate the percent by mass of calcium carbonate in the sample. State any assumptions.

11.88 Calculate the mass in grams of hydrogen chloride produced when 5.6 L of molecular hydrogen measured at STP react with an excess of molecular chlorine gas.

11.89 Ethanol (C_2H_5OH) burns in air:

$$C_2H_5OH(l) + O_2(g) \longrightarrow CO_2(g) + H_2O(l)$$

Balance the equation and determine the volume of air in liters at 45.0°C and 793 mmHg required to burn 185 g of ethanol. Assume that air is 21.0 percent O_2 by volume.

11.90 A piece of sodium metal reacts completely with water as follows:

$$2Na(s) + 2H_2O(l) \longrightarrow 2NaOH(aq) + H_2(g)$$

The hydrogen gas generated is collected over water at 25.0°C. The volume of the gas is 246 mL measured at 1.00 atm. Calculate the number of grams of sodium used in the reaction. (Vapor pressure of water at 25°C = 0.0313 atm.)

11.91 A sample of zinc metal reacts completely with an excess of hydrochloric acid:

$$Zn(s) + 2HCl(aq) \longrightarrow ZnCl_2(aq) + H_2(g)$$

The hydrogen gas produced is collected over water at 25.0°C using an arrangement similar to that shown in Figure 11.23(a). The volume of the gas is 7.80 L, and the pressure is 0.980 atm. Calculate the amount of zinc metal in grams consumed in the reaction. (Vapor pressure of water at 25°C = 23.8 mmHg.)

ADDITIONAL PROBLEMS

11.92   Under the same conditions of temperature and pressure, which of the following gases would behave most ideally: Ne, N_2, or CH_4? Explain.

11.93   Nitroglycerin, an explosive compound, decomposes according to the equation

$$4C_3H_5(NO_3)_3(s) \longrightarrow 12CO_2(g) + 10H_2O(g) + 6N_2(g) + O_2(g)$$

Calculate the total volume of gases when collected at 1.2 atm and 25°C from 2.6×10^2 g of nitroglycerin. What are the partial pressures of the gases under these conditions?

11.94   The empirical formula of a compound is CH. At 200°C, 0.145 g of this compound occupies 97.2 mL at a pressure of 0.74 atm. What is the molecular formula of the compound?

11.95   When ammonium nitrite (NH_4NO_2) is heated, it decomposes to give nitrogen gas. This property is used to inflate some tennis balls. (a) Write a balanced equation for the reaction. (b) Calculate the quantity (in grams) of NH_4NO_2 needed to inflate a tennis ball to a volume of 86.2 mL at 1.20 atm and 22°C.

11.96   The percent by mass of bicarbonate (HCO_3^-) in a certain Alka-Seltzer product is 32.5 percent. Calculate the volume of CO_2 generated (in mL) at 37°C and 1.00 atm when a person ingests a 3.29-g tablet. (*Hint:* The reaction is between HCO_3^- and HCl acid in the stomach.)

11.97   Three flasks containing gases A (red) and B (blue) are shown here. (a) If the total pressure in (i) is 2.0 atm, what are the pressures in (ii) and (iii)? (b) Calculate the total pressure and the partial pressure of each gas after the valves are opened. The volumes of (i) and (iii) are 2.0 L each, and the volume of (ii) is 1.0 L. The temperature is the same throughout.

(i)   (ii)   (iii)

11.98   Referring to the hyperbaric chamber in problem 11.78, in one treatment protocol, the chamber is pressurized to 6.0 atm with compressed air and the patient breathes a mixture of gases that is 47 percent oxygen by volume. In another protocol, the chamber is pressurized with compressed air to 2.8 atm and the patient breathes pure O_2. Determine the partial pressure of O_2 in each treatment protocol and compare the results.

11.99   In the metallurgical process of refining nickel, the metal is first combined with carbon monoxide to form tetracarbonylnickel, which is a gas at 43°C:

$$Ni(s) + 4CO(g) \longrightarrow Ni(CO)_4(g)$$

This reaction separates nickel from other solid impurities. (a) Starting with 86.4 g of Ni, calculate the pressure of $Ni(CO)_4$ in a container of volume 4.00 L. (Assume the preceding reaction goes to completion.) (b) At temperatures above 43°C, the pressure of the gas is observed to increase much more rapidly than predicted by the ideal gas equation. Explain.

11.100   The partial pressure of carbon dioxide varies with seasons. Would you expect the partial pressure in the Northern Hemisphere to be higher in the summer or winter? Explain.

11.101   A healthy adult exhales about 5.0×10^2 mL of a gaseous mixture with each breath. Calculate the number of molecules present in this volume at 37°C and 1.1 atm. List the major components of this gaseous mixture.

11.102   Sodium bicarbonate ($NaHCO_3$) is called baking soda because when heated, it releases carbon dioxide gas, which is responsible for the rising of cookies, some doughnuts, and cakes. (a) Calculate the volume (in liters) of CO_2 produced by heating 5.0 g of $NaHCO_3$ at 180°C and 1.3 atm. (b) Ammonium bicarbonate (NH_4HCO_3) has also been used for the same purpose. Suggest one advantage and one disadvantage of using NH_4HCO_3 instead of $NaHCO_3$ for baking.

11.103   On heating, potassium chlorate ($KClO_3$) decomposes to yield potassium chloride and oxygen gas. In one experiment, a student heated 20.4 g of $KClO_3$ until the decomposition was complete. (a) Write a balanced equation for the reaction. (b) Calculate the volume of oxygen (in liters) if it was collected at 0.962 atm and 18.3°C.

11.104   Some commercial drain cleaners contain a mixture of sodium hydroxide and aluminum powder. When the mixture is poured down a clogged drain, the following reaction occurs:

$$2NaOH(aq) + 2Al(s) + 6H_2O(l) \longrightarrow$$
$$2NaAl(OH)_4(aq) + 3H_2(g)$$

The heat generated in this reaction helps melt away obstructions such as grease, and the hydrogen gas released stirs up the solids clogging the drain. Calculate the volume of H_2 formed at 23°C and 1.00 atm if 3.12 g of Al are treated with an excess of NaOH.

11.105   The volume of a sample of pure HCl gas was 189 mL at 25°C and 108 mmHg. It was completely dissolved in about 60 mL of water and titrated with an NaOH solution; 15.7 mL of the NaOH solution was required to neutralize the HCl. Calculate the molarity of the NaOH solution.

11.106   Propane (C_3H_8) burns in oxygen to produce carbon dioxide gas and water vapor. (a) Write a balanced equation for this reaction. (b) Calculate the number of liters of carbon dioxide measured at STP that could be produced from 7.45 g of propane.

11.107 Consider the following apparatus. Calculate the partial pressures of helium and neon after the stopcock is open. The temperature remains constant at 16°C.

1.2 L
0.63 atm

3.4 L
2.8 atm

11.108 Nitric oxide (NO) reacts with molecular oxygen as follows:

$$2NO(g) + O_2(g) \longrightarrow 2NO_2(g)$$

Initially NO and O_2 are separated as shown here. When the valve is opened, the reaction quickly goes to completion. Determine what gases remain at the end and calculate their partial pressures. Assume that the temperature remains constant at 25°C.

4.00 L at
0.500 atm

2.00 L at
1.00 atm

11.109 Consider the apparatus shown here. When a small amount of water is introduced into the flask by squeezing the bulb of the medicine dropper, water is squirted upward out of the long glass tubing. Explain this observation. (*Hint:* Hydrogen chloride gas is soluble in water.)

HCl gas

H₂O

Rubber bulb

H₂O

11.110 A 180.0-mg sample of an alloy of iron and metal X is treated with dilute sulfuric acid, liberating hydrogen and yielding Fe^{2+} and X^{3+} ions in solution. It is known that the alloy contains 20.0 percent iron by mass. The alloy yields 50.9 mL of hydrogen collected over water at 22°C and a total pressure of 750.0 torr. What is element X?

11.111 A certain hydrate has the formula $MgSO_4 \cdot xH_2O$. A quantity of 54.2 g of the compound is heated in an oven to drive off the water. If the steam generated exerts a pressure of 24.8 atm in a 2.00-L container at 120°C, calculate *x*.

11.112 A mixture of Na_2CO_3 and $MgCO_3$ of mass 7.63 g is combined with an excess of hydrochloric acid. The CO_2 gas generated occupies a volume of 1.67 L at 1.24 atm and 26°C. From these data, calculate the percent composition by mass of Na_2CO_3 in the mixture.

11.113 The apparatus shown below can be used to measure atomic and molecular speeds. Suppose that a beam of metal atoms is directed at a rotating cylinder in a vacuum. A small opening in the cylinder allows the atoms to strike a target area. Because the cylinder is rotating, atoms traveling at different speeds will strike the target at different positions. In time, a layer of the metal will deposit on the target area, and the variation in its thickness is found to correspond to Maxwell's speed distribution. In one experiment, it is found that at 850°C some bismuth (Bi) atoms struck the target at a point 2.80 cm from the spot directly opposite the slit. The diameter of the cylinder is 15.0 cm, and it is rotating at 130 revolutions per second. (a) Calculate the speed (in m/s) at which the target is moving. (*Hint:* The circumference of a circle is given by $2\pi r$, where *r* is the radius.) (b) Calculate the time (in seconds) it takes for the target to travel 2.80 cm. (c) Determine the speed of the Bi atoms. Compare your result in part (c) with the u_{rms} of Bi at 850°C. Comment on the difference.

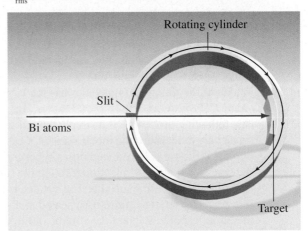

Rotating cylinder

Slit

Bi atoms

Target

11.114 If 10.00 g of water is introduced into an evacuated flask of volume 2.500 L at 65°C, calculate the mass of water vaporized. (*Hint:* Assume that the volume of the remaining liquid water is negligible; the vapor pressure of water at 65°C is 187.5 mmHg.)

11.115 Commercially, compressed oxygen is sold in metal cylinders. If a 120-L cylinder is filled with oxygen to a pressure of 132 atm at 22°C, what is the mass of O_2 present? How many liters of O_2 gas at 1.00 atm and 22°C could the cylinder produce? (Assume ideal behavior.)

11.116   The shells of hard-boiled eggs sometimes crack due to the rapid thermal expansion of the shells at high temperatures. Suggest another reason why the shells may crack.

11.117   Ethylene gas (C_2H_4) is emitted by fruits and is known to be responsible for their ripening. Based on this information, explain why a bunch of bananas ripens faster in a closed paper bag than in an open bowl.

11.118   About 8.0×10^6 tons of urea [$(NH_2)_2CO$] are used annually as a fertilizer. The urea is prepared at 200°C and under high-pressure conditions from carbon dioxide and ammonia (the products are urea and steam). Calculate the volume of ammonia (in liters) measured at 150 atm needed to prepare 1.0 ton of urea.

11.119   Some ballpoint pens have a small hole in the main body of the pen. What is the purpose of this hole?

11.120   The gas laws are vitally important to scuba divers. The pressure exerted by 33 ft of seawater is equivalent to 1 atm pressure. (a) A diver ascends quickly to the surface of the water from a depth of 36 ft without exhaling gas from his lungs. By what factor will the volume of his lungs increase by the time he reaches the surface? Assume that the temperature is constant. (b) The partial pressure of oxygen in air is about 0.20 atm. (Air is 20 percent oxygen by volume.) In deep-sea diving, the composition of air the diver breathes must be changed to maintain this partial pressure. What must the oxygen content (in percent by volume) be when the total pressure exerted on the diver is 4.0 atm? (At constant temperature and pressure, the volume of a gas is directly proportional to the number of moles of gases.)

11.121   Nitrous oxide (N_2O) can be obtained by the thermal decomposition of ammonium nitrate (NH_4NO_3). (a) Write a balanced equation for the reaction. (b) In a certain experiment, a student obtains 0.340 L of the gas at 718 mmHg and 24°C. If the gas weighs 0.580 g, calculate the value of the gas constant.

11.122   Two vessels are labeled A and B. Vessel A contains NH_3 gas at 70°C, and vessel B contains Ne gas at the same temperature. If the average kinetic energy of NH_3 is 7.1×10^{-21} J/molecule, calculate the root-mean-square speed of Ne atoms in m^2/s^2.

11.123   Which of the following molecules has the largest a value: CH_4, F_2, C_6H_6, Ne?

11.124   The following procedure is a simple though somewhat crude way to measure the molar mass of a gas. A liquid of mass 0.0184 g is introduced into a syringe like the one shown here by injection through the rubber tip using a hypodermic needle. The syringe is then transferred to a temperature bath heated to 45°C, and the liquid vaporizes. The final volume of the vapor (measured by the outward movement of the plunger) is 5.58 mL, and the atmospheric pressure is 760 mmHg. Given that the compound's empirical formula is CH_2, determine the molar mass of the compound.

Rubber tip

11.125   In 1995, a man suffocated as he walked by an abandoned mine in England. At that moment there was a sharp drop in atmospheric pressure due to a change in the weather. Suggest what might have caused the man's death.

11.126   Acidic oxides such as carbon dioxide react with basic oxides like calcium oxide (CaO) and barium oxide (BaO) to form salts (metal carbonates). (a) Write equations representing these two reactions. (b) A student placed a mixture of BaO and CaO of combined mass 4.88 g in a 1.46-L flask containing carbon dioxide gas at 35°C and 746 mmHg. After the reactions were complete, she found that the CO_2 pressure had dropped to 252 mmHg. Calculate the percent composition by mass of the mixture. Assume that the volumes of the solids are negligible.

11.127   (a) What volume of air at 1.0 atm and 22°C is needed to fill a 0.98-L bicycle tire to a pressure of 5.0 atm at the same temperature? (Note that the 5.0 atm is the gauge pressure, which is the difference between the pressure in the tire and atmospheric pressure. Before filling, the pressure in the tire was 1.0 atm.) (b) What is the total pressure in the tire when the gauge pressure reads 5.0 atm? (c) The tire is pumped by filling the cylinder of a hand pump with air at 1.0 atm and then, by compressing the gas in the cylinder, adding all the air in the pump to the air in the tire. If the volume of the pump is 33 percent of the tire's volume, what is the gauge pressure in the tire after three full strokes of the pump? Assume constant temperature.

11.128   The running engine of an automobile produces carbon monoxide (CO), a toxic gas, at the rate of about 188 g CO per hour. A car is left idling in a poorly ventilated garage that is 6.0 m long, 4.0 m wide, and 2.2 m high at 20°C. (a) Calculate the rate of CO production in mol/min. (b) How long would it take to build up a lethal concentration of CO of 1000 ppmv (parts per million by volume)?

11.129   Interstellar space contains mostly hydrogen atoms at a concentration of about 1 atom/cm^3. (a) Calculate the pressure of the H atoms. (b) Calculate the volume (in liters) that contains 1.0 g of H atoms. The temperature is 3 K.

11.130   Atop Mt. Everest, the atmospheric pressure is 210 mmHg and the air density is 0.426 kg/m^3. (a) Calculate the air temperature, given that the molar mass of air is 29.0 g/mol. (b) Assuming no change in air composition, calculate the percent decrease in oxygen gas from sea level to the top of Mt. Everest.

11.131   Relative humidity is defined as the ratio (expressed as a percentage) of the partial pressure of water vapor in the air to the equilibrium vapor pressure (see Table 11.6) at a given temperature. On a certain summer day in North Carolina, the partial pressure of water vapor in the air is 3.9×10^3 Pa at 30°C. Calculate the relative humidity.

11.132   Under the same conditions of temperature and pressure, why does 1 L of moist air weigh less than 1 L of dry air? In weather forecasts, an oncoming low-pressure front usually means imminent rainfall. Explain.

11.133 Air entering the lungs ends up in tiny sacs called alveoli. It is from the alveoli that oxygen diffuses into the blood. The average radius of the alveoli is 0.0050 cm, and the air inside contains 14 percent oxygen. Assuming that the pressure in the alveoli is 1.0 atm and the temperature is 37°C, calculate the number of oxygen molecules in one of the alveoli. (*Hint:* The volume of a sphere of radius r is $\frac{4}{3}\pi r^3$.)

11.134 A student breaks a thermometer and spills most of the mercury (Hg) onto the floor of a laboratory that measures 15.2 m long, 6.6 m wide, and 2.4 m high. (a) Calculate the mass of mercury vapor (in grams) in the room at 20°C. The vapor pressure of mercury at 20°C is 1.7×10^{-6} atm. (b) Does the concentration of mercury vapor exceed the air quality regulation of 0.050 mg Hg/m^3 of air? (c) One way to deal with small quantities of spilled mercury is to spray sulfur powder over the metal. Suggest a physical and a chemical reason for this action.

11.135 Nitrogen forms several gaseous oxides. One of them has a density of 1.33 g/L measured at 764 mmHg and 150°C. Write the formula of the compound.

11.136 Nitrogen dioxide (NO_2) cannot be obtained in a pure form in the gas phase because it exists as a mixture of NO_2 and N_2O_4. At 25°C and 0.98 atm, the density of this gas mixture is 2.7 g/L. What is the partial pressure of each gas?

11.137 Lithium hydride reacts with water as follows:

$$LiH(s) + H_2O(l) \longrightarrow LiOH(aq) + H_2(g)$$

During World War II, U.S. pilots carried LiH tablets. In the event of a crash landing at sea, the LiH would react with the seawater and fill their life jackets and lifeboats with hydrogen gas. How many grams of LiH are needed to fill a 4.1-L life jacket at 0.97 atm and 12°C?

11.138 The atmosphere on Mars is composed mainly of carbon dioxide. The surface temperature is 220 K, and the atmospheric pressure is about 6.0 mmHg. Taking these values as Martian "STP," calculate the molar volume in liters of an ideal gas on Mars.

11.139 Venus's atmosphere is composed of 96.5 percent CO_2, 3.5 percent N_2, and 0.015 percent SO_2 by volume. Its standard atmospheric pressure is 9.0×10^6 Pa. Calculate the partial pressures of the gases in pascals.

11.140 A student tries to determine the volume of a bulb like the one shown in Figure 11.18. These are her results: mass of the bulb filled with dry air at 23°C and 744 mmHg = 91.6843 g; mass of evacuated bulb = 91.4715 g. Assume the composition of air is 78 percent N_2, 21 percent O_2, and 1 percent argon by volume. What is the volume (in mL) of the bulb? (*Hint:* First calculate the average molar mass of air, as shown in Problem 5.137.)

11.141 Apply your knowledge of the kinetic theory of gases to the following situations. (a) Two flasks of volumes V_1 and V_2 ($V_2 > V_1$) contain the same number of helium atoms at the same temperature. (i) Compare the root-mean-square (rms) speeds and average kinetic energies of the helium (He) atoms in the flasks. (ii) Compare the frequency and the force with which the He atoms collide with the walls of their containers. (b) Equal numbers of He atoms are placed in two flasks of the same volume at temperatures T_1 and T_2 ($T_2 > T_1$). (i) Compare the rms speeds of the atoms in the two flasks. (ii) Compare the frequency and the force with which the He atoms collide with the walls of their containers. (c) Equal numbers of He and neon (Ne) atoms are placed in two flasks of the same volume, and the temperature of both gases is 74°C. Comment on the validity of the following statements: (i) The rms speed of He is equal to that of Ne. (ii) The average kinetic energies of the two gases are equal. (iii) The rms speed of each He atom is 1.47×10^3 m/s.

11.142 At what temperature will He atoms have the same u_{rms} value as N_2 molecules at 25°C?

11.143 Estimate the distance (in nm) between molecules of water vapor at 100°C and 1.0 atm. Assume ideal behavior. Repeat the calculation for liquid water at 100°C, given that the density of water is 0.96 g/cm^3 at that temperature. Comment on your results. (Assume each water molecule to be a sphere with a diameter of 0.3 nm.) (*Hint:* First calculate the number density of water molecules. Next, convert the number density to linear density, that is, the number of molecules in one direction.)

11.144 Which of the noble gases would not behave ideally under any conditions? Explain.

11.145 A 5.72-g sample of graphite was heated with 68.4 g of O_2 in a 8.00-L flask. The reaction that took place was

$$C(graphite) + O_2(g) \longrightarrow CO_2(g)$$

After the reaction was complete, the temperature in the flask was 182°C. What was the total pressure inside the flask?

11.146 A 6.11-g sample of a Cu-Zn alloy reacts with HCl acid to produce hydrogen gas. If the hydrogen gas has a volume of 1.26 L at 22°C and 728 mmHg, what is the percent of Zn in the alloy? (*Hint:* Cu does not react with HCl.)

11.147 A stockroom supervisor measured the contents of a 25.0-gal drum partially filled with acetone on a day when the temperature was 18.0°C and atmospheric pressure was 750 mmHg, and found that 15.4 gal of the solvent remained. After tightly sealing the drum, an assistant dropped the drum while carrying it upstairs to the organic laboratory. The drum was dented, and its internal volume was decreased to 20.4 gal. What is the total pressure inside the drum after the accident? The vapor pressure of acetone at 18.0°C is 400 mmHg. (*Hint:* At the time the drum was sealed, the pressure inside the drum, which is equal to the sum of the pressures of air and acetone, was equal to the atmospheric pressure.)

11.148 In 2.00 min., 29.7 mL of He effuses through a small hole. Under the same conditions of pressure and temperature, 10.0 mL of a mixture of CO and CO_2 effuses through the hole in the same amount of time. Calculate the percent composition by volume of the mixture.

11.149 A mixture of methane (CH_4) and ethane (C_2H_6) is stored in a container at 294 mmHg. The gases are burned in air to form CO_2 and H_2O. If the pressure of CO_2 is 356 mmHg measured at the same temperature and volume as the original mixture, calculate the mole fractions of the gases.

11.150 Use the kinetic theory of gases to explain why hot air rises.

11.151 One way to gain a physical understanding of b in the van der Waals equation is to calculate the "excluded volume." Assume that the distance of closest approach between two similar atoms is the sum of their radii ($2r$). (a) Calculate the volume around each atom into which the center of another atom cannot penetrate. (b) From your result in part (a), calculate the excluded volume for 1 mole of the atoms, which is the constant b. How does this volume compare with the sum of the volumes of 1 mole of the atoms?

11.152 A 5.00-mole sample of NH_3 gas is kept in a 1.92-L container at 300 K. If the van der Waals equation is assumed to give the correct answer for the pressure of the gas, calculate the percent error made in using the ideal gas equation to calculate the pressure.

11.153 The root-mean-square speed of a certain gaseous oxide is 493 m/s at 20°C. What is the molecular formula of the compound?

11.154 Referring to Figure 11.4, we see that the maximum of each speed distribution plot is called the most probable speed (u_{mp}) because it is the speed possessed by the largest number of molecules. It is given by $u_{mp} = \sqrt{2RT/\mathscr{M}}$. (a) Compare u_{mp} with u_{rms} for nitrogen at 25°C. (b) The following diagram shows the Maxwell speed distribution curves for an ideal gas at two different temperatures T_1 and T_2. Calculate the value of T_2.

11.155 A gaseous reaction takes place at constant volume and constant pressure in a cylinder as shown here. Which of the following equations best describes the reaction?

The initial temperature (T_1) is twice that of the final temperature (T_2).
(a) A + B $\longrightarrow$ C
(b) AB $\longrightarrow$ C + D
(c) A + B $\longrightarrow$ C + D
(d) A + B $\longrightarrow$ 2C + D

11.156 Assuming ideal behavior, which of the following gases will have the greatest volume at STP? (a) 0.82 mole of He, (b) 24 g of N_2, or (c) 5.0×10^{23} molecules of Cl_2.

11.157 Calculate the density of helium in a helium balloon at 25.0°C. (Assume that the pressure inside the balloon is 1.10 atm.)

11.158 Helium atoms in a closed container at room temperature are constantly colliding with one another and with the walls of their container. Does this "perpetual motion" violate the law of conservation of energy? Explain.

11.159 Sulfur hexafluoride (SF_6) has a molar mass of 146 g/mol and neon (Ne) has a molar mass of 20 g/mol. However, the average kinetic energies of these two gases at the same temperature are the same. Explain.

11.160 Consider the molar volumes shown in Figure 11.19. (a) Explain why Cl_2 and NH_3 have molar volumes significantly smaller from that of an ideal gas. (b) Explain why H_2, He, and Ne have molar volumes greater than that of an ideal gas. (*Hint:* Look up the boiling points of the gases shown in the figure.)

11.161 The plot of Z versus P for a gas at 0°C is shown. Explain the causes of the negative deviation from ideal behavior at lower pressures and the positive deviation from ideal behavior at higher pressures.

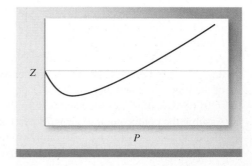

Answers to In-Chapter Materials

PRACTICE PROBLEMS

11.1A 2.137. **11.1B** 2.02 g/mol, H_2. **11.2A** 1.32 atm. **11.2B** 9.52 m. **11.3A** 2.23 L. **11.3B** 1.80 atm. **11.4A** 30.7 L. **11.4B** 300°C. **11.5A** 34 L. **11.5B** 3.16 L CO, 1.58 L O_2. **11.6A** 5.09 L. **11.6B** 85.0 m. A common mistake in this problem is failure to subtract the atmospheric pressure (0.965 atm) from the total pressure at the bottom of the lake (9.19 atm). The pressure due to the *water* is only 8.23 atm. **11.7A** 128 L. **11.7B** 336°C. **11.8A** 0.180 g/L. **11.8B** 1.29 g/L. **11.9A** 55.2 g/mol. **11.9B** 146 g/mol. **11.10A** 50.6 atm, 51.6 atm. **11.10B** 1.3 atm, 1.3 atm. **11.11A** 0.0453 L/mol, 0.0113 L. **11.11B** 146 pm. **11.12A** $P_{He} = 0.184$ atm, $P_{H_2} = 0.390$ atm, $P_{Ne} = 1.60$ atm, $P_{total} = 2.18$ atm. **11.12B** 0.032 mol CH_4, 0.091 mol C_2H_6, 0.123 mol total. **11.13A** $\chi_{CO_2} = 0.0495$, $\chi_{CH_4} = 0.255$, $\chi_{He} = 0.695$, $P_{CO_2} = 0.286$ atm, $P_{CH_4} = 1.47$ atm, $P_{He} = 4.02$ atm. **11.13B** $P_{Xe} = 4.95$ atm, $P_{Ne} = 1.55$ atm, $n_{Xe} = 3.13$, $n_{Ne} = 0.984$. **11.14A** 151 mL. **11.14B** 3.48 g. **11.15A** 1.0×10^2 mol. **11.15B** 0.0052 atm. **11.16A** 1.03 g. **11.16B** 0.386 L.

SECTION REVIEW

11.2.1 94.95 g/mol, CH_3Br. **11.2.2** He effuses 3.16 times as fast as Ar. **11.3.1** 1.17 bar. **11.3.2** 2.300 atm. **11.3.3** 13.1 m. **11.3.4** 4.84 atm. **11.3.5** iii < i = ii. **11.4.1** 47.4 mL. **11.4.2** 50.0 mL. **11.4.3** 203°C. **11.4.4** 120 mL. **11.4.5** ii only. **11.4.6** i, ii, and iii. **11.5.1** 196 L. **11.5.2** 52 atm. **11.5.3** 4.77 g/L. **11.5.4** 60.1 g/mol. **11.6.1** 8.9 atm. **11.6.2** −183.6°C. **11.7.1** 0.201 atm. **11.7.2** 0.0138. **11.7.3** 1.60 atm. **11.7.4** $\chi_{red} = 0.3125$, $\chi_{blue} = 0.25$, $\chi_{green} = 0.4375$. **11.7.5** $P_{red} = 2.57$ atm, $P_{blue} = 2.05$ atm, $P_{green} = 3.59$ atm. **11.8.1** 11.2 L. **11.8.2** 148 g. **11.8.3** 0.424 g.

KEY SKILLS

Mole Fractions

Most of the gases that we encounter are mixtures of two or more different gases. The concentrations of gases in a mixture are typically expressed using mole fractions, which are calculated using Equation 11.15:

$$\chi_i = \frac{n_i}{n_{total}}$$

Depending on the information given in a problem, calculating mole fractions may require you to determine molar masses and carry out mass-to-mole conversions [◄◄ Section 5.10].

For example, consider a mixture that consists of known masses of three different gases: 5.50 g He, 7.75 g N_2O, and 10.00 g SF_6. Molar masses of the components are

He: $4.003 = $ $\boxed{\dfrac{4.003 \text{ g}}{\text{mol}}}$ N_2O: $2(14.01) + (16.00) = $ $\boxed{\dfrac{44.02 \text{ g}}{\text{mol}}}$ SF_6: $32.07 + 6(19.00) = $ $\boxed{\dfrac{146.1 \text{ g}}{\text{mol}}}$

We convert each of the masses given in the problem to moles by dividing each by the corresponding molar mass:

$\dfrac{5.50 \text{ g He}}{4.003 \text{ g/mol}}$ = 1.374 mol He $\dfrac{7.75 \text{ g } N_2O}{44.02 \text{ g/mol}}$ = 0.1761 mol N_2O $\dfrac{10.00 \text{ g } SF_6}{146.1 \text{ g/mol}}$ = 0.06846 mol SF_6

We then determine the total number of moles in the mixture:

1.374 mol He + 0.1761 mol N_2O + 0.06846 mol SF_6 = 1.619 moles

We divide the number of moles of each component by the total number of moles to get each component's mole fraction.

$\chi_{He} = \dfrac{1.374 \text{ mol He}}{1.619 \text{ moles}}$ = 0.849 $\chi_{N_2O} = \dfrac{0.1761 \text{ mol } N_2O}{1.619 \text{ moles}}$ = 0.109 $\chi_{SF_6} = \dfrac{0.06846 \text{ mol } SF_6}{1.619 \text{ moles}}$ = 0.0423

The resulting mole fractions have no units; and for any mixture, the sum of mole fractions of all components is 1. Rounding error may result in the overall sum of mole fractions not being exactly 1. In this case, to the appropriate number of significant figures [◄◄ Section 1.5], the sum is 1.00. (Note that we kept an extra digit throughout the calculations.)

Because at a given temperature, pressure is proportional to the number of moles, mole fractions can also be calculated using the partial pressures of the gaseous components using Equation 11.16:

$$\chi_i = \frac{P_i}{P_{total}}$$

Because gases that do not react with one another are all mutually miscible [◄◄ Section 11.1], gas mixtures are homogeneous—and can also be referred to as *solutions*. And although we first encounter mole fractions in the context of gases, they are also used extensively in the context of other solutions—including *aqueous* solutions [►► Section 13.5]. Determination of mole fraction is done the same way, regardless of the nature of the solution. When liquids are involved, it is sometimes necessary to convert from volume to mass using the liquid's *density* [◄◄ Section 1.4].

volume of liquid (mL) × density of liquid (g/mL) = mass of liquid (g)

Consider the following example: 5.75 g of sugar (sucrose, $C_{12}H_{22}O_{11}$) is dissolved in 100.0 mL of water at 25°C. We first determine the molar masses of sucrose and water.

$$H_2O: 2(1.008) + 16.00 = \boxed{\dfrac{18.02\ g}{mol}} \qquad C_{12}H_{22}O_{11}: 12(12.01) + 11(16.00) = \boxed{\dfrac{342.3\ g}{mol}}$$

Then we use the density of water to convert the volume given to a mass. The density of water at 25°C is 0.9970 g/mL.

$$\boxed{100.0\ mL\ H_2O} \times \boxed{\dfrac{0.9970\ g}{mL}} = \boxed{99.70\ g\ H_2O}$$

We convert the masses of both solution components to moles:

$$\boxed{\dfrac{5.75\ g\ C_{12}H_{22}O_{11}}{342.3\ g/mol}} = \boxed{0.01680\ mol\ C_{12}H_{22}O_{11}} \qquad \boxed{\dfrac{99.70\ g\ H_2O}{18.02\ g/mol}} = \boxed{5.5327\ mol\ H_2O}$$

We then sum the number of moles and divide moles of each individual component by the total.

$$\boxed{0.01680\ mol\ C_{12}H_{22}O_{11}} + \boxed{5.5327\ mol\ H_2O} = \boxed{5.5495\ moles}$$

$$\chi_{C_{12}H_{22}O_{11}} = \boxed{\dfrac{0.01680\ mol\ C_{12}H_{22}O_{11}}{5.5495\ moles}} = \boxed{0.00303} \qquad \chi_{H_2O} = \boxed{\dfrac{5.5327\ mol\ H_2O}{5.5495\ moles}} = \boxed{0.997}$$

To the appropriate number of significant figures, the mole fractions sum to 1.

Key Skills Problems

11.1
Determine the mole fraction of helium in a gaseous mixture consisting of 0.524 g He, 0.275 Ar, and 2.05 g CH_4.

(a) 0.0069   (b) 0.0259   (c) 0.481   (d) 0.493   (e) 0.131

11.2
Determine the mole fraction of argon in a gaseous mixture in which the partial pressures of H_2, N_2, and Ar are 0.01887 atm, 0.3105 atm, and 1.027 atm, respectively.

(a) 0.01391   (b) 0.2289   (c) 0.7572   (d) 0.01887   (e) 1.027

11.3
Determine the mole fraction of *water* in a solution consisting of 5.00 g glucose ($C_6H_{12}O_6$) and 250.0 g water.

(a) 0.00200   (b) 0.998   (c) 0.0278   (d) 1.00   (e) 0.907

11.4
Determine the mole fraction of ethanol in a solution containing 15.50 mL ethanol (C_2H_5OH) and 110.0 mL water. (The density of ethanol is 0.789 g/mL; the density of water is 0.997 g/mL.)

(a) 0.0436   (b) 6.08   (c) 0.265   (d) 0.958   (e) 0.0418

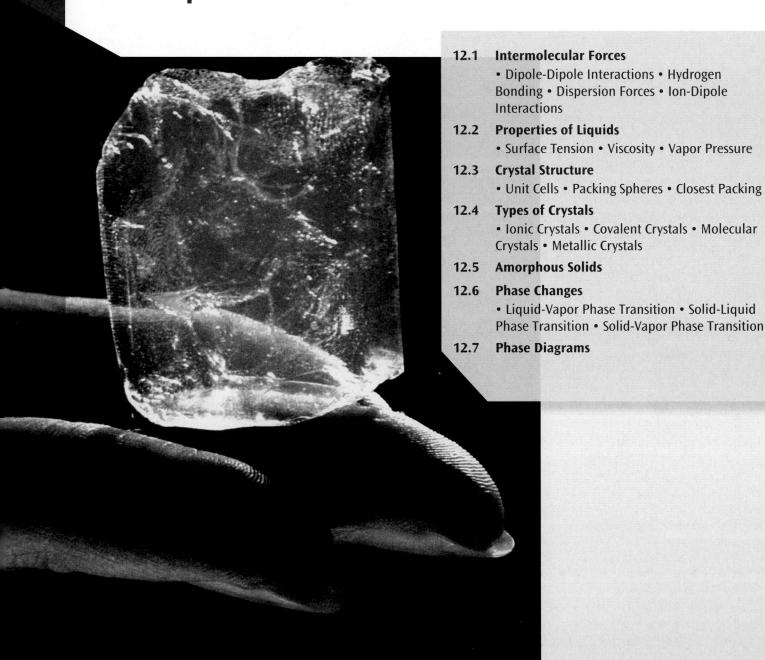

CHAPTER 12

Intermolecular Forces and the Physical Properties of Liquids and Solids

12.1 Intermolecular Forces
• Dipole-Dipole Interactions • Hydrogen Bonding • Dispersion Forces • Ion-Dipole Interactions

12.2 Properties of Liquids
• Surface Tension • Viscosity • Vapor Pressure

12.3 Crystal Structure
• Unit Cells • Packing Spheres • Closest Packing

12.4 Types of Crystals
• Ionic Crystals • Covalent Crystals • Molecular Crystals • Metallic Crystals

12.5 Amorphous Solids

12.6 Phase Changes
• Liquid-Vapor Phase Transition • Solid-Liquid Phase Transition • Solid-Vapor Phase Transition

12.7 Phase Diagrams

Discovered in 1931, aerogels were originally thought to be nothing more than chemical anomalies—due to their extremely low densities. (The lowest known density of an aerogel is actually less than the density of *air*.) After recognizing their unusual properties, chemists and physicists have applied aerogels to a number of important uses, including as chemical adsorbers for cleaning up chemical and oil spills, thermal insulation for the Mars rover and space suits, biocompatible drug delivery systems, and particle traps for space dust aboard spacecraft.

12.1 INTERMOLECULAR FORCES

In Chapter 11, we learned that gases consist of rapidly moving particles (molecules or atoms), separated by relatively large distances. Liquids and solids, the *condensed* phases [◄◄ margin note on page 5], consist of particles (molecules, atoms, or ions) that are touching one another. The attractive forces that hold particles together in the condensed phases are called ***intermolecular forces.*** The *magnitude* of intermolecular forces is what determines whether the particles that make up a substance are a gas, liquid, or solid.

Gas	Liquid	Solid
Particles in a gas are separated by large distances and free to move entirely independently of one another.	Particles in a liquid are touching one another but free to move about.	Particles in a solid are essentially locked in place with respect to one another.

We have already encountered an example of "intermolecular" forces in the form of ionic bonding [◄◄ Section 5.3], where the magnitude of attraction between oppositely charged particles is governed by Coulomb's law [◄◄ Section 4.4]. Because the particles that make up an ionic compound have discrete (*full*) charges, the attractive forces that hold them together are especially powerful. In fact, that's the reason that they're solids at room temperature. The intermolecular forces that we will encounter in this chapter are also the result of Coulombic attractions, but the attractions involve only partial charges [◄◄ Section 6.2] rather than discrete charges and are therefore weaker than the forces involved in ionic bonding.

We will begin our discussion of intermolecular forces with the attractive forces that act between atoms or molecules in a pure substance. These forces are known collectively as ***van der Waals forces,*** and they include *dipole-dipole interactions,* including *hydrogen bonding* and *dispersion forces.*

Student Annotation: The term *intermolecular* is used to refer to attractive forces between molecules, atoms, or ions.

Student Annotation: Hydrogen bonding constitutes a special type of dipole-dipole interaction and is discussed separately.

HCl

Dipole-Dipole Interactions

Dipole-dipole interactions are attractive forces that act between *polar molecules*. Recall that a diatomic molecule containing elements of significantly different electronegativities, such as HCl, has an unequal distribution of electron density and therefore has partial charges, positive (δ+) at one end and negative (δ−) at the other. The partial positive charge on one molecule is attracted to the partial negative charge on a neighboring molecule. Figure 12.1 shows the orientation of polar molecules in a solid and in a liquid. The arrangement is somewhat less orderly in the liquid than it is in the solid.

Because this attractive force between polar molecules is Coulombic, the magnitude of the attractive forces depends on the magnitude of the dipole. In general, the larger the dipole, the larger the attractive force. Certain physical properties such as boiling point *reflect* the magnitude of intermolecular forces. A substance in which the particles are held together by larger intermolecular attractions will require more energy to *separate* the particles and will therefore boil at a higher temperature. Table 12.1 lists several compounds with similar molar masses along with their dipole moments and boiling points.

Hydrogen Bonding

Hydrogen bonding is a special type of dipole-dipole interaction. But, whereas dipole-dipole interactions act between any polar molecules, hydrogen bonding occurs only in molecules that contain H bonded to a small, highly electronegative atom, such as N, O, or F. In a molecule such as HF, which is shown in Figure 12.2, the F atom to which H is bonded draws electron density toward itself. Being small and very electronegative, the F atom draws electron density away from H very effectively. Because H has only one electron, this leaves the hydrogen nucleus practically unshielded—giving H a very large partial positive charge. This large partial positive charge is powerfully attracted to the large partial negative charge (lone pairs) on the small, highly electronegative F atom of a neighboring HF molecule. The result is an especially strong dipole-dipole attraction.

In Worked Example 6.2 we calculated the partial charges on H and F as +0.41 and −0.41, respectively. The partial charges on H and Cl, by contrast, are only +0.18 and −0.18, respectively. They are smaller in HCl because Cl is larger and less electronegative than F. Because of the very high electronegativity of F, and the high partial positive charges that result, HF exhibits significant hydrogen bonding, whereas HCl does not.

Student Annotation: It is a common error to assume that hydrogen bonding occurs in any molecule that contains hydrogen. It *only* occurs to a significant degree in molecules with N—H, O—H, or F—H bonds.

Student Annotation: Strictly speaking, HCl does exhibit hydrogen bonding to a very small degree. But only molecules containing an N—H, O—H, or F—H bond exhibit significant hydrogen bonding.

Figure 12.1 Arrangement of polar molecules in a liquid (left) and in a solid (right).

Liquid

Solid

TABLE 12.1	Dipole Moments and Boiling Points of Compounds with Similar Molecular Masses		
Compound	**Structural formula**	**Dipole moment (D)**	**Boiling point (°C)**
Propane	$CH_3CH_2CH_3$	0.1	−42
Dimethyl ether	CH_3OCH_3	1.3	−25
Methyl chloride	CH_3Cl	1.9	−24
Acetaldehyde	CH_3CHO	2.7	21
Acetonitrile	CH_3CN	2.9	82

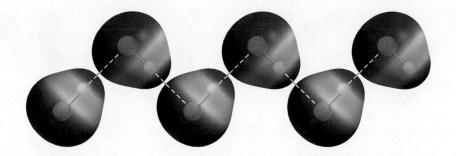

Figure 12.2 Hydrogen bonds between HF molecules.

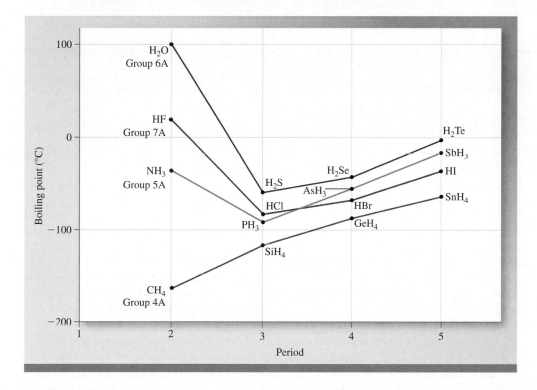

Figure 12.3 Boiling points of the hydrogen compounds of elements from Groups 4A through 7A. Although normally the boiling point increases with increasing mass within a group, the *lightest* compound has the *highest* boiling point in Groups 5A through 7A. This departure from the observed trend is due to hydrogen bonding.

Figure 12.3 shows the boiling points of the binary hydrogen compounds of Groups 4A through 7A. Within the series of hydrogen compounds of Group 4A, the boiling point increases with increasing molar mass. For Groups 5A through 7A, the same trend is observed for all but the smallest member of each series, which has what appears to be an unexpectedly high boiling point. This departure from the trend in boiling points illustrates how powerful hydrogen bonding can be. NH_3 (Group 5A), HF (Group 7A), and H_2O (Group 6A) have anomalously high boiling points because they exhibit strong hydrogen bonding. CH_4 (the smallest member of the Group 4A series) does not exhibit hydrogen bonding because it does not contain an N—H, O—H, or F—H bond; hence, it has the lowest boiling point of that group.

Student Annotation: Hydrogen bonding also occurs in mixtures, between solute and solvent molecules that contain N—H, F—H, or O—H bonds.

Dispersion Forces

Nonpolar gases, such as N_2 and O_2, can be liquefied under the right conditions of pressure and temperature, so nonpolar molecules must also exhibit attractive intermolecular forces. These intermolecular forces are Coulombic in nature (as are all intermolecular forces), but they differ from other intermolecular forces because they arise from the movement of electrons in nonpolar molecules.

On average, the distribution of electron density in a nonpolar molecule is uniform and symmetrical (which is why a nonpolar molecule has no dipole moment). However, because electrons in a molecule have some freedom to move about, at any given point in time the molecule may have a nonuniform distribution of electron density, giving it a fleeting, temporary dipole—called an ***instantaneous dipole.*** An instantaneous dipole in one molecule can induce dipoles in neighboring molecules. For example, the temporary partial negative charge on a molecule repels the electrons

Figure 12.4 Instantaneous dipoles in ordinarily nonpolar molecules can induce temporary dipoles in neighboring molecules, causing the molecules to be attracted to one another. This type of interaction is responsible for the condensation of nonpolar gases.

TABLE 12.2	Molar Masses, Boiling Points, and States of the Halogens at Room Temperature		
Molecule	**Molar mass (g/mol)**	**Boiling point (°C)**	**State (room temp.)**
F_2	38.0	−188	Gas
Cl_2	70.9	−34	Gas
Br_2	159.8	59	Liquid
I_2	253.8	184	Solid

in a molecule next to it. This repulsion polarizes the second molecule, which then acquires a temporary dipole. It in turn polarizes the next molecule and so on, leaving a collection of ordinarily nonpolar molecules with partial positive and negative charges and Coulombic attractions between them as shown in Figure 12.4. The resulting attractive forces are called ***London*[1] *dispersion forces*** or simply ***dispersion forces.***

The magnitude of dispersion forces depends on how mobile the electrons in the molecule are. In small molecules, such as F_2, the electrons are relatively close to the nuclei and cannot move about very freely; thus, the electron distribution in F_2 is not easily *polarized.* In larger molecules, such as Cl_2, the electrons are somewhat farther away from the nuclei and therefore move about more freely. The electron density in Cl_2 is more easily polarized than that in F_2, resulting in larger instantaneous dipoles, larger induced dipoles, and larger intermolecular attractions overall. The trend in magnitude of dispersion forces with increasing molecular size is illustrated by the data in Table 12.2. (It is also illustrated by the correlation between molar mass and boiling point in Figure 12.3.) Dispersion forces act not only between nonpolar molecules, but between *all* molecules.

Worked Example 12.1 lets you practice determining what kinds of forces exist between particles in liquids and solids.

> **Student Annotation:** Molecules that more readily acquire an instantaneous dipole are said to be *polarizable.* In general, larger molecules have greater *polarizability* than small ones.

Worked Example 12.1

What kind(s) of intermolecular forces exist in (a) $CCl_4(l)$, (b) $CH_3COOH(l)$, (c) $CH_3COCH_3(l)$, and (d) $H_2S(l)$?

Strategy Draw Lewis dot structures and apply VSEPR theory [◄◄ Section 7.1] to determine whether each molecule is polar or nonpolar. Nonpolar molecules exhibit dispersion forces only. Polar molecules exhibit both dipole-dipole interactions and dispersion forces. Polar molecules with N—H, F—H, or O—H bonds exhibit dipole-dipole interactions (including hydrogen bonding) and dispersion forces.

---

[1] Fritz London (1900–1954), a German physicist, was a theoretical physicist whose major work was on superconductivity in liquid helium.

Setup The Lewis dot structures for molecules (a) to (d) are:

(a)   (b)   (c)   (d)

Solution

(a) CCl_4 is nonpolar, so the only intermolecular forces are dispersion forces.

(b) CH_3COOH is polar and contains an O—H bond, so it exhibits dipole-dipole interactions (including hydrogen bonding) and dispersion forces.

(c) CH_3COCH_3 is polar but does *not* contain N—H, O—H, or F—H bonds, so it exhibits dipole-dipole interactions and dispersion forces.

(d) H_2S is polar but does not contain N—H, O—H, or F—H bonds, so it exhibits dipole-dipole interactions and dispersion forces.

> **Think About It**
> Being able to draw correct Lewis structures is, once again, vitally important. Review, if you need to, the procedure for drawing them [◀◀ Section 6.3].

Practice Problem A What kind(s) of intermolecular forces exist in (a) $CH_3CH_2CH_2CH_2CH_3(l)$, (b) $CH_3CH_2OH(l)$, (c) $H_2CO(l)$, and (d) $O_2(l)$?

Practice Problem B What kind(s) of intermolecular forces exist in (a) $CH_2Cl_2(l)$, (b) $CH_3CH_2CH_2OH(l)$, (c) $H_2O_2(l)$, and (d) $N_2(l)$?

Ion-Dipole Interactions

Ion-dipole interactions are Coulombic attractions between ions (either positive or negative) and polar molecules. These interactions occur in mixtures of ionic and polar species such as an aqueous solution of sodium chloride. The magnitude of ion-dipole interactions depends on the charge and the size of the ion, and on the dipole moment and size of the polar molecule. Cations generally interact more strongly with dipoles than anions (of the same magnitude charge) because they tend to be smaller.

Figure 12.5 shows the ion-dipole interaction between the Na^+ and Mg^{2+} ions with a water molecule, which has a large dipole moment (1.87 D). Because the Mg^{2+} ion has a *higher charge* and a *smaller size* [◀◀ Section 4.6] than the Na^+ ion (the ionic radii of Mg^{2+} and Na^+ are 72 and 102 pm, respectively), Mg^{2+} interacts more strongly with water molecules. The properties of solutions are discussed in Chapter 13.

Although the intermolecular forces discussed so far are all *attractive* forces, molecules also exert repulsive forces on one another (when *like* charges approach one another). When two molecules approach each other closely, the repulsions between electrons and between nuclei in the molecules become significant. The magnitude of these repulsive forces rises very steeply as the distance separating the molecules in a condensed phase decreases. This is the reason that liquids and solids are so hard to compress. In these phases, the molecules are already in close contact with one another, and so they greatly resist being compressed further.

> **Student Annotation:** Hydration [◀◀ Section 9.2] is one example of an ion-dipole interaction.

Figure 12.5 Ion-dipole interactions between ions and water molecules. In each case the positive charge on the ion is attracted to the partial negative charge on the oxygen atom in the water molecule. The attraction is stronger when the distance between the two species is smaller.

SECTION 12.1 REVIEW

Intermolecular Forces

12.1.1 Describe the intermolecular forces that exist between molecules of (a) C_6H_6, (b) HBr, (c) H_2CF_2, (d) H_2, (e) H_2O_2, and (f) CH_3CN.

12.1.2 Using intermolecular forces, explain why methane (CH_4) is a gas and hexane (C_6H_{14}) is a liquid.

Figure 12.6 Intermolecular forces acting on a molecule in the surface layer of a liquid and in the interior region of the liquid.

Student Annotation: *Cohesion* and *adhesion* are also called *cohesive forces* and *adhesive forces.*

Blood being drawn from a finger into a capillary tube.

Figure 12.7 Surface tension causes water to bead up on a just-washed car.

12.2 PROPERTIES OF LIQUIDS

Several of the physical properties of a liquid depend on the magnitude of its intermolecular forces. In this section we consider three such properties: surface tension, viscosity, and vapor pressure.

Surface Tension

A molecule within a liquid is pulled in all directions by the intermolecular forces between it and the other molecules that surround it. There is no *net* pull in any one direction. A molecule at the surface of the liquid is similarly pulled down and to the sides by neighboring molecules, but Figure 12.6 shows there is no upward pull to balance the downward or inward pull (into the bulk of the liquid). This results in a net pull inward on molecules at the surface, causing the surface of a liquid to tighten like an elastic film, thus minimizing its surface area. The "beading" of water on the surface of a freshly washed car, shown in Figure 12.7, is an illustration of this phenomenon.

A quantitative measure of the elastic force in the surface of a liquid is the ***surface tension,*** the amount of energy required to stretch or increase the surface of a liquid by a unit area (for example, by 1 cm^2). A liquid with strong intermolecular forces has a high surface tension. Water, for instance, with its strong hydrogen bonds, has a very high surface tension.

Another illustration of surface tension is the *meniscus,* the curved surface of a liquid contained in a narrow tube. Figure 12.8(a) shows the concave surface of water in a graduated cylinder. (You probably know from your laboratory class that you are to read the volume level with the bottom of the meniscus.) This is caused by a thin film of water adhering to the wall of the glass cylinder. The surface tension of water causes this film to contract, and as it does, it pulls the water up the cylinder. This effect, known as ***capillary action,*** is more pronounced in a cylinder with a very small diameter, such as a capillary tube used to draw a small amount of blood. Two types of forces bring about capillary action. One is ***cohesion,*** the attractions between *like* molecules (in this case, between water molecules). The other is ***adhesion,*** the attractions between *unlike* molecules (in this case, between water molecules and the molecules that make up the interior surface of the graduated cylinder). If adhesion is stronger than cohesion, as it is in Figure 12.8(a), the contents of the tube will be pulled upward. The upward movement is limited by the weight of the liquid in the tube. In the case of mercury, shown in Figure 12.8(b), the cohesive forces are stronger than the adhesive forces, resulting in a convex meniscus in which the liquid level at the glass wall is lower than that in the middle.

Viscosity

Another property determined by the magnitude of intermolecular forces in a liquid is viscosity. *Viscosity,* with units of N · s/m^2, is a measure of a fluid's resistance to flow. The higher the viscosity, the more slowly a liquid flows. The viscosity of a liquid typically decreases with increasing temperature. The phrase "slow as molasses in winter" refers to the fact that molasses pours more slowly (has a higher viscosity) in cold weather. You may also have noticed that honey and maple syrup seem thinner when they are heated.

(a)

(b)

Figure 12.8 (a) When water is measured in a glass graduated cylinder, the adhesive forces are greater than the cohesive forces and the meniscus is concave. (b) When mercury is measured in a glass graduated cylinder, cohesive forces are greater than adhesive forces and the meniscus is convex.

TABLE 12.3	Viscosities of Some Familiar Liquids at 20°C
Liquid	**Viscosity (N · s/m²)**
Acetone (C_3H_6O)	3.16×10^{-4}
Water (H_2O)	1.01×10^{-3}
Ethanol (C_2H_5OH)	1.20×10^{-3}
Mercury (Hg)	1.55×10^{-3}
Blood	4×10^{-3}
Glycerol ($C_3H_8O_3$)	1.49

Liquids that have strong intermolecular forces have higher viscosities than those that have weaker intermolecular forces. Table 12.3 lists the viscosities of some liquids that may be familiar to you. Water's high viscosity, like its high surface tension, is the result of hydrogen bonding. Note how large the viscosity of glycerol is compared to the other liquids listed in Table 12.3. The structure of glycerol, which is a sweet tasting, syrupy liquid used for a wide variety of things including the manufacture of candy and antibiotics, is

$$
\begin{array}{c}
\text{H} \\
| \\
\text{H}-\text{C}-\text{O}-\text{H} \\
| \\
\text{H}-\text{C}-\text{O}-\text{H} \\
| \\
\text{H}-\text{C}-\text{O}-\text{H} \\
| \\
\text{H}
\end{array}
$$

Glycerol

Like water, glycerol can form hydrogen bonds. Each glycerol molecule has three —OH groups that can participate in hydrogen bonding with other glycerol molecules. Furthermore, because of their shape, the molecules have a great tendency to become entangled rather than to slip past one another as the molecules of less viscous liquids do. These interactions contribute to its high viscosity.

Vapor Pressure

In Chapter 11 we encountered the term *vapor pressure,* referring to the temperature-dependent partial pressure of water [◀◀ Section 11.8]. In fact, vapor pressure is another property of liquids that depends on the magnitude of intermolecular forces. The molecules in a liquid are in constant

Student Annotation: Substances that have *high* vapor pressures at room temperature are said to be *volatile.* Note that this does *not* mean that a substance is explosive— only that it has a high vapor pressure.

motion, and, like the molecules in a gas, they have a distribution of kinetic energies. The most probable kinetic energy for molecules in a sample of liquid increases with increasing temperature, as shown in Figure 12.9. If a molecule at the surface of a liquid has sufficient kinetic energy, it can escape from the liquid phase into the gas phase. This phenomenon is known as ***evaporation*** or ***vaporization.*** Consider the apparatus shown in Figure 12.10. As a liquid begins to evaporate, molecules leave the liquid phase and become part of the gas phase in the space above the liquid. Molecules in the gas phase can return to the liquid phase if they strike the liquid surface and again become trapped by intermolecular forces, a process known as ***condensation.*** Initially, evaporation occurs more rapidly than condensation. As the number of molecules in the gas phase increases, however, so does the rate of condensation. The vapor pressure over the liquid increases until the rate of condensation is equal to the rate of evaporation, which is constant at any given temperature (Figure 12.11). This (or any other) situation, wherein a forward process and reverse process are occurring at the same rate, is called a ***dynamic equilibrium.*** Although both processes are ongoing (*dynamic*), the number of molecules in the gas phase at any given point in time does not change (*equilibrium*). The pressure exerted by the molecules that have escaped to the gas phase, once the pressure has stopped increasing, is the ***equilibrium vapor pressure.***

The average kinetic energy of molecules in a liquid increases with increasing temperature (see Figure 12.9). At a higher temperature, therefore, a greater percentage of molecules at the liquid surface will possess sufficient kinetic energy to escape into the gas phase. Consequently, as we have already seen with water in Table 11.6, vapor pressure increases with increasing temperature. Figure 12.12 shows the plots of vapor pressure versus temperature for three different liquids.

Student Annotation: The processes of vaporization and condensation are examples of *phase changes*. These and other phase changes are discussed in detail in Section 12.6.

Student Annotation: We often use the simpler term *vapor pressure* to mean *equilibrium vapor pressure.*

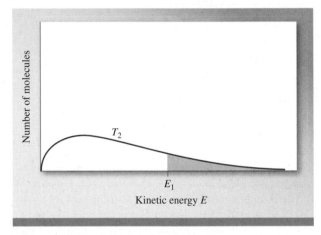

Figure 12.9 Kinetic energy distribution curves for molecules in a liquid (a) at temperature T_1 and (b) at a higher temperature T_2. Note that at the higher temperature, the curve flattens out. The shaded areas represent the number of molecules possessing kinetic energy equal to or greater than a certain kinetic energy E_1. The higher the temperature, the greater the number of molecules with high kinetic energy.

Figure 12.10 Establishment of equilibrium vapor pressure. (a) Initially, there are no molecules in the gas phase. (b) Molecules enter the gas phase, increasing the total pressure above the liquid. (c) The partial pressure of the liquid continues to increase until the rates of vaporization and condensation are equal. (d) Vaporization and condensation continue to occur at the same rate, and there is no further net change in pressure.

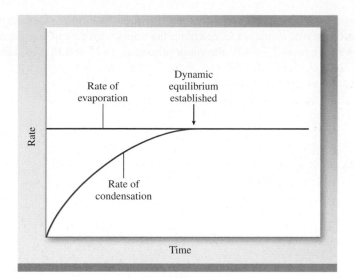

Figure 12.11 Comparison of the rates of vaporization and condensation at constant temperature.

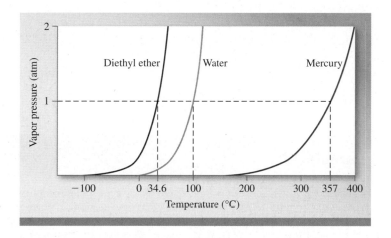

Figure 12.12 The increase in vapor pressure with temperature for three liquids. The normal boiling points of the liquids (at 1 atm) are shown on the horizontal axis. The strong metallic bonding in mercury results in its having a very low vapor pressure at room temperature.

The plots in Figure 12.12 of vapor pressure as a function of temperature are not linear. However, a linear relationship does exist between the natural log of vapor pressure and the reciprocal of absolute temperature. This relationship is called the **Clausius[2]-Clapeyron[3] equation:**

$$\ln P = -\frac{\Delta H_{vap}}{RT} + C \qquad \textbf{Equation 12.1}$$

where $\ln P$ is the natural logarithm of the vapor pressure, ΔH_{vap} is the molar heat of vaporization (kJ/mol), R is the gas constant (8.314 J/K · mol), and C is a constant that must be determined experimentally for each different compound. The Clausius-Clapeyron equation has the form of the general linear equation $y = mx + b$:

$$\ln P = \left(-\frac{\Delta H_{vap}}{R}\right)\left(\frac{1}{T}\right) + C$$
$$y = mx + b$$

By measuring the vapor pressure of a liquid at several different temperatures and plotting $\ln P$ versus $1/T$, we can determine the slope of the line, which is equal to $-\Delta H_{vap}/R$. (ΔH_{vap} is assumed to be independent of temperature.)

Student Annotation: The units of R are those that enable us to cancel the units of J/mol (or kJ/mol) associated with ΔH_{vap} [◀◀ Section 11.5, Table 11.4].

---

[2]Rudolf Julius Emanuel Clausius (1822–1888), a German physicist, worked mainly in electricity, kinetic theory of gases, and thermodynamics.

[3]Benoit Paul Emile Clapeyron (1799–1864), a French engineer, made contributions to the thermodynamics of steam engines.

If we know the value of ΔH_{vap} and the vapor pressure of a liquid at one temperature, we can use the Clausius-Clapeyron equation to calculate the vapor pressure of the liquid at a different temperature. At temperatures T_1 and T_2, the vapor pressures are P_1 and P_2. From Equation 12.1 we can write

Equation 12.2
$$\ln P_1 = -\frac{\Delta H_{vap}}{RT_1} + C$$

Equation 12.3
$$\ln P_2 = -\frac{\Delta H_{vap}}{RT_2} + C$$

Subtracting Equation 12.3 from Equation 12.2 we get

$$\ln P_1 - \ln P_2 = -\frac{\Delta H_{vap}}{RT_1} - \left(-\frac{\Delta H_{vap}}{RT_2} \right)$$

$$= \frac{\Delta H_{vap}}{R} \left(\frac{1}{T_2} - \frac{1}{T_1} \right)$$

and finally

Equation 12.4
$$\ln \frac{P_1}{P_2} = \frac{\Delta H_{vap}}{R} \left(\frac{1}{T_2} - \frac{1}{T_1} \right)$$

Worked Example 12.2 shows how to use Equation 12.4.

Worked Example 12.2

Diethyl ether is a volatile, highly flammable organic liquid that today is used mainly as a solvent. (It was used as an anesthetic during the nineteenth century and as a recreational intoxicant early in the twentieth century during prohibition, when ethanol was difficult to obtain.) The vapor pressure of diethyl ether is 401 mmHg at 18°C, and its molar heat of vaporization is 26 kJ/mol. Calculate its vapor pressure at 32°C.

Strategy Given the vapor pressure at one temperature, P_1, use Equation 12.4 to calculate the vapor pressure at a second temperature, P_2.

$$\ln \frac{P_1}{P_2} = \frac{\Delta H_{vap}}{R} \left(\frac{1}{T_2} - \frac{1}{T_1} \right)$$

Setup Temperature must be expressed in kelvins, so $T_1 = 291.15$ K and $T_2 = 305.15$ K. Because the molar heat of vaporization is given in kJ/mol, we will have to convert it to J/mol for the units of R to cancel properly: $\Delta H_{vap} = 2.6 \times 10^4$ J/mol. The inverse function of $\ln x$ is e^x.

Solution

$$\ln \frac{P_1}{P_2} = \frac{2.6 \times 10^4 \text{ J/mol}}{8.314 \text{ J/K} \cdot \text{mol}} \left(\frac{1}{305.15 \text{ K}} - \frac{1}{291.15 \text{ K}} \right)$$

$$= -0.4928$$

$$\frac{P_1}{P_2} = e^{-0.4928} = 0.6109$$

$$\frac{P_1}{0.6109} = P_2$$

$$P_2 = \frac{401 \text{ mmHg}}{0.6109} = 6.6 \times 10^2 \text{ mmHg}$$

Think About It
It is easy to switch P_1 and P_2 or T_1 and T_2 accidentally and get the wrong answer to a problem such as this. One way to help safeguard against this common error is to verify that the vapor pressure is *higher* at the higher temperature.

Practice Problem A The vapor pressure of ethanol is 1.00×10^2 mmHg at 34.9°C. What is its vapor pressure at 55.8°C? (ΔH_{vap} for ethanol is 39.3 kJ/mol.)

Practice Problem B Estimate the molar heat of vaporization of a liquid whose vapor pressure doubles when the temperature is raised from 85°C to 95°C. At what temperature will the vapor pressure be five times the value at 85°?

SECTION 12.2 REVIEW

Properties of Liquids

12.2.1 At what temperature would diethyl ether have a vapor pressure of 250 mmHg? Use the vapor pressure at 18°C and ΔH_{vap} given in Worked Example 12.2.

12.2.2 Given the following information for C_6F_6, calculate its ΔH_{vap}. At 300 K, the vapor pressure is 92.47 mmHg, and at 320 K, the vapor pressure is 225.1 mmHg.

12.2.3 Using the graph, estimate the vapor pressure of the liquid at 100°C.

12.2.4 Using the result from Question 12.2.3 and another point from the graph, estimate ΔH_{vap} for the liquid.

12.3 CRYSTAL STRUCTURE

Solids can be categorized as either crystalline or amorphous. A ***crystalline solid*** possesses rigid and long-range order; its atoms, molecules, or ions occupy specific positions. The arrangement of the particles in a crystalline solid, which we call the ***lattice structure,*** depends on the nature and the size of the particles involved. The forces responsible for the stability of a crystal can be ionic forces, covalent bonds, van der Waals forces, hydrogen bonds, or a combination of some of these forces. Amorphous solids lack a well-defined arrangement and long-range molecular order. In this section, we will concentrate on the nature of crystalline solids. (Amorphous solids are discussed in Section 12.5.)

> **Student Annotation:** Ice is a crystalline solid. Glass is an amorphous solid.

Unit Cells

A ***unit cell*** is the basic repeating structural unit of a crystalline solid. Figure 12.13 shows a unit cell and its extension in three dimensions. Each sphere represents an atom, ion, or molecule and is called a ***lattice point.*** For the purpose of clarity, we will limit our discussion in this section to metal crystals in which each lattice point is occupied by an atom.

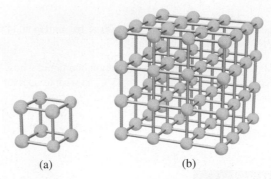

Figure 12.13 (a) A single unit cell and (b) a lattice (three-dimensional array) made up of many unit cells. Each sphere represents a lattice point, which may be an atom, a molecule, or an ion.

Simple cubic
$a = b = c$
$\alpha = \beta = \gamma = 90°$

Tetragonal
$a = b \neq c$
$\alpha = \beta = \gamma = 90°$

Orthorhombic
$a \neq b \neq c$
$\alpha = \beta = \gamma = 90°$

Rhombohedral
$a = b = c$
$\alpha = \beta = \gamma \neq 90°$

Monoclinic
$a \neq b \neq c$
$\gamma \neq \alpha = \beta = 90°$

Triclinic
$a \neq b \neq c$
$\alpha \neq \beta \neq \gamma \neq 90°$

Hexagonal
$a = b \neq c$
$\alpha = \beta = 90°, \gamma = 120°$

Figure 12.14 The seven types of unit cells. Angle α is defined by edges b and c, angle β by edges a and c, and angle γ by edges a and b.

Every crystalline solid can be described in terms of one of the seven types of unit cells shown in Figure 12.14. The geometry of the cubic unit cell is particularly simple because all sides and all angles are equal. Any of the unit cells, when repeated in space in all three dimensions, forms the lattice structure characteristic of a crystalline solid.

Packing Spheres

We can understand the geometric requirements for crystal formation by considering the different ways of packing a number of identical atoms to form an ordered three-dimensional structure. The way the atoms are arranged in layers determines the type of unit cell.

In the simplest case, a layer of atoms can be arranged as shown in Figure 12.15(a). The three-dimensional structure can be generated by placing a layer above and below this layer in such a way that atoms in one layer are directly over the atoms in the layer below. This procedure can be extended to generate many, many layers, as in the case of a crystal. Focusing on the atom labeled with an "*x*," we see that it is in contact with four atoms in its own layer, one atom in the layer above it, and one atom in the layer below it. Each atom in this arrangement is said to have a coordination number of 6 because it has six immediate neighbors. The ***coordination number*** is defined as the number of atoms surrounding an atom in a crystal lattice. The value of the coordination number indicates how tightly the atoms are packed together—the larger the coordination

Student Annotation: Depending on the type of particles that make up a solid, the coordination number can also refer to the number of surrounding molecules or ions.

Figure 12.15 Arrangement of identical spheres in a simple cubic cell. (a) Top view of one layer of spheres. (b) Definition of a simple cubic cell.

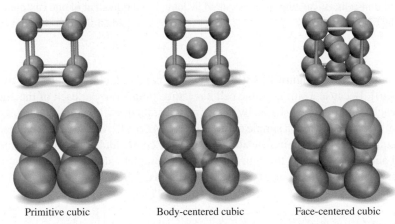

Primitive cubic   Body-centered cubic   Face-centered cubic

Figure 12.16 Three types of cubic cells. The top view makes it easier to see the locations of the lattice points, but the bottom view is more realistic, with the spheres touching one another.

Figure 12.17 In the body-centered cubic arrangement, the spheres in each layer rest in the depressions between spheres in the previous layer.

number, the closer the atoms are to one another. The basic repeating unit in the array of atoms is called a ***simple cubic cell*** (scc) [Figure 12.15(b)].

The other types of cubic cells, shown in Figure 12.16, are the ***body-centered cubic cell*** (bcc) and the ***face-centered cubic cell*** (fcc). Unlike the simple cube, the second layer of atoms in the body-centered cubic arrangement fits into the depressions of the first layer and the third layer fits into the depressions of the second layer (Figure 12.17).

The coordination number of each atom in the bcc structure is 8 (each sphere is in contact with four others in the layer above and four others in the layer below). In the face-centered cubic cell, there are atoms at the center of each of the six faces of the cube, in addition to the eight corner atoms. The coordination number in the face-centered cubic cell is 12 (each sphere is in contact with four others in its own layer, four others in the layer above, and four others in the layer below).

Because every unit cell in a crystalline solid is adjacent to other unit cells, most of a cell's atoms are shared by neighboring cells. (The atom at the center of the body-centered cubic cell is an exception.) In all types of cubic cells, for example, each corner atom belongs to eight unit cells whose corners all touch [Figure 12.18(a)]. An atom that lies on an edge, on the other hand,

Student Annotation: The simple cubic cell is also called the *primitive* cubic cell.

Figure 12.18 (a) A corner atom in any cell is shared by eight unit cells. (b) An edge atom is shared by four unit cells. (c) A face-centered atom in a cubic cell is shared by two unit cells.

Figure 12.19 Because each sphere is shared by eight unit cells and there are eight corners in a cube, there is the equivalent of one complete sphere inside a simple cubic unit cell.

is shared by four unit cells [Figure 12.18(b)], and a face-centered atom is shared by two unit cells [Figure 12.18(c)]. Because a simple cubic cell has lattice points only at each of the eight corners, and because each corner atom is shared by eight unit cells, there will be the equivalent of only *one* complete atom contained within a simple cubic unit cell (Figure 12.19). A body-centered cubic cell contains the equivalent of two complete atoms, one in the center and eight shared corner atoms. A face-centered cubic cell contains the equivalent of four complete atoms—three from the six face-centered atoms and one from the eight shared corner atoms.

Closest Packing

There is more empty space in the simple cubic and body-centered cubic cells than in the face-centered cubic cell. Closest packing, the most efficient arrangement of atoms, starts with the structure shown in Figure 12.20(a), which we call layer A. Focusing on the only atom that is surrounded completely by other atoms, we see that it has six immediate neighbors in its own layer. In the second layer, which we call layer B, atoms are packed into the depressions between the atoms in the first layer so that all the atoms are as close together as possible [Figure 12.20(b)].

There are two ways that a third layer of atoms can be arranged. They may sit in the depressions between second-layer atoms such that the third-layer atoms lie directly over atoms in the first layer [Figure 12.20(c)]. In this case, the third layer is also labeled A. Alternatively, atoms in the third layer may sit in a *different* set of depressions such that they do not lie directly over atoms in the first layer [Figure 12.20(d)]. In this case, we label the third layer C.

Figure 12.21 shows the exploded views and the structures resulting from these two arrangements. The ABA arrangement [Figure 12.21(a)] is known as the *hexagonal close-packed (hcp) structure,* and the ABC arrangement [Figure 12.21(b)] is the *cubic close-packed (ccp) structure,*

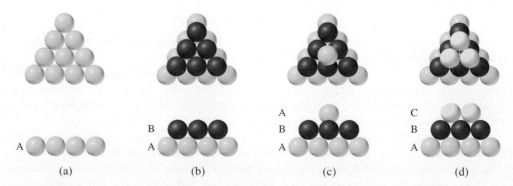

Figure 12.20 (a) In a close-packed layer, each sphere is in contact with six others. (b) Spheres in the second layer fit into the depressions between the first-layer spheres. (c) In the hexagonal close-packed structure, each third-layer sphere is directly over a first-layer sphere. (d) In the cubic close-packed structure, each third-layer sphere fits into a depression that is directly over a depression in the first layer.

(a)

(b)

Figure 12.21 Exploded views of (a) a hexagonal close-packed structure and (b) a cubic close-packed structure. This view is tilted to show the face-centered cubic unit cell more clearly. Note that this arrangement is the same as the face-centered unit cell.

which corresponds to the face-centered cube already described. In the hcp structure, the spheres in every other layer occupy the same vertical position (ABABAB . . .), while in the ccp structure, the spheres in every fourth layer occupy the same vertical position (ABCABCA . . .). In both structures, each sphere has a coordination number of 12 (each sphere is in contact with six spheres in its own layer, three spheres in the layer above, and three spheres in the layer below). Both the hcp and ccp structures represent the most efficient way of packing identical spheres in a unit cell, and the coordination number cannot exceed 12.

Many metals form crystals with hcp or ccp structures. For example, magnesium, titanium, and zinc crystallize with their atoms in an hcp array, while aluminum, nickel, and silver crystallize in the ccp arrangement. A substance will crystallize with the arrangement that maximizes the stability of the solid.

Figure 12.22 summarizes the relationship between the atomic radius r and the edge length a of a simple cubic cell, a body-centered cubic cell, and a face-centered cubic cell. This relationship can be used to determine the atomic radius of a sphere in which the density of the crystal is known.

Student Annotation: The noble gases, which are monatomic, crystallize in the ccp structure, with the exception of helium, which crystallizes in the hcp structure.

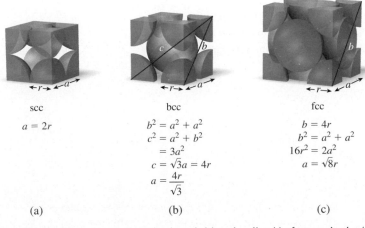

scc

$a = 2r$

bcc

$b^2 = a^2 + a^2$
$c^2 = a^2 + b^2$
$= 3a^2$
$c = \sqrt{3}a = 4r$
$a = \dfrac{4r}{\sqrt{3}}$

fcc

$b = 4r$
$b^2 = a^2 + a^2$
$16r^2 = 2a^2$
$a = \sqrt{8}r$

(a)   (b)   (c)

Figure 12.22 The relationship between the edge length (a) and radius (r) of atoms in the (a) simple cubic cell, (b) body-centered cubic cell, and (c) face-centered cubic cell.

Thinking Outside the Box

X-ray Diffraction

Virtually all we know about crystal structure has been learned from X-ray diffraction studies. X-ray diffraction is the scattering of X rays by the units of a crystalline solid. The scattering, or *diffraction patterns,* produced are used to deduce the arrangement of particles in the solid lattice.

In Section 3.2 we discussed the interference phenomenon associated with waves (see Figure 3.4). Because X rays are a form of electromagnetic radiation (i.e., they are *waves*), they exhibit interference phenomena under suitable conditions. In 1912 Max von Laue[4] correctly suggested that, because the wavelength of X rays is comparable in magnitude to the distances between lattice points in a crystal, the lattice should be able to diffract X rays. An X-ray diffraction pattern is the result of interference in the waves associated with X rays.

The figure here shows a typical X-ray diffraction setup. A beam of X rays is directed at a mounted crystal. When X-ray photons encounter the electrons in the atoms of a crystalline solid, some of the incoming radiation is reflected, much as visible light is reflected by a mirror; the process is called the scattering of X rays.

(a)

(a) Arrangement for obtaining the X-ray diffraction pattern of a crystal. The shield prevents the intense beam of undiffracted X rays from damaging the photographic plate. (b) X-ray diffraction pattern.

(b)

---

[4]Max Theodor Felix von Laue (1879–1960), a German physicist, received the Nobel Prize in Physics in 1914 for his discovery of X-ray diffraction.

To understand how a diffraction pattern arises, consider the scattering of X rays by the atoms in two parallel planes (below). Initially, the two incident rays are in phase with each other (their maxima and minima occur at the same positions). The upper wave is scattered, or reflected, by an atom in the first layer, while the lower wave is scattered by an atom in the second layer. For these two scattered waves to be in phase again, the extra distance traveled by the lower wave (the sum of the distance between points B and C and the distance between points C and D) must be an integral multiple of the wavelength (λ) of the X ray; that is,

$$BC + CD = 2d \sin \theta = n\lambda \qquad n = 1, 2, 3, \ldots$$

where θ is the angle between the X rays and the plane of the crystal and d is the distance between adjacent planes. This is known as the Bragg equation, after William H. Bragg and Sir William L. Bragg.[5] The reinforced waves produce a dark spot on a photographic film for each value of θ that satisfies the Bragg equation.

The X-ray diffraction technique offers the most accurate method for determining bond lengths and bond angles in molecules in solids. Because X rays are scattered by electrons, chemists can construct an electron-density contour map from the diffraction patterns by using a complex mathematical procedure. Basically, an electron-density contour map tells us the relative electron densities at various locations in a molecule. The densities reach a maximum near the center of each atom. In this manner, we can determine the positions of the nuclei and hence the geometric parameters of the molecule.

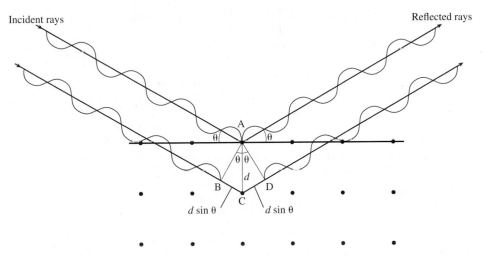

Reflection of X rays from two layers of atoms. The lower wave travels a distance $2d \sin \theta$ longer than the upper wave does. For the two waves to be in phase again after reflection, it must be true that $2d \sin \theta = n\lambda$, where λ is the wavelength of the X ray and $n = 1, 2, 3, \ldots$ The sharply defined spots in the X-ray diffraction figure are observed only if the crystal is large enough to consist of hundreds of parallel layers.

---

[5]William Henry Bragg (1862–1942) and Sir William Lawrence Bragg (1890–1972) were English physicists, father and son. Both worked on X-ray crystallography. The younger Bragg formulated the fundamental equation for X-ray diffraction. The two shared the Nobel Prize in Physics in 1915.

Worked Example 12.3 illustrates the relationships between the unit cell type, cell dimensions, and density of a metal.

Worked Example 12.3

Gold crystallizes in a cubic close-packed structure (face-centered cubic unit cell) and has a density of 19.3 g/cm³. Calculate the atomic radius of an Au atom in angstroms (Å).

Strategy Using the given density and the mass of gold contained within a face-centered cubic unit cell, determine the volume of the unit cell. Then, use the volume to determine the value of a, and use the equation supplied in Figure 12.22(c) to find r. Be sure to use consistent units for mass, length, and volume.

(Continued on next page)

Setup The face-centered cubic unit cell contains a total of four atoms of gold [six faces, each shared by two unit cells, and eight corners, each shared by eight unit cells—Figure 12.22(c)]. $d = m/V$ and $V = a^3$.

Solution First, we determine the mass of gold (in grams) contained within a unit cell:

$$m = \frac{4 \text{ atoms}}{\text{unit cell}} \times \frac{1 \text{ mol}}{6.022 \times 10^{23} \text{ atoms}} \times \frac{197.0 \text{ g Au}}{1 \text{ mol Au}} = 1.31 \times 10^{-21} \text{ g/unit cell}$$

Then we calculate the volume of the unit cell in cm^3:

$$V = \frac{m}{d} = \frac{1.31 \times 10^{-21} \text{ g}}{19.3 \text{ g/cm}^3} = 6.78 \times 10^{-23} \text{ cm}^3$$

Using the calculated volume and the relationship $V = a^3$ (rearranged to solve for a), we determine the length of a side of a unit cell:

$$a = \sqrt[3]{V} = \sqrt[3]{6.78 \times 10^{-23} \text{ cm}^3} = 4.08 \times 10^{-8} \text{ cm}$$

Using the relationship provided in Figure 12.22(c) (rearranged to solve for r), we determine the radius of a gold atom in centimeters:

$$r = \frac{a}{\sqrt{8}} = \frac{4.08 \times 10^{-8} \text{ cm}}{\sqrt{8}} = 1.44 \times 10^{-8} \text{ cm}$$

Finally, we convert centimeters to angstroms:

$$1.44 \times 10^{-8} \text{ cm} \times \frac{1 \times 10^{-2} \text{ m}}{1 \text{ cm}} \times \frac{1 \text{ Å}}{1 \times 10^{-10} \text{ m}} = 1.44 \text{ Å}$$

Think About It
Atomic radii tend to be on the order of 1 Å, so this answer is reasonable.

Practice Problem A When silver crystallizes, it forms face-centered cubic cells. The unit cell edge length is 4.087 Å. Calculate the density of silver.

Practice Problem B The density of sodium metal is 0.971 g/cm³, and the unit cell edge length is 4.285 Å. Determine the unit cell (simple, body-centered, or face-centered cubic) of sodium metal.

SECTION 12.3 REVIEW

Crystal Structure

12.3.1   Nickel has a face-centered cubic unit cell with an edge length of 352.4 pm. Calculate the density of nickel.

12.3.2   A metal crystallizes in a body-centered cubic unit cell with an edge length of 5.24×10^4 cm and has a density of 0.9 g/cm³. Determine the approximate molar mass and the identity of the metal.

12.4 TYPES OF CRYSTALS

The structures and properties of crystalline solids, such as melting point, density, and hardness, are determined by the kinds of forces that hold the particles together. We can classify any crystal as one of four types: ionic, covalent, molecular, or metallic.

Ionic Crystals

Ionic crystals are composed of charged spheres (cations and anions) that are held together by Coulombic attraction. Anions typically are considerably bigger than cations [◄◄ Section 4.6], and the relative sizes and relative numbers of the ions in a compound determine how the ions are arranged

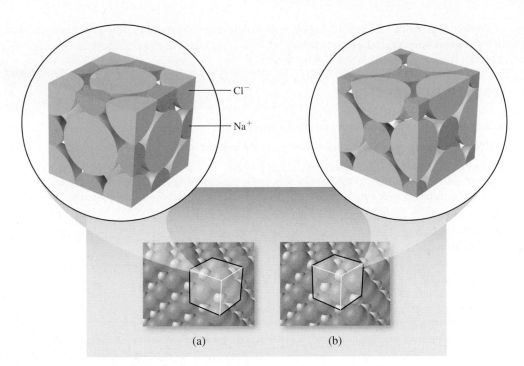

Figure 12.23 The unit cell of an ionic compound can be defined either by (a) the positions of anions or (b) the positions of cations.

Cl⁻

Na⁺

(a)   (b)

in the solid lattice. NaCl adopts a face-centered cubic arrangement as shown in Figure 12.23. Note the positions of ions within the unit cell, and within the lattice overall. Both the Na^+ ions and the Cl^- ions adopt face-centered cubic arrangements, and the unit cell defined by the arrangement of cations overlaps with the unit cell defined by the arrangement of anions. Look closely at the unit cell shown in Figure 12.23(a). It is defined as fcc by the positions of the Cl^- ions. Recall that there is the equivalent of four spheres contained in the fcc unit cell (half a sphere at each of six faces and one-eighth of a sphere at each of eight corners). In this case the spheres are Cl^- ions, so the unit cell of NaCl contains four Cl^- ions. Now look at the positions of the Na^+ ions. There are Na^+ ions centered on each edge of the cube, in addition to one Na^+ at the center. Each sphere on the cube's edge is shared by four unit cells, and there are 12 such edges. Thus, the unit cell in Figure 12.23(a) also contains four Na^+ ions (one-quarter sphere at each of 12 edges, giving three spheres, and one sphere at the center). The unit cell of an ionic compound always contains the same ratio of cations to anions as the empirical formula of the compound.

Figure 12.24 shows the crystal structures of three ionic compounds: CsCl, ZnS, and CaF_2. Cesium chloride [Figure 12.24(a)] has the simple cubic lattice. Despite the apparent similarity of the formulas of CsCl and NaCl, CsCl adopts a different arrangement because the Cs^+ ion is much larger than the Na^+ ion. Zinc sulfide [Figure 12.24(b)] has the *zincblende* structure, which is based on the face-centered cubic lattice. If the S^{2-} ions occupy the lattice points, the smaller Zn^{2+} ions are arranged tetrahedrally about each S^{2-} ion. Other ionic compounds that have the zincblende structure include CuCl, BeS, CdS, and HgS. Calcium fluoride [Figure 12.24(c)] has the *fluorite* structure. The unit cell in Figure 12.24(c) is defined based on the positions of the cations, rather than the positions of the anions. The Ca^{2+} ions occupy the lattice points, and each F^- ion is surrounded tetrahedrally by four Ca^{2+} ions. The compounds SrF_2, BaF_2, $BaCl_2$, and PbF_2 also have the fluorite structure.

Student Annotation: It is important to realize that the lattice points used to define a unit cell must all be identical. We can define the unit cell of NaCl based on the positions of the Na^+ ions or the positions of the Cl^- ions.

Student Annotation: It is a common mistake to identify the CsCl structure as body-centered cubic. Remember that the lattice points used to define a unit cell must all be identical. In this case, they are all Cl^- ions. CsCl has a simple cubic unit cell.

Figure 12.24 Crystal structures of (a) CsCl, (b) ZnS, and (c) CaF_2. In each case, the smaller sphere represents the cation.

(a)   (b)   (c)

Worked Examples 12.4 and 12.5 show how to determine the number of ions in a unit cell and the density of an ionic crystal, respectively.

Worked Example 12.4

How many of each ion are contained within a unit cell of ZnS?

Strategy Determine the contribution of each ion in the unit cell based on its position.

Setup Referring to Figure 12.24, the unit cell has four Zn^{2+} ions completely contained within the unit cell, and S^{2-} ions at each of the eight corners and at each of the six faces. Interior ions (those completely contained within the unit cell) contribute one, those at the corners each contribute one-eighth, and those on the faces each contribute one-half.

Solution The ZnS unit cell contains four Zn^{2+} ions (interior) and four S^{2-} ions [$8 \times \frac{1}{8}$(corners) and $6 \times \frac{1}{2}$(faces)].

Think About It
Make sure that the ratio of cations to anions that you determine for a unit cell matches the ratio expressed in the compound's empirical formula.

Practice Problem A Referring to Figure 12.24, determine how many of each ion are contained within a unit cell of CaF_2.

Practice Problem B Referring to Figure 12.24, determine how many of each ion are contained within a unit cell of CsCl.

Worked Example 12.5

The edge length of the NaCl unit cell is 564 pm. Determine the density of NaCl in g/cm^3.

Strategy Use the number of Na^+ and Cl^- ions in a unit cell (four of each) to determine the mass of a unit cell. Calculate volume using the edge length given in the problem statement. Density is mass divided by volume ($d = m/V$). Be careful to use units consistently.

Setup The masses of Na^+ and Cl^- ions are 22.99 amu and 35.45 amu, respectively. The conversion factor from amu to grams is

$$\frac{1 \text{ g}}{6.022 \times 10^{23} \text{ amu}}$$

so the masses of the Na^+ and Cl^- ions are 3.818×10^{-23} g and 5.887×10^{-23} g, respectively. The unit cell length is

$$564 \text{ pm} \times \frac{1 \times 10^{-12} \text{ m}}{1 \text{ pm}} \times \frac{1 \text{ cm}}{1 \times 10^{-2} \text{ m}} = 5.64 \times 10^{-8} \text{ cm}$$

Solution The mass of a unit cell is 3.882×10^{-22} g ($4 \times 3.818 \times 10^{-23}$ g $+ 4 \times 5.887 \times 10^{-23}$ g). The volume of a unit cell is 1.794×10^{-22} cm^3 [$(5.64 \times 10^{-8}$ cm$)^3$]. Therefore, the density is given by

$$d = \frac{3.882 \times 10^{-22} \text{ g}}{1.794 \times 10^{-22} \text{ cm}^3} = 2.16 \text{ g/cm}^3$$

Think About It
If you were to hold a cubic centimeter (1 cm^3) of salt in your hand, how heavy would you expect it to be? Common errors in this type of problem include errors of unit conversion—especially with regard to length and volume. Such errors can lead to results that are off by many orders of magnitude. Often you can use common sense to gauge whether or not a calculated answer is reasonable. For instance, simply getting the centimeter-meter conversion upside down would result in a calculated density of 2.16×10^{12} g/cm^3! You *know* that a cubic centimeter of salt doesn't have a mass that large. (That's billions of kilograms!) If the magnitude of a result is not reasonable, go back and check your work.

Practice Problem A LiF has the same unit cell as NaCl (fcc). The edge length of the LiF unit cell is 402 pm. Determine the density of LiF in g/cm^3.

Practice Problem B NiO also adopts the face-centered-cubic arrangement. Given that the density of NiO is 6.67 g/cm^3, calculate the length of the edge of its unit cell (in pm).

Most ionic crystals have high melting points, which is an indication of the strong cohesive forces holding the ions together. A measure of the stability of ionic crystals is the lattice energy [◄◄ Section 5.3]; the higher the lattice energy, the more stable the compound. Ionic solids do not conduct electricity well because the ions are fixed in position. In the molten (melted) state or when dissolved in water, however, the compound's ions are free to move and the resulting liquid conducts electricity.

Covalent Crystals

In covalent crystals, atoms are held together in an extensive three-dimensional network entirely by covalent bonds. Well-known examples are two of carbon's allotropes: diamond and graphite. In diamond, each carbon atom is sp^3-hybridized and bonded to four other carbon atoms [Figure 12.25(a)]. The strong covalent bonds in three dimensions contribute to diamond's unusual hardness (it is the hardest material known) and very high melting point (3550°C). In graphite, carbon atoms are arranged in six-membered rings [Figure 12.25(b)]. The atoms are all sp^2-hybridized, and each atom is bonded to three other atoms. The remaining unhybridized $2p$ orbital on each carbon atom is used in pi bonding. In fact, each layer of graphite has the kind of delocalized molecular orbital that is present in benzene [◄◄ Section 7.7]. Because electrons are free to move around in this extensively delocalized molecular orbital, graphite is a good conductor of electricity in directions along the planes of the carbon atoms. The layers are held together by weak van der Waals forces. The covalent bonds in graphite account for its hardness; however, because the layers can slide past one another, graphite is slippery to the touch and is effective as a lubricant. It is also used as the "lead" in pencils.

Another covalent crystal is quartz (SiO_2). The arrangement of silicon atoms in quartz is similar to that of carbon in diamond, but in quartz there is an oxygen atom between each pair of Si atoms. Because Si and O have different electronegativities, the Si—O bond is polar. Nevertheless, SiO_2 is similar to diamond in many respects, such as being very hard and having a high melting point (1610°C).

335 pm

(a)   (b)

Figure 12.25 Structures of (a) diamond and (b) graphite. Note that in diamond, each carbon atom is bonded in a tetrahedral arrangement to four other carbon atoms. In graphite, each carbon atom is bonded in a trigonal planar arrangement to three other carbon atoms. The distance between layers in graphite is 335 pm.

Figure 12.26 The three-dimensional structure of ice. The covalent bonds are shown by short solid lines and the weaker hydrogen bonds by long dotted lines between O and H. The empty space in the structure accounts for the low density of ice, relative to liquid water.

Molecular Crystals

In a molecular crystal, the lattice points are occupied by molecules, so the attractive forces between them are van der Waals forces and/or hydrogen bonding. An example of a molecular crystal is solid sulfur dioxide (SO_2), in which the predominant attractive force is a dipole-dipole interaction. Intermolecular hydrogen bonding is mainly responsible for maintaining the three-dimensional lattice of ice (Figure 12.26). Other examples of molecular crystals are I_2, P_4, and S_8.

Except in ice, molecules in molecular crystals are generally packed together as closely as their size and shape allow. Because van der Waals forces and hydrogen bonding are usually quite weak compared with covalent and ionic bonds, molecular crystals are more easily broken apart than ionic and covalent crystals. Indeed, most molecular crystals melt at temperatures below 100°C.

Metallic Crystals

Every lattice point in a metallic crystal is occupied by an atom of the same metal. Metallic crystals are generally body-centered cubic, face-centered cubic, or hexagonal close-packed. Consequently, metallic elements are usually very dense.

The bonding in metals is quite different from that in other types of crystals. In a metal, the bonding electrons are delocalized over the entire crystal. In fact, metal atoms in a crystal can be imagined as an array of positive ions immersed in a sea of delocalized valence electrons (Figure 12.27). The great cohesive force resulting from delocalization is responsible for a metal's strength, whereas the mobility of the delocalized electrons makes metals good conductors of heat and electricity. Table 12.4 summarizes the properties of the four different types of crystals discussed. Note that the data in Table 12.4 refer to the solid phase of each substance listed.

Figure 12.27 A cross section of a metallic crystal. Each circled positive charge represents the nucleus and inner electrons of a metal atom. The grey area surrounding the positive metal ions indicates the mobile "sea" of electrons.

TABLE 12.4	Types of Crystals and Their General Properties		
Type of crystal	**Cohesive forces**	**General properties**	**Examples**
Ionic	Coulombic attraction and dispersion forces	Hard, brittle, high melting point, poor conductor of heat and electricity	NaCl, LiF, MgO, $CaCO_3$
Covalent	Covalent bonds	Hard, brittle, high melting point, poor conductor of heat and electricity	C (diamond),* SiO_2 (quartz)
Molecular†	Dispersion and dipole-dipole forces, hydrogen bonds	Soft, low melting point, poor conductor of heat and electricity	Ar, CO_2, I_2, H_2O, $C_{12}H_{22}O_{11}$
Metallic	Metallic bonds	Variable hardness and melting point, good conductor of heat and electricity	All metallic elements, such as Na, Mg, Fe, Cu

*Diamond is a good conductor of heat.
†Included in this category are crystals made up of individual atoms.

Worked Example 12.6 lets you practice using unit-cell data to determine the density of a metal.

Worked Example 12.6

The metal iridium (Ir) crystallizes with a face-centered cubic unit cell. Given that the length of the edge of a unit cell is 383 pm, determine the density of iridium in g/cm^3.

Strategy A face-centered metallic crystal contains four atoms per unit cell [$8 \times \frac{1}{8}$(corners) and $6 \times \frac{1}{2}$(faces)]. Use the number of atoms per cell and the atomic mass to determine the mass of a unit cell. Calculate volume using the edge length given in the problem statement. Density is then mass divided by volume ($d = m/V$). Be sure to make all necessary unit conversions.

Setup The mass of an Ir atom is 192.2 amu. The conversion factor from amu to grams is

$$\frac{1 \text{ g}}{6.022 \times 10^{23} \text{ amu}}$$

so the mass of an Ir atom is 3.192×10^{-22} g. The unit cell length is

$$383 \text{ pm} \times \frac{1 \times 10^{-12} \text{ m}}{1 \text{ pm}} \times \frac{1 \text{ cm}}{1 \times 10^{-2} \text{ m}} = 3.83 \times 10^{-8} \text{ cm}$$

Solution The mass of a unit cell is 1.277×10^{-21} g ($4 \times 3.192 \times 10^{-22}$ g). The volume of a unit cell is 5.618×10^{-23} cm³ [$(3.83 \times 10^{-8}$ cm$)^3$]. Therefore, the density is given by

$$d = \frac{1.277 \times 10^{-21} \text{ g}}{5.62 \times 10^{-23} \text{ cm}^3} = 22.7 \text{ g/cm}^3$$

> **Think About It**
> Metals typically have high densities, so common sense can help you decide whether or not your calculated answer is reasonable.

Practice Problem A Aluminum metal crystallizes in a face-centered cubic unit cell. If the length of the cell edge is 404 pm, what is the density of aluminum in g/cm^3?

Practice Problem B Copper crystallizes in a face-centered cubic lattice. If the density of the metal is 8.96 g/cm^3, what is the length of the unit cell edge in picometers?

12.5 AMORPHOUS SOLIDS

Solids are most stable in crystalline form. However, if a solid is formed rapidly (e.g., when a liquid is cooled quickly), its atoms or molecules do not have time to align themselves and may become locked in positions other than those of a regular crystal. The resulting solid is said to be amorphous. *Amorphous solids,* such as glass, lack a regular three-dimensional arrangement of atoms. In this section, we will briefly discuss the properties of glass.

Glass is one of civilization's most valuable and versatile materials. It is also one of the oldest—glass articles date back as far as 1000 B.C. *Glass* commonly refers to an optically transparent fusion product of inorganic materials that has cooled to a rigid state without crystallizing. By fusion product we mean that the glass is formed by mixing molten silicon dioxide (SiO_2), its chief component, with compounds such as sodium oxide (Na_2O), boron oxide (B_2O_3), and certain transition metal oxides for color and other properties. In some respects, glass behaves more like a liquid than a solid.

There are about 800 different types of glass in common use today. Figure 12.28 shows two-dimensional schematic representations of crystalline quartz and amorphous quartz glass. Table 12.5 lists the composition and properties of quartz, Pyrex, and soda-lime glass. The color of glass is due largely to the presence of oxides of metal ions—mostly transition metal ions. For example, green glass contains iron(III) oxide (Fe_2O_3) or copper(II) oxide (CuO), yellow glass contains uranium(IV) oxide (UO_2), blue glass contains cobalt(II) and copper(II) oxides (CoO and CuO), and red glass contains small particles of gold and copper.

Figure 12.28 Two-dimensional representation of (a) crystalline quartz and (b) noncrystalline (amorphous) quartz glass. The small spheres represent silicon. In reality, the structure of quartz is three dimensional. Each Si atom is bonded in a tetrahedral arrangement to four O atoms.

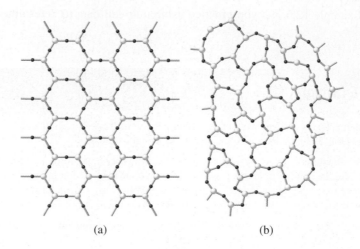

(a)   (b)

TABLE 12.5		Composition and Properties of Three Types of Glass
Pure quartz glass	100% SiO_2	Low thermal expansion, transparent to a wide range of wavelengths. Used in optical research.
Pyrex glass	60%–80% SiO_2, 10%–25% B_2O_3, some Al_2O_3	Low thermal expansion; transparent to visible and infrared, but not to ultraviolet light. Used in cookware and laboratory glassware.
Soda-lime glass	75% SiO_2, 15% Na_2O, 10% CaO	Easily attacked by chemicals and sensitive to thermal shocks. Transmits visible light but absorbs ultraviolet light. Used in windows and bottles.

12.6 PHASE CHANGES

A *phase* is a homogeneous part of a system that is separated from the rest of the system by a well-defined boundary. When an ice cube floats in a glass of water, for example, the liquid water is one phase and the solid water (the ice cube) is another. Although the chemical properties of water are the same in both phases, the physical properties of a solid are different from those of a liquid.

When a substance goes from one phase to another phase, we say that it has undergone a ***phase change.*** Phase changes in a system are generally caused by the addition or removal of energy, usually in the form of heat. Familiar examples of phase changes include the following:

> **Student Annotation:** Phase changes are *physical* changes [◄◄ Section 1.3].

Example	Phase Change
Freezing of water	$H_2O(l) \longrightarrow H_2O(s)$
Evaporation (or vaporization) of water	$H_2O(l) \longrightarrow H_2O(g)$
Melting (fusion) of ice	$H_2O(s) \longrightarrow H_2O(l)$
Condensation of water vapor	$H_2O(g) \longrightarrow H_2O(l)$
Sublimation of dry ice	$CO_2(s) \longrightarrow CO_2(g)$

The establishment of an equilibrium vapor pressure, as described in Section 12.2, involved two of these phase changes: vaporization and condensation. Figure 12.29 summarizes the various types of phase changes.

Liquid-Vapor Phase Transition

> **Student Annotation:** The temperature at which the vapor pressure of a liquid is equal to 1 atm is called the ***normal boiling point.***

In Section 12.2 we learned that the vapor pressure of a liquid increases with increasing temperature. When the vapor pressure reaches the external pressure, the liquid boils. In fact, the ***boiling point*** of a substance is defined as the temperature at which its vapor pressure equals the external, atmospheric pressure. As a result, the boiling point of a substance varies with the external pressure. At the top of a mountain, for example, where the atmospheric pressure is lower than that at sea

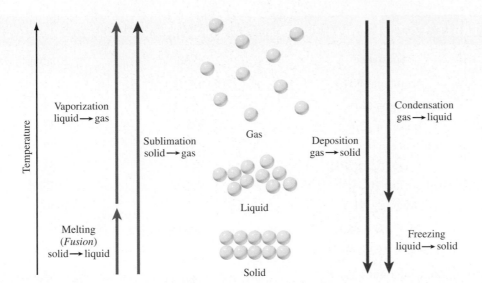

Figure 12.29 The six possible phase changes: melting (fusion), vaporization, sublimation, deposition, condensation, and freezing.

TABLE 12.6	Molar Heats of Vaporization for Selected Liquids	
Substance	**Boiling point (°C)**	**ΔH_{vap} (kJ/mol)**
Argon (Ar)	−186	6.3
Benzene (C_6H_6)	80.1	31.0
Ethanol (C_2H_5OH)	78.3	39.3
Diethyl ether ($C_2H_5OC_2H_5$)	34.6	26.0
Mercury (Hg)	357	59.0
Methane (CH_4)	−164	9.2
Water (H_2O)	100	40.79

level, the vapor pressure of water (or any liquid) reaches the external pressure at a lower temperature. Thus, the boiling point is lower than it would be at sea level.

Because the boiling point is defined in terms of the vapor pressure of the liquid, the boiling point is related to the ***molar heat of vaporization*** (ΔH_{vap}), the amount of heat required to vaporize a mole of substance at its boiling point. Indeed, the data in Table 12.6 show that the boiling point generally increases as ΔH_{vap} increases. Ultimately, both the boiling point and ΔH_{vap} are determined by the strength of intermolecular forces. For example, argon (Ar) and methane (CH_4), which have only relatively weak dispersion forces, have low boiling points and small molar heats of vaporization. Diethyl ether ($C_2H_5OC_2H_5$) has a dipole moment, and the dipole-dipole forces account for its moderately high boiling point and ΔH_{vap}. Both ethanol (C_2H_5OH) and water have strong hydrogen bonding, which accounts for their high boiling points and large ΔH_{vap} values. Strong metallic bonding causes mercury to have the highest boiling point and ΔH_{vap} of the liquids in Table 12.6. Interestingly, benzene (C_6H_6), although nonpolar, has a high *polarizability* due to the distribution of its electrons in delocalized π molecular orbitals [◄◄ Section 7.7]. The dispersion forces that result can be as strong as (or even stronger than) dipole-dipole forces and/or hydrogen bonds.

The opposite of vaporization is condensation. In principle, a gas can be liquefied (made to condense) either by cooling or by applying pressure. Cooling a sample of gas decreases the kinetic energy of its molecules, so eventually the molecules aggregate to form small drops of liquid. Applying pressure to the gas (compression), on the other hand, reduces the distance between molecules, so they can be pulled together by intermolecular attractions. Many liquefaction processes use a combination of reduced temperature and increased pressure.

Every substance has a ***critical temperature*** (T_c) above which its gas phase cannot be liquefied, no matter how great the applied pressure. ***Critical pressure*** (P_c) is the minimum pressure that must be applied to liquefy a substance *at* its critical temperature. At temperatures above the critical temperature, there is no fundamental distinction between a liquid and a gas—we simply have a fluid. A fluid at a temperature and pressure that exceed T_c and P_c, respectively, is called a ***supercritical fluid.*** Supercritical fluids have some remarkable properties and are used as solvents

Student Annotation: T_c is the *highest* temperature at which a substance can exist as a liquid.

TABLE 12.7	Critical Temperatures and Critical Pressures of Selected Substances	
Substance	T_c (°C)	P_c (atm)
Ammonia (NH_3)	132.4	111.5
Argon (Ar)	−122.2	6.3
Benzene (C_6H_6)	288.9	47.9
Carbon dioxide (CO_2)	31.0	73.0
Ethanol (C_2H_5OH)	243	63.0
Diethyl ether ($C_2H_5OC_2H_5$)	192.6	35.6
Mercury (Hg)	1462	1036
Methane (CH_4)	−83.0	45.6
Molecular hydrogen (H_2)	−239.9	12.8
Molecular nitrogen (N_2)	−147.1	33.5
Molecular oxygen (O_2)	−118.8	49.7
Sulfur hexafluoride (SF_6)	45.5	37.6
Water (H_2O)	374.4	219.5

in a wide variety of industrial applications. The first such large-scale industrial use was the decaffeination of coffee with supercritical CO_2.

Table 12.7 lists the critical temperatures and critical pressures of a number of common substances. The critical temperature of a substance reflects the strength of its intermolecular forces. Benzene, ethanol, mercury, and water, which have strong intermolecular forces, also have high critical temperatures compared with the other substances listed in the table.

Solid-Liquid Phase Transition

The transformation of liquid to solid is called *freezing,* and the reverse process is called *melting,* or *fusion.* The **melting point** of a solid or the *freezing point* of a liquid is the temperature at which solid and liquid phases coexist in equilibrium. The normal melting (or freezing) point of a substance is the temperature at which it melts (or freezes) at 1 atm.

The most familiar liquid-solid equilibrium is probably that of water and ice. At 0°C and 1 atm, the dynamic equilibrium is represented by

$$ice \rightleftharpoons water$$

or

$$H_2O(s) \rightleftharpoons H_2O(l)$$

Student Annotation: In most cases a glass of ice water would not be a *true* example of a dynamic equilibrium because it would not be kept at 0°C. At room temperature, all the ice eventually melts.

A glass of ice water at 0°C provides a practical illustration of this dynamic equilibrium. As the ice cubes melt to form water, some of the water between ice cubes may freeze, thus joining the cubes together. Remember that in a dynamic equilibrium, forward and reverse processes are occurring at the same rate [◄◄ Section 9.1].

Because molecules are more strongly held in the solid phase than in the liquid phase, heat is required to melt a solid into a liquid. The heating curve in Figure 12.30 shows that when a solid is heated, its temperature increases gradually until point A is reached. At this point, the solid begins to melt. During the melting period (A ⟶ B), the first flat portion of the curve in Figure 12.30, heat is being absorbed by the system, yet its temperature remains constant. The heat helps the molecules overcome the attractive forces in the solid. Once the sample has melted completely (point B), the heat absorbed increases the average kinetic energy of the liquid molecules and the liquid temperature rises (B ⟶ C). The vaporization process (C ⟶ D) can be explained similarly. The temperature remains constant during the period when the increased kinetic energy is used to overcome the cohesive forces in the liquid. When all molecules are in the gas phase, the temperature rises again.

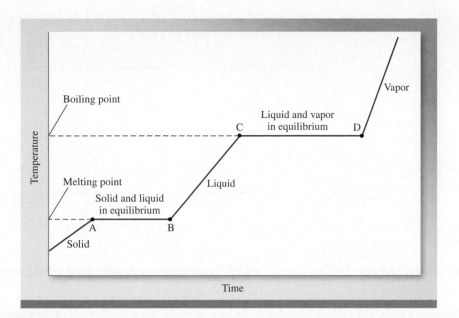

Figure 12.30 A typical heating curve, from the solid phase through the liquid phase to the gas phase of a substance. Because ΔH_{fus} is smaller than ΔH_{vap}, a substance melts in less time than it takes to vaporize. This explains why AB is shorter than CD. The steepness of the solid, liquid, and vapor heating lines is determined by the specific heat of the substance in each state.

TABLE 12.8	Molar Heats of Fusion for Selected Substances	
Substance	**Melting point (°C)**	**ΔH_{fus} (kJ/mol)**
Argon (Ar)	−190	1.3
Benzene (C_6H_6)	5.5	10.9
Ethanol (C_2H_5OH)	−117.3	7.61
Diethyl ether ($C_2H_5OC_2H_5$)	−116.2	6.90
Mercury (Hg)	−39	23.4
Methane (CH_4)	−183	0.84
Water (H_2O)	0	6.01

The ***molar heat of fusion*** (ΔH_{fus}) is the energy, usually expressed in kJ/mol, required to melt 1 mole of a solid. Table 12.8 lists the molar heats of fusion for the substances in Table 12.6. A comparison of the data in the two tables shows that ΔH_{fus} is smaller than ΔH_{vap} for each substance. This is consistent with the fact that molecules in a liquid are still fairly closely packed together, so some energy (but not a lot of energy, relatively speaking) is needed to bring about the rearrangement from solid to liquid. When a liquid is vaporized, on the other hand, its molecules become completely separated from one another, so considerably more energy is required to overcome the intermolecular attractive forces.

Cooling a substance has the opposite effect of heating it. If we remove heat from a gas sample at a steady rate, its temperature decreases. As the liquid is being formed, heat is given off by the system, because its potential energy is decreasing. For this reason, the temperature of the system remains constant over the condensation period (D ⟶ C). After all the vapor has condensed, the temperature of the liquid begins to drop again. Continued cooling of the liquid finally leads to freezing (B ⟶ A).

Supercooling is a phenomenon in which a liquid can be temporarily cooled to below its freezing point. Supercooling occurs when heat is removed from a liquid so rapidly that the molecules literally have no time to assume the ordered structure of a solid. A supercooled liquid is unstable. Gentle stirring or the addition to it of a small "seed" crystal of the same substance will cause it to solidify quickly.

Solid-Vapor Phase Transition

Solids can be vaporized, so solids, too, have a vapor pressure. ***Sublimation*** is the process by which molecules go directly from the solid phase to the vapor phase. The reverse process, in which molecules go directly from the vapor phase to the solid phase, is called ***deposition***.

Figure 12.31 Heating curve of water.

Solid iodine in equilibrium with its vapor.

Student Annotation: Equation 12.5 is generally used to approximate ΔH_{sub}. It only holds strictly when all the phase changes occur at the same temperature.

Naphthalene, which is the substance used to make mothballs, has a fairly high vapor pressure for a solid (1 mmHg at 53°C); thus, its pungent vapor quickly permeates an enclosed space. Iodine also sublimes. At room temperature, the violet color of iodine vapor is easily visible in a closed container.

Because molecules are more tightly held in a solid, the vapor pressure of a solid is generally much less than that of the corresponding liquid. The ***molar enthalpy of sublimation*** (ΔH_{sub}) of a substance is the energy, usually expressed in kilojoules, required to sublime 1 mole of a solid. It is equal to the sum of the molar enthalpies of fusion and vaporization:

Equation 12.5
$$\Delta H_{sub} = \Delta H_{fus} + \Delta H_{vap}$$

Equation 12.5 is an illustration of Hess's law [◄◄ Section 10.5]. The enthalpy, or heat change, for the overall process is the same whether the substance changes directly from the solid to the vapor phase or if it changes from the solid to the liquid and then to the vapor phase.

Phase changes can be of significant consequence in biological systems. If you have ever suffered a steam burn, you know that it can be far more serious than a burn caused simply by boiling water—even though steam and boiling water are both at the same temperature. A heating curve helps explain why this is so (see Figure 12.31). When boiling water touches your skin, it is cooled to body temperature because it deposits the heat it contains on your skin. The heat deposited on your skin by a sample of boiling water at 100°C can be represented by the orange line under the curve. When an equivalent mass of steam contacts your skin, it first deposits heat as it condenses and *then* cools to body temperature. The heat deposited on your skin by a sample of steam is represented by the red line under the curve. Notice how much more heat is deposited by steam than by liquid water at the same temperature. The steam contains more heat because it has been heated *and* vaporized. The additional heat that was absorbed by the water to vaporize it is what makes a steam burn worse than a burn from boiling water.

A heating curve can also be used to explain why hikers stranded by blizzards are warned not to consume snow in an effort to stay hydrated. When you drink cold water, your body expends energy to warm the water you consume to body temperature. If you consume snow, your body must first expend the energy necessary to melt the snow, and then to warm it. Because a phase change is involved, the amount of energy required to assimilate snow is much greater than the amount necessary to assimilate an equal mass of water—even if the water is ice-cold. This can contribute to *hypothermia,* a potentially dangerous drop in body temperature.

Worked Example 12.7

Student Annotation: You may want to review the calculation of the heat exchanged between the system and surroundings for temperature changes and phase changes [◄◄ Sections 10.3 and 10.4].

(a) Calculate the amount of heat deposited on the skin of a person burned by 1.00 g of liquid water at 100.0°C and (b) the amount of heat deposited by 1.00 g of steam at 100.0°C. (c) Calculate the amount of energy necessary to warm 100.0 g of water from 0.0°C to body temperature and (d) the amount of heat required to melt 100.0 g of ice at 0.0°C and then warm it to body temperature. (Assume that body temperature is 37.0°C.)

Strategy For the purpose of following the sign conventions, we can designate the water as the *system* and the body as the *surroundings*. (a) Heat is transferred from hot water to the skin in a single step: a temperature change. (b) The transfer of heat from steam to the skin takes place in two steps: a phase change and a temperature change. (c) Cold water is warmed to body temperature in a single step: a temperature change. (d) The melting of ice and the subsequent warming of the resulting liquid water takes place in two steps: a phase change and a temperature change. In each case, the heat transferred during a temperature change depends on the mass of the water, the specific heat of water, and the change in temperature. For the phase changes, the heat transferred depends on the amount of water (in moles) and the molar heat of vaporization (ΔH_{vap}) or molar heat of fusion (ΔH_{fus}). In each case, the total energy transferred or required is the sum of the energy changes for the individual steps.

Setup The required specific heats (s) are 4.184 J/g · °C for water and 1.99 J/g · °C for steam. (Assume that the specific heat values do not change over the range of temperatures in the problem.) From Table 12.6, the molar heat of vaporization (ΔH_{vap}) of water is 40.79 kJ/mol, and from Table 12.8, the molar heat of fusion (ΔH_{fus}) of water is 6.01 kJ/mol. The molar mass of water is 18.02 g/mol. *Note:* The ΔH_{vap} of water is the amount of heat required to vaporize a mole of water. In this problem, however, we want to know how much heat is deposited when water vapor *condenses,* so we must use the negative, −40.79 kJ/mol.

Solution
(a) $\Delta T = 37.0°C - 100.0°C = -63.0°C$
From Equation 10.13, we write

$$q = ms\Delta T = 1.00\ g \times \frac{4.184\ J}{g \cdot °C} \times -63.0°C = -2.64 \times 10^2\ J = -0.264\ kJ$$

Thus, 1.00 g of water at 100.0°C deposits 0.264 kJ of heat on the skin. (The negative sign indicates that heat is given off by the system and absorbed by the surroundings.)

(b) $\dfrac{1.00\ g}{18.02\ g/mol} = 0.0555\ mol$ water

$$q_1 = n\Delta H_{vap} = 0.0555\ mol \times \frac{-40.79\ kJ}{mol} = -2.26\ kJ$$

$$q_2 = ms\Delta T = 1.00\ g \times \frac{4.184\ J}{g \cdot °C} \times -63.0°C = -2.64 \times 10^2\ J = -0.264\ kJ$$

The overall energy deposited on the skin by 1.00 g of steam is the sum of q_1 and q_2:

$$-2.26\ kJ + (-0.264\ kJ) = -2.53\ kJ$$

The negative sign indicates that the system (steam) gives off the energy.

(c) $\Delta T = 37.0°C - 0.0°C = 37.0°C$

$$q = ms\Delta T = 100.0\ g \times \frac{4.184\ J}{g \cdot °C} \times 37.0°C = 1.55 \times 10^4\ J = 15.5\ kJ$$

The energy required to warm 100.0 g of water from 0.0°C to 37.0°C is 15.5 kJ.

(d) $\dfrac{100.0\ g}{18.02\ g/mol} = 5.55\ mol$

$$q_1 = n\Delta H_{fus} = 5.55\ mol \times \frac{6.01\ kJ}{mol} = 33.4\ kJ$$

$$q_2 = ms\Delta T = 100.0\ g \times \frac{4.184\ J}{g \cdot °C} \times 37.0°C = 1.55 \times 10^4\ J = 15.5\ kJ$$

The energy required to melt 100.0 g of ice at 0.0°C and warm it to 37.0°C is the sum of q_1 and q_2:

$$33.4\ kJ + 15.5\ kJ = 48.9\ kJ$$

Think About It
In problems that include phase changes, the q values corresponding to the phase-change steps will be the largest contributions to the total. If you find that this is not the case in your solution, check to see if you have made the common error of neglecting to convert the q values corresponding to temperature changes from J to kJ.

Practice Problem A Calculate the amount of energy (in kJ) necessary to convert 346 g of liquid water from 0°C to water vapor at 182°C.

Practice Problem B Determine the final state and temperature of 100 g of water originally at 25.0°C after 50.0 kJ of heat have been added to it.

SECTION 12.6 REVIEW

Phase Changes

12.6.1   How much energy (in kJ) is required to convert 25.0 g of liquid water at room temperature (25°C) to steam at 110°C?

12.6.2   How much energy (in kJ) is given off when 1.00 g of steam at 100.0°C cools to room temperature (25.0°C)?

12.7   PHASE DIAGRAMS

The relationships between the phases of a substance can be represented in a single graph known as a phase diagram. A ***phase diagram*** summarizes the conditions (temperature and pressure) at which a substance exists as a solid, liquid, or gas. Figure 12.32(a) shows the phase diagram of CO_2, which is typical of many substances. The graph is divided into three regions, each of which represents a pure phase. The line separating any two regions, called a *phase boundary line,* indicates conditions under which these two phases can exist in equilibrium. The point at which all three phase boundary lines meet is called the ***triple point.*** The triple point is the only combination of temperature and pressure at which all three phases of a substance can be in equilibrium with one another. The point at which the liquid-vapor phase boundary line abruptly ends is the critical point, corresponding to the critical temperature (T_c) and the critical pressure (P_c).

In order to understand the information in a phase diagram, consider the dashed lines between numbered points in Figure 12.32(b). If we start with a sample of CO_2 at 1 atm and −100°C, the sample is initially a solid (point 1). If we then add heat to the sample at 1 atm, its temperature increases until it reaches −78°C, the sublimation point of CO_2 at 1 atm (point 2). When the entire sample has sublimed at −78°C, the temperature of the resulting vapor will begin to increase. We continue adding heat until the temperature of the vapor is −25°C (point 3). At this point, we maintain the temperature at −25°C and begin increasing the pressure until the vapor condenses, which would occur at a pressure of about 70 atm (point 4). With a phase diagram, we can tell in what phase a substance will exist at any given temperature and pressure. Furthermore, we can tell what phase changes will occur as the result of increases or decreases in temperature, pressure, or both.

One of the interesting things about the phase diagram of CO_2 is that its triple point occurs above atmospheric pressure −57°C, 5.2 atm. This means that there is no liquid phase at atmospheric pressure, the condition that makes dry ice "dry." At elevated pressure, solid CO_2 does melt. In fact, liquid CO_2 is used as the solvent in many dry-cleaning operations.

The phase diagram of water (Figure 12.33) is unusual because the solid-liquid phase-boundary line has a negative slope. (Compare this with the solid-liquid phase boundary line of CO_2 in Figure 12.32.) As a result, ice can be liquefied within a narrow temperature range by applying pressure.

Student Annotation: Bismuth is another example of a substance whose solid-liquid phase boundary (under ordinary atmospheric conditions) has a negative slope. Like water, bismuth has a liquid density (1.005 g/cm³ at room temperature) that is higher than its solid density (0.9780 g/cm³ at its melting point of 271°C).

Figure 12.32 (a) The phase diagram of carbon dioxide. Note that the solid-liquid boundary line has a positive slope. There is no liquid phase below 5.2 atm, so only the solid and vapor phases can exist under ordinary atmospheric conditions. (b) Heating solid CO_2 initially at −100°C and 1 atm (point 1) causes it to sublime when it reaches −78°C (point 2). At −25°C, increasing the pressure from 1 atm (point 3) to about 70 (point 4) will cause CO_2 to condense to a liquid.

(a)

(b)

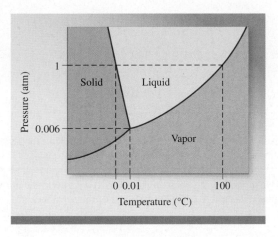

Figure 12.33 The phase diagram of water. Each solid line between two phases specifies the conditions of pressure and temperature under which the two phases can exist in equilibrium. The point at which all three phases can exist in equilibrium (0.006 atm and 0.01°C) is called the triple point.

Worked Example 12.8 lets you practice interpreting the information in a phase diagram.

Worked Example 12.8

Using the following phase diagram, (a) determine the normal boiling point and the normal melting point of the substance, (b) determine the physical state of the substance at 2 atm and 110°C, and (c) determine the pressure and temperature that correspond to the triple point of the substance.

Strategy Each point on the phase diagram corresponds to a pressure-temperature combination. The normal boiling and melting points are the temperatures at which the substance undergoes phase changes. These points fall on the phase boundary lines. The triple point is where the three phase boundaries meet.

Setup By drawing lines corresponding to a given pressure and/or temperature, we can determine the temperature at which a phase change occurs, or the physical state of the substance under specified conditions.

| (a) | (b) | (c) |

(Continued on next page)

Solution

(a) The normal boiling and melting points are ~140°C and ~205°C, respectively.

(b) At 2 atm and 110°C the substance is a solid.

(c) The triple point occurs at ~0.8 atm and ~115°C.

Think About It
The triple point of this substance occurs at a pressure below atmospheric pressure. Therefore, it will melt rather than sublime when it is heated under ordinary conditions.

Practice Problem A Use the following phase diagram to (a) determine the normal boiling point and melting point of the substance, and (b) the physical state of the substance at 1.2 atm and 100°C.

Practice Problem B Sketch the phase diagram of a substance using the following data:

Pressure (atm)	Melting point (°C)	Boiling point (°C)	Sublimation point (°C)
0.5	—	—	0
1.0	60	110	—
1.5	75	200	—
2.0	105	250	—
2.5	125	275	—

The triple point is at 0.75 atm and 45°C.

SECTION 12.7 REVIEW

Phase Diagrams

12.7.1   For each one of the following phase diagrams, indicate whether the substance represented (a) will melt or sublime as it is heated at 1 atm, and (b) can be liquefied by increased pressure below its normal freezing point.

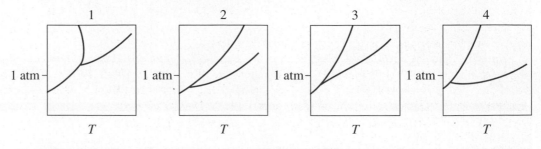

Learning Outcomes

- List and briefly describe the different types of intermolecular forces: dipole-dipole, hydrogen bonding, dispersion forces, and ion-dipole.
- Identify the intermolecular forces present in a given substance.
- Define surface tension, viscosity, and vapor pressure.
- Rank molecules based upon relative strength of intermolecular forces as well as surface tension, viscosity, and vapor pressure.
- Use the Clausius-Clapeyron equation to calculate the vapor pressure of a liquid at a given temperature.
- Define unit cell and lattice point.

- Calculate the atomic radius of an atom given its density and type of crystal.
- Identify key characteristics and examples of the major types of crystal: ionic, covalent, molecular, or metallic.
- Calculate the amount of heat lost or gained when a substance undergoes a series of phase and/or temperature changes.
- Define phase boundary, triple point, and critical point.
- Use phase diagrams to determine the phase of a substance at a given temperature and pressure.

Chapter Summary

SECTION 12.1

- The particles (atoms, molecules, or ions) in the condensed phases (solids and liquids) are held together by **intermolecular forces.** Intermolecular forces are electrostatic attractions between opposite charges or partial charges.
- Intermolecular forces acting between atoms or molecules in a pure substance are called **van der Waals forces** and include **dipole-dipole interactions** (including **hydrogen bonding**) and **London dispersion forces** (also called simply **dispersion forces**).
- Dipole-dipole interactions exist between *polar* molecules, whereas *nonpolar* molecules are held together by *dispersion* forces alone. Dispersion forces are those between **instantaneous dipoles** and *induced* dipoles. When a nonpolar molecule acquires an instantaneous dipole, it is said to be **polarized.** Dispersion forces act between all molecules, nonpolar and polar.
- Hydrogen bonding is an especially strong type of dipole-dipole interaction that occurs in molecules that contain H−N, H−O, or H−F bonds.
- **Ion-dipole interactions** are those that occur (in solutions) between ions and polar molecules.

SECTION 12.2

- Physical properties of liquids that result from intermolecular forces include surface tension, viscosity, and vapor pressure.
- **Surface tension** is the net pull inward on molecules at the surface of a liquid. Surface tension is related to **cohesion,** the attractive forces between molecules within a substance, and **adhesion,** the attractive forces between molecules in a substance and their container. The balance between cohesion and adhesion determines whether a liquid meniscus is concave or convex. It also gives rise to **capillary action,** in which liquid is drawn upward into a narrow tube against gravity.
- **Viscosity** is resistance to flow, reflecting how easily molecules move past one another.

- **Evaporation** (also known as **vaporization**) is the phase change from liquid to vapor. **Condensation** is the phase change from vapor to liquid. In a closed system, when vaporization and condensation are occurring at the same rate, a state of **dynamic equilibrium** exists and the *vapor pressure* is equal to the **equilibrium vapor pressure.** Vapor pressure measures how easily molecules escape to the vapor phase. A **volatile** substance has a high vapor pressure.
- Surface tension, viscosity, and vapor pressure are all temperature dependent. The **Clausius-Clapeyron equation** relates the vapor pressure of a substance to its absolute temperature.

SECTION 12.3

- The spheres (molecules, atoms, or ions) in a **crystalline solid** are arranged in a three-dimensional **lattice structure** consisting of a repeating pattern of **unit cells.** The type of unit cell is determined by the positions of the **lattice points.**
- Cubic unit cells may be **simple cubic, body-centered cubic,** or **face-centered cubic,** containing a total of one, two, or four spheres, respectively. The **coordination number** is the number of spheres surrounding each sphere.
- *Closest packing* is the most efficient arrangement of spheres in a solid. It may be *hexagonal* or *cubic*. Each has a coordination number of 12.

SECTION 12.4

- Crystals may be ionic, covalent, molecular, or metallic. Each type of crystalline solid has characteristics determined in part by the types of interactions holding it together.

SECTION 12.5

- **Amorphous solids** such as **glass** lack regular three-dimensional structure.

SECTION 12.6

- The possible *phase changes* are melting or *fusion* ($s \longrightarrow l$), freezing ($l \longrightarrow s$), vaporization ($l \longrightarrow g$), *condensation* ($g \longrightarrow l$), *sublimation* ($s \longrightarrow g$), and *deposition* ($g \longrightarrow s$).
- The *boiling point* of a substance is the temperature at which its vapor pressure equals the external pressure. The *normal boiling point* is the temperature at which its vapor pressure equals 1 atm. Boiling point is pressure dependent. The *molar heat of vaporization* (ΔH_{vap}) is the amount of heat required to vaporize 1 mole of a substance at its boiling point.
- The *critical temperature* (T_c) is the temperature above which a gas cannot be liquefied by applying pressure. The *critical pressure* (P_c) is the pressure necessary to liquefy a gas at its critical temperature. A substance above its critical temperature and pressure is a *supercritical fluid.*

- The *melting point* or *freezing point* is the temperature at which the solid and liquid phases are in equilibrium. The *molar heat of fusion* (ΔH_{fus}) is the amount of heat required to melt 1 mole of a substance at its melting point. *Supercooling* is the process of rapidly lowering a liquid's temperature below its freezing point.
- The *molar heat of sublimation* (ΔH_{sub}) is equal to the sum of the molar heats of fusion and vaporization: $\Delta H_{sub} = \Delta H_{fus} + \Delta H_{vap}$

SECTION 12.7

- A *phase diagram* indicates the phase of a substance under any combination of temperature and pressure. Lines between phases are called *phase boundaries.*
- The *triple point* is where all three phase boundaries meet. This is the temperature and pressure combination at which all three phases are in equilibrium.

Key Words

Adhesion, 470	Dipole-dipole interactions, 466	Lattice point, 475	Simple cubic cell, 477
Amorphous solid, 487	Dispersion forces, 468	Lattice structure, 475	Sublimation, 491
Body-centered cubic cell, 477	Dynamic equilibrium, 472	London dispersion forces, 468	Supercooling, 491
Boiling point, 488	Equilibrium vapor	Melting point, 490	Supercritical fluid, 489
Capillary action, 470	pressure, 472	Molar enthalpy of sublimation	Surface tension, 470
Clausius-Clapeyron	Evaporation, 472	(ΔH_{sub}), 492	Triple point, 494
equation, 473	Face-centered cubic cell, 477	Molar heat of fusion	Unit cell, 475
Cohesion, 470	Freezing point, 490	(ΔH_{fus}), 491	van der Waals forces, 465
Condensation, 472	Fusion, 490	Molar heat of vaporization	Vaporization, 472
Coordination number, 476	Glass, 487	(ΔH_{vap}), 489	Viscosity, 470
Critical pressure (P_c), 489	Hydrogen bonding, 466	Normal boiling point, 488	Volatile, 471
Critical temperature (T_c), 489	Instantaneous dipole, 467	Phase change, 488	
Crystalline solid, 475	Intermolecular forces, 465	Phase diagram, 494	
Deposition, 491	Ion-dipole interactions, 469	Polarized, 468	

Key Equations

12.1 $\quad \ln P = -\dfrac{\Delta H_{vap}}{RT} + C$

12.2 $\quad \ln P_1 = -\dfrac{\Delta H_{vap}}{RT_1} + C$

12.3 $\quad \ln P_2 = -\dfrac{\Delta H_{vap}}{RT_2} + C$

12.4 $\quad \ln \dfrac{P_1}{P_2} = \dfrac{\Delta H_{vap}}{R}\left(\dfrac{1}{T_2} - \dfrac{1}{T_1}\right)$

12.5 $\quad \Delta H_{sub} = \Delta H_{fus} + \Delta H_{vap}$

Questions and Problems

SECTION 12.1:   INTERMOLECULAR FORCES

Review Questions

12.1   Give an example for each type of intermolecular force: (a) dipole-dipole interaction, (b) ion-dipole interaction, (c) dispersion forces, (d) van der Waals forces.

12.2   Explain the term *polarizability*. What kind of molecules tend to have high polarizabilities? What is the relationship between polarizability and intermolecular forces?

12.3   Explain the difference between a temporary dipole moment and a permanent dipole moment.

12.4   What evidence can you cite that all molecules exert attractive forces on one another?

12.5   What physical properties are determined by the strength of intermolecular forces in solids and in liquids?

12.6   Explain why hydrogen bonding is exhibited by some hydrogen-containing compounds and not by others.

12.7   Describe the types of intermolecular forces that govern the folding of a protein molecule into its physiologically functioning three-dimensional state.

Problems

12.8   The compounds Br_2 and ICl are isoelectronic (have the same number of electrons) and have similar molar masses, yet Br_2 melts at $-7.2°C$ and ICl melts at $27.2°C$. Explain.

12.9   If you lived in Alaska, which of the following natural gases could you keep in an outdoor storage tank in winter: methane (CH_4), propane (C_3H_8), or butane (C_4H_{10})? Explain why.

12.10   The binary hydrogen compounds of the Group 4A elements and their boiling points are: CH_4, $-162°C$; SiH_4, $-112°C$; GeH_4, $-88°C$; and SnH_4, $-52°C$. Explain the increase in boiling points from CH_4 to SnH_4.

12.11   List the types of intermolecular forces that exist between molecules (or atoms or ions) in each of the following species: (a) benzene (C_6H_6), (b) CH_3Cl, (c) PF_3, (d) NaCl, (e) CS_2.

12.12   Ammonia is both a donor and an acceptor of hydrogen in hydrogen-bond formation. Draw a diagram showing the hydrogen bonding of an ammonia molecule with two other ammonia molecules.

12.13   Which of the following species are capable of hydrogen bonding among themselves: (a) C_2H_6, (b) HI, (c) KF, (d) BeH_2, (e) CH_3COOH?

12.14   Arrange the following in order of increasing boiling point: RbF, CO_2, CH_3OH, CH_3Br. Explain your reasoning.

12.15   Diethyl ether has a boiling point of $34.5°C$, and 1-butanol has a boiling point of $117°C$:

$$\begin{array}{ccccc} & H & H & & H & H \\ & | & | & & | & | \\ H- & C- & C- & O- & C- & C-H \\ & | & | & & | & | \\ & H & H & & H & H \end{array} \qquad \begin{array}{cccc} H & H & H & H \\ | & | & | & | \\ H-C- & C- & C- & C-OH \\ | & | & | & | \\ H & H & H & H \end{array}$$

    Diethyl ether   1-Butanol

Both of these compounds have the same numbers and types of atoms. Explain the difference in their boiling points.

12.16   Which member of each of the following pairs of substances would you expect to have a higher boiling point: (a) O_2 and Cl_2, (b) SO_2 and CO_2, (c) HF and HI?

12.17   Which substance in each of the following pairs would you expect to have the higher boiling point: (a) Ne or Xe, (b) CO_2 or CS_2, (c) CH_4 or Cl_2, (d) F_2 or LiF, (e) NH_3 or PH_3? Explain why.

12.18   Explain in terms of intermolecular forces why (a) NH_3 has a higher boiling point than CH_4 and (b) KCl has a higher melting point than I_2.

12.19   What kind of attractive forces must be overcome to (a) melt ice, (b) boil molecular bromine, (c) melt solid iodine, and (d) dissociate F_2 into F atoms?

12.20   The following compounds have the same molecular formulas (C_4H_{10}). Which one would you expect to have a higher boiling point?

12.21   Explain the difference in the melting points of the following compounds:

$$\begin{array}{cc} NO_2 & NO_2 \\ \text{(}ortho\text{-OH)} & \\ \text{m.p. } 45°C & \text{m.p. } 115°C \\ & \text{(}para\text{-OH)} \end{array}$$

(*Hint:* One of the two can form *intra*molecular hydrogen bonds.)

SECTION 12.2:   PROPERTIES OF LIQUIDS

Review Questions

12.22   Explain why liquids, unlike gases, are virtually incompressible.

12.23   What is surface tension? What is the relationship between intermolecular forces and surface tension? How does surface tension change with temperature?

12.24   Despite the fact that stainless steel is much denser than water, a stainless-steel razor blade can be made to float on water. Why?

12.25   Use water and mercury as examples to explain adhesion and cohesion.

12.26   A glass can be filled slightly above the rim with water. Explain why the water does not overflow.

12.27   Draw diagrams showing the capillary action of (a) water and (b) mercury in three tubes of different radii.

12.28   What is viscosity? What is the relationship between intermolecular forces and viscosity?

12.29   Why does the viscosity of a liquid decrease with increasing temperature?

12.30   Why is ice less dense than water?

12.31   Outdoor water pipes have to be drained or insulated in winter in a cold climate. Why?

Problems

12.32   Predict which of the following liquids has greater surface tension: ethanol (C_2H_5OH) or dimethyl ether (CH_3OCH_3).

12.33   Predict the viscosity of ethylene glycol relative to that of ethanol and glycerol (see Table 12.3).

$$CH_2-OH$$
$$|$$
$$CH_2-OH$$

Ethylene glycol

12.34   Vapor pressure measurements at several different temperatures are shown for mercury. Determine graphically the molar heat of vaporization for mercury.

$T(°C)$	200	250	300	320	340
P(mmHg)	17.3	74.4	246.8	376.3	557.9

12.35   The vapor pressure of benzene (C_6H_6) is 40.1 mmHg at 7.6°C. What is its vapor pressure at 60.6°C? The molar heat of vaporization of benzene is 31.0 kJ/mol.

12.36   The vapor pressure of liquid X is lower than that of liquid Y at 20°C, but higher at 60°C. What can you deduce about the relative magnitude of the molar heats of vaporization of X and Y?

12.37   Estimate the molar heat of vaporization of a liquid whose vapor pressure doubles when the temperature is raised from 75°C to 100°C.

SECTION 12.3:   CRYSTAL STRUCTURE

Review Questions

12.38   Define the following terms: *crystalline solid, lattice point, unit cell, coordination number, closest packing.*

12.39   Describe the geometries of the following cubic cells: simple cubic, body-centered cubic, face-centered cubic. Which of these structures would give the highest density for the same type of atoms? Which the lowest?

12.40   Classify the solid states in terms of crystal types of the elements in the third period of the periodic table. Predict the trends in their melting points and boiling points.

12.41   The melting points of the oxides of the third-period elements are given in parentheses: Na_2O (1275°C), MgO (2800°C), Al_2O_3 (2045°C), SiO_2 (1610°C), P_4O_{10} (580°C), SO_3 (16.8°C), Cl_2O_7 (−91.5°C). Classify these solids in terms of crystal types.

12.42   Define X-ray diffraction. What are the typical wavelengths (in nm) of X rays? (See Figure 3.1.)

12.43   Write the Bragg equation. Define every term and describe how this equation can be used to measure interatomic distances.

Problems

12.44   What is the coordination number of each sphere in (a) a simple cubic cell, (b) a body-centered cubic cell, and (c) a face-centered cubic cell? Assume the spheres are all the same.

12.45   Calculate the number of spheres that would be found within a simple cubic cell, body-centered cubic cell, and face-centered cubic cell. Assume that the spheres are the same.

12.46   Metallic iron crystallizes in a cubic lattice. The unit cell edge length is 287 pm. The density of iron is 7.87 g/cm^3. How many iron atoms are within a unit cell?

12.47   Barium metal crystallizes in a body-centered cubic lattice (the Ba atoms are at the lattice points only). The unit cell edge length is 502 pm, and the density of the metal is 3.50 g/cm^3. Using this information, calculate Avogadro's number. [*Hint:* First calculate the volume (in cm^3) occupied by 1 mole of Ba atoms in the unit cells. Next calculate the volume (in cm^3) occupied by one Ba atom in the unit cell. Assume that 68 percent of the unit cell is occupied by Ba atoms.]

12.48   Vanadium crystallizes in a body-centered cubic lattice (the V atoms occupy only the lattice points). How many V atoms are present in a unit cell?

12.49   Europium crystallizes in a body-centered cubic lattice (the Eu atoms occupy only the lattice points). The density of Eu is 5.26 g/cm^3. Calculate the unit cell edge length in picometers.

12.50   Crystalline silicon has a cubic structure. The unit cell edge length is 543 pm. The density of the solid is 2.33 g/cm^3. Calculate the number of Si atoms in one unit cell.

12.51   A face-centered cubic cell contains 8 X atoms at the corners of the cell and 6 Y atoms at the faces. What is the empirical formula of the solid?

12.52   When X rays of wavelength 0.090 nm are diffracted by a metallic crystal, the angle of first-order diffraction ($n = 1$) is measured to be 15.2°. What is the distance (in pm) between the layers of atoms responsible for the diffraction?

12.53   The distance between layers in an NaCl crystal is 282 pm. X rays are diffracted from these layers at an angle of 23.0°. Assuming that $n = 1$, calculate the wavelength of the X rays in nanometers.

12.54   Identify the unit cell of molecular iodine (I_2) shown here. (*Hint:* Consider the position of iodine molecules, not individual iodine atoms.)

12.55   Shown here is a zinc oxide unit cell. What is the formula of zinc oxide?

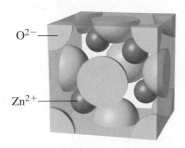

SECTION 12.4:   TYPES OF CRYSTALS

Review Questions

12.56   Describe and give examples of the following types of crystals: (a) ionic crystals, (b) covalent crystals, (c) molecular crystals, (d) metallic crystals.

12.57   Why are metals good conductors of heat and electricity? Why does the ability of a metal to conduct electricity decrease with increasing temperature?

Problems

12.58   A solid is hard, brittle, and electrically nonconducting. Its melt (the liquid form of the substance) and an aqueous solution containing the substance conduct electricity. Classify the solid.

12.59   A solid is soft and has a low melting point (below 100°C). The solid, its melt, and an aqueous solution containing the substance are all nonconductors of electricity. Classify the solid.

12.60   A solid is very hard and has a high melting point. Neither the solid nor its melt conducts electricity. Classify the solid.

12.61   Which of the following are molecular solids and which are covalent solids: Se_8, HBr, Si, CO_2, C, P_4O_6, SiH_4?

12.62   Classify the solid state of the following substances as ionic crystals, covalent crystals, molecular crystals, or metallic crystals: (a) CO_2, (b) B_{12}, (c) S_8, (d) KBr, (e) Mg, (f) SiO_2, (g) LiCl, (h) Cr.

12.63   Explain why diamond is harder than graphite. Why is graphite an electrical conductor but diamond is not?

SECTION 12.5:   AMORPHOUS SOLIDS

Review Questions

12.64   What is an amorphous solid? How does it differ from a crystalline solid?

12.65   Define glass. What is the chief component of glass? Name three types of glass.

SECTION 12.6:   PHASE CHANGES

Review Questions

12.66   What is a phase change? Name all possible changes that can occur among the vapor, liquid, and solid phases of a substance.

12.67   What is the equilibrium vapor pressure of a liquid? How is it measured, and how does it change with temperature?

12.68   Use any one of the phase changes to explain what is meant by dynamic equilibrium.

12.69   Define the following terms: (a) molar heat of vaporization, (b) molar heat of fusion, (c) molar heat of sublimation. What are their typical units?

12.70   How is the molar heat of sublimation related to the molar heats of vaporization and fusion? On what law are these relationships based?

12.71   What can we learn about the intermolecular forces in a liquid from the molar heat of vaporization?

12.72   The greater the molar heat of vaporization of a liquid, the greater its vapor pressure. True or false?

12.73   Define boiling point. How does the boiling point of a liquid depend on external pressure? Referring to Table 11.5, what is the boiling point of water when the external pressure is 187.5 mmHg?

12.74   As a liquid is heated at constant pressure, its temperature rises. This trend continues until the boiling point of the liquid is reached. No further rise in temperature of the liquid can be induced by heating. Explain.

12.75   What is critical temperature? What is the significance of critical temperature in condensation of gases?

12.76   What is the relationship between intermolecular forces in a liquid and the liquid's boiling point and critical temperature? Why is the critical temperature of water greater than that of most other substances?

12.77   How do the boiling points and melting points of water and carbon tetrachloride vary with pressure? Explain any difference in behavior of these two substances.

12.78   Why is solid carbon dioxide called dry ice?

12.79   The vapor pressure of a liquid in a closed container depends on which of the following: (a) the volume above the liquid, (b) the amount of liquid present, (c) temperature, (d) intermolecular forces between the molecules in the liquid?

12.80   Wet clothes dry more quickly on a hot, dry day than on a hot, humid day. Explain.

12.81   Which of the following phase transitions gives off more heat: (a) 1 mole of steam to 1 mole of water at 100°C, or (b) 1 mole of water to 1 mole of ice at 0°C?

12.82   A beaker of water is heated to boiling by a Bunsen burner. Would adding another burner raise the temperature of the boiling water? Explain.

12.83   Explain why splashing a small amount of liquid nitrogen (b.p. 77 K) is not as harmful as splashing boiling water on your skin.

Problems

12.84   Calculate the amount of heat (in kJ) required to convert 150.2 g of water to steam at 100°C.

12.85   How much heat (in kJ) is needed to convert 866 g of ice at −15°C to steam at 146°C? (The specific heats of ice and steam are 2.03 and 1.99 J/g · °C, respectively.)

12.86   How is the rate of evaporation of a liquid affected by (a) temperature, (b) the surface area of a liquid exposed to air, (c) intermolecular forces?

12.87   The molar heats of fusion and sublimation of molecular iodine are 15.27 and 62.30 kJ/mol, respectively. Estimate the molar heat of vaporization of liquid iodine.

12.88   The following compounds, listed with their boiling points, are liquid at −10°C: butane, −0.5°C; ethanol, 78.3°C; toluene, 110.6°C. At −10°C, which of these liquids would you expect to have the highest vapor pressure? Which the lowest? Explain.

12.89   Freeze-dried coffee is prepared by freezing brewed coffee and then removing the ice component with a vacuum pump. Describe the phase changes taking place during these processes.

12.90   A student hangs wet clothes outdoors on a winter day when the temperature is −15°C. After a few hours, the clothes are found to be fairly dry. Describe the phase changes in this drying process.

12.91   Explain why steam at 100°C causes more serious burns than water at 100°C.

SECTION 12.7:   PHASE DIAGRAMS

Review Questions

12.92   What is a phase diagram? What useful information can be obtained from studying a phase diagram?

12.93   Explain how water's phase diagram differs from those of most substances. What property of water causes the difference?

Problems

12.94   The blades of ice skates are quite thin, so the pressure exerted on ice by a skater can be substantial. Explain how this facilitates skating on ice.

12.95   A length of wire is placed on top of a block of ice. The ends of the wire extend over the edges of the ice, and a heavy weight is attached to each end. It is found that the ice under the wire gradually melts, so the wire slowly moves through the ice block. At the same time, the water above the wire refreezes. Explain the phase changes that accompany this phenomenon.

12.96   The boiling point and freezing point of sulfur dioxide are −10°C and −72.7°C (at 1 atm), respectively. The

triple point is −75.5°C and 1.65 × 10⁻³ atm, and its critical point is at 157°C and 78 atm. On the basis of this information, draw a rough sketch of the phase diagram of SO_2.

12.97   A phase diagram of water is shown. Label the regions. Predict what would happen as a result of the following changes: (a) Starting at A, we raise the temperature at constant pressure. (b) Starting at B, we lower the pressure at constant temperature. (c) Starting at C, we lower the temperature at constant pressure.

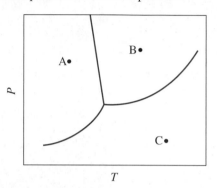

ADDITIONAL PROBLEMS

12.98   Name the kinds of attractive forces that must be overcome to (a) boil liquid ammonia, (b) melt solid phosphorus (P_4), (c) dissolve CsI in liquid HF, (d) melt potassium metal.

12.99   Which of the following properties indicates very strong intermolecular forces in a liquid: (a) very low surface tension, (b) very low critical temperature, (c) very low boiling point, (d) very low vapor pressure?

12.100   At −35°C, liquid HI has a higher vapor pressure than liquid HF. Explain.

12.101   Based on the following properties of elemental boron, classify it as one of the crystalline solids discussed in Section 12.4: high melting point (2300°C), poor conductor of heat and electricity, insoluble in water, very hard substance.

12.102   Referring to Figure 12.32, determine the stable phase of CO_2 at (a) 4 atm and −60°C and (b) 0.5 atm and −20°C.

12.103   Which of the following substances has the highest polarizability: CH_4, H_2, CCl_4, SF_6, H_2S?

12.104   Given two complementary strands of DNA containing 100 base pairs each, calculate the ratio of two separate strands to hydrogen-bonded double helix in solution at 300 K. (*Hint:* The formula for calculating this ratio is $e^{-\Delta E/RT}$, where ΔE is the energy difference between hydrogen-bonded double-strand DNAs and single-strand DNAs and R is the gas constant.) Assume the energy of hydrogen bonds per base pair to be 10 kJ/mol.

12.105   The average distance between base pairs measured parallel to the axis of a DNA molecule is 3.4 Å. The average molar mass of a pair of nucleotides is 650 g/mol. Estimate the length in centimeters of a DNA molecule of molar mass 5.0 × 10⁹ g/mol. Roughly how many base pairs are contained in this molecule?

12.106   A CO_2 fire extinguisher is located on the outside of a building in Massachusetts. During the winter months, one can hear a sloshing sound when the extinguisher is gently shaken. In the summertime there is often no sound when it is shaken. Explain. Assume that the extinguisher has no leaks and that it has not been used.

12.107   What is the vapor pressure of mercury at its normal boiling point (357°C)?

12.108   A flask of water is connected to a powerful vacuum pump. When the pump is turned on, the water begins to boil. After a few minutes, the same water begins to freeze. Eventually, the ice disappears. Explain what happens at each step.

12.109   The liquid-vapor boundary line in the phase diagram of any substance always stops abruptly at a certain point. Why?

12.110   The interionic distances of several alkali halide crystals are as follows:

Crystal	NaCl	NaBr	NaI	KCl	KBr	KI
Interionic distance (pm)	282	299	324	315	330	353

Plot lattice energy versus the reciprocal interionic distance. How would you explain the plot in terms of the dependence of lattice energy on the distance of separation between ions? What law governs this interaction? (For lattice energies, see Table 5.1.)

12.111   Which has a greater density, crystalline SiO_2 or amorphous SiO_2? Why?

12.112   A student is given four solid samples labeled W, X, Y, and Z. All have a metallic luster. She is told that the solids could be gold, lead sulfide, mica (which is quartz, or SiO_2), and iodine. The results of her investigations are: (a) W is a good electrical conductor; X, Y, and Z are poor electrical conductors. (b) When the solids are hit with a hammer, W flattens out, X shatters into many pieces, Y is smashed into a powder, and Z is not affected. (c) When the solids are heated with a Bunsen burner, Y melts with some sublimation, but X, W, and Z do not melt. (d) In treatment with 6 *M* HNO_3, X dissolves; there is no effect on W, Y, or Z. On the basis of these test results, identify the solids.

12.113   Which of the following statements are false? (a) Dipole-dipole interactions between molecules are greatest if the molecules possess only temporary dipole moments. (b) All compounds containing hydrogen atoms can participate in hydrogen-bond formation. (c) Dispersion forces exist between all atoms, molecules, and ions.

12.114   The diagram shows a kettle of boiling water. Identify the phases in regions A and B.

12.115   The south pole of Mars is covered with solid carbon dioxide, which partly sublimes during the summer. The CO_2 vapor recondenses in the winter when the temperature drops to 150 K. Given that the heat of sublimation of CO_2 is 25.9 kJ/mol, calculate the atmospheric pressure on the surface of Mars. [*Hint:* Use Figure 12.32 to determine the normal sublimation temperature of dry ice and Equation 12.4, which also applies to sublimations.]

12.116   The properties of gases, liquids, and solids differ in a number of respects. How would you use the kinetic molecular theory (see Section 11.2) to explain the following observations? (a) Ease of compressibility decreases from gas to liquid to solid. (b) Solids retain a definite shape, but gases and liquids do not. (c) For most substances, the volume of a given amount of material increases as it changes from solid to liquid to gas.

12.117   Select the substance in each pair that should have the higher boiling point. In each case identify the principal intermolecular forces involved and account briefly for your choice: (a) K_2S or $(CH_3)_3N$, (b) Br_2 or $CH_3CH_2CH_2CH_3$.

12.118   A small drop of oil in water assumes a spherical shape. Explain. (*Hint:* Oil is made up of nonpolar molecules, which tend to avoid contact with water.)

12.119   Under the same conditions of temperature and density, which of the following gases would you expect to behave less ideally: CH_4 or SO_2? Explain.

12.120   The fluorides of the second period elements and their melting points are: LiF, 845°C; BeF_2, 800°C; BF_3, −126.7°C; CF_4, −184°C; NF_3, −206.6°C; OF_2, −223.8°C; F_2, −219.6°C. Classify the type(s) of intermolecular forces present in each compound.

12.121   The standard enthalpy of formation of gaseous molecular iodine is 62.4 kJ/mol. Use this information to calculate the molar heat of sublimation of molecular iodine at 25°C.

12.122   The distance between Li^+ and Cl^- is 257 pm in solid LiCl and 203 pm in an LiCl unit in the gas phase. Explain the difference in the bond lengths.

12.123   Heat of hydration, that is, the heat change that occurs when ions become hydrated in solution, is largely due to ion-dipole interactions. The heats of hydration for the alkali metal ions are Li^+, −520 kJ/mol; Na^+, −405 kJ/mol; K^+, −321 kJ/mol. Account for the trend in these values.

12.124   If water were a linear molecule, (a) would it still be polar, and (b) would the water molecules still be able to form hydrogen bonds with one another?

12.125   Calculate the $\Delta H°$ for the following processes at 25°C: (a) $Br_2(l) \longrightarrow Br_2(g)$ and (b) $Br_2(g) \longrightarrow 2Br(g)$. Comment on the relative magnitudes of these $\Delta H°$ values in terms of the forces involved in each case. (*Hint:* See Table 10.4.)

12.126   Which liquid would you expect to have a greater viscosity, water or diethyl ether? The structure of diethyl ether is shown in Problem 12.15.

12.127   A beaker of water is placed in a closed container. Predict the effect on the vapor pressure of the water when (a) its temperature is lowered, (b) the volume of the container is doubled, (c) more water is added to the beaker.

12.128   Ozone (O_3) is a strong oxidizing agent that can oxidize all the common metals except gold and platinum. A convenient test for ozone is based on its action on mercury. When exposed to ozone, mercury becomes dull looking and sticks to glass tubing (instead of flowing freely through it). Write a balanced equation for the reaction. What property of mercury is altered by its interaction with ozone?

12.129   A sample of limestone ($CaCO_3$) is heated in a closed vessel until it is partially decomposed. Write an equation for the reaction, and state how many phases are present.

12.130   Carbon and silicon belong to Group 4A of the periodic table and have the same valence electron configuration (ns^2np^2). Why does silicon dioxide (SiO_2) have a much higher melting point than carbon dioxide (CO_2)?

12.131   Gaseous or highly volatile liquid anesthetics are often preferred in surgical procedures because once inhaled, these vapors can quickly enter the bloodstream through the alveoli and then enter the brain. Several common gaseous anesthetics are shown with their boiling points:

Halothane	Isoflurane	Enflurane
50°C	48.5°C	56.5°C

Based on intermolecular force considerations, explain the advantages of using these anesthetics. (*Hint:* The brain barrier is made of membranes that have a nonpolar interior region.)

12.132   Given the general properties of water and ammonia, comment on the problems that a biological system (as we know it) would have developing in an ammonia medium.

	H_2O	NH_3
Boiling point	373.15 K	239.65 K
Melting point	273.15 K	195.3 K
Molar heat capacity	75.3 J/K · mol	8.53 J/K · mol
Molar heat of vaporization	40.79 kJ/mol	23.3 kJ/mol
Molar heat of fusion	6.0 kJ/mol	5.9 kJ/mol
Viscosity	0.001 N · s/m²	0.0254 N · s/m² (at 240 K)
Dipole moment	1.82 D	1.46 D
Phase at 300 K	Liquid	Gas

12.133   A pressure cooker is a sealed container that allows steam to escape when it exceeds a predetermined pressure. How does this device reduce the time needed for cooking?

12.134   A 1.20-g sample of water is injected into an evacuated 5.00-L flask at 65°C. What percentage of the water will be vapor when the system reaches equilibrium? Assume ideal behavior of water vapor and that the volume of liquid water is negligible. The vapor pressure of water at 65°C is 187.5 mmHg.

12.135   What are the advantages of cooking the vegetable broccoli with steam instead of boiling it in water?

12.136   A quantitative measure of how efficiently spheres pack into unit cells is called *packing efficiency,* which is the percentage of the cell space occupied by the spheres.

Calculate the packing efficiencies of a simple cubic cell, a body-centered cubic cell, and a face-centered cubic cell. (*Hint:* Refer to Figure 12.22 and use the relationship that the volume of a sphere is $\frac{4}{3}\pi r^3$, where r is the radius of the sphere.)

12.137   The phase diagram of helium is shown. Helium is the only known substance that has two different liquid phases: helium-I and helium-II. (a) What is the maximum temperature at which helium-II can exist? (b) What is the minimum pressure at which solid helium can exist? (c) What is the normal boiling point of helium-I? (d) Can solid helium sublime?

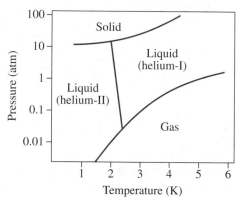

12.138   The phase diagram of sulfur is shown. (a) How many triple points are there? (b) Which is the more stable allotrope under ordinary atmospheric conditions? (c) Describe what happens when sulfur at 1 atm is heated from 80°C to 200°C.

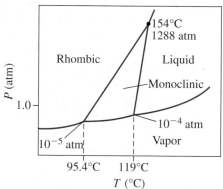

12.139   Provide an explanation for each of the following phenomena: (a) Solid argon (m.p. −189.2°C; b.p. −185.7°C) can be prepared by immersing a flask containing argon gas in liquid nitrogen (b.p. −195.8°C) until it liquefies and then connecting the flask to a vacuum pump. (b) The melting point of cyclohexane (C_6H_{12}) increases with increasing pressure exerted on the solid cyclohexane. (c) Certain high-altitude clouds contain water droplets at −10°C. (d) When a piece of dry ice is added to a beaker of water, fog forms above the water.

12.140   Argon crystallizes in the face-centered cubic arrangement at 40 K. Given that the atomic radius of argon is 191 pm, calculate the density of solid argon.

12.141   Given the phase diagram of carbon, answer the following questions: (a) How many triple points are there and what are the phases that can coexist at each triple point? (b) Which has a higher density, graphite or diamond? (c) Synthetic diamond can be made from graphite. Using the phase diagram, how would you go about making diamond?

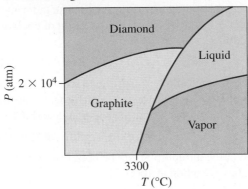

12.142   A chemistry instructor performed the following mystery demonstration. Just before the students arrived in class, she heated some water to boiling in an Erlenmeyer flask. She then removed the flask from the flame and closed the flask with a rubber stopper. After the class commenced, she held the flask in front of the students and announced that she could make the water boil simply by rubbing an ice cube on the outside walls of the flask. To the amazement of everyone, it worked. Give an explanation for this phenomenon.

12.143   Swimming coaches sometimes suggest that a drop of alcohol (ethanol) placed in an ear plugged with water "draws out the water." Explain this action from a molecular point of view.

12.144   Two of the drugs that are prescribed for the treatment and prevention of kidney stones are hydrochlorothiazide and chlorthalidone, shown here. What types of intermolecular forces exist between chlorthalidone molecules and between hydrochlorothiazide molecules?

Hydrochlorothiazide

Chlorthalidone

12.145   Why do citrus growers spray their trees with water to protect them from freezing?

12.146   Calcium metal crystallizes in a face-centered cubic unit cell with a cell edge length of 558.84 pm. Calculate (a) the radius of a calcium atom in angstroms (Å) and (b) the density of calcium metal in g/cm³.

12.147   A student heated a beaker of cold water (on a tripod) with a Bunsen burner. When the gas was ignited, she noticed that there was water condensed on the outside of the beaker. Explain what happened.

12.148   The compound dichlorodifluoromethane (CCl_2F_2) has a normal boiling point of −30°C, a critical temperature of 112°C, and a corresponding critical pressure of 40 atm. If the gas is compressed to 18 atm at 20°C, will the gas condense? Your answer should be based on a graphical interpretation.

12.149   Iron crystallizes in a body-centered cubic lattice. The cell length as determined by X-ray diffraction is 286.7 pm. Given that the density of iron is 7.874 g/cm³, calculate Avogadro's number.

12.150   Sketch the cooling curves of water from about 110°C to about −10°C. How would you also show the formation of supercooled liquid below 0°C that then freezes to ice? The pressure is at 1 atm throughout the process. The curves need not be drawn quantitatively.

12.151   The boiling point of methanol is 65.0°C, and the standard enthalpy of formation of methanol vapor is −201.2 kJ/mol. Calculate the vapor pressure of methanol (in mmHg) at 25°C. (*Hint:* See Appendix 2 for other thermodynamic data of methanol.)

12.152   A sample of water shows the following behavior as it is heated at a constant rate:

Heat added

If twice the mass of water has the same amount of heat transferred to it, which of the following graphs best describes the temperature variation? Note that the scales for all the graphs are the same.

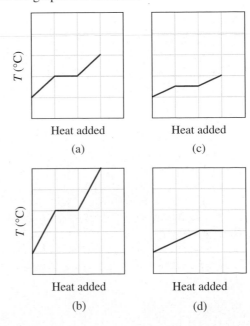

12.153 A closed vessel of volume 9.6 L contains 2.0 g of water. Calculate the temperature (in °C) at which only half of the water remains in the liquid phase. (See Table 11.5 for vapor pressures of water at different temperatures.)

12.154 The electrical conductance of copper metal decreases with increasing temperature, but that of a $CuSO_4$ solution increases with increasing temperature. Explain.

12.155 Assuming ideal behavior, calculate the density of gaseous HF at its normal boiling point (19.5°C). The experimentally measured density under the same conditions is 3.10 g/L. Account for the difference between your calculated result and the experimental value.

12.156 Explain why drivers are advised to use motor oil with lower viscosity in the winter and higher viscosity in the summer.

12.157 Which of the following compounds is most likely to exist as a liquid at room temperature: ethane (C_2H_6), hydrazine (N_2H_4), fluoromethane (CH_3F)? Explain.

12.158 At what angle would you expect X rays of wavelength 0.154 nm to be reflected from a crystal in which the distance between layers is 312 pm? (Assume $n = 1$.)

12.159 Patients who have suffered from kidney stones often are advised to drink extra water to help prevent the formation of additional stones. An article on WebMD.com recommends drinking at least 3 quarts (2.84 L) of water every day—nearly 50 percent more than the amount recommended for healthy adults. How much energy must the body expend to warm this amount of water consumed at 10°C to body temperature (37°C)? How much *more* energy would have to be expended if the same quantity of water were consumed as *ice* at 0°C? ΔH_{fus} for water is 6.01 kJ/mol. Assume the density and specific heat of water are 1.00 g/cm^3 and 4.184 J/g · °C, respectively, and that both quantities are independent of temperature.

12.160 Silicon used in computer chips must have an impurity level below 10^{-9} (that is, fewer than one impurity atom for every 10^9 Si atoms). Silicon is prepared by the reduction of quartz (SiO_2) with coke (a form of carbon made by the destructive distillation of coal) at about 2000°C:

$$SiO_2(s) + 2C(s) \longrightarrow Si(l) + 2CO(g)$$

Next, solid silicon is separated from other solid impurities by treatment with hydrogen chloride at 350°C to form gaseous trichlorosilane ($SiCl_3H$):

$$Si(s) + 3HCl(g) \longrightarrow SiCl_3H(g) + H_2(g)$$

Finally, ultrapure Si can be obtained by reversing the above reaction at 1000°C:

$$SiCl_3H(g) + H_2(g) \longrightarrow Si(s) + 3HCl(g)$$

The molar heat of vaporization of trichlorosilane is 28.8 kJ/mol and its vapor pressure at 2°C is 0.258 atm. (a) Using this information and the equation

$$\ln \frac{P_1}{P_2} = \frac{\Delta H_{vap}}{R} \left(\frac{1}{T_2} - \frac{1}{T_1} \right)$$

determine the normal boiling point of trichlorosilane. (b) What kind(s) of intermolecular forces exist between trichlorosilane molecules? (c) Each cubic unit cell (edge length $a = 543$ pm) contains eight Si atoms. If there are 1.0×10^{13} boron atoms per cubic centimeter in a sample of pure silicon, how many Si atoms are there for every B atom in the sample? (d) Calculate the density of pure silicon.

Answers to In-Chapter Materials

PRACTICE PROBLEMS

12.1A (a) Dispersion forces, (b) dipole-dipole forces, H bonding, and dispersion forces, (c) dipole-dipole and dispersion forces, (d) dispersion forces. **12.1B** (a) Dipole-dipole and dispersion forces, (b) dipole-dipole forces, H bonding, and dispersion forces, (c) dipole-dipole forces, H bonding, and dispersion forces, (d) dispersion forces. **12.2A** 265 mmHg. **12.2B** 75.9 kJ/mol, 109°C. **12.3A** 10.5 g/cm³. **12.3B** Body-centered cubic. **12.4A** 4 Ca, 8 F. **12.4B** 1 Cs, 1 Cl. **12.5A** 2.65 g/cm³. **12.5B** 421 pm. **12.6A** 2.72 g/cm³. **12.6B** 361 pm. **12.7A** 984 kJ. **12.7B** 100°C, liquid and vapor in equilibrium. **12.8A** (a) ~110°C, ~−10°C, (b) liquid.

12.8B

SECTION REVIEW

12.1.1 (a) Dispersion forces, (b) dipole-dipole and dispersion forces, (c) dipole-dipole and dispersion forces, (d) dispersion forces, (e) dipole-dipole forces, H bonding, and dispersion forces, (f) dipole-dipole and dispersion forces. **12.1.2** Hexane is larger and therefore has greater dispersion forces. **12.2.1** 5.6°C. **12.2.2** 35.5 kJ/mol. **12.2.3** 0.75 atm. **12.2.4** 35 kJ/mol. **12.3.1** 8.908 g/cm³. **12.3.2** Molar mass ≈ 40 g/mol. The metal is either K or Ca. **12.6.1** 64.9 kJ. **12.6.2** 2.58 kJ. **12.7.1** (a) 1 = sublime, 2 = melt, 3 = melt, 4 = melt; (b) 1 = no, 2 = no, 3 = no, 4 = no.

KEY SKILLS

Intermolecular Forces

Most of the intermolecular forces discussed in Chapter 12 are those between particles (atoms, molecules, or ions) in a pure substance. However, our ability to predict how easily a substance can be dissolved in a particular solvent relies on our understanding of the forces between the particles of two *different* substances. The axiom "like dissolves like" refers to *polar* (or ionic) substances being more soluble in *polar* solvents, and *nonpolar* substances being more soluble in *nonpolar* solvents. To assess the solubility of a substance, we must identify it as ionic, polar, or nonpolar. The following flowchart illustrates this identification process and the conclusions we can draw about solubility.

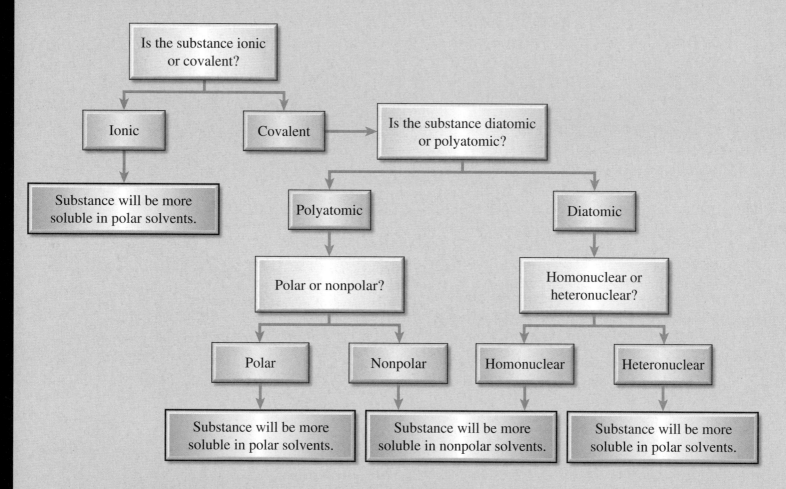

To determine whether or not a substance is ionic, we examine its chemical formula. If the formula contains either a metal cation or the ammonium ion (NH_4^+), it is ionic. Recall that there are some ionic compounds that are considered insoluble in water [◄◄ Table 9.3, page 313]. However, even these compounds are more soluble in *water* than they are in *non*polar solvents.

If a substance is not ionic, it is covalent. Covalent substances may be polar or nonpolar, depending on the electronegativities of the atoms involved—and on molecular geometry [◄◄ Chapter 7 Key Skills]. Polar species will be more soluble in polar solvents, such as water; and nonpolar species will be more soluble in nonpolar solvents, such as benzene.

In addition to deciding whether a substance will be more soluble in polar or nonpolar solvents, it is possible to assess *relative* solubilities of two different solutes in the same solvent. For example, we may be asked to compare the solubilities (in water and in benzene) of two different molecules. If one of the molecules is polar and the other is nonpolar, we should expect the *polar* molecule to be more soluble in *water*—and the *nonpolar* one to be more soluble in *benzene*.

Further, some nonpolar substances do dissolve in water because dispersion forces, which are stronger in larger molecules with greater *polarizability* [◄◄ Section 12.1]. Therefore, we should expect the larger of two nonpolar molecules to be more soluble in water.

Key Skills Problems

12.1
Which of the following would you expect to be more soluble in water than in benzene? (Select all that apply.)

(a) CH_3OH (b) CCl_4 (c) [structure: $C=C$ with H, Cl top and Cl, H bottom]   (d) [structure: $C=C$ with Cl, Cl top and H, H bottom]   (e) KI

12.2
Which of the following would you expect to be more soluble in benzene than in water? (Select all that apply.)

(a) Br_2 (b) KBr   (c) NH_3 (d) [structure: $C=C$ with H, Cl top and Cl, H bottom]   (e) [structure: $C-C$ with H, Cl top and H, Cl bottom]

12.3
Arrange the following substances in order of *decreasing* solubility in water: Kr, O_2, N_2.

(a) $Kr \approx O_2 > N_2$
(b) $Kr > O_2 \approx N_2$
(c) $Kr \approx N_2 > O_2$
(d) $Kr > N_2 > O_2$
(e) $Kr \approx N_2 \approx O_2$

12.4
Arrange the following substances in order of *increasing* solubility in water: C_2H_5OH, CO_2, N_2O

(a) $C_2H_5OH < CO_2 < N_2O$
(b) $CO_2 < N_2O < C_2H_5OH$
(c) $N_2O < C_2H_5OH < CO_2$
(d) $CO_2 \approx N_2O < C_2H_5OH$
(e) $CO_2 < C_2H_5OH < N_2O$

CHAPTER 13

Physical Properties of Solutions

13.1 Types of Solutions

13.2 A Molecular View of the Solution Process
• The Importance of Intermolecular Forces
• Energy and Entropy in Solution Formation

13.3 Concentration Units
• Molality • Percent by Mass • Comparison of Concentration Units

13.4 Factors That Affect Solubility
• Temperature • Pressure

13.5 Colligative Properties
• Vapor-Pressure Lowering • Boiling-Point Elevation • Freezing-Point Depression • Osmotic Pressure • Electrolyte Solutions

13.6 Calculations Using Colligative Properties

13.7 Colloids

A colloid is a uniform dispersion of one substance in another substance. Liquid magnets or *ferrofluids* represent an unusual type of colloid wherein nanoscale ferromagnetic particles are suspended in a carrier fluid, such as an organic solvent or water. When no external magnetic field is present, the fluid is not magnetic. However, when an external magnetic field is applied, the paramagnetic nanoparticles align with the magnet. Depending on the strength of the magnetic field applied, the density and shape of the ferrofluid can change. Chemists and materials scientists have found uses for ferrofluids in magnetic liquid sealants, low friction seals for rotating shafts, stereo speakers and computer hard drives.

Before You Begin, Review These Skills

- Intermolecular forces [◄◄ Section 12.1]
- Molecular geometry and polarity [◄◄ Section 7.2]
- Solution stoichiometry [◄◄ Section 9.5]

13.1 TYPES OF SOLUTIONS

As we noted in Section 1.2, a solution is a homogeneous mixture of two or more substances. Recall that a solution consists of a *solvent* and one or more *solutes* [◄◄ Section 9.1]. Although many of the most familiar solutions are those in which a solid is dissolved in a liquid (e.g., saltwater or sugar water), the components of a solution may be solid, liquid, or gas. The possible combinations give rise to seven distinct types of solutions, which we classify by the original states of the solution components. Table 13.1 gives an example of each type.

In this chapter, we will focus on solutions in which the solvent is a liquid; and the liquid solvent we will encounter most often is water. Recall that solutions in which water is the solvent are called *aqueous* solutions [◄◄ Section 9.1].

Solutions can also be classified by the amount of solute dissolved relative to the maximum amount that can be dissolved. A ***saturated solution*** is one that contains the maximum amount of a solute that will dissolve in a solvent at a specific temperature. The amount of solute dissolved in a given volume of a saturated solution is called the ***solubility.*** It is important to realize that solubility refers to a specific solute, a specific solvent, and a specific *temperature*. For example, the solubility of NaCl in water at 20°C is 36 g per 100 mL. The solubility of NaCl at another temperature, or in another solvent, would be different. An ***unsaturated solution*** is one that contains less solute than it has the capacity to dissolve. A ***supersaturated solution,*** on the other hand, contains *more* dissolved solute than is present in a saturated solution (Figure 13.1). It is generally not stable, and eventually the dissolved solute will come out of solution. An example of this phenomenon is shown in Figure 13.2.

Student Annotation: The term *solubility* was also defined in Section 9.2.

TABLE 13.1	Types of Solutions		
Solute	**Solvent**	**State of resulting solution**	**Example**
Gas	Gas	Gas*	Air
Gas	Liquid	Liquid	Carbonated water
Gas	Solid	Solid	H_2 gas in palladium
Liquid	Liquid	Liquid	Ethanol in water
Liquid	Solid	Solid	Mercury in silver
Solid	Liquid	Liquid	Saltwater
Solid	Solid	Solid	Brass (Cu/Zn)

*Gaseous solutions can only contain gaseous solutes.

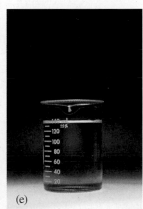

(a) (b) (c) (d) (e)

Figure 13.1 (a) Many solutions consist of a solid dissolved in water. (b) When all the solid dissolves, the solution is unsaturated. (c) If more solid is added than will dissolve, the solution is saturated. (d) A saturated solution is, by definition, in contact with undissolved solid. (e) Some saturated solutions can be made into supersaturated solutions by heating to dissolve more solid, and cooling carefully to prevent crystallization.

Figure 13.2 In a supersaturated solution, (a) addition of a tiny seed crystal initiates crystallization of excess solute. (b)–(e) Crystallization proceeds rapidly to give a *saturated* solution and the crystallized solid.

13.2 A MOLECULAR VIEW OF THE SOLUTION PROCESS

In Chapter 9, we learned guidelines that helped us predict whether or not an ionic solid is soluble in water. We now take a more general look at the factors that determine solubility at the molecular level. This discussion will enable us to understand why so many ionic substances are soluble in water, which is a polar solvent; and it will help us to predict the solubility of ionic and molecular compounds in both polar and nonpolar solvents.

The Importance of Intermolecular Forces

The intermolecular forces that hold molecules together in liquids and solids play a central role in the solution process. When the solute dissolves in the solvent, molecules of the solute disperse throughout the solvent. They are, in effect, *separated* from one another and each solute molecule is *surrounded* by solvent molecules—a process known as ***solvation.*** The ease with which solute molecules are separated from one another and surrounded by solvent molecules depends on the relative strengths of three types of interactions:

1. Solute-solute interactions
2. Solvent-solvent interactions
3. Solute-solvent interactions

Unlike most of the intermolecular forces covered in Chapter 12, which were between the molecules, atoms, or ions of a pure substance, solute-solvent interactions are those that exist in a mixture of different substances. Because the components of a mixture can have different properties, there is a greater variety of intermolecular forces to consider. In addition to dispersion forces, which exist between all substances, dipole-dipole forces, which exist between polar molecules, and ion-ion forces, which exist between ions, solutions can exhibit the following intermolecular forces:

Student Annotation: A hemoglobin molecule contains four Fe^{2+} ions. In the early stages of O_2 binding, oxygen molecules are attracted to the Fe^{2+} ions by an ion-induced dipole interaction.

Intermolecular forces	Example	Model
Ion-dipole. The charge of an ion is attracted to the partial charge on a polar molecule.	NaCl or KI in H_2O	
Dipole-induced dipole. The partial charge on a polar molecule induces a temporary partial charge on a neighboring nonpolar molecule or atom.	He or CO_2 in H_2O	
Ion-induced dipole. The charge of an ion induces a temporary partial charge on a neighboring nonpolar molecule or atom.	Fe^{2+} and O_2	

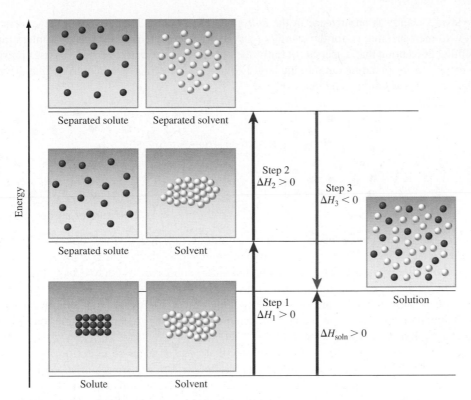

Figure 13.3 A molecular view of the solution process portrayed as taking place in three steps: First the solute and solvent molecules are separated (steps 1 and 2, respectively—both endothermic). Then the solvent and solute molecules mix (step 3—exothermic).

For simplicity, we can imagine the solution process taking place in the three distinct steps shown in Figure 13.3. Step 1 is the separation of solute molecules from one another, and step 2 is the separation of solvent molecules from one another. Both of these steps require an input of energy to overcome intermolecular attractions, so they are *endothermic*. In step 3 the solvent and solute molecules mix. This process is usually *exothermic*. The enthalpy change for the overall process, ΔH_{soln}, is given by

$$\Delta H_{soln} = \Delta H_1 + \Delta H_2 + \Delta H_3$$

The overall solution-formation process is exothermic ($\Delta H_{soln} < 0$) when the energy given off in step 3 is greater than the sum of energy required for steps 1 and 2. The overall process is endothermic ($\Delta H_{soln} > 0$) when the energy given off in step 3 is less than the total required for steps 1 and 2. (Figure 13.3 depicts a solution formation that is endothermic overall.)

Student Annotation: Like the formation of chemical bonds [◄◄ Section 10.7], the formation of intermolecular attractions is exothermic. If that isn't intuitively obvious, think of it this way: It would require energy to *separate* molecules that are attracted to each other. The reverse process, the *combination* of molecules that attract each other, would give off an equal amount of energy [◄◄ Section 10.3].

Energy and Entropy in Solution Formation

Previously, we learned that the driving force behind some processes is the lowering of the system's potential energy. Recall the minimization of potential energy when two hydrogen atoms are 74 pm apart [◄◄ Section 7.3]. However, because there are substances that dissolve endothermically, meaning that the process increases the system's potential energy, something else must be involved in determining whether or not a substance will dissolve. That something else is *entropy*.

The **entropy** of a system is a measure of how *dispersed* or *spread out* its energy is. Consider two samples of different gases separated by a physical barrier. When we remove the barrier, the gases mix, forming a solution. Under ordinary conditions, we can treat the gases as ideal, meaning we can assume that there are no attractive forces between the molecules in either sample before they mix (no solute-solute or solvent-solvent attractions to break)—and no attractive forces between the molecules in the mixture (no solute-solvent attractions form). The energy of the system does not change—and yet the gases mix spontaneously. The reason such a solution forms is that, although there is no change in the energy of either of the original samples of gas, the energy possessed by each sample of gas spreads out into a larger volume. This increased dispersal of the system's energy is an increase in the *entropy* of the system. There is a natural tendency for entropy to increase; that is, for the energy of a system to become more dispersed—unless there is something preventing that dispersal. Initially, the physical barrier between the two gases prevented their energy from spreading out into the larger volume. It is the increase in entropy that drives the formation of this solution—and many others.

Separate gases   Mixture of gases

Now consider the case of solid ammonium nitrate (NH_4NO_3), which dissolves in water in an *endothermic* process. In this case, the dissolution *increases* the potential energy of the system. However, the energy possessed by the ammonium nitrate solid spreads out to occupy the volume of the resulting solution causing the entropy of the system to increase. Ammonium nitrate dissolves in water because the favorable increase in the system's entropy outweighs the unfavorable increase in its potential energy. Although the process being endothermic is a barrier to solution formation, it is not enough of a barrier to prevent it.

In some cases, a process is so endothermic that even an increase in entropy is not enough to allow it to happen spontaneously. Sodium chloride (NaCl) is not soluble in a nonpolar solvent such as benzene, for example, because the solvent-solute interactions that would result are too weak to compensate for the energy required to separate the network of positive and negative ions in sodium chloride. The magnitude of the exothermic step in solution formation (ΔH_3) is so small compared to the combined magnitude of the endothermic steps (ΔH_1 and ΔH_2) that the overall process is *very* endothermic and does not happen to any significant degree despite the increase in entropy that would result.

The saying "like dissolves like" is useful in predicting the solubility of a substance in a given solvent. What this expression means is that two substances with intermolecular forces of similar type and magnitude are likely to be soluble in each other. For example, both carbon tetrachloride (CCl_4) and benzene (C_6H_6) are nonpolar liquids. The only intermolecular forces present in these substances are dispersion forces [◄◄ Section 12.1]. When these two liquids are mixed, they readily dissolve in each other, because the attraction between CCl_4 and C_6H_6 molecules is comparable in magnitude to the forces between molecules in pure CCl_4 and those between molecules in pure C_6H_6. Two liquids are said to be ***miscible*** if they are completely soluble in each other in all proportions. Alcohols such as methanol, ethanol, and 1,2-ethylene glycol are miscible with water because they can form hydrogen bonds with water molecules:

$$\begin{array}{ccc}
\overset{\displaystyle H}{\underset{\displaystyle H}{H-C-O-H}} & \overset{\displaystyle H\ \ H}{\underset{\displaystyle H\ \ H}{H-C-C-O-H}} & \overset{\displaystyle H\ \ H}{\underset{\displaystyle H\ \ H}{H-O-C-C-O-H}} \\[1em]
\text{Methanol} & \text{Ethanol} & \text{1,2-Ethylene glycol}
\end{array}$$

Student Annotation: *Solvation* refers in a general way to solute particles being surrounded by solvent molecules. When the solvent is water, we use the more specific term *hydration* [◄◄ Section 9.2].

The guidelines listed in Tables 9.2 and 9.3 enable us to predict the solubility of a particular ionic compound in water. When sodium chloride dissolves in water, the ions are stabilized in solution by *hydration*, which involves ion-dipole interactions. In general, ionic compounds are much more soluble in polar solvents, such as water, liquid ammonia, and liquid hydrogen fluoride, than in nonpolar solvents. Because the molecules of nonpolar solvents, such as benzene and carbon tetrachloride, do not have a dipole moment, they cannot effectively solvate the Na^+ and Cl^- ions. The predominant intermolecular interaction between ions and nonpolar compounds is an ion-induced dipole interaction, which typically is much weaker than ion-dipole interactions. Consequently, ionic compounds usually have extremely low solubility in nonpolar solvents.

Worked Example 13.1 lets you practice predicting solubility based on intermolecular forces.

Worked Example 13.1

Determine for each solute whether the solubility will be greater in water, which is polar, or in benzene (C_6H_6), which is nonpolar: (a) bromine (Br_2), (b) sodium iodide (NaI), (c) carbon tetrachloride (CCl_4), and (d) formaldehyde (CH_2O).

Strategy Consider the structure of each solute to determine whether or not it is polar. For molecular solutes, start with a Lewis structure and apply the VSEPR theory [◄◄ Section 7.1]. We expect polar solutes, including ionic compounds, to be more soluble in water. Nonpolar solutes will be more soluble in benzene.

Setup

(a) Bromine is a homonuclear diatomic molecule and is nonpolar.

(b) Sodium iodide is ionic.

(c) Carbon tetrachloride has the following Lewis structure:

$$:\ddot{C}l:$$
$$:\ddot{C}l - C - \ddot{C}l:$$
$$:\ddot{C}l:$$

With four electron domains around the central atom, we expect a tetrahedral arrangement. A symmetrical arrangement of identical bonds results in a nonpolar molecule.

(d) Formaldehyde has the following Lewis structure:

$$\overset{\ddot{O}}{\underset{H \nearrow C \nwarrow H}{\|}}$$

Crossed arrows can be used to represent the individual bond dipoles [◄◄ Section 7.2]. This molecule is polar and can form hydrogen bonds with water.

Solution

(a) Bromine is more soluble in benzene.
(b) Sodium iodide is more soluble in water.
(c) Carbon tetrachloride is more soluble in benzene.
(d) Formaldehyde is more soluble in water.

> **Think About It**
> Remember that molecular formula alone is not sufficient to determine the shape or the polarity of a polyatomic molecule. It must be determined by starting with a correct Lewis structure and applying the VSEPR theory [◄◄ Section 7.2].

Practice Problem A Predict whether iodine (I_2) is more soluble in liquid ammonia (NH_3) or in carbon disulfide (CS_2).

Practice Problem B Which of the following should you expect to be more soluble in benzene than in water: C_3H_8, HCl, I_2, CS_2?

SECTION 13.2 REVIEW

A Molecular View of the Solution Process

13.2.1 Which of the following compounds do you expect to be more soluble in benzene than in water? (Select all that apply.) SO_2, CO_2, Na_2SO_4, C_2H_6, Br_2.

13.2.2 Which of the following compounds dissolved in water would exhibit hydrogen bonding between the solute and solvent? H_2, CH_3OH, CO_2, NH_3, NaCl.

13.3 CONCENTRATION UNITS

We learned in Chapter 9 that chemists often express concentration of solutions in units of *molarity*. Recall that molarity, *M*, is defined as the number of moles of solute divided by the number of liters of solution [◀◀ Section 9.5].

$$\text{molarity} = M = \frac{\text{moles of solute}}{\text{liters of solution}}$$

Mole fraction, χ, which is defined as the number of moles of solute divided by the total number of moles, is also an expression of concentration [◀◀ Section 11.7].

$$\text{mole fraction of component A} = \chi_A = \frac{\text{moles of A}}{\text{sum of moles of all components}}$$

> **Student Annotation:** We have already used percent by mass to describe the composition of a pure substance [◀◀ Section 5.9]. In this chapter, we will use percent by mass to describe *solutions*.

In this section, we will learn about *molality* and *percent by mass,* two additional ways to express the concentration of a mixture component. How a chemist expresses concentration depends on the type of problem being solved.

Molality

Molality (*m*) is the number of moles of solute dissolved in 1 kg (1000 g) of solvent:

> **Student Annotation:** It is a common mistake to confuse molarity and molality. Molarity depends on the *volume* of the solution. Molality depends on the *mass* of the solvent.

Equation 13.1	$\text{molality} = m = \dfrac{\text{moles of solute}}{\text{mass of solvent (in kg)}}$

For example, to prepare a 1 molal (1 *m*) aqueous sodium sulfate solution, we must dissolve 1 mole (142.0 g) of Na_2SO_4 in 1 kg of water.

Percent by Mass

The ***percent by mass*** (also called *percent by weight*) is the ratio of the mass of a solute to the mass of the solution, multiplied by 100 percent. Because the units of mass cancel on the top and bottom of the fraction, any units of mass can be used—provided they are used consistently:

Equation 13.2	percent by mass $= \dfrac{\text{mass of solute}}{\text{mass of solute} + \text{mass of solvent}} \times 100\%$

For example, we can express the concentration of the 1 *m* aqueous sodium sulfate solution as

$$\text{percent by mass } Na_2SO_4 = \frac{\text{mass of } Na_2SO_4}{\text{mass of } Na_2SO_4 + \text{mass of water}} \times 100\%$$

$$= \frac{142.0 \text{ g}}{1142.0 \text{ g}} \times 100\% = 12.4\%$$

The term *percent* literally means "parts per hundred." If we were to use Equation 13.2 but multiply by 1000 instead of 100, we would get "parts per thousand"; multiplying by 1,000,000 would give "parts per million" or *ppm;* and so on. Parts per million, parts per billion, parts per trillion, and so forth, usually are used to express very low concentrations, such as those of some pollutants in the atmosphere or a body of water. For example, if a 1-kg sample of water is found to contain 3 μg (3×10^{-6} g) of arsenic, its concentration can be expressed in parts per billion (ppb) as follows:

$$\frac{3 \times 10^{-6} \text{ g}}{1000 \text{ g}} \times 10^9 = 3 \text{ ppb}$$

Worked Example 13.2 shows how to calculate the concentration in molality and in percent by mass.

Worked Example 13.2

A solution is made by dissolving 170.1 g of glucose ($C_6H_{12}O_6$) in enough water to make a liter of solution. The density of the solution is 1.062 g/mL. Express the concentration of the solution in (a) molality, (b) percent by mass, and (c) parts per million.

Strategy Use the molar mass of glucose to determine the number of moles of glucose in a liter of solution. Use the density (in g/L) to calculate the mass of a liter of solution. Subtract the mass of glucose from the mass of solution to determine the mass of water. Use Equation 13.1 to determine the molality. Knowing the mass of glucose and the total mass of solution in a liter, use Equation 13.2 to calculate the percent concentration by mass.

Setup The molar mass of glucose is 180.2 g/mol; the density of the solution is 1.062 g/mL.

Solution

(a)
$$\frac{170.1 \text{ g}}{180.2 \text{ g/mol}} = 0.9440 \text{ mol glucose per liter of solution}$$

$$1 \text{ liter of solution} \times \frac{1062 \text{ g}}{\text{L}} = 1062 \text{ g}$$

$$1062 \text{ g solution} - 170.1 \text{ g glucose} = 892 \text{ g water} = 0.892 \text{ kg water}$$

$$\frac{0.9440 \text{ mol glucose}}{0.892 \text{ kg water}} = 1.06 \text{ } m$$

(b) $\dfrac{170.1 \text{ g glucose}}{1062 \text{ g solution}} \times 100\% = 16.02\%$ glucose by mass

(c) $\dfrac{170.1 \text{ g glucose}}{1062 \text{ g solution}} \times 1{,}000{,}000 = 1.602 \times 10^5$ ppm glucose

---

Think About It

Pay careful attention to units in problems such as this. Most require conversions between grams and kilograms and/or liters and milliliters.

Practice Problem A Determine (a) the molality and (b) the percent by mass of urea for a solution prepared by dissolving 5.46 g urea [$(NH_2)_2CO$] in 215 g of water.

Practice Problem B Determine the molality of an aqueous solution that is 4.5 percent urea by mass.

Comparison of Concentration Units

The choice of a concentration unit is based on the purpose of the experiment. For instance, we typically use molarity to express the concentrations of solutions for titrations and gravimetric analyses. *Mole fractions* are used to express the concentrations of gases—and of solutions when we are working with vapor pressures, which we will discuss in Section 13.5.

The advantage of molarity is that it is generally easier to measure the volume of a solution, using precisely calibrated volumetric flasks, than to weigh the solvent. Molality, on the other hand, has the advantage of being temperature independent. The volume of a solution typically increases slightly with increasing temperature, which would change the molarity. The mass of solvent in a solution, however, does *not* change with temperature.

Percent by mass is similar to molality in that it is independent of temperature. Furthermore, because it is defined in terms of the ratio of the mass of solute to the mass of solution, we do not need to know the molar mass of the solute to calculate the percent by mass.

Often it is necessary to convert the concentration of a solution from one unit to another. For example, the same solution may be used for different experiments that require different concentration units for calculations. Suppose we want to express the concentration of a 0.396 m aqueous glucose ($C_6H_{12}O_6$) solution (at 25°C) in molarity. We know there is 0.396 mole of glucose in 1000 g of

Student Annotation: For very dilute aqueous solutions, molarity and molality have the same value. The mass of a liter of water is 1 kg, and in a very dilute solution, the mass of solute is negligible compared to that of the solvent.

the solvent. We need to determine the *volume* of this solution to calculate molarity. To determine volume, we must first calculate its mass:

$$0.396 \text{ mol } C_6H_{12}O_6 \times \frac{180.2 \text{ g}}{1 \text{ mol } C_6H_{12}O_6} = 71.4 \text{ g } C_6H_{12}O_6$$

$$71.4 \text{ g } C_6H_{12}O_6 + 1000 \text{ g } H_2O = 1071 \text{ g solution}$$

Student Annotation: Problems that require conversions between molarity and molality must provide density or sufficient information to determine density.

Once we have determined the mass of the solution, we use the *density* of the solution, which is typically determined experimentally, to determine its volume. The density of a 0.396 *m* glucose solution is 1.16 g/mL at 25°C. Therefore, its volume is

$$\text{volume} = \frac{\text{mass}}{\text{density}}$$

$$= \frac{1071 \text{ g}}{1.16 \text{ g/mL}} \times \frac{1 \text{ L}}{1000 \text{ mL}}$$

$$= 0.923 \text{ L}$$

Having determined the volume of the solution, the molarity is given by

$$\text{molarity} = \frac{\text{moles of solute}}{\text{liters of solution}}$$

$$= \frac{0.396 \text{ mol}}{0.923 \text{ L}}$$

$$= 0.429 \text{ mol/L} = 0.429 \text{ } M$$

Worked Example 13.3 shows how to convert from one unit of concentration to another.

Worked Example 13.3

"Rubbing alcohol" is a mixture of isopropyl alcohol (C_3H_7OH) and water that is 70 percent isopropyl alcohol by mass (density = 0.79 g/mL at 20°C). Express the concentration of rubbing alcohol in (a) molarity and (b) molality.

Strategy

Student Annotation: You can choose to start with any volume in a problem like this. Choosing 1 L simplifies the math.

(a) Use density to determine the total mass of a liter of solution, and use percent by mass to determine the mass of isopropyl alcohol in a liter of solution. Convert the mass of isopropyl alcohol to moles, and divide moles by liters of solution to get molarity.

(b) Subtract the mass of C_3H_7OH from the mass of solution to get the mass of water. Divide moles of C_3H_7OH by the mass of water (in kg) to get molality.

Setup   The mass of a liter of rubbing alcohol is 790 g, and the molar mass of isopropyl alcohol is 60.09 g/mol.

Solution

(a) $$\frac{790 \text{ g solution}}{\text{L solution}} \times \frac{70 \text{ g } C_3H_7OH}{100 \text{ g solution}} = \frac{553 \text{ g } C_3H_7OH}{\text{L solution}}$$

$$\frac{553 \text{ g } C_3H_7OH}{\text{L solution}} \times \frac{1 \text{ mol}}{60.09 \text{ g } C_3H_7OH} = \frac{9.20 \text{ mol } C_3H_7OH}{\text{L solution}} = 9.2 \text{ } M$$

(b) 790 g solution − 553 g C_3H_7OH = 237 g water = 0.237 kg water

$$\frac{9.20 \text{ mol } C_3H_7OH}{0.237 \text{ kg water}} = 39 \text{ } m$$

Rubbing alcohol is 9.2 *M* and 39 *m* in isopropyl alcohol.

Think About It
Note the large difference between molarity and molality in this case. Molarity and molality are the same (or similar) only for very dilute aqueous solutions.

Practice Problem A An aqueous solution that is 16 percent sulfuric acid (H_2SO_4) by mass has a density of 1.109 g/mL at 25°C. Determine (a) the molarity and (b) the molality of the solution at 25°C.

Practice Problem B Determine the percent sulfuric acid by mass of a 1.49 *m* aqueous solution of H_2SO_4.

Concentration Units

13.3.1 Determine the percent by mass of KCl in a solution prepared by dissolving 1.18 g of KCl in 86.3 g of water.

13.3.2 What is the molality of a solution prepared by dissolving 6.44 g of naphthalene ($C_{10}H_8$) in 80.1 g benzene?

13.3.3 At 20.0°C, a 0.258 *m* aqueous solution of glucose ($C_6H_{12}O_6$) has a density of 1.0173 g/mL. Calculate the molarity of this solution.

13.3.4 At 25.0°C, an aqueous solution that is 25.0 percent H_2SO_4 by mass has a density of 1.178 g/mL. Calculate the molarity and the molality of this solution.

13.4 FACTORS THAT AFFECT SOLUBILITY

Recall that solubility is defined as the maximum amount of solute that will dissolve in a given quantity of solvent at a specific *temperature*. Temperature affects the solubility of most substances. In this section we will consider the effects of temperature on the aqueous solubility of solids and gases, and the effect of *pressure* on the aqueous solubility of gases.

Temperature

More sugar dissolves in hot tea than in iced tea because the aqueous solubility of sugar, like that of most solid substances, increases as the temperature increases. Figure 13.4 shows the solubility of some common solids in water as a function of temperature. Note how the solubility of a solid and the *change* in solubility over a particular temperature range vary considerably. The relationship between temperature and solubility is complex and often nonlinear.

The relationship between temperature and the aqueous solubility of gases is somewhat simpler than that of solids. Most gaseous solutes become less soluble in water as temperature increases. If you get a glass of water from your faucet and leave it on the kitchen counter for a while, you will see bubbles forming in the water as it warms to room temperature. As the temperature of the

Figure 13.4 Temperature dependence of the solubility of glucose and several ionic compounds in water.

water increases, dissolved gases become less soluble and come out of solution—resulting in the formation of bubbles.

One of the more important consequences of the reduced solubility of gases in water at elevated temperature is *thermal pollution.* Hundreds of billions of gallons of water are used every year for industrial cooling, mostly in electric power and nuclear power production. This process heats the water, which is then returned to the rivers and lakes from which it was taken. The increased water temperature has a twofold impact on aquatic life. The rate of metabolism of cold-blooded species such as fish increases with increasing temperature, thereby increasing their need for oxygen. At the same time, the increased water temperature causes a decrease in the solubility of oxygen—making less oxygen available. The result can be disastrous for fish populations.

Pressure

Although pressure does not influence the solubility of a liquid or a solid significantly, it does greatly affect the solubility of a gas. The quantitative relationship between gas solubility and pressure is given by ***Henry's***[1] ***law,*** which states that the solubility of a gas in a liquid is proportional to the pressure of the gas over the solution,

> **Student Annotation:** Henry's law means that if we double the pressure of a gas over a solution (at constant temperature), we double the concentration of gas dissolved in the solution; triple the pressure, triple the concentration; and so on.

$$c \propto P$$

and is expressed as

Equation 13.3	$c = kP$

where c is the molar concentration (mol/L) of the dissolved gas, P is the pressure (in atm) of the gas over the solution, and k is a proportionality constant called the ***Henry's law constant.*** Henry's law constants are specific to the gas-solvent combination and vary with temperature. The units of k are mol/L · atm. If there is a mixture of gases over the solution, then P in Equation 13.3 is the partial pressure of the gas in question.

Henry's law can be understood qualitatively in terms of the kinetic molecular theory [◄◄ Section 11.2]. The amount of gas that will dissolve in a solvent depends on how frequently the gas molecules collide with the liquid surface and become trapped by the condensed phase. Suppose we have a gas in dynamic equilibrium [◄◄ Section 12.2] with a solution, as shown in Figure 13.5(a). At any point in time, the number of gas molecules entering the solution is equal to the number of dissolved gas molecules leaving the solution and entering the vapor phase. If the partial pressure of the gas is increased [Figure 13.5(b)], more molecules strike the liquid surface, causing more of them to dissolve. As the concentration of dissolved gas increases, the number of gas molecules leaving the solution also increases. These processes continue until the concentration of dissolved gas in the solution reaches the point again where the number of molecules leaving the solution per second equals the number entering the solution per second.

Figure 13.5 A molecular view of Henry's law. When the partial pressure of the gas over the solution increases from (a) to (b), the concentration of the dissolved gas also increases according to Equation 13.3.

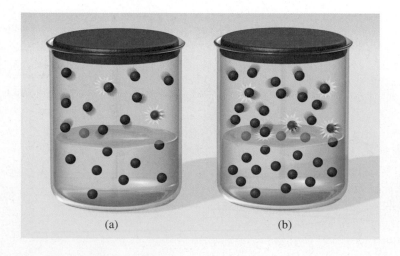

(a)   (b)

---

[1]William Henry (1775–1836) was an English chemist whose major contribution to science was his discovery of the law describing the solubility of gases, which now bears his name.

One interesting application of Henry's law is the production of carbonated beverages. Manufacturers put the "fizz" in soft drinks using pressurized carbon dioxide. The pressure of CO_2 applied (typically on the order of 5 atm) is many thousands of times greater than the partial pressure of CO_2 in the air. Thus, when a can or bottle of soda is opened, the CO_2 dissolved under high-pressure conditions comes out of solution—resulting in the bubbles that make carbonated drinks appealing.

Worked Example 13.4 illustrates the use of Henry's law.

Worked Example 13.4

Calculate the concentration of carbon dioxide in a soft drink that was bottled under a partial pressure of 5.0 atm CO_2 at 25°C (a) before the bottle is opened and (b) after the soda has gone "flat" at 25°C. The Henry's law constant for CO_2 in water at this temperature is 3.1×10^{-2} mol/L · atm. Assume that the partial pressure of CO_2 in air is 0.0003 atm and that the Henry's law constant for the soft drink is the same as that for water.

Strategy Use Equation 13.3 and the given Henry's law constant to solve for the molar concentration (mol/L) of CO_2 at 25°C and the two CO_2 pressures given.

Setup At 25°C, the Henry's law constant for CO_2 in water is 3.1×10^{-2} mol/L · atm.

Solution (a) $c = (3.1 \times 10^{-2}$ mol/L · atm$)(5.0$ atm$) = 1.6 \times 10^{-1}$ mol/L

(b) $c = (3.1 \times 10^{-2}$ mol/L · atm$)(0.0003$ atm$) = 9 \times 10^{-6}$ mol/L

> **Think About It**
> With a pressure approximately 15,000 times smaller in part (b) than in part (a), we expect the concentration of CO_2 to be approximately 15,000 times smaller—and it is.

Practice Problem A Calculate the concentration of CO_2 in water at 25°C when the pressure of CO_2 over the solution is 4.0 atm.

Practice Problem B Calculate the pressure of O_2 necessary to generate an aqueous solution that is 3.4×10^{-2} M in O_2 at 25°C. The Henry's law constant for O_2 in water at 25°C is 1.3×10^{-3} mol/L · atm.

SECTION 13.4 REVIEW

Factors That Affect Solubility

13.4.1 The solubility of N_2 in water at 25°C and an N_2 pressure of 1 atm is 6.8×10^{-4} mol/L. Calculate the concentration of dissolved N_2 in water under atmospheric conditions where the partial pressure of N_2 is 0.78 atm.

13.4.2 Calculate the molar concentration of O_2 in water at 25°C under atmospheric conditions where the partial pressure of O_2 is 0.22 atm. The Henry's law constant for O_2 is 1.3×10^{-3} mol/L · atm.

13.5 COLLIGATIVE PROPERTIES

Colligative properties are properties that depend on the number of solute particles in solution but do not depend on the nature of the solute particles. That is, colligative properties depend on the concentration of solute particles regardless of whether those particles are atoms, molecules, or ions. The colligative properties are vapor-pressure lowering, boiling-point elevation, freezing-point depression, and osmotic pressure. We begin by considering the colligative properties of relatively dilute solutions (≤ 0.2 M) of nonelectrolytes.

Vapor-Pressure Lowering

We have seen that a liquid exerts a characteristic vapor pressure [◄◄ Section 12.2]. When a ***non-volatile*** solute (one that does *not* exert a vapor pressure) is dissolved in a liquid, the vapor pressure exerted by the liquid decreases. The difference between the vapor pressure of a pure solvent and that of the corresponding solution depends on the concentration of the solute in the solution. This relationship is expressed by ***Raoult's[2] law,*** which states that the partial pressure of a solvent over a solution, P_1, is given by the vapor pressure of the pure solvent, P_1°, times the mole fraction of the solvent in the solution, χ_1:

Student Annotation: Table 11.6 (page 448) gives the vapor pressure of water at various temperatures.

Equation 13.4
$$P_1 = \chi_1 P_1^\circ$$

In a solution containing only one solute, $\chi_1 = 1 - \chi_2$, where χ_2 is the mole fraction of the solute. Equation 13.4 can therefore be rewritten as

$$P_1 = (1 - \chi_2)P_1^\circ$$

or

$$P_1 = P_1^\circ - \chi_2 P_1^\circ$$

so that

Equation 13.5
$$P_1^\circ - P_1 = \Delta P = \chi_2 P_1^\circ$$

Thus, the decrease in vapor pressure, ΔP, is directly proportional to the solute concentration expressed as a *mole fraction.*

To understand the phenomenon of vapor-pressure lowering, we must understand the degree of *order* associated with the states of matter involved. As we saw in Section 13.2, molecules in the liquid state are fairly highly ordered; that is, they have low entropy. Molecules in the gas phase have significantly less order—they have high entropy. Because there is a natural tendency toward increased entropy, molecules have a certain tendency to leave the region of lower entropy and enter the region of higher entropy. This corresponds to molecules leaving the liquid and entering the gas phase. As we have seen, when a solute is added to a liquid, the liquid's order is disrupted. Thus, the solution has greater entropy than the pure liquid. Because there is a smaller difference in entropy between the solution and the gas phase than there was between the pure liquid and the gas phase, there is a decreased tendency for molecules to leave the solution and enter the gas phase—resulting in a lower vapor pressure exerted by the solvent. This qualitative explanation of vapor-pressure lowering is illustrated in Figure 13.6. The smaller difference in entropy between the solution and gas phases, relative to that between the pure liquid and gas phases, results in a decreased tendency for solvent molecules to enter the gas phase. This results in a lowering of vapor pressure. The solvent in a solution will always exert a lower vapor pressure than the pure solvent.

Worked Example 13.5 shows how to use Raoult's law.

Figure 13.6 The smaller difference in entropy between the solution and gas phases, relative to that between the pure liquid and gas phases, results in a decreased tendency for solvent molecules to enter the gas phase. This results in a lowering of vapor pressure. The solvent in a solution always exerts a lower vapor pressure than the pure solvent.

---

[2]François Marie Raoult (1839–1901), a French chemist, worked mainly in solution properties and electrochemistry.

Worked Example 13.5

Calculate the vapor pressure of water over a solution made by dissolving 225 g of glucose in 575 g of water at 35°C. (At 35°C, $P_{H_2O}^\circ = 42.2$ mmHg.)

Strategy Convert the masses of glucose and water to moles, determine the mole fraction of water, and use Equation 13.4 to find the vapor pressure over the solution.

Setup The molar masses of glucose and water are 180.2 and 18.02 g/mol, respectively.

Solution

$$\frac{225 \text{ g glucose}}{180.2 \text{ g/mol}} = 1.25 \text{ mol glucose} \quad \text{and} \quad \frac{575 \text{ g water}}{18.02 \text{ g/mol}} = 31.9 \text{ mol water}$$

$$\chi_{water} = \frac{31.9 \text{ mol water}}{1.25 \text{ mol glucose} + 31.9 \text{ mol water}} = 0.962$$

$$P_{H_2O} = \chi_{water} \times P_{H_2O}^\circ = 0.962 \times 42.2 \text{ mmHg} = 40.6 \text{ mmHg}$$

The vapor pressure of water over the solution is 40.6 mmHg.

Think About It
This problem can also be solved using Equation 13.5 to calculate the vapor-pressure lowering, ΔP.

Practice Problem A Calculate the vapor pressure of a solution made by dissolving 115 g of urea [$(NH_2)_2CO$; molar mass = 60.06 g/mol] in 485 g of water at 25°C. (At 25°C, $P_{H_2O}^\circ = 23.8$ mmHg.)

Practice Problem B Calculate the mass of urea that should be dissolved in 225 g of water at 35°C to produce a solution with a vapor pressure of 37.1 mmHg. (At 35°C, $P_{H_2O}^\circ = 42.2$ mmHg.)

If both components of a solution are **volatile** (i.e., have measurable vapor pressure), the vapor pressure of the solution is the sum of the individual partial pressures exerted by the solution components. Raoult's law holds equally well in this case:

$$P_A = \chi_A P_A^\circ$$

$$P_B = \chi_B P_B^\circ$$

where P_A and P_B are the partial pressures over the solution for components A and B, P_A° and P_B° are the vapor pressures of the pure substances A and B, and χ_A and χ_B are their mole fractions. The total pressure is given by Dalton's law of partial pressures [◄◄ Section 11.7]:

$$P_T = P_A + P_B$$

or

$$P_T = \chi_A P_A^\circ + \chi_B P_B^\circ$$

For example, benzene and toluene are volatile components that have similar structures and therefore similar intermolecular forces:

Benzene   Toluene

In a solution of benzene and toluene, the vapor pressure of each component obeys Raoult's law. Figure 13.7 shows the dependence of the total vapor pressure (P_T) in a benzene-toluene solution on the composition of the solution. Because there are only two components in the solution, we need only express the composition of the solution in terms of the mole fraction of *one* component. For any value of $\chi_{benzene}$, the mole fraction of toluene, $\chi_{toluene}$, is given by the equation $(1 - \chi_{benzene})$. The

Figure 13.7 The dependence of partial pressures of benzene and toluene on their mole fractions in a benzene-toluene solution ($\chi_{\text{toluene}} = 1 - \chi_{\text{benzene}}$) at 80°C. This solution is said to be ideal because the vapor pressures obey Raoult's law.

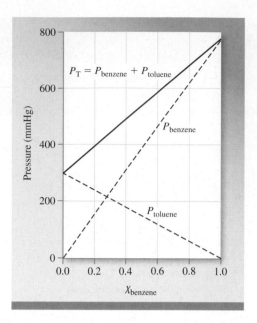

benzene-toluene solution is an example of an ***ideal solution,*** which is simply a solution that *obeys* Raoult's law.

Note that for a mixture in which the mole fractions of benzene and toluene are both 0.5, although the liquid mixture is equimolar, the vapor above the solution is not. Because pure benzene has a higher vapor pressure (75 mmHg at 20°C) than pure toluene (22 mmHg at 20°C), the vapor phase over the mixture will contain a higher concentration of the more volatile benzene molecules than it will the less volatile toluene molecules.

Boiling-Point Elevation

Recall that the *boiling point* of a substance is the temperature at which its vapor pressure equals the external atmospheric pressure [◄◄ Section 12.6]. Because the presence of a nonvolatile solute lowers the vapor pressure of a solution, it also affects the boiling point of the solution—relative to that of the pure liquid. Figure 13.8 shows the phase diagram of water and the changes that occur when a nonvolatile solute is added to it. At any temperature the vapor pressure over a solution is lower than that over the pure liquid, so the liquid-vapor curve for the solution lies below that for the pure solvent. Consequently, the dashed solution curve intersects the horizontal line that marks $P = 1$ atm at a higher temperature than the normal boiling point of the pure solvent. That is, a higher temperature is needed to make the solvent's vapor pressure equal to atmospheric pressure.

Figure 13.8 Phase diagram illustrating the boiling-point elevation and freezing-point depression of aqueous solutions. The dashed curves pertain to the solution, and the solid curves to the pure solvent. As this diagram shows, the boiling point of the solution is higher than that of water, and the freezing point of the solution is lower than that of water.

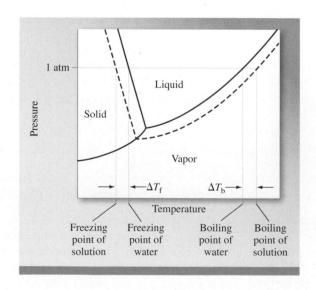

The boiling-point elevation (ΔT_b) is defined as the difference between the boiling point of the solution (T_b) and the boiling point of the pure solvent (T_b°):

$$\Delta T_b = T_b - T_b^\circ$$

Student Annotation: Rearranging this equation, we get the boiling point of the solution by adding ΔT_b to the boiling point of the pure solvent: $T_b = T_b^\circ + \Delta T_b$.

Because $T_b > T_b^\circ$, ΔT_b is a positive quantity.

The value of ΔT_b is proportional to the concentration, expressed in molality, of the solute in the solution.

$$\Delta T_b \propto m$$

or

$$\Delta T_b = K_b m \qquad\qquad \textbf{Equation 13.6}$$

where m is the molality of the solution and K_b is the molal boiling-point elevation constant. The units of K_b are °C/m. Table 13.2 lists values of K_b for several common solvents. Using the boiling-point elevation constant for water and Equation 13.6, you can show that the boiling point of a 1.00 m aqueous solution of a nonvolatile, nonelectrolyte would be 100.5°C:

$$\Delta T_b = K_b m = (0.52°C/m)(1.00\ m) = 0.52°C$$

$$T_b = T_b^\circ + \Delta T_b = 100.0°C + 0.52°C = 100.5°C$$

Student Annotation: The practice of adding salt to water in which food is cooked is for the purpose of increasing the boiling point, thereby cooking the food at a higher temperature.

Freezing-Point Depression

If you have ever lived in a cold climate, you may have seen roads and sidewalks that were "salted" in the winter. The application of a salt such as NaCl or CaCl$_2$ thaws ice (or prevents its formation) by lowering the freezing point of water.

The phase diagram in Figure 13.8 shows that in addition to shifting the liquid-vapor phase boundary down, the addition of a nonvolatile solute also shifts the solid-liquid phase boundary to the left. Consequently, this dashed line intersects the solid horizontal line at 1 atm at a temperature lower than the freezing point of pure water. The freezing-point depression (ΔT_f) is defined as the difference between the freezing point of the pure solvent and the freezing point of the solution:

$$\Delta T_f = T_f^\circ - T_f$$

Student Annotation: We get the freezing point of the solution by *subtracting* ΔT_f from the freezing point of the pure solvent: $T_f = T_f^\circ - \Delta T_f$.

Because $T_f^\circ > T_f$, ΔT_f is a positive quantity. Again, the change in temperature is proportional to the molal concentration of the solution:

$$\Delta T_f \propto m$$

or

$$\Delta T_f = K_f m \qquad\qquad \textbf{Equation 13.7}$$

where m is the concentration of solute expressed in molality and K_f is the molal freezing-point depression constant (see Table 13.2). Like K_b, K_f has units of °C/m.

TABLE 13.2	Molal Boiling-Point Elevation and Freezing-Point Depression Constants of Several Common Solvents			
Solvent	Normal boiling point (°C)	K_b (°C/m)	Normal freezing point (°C)	K_f (°C/m)
Water	100.0	0.52	0.0	1.86
Benzene	80.1	2.53	5.5	5.12
Ethanol	78.4	1.22	−117.3	1.99
Acetic acid	117.9	2.93	16.6	3.90
Cyclohexane	80.7	2.79	6.6	20.0

Figure 13.9 The solution has greater entropy than the pure solvent. The bigger difference in entropy between the solution and the solid means that more energy must be removed from the solution for it to freeze. Thus, the solution freezes at a lower temperature than the pure solvent.

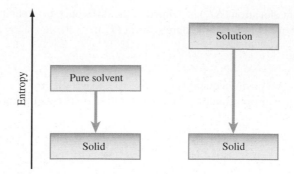

Student Annotation: When a solution freezes, the solid that separates out is actually pure solvent. The solute remains in the liquid solution.

Like boiling-point elevation, freezing-point depression can be explained in terms of differences in entropy. Freezing involves a transition from the more disordered liquid state to the more ordered solid state. For this to happen, energy must be removed from the system. Because a solution has greater disorder than the solvent, there is a bigger difference in entropy between the solution and the solid than there is between the pure solvent and the solid (Figure 13.9). The larger difference in entropy means that more energy must be removed for the liquid-solid transition to happen. Thus, the solution freezes at a lower temperature than does the pure solvent. Boiling-point elevation occurs only when the solute is nonvolatile. Freezing-point depression occurs regardless of the solute's volatility.

Worked Example 13.6 demonstrates a practical application of freezing-point depression and boiling-point elevation.

Worked Example 13.6

Ethylene glycol [CH$_2$(OH)CH$_2$(OH)] is a common automobile antifreeze. It is water soluble and fairly nonvolatile (b.p. 197°C). Calculate (a) the freezing point and (b) the boiling point of a solution containing 685 g of ethylene glycol in 2075 g of water.

Strategy Convert grams of ethylene glycol to moles, and divide by the mass of water in kilograms to get molal concentration. Use molal concentration in Equations 13.7 and 13.6 to determine ΔT_f and ΔT_b, respectively.

Setup The molar mass of ethylene glycol (C$_2$H$_6$O$_2$) is 62.07 g/mol. K_f and K_b for water are 1.86°C/m and 0.52°C/m, respectively.

Solution

$$\frac{685 \text{ g C}_2\text{H}_6\text{O}_2}{62.07 \text{ g/mol}} = 11.04 \text{ mol C}_2\text{H}_6\text{O}_2 \quad \text{and} \quad \frac{11.04 \text{ mol C}_2\text{H}_6\text{O}_2}{2.075 \text{ kg H}_2\text{O}} = 5.32 \text{ } m \text{ C}_2\text{H}_6\text{O}_2$$

(a) $\Delta T_f = K_f m = (1.86°C/m)(5.32 \text{ } m) = 9.89°C$

The freezing point of the solution is $(0 - 9.89)°C = -9.89°C$.

(b) $\Delta T_b = K_b m = (0.52°C/m)(5.32 \text{ } m) = 2.8°C$

The boiling point of the solution is $(100.0 + 2.8)°C = 102.8°C$.

Think About It
Because it both lowers the freezing point and raises the boiling point, antifreeze is useful at both temperature extremes.

Practice Problem A Calculate the freezing point and boiling point of a solution containing 268 g of ethylene glycol and 1015 g of water.

Practice Problem B What mass of ethylene glycol must be added to 1525 g of water to raise the boiling point to 103.9°C?

Figure 13.10 Osmotic pressure. (a) The levels of the pure solvent (left) and of the solution (right) are equal at the start. (b) During osmosis, the level on the solution side rises as a result of the net flow of solvent from left to right.

Osmotic Pressure

Many chemical and biological processes depend on *osmosis,* the selective passage of solvent molecules through a porous membrane from a more dilute solution to a more concentrated one. Figure 13.10 illustrates osmosis. The left compartment of the apparatus contains pure solvent; the right compartment contains a solution made with the same solvent. The two compartments are separated by a *semipermeable membrane,* which allows the passage of solvent molecules but blocks the passage of solute molecules. At the beginning, the liquid levels in the two tubes are equal [Figure 13.10(a)]. As time passes, the level in the right tube rises. It continues to rise until equilibrium is reached, after which no further net change in levels is observed. The *osmotic pressure* (π) of a solution is the pressure required to stop osmosis. As shown in Figure 13.10(b), this pressure can be measured directly from the difference in the final liquid levels.

The osmotic pressure of a solution is directly proportional to the concentration, expressed in *molarity,* of the solute in solution:

$$\pi \propto M$$

and is given by

$$\pi = MRT \qquad \textbf{Equation 13.8}$$

Multi 13.1
Osmosis.

where M is the molarity of the solution, R is the gas constant (0.08206 L · atm/K · mol), and T is the absolute temperature. The osmotic pressure (π) is typically expressed in atmospheres.

Like boiling-point elevation and freezing-point depression, osmotic pressure is directly proportional to the concentration of the solution. This is what we would expect, though, because all colligative properties depend only on the number of solute particles in solution, not on the identity of the solute particles. Two solutions of equal concentration have the same osmotic pressure and are said to be *isotonic* to each other.

Electrolyte Solutions

So far we have discussed the colligative properties of nonelectrolyte solutions. Because electrolytes undergo *dissociation* when dissolved in water [◄◄ Section 9.1], we must consider them separately. Recall, for example, that when NaCl dissolves in water, it dissociates into $Na^+(aq)$ and $Cl^-(aq)$. For every mole of NaCl dissolved, we get two moles of ions in solution. Similarly, when a formula unit of $CaCl_2$ dissolves, we get three ions: one Ca^{2+} ion and two Cl^- ions. Thus, for every mole of $CaCl_2$ dissolved, we get three moles of ions in solution. Colligative properties depend only on the number of dissolved particles—not on the type of particles. This means that a 0.1 m solution of NaCl will exhibit a freezing-point depression twice that of a 0.1 m solution of a nonelectrolyte, such as sucrose. Similarly, we expect a 0.1 m solution of $CaCl_2$ to depress the freezing point of water three times as much as a 0.1 m sucrose solution. To account for this effect, we introduce and define a quantity called the ***van't Hoff***[3] ***factor (i),*** which is given by

$$i = \frac{\text{actual number of particles in solution after dissociation}}{\text{number of formula units initially dissolved in solution}}$$

Thus, i is 1 for all nonelectrolytes. For strong electrolytes such as NaCl and KNO_3, i should be 2, and for strong electrolytes such as Na_2SO_4 and $CaCl_2$, i should be 3. Consequently, the equations for colligative properties must be modified as follows:

Student Annotation: The amount of vapor-pressure lowering would also be affected by dissociation of an electrolyte. In calculating the mole fraction of solute and solvent, the number of moles of solute would have to be multiplied by the appropriate van't Hoff factor.

Equation 13.9	$\Delta T_f = iK_f m$

Equation 13.10	$\Delta T_b = iK_b m$

Equation 13.11	$\pi = iMRT$

In reality, the colligative properties of electrolyte solutions are usually smaller than predicted by Equations 13.9 through 13.11, especially at higher concentrations, because of the formation of *ion pairs*. An ***ion pair*** is made up of one or more cations and one or more anions held together by electrostatic forces (Figure 13.11). The presence of an ion pair reduces the number of particles in solution, thus reducing the observed colligative properties. Tables 13.3 and 13.4 list van't Hoff factors calculated from balanced equations and those measured experimentally.

Student Annotation: A van't Hoff factor calculated using the coefficients in a balanced equation is an exact number [◄◄ Section 1.5].

(a)   (b)

Figure 13.11 (a) Free ions and (b) ion pairs in solution. Ion pairing reduces the number of dissolved particles in a solution, causing a decrease in the observed colligative properties. Furthermore, an ion pair bears no net charge and therefore cannot conduct electricity in solution.

TABLE 13.3	Calculated and Measured van't Hoff Factors of 0.0500 M Electrolyte Solutions at 25°C	
Electrolyte	**i (Calculated)**	**i (Measured)**
Sucrose*	1	1.0
HCl	2	1.9
NaCl	2	1.9
$MgSO_4$	2	1.3
$MgCl_2$	3	2.7
$FeCl_3$	4	3.4

*Sucrose is a nonelectrolyte. It is listed here for comparison only.

[3]Jacobus Henricus van't Hoff (1852–1911). One of the most prominent chemists of his time, van't Hoff, a Dutch chemist, did significant work in thermodynamics, molecular structure and optical activity, and solution chemistry. In 1901 he received the first Nobel Prize in Chemistry.

TABLE 13.4	Experimentally Measured van't Hoff Factors of Sucrose and NaCl Solutions at 25°C		
	Concentration		
Compound	**0.100 *m***	**0.00100 *m***	**0.000100 *m***
Sucrose	1.00	1.00	1.00
NaCl	1.87	1.94	1.97

Worked Example 13.7 demonstrates the experimental determination of a van't Hoff factor.

Worked Example 13.7

The osmotic pressure of a 0.0100 M potassium iodide (KI) solution at 25°C is 0.465 atm. Determine the experimental van't Hoff factor for KI at this concentration.

Strategy Use osmotic pressure to calculate the molar concentration of KI, and divide by the *nominal* concentration of 0.0100 M.

Setup $R = 0.08206$ L · atm/K · mol, and $T = 298$ K.

Solution Solving Equation 13.8 for M,

$$M = \frac{\pi}{RT} = \frac{0.465 \text{ atm}}{(0.08206 \text{ L} \cdot \text{atm/K} \cdot \text{mol})(298 \text{ K})} = 0.0190 \text{ } M$$

$$i = \frac{0.0190 \text{ } M}{0.0100 \text{ } M} = 1.90$$

The experimental van't Hoff factor for KI at this concentration is 1.90.

Think About It
The calculated van't Hoff factor for KI is 2. The experimentally determined van't Hoff factor must be less than or equal to the calculated value.

Practice Problem A The freezing-point depression of a 0.100 m MgSO$_4$ solution is 0.225°C. Determine the experimental van't Hoff factor of MgSO$_4$ at this concentration.

Practice Problem B Using the experimental van't Hoff factor from Table 13.4, determine the freezing point of a 0.100 m aqueous solution of NaCl. (Assume that the van't Hoff factors do not change with temperature.)

SECTION 13.5 REVIEW

Colligative Properties

13.5.1 A solution contains 75.0 g of glucose (molar mass 180.2 g/mol) in 425 g of water. Determine the vapor pressure of water over the solution at 35°C. ($P^\circ_{\text{H}_2\text{O}} = 42.2$ mmHg at 35°C.)

13.5.2 Determine the boiling point and the freezing point of a solution prepared by dissolving 678 g of glucose in 2.0 kg of water. For water, $K_b = 0.52$°C/m and $K_f = 1.86$°C/m.

13.5.3 Calculate the osmotic pressure of a solution prepared by dissolving 65.0 g of Na$_2$SO$_4$ in enough water to make 500 mL of solution at 20°C. (Assume no ion pairing.)

13.5.4 A 1.00 m solution of HCl has a freezing point of −3.30°C. Determine the experimental van't Hoff factor for HCl at this concentration.

Thinking Outside the Box

Intravenous Fluids

Human blood consists of red blood cells (*erythrocytes*), white blood cells (*leukocytes*), and platelets (*thrombocytes*) suspended in plasma, an aqueous solution containing a variety of solutes including salts and proteins. Each red blood cell is surrounded by a protective semipermeable membrane. Inside this membrane, the concentration of dissolved substances is about 0.3 *M.* Likewise, the concentration of dissolved substances in plasma is also about 0.3 *M.* Having the same concentration (and therefore the same osmotic pressure of ~7.6 atm at 37°C) inside and outside the red blood cell prevents a net movement of water into or out of the cell through the protective semipermeable membrane. To maintain this balance of osmotic pressure, fluids that are given intravenously must be *isotonic* to plasma. Five percent dextrose (sugar) and normal saline, which is 0.9% sodium chloride, are two of the most commonly used isotonic intravenous fluids.

(a)   (b)   (c)

A cell in (a) a hypotonic solution, (b) an isotonic solution, and (c) a hypertonic solution. The cell swells and may eventually burst in (a); it shrinks in (c).

A solution that has a lower concentration of dissolved substances than plasma is said to be **hypotonic** to plasma. If a significant volume of pure water were administered intravenously, it would dilute the plasma, lowering its concentration and making it hypotonic to the solution inside the red blood cells. If this were to happen, water would enter the red blood cells via osmosis. The cells would swell and could potentially burst, a process called *hemolysis.* On the other hand, if red blood cells were placed in a solution with a higher concentration of dissolved substances than plasma, a solution said to be **hypertonic** to plasma, water would leave the cells via osmosis. The cells would shrink, a process called *crenation,* which is also potentially dangerous. The osmotic pressure of human plasma must be maintained within a very narrow range to prevent damage to red blood cells. Hypotonic and hypertonic solutions can be administered intravenously to treat specific medical conditions, but the patient must be carefully monitored throughout the treatment.

Interestingly, humans have for centuries exploited the sensitivity of cells to osmotic pressure. The process of "curing" meat with salt or with sugar causes crenation of the bacteria cells that would otherwise cause spoilage.

Thinking Outside the Box

Fluoride Poisoning

In 1993, nine patients who had undergone routine hemodialysis treatment at the University of Chicago Hospitals became seriously ill, and three of them died. The illnesses and deaths were attributed to fluoride poisoning, which occurred when the equipment meant to remove fluoride from the water failed. Although hemodialysis is supposed to remove impurities from the blood, the inadvertent use of fluoridated water in the process actually added a toxin to the patients' blood.

Hemodialysis, often called simply *dialysis,* is the cleansing of toxins from the blood of patients whose kidneys have failed. It works by routing a patient's blood temporarily through a special filter called a *dialyzer.* Inside the dialyzer, the blood is separated (by an artificial porous membrane) from an aqueous solution called the *dialysate.* The dialysate contains a variety of dissolved substances, typically including sodium chloride, sodium bicarbonate or sodium acetate, calcium chloride, potassium chloride, magnesium chloride, and sometimes glucose. Its composition mimics that of blood plasma. When the two solutions, blood and dialysate, are separated by a porous membrane, the smallest of the dissolved solutes pass through the membrane from the side where the concentration is high to the side where the concentration is low. Because the dialysate contains vital components of blood in concentrations equal to those in blood, no net passage of these substances occurs through the membrane. However, the harmful substances that accumulate in the blood of patients whose kidneys do not function properly pass through the membrane into the dialysate, in which their concentration is initially zero, and are thereby removed from the blood. Properly done, hemodialysis therapy can add years to the life of a patient with kidney failure.

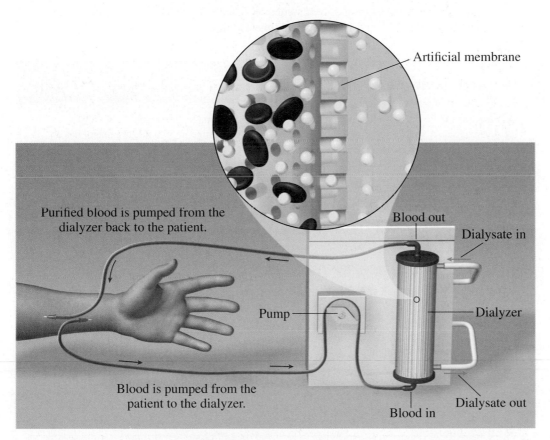

Osmosis refers to the movement of solvent through a membrane from the side where the solute concentration is lower to the side where the solute concentration is higher. Hemodialysis involves a more porous membrane, through which both solvent (water) and small solute particles can pass. The size of the membrane pores is such that only small waste products such as excess potassium ion, creatinine, urea, and extra fluid can pass through. Larger components in blood, such as blood cells and proteins, are too large to pass through the membrane. A solute will pass through the membrane from the side where its concentration is higher to the side where its concentration is lower. The composition of the dialysate ensures that the necessary solutes in the blood (e.g., sodium and calcium ions) are not removed. Because it is not normally found in blood, fluoride ion, if present in the dialysate, will flow across the membrane into the blood. In fact, this is true of any sufficiently small solute that is not normally found in blood—necessitating requirements for the purity of water used to prepare dialysate solutions that far exceed those for drinking water.

(Continued on next page)

Despite the use of fluoride in municipal water supplies and many topical dental products, acute fluoride poisoning is relatively rare. Fluoride is now routinely removed from the water used to prepare dialysate solutions. However, water-supply fluoridation became common during the 1960s and 1970s—just when hemodialysis was first being made widely available to patients. This unfortunate coincidence resulted in large numbers of early dialysis patients suffering the effects of fluoride poisoning, before the danger of introducing fluoride via dialysis was recognized. The level of fluoride considered safe for the drinking water supply is based on the presumed ingestion by a healthy person of 14 L of water per week. Many dialysis patients routinely are exposed to as much as *50 times* that volume, putting them at significantly increased risk of absorbing toxic amounts of fluoride.

13.6 CALCULATIONS USING COLLIGATIVE PROPERTIES

The colligative properties of nonelectrolyte solutions provide a means of determining the molar mass of a solute. Although any of the four colligative properties can be used in theory for this purpose, only freezing-point depression and osmotic pressure are used in practice because they show the most pronounced, and therefore the most easily measured, changes. From the experimentally determined freezing-point depression or osmotic pressure, we can calculate the solution's molality or molarity, respectively. Knowing the mass of dissolved solute, we can readily determine its molar mass. Worked Examples 13.8 and 13.9 illustrate this technique.

Worked Example 13.8

Quinine was the first drug widely used to treat malaria, and it remains the treatment of choice for severe cases. A solution prepared by dissolving 10.0 g of quinine in 50.0 mL of ethanol has a freezing point 1.55°C below that of pure ethanol. Determine the molar mass of quinine. (The density of ethanol is 0.789 g/mL.) Assume that quinine is a nonelectrolyte.

Strategy Use Equation 13.7 to determine the molal concentration of the solution. Use the density of ethanol to determine the mass of solvent. The molal concentration of quinine multiplied by the mass of ethanol (in kg) gives moles of quinine. The mass of quinine (in grams) divided by moles of quinine gives the molar mass.

Setup   mass of ethanol = 50.0 mL $\times$ 0.789 g/mL = 39.5 g   or 3.95×10^{-2} kg

K_f for ethanol (from Table 13.2) is 1.99°C/m.

Solution Solving Equation 13.7 for molal concentration,

$$m = \frac{\Delta T_f}{K_f} = \frac{1.55°C}{1.99°C/m} = 0.779\ m$$

The solution is 0.779 m in quinine (i.e., 0.779 mol quinine/kg ethanol solvent).

$$\left(\frac{0.779\ \text{mol quinine}}{\text{kg ethanol}}\right)(3.95 \times 10^{-2}\ \text{kg ethanol}) = 0.0308\ \text{mol quinine}$$

$$\text{molar mass of quinine} = \frac{10.0\ \text{g quinine}}{0.0308\ \text{mol quinine}} = 325\ \text{g/mol}$$

> **Think About It**
> Check the result using the molecular formula of quinine: $C_{20}H_{24}N_2O_2$ (324.4 g/mol). Multistep problems such as this one require careful tracking of units at each step.

Practice Problem A Calculate the molar mass of naphthalene, the organic compound in "mothballs," if a solution prepared by dissolving 5.00 g of naphthalene in exactly 100 g of benzene has a freezing point 2.00°C below that of pure benzene.

Practice Problem B What mass of naphthalene must be dissolved in 2.00×10^2 g of benzene to give a solution with a freezing point 2.50°C below that of pure benzene?

Worked Example 13.9

A solution is prepared by dissolving 50.0 g of hemoglobin (Hb) in enough water to make 1.00 L of solution. The osmotic pressure of the solution is measured and found to be 14.3 mmHg at 25°C. Calculate the molar mass of hemoglobin. (Assume that there is no change in volume when the hemoglobin is added to the water.)

Strategy Use Equation 13.8 to calculate the molarity of the solution. Because the solution volume is 1 L, the molarity is equal to the number of moles of hemoglobin. Dividing the mass of hemoglobin, which is given in the problem statement, by the number of moles gives the molar mass.

Setup $R = 0.08206$ L · atm/K · mol, $T = 298$ K, and $\pi = 14.3$ mmHg/(760 mmHg/atm) $= 1.88 \times 10^{-2}$ atm.

Solution Rearranging Equation 13.8 to solve for molarity, we get

$$M = \frac{\pi}{RT} = \frac{1.88 \times 10^{-2} \text{ atm}}{(0.08206 \text{ L} \cdot \text{atm/K} \cdot \text{mol})(298 \text{ K})} = 7.69 \times 10^{-4} \, M$$

Thus, the solution contains 7.69×10^{-4} mole of hemoglobin.

$$\text{molar mass of hemoglobin} = \frac{50.0 \text{ g}}{7.69 \times 10^{-4} \text{ mol}} = 6.50 \times 10^{4} \text{ g/mol}$$

Think About It
Biological molecules can have *very* high molar masses.

Practice Problem A A solution made by dissolving 25 mg of insulin in 5.0 mL of water has an osmotic pressure of 15.5 mmHg at 25°C. Calculate the molar mass of insulin. (Assume that there is no change in volume when the insulin is added to the water.)

Practice Problem B What mass of insulin must be dissolved in 50.0 mL of water to produce a solution with an osmotic pressure of 16.8 mmHg at 25°C?

The colligative properties of an electrolyte solution can be used to determine percent dissociation. *Percent dissociation* is the percentage of dissolved molecules (or formula units, in the case of an ionic compound) that separate into ions in solution. For a strong electrolyte such as NaCl, there should be *complete,* or 100 percent, dissociation. However, the data in Table 13.4 indicate that this is not necessarily the case. An experimentally determined van't Hoff factor smaller than the corresponding calculated value indicates less than 100 percent dissociation. As the experimentally determined van't Hoff factors for NaCl indicate, dissociation of a strong electrolyte is more complete at lower concentration. The *percent ionization* of a weak electrolyte, such as a weak acid, also depends on the concentration of the solution.

Worked Example 13.10 shows how to use colligative properties to determine the percent dissociation of a weak electrolyte.

Student Annotation: Recall that the term *dissociation* is used for ionic electrolytes and the term *ionization* is used for molecular electrolytes. In this context, they mean essentially the same thing.

Worked Example 13.10

A solution that is 0.100 M in hydrofluoric acid (HF) has an osmotic pressure of 2.64 atm at 25°C. Calculate the percent ionization of HF at this concentration.

Strategy Use the osmotic pressure and Equation 13.8 to determine the molar concentration of the particles in solution. Compare the concentration of particles to the *nominal* concentration (0.100 M) to determine what percentage of the original HF molecules are ionized.

Setup $R = 0.08206$ L · atm/K · mol, and $T = 298$ K.

Solution Rearranging Equation 13.8 to solve for molarity,

$$M = \frac{\pi}{RT} = \frac{2.64 \text{ atm}}{(0.08206 \text{ L} \cdot \text{atm/K} \cdot \text{mol})(298 \text{ K})} = 0.108 \, M$$

(Continued on next page)

The concentration of dissolved particles is 0.108 M. Consider the ionization of HF [◄◄ Section 9.3]:

$$HF(aq) \rightleftharpoons H^+(aq) + F^-(aq)$$

According to this equation, if x HF molecules ionize, we get x H$^+$ ions and x F$^-$ ions. Thus, the total concentration of particles in solution will be the original concentration of HF minus x, which gives the concentration of intact HF molecules, plus $2x$, which is the concentration of ions (H$^+$ and F$^-$):

$$(0.100 - x) + 2x = 0.100 + x$$

Therefore, $0.108 = 0.100 + x$ and $x = 0.008$. Because we earlier defined x as the amount of HF ionized, the percent ionization is given by

$$\text{percent ionization} = \frac{0.008\ M}{0.100\ M} \times 100\% = 8\%$$

At this concentration HF is 8 percent ionized.

Think About It

For weak acids, the lower the concentration, the greater the percent ionization. A 0.010 M solution of HF has an osmotic pressure of 0.30 atm, corresponding to 23 percent ionization. A 0.0010 M solution of HF has an osmotic pressure of 3.8×10^{-2} atm, corresponding to 56 percent ionization.

Practice Problem A An aqueous solution that is 0.0100 M in acetic acid (HC$_2$H$_3$O$_2$) has an osmotic pressure of 0.255 atm at 25°C. Calculate the percent ionization of acetic acid at this concentration.

Practice Problem B An aqueous solution that is 0.015 M in acetic acid (HC$_2$H$_3$O$_2$) is 3.5 percent ionized at 25°C. Calculate the osmotic pressure of this solution.

SECTION 13.6 REVIEW

Calculations Using Colligative Properties

13.6.1 A solution made by dissolving 14.2 g of sucrose in 100 g of water exhibits a freezing-point depression of 0.77°C. Calculate the molar mass of sucrose.

13.6.2 A 0.010 M solution of the weak electrolyte HA has an osmotic pressure of 0.27 atm at 25°C. What is the percent ionization of the electrolyte at this concentration?

13.7 COLLOIDS

Student Annotation: The substance dispersed is called the *dispersed phase;* the substance in which it is dispersed is called the *dispersing medium.*

The solutions discussed so far in this chapter are true homogeneous mixtures. Now consider what happens if we add fine sand to a beaker of water and stir. The sand particles are suspended at first but gradually settle to the bottom of the beaker. This is an example of a heterogeneous mixture. Between the two extremes of homogeneous and heterogeneous mixtures is an intermediate state called a colloidal suspension, or simply, a colloid. A *colloid* is a dispersion of particles of one substance throughout another substance. Colloidal particles are much larger than the normal solute molecules; they range from 1×10^3 pm to 1×10^6 pm. Also, a colloidal suspension lacks the homogeneity of a true solution.

Colloids can be further categorized as aerosols (liquid or solid dispersed in gas), foams (gas dispersed in liquid or solid), emulsions (liquid dispersed in another liquid), sols (solid dispersed in liquid or in another solid), and gels (liquid dispersed in a solid). Table 13.5 lists the different types of colloids and gives one or more examples of each.

One way to distinguish a solution from a colloid is by the ***Tyndall***[4] ***effect.*** When a beam of light passes through a colloid, it is scattered by the dispersed phase (Figure 13.12). No such

---

[4]John Tyndall (1820–1893), an Irish physicist, did important work in magnetism and also explained glacier motion.

TABLE 13.5	Types of Colloids		
Dispersing medium	**Dispersed phase**	**Name**	**Example**
Gas	Liquid	Aerosol	Fog, mist
Gas	Solid	Aerosol	Smoke
Liquid	Gas	Foam	Whipped cream, meringue
Liquid	Liquid	Emulsion	Mayonnaise
Liquid	Solid	Sol	Milk of magnesia
Solid	Gas	Foam	Styrofoam
Solid	Liquid	Gel	Jelly, butter
Solid	Solid	Solid sol	Alloys such as steel, gemstones (glass with dispersed metal)

Student Annotation: Styrofoam is a registered trademark of the Dow Chemical Company. It refers specifically to extruded polystyrene used for insulation in home construction. "Styrofoam" cups, coolers, and packing peanuts are not really made of Styrofoam.

Figure 13.12 The Tyndall effect. Light is scattered by colloidal particles (left) but not by dissolved particles (right).

Figure 13.13 A familiar example of the Tyndall effect: headlights illuminating fog.

visible light. Another demonstration of the Tyndall effect is the scattering of light from automobile headlights in fog (Figure 13.13).

Among the most important colloids are those in which the dispersing medium is water. Such colloids can be categorized as **hydrophilic** (*water loving*) or **hydrophobic** (*water fearing*). Hydrophilic colloids contain extremely large molecules such as proteins. In the aqueous phase, a protein like hemoglobin folds in such a way that the hydrophilic parts of the molecule, the parts that can

Figure 13.14 Hydrophilic groups on the surface of a large molecule such as a protein stabilize the molecule in water. Note that all the hydrophilic groups can form hydrogen bonds with water.

Figure 13.15 Diagram showing the stabilization of hydrophobic colloids. Negative ions are adsorbed onto the surface, and the repulsion between like charges prevents aggregation of the particles.

interact favorably with water molecules by ion-dipole forces or hydrogen-bond formation, are on the outside surface (Figure 13.14).

A hydrophobic colloid normally would not be stable in water, and the particles would clump together, like droplets of oil in water merging to form a film at the water's surface. They can be stabilized, however, by the adsorption of ions on their surface (Figure 13.15). Material that collects on the surface is *adsorbed,* whereas material that passes to the interior is *absorbed.* The adsorbed ions are hydrophilic and can interact with water to stabilize the colloid. In addition, because adsorption of ions leaves the colloid particles *charged,* electrostatic repulsion prevents them from clumping together. Soil particles in rivers and streams are hydrophobic particles that are stabilized in this way. When river water enters the sea, the charges on the dispersed particles are neutralized by the high-salt medium. With the charges on their surfaces neutralized, the particles no longer repel one another and they clump together to form the silt that is seen at the mouth of the river.

Another way hydrophobic colloids can be stabilized is by the presence of other hydrophilic groups on their surfaces. Consider sodium stearate, a soap molecule that has a polar group at one end, often called the "head," and a long hydrocarbon "tail" that is nonpolar (Figure 13.16). The cleansing action of soap is due to the dual nature of the hydrophobic tail and the hydrophilic head. The hydrocarbon tail is readily soluble in oily substances, which are also nonpolar, while the ionic $-COO^-$ group remains outside the oily surface. When enough soap molecules have surrounded an oil droplet, as shown in Figure 13.17, the entire system becomes stabilized in water because the exterior portion is now largely hydrophilic. This is how greasy substances are removed by the action of soap. In general, the process of stabilizing a colloid that would otherwise not stay

> **Student Annotation:** A hydrophobic colloid must be *stabilized* to remain suspended in water.

Figure 13.16 (a) A sodium stearate molecule. (b) The simplified representation of the molecule that shows a hydrophilic head and a hydrophobic tail.

Sodium stearate ($C_{17}H_{35}COO^-Na^+$)

(a)

Hydrophilic head

Hydrophobic tail

(b)

(a) Grease
(b)
(c)

Figure 13.17 The mechanism by which soap removes grease. (a) Grease (oily substance) is not soluble in water. (b) When soap is added to water, the nonpolar tails of soap molecules dissolve in grease. (c) The grease can be washed away when the polar heads of the soap molecules stabilize it in water.

Figure 13.18 Structure of sodium glycocholate. The hydrophobic tail of sodium glycocholate dissolves in ingested fats, stabilizing them on the aqueous medium of the digestive system.

dispersed is called *emulsification,* and a substance used for such stabilization is called an *emulsifier* or *emulsifying agent.*

A mechanism similar to that involving sodium stearate makes it possible for us to digest dietary fat. When we ingest fat, the gallbladder excretes a substance known as bile. Bile contains a variety of substances including bile salts. A *bile salt* is a derivative of cholesterol with an attached amino acid. Like sodium stearate, a bile salt has both a hydrophobic end and a hydrophilic end. (Figure 13.18 shows the bile salt sodium glycocholate.) The bile salts surround fat particles with their hydrophobic ends oriented toward the fat and their hydrophilic ends facing the water, emulsifying the fat in the aqueous medium of the digestive system. This process allows fats to be digested and other nonpolar substances such as fat-soluble vitamins to be absorbed through the wall of the small intestine.

Student Annotation: It is being nonpolar that makes some vitamins soluble in fat. Remember the axiom "like dissolves like."

Learning Outcomes

- Define solubility.
- Define saturated, unsaturated, and supersaturated solution.
- Describe the three types of interactions that determine the extent to which a solute is dissolved in solution.
- Use concentration units to express the concentration of a given solution or to interchange concentration units.
- List and describe the factors that affect the solubility of a solute.
- Use Henry's law to determine the solubility of a gas in solution.

- List, describe, and perform calculations involving colligative properties: vapor-pressure lowering, boiling-point elevation, freezing-point depression, and osmotic pressure.
- Use van't Hoff factors to determine the colligative properties of electrolyte solutions.
- Define isotonic, hypertonic, and hypotonic.
- Use colligative properties to determine the percent dissociation (or percent ionization) of an electrolyte in solution.
- Define colloid and provide examples.

Chapter Summary

SECTION 13.1

- Solutions are homogeneous mixtures of two or more substances, which may be solids, liquids, or gases.
- *Saturated solutions* contain the maximum possible amount of dissolved solute.
- The amount of solute dissolved in a saturated solution is the *solubility* of the solute in the specified solvent at the specified temperature.
- *Unsaturated solutions* contain less than the maximum possible amount of solute.
- *Supersaturated solutions* contain more solute than specified by the solubility.

SECTION 13.2

- Substances with similar intermolecular forces tend to be soluble in one another. "Like dissolves like." Two liquids that are soluble in each other are called *miscible.*
- Solution formation may be endothermic or exothermic overall. An increase in *entropy* is the driving force for solution formation. Solute particles are surrounded by solvent molecules in a process called *solvation.*

SECTION 13.3

- In addition to molarity (M) and mole fraction (χ), *molality (m)* and *percent by mass* are used to express the concentrations of solutions.
- *Molality* is defined as the number of moles of solute per kilogram of solvent. *Percent by mass* is defined as the mass of solute divided by the total mass of the solution, all multiplied by 100 percent.
- Molality and percent by mass have the advantage of being temperature independent. Conversion among molarity, molality, and percent by mass requires solution *density*.
- The units of concentration used depend on the type of problem to be solved.

SECTION 13.4

- Increasing the temperature *increases* the solubility of most solids in water and *decreases* the solubility of most gases in water.
- Increasing the pressure increases the solubility of gases in water but does not affect the solubility of solids.
- According to *Henry's law,* the solubility of a gas in a liquid is directly proportional to the partial pressure of the gas over the solution: $c = kP$.
- The proportionality constant k is the *Henry's law constant.* Henry's law constants are specific to the gas and solvent, and they are temperature dependent.

SECTION 13.5

- *Colligative properties* depend on the *number* (but not on the *type*) of dissolved particles. The colligative properties are *vapor-pressure lowering, boiling-point elevation, freezing-point depression,* and *osmotic pressure.*
- A *volatile* substance is one that has a measurable vapor pressure. A *nonvolatile* substance is one that does not have a measurable vapor pressure.
- According to *Raoult's law,* the partial pressure of a substance over a solution is equal to the *mole fraction* (χ) of the substance times its *pure vapor pressure* ($P°$). An *ideal solution* is one that obeys Raoult's law.
- *Osmosis* is the flow of solvent through a *semipermeable membrane,* one that allows solvent molecules but not solute particles to pass, from a more dilute solution to a more concentrated one.
- *Osmotic pressure* (π) is the pressure required to prevent osmosis from occurring.
- Two solutions with the same osmotic pressure are called *isotonic. Hypotonic* refers to a solution with a *lower* osmotic pressure. *Hypertonic* refers to a solution with a *higher* osmotic pressure. These terms are often used in reference to human plasma, which has an osmotic pressure of 7.6 atm.
- In electrolyte solutions, the number of dissolved particles is increased by dissociation or ionization. The magnitudes of colligative properties are increased by the *van't Hoff factor (i),* which indicates the degree of dissociation or ionization.
- The experimentally determined van't Hoff factor is generally smaller than the calculated value due to the formation of *ion pairs*—especially at high concentrations. Ion pairs are oppositely charged ions that are attracted to each other and effectively become a single "particle" in solution.

SECTION 13.6

- Experimentally determined colligative properties can be used to calculate the molar mass of a nonelectrolyte or the *percent dissociation* (or *percent ionization*) of a weak electrolyte.

SECTION 13.7

- A *colloid* is a dispersion of particles (about 1×10^3 pm to 1×10^6 pm) of one substance in another substance.
- Colloids can be distinguished from true solutions by the *Tyndall effect,* which is the scattering of visible light by colloidal particles.
- Colloids are classified either as *hydrophilic* (water loving) or *hydrophobic* (water fearing).
- Hydrophobic colloids can be stabilized in water by surface interactions with ions or polar molecules.

Key Words

Colligative properties, 521
Colloid, 534
Entropy, 513
Henry's law, 520
Henry's law constant (k), 520
Hydrophilic, 535
Hydrophobic, 535
Hypertonic, 530

Hypotonic, 530
Ideal solution, 524
Ion pair, 528
Isotonic, 527
Miscible, 514
Molality (m), 516
Nonvolatile, 522
Osmosis, 527

Osmotic pressure (π), 527
Percent by mass, 516
Percent dissociation, 533
Percent ionization, 533
Raoult's law, 522
Saturated solution, 511
Semipermeable
    membrane, 527

Solubility, 511
Solvation, 512
Supersaturated solution, 511
Tyndall effect, 534
Unsaturated solution, 511
van't Hoff factor (i), 528
Volatile, 523

Key Equations

13.1 $\text{molality} = m = \dfrac{\text{moles of solute}}{\text{mass of solvent (in kg)}}$

13.2 $\text{percent by mass} = \dfrac{\text{mass of solute}}{\text{mass of solute} + \text{mass of solvent}} \times 100\%$

13.3 $c = kP$

13.4 $P_1 = \chi_1 P_1^\circ$

13.5 $P_1^\circ - P_1 = \Delta P = \chi_2 P_1^\circ$

13.6 $\Delta T_b = K_b m$

13.7 $\Delta T_f = K_f m$

13.8 $\pi = MRT$

13.9 $\Delta T_f = iK_f m$

13.10 $\Delta T_b = iK_b m$

13.11 $\pi = iMRT$

Questions and Problems

SECTION 13.1:   TYPES OF SOLUTIONS

Review Questions

13.1   Distinguish between an unsaturated solution, a saturated solution, and a supersaturated solution.

13.2   Describe the different types of solutions that can be formed by the combination of solids, liquids, and gases. Give examples of each type of solution.

SECTION 13.2:   A MOLECULAR VIEW OF THE SOLUTION PROCESS

Review Questions

13.3   Briefly describe the solution process at the molecular level. Use the dissolution of a solid in a liquid as an example.

13.4   Basing your answer on intermolecular force considerations, explain what "like dissolves like" means.

13.5   What is solvation? What factors influence the extent to which solvation occurs? Give two examples of solvation; include one that involves ion-dipole interaction and one in which dispersion forces come into play.

13.6   As you know, some solution processes are endothermic and others are exothermic. Provide a molecular interpretation for the difference.

13.7   Explain why dissolving a solid almost always leads to an increase in disorder.

13.8   Describe the factors that affect the solubility of a solid in a liquid. What does it mean to say that two liquids are miscible?

Problems

13.9   Why is naphthalene ($C_{10}H_8$) more soluble than CsF in benzene?

13.10   Explain why ethanol (C_2H_5OH) is not soluble in cyclohexane (C_6H_{12}).

13.11 Arrange the following compounds in order of increasing solubility in water: O_2, LiCl, Br_2, methanol (CH_3OH).

13.12 Explain the variations in solubility in water of the listed alcohols:

Compound	Solubility in water (g/100 g) at 20°C
CH_3OH	∞
CH_3CH_2OH	∞
$CH_3CH_2CH_2OH$	∞
$CH_3CH_2CH_2CH_2OH$	9
$CH_3CH_2CH_2CH_2CH_2OH$	2.7

Note: ∞ means that the alcohol and water are completely miscible in all proportions.

SECTION 13.3: CONCENTRATION UNITS

Review Questions

13.13 Define the following concentration terms and give their units: *percent by mass, mole fraction, molarity, molality.* Compare their advantages and disadvantages.

13.14 Outline the steps required for conversion between molarity, molality, and percent by mass.

13.15 A solution of a particular concentration is prepared at 20°C. Of *molarity, molality, percent by mass,* and *mole fraction,* which will change when the solution is heated to 75°C? Explain.

Problems

13.16 Calculate the amount of water (in grams) that must be added to (a) 5.00 g of urea ($NH_2)_2CO$ in the preparation of a 16.2 percent by mass solution, and (b) 26.2 g of $MgCl_2$ in the preparation of a 1.5 percent by mass solution.

13.17 Calculate the molality of each of the following solutions: (a) 14.3 g of sucrose ($C_{12}H_{22}O_{11}$) in 685 g of water, (b) 7.15 moles of ethylene glycol ($C_2H_6O_2$) in 3505 g of water.

13.18 Calculate the molality of each of the following aqueous solutions: (a) 2.55 *M* NaCl solution (density of solution = 1.08 g/mL), (b) 45.2 percent by mass KBr solution.

13.19 Calculate the molalities of the following aqueous solutions: (a) 1.22 *M* sugar ($C_{12}H_{22}O_{11}$) solution (density of solution = 1.12 g/mL), (b) 0.87 *M* NaOH solution (density of solution = 1.04 g/mL), (c) 5.24 *M* $NaHCO_3$ solution (density of solution = 1.19 g/mL).

13.20 For dilute aqueous solutions in which the density of the solution is roughly equal to that of the pure solvent, the molarity of the solution is equal to its molality. Show that this statement is correct for a 0.010 *M* aqueous urea ($NH_2)_2CO$ solution.

13.21 The alcohol content of hard liquor is normally given in terms of the "proof," which is defined as twice the percentage by volume of ethanol (C_2H_5OH) present. Calculate the number of grams of alcohol present in 1.00 L of 75-proof gin. The density of ethanol is 0.798 g/mL.

13.22 The concentrated sulfuric acid we use in the laboratory is 98.0 percent H_2SO_4 by mass. Calculate the molality and molarity of the acid solution. The density of the solution is 1.83 g/mL.

13.23 Calculate the molarity and molality of an NH_3 solution made up of 35.0 g of NH_3 in 75.0 g of water. The density of the solution is 0.982 g/mL.

13.24 The density of an aqueous solution containing 15.0 percent of ethanol (C_2H_5OH) by mass is 0.984 g/mL. (a) Calculate the molality of this solution. (b) Calculate its molarity. (c) What volume of the solution would contain 0.250 mole of ethanol?

13.25 Fish breathe the dissolved air in water through their gills. Assuming the partial pressures of oxygen and nitrogen in air to be 0.20 and 0.80 atm, respectively, calculate the mole fractions of oxygen and nitrogen in the air dissolved in water at 298 K. The solubilities of O_2 and N_2 in water at 298 K are 1.3×10^{-3} mol/L · atm and 6.8×10^{-4} mol/L · atm, respectively. Comment on your results.

SECTION 13.4: FACTORS THAT AFFECT SOLUBILITY

Review Questions

13.26 How do the solubilities of most ionic compounds in water change with temperature? With pressure?

13.27 Discuss the factors that influence the solubility of a gas in a liquid.

13.28 What is thermal pollution? Why is it harmful to aquatic life?

13.29 What is Henry's law? Define each term in the equation, and give its units. How would you account for the law in terms of the kinetic molecular theory of gases? Give two exceptions to Henry's law.

13.30 A student is observing two beakers of water. One beaker is heated to 30°C, and the other is heated to 100°C. In each case, bubbles form in the water. Are these bubbles of the same origin? Explain.

13.31 A man bought a goldfish in a pet shop. Upon returning home, he put the goldfish in a bowl of recently boiled water that had been cooled quickly. A few minutes later the fish was found dead. Explain what happened to the fish.

Problems

13.32 A 3.20-g sample of a salt dissolves in 9.10 g of water to give a saturated solution at 25°C. What is the solubility (in g salt/100 g of H_2O) of the salt?

13.33 The solubility of KNO_3 is 155 g per 100 g of water at 75°C and 38.0 g at 25°C. What mass (in grams) of KNO_3 will crystallize out of solution if exactly 100 g of its saturated solution at 75°C is cooled to 25°C?

13.34 A 50-g sample of impure $KClO_3$ (solubility = 7.1 g per 100 g H_2O at 20°C) is contaminated with 10 percent of KCl (solubility = 25.5 g per 100 g of H_2O at 20°C). Calculate the minimum quantity of 20°C water needed to dissolve all the KCl from the sample. How much $KClO_3$ will be left after this treatment? (Assume that the solubilities are unaffected by the presence of the other compound.)

13.35 The difference between water-soluble and fat-soluble vitamins is their molecular structures. Water-soluble vitamins tend to have multiple polar groups that can interact with water to form hydrogen bonds, whereas fat-soluble vitamins tend to be nonpolar molecules consisting predominately of hydrocarbon chains. This is an example of what is meant by the expression "like dissolves like." Predict whether vitamin C and vitamin E will be water soluble or fat soluble.

Vitamin C

Vitamin E

13.36 Predict whether each vitamin will be water soluble or fat soluble. (See Problem 13.35.)

Vitamin D

Vitamin B$_2$ (riboflavin)

13.37 The solubility of CO_2 in water at 25°C and 1 atm is 0.034 mol/L. What is its solubility under atmospheric conditions? (The partial pressure of CO_2 in air is 0.0003 atm.) Assume that CO_2 obeys Henry's law.

13.38 The solubility of N_2 in blood at 37°C and at a partial pressure of 0.80 atm is 5.6×10^{-4} mol/L. A deep-sea diver breathes compressed air with the partial pressure of N_2 equal to 4.0 atm. Assume that the total volume of blood in the body is 5.0 L. Calculate the amount of N_2 gas released (in liters at 37°C and 1 atm) when the diver returns to the surface of the water, where the partial pressure of N_2 is 0.80 atm.

13.39 A student carried out the following experiment to measure the pressure of carbon dioxide in the space above the carbonated soft drink in a bottle. First, she weighed the bottle (853.5 g). Next, she carefully removed the cap to let the CO_2 gas escape. She then reweighed the bottle with the cap (851.3 g). Finally, she measured the volume of the soft drink (452.4 mL). Given that the Henry's law constant for CO_2 in water at 25°C is 3.4×10^{-2} mol/L · atm, calculate the pressure of CO_2 over the soft drink in the bottle before it was opened. Explain why this pressure is only an estimate of the true value.

SECTION 13.5:   COLLIGATIVE PROPERTIES

Review Questions

13.40 What are colligative properties? What is the meaning of the word *colligative* in this context?

13.41 Give two examples of (a) a volatile liquid and (b) a nonvolatile liquid.

13.42 Write the equation representing Raoult's law, and express it in words.

13.43 Use a solution of benzene in toluene to explain what is meant by an ideal solution.

13.44 Write the equations relating boiling-point elevation and freezing-point depression to the concentration of the solution. Define all the terms, and give their units.

13.45 How is vapor-pressure lowering related to a rise in the boiling point of a solution?

13.46 Use a phase diagram to show the difference in freezing points and boiling points between an aqueous urea solution and pure water.

13.47 What is osmosis? What is a semipermeable membrane?

13.48 Write the equation relating osmotic pressure to the concentration of a solution. Define all the terms, and specify their units.

13.49 What does it mean when we say that the osmotic pressure of a sample of seawater is 25 atm at a certain temperature?

13.50 Explain why molality is used for boiling-point elevation and freezing-point depression calculations and molarity is used in osmotic pressure calculations.

13.51 Why is the discussion of the colligative properties of electrolyte solutions more involved than that of nonelectrolyte solutions?

13.52 What are ion pairs? What effect does ion-pair formation have on the colligative properties of a solution? How does the ease of ion-pair formation depend on (a) charges on the ions, (b) size of the ions, (c) nature of the solvent (polar versus nonpolar), (d) concentration?

13.53 Indicate which compound in each of the following pairs is more likely to form ion pairs in water: (a) NaCl or Na_2SO_4, (b) $MgCl_2$ or $MgSO_4$, (c) LiBr or KBr.

13.54 What is the van't Hoff factor? What information does it provide?

13.55 For most intravenous injections, great care is taken to ensure that the concentration of solutions to be injected is comparable to that of blood plasma. Explain.

Problems

13.56 A solution is prepared by dissolving 396 g of sucrose $(C_{12}H_{22}O_{11})$ in 624 g of water. What is the vapor pressure of this solution at 30°C? (The vapor pressure of water is 31.8 mmHg at 30°C.)

13.57 How many grams of sucrose $(C_{12}H_{22}O_{11})$ must be added to 552 g of water to give a solution with a vapor pressure 2.0 mmHg less than that of pure water at 20°C? (The vapor pressure of water at 20°C is 17.5 mmHg.)

13.58 The vapor pressure of benzene is 100.0 mmHg at 26.1°C. Calculate the vapor pressure of a solution containing 24.6 g of camphor $(C_{10}H_{16}O)$ dissolved in 98.5 g of benzene. (Camphor is a low-volatility solid.)

13.59 The vapor pressures of ethanol (C_2H_5OH) and 1-propanol (C_3H_7OH) at 35°C are 100 and 37.6 mmHg, respectively. Assume ideal behavior and calculate the partial pressures of ethanol and 1-propanol at 35°C over a solution of ethanol in 1-propanol, in which the mole fraction of ethanol is 0.300.

13.60 The vapor pressure of ethanol (C_2H_5OH) at 20°C is 44 mmHg, and the vapor pressure of methanol (CH_3OH) at the same temperature is 94 mmHg. A mixture of 30.0 g of methanol and 45.0 g of ethanol is prepared (and can be assumed to behave as an ideal solution). (a) Calculate the vapor pressure of methanol and ethanol above this solution at 20°C. (b) Calculate the mole fraction of methanol and ethanol in the vapor above this solution at 20°C. (c) Suggest a method for separating the two components of the solution.

13.61 How many grams of urea $[(NH_2)_2CO]$ must be added to 658 g of water to give a solution with a vapor pressure 2.50 mmHg lower than that of pure water at 30°C? (The vapor pressure of water at 30°C is 31.8 mmHg.)

13.62 What are the boiling point and freezing point of a 3.12 m solution of naphthalene in benzene? (The boiling point and freezing point of benzene are 80.1°C and 5.5°C, respectively.)

13.63 An aqueous solution contains the amino acid glycine (NH_2CH_2COOH). Assuming that the acid does not ionize in water, calculate the molality of the solution if it freezes at −1.1°C.

13.64 How many liters of the antifreeze ethylene glycol $[CH_2(OH)CH_2(OH)]$ would you add to a car radiator containing 6.50 L of water if the coldest winter temperature in your area is −20°C? Calculate the boiling point of this water-ethylene glycol mixture. (The density of ethylene glycol is 1.11 g/mL.)

13.65 A solution is prepared by condensing 4.00 L of a gas, measured at 27°C and 748 mmHg pressure, into 75.0 g of benzene. Calculate the freezing point of this solution.

13.66 What is the osmotic pressure (in atm) of a 1.57 M aqueous solution of urea $[(NH_2)_2CO]$ at 27.0°C?

13.67 Which of the following aqueous solutions has (a) the higher boiling point, (b) the higher freezing point, and (c) the lower vapor pressure: 0.35 m $CaCl_2$ or 0.90 m urea? Explain. Assume complete dissociation.

13.68 Consider two aqueous solutions, one of sucrose $(C_{12}H_{22}O_{11})$ and the other of nitric acid (HNO_3). Both solutions freeze at −1.5°C. What other properties do these solutions have in common?

13.69 Arrange the following solutions in order of decreasing freezing point: 0.10 m Na_3PO_4, 0.35 m NaCl, 0.20 m $MgCl_2$, 0.15 m $C_6H_{12}O_6$, 0.15 m CH_3COOH.

13.70 Arrange the following aqueous solutions in order of decreasing freezing point, and explain your reasoning: 0.50 m HCl, 0.50 m glucose, 0.50 m acetic acid.

13.71 What are the normal freezing points and boiling points of the following solutions: (a) 21.2 g NaCl in 135 mL of water and (b) 15.4 g of urea in 66.7 mL of water?

13.72 At 25°C, the vapor pressure of pure water is 23.76 mmHg and that of seawater is 22.98 mmHg. Assuming that seawater contains only NaCl, estimate its molal concentration.

13.73 Both NaCl and $CaCl_2$ are used to melt ice on roads and sidewalks in winter. What advantages do these substances have over sucrose or urea in lowering the freezing point of water?

13.74 A 0.86 percent by mass solution of NaCl is called "physiological saline" because its osmotic pressure is equal to that of the solution in blood cells. Calculate the osmotic pressure of this solution at normal body temperature (37°C). Note that the density of the saline solution is 1.005 g/mL.

13.75 The osmotic pressure of 0.010 M solutions of $CaCl_2$ and urea at 25°C are 0.605 and 0.245 atm, respectively. Calculate the van't Hoff factor for the $CaCl_2$ solution.

13.76 Calculate the osmotic pressure of a 0.0500 M $MgSO_4$ solution at 25°C. (*Hint:* See Table 13.3.)

13.77 The tallest trees known are the redwoods in California. Assuming the height of a redwood to be 105 m (about 350 ft), estimate the osmotic pressure required to push water up to the tree top.

13.78 Calculate the difference in osmotic pressure (in atm) at the normal body temperature between the blood plasma of a diabetic patient and that of a healthy adult. Assume that the sole difference between the two people is due to the higher glucose level in the diabetic patient. The glucose levels are 1.75 and 0.84 g/L, respectively. Based on your result, explain why such a patient frequently feels thirsty.

SECTION 13.6: CALCULATIONS USING COLLIGATIVE PROPERTIES

Review Questions

13.79 Describe how you would use freezing-point depression and osmotic pressure measurements to determine the molar mass of a compound. Why are boiling-point elevation and vapor-pressure lowering normally not used for this purpose?

13.80 Describe how you would use the osmotic pressure to determine the percent ionization of a weak, monoprotic acid.

13.81 Explain why we cannot use osmotic pressure to determine both molar mass and percent ionization for an unknown monoprotic acid.

Problems

13.82 The elemental analysis of an organic solid extracted from gum arabic (a gummy substance used in adhesives, inks, and pharmaceuticals) showed that it contained 40.0 percent C, 6.7 percent H, and 53.3 percent O. A solution of 0.650 g of the solid in 27.8 g of the solvent diphenyl gave a freezing-point depression of 1.56°C. Calculate the molar mass and molecular formula of the solid. (K_f for diphenyl is 8.00°C/m.)

13.83 A solution of 2.50 g of a compound having the empirical formula C_6H_5P in 25.0 g of benzene is observed to freeze at 4.3°C. Calculate the molar mass of the solute and its molecular formula.

13.84 The molar mass of benzoic acid (C_6H_5COOH) determined by measuring the freezing-point depression in benzene is twice what we would expect for the molecular formula, $C_7H_6O_2$. Explain this apparent anomaly.

13.85 A solution containing 0.8330 g of a polymer of unknown structure in 170.0 mL of an organic solvent was found to have an osmotic pressure of 5.20 mmHg at 25°C. Determine the molar mass of the polymer.

13.86 A quantity of 7.480 g of an organic compound is dissolved in water to make 300.0 mL of solution. The solution has an osmotic pressure of 1.43 atm at 27°C. The analysis of this compound shows that it contains 41.8 percent C, 4.7 percent H, 37.3 percent O, and 16.3 percent N. Calculate the molecular formula of the compound.

13.87 A solution of 6.85 g of a carbohydrate in 100.0 g of water has a density of 1.024 g/mL and an osmotic pressure of 4.61 atm at 20.0°C. Calculate the molar mass of the carbohydrate.

13.88 A 0.036 M aqueous nitrous acid (HNO_2) solution has an osmotic pressure of 0.93 atm at 25°C. Calculate the percent ionization of the acid.

13.89 A 0.100 M aqueous solution of the base HB has an osmotic pressure of 2.83 atm at 25°C. Calculate the percent ionization of the base.

13.90 Hydrofluoric acid (HF) can be used in the fluoridation of water. HF is a weak acid that only partially ionizes in solution. If an aqueous solution that is 0.15 M in HF has an osmotic pressure of 3.9 atm at 25°C, what is the percent ionization of HF at this concentration?

SECTION 13.7: COLLOIDS

Review Questions

13.91 What are colloids? Referring to Table 13.5, why is there no colloid in which both the dispersed phase and the dispersing medium are gases?

13.92 Describe how hydrophilic and hydrophobic colloids are stabilized in water.

13.93 Describe and give an everyday example of the Tyndall effect.

ADDITIONAL PROBLEMS

13.94 Lysozyme is an enzyme that cleaves bacterial cell walls. A sample of lysozyme extracted from egg white has a molar mass of 13,930 g. A quantity of 0.100 g of this enzyme is dissolved in 150 g of water at 25°C. Calculate the vapor-pressure lowering, the depression in freezing point, the elevation in boiling point, and the osmotic pressure of this solution. (The vapor pressure of water at 25°C is 23.76 mmHg.)

13.95 The blood sugar (glucose) level of a diabetic patient is approximately 0.140 g of glucose/100 mL of blood. Every time the patient ingests 40 g of glucose, her blood glucose level rises to approximately 0.240 g/100 mL of blood. Calculate the number of moles of glucose per milliliter of blood and the total number of moles and grams of glucose in the blood before and after consumption of glucose. (Assume that the total volume of blood in her body is 5.0 L.)

13.96 Trees in cold climates may be subjected to temperatures as low as −60°C. Estimate the concentration of an aqueous solution in the body of the tree that would remain unfrozen at this temperature. Is this a reasonable concentration? Comment on your result.

13.97 A cucumber placed in concentrated brine (saltwater) shrivels into a pickle. Explain.

13.98 Two liquids A and B have vapor pressures of 76 and 132 mmHg, respectively, at 25°C. What is the total vapor pressure of the ideal solution made up of (a) 1.00 mole of A and 1.00 mole of B and (b) 2.00 moles of A and 5.00 moles of B?

13.99 Determine the van't Hoff factor of Na_3PO_4 in a 0.40 m solution whose freezing point is −2.6°C.

13.100 A 262-mL sample of a sugar solution containing 1.22 g of the sugar has an osmotic pressure of 30.3 mmHg at 35°C. What is the molar mass of the sugar?

13.101 Consider the three mercury manometers shown in the diagram. One of them has 1 mL of water on top of the mercury, another has 1 mL of a 1 m urea solution on top of the mercury, and the third one has 1 mL of a 1 m NaCl solution placed on top of the mercury. Which of these solutions is in the tube labeled X, which is in Y, and which is in Z?

13.102 A forensic chemist is given a white powder for analysis. She dissolves 0.50 g of the substance in 8.0 g of benzene. The solution freezes at 3.9°C. Can the chemist conclude that the compound is cocaine ($C_{17}H_{21}NO_4$)? What assumptions are made in the analysis?

13.103 "Time-release" drugs have the advantage of releasing the drug to the body at a constant rate so that the drug concentration at any time is not too high as to have harmful side effects or too low as to be ineffective. A schematic diagram of a pill that works on this basis is shown. Explain how it works.

13.104   A solution of 1.00 g of anhydrous aluminum chloride ($AlCl_3$) in 50.0 g of water freezes at $-1.11°C$. Does the molar mass determined from this freezing point agree with that calculated from the formula? Why?

13.105   Explain why reverse osmosis is (theoretically) more desirable as a desalination method than distillation or freezing. What minimum pressure must be applied to seawater at 25°C for reverse osmosis to occur? (Treat seawater as a 0.70 *M* NaCl solution.)

13.106   What masses of sodium chloride, magnesium chloride, sodium sulfate, calcium chloride, potassium chloride, and sodium bicarbonate are needed to produce 1 L of artificial seawater for an aquarium? The required ionic concentrations are $[Na^+] = 2.56\ M$, $[K^+] = 0.0090\ M$, $[Mg^{2+}] = 0.054\ M$, $[Ca^{2+}] = 0.010\ M$, $[HCO_3^-] = 0.0020\ M$, $[Cl^-] = 2.60\ M$, $[SO_4^{2-}] = 0.051\ M$.

13.107   The osmotic pressure of blood plasma is approximately 7.5 atm at 37°C. Estimate the total concentration of dissolved species and the freezing point of blood.

13.108   The antibiotic gramicidin A can transport Na^+ ions into a certain cell at the rate of $5.0 \times 10^7\ Na^+$ ions/channel · s. Calculate the time in seconds to transport enough Na^+ ions to increase its concentration by $8.0 \times 10^{-3}\ M$ in a cell whose intracellular volume is 2.0×10^{-10} mL.

13.109   A protein has been isolated as a salt with the formula $Na_{20}P$ (this notation means that there are 20 Na^+ ions associated with a negatively charged protein P^{20-}). The osmotic pressure of a 10.0-mL solution containing 0.225 g of the protein is 0.257 atm at 25.0°C. (a) Calculate the molar mass of the protein from these data. (b) Calculate the actual molar mass of the protein.

13.110   A nonvolatile organic compound Z was used to make up two solutions. Solution A contains 5.00 g of Z dissolved in 100 g of water, and solution B contains 2.31 g of Z dissolved in 100 g of benzene. Solution A has a vapor pressure of 754.5 mmHg at the normal boiling point of water, and solution B has the same vapor pressure at the normal boiling point of benzene. Calculate the molar mass of Z in solutions A and B, and account for the difference.

13.111   Hydrogen peroxide with a concentration of 3.0 percent (3.0 g of H_2O_2 in 100 mL of solution) is sold in drugstores for use as an antiseptic. For a 10.0-mL 3.0 percent H_2O_2 solution, calculate (a) the oxygen gas produced (in liters) at STP when the compound undergoes complete decomposition and (b) the ratio of the volume of O_2 collected to the initial volume of the H_2O_2 solution.

13.112   State which of the alcohols listed in Problem 13.12 you would expect to be the best solvent for each of the following substances, and explain why: (a) I_2, (b) KBr, (c) $CH_3CH_2CH_2CH_2CH_3$.

13.113   Before a carbonated beverage bottle is sealed, it is pressurized with a mixture of air and carbon dioxide. (a) Explain the effervescence that occurs when the cap of the bottle is removed. (b) What causes the fog to form near the mouth of the bottle right after the cap is removed?

13.114   Iodine (I_2) is only sparingly soluble in water (left photo). Yet upon the addition of iodide ions (for example, from KI), iodine is converted to the triiodide ion, which readily dissolves (right photo):

$$I_2(s) + I^-(aq) \rightleftharpoons I_3^-(aq)$$

Describe the change in solubility of I_2 in terms of the change in intermolecular forces.

13.115   (a) The root cells of plants contain a solution that is hypertonic in relation to water in the soil. Thus, water can move into the roots by osmosis. Explain why salts such as NaCl and $CaCl_2$ spread on roads to melt ice can be harmful to nearby trees. (b) Just before urine leaves the human body, the collecting ducts in the kidney (which contain the urine) pass through a fluid whose salt concentration is considerably greater than is found in the blood and tissues. Explain how this action helps conserve water in the body.

13.116   Hemoglobin, the oxygen-transport protein, binds about 1.35 mL of oxygen per gram of the protein. The concentration of hemoglobin in normal blood is 150 g/L blood. Hemoglobin is about 95 percent saturated with O_2 in the lungs and only 74 percent saturated with O_2 in the capillaries. Calculate the volume of O_2 released by hemoglobin when 100 mL of blood flows from the lungs to the capillaries.

13.117 Two beakers, one containing a 50-mL aqueous 1.0 *M* glucose solution and the other a 50-mL aqueous 2.0 *M* glucose solution, are placed under a tightly sealed bell jar at room temperature. What are the volumes in these two beakers at equilibrium?

13.118 In the apparatus shown, what will happen if the membrane is (a) permeable to both water and the Na^+ and Cl^- ions, (b) permeable to water and the Na^+ ions but not to the Cl^- ions, (c) permeable to water but not to the Na^+ and Cl^- ions?

Membrane

0.01 *M* NaCl

0.1 *M* NaCl

13.119 Concentrated hydrochloric acid is usually available at a concentration of 37.7 percent by mass. What is its molar concentration? (The density of the solution is 1.19 g/mL.)

13.120 Explain each of the following statements: (a) The boiling point of seawater is higher than that of pure water. (b) Carbon dioxide escapes from the solution when the cap is removed from a carbonated soft drink bottle. (c) Molal and molar concentrations of dilute aqueous solutions are approximately equal. (d) In discussing the colligative properties of a solution (other than osmotic pressure), it is preferable to express the concentration in units of molality rather than in molarity. (e) Methanol (b.p. 65°C) is useful as an antifreeze, but it should be removed from the car radiator during the summer season.

13.121 A mixture of NaCl and sucrose ($C_{12}H_{22}O_{12}$) of combined mass 10.2 g is dissolved in enough water to make up a 250-mL solution. The osmotic pressure of the solution is 7.32 atm at 23°C. Calculate the mass percent of NaCl in the mixture.

13.122 A 1.32-g sample of a mixture of cyclohexane (C_6H_{12}) and naphthalene ($C_{10}H_8$) is dissolved in 18.9 g of benzene (C_6H_6). The freezing point of the solution is 2.2°C. Calculate the mass percent of the mixture. (See Table 13.2 for constants.)

13.123 How does each of the following affect the solubility of an ionic compound: (a) lattice energy, (b) solvent (polar versus nonpolar), (c) enthalpies of hydration of cation and anion?

13.124 A solution contains two volatile liquids A and B. Complete the following table, in which the symbol ⟷ indicates attractive intermolecular forces.

Attractive forces	Deviation from Raoult's law	ΔH_{soln}
A ⟷ A, B ⟷ B > A ⟷ B		
	Negative	
		Zero

13.125 The concentration of commercially available concentrated nitric acid is 70.0 percent by mass, or 15.9 *M*. Calculate the density and the molality of the solution.

13.126 A mixture of ethanol and 1-propanol behaves ideally at 36°C and is in equilibrium with its vapor. If the mole fraction of ethanol in the solution is 0.62, calculate its mole fraction in the vapor phase at this temperature. (The vapor pressures of pure ethanol and 1-propanol at 36°C are 108 and 40.0 mmHg, respectively.)

13.127 Ammonia (NH_3) is very soluble in water, but nitrogen trichloride (NCl_3) is not. Explain.

13.128 For ideal solutions, the volumes are additive. This means that if 5 mL of A and 5 mL of B form an ideal solution, the volume of the solution is 10 mL. Provide a molecular interpretation for this observation. When 500 mL of ethanol (C_2H_5OH) is mixed with 500 mL of water, the final volume is less than 1000 mL. Why?

13.129 Acetic acid is a weak acid that ionizes in solution as follows:

$$CH_3COOH(aq) \rightleftharpoons CH_3COO^-(aq) + H^+(aq)$$

If the freezing point of a 0.106 *m* CH_3COOH solution is −0.203°C, calculate the percent of the acid that has undergone ionization.

13.130 Which vitamins (see the given structures) do you expect to be water soluble? (See Problem 13.35.)

Pantothenic acid

Nicotinic acid

Vitamin K

13.131   Calculate the percent by mass of the solute in each of the following aqueous solutions: (a) 5.75 g of NaBr in 67.9 g of solution, (b) 24.6 g of KCl in 114 g of water, (c) 4.8 g of toluene in 39 g of benzene.

13.132   Acetic acid is a polar molecule and can form hydrogen bonds with water molecules. Therefore, it has a high solubility in water. Yet acetic acid is also soluble in benzene (C_6H_6), a nonpolar solvent that lacks the ability to form hydrogen bonds. A solution of 3.8 g of CH_3COOH in 80 g C_6H_6 has a freezing point of 3.5°C. Calculate the molar mass of the solute, and suggest what its structure might be. (*Hint:* Acetic acid molecules can form hydrogen bonds between themselves.)

13.133   A 2.6-L sample of water contains 192 μg of lead. Does this concentration of lead exceed the safety limit of 0.050 ppm of lead per liter of drinking water?

13.134   Fish in the Antarctic Ocean swim in water at about −2°C. (a) To prevent their blood from freezing, what must be the concentration (in molality) of the blood? Is this a reasonable physiological concentration? (b) In recent years, scientists have discovered a special type of protein in the blood of these fish that, although present in quite low concentrations (≤ 0.001 m), has the ability to prevent the blood from freezing. Suggest a mechanism for its action.

13.135   Why are ice cubes (for example, those you see in the trays in the freezer of a refrigerator) cloudy inside?

13.136   If a soft drink can is shaken and then opened, the drink escapes violently. However, if after shaking the can, we tap it several times with a metal spoon, no such "explosion" of the drink occurs. Why?

13.137   Two beakers are placed in a closed container. Beaker A initially contains 0.15 mole of naphthalene ($C_{10}H_8$) in 100 g of benzene (C_6H_6), and beaker B initially contains 31 g of an unknown compound dissolved in 100 g of benzene. At equilibrium, beaker A is found to have lost 7.0 g of benzene. Assuming ideal behavior, calculate the molar mass of the unknown compound. State any assumptions made.

13.138   (a) Derive the equation relating the molality (m) of a solution to its molarity (M)

$$m = \frac{M}{d - \frac{M\mathcal{M}}{1000}}$$

where d is the density of the solution (g/mL) and $\mathcal{M}$ is the molar mass of the solute (g/mol). (*Hint:* Start by expressing the solvent in kilograms in terms of the difference between the mass of the solution and the mass of the solute.) (b) Show that, for dilute aqueous solutions, m is approximately equal to M.

13.139   At 27°C, the vapor pressure of pure water is 23.76 mmHg and that of an aqueous solution of urea is 22.98 mmHg. Calculate the molality of urea in the solution.

13.140   A very long pipe is capped at one end with a semipermeable membrane. How deep (in meters) must the pipe be immersed into the sea for fresh water to begin to pass through the membrane? Assume the water to be at 20°C, and treat it as a 0.70 M NaCl solution. The density of seawater is 1.03 g/cm³, and the acceleration due to gravity is 9.81 m/s².

13.141   A mixture of liquids A and B exhibits ideal behavior. At 84°C, the total vapor pressure of a solution containing 1.2 moles of A and 2.3 moles of B is 331 mmHg. Upon the addition of another mole of B to the solution, the vapor pressure increases to 347 mmHg. Calculate the vapor pressure of pure A and B at 84°C.

13.142   Use Henry's law and the ideal gas equation to prove the statement that the volume of a gas that dissolves in a given amount of solvent is *independent* of the pressure of the gas. (*Hint:* Henry's law can be modified as $n = kP$, where n is the number of moles of the gas dissolved in the solvent.)

13.143   At 298 K, the osmotic pressure of a glucose solution is 10.50 atm. Calculate the freezing point of the solution. The density of the solution is 1.16 g/mL.

13.144   *Ringer's lactate*, a solution containing several different salts, is often administered intravenously for the initial treatment of trauma patients. One liter of Ringer's lactate contains 0.102 mole of sodium chloride, 4×10^{-3} mole of potassium chloride, 1.5×10^{-3} mole of calcium chloride, and 2.8×10^{-2} mole of sodium lactate. Determine the osmotic pressure of this solution at normal body temperature (37°C). Assume no ion pairing. (The formula of the lactate ion is $CH_3CH_2COO^-$.)

13.145   The diagram here shows vapor pressure curves for pure benzene and a solution of a nonvolatile solute in benzene. Estimate the molality of the solution.

13.146   Valinomycin is an antibiotic. It functions by binding K^+ ions and transporting them across the membrane into cells to offset the ionic balance. The molecule is represented here by its skeletal structure in which the end of each straight line corresponds to a carbon atom (unless a different atom is shown at the end of the line). There are as many H atoms attached to each C atom as necessary to give each C atom a total of four bonds.

Using the "like dissolves like" principle, explain how the molecule functions. (*Hint:* The −CH₃ groups at the two ends of each Y shape are nonpolar.)

13.147 Early fluoridation of municipal water supplies was done by dissolving enough sodium fluoride to achieve a 1-ppm concentration of fluoride ion. Convert 1.0 ppm F⁻ to *percent by mass* F⁻ and *molality* of NaF.

13.148 Many fluoridation facilities now use fluorosilicic acid instead of sodium fluoride. Fluorosilicic acid typically is distributed as a 23 percent (1.596 *m*) aqueous solution. (a) Calculate the van't Hoff factor of fluorosilicic acid given that a 23 percent solution has a freezing point of −15.5°C. (b) The density of 23 percent fluorosilicic acid is 1.19 g/mL. Given that the osmotic pressure of the solution at 25°C is 242 atm, calculate the molar mass of fluorosilicic acid.

13.149 A mixture of two volatile liquids is said to be ideal if each component obeys Raoult's law:

$$P_i = \chi_i P_i^\circ$$

Two volatile liquids A (molar mass 100 g/mol) and B (molar mass 110 g/mol) form an ideal solution. At 55°C, A has a vapor pressure of 98 mmHg and B has a vapor pressure of 42 mmHg. A solution is prepared by mixing equal masses of A and B. (a) Calculate the mole fraction of each component in the solution. (b) Calculate the partial pressures of A and B over the solution at 55°C. (c) Suppose that some of the vapor over the solution at 55°C is condensed to a liquid. Calculate the mole fraction of each component in the condensed liquid. (d) Calculate the partial pressures of the components above the condensed liquid at 55°C.

Answers to In-Chapter Problems

PRACTICE PROBLEMS

13.1A CS₂. **13.1B** C₃H₈, I₂, CS₂. **13.2A** (a) 0.423 *m*, (b) 2.48%.
13.2B 0.78 *m*. **13.3A** (a) 1.8 *M*, (b) 1.9 *m*. **13.3B** 12.8%. **13.4A** 0.12 *M*.
13.4B 26 atm. **13.5A** 22.2 mmHg. **13.5B** 103 g. **13.6A** f.p. = −7.91°C,
b.p. = 102.2°C. **13.6B** 710 g. **13.7A** *i* = 1.21. **13.7B** f.p. = −0.35°C.
13.8A 128 g/mol. **13.8B** 12.5 g. **13.9A** 6.0 × 10³ g/mol. **13.9B** 0.27 g.
13.10A 4%. **13.10B** 0.38 atm.

SECTION REVIEW

13.2.1 CO₂, C₂H₆, Br₂. **13.2.2** CH₃OH, NH₃. **13.3.1** 1.35%.
13.3.2 0.627 *m*. **13.3.3** 0.251 *M*. **13.3.4** 3.00 *M* and 3.40 *m*.
13.4.1 5.3 × 10⁻⁴ *M*. **13.4.2** 2.9 × 10⁻⁴ *M*. **13.5.1** 41.5 mmHg.
13.5.2 b.p. = 101°C, f.p. = −3.5°C. **13.5.3** 66 atm. **13.5.4** *i* = 1.77.
13.6.1 3.4 × 10² g/mol. **13.6.2** 10%.

KEY SKILLS

Entropy as a Driving Force

We have seen that although a decrease in system energy can be the driving force for a process [◄◄ Section 7.3], entropy also plays a role in determining whether or not a process will occur. Recall that entropy is a measure of how spread out a system's energy is. The simplest way to interpret this is to consider how spread out a system's energy is in *space*. Consider the example of a compressed gas in one side of a divided container. If the barrier between the two compartments is removed, the compressed gas will expand to fill the new, larger volume.

The energy possessed by the gas molecules was originally contained within a smaller volume. After the expansion, the energy possessed by the molecules occupies a larger volume, meaning that the energy is more spread out in space. This spreading out in space of the system's energy is an increase in entropy.

In addition to applying this interpretation of entropy to gas expansion and solution formation [◄◄ Pages 513 and 514], we can apply it to phase changes, such as the sublimation of dry ice [$CO_2(s)$].

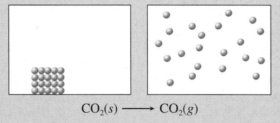

$$CO_2(s) \longrightarrow CO_2(g)$$

The CO_2 molecules in a sample of dry ice possess energy that is confined to the volume of the solid. Sublimation of the sample results in the molecules (and the energy they possess) occupying a much larger volume—corresponding to an increase in entropy. Because of this increase in entropy, although it is endothermic, the sublimation of dry ice does happen spontaneously.

For any process to happen, it must be exothermic, or be accompanied by an entropy increase, or both. An endothermic process (one in which system energy increases) may occur if there is a sufficient increase in the system's entropy. For example, although the dissolution of sucrose ($C_{12}H_{22}O_{11}$) is endothermic, sucrose dissolves in water because of the resulting increase in entropy.

$$C_{12}H_{22}O_{11}(s) \longrightarrow C_{12}H_{22}O_{11}(aq)$$

Likewise, a process that results in an entropy *decrease* may occur if it is sufficiently exothermic. An example of this is the condensation of water vapor on a cool surface. Although the energy of the water molecules is less spread out when it condenses, the condensation process is exothermic enough to compensate for the entropy decrease—and it does happen.

Student Annotation: Condensation is the reverse of vaporization. The molar enthalpy of vaporization of water (ΔH_{vap}) is 40.79 kJ/mol [◄◄ Section 12.6]. Therefore, the molar enthalpy of condensation is −40.79 kJ/mol.

$$H_2O(g) \longrightarrow H_2O(l)$$

Processes that are neither exothermic nor accompanied by an entropy increase do not occur.

Being able to make a qualitative assessment of the entropy change associated with a process, and being able to determine whether a process is exothermic or endothermic, can help us predict which processes are likely to happen, and which are not.

Key Skills Problems

13.1
Which of the following processes is accompanied by an increase in entropy? (Select all that apply.)

(a) $Br_2(l) \longrightarrow Br_2(g)$
(b) $NH_3(g) + HCl(g) \longrightarrow NH_4Cl(s)$
(c) $NaCl(s) \longrightarrow Na^+(g) + Cl^-(g)$
(d) $H_2(g) + O_2(g) \longrightarrow 2H_2O(l)$

13.2
For each of the processes depicted here, determine if it is endothermic or exothermic, or if there is not enough information to determine.

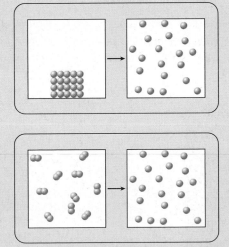

(a) Endothermic, exothermic
(b) Exothermic, endothermic
(c) Endothermic, not enough information to determine
(d) Endothermic, endothermic
(e) Exothermic, not enough information to determine

13.3
For each of the processes depicted here, determine if it is endothermic or exothermic, or if there is not enough information to determine.

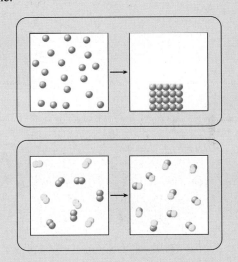

(a) Endothermic, exothermic
(b) Exothermic, endothermic
(c) Endothermic, not enough information to determine
(d) Endothermic, endothermic
(e) Exothermic, not enough information to determine

13.4
For some ionic solutes, dissolution actually causes an overall decrease in entropy. In order for such a dissolution to occur spontaneously, it must be _____.

(a) Exothermic
(b) Endothermic
(c) There is not enough information to determine this.

CHAPTER 14

Chemical Kinetics

14.1 Reaction Rates

14.2 Collision Theory of Chemical Reactions

14.3 Measuring Reaction Progress and Expressing Reaction Rate
• Average Reaction Rate • Instantaneous Rate
• Stoichiometry and Reaction Rate

14.4 Dependence of Reaction Rate on Reactant Concentration
• The Rate Law • Experimental Determination of the Rate Law

14.5 Dependence of Reactant Concentration on Time
• First-Order Reactions • Second-Order Reactions

14.6 Dependence of Reaction Rate on Temperature
• The Arrhenius Equation

14.7 Reaction Mechanisms
• Elementary Reactions • Rate-Determining Step • Mechanisms with a Fast First Step • Experimental Support for Reaction Mechanisms

14.8 Catalysis
• Heterogeneous Catalysis • Homogeneous Catalysis • Enzymes: Biological Catalysts

Living cells contain thousands of different enzymes, *proteins* that serve as natural catalysts for a wide variety of biochemical processes. Chemists have succeeded in using enzymes to catalyze a number of simpler chemical reactions in the laboratory—*outside* of living cells. Shown here are researchers Arun Goyal (left) and Neil Nelson (right) with tissue samples of a hybrid poplar tree, which was genetically modified to produce a specific enzyme. This enzyme can be used in place of the highly toxic chlorine gas traditionally used in the pulp-bleaching process—one step in the production of paper. Replacement of chlorine in the process results in reduced cost and reduced environmental impact for the papermaking industry. More widespread use of enzymes in chemical reactions will ultimately lead to more efficient, less expensive, and less hazardous industrial processes.

REACTION RATES

Chemical kinetics is the study of how fast reactions take place. Many familiar reactions, such as the initial steps in vision and photosynthesis, happen almost instantaneously. Others, such as the rusting of iron or the conversion of diamond to graphite, take place on a timescale of days or even millions of years.

Knowledge of kinetics is important to many scientific endeavors, including drug design, pollution control, and food processing. The job of an industrial chemist often is to work on increasing the *rate* of a reaction rather than maximizing its yield or developing a new process. Among the factors that can increase reaction rate are increased reactant concentration, increased temperature, increased surface area of a solid reactant, and the presence of a catalyst. After examining how these things affect reaction rate at the molecular level, we will look at the quantitative impact of each factor in more detail.

14.2 COLLISION THEORY OF CHEMICAL REACTIONS

A chemical reaction can be represented by the general equation

$$\text{reactants} \longrightarrow \text{products}$$

This equation tells us that during the course of a reaction, reactants are consumed while products are formed. Chemical reactions generally occur as a result of collisions between reacting molecules. A greater frequency of collisions usually leads to a higher reaction rate. According to the *collision theory* of chemical kinetics, the reaction rate is directly proportional to the number of molecular collisions per second:

$$\text{rate} \propto \frac{\text{number of collisions}}{\text{s}}$$

Consider the reaction of A molecules with B molecules to form some product. Suppose that each product molecule is formed by the direct combination of an A molecule and a B molecule. If we doubled the concentration of A, then the number of A-B collisions would also double, because there would be twice as many A molecules that could collide with B molecules in any given volume. Consequently, the rate would increase by a factor of 2. Similarly, doubling the concentration of B molecules would increase the rate twofold.

This view of collision theory is something of a simplification, though, because not every collision between molecules results in a reaction. A collision that *does* result in a reaction is called an *effective collision.* A molecule in motion possesses kinetic energy; the faster it is moving, the greater its kinetic energy. When molecules collide, part of their kinetic energy is converted to *vibrational* energy. If the initial kinetic energies are large, then the colliding molecules will vibrate so strongly as to break some of the chemical bonds. This bond breaking is the first step toward product formation. If the initial kinetic energies are small, the molecules will merely bounce off of each other intact. There is a minimum amount of energy, the *activation energy* (*E*a) [►► Section 14.6], required to initiate a chemical reaction. Without this minimum amount of energy at impact, a collision will be ineffective; that is, it will not result in a reaction.

Student Annotation: Kinetic energy is the result of motion of the whole molecule, relative to its surroundings. Vibrational energy is the result of motion of the atoms in a molecule, relative to one another.

When molecules react (as opposed to when *atoms* react), having sufficient kinetic energy is not the only requirement for a collision to be effective. Molecules must also be oriented in a way that favors reaction. The reaction between chlorine atoms and nitrosyl chloride (NOCl) illustrates this point:

$$Cl + NOCl \longrightarrow Cl_2 + NO$$

This reaction is most favorable when a free Cl atom collides directly with the Cl atom in the NOCl molecule [Figure 14.1(a)]. Otherwise, the reactants simply bounce off of each other and no reaction occurs [Figure 14.1(b)].

When an effective collision occurs between reactant molecules, they form an ***activated complex*** (a state also known as the ***transition state***), a temporary species formed by the reactant molecules as a result of the collision. Figure 14.2 shows a potential energy profile for the reaction between Cl and NOCl.

We can think of the activation energy as an energy *barrier* that prevents less energetic molecules from reacting. Because the number of reactant molecules in an ordinary reaction is very large, the speeds, and therefore also the kinetic energies of the molecules, vary greatly. Normally, only a small fraction of the colliding molecules—the fastest-moving ones—have sufficient kinetic energy to exceed the activation energy. These molecules can therefore take part in the reaction. This explains why reaction rates typically increase with increasing temperature. According to kinetic molecular theory, the average kinetic energy of a sample of molecules increases as the temperature increases [◄◄ Section 11.2, Figure 11.4]. Thus, at a higher temperature, more of the molecules in the sample have sufficient kinetic energy to exceed the activation energy (Figure 14.3), and the reaction rate increases. Figure 14.4 (pages 554–555) summarizes the factors that affect reaction rate.

Multi 14.1
Collision theory

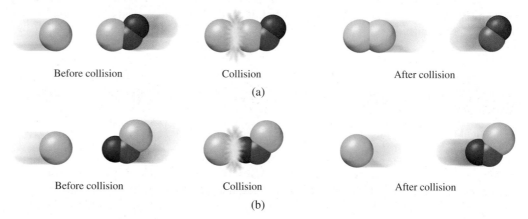

Figure 14.1 (a) For an effective collision to take place, the free Cl atom must collide directly with the Cl atom in NOCl. (b) Otherwise, the reactants bounce off of one another and the collision is ineffective—no reaction takes place.

Figure 14.2 Energy profile for the reaction of Cl with NOCl. In addition to being oriented properly, reactant molecules must possess sufficient energy to overcome the activation energy.

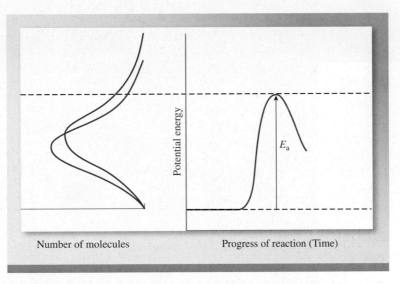

Number of molecules   Progress of reaction (Time)

Figure 14.3 Kinetic molecular theory shows that the average speed and therefore average kinetic energy of a collection of molecules increases with increasing temperature. The blue line represents a collection of molecules at lower temperature; the red line represents the collection of molecules at higher temperature. At higher temperature, more molecules have sufficient kinetic energy to exceed the activation energy and undergo effective collision.

14.3 MEASURING REACTION PROGRESS AND EXPRESSING REACTION RATE

We can follow the progress of a reaction by monitoring either the decrease in concentration of the reactants or the increase in the concentrations of the products. The method used to monitor changes in reactant or product concentrations depends on the specific reaction. In a reaction that either consumes or produces a colored species, we can measure the intensity of the color over time with a spectrometer. In a reaction that either consumes or produces a gas, we can measure the change in pressure over time with a manometer. Electrical conductance measurement can be used to monitor the progress if ionic species are consumed or produced.

Average Reaction Rate

Consider the hypothetical reaction represented by

$$A \longrightarrow B$$

in which A molecules are converted to B molecules. Figure 14.5 (page 556) shows the progress of this reaction as a function of time. The decrease in the number of A molecules and the increase in the number of B molecules with time are also shown graphically in Figure 14.6 (page 556).

It is generally convenient to express the rate in terms of the change in concentration with time. Thus, for the reaction $A \longrightarrow B$, we can express the rate as

$$\text{rate} = -\frac{\Delta[A]}{\Delta t} \quad \text{or} \quad \text{rate} = \frac{\Delta[B]}{\Delta t}$$

where $\Delta[A]$ and $\Delta[B]$ are the changes in concentration (molarity) over a time period Δt. The rate expression containing $\Delta[A]$ has a minus sign because the concentration of A decreases during the time interval—that is, $\Delta[A]$ is a negative quantity. The rate expression containing $\Delta[B]$ does not have a minus sign because the concentration of B increases during the time interval. Rate is always a positive quantity, so when it is expressed in terms of the change in a reactant concentration, a minus sign is needed in the rate expression to make the rate positive. When the rate is expressed in terms of the change in a product concentration, no negative sign is needed to make the rate positive because the product concentration increases with time. Rates calculated in this way are average rates over the time period Δt.

Figure 14.4

Collision Theory

At higher concentration, reactant molecules collide more often, giving rise to a greater number of effective collisions—thereby increasing reaction rate.

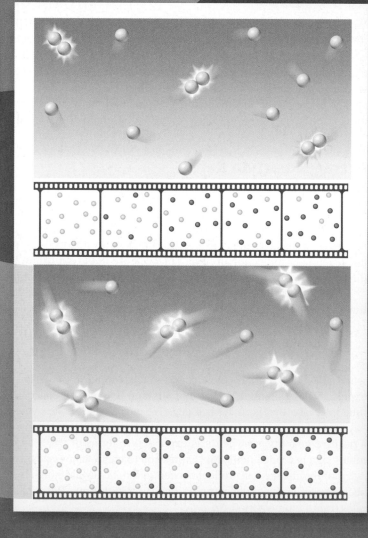

At higher temperature, reactant molecules are moving faster, causing more frequent collisions and greater energy at impact. Both factors increase the number of effective collisions and rate increases.

To be effective, a collision must occur between reactants with proper orientation. In the reaction of Cl and NOCl, collisions can be effective only when a Cl atom collides with the Cl atom in NOCl. (Effective collisions are identified by yellow.)

Product formation only occurs as the result of effective collision. Other collisions result in reactants simply bouncing off of one another. (Note that each effective collision resulted in the formation of one Cl_2 molecule and one NO molecule.)

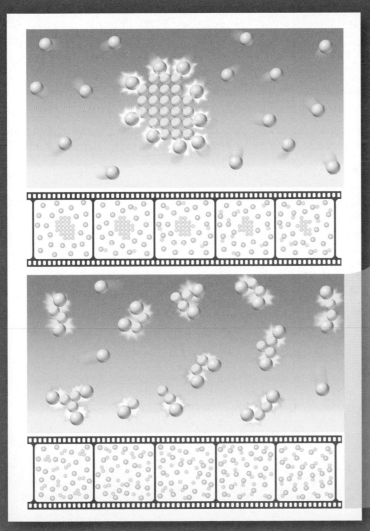

More finely divided solid reactant has more surface area where molecular collisions can occur. With greater surface area, reactant molecules can collide more frequently, giving rise to a greater number of effective collisions   thereby increasing reaction rate.

What's the point?

Several factors can influence the rate at which a chemical reaction ocurs including *reactant concentration*, *temperature*, *molecular orientation*, and *surface area*. In general:

- Reaction rate increases as reactant concentration increases
- Reaction rate increases as temperature increases
- Reaction rate increases as the surface area of a solid reactant increases
- Only molecules oriented properly at collision will react

Figure 14.5 The progress of the reaction A ⟶ B. Initially, only A molecules (grey spheres) are present. As time progresses, there are more and more B molecules (red spheres).

Figure 14.6 The rate of reaction A ⟶ B represented as the decrease of A molecules with time and as the increase of B molecules with time.

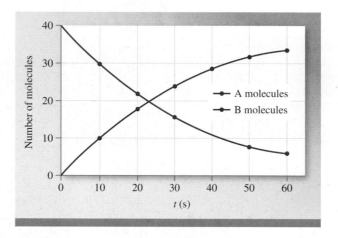

To understand rates of chemical reactions and how they are determined, it is useful to consider some specific reactions. First, we consider the aqueous reaction of molecular bromine (Br_2) with formic acid (HCOOH):

$$Br_2(aq) + HCOOH(aq) \longrightarrow 2Br^-(aq) + 2H^+(aq) + CO_2(g)$$

Molecular bromine is reddish-brown, whereas all the other species in the reaction are colorless. As the reaction proceeds, the concentration of bromine decreases and its color fades (Figure 14.7). The decrease in intensity of the color (and, therefore in the concentration of bromine) can be monitored with a spectrometer, which registers the amount of visible light absorbed by bromine (Figure 14.8).

Measuring the bromine concentration at some initial time and then at some final time enables us to determine the average rate of the reaction during that time interval:

$$\text{average rate} = -\frac{\Delta[Br_2]}{\Delta t}$$

$$= -\frac{[Br_2]_{final} - [Br_2]_{initial}}{t_{final} - t_{initial}}$$

Using data from Table 14.1, we can calculate the average rate over the first 50-s time interval as follows:

$$\text{average rate} = -\frac{(0.0101 - 0.0120)\,M}{50.0} = 3.80 \times 10^{-5}\,M/s$$

If we had chosen the first 100 s as our time interval, the average rate would then be given by

$$\text{average rate} = -\frac{(0.00846 - 0.0120)\,M}{100.0} = 3.54 \times 10^{-5}\,M/s$$

Figure 14.7 From left to right: The decrease in bromine concentration as time elapses is indicated by the loss of color.

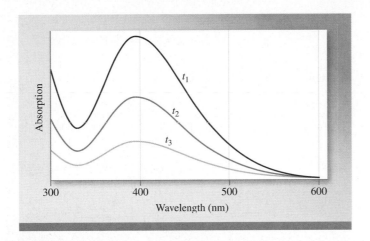

Figure 14.8 Plot of the absorption of bromine versus wavelength. The maximum absorption of visible light by bromine occurs at 393 nm. As the reaction progresses (t_1 to t_3), the absorption, which is proportional to [Br_2], decreases.

TABLE 14.1	Rates of the Reaction of Molecular Bromine and Formic Acid at 25°C		
Time (s)	**[Br$_2$] (M)**	**Rate (M/s)**	
0.0	0.0120	4.20×10^{-5}	
50.0	0.0101	3.52×10^{-5}	
100.0	0.00846	2.96×10^{-5}	
150.0	0.00710	2.49×10^{-5}	
200.0	0.00596	2.09×10^{-5}	
250.0	0.00500	1.75×10^{-5}	
300.0	0.00420	1.48×10^{-5}	
350.0	0.00353	1.23×10^{-5}	
400.0	0.00296	1.04×10^{-5}	

These calculations demonstrate that the average rate of this reaction depends on the time interval we choose. In other words, the rate changes over time. This is why a plot of the concentration of a reactant or product as a function of time is a curve rather than a straight line [Figure 14.9(a)].

Instantaneous Rate

If we were to calculate the average rate over shorter and shorter time intervals, we could obtain the ***instantaneous rate,*** which is the rate for a specific instant in time. Figure 14.10 shows the plot of [Br_2] versus time based on the data from Table 14.1. The instantaneous rate is equal to the slope of a tangent to the curve at any particular time. Note that we can pick *any* two points along a tangent to calculate its slope. For a chemist, the instantaneous rate is generally a more useful quantity than

Figure 14.9 (a) The plot of $[Br_2]$ against time is a curve because the reaction rate changes as $[Br_2]$ changes with time. (b) The plot of the reaction rate against $[Br_2]$ is a straight line because the rate is proportional to $[Br_2]$.

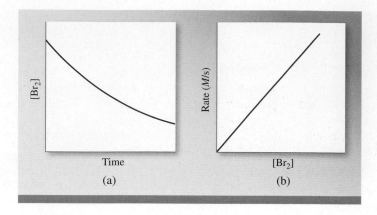

(a)   (b)

Figure 14.10 The instantaneous rates of the reaction between molecular bromine and formic acid at $t = 100$, 200, and 300 s are given by the slopes of the tangents at these times.

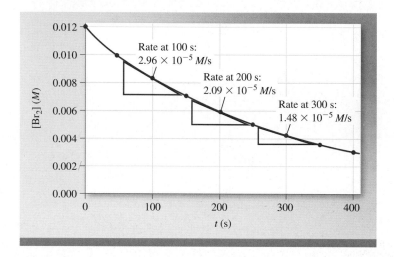

the average rate. For the remainder of this chapter, therefore, the term *rate* will be used to mean "instantaneous rate" (unless otherwise stated).

The slope of the tangent, and therefore the reaction *rate*, diminishes with time because the concentration of bromine decreases with time [Figure 14.9(a)]. The data in Table 14.1 show how the rate of this reaction depends on the concentration of bromine. At 50 s, for example, when the concentration of bromine is 0.0101 *M*, the rate is 3.52×10^{-5} *M*/s. When the concentration of bromine has been reduced by half (i.e., reduced to 0.00500 *M*), at 250 s, the rate is also reduced by half (i.e., reduced to 1.75×10^{-5} *M*/s):

$$\frac{[Br_2]_{50s}}{[Br_2]_{250s}} \approx 2 \quad \text{and} \quad \frac{\text{rate at 50.0 s}}{\text{rate at 250.0 s}} = \frac{3.52 \times 10^{-5} \ M/s}{1.75 \times 10^{-5} \ M/s} \approx 2$$

Thus, the rate is directly proportional to the concentration of bromine:

$$\text{rate} \propto [Br_2]$$

$$\text{rate} = k[Br_2]$$

where k, the proportionality constant, is called the ***rate constant.***

Rearranging the preceding equation gives

$$k = \frac{\text{rate}}{[Br_2]}$$

We can use the concentration and rate data from Table 14.1 for any value of t to calculate the value of k for this reaction. For example, using the data for $t = 50.0$ s gives

$$k = \frac{3.52 \times 10^{-5} \ M/s}{0.0101 \ M} = 3.49 \times 10^{-3} \ s^{-1} \ (\text{at } t = 50.0 \text{ s})$$

Likewise, using the data for $t = 300.0$ s gives

$$k = \frac{1.48 \times 10^{-5} \ M/s}{0.00420 \ M} = 3.52 \times 10^{-3} \ s^{-1} \ (\text{at } t = 300.0 \text{ s})$$

Slight variations in the calculated values of k are due to experimental deviations in rate measurements. To two significant figures, we get $k = 3.5 \times 10^{-3} \ s^{-1}$ for this reaction, regardless of which line of data we chose from Table 14.1. It is important to note that the value of k does not depend on the concentration of bromine. The rate constant is *constant* at constant temperature. (In Section 14.6, we discuss how k depends on temperature.)

We now consider another specific reaction, the decomposition of hydrogen peroxide:

$$2H_2O_2(aq) \longrightarrow 2H_2O(l) + O_2(g)$$

Because one of the products is a gas, we can monitor the progress of this reaction by measuring the pressure with a manometer. Pressure is converted to concentration using the ideal gas equation:

$$PV = nRT$$

or

$$P_{O_2} = \frac{n}{V}RT = [O_2]RT$$

where n/V gives the molarity of the oxygen gas. Rearranging the equation and solving for $[O_2]$, we get

$$[O_2] = \frac{1}{RT}P_{O_2}$$

The reaction rate, which is expressed as the rate of oxygen production, can now be written as

$$\text{rate} = \frac{\Delta[O_2]}{\Delta t} = \frac{1}{RT}\frac{\Delta P_{O_2}}{\Delta t}$$

Student Annotation: Many students prefer simply to convert pressures to concentrations using the ideal gas equation [◄◄ Section 11.5] and then determine the rate using the familiar form the equation: rate = Δ[O₂]/Δt.

Determining the rate from pressure data is possible only if the temperature (in kelvins) at which the reaction is carried out is known. Figure 14.11(a) shows the apparatus used to monitor the pressure change in the decomposition of hydrogen peroxide. Figure 14.11(b) shows the plot of oxygen pressure, P_{O_2}, versus time. As we did in Figure 14.10, we can draw a tangent to the curve in Figure 14.11(b) to determine the instantaneous rate at any point.

(a)

P_{O_2}

Time

$$2H_2O_2(aq) \longrightarrow 2H_2O(l) + O_2(g)$$

(b)

Figure 14.11 (a) The rate of hydrogen peroxide decomposition can be measured with a manometer, which (b) shows the increase in the oxygen gas pressure with time.

Stoichiometry and Reaction Rate

For stoichiometrically simple reactions of the type A ⟶ B, the rate can be expressed either in terms of the decrease in reactant concentration with time, $-\Delta[A]/\Delta t$, or in terms of the increase in product concentration with time, $\Delta[B]/\Delta t$—both expressions give the same result. For reactions in which one or more of the stoichiometric coefficients is something other than 1, we must take extra care in expressing the rate. For example, consider again the reaction between molecular bromine and formic acid:

$$Br_2(aq) + HCOOH(aq) \longrightarrow 2Br^-(aq) + 2H^+(aq) + CO_2(g)$$

We have expressed the rate of this reaction in terms of the disappearance of bromine. But what if we chose instead to express the rate in terms of the appearance of bromide ion? According to the balanced equation, 2 moles of Br^- are generated for each mole of Br_2 consumed. Thus, Br^- appears at twice the rate that Br_2 disappears. To avoid the potential ambiguity of reporting the rate of disappearance or appearance of a specific chemical *species,* we report the ***rate of reaction.*** We determine the rate of reaction such that the result is the same regardless of which species we monitor. For the hypothetical reaction,

$$A \longrightarrow 2B$$

the rate of reaction can be written as either

$$rate = -\frac{\Delta[A]}{\Delta t} \quad or \quad rate = \frac{1}{2}\frac{\Delta[B]}{\Delta t}$$

both of which give the same result. For the bromine and formic acid reaction, we can write the rate of reaction as either

$$rate = -\frac{\Delta[Br_2]}{\Delta t}$$

as we did earlier, or

$$rate = \frac{1}{2}\frac{\Delta[Br^-]}{\Delta t}$$

In general, for the reaction

$$aA + bB \longrightarrow cC + dD$$

the rate is given by

Equation 14.1 $$rate = -\frac{1}{a}\frac{\Delta[A]}{\Delta t} = -\frac{1}{b}\frac{\Delta[B]}{\Delta t} = \frac{1}{c}\frac{\Delta[C]}{\Delta t} = \frac{1}{d}\frac{\Delta[D]}{\Delta t}$$

Student Annotation: The rate of change in concentration of each species is divided by the coefficient of that species in the balanced equation.

Expressing the rate in this fashion ensures that the rate of reaction is the same regardless of which species we measure to monitor the reaction's progress.

Worked Examples 14.1 and 14.2 show how to write expressions for reaction rates and how to take stoichiometry into account in rate expressions.

Worked Example 14.1

Write the rate expressions for each of the following reactions:

(a) $I^-(aq) + OCl^-(aq) \longrightarrow Cl^-(aq) + OI^-(aq)$

(b) $2O_3(g) \longrightarrow 3O_2(g)$

(c) $4NH_3(g) + 5O_2(g) \longrightarrow 4NO(g) + 6H_2O(g)$

Strategy Use Equation 14.1 to write rate expressions for each of the reactions.

Setup For reactions containing gaseous species, progress is generally monitored by measuring pressure. Pressures are converted to molar concentrations using the ideal gas equation, and rate expressions are written in terms of molar concentrations.

Solution

(a) All the coefficients in this equation are 1. Therefore,

$$\text{rate} = -\frac{\Delta[I^-]}{\Delta t} = -\frac{\Delta[OCl^-]}{\Delta t} = \frac{\Delta[Cl^-]}{\Delta t} = \frac{\Delta[OI^-]}{\Delta t}$$

(b) $\text{rate} = -\dfrac{1}{2}\dfrac{\Delta[O_3]}{\Delta t} = \dfrac{1}{3}\dfrac{\Delta[O_2]}{\Delta t}$

(c) $\text{rate} = -\dfrac{1}{4}\dfrac{\Delta[NH_3]}{\Delta t} = -\dfrac{1}{5}\dfrac{\Delta[O_2]}{\Delta t} = \dfrac{1}{4}\dfrac{\Delta[NO]}{\Delta t} = \dfrac{1}{6}\dfrac{\Delta[H_2O]}{\Delta t}$

> **Think About It**
> Make sure that the change in concentration of each species is divided by the corresponding coefficient in the balanced equation. Also make sure that the rate expressions written in terms of reactant concentrations have a negative sign in order to make the resulting rate positive.

Practice Problem A Write the rate expressions for each of the following reactions:

(a) $CO_2(g) + 2H_2O(g) \longrightarrow CH_4(g) + 2O_2(g)$

(b) $3O_2(g) \longrightarrow 2O_3(g)$

(c) $2NO(g) + O_2(g) \longrightarrow 2NO_2(g)$

Practice Problem B Write the balanced equation corresponding to the following rate expressions:

(a) $\text{rate} = -\dfrac{1}{3}\dfrac{\Delta[CH_4]}{\Delta t} = -\dfrac{1}{2}\dfrac{\Delta[H_2O]}{\Delta t} = -\dfrac{\Delta[CO_2]}{\Delta t} = \dfrac{1}{4}\dfrac{\Delta[CH_3OH]}{\Delta t}$

(b) $\text{rate} = -\dfrac{1}{2}\dfrac{\Delta[N_2O_5]}{\Delta t} = \dfrac{1}{2}\dfrac{\Delta[N_2]}{\Delta t} = \dfrac{1}{5}\dfrac{\Delta[O_2]}{\Delta t}$

(c) $\text{rate} = -\dfrac{\Delta[H_2]}{\Delta t} = -\dfrac{\Delta[CO]}{\Delta t} = \dfrac{\Delta[O_2]}{\Delta t} = \dfrac{\Delta[H_2CO_3]}{\Delta t}$

Worked Example 14.2

Consider the reaction

$$4NO_2(g) + O_2(g) \longrightarrow 2N_2O_5(g)$$

At a particular time during the reaction, nitrogen dioxide is being consumed at the rate of 0.00130 M/s. (a) At what rate is molecular oxygen being consumed? (b) At what rate is dinitrogen pentoxide being produced?

Strategy Determine the rate of reaction using Equation 14.1, and, using the stoichiometry of the reaction, convert to rates of change for the specified individual species.

Setup

$$\text{rate} = -\frac{1}{4}\frac{\Delta[NO_2]}{\Delta t} = -\frac{\Delta[O_2]}{\Delta t} = \frac{1}{2}\frac{\Delta[N_2O_5]}{\Delta t}$$

We are given

$$\frac{\Delta[NO_2]}{\Delta t} = -0.00130 \; M/\text{s}$$

where the minus sign indicates that the concentration of NO_2 is decreasing with time. The rate of reaction, therefore, is

$$\text{rate} = -\frac{1}{4}\frac{\Delta[NO_2]}{\Delta t} = -\frac{1}{4}(-0.00130 \; M/\text{s})$$

$$= 3.25 \times 10^{-4} \; M/\text{s}$$

(Continued on next page)

Solution

(a) $3.25 \times 10^{-4} \, M/s = -\dfrac{\Delta[O_2]}{\Delta t}$

$\dfrac{\Delta[O_2]}{\Delta t} = -3.25 \times 10^{-4} \, M/s$

Molecular oxygen is being consumed at a rate of $3.25 \times 10^{-4} \, M/s$.

(b) $3.25 \times 10^{-4} \, M/s = \dfrac{1}{2} \dfrac{\Delta[N_2O_5]}{\Delta t}$

$2(3.25 \times 10^{-4} \, M/s) = \dfrac{\Delta[N_2O_5]}{\Delta t}$

$\dfrac{\Delta[N_2O_5]}{\Delta t} = 6.50 \times 10^{-4} \, M/s$

Dinitrogen pentoxide is being produced at a rate of $6.50 \times 10^{-4} \, M/s$.

> **Think About It**
> Remember that the negative sign in a rate expression indicates that a species is being consumed rather than produced. Rates are always expressed as positive quantities.

Practice Problem A Consider the reaction

$$4PH_3(g) \longrightarrow P_4(g) + 6H_2(g)$$

At a particular point during the reaction, molecular hydrogen is being formed at the rate of 0.168 M/s. (a) At what rate is P_4 being produced? (b) At what rate is PH_3 being consumed?

Practice Problem B Consider the following unbalanced equation:

$$A + B \longrightarrow C$$

When C is being formed at the rate of 0.086 M/s, A is being consumed at a rate of 0.172 M/s and B is being consumed at a rate of 0.258 M/s. Balance the equation based on the relative rates of formation and consumption of products and reactants.

SECTION 14.3 REVIEW

Measuring Reaction Progress and Expressing Reaction Rate

14.3.1 Write the rate expressions for the following reaction.

$$A + 2B \longrightarrow C + D$$

14.3.2 In the same reaction,

$$A + 2B \longrightarrow C + D$$

if the concentration of A is changing at a rate of 0.026 M/s, what is the rate of change in the concentration of B?

14.4 DEPENDENCE OF REACTION RATE ON REACTANT CONCENTRATION

We saw in Section 14.3 that the rate of reaction between bromine and formic acid is proportional to the concentration of bromine and that the proportionality constant k is the rate constant. We will now explore in more detail how the rate, the rate constant, and the reactant concentrations are related.

The Rate Law

The equation relating the rate of reaction to the concentration of molecular bromine,

$$\text{rate} = k[\text{Br}_2]$$

is an example of a ***rate law.*** The rate law is an equation that relates the rate of reaction to the concentrations of reactants. For the general reaction,

$$a\text{A} + b\text{B} \longrightarrow c\text{C} + d\text{D}$$

the rate law is

$$\text{rate} = k[\text{A}]^x[\text{B}]^y \qquad \textbf{Equation 14.2}$$

where k is the rate constant and the exponents x and y are numbers that must be determined experimentally. When we know the values of k, x, and y, we can use Equation 14.2 to calculate the rate of the reaction, given the concentrations of A and B.

In the case of the reaction of molecular bromine and formic acid, the rate law is

$$\text{rate} = k[\text{Br}_2]^x[\text{HCOOH}]^y$$

where $x = 1$ and $y = 0$.

The values of the exponents in the rate law indicate the *order* of the reaction with respect to each reactant. In the reaction of bromine and formic acid, for example, the exponent for the bromine concentration, $x = 1$, means that the reaction is *first order* with respect to bromine. The exponent of 0 for the formic acid concentration indicates that the reaction is *zeroth order* with respect to formic acid. The sum of x and y is called the overall ***reaction order.*** Thus, the reaction of bromine and formic acid is first order in bromine, zeroth order in formic acid, and first order $(1 + 0 = 1)$ overall.

Student Annotation: It is important to emphasize that the exponents in a rate law must be determined from experimental data and that, in general, they are *not* equal to the coefficients from the chemical equation.

Experimental Determination of the Rate Law

To see how a rate law is determined from experimental data, consider the following reaction between fluorine and chlorine dioxide:

$$\text{F}_2(g) + 2\text{ClO}_2(g) \longrightarrow 2\text{FClO}_2(g)$$

Rate laws are commonly determined using a table of starting reactant concentrations and initial rates. The ***initial rate*** is the instantaneous rate at the beginning of the reaction. By varying the starting concentrations of reactants and observing the changes that result in the initial rate, we can determine how the rate depends on each reactant concentration.

Table 14.2 shows the initial rate data for the reaction of fluorine and chlorine dioxide being carried out three different times. Each time, the combination of reactant concentrations is different, and each time the initial rate is different.

To determine the values of the exponents x and y in the rate law,

$$\text{rate} = k[\text{F}_2]^x[\text{ClO}_2]^y$$

TABLE 14.2	Initial Rate Data for the Reaction Between F_2 and ClO_2		
Experiment	**[F$_2$] (M)**	**[ClO$_2$] (M)**	**Initial rate (M/s)**
1	0.10	0.010	1.2×10^{-3}
2	0.10	0.040	4.8×10^{-3}
3	0.20	0.010	2.4×10^{-3}

we must compare two experiments in which one reactant concentration *changes,* and the other remains constant. For example, we first compare the data from experiments 1 and 3:

Experiment	$[F_2]$ (*M*)	$[ClO_2]$ (*M*)	Initial rate (*M*/s)
1	0.10	0.010	1.2×10^{-3}
2	[F₂] doubles 0.10	[ClO₂] unchanged 0.040	Rate doubles 4.8×10^{-3}
3	0.20	0.010	2.4×10^{-3}

When the concentration of fluorine doubles, with the chlorine dioxide concentration held constant, the rate doubles.

$$\frac{[F_2]_3}{[F_2]_1} = \frac{0.20\ M}{0.10\ M} = 2 \qquad \frac{\text{rate}_3}{\text{rate}_1} = \frac{2.4 \times 10^{-3}\ M/s}{1.2 \times 10^{-3}\ M/s} = 2$$

This indicates that the rate is directly proportional to the concentration of fluorine and the value of *x* is 1.

Student Annotation: Recall that when an exponent is 1, it need not be shown [◀◀ Section 8.1].

$$\text{rate} = k[F_2][ClO_2]^y$$

Similarly, we can compare experiments 1 and 2:

Experiment	$[F_2]$ (*M*)	$[ClO_2]$ (*M*)	Initial rate (*M*/s)
1	[F₂] unchanged 0.10	[ClO₂] quadruples 0.010	Rate quadruples 1.2×10^{-3}
2	0.10	0.040	4.8×10^{-3}
3	0.20	0.010	2.4×10^{-3}

We find that the rate quadruples when the concentration of chlorine dioxide is quadrupled, but the fluorine concentration is held constant.

$$\frac{[ClO_2]_2}{[ClO_2]_1} = \frac{0.040\ M}{0.010\ M} = 4 \qquad \frac{\text{rate}_2}{\text{rate}_1} = \frac{4.8 \times 10^{-3}\ M/s}{1.2 \times 10^{-3}\ M/s} = 4$$

This indicates that the rate is also directly proportional to the concentration of chlorine dioxide, so the value of *y* is also 1. Thus, we can write the rate law as follows:

$$\text{rate} = k[F_2][ClO_2]$$

Because the concentrations of F_2 and ClO_2 are each raised to the first power, we say that the reaction is first order in F_2 and first order in ClO_2. The reaction is second order overall.

Knowing the rate law, we can then use the data from any one of the experiments to calculate the rate constant. Using the data for the first experiment in Table 14.2, we can write

$$k = \frac{\text{rate}}{[F_2][ClO_2]} = \frac{1.2 \times 10^{-3}\ M/s}{(0.10\ M)(0.010\ M)} = 1.2\ M^{-1} \cdot s^{-1}$$

Table 14.3 contains initial rate data for the hypothetical reaction

$$aA + bB \longrightarrow cC + dD$$

which has the general rate law

$$\text{rate} = k[A]^x[B]^y$$

TABLE 14.3	Initial Rate Data for the Reaction Between A and B		
Experiment	[A] (*M*)	[B] (*M*)	Initial rate (*M*/s)
1	0.10	0.015	2.1×10^{-4}
2	0.20	0.015	4.2×10^{-4}
3	0.10	0.030	8.4×10^{-4}

Comparing experiments 1 and 2, we see that when [A] doubles, with [B] unchanged, the rate also doubles.

Experiment		[A] (M)		[B] (M)		Initial rate (M/s)
1	[A] doubles {	0.10	[B] unchanged {	0.015	Rate doubles {	2.1 × 10⁻⁴
2		0.20		0.015		4.2 × 10⁻⁴
3		0.10		0.030		8.4 × 10⁻⁴

Thus, $x = 1$.

Comparing experiments 1 and 3, when [B] doubles with [A] unchanged, the rate quadruples.

Experiment		[A] (M)		[B] (M)		Initial rate (M/s)
1		0.10		0.015		2.1 × 10⁻⁴
2	[A] unchanged {	0.20	[B] doubles {	0.015	Rate quadruples {	4.2 × 10⁻⁴
3		0.10		0.030		8.4 × 10⁻⁴

Thus, the rate is *not* directly proportional to [B] to the first power, but rather it is directly proportional to [B] to the second power (i.e., $y = 2$):

$$\text{rate} \propto [B]^2$$

The overall rate law is

$$\text{rate} = k[A][B]^2$$

This reaction is therefore first order in A, second order in B, and third order overall.

Once again, knowing the rate law, we can use data from any of the experiments in the table to calculate the rate constant. Rearranging the rate law and using the data from experiment 1, we get

$$k = \frac{\text{rate}}{[A][B]^2} = \frac{2.1 \times 10^{-4}\ M/s}{(0.10\ M)(0.015\ M)^2} - 9.3\ M^{-2} \cdot s^{-1}$$

Note that the units of this rate constant are different from those for the rate constant we calculated for the F_2-ClO_2 reaction and the bromine reaction. In fact, the units of a rate constant depend on the *overall* order of the reaction. Table 14.4 compares the units of the rate constant for reactions that are zeroth, first, second, and third order overall.

The following are three important things to remember about the rate law:

1. The exponents in a rate law must be determined from a table of experimental data—in general, they are not related to the stoichiometric coefficients in the balanced chemical equation.
2. Comparing changes in individual reactant concentrations with changes in rate shows how the rate depends on each reactant concentration.
3. Reaction order is always defined in terms of reactant concentrations, never product concentrations.

TABLE 14.4	Units of the Rate Constant k for Reactions of Various Overall Orders	
Overall reaction order	**Sample rate law**	**Units of k**
0	rate = k	$M \cdot s^{-1}$
1	rate = $k[A]$ or rate = $k[B]$	s^{-1}
2	rate = $k[A]^2$, rate = $k[B]^2$, or rate = $k[A][B]$	$M^{-1} \cdot s^{-1}$
3*	rate = $k[A]^2[B]$ or rate = $k[A][B]^2$	$M^{-2} \cdot s^{-1}$

*Another possibility for a third-order reaction is rate = $k[A][B][C]$, although such reactions are very rare.

Worked Example 14.3 shows how to use initial rate data to determine a rate law.

Worked Example 14.3

The gas-phase reaction of nitric oxide with hydrogen at 1280°C is

$$2NO(g) + 2H_2(g) \longrightarrow N_2(g) + 2H_2O(g)$$

From the following data collected at 1280°C, determine (a) the rate law, (b) the rate constant, including units, and (c) the rate of the reaction when $[NO] = 4.8 \times 10^{-3}\ M$ and $[H_2] = 6.2 \times 10^{-3}\ M$.

Experiment	[NO] (M)	[H$_2$] (M)	Initial rate (M/s)
1	5.0×10^{-3}	2.0×10^{-3}	1.3×10^{-5}
2	1.0×10^{-2}	2.0×10^{-3}	5.0×10^{-5}
3	1.0×10^{-2}	4.0×10^{-3}	1.0×10^{-4}

Strategy Compare two experiments at a time to determine how the rate depends on the concentration of each reactant.

Setup The rate law is rate $= k[NO]^x[H_2]^y$. Comparing experiments 1 and 2, we see that the rate increases by approximately a factor of 4 when [NO] is doubled but [H$_2$] is held constant. Comparing experiments 2 and 3 shows that the rate doubles when [H$_2$] doubles but [NO] is held constant.

Solution

(a) Dividing the rate from experiment 2 by the rate from experiment 1, we get

$$\frac{\text{rate}_2}{\text{rate}_1} = \frac{5.0 \times 10^{-5}\ M \cdot s^{-1}}{1.3 \times 10^{-5}\ M \cdot s^{-1}} \approx 4 = \frac{k(1.0 \times 10^{-2}\ M)^x(2.0 \times 10^{-3}\ M)^y}{k(5.0 \times 10^{-3}\ M)^x(2.0 \times 10^{-3}\ M)^y}$$

Canceling identical terms in the numerator and denominator gives

$$\frac{(1.0 \times 10^{-2}\ M)^x}{(5.0 \times 10^{-3}\ M)^x} = 2^x = 4$$

Therefore, $x = 2$. The reaction is second order in NO.
Dividing the rate from experiment 3 by the rate from experiment 2, we get

$$\frac{\text{rate}_3}{\text{rate}_2} = \frac{1.0 \times 10^{-4}\ M \cdot s^{-1}}{5.0 \times 10^{-5}\ M \cdot s^{-1}} = 2 = \frac{k(1.0 \times 10^{-2}\ M)^x(4.0 \times 10^{-3}\ M)^y}{k(1.0 \times 10^{-2}\ M)^x(2.0 \times 10^{-3}\ M)^y}$$

Canceling identical terms in the numerator and denominator gives

$$\frac{(4.0 \times 10^{-3}\ M)^y}{(2.0 \times 10^{-3}\ M)^y} = 2^y = 2$$

Therefore, $y = 1$. The reaction is first order in H$_2$. The overall rate law is

$$\text{rate} = k[NO]^2[H_2]$$

(b) We can use data from any of the experiments to calculate the value and units of k. Using the data from experiment 1 gives

$$k = \frac{\text{rate}}{[NO]^2[H_2]} = \frac{1.3 \times 10^{-5}\ M/s}{(5.0 \times 10^{-3}\ M)^2(2.0 \times 10^{-3}\ M)} = 2.6 \times 10^2\ M^{-2} \cdot s^{-1}$$

(c) Using the rate constant determined in part (b) and the concentrations of NO and H$_2$ given in the problem statement, we can determine the reaction rate as follows:

$$\text{rate} = (2.6 \times 10^2\ M^{-2} \cdot s^{-1})(4.8 \times 10^{-3}\ M)^2(6.2 \times 10^{-3}\ M)$$

$$= 3.7 \times 10^{-5}\ M/s$$

Think About It
The exponent for the concentration of H$_2$ in the rate law is 1, whereas the coefficient for H$_2$ in the balanced equation is 2. It is a common error to try to write a rate law using the stoichiometric coefficients as the exponents. Remember that, in general, the exponents in the rate law are not related to the coefficients in the balanced equation. Rate laws must be determined by examining a table of experimental data.

Practice Problem A The reaction of peroxydisulfate ion ($S_2O_8^{2-}$) with iodide ion (I^-) is

$$S_2O_8^{2-}(aq) + 3I^-(aq) \longrightarrow 2SO_4^{2-}(aq) + I_3^-(aq)$$

From the following data collected at a certain temperature, determine the rate law and calculate the rate constant, including its units.

Experiment	$[S_2O_8^{2-}]$ (M)	$[I^-]$ (M)	Initial rate (M/s)
1	0.080	0.034	2.2×10^{-4}
2	0.080	0.017	1.1×10^{-4}
3	0.16	0.017	2.2×10^{-4}

Practice Problem B For the following general reaction, rate = $k[A]^2$ and $k = 1.3 \times 10^{-2} \, M^{-1} \cdot s^{-1}$:

$$A + B \longrightarrow 2C$$

Use this information to fill in the missing table entries.

Experiment	[A] (M)	[B] (M)	Initial rate (M/s)
1	0.013	0.250	2.20×10^{-6}
2	0.026	0.250	
3		0.500	2.20×10^{-6}

SECTION 14.4 REVIEW

Dependence of Reaction Rate on Reactant Concentration

Answer questions 14.4.1 through 14.4.4 using the table of initial rate data for the reaction

$$A + 2B \longrightarrow 2C + D$$

Experiment	[A] (M)	[B] (M)	Initial rate (M/s)
1	0.12	0.010	2.2×10^{-3}
2	0.36	0.010	6.6×10^{-3}
3	0.12	0.020	2.2×10^{3}

14.4.1 What is rate law for the reaction?

14.4.2 Calculate the rate constant.

14.4.3 What is the overall order of the reaction?

14.4.4 Determine the rate when [A] = 0.50 M and [B] = 0.25 M.

14.4.5 The diagrams represent three experiments in which the reaction A + B ⟶ C is carried out with varied initial concentrations of A and B. Determine the rate law for the reaction. (A = green, B = yellow, C = red.)

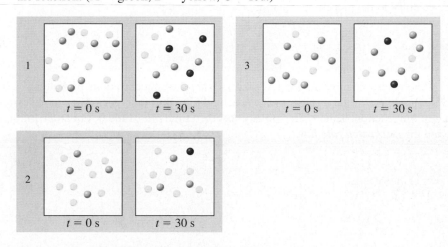

14.5 DEPENDENCE OF REACTANT CONCENTRATION ON TIME

We can use the rate law to determine the rate of a reaction using the rate constant and the reactant concentrations:

$$\overset{\text{rate law}}{\underset{\underset{\text{rate}}{\uparrow}\quad\underset{\text{rate constant}}{\uparrow}}{\text{rate} = k[A]^x[B]^y}}$$

A rate law can also be used to determine the remaining concentration of a reactant at a specific time during a reaction. We will illustrate this use of rate laws using reactions that are first order overall and reactions that are second order overall.

First-Order Reactions

A *first-order reaction* is a reaction whose rate depends on the concentration of one of the reactants raised to the first power. Two examples are the decomposition of ethane (C_2H_6) into highly reactive fragments called methyl radicals ($\cdot CH_3$), and the decomposition of dinitrogen pentoxide (N_2O_5) into nitrogen dioxide (NO_2) and molecular oxygen (O_2):

$$C_2H_6 \longrightarrow 2 \cdot CH_3 \qquad\qquad \text{rate} = k[C_2H_6]$$

$$2N_2O_5(g) \longrightarrow 4NO_2(g) + O_2(g) \qquad\qquad \text{rate} = k[N_2O_5]$$

In a first-order reaction of the type

$$A \longrightarrow \text{products}$$

the rate can be expressed as the rate of change in reactant concentration,

$$\text{rate} = -\frac{\Delta[A]}{\Delta t}$$

as well as in the form of the rate law:

$$\text{rate} = k[A]$$

Setting these two expressions of the rate equal to each other we get

$$-\frac{\Delta[A]}{\Delta t} = k[A]$$

Applying calculus to the preceding equation, we can show that

Equation 14.3	$\ln\dfrac{[A]_t}{[A]_0} = -kt$

where ln is the natural logarithm, and $[A]_0$ and $[A]_t$ are the concentrations of A at times 0 and t, respectively. In general, time 0 refers to any specified time during a reaction—not necessarily the beginning of the reaction. Time t refers to any specified time *after* time 0. Equation 14.3 is sometimes called the *integrated rate law.*

Student Annotation: In differential form, the preceding equation becomes

$$-\frac{d[A]}{dt} = k[A]$$

Rearranging, we get

$$\frac{d[A]}{[A]} = -kdt$$

Integrating between $t = 0$ and $t = t$ gives

$$\int_{[A]_0}^{[A]_t} \frac{d[A]}{[A]} = -k\int_0^t dt$$

$$\ln[A]_t - \ln[A]_0 = -kt$$

or

$$\ln\frac{[A]_t}{[A]_0} = -kt$$

Student Annotation: It is not necessary for you to be able to do the calculus required to arrive at Equation 14.3, but it is very important that you know how to *use* Equation 14.3.

In Worked Example 14.4 we apply Equation 14.3 to a specific reaction.

Worked Example 14.4

The decomposition of hydrogen peroxide is first order in H_2O_2.

$$2H_2O_2(aq) \longrightarrow 2H_2O(l) + O_2(g)$$

The rate constant for this reaction at 20°C is 1.8×10^{-5} s^{-1}. If the starting concentration of H_2O_2 is 0.75 M, determine (a) the concentration of H_2O_2 remaining after 3 h and (b) how long it will take for the H_2O_2 concentration to drop to 0.10 M.

Strategy Use Equation 14.3 to find $[H_2O_2]_t$ where t = 3 h, and then solve Equation 14.3 for t to determine how much time must pass for $[H_2O_2]_t$ to equal 0.10 M.

Setup $[H_2O_2]_0$ = 0.75 M; time t for part (a) is (3 h)(60 min/h)(60 s/min) = 10,800 s.

Solution

(a) $\ln \dfrac{[H_2O_2]_t}{[H_2O_2]_0} = -kt$

$\ln \dfrac{[H_2O_2]_t}{0.75\ M} = -(1.8 \times 10^{-5}\ s^{-1})(10,800\ s) = -0.1944$

Take the inverse natural logarithm of both sides of the equation to get

$$\frac{[H_2O_2]_t}{0.75\ M} = e^{-0.1944} = 0.823$$

$$[H_2O_2]_t = (0.823)(0.75\ M) = 0.62\ M$$

The concentration of H_2O_2 after 3 h is 0.62 M.

> **Student Annotation:** The inverse of $\ln x$ is e^x [▶▶ Appendix 1].

(b) $\ln\left(\dfrac{0.10\ M}{0.75\ M}\right) = -2.015 = -(1.8 \times 10^{-5}\ s^{-1})t$

$\dfrac{2.015}{1.8 \times 10^{-5}\ s^{-1}} = t = 1.12 \times 10^5\ s$

The time required for the peroxide concentration to drop to 0.10 M is 1.1×10^5 s or about 31 h.

Think About It
Don't forget the minus sign in Equation 14.3. If you calculate a concentration at time t that is greater than the concentration at time 0 (or if you get a negative time required for the concentration to drop to a specified level), check your solution for this common error.

Practice Problem A The rate constant for the reaction 2A $\longrightarrow$ B is 7.5×10^{-3} s^{-1} at 110°C. The reaction is first order in A. How long (in seconds) will it take for [A] to decrease from 1.25 M to 0.71 M?

Practice Problem B Refer again to the reaction 2A $\longrightarrow$ B, for which $k = 7.5 \times 10^{-3}$ s^{-1} at 110°C. With a starting concentration of [A] = 2.25 M, what will [A] be after 2.0 min?

Equation 14.3 can be rearranged as follows:

$$\ln[A]_t = -kt + \ln[A]_0 \qquad \textbf{Equation 14.4}$$

Equation 14.4 has the form of the linear equation $y = mx + b$:

$$\ln[A]_t = (-k)(t) + \ln[A]_0$$

$$y\ \ =\ \ m\ x\ +\ \ b$$

> **Student Annotation:** Because pressure is proportional to concentration, for gaseous reactions [◀◀ Section 11.8] Equations 14.3 and 14.4 can be written as
>
> $$\ln\frac{P_t}{P_0} = -kt$$
>
> and
>
> $$\ln P_t = -kt + \ln P_0$$
>
> respectively, where P_0 and P_t are the pressures of reactant A at times 0 and t, respectively.

Figure 14.12(a) shows the decrease in concentration of reactant A during the course of the reaction. As we saw in Section 14.2, the plot of reactant concentration as a function of time is not a straight line. For a first-order reaction, however, we do get a straight line if we plot the natural log of reactant concentration ($\ln[A]_t$) versus time (y versus x). The slope of the line is equal to $-k$ [Figure 14.12(b)], so we can determine the rate constant from the slope of this plot.

> **Student Annotation:** This graphical determination is an alternative to using the method of initial rates to determine the value of k.

Figure 14.12 First-order reaction characteristics: (a) Decrease of reactant concentration with time. (b) A plot of $\ln[A]_t$ versus t. The slope of the line is equal to $-k$ and the y intercept is equal to $\ln[A]_0$.

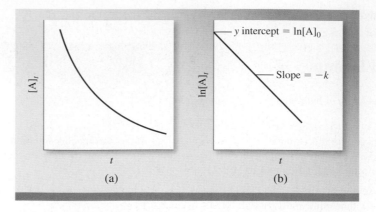

Worked Example 14.5 shows how a rate constant can be determined from experimental data.

Worked Example 14.5

The rate of decomposition of azomethane is studied by monitoring the partial pressure of the reactant as a function of time:

$$CH_3-N=N-CH_3(g) \longrightarrow N_2(g) + C_2H_6(g)$$

The data obtained at 300°C are listed in the following table:

Time (s)	$P_{azomethane}$ (mmHg)
0	284
100	220
150	193
200	170
250	150
300	132

Determine the rate constant of the reaction at this temperature.

Strategy We can use Equation 14.3 only for first-order reactions, so we must first determine if the decomposition of azomethane is first order. We do this by plotting $\ln P$ against time. If the reaction is first order, we can use Equation 14.3 and the data at any two of the times in the table to determine the rate constant.

Setup The table expressed as $\ln P$ is

Time (s)	$\ln P$
0	5.649
100	5.394
150	5.263
200	5.136
250	5.011
300	4.883

Plotting these data gives a straight line, indicating that the reaction is indeed first order. Thus, we can use Equation 14.3 expressed in terms of pressure.

$$\ln\frac{P_t}{P_0} = -kt$$

P_t and P_0 can be pressures at any two times during the experiment. P_0 need not be the pressure at 0 s—it need only be at the earlier of the two times.

Solution Using data from times 100 s and 250 s of the original table ($P_{azomethane}$ versus t), we get

$$\ln\frac{150 \text{ mmHg}}{220 \text{ mmHg}} = -k(150 \text{ s})$$

$$\ln 0.682 = -k(150 \text{ s})$$

$$k = 2.55 \times 10^{-3} \text{ s}^{-1}$$

Think About It

We could equally well have determined the rate constant by calculating the slope of the plot of ln P versus t. Using the two points labeled on the plot, we get

$$\text{slope} = \frac{5.011 - 5.394}{250 - 100}$$

$$= -2.55 \times 10^{-3}\ \text{s}^{-1}$$

Remember that slope $= -k$, so $k = 2.55 \times 10^{-3}\ \text{s}^{-1}$.

Practice Problem A Ethyl iodide (C_2H_5I) decomposes at a certain temperature in the gas phase as follows:

$$C_2H_5I(g) \longrightarrow C_2H_4(g) + HI(g)$$

From the following data, determine the rate constant of this reaction. Begin by constructing a plot to verify that the reaction is first order.

Time (min)	$[C_2H_5I]$ (M)
0	0.36
15	0.30
30	0.25
48	0.19
75	0.13

Practice Problem B Use the calculated k from Practice Problem A to fill in the missing values in the following table:

Time (min)	$[C_2H_5I]$ (M)
0	0.45
10	—
20	—
30	—
40	—

We often describe the rate of a reaction using the half-life. The **half-life** ($t_{1/2}$) is the time required for the reactant concentration to drop to *half* its original value. We obtain an expression for $t_{1/2}$ for a first-order reaction as follows:

$$t = \frac{1}{k} \ln \frac{[A]_0}{[A]_t}$$

According to the definition of half-life, $t = t_{1/2}$ when $[A]_t = \frac{1}{2}[A]_0$, so

$$t_{1/2} = \frac{1}{k} \ln \frac{[A]_0}{\frac{1}{2}[A]_0}$$

Because $\dfrac{[A]_0}{\frac{1}{2}[A]_0} = 2$, and ln 2 = 0.693, the expression for $t_{1/2}$ simplifies to

$$t_{1/2} = \frac{0.693}{k} \qquad\qquad \textbf{Equation 14.5}$$

According to Equation 14.5, the half-life of a first-order reaction is independent of the initial concentration of the reactant. Thus, it takes the same time for the concentration of the reactant to decrease from 1.0 M to 0.50 M as it does for the concentration to decrease from 0.10 M to 0.050 M (Figure 14.13). Measuring the half-life of a reaction is one way to determine the rate constant of a first-order reaction.

The half-life of a first-order reaction is inversely proportional to its rate constant, so a short half-life corresponds to a large rate constant. Consider, for example, two radioactive isotopes used in nuclear medicine: ^{24}Na ($t_{1/2} = 14.7$ h) and ^{60}Co ($t_{1/2} = 5.3$ yr). Sodium-24, with the shorter half-life, decays faster. If we started with an equal number of moles of each isotope, most of the sodium-24 would be gone in a week whereas most of the cobalt-60 would remain unchanged.

Figure 14.13 A plot of [A] versus time for the first-order reaction A ⟶ products. The half-life of the reaction is 1 min. The concentration of A is halved every half-life.

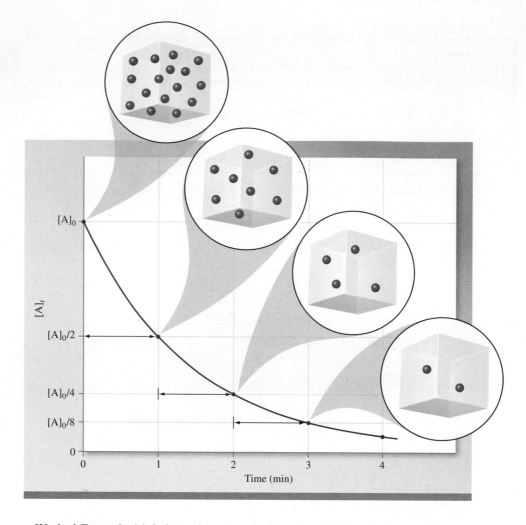

Worked Example 14.6 shows how to calculate the half-life of a first-order reaction, given the rate constant.

Worked Example 14.6

The decomposition of ethane (C_2H_6) to methyl radicals (CH_3) is a first-order reaction with a rate constant of 5.36×10^{-4} s^{-1} at 700°C:

$$C_2H_6 \longrightarrow 2CH_3$$

Calculate the half-life of the reaction in minutes.

Strategy Use Equation 14.5 to calculate $t_{1/2}$ in seconds, and then convert to minutes.

Setup $\text{seconds} \times \dfrac{1 \text{ minute}}{60 \text{ seconds}} = \text{minutes}$

Solution

$$t_{1/2} = \frac{0.693}{k} = \frac{0.693}{5.36 \times 10^{-4} \text{ s}^{-1}} = 1293 \text{ s}$$

$$1293 \text{ s} \times \frac{1 \text{ min}}{60 \text{ s}} = 21.5 \text{ min}$$

The half-life of ethane decomposition at 700°C is 21.5 min.

Think About It
Half-lives and rate constants can be expressed using any units of time and reciprocal time, respectively. Track units carefully when you convert from one unit of time to another.

Practice Problem A Calculate the half-life of the decomposition of azomethane, discussed in Worked Example 14.5.

Practice Problem B Calculate the rate constant for the first-order decay of ^{24}Na ($t_{1/2} = 14.7$ h).

Second-Order Reactions

A *second-order reaction* is a reaction whose rate depends on the concentration of one reactant raised to the second power or on the product of the concentrations of two different reactants (each raised to the first power). For simplicity, we will consider only the first type of reaction:

$$A \longrightarrow \text{product}$$

where the rate can be expressed as

$$\text{rate} = -\frac{\Delta[A]}{\Delta t}$$

or as

$$\text{rate} = k[A]^2$$

As before, we can combine the two expressions of the rate:

$$-\frac{\Delta[A]}{\Delta t} = k[A]^2$$

Again, using calculus, we obtain the following integrated rate law:

$$\frac{1}{[A]_t} = kt + \frac{1}{[A]_0} \qquad \textbf{Equation 14.6}$$

Student Annotation: Equation 14.6 is the result of

$$\int_{[A]_0}^{[A]_t} \frac{d[A]}{[A]^2} = -k \int_0^t dt$$

Again: It is not necessary that you be able to derive Equation 14.6, only that you be able to use it to solve second-order kinetics problems.

Thus, for a second-order reaction, we obtain a straight line when we plot the reciprocal of concentration ($1/[A]_t$) against time (Figure 14.14), and the slope of the line is equal to the rate constant, k. As before, we can obtain the expression for the half-life by setting $[A]_t = \frac{1}{2}[A]_0$ in Equation 14.6.

$$\frac{1}{\frac{1}{2}[A]_0} = kt_{1/2} + \frac{1}{[A]_0}$$

Solving for $t_{1/2}$, we obtain

$$t_{1/2} = \frac{1}{k[A]_0} \qquad \textbf{Equation 14.7}$$

Note that unlike the half-life of a first-order reaction, which is independent of the starting concentration, the half-life of a second-order reaction is inversely proportional to the initial reactant concentration. Determining the half-life at several different initial concentrations is one way to distinguish between first-order and second-order reactions.

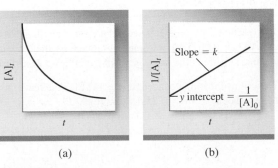

(a)   (b)

Figure 14.14 Second-order reaction characteristics: (a) Decrease of reactant concentration with time.

(b) A plot of $\frac{1}{[A]_t}$ versus t. The slope of the line is equal to k, and the y intercept is equal to $\frac{1}{[A]_0}$.

Worked Example 14.7 shows how to use Equations 14.6 and 14.7 to calculate reactant concentrations and the half-life of a second-order reaction.

Worked Example 14.7

Student Annotation: This equation can also be written as $2I(g) \longrightarrow I_2(g)$.

Iodine atoms combine to form molecular iodine in the gas phase:

$$I(g) + I(g) \longrightarrow I_2(g)$$

This reaction is second order and has a rate constant of $7.0 \times 10^9 \ M^{-1} \cdot s^{-1}$ at 23°C. (a) If the initial concentration of I is 0.086 M, calculate the concentration after 2.0 min. (b) Calculate the half-life of the reaction when the initial concentration of I is 0.60 M and when the initial concentration of I is 0.42 M.

Strategy Use Equation 14.6 to determine $[I]_t$ at $t = 2.0$ min; use Equation 14.7 to determine $t_{1/2}$ when $[I]_0 = 0.60 \ M$ and when $[I]_0 = 0.42 \ M$.

Setup

$$t = (2.0 \ \text{min})(60 \ \text{s/min}) = 120 \ \text{s}.$$

Solution

(a) $\dfrac{1}{[A]_t} = kt + \dfrac{1}{[A]_0}$

$\qquad = (7.0 \times 10^9 \ M^{-1} \cdot s^{-1})(120 \ s) + \dfrac{1}{0.086 \ M}$

$\qquad = 8.4 \times 10^{11} \ M^{-1}$

$[A]_t = \dfrac{1}{8.4 \times 10^{11} \ M^{-1}} = 1.2 \times 10^{-12} \ M$

The concentration of atomic iodine after 2 min is $1.2 \times 10^{-12} \ M$.

(b) When $[I]_0 = 0.60 \ M$,

$$t_{1/2} = \frac{1}{k[A]_0} = \frac{1}{(7.0 \times 10^9 \ M^{-1} \cdot s^{-1})(0.60 \ M)} = 2.4 \times 10^{-10} \ s$$

When $[I]_0 = 0.42 \ M$,

$$t_{1/2} = \frac{1}{k[A]_0} = \frac{1}{(7.0 \times 10^9 \ M^{-1} \cdot s^{-1})(0.42 \ M)} = 3.4 \times 10^{-10} \ s$$

Think About It
(a) Iodine, like the other halogens, exists as diatomic molecules at room temperature. It makes sense, therefore, that atomic iodine would react quickly, and essentially completely, to form I_2 at room temperature. The very low remaining concentration of I after 2 min makes sense.
(b) As expected, the half-life of this second-order reaction is not constant. (A constant half-life is a characteristic of first-order reactions.)

Practice Problem A The reaction $2A \longrightarrow B$ is second order in A with a rate constant of $32 \ M^{-1} \cdot s^{-1}$ at 25°C. (a) Starting with $[A]_0 = 0.0075 \ M$, how long will it take for the concentration of A to drop to 0.0018 M? (b) Calculate the half-life of the reaction for $[A]_0 = 0.0075 \ M$ and for $[A]_0 = 0.0025 \ M$.

Practice Problem B Determine the initial concentration, $[A]_0$, for the reaction in Practice Problem A necessary for the half-life to be (a) 1.50 s, (b) 25.0 s, and (c) 175 s.

First- and second-order reactions are the most common reaction types. Reactions of overall order zero exist but are relatively rare. For a zeroth-order reaction

$$A \longrightarrow \text{products}$$

the rate law is given by

$$\text{rate} = k[A]^0 = k$$

TABLE 14.5	Summary of the Kinetics of Zeroth-Order, First-Order, and Second-Order Reactions		
Order	**Rate law**	**Integrated rate law**	**Half-Life**
0	rate = k	$[A]_t = -kt + [A]_0$	$\dfrac{[A]_0}{2k}$
1	rate = $k[A]$	$\ln\dfrac{[A]_t}{[A]_0} = -kt$	$\dfrac{0.693}{k}$
2	rate = $k[A]^2$	$\dfrac{1}{[A]_t} = kt + \dfrac{1}{[A]_0}$	$\dfrac{1}{k[A]_0}$

Thus, the rate of a *zeroth-order reaction* is a constant, independent of reactant concentration. Third-order and higher-order reactions are quite rare and too complex to be covered in this book. Table 14.5 summarizes the kinetics for zeroth-order, first-order, and second-order reactions of the type A ⟶ products.

SECTION 14.5 REVIEW

Dependence of Reactant Concentration on Time

The first-order decomposition of dinitrogen pentoxide (N_2O_5) is represented by

$$2N_2O_5(g) \longrightarrow 4NO_2(g) + O_2(g)$$

Use the table of data to answer questions 14.5.1 and 14.5.2:

t (s)	$[N_2O_5]$ (M)
0	0.91
300	0.75
600	0.64
1200	0.44
3000	0.16

14.5.1   What is the rate constant for the decomposition of N_2O_5?

14.5.2   Approximately how long will it take for $[N_2O_5]$ to fall from 0.62 M to 0.10 M?

14.5.3   Consider the first-order reaction A ⟶ B in which A molecules (blue spheres) are converted to B molecules (yellow spheres). What is the half-life for the reaction?

$t = 0\text{ s}$ $t = 10\text{ s}$

14.5.4   A ⟶ 2B is a second-order reaction for which $k = 5.3 \times 10^{-1}\ M^{-1} \cdot s^{-1}$. Calculate $t_{1/2}$ when $[A]_0 = 0.55\ M$.

14.6 DEPENDENCE OF REACTION RATE ON TEMPERATURE

Nearly all reactions happen faster at higher temperatures. For example, the time required to cook food depends largely on the boiling point of water. The reaction involved in hard-boiling an egg happens faster at 100°C (about 10 min) than at 80°C (about 30 min). The dependence of reaction rate on temperature is the reason we keep food in a refrigerator—and why food keeps even longer in a freezer. The lower the temperature, the slower the processes that cause food to spoil.

The Arrhenius Equation

The dependence of the rate constant of a reaction on temperature can be expressed by the *Arrhenius equation,*

| Equation 14.8 | $$k = Ae^{-E_a/RT}$$ |

where E_a is the activation energy of the reaction (in kJ/mol), R is the gas constant (8.314 J/K · mol), T is the absolute temperature, and e is the base of the natural logarithm [►► Appendix 1]. The quantity A represents the collision frequency and is called the frequency factor. It can be treated as a constant for a given reaction over a reasonably wide temperature range. Equation 14.8 shows that the rate constant decreases with increasing activation energy and increases with increasing temperature. This equation can be expressed in a more useful form by taking the natural logarithm of both sides:

$$\ln k = \ln Ae^{-E_a/RT}$$

or

| Equation 14.9 | $$\ln k = \ln A - \frac{E_a}{RT}$$ |

which can be rearranged to give the following linear equation:

| Equation 14.10 | $$\ln k = \left(-\frac{E_a}{R}\right)\left(\frac{1}{T}\right) + \ln A$$
 $$y = \quad m \quad x \ + \ b$$ |

Thus, a plot of $\ln k$ versus $1/T$ gives a straight line whose slope is equal to $-E_a/R$ and whose y intercept (b) is equal to $\ln A$.

Worked Example 14.8 demonstrates a graphical method for determining the activation energy of a reaction.

Worked Example 14.8

Rate constants for the reaction

$$CO(g) + NO_2(g) \longrightarrow CO_2(g) + NO(g)$$

were measured at four different temperatures. The data are shown in the table. Plot $\ln k$ versus $1/T$, and determine the activation energy (in kJ/mol) for the reaction.

k (M^{-1} · s^{-1})	T (K)
0.0521	288
0.101	298
0.184	308
0.332	318

Strategy Plot $\ln k$ versus $1/T$, and determine the slope of the resulting line. According to Equation 14.10, slope = $-E_a/R$.

Setup $R = 8.314$ J/mol $\cdot$ K. Taking the natural log of each value of k and the inverse of each value of T gives

ln k	1/T (K^{-1})
-2.95	3.47×10^{-3}
-2.29	3.36×10^{-3}
-1.69	3.25×10^{-3}
-1.10	3.14×10^{-3}

Solution A plot of these data yields the following graph:

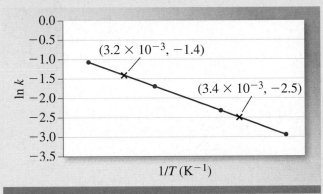

The slope is determined using the x and y coordinates of any two points on the line. Using the points that are labeled on the graph gives

$$\text{slope} = \frac{-1.4 - (-2.5)}{3.2 \times 10^{-3} \text{ K}^{-1} - 3.4 \times 10^{-3} \text{ K}^{-1}} - -5.5 \times 10^{3} \text{ K}$$

The value of the slope is -5.5×10^{3} K. Because slope $= -E_a/R$,

$$E_a = -(\text{slope})(R)$$
$$= -(-5.5 \times 10^{3} \text{ K})(8.314 \text{ J/K} \cdot \text{mol})$$
$$= 4.6 \times 10^{4} \text{ J/mol or 46 kJ/mol}$$

The activation energy is 46 kJ/mol.

Think About It
Note that while k has units of $M^{-1} \cdot s^{-1}$, ln k has no units.

Practice Problem A The second-order rate constant for the decomposition of nitrous oxide to nitrogen molecules and oxygen atoms has been determined at various temperatures:

k ($M^{-1} \cdot s^{-1}$)	T (°C)
1.87×10^{-3}	600
0.0113	650
0.0569	700
0.244	750

Determine the activation energy graphically.

Practice Problem B Each line in the graph shown here represents a different reaction. List the reactions in order of increasing activation energy.

We can derive an even more useful form of the Arrhenius equation starting with Equation 14.9 written for two different temperatures, T_1 and T_2:

$$\ln k_1 = \ln A - \frac{E_a}{RT_1}$$

$$\ln k_2 = \ln A - \frac{E_a}{RT_2}$$

Subtracting $\ln k_2$ from $\ln k_1$ gives

$$\ln k_1 - \ln k_2 = \left(\ln A - \frac{E_a}{RT_1}\right) - \left(\ln A - \frac{E_a}{RT_2}\right)$$

$$\ln \frac{k_1}{k_2} = \frac{E_a}{R}\left(-\frac{1}{T_1} + \frac{1}{T_2}\right)$$

Equation 14.11
$$\ln \frac{k_1}{k_2} = \frac{E_a}{R}\left(\frac{1}{T_2} - \frac{1}{T_1}\right)$$

Equation 14.11 enables us to do two things:

1. If we know the rate constant at two different temperatures, we can calculate the activation energy.
2. If we know the activation energy and the rate constant at one temperature, we can determine the value of the rate constant at any other temperature.

Worked Examples 14.9 and 14.10 show how to use Equation 14.11.

Worked Example 14.9

The rate constant for a particular first-order reaction is given for three different temperatures:

T (K)	k (s^{-1})
400	2.9×10^{-3}
450	6.1×10^{-2}
500	7.0×10^{-1}

Using these data, calculate the activation energy of the reaction.

Strategy Use Equation 14.11 to solve for E_a.

Setup Solving Equation 14.11 for E_a gives

$$E_a = R\left(\frac{\ln \dfrac{k_1}{k_2}}{\dfrac{1}{T_2} - \dfrac{1}{T_1}}\right)$$

Solution Using the rate constants for 400 K (T_1) and 450 K (T_2), we get

$$E_a = \frac{8.314 \text{ J}}{\text{K} \cdot \text{mol}}\left(\frac{\ln \dfrac{2.9 \times 10^{-3} \text{ s}^{-1}}{6.1 \times 10^{-2} \text{ s}^{-1}}}{\dfrac{1}{450 \text{ K}} - \dfrac{1}{400 \text{ K}}}\right)$$

$$= 91,173 \text{ J/mol} = 91 \text{ kJ/mol}$$

The activation energy of the reaction is 91 kJ/mol.

Think About It
A good way to check your work is to use the value of E_a that you calculated (and Equation 14.11) to determine the rate constant at 500 K. Make sure it agrees with the value in the table.

Practice Problem A Use the data in the following table to determine the activation energy of the reaction:

T (K)	k (s^{-1})
625	1.1×10^{-4}
635	1.5×10^{-4}
645	2.0×10^{-4}

Practice Problem B Based on the data shown in Practice Problem A, what will be the value of k at 655 K?

Worked Example 14.10

A certain first-order reaction has an activation energy of 83 kJ/mol. If the rate constant for this reaction is 2.1×10^{-2} s^{-1} at 150°C, what is the rate constant at 300°C?

Strategy Use Equation 14.11 to solve for k_2. Pay particular attention to units in this type of problem.

Setup Solving Equation 14.11 for k_2 gives

$$k_2 = \frac{k_1}{e^{\left(\frac{E_a}{R}\right)\left(\frac{1}{T_2} - \frac{1}{T_1}\right)_2}}$$

$E_a = 8.3 \times 10^4$ J/mol, $T_1 = 423$ K, $T_2 = 573$ K, $R = 8.314$ J/K · mol, and $k_1 = 2.1 \times 10^{-2}$ s^{-1}.

Solution

$$k_2 = \frac{2.1 \times 10^{-2} \text{ s}^{-1}}{e^{\left(\frac{8.3 \times 10^4 \text{ J/mol}}{8.314 \text{ J/K} \cdot \text{mol}}\right)\left(\frac{1}{573 \text{ K}} - \frac{1}{423 \text{ K}}\right)}}$$

$$= 1.0 \times 10^1 \text{ s}^{-1}$$

The rate constant at 300°C is 10 s^{-1}.

> **Student Annotation:** Note that E_a is converted to joules so that the units will cancel properly. Alternatively, the R could be expressed as 0.008314 kJ/K · mol. Also note again that T must be expressed in kelvins.

> **Think About It**
> Make sure that the rate constant you calculate at a higher temperature is in fact higher than the original rate constant. According to the Arrhenius equation, the rate constant always increases with increasing temperature. If you get a smaller k at a higher temperature, check your solution for mathematical errors.

Practice Problem A Calculate the rate constant at 200°C for a reaction that has a rate constant of 8.1×10^{-4} s^{-1} at 90°C and an activation energy of 99 kJ/mol.

Practice Problem B Calculate the rate constant at 200°C for a reaction that has a rate constant of 8.1×10^{-4} s^{-1} at 90°C and an activation energy of 59 kJ/mol.

SECTION 14.6 REVIEW

Dependence of Reaction Rate on Temperature

Use the table of data collected for a first-order reaction to answer Questions 14.6.1 and 14.6.2:

T (K)	k (s^{-1})
300	3.9×10^{-2}
310	1.1×10^{-1}
320	2.8×10^{-1}

14.6.1 What is the activation energy of the reaction?

14.6.2 What is the rate constant at 80°C?

Thinking Outside the Box

Surface Area

As we saw in Section 14.2, one of the factors that can influence the rate of reaction is the surface area of a solid reactant. The reason is simple: aqueous or gaseous reactant molecules can only encounter and collide with solid reactant molecules at the surface of the solid. The more finely divided a solid reactant is, the more surface area is exposed, and the more collisions can take place. To illustrate this, we can compare the rate at which an Alka-Seltzer tablet reacts with water. In the first photo in each series, an Alka-Seltzer tablet is being added to a glass of lukewarm water. The top series of photos shows the reaction of a whole tablet; the bottom series shows the reaction of a tablet that has been ground to a powder. In the case of the powder, the reaction occurs much more rapidly.

At the end of 30 seconds, the powder has reacted completely, while the *whole tablet* continues to react, as evidenced by its continued effervescence and the remaining tablet.

The effect of increased surface area on reaction rate can be dramatic and even dangerous. A tragic example of this occurred recently at the Imperial Sugar refinery (right) in Savannah, Georgia. On February 7, 2008, finely divided sugar dust in a storage silo was ignited by an unknown source, causing a series of violent explosions that destroyed the facility and killed more than a dozen workers.

14.7 REACTION MECHANISMS

A balanced chemical equation does not tell us much about *how* a reaction actually takes place. In many cases, the balanced equation is simply the sum of a series of steps. Consider the following hypothetical example. In the first step of a reaction, a molecule of reactant A combines with a molecule of reactant B to form a molecule of C:

$$A + B \longrightarrow C$$

In the second step, the molecule of C combines with another molecule of B to produce D:

$$C + B \longrightarrow D$$

The overall balanced equation is the sum of these two equations:

$$
\begin{aligned}
\textit{Step 1:} \quad & A + B \longrightarrow \cancel{C} \\
\textit{Step 2:} \quad & \cancel{C} + B \longrightarrow D \\
\hline
& A + 2B \longrightarrow D
\end{aligned}
$$

The sequence of steps that sum to give the overall reaction is called the **reaction mechanism.** A reaction mechanism is comparable to the *route* traveled during a trip, whereas the overall balanced chemical equation specifies only the *origin* and the *destination*.

For a specific example of a reaction mechanism, we consider the reaction between nitric oxide and oxygen:

$$2NO(g) + O_2(g) \longrightarrow 2NO_2(g)$$

We know that NO_2 does not form as the result of a single collision between two NO molecules and one O_2 molecule because N_2O_2 is detected during the course of the reaction. We can envision the reaction taking place via the following two steps:

$$2NO(g) \longrightarrow N_2O_2(g)$$

$$N_2O_2(g) + O_2(g) \longrightarrow 2NO_2(g)$$

In the first step, two NO molecules collide to form an N_2O_2 molecule. This is followed by the step in which N_2O_2 and O_2 combine to give two molecules of NO_2. The net chemical equation, which represents the overall change, is given by the sum of the first and second steps:

$$
\begin{aligned}
\textit{Step 1:} \quad & NO + NO \longrightarrow N_2O_2 \\
\textit{Step 2:} \quad & N_2O_2 + O_2 \longrightarrow 2NO_2 \\
\hline
\textit{Overall reaction:} \quad & 2NO(g) + O_2(g) \longrightarrow 2NO_2(g)
\end{aligned}
$$

Species such as N_2O_2 (and C in the hypothetical equation) are called **intermediates** because they appear in the mechanism of the reaction but not in the overall balanced equation. An intermediate is produced in an early step in the reaction and consumed in a later step.

Elementary Reactions

Each step in a reaction mechanism represents an **elementary reaction,** one that occurs in a single collision of the reactant molecules. The **molecularity** of an elementary reaction is essentially the *number* of reactant molecules involved in the collision. Elementary reactions may be **unimolecular** (one reactant molecule), **bimolecular** (two reactant molecules), or **termolecular** (three reactant molecules). These molecules may be of the same or different types. Each of the elementary steps in the formation of NO_2 from NO and O_2 is bimolecular, because there are *two* reactant molecules in each step. Likewise, each of the steps in the hypothetical $A + 2B \longrightarrow D$ reaction is bimolecular.

Knowing the steps of a reaction enables us to deduce the rate law. Suppose we have the following elementary reaction:

$$A \longrightarrow products$$

Student Annotation: Termolecular reactions actually are quite rare simply because the simultaneous encounter of three molecules is far less likely than that of two molecules.

Student Annotation: The overall equation has three reactant molecules. Because it is not an elementary reaction, though, we do not classify it as a termolecular reaction. Rather, it is the combination of two bimolecular reactions (steps 1 and 2).

Because there is only one molecule present, this is a unimolecular reaction. It follows that the larger the number of A molecules present, the faster the rate of product formation. Thus, the rate of a unimolecular reaction is directly proportional to the concentration of A—the reaction is first order in A:

$$\text{rate} = k[\text{A}]$$

For a bimolecular elementary reaction involving A and B molecules,

$$\text{A} + \text{B} \longrightarrow \text{products}$$

the rate of product formation depends on how frequently A and B collide, which in turn depends on the concentrations of A and B. Thus, we can express the rate as

$$\text{rate} = k[\text{A}][\text{B}]$$

Therefore, this is a second-order reaction. Similarly, for a bimolecular elementary reaction of the type

$$\text{A} + \text{A} \longrightarrow \text{products}$$

or

$$2\text{A} \longrightarrow \text{products}$$

the rate becomes

$$\text{rate} = k[\text{A}]^2$$

Student Annotation: It is important to remember that this is not the case in general. It only applies to elementary reactions—and whether or not a reaction is elementary must be determined experimentally.

which is also a second-order reaction. The preceding examples show that the reaction order for each reactant in an elementary reaction is equal to its stoichiometric coefficient in the chemical equation for that step. In general, we cannot tell just by looking at the balanced equation whether the reaction occurs as shown or in a series of steps. This determination must be made using data obtained experimentally.

Rate-Determining Step

In a reaction mechanism consisting of more than one elementary step, the rate law for the overall process is given by the ***rate-determining step,*** which is the *slowest* step in the sequence. An analogy for a process in which there is a rate-determining step is the amount of time required to buy stamps at the post office when there is a long line of customers. The process consists of several steps: waiting in line, requesting the stamps, receiving the stamps, and paying for the stamps. At a time when the line is very long, the amount of time spent waiting in line (step 1) largely determines how much time the overall process takes.

To study reaction mechanisms, we first do a series of experiments to establish initial rates at various reactant concentrations. We then analyze the data to determine the rate constant and overall order of the reaction, and we write the rate law. Finally, we propose a plausible mechanism for the reaction in terms of logical elementary steps. The steps of the proposed mechanism must satisfy two requirements:

1. The sum of the elementary reactions must be the overall balanced equation for the reaction.
2. The rate-determining step must have the same rate law as that determined from the experimental data.

Let's consider the gas-phase reaction of hydrogen with iodine monochloride to form hydrogen chloride and iodine.

$$\text{H}_2 + 2\text{ICl} \longrightarrow 2\text{HCl} + \text{I}_2$$

The experimentally determined rate law for this reaction is rate = $k[\text{H}_2][\text{ICl}]$. Here are four different proposed mechanisms.

Mechanism 1

Step 1: $\text{ICl} + \text{ICl} \longrightarrow \text{I}_2 + \text{Cl}_2$ (slow)
Step 2: $\text{Cl}_2 + \text{H}_2 \longrightarrow 2\text{HCl}$

The steps in mechanism 1 sum to the correct overall reaction:

$$\text{ICl} + \text{ICl} \longrightarrow \text{I}_2 + \cancel{\text{Cl}_2} \text{ (slow)}$$
$$\cancel{\text{Cl}_2} + \text{H}_2 \longrightarrow 2\text{HCl}$$
$$\overline{\text{Sum: } \text{H}_2 + 2\text{ICl} \longrightarrow 2\text{HCl} + \text{I}_2}$$

However, the rate law of the rate-determining step is rate $= k[\text{ICl}]^2$. Therefore, mechanism 1 is not plausible. It meets the first requirement for a plausible mechanism, but it does not meet the second requirement.

Mechanism 2

Step 1: $\text{H}_2 + \text{ICl} \longrightarrow \text{HI} + \text{HCl}$ (slow)
Step 2: $\text{ICl} + \text{HCl} \longrightarrow \text{HI} + \text{Cl}_2$

The rate-determining step in mechanism 2 has the correct rate law:

$$\text{rate} = k[\text{H}_2][\text{HCl}]$$

However, the steps do not sum to the correct overall reaction:

$$\text{H}_2 + \text{ICl} \longrightarrow \text{HI} + \cancel{\text{HCl}} \text{ (slow)}$$
$$\text{ICl} + \cancel{\text{HCl}} \longrightarrow \text{HI} + \text{Cl}_2$$
$$\overline{\text{Sum: } \text{H}_2 + 2\text{ICl} \longrightarrow 2\text{HI} + \text{Cl}_2}$$

Therefore, mechanism 2 is not plausible. It meets the second requirement, but it does not meet the first requirement.

Mechanism 3

Step 1: $\text{H}_2 \longrightarrow 2\text{H}$ (slow)
Step 2: $\text{ICl} + \text{H} \longrightarrow \text{HCl} + \text{I}$
Step 3: $\text{H} + \text{I} \longrightarrow \text{HI}$

The rate law for the rate-determining step in mechanism 3 (rate $= k[\text{H}_2]$) is not correct. Furthermore, the steps do not sum to the correct overall reaction:

$$\text{H}_2 \longrightarrow 2\cancel{\text{H}} \text{ (slow)}$$
$$\text{ICl} + \cancel{\text{H}} \longrightarrow \text{HCl} + \cancel{\text{I}}$$
$$\cancel{\text{H}} + \cancel{\text{I}} \longrightarrow \text{HI}$$
$$\overline{\text{Sum: } \text{H}_2 + \text{ICl} \longrightarrow \text{HCl} + \text{HI}}$$

Therefore, mechanism 3 is not plausible. It meets neither requirement 1 nor requirement 2.

Mechanism 4

Step 1: $\text{H}_2 + \text{ICl} \longrightarrow \text{HCl} + \text{HI}$ (slow)
Step 2: $\text{HI} + \text{ICl} \longrightarrow \text{HCl} + \text{I}_2$

The rate-determining step in mechanism 4 has the correct rate law:

$$\text{rate} = k[\text{H}_2][\text{ICl}]$$

Furthermore, the steps in mechanism 4 sum to the correct overall reaction:

$$\text{H}_2 + \text{ICl} \longrightarrow \text{HCl} + \cancel{\text{HI}} \text{ (slow)}$$
$$\cancel{\text{HI}} + \text{ICl} \longrightarrow \text{HCl} + \text{I}_2$$
$$\overline{\text{Sum: } \text{H}_2 + 2\text{ICl} \longrightarrow 2\text{HCl} + \text{I}_2}$$

Therefore, mechanism 4 is plausible. It meets both requirements.

Figure 14.15 The decomposition of hydrogen peroxide is catalyzed by the addition of an iodide salt. Some of the iodide ions are oxidized to molecular iodine, which then reacts with iodide ions to form the brown triiodide ion (I_3^-).

The decomposition of hydrogen peroxide can be facilitated by iodide ions (Figure 14.15). The overall reaction is

$$2H_2O_2(aq) \longrightarrow 2H_2O(l) + O_2(g)$$

By experiment, we find the rate law to be

$$\text{rate} = k[H_2O_2][I^-]$$

Thus, the reaction is first order with respect to both H_2O_2 and I^-.

The decomposition of H_2O_2 is not an elementary reaction, because it does not occur in a single step. If it did, the reaction would be second order in H_2O_2 (as a result of the collision of two H_2O_2 molecules). What's more, the I^- ion, which is not even part of the overall equation, would not appear in the rate law expression. How can we reconcile these facts? First, we can account for the observed rate law by assuming that the reaction takes place in two separate elementary steps, each of which is bimolecular.

$$\textit{Step 1:} \quad H_2O_2 + I^- \xrightarrow{k_1} H_2O + IO^-$$
$$\textit{Step 2:} \quad H_2O_2 + IO^- \xrightarrow{k_2} H_2O + O_2 + I^-$$

If we further assume that step 1 is the rate-determining step, then the rate of the reaction can be determined from the first step alone:

$$\text{rate} = k_1[H_2O_2][I^-]$$

where $k_1 = k$. The IO^- ion is an intermediate because it is produced in the first step and consumed in the second step. It does not appear in the overall balanced equation. The I^- ion also does not appear in the overall equation, but it is consumed in the first step and then produced in the second step. In other words, it is present at the start of the reaction, and it is present at the end. The I^- ion is a *catalyst,* and its function is to *speed up* the reaction. Catalysts are discussed in greater detail in Section 14.8. Figure 14.16 shows the potential energy profile for a reaction like the decomposition of H_2O_2. The first step, which is the rate-determining step, has a larger activation energy than the second step. The intermediate, although stable enough to be observed, reacts quickly to form the products. Its existence is only fleeting.

Worked Example 14.11 lets you practice determining if a proposed reaction mechanism is plausible.

Worked Example 14.11

The gas-phase decomposition of nitrous oxide (N_2O) is believed to occur in two steps:

$$\text{Step 1:} \quad N_2O \xrightarrow{k_1} N_2 + O$$

$$\text{Step 2:} \quad N_2O + O \xrightarrow{k_2} N_2 + O_2$$

Experimentally the rate law is found to be rate $= k[N_2O]$. (a) Write the equation for the overall reaction. (b) Identify the intermediate(s). (c) Identify the rate-determining step.

Strategy Add the two equations, canceling identical terms on opposite sides of the arrow, to obtain the overall reaction. The canceled terms will be the intermediates if they were first generated and then consumed. Write rate laws for each elementary step; the one that matches the experimental rate law will be the rate-determining step.

Setup Intermediates are species that are generated in an earlier step and consumed in a later step. We can write rate laws for elementary reactions simply by using the stoichiometric coefficient for each species as its exponent in the rate law.

$$\text{Step 1:} \qquad N_2O \xrightarrow{k_1} N_2 + O \qquad \text{rate} = k[N_2O]$$

$$\text{Step 2:} \quad N_2O + O \xrightarrow{k_2} N_2 + O_2 \qquad \text{rate} = k[N_2O][O]$$

Solution

(a) $2N_2O \longrightarrow 2N_2 + O_2$

(b) O (atomic oxygen) is the intermediate.

(c) Step 1 is the rate-determining step because its rate law is the same as the experimental rate law: rate $= k[N_2O]$.

> **Think About It**
> A species that gets canceled when steps are added may be an intermediate or a catalyst. In this case, the canceled species is an intermediate because it was first generated and then consumed. A species that is first consumed and then generated, but doesn't appear in the overall equation, is a catalyst.

Practice Problem A The reaction between NO_2 and CO to produce NO and CO_2 is thought to occur in two steps:

$$\text{Step 1:} \quad NO_2 + NO_2 \xrightarrow{k_1} NO + NO_3$$

$$\text{Step 2:} \quad NO_3 + CO \xrightarrow{k_2} NO_2 + CO_2$$

The experimental rate law is rate $= k[NO_2]^2$. (a) Write the equation for the overall reaction. (b) Identify the intermediate(s). (c) Identify the rate-determining step.

Practice Problem B Propose a plausible mechanism for the reaction $A + 2B \longrightarrow C + D$ given that the rate law for the reaction is rate $= k[A][B]$.

Mechanisms with a Fast First Step

For first- and second-order reactions, it is reasonably straightforward to propose a plausible mechanism. We simply use the experimentally determined rate law to write the rate-determining step as the first step, and then write one or more additional steps such that the appropriate species will cancel to give the correct overall equation. Sometimes, however, we will encounter a reaction with an experimentally determined rate law that suggests an unlikely scenario. For example, consider the gaseous reaction of nitric oxide with chlorine to produce nitrosyl chloride,

$$2NO(g) + Cl_2(g) \longrightarrow 2NOCl(g)$$

for which the experimentally determined rate law $= k[NO]^2[Cl_2]$. Note that the exponents in the rate law are the same as the coefficients in the balanced equation—making this reaction *third order* overall. Although one possibility is that the reaction is an elementary process, this would require the simultaneous collision of three molecules. As we noted on page 581, such a termolecular reaction is unlikely. A more reasonable mechanism would be one in which a fast first step is followed by the slower, rate-determining step.

Step 1: $NO(g) + Cl_2(g) \xrightarrow{k_1} NOCl_2(g)$ (fast)
Step 2: $NOCl_2(g) + NO(g) \xrightarrow{k_2} 2NOCl(g)$ (slow)

However, when we write the overall rate law using the equation for the rate-determining step, as we have done previously, the resulting rate law

$$\text{rate} = k_2[NOCl_2][NO]$$

includes the concentration of an *intermediate* ($NOCl_2$). Although this rate law is correct for the proposed mechanism, in this form it does not enable us to determine the plausibility of the mechanism by comparison to the experimentally determined rate law. To do this, we must derive a rate law in which only *reactants* from the overall equation appear.

When the intermediate ($NOCl_2$) is not consumed by step 2 as fast as it is produced by step 1, its concentration builds up, causing step 1 to happen in *reverse*; that is, $NOCl_2$ reacts to produce NO and Cl_2. This results in the establishment of a dynamic equilibrium [◀◀ Section 9.1], where the forward and reverse of step 1 are occurring at the same rate. We denote this by changing the single reaction arrow in step 1 to equilibrium arrows:

$$NO(g) + Cl_2(g) \underset{k_{-1}}{\overset{k_1}{\rightleftharpoons}} NOCl_2(g)$$

We can write the rate laws for the forward and reverse of step 1, both elementary processes, as

$$\text{rate}_{\text{forward}} = k_1[NO][Cl_2] \qquad \text{and} \qquad \text{rate}_{\text{reverse}} = k_{-1}[NOCl_2]$$

where k_1 and k_{-1} are the individual rate constants for the forward and reverse processes, respectively. Because the two rates are equal, we can write

$$k_1[NO][Cl_2] = k_{-1}[NOCl_2]$$

Rearranging to solve for the concentration of $NOCl_2$ gives

$$\frac{k_1}{k_{-1}}[NO][Cl_2] = [NOCl_2]$$

When we substitute the result into the original rate law for the concentration of $NOCl_2$, we get

$$\text{rate} = k_2[NOCl_2][NO] = k_2\frac{k_1}{k_{-1}}[NO]^2[Cl_2]$$

which agrees with the experimentally determined rate law, rate $= k[NO]^2[Cl_2]$, where k is equal to $\frac{k_2k_1}{k_{-1}}$.

Worked Example 14.12 lets you practice relating the experimentally determined rate law to a reaction mechanism in which a fast first step is followed by a slower, rate-determining step.

Worked Example 14.12

Consider the gas-phase reaction of nitric oxide and oxygen that was described at the beginning of Section 14.5.

$$2NO(g) + O_2(g) \longrightarrow 2NO_2(g)$$

Show that the following mechanism is plausible. The experimentally determined rate law is rate = $k[NO]^2[O_2]$.

Step 1: $NO(g) + NO(g) \underset{k_{-1}}{\overset{k_1}{\rightleftharpoons}} N_2O_2(g)$ (fast)

Step 2: $N_2O_2(g) + O_2(g) \overset{k_2}{\longrightarrow} 2NO_2(g)$ (slow)

Strategy To establish the plausibility of a mechanism, we must compare the rate law of the rate-determining step to the experimentally determined rate law. In this case, the rate-determining step has an intermediate (N_2O_2) as one of its reactants, giving us a rate law of rate = $k_2[N_2O_2][O_2]$. Because we cannot compare this directly to the experimental rate law, we must solve for the intermediate concentration in terms of *reactant* concentrations.

Setup The first step is a rapidly established equilibrium. Both the forward and reverse of step 1 are elementary processes, which enables us to write their rate laws from the balanced equation.

$$rate_{forward} = k_1[NO]^2 \quad \text{and} \quad rate_{reverse} = k_{-1}[N_2O_2]$$

Solution Because at equilibrium the forward and reverse processes are occurring at the same rate, we can set their rates equal to each other and solve for the intermediate concentration.

$$k_1[NO]^2 = k_{-1}[N_2O_2]$$

$$[N_2O_2] = \frac{k_1[NO]^2}{k_{-1}}$$

Substituting the solution into the original rate law (rate = $k[N_2O_2][O_2]$) gives

$$rate = k_2 \frac{k_1[NO]^2}{k_{-1}}[O_2] = k[NO]^2[O_2] \quad \text{where } k = \frac{k_2 k_1}{k_{-1}}$$

Think About It
Not all reactions have a single rate-determining step. Analyzing the kinetics of reactions with two or more comparably slow steps is beyond the scope of this book.

Practice Problem A Show that the following mechanism is consistent with the experimentally determined rate law of rate = $k[NO]^2[Br_2]$ for the reaction of nitric oxide and bromine: $2NO(g) + Br_2(g) \longrightarrow 2NOBr(g)$.

Step 1: $NO(g) + Br_2(g) \underset{k_{-1}}{\overset{k_1}{\rightleftharpoons}} NOBr_2(g)$ (fast)

Step 2: $NOBr_2(g) + NO(g) \overset{k_2}{\longrightarrow} 2NOBr(g)$ (slow)

Practice Problem B The reaction $H_2(g) + I_2(g) \longrightarrow 2HI(g)$ proceeds via a two-step mechanism in which the rate law for the rate-determining step is rate = $k[H_2][I]^2$. Write the mechanism and rewrite the rate law using only reactant concentrations.

Experimental Support for Reaction Mechanisms

When you propose a mechanism based on experimental rate data, and your mechanism satisfies the two requirements listed on page 582, you can say that the proposed mechanism is *plausible*—not that it is necessarily *correct*. It is not possible to prove that a mechanism is correct using rate data alone. To determine whether or not a proposed reaction mechanism is actually correct, we must conduct other experiments. In the case of hydrogen peroxide decomposition, we might try to detect the presence of the IO^- ions. If we can detect them, it will support the proposed mechanism.

$$H_2(g) + I_2(g) \longrightarrow 2HI(g)$$

rate $= k[H_2][I_2]$

Proposed mechanism

Step 1: $I_2 \underset{k_{-1}}{\overset{k_1}{\rightleftharpoons}} 2I$

Step 2: $H_2 + 2I \xrightarrow{k_2} 2HI$

Similarly, for the reaction of hydrogen and iodine to form hydrogen iodide, detection of iodine atoms would lend support to the proposed two-step mechanism shown in the margin. For example, I_2 dissociates into atoms when it is irradiated with visible light. Thus, we might predict that the formation of HI from H_2 and I_2 would speed up as the intensity of light is increased—because that would increase the concentration of I atoms. Indeed, this is just what is observed.

In one case, chemists wanted to know which C—O bond was broken in the reaction between methyl acetate and water to better understand the reaction

$$CH_3 \overset{\overset{O}{\|}}{C}-O-CH_3 \ + \ H_2O \longrightarrow CH_3-\overset{\overset{O}{\|}}{C}-OH \ + \ CH_3OH$$

The two possibilities of bond breaking are

$$CH_3-\overset{\overset{O}{\|}}{C}\text{-}\!\downarrow\text{-}O-CH_3 \quad \text{and} \quad CH_3-\overset{\overset{O}{\|}}{C}-O\text{-}\!\downarrow\text{-}CH_3$$
$$\text{(a)} \qquad\qquad\qquad\qquad \text{(b)}$$

To distinguish between schemes (a) and (b), chemists used water containing the oxygen-18 isotope instead of ordinary water, which contains the oxygen-16 isotope. When the ^{18}O water was used, only the acetic acid formed contained ^{18}O:

$$CH_3-\overset{\overset{O}{\|}}{C}-^{18}O-H$$

Thus, the reaction must have occurred via bond-breaking scheme (a), because the product formed via scheme (b) would have retained both of its original oxygen atoms and would contain no ^{18}O.

Another example is photosynthesis, the process by which green plants produce glucose from carbon dioxide and water:

$$6CO_2 + 6H_2O \longrightarrow C_6H_{12}O_6 + 6O_2$$

A question that arose early in the studies of photosynthesis was whether the molecular oxygen produced came from the water, the carbon dioxide, or both. By using water containing only the oxygen-18 isotope, it was concluded that all the oxygen produced by photosynthesis came from the water and none came from the carbon dioxide, because the O_2 produced contained only ^{18}O.

These examples illustrate how creative chemists must be in order to study reaction mechanisms.

SECTION 14.7 REVIEW

Reaction Mechanisms

Use the following information to answer questions 14.7.1 to 14.7.3: For the reaction

$$A + B \longrightarrow C + D$$

the experimental rate law is rate $= k[B]^2$.

14.7.1 What is the order of the reaction with respect to A and B, respectively?

14.7.2 What is the overall order of the reaction?

14.7.3 Show how the following mechanism is plausible for this reaction.

Step 1: $B + B \longrightarrow C + E$ (slow)

Step 2: $E + A \longrightarrow D + B$ (fast)

14.7.4 A plausible mechanism for the reaction

$$H_2 + 2IBr \longrightarrow I_2 + 2HBr$$

is the following:

Step 1: $H_2 + IBr \xrightarrow{k_1} HI + HBr$ (slow)

Step 2: $HI + IBr \xrightarrow{k_2} I_2 + HBr$ (fast)

What is the rate law that will be determined experimentally?

14.8 CATALYSIS

Multi 14.2
Catalysis

Recall from Section 14.7 that the reaction rate for the decomposition of hydrogen peroxide depends on the concentration of iodide ions, even though I^- does not appear in the overall equation. Instead, I^- acts as a catalyst for the reaction. A *catalyst* is a substance that increases the rate of a chemical reaction without itself being consumed. The catalyst may react to form an intermediate, but it is regenerated in a subsequent step of the reaction.

Molecular oxygen is prepared in the laboratory by heating potassium chlorate. The reaction is

$$2KClO_3(s) \longrightarrow 2KCl(s) + 3O_2(g)$$

However, this thermal decomposition process is very slow in the absence of a catalyst. The rate of decomposition can be increased dramatically by adding a small amount of manganese(IV) dioxide (MnO_2), a black powdery substance. All the MnO_2 can be recovered at the end of the reaction, just as all the I^- ions remain following the decomposition of H_2O_2.

A catalyst speeds up a reaction by providing a set of elementary steps with more favorable kinetics than those that exist in its absence. From Equation 14.8, we know that the rate constant k (and hence the rate) of a reaction depends on the frequency factor (A) and the activation energy (E_a)—the larger the value of A (or the smaller the value of E_a), the greater the rate. In many cases, a catalyst increases the rate by lowering the activation energy for the reaction.

Let's assume that the following reaction has a certain rate constant k and an activation energy E_a.

$$A + B \xrightarrow{\ k\ } C + D$$

In the presence of a catalyst, however, the rate constant is k_c, called the *catalytic rate constant*.

By the definition of a catalyst,

$$\text{rate}_{catalyzed} > \text{rate}_{uncatalyzed}$$

Figure 14.17 shows the potential energy profiles for both reactions. The total energies of the reactants (A and B) and those of the products (C and D) are unaffected by the catalyst; the only difference between the two is a lowering of the activation energy from E_a to E_a'. Because the activation energy for the reverse reaction is also lowered, a catalyst enhances the rates of the forward and reverse reactions equally.

There are three general types of catalysis, depending on the nature of the rate-increasing substance: heterogeneous catalysis, homogeneous catalysis, and enzyme catalysis.

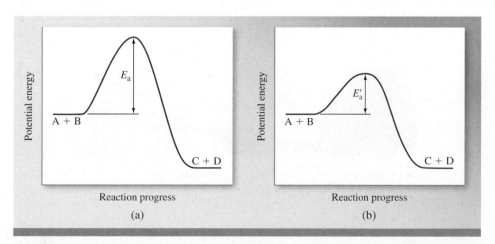

Figure 14.17 Comparison of the activation energy barriers of (a) an uncatalyzed reaction and (b) the same reaction with a catalyst. A catalyst lowers the energy barrier but does not affect the energies of the reactants or products. Although the reactants and products are the same in both cases, the reaction mechanisms and rate laws are different in (a) and (b).

Heterogeneous Catalysis

In *heterogeneous catalysis,* the reactants and the catalyst are in different phases. The catalyst is usually a solid, and the reactants are either gases or liquids. Heterogeneous catalysis is by far the most important type of catalysis in industrial chemistry, especially in the synthesis of many important chemicals. Heterogeneous catalysis is also used in the catalytic converters in automobiles.

At high temperatures inside a car's engine, nitrogen and oxygen gases react to form nitric oxide:

$$N_2(g) + O_2(g) \longrightarrow 2NO(g)$$

When released into the atmosphere, NO rapidly combines with O_2 to form NO_2. Nitrogen dioxide and other gases emitted by automobiles, such as carbon monoxide (CO) and various unburned hydrocarbons, make automobile exhaust a major source of air pollution.

Most new cars are equipped with catalytic converters [Figure 14.18(a)]. An efficient catalytic converter serves two purposes: It oxidizes CO and unburned hydrocarbons to CO_2 and H_2O, and it converts NO and NO_2 to N_2 and O_2. Hot exhaust gases into which air has been injected are passed through the first chamber of one converter to accelerate the complete burning of hydrocarbons and to decrease CO emissions. Because high temperatures increase NO production, however, a second chamber containing a different catalyst (a transition metal or a transition metal oxide such as CuO or Cr_2O_3) and operating at a lower temperature is required to dissociate NO into N_2 and O_2 before the exhaust is discharged through the tailpipe [Figure 14.18(b)].

Homogeneous Catalysis

In *homogeneous catalysis* the reactants and the catalyst are dispersed in a single phase, usually liquid. Acid and base catalyses are the most important types of homogeneous catalysis in liquid solution. For example, the reaction of ethyl acetate with water to form acetic acid and ethanol normally occurs too slowly to be measured.

$$CH_3COOC_2H_5 + H_2O \longrightarrow CH_3COOH + C_2H_5OH$$

In the absence of the catalyst, the rate law is given by

$$\text{rate} = k[CH_3COOC_2H_5]$$

The reaction, however, can be catalyzed by an acid. Often a catalyst is shown above the arrow in a chemical equation:

$$CH_3COOC_2H_5 + H_2O \xrightarrow{\text{H}^+} CH_3COOH + C_2H_5OH$$

Figure 14.18 (a) A two-stage catalytic converter for an automobile. (b) In the second stage, NO molecules bind to the surface of the catalyst. The N atoms bond to each other and the O atoms bond to each other, producing N_2 and O_2, respectively.

In the presence of acid, the rate is faster and the rate law is given by

$$\text{rate} = k_c[\text{CH}_3\text{COOC}_2\text{H}_5][\text{H}^+]$$

Because $k_c > k$ in magnitude, the rate is determined solely by the catalyzed portion of the reaction.

Homogeneous catalysis has several advantages over heterogeneous catalysis. For one thing, the reactions can often be carried out under atmospheric conditions, thus reducing production costs and minimizing the decomposition of products at high temperatures. In addition, homogeneous catalysts can be designed to function selectively for particular types of reactions, and homogeneous catalysts cost less than the precious metals (e.g., platinum and gold) used in heterogeneous catalysis.

Enzymes: Biological Catalysts

Of all the intricate processes that have evolved in living systems, none is more striking or more essential than enzyme catalysis. **Enzymes** are *biological* catalysts. The amazing fact about enzymes is that not only can they increase the rate of biochemical reactions by factors ranging from 10^6 to 10^{18}, but they are also highly specific. An enzyme acts only on certain reactant molecules, called *substrates,* while leaving the rest of the system unaffected. It has been estimated that an average living cell may contain some 3000 different enzymes, each of them catalyzing a specific reaction in which a substrate is converted into the appropriate product(s). Enzyme catalysis is usually homogeneous because the substrate and enzyme are present in aqueous solution.

An enzyme is typically a large protein molecule that contains one or more active sites where interactions with substrates take place. These sites are structurally compatible with specific substrate molecules, in much the same way that a key fits a particular lock. In fact, the notion of a rigid enzyme structure that binds only to molecules whose shape exactly matches that of the active site was the basis of an early theory of enzyme catalysis, the so-called lock-and-key theory developed by Emil Fischer[1] in 1894 (Figure 14.19). Fischer's hypothesis accounts for the specificity of enzymes, but it contradicts research evidence that a single enzyme binds to substrates of different sizes and shapes. Chemists now know that an enzyme molecule (or at least its active site) has a fair amount of structural flexibility and can modify its shape to accommodate more than one type of substrate. Figure 14.20 shows a molecular model of an enzyme in action.

The mathematical treatment of enzyme kinetics is quite complex, even when we know the basic steps involved in the reaction. A simplified scheme is given by the following elementary steps:

$$\text{E} + \text{S} \underset{k_{-1}}{\overset{k_1}{\rightleftharpoons}} \text{ES}$$

$$\text{ES} \xrightarrow{k_2} \text{E} + \text{P}$$

Substrate

+

Enzyme

Enzyme-substrate complex

Products

+

Enzyme

Figure 14.19 The lock-and-key model of an enzyme's specificity for substrate molecules.

[1]Emil Fischer (1852–1919), a German chemist, is regarded by many as the greatest organic chemist of the nineteenth century. Fischer made many significant contributions in the synthesis of sugars and other important molecules. He was awarded the Nobel Prize in Chemistry in 1902.

Figure 14.20 Left to right: The binding of glucose molecule (red) to hexokinase (an enzyme in the metabolic pathway). Note how the region at the active site closes around glucose after binding. Often, the geometries of both the substrate and the active site are altered to fit each other.

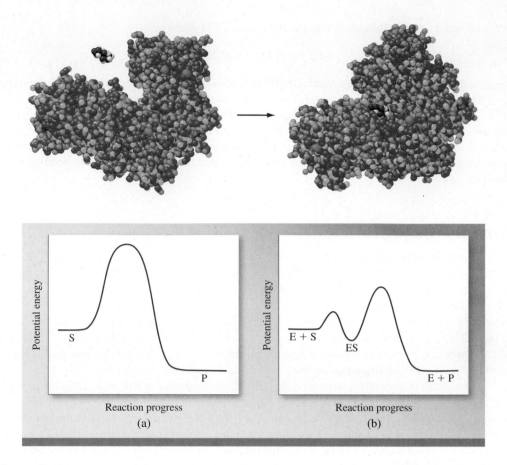

Figure 14.21 Comparison of (a) an uncatalyzed reaction and (b) the same reaction catalyzed by an enzyme. The plot in (b) assumes that the catalyzed reaction has a two-step mechanism, in which the second step (ES ⟶ E + P) is rate determining.

where E, S, and P represent enzyme, substrate, and product, respectively, and ES is the enzyme-substrate intermediate. It is often assumed that the formation of ES and its decomposition back to enzyme and substrate molecules occur rapidly and that the rate-determining step is the formation of product. Figure 14.21 shows the potential energy profile for the reaction.

In general, the rate of such a reaction is given by the equation

$$\text{rate} = \frac{\Delta[P]}{\Delta t}$$

$$= k[ES]$$

The concentration of the ES intermediate is itself proportional to the amount of the substrate present, and a plot of the rate versus the concentration of substrate typically yields a curve like that shown in Figure 14.22. Initially the rate rises rapidly with increasing substrate concentration.

Above a certain concentration, however, all the active sites are occupied, and the reaction becomes zeroth order in the substrate. In other words, the rate remains the same even though the substrate concentration increases. At and beyond this point, the rate of formation of product depends only on how fast the ES intermediate breaks down, not on the number of substrate molecules present.

Figure 14.22 Plot of the rate of product formation versus substrate concentration in an enzyme-catalyzed reaction.

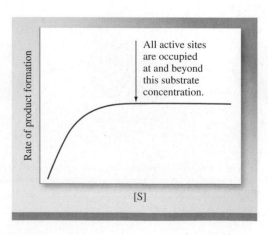

Learning Outcomes

- Describe the main factors that can increase the rate of a reaction.
- Describe the collision theory of chemical kinetics.
- Define effective collision and activation energy.
- Determine the average rate of a reaction given appropriate data.
- Determine the instantaneous rate of a reaction given a graph.
- Use the stoichiometry of a reaction to express the rate of a reaction in terms of a reactant or product.
- Define reaction order and provide examples of a zeroth-, first- and second-order reaction rate law.
- Produce the rate law of a reaction given experimental data.
- Predict the units of the rate constant k for a reaction.
- Determine the order of a reaction from its rate law.

- Determine the concentration of reactant using the integrated rate law for the reaction.
- Calculate the half-life $(t_{1/2})$ of a reaction.
- Calculate the amount of reactant remaining after a certain period of time given the half-life and order of the reaction.
- Determine the rate constant or activation energy of a reaction using the Arrhenius equation.
- Define reaction mechanism.
- Determine the rate law of a reaction given its rate-determining step.
- Understand the criteria that must be met for a proposed mechanism to be plausible.
- Define elementary reaction.
- Define catalyst and intermediate.
- Describe the major types of catalysis: heterogeneous, homogeneous, and enzymatic.

Chapter Summary

SECTION 14.1

- Reaction rate refers to the speed at which a chemical reaction occurs. Factors that influence reaction rate are reactant concentration, temperature, surface area, and catalysis.

SECTION 14.2

- *Collision theory* explains why the rate constant, and therefore the reaction rate, increases with increasing temperature.
- The *activation energy* (E_a) is the minimum energy that colliding molecules must possess in order for the collision to be effective.
- Reactions occur when molecules of sufficient energy (and appropriate orientation) collide. *Effective collisions* are those that result in the formation of an *activated complex,* also called a *transition state.* Only *effective* collisions can result in product formation.

SECTION 14.3

- The rate of a chemical reaction is the change in concentration of reactants or products over time. Rates may be expressed as an *average* rate over a given time interval or as an *instantaneous rate.*
- The *rate constant* (k) is a proportionality constant that relates the *rate of reaction* with the concentration(s) of reactant(s). The rate constant k for a given reaction changes only with temperature.

SECTION 14.4

- The *rate law* is an equation that expresses the relationship between rate and reactant concentration(s). In general, the rate law for the reaction of A and B is rate = $k[A]^x[B]^y$.

- The *reaction order* is the power to which the concentration of a given reactant is raised in the rate law equation. The overall reaction order is the sum of the powers to which reactant concentrations are raised in the rate law.
- The *initial rate* is the instantaneous rate of reaction when the reactant concentrations are *starting* concentrations.
- The rate law and reaction order must be determined by comparing changes in the initial rate with changes in starting reactant concentrations. In general, the rate law cannot be determined solely from the balanced equation.

SECTION 14.5

- The *integrated rate law* can be used to determine reactant concentrations after a specified period of time. It can also be used to determine how long it will take to reach a specified reactant concentration.
- The rate of a *first-order reaction* is proportional to the concentration of a single reactant. The rate of a *second-order reaction* is proportional to the product of two reactant concentrations ($[A][B]$), or on the concentration of a single reactant squared ($[A]^2$ or $[B]^2$). The rate of a *zeroth-order reaction* does not depend on reactant concentration.
- The *half-life* $(t_{1/2})$ of a reaction is the time it takes for half of a reactant to be consumed. The half-life is *constant* for first-order reactions, and it can be used to determine the rate constant of the reaction.

SECTION 14.6

• The relationship between temperature and the rate constant is expressed by the *Arrhenius equation.*

SECTION 14.7

• A *reaction mechanism* may consist of a series of *steps,* called *elementary reactions.* Unlike rate laws in general, the rate law for an elementary reaction can be written from the balanced equation, using the stoichiometric coefficient for each reactant species as its exponent in the rate law.

• A species that is produced in one step of a reaction mechanism and subsequently consumed in another step is called an *intermediate.* A species that is first consumed and later regenerated is called a *catalyst.* Neither intermediates nor catalysts appear in the overall balanced equation.

• The rate law of each step in a reaction mechanism indicates the *molecularity* or overall *order* of the step. A *unimolecular* step is first order, involving just one molecule; a *bimolecular* step is second order, involving the collision of two molecules; and a *termolecular* step is third order, involving the collision of three molecules. Termolecular processes are relatively rare.

• If one step in a reaction is much slower than all the other steps, it is the *rate-determining step.* The rate-determining step has a rate law identical to the experimental rate law.

SECTION 14.8

• A *catalyst* speeds up a reaction, usually by lowering the value of the activation energy. *Catalysis* refers to the process by which a catalyst increases the reaction rate.

• Catalysis may be *heterogeneous,* in which the catalyst and reactants exist in different phases, or *homogeneous,* in which the catalyst and reactants exist in the same phase.

• *Enzymes* are biological catalysts with high specificity for the reactions that they catalyze.

Key Words

Activated complex, 552	Enzymes, 591	Intermediate, 581	Second-order reaction, 573
Activation energy (E_a), 551	First-order reaction, 568	Molecularity, 581	Termolecular, 581
Arrhenius equation, 576	Half-life ($t_{1/2}$), 571	Rate constant, 558	Transition state, 552
Bimolecular, 581	Heterogeneous catalysis, 590	Rate-determining step, 582	Unimolecular, 581
Catalyst, 589	Homogeneous catalysis, 590	Rate law, 563	Zeroth-order reaction, 575
Collision theory, 551	Initial rate, 563	Rate of reaction, 560	
Effective collision, 551	Instantaneous rate, 557	Reaction mechanism, 581	
Elementary reaction, 581	Integrated rate law, 568	Reaction order, 563	

Key Equations

14.1 $\quad \text{rate} = -\dfrac{1}{a}\dfrac{\Delta[A]}{\Delta t} = -\dfrac{1}{b}\dfrac{\Delta[B]}{\Delta t} = \dfrac{1}{c}\dfrac{\Delta[C]}{\Delta t} = \dfrac{1}{d}\dfrac{\Delta[D]}{\Delta t}$

14.2 $\quad \text{rate} = k[A]^x[B]^y$

14.3 $\quad \ln\dfrac{[A]_t}{[A]_0} = -kt$

14.4 $\quad \ln[A]_t = -kt + \ln[A]_0$

14.5 $\quad t_{1/2} = \dfrac{0.693}{k}$

14.6 $\quad \dfrac{1}{[A]_t} = kt + \dfrac{1}{[A]_0}$

14.7 $\quad t_{1/2} = \dfrac{1}{k[A]_0}$

14.8 $\quad k = Ae^{-E_a/RT}$

14.9 $\quad \ln k = \ln A - \dfrac{E_a}{RT}$

14.10 $\quad \ln k = \left(-\dfrac{E_a}{R}\right)\left(\dfrac{1}{T}\right) + \ln A$

14.11 $\quad \ln\dfrac{k_1}{k_2} = \dfrac{E_a}{R}\left(\dfrac{1}{T_2} - \dfrac{1}{T_1}\right)$

Questions and Problems

SECTION 14.2: COLLISION THEORY OF CHEMICAL REACTIONS

Visualizing Chemistry
Figure 14.4

VC 14.1 The rate of a reaction in which the reactant concentration is reduced and the temperature is increased will
(a) increase.
(b) decrease.
(c) It is not possible to determine the effect on rate without additional information.

VC 14.2 The rate of a reaction in which the reactant concentration is reduced and the temperature is reduced will
(a) increase.
(b) decrease.
(c) It is not possible to determine the effect on rate without additional information.

VC 14.3 The rate of a reaction in which the reactant concentration is increased and the temperature is increased will
(a) increase.
(b) decrease.
(c) It is not possible to determine the effect on rate without additional information.

VC 14.4 Increasing the temperature of a reaction increases
(a) the number of collisions between reactant molecules.
(b) the kinetic energy of colliding molecules.
(c) both the number of collisions between reactant molecules and the kinetic energy of colliding molecules.

Review Questions

14.1 Define *activation energy*. What role does activation energy play in chemical kinetics?

14.2 Sketch a potential energy versus reaction progress plot for the following reactions:
(a) $S(s) + O_2(g) \longrightarrow SO_2(g)$ $\Delta H° = -296$ kJ/mol
(b) $Cl_2(g) \longrightarrow Cl(g) + Cl(g)$ $\Delta H° = 243$ kJ/mol

14.3 The reaction $H + H_2 \longrightarrow H_2 + H$ has been studied for many years. Sketch a potential energy versus reaction progress diagram for this reaction.

SECTION 14.3: MEASURING REACTION PROGRESS AND EXPRESSING REACTION RATE

Review Questions

14.4 What is meant by the *rate* of a chemical reaction? What are the units of the rate of a reaction?

14.5 Distinguish between average rate and instantaneous rate. Which of the two rates gives us an unambiguous measurement of reaction rate? Why?

14.6 What are the advantages of measuring the initial rate of a reaction?

14.7 Identify two reactions that are very slow (take days or longer to complete) and two reactions that are very fast (reactions that are over in minutes or seconds).

Problems

14.8 Write the reaction rate expressions for the following reactions in terms of the disappearance of the reactants and the appearance of products:
(a) $2H_2(g) + O_2(g) \longrightarrow 2H_2O(g)$
(b) $4NH_3(g) + 5O_2(g) \longrightarrow 4NO(g) + 6H_2O(g)$

14.9 Write the reaction rate expressions for the following reactions in terms of the disappearance of the reactants and the appearance of products:
(a) $H_2(g) + I_2(g) \longrightarrow 2HI(g)$
(b) $5Br^-(aq) + BrO_3^-(aq) + 6H^+(aq) \longrightarrow$
$3Br_2(aq) + 3H_2O(l)$

14.10 Consider the reaction

$$N_2(g) + 3H_2(g) \longrightarrow 2NH_3(g)$$

Suppose that at a particular moment during the reaction molecular hydrogen is reacting at the rate of 0.082 M/s. (a) At what rate is ammonia being formed? (b) At what rate is molecular nitrogen reacting?

14.11 Consider the reaction

$$2NO(g) + O_2(g) \longrightarrow 2NO_2(g)$$

Suppose that at a particular moment during the reaction nitric oxide (NO) is reacting at the rate of 0.066 M/s. (a) At what rate is NO_2 being formed? (b) At what rate is molecular oxygen reacting?

SECTION 14.4: DEPENDENCE OF REACTION RATE ON REACTANT CONCENTRATION

Review Questions

14.12 Explain what is meant by the *rate law* of a reaction.

14.13 Explain what is meant by the *order* of a reaction.

14.14 What are the units for the rate constants of first-order and second-order reactions?

14.15 Consider the zeroth-order reaction: A $\longrightarrow$ product. (a) Write the rate law for the reaction. (b) What are the units for the rate constant? (c) Plot the rate of the reaction versus [A].

14.16 The rate constant of a first-order reaction is 66 s^{-1}. What is the rate constant in units of minutes?

14.17 On which of the following properties does the rate constant of a reaction depend: (a) reactant concentrations, (b) nature of reactants, (c) temperature?

Problems

14.18 Use the data in Table 14.2 to calculate the rate of the reaction at the time when $[F_2] = 0.020$ M and $[ClO_2] = 0.035$ M.

14.19 The rate law for the reaction

$$NH_4^+(aq) + NO_2^-(aq) \longrightarrow N_2(g) + 2H_2O(l)$$

is given by rate = $k[NH_4^+][NO_2^-]$. At 25°C, the rate constant is $3.0 \times 10^{-4}/M \cdot s$. Calculate the rate of the reaction at this temperature if $[NH_4^+] = 0.36\ M$ and $[NO_2^-] = 0.075\ M$.

14.20 Consider the reaction

$$X + Y \longrightarrow Z$$

From the following data, obtained at 360 K, (a) determine the order of the reaction, and (b) determine the initial rate of disappearance of X when the concentration of X is 0.30 M and that of Y is 0.40 M.

Initial rate of disappearance of X (M/s)	[X] (M)	[Y] (M)
0.053	0.10	0.50
0.127	0.20	0.30
1.02	0.40	0.60
0.254	0.20	0.60
0.509	0.40	0.30

14.21 Consider the reaction

$$A + B \longrightarrow products$$

From the following data obtained at a certain temperature, determine the order of the reaction and calculate the rate constant.

[A] (M)	[B] (M)	Rate (M/s)
1.50	1.50	3.20×10^{-1}
1.50	2.50	3.20×10^{-1}
3.00	1.50	6.40×10^{-1}

14.22 Consider the reaction

$$A \longrightarrow B$$

The rate of the reaction is $1.6 \times 10^{-2}\ M$/s when the concentration of A is 0.15 M. Calculate the rate constant if the reaction is (a) first order in A and (b) second order in A.

14.23 Determine the overall orders of the reactions to which the following rate laws apply: (a) rate = $k\ [NO_2]^2$, (b) rate = k, (c) rate = $k\ [H_2]^2[Br_2]^{1/2}$, (d) rate = $k\ [NO]^2[O_2]$.

14.24 The following gas-phase reaction was studied at 290°C by observing the change in pressure as a function of time in a constant-volume vessel:

$$ClCO_2CCl_3(g) \longrightarrow 2COCl_2(g)$$

Determine the order of the reaction and the rate constant based on the following data.

Time (s)	P (mmHg)
0	15.76
181	18.88
513	22.79
1164	27.08

where P is the total pressure.

14.25 Cyclobutane decomposes to ethylene according to the equation

$$C_4H_8(g) \longrightarrow 2C_2H_4(g)$$

Determine the order of the reaction and the rate constant based on the following pressures, which were recorded when the reaction was carried out at 430°C in a constant-volume vessel.

Time (s)	$P_{C_4H_8}$ (mmHg)
0	400
2,000	316
4,000	248
6,000	196
8,000	155
10,000	122

SECTION 14.5: DEPENDENCE OF REACTANT CONCENTRATION ON TIME

Review Questions

14.26 Write an equation relating the concentration of a reactant A at $t = 0$ to that at $t = t$ for a first-order reaction. Define all the terms, and give their units. Do the same for a second-order reaction.

14.27 Define *half-life*. Write the equation relating the half-life of a first-order reaction to the rate constant.

14.28 Write the equations relating the half-life of a second-order reaction to the rate constant. How does it differ from the equation for a first-order reaction?

14.29 For a first-order reaction, how long will it take for the concentration of reactant to fall to one-eighth its original value? Express your answer in terms of the half-life ($t_{1/2}$) and in terms of the rate constant k.

Problems

14.30 The thermal decomposition of phosphine (PH_3) into phosphorus and molecular hydrogen is a first-order reaction:

$$4PH_3(g) \longrightarrow P_4(g) + 6H_2(g)$$

The half-life of the reaction is 35.0 s at 680°C. Calculate (a) the first-order rate constant for the reaction and (b) the time required for 95 percent of the phosphine to decompose.

14.31 What is the half-life of a compound if 75 percent of a given sample of the compound decomposes in 60 min? Assume first-order kinetics.

14.32 The rate constant for the second-order reaction

$$2NO_2(g) \longrightarrow 2NO(g) + O_2(g)$$

is 0.54/$M \cdot s$ at 300°C. How long (in seconds) would it take for the concentration of NO_2 to decrease from 0.65 M to 0.18 M?

14.33 The rate constant for the second-order reaction

$$2NOBr(g) \longrightarrow 2NO(g) + Br_2(g)$$

is 0.80/$M \cdot$ s at 10°C. (a) Starting with a concentration of 0.086 M, calculate the concentration of NOBr after 22 s. (b) Calculate the half-lives when $[NOBr]_0 = 0.072$ M and $[NOBr]_0 = 0.054$ M.

14.34 Consider the first-order reaction X $\longrightarrow$ Y shown here. (a) What is the half-life of the reaction? (b) Draw pictures showing the number of X (red) and Y (blue) molecules at 20 s and at 30 s.

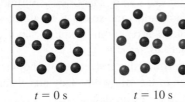

$t = 0$ s $\qquad$ $t = 10$ s

14.35 The reaction A $\longrightarrow$ B shown here follows first-order kinetics. Initially different amounts of A molecules are placed in three containers of equal volume at the same temperature. (a) What are the relative rates of the reaction in these three containers? (b) How would the relative rates be affected if the volume of each container were doubled? (c) What are the relative half-lives of the reactions in (i) to (iii)?

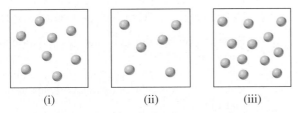

(i) $\qquad$ (ii) $\qquad$ (iii)

14.36 Consider the first-order reaction A $\longrightarrow$ B in which A molecules (blue spheres) are converted to B molecules (yellow spheres). The figure shows the progress of the reaction after 10 s.

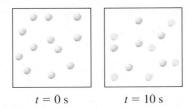

$t = 0$ s $\qquad$ $t = 10$ s

Which figure represents the numbers of molecules present after 20 s for the reaction above?

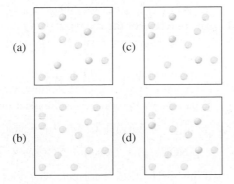

(a) $\qquad$ (c)

(b) $\qquad$ (d)

14.37 Considering the plots shown, which corresponds to a zeroth-order reaction, which corresponds to a first-order reaction, and which corresponds to a second-order reaction?

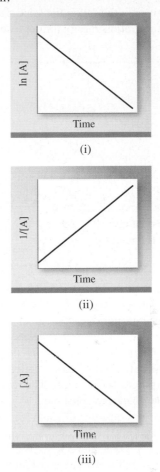

(i)

(ii)

(iii)

SECTION 14.6: DEPENDENCE OF REACTION RATE ON TEMPERATURE

Review Questions

14.38 Write the Arrhenius equation, and define all terms.

14.39 Use the Arrhenius equation to show why the rate constant of a reaction (a) decreases with increasing activation energy and (b) increases with increasing temperature.

14.40 The burning of methane in oxygen is a highly exothermic reaction. Yet a mixture of methane and oxygen gas can be kept indefinitely without any apparent change. Explain.

14.41 Over the range of about ±3°C from normal body temperature, the metabolic rate, M_T, is given by $M_T = M_{37}(1.1)^{\Delta T}$, where M_{37} is the normal rate (at 37°C) and ΔT is the change in T. Discuss this equation in terms of a possible molecular interpretation.

Problems

14.42 Given the same reactant concentrations, the reaction

$$CO(g) + Cl_2(g) \longrightarrow COCl_2(g)$$

at 250°C is 1.50×10^3 times as fast as the same reaction at 150°C. Calculate the activation energy for this reaction. Assume that the frequency factor is constant.

14.43 Variation of the rate constant with temperature for the first-order reaction

$$2N_2O_5(g) \longrightarrow 2N_2O_4(g) + O_2(g)$$

is given in the following table. Determine graphically the activation energy for the reaction.

T (K)	k (s^{-1})
298	1.74×10^{-5}
308	6.61×10^{-5}
318	2.51×10^{-4}
328	7.59×10^{-4}
338	2.40×10^{-3}

14.44 The rate constant of a first-order reaction is 4.60×10^{-4} s^{-1} at 350°C. If the activation energy is 104 kJ/mol, calculate the temperature at which its rate constant is 8.80×10^{-4} s^{-1}.

14.45 For the reaction

$$NO(g) + O_3(g) \longrightarrow NO_2(g) + O_2(g)$$

the frequency factor A is 8.7×10^{12} s^{-1} and the activation energy is 63 kJ/mol. What is the rate constant for the reaction at 75°C?

14.46 The rate at which tree crickets chirp is 2.0×10^2 per minute at 27°C but only 39.6 per minute at 5°C. From these data, calculate the "activation energy" for the chirping process. (*Hint:* The ratio of rates is equal to the ratio of rate constants.)

14.47 The rate constants of some reactions double with every 10° rise in temperature. Assume that a reaction takes place at 295 K and 305 K. What must the activation energy be for the rate constant to double as described?

14.48 The activation energy for the denaturation of a protein is 396 kJ/mol. At what temperature will the rate of denaturation be 20 percent greater than its rate at 25°C?

14.49 The rate of bacterial hydrolysis of fish muscle is twice as great at 2.2°C as at −1.1°C. Estimate an E_a value for this reaction. Is there any relation to the problem of storing fish for food?

14.50 A chemist orders three different samples of zinc metal from a chemical supply company to try in an experiment where zinc metal is allowed to react with hydrochloric acid. The three types of zinc ordered are (a) zinc dust (particle size with a diameter of 0.044 mm), (b) zinc shot (particle size with a diameter of 1.40 mm), and (c) zinc powder (particle size with a diameter of 0.422 mm). Rank in order of increasing rate of reaction the various zinc samples used in the experiment.

14.51 The directions for using Alka-Seltzer call for dropping two tablets into six ounces of lukewarm water, and drinking the mixture once the effervescence stops. Compare the time required for the effervescence to stop for the following scenarios: (a) Two whole tablets are dropped into lukewarm water, (b) two tablets each broken into two pieces are dropped into lukewarm water, (c) two whole tablets are dropped into cold water, (d) two crushed tablets are dropped into lukewarm water, (e) two crushed tablets are dropped into very warm water.

SECTION 14.7:   REACTION MECHANISMS

Review Questions

14.52 What do we mean by the *mechanism* of a reaction?

14.53 What is an elementary step? What is the molecularity of a reaction?

14.54 Classify the following elementary reactions as unimolecular, bimolecular, or termolecular:
(a) $2NO + Br_2 \longrightarrow 2NOBr$
(b) $CH_3NC \longrightarrow CH_3CN$
(c) $SO + O_2 \longrightarrow SO_2 + O$

14.55 Reactions can be classified as unimolecular, bimolecular, and so on. Why are there no zero-molecular reactions? Explain why termolecular reactions are rare.

14.56 Determine the molecularity, and write the rate law for each of the following elementary steps:
(a) $X \longrightarrow$ products
(b) $X + Y \longrightarrow$ products
(c) $X + Y + Z \longrightarrow$ products
(d) $X + X \longrightarrow$ products
(e) $X + 2Y \longrightarrow$ products

14.57 What is the rate-determining step of a reaction? Give an everyday analogy to illustrate the meaning of *rate determining*.

14.58 The equation for the combustion of ethane (C_2H_6) is

$$2C_2H_6(g) + 7O_2(g) \longrightarrow 4CO_2(g) + 6H_2O(l)$$

Explain why it is unlikely that this equation also represents the elementary step for the reaction.

14.59 Specify which of the following species cannot be isolated in a reaction: activated complex, product, intermediate.

Problems

14.60 Classify each of the following elementary steps as unimolecular, bimolecular, or termolecular.

14.61 The rate law for the reaction

$$2NO(g) + Cl_2(g) \longrightarrow 2NOCl(g)$$

is given by rate = $k[NO][Cl_2]$. (a) What is the order of the reaction? (b) A mechanism involving the following steps has been proposed for the reaction:

$$NO(g) + Cl_2(g) \longrightarrow NOCl_2(g)$$

$$NOCl_2(g) + NO(g) + NO(g) \longrightarrow 2NOCl(g)$$

If this mechanism is correct, what does it imply about the relative rates of these two steps?

14.62 For the reaction $X_2 + Y + Z \longrightarrow XY + XZ$, it is found that doubling the concentration of X_2 doubles the reaction rate, tripling the concentration of Y triples the rate, and doubling the concentration of Z has no effect. (a) What is the rate law for this reaction? (b) Why is it that the change in the concentration of Z has no effect on the rate? (c) Suggest a mechanism for the reaction that is consistent with the rate law.

14.63 The rate law for the reaction

$$2H_2(g) + 2NO(g) \longrightarrow N_2(g) + 2H_2O(g)$$

is rate $= k[H_2][NO]^2$. Which of the following mechanisms can be ruled out on the basis of the observed rate expression?

Mechanism I
$$H_2 + NO \longrightarrow H_2O + N \quad \text{(slow)}$$
$$N + NO \longrightarrow N_2 + O \quad \text{(fast)}$$
$$O + H_2 \longrightarrow H_2O \quad \text{(fast)}$$

Mechanism II
$$H_2 + 2NO \longrightarrow N_2O + H_2O \quad \text{(slow)}$$
$$N_2O + H_2 \longrightarrow N_2 + H_2O \quad \text{(fast)}$$

Mechanism III
$$2NO \rightleftharpoons N_2O_2 \quad \text{(fast equilibrium)}$$
$$N_2O_2 + H_2 \longrightarrow N_2O + H_2O \quad \text{(slow)}$$
$$N_2O + H_2 \longrightarrow N_2 + H_2O \quad \text{(fast)}$$

14.64 The rate law for the decomposition of ozone to molecular oxygen

$$2O_3(g) \longrightarrow 3O_2(g)$$

is

$$\text{rate} = k\frac{[O_3]^2}{[O_2]}$$

The mechanism proposed for this process is

$$O_3 \underset{k_{-1}}{\overset{k_1}{\rightleftharpoons}} O + O_2$$

$$O + O_3 \overset{k_2}{\longrightarrow} 2O_2$$

Derive the rate law from these elementary steps. Clearly state the assumptions you use in the derivation. Explain why the rate decreases with increasing O_2 concentration.

SECTION 14.8: CATALYSIS

Review Questions

14.65 How does a catalyst increase the rate of a reaction?

14.66 What are the characteristics of a catalyst?

14.67 Distinguish between homogeneous catalysis and heterogeneous catalysis.

14.68 Are enzyme-catalyzed reactions examples of homogeneous or heterogeneous catalysis? Explain.

14.69 The concentrations of enzymes in cells are usually quite small. What is the biological significance of this fact?

14.70 When fruits such as apples and pears are cut, the exposed areas begin to turn brown. This is the result of an enzyme-catalyzed reaction. Often the browning can be prevented or slowed by adding a few drops of lemon juice. What is the chemical basis of this treatment?

14.71 The first-order rate constant for the dehydration of carbonic acid

$$H_2CO_3 \longrightarrow CO_2 + H_2O$$

is about $1 \times 10^2 \text{ s}^{-1}$. In view of this rather high rate constant, explain why it is necessary to have the enzyme carbonic anhydrase to enhance the rate of dehydration in the lungs.

Problems

14.72 Consider the following mechanism for the enzyme-catalyzed reaction:

$$E + S \underset{k_{-1}}{\overset{k_1}{\rightleftharpoons}} ES \quad \text{(fast equilibrium)}$$

$$ES \overset{k_2}{\longrightarrow} E + P \quad \text{(slow)}$$

Derive an expression for the rate law of the reaction in terms of the concentrations of E and S. (*Hint:* To solve for [ES], make use of the fact that, at equilibrium, the rate of the forward reaction is equal to the rate of the reverse reaction.)

14.73 Most reactions, including enzyme-catalyzed reactions, proceed faster at higher temperatures. However, for a given enzyme, the rate drops off abruptly at a certain temperature. Account for this behavior.

ADDITIONAL PROBLEMS

14.74 Suggest experimental means by which the rates of the following reactions could be followed:
(a) $CaCO_3(s) \longrightarrow CaO(s) + CO_2(g)$
(b) $Cl_2(g) + 2Br^-(aq) \longrightarrow Br_2(aq) + 2Cl^-(aq)$
(c) $C_2H_6(g) \longrightarrow C_2H_4(g) + H_2(g)$
(d) $C_2H_5I(g) + H_2O(l) \longrightarrow$
$$C_2H_5OH(aq) + H^+(aq) + I^-(aq)$$

14.75 "The rate constant for the reaction

$$NO_2(g) + CO(g) \longrightarrow NO(g) + CO_2(g)$$

is $1.64 \times 10^{-6}\,/M \cdot \text{s}$." What is incomplete about this statement?

14.76 In a certain industrial process involving a heterogeneous catalyst, the volume of the catalyst (in the shape of a sphere) is 10.0 cm^3. Calculate the surface area of the catalyst. If the sphere is broken down into eight smaller spheres, each having a volume of 1.25 cm^3, what is the total surface area of the spheres? Which of the two geometric configurations of the catalyst is more effective? (The surface area of a sphere is $4\pi r^2$, where r is the radius of the sphere.) Based on your analysis here, explain why it is sometimes dangerous to work in grain elevators.

14.77 The following pictures represent the progress of the reaction A $\longrightarrow$ B where the red spheres represent A molecules and the green spheres represent B molecules. Calculate the rate constant of the reaction.

| $t = 0$ s | $t = 20$ s | $t = 40$ s |

14.78   The following pictures show the progress of the reaction $2A \longrightarrow A_2$. Determine whether the reaction is first order or second order, and calculate the rate constant.

| $t = 0$ min | $t = 15$ min | $t = 30$ min |

14.79   Explain why most metals used in catalysis are transition metals.

14.80   The following data were collected for the reaction between hydrogen and nitric oxide at 700°C:

$$2H_2(g) + 2NO(g) \longrightarrow 2H_2O(g) + N_2(g)$$

Experiment	[H₂] (M)	[NO] (M)	Initial rate (M/s)
1	0.010	0.025	2.4×10^{-6}
2	0.0050	0.025	1.2×10^{-6}
3	0.010	0.0125	0.60×10^{-6}

(a) Determine the order of the reaction. (b) Calculate the rate constant. (c) Suggest a plausible mechanism that is consistent with the rate law. (*Hint:* Assume that the oxygen atom is the intermediate.)

14.81   When methyl phosphate is heated in acid solution, it reacts with water:

$$CH_3OPO_3H_2 + H_2O \longrightarrow CH_3OH + H_3PO_4$$

If the reaction is carried out in water enriched with ^{18}O, the oxygen-18 isotope is found in the phosphoric acid product but not in the methanol. What does this tell us about the mechanism of the reaction?

14.82   The rate of the reaction

$$CH_3COOC_2H_5(aq) + H_2O(l) \longrightarrow$$
$$CH_3COOH(aq) + C_2H_5OH(aq)$$

shows first-order characteristics—that is, rate = $k[CH_3COOC_2H_5]$—even though this is a second-order reaction (first order in $CH_3COOC_2H_5$ and first order in H_2O). Explain.

14.83   List four factors that influence the rate of a reaction.

14.84   The reaction $2A + 3B \longrightarrow C$ is first order with respect to A and B. When the initial concentrations are $[A] = 1.6 \times 10^{-2} M$ and $[B] = 2.4 \times 10^{-3} M$, the rate is $4.1 \times 10^{-4} M/s$. Calculate the rate constant of the reaction.

14.85   The bromination of acetone is acid-catalyzed:

$$CH_3COCH_3 + Br_2 \xrightarrow[H^+]{\text{catalyst}} CH_3COCH_2Br + H^+ + Br^-$$

The rate of disappearance of bromine was measured for several different concentrations of acetone, bromine, and H^+ ions at a certain temperature:

	[CH₃COCH₃] (M)	[Br₂] (M)	[H⁺] (M)	Rate of disappearance of Br₂ (M/s)
(1)	0.30	0.050	0.050	5.7×10^{-5}
(2)	0.30	0.10	0.050	5.7×10^{-5}
(3)	0.30	0.050	0.10	1.2×10^{-4}
(4)	0.40	0.050	0.20	3.1×10^{-4}
(5)	0.40	0.050	0.050	7.6×10^{-5}

(a) What is the rate law for the reaction? (b) Determine the rate constant. (c) The following mechanism has been proposed for the reaction:

$$CH_3\overset{\overset{\displaystyle O}{\|}}{-C}-CH_3 + H_3O^+ \rightleftharpoons CH_3\overset{\overset{\displaystyle ^+OH}{\|}}{-C}-CH_3 + H_2O \quad \text{(fast equilibrium)}$$

$$CH_3\overset{\overset{\displaystyle ^+OH}{\|}}{-C}-CH_3 + H_2O \longrightarrow CH_3\overset{\overset{\displaystyle OH}{|}}{-C}=CH_2 + H_3O^+ \quad \text{(slow)}$$

$$CH_3\overset{\overset{\displaystyle OH}{|}}{-C}=CH_2 + Br_2 \longrightarrow CH_3\overset{\overset{\displaystyle O}{\|}}{-C}-CH_2Br + HBr \quad \text{(fast)}$$

Show that the rate law deduced from the mechanism is consistent with that shown in part (a).

14.86   The decomposition of N_2O to N_2 and O_2 is a first-order reaction. At 730°C, the half-life of the reaction is 3.58×10^3 min. If the initial pressure of N_2O is 2.10 atm at 730°C, calculate the total gas pressure after one half-life. Assume that the volume remains constant.

14.87   The reaction $S_2O_8^{2-} + 2I^- \longrightarrow 2SO_4^{2-} + I_2$ proceeds slowly in aqueous solution, but it can be catalyzed by the Fe^{3+} ion. Given that Fe^{3+} can oxidize I^- and Fe^{2+} can reduce $S_2O_8^{2-}$, write a plausible two-step mechanism for this reaction. Explain why the uncatalyzed reaction is slow.

14.88   What are the units of the rate constant for a third-order reaction?

14.89   The integrated rate law for the zeroth-order reaction $A \longrightarrow B$ is $[A]_t = [A]_0 - kt$. (a) Sketch the following plots: (i) rate versus $[A]_t$ and (ii) $[A]_t$ versus t. (b) Derive an expression for the half-life of the reaction. (c) Calculate the time in half-lives when the integrated rate law is no longer valid, that is, when $[A]_t = 0$.

14.90   A flask contains a mixture of compounds A and B. Both compounds decompose by first-order kinetics. The half-lives are 50.0 min for A and 18.0 min for B. If the concentrations of A and B are equal initially, how long will it take for the concentration of A to be four times that of B?

14.91   Referring to Worked Example 14.5, explain how you would measure the partial pressure of azomethane experimentally as a function of time.

14.92 The rate law for the reaction $2NO_2(g) \longrightarrow N_2O_4(g)$ is rate = $k[NO_2]^2$. Which of the following changes will change the value of k? (a) The pressure of NO_2 is doubled. (b) The reaction is run in an organic solvent. (c) The volume of the container is doubled. (d) The temperature is decreased. (e) A catalyst is added to the container.

14.93 The reaction of G_2 with E_2 to form 2EG is exothermic, and the reaction of G_2 with X_2 to form 2XG is endothermic. The activation energy of the exothermic reaction is greater than that of the endothermic reaction. Sketch the potential energy profile diagrams for these two reactions on the same graph.

14.94 In the nuclear industry, workers use a rule of thumb that the radioactivity from any sample will be relatively harmless after 10 half-lives. Calculate the fraction of a radioactive sample that remains after this time period. (*Hint:* Radioactive decays obey first-order kinetics.)

14.95 Briefly comment on the effect of a catalyst on each of the following: (a) activation energy, (b) reaction mechanism, (c) enthalpy of reaction, (d) rate of forward reaction, (e) rate of reverse reaction.

14.96 When 6 g of granulated Zn is added to a solution of 2 *M* HCl in a beaker at room temperature, hydrogen gas is generated. For each of the following changes (at constant volume of the acid), state whether the rate of hydrogen gas evolution will be increased, decreased, or unchanged: (a) 6 g of powdered Zn is used, (b) 4 g of granulated Zn is used, (c) 2 *M* acetic acid is used instead of 2 *M* HCl, (d) temperature is raised to 40°C.

14.97 Strictly speaking, the rate law derived for the reaction in Problem 14.80 applies only to certain concentrations of H_2. The general rate law for the reaction takes the form

$$\text{rate} = \frac{k_1[NO]^2[H_2]}{1 + k_2[H_2]}$$

where k_1 and k_2 are constants. Derive rate law expressions under the conditions of very high and very low hydrogen concentrations. Does the result from Problem 14.80 agree with one of the rate expressions here?

14.98 A certain first-order reaction is 35.5 percent complete in 4.90 min at 25°C. What is its rate constant?

14.99 The decomposition of dinitrogen pentoxide has been studied in carbon tetrachloride solvent (CCl_4) at a certain temperature:

$$2N_2O_5 \longrightarrow 4NO_2 + O_2$$

$[N_2O_5]$ (*M*)	Initial rate (*M*/s)
0.92	0.95×10^{-5}
1.23	1.20×10^{-5}
1.79	1.93×10^{-5}
2.00	2.10×10^{-5}
2.21	2.26×10^{-5}

Determine graphically the rate law for the reaction, and calculate the rate constant.

14.100 The thermal decomposition of N_2O_5 obeys first-order kinetics. At 45°C, a plot of ln $[N_2O_5]$ versus t gives a slope of -6.18×10^{-4} min^{-1}. What is the half-life of the reaction?

14.101 When a mixture of methane and bromine is exposed to light, the following reaction occurs slowly:

$$CH_4(g) + Br_2(g) \longrightarrow CH_3Br(g) + HBr(g)$$

Suggest a reasonable mechanism for this reaction. (*Hint:* Bromine vapor is deep red; methane is colorless.)

14.102 The rate of the reaction between H_2 and I_2 to form HI (discussed on page 588) increases with the intensity of visible light. (a) Explain why this fact supports the two-step mechanism given. (I_2 vapor is purple.) (b) Explain why the visible light has no effect on the formation of H atoms.

14.103 To prevent brain damage, a standard procedure is to lower the body temperature of someone who has been resuscitated after suffering cardiac arrest. What is the physiochemical basis for this procedure?

14.104 The second-order rate constant for the dimerization of a protein (P)

$$P + P \longrightarrow P_2$$

is 6.2×10^{-3}/*M* · s at 25°C. If the concentration of the protein is 2.7×10^{-4} *M*, calculate the initial rate (*M*/s) of formation of P_2. How long (in seconds) will it take to decrease the concentration of P to 2.7×10^{-5} *M?*

14.105 Consider the following elementary step:

$$X + 2Y \longrightarrow XY_2$$

(a) Write a rate law for this reaction. (b) If the initial rate of formation of XY_2 is 3.8×10^{-3} *M*/s and the initial concentrations of X and Y are 0.26 *M* and 0.88 *M*, respectively, what is the rate constant of the reaction?

14.106 In recent years, ozone in the stratosphere has been depleted at an alarmingly fast rate by chlorofluorocarbons (CFCs). A CFC molecule such as $CFCl_3$ is first decomposed by UV radiation:

$$CFCl_3 \longrightarrow CFCl_2 + Cl$$

The chlorine radical then reacts with ozone as follows:

$$Cl + O_3 \longrightarrow ClO + O_2$$
$$ClO + O \longrightarrow Cl + O_2$$

(a) Write the overall reaction for the last two steps. (b) What are the roles of Cl and ClO? (c) Why is the fluorine radical not important in this mechanism? (d) One suggestion to reduce the concentration of chlorine radicals is to add hydrocarbons such as ethane (C_2H_6) to the stratosphere. How will this work? (e) Draw potential energy versus reaction progress diagrams for the uncatalyzed and catalyzed (by Cl) destruction of ozone: $O_3 + O \longrightarrow 2O_2$. Use the thermodynamic data in Appendix 2 to determine whether the reaction is exothermic or endothermic.

14.107 Chlorine oxide (ClO), which plays an important role in the depletion of ozone (see Problem 14.106), decays rapidly at room temperature according to the equation

$$2ClO(g) \longrightarrow Cl_2(g) + O_2(g)$$

From the following data, determine the reaction order and calculate the rate constant of the reaction.

Time (s)	[ClO] (M)
0.12×10^{-3}	8.49×10^{-6}
0.96×10^{-3}	7.10×10^{-6}
2.24×10^{-3}	5.79×10^{-6}
3.20×10^{-3}	5.20×10^{-6}
4.00×10^{-3}	4.77×10^{-6}

14.108 A compound X undergoes two *simultaneous* first-order reactions as follows: X $\longrightarrow$ Y with rate constant k_1 and X $\longrightarrow$ Z with rate constant k_2. The ratio of k_1/k_2 at 40°C is 8.0. What is the ratio at 300°C? Assume that the frequency factors of the two reactions are the same.

14.109 Consider a car fitted with a catalytic converter. The first 5 min or so after it is started are the most polluting. Why?

14.110 The following scheme in which A is converted to B, which is then converted to C, is known as a consecutive reaction.

$$A \longrightarrow B \longrightarrow C$$

Assuming that both steps are first order, sketch on the same graph the variations of [A], [B], and [C] with time.

14.111 (a) What can you deduce about the activation energy of a reaction if its rate constant changes significantly with a small change in temperature? (b) If a bimolecular reaction occurs every time an A and a B molecule collide, what can you say about the orientation factor and activation energy of the reaction?

14.112 The rate law for the following reaction

$$CO(g) + NO_2(g) \longrightarrow CO_2(g) + NO(g)$$

is rate = $k[NO_2]^2$. Suggest a plausible mechanism for the reaction, given that the unstable species NO_3 is an intermediate.

14.113 Radioactive plutonium-239 ($t_{1/2} = 2.44 \times 10^5$ yr) is used in nuclear reactors and atomic bombs. If there are 5.0×10^2 g of the isotope in a small atomic bomb, how long will it take for the substance to decay to 1.0×10^2 g, too small an amount for an effective bomb?

14.114 Many reactions involving heterogeneous catalysts are zeroth order; that is, rate = k. An example is the decomposition of phosphine (PH_3) over tungsten (W):

$$4PH_3(g) \longrightarrow P_4(g) + 6H_2(g)$$

It is found that the reaction is independent of $[PH_3]$ as long as phosphine's pressure is sufficiently high (≥ 1 atm). Explain.

14.115 Thallium(I) is oxidized by cerium(IV) as follows:

$$Tl^+ + 2Ce^{4+} \longrightarrow Tl^{3+} + 2Ce^{3+}$$

The elementary steps, in the presence of Mn(II), are as follows:

$$Ce^{4+} + Mn^{2+} \longrightarrow Ce^{3+} + Mn^{3+}$$

$$Ce^{4+} + Mn^{3+} \longrightarrow Ce^{3+} + Mn^{4+}$$

$$Tl^+ + Mn^{4+} \longrightarrow Tl^{3+} + Mn^{2+}$$

(a) Identify the catalyst, intermediates, and the rate-determining step if the rate law is rate = $k[Ce^{4+}][Mn^{2+}]$. (b) Explain why the reaction is slow without the catalyst. (c) Classify the type of catalysis (homogeneous or heterogeneous).

14.116 Sucrose ($C_{12}H_{22}O_{11}$), commonly called table sugar, undergoes hydrolysis (reaction with water) to produce fructose ($C_6H_{12}O_6$) and glucose ($C_6H_{12}O_6$):

$$\underset{}{C_{12}H_{22}O_{11}} + H_2O \longrightarrow \underset{\text{fructose}}{C_6H_{12}O_6} + \underset{\text{glucose}}{C_6H_{12}O_6}$$

This reaction is of considerable importance in the candy industry. First, fructose is sweeter than sucrose. Second, a mixture of fructose and glucose, called *invert sugar,* does not crystallize, so the candy containing this sugar would be chewy rather than brittle as candy containing sucrose crystals would be. (a) From the following data, determine the order of the reaction. (b) How long does it take to hydrolyze 95 percent of sucrose? (c) Explain why the rate law does not include $[H_2O]$ even though water is a reactant.

Time (min)	$[C_{12}H_{22}O_{11}]$ (M)
0	0.500
60.0	0.400
96.4	0.350
157.5	0.280

14.117 The first-order rate constant for the decomposition of dimethyl ether

$$(CH_3)_2O(g) \longrightarrow CH_4(g) + H_2(g) + CO(g)$$

is 3.2×10^{-4} s^{-1} at 450°C. The reaction is carried out in a constant-volume flask. Initially only dimethyl ether is present and the pressure is 0.350 atm. What is the pressure of the system after 8.0 min? Assume ideal behavior.

14.118 At 25°C, the rate constant for the ozone-depleting reaction

$$O(g) + O_3(g) \longrightarrow 2O_2(g)$$

is 7.9×10^{-15} cm^3/molecule $\cdot$ s. Express the rate constant in units of $1/M \cdot$ s.

14.119 Consider the following elementary steps for a consecutive reaction:

$$A \xrightarrow{k_1} B \xrightarrow{k_2} C$$

(a) Write an expression for the rate of change of B.
(b) Derive an expression for the concentration of B under "steady-state" conditions; that is, when B is decomposing to C at the same rate as it is formed from A.

14.120 Ethanol is a toxic substance that, when consumed in excess, can impair respiratory and cardiac functions by interference with the neurotransmitters of the nervous system. In the human body, ethanol is metabolized by the enzyme alcohol dehydrogenase to acetaldehyde, which causes hangovers. Based on your knowledge of enzyme kinetics, explain why binge drinking (that is, consuming too much alcohol too fast) can prove fatal.

14.121 Strontium-90, a radioactive isotope, is a major product of an atomic bomb explosion. It has a half-life of 28.1 yr. (a) Calculate the first-order rate constant for the nuclear decay. (b) Calculate the fraction of ^{90}Sr that remains after 10 half-lives. (c) Calculate the number of years required for 99.0 percent of ^{90}Sr to disappear.

14.122 Consider the potential energy profiles for the following three reactions (from left to right). (1) Rank the rates (slowest to fastest) of the reactions. (2) Calculate ΔH for each reaction, and determine which reaction(s) are exothermic and which reaction(s) are endothermic. Assume the reactions have roughly the same frequency factors.

Reaction progress	Reaction progress	Reaction progress
(a)	(b)	(c)

14.123 Consider the following potential energy profile for the A $\longrightarrow$ D reaction. (a) How many elementary steps are there? (b) How many intermediates are formed? (c) Which step is rate determining? (d) Is the overall reaction exothermic or endothermic?

Reaction progress

14.124 A factory that specializes in the refinement of transition metals such as titanium was on fire. The firefighters were advised not to douse the fire with water. Why?

14.125 The activation energy for the decomposition of hydrogen peroxide

$$2H_2O_2(aq) \longrightarrow 2H_2O(l) + O_2(g)$$

is 42 kJ/mol, whereas when the reaction is catalyzed by the enzyme catalase, it is 7.0 kJ/mol. Calculate the temperature that would cause the uncatalyzed decomposition to proceed as rapidly as the enzyme-catalyzed decomposition at 20°C. Assume the frequency factor A to be the same in both cases.

14.126 The *activity* of a radioactive sample is the number of nuclear disintegrations per second, which is equal to the first-order rate constant times the number of radioactive nuclei present. The fundamental unit of radioactivity is the *curie* (Ci), where 1 Ci corresponds to exactly 3.70×10^{10} disintegrations per second. This decay rate is equivalent to that of 1 g of radium-226. Calculate the rate constant and half-life for the radium decay. Starting with 1.0 g of the radium sample, what is the activity after 500 yr? The molar mass of Ra-226 is 226.03 g/mol.

14.127 To carry out metabolism, oxygen is taken up by hemoglobin (Hb) to form oxyhemoglobin (HbO$_2$) according to the simplified equation

$$Hb(aq) + O_2(aq) \xrightarrow{k} HbO_2(aq)$$

where the second-order rate constant is $2.1 \times 10^6 / M \cdot s$ at 37°C. For an average adult, the concentrations of Hb and O$_2$ in the blood at the lungs are $8.0 \times 10^{-6} M$ and $1.5 \times 10^{-6} M$, respectively. (a) Calculate the rate of formation of HbO$_2$. (b) Calculate the rate of consumption of O$_2$. (c) The rate of formation of HbO$_2$ increases to 1.4×10^{-4} M/s during exercise to meet the demand of the increased metabolism rate. Assuming the Hb concentration to remain the same, what must the oxygen concentration be to sustain this rate of HbO$_2$ formation?

14.128 At a certain elevated temperature, ammonia decomposes on the surface of tungsten metal as follows:

$$2NH_3 \longrightarrow N_2 + 3H_2$$

From the following plot of the rate of the reaction versus the pressure of NH$_3$, describe the mechanism of the reaction.

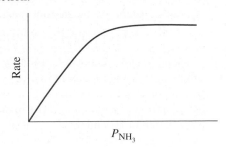

14.129 The following expression shows the dependence of the half-life of a reaction ($t_{1/2}$) on the initial reactant concentration $[A]_0$:

$$t_{1/2} \propto \frac{1}{[A]_0^{n-1}}$$

where n is the order of the reaction. Verify this dependence for zeroth-, first-, and second-order reactions.

14.130 Polyethylene is used in many items, including water pipes, bottles, electrical insulation, toys, and mailer envelopes. It is a *polymer*, a molecule with a very high molar mass made by joining many ethylene molecules together. (Ethylene is the basic unit, or monomer for polyethylene.) The initiation step is

$$R_2 \xrightarrow{k_1} 2R\cdot \quad \text{(initiation)}$$

The R· species (called a radical) reacts with an ethylene molecule (M) to generate another radical

$$R\cdot + M \longrightarrow M_1\cdot$$

The reaction of $M_1\cdot$ with another monomer leads to the growth or propagation of the polymer chain:

$$M_1\cdot + M \xrightarrow{k_p} M_2\cdot \quad \text{(propagation)}$$

This step can be repeated with hundreds of monomer units. The propagation terminates when two radicals combine

$$M'\cdot + M''\cdot \xrightarrow{k_t} M' - M'' \quad \text{(termination)}$$

The initiator frequently used in the polymerization of ethylene is benzoyl peroxide $[(C_6H_5COO)_2]$:

$$(C_6H_5COO)_2 \longrightarrow 2C_6H_5COO$$

This is a first-order reaction. The half-life of benzoyl peroxide at 100°C is 19.8 min. (a) Calculate the rate constant (in min^{-1}) of the reaction. (b) If the half-life of benzoyl peroxide is 7.30 h, or 438 min, at 70°C, what is the activation energy (in kJ/mol) for the decomposition of benzoyl peroxide? (c) Write the rate laws for the elementary steps in the preceding polymerization process, and identify the reactant, product, and intermediates. (d) What condition would favor the growth of long, high-molar-mass polyethylenes?

14.131 The rate constant for the gaseous reaction

$$H_2(g) + I_2(g) \longrightarrow 2HI(g)$$

is $2.42 \times 10^{-2}/M \cdot s$ at 400°C. Initially an equimolar sample of H_2 and I_2 is placed in a vessel at 400°C, and the total pressure is 1658 mmHg. (a) What is the initial rate (M/min) of formation of HI? (b) What are the rate of formation of HI and the concentration of HI (in molarity) after 10.0 min?

14.132 A protein molecule P of molar mass $\mathcal{M}$ dimerizes when it is allowed to stand in solution at room temperature. A plausible mechanism is that the protein molecule is first denatured (that is, loses its activity due to a change in overall structure) before it dimerizes:

$$P \xrightarrow{k} P^* \text{ (denatured)} \quad \text{slow}$$

$$2P^* \longrightarrow P_2 \quad \text{fast}$$

where the asterisk denotes a denatured protein molecule. Derive an expression for the average molar mass (of P and P_2), $\overline{\mathcal{M}}$, in terms of the initial protein concentration $[P]_0$ and the concentration at time t, $[P]$, and $\mathcal{M}$. Describe how you would determine k from molar mass measurements.

14.133 When the concentration of A in the reaction A $\longrightarrow$ B was changed from 1.20 M to 0.60 M, the half-life increased from 2.0 min to 4.0 min at 25°C. Calculate the order of the reaction and the rate constant. (*Hint:* Use the equation in Problem 14.129.)

14.134 At a certain elevated temperature, ammonia decomposes on the surface of tungsten metal as follows:

$$NH_3 \longrightarrow \tfrac{1}{2}N_2 + \tfrac{3}{2}H_2$$

The kinetic data are expressed as the variation of the half-life with the initial pressure of NH_3:

P (mmHg)	$t_{1/2}$ (s)
264	456
130	228
59	102
16	60

(a) Determine the order of the reaction. (b) How does the order depend on the initial pressure? (c) How does the mechanism of the reaction vary with pressure? (*Hint:* You need to use the equation in Problem 14.129 and plot $\log t_{1/2}$ versus $\log P$.)

14.135 The activation energy for the reaction

$$N_2O(g) \longrightarrow N_2(g) + O(g)$$

is 2.4×10^2 kJ/mol at 600 K. Calculate the percentage of the increase in rate from 600 K to 606 K. Comment on your results.

14.136 The rate of a reaction was followed by the absorption of light by the reactants and products as a function of wavelengths ($\lambda_1, \lambda_2, \lambda_3$) as time progresses. Which of the following mechanisms is consistent with the experimental data?
(a) A $\longrightarrow$ B, A $\longrightarrow$ C
(b) A $\longrightarrow$ B + C
(c) A $\longrightarrow$ B, B $\longrightarrow$ C + D
(d) A $\longrightarrow$ B, B $\longrightarrow$ C

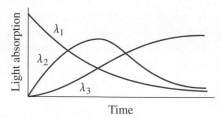

14.137 Magnesium reacts with strong acid to form Mg^{2+} ions and hydrogen gas. Which of the following forms of solid magnesium would react fastest with acid?

(a)   (b)   (c)

14.138 Use the data in Worked Example 14.5 to determine graphically the half-life of the reaction.

14.139 Diagram A describes the initial state of reaction

H_2
Cl_2
HCl

Diagram A

Suppose the reaction is carried out at two different temperatures as shown in diagram B. Which picture represents the result at the higher temperature? (The reaction proceeds for the same amount of time at both temperatures.)

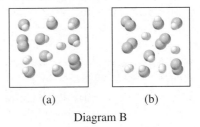

(a)   (b)

Diagram B

Answers to In-Chapter Materials

PRACTICE PROBLEMS

14.1A (a) rate $= -\dfrac{\Delta[CO_2]}{\Delta t} = -\dfrac{1}{2}\dfrac{\Delta[H_2O]}{\Delta t} = \dfrac{\Delta[CH_4]}{\Delta t} = \dfrac{1}{2}\dfrac{\Delta[O_2]}{\Delta t}$,

(b) rate $= -\dfrac{1}{3}\dfrac{\Delta[O_2]}{\Delta t} = \dfrac{1}{2}\dfrac{\Delta[O_3]}{\Delta t}$, (c) rate $= -\dfrac{1}{2}\dfrac{\Delta[NO]}{\Delta t} = -\dfrac{\Delta[O_2]}{\Delta t}$

$= \dfrac{1}{2}\dfrac{\Delta[NO_2]}{\Delta t}$. **14.1B** (a) $3CH_4 + 2H_2O + CO_2 \longrightarrow 4CH_3OH$,

(b) $2N_2O_5 \longrightarrow 2N_2 + 5O_2$, (c) $H_2 + CO + O_2 \longrightarrow H_2CO_3$.
14.2A (a) 0.0280 M/s, (b) 0.112 M/s. **14.2B** $2A + 3B \longrightarrow C$.
14.3A rate $= k[S_2O_8^{2-}][I^-]$, $k = 8.1 \times 10^{-2}/M \cdot s$. **14.3B** 0.013 M,
8.8×10^{-6} M/s. **14.4A** 75 s. **14.4B** 0.91 M.
14.5A

$k = 1.4 \times 10^{-2}$/min. **14.5B** 0.39 M, 0.34 M, 0.30 M, 0.26 M.
14.6A $t_{1/2} = 272$ s. **14.6B** $k = 4.71 \times 10^{-2}$/h. **14.7A** (a) 13.2 s,

(b) $t_{1/2} = 4.2$ s, 13 s. **14.7B** (a) 0.0208 M, (b) 1.25×10^{-3} M,
(c) 1.79×10^{-4} M. **14.8A** 241 kJ/mol. **14.8B** Red < green < blue.
14.9A 1.0×10^2 kJ/mol. **14.9B** 2.7×10^{-4}/s. **14.10A** 1.7/s.
14.10B 7.6×10^{-2}/s. **14.11A** (a) $NO_2 + CO \longrightarrow NO + CO_2$,
(b) NO_3, (c) step 1 is rate determining. **14.11B** $A + B \longrightarrow 2C$ (slow),
$C + B \longrightarrow D$. **14.12A** The first step is a rapidly established equilibrium.
Setting the rates of forward and reverse reactions equal to each other gives
$k_1[NO][Br_2] = k_{-1}[NOBr_2]$. Solving for $[NOBr_2]$ gives $k_1[NO][Br_2]/k_{-1}$.
Substituting this into the rate law for the rate-determining step,
rate $= k_2[NOBr_2][NO]$, gives rate $= (k_1k_2/k_{-1})[NO]^2[Br_2]$ or $k[NO]^2[Br_2]$.

14.12B *Step 1:* $I_2(g) \underset{k_{-1}}{\overset{k_1}{\rightleftharpoons}} 2I(g)$. *Step 2:* $H_2(g) + 2I(g) \longrightarrow 2HI(g)$,

rate $= k[H_2][I_2]$.

SECTION REVIEW

14.3.1 rate $= -\dfrac{\Delta[A]}{\Delta t} = -\dfrac{1}{2}\dfrac{\Delta[B]}{\Delta t} = \dfrac{\Delta[C]}{\Delta t} = \dfrac{\Delta[D]}{\Delta t}$. **14.3.2** 0.052 M/s.
14.4.1 rate $= k[A]$. **14.4.2** 0.018 s^{-1}. **14.4.3** 1. **14.4.4** 9.2×10^{-3} M/s.
14.4.5 rate $= k[A]^2[B]$. **14.5.1** 6×10^{-4} s^{-1}. **14.5.2** 3×10^3 s.
14.5.3 10 s. **14.5.4** 3.4 s. **14.6.1** 80 kJ/mol. **14.6.2** 4.8 s^{-1}. **14.7.1** 0 and 2.
14.7.2 2. **14.7.3** The rate-determining step is *Step 1*. Therefore, the rate
law is rate $= k[B]^2$. **14.7.4** rate $= k[H_2][IBr]$.

KEY SKILLS

First-Order Kinetics

One of the important applications of kinetics is the analysis of radioactive decay, which is first order. Although the equations are the same as those we have already derived for first-order kinetics, the terms and symbols vary slightly from what we have seen to this point. For example, the amount of radioactive material is typically expressed using *activity* (A) in *disintegrations per second* (dps), or in numbers of nuclei (N), rather than in units of concentration. Thus, Equation 14.3 becomes

$$\ln \frac{A_t}{A_0} = -kt \qquad \text{or} \qquad \ln \frac{N_t}{N_0} = -kt$$

The use of activity is very similar to the use of concentration. As with other kinetics problems, we may be given the initial activity (A_0), the rate constant (k), and the time elapsed (t)—and be asked to determine the new activity (A_t). Or we may be asked to solve for one of the other parameters, which simply requires manipulation of the original equation. For example, we may be given A_0, A_t, and t and be asked to determine the rate constant—or the half-life. (Recall that for any first-order process, the half-life is constant, and is related to the rate constant by Equation 14.5.) In this case, we solve Equation 14.3 for k, or for $t_{1/2}$—or for whichever parameter we need to find.

When the missing parameter is either A_0 or A_t, we must pay special attention to the manipulation of logarithms [▶▶ Appendix 1]. Solving the activity version of Equation 14.3 for A_t, for example, gives

$$A_t = A_0(e^{-kt})$$

Student Annotation: Note that because mass is proportional to the number of nuclei for a given isotope, we can use masses in the number-of-nuclei version of Equation 14.3—as long as they are mass amounts of the same nucleus.

When radioactive decay is quantified using numbers of nuclei (N), some additional thought must to go into determining the "known" parameters. Rocks that contain uranium, for example, can be dated by measuring the amounts of uranium-238 and lead-206 they contain. ^{238}U is unstable and undergoes a series of radioactive decay steps [▶▶ Section 20.3], ultimately producing a ^{206}Pb nucleus for every ^{238}U nucleus that decays. Although rocks may contain other isotopes of lead, ^{206}Pb results strictly from the decay of ^{238}U. Therefore, we can assume that every ^{206}Pb nucleus was originally a ^{238}U nucleus. If we know the mass of ^{238}U (N_t) and the mass of ^{206}Pb in the rock, we can determine N_0 as follows:

$$\text{mass of } ^{206}Pb \quad \times \quad \frac{1}{\text{atomic mass of } ^{206}Pb} \quad = \quad \text{number of } ^{206}Pb \text{ nuclei}$$

Because every ^{206}Pb nucleus was originally a ^{238}U nucleus,

$$\text{number of } ^{206}Pb \text{ nuclei} \quad = \quad \text{number of } ^{238}U \text{ nuclei}$$

$$\text{number of } ^{238}U \text{ nuclei} \quad \times \quad \text{atomic mass of } ^{238}U \quad = \quad \text{mass of } ^{238}U$$

These operations condense to give

$$\boxed{\text{mass of } ^{206}\text{Pb}} \times \boxed{\dfrac{\text{atomic mass of } ^{238}\text{U}}{\text{atomic mass of } ^{206}\text{Pb}}} = \boxed{\text{mass of } ^{238}\text{U}}$$

This gives the mass of ^{238}U *not* accounted for in the mass of ^{238}U found in the rock. Adding this mass to the mass of ^{238}U in the rock gives the mass of ^{238}U *originally* present (N_0). When we have both N_t and N_0, given the rate constant for decay of ^{238}U ($1.54 \times 10^{-10} \text{ yr}^{-1}$), we can determine the age of the rock (t).

Consider the following example:

A rock is found to contain 23.17 g ^{238}U and 2.02 g ^{206}Pb. Its age is determined as follows:

$$\boxed{2.02 \text{ g } ^{206}\text{Pb}} \times \boxed{\dfrac{238 \text{ g } ^{238}\text{U}}{206 \text{ g } ^{206}\text{Pb}}} = \boxed{2.334 \text{ g } ^{238}\text{U}}$$

$$\boxed{N_0 = (23.17 + 2.334) = 25.50 \text{ g}} \qquad \boxed{N_t = 23.17 \text{ g}}$$

Solving Equation 14.3 for t gives

$$\boxed{t = -\left(\dfrac{\ln \dfrac{N_t}{N_0}}{k} \right)}$$

and

$$\boxed{t = -\left(\dfrac{\ln \dfrac{23.17 \text{ g}}{25.50 \text{ g}}}{1.54 \times 10^{-10} \text{ yr}^{-1}} \right)} = \boxed{6.22 \times 10^8 \text{ yr}}$$

Therefore, the rock is 622 million years old.

Key Skills Problems

14.1
It takes 218 hours for the activity of a certain radioactive isotope to fall to one-tenth of its original value. Calculate the half-life of the isotope.

(a) 3.18×10^{-4} h (b) 21.8 h (c) 0.0152 h (d) 65.6 h (e) 0.0106 h

14.2
^{61}Cu decays with a half-life of 3.35 h. Determine the original mass of a sample of ^{61}Cu if 612.8 mg remains after exactly 24 hours.

(a) 85.5 mg (b) 4.39×10^3 mg (c) 736 mg (d) 6.40×10^3 mg (e) 8.78×10^4 mg

14.3
The rate constant for the radioactive decay of iodine-126 is 0.0533 d^{-1}. How much ^{126}I remains of a 2.55-g sample of ^{126}I after exactly 24 hours?

(a) 0.948 g (b) 2.42 g (c) 0.136 g (d) 0.710 g (e) 0.873 g

14.4
Determine the age of a rock that contains 45.7 mg ^{238}U and 1.02 mg ^{206}Pb.

(a) 165 million years (b) 2.50 billion years (c) 143 million years (d) 6.49 billion years (e) 63.7 million years

CHAPTER 15

Chemical Equilibrium

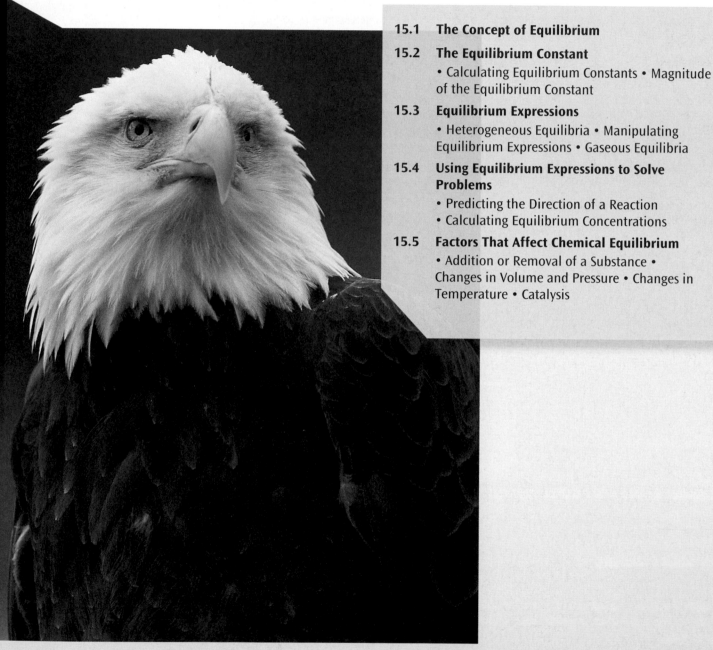

15.1 **The Concept of Equilibrium**

15.2 **The Equilibrium Constant**
• Calculating Equilibrium Constants • Magnitude of the Equilibrium Constant

15.3 **Equilibrium Expressions**
• Heterogeneous Equilibria • Manipulating Equilibrium Expressions • Gaseous Equilibria

15.4 **Using Equilibrium Expressions to Solve Problems**
• Predicting the Direction of a Reaction
• Calculating Equilibrium Concentrations

15.5 **Factors That Affect Chemical Equilibrium**
• Addition or Removal of a Substance • Changes in Volume and Pressure • Changes in Temperature • Catalysis

The majestic bald eagle, once again common in North America, neared the brink of extinction during the mid twentieth century. Biomagnification of the pesticide *dichlorodiphenyltrichloroethane* (DDT) in the food chain had led to significant weakening of the eggshells of this apex predator—making successful reproduction nearly impossible. Although DDT was banned in the United States in the 1970s (and in Canada in the 1980s) its use continues in some parts of the world. To study the phenomenon of biomagnification, wherein species higher in the food chain are exposed to greater and greater levels of a pesticide or other toxin, chemists have developed a laboratory equilibrium system. Using this system, which consists of octanol and water, scientists can model the selective absorption of substances such as DDT into the fatty tissues of birds, fish, and mammals.

15.1 THE CONCEPT OF EQUILIBRIUM

Up until now, we have treated chemical equations as though they go to completion; that is, we start with only *reactants* and end up with only *products*. In fact, this is not the case with most chemical reactions. Instead, if we start with only reactants, the reaction will proceed, causing reactant concentrations to decrease (as reactants are consumed) and product concentrations to increase (as products are produced). Eventually, though, the concentrations of reactants and products will stop changing. The reaction will appear to have stopped, and we will be left with a *mixture* of reactants and products.

As an example, consider the decomposition of dinitrogen tetroxide (N_2O_4) to yield nitrogen dioxide (NO_2):

$$N_2O_4(g) \rightleftharpoons 2NO_2(g)$$

N_2O_4 is a colorless gas, whereas NO_2 is brown. If we begin by placing a sample of pure N_2O_4 in an evacuated flask, the contents of the flask change from colorless to brown as the decomposition produces NO_2 (Figure 15.1). At first, the brown color intensifies as the concentration of NO_2 increases. After some time has passed, though, the intensity of the brown color stops increasing, indicating that the concentration of NO_2 has stopped increasing.

Student Annotation: NO_2 is the cause of the brown appearance of some polluted air.

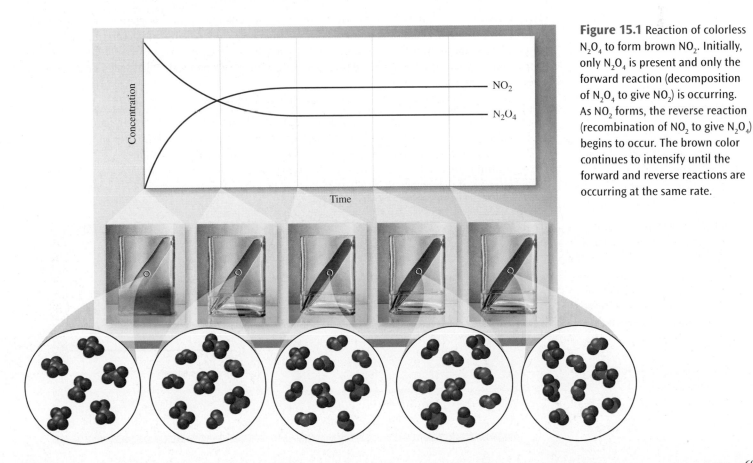

Figure 15.1 Reaction of colorless N_2O_4 to form brown NO_2. Initially, only N_2O_4 is present and only the forward reaction (decomposition of N_2O_4 to give NO_2) is occurring. As NO_2 forms, the reverse reaction (recombination of NO_2 to give N_2O_4) begins to occur. The brown color continues to intensify until the forward and reverse reactions are occurring at the same rate.

609

Although the concentration of the product (and of the reactant) has stopped changing, the reaction has not actually stopped. Like most chemical reactions, the decomposition of N_2O_4 is a ***reversible process,*** meaning that the products of the reaction can react to form *reactants*. Thus, as the decomposition of N_2O_4 continues, the reverse reaction, the combination of NO_2 molecules to produce N_2O_4, is also occurring. Eventually, the concentrations of both species reach levels where they remain constant because the two processes are occurring at the same rate—and the system is said to have achieved *dynamic equilibrium* or simply **equilibrium.**

In this case, both the forward and reverse reactions are *elementary* reactions, so we can write their rate laws from the balanced equation:

$$\text{rate}_{\text{forward}} = k_f[N_2O_4] \qquad \text{and} \qquad \text{rate}_{\text{reverse}} = k_r[NO_2]^2$$

where k_f and k_r are the rate constants for the forward and reverse reactions, respectively [◄◄ Section 14.7]. As always, the square brackets denote *molar concentration.* In the experiment shown in Figure 15.1, initially:

- N_2O_4 concentration is high, and the rate of the forward reaction is high.
- NO_2 concentration is zero, making the rate of the reverse reaction zero.

As the reaction proceeds:

- N_2O_4 concentration falls, decreasing the rate of the forward reaction.
- NO_2 concentration rises, increasing the rate of the reverse reaction.

Figure 15.2(a) shows how the rates of these forward and reverse reactions change over time, and how they eventually become equal as equilibrium is established.

We could equally well have started the N_2O_4-NO_2 experiment with pure NO_2 in a flask. Figure 15.3 shows how the brown color, initially intense, fades as NO_2 combines to form N_2O_4. As before, the intensity stops changing after a period of time. When we start the experiment with pure NO_2, initially:

- NO_2 concentration is high, and the rate of the reverse reaction is high.
- N_2O_4 concentration is zero, making the rate of the forward reaction zero.

As the reaction proceeds:

- NO_2 concentration falls, decreasing the rate of the reverse reaction.
- N_2O_4 concentration rises, increasing the rate of the forward reaction.

Figure 15.2(b) shows how the forward and reverse rates change over time when we start with NO_2 instead of N_2O_4. We could also conduct this kind of experiment starting with a mixture of NO_2 and N_2O_4. Again, the forward and reverse reactions would occur, initially at rates determined by the corresponding starting concentrations, and equilibrium would be established when both reactions were occurring at the same rate.

Some important things to remember about equilibrium are:

- Equilibrium is a *dynamic* state—both forward and reverse reactions continue to occur, although there is no net change in reactant and product concentrations over time.
- At equilibrium, the rates of the forward and reverse reactions are equal.
- Equilibrium can be established starting with only *reactants,* with only *products,* or with any *mixture* of reactants and products.

Figure 15.2 (a) Starting with just N_2O_4, the rate of the reverse reaction (formation of N_2O_4) is initially zero. The rate of the reverse reaction rises and the rate of the forward reaction falls until both rates are equal. (b) Starting with NO_2, the rate of the forward reaction is initially zero.

Figure 15.3 N_2O_4/NO_2 equilibrium starting with NO_2. Initially, only NO_2 is present and only the reverse reaction (recombination of NO_2 to give N_2O_4) is occurring. As N_2O_4 forms, the forward reaction (decomposition of N_2O_4) begins to occur. The brown color continues to fade until the forward and reverse reactions are occurring at the same rate.

Finally, it is important to understand that the principles of equilibrium apply not only to reversible chemical reactions, but also to reversible physical processes such as phase changes. In this chapter, we will limit our discussion to *chemical* equilibria. We explore reversible *physical* processes in some detail in Chapter 18.

15.2 THE EQUILIBRIUM CONSTANT

We have defined equilibrium as the state in which the opposing forward and reverse reactions are occurring at the same rate:

$$\text{rate}_{\text{forward}} = \text{rate}_{\text{reverse}}$$

Thus, using the N_2O_4-NO_2 system as an example again,

$$k_f[N_2O_4]_{eq} = k_r[NO_2]^2_{eq}$$

where the subscript "eq" denotes a concentration at equilibrium. Rearranging this expression gives

$$\frac{k_f}{k_r} = \frac{[NO_2]^2_{eq}}{[N_2O_4]_{eq}}$$

and because the ratio of two constants (k_f/k_r) is also a constant, we have

equilibrium expression

$$K_c = \frac{[NO_2]^2_{eq}}{[N_2O_4]_{eq}}$$

equilibrium constant

TABLE 15.1	Initial and Equilibrium Concentrations of N_2O_4 and NO_2 at 25°C				
	Initial concentrations (_M_)		**Equilibrium concentrations (_M_)**		
Experiment	$[N_2O_4]_i$	$[NO_2]_i$	$[N_2O_4]$	$[NO_2]$	$\dfrac{[NO_2]^2}{[N_2O_4]}$
1	0.670	0.00	0.643	0.0547	4.65×10^{-3}
2	0.446	0.0500	0.448	0.0457	4.66×10^{-3}
3	0.500	0.0300	0.491	0.0475	4.60×10^{-3}
4	0.600	0.0400	0.594	0.0523	4.60×10^{-3}
5	0.000	0.200	0.0898	0.0204	4.63×10^{-3}

Student Annotation: From this point on, we will no longer show the "eq" subscript for concentrations in equilibrium expressions—although you should know that every concentration in an equilibrium expression is the concentration *at equilibrium*.

where K_c is the **equilibrium constant** and the equation is known as the **equilibrium expression.** (The subscript "c" stands for *concentration*, referring to the molar concentrations in the expression.) Note the relationship between the equilibrium expression and the balanced chemical equation for the reaction: the numerator contains the product concentration raised to a power equal to its stoichiometric coefficient in the balanced chemical equation:

$$K_c = \frac{\left[NO_2\right]^2_{eq}}{\left[N_2O_4\right]_{eq}} \qquad N_2O_4(g) \rightleftharpoons 2NO_2(g)$$

The denominator, moreover, contains the reactant concentration raised to a power equal to its stoichiometric coefficient in the balanced chemical equation. (In this equation the coefficient of N_2O_4 is 1, which generally is not written either as a coefficient or as an exponent.) Table 15.1 lists the starting and equilibrium concentrations of N_2O_4 and NO_2 in a series of experiments carried out at 25°C. Using the equilibrium concentrations from each of the experiments in the table, the value of the expression $[NO_2]^2/[N_2O_4]$ is indeed constant (the average is 4.63×10^{-3}) within the limits of experimental error.

Calculating Equilibrium Constants

In the mid-nineteenth century, Cato Guldberg[1] and Peter Waage[2] studied the equilibrium mixtures of a wide variety of chemical reactions. They observed that at a constant temperature in an equilibrium mixture of reactants and products regardless of the initial concentrations, the *reaction quotient* has a constant value. The **reaction quotient (Q_c)** is a fraction with product concentrations in the numerator and reactant concentrations in the denominator—with each concentration raised to a power equal to the corresponding stoichiometric coefficient in the balanced chemical equation. For the general reaction,

$$a\text{A} + b\text{B} \rightleftharpoons c\text{C} + d\text{D}$$

at equilibrium, the reaction quotient Q_c is equal to the equilibrium constant K_c.

Equation 15.1	$Q_c = \dfrac{[C]^c[D]^d}{[A]^a[B]^b} = K_c$ (at equilibrium)

Student Annotation: In our first example, there was just one reactant and one product. When there are multiple species on either side of the equation, the numerator is the *product* of product concentrations and the denominator is the product of *reactant* concentrations—with each concentration raised to the appropriate power, that is, the stoichiometric coefficient.

This expression is known as the **law of mass action.** Like the equilibrium constant K, Q is subscripted with a "c" to indicate that the quotient is defined in terms of *concentrations*. For the N_2O_4-NO_2 system, this approach gives the same equilibrium expression as we got from our kinetics

---

[1]Cato Maximilian Guldberg (1836–1902), a Norwegian chemist and mathematician, conducted research primarily in the field of thermodynamics.

[2]Peter Waage (1833–1900), a Norwegian chemist, who—like his coworker, Guldberg—did research in thermodynamics.

approach: $[NO_2]^2_{eq}/[N_2O_4]_{eq}$. But the law of mass action was developed *empirically* from countless observations of many different reactions—long before the principles of kinetics were developed. Additionally, it applies not only to elementary reactions, but also to more complex reactions that occur via a series of steps. Furthermore, the law of mass action enables us to write the equilibrium expression for any reaction for which we know the balanced equation. Knowing the equilibrium expression for a reaction, we can use equilibrium concentrations to calculate the value of the equilibrium constant.

Worked Example 15.1 shows how to use equilibrium concentrations and the law of mass action to calculate the value of an equilibrium constant.

Worked Example 15.1

Carbonyl chloride ($COCl_2$), also called phosgene, is a highly poisonous gas that was used on the battlefield in World War I. It is produced by the reaction of carbon monoxide with chlorine gas:

$$CO(g) + Cl_2(g) \rightleftharpoons COCl_2(g)$$

In an experiment conducted at 74°C, the equilibrium concentrations of the species involved in the reaction were as follows: $[CO] = 1.2 \times 10^{-2}\ M$, $[Cl_2] = 0.054\ M$, and $[COCl_2] = 0.14\ M$. (a) Write the equilibrium expression, and (b) determine the value of the equilibrium constant for this reaction at 74°C.

Strategy Use the law of mass action to write the equilibrium expression and plug in the equilibrium concentrations of all three species to evaluate K_c.

Setup The equilibrium expression has the form of concentrations of products over concentrations of reactants, each raised to the appropriate power—in the case of this reaction, all the coefficients are 1, so all the powers will be 1.

Solution

(a) $K_c = \dfrac{[COCl_2]}{[CO][Cl_2]}$

(b) $K_c = \dfrac{(0.14)}{(1.2 \times 10^{-2})(0.054)} = 216$ or 2.2×10^2

K_c for this reaction at 74°C is 2.2×10^2.

> **Think About It**
> When putting the equilibrium concentrations into the equilibrium expression, we leave out the units. It is common practice to express equilibrium constants without units.

Practice Problem A In an analysis of the following reaction at 100°C,

$$Br_2(g) + Cl_2(g) \rightleftharpoons 2BrCl(g)$$

the equilibrium concentrations were found to be $[Br_2] = 2.3 \times 10^{-3}\ M$, $[Cl_2] = 1.2 \times 10^{-2}\ M$, and $[BrCl] = 1.4 \times 10^{-2}\ M$. Write the equilibrium expression, and calculate the equilibrium constant for this reaction at 100°C.

Practice Problem B In another analysis at 100°C involving the same reaction, the equilibrium concentrations of the reactants were found to be $[Br_2] = 4.1 \times 10^{-3}\ M$ and $[Cl_2] = 8.3 \times 10^{-3}\ M$. Determine the value of $[BrCl]$.

Guldberg and Waage's work involved calculating reaction quotients at equilibrium, but the numerical value of the reaction quotient can be determined using starting concentrations or final (equilibrium) concentrations, or concentrations at any time during the reaction (provided that the concentrations are known). The value of Q_c changes as the reaction progresses (Figure 15.4), and Q_c is equal to K_c only when a system is at equilibrium. However, we often find it useful to calculate the value of Q_c for a system that is not at equilibrium. At any point during the progress of a reaction, therefore,

$$Q_c = \frac{[C]^c[D]^d}{[A]^a[B]^b}$$

Equation 15.2

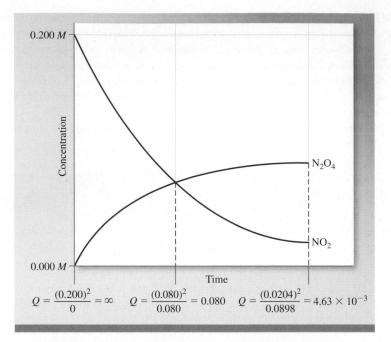

$$Q = \frac{(0.200)^2}{0} = \infty \qquad Q = \frac{(0.080)^2}{0.080} = 0.080 \qquad Q = \frac{(0.0204)^2}{0.0898} = 4.63 \times 10^{-3}$$

Figure 15.4 The value of the reaction quotient, Q, changes as the reaction (experiment 5 from Table 15.1) progresses. When the system reaches equilibrium, Q is equal to the equilibrium constant.

Worked Example 15.2 lets you practice writing reaction quotients for a variety of balanced equations.

Worked Example 15.2

Write reaction quotients for the following reactions:

(a) $N_2(g) + 3H_2(g) \rightleftharpoons 2NH_3(g)$

(b) $H_2(g) + I_2(g) \rightleftharpoons 2HI(g)$

(c) $Ag^+(aq) + 2NH_3(aq) \rightleftharpoons Ag(NH_3)_2^+(aq)$

(d) $2O_3(g) \rightleftharpoons 3O_2(g)$

(e) $Cd^{2+}(aq) + 4Br^-(aq) \rightleftharpoons CdBr_4^{2-}(aq)$

(f) $2NO(g) + O_2(g) \rightleftharpoons 2NO_2(g)$

Strategy Use the law of mass action to write reaction quotients.

Setup The reaction quotient for each reaction has the form of the concentrations of *products* over the concentrations of *reactants*, each raised to a power equal to its stoichiometric coefficient in the balanced chemical equation.

Solution

(a) $Q_c = \dfrac{[NH_3]^2}{[N_2][H_2]^3}$

(d) $Q_c = \dfrac{[O_2]^3}{[O_3]^2}$

(b) $Q_c = \dfrac{[HI]^2}{[H_2][I_2]}$

(e) $Q_c = \dfrac{[CdBr_4^{2-}]}{[Cd^{2+}][Br^-]^4}$

(c) $Q_c = \dfrac{[Ag(NH_3)_2^+]}{[Ag^+][NH_3]^2}$

(f) $Q_c = \dfrac{[NO_2]^2}{[NO]^2[O_2]}$

Student Annotation: The molar concentrations in a reaction quotient may be concentrations of *gases* or *aqueous* species.

Think About It

With practice, writing reaction quotients becomes second nature. Without sufficient practice, it will seem inordinately difficult. It is important that you become proficient at this. It is very often the first step in solving equilibrium problems.

Practice Problem A Write the reaction quotient for each of the following reactions:

(a) $2N_2O(g) \rightleftharpoons 2N_2(g) + O_2(g)$

(b) $2NOBr(g) \rightleftharpoons 2NO(g) + Br_2(g)$

(c) $HF(aq) \rightleftharpoons H^+(aq) + F^-(aq)$

(d) $CO(g) + H_2O(g) \rightleftharpoons CO_2(g) + H_2(g)$

(e) $CH_4(g) + 2H_2S(g) \rightleftharpoons CS_2(g) + 4H_2(g)$

(f) $H_2C_2O_4(aq) \rightleftharpoons 2H^+(aq) + C_2O_4^{2-}(aq)$

Practice Problem B Write the equation for the equilibrium that corresponds to each of the following reaction quotients:

(a) $Q_c = \dfrac{[HCl]^2}{[H_2][Cl_2]}$

(d) $Q_c = \dfrac{[H^+][ClO^-]}{[HClO]}$

(b) $Q_c = \dfrac{[HF]}{[H^+][F^-]}$

(e) $Q_c = \dfrac{[H^+][HSO_3^-]}{[H_2SO_3]}$

(c) $Q_c = \dfrac{[Cr(OH)_4^-]}{[Cr^{3+}][OH^-]^4}$

(f) $Q_c = \dfrac{[NOBr]^2}{[NO]^2[Br_2]}$

Magnitude of the Equilibrium Constant

One of the things the equilibrium constant tells us is the extent to which a reaction proceeds at a particular temperature. If we combine stoichiometric amounts of the reactants in a reaction, three outcomes are possible:

1. The reaction will go essentially to completion, and the equilibrium mixture will consist predominantly of products.
2. The reaction will not occur to any significant degree, and the equilibrium mixture will consist predominantly of reactants.
3. The reaction will proceed to a significant degree but will not go to completion, and the equilibrium mixture will contain comparable amounts of both reactants and products.

When the magnitude of K_c is very large, we expect the first outcome. The formation of the $Ag(NH_3)_2^+$ ion is an example of this possibility.

$$Ag^+(aq) + 2NH_3(aq) \rightleftharpoons Ag(NH_3)_2^+(aq) \qquad K_c = 1.5 \times 10^7 \text{ (at 25°C)}$$

If we were to combine aqueous Ag^+ and aqueous NH_3 in a mole ratio of 1:2, the resulting equilibrium mixture would contain mostly $Ag(NH_3)_2^+$ with only very small amounts of reactants remaining. A reaction with a very large equilibrium constant is sometimes said to "lie to the right" or to "favor products."

When the magnitude of K_c is very small, we expect the second outcome. The chemical combination of nitrogen and oxygen gases to give nitrogen monoxide is an example of this possibility.

$$N_2(g) + O_2(g) \rightleftharpoons 2NO(g) \qquad K_c = 4.3 \times 10^{-25} \text{ (at 25°C)}$$

Nitrogen and oxygen gases do not react to any significant extent at room temperature. If we were to place a mixture of N_2 and O_2 in an evacuated flask and allow the system to reach equilibrium, the resulting mixture would be predominantly N_2 and O_2 with only a *very* small amount of NO. A reaction with a very small equilibrium constant is said to "lie to the left" or to "favor reactants."

The terms *very large* and *very small* are somewhat arbitrary when applied to equilibrium constants. Generally speaking, an equilibrium constant with a magnitude greater than about 1×10^2 can be considered large; one with a magnitude smaller than about 1×10^{-2} can be considered small.

An equilibrium constant that falls between 1×10^2 and 1×10^{-2} indicates that neither products nor reactants are strongly favored. In this case, a system at equilibrium will contain a *mixture* of reactants and products, the exact composition of which will depend on the stoichiometry of the reaction.

SECTION 15.2 REVIEW

The Equilibrium Constant

15.2.1   Write the equilibrium expression for the reaction

$$2CO(g) + O_2(g) \rightleftharpoons 2CO_2(g)$$

15.2.2   Determine the value of the equilibrium constant, K_c, for the reaction

$$A + 2B \rightleftharpoons C + D$$

if the equilibrium concentrations are
$[A] = 0.0115 \ M$, $[B] = 0.0253 \ M$, $[C] = 0.109 \ M$, and $[D] = 0.0110 \ M$.

15.3   EQUILIBRIUM EXPRESSIONS

The equilibria we have discussed so far have all been *homogeneous;* that is, the reactants and products have all existed in the same phase—either gaseous or aqueous. In these cases, the equilibrium expression consists of writing the product of the product concentrations at equilibrium over the product of the reactant concentrations at equilibrium, with each concentration raised to a power equal to its stoichiometric coefficient in the balanced chemical equation (Equation 15.2). When the species in a reversible chemical reaction are not all in the same phase, the equilibrium is *heterogeneous.*

Heterogeneous Equilibria

Writing equilibrium expressions for heterogeneous equilibria is also straightforward, but it is slightly different from what we have done so far for homogeneous equilibria. For example, carbon dioxide can combine with elemental carbon to produce carbon monoxide:

$$CO_2(g) + C(s) \rightleftharpoons 2CO(g)$$

The two gases and one solid constitute two separate phases. If we were to write the equilibrium expression for this reaction as we have done previously for homogeneous reactions, including all product concentrations in the numerator and all reactant concentrations in the denominator, we would have

$$K_c^* = \frac{[CO]^2}{[CO_2][C]}$$

(K_c^* is superscripted with an asterisk to distinguish it from the equilibrium constant that we are about to derive.) The "concentration" of a solid, however, is a constant. If we were to double the number of moles of elemental carbon (C) in the preceding reaction, we would also double its volume. The ratio of moles to volume, which is how we define the concentration, remains the same. Because the concentration of solid carbon is a constant, it is incorporated into the value of the equilibrium constant and does not appear explicitly in the equilibrium expression.

$$K_c^* \times [C] = \frac{[CO]^2}{[CO_2]}$$

The product of K_c^* and $[C]_{eq}$ gives the *real* equilibrium constant for this reaction. The corresponding equilibrium expression is

$$K_c = \frac{[CO]^2}{[CO_2]}$$

The same argument applies to the concentrations of pure liquids in heterogeneous equilibria. Only gaseous species and aqueous species appear in equilibrium expressions.

Worked Example 15.3 lets you practice writing equilibrium expressions for heterogeneous equilibria.

Worked Example 15.3

Write equilibrium expressions for each of the following reactions:

(a) $CaCO_3(s) \rightleftharpoons CaO(s) + CO_2(g)$

(b) $Hg(l) + Hg^{2+}(aq) \rightleftharpoons Hg_2^{2+}(aq)$

(c) $2Fe(s) + 3H_2O(l) \rightleftharpoons Fe_2O_3(s) + 2H_2(g)$

(d) $O_2(g) + 2H_2(g) \rightleftharpoons 2H_2O(l)$

Strategy Use the law of mass action to write the equilibrium expression for each reaction. Only gases and aqueous species appear in the expression.

Setup

(a) Only CO_2 will appear in the expression.

(b) Hg^{2+} and Hg_2^{2+} will appear in the expression.

(c) Only H_2 will appear in the expression.

(d) O_2 and H_2 will appear in the expression.

Solution

(a) $K_c = [CO_2]$

(b) $K_c = \dfrac{[Hg_2^{2+}]}{[Hg^{2+}]}$

(c) $K_c = [H_2]^2$

(d) $K_c = \dfrac{1}{[O_2][H_2]^2}$

Think About It
Like writing equilibrium expressions for homogeneous equilibria, writing equilibrium expressions for heterogeneous equilibria becomes second nature if you practice. The importance of developing this skill now cannot be overstated. Your ability to understand the principles and to solve many of the problems in this and Chapters 16 to 19 depends on your ability to write equilibrium expressions *correctly* and *easily*.

Practice Problem A Write equilibrium expressions for each of the following reactions:

(a) $SiCl_4(g) + 2H_2(g) \rightleftharpoons Si(s) + 4HCl(g)$

(b) $Hg^{2+}(aq) + 2Cl^-(aq) \rightleftharpoons HgCl_2(s)$

(c) $Ni(s) + 4CO(g) \rightleftharpoons Ni(CO)_4(g)$

(d) $Zn(s) + Fe^{2+}(aq) \rightleftharpoons Zn^{2+}(aq) + Fe(s)$

Practice Problem B Which of the following equilibrium expressions corresponds to a heterogeneous equilibrium? How can you tell?

(a) $K_c = [NH_3][HCl]$

(b) $K_c = \dfrac{[H^+][C_2H_3O_2]}{[HC_2H_3O_2]}$

(c) $K_c = \dfrac{[Ag(NH_3)_2^+][Cl^-]}{[NH_3]^2}$

(d) $K_c = [Ba^{2+}][F^-]^2$

Manipulating Equilibrium Expressions

In our study of enthalpy, we learned that it is possible to manipulate chemical equations to solve thermochemistry problems [◄◄ Section 10.3]. Recall that when we made a change in a thermochemical equation, we had to make the corresponding change in the ΔH of the reaction. When we reversed a reaction, for example, we had to change the sign of its ΔH. When we change something about how an equilibrium reaction is expressed, we must also make the appropriate changes to the equilibrium expression and the equilibrium constant. Consider the reaction of nitric oxide and oxygen to produce nitrogen dioxide:

$$2NO(g) + O_2(g) \rightleftharpoons 2NO_2(g)$$

The equilibrium expression is

$$K_c = \frac{[NO_2]^2}{[NO]^2[O_2]}$$

and the equilibrium constant at 500 K is 6.9×10^5. If we were to reverse this equation, writing the equation for the decomposition of NO_2 to produce NO and O_2,

$$2NO_2(g) \rightleftharpoons 2NO(g) + O_2(g)$$

the new equilibrium expression would be the reciprocal of the original equilibrium expression:

$$K_c' = \frac{[NO]^2[O_2]}{[NO_2]^2}$$

Because the equilibrium expression is the reciprocal of the original, the equilibrium constant is also the reciprocal of the original. At 500 K, therefore, the equilibrium constant for the new equation is $1/(6.9 \times 10^5)$ or 1.5×10^{-6}.

Alternatively, if instead of reversing the original equation, we were to multiply it by 2,

$$4NO(g) + 2O_2(g) \rightleftharpoons 4NO_2(g)$$

the new equilibrium expression would be

$$K_c'' = \frac{[NO_2]^4}{[NO]^4[O_2]^2}$$

which is the original equilibrium expression squared. Again, because the new equilibrium expression is the square of the original, the new equilibrium constant is the square of the original: $K_c = (6.9 \times 10^5)^2$ or 4.8×10^{11}.

Finally, if we were to add the reverse of the original equation,

$$2NO_2(g) \rightleftharpoons 2NO(g) + O_2(g)$$

(for which $K_c = 1.6 \times 10^{-6}$ at 500 K) to the equation

$$2H_2(g) + O_2(g) \rightleftharpoons 2H_2O(g)$$

(for which $K_c = 2.4 \times 10^{47}$ at 500 K), the sum of the equations and the equilibrium expression (prior to the cancellation of identical terms) would be

$$2NO_2(g) + 2H_2(g) + O_2(g) \rightleftharpoons 2NO(g) + O_2(g) + 2H_2O(g)$$

and

$$K_c = \frac{[NO]^2[O_2][H_2O]^2}{[NO_2]^2[H_2]^2[O_2]}$$

It may be easier to see before canceling identical terms that for the *sum* of two equations, the equilibrium expression is the *product* of the two corresponding equilibrium expressions.

$$\frac{[NO]^2[O_2][H_2O]^2}{[NO_2]^2[H_2]^2[O_2]} = \frac{[NO]^2[O_2]}{[NO_2]^2} \times \frac{[H_2O]^2}{[H_2]^2[O_2]}$$

Canceling identical terms on the left and right sides of the equation, and on the top and bottom of the equilibrium expression, gives

$$2NO_2(g) + 2H_2(g) \rightleftharpoons 2NO(g) + 2H_2O(g) \qquad \text{and} \qquad K_c = \frac{[NO]^2[H_2O]^2}{[NO_2]^2[H_2]^2}$$

TABLE 15.2	Manipulation of Equilibrium Constant Expressions

$$A(g) + B(g) \rightleftharpoons 2C(g) \qquad K_{c_1} = 4.39 \times 10^{-3}$$

$$2C(g) \rightleftharpoons D(g) + E(g) \qquad K_{c_2} = 1.15 \times 10^4$$

Equation	Equilibrium expression	Relationship to original K_c	Equilibrium constant
$2C(g) \rightleftharpoons A(g) + B(g)$ Original equation is reversed.	$K'_{c_1} = \dfrac{[A][B]}{[C]^2}$	$\dfrac{1}{K_{c_1}}$	2.28×10^2 New constant is the reciprocal of the original.
$2A(g) + 2B(g) \rightleftharpoons 4C(g)$ Original equation is multiplied by a number.	$K''_{c_1} = \dfrac{[C]^4}{[A]^2[B]^2}$	$(K_{c_1})^2$	1.93×10^{-5} New constant is the original raised to the same number.
$\frac{1}{2}A(g) + \frac{1}{2}B(g) \rightleftharpoons C(g)$ Original equation is divided by 2.	$K'''_{c_1} = \dfrac{[C]}{[A]^{1/2}[B]^{1/2}}$	$\sqrt{K_{c_1}}$	6.63×10^{-2} New constant is the square root of the original.
$A(g) + B(g) \rightleftharpoons D(g) + E(g)$ Two equations are added.	$K_{c_3} = \dfrac{[D][E]}{[A][B]}$	$K_{c_1} \times K_{c_2}$	50.5 New constant is the product of the two original constants.

*Temperature is the same for both reactions.

And, because the new equilibrium expression is the product of the individual expressions, the new equilibrium constant is the product of the individual constants. Therefore, for the reaction

$$2NO_2(g) + 2H_2(g) \rightleftharpoons 2NO(g) + 2H_2O(g)$$

at 500 K, $K_c = (1.6 \times 10^{-6})(2.4 \times 10^{47}) = 3.8 \times 10^{41}$.

Using hypothetical equilibria, Table 15.2 summarizes the various ways that chemical equations can be manipulated and the corresponding changes that must be made to the equilibrium expression and equilibrium constant.

Worked Example 15.4 shows how to manipulate chemical equations and make the corresponding changes to their equilibrium constants.

Worked Example 15.4

The following reactions have the indicated equilibrium constants at 100°C:

$$(1) \qquad 2NOBr(g) \rightleftharpoons 2NO(g) + Br_2(g) \qquad K_c = 0.014$$

$$(2) \qquad Br_2(g) + Cl_2(g) \rightleftharpoons 2BrCl(g) \qquad K_c = 7.2$$

Determine the value of K_c for the following reactions at 100°C:

(a) $2NO(g) + Br_2(g) \rightleftharpoons 2NOBr(g)$ (d) $2NOBr(g) + Cl_2(g) \rightleftharpoons 2NO(g) + 2BrCl(g)$

(b) $4NOBr(g) \rightleftharpoons 4NO(g) + 2Br_2(g)$ (e) $NO(g) + BrCl(g) \rightleftharpoons NOBr(g) + \frac{1}{2}Cl_2(g)$

(c) $NOBr(g) \rightleftharpoons NO(g) + \frac{1}{2}Br_2(g)$

Strategy Begin by writing the equilibrium expressions for the reactions that are given. Then, determine the relationship of each equation's equilibrium expression to the equilibrium expression of the original equations, and make the corresponding change to the equilibrium constant for each.

Setup The equilibrium expressions for the reactions that are given are

$$K_c = \frac{[NO]^2[Br_2]}{[NOBr]^2} \qquad \text{and} \qquad K_c = \frac{[BrCl]^2}{[Br_2][Cl_2]}$$

(a) This equation is the reverse of original equation 1. Its equilibrium expression is the reciprocal of that for the original equation:

$$2NO(g) + Br_2(g) \rightleftharpoons 2NOBr(g) \qquad K_c = \frac{[NOBr]^2}{[NO]^2[Br_2]}$$

(Continued on next page)

(b) This is original equation 1 multiplied by a factor of 2. Its equilibrium expression is the original expression squared:

$$4NOBr(g) \rightleftharpoons 4NO(g) + 2Br_2(g) \qquad K_c = \left(\frac{[NO]^2[Br_2]}{[NOBr]^2}\right)^2$$

(c) This is original equation 1 multiplied by $\frac{1}{2}$. Its equilibrium expression is the square root of the original:

$$NOBr(g) \rightleftharpoons NO(g) + \tfrac{1}{2}Br_2(g) \qquad K_c = \sqrt{\frac{[NO]^2[Br_2]}{[NOBr]^2}} \quad or \quad K_c = \left(\frac{[NO]^2[Br_2]}{[NOBr]^2}\right)^{1/2}$$

(d) This is the sum of original equations 1 and 2. Its equilibrium expression is the product of the two individual expressions:

$$2NOBr(g) + Cl_2(g) \rightleftharpoons 2NO(g) + 2BrCl(g) \qquad K_c = \frac{[NO]^2[BrCl]^2}{[NOBr]^2[Cl_2]}$$

(e) Probably the simplest way to analyze this reaction is to recognize that it is the reverse of the reaction in part (d), multiplied by $\frac{1}{2}$. Its equilibrium expression is the square root of the reciprocal of the expression in part (d):

$$NO(g) + BrCl(g) \rightleftharpoons NOBr(g) + \tfrac{1}{2}Cl_2(g)$$

$$K_c = \sqrt{\frac{[NOBr]^2[Cl_2]}{[NO]^2[BrCl]^2}} \quad or \quad K_c = \left(\frac{[NOBr]^2[Cl_2]}{[NO]^2[BrCl]^2}\right)^{1/2}$$

Each equilibrium constant will bear the same relationship to the original as the equilibrium expression bears to the original.

Solution

(a) $K_c = 1/0.014 = 71$ (c) $K_c = (0.014)^{1/2} = 0.12$ (e) $K_c = (1/0.10)^{1/2} = 3.2$

(b) $K_c = (0.014)^2 = 2.0 \times 10^{-4}$ (d) $K_c = (0.014)(7.2) = 0.10$

Think About It

The magnitude of an equilibrium constant reveals whether products or reactants are favored, so the reciprocal relationship between K_c values of forward and reverse reactions should make sense. A very large K_c value means that products are favored. In the reaction of hydrogen ion and hydroxide ion to form water, the value of K_c is very large, indicating that the product, water, is favored.

$$H^+(aq) + OH^-(aq) \rightleftharpoons H_2O(l) \qquad K_c = 1.0 \times 10^{14} \text{ (at 25°C)}$$

Simply writing the equation backward doesn't change the fact that water is the predominate species. In the reverse reaction, therefore, the favored species is on the reactant side:

$$H_2O(l) \rightleftharpoons H^+(aq) + OH^-(aq) \qquad K_c = 1.0 \times 10^{-14} \text{ (at 25°C)}$$

As a result, the magnitude of K_c should correspond to reactants being favored; that is, it should be very small.

Practice Problem A The following reactions have the indicated equilibrium constants at a particular temperature:

$$N_2(g) + O_2(g) \rightleftharpoons 2NO(g) \qquad\qquad K_c = 4.3 \times 10^{-25}$$

$$2NO(g) + O_2(g) \rightleftharpoons 2NO_2(g) \qquad\qquad K_c = 6.4 \times 10^{9}$$

Determine the values of the equilibrium constants for the following equations at the same temperature: (a) $2NO(g) \rightleftharpoons N_2(g) + O_2(g)$, (b) $\frac{1}{2}N_2(g) + \frac{1}{2}O_2(g) \rightleftharpoons NO(g)$, and (c) $N_2(g) + 2O_2(g) \rightleftharpoons 2NO_2(g)$.

Practice Problem B Using the data from Practice Problem A, determine the values of the equilibrium constants for the following equations: (a) $4NO(g) \rightleftharpoons N_2(g) + 2NO_2(g)$, (b) $4NO_2(g) \rightleftharpoons 2N_2(g) + 4O_2(g)$, and (c) $2NO(g) + 2NO_2(g) \rightleftharpoons 3O_2(g) + 2N_2(g)$.

Gaseous Equilibria

When an equilibrium expression contains only gases, we can write an alternate form of the expression in which the concentrations of gases are expressed as partial pressures (atm). Thus, for the equilibrium

$$N_2O_4(g) \rightleftharpoons 2NO_2(g)$$

we can either write the equilibrium expression as

$$K_c = \frac{[NO_2]^2}{[N_2O_4]}$$

or as

$$K_P = \frac{\left(P_{NO_2}\right)^2}{P_{N_2O_4}}$$

where the subscript "P" in K_P stands for *pressure*, and P_{NO_2} and $P_{N_2O_4}$ are the equilibrium partial pressures of NO_2 and N_2O_4, respectively. In general, K_c is not equal to K_P because the partial pressures of reactants and products expressed in atmospheres are not equal to their concentrations expressed in mol/L. However, a simple relationship between K_P and K_c can be derived using the following equilibrium:

$$aA(g) \rightleftharpoons bB(g)$$

where a and b are the stoichiometric coefficients. The equilibrium constant K_c is given by

$$K_c = \frac{[B]^b}{[A]^a}$$

and the expression for K_P is

$$K_P = \frac{(P_B)^b}{(P_A)^a}$$

where P_A and P_B are the partial pressures of A and B. Assuming ideal gas behavior,

$$P_A V = n_A RT$$

$$P_A = \frac{n_A RT}{V} = \left(\frac{n_A}{V}\right)RT$$

and

$$P_A = [A]RT$$

where [A] is the molar concentration of A. Likewise,

$$P_B V = n_B RT$$

$$P_B = \frac{n_B RT}{V} = \left(\frac{n_B}{V}\right)RT$$

and

$$P_B = [B]RT$$

Substituting the expressions for P_A and P_B into the expression for K_P gives

$$K_P = \frac{(P_B)^b}{(P_A)^a}$$

$$= \frac{[B]^b}{[A]^a}(RT)^{b-a}$$

which simplifies to

$$K_P = K_c(RT)^{\Delta n}$$

where $\Delta n = b - a$. In general,

$$\Delta n = \text{moles of gaseous products} - \text{moles of gaseous reactants} \qquad \textbf{Equation 15.3}$$

Because pressures are usually expressed in atmospheres, the gas constant R is expressed as 0.08206 L · atm/K · mol, and we can write the relationship between K_P and K_c as

Equation 15.4 $$K_P = K_c[(0.08206 \text{ L} \cdot \text{atm/K} \cdot \text{mol}) \times T]^{\Delta n}$$

K_P is equal to K_c only in the special case where $\Delta n = 0$, as in the following equilibrium reaction:

$$H_2(g) + Br_2(g) \rightleftharpoons 2HBr(g)$$

In this case, Equation 15.4 can be written as

$$K_P = K_c[(0.08206 \text{ L} \cdot \text{atm/K} \cdot \text{mol}) \times T]^0$$
$$= K_c$$

Keep in mind that K_P expressions can only be written for reactions in which every species in the equilibrium expression is a gas. (Remember that solids and pure liquids do not appear in the equilibrium expression.)

Worked Examples 15.5 and 15.6 let you practice writing K_P expressions and illustrate the conversion between K_c and K_P.

Worked Example 15.5

Write K_P expressions for (a) $PCl_3(g) + Cl_2(g) \rightleftharpoons PCl_5(g)$, (b) $O_2(g) + 2H_2(g) \rightleftharpoons 2H_2O(l)$, and (c) $F_2(g) + H_2(g) \rightleftharpoons 2HF(g)$.

Strategy Write equilibrium expressions for each equation, expressing the concentrations of the gases in partial pressures.

Setup (a) All the species in this equation are gases, so they will all appear in the K_P expression.
(b) Only the reactants are gases.
(c) All species are gases.

Solution

$$\text{(a) } K_P = \frac{(P_{PCl_5})}{(P_{PCl_3})(P_{Cl_2})} \qquad \text{(b) } K_P = \frac{1}{(P_{O_2})(P_{H_2})^2} \qquad \text{(c) } K_P = \frac{(P_{HF})^2}{(P_{F_2})(P_{H_2})}$$

Think About It
It isn't necessary for every species in the reaction to be a gas—only those species that appear in the equilibrium expression.

Practice Problem A Write K_P expressions for (a) $2CO(g) + O_2(g) \rightleftharpoons 2CO_2(g)$, (b) $CaCO_3(s) \rightleftharpoons CaO(s) + CO_2(g)$, and (c) $N_2(g) + 3H_2(g) \rightleftharpoons 2NH_3(g)$.

Practice Problem B Write the equation for the gaseous equilibrium corresponding to each of the following K_P expressions:

$$\text{(a) } K_P = \frac{(P_{NO_3})^2}{(P_{NO_2})^2(P_{O_2})} \qquad \text{(b) } K_P = \frac{(P_{CO_2})(P_{H_2})^4}{(P_{CH_4})(P_{H_2O})^2} \qquad \text{(c) } K_P = \frac{(P_{HI})^2}{(P_{I_2})(P_{H_2})}$$

Worked Example 15.6

The equilibrium constant, K_c, for the reaction

$$N_2O_4(g) \rightleftharpoons 2NO_2(g)$$

is 4.63×10^{-3} at 25°C. What is the value of K_P at this temperature?

Strategy Use Equation 15.4 to convert from K_c to K_P. Be sure to convert temperature in degrees Celsius to kelvins.

Setup Using Equation 15.3,

$$\Delta n = 2(NO_2) - 1(N_2O_4) = 1$$

$T = 298$ K.

Solution $K_P = \left[K_c \left(\dfrac{0.08206 \text{ L} \cdot \text{atm}}{\text{K} \cdot \text{mol}} \right) \times T \right]$

$\qquad = (4.63 \times 10^{-3})(0.08206 \times 298)$

$\qquad = 0.113$

Think About It

Note that we have essentially disregarded the units of R and T so that the resulting equilibrium constant, K_P, is unitless. Equilibrium constants commonly are treated as unitless quantities.

Practice Problem A For the reaction

$$N_2(g) + 3H_2(g) \rightleftharpoons 2NH_3(g)$$

K_c is 2.3×10^{-2} at 375°C. Calculate K_P for the reaction at this temperature.

Practice Problem B $K_P = 2.79 \times 10^{-5}$ for the reaction in Practice Problem A at 472°C. What is K_c for this reaction at 472°C?

SECTION 15.3 REVIEW

Equilibrium Expressions

15.3.1   Write the equilibrium expression for the reaction

$$H^+(aq) + OH^-(aq) \rightleftharpoons H_2O(l)$$

15.3.2   Write the equilibrium expression for the reaction

$$CaO(s) + CO_2(g) \rightleftharpoons CaCO_3(s)$$

15.3.3   Given the following information,

$$HF(aq) \rightleftharpoons H^+(aq) + F^-(aq) \qquad K_c = 6.8 \times 10^{-4} \text{ (at 25°C)}$$

$$H_2C_2O_4(aq) \rightleftharpoons 2H^+(aq) + C_2O_4^{2-}(aq) \qquad K_c = 3.8 \times 10^{-6} \text{ (at 25°C)}$$

determine the value of K_c for the following reaction at 25°C:

$$C_2O_4^{2-}(aq) + 2HF(aq) \rightleftharpoons 2F^-(aq) + H_2C_2O_4(aq)$$

15.3.4 K_c for the reaction

$$Br_2(g) \rightleftharpoons 2Br(g)$$

is 1.1×10^{-3} at 1280°C. Calculate the value of K_P for this reaction at this temperature.

15.4   USING EQUILIBRIUM EXPRESSIONS TO SOLVE PROBLEMS

We have already used equilibrium expressions to determine the value of an equilibrium constant using equilibrium concentrations. In this section, we will learn how to use equilibrium expressions to predict the direction of a reaction and to calculate equilibrium concentrations.

Predicting the Direction of a Reaction

If we start an experiment with only reactants, we know that the reactant concentrations will decrease and the product concentrations will increase; that is, the reaction must proceed in the *forward* direction for equilibrium to be established. Likewise, if we start an experiment with only products, we know that the product concentrations will decrease and the reactant concentrations will increase. In this case, the reaction must proceed in the *reverse* direction to achieve equilibrium. But often we must predict the direction in which a reaction will proceed when we start with a mixture of reactants and products. For this situation, we calculate the value of the reaction quotient, Q_c, and compare it to the value of the equilibrium constant, K_c.

The equilibrium constant, K_c, for the gaseous formation of hydrogen iodide from molecular hydrogen and molecular iodine,

$$H_2(g) + I_2(g) \rightleftharpoons 2HI(g)$$

is 54.3 at 430°C. If we were to conduct an experiment starting with a mixture of 0.243 mole of H_2, 0.146 mole of I_2, and 1.98 moles of HI in a 1.00-L container at 430°C, would more HI form or would HI be consumed and more H_2 and I_2 form? Using the starting concentrations, we can calculate the reaction quotient as follows:

$$Q_c = \frac{[HI]_i^2}{[H_2]_i[I_2]_i} = \frac{(1.98)^2}{(0.243)(0.146)} = 111$$

where the subscript "i" indicates *initial* concentration. Because the reaction quotient does not equal K_c ($Q_c = 111$, $K_c = 54.3$), the reaction is not at equilibrium. To establish equilibrium, the reaction will proceed to the left, consuming HI and producing H_2 and I_2, decreasing the value of the numerator and increasing the value in the denominator until the value of the reaction quotient equals that of the equilibrium constant. Thus, the reaction proceeds in the reverse direction (from right to left) to reach equilibrium.

There are three possibilities when we compare Q with K:

$Q < K$ The ratio of initial concentrations of products to reactants is too small. To reach equilibrium, reactants must be converted to products. The system proceeds in the forward direction (from left to right).

$Q = K$ The initial concentrations are equilibrium concentrations. The system is already at equilibrium, and there will be no net reaction in either direction.

$Q > K$ The ratio of initial concentrations of products to reactants is too large. To reach equilibrium, products must be converted to reactants. The system proceeds in the reverse direction (from right to left).

Worked Example 15.7 shows how the value of Q is used to determine the direction of a reaction that is not at equilibrium.

Student Annotation: Q_c is calculated using the initial concentrations of reactants and products. Similarly, Q_P can be calculated using the initial partial pressures of reactants and products.

Student Annotation: Remember that calculating Q_c is just like calculating K_c: products over reactants, each raised to the appropriate power—except that the concentrations we use to calculate Q_c are the *starting* concentrations. To calculate K_c we must use *equilibrium* concentrations.

Student Annotation: The comparison of Q with K can refer either to Q_c and K_c or Q_P and K_P.

Worked Example 15.7

At 375°C, the equilibrium constant for the reaction

$$N_2(g) + 3H_2(g) \rightleftharpoons 2NH_3(g)$$

is 1.2. At the start of a reaction, the concentrations of N_2, H_2, and NH_3 are 0.071 M, 9.2×10^{-3} M, and 1.83×10^{-4} M, respectively. Determine whether this system is at equilibrium, and if not, determine in which direction it must proceed to establish equilibrium.

Strategy Use the initial concentrations to calculate Q_c, and then compare Q_c with K_c.

Setup

$$Q_c = \frac{[NH_3]_i^2}{[N_2]_i[H_2]_i^3} = \frac{(1.83 \times 10^{-4})^2}{(0.071)(9.2 \times 10^{-3})^3} = 0.61$$

Solution The calculated value of Q_c is less than K_c. Therefore, the reaction is not at equilibrium and must proceed to the right to establish equilibrium.

Think About It

In proceeding to the right, a reaction consumes reactants and produces more products. This increases the numerator in the reaction quotient and decreases the denominator. The result is an increase in Q_c until it is equal to K_c, at which point equilibrium will be established.

Practice Problem A The equilibrium constant, K_c, for the formation of nitrosyl chloride from nitric oxide and chlorine,

$$2NO(g) + Cl_2(g) \rightleftharpoons 2NOCl(g)$$

is 6.5×10^4 at 35°C. In which direction will the reaction proceed to reach equilibrium if the starting concentrations of NO, Cl_2, and NOCl are 1.1×10^{-3} M, 3.5×10^{-4} M, and 1.9 M, respectively?

Practice Problem B Calculate K_p for the formation of nitrosyl chloride from nitric oxide and chlorine at 35°C, and determine whether the reaction will proceed to the right or the left to achieve equilibrium when the starting pressures are $P_{NO} = 1.01$ atm, $P_{Cl_2} = 0.42$ atm, and $P_{NOCl} = 1.76$ atm.

Calculating Equilibrium Concentrations

If we know the equilibrium constant for a reaction, we can calculate the concentrations in the equilibrium mixture from the initial reactant concentrations. Consider the following system involving two organic compounds, *cis*- and *trans*-stilbene:

cis-Stilbene   trans-Stilbene

The equilibrium constant (K_c) for this system is 24.0 at 200°C. If we know that the starting concentration of *cis*-stilbene is 0.850 M, we can use the equilibrium expression to determine the equilibrium concentrations of both species. The stoichiometry of the reaction tells us that for every mole of *cis*-stilbene converted, 1 mole of *trans*-stilbene is produced. We will let x be the equilibrium concentration of *trans*-stilbene in mol/L; therefore, the equilibrium concentration of *cis*-stilbene must be $(0.850 - x)$ mol/L. It is useful to summarize these changes in concentrations in an equilibrium table:

$$cis\text{-stilbene} \rightleftharpoons trans\text{-stilbene}$$

	cis-stilbene	*trans*-stilbene
Initial concentration (M):	0.850	0
Change in concentration (M):	$-x$	$+x$
Equilibrium concentration (M):	$0.850 - x$	x

We then use the equilibrium concentrations, defined in terms of x, in the equilibrium expression:

$$K_c = \frac{[trans\text{-stilbene}]}{[cis\text{-stilbene}]}$$

$$24.0 = \frac{x}{0.850 - x}$$

$$x = 0.816 \, M$$

Having solved for x, we calculate the equilibrium concentrations of *cis*- and *trans*-stilbene as follows:

$$[cis\text{-stilbene}] = (0.850 - x) \, M = 0.034 \, M$$

$$[trans\text{-stilbene}] = x \, M = 0.816 \, M$$

A good way to check the answer to a problem such as this is to use the calculated equilibrium concentrations in the equilibrium expression and make sure that we get the correct K_c value.

$$K_c = \frac{0.816}{0.034} = 24$$

Worked Examples 15.8 and 15.9 provide additional examples of this kind of problem.

Worked Example 15.8

K_c for the reaction of hydrogen and iodine to produce hydrogen iodide,

$$H_2(g) + I_2(g) \rightleftharpoons 2HI(g)$$

is 54.3 at 430°C. What will the concentrations be at equilibrium if we start with 0.240 M concentrations of both H_2 and I_2?

Strategy Construct an equilibrium table to determine the equilibrium concentration of each species in terms of an unknown (x); solve for x, and use it to calculate the equilibrium molar concentrations.

Setup Insert the starting concentrations that we know into the equilibrium table:

$$H_2(g) + I_2(g) \rightleftharpoons 2HI(g)$$

Initial concentration (M):	0.240	0.240	0
Change in concentration (M):			
Equilibrium concentration (M):			

Solution We define the change in concentration of one of the reactants as x. Because there is no product at the start of the reaction, the reactant concentration must decrease; that is, this reaction must proceed in the forward direction to reach equilibrium. According to the stoichiometry of the chemical reaction, the reactant concentrations will both decrease by the same amount (x), and the product concentration will increase by twice that amount ($2x$). Combining the initial concentration and the change in concentration for each species, we get expressions (in terms of x) for the equilibrium concentrations:

	$H_2(g)$	$+$	$I_2(g)$	$\rightleftharpoons$	$2HI(g)$
Initial concentration (M):	0.240		0.240		0
Change in concentration (M):	$-x$		$-x$		$+2x$
Equilibrium concentration (M):	$0.240 - x$		$0.240 - x$		$2x$

Next, we insert these expressions for the equilibrium concentrations into the equilibrium expression and solve for x.

$$K_c = \frac{[HI]^2}{[H_2][I_2]}$$

$$54.3 = \frac{(2x)^2}{(0.240 - x)(0.240 - x)} = \frac{(2x)^2}{(0.240 - x)^2}$$

$$\sqrt{54.3} = \frac{2x}{0.240 - x}$$

$$x = 0.189$$

Using the calculated value of x, we can determine the equilibrium concentration of each species as follows:

$$[H_2] = (0.240 - x)\ M = 0.051\ M$$

$$[I_2] = (0.240 - x)\ M = 0.051\ M$$

$$[HI] = 2x = 0.378\ M$$

Think About It
Always check your answer by inserting the calculated concentrations into the equilibrium expression:

$$\frac{[HI]^2}{[H_2][I_2]} = \frac{(0.378)^2}{(0.051)^2} = 54.9 \approx K_c$$

The small difference between the calculated K_c and the one given in the problem statement is due to rounding.

Practice Problem A Calculate the equilibrium concentrations of H_2, I_2, and HI at 430°C if the initial concentrations are $[H_2] = [I_2] = 0\ M$, and $[HI] = 0.525\ M$.

Practice Problem B Determine the initial concentration of HI if the initial concentrations of H_2 and I_2 are both 0.10 M and their equilibrium concentrations are both 0.043 M at 430°C.

Worked Example 15.9

For the same reaction and temperature as in Worked Example 15.8, calculate the equilibrium concentrations of all three species if the starting concentrations are as follows: $[H_2] = 0.00623\ M$, $[I_2] = 0.00414\ M$, and $[HI] = 0.0424\ M$.

Strategy Using the initial concentrations, calculate the reaction quotient, Q_c, and compare it to the value of K_c (given in the problem statement of Worked Example 15.8) to determine which direction the reaction will proceed to establish equilibrium. Then, construct an equilibrium table to determine the equilibrium concentrations.

Setup

$$\frac{[HI]^2}{[H_2][I_2]} = \frac{(0.0424)^2}{(0.00623)(0.00414)} = 69.7$$

Therefore, $Q_c > K_c$, so the system will have to proceed to the *left* (reverse) to reach equilibrium. The equilibrium table is

$$H_2(g) + I_2(g) \rightleftharpoons 2HI(g)$$

Initial concentration (M):	0.00623	0.00414	0.0424
Change in concentration (M):			
Equilibrium concentration (M):			

Solution Because we know the reaction must proceed from right to left, we know that the concentration of HI will decrease and the concentrations of H_2 and I_2 will increase. Therefore, the table should be filled in as follows:

$$H_2(g) \quad + \quad I_2(g) \quad \rightleftharpoons \quad 2HI(g)$$

	$H_2(g)$	$I_2(g)$	$2HI(g)$
Initial concentration (M):	0.00623	0.00414	0.0424
Change in concentration (M):	$+x$	$+x$	$-2x$
Equilibrium concentration (M):	$0.00623 + x$	$0.00414 + x$	$0.0424 - 2x$

Next, we insert these expressions for the equilibrium concentrations into the equilibrium expression and solve for x.

$$K_c = \frac{[HI]^2}{[H_2][I_2]}$$

$$54.3 = \frac{(0.0424 - 2x)^2}{(0.00623 + x)(0.00414 + x)}$$

It isn't possible to solve this equation the way we did in Worked Example 15.8 (by taking the square root of both sides) because the concentrations of H_2 and I_2 are unequal. Instead, we have to carry out the multiplications,

$$54.3(2.58 \times 10^{-5} + 1.04 \times 10^{-2}x + x^2) = 1.80 \times 10^{-3} - 1.70 \times 10^{-1}x + 4x^2$$

Collecting terms we get

$$50.3x^2 + 0.735x - 4.00 \times 10^{-4} = 0$$

This is a quadratic equation of the form $ax^2 + bx + c = 0$. The solution for the quadratic equation [▶ Appendix 1] is

$$x = \frac{-b \pm \sqrt{b^2 - 4ac}}{2a}$$

(Continued on next page)

Here we have $a = 50.3$, $b = 0.735$, and $c = -4.00 \times 10^{-4}$, so

$$x = \frac{-0.735 \pm \sqrt{(0.735)^2 - 4(50.3)(-4.00 \times 10^{-4})}}{2(50.3)}$$

$$x = 5.25 \times 10^{-4} \quad \text{or} \quad x = -0.0151$$

Only the first of these values, 5.25×10^{-4}, makes sense because concentration cannot be a negative number. Using the calculated value of x, we can determine the equilibrium concentration of each species as follows:

$$[H_2] = (0.00623 + x)\,M = 0.00676\,M$$

$$[I_2] = (0.00414 + x)\,M = 0.00467\,M$$

$$[HI] = (0.0424 - 2x)\,M = 0.0414\,M$$

> **Think About It**
> Checking this result gives $\quad K_c = \dfrac{[HI]^2}{[H_2][I_2]} = \dfrac{(0.0414)^2}{(0.00676)(0.00467)} = 54.3$

Practice Problem A At 1280°C the equilibrium constant K_c for the reaction

$$Br_2(g) \rightleftharpoons 2Br(g)$$

is 1.1×10^{-3}. If the initial concentrations are $[Br_2] = 6.3 \times 10^{-2}\,M$ and $[Br] = 1.2 \times 10^{-2}\,M$, calculate the concentrations of these two species at equilibrium.

Practice Problem B Using information from Practice Problem A, determine the initial and equilibrium concentrations of Br if the initial and equilibrium concentrations of Br_2 are $5.7 \times 10^{-3}\,M$ and $5.3 \times 10^{-3}\,M$, respectively.

Here is a summary of the use of initial reactant concentrations to determine equilibrium concentrations:

Student Annotation: If $Q < K$, the reaction will occur as written. If $Q > K$, the reverse reaction will occur.

1. Construct an equilibrium table, and fill in the initial concentrations (including any that are zero).
2. Use initial concentrations to calculate the reaction quotient, Q, and compare Q to K to determine the direction in which the reaction will proceed.
3. Define x as the amount of a particular species consumed, and use the stoichiometry of the reaction to define (in terms of x) the amount of other species consumed or produced.
4. For each species in the equilibrium, add the change in concentration to the initial concentration to get the equilibrium concentration.
5. Use the equilibrium concentrations and the equilibrium expression to solve for x.
6. Using the calculated value of x, determine the concentrations of all species at equilibrium.
7. Check your work by plugging the calculated equilibrium concentrations into the equilibrium expression. The result should be very close to the K_c stated in the problem.

The same procedure applies to K_P.

Worked Example 15.10 shows how to solve an equilibrium problem using partial pressures.

Worked Example 15.10

Student Annotation: For this reaction, $\Delta n = 0$; therefore, K_c is equal to K_P.

A mixture of 5.75 atm of H_2 and 5.75 atm of I_2 is contained in a 1.0-L vessel at 430°C. The equilibrium constant (K_P) for the reaction

$$H_2(g) + I_2(g) \rightleftharpoons 2HI(g)$$

at this temperature is 54.3. Determine the equilibrium partial pressures of H_2, I_2, and HI.

Strategy Construct an equilibrium table to determine the equilibrium partial pressures.

Setup The equilibrium table is

	$H_2(g)$	+	$I_2(g)$	$\rightleftharpoons$	$2HI(g)$
Initial partial pressure (atm):	5.75		5.75		0
Change in partial pressure (atm):	$-x$		$-x$		$+2x$
Equilibrium partial pressure (atm):	$5.75 - x$		$5.75 - x$		$2x$

Solution Setting the equilibrium expression equal to K_P,

$$54.3 = \frac{(2x)^2}{(5.75 - x)^2}$$

Taking the square root of both sides of the equation gives

$$\sqrt{54.3} = \frac{2x}{5.75 - x}$$

$$7.369 = \frac{2x}{5.75 - x}$$

$$7.369(5.75 - x) = 2x$$

$$42.37 - 7.369x = 2x$$

$$42.37 = 9.369x$$

$$x = 4.52$$

The equilibrium partial pressures are $P_{H_2} = P_{I_2} = 5.75 - 4.52 = 1.23$ atm, and $P_{HI} = 9.04$ atm.

Think About It

Plugging the calculated partial pressures into the equilibrium expression gives

$$\frac{(P_{HI})^2}{(P_{H_2})(P_{I_2})} = \frac{(9.04)^2}{(1.23)^2} = 54.0$$

The small difference between this result and the equilibrium constant given in the problem statement is due to rounding.

Practice Problem A Determine the equilibrium partial pressures of H_2, I_2, and HI if we begin the experiment with 1.75 atm each of H_2 and I_2 at 430°C.

Practice Problem B Determine the equilibrium partial pressures of H_2, I_2, and HI if we begin the experiment with 2.75 atm HI at 430°C.

Student Annotation: When a reaction starts with reactants and products, be sure to calculate Q and compare it to K to determine which direction the reaction will proceed to reach equilibrium.

SECTION 15.4 REVIEW

Using Equilibrium Expressions to Solve Problems

Use the following information to answer questions 15.4.1 and 15.4.2:
K_c for the reaction

$$A + B \rightleftharpoons 2C$$

is 1.7×10^{-2} at 250°C.

15.4.1 What will the equilibrium concentrations of A, B, and C be at this temperature if $[A]_i = [B]_i = 0.750\ M$ ($[C]_i = 0$)?

15.4.2 What will the equilibrium concentrations of A, B, and C be at this temperature if $[C]_i = 0.875\ M$ ($[A]_i = [B]_i = 0$)?

15.4.3 If $K_c = 3$ for the reaction $X + 2Y \rightleftharpoons Z$ at a certain temperature, then for each of the mixtures of X, Y, and Z shown here, in what direction must the reaction proceed to achieve equilibrium?

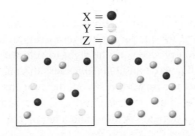

$X = \bullet$
$Y = \circ$
$Z = \circ$

15.5 **FACTORS THAT AFFECT CHEMICAL EQUILIBRIUM**

One of the interesting and useful features of chemical equilibria is that they can be manipulated in specific ways to maximize production of a desired substance. Consider, for example, the industrial production of ammonia from its constituent elements by the Haber process:

$$N_2(g) + 3H_2(g) \rightleftharpoons 2NH_3(g)$$

More than 100 million tons of ammonia is produced annually by this reaction, with most of the resulting ammonia being used for fertilizers to enhance crop production. Clearly it would be in the best interest of industry to maximize the yield of NH_3. In this section, we will learn about the various ways in which an equilibrium can be manipulated to accomplish this goal.

Le Châtelier's principle states that when a *stress* is applied to a system at equilibrium, the system will respond by *shifting* in the direction that minimizes the effect of the stress. In this context, "stress" refers to a disturbance of the system at equilibrium by any of the following means:

- The addition of a reactant or product
- The removal of a reactant or product
- A change in volume of the system, resulting in a change in concentration or partial pressure of the reactants and products
- A change in temperature

"Shifting" refers to the occurrence of either the forward or reverse reaction such that the effect of the stress is partially offset as the system reestablishes equilibrium. An equilibrium that shifts to the right is one in which more products are produced by the forward reaction. An equilibrium that shifts to the left is one in which more reactants are produced by the reverse reaction. Using Le Châtelier's principle, we can predict the direction in which an equilibrium will shift, given the specific stress that is applied.

Addition or Removal of a Substance

Again using the Haber process as an example,

$$N_2(g) + 3H_2(g) \rightleftharpoons 2NH_3(g)$$

consider a system at 700 K, in which the equilibrium concentrations are as follows:

$$[N_2] = 2.05\ M \qquad [H_2] = 1.56\ M \qquad [NH_3] = 1.52\ M$$

Student Annotation: Remember that at equilibrium, the reaction quotient, Q_c, is equal to the equilibrium constant, K_c.

Using these concentrations in the reaction quotient expression, we can calculate the value of K_c for the reaction at this temperature as follows:

$$Q_c = \frac{[NH_3]^2}{[N_2][H_2]^3} = \frac{(1.52)^2}{(2.05)(1.56)^3} = 0.297 = K_c$$

If we were to apply stress to this system by adding more N_2, increasing its concentration from 2.05 M to 3.51 M, the system would no longer be at equilibrium. To see that this is true, use the new concentration of nitrogen in the reaction quotient expression. The new calculated value of Q_c (0.173) is no longer equal to the value of K_c (0.297).

$$Q_c = \frac{[NH_3]^2}{[N_2][H_2]^3} = \frac{(1.52)^2}{(3.51)(1.56)^3} = 0.173 \neq K_c$$

Student Annotation: While reestablishing equilibrium causes a decrease in the N_2 concentration, the final concentration will still be higher than that in the original equilibrium mixture. The system responds to the stress of the added reactant by consuming part of it.

For this system to reestablish equilibrium, the net reaction will have to shift in such a way that Q_c is again equal to K_c, which is constant at a given temperature. Recall from Section 15.4 that when Q is less than K, the reaction proceeds to the right to achieve equilibrium. Likewise, an equilibrium that is stressed in such a way that Q *becomes* less than K will *shift* to the right to reestablish equilibrium. This means that the forward reaction, the consumption of N_2 and H_2 to produce NH_3, will occur. The result will be a net decrease in the concentrations of N_2 and H_2 (thus making the denominator of the reaction quotient smaller), and a net increase in the concentration of NH_3 (thus

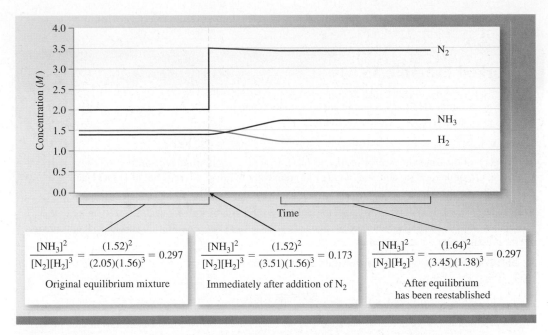

$$\frac{[NH_3]^2}{[N_2][H_2]^3} = \frac{(1.52)^2}{(2.05)(1.56)^3} = 0.297$$

Original equilibrium mixture

$$\frac{[NH_3]^2}{[N_2][H_2]^3} = \frac{(1.52)^2}{(3.51)(1.56)^3} = 0.173$$

Immediately after addition of N_2

$$\frac{[NH_3]^2}{[N_2][H_2]^3} = \frac{(1.64)^2}{(3.45)(1.38)^3} = 0.297$$

After equilibrium
has been reestablished

Figure 15.5 Adding more of a reactant to a system at equilibrium causes the equilibrium position to shift toward product. The system responds to the addition of N_2 by consuming some of the added N_2 (and some of the other reactant, H_2) to produce more NH_3.

making the numerator larger). When the concentrations of all species are such that Q_c is again equal to K_c, the system will have established a new *equilibrium position,* meaning that it will have shifted in one direction or the other, resulting in a new equilibrium concentration for each species. Figure 15.5 shows how the concentrations of N_2, H_2, and NH_3 change when N_2 is added to the original equilibrium mixture.

Conversely, if we were to remove N_2 from the original equilibrium mixture, the lower concentration in the denominator of the reaction quotient would result in Q_c being greater than K_c. In this case the reaction will shift to the left. That is, the reverse reaction will take place, thereby increasing the concentrations of N_2 and H_2 and decreasing the concentration of NH_3 until Q_c is once again equal to K_c.

The addition or removal of NH_3 will cause a shift in the equilibrium, too. The addition of NH_3 will cause a shift to the left; the removal of NH_3 will cause a shift to the right. Figure 15.6(a) shows the additions and removals that cause this equilibrium to shift to the right. Figure 15.6(b) shows those that cause it to shift to the left.

In essence, a system at equilibrium will respond to the addition of a species by consuming some of that species, and it will respond to the removal of a species by producing more of that species. It is important to remember that the addition or removal of a species from an equilibrium mixture does not change the value of the equilibrium constant, K. Rather, it changes temporarily the value of the reaction quotient, Q. Furthermore, to cause a shift in the equilibrium, the species added or removed must be one that appears in the reaction quotient expression. In the case of a heterogeneous equilibrium, altering the amount of a solid or liquid species does not change the position of the equilibrium because doing so does not change the value of Q.

(a)

(b)

Figure 15.6 (a) Addition of a reactant or removal of a product will cause an equilibrium to shift to the right. (b) Addition of a product or removal of a reactant will cause an equilibrium to shift to the left.

Worked Example 15.11 shows the effects of stress on a system at equilibrium.

Worked Example 15.11

Hydrogen sulfide (H_2S) is a contaminant commonly found in natural gas. It is removed by reaction with oxygen to produce elemental sulfur.

$$2H_2S(g) + O_2(g) \rightleftharpoons 2S(s) + 2H_2O(g)$$

For each of the following scenarios, determine whether the equilibrium will shift to the right, shift to the left, or neither: (a) addition of $O_2(g)$, (b) removal of $H_2S(g)$, (c) removal of $H_2O(g)$, and (d) addition of $S(s)$.

Strategy Use Le Châtelier's principle to predict the direction of shift for each case. Remember that the position of the equilibrium is only changed by the addition or removal of a species that appears in the reaction quotient expression.

Setup Begin by writing the reaction quotient expression:

$$Q_c = \frac{[H_2O]^2}{[H_2S]^2[O_2]}$$

Because sulfur is a solid, it does not appear in the expression. Changes in the concentration of any of the other species will cause a change in the equilibrium position. Addition of a reactant or removal of a product that appears in the expression for Q_c will shift the equilibrium to the right:

addition   addition

$$2H_2S(g) \;+\; O_2(g) \;\longrightarrow\; 2S(s) \;+\; 2H_2O(g)$$

removal

Removal of a reactant or addition of a product that appears in the expression for Q_c will shift the equilibrium to the left:

addition

$$2H_2S(g) \;+\; O_2(g) \;\longleftarrow\; 2S(s) \;+\; 2H_2O(g)$$

removal   removal

Solution

(a) Shift to the right

(b) Shift to the left

(c) Shift to the right

(d) No change

Think About It

In each case, analyze the effect the change will have on the value of Q_c. In part (a), for example, O_2 is added, so its concentration increases. Looking at the reaction quotient expression, we can see that a larger concentration of oxygen corresponds to a larger overall denominator—giving the overall fraction a smaller value. Thus, Q will temporarily be smaller than K and the reaction will have to shift to the right, consuming some of the added O_2 (along with some of the H_2S in the mixture) to reestablish equilibrium.

Practice Problem A For each change indicated, determine whether the equilibrium

$$PCl_3(g) + Cl_2(g) \rightleftharpoons PCl_5(g)$$

will shift to the right, shift to the left, or neither: (a) addition of $PCl_3(g)$, (b) removal of $PCl_3(g)$, (c) removal of $PCl_5(g)$, and (d) removal of $Cl_2(g)$.

Practice Problem B What can be added to the equilibrium that will (a) shift it to the left, (b) shift it to the right, (c) not shift it in either direction?

$$AgCl(s) + 2NH_3(aq) \rightleftharpoons Ag(NH_3)_2^+(aq) + Cl^-(aq)$$

Changes in Volume and Pressure

If we were to start with a gaseous system at equilibrium in a cylinder with a movable piston, we could change the volume of the system, thereby changing the concentrations of the reactants and products.

Consider again the equilibrium between N_2O_4 and NO_2:

$$N_2O_4(g) \rightleftharpoons 2NO_2(g)$$

At 25°C the equilibrium constant for this reaction is 4.63×10^{-3}. Suppose we have an equilibrium mixture of 0.643 M N_2O_4 and 0.0547 M NO_2 in a cylinder fitted with a movable piston. If we push down on the piston, the equilibrium will be disturbed and will shift in the direction that minimizes the effect of this disturbance. Consider what happens to the concentrations of both species if we decrease the volume of the cylinder by half. Both concentrations are initially *doubled:* $[N_2O_4] = 1.286$ M and $[NO_2] = 0.1094$ M. If we plug the new concentrations into the reaction quotient expression, we get

$$Q_c = \frac{[NO_2]^2_{eq}}{[N_2O_4]_{eq}} = \frac{(0.1094)^2}{1.286} = 9.31 \times 10^{-3}$$

which is not equal to K_c, so the system is no longer at equilibrium. Because Q_c is greater than K_c, the equilibrium will have to shift to the left for equilibrium to be reestablished (Figure 15.7).

In general, a decrease in volume of a reaction vessel will cause a shift in the equilibrium in the direction that minimizes the total number of moles of gas. Conversely, an increase in volume will cause a shift in the direction that maximizes the total number of moles of gas.

Worked Example 15.12 shows how to predict the equilibrium shift that will be caused by a volume change.

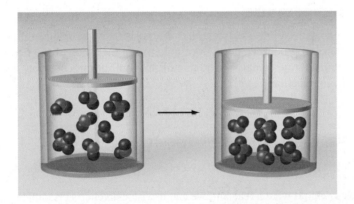

Figure 15.7 The effect of a volume decrease (pressure increase) on the $N_2O_4(g) \rightleftharpoons 2NO_2(g)$ equilibrium. When volume is decreased, the equilibrium is driven toward the side with the smallest number of moles of gas.

Worked Example 15.12

For each reaction, predict in what direction the equilibrium will shift when the volume of the reaction vessel is decreased.

(a) $PCl_5(g) \rightleftharpoons PCl_3(g) + Cl_2(g)$

(b) $2PbS(s) + 3O_2(g) \rightleftharpoons 2PbO(s) + 2SO_2(g)$

(c) $H_2(g) + I_2(g) \rightleftharpoons 2HI(g)$

Strategy Determine which direction minimized the number of moles of gas in the reaction. Count only moles of *gas*.

Setup We have (a) 1 mole of gas on the reactant side and 2 moles of gas on the product side, (b) 3 moles of gas on the reactant side and 2 moles of gas on the product side, and (c) 2 moles of gas on each side.

Solution

(a) Shift to the left

(b) Shift to the right

(c) No shift

Student Annotation: It is a common error to count all the species in a reaction to determine which side has fewer moles. To determine what direction shift a volume change will cause, it is only the number of moles of *gas* that matters.

(Continued on next page)

(a)

(b)

Figure 15.8 (a) N_2O_4-NO_2 equilibrium. (b) Because the reaction is endothermic, at higher temperature, the $N_2O_4(g) \rightleftharpoons 2NO_2(g)$ equilibrium shifts toward product, making the reaction mixture darker.

Multi 15.1
Le Châtelier's principle
Figures 15.10 and 15.11

Think About It
When there is no difference in the number of moles of gas, changing the volume of the reaction vessel will change the concentrations of reactant(s) and product(s)—but the system will remain at equilibrium. (Q will remain equal to K.)

Practice Problem A For each reaction, predict the direction of shift caused by increasing the volume of the reaction vessel.

(a) $2NOCl(g) \rightleftharpoons 2NO(g) + Cl_2(g)$

(b) $CaCO_3(s) \rightleftharpoons CaO(s) + CO_2(g)$

(c) $Zn(s) + 2H^+(aq) \rightleftharpoons Zn^{2+}(aq) + H_2(g)$

Practice Problem B For the following equilibrium, give an example of a stress that will cause a shift to the right, a stress that will cause a shift to the left, and one that will cause no shift:

$$H_2(g) + F_2(g) \rightleftharpoons 2HF(g)$$

It is possible to change the total pressure of a system without changing its volume—by adding an inert gas such as helium to the reaction vessel. Because the total volume remains the same, the concentrations of reactant and product gases do not change. Therefore, the equilibrium is not disturbed and no shift will occur.

Changes in Temperature

A change in concentration or volume may alter the position of an equilibrium (i.e., the relative amounts of reactants and products), but it does not change the value of the equilibrium constant. Only a change in temperature can alter the value of the equilibrium constant. To understand why, consider the following reaction:

$$N_2O_4(g) \rightleftharpoons 2NO_2(g)$$

The forward reaction is endothermic (absorbs heat, $\Delta H > 0$):

$$\text{Heat} + N_2O_4(g) \rightleftharpoons 2NO_2(g) \qquad \Delta H° = 58.0 \text{ kJ/mol}$$

If we treat heat as though it were a reactant, we can use Le Châtelier's principle to predict what will happen if we add or remove heat. Increasing the temperature (adding heat) will shift the reaction in the forward direction because heat appears on the reactant side. Lowering the temperature (removing heat) will shift the reaction in the reverse direction. Consequently, the equilibrium constant, given by

$$K_c = \frac{[NO_2]^2}{[N_2O_4]}$$

increases when the system is heated and decreases when the system is cooled (Figure 15.8). A similar argument can be made in the case of an exothermic reaction, where heat can be considered to be a product. Increasing the temperature of an exothermic reaction causes the equilibrium constant to decrease, shifting the equilibrium toward reactants.

Another example of this phenomenon is the equilibrium between the following ions:

$$\underset{\text{blue}}{CoCl_4^{2-}} + 6H_2O \rightleftharpoons \underset{\text{pink}}{Co(H_2O)_6^{2+}} + 4Cl^- + \text{heat}$$

The reaction as written, the formation of $Co(H_2O)_6^{2+}$, is exothermic. Thus, the reverse reaction, the formation of $CoCl_4^{2-}$, is endothermic. On heating, the equilibrium shifts to the left and the solution turns blue. Cooling favors the exothermic reaction [the formation of $Co(H_2O)_6^{2+}$] and the solution turns pink (Figure 15.9).

In summary, a temperature increase favors an endothermic reaction, and a temperature decrease favors an exothermic process. Temperature affects the position of an equilibrium by changing the value of the equilibrium constant. Figures 15.10 and 15.11 (pages 636–639) illustrate the effects of various stresses on systems at equilibrium.

(a)   (b)   (c)

Figure 15.9 (a) An equilibrium mixture of $CoCl_4^{2-}$ ions and $Co(H_2O)_6^{2+}$ ions appears violet. (b) Heating favors the formation of $CoCl_4^{2-}$, making the solution look more blue. (c) Cooling favors the formation of $Co(H_2O)_6^{2+}$, making the solution look more pink.

Catalysis

A catalyst speeds up a reaction by lowering the reaction's activation energy [◄◄ Section 14.8]. However, a catalyst lowers the activation energy of the forward and reverse reactions to the same extent (see Figure 14.17). The presence of a catalyst, therefore, does not alter the equilibrium constant, nor does it shift the position of an equilibrium system. Adding a catalyst to a reaction mixture that is not at equilibrium will simply cause the mixture to reach equilibrium sooner. The same equilibrium mixture could be obtained without the catalyst, but it might take a much longer time.

SECTION 15.5 REVIEW

Factors That Affect Chemical Equilibrium

15.5.1   Indicate in which direction the following equilibrium will shift in response to each change:

$$XY_2(s) \rightleftharpoons X(s) + Y_2(g)$$

(a) Addition of $XY_2(s)$, (b) removal of $Y_2(g)$, (c) decrease in container volume, (d) addition of $X(s)$.

15.5.2   Indicate in which direction the following equilibrium will shift in response to each change:

$$A_2(g) + B_2(g) \rightleftharpoons 2AB(g)$$

(a) Addition of $A_2(g)$, (b) removal of $B_2(g)$, (c) increase in container volume, (d) addition of $AB(g)$.

15.5.3   The diagram shows the gaseous reaction $2A \rightleftharpoons A_2$ at equilibrium. How will the numbers of A and A_2 change if the volume of the container is increased at constant temperature?

15.5.4   The diagrams show equilibrium mixtures of A_2, B_2, and AB at two different temperatures $(T_2 > T_1)$. Is the reaction $A_2 + B_2 \rightleftharpoons 2AB$ endothermic or exothermic?

A = ●
B = ◐

T_1 T_2

Figure 15.10 Le Châtelier's principle.

Effect of Addition to an Equilibrium Mixture

$$H_2(g) + I_2(g) \rightleftharpoons 2HI(g)$$

$$[H_2] = 0.112\ M$$
$$[I_2] = 0.112\ M$$
$$[HI] = 0.825\ M$$

$$Q_c = \frac{[HI]^2}{[H_2][I_2]} = \frac{(0.825)^2}{(0.112)(0.112)} = 54.3$$

$$Q_c = K_c$$

$$[H_2] = 0.112\ M$$
$$[I_2] = 0.112\ M$$
$$[HI] = 0.825\ M$$

$$Q_c = \frac{[HI]^2}{[H_2][I_2]} = \frac{(0.825)^2}{(0.112)(0.112)} = 54.3$$

$$Q_c = K_c$$

$$[H_2] = 0.112\ M$$
$$[I_2] = 0.112\ M$$
$$[HI] = 0.825\ M$$

$$Q_c = \frac{[HI]^2}{[H_2][I_2]} = \frac{(0.825)^2}{(0.112)(0.112)} = 54.3$$

$$Q_c = K_c$$

Add a reactant—$I_2(g)$.

Add a product—$HI(g)$.

Add a species not involved in the equilibrium—$He(g)$.

$$[H_2] = 0.112\ M$$
$$[I_2] = 0.499\ M$$
$$[HI] = 0.825\ M$$

$$Q_c = \frac{(0.825)^2}{(0.112)(0.499)} = 12$$

$$Q_c \neq K_c$$

$$[H_2] = 0.112\ M$$
$$[I_2] = 0.112\ M$$
$$[HI] = 3.17\ M$$

$$Q_c = \frac{(3.17)^2}{(0.112)(0.112)} = 801$$

$$Q_c \neq K_c$$

$$[H_2] = 0.112\ M$$
$$[I_2] = 0.112\ M$$
$$[HI] = 0.825\ M$$
$$[He] = 0.565\ M$$

$$Q_c = \frac{(0.825)^2}{(0.112)(0.112)} = 54.3$$

$$Q_c = K_c$$

Equilibrium shifts toward product.

Equilibrium shifts toward reactant.

Equilibrium does not shift in either direction.

$$[H_2] = 0.0404\ M$$
$$[I_2] = 0.427\ M$$
$$[HI] = 0.968\ M$$

$$Q_c = \frac{(0.968)^2}{(0.0404)(0.427)} = 54.3$$

$$Q_c = K_c$$

$$[H_2] = 0.362\ M$$
$$[I_2] = 0.362\ M$$
$$[HI] = 2.67\ M$$

$$Q_c = \frac{(2.67)^2}{(0.362)(0.362)} = 54.4$$

$$Q_c = K_c$$

$$[H_2] = 0.112\ M$$
$$[I_2] = 0.112\ M$$
$$[HI] = 0.825\ M$$
$$[He] = 0.565\ M$$

What's the point?

Adding a reactant to an equilibrium mixture shifts the equilibrium toward the product side of the equation. Adding a product shifts the equilibrium toward the reactant side. Adding a species that is neither a reactant nor a product does not cause a shift in the equilibrium.

Effect of Temperature Change

$$N_2O_4(g) \rightleftharpoons 2NO_2(g) \quad \Delta H° = 58.04 \text{ kJ/mol}$$

Temperature decrease drives an endothermic equilibrium toward reactants.

Temperature increase drives an endothermic equilibrium toward products.

$$H_2(g) + I_2(g) \rightleftharpoons 2HI(g) \quad \Delta H° = -9.4 \text{ kJ/mol}$$

Temperature increase drives an exothermic equilibrium toward reactants.

Temperature decrease drives an exothermic equilibrium toward products.

What's the point?

Increasing the temperature of an equilibrium mixture causes a shift toward the product side for an endothermic reaction, and a shift toward the reactant side for an exothermic reaction.

Figure 15.11 Le Châtelier's principle.

Effect of Volume Change

$[N_2O_4] = 1.08\ M$
$[NO_2] = 0.0707\ M$

$$Q_c = \frac{[NO_2]^2}{[N_2O_4]} = \frac{(0.0707)^2}{1.08} = 4.63 \times 10^{-3}$$

$$Q_c = K_c$$

$[N_2O_4] = 0.540\ M$
$[NO_2] = 0.0354\ M$

$$Q_c = \frac{(0.0354)^2}{0.540} = 2.3 \times 10^{-3}$$

$$Q_c \neq K_c$$

$[N_2O_4] = 2.16\ M$
$[NO_2] = 0.141\ M$

$$Q_c = \frac{(0.141)^2}{2.16} = 9.2 \times 10^{-3}$$

$$Q_c \neq K_c$$

What's the point?

Increasing the volume causes a shift toward the side with the *larger* number of moles of gas. Decreasing the volume of an equilibrium mixture causes a shift toward the side of the equation with the *smaller* number of moles of gas.

$[N_2O_4] = 0.533\ M$
$[NO_2] = 0.0497\ M$

$$Q_c = \frac{(0.0497)^2}{0.533} = 4.6 \times 10^{-3}$$

$$Q_c = K_c$$

$[N_2O_4] = 2.18\ M$
$[NO_2] = 0.100\ M$

$$Q_c = \frac{(0.100)^2}{2.18} = 4.6 \times 10^{-3}$$

$$Q_c = K_c$$

$[H_2] = 0.112\ M$
$[I_2] = 0.112\ M$
$[HI] = 0.825\ M$

$$Q_c = \frac{[HI]^2}{[H_2][I_2]} = \frac{(0.825)^2}{(0.112)(0.112)} = 54.3$$

$$Q_c = K_c$$

$[H_2] = 0.056\ M$
$[I_2] = 0.056\ M$
$[HI] = 0.413\ M$

$$Q_c = \frac{(0.413)^2}{(0.056)(0.056)} = 54.3$$

$$Q_c = K_c$$

$[H_2] = 0.224\ M$
$[I_2] = 0.224\ M$
$[HI] = 1.65\ M$

$$Q_c = \frac{(1.65)^2}{(0.224)(0.224)} = 54.3$$

$$Q_c = K_c$$

What's the point?

For an equilibrium with equal numbers of gaseous moles on both sides, a change in volume does not cause the equilibrium to shift in either direction.

$[H_2] = 0.056\ M$
$[I_2] = 0.056\ M$
$[HI] = 0.413\ M$

$$Q_c = \frac{(0.413)^2}{(0.056)(0.056)} = 54.3$$

$$Q_c = K_c$$

$[H_2] = 0.224\ M$
$[I_2] = 0.224\ M$
$[HI] = 1.65\ M$

$$Q_c = \frac{(1.65)^2}{(0.224)(0.224)} = 54.3$$

$$Q_c = K_c$$

Thinking Outside the Box

Biological Equilibria

In chemistry, and in biology, when a necessary ingredient for a process is in short supply, nature sometimes responds in a way that compensates for the shortage.

An important example of nature responding to a shortage is the production of extra red blood cells in individuals who reside at high elevation—where the concentration of oxygen is lower than at sea level. Extra red blood cells enable the blood to transport adequate oxygen from the lungs to the rest of the body, despite the low oxygen concentration. Enhanced oxygen-carrying capacity of the blood can give an athlete greater aerobic capacity and stamina (at normal oxygen concentrations). This has given rise to attempts by some athletes to increase their red blood count (RBC) artificially—a practice known as "blood doping."

Historically, blood doping has been done with blood infusions or with the drug *erythropoietin*—both of which have been banned by the World Anti-Doping Agency (WADA). In recent years, however, the use of hypoxic sleeping tents has grown in popularity. These tents are kept filled with a mixture of nitrogen and oxygen in which the oxygen concentration is lower than that in natural air. Just as the bodies of people who reside at high elevations naturally produce additional red blood cells to compensate for the lower partial pressure of oxygen in the air, the body of an athlete who spends his or her sleeping hours in a hypoxic tent adjusts in the same way, increasing the athlete's RBC. Those who "live high and train low" are believed to have an advantage over athletes who reside and train at or near sea level.

The combination of oxygen with the hemoglobin (Hb) molecule, which carries oxygen through the blood, is a complex reaction, but for our purposes it can be represented by the following simplified equation:*

$$Hb(aq) + O_2(aq) \rightleftharpoons HbO_2(aq)$$

where HbO_2 is oxyhemoglobin, the hemoglobin-oxygen complex that actually transports oxygen to tissues. The equilibrium expression for this process is

$$K_c = \frac{[HbO_2]}{[Hb][O_2]}$$

At an altitude of 3 km, the partial pressure of oxygen is only about 0.14 atm, compared with 0.20 atm at sea level. According to Le Châtelier's principle, a decrease in oxygen concentration will shift the hemoglobin-oxyhemoglobin equilibrium from right to left. This change depletes the supply of oxyhemoglobin, causing hypoxia. Over time, the body copes with this problem by producing more hemoglobin molecules. As the concentration of Hb increases, the equilibrium gradually shifts back toward the right (toward the formation of oxyhemoglobin). It can take several weeks for the increase in hemoglobin production to meet the body's oxygen needs adequately. A return to full capacity may require several years to occur. Studies show that long-time residents of high-altitude areas have high hemoglobin levels in their blood—sometimes as much as 50 percent more than individuals living at sea level. The production of more hemoglobin and the resulting increased capacity of the blood to deliver oxygen to the body have made high-altitude training and hypoxic tents popular among some athletes.

*Biological processes such as this are not true equilibria, but rather they are *steady-state* situations. In a steady state, the constant concentrations of reactants and products are not the result of forward and reverse reactions occurring at the same rate. Instead, reactant concentration is replenished by a previous reaction and product concentration is maintained by a subsequent reaction. Nevertheless, many of the principles of equilibrium, including Le Châtelier's principle, still apply.

Learning Outcomes

- Define reversible process.
- Define equilibrium.
- Write the equilibrium constant expression for a given reaction.
- Determine the value of the equilibrium constant given equilibrium concentrations of reactants and products.
- Differentiate between equilibrium constant and reaction quotient.
- Use the equilibrium constant to predict the relative amounts of reactants and products at equilibrium.
- Differentiate between heterogeneous and homogeneous equilibria.
- Convert between K_c and K_P for a reaction involving gases.

- Predict the direction of a reaction given initial concentrations of reactants and products and the value of the equilibrium constant.
- Calculate the equilibrium concentration of reactants or products given initial concentrations.
- Construct an equilibrium table for a reaction and use it to determine equilibrium, initial or final concentrations of a reactant or product.
- Give in your own words the meaning of Le Châtelier's principle.
- Apply Le Châtelier's principle toward determining the shift of a reaction at equilibrium given a change in one of the following: removal or addition of reactant or product, change in volume or pressure, and temperature change.

Chapter Summary

SECTION 15.1

- By our definition of a chemical reaction, reactants are consumed and products are produced. This is known as the *forward* reaction. A **reversible process** is one in which the products can also be consumed to produce reactants, a process known as the *reverse* reaction.
- *Equilibrium* is the condition where the forward and reverse reactions are occurring at the same rate and there is no net change in the reactant and product concentrations over time.
- In theory, equilibrium can be established starting with just reactants, with just products, or with a combination of reactants and products.

SECTION 15.2

- The **reaction quotient** (Q_c) is the product of the *product concentrations* over the product of the *reactant concentrations,* with each concentration raised to a power equal to the corresponding stoichiometric coefficient in the balanced chemical equation. This is known as the **law of mass action.**
- At equilibrium, the reaction quotient is equal to a constant value, the **equilibrium constant (K_c).**
- At equilibrium, concentrations in the reaction quotient are *equilibrium* concentrations and the quotient is called the **equilibrium expression.**

- K_c is constant at constant temperature. The value of K_c can be calculated by plugging equilibrium concentrations into the equilibrium expression.
- A large equilibrium constant ($K_c > 10^2$) indicates that products are favored at equilibrium. A small equilibrium constant ($K_c < 10^{-2}$) indicates that reactants are favored at equilibrium.

SECTION 15.3

- Solids and liquids do not appear in the equilibrium expression for a heterogeneous reaction.
- When chemical equations that represent equilibria are reversed, multiplied, combined with other equations, or any combination of these processes, the corresponding changes must be made to the equilibrium constants.
- Equilibrium expressions that contain only gases can be written either as K_c expressions or as K_P expressions. K_P expressions have the same form as K_c expressions but contain partial pressures rather than molar concentrations. The reaction quotient, Q, can also be expressed in terms of the pressures of products and reactants. In this case it is labeled Q_P.
- K_c and K_P are not usually equal. The values are the same *only* when the reaction results in no net change in the number of moles of gas.

SECTION 15.4

- We can predict in which direction a reaction must proceed to achieve equilibrium by comparing the values of Q_c and K_c (or of Q_P and K_P).
- Starting concentrations can be used, along with the equilibrium expression and equilibrium constant, to determine equilibrium concentrations.

SECTION 15.5

- According to *Le Châtelier's principle,* a system at equilibrium will react to stress by shifting in the direction that will partially offset the effect of the stress.
- The stresses that can be applied to a system at equilibrium include the addition or removal of a substance, changes in the volume of the reaction vessel, and changes in the temperature.
- The addition of a catalyst does not shift the equilibrium in either direction.

Key Words

Equilibrium, 610
Equilibrium constant
(K_c or K_P), 612

Equilibrium expression, 612
Law of mass action, 612
Le Châtelier's principle, 630

Reaction quotient
(Q_c or Q_P), 612

Reversible process, 610

Key Equations

15.1 $\quad Q_c = \dfrac{[C]^c[D]^d}{[A]^a[B]^b} = K_c$ (at equilibrium)

15.2 $\quad Q_c = \dfrac{[C]^c[D]^d}{[A]^a[B]^b}$

15.3 $\quad \Delta n = $ moles of gaseous products $-$ moles of gaseous reactants

15.4 $\quad K_P = K_c\,[(0.08206 \text{ L} \cdot \text{atm/K} \cdot \text{mol}) \times T]^{\Delta n}$

Questions and Problems

SECTION 15.1:   THE CONCEPT OF EQUILIBRIUM

Review Questions

15.1   Define *equilibrium*. Give two examples of a dynamic equilibrium.

15.2   Which of the following statements is correct about a reacting system at equilibrium: (a) the concentrations of reactants are equal to the concentrations of products, (b) the rate of the forward reaction is equal to the rate of the reverse reaction.

15.3   Consider the reversible reaction A $\rightleftharpoons$ B. Explain how equilibrium can be reached by starting with only A, only B, or a mixture of A and B.

SECTION 15.2:   THE EQUILIBRIUM CONSTANT

Review Questions

15.4   What is the law of mass action?

15.5   Briefly describe the importance of equilibrium in the study of chemical reactions.

15.6   Define *reaction quotient*. How does it differ from the equilibrium constant?

15.7   Write reaction quotients for the following reactions: (a) $2NO(g) + O_2(g) \rightleftharpoons N_2O_4(g)$, (b) $S(s) + 3F_2(g) \rightleftharpoons SF_6(g)$, (c) $Co^{3+}(aq) + 6NH_3(aq) \rightleftharpoons Co(NH_3)_6^{3+}(aq)$, (d) $HCOOH(aq) \rightleftharpoons HCOO^-(aq) + H^+(aq)$.

15.8   Write the equation for the reaction that corresponds to each of the following reaction quotients:

(a) $Q_c = \dfrac{[H_2]^2[S_2]}{[H_2S]^2}$

(b) $Q_c = \dfrac{[NO_2]^2[Cl_2]}{[NClO_2]^2}$

(c) $Q_c = \dfrac{[HgI_4^{2-}]}{[Hg^{2+}][I^-]^4}$

(d) $Q_c = \dfrac{[NO]^2[Br_2]}{[NOBr]^2}$

Problems

15.9 Consider the reaction

$$2NO(g) + 2H_2(g) \rightleftharpoons N_2(g) + 2H_2O(g)$$

At a certain temperature, the equilibrium concentrations are [NO] = 0.31 M, [H$_2$] = 0.16 M, [N$_2$] = 0.082 M, and [H$_2$O] = 4.64 M. (a) Write the equilibrium expression for the reaction. (b) Determine the value of the equilibrium constant.

15.10 The equilibrium constant for the reaction

$$2SO_2(g) + O_2(g) \rightleftharpoons 2SO_3(g)$$

is 2.8 × 10^2 at a certain temperature. If [SO$_2$] = 0.0124 M and [O$_2$] = 0.031 M, what is [SO$_3$]?

15.11 Consider the following equilibrium process at 700°C:

$$2H_2(g) + S_2(g) \rightleftharpoons 2H_2S(g)$$

Analysis shows that there are 2.50 moles of H$_2$, 1.35 × 10^{-5} mole of S$_2$, and 8.70 moles of H$_2$S present in a 12.0-L flask. Calculate the equilibrium constant K_c for the reaction.

15.12 The equilibrium constant for the reaction

$$2H_2(g) + CO(g) \rightleftharpoons CH_3OH(g)$$

is 1.6 × 10^{-2} at a certain temperature. If there are 1.17 × 10^{-2} mole of H$_2$ and 3.46 × 10^{-3} mole of CH$_3$OH at equilibrium in a 5.60-L flask, what is the concentration of CO?

SECTION 15.3: EQUILIBRIUM EXPRESSIONS

Review Questions

15.13 Define *homogeneous* equilibrium and *heterogeneous* equilibrium. Give two examples of each.

15.14 What do the symbols K_c and K_p represent?

15.15 Write the expressions for the equilibrium constants K_P of the following thermal decomposition reactions:
(a) 2NaHCO$_3$(s) $\rightleftharpoons$ Na$_2$CO$_3$(s) + CO$_2$(g) + H$_2$O(g)
(b) 2CaSO$_4$(s) $\rightleftharpoons$ 2CaO(s) + 2SO$_2$(g) + O$_2$(g)

15.16 Write equilibrium constant expressions for K_c and for K_P, if applicable, for the following processes:
(a) 2CO$_2$(g) $\rightleftharpoons$ 2CO(g) + O$_2$(g)
(b) 3O$_2$(g) $\rightleftharpoons$ 2O$_3$(g)
(c) CO(g) + Cl$_2$(g) $\rightleftharpoons$ COCl$_2$(g)
(d) H$_2$O(g) + C(s) $\rightleftharpoons$ CO(g) + H$_2$(g)
(e) HCOOH(aq) $\rightleftharpoons$ H$^+$(aq) + HCOO$^-$(aq)
(f) 2HgO(s) $\rightleftharpoons$ 2Hg(l) + O$_2$(g)

15.17 Write the equilibrium constant expressions for K_c and for K_P, if applicable, for the following reactions:
(a) 2NO$_2$(g) + 7H$_2$(g) $\rightleftharpoons$ 2NH$_3$(g) + 4H$_2$O(l)
(b) 2ZnS(s) + 3O$_2$(g) $\rightleftharpoons$ 2ZnO(s) + 2SO$_2$(g)
(c) C(s) + CO$_2$(g) $\rightleftharpoons$ 2CO(g)
(d) C$_6$H$_5$COOH(aq) $\rightleftharpoons$ C$_6$H$_5$COO$^-$(aq) + H$^+$(aq)

15.18 Write the equation relating K_c to K_P, and define all the terms.

15.19 What is the rule for writing the equilibrium constant for the overall reaction that is the sum of two or more reactions?

15.20 Give an example of a multiple equilibria reaction.

Problems

15.21 The equilibrium constant for the reaction A $\rightleftharpoons$ B is K_c = 10 at a certain temperature. (1) Starting with only reactant A, which of the diagrams shown here best represents the system at equilibrium? (2) Which of the diagrams best represents the system at equilibrium if K_c = 0.10? Explain why you can calculate K_c in each case without knowing the volume of the container. The grey spheres represent the A molecules, and the green spheres represent the B molecules.

(a)   (b)   (c)   (d)

15.22 The following diagrams represent the equilibrium state for three different reactions of the type

$$A + X \rightleftharpoons AX \ (X = B, C, \text{ or } D)$$

A + B $\rightleftharpoons$ AB   A + C $\rightleftharpoons$ AC   A + D $\rightleftharpoons$ AD

(a) Which reaction has the largest equilibrium constant? (b) Which reaction has the smallest equilibrium constant?

15.23 The equilibrium constant (K_c) for the reaction

$$2HCl(g) \rightleftharpoons H_2(g) + Cl_2(g)$$

is 4.17 × 10^{-34} at 25°C. What is the equilibrium constant for the reaction

$$H_2(g) + Cl_2(g) \rightleftharpoons 2HCl(g)$$

at the same temperature?

15.24 What is K_P at 1273°C for the reaction

$$2CO(g) + O_2(g) \rightleftharpoons 2CO_2(g)$$

if K_c is 2.24 × 10^{22} at the same temperature?

15.25 The equilibrium constant K_P for the reaction

$$2SO_3(g) \rightleftharpoons 2SO_2(g) + O_2(g)$$

is 1.8 × 10^{-5} at 350°C. What is K_c for this reaction?

15.26 Consider the reaction

$$N_2(g) + O_2(g) \rightleftharpoons 2NO(g)$$

If the equilibrium partial pressures of N$_2$, O$_2$, and NO are 0.15, 0.33, and 0.050 atm, respectively, at 2200°C, what is K_P?

15.27 A reaction vessel contains NH$_3$, N$_2$, and H$_2$ at equilibrium at a certain temperature. The equilibrium concentrations are [NH$_3$] = 0.25 M, [N$_2$] = 0.11 M, and [H$_2$] = 1.91 M. Calculate the equilibrium constant

K_c for the synthesis of ammonia if the reaction is represented as

(a) $N_2(g) + 3H_2(g) \rightleftharpoons 2NH_3(g)$

(b) $\frac{1}{2}N_2(g) + \frac{1}{2}H_2(g) \rightleftharpoons NH_3(g)$

15.28 The equilibrium constant K_c for the reaction

$$I_2(g) \rightleftharpoons 2I(g)$$

is 3.8×10^{-5} at 727°C. Calculate K_c and K_P for the equilibrium

$$2I(g) \rightleftharpoons I_2(g)$$

at the same temperature.

15.29 At equilibrium, the pressure of the reacting mixture

$$CaCO_3(s) \rightleftharpoons CaO(s) + CO_2(g)$$

is 0.105 atm at 350°C. Calculate K_P and K_c for this reaction.

15.30 The equilibrium constant K_P for the reaction

$$PCl_5(g) \rightleftharpoons PCl_3(g) + Cl_2(g)$$

is 1.05 at 250°C. The reaction starts with a mixture of PCl_5, PCl_3, and Cl_2 at pressures of 0.177, 0.223, and 0.111 atm, respectively, at 250°C. When the mixture comes to equilibrium at that temperature, which pressures will have decreased and which will have increased? Explain why.

15.31 Ammonium carbamate ($NH_4CO_2NH_2$) decomposes as follows:

$$NH_4CO_2NH_2(s) \rightleftharpoons 2NH_3(g) + CO_2(g)$$

Starting with only the solid, it is found that when the system reaches equilibrium at 40°C, the total gas pressure (NH_3 and CO_2) is 0.363 atm. Calculate the equilibrium constant K_P.

15.32 Pure phosgene gas ($COCl_2$), 3.00×10^{-2} mol, was placed in a 1.50-L container. It was heated to 800 K, and at equilibrium the pressure of CO was found to be 0.497 atm. Calculate the equilibrium constant K_P for the reaction

$$CO(g) + Cl_2(g) \rightleftharpoons COCl_2(g)$$

15.33 Consider the equilibrium

$$2NOBr(g) \rightleftharpoons 2NO(g) + Br_2(g)$$

If nitrosyl bromide (NOBr) is 34 percent dissociated at 25°C and the total pressure is 0.25 atm, calculate K_P and K_c for the dissociation at this temperature.

15.34 The following equilibrium constants have been determined for hydrosulfuric acid at 25°C:

$$H_2S(aq) \rightleftharpoons H^+(aq) + HS^-(aq) \quad K_c' = 9.5 \times 10^{-8}$$

$$HS^-(aq) \rightleftharpoons H^+(aq) + S^{2-}(aq) \quad K_c'' = 1.0 \times 10^{-19}$$

Calculate the equilibrium constant for the following reaction at the same temperature:

$$H_2S(aq) \rightleftharpoons 2H^+(aq) + S^{2-}(aq)$$

15.35 The following equilibrium constants have been determined for oxalic acid at 25°C:

$$H_2C_2O_4(aq) \rightleftharpoons H^+(aq) + HC_2O_4^-(aq) \quad K_c' = 6.5 \times 10^{-2}$$

$$HC_2O_4^-(aq) \rightleftharpoons H^+(aq) + C_2O_4^{2-}(aq) \quad K_c'' = 6.1 \times 10^{-5}$$

Calculate the equilibrium constant for the following reaction at the same temperature:

$$H_2C_2O_4(aq) \rightleftharpoons 2H^+(aq) + C_2O_4^{2-}(aq)$$

15.36 The following equilibrium constants were determined at 1123 K:

$$C(s) + CO_2(g) \rightleftharpoons 2CO(g) \quad K_P' = 1.3 \times 10^{14}$$

$$CO(g) + Cl_2(g) \rightleftharpoons COCl_2(g) \quad K_P'' = 6.0 \times 10^{-3}$$

Write the equilibrium constant expression K_P, and calculate the equilibrium constant at 1123 K for

$$C(s) + CO_2(g) + 2Cl_2(g) \rightleftharpoons 2COCl_2(g)$$

15.37 At a certain temperature, the following reactions have the constants shown:

$$S(s) + O_2(g) \rightleftharpoons SO_2(g) \quad K_c' = 4.2 \times 10^{52}$$

$$2S(s) + 3O_2(g) \rightleftharpoons 2SO_3(g) \quad K_c'' = 9.8 \times 10^{128}$$

Calculate the equilibrium constant K_c for the following reaction at that temperature:

$$2SO_2(g) + O_2(g) \rightleftharpoons 2SO_3(g)$$

SECTION 15.4: USING EQUILIBRIUM EXPRESSIONS TO SOLVE PROBLEMS

Review Questions

15.38 Outline the steps for calculating the concentrations of reacting species in an equilibrium reaction.

Problems

15.39 If $K_c = 2$ for the reaction $A_2 + B_2 \rightleftharpoons 2AB$ at a certain temperature, which of the following diagrams represents an equilibrium mixture of A_2, B_2, and AB? (Select all that apply.)

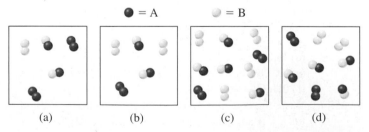

● = A   ◐ = B

(a)   (b)   (c)   (d)

15.40 A and B react to form A_2B according to the following equation:

$$2A + B \rightleftharpoons A_2B$$

All but one of the figures below represent equilibrium mixtures of A, B, and A_2B. Identify the figure in which the mixture is not at equilibrium.

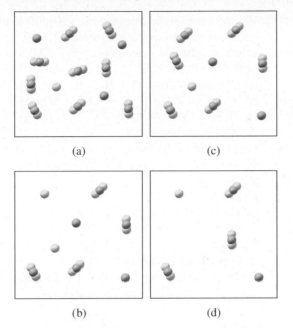

(a)   (c)

(b)   (d)

15.41 For the reaction

$$H_2(g) + CO_2(g) \rightleftharpoons H_2O(g) + CO(g)$$

at 700°C, $K_c = 0.534$. Calculate the number of moles of H_2 that are present at equilibrium if a mixture of 0.300 mole of CO and 0.300 mole of H_2O is heated to 700°C in a 10.0-L container.

15.42 At 1000 K, a sample of pure NO_2 gas decomposes:

$$2NO_2(g) \rightleftharpoons 2NO(g) + O_2(g)$$

The equilibrium constant K_P is 158. Analysis shows that the partial pressure of O_2 is 0.25 atm at equilibrium. Calculate the pressure of NO and NO_2 in the mixture.

15.43 The equilibrium constant K_c for the reaction

$$H_2(g) + Br_2(g) \rightleftharpoons 2HBr(g)$$

is 2.18×10^6 at 730°C. Starting with 3.20 moles of HBr in a 12.0-L reaction vessel, calculate the concentrations of H_2, Br_2, and HBr at equilibrium.

15.44 The dissociation of molecular iodine into iodine atoms is represented as

$$I_2(g) \rightleftharpoons 2I(g)$$

At 1000 K, the equilibrium constant K_c for the reaction is 3.80×10^{-5}. Suppose you start with 0.0456 mole of I_2 in a 2.30-L flask at 1000 K. What are the concentrations of the gases at equilibrium?

15.45 The equilibrium constant K_c for the decomposition of phosgene ($COCl_2$) is 4.63×10^{-3} at 527°C:

$$COCl_2(g) \rightleftharpoons CO(g) + Cl_2(g)$$

Calculate the equilibrium partial pressures of all the components, starting with pure phosgene at 0.760 atm.

15.46 Consider the following equilibrium process at 686°C:

$$CO_2(g) + H_2(g) \rightleftharpoons CO(g) + H_2O(g)$$

The equilibrium concentrations of the reacting species are [CO] = 0.050 M, [H_2] = 0.045 M, [CO_2] = 0.086 M, and [H_2O] = 0.040 M. (a) Calculate K_c for the reaction at 686°C. (b) If we add CO_2 to increase its concentration to 0.50 mol/L, what will the concentrations of all the gases be when equilibrium is reestablished?

15.47 Consider the heterogeneous equilibrium process:

$$C(s) + CO_2(g) \rightleftharpoons 2CO(g)$$

At 700°C, the total pressure of the system is found to be 4.50 atm. If the equilibrium constant K_P is 1.52, calculate the equilibrium partial pressures of CO_2 and CO.

15.48 The equilibrium constant K_c for the reaction

$$H_2(g) + CO_2(g) \rightleftharpoons H_2O(g) + CO(g)$$

is 4.2 at 1650°C. Initially 0.80 mol H_2 and 0.80 mol CO_2 are injected into a 5.0-L flask. Calculate the concentration of each species at equilibrium.

15.49 The aqueous reaction

L-glutamate + pyruvate $\rightleftharpoons$ α-ketoglutarate + L-alanine

is catalyzed by the enzyme L-glutamate–pyruvate aminotransferase. At 300 K, the equilibrium constant for the reaction is 1.11. Predict whether the forward reaction will occur if the concentrations of the reactants and products are [L-glutamate] = 3.0×10^{-5} M, [pyruvate] = 3.3×10^{-4} M, [α-ketoglutarate] = 1.6×10^{-2} M, and [L-alanine] = 6.25×10^{-3} M.

SECTION 15.5: FACTORS THAT AFFECT CHEMICAL EQUILIBRIUM

 Visualizing Chemistry
Figure 15.10 and Figure 15.11

Solid calcium carbonate decomposes to form solid calcium oxide and carbon dioxide gas.

$$CaCO_3(s) \rightleftharpoons CaO(s) + CO_2(g) \qquad \Delta H° = 177.8 \text{ kJ/mol}$$

Consider an equilibrium mixture of calcium carbonate and its decomposition products in a container.

VC 15.1 Which of the following changes will result in the formation of more CaO(s)?
(a) addition of more $CaCO_3$(s)
(b) addition of more CO_2(g)
(c) removal of some of the CO_2(g)

VC 15.2 Which of the following changes will result in the formation of more $CaCO_3$(s)?
(a) addition of more CaO(s)
(b) addition of more CO_2(g)
(c) removal of some of the $CaCO_3$(s)

VC 15.3 Which of the following changes will not cause the equilibrium to shift in either direction? (Select all that apply.)
(a) removal of some of the $CaCO_3(s)$
(b) removal of some of the $CO_2(g)$
(c) addition of more $CaO(s)$

VC 15.4 Which of the following will be affected by a change in the system's temperature? (Select all that apply.)
(a) the amount of $CaCO_3(s)$
(b) the amount of $CaO(s)$
(c) the amount of $CO_2(g)$

A sample of calcium carbonate is in equilibrium with its decomposition products in a closed system:
$CaCO_3(s) \rightleftharpoons CaO(s) + CO_2(g)$.

VC 15.5 If the volume of the system is increased at constant temperature, relative to the original equilibrium mixture, which of the following will be true when equilibrium is reestablished? (Select all that apply.)
(a) There will be a higher concentration of $CO_2(g)$.
(b) There will be a lower concentration of $CO_2(g)$.
(c) There will be more $CO_2(g)$.

VC 15.6 If the volume of the system is decreased at constant temperature, relative to the original equilibrium mixture, which of the following will be true when equilibrium is reestablished? (Select all that apply.)
(a) There will be more $CaCO_3(s)$.
(b) There will be more $CaO(s)$.
(c) There will be more $CO_2(g)$.

A sample of gaseous hydrogen iodide is in equilibrium with its decomposition products in a closed system:
$2HI(g) \rightleftharpoons H_2(g) + I_2(g)$.

VC 15.7 If the volume of the system is increased at constant temperature, relative to the original equilibrium mixture, which of the following will be true when equilibrium is reestablished?
(a) The concentration of HI will increase and the concentrations of H_2 and I_2 will decrease.
(b) The concentration of all three species will be lower.
(c) The concentration of all three species will be unchanged.

VC 15.8 If the volume of the system is decreased at constant temperature, relative to the original equilibrium mixture, which of the following will be true when equilibrium is reestablished?
(a) There will be more HI.
(b) There will be less HI.
(c) The amount of HI will be unchanged.

Review Questions

15.50   Explain Le Châtelier's principle. How does this principle enable us to maximize the yields of desirable reactions and minimize the effect of undesirable ones?

15.51   Use Le Châtelier's principle to explain why the equilibrium vapor pressure of a liquid increases with increasing temperature.

15.52   List four factors that can shift the position of an equilibrium. Only one of these factors can alter the value of the equilibrium constant. Which one is it?

15.53   Does the addition of a catalyst have any effects on the position of an equilibrium?

Problems

15.54   Which of the following equilibria will shift to the left when the temperature is increased? [ΔH (kJ/mol) values are given in parentheses.] (Select all that apply.)
(a) $S + H_2 \rightleftharpoons H_2S$ ΔH (−20)
(b) $C + H_2O \rightleftharpoons CO + H_2$ ΔH (131)
(c) $H_2 + CO_2 \rightleftharpoons H_2O + CO$ ΔH (41)
(d) $MgO + CO_2 \rightleftharpoons MgCO_3$ ΔH (−117)
(e) $2CO + O_2 \rightleftharpoons 2CO_2$ ΔH (−566)

15.55   For which of the following reactions will a change in volume *not* affect the position of the equilibrium? (Select all that apply.)
(a) $MgO(s) + CO_2(g) \rightleftharpoons MgCO_3(s)$
(b) $H_2(g) + Cl_2(g) \rightleftharpoons 2HCl(g)$
(c) $BaCO_3(s) \rightleftharpoons BaO(s) + CO_2(g)$
(d) $Br_2(l) + H_2(g) \rightleftharpoons 2HBr(g)$
(e) $C(graphite) + CO_2(g) \rightleftharpoons 2CO(g)$

15.56   Which of the following equilibria will shift to the right when H_2 is added? (Select all that apply.)
(a) $2H_2 + O_2 \rightleftharpoons 2H_2O$
(b) $2HI \rightleftharpoons H_2 + I_2$
(c) $H_2 + CO_2 \rightleftharpoons H_2O + CO$
(d) $2NaHCO_3 \rightleftharpoons Na_2CO_3 + H_2O + CO_2$
(e) $2CO + O_2 \rightleftharpoons 2CO_2$

15.57   Which of the following will cause the equilibrium

$$C(graphite) + CO_2(g) \rightleftharpoons 2CO(g)$$

to shift to the right? (Select all that apply.)
(a) decreasing the volume
(b) increasing the volume
(c) adding more C(graphite)
(d) adding more $CO_2(g)$
(e) removing $CO(g)$ as it forms

15.58   Consider the following equilibrium system involving SO_2, Cl_2, and SO_2Cl_2 (sulfuryl dichloride):

$$SO_2(g) + Cl_2(g) \rightleftharpoons SO_2Cl_2(g)$$

Predict how the equilibrium position would change if (a) Cl_2 gas were added to the system, (b) SO_2Cl_2 were removed from the system, (c) SO_2 were removed from the system. The temperature remains constant in each case.

15.59   Heating solid sodium bicarbonate in a closed vessel establishes the following equilibrium:

$$2NaHCO_3(s) \rightleftharpoons Na_2CO_3(s) + H_2O(g) + CO_2(g)$$

What would happen to the equilibrium position if (a) some of the CO_2 were removed from the system, (b) some solid Na_2CO_3 were added to the system, (c) some of the solid $NaHCO_3$ were removed from the system? The temperature remains constant.

15.60   Consider the following equilibrium systems:
(a) $A \rightleftharpoons 2B$ $\Delta H° = 20.0$ kJ/mol
(b) $A + B \rightleftharpoons C$ $\Delta H° = -5.4$ kJ/mol
(c) $A \rightleftharpoons B$ $\Delta H° = 0.0$ kJ/mol
Predict the change in the equilibrium constant K_c that would occur in each case if the temperature of the reacting system were raised.

15.61 What effect does an increase in pressure have on each of the following systems at equilibrium? The temperature is kept constant, and, in each case, the reactants are in a cylinder fitted with a movable piston.
(a) $A(s) \rightleftharpoons 2B(s)$
(b) $2A(l) \rightleftharpoons B(l)$
(c) $A(s) \rightleftharpoons B(g)$
(d) $A(g) \rightleftharpoons B(g)$
(e) $A(g) \rightleftharpoons 2B(g)$

15.62 Consider the equilibrium

$$2I(g) \rightleftharpoons I_2(g)$$

What would be the effect on the position of equilibrium of (a) increasing the total pressure on the system by decreasing its volume, (b) adding I_2 to the reaction mixture, and (c) decreasing the temperature?

15.63 Consider the following equilibrium process:

$$PCl_5(g) \rightleftharpoons PCl_3(g) + Cl_2(g) \quad \Delta H° = 92.5 \text{ kJ/mol}$$

Predict the direction of the shift in equilibrium when (a) the temperature is raised, (b) more chlorine gas is added to the reaction mixture, (c) some PCl_3 is removed from the mixture, (d) the pressure on the gases is increased, (e) a catalyst is added to the reaction mixture.

15.64 Consider the reaction

$$2SO_2(g) + O_2(g) \rightleftharpoons 2SO_3(g) \quad \Delta H° = -198.2 \text{ kJ/mol}$$

Comment on the changes in the concentrations of SO_2, O_2, and SO_3 at equilibrium if we were to (a) increase the temperature, (b) increase the pressure, (c) increase SO_2, (d) add a catalyst, (e) add helium at constant volume.

15.65 In the uncatalyzed reaction

$$N_2O_4(g) \rightleftharpoons 2NO_2(g)$$

the pressure of the gases at equilibrium are $P_{N_2O_4} = 0.377$ atm and $P_{NO_2} = 1.56$ atm at 100°C. What would happen to these pressures if a catalyst were added to the mixture?

15.66 Consider the gas-phase reaction

$$2CO(g) + O_2(g) \rightleftharpoons 2CO_2(g)$$

Predict the shift in the equilibrium position when helium gas is added to the equilibrium mixture (a) at constant pressure and (b) at constant volume.

15.67 Consider the following equilibrium reaction in a closed container:

$$CaCO_3(s) \rightleftharpoons CaO(s) + CO_2(g)$$

What will happen if (a) the volume is increased, (b) some CaO is added to the mixture, (c) some $CaCO_3$ is removed, (d) some CO_2 is added to the mixture, (e) a few drops of an NaOH solution are added to the mixture, (f) a few drops of an HCl solution are added to the mixture (ignore the reaction between CO_2 and water), (g) temperature is increased?

15.68 The following diagrams show the reaction $A + B \rightleftharpoons AB$ at two different temperatures. Is the forward reaction endothermic or exothermic?

600 K   800 K

15.69 The following diagrams show an equilibrium mixture of O_2 and O_3 at temperatures T_1 and T_2 ($T_2 > T_1$). (a) Write an equilibrium equation showing the forward reaction to be exothermic. (b) Predict how the number of O_2 and O_3 molecules would change if the volume were decreased at constant temperature.

T_1 T_2

15.70 The simplified equation representing the binding of oxygen by hemoglobin (Hb) is

$$Hb(aq) + O_2(aq) \rightleftharpoons HbO_2(aq) \quad \Delta H < 0$$

Determine how each of the following affects the amount of HbO_2: (a) decreasing the temperature; (b) increasing the pressure of O_2; (c) decreasing the amount of hemoglobin.

15.71 The effect of acid (H^+) on the binding of oxygen to hemoglobin can be summarized as follows:

$$HbH^+(aq) + O_2(aq) \rightleftharpoons HbO_2(aq) + H^+(aq)$$

During strenuous exercise, acid can build up in a condition known as *acidosis*. What happens to the concentration of oxyhemoglobin as acidosis occurs?

ADDITIONAL PROBLEMS

15.72 Consider the following reaction at equilibrium:

$$A(g) \rightleftharpoons 2B(g)$$

From the data shown here, calculate the equilibrium constant (both K_p and K_c) at each temperature. Is the reaction endothermic or exothermic?

Temperature (°C)	[A] (M)	[B] (M)
200	0.0125	0.843
300	0.171	0.764
400	0.250	0.724

15.73 The equilibrium constant K_P for the reaction

$$2H_2O(g) \rightleftharpoons 2H_2(g) + O_2(g)$$

is 2×10^{-42} at 25°C. (a) What is K_c for the reaction at the same temperature? (b) The very small value of K_P (and

K_c) indicates that the reaction overwhelmingly favors the formation of water molecules. Explain why, despite this fact, a mixture of hydrogen and oxygen gases can be kept at room temperature without any change.

15.74   Consider the following reacting system:

$$2NO(g) + Cl_2(g) \rightleftharpoons 2NOCl(g)$$

What combination of temperature and pressure would maximize the yield of nitrosyl chloride (NOCl)? [*Hint:* $\Delta H_f^\circ(NOCl) = 51.7$ kJ/mol.]

15.75   At a certain temperature and a total pressure of 1.2 atm, the partial pressures of an equilibrium mixture

$$2A(g) \rightleftharpoons B(g)$$

are $P_A = 0.60$ atm and $P_B = 0.60$ atm. (a) Calculate the K_P for the reaction at this temperature. (b) If the total pressure were increased to 1.5 atm, what would be the partial pressures of A and B at equilibrium?

15.76   The decomposition of ammonium hydrogen sulfide

$$NH_4HS(s) \rightleftharpoons NH_3(g) + H_2S(g)$$

is an endothermic process. A 6.1589-g sample of the solid is placed in an evacuated 4.000-L vessel at exactly 24°C. After equilibrium has been established, the total pressure inside is 0.709 atm. Some solid NH_4HS remains in the vessel. (a) What is the K_P for the reaction? (b) What percentage of the solid has decomposed? (c) If the volume of the vessel were doubled at constant temperature, what would happen to the amount of solid in the vessel?

15.77   Consider the reaction

$$2NO(g) + O_2(g) \rightleftharpoons 2NO_2(g)$$

At 430°C, an equilibrium mixture consists of 0.020 mole of O_2, 0.040 mole of NO, and 0.96 mole of NO_2. Calculate K_P for the reaction, given that the total pressure is 0.20 atm.

15.78   When heated, ammonium carbamate decomposes as follows:

$$NH_4CO_2NH_2(s) \rightleftharpoons 2NH_3(g) + CO_2(g)$$

At a certain temperature, the equilibrium pressure of the system is 0.318 atm. Calculate K_P for the reaction.

15.79   A mixture of 0.47 mole of H_2 and 3.59 moles of HCl is heated to 2800°C. Calculate the equilibrium partial pressures of H_2, Cl_2, and HCl if the total pressure is 2.00 atm. For the reaction

$$H_2(g) + Cl_2(g) \rightleftharpoons 2HCl(g)$$

K_P is 193 at 2800°C.

15.80   When heated at high temperatures, iodine vapor dissociates as follows:

$$I_2(g) \rightleftharpoons 2I(g)$$

In one experiment, a chemist finds that when 0.054 mole of I_2 was placed in a flask of volume 0.48 L at 587 K, the degree of dissociation (that is, the fraction of I_2 dissociated) was 0.0252. Calculate K_c and K_P for the reaction at this temperature.

15.81   One mole of N_2 and three moles of H_2 are placed in a flask at 375°C. Calculate the total pressure of the system at equilibrium if the mole fraction of NH_3 is 0.21. The K_P for the reaction is 4.31×10^{-4}.

15.82   At 1130°C, the equilibrium constant (K_c) for the reaction

$$2H_2S(g) \rightleftharpoons 2H_2(g) + S_2(g)$$

is 2.25×10^{-4}. If $[H_2S] = 4.84 \times 10^{-3}$ M and $[H_2] = 1.50 \times 10^{-3}$ M, calculate $[S_2]$.

15.83   A quantity of 6.75 g of SO_2Cl_2 was placed in a 2.00-L flask. At 648 K, there is 0.0345 mole of SO_2 present. Calculate K_c for the reaction

$$SO_2Cl_2(g) \rightleftharpoons SO_2(g) + Cl_2(g)$$

15.84   The following diagram represents a gas-phase equilibrium mixture for the reaction $AB \rightleftharpoons A + B$ at a certain temperature. Describe what would happen to the system after each of the following changes: (a) the temperature is decreased, (b) the volume is increased, (c) He atoms are added to the mixture at constant volume, (d) a catalyst is added to the mixture.

15.85   The formation of SO_3 from SO_2 and O_2 is an intermediate step in the manufacture of sulfuric acid, and it is also responsible for the acid rain phenomenon. The equilibrium constant K_P for the reaction

$$2SO_2(g) + O_2(g) \rightleftharpoons 2SO_3(g)$$

is 0.13 at 830°C. In one experiment, 2.00 mol SO_2 and 2.00 mol O_2 were initially present in a flask. What must the total pressure at equilibrium be to have an 80.0 percent yield of SO_3?

15.86   Consider the dissociation of iodine:

$$I_2(g) \rightleftharpoons 2I(g)$$

A 1.00-g sample of I_2 is heated to 1200°C in a 500-mL flask. At equilibrium, the total pressure is 1.51 atm. Calculate K_P for the reaction at this temperature.

15.87   Consider the following reaction at 1600°C:

$$Br_2(g) \rightleftharpoons 2Br(g)$$

When 1.05 moles of Br_2 are put in a 0.980-L flask, 1.20 percent of the Br_2 undergoes dissociation. Calculate the equilibrium constant K_c for the reaction.

15.88   Eggshells are composed mostly of calcium carbonate ($CaCO_3$) formed by the reaction

$$Ca^{2+}(aq) + CO_3^{2-}(aq) \rightleftharpoons CaCO_3(s)$$

The carbonate ions are supplied by carbon dioxide produced as a result of metabolism. Explain why eggshells are thinner in the summer when the rate of panting by chickens is greater. Suggest a remedy for this situation.

15.89 The equilibrium constant K_p for the following reaction is 4.31×10^{-4} at 375°C:

$$N_2(g) + 3H_2(g) \rightleftharpoons 2NH_3(g)$$

In a certain experiment a student starts with 0.862 atm of N_2 and 0.373 atm of H_2 in a constant-volume vessel at 375°C. Calculate the partial pressures of all species when equilibrium is reached.

15.90 A quantity of 0.20 mole of carbon dioxide was heated to a certain temperature with an excess of graphite in a closed container until the following equilibrium was reached:

$$C(s) + CO_2(g) \rightleftharpoons 2CO(g)$$

Under these conditions, the average molar mass of the gases was 35 g/mol. (a) Calculate the mole fractions of CO and CO_2. (b) What is K_p if the total pressure is 11 atm? (*Hint:* The average molar mass is the sum of the products of the mole fraction of each gas and its molar mass.)

15.91 When dissolved in water, glucose (corn sugar) and fructose (fruit sugar) exist in equilibrium as follows:

$$\text{fructose} \rightleftharpoons \text{glucose}$$

A chemist prepared a 0.244 M fructose solution at 25°C. At equilibrium, it was found that its concentration had decreased to 0.113 M. (a) Calculate the equilibrium constant for the reaction. (b) At equilibrium, what percentage of fructose was converted to glucose?

15.92 At room temperature, solid iodine is in equilibrium with its vapor through sublimation and deposition. Describe how you would use radioactive iodine, in either solid or vapor form, to show that there is a dynamic equilibrium between these two phases.

15.93 At 1024°C, the pressure of oxygen gas from the decomposition of copper(II) oxide (CuO) is 0.49 atm:

$$4CuO(s) \rightleftharpoons 2Cu_2O(s) + O_2(g)$$

(a) What is K_p for the reaction? (b) Calculate the fraction of CuO that will decompose if 0.16 mole of it is placed in a 2.0-L flask at 1024°C. (c) What would the fraction be if a 1.0-mole sample of CuO were used? (d) What is the smallest amount of CuO (in moles) that would establish the equilibrium?

15.94 A mixture containing 3.9 moles of NO and 0.88 mole of CO_2 was allowed to react in a flask at a certain temperature according to the equation

$$NO(g) + CO_2(g) \rightleftharpoons NO_2(g) + CO(g)$$

At equilibrium, 0.11 mole of CO_2 was present. Calculate the equilibrium constant K_c of this reaction.

15.95 The equilibrium constant K_c for the reaction

$$H_2(g) + I_2(g) \rightleftharpoons 2HI(g)$$

is 54.3 at 430°C. At the start of the reaction, there are 0.714 mole of H_2, 0.984 mole of I_2, and 0.886 mole of HI in a 2.40-L reaction chamber. Calculate the concentrations of the gases at equilibrium.

15.96 When heated, a gaseous compound A dissociates as follows:

$$A(g) \rightleftharpoons B(g) + C(g)$$

In an experiment, A was heated at a certain temperature until its equilibrium pressure reached 0.14 P, where P is the total pressure. Calculate the equilibrium constant K_p of this reaction.

15.97 When a gas was heated under atmospheric conditions, its color deepened. Heating above 150°C caused the color to fade, and at 550°C the color was barely detectable. However, at 550°C, the color was partially restored by increasing the pressure of the system. Which of the following best fits the preceding description: (a) a mixture of hydrogen and bromine, (b) pure bromine, (c) a mixture of nitrogen dioxide and dinitrogen tetroxide. (*Hint:* Bromine has a reddish color, and nitrogen dioxide is a brown gas. The other gases are colorless.) Justify your choice.

15.98 Both Mg^{2+} and Ca^{2+} are important biological ions. One of their functions is to bind to the phosphate group of ATP molecules or amino acids of proteins. For Group 2A metals in general, the equilibrium constant for binding to the anions increases in the order $Ba^{2+} < Sr^{2+} < Ca^{2+} < Mg^{2+}$. What property of the Group 2A metal cations might account for this trend?

15.99 The equilibrium constant K_c for the following reaction is 1.2 at 375°C.

$$N_2(g) + 3H_2(g) \rightleftharpoons 2NH_3(g)$$

(a) What is the value of K_p for this reaction? (b) What is the value of the equilibrium constant K_c for $2NH_3(g) \rightleftharpoons N_2(g) + 3H_2(g)$? (c) What is K_c for $\frac{1}{2}N_2(g) + \frac{3}{2}H_2(g) \rightleftharpoons NH_3(g)$? (d) What are the values of K_p for the reactions described in parts (b) and (c)?

15.100 The equilibrium constant (K_p) for the formation of the air pollutant nitric oxide (NO) in an automobile engine at 530°C is 2.9×10^{-11}.

$$N_2(g) + O_2(g) \rightleftharpoons 2NO(g)$$

(a) Calculate the partial pressure of NO under these conditions if the partial pressures of nitrogen and oxygen are 3.0 and 0.012 atm, respectively. (b) Repeat the calculation for atmospheric conditions where the partial pressures of nitrogen and oxygen are 0.78 and 0.21 atm and the temperature is 25°C. (The K_p for the reaction is 4.0×10^{-31} at this temperature.) (c) Is the formation of NO endothermic or exothermic? (d) What natural phenomenon promotes the formation of NO? Why?

15.101 A sealed glass bulb contains a mixture of NO_2 and N_2O_4 gases. Describe what happens to the following properties of the gases when the bulb is heated from 20°C to 40°C: (a) color, (b) pressure, (c) average molar mass, (d) degree of dissociation (from N_2O_4 to NO_2), (e) density. Assume that volume remains constant. (*Hint:* NO_2 is a brown gas; N_2O_4 is colorless.)

15.102 At 20°C, the vapor pressure of water is 0.0231 atm. Calculate K_p and K_c for the process

$$H_2O(l) \rightleftharpoons H_2O(g)$$

15.103 Industrially, sodium metal is obtained by electrolyzing molten sodium chloride. The reaction at the cathode is $Na^+ + e^- \longrightarrow Na$. We might expect that potassium metal would also be prepared by electrolyzing molten potassium chloride. However, potassium metal is soluble in molten potassium chloride and therefore is hard to recover. Furthermore, potassium vaporizes readily at the operating temperature, creating hazardous conditions. Instead, potassium is prepared by the distillation of molten potassium chloride in the presence of sodium vapor at 892°C:

$$Na(g) + KCl(l) \rightleftharpoons NaCl(l) + K(g)$$

In view of the fact that potassium is a stronger reducing agent than sodium, explain why this approach works. (The boiling points of sodium and potassium are 892°C and 770°C, respectively.)

15.104 In the gas phase, nitrogen dioxide is actually a mixture of nitrogen dioxide (NO_2) and dinitrogen tetroxide (N_2O_4). If the density of such a mixture is 2.3 g/L at 74°C and 1.3 atm, calculate the partial pressures of the gases and K_P for the dissociation of N_2O_4.

15.105 A 2.50-mole sample of NOCl was initially in a 1.50-L reaction chamber at 400°C. After equilibrium was established, it was found that 28.0 percent of the NOCl had dissociated:

$$2NOCl(g) \rightleftharpoons 2NO(g) + Cl_2(g)$$

Calculate the equilibrium constant K_c for the reaction.

15.106 About 75 percent of hydrogen for industrial use is produced by the *steam-reforming* process. This process is carried out in two stages called primary and secondary reforming. In the primary stage, a mixture of steam and methane at about 30 atm is heated over a nickel catalyst at 800°C to give hydrogen and carbon monoxide:

$$CH_4(g) + H_2O(g) \rightleftharpoons CO(g) + 3H_2(g)$$
$$\Delta H° = 206 \text{ kJ/mol}$$

The secondary stage is carried out at about 1000°C, in the presence of air, to convert the remaining methane to hydrogen:

$$CH_4(g) + \frac{1}{2}O_2(g) \rightleftharpoons CO(g) + 2H_2(g)$$
$$\Delta H° = 35.7 \text{ kJ/mol}$$

(a) What conditions of temperature and pressure would favor the formation of products in both the primary and secondary stages? (b) The equilibrium constant K_c for the primary stage is 18 at 800°C. (i) Calculate K_P for the reaction. (ii) If the partial pressures of methane and steam were both 15 atm at the start, what are the pressures of all the gases at equilibrium?

15.107 Photosynthesis can be represented by

$$6CO_2(g) + 6H_2O(l) \rightleftharpoons C_6H_{12}O_6(s) + 6O_2(g)$$
$$\Delta H° = 2801 \text{ kJ/mol}$$

Explain how the equilibrium would be affected by the following changes: (a) partial pressure of CO_2 is increased, (b) O_2 is removed from the mixture,

(c) $C_6H_{12}O_6$ (glucose) is removed from the mixture, (d) more water is added, (e) a catalyst is added, (f) temperature is decreased.

15.108 Consider the decomposition of ammonium chloride at a certain temperature:

$$NH_4Cl(s) \rightleftharpoons NH_3(g) + HCl(g)$$

Calculate the equilibrium constant K_P if the total pressure is 2.2 atm at that temperature.

15.109 Water is a very weak electrolyte that undergoes the following ionization (called *autoionization*):

$$H_2O(l) \underset{k_{-1}}{\overset{k_1}{\rightleftharpoons}} H^+(aq) + OH^-(aq)$$

(a) If $k_1 = 2.4 \times 10^{-5} \text{ s}^{-1}$ and $k_{-1} = 1.3 \times 10^{11}/M \cdot s$, calculate the equilibrium constant K where $K = [H^+][OH^-]/[H_2O]$. (b) Calculate the product $[H^+][OH^-]$, $[H^+]$, and $[OH^-]$. (*Hint:* Calculate the concentration of liquid water using its density, 1.0 g/mL.)

15.110 Consider the following reaction, which takes place in a single elementary step:

$$2A + B \underset{k_{-1}}{\overset{k_1}{\rightleftharpoons}} A_2B$$

If the equilibrium constant K_c is 12.6 at a certain temperature and if $k_1 = 5.1 \times 10^{-2} \text{ s}^{-1}$, calculate the value of k_{-1}.

15.111 At 25°C, the equilibrium partial pressures of NO_2 and N_2O_4 are 0.15 atm and 0.20 atm, respectively. If the volume is doubled at constant temperature, calculate the partial pressures of the gases when a new equilibrium is established.

15.112 In 1899 the German chemist Ludwig Mond developed a process for purifying nickel by converting it to the volatile nickel tetracarbonyl [$Ni(CO)_4$] (b.p. = 42.2°C):

$$Ni(s) + 4CO(g) \rightleftharpoons Ni(CO)_4(g)$$

(a) Describe how you can separate nickel and its solid impurities. (b) How would you recover nickel? [$\Delta H°_f$ for $Ni(CO)_4$ is −602.9 kJ/mol.]

15.113 Consider the equilibrium reaction described in Problem 15.30. A quantity of 2.50 g of PCl_5 is placed in an evacuated 0.500-L flask and heated to 250°C. (a) Calculate the pressure of PCl_5, assuming it does not dissociate. (b) Calculate the partial pressure of PCl_5 at equilibrium. (c) What is the total pressure at equilibrium? (d) What is the degree of dissociation of PCl_5? (The degree of dissociation is given by the fraction of PCl_5 that has undergone dissociation.)

15.114 Consider the equilibrium system $3A \rightleftharpoons B$. Sketch the changes in the concentrations of A and B over time for the following situations: (a) initially only A is present, (b) initially only B is present, (c) initially both A and B are present (with A in higher concentration). In each case, assume that the concentration of B is higher than that of A at equilibrium.

15.115 The vapor pressure of mercury is 0.0020 mmHg at 26°C. (a) Calculate K_c and K_P for the process $Hg(l) \rightleftharpoons Hg(g)$. (b) A chemist breaks a thermometer and spills mercury onto the floor of a laboratory measuring 6.1 m long, 5.3 m wide, and 3.1 m high. Calculate the mass of mercury (in grams) vaporized at equilibrium and the concentration of mercury vapor (in mg/m³). Does this concentration exceed the safety limit of 0.05 mg/m³? (Ignore the volume of furniture and other objects in the laboratory.)

15.116   At 25°C, a mixture of NO_2 and N_2O_4 gases are in equilibrium in a cylinder fitted with a movable piston. The concentrations are $[NO_2] = 0.0475\ M$ and $[N_2O_4] = 0.487\ M$. The volume of the gas mixture is halved by pushing down on the piston at constant temperature. Calculate the concentrations of the gases when equilibrium is reestablished. Will the color become darker or lighter after the change? [*Hint:* K_c for the dissociation of N_2O_4 is 4.63×10^{-3}. $N_2O_4(g)$ is colorless, and $NO_2(g)$ has a brown color.]

15.117   A student placed a few ice cubes in a drinking glass with water. A few minutes later she noticed that some of the ice cubes were fused together. Explain what happened.

15.118   Consider the potential-energy diagrams for two types of reactions A $\rightleftharpoons$ B. In each case, answer the following questions for the system at equilibrium. (a) How would a catalyst affect the forward and reverse rates of the reaction? (b) How would a catalyst affect the energies of the reactant and product? (c) How would an increase in temperature affect the equilibrium constant? (d) If the only effect of a catalyst is to lower the activation energies for the forward and reverse reactions, show that the equilibrium constant remains unchanged if a catalyst is added to the reacting mixture.

15.119   The equilibrium constant K_c for the reaction

$$2NH_3(g) \rightleftharpoons N_2(g) + 3H_2(g)$$

is 0.83 at 375°C. A 14.6-g sample of ammonia is placed in a 4.00-L flask and heated to 375°C. Calculate the concentrations of all the gases when equilibrium is reached.

15.120   The dependence of the equilibrium constant of a reaction on temperature is given by the van't Hoff equation:

$$\ln K = \frac{-\Delta H°}{RT} + C$$

where C is a constant. The following table gives the equilibrium constant (K_p) for the reaction at various temperatures.

$$2NO(g) + O_2(g) \rightleftharpoons 2NO_2(g)$$

K_P	138	5.12	0.436	0.0626	0.0130
T(K)	600	700	800	900	1000

Determine graphically the $\Delta H°$ for the reaction.

15.121   Consider the reaction between NO_2 and N_2O_4 in a closed container:

$$N_2O_4(g) \rightleftharpoons 2NO_2(g)$$

Initially, 1 mole of N_2O_4 is present. At equilibrium, x mole of N_2O_4 has dissociated to form NO_2. (a) Derive an expression for K_p in terms of x and P, the total pressure. (b) How does the expression in part (a) help you predict the shift in equilibrium due to an increase in P? Does your prediction agree with Le Châtelier's principle?

15.122   (a) Use the van't Hoff equation in Problem 15.120 to derive the following expression, which relates the equilibrium constants at two different temperatures:

$$\ln \frac{K_1}{K_2} = \frac{\Delta H°}{R}\left(\frac{1}{T_2} - \frac{1}{T_1}\right)$$

How does this equation support the prediction based on Le Châtelier's principle about the shift in equilibrium with temperature? (b) The vapor pressures of water are 31.82 mmHg at 30°C and 92.51 mmHg at 50°C. Calculate the molar heat of vaporization of water.

15.123   The K_p for the reaction

$$SO_2Cl_2(g) \rightleftharpoons SO_2(g) + Cl_2(g)$$

is 2.05 at 648 K. A sample of SO_2Cl_2 is placed in a container and heated to 648 K, while the total pressure is kept constant at 9.00 atm. Calculate the partial pressures of the gases at equilibrium.

15.124   The "boat" form and the "chair" form of cyclohexane (C_6H_{12}) interconvert as shown here:

Boat   Chair

In this representation, the H atoms are omitted and a C atom is assumed to be at each intersection of two lines (bonds). The conversion is first order in each direction. The activation energy for the chair $\longrightarrow$ boat conversion is 41 kJ/mol. If the frequency factor is $1.0 \times 10^{12}\ s^{-1}$, what is k_1 at 298 K? The equilibrium constant K_c for the reaction is 9.83×10^3 at 298 K.

15.125   Consider the following reaction at a certain temperature

$$A_2 + B_2 \rightleftharpoons 2AB$$

The mixing of 1 mole of A_2 with 3 moles of B_2 gives rise to x mole of AB at equilibrium. The addition of two more moles of A_2 produces another x mole of AB. What is the equilibrium constant for the reaction?

15.126   Iodine is sparingly soluble in water but much more so in carbon tetrachloride (CCl_4). The equilibrium constant, also called the partition coefficient, for the distribution of I_2 between these two phases

$$I_2(aq) \rightleftharpoons I_2(CCl_4)$$

is 83 at 20°C. (a) A student adds 0.030 L of CCl_4 to 0.200 L of an aqueous solution containing 0.032 g of

I_2. The mixture at 20°C is shaken, and the two phases are then allowed to separate. Calculate the fraction of I_2 remaining in the aqueous phase. (b) The student now repeats the extraction of I_2 with another 0.030 L of CCl_4. Calculate the fraction of the I_2 from the original solution that remains in the aqueous phase. (c) Compare the result in part (b) with a single extraction using 0.060 L of CCl_4. Comment on the difference.

15.127   For the purpose of determining K_p using Equation 15.4, what is Δn for the following equation?

$$C_3H_8(g) + 5O_2(g) \rightleftharpoons 3CO_2(g) + 4H_2O(l)$$

15.128   Industrial production of ammonia from hydrogen and nitrogen gases is done using the Haber process.

$$N_2(g) + 3H_2(g) \rightleftharpoons 2NH_3(g)$$

$$\Delta H° = -92.6 \text{ kJ/mol}$$

Based on your knowledge of the principles of equilibrium, what would the optimal temperature and pressure conditions be for production of ammonia on a large scale? Are the same conditions also optimal from the standpoint of kinetics? Explain.

15.129   For which of the following reactions is K_c equal to K_p? For which can we not write a K_p expression?
(a) $4NH_3(g) + 5O_2(g) \rightleftharpoons 4NO(g) + 6H_2O(g)$
(b) $CaCO_3(s) \rightleftharpoons CaO(s) + CO_2(g)$
(c) $Zn(s) + 2H^+(aq) \rightleftharpoons Zn^{2+}(aq) + H_2(g)$
(d) $PCl_3(g) + 3NH_3(g) \rightleftharpoons 3HCl(g) + P(NH_2)_3(g)$
(e) $NH_3(g) + HCl(g) \rightleftharpoons NH_4Cl(s)$
(f) $NaHCO_3(s) + H^+(aq) \rightleftharpoons H_2O(l) + CO_2(g) + Na^+(aq)$
(g) $H_2(g) + F_2(g) \rightleftharpoons 2HF(g)$
(h) $C(\text{graphite}) + CO_2(g) \rightleftharpoons 2CO(g)$

15.130   At present, the World Anti-Doping Agency has no way to detect the use of hypoxic sleeping tents, other than inspection of an athlete's home. Imagine, however, that a biochemical analysis company is developing a way to determine whether an elevated red blood cell count in an athlete's blood is the result of such a practice. A key substance in the detection process is the proprietary compound OD17X, which is produced by the combination of two other proprietary compounds, OD1A and OF2A. The aqueous reaction is represented by the equation

$$OD1A(aq) + OF2A(aq) \rightleftharpoons OD17X(aq)$$

$$\Delta H = 29 \text{ kJ/mol}$$

(a) Write the equilibrium expression for the reaction shown above. (b) Given the equilibrium concentrations at room temperature of [OD1A] = 2.12 M, [OF2A] = 1.56 M, and [OD17X] = 1.01 × 10^{-4} M, calculate the value of the equilibrium constant (K_c) at room temperature. (c) The OD17X produced is precipitated with another proprietary substance according to the equation

$$OD17X(aq) + A771A(aq) \rightleftharpoons OD17X\text{-}A77(s)$$

K_c for the precipitation equilibrium is 1.0 × 10^6 at room temperature. Write the equilibrium expression for the sum of the two reactions and determine the value of the overall equilibrium constant. (d) Determine whether or not a mixture with [OD1A] = 3.00 M, [OF2A] = 2.50 M, and [OD17X] = 2.7 × 10^{-4} M is at equilibrium and, if not, which direction it will have to proceed in order to achieve equilibrium. (e) Because the production of OD17X is endothermic, it can be enhanced by increasing the temperature. At 250°C, the equilibrium constant for the reaction

$$OD1A(aq) + OF2A(aq) \rightleftharpoons OD17X(aq)$$

is 3.8 × 10^2. If a synthesis at 250°C begins with 1.0 M of each reactant, what will the equilibrium concentrations of reactants and products be?

Answers to In-Chapter Materials

PRACTICE PROBLEMS

15.1A $K_c = \dfrac{[BrCl]^2}{[Br_2][Cl_2]}$, $K_c = 7.1$. **15.1B** $0.016\ M$.

15.2A (a) $Q_c = \dfrac{[N_2]^2[O_2]}{[N_2O]^2}$, (b) $Q_c = \dfrac{[NO]^2[Br_2]}{[NOBr]^2}$, (c) $Q_c = \dfrac{[H^+][F^-]}{[HF]}$,

(d) $Q_c = \dfrac{[CO_2][H_2]}{[CO][H_2O]}$, (e) $Q_c = \dfrac{[CS_2][H_2]^4}{[CH_4][H_2S]^2}$, (f) $Q_c = \dfrac{[H^+]^2[C_2O_4^{2-}]}{[H_2C_2O_4]}$.

15.2B (a) $H_2 + Cl_2 \rightleftharpoons 2HCl$, (b) $H^+ + F^- \rightleftharpoons HF$,
(c) $Cr^{3+} + 4OH^- \rightleftharpoons Cr(OH)_4^-$, (d) $HClO \rightleftharpoons H^+ + ClO^-$,
(e) $H_2SO_3 \rightleftharpoons H^+ + HSO_3^-$, (f) $2NO + Br_2 \rightleftharpoons 2NOBr$.

15.3A (a) $K_c = \dfrac{[HCl]^4}{[SiCl_4][H_2]^2}$, (b) $K_c = \dfrac{1}{[Hg^{2+}][Cl^-]^2}$, (c) $K_c = \dfrac{[Ni(CO)_4]}{[CO]^4}$,

(d) $K_c = \dfrac{[Zn^{2+}]}{[Fe^{2+}]}$. **15.3B** The expressions in (a), (c), and (d) correspond

to heterogeneous equilibria. It would be impossible to write a balanced
chemical equation using only the species in each of these expressions,
indicating that there are species in each reaction (solids or liquids) that
do not appear in the equilibrium expressions. **15.4A** (a) 2.3×10^{24},
(b) 6.6×10^{-13}, (c) 2.8×10^{-15}. **15.4B** (a) 1.5×10^{34}, (b) 1.3×10^{29},

(c) 8.5×10^{38}. **15.5A** (a) $K_P = \dfrac{(P_{CO_2})^2}{(P_{CO})^2(P_{O_2})}$, (b) $K_P = P_{CO_2}$,

(c) $K_P = \dfrac{(P_{NH_3})^2}{(P_{N_2})(P_{H_2})^3}$. **15.5B** (a) $2NO_2 + O_2 \rightleftharpoons 2NO_3$,

(b) $CH_4 + 2H_2O \rightleftharpoons CO_2 + 4H_2$, (c) $I_2 + H_2 \rightleftharpoons 2HI$.
15.6A 8.1×10^{-6}. **15.6B** 0.104. **15.7A** left. **15.7B** right.
15.8A $[H_2] = [I_2] = 0.056\ M$; $[HI] = 0.413\ M$. **15.8B** $0.20\ M$.
15.9A $[Br] = 8.4 \times 10^{-3}\ M$, $[Br_2] = 6.5 \times 10^{-2}\ M$.
15.9B $[Br] = 1.6 \times 10^{-3}\ M$ initially and $2.4 \times 10^{-3}\ M$ at
equilibrium. **15.10A** $P_{H_2} = P_{I_2} = 0.37$ atm, $P_{HI} = 2.75$ atm.
15.10B $P_{H_2} = P_{I_2} = 0.294$ atm, $P_{HI} = 2.16$ atm. **15.11A** (a) right, (b) left,
(c) right, (d) left. **15.11B** (a) $Ag(NH_3)_2^+\ (aq)$ or $Cl^-(aq)$, (b) $NH_3(aq)$,
(c) $AgCl(s)$. **15.12A** (a) right, (b) right, (c) right. **15.12B** right shift: remove
HF; left shift: remove H_2; no shift: reduce volume of container.

SECTION REVIEW

15.2.1 $K_c = \dfrac{[CO_2]^2}{[CO]^2[O_2]}$. **15.2.2** 163. **15.3.1** $K_c = \dfrac{1}{[H^+][OH^-]}$.

15.3.2 $K_c = \dfrac{1}{[CO_2]}$. **15.3.3** 1.2×10^{-1}. **15.3.4** 0.14. **15.4.1** $0.70\ M$,

$0.70\ M$, $0.092\ M$. **15.4.2** $0.41\ M$, $0.41\ M$, $0.054\ M$. **15.4.3** right, neither.
15.5.1 (a) neither, (b) right, (c) left, (d) neither. **15.5.2** (a) right, (b) left,
(c) neither, (d) left. **15.5.3** A will increase and A_2 will decrease.
15.5.4 exothermic.

Equilibrium Problems

The principles of equilibrium were introduced in Chapter 15 largely through the use of examples involving gases. However, it is important to recognize that these principles apply to *all* types of equilibria; and that the approach to solving an equilibrium problem is always the same. Many of the important reactions and processes that we will study occur in water (i.e., they are *aqueous equilibria*). Common examples of aqueous equilibria include the ionization of a weak acid such as hydrofluoric acid

$$HF(aq) \rightleftharpoons H^+(aq) + F^-(aq) \qquad\qquad K_a = 7.1 \times 10^{-4}$$

and the dissolution of a slightly soluble salt such as lead(II) chloride

$$PbCl_2(s) \rightleftharpoons Pb^{2+}(aq) + 2Cl^-(aq) \qquad\qquad K_{sp} = 2.4 \times 10^{-4}$$

Each of these equilibria has an equilibrium constant (K_c) associated with it—although they are shown, respectively, as K_a and K_{sp}. The subscripts a and sp simply identify the specific *type* of equilibrium to which the equilibrium constants refer: ionization of a weak _acid_, or _solubility product_ of a slightly soluble salt.

When solving an equilibrium problem, we start with a balanced chemical equation, and use it to write an equilibrium expression. We then construct an equilibrium table and fill in the known concentrations. Often, these are the *initial* concentrations; but they can also be *equilibrium* concentrations, depending on what information is given in the problem. Then, using stoichiometry, we determine the changes in concentrations of reactants and products, and we use the equilibrium *expression* and equilibrium *constant* to solve for the unknown concentrations.

Consider a solution that is 0.15 M in HF. We may wish to know the concentration of H$^+$ ion at equilibrium. We construct an equilibrium table and write the equilibrium expression.

$$HF(aq) \rightleftharpoons H^+(aq) + F^-(aq)$$

	HF	H$^+$	F$^-$
i	0.15	0	0
c			
e			

$$7.1 \times 10^{-4} = \frac{[H^+][F^-]}{[HF]}$$

Student Annotation: The initials i, c, and e stand for *initial, change,* and *equilibrium.*

As we will see in Chapter 16, the initial concentration of H$^+$ in a problem such as this is not really zero, but it is *very* small and can be neglected in most cases. Using the stoichiometry of the balanced equation, we determine that the concentration of HF will decrease by some unknown amount, which we designate x, and that the concentrations of H$^+$ and F$^-$ will each increase by the same amount.

$$HF(aq) \rightleftharpoons H^+(aq) + F^-(aq)$$

	HF	H$^+$	F$^-$
i	0.15	0	0
c	$-x$	$+x$	$+x$
e	$0.15 - x$	x	x

$$7.1 \times 10^{-4} = \frac{[H^+][F^-]}{[HF]}$$

We enter the equilibrium concentrations (in this case, in terms of the unknown x) into the equilibrium expression and set it equal to the equilibrium constant.

$$7.1 \times 10^{-4} = \frac{x \cdot x}{0.15 - x}$$

In this case, because the equilibrium constant is so small, we neglect the x in the denominator and solving for x gives 0.010 M. This is the concentration of both the H$^+$ ion and the F$^-$ ion.

Next, consider a saturated solution of $PbCl_2$. We may wish to know the concentrations of Pb^{2+} and Cl^- ions in the solution. In this case, we proceed in the same way by constructing an equilibrium table and writing an equilibrium expression. Recall that solids, such as $PbCl_2$, do not appear in the equilibrium expression. Before the $PbCl_2$ dissolves, the concentrations of lead(II) ion and chloride ion are zero.

$$PbCl_2(s) \rightleftharpoons Pb^{2+}(aq) + 2Cl^-(aq)$$

		0	0
i			
c			
e			

$$2.4 \times 10^{-4} = [Pb^{2+}][Cl^-]^2$$

The stoichiometry indicates that $[Pb^{2+}]$ will increase and that $[Cl^-]$ will increase by twice as much. In the case of solubility equilibria, we can use s in place of x, to remind us that the result is the "solubility" of the salt.

$$PbCl_2(s) \rightleftharpoons Pb^{2+}(aq) + 2Cl^-(aq)$$

		0	0
i			
c		$+s$	$+2s$
e		s	$2s$

$$2.4 \times 10^{-4} = [Pb^{2+}][Cl^-]^2$$

We enter the equilibrium concentrations (in this case, in terms of the unknown s) into the equilibrium expression and set it equal to the equilibrium constant.

$$2.4 \times 10^{-4} = (s) \cdot (2s)^2$$

Solving for s gives $0.039\ M$. This is the concentration Pb^{2+} ion, but the concentration of Cl^- ion is $2s = 0.078\ M$.

Key Skills Problems

15.1
The K_a for hydrocyanic acid (HCN) is 4.9×10^{-10}. Determine the concentration of H^+ in a solution that is $0.25\ M$ in HCN.

(a) $1.2 \times 10^{-10}\ M$ (b) $5.0 \times 10^{-4}\ M$ (c) $2.2 \times 10^{-5}\ M$ (d) $2.5 \times 10^{-5}\ M$ (e) $1.1 \times 10^{-5}\ M$

15.2
Determine the concentrations of Pb^{2+} and I^- in a saturated solution of PbI_2. (K_{sp} for PbI_2 is 1.4×10^{-8}.)

(a) $0.0015\ M$ and $0.0030\ M$ (b) $0.0015\ M$ and $0.0015\ M$
(c) $0.0015\ M$ and $0.00075\ M$ (d) $0.0019\ M$ and $0.0019\ M$
(e) $0.0019\ M$ and $0.0038\ M$

15.3
Determine the K_a for a weak acid if a 0.10-M solution of the acid has $[H^+] = 4.6 \times 10^{-4}\ M$.

(a) 2.1×10^{-7} (b) 2.1×10^{-6} (c) 0.32 (d) 4.6×10^{-2} (e) 0.046

15.4
Determine the K_{sp} for the slightly soluble salt A_2X, if $[A^+] = 0.019\ M$.

(a) 9.5×10^{-3} (b) 3.6×10^{-4} (c) 1.8×10^{-4} (d) 3.4×10^{-6}
(e) 6.9×10^{-5}

Acids and Bases

16.1   **Brønsted Acids and Bases**

16.2   **Molecular Structure and Acid Strength**
• Hydrohalic Acids • Oxoacids • Carboxylic Acids

16.3   **The Acid-Base Properties of Water**

16.4   **The pH Scale**

16.5   **Strong Acids and Bases**
• Strong Acids • Strong Bases

16.6   **Weak Acids and Acid Ionization Constants**
• The Ionization Constant, K_a • Calculating pH from K_a • Percent Ionization • Using pH to Determine K_a

16.7   **Weak Bases and Base Ionization Constants**
• The Ionization Constant, K_b • Calculating pH from K_b • Using pH to Determine K_b

16.8   **Conjugate Acid-Base Pairs**
• The Strength of a Conjugate Acid or Base
• The Relationship Between K_a and K_b of a Conjugate Acid-Base Pair

16.9   **Diprotic and Polyprotic Acids**

16.10 **Acid-Base Properties of Salt Solutions**
• Basic Salt Solutions • Acidic Salt Solutions
• Neutral Salt Solutions • Salts in Which Both the Cation and the Anion Hydrolyze

16.11 **Acid-Base Properties of Oxides and Hydroxides**
• Oxides of Metals and Nonmetals • Basic and Amphoteric Hydroxides

16.12 **Lewis Acids and Bases**

A *superacid*, derived from the reaction of a strong Lewis base with a strong Brønsted acid, may be thousands of times stronger than the original Brønsted acid. For many years, the utility of superacids eluded scientists—who were nonetheless fascinated by their ability to dissolve notoriously insoluble substances, including *candle wax.* In recent years, however, chemists have used superacids in some unusual chemical transformations, generating chemical species that were ordinarily too elusive to be studied easily. Superacids now feature prominently in some important industrial processes, including the manufacture of plastics and production of high-octane gasoline.

Before You Begin, Review These Skills

- The list of strong acids and the list of strong bases [◄◄ Section 9.3]
- How to solve equilibrium problems [◄◄ Section 15.4]

16.1 BRØNSTED ACIDS AND BASES

In Chapter 9, we learned that a Brønsted acid is a substance that can donate a proton and a Brønsted base is a substance that can accept a proton [◄◄ Section 9.3]. In this chapter, we extend our discussion of Brønsted acid-base theory to include conjugate acids and conjugate bases.

When a Brønsted acid donates a proton, what remains of the acid is known as a *conjugate base.* For example, in the ionization of HCl in water,

$$HCl(aq) + H_2O(l) \rightleftharpoons H_3O^+(aq) + Cl^-(aq)$$

acid   conjugate base

HCl donates a proton to water, producing the hydronium ion (H_3O^+) and the chloride ion (Cl^-), which is the conjugate base of HCl. The two species, HCl and Cl^-, are known as a *conjugate acid-base pair* or simply a *conjugate pair.* Table 16.1 lists the conjugate bases of several familiar species.

Conversely, when a Brønsted base *accepts* a proton, the newly formed *protonated* species is known as a *conjugate acid.* When ammonia (NH_3) ionizes in water,

$$NH_3(aq) + H_2O(l) \rightleftharpoons NH_4^+(aq) + OH^-(aq)$$

base   conjugate acid

NH_3 accepts a proton from water to become the ammonium ion (NH_4^+). The ammonium ion is the conjugate acid of ammonia. Table 16.2 lists the conjugate acids of several common species.

Any reaction that we describe using Brønsted acid-base theory involves an acid and a base. The acid donates the proton, and the base accepts it. Furthermore, the products of such a reaction are always a conjugate base and a conjugate acid. It is useful to identify and label each species in a Brønsted acid-base reaction. For the ionization of HCl in water, the species are labeled as follows:

TABLE 16.1	Conjugate Bases of Some Common Species	
Species	**Conjugate base**	
CH_3COOH	CH_3COO^-	
H_2O	OH^-	
NH_3	NH_2^-	
H_2SO_4	HSO_4^-	

TABLE 16.2	Conjugate Acids of Some Common Species	
Species	**Conjugate acid**	
NH_3	NH_4^+	
H_2O	H_3O^+	
OH^-	H_2O	
H_2NCONH_2 (urea)	$H_2NCONH_3^+$	

loses a proton
gains a proton

$$HCl(aq) + H_2O(l) \rightleftharpoons H_3O^+(aq) + Cl^-(aq)$$

acid   base   conjugate   conjugate
                            acid   base

And for the ionization of NH_3 in water,

gains a proton
loses a proton

$$NH_3(aq) + H_2O(l) \rightleftharpoons NH_4^+(aq) + OH^-(aq)$$

base   acid   conjugate   conjugate
                            acid   base

Worked Examples 16.1 and 16.2 let you practice identifying conjugate pairs and the species in a Brønsted acid-base reaction.

Worked Example 16.1

What is (a) the conjugate base of HNO_3, (b) the conjugate acid of O^{2-}, (c) the conjugate base of HSO_4^-, and (d) the conjugate acid of HCO_3^-?

Strategy To find the conjugate base of a species, *remove* a proton from the formula. To find the conjugate acid of a species, *add* a proton to the formula.

Setup The word *proton*, in this context, refers to H^+. Thus, the formula and the charge will both be affected by the addition or removal of H^+.

Solution

(a) NO_3^- (b) OH^- (c) SO_4^{2-} (d) H_2CO_3

> **Think About It**
> A species does not need to be what we think of as an acid in order for it to have a conjugate base. For example, we would not refer to the hydroxide ion (OH^-) as an acid—but it does have a conjugate base, the oxide ion (O^{2-}). Furthermore, a species that can either lose or gain a proton, such as HCO_3^-, has both a conjugate base (CO_3^{2-}) and a conjugate acid (H_2CO_3).

Practice Problem A What is (a) the conjugate acid of ClO_4^-, (b) the conjugate acid of S^{2-}, (c) the conjugate base of H_2S, and (d) the conjugate base of $H_2C_2O_4$?

Practice Problem B HSO_3^- is the conjugate acid of what species? HSO_3^- is the conjugate base of what species?

Worked Example 16.2

Label each of the species in the following equations as an acid, base, conjugate base, or conjugate acid:

(a) $HF(aq) + NH_3(aq) \rightleftharpoons F^-(aq) + NH_4^+(aq)$

(b) $CH_3COO^-(aq) + H_2O(l) \rightleftharpoons CH_3COOH(aq) + OH^-(aq)$

Strategy In each equation, the reactant that loses a proton is the acid and the reactant that gains a proton is the base. Each product is the conjugate of one of the reactants. Two species that differ only by a proton constitute a conjugate pair.

Setup

(a) HF loses a proton and becomes F^-; NH_3 gains a proton and becomes NH_4^+.

(b) CH_3COO^- gains a proton to become CH_3COOH; H_2O loses a proton to become OH^-.

Solution

(a) $HF(aq) + NH_3(aq) \rightleftharpoons F^-(aq) + NH_4^+(aq)$

     acid   base   conjugate base   conjugate acid

(b) $CH_3COO^-(aq) + H_2O(l) \rightleftharpoons CH_3COOH(aq) + OH^-(aq)$

     base   acid   conjugate acid   conjugate base

> **Think About It**
> In a Brønsted acid-base reaction, there is always an acid and a base, and whether a substance behaves as an acid or a base depends on what it is combined with. Water, for example, behaves as a base when combined with HCl but behaves as an acid when combined with NH_3.

Practice Problem A Identify and label the species in each reaction.

(a) $NH_4^+(aq) + H_2O(l) \rightleftharpoons NH_3(aq) + H_3O^+(aq)$

(b) $CN^-(aq) + H_2O(l) \rightleftharpoons HCN(aq) + OH^-(aq)$

Practice Problem B (a) Write an equation in which HSO_4^- reacts (with water) to form its conjugate base. (b) Write an equation in which HSO_4^- reacts (with water) to form its conjugate acid.

Brønsted Acids and Bases

16.1.1 Determine the conjugate bases of the following acids: H_2S, HBr, H_2SO_4.

16.1.2 Determine the conjugate acids of the following bases: OH^-, CO_3^{2-}, $HC_2O_4^-$.

16.2 MOLECULAR STRUCTURE AND ACID STRENGTH

The strength of an acid is measured by its tendency to ionize:

$$HX \longrightarrow H^+ + X^-$$

Two factors influence the extent to which the acid undergoes ionization. One is the strength of the H—X bond. The stronger the bond, the more difficult it is for the HX molecule to break up and hence the weaker the acid. The other factor is the polarity of the H—X bond. The difference in the electronegativities between H and X results in a polar bond like

$$\delta+ \quad \delta-$$
$$H-X$$

If the bond is highly polarized (i.e., if there is a large accumulation of positive and negative charges on the H and X atoms, respectively), HX will tend to break up into H^+ and X^- ions. A high degree of polarity, therefore, gives rise to a stronger acid. In this section, we consider the roles of bond strength and bond polarity in determining the strength of an acid.

> **Student Annotation:** Remember that protons are *hydrated* in aqueous solution [◄◄ Section 9.3] and that they can also be represented by the formula H_3O^+. Thus, this equation could also be written as:
> $$HX + H_2O \longrightarrow H_3O^+ + X^-$$

Hydrohalic Acids

The halogens form a series of binary acids called the hydrohalic acids (HF, HCl, HBr, and HI). Table 16.3 shows that of this series only HF is a weak acid. The data in the table indicate that the predominant factor in determining the strength of the hydrohalic acids is bond strength. HF has the largest bond enthalpy, making its bond the most difficult to break. In this series of binary acids, acid strength increases as bond strength decreases. The strength of the acids increases as follows:

$$HF \ll HCl < HBr < HI$$

> **Student Annotation:** The polarity of the H—X bond actually decreases from H—F to H—I, largely because F is the most electronegative element. This would suggest that HF would be the strongest of the hydrohalic acids. Based on the data in Table 16.3, however, bond enthalpy is the more important factor in determining the strengths of these acids.

Oxoacids

An oxoacid, as we learned in Chapter 5, contains hydrogen, oxygen, and a central, nonmetal atom [◄◄ Section 5.7]. As the Lewis structures in Figure 16.1 show, oxoacids contain one or more O—H bonds. If the central atom is an electronegative element, or is in a high oxidation state, it will attract electrons, causing the O—H bond to be more polar. This makes it easier for the hydrogen to be lost as H^+, making the acid stronger.

TABLE 16.3	Bond Enthalpies for Hydrogen Halides and Acid Strengths for Hydrohalic Acids		
Bond	**Bond enthalpy (kJ/mol)**	**Acid strength**	
H—F	562.8	Weak	
H—Cl	431.9	Strong	
H—Br	366.1	Strong	
H—I	298.3	Strong	

Figure 16.1 Lewis structures of some common oxoacids. Recall that there is more than one possible Lewis structure for oxoacids in which the central atom is from period 3 or below on the periodic table [◄◄ Section 6.6].

H—Ö—Cl̈:

Hypochlorous acid (+1)

H—Ö—Cl̈—Ö:

Chlorous acid (+3)

:Ö:
|
H—Ö—Cl—Ö:

Chloric acid (+5)

:Ö:
‖
H—Ö—Cl—Ö:
|
:Ö:

Perchloric acid (+7)

Figure 16.2 Lewis structures of the oxoacids of chlorine. The oxidation number of the Cl atom is shown in parentheses. Note that although hypochlorous acid is written as HClO, the H atom is bonded to the O atom.

Student Annotation: As the number of attached oxygen atoms increases, the oxidation number of the central atom also increases [◄◄ Section 9.4].

To compare their strengths, it is convenient to divide the oxoacids into two groups:

1. *Oxoacids having different central atoms that are from the same group of the periodic table and that have the same oxidation number.* Two examples are

:Ö:
|
H—Ö—Cl—Ö:

$HClO_3$

:Ö:
|
H—Ö—Br—Ö:

$HBrO_3$

Within this group, acid strength increases with increasing electronegativity of the central atom. Cl and Br have the same oxidation number in these acids, +5. However, because Cl is more electronegative than Br, it attracts the electron pair it shares with oxygen (in the Cl—O—H group) to a greater extent than Br does (in the corresponding Br—O—H group). Consequently, the O—H bond is more polar in chloric acid than in bromic acid and ionizes more readily. The relative acid strengths are

$$HClO_3 > HBrO_3$$

2. *Oxoacids having the same central atom but different numbers of oxygen atoms.* Within this group, acid strength increases with increasing oxidation number of the central atom. Consider the oxoacids of chlorine shown in Figure 16.2. In this series, the ability of chlorine to draw electrons away from the OH group (thus making the O—H bond more polar) increases with the number of electronegative O atoms attached to Cl. Thus, $HClO_4$ is the strongest acid because it has the largest number of oxygen atoms attached to Cl. The acid strength decreases as follows:

$$HClO_4 > HClO_3 > HClO_2 > HClO$$

Worked Example 16.3 compares acid strengths based on molecular structure.

Worked Example 16.3

Predict the relative strengths of the oxoacids in each of the following groups:

(a) HClO, HBrO, and HIO; (b) HNO_3 and HNO_2.

Strategy In each group, compare the electronegativities or oxidation numbers of the central atoms to determine which O—H bonds are the most polar. The more polar the O—H bond, the more readily it is broken and the stronger the acid.

Setup

(a) In a group with different central atoms, we must compare electronegativities. The electronegativities of the central atoms in this group decrease as follows: Cl > Br > I.

(b) These two acids have the same central atom but differ in the number of attached oxygen atoms. In a group such as this, the greater the number of attached oxygen atoms, the higher the oxidation number of the central atom and the stronger the acid.

Solution

(a) Acid strength decreases as follows: HClO > HBrO > HIO.

(b) HNO_3 is a stronger acid than HNO_2.

Student Annotation: Another way to compare the strengths of these two is to remember that HNO_3 is one of the seven strong acids. HNO_2 is not.

Think About It
Four of the strong acids are oxoacids: HNO_3, $HClO_4$, $HClO_3$, and H_2SO_4.

Practice Problem A Indicate which is the stronger acid: (a) $HBrO_3$ or $HBrO_4$; (b) H_2SeO_4 or H_2SO_4.

Practice Problem B Based on the information in this section, which is the predominant factor in determining the strength of an oxoacid: electronegativity of the central atom or oxidation state of the central atom? Explain.

Carboxylic Acids

So far our discussion has focused on inorganic acids. A particularly important group of organic acids is the *carboxylic acids,* whose Lewis structures can be represented by

$$R-\overset{\overset{\ddot{O}}{\|}}{C}-\ddot{O}-H$$

where R is part of the acid molecule and the shaded portion represents the carboxyl group, —COOH.
    The conjugate base of a carboxylic acid, called a carboxylate anion, RCOO⁻, can be represented by more than one resonance structure:

$$R-\overset{\overset{\ddot{O}}{\|}}{C}-\ddot{O}\colon^- \quad\longleftrightarrow\quad R-\overset{\colon\ddot{O}\colon^-}{\underset{}{C}}=\ddot{O}\colon$$

In terms of molecular orbital theory [◄◄ Section 7.6], we attribute the stability of the anion to its ability to spread out or delocalize the electron density over several atoms. The greater the extent of electron delocalization, the more stable the anion and the greater the tendency for the acid to undergo ionization—that is, the stronger the acid.
    The strength of carboxylic acids depends on the nature of the R group. Consider, for example, acetic acid and chloroacetic acid:

Acetic acid   Chloroacetic acid

The presence of the electronegative Cl atom in chloroacetic acid shifts the electron density toward the R group, thereby making the O—H bond more polar. Consequently, there is a greater tendency for chloroacetic acid to ionize:

Chloroacetic acid is the stronger of the two acids.

Student Annotation: You learned in Chapter 9 [◄◄ Section 9.3, Figure 9.5] that carboxylic acid formulas are often written with the ionizable H atom last, in order to keep the functional group together. You should recognize the formulas for organic acids written either way. For example, acetic acid may be written as $HC_2H_3O_2$ or as CH_3COOH.

SECTION 16.2 REVIEW

Molecular Structure and Acid Strength

16.2.1   Arrange the following organic acids in order of increasing strength: bromoacetic acid ($CH_2BrCOOH$), chloroacetic acid ($CH_2ClCOOH$), fluoroacetic acid (CH_2FCOOH), iodoacetic acid (CH_2ICOOH).

16.2.2   Arrange the following acids in order of increasing strength: $HBrO_3$, $HBrO$, $HBrO_4$.

16.2.3   Consider the following three acids and their bond enthalpies: H_2A (268 kJ/mol), H_2B (344 kJ/mol), H_2C (314 kJ/mol). Which of the three acids is strongest, and which is the weakest?

16.3   THE ACID-BASE PROPERTIES OF WATER

Water is often referred to as the "universal solvent," because it is so common and so important to life on Earth. In addition, most of the acid-base chemistry that you will encounter takes place in aqueous solution. In this section, we take a closer look at water's ability to act as either a Brønsted acid (as in the ionization of NH_3) or a Brønsted base (as in the ionization of HCl). A species that

Multi 16.1
Chemical equilibrium—equilibrium
(interactive)

can behave either as a Brønsted acid or a Brønsted base is called *amphoteric.* Water is a very weak electrolyte, but it does undergo ionization to a small extent:

$$H_2O(l) \rightleftharpoons H^+(aq) + OH^-(aq)$$

This reaction is known as the *autoionization of water.* Because we can represent the aqueous proton as either H^+ or H_3O^+ [◄◄ Section 9.3], we can also write the autoionization of water as

$$2H_2O(l) \rightleftharpoons H_3O^+(aq) + OH^-(aq)$$

acid   base   conjugate acid   conjugate base

> **Student Annotation:** Recall that in a heterogeneous equilibrium such as this, liquids and solids do not appear in the equilibrium expression [◄◄ Section 15.3].

where one water molecule acts as an acid and the other acts as a base.

As indicated by the double arrow in the equation, the reaction is an equilibrium. The equilibrium expression for the autoionization of water is

$$K_w = [H_3O^+][OH^-] \text{ or } K_w = [H^+][OH^-]$$

Because the autoionization of water is an important equilibrium that you will encounter frequently in the study of acids and bases, we use the subscript w to indicate that the equilibrium constant is that specifically for the autoionization of *water.* It is important to realize, though, that K_w is simply a K_c for a *specific reaction.* We will frequently replace the c in K_c expressions with a letter or a series of letters to indicate the specific type of reaction to which the K_c refers. For example, K_c for the ionization of a weak acid is called K_a, and K_c for the ionization of a weak base is called K_b. In Chapter 17, we will encounter K_{sp}, where "sp" stands for "solubility product." Each specially subscripted K is simply a K_c for a specific type of reaction. The constant K_w is sometimes referred to as the *ion-product constant.*

> **Student Annotation:** Recall that we disregard the units when we substitute concentrations into an equilibrium expression [◄◄ Section 15.2].

In pure water, autoionization is the only source of H_3O^+ and OH^-, and the stoichiometry of the reaction tells us that their concentrations are equal. At 25°C, the concentrations of hydronium and hydroxide ions in pure water are $[H_3O^+] = [OH^-] = 1.0 \times 10^{-7}$ M. Using the equilibrium expression, we can calculate the value of K_w at 25°C as follows:

$$K_w = [H_3O^+][OH^-] = (1.0 \times 10^{-7})(1.0 \times 10^{-7}) = 1.0 \times 10^{-14}$$

Furthermore, in any aqueous solution at 25°C, the product of H_3O^+ and OH^- concentrations is equal to 1.0×10^{-14}.

Equation 16.1	$K_w = [H_3O^+][OH^-] = 1.0 \times 10^{-14}$ (at 25°C)

Although their product is a constant, the individual concentrations of hydronium and hydroxide can be influenced by the addition of an acid or a base. The relative amounts of H_3O^+ and OH^- determine whether a solution is neutral, acidic, or basic.

> **Student Annotation:** Because the product of H_3O^+ and OH^- concentrations is a constant, we cannot alter the concentrations independently. Any change in one also affects the other.

- When $[H_3O^+] = [OH^-]$, the solution is neutral.
- When $[H_3O^+] > [OH^-]$, the solution is acidic.
- When $[H_3O^+] < [OH^-]$, the solution is basic.

Worked Example 16.4 shows how to use Equation 16.1.

Worked Example 16.4

The concentration of hydronium ions in stomach acid is 0.10 *M.* Calculate the concentration of hydroxide ions in stomach acid at 25°C.

Strategy Use the value of K_w to determine $[OH^-]$ when $[H_3O^+] = 0.10$ *M.*

Setup $K_w = [H_3O^+][OH^-] = 1.0 \times 10^{-14}$ at 25°C. Rearranging Equation 16.1 to solve for $[OH^-]$,

$$[OH^-] = \frac{1.0 \times 10^{-14}}{[H_3O^+]}$$

Solution

$$[OH^-] = \frac{1.0 \times 10^{-14}}{0.10} = 1.0 \times 10^{-13} \, M$$

> **Think About It**
> Remember that equilibrium constants are temperature dependent. The value of K_w is 1.0×10^{-14} only at 25°C.

Practice Problem A The concentration of hydroxide ions in the antacid milk of magnesia is $5.0 \times 10^{-4} \, M$. Calculate the concentration of hydronium ions at 25°C.

Practice Problem B The value of K_w at normal body temperature (37°C) is 2.8×10^{-14}. Calculate the concentration of hydroxide ions in stomach acid at body temperature ($[H_3O^+] = 0.10 \, M$).

SECTION 16.3 REVIEW

The Acid-Base Properties of Water

16.3.1 Calculate $[OH^-]$ in a solution in which $[H_3O^+] = 0.0012 \, M$ at 25°C.

16.3.2 Calculate $[H_3O^+]$ in a solution in which $[OH^-] = 0.25 \, M$ at 25°C.

16.4 THE pH SCALE

The acidity of an aqueous solution depends on the concentration of hydronium ions $[H_3O^+]$. This concentration can range over many orders of magnitude, which can make reporting the numbers cumbersome. To describe the acidity of a solution, rather than report the molar concentration of hydronium ions, we typically use the more convenient pH scale. The **pH** of a solution is defined as the negative base-10 logarithm of the hydronium ion concentration (in mol/L).

$$pH = -\log [H_3O^+] \text{ or } pH = -\log [H^+] \qquad \textbf{Equation 16.2}$$

> **Student Annotation:** Equation 16.2 converts numbers that can span an enormous range ($\sim 10^{-1}$ to 10^{-14}) to numbers generally ranging from ~ 1 to 14.

The pH of a solution is a dimensionless quantity, so the units of concentration must be removed from $[H_3O^+]$ before taking the logarithm. Because $[H_3O^+] = [OH^-] = 1.0 \times 10^{-7} \, M$ in pure water at 25°C, the pH of pure water at 25°C is

$$-\log (1.0 \times 10^{-7}) = 7.00$$

> **Student Annotation:** A word about significant figures: When we take the log of a number with two significant figures, we report the result to two places past the decimal point. Thus, pH 7.00 has *two* significant figures, not three.

Remember, too, that a solution in which $[H_3O^+] = [OH^-]$ is neutral. At 25°C, therefore, a neutral solution has pH 7.00. An acidic solution, one in which $[H_3O^+] > [OH^-]$, has pH < 7.00, whereas a basic solution, in which $[H_3O^+] < [OH^-]$, has pH > 7.00. Table 16.4 shows the calculation of pH for solutions ranging from 0.10 M to $1.0 \times 10^{-14} \, M$.

In the laboratory, pH is measured with a pH meter (Figure 16.3). Table 16.5 lists the pH values of a number of common fluids. Note that the pH of body fluids varies greatly, depending on the location and function of the fluid. The low pH (high acidity) of gastric juices is vital for digestion of food, whereas the higher pH of blood is required to facilitate the transport of oxygen.

A measured pH can be used to determine experimentally the concentration of hydronium ion in solution. Solving Equation 16.2 for $[H_3O^+]$ gives

> **Student Annotation:** 10^x is the inverse function of log. (It is the second function on the same key on most calculators.) You must be comfortable performing these operations on your calculator.

$$[H_3O^+] = 10^{-pH} \qquad \textbf{Equation 16.3}$$

Figure 16.3 A pH meter is commonly used in the laboratory to determine the pH of a solution. Although many pH meters have a range of 1 to 14, pH values can actually be less than 1 and greater than 14.

TABLE 16.4	Benchmark pH Values for a Range of Hydronium Ion Concentrations at 25°C		
[H₃O⁺] (M)	**−log [H₃O⁺]**	**pH**	
0.10	$-\log (1.0 \times 10^{-1})$	1.00	
0.010	$-\log (1.0 \times 10^{-2})$	2.00	
1.0×10^{-3}	$-\log (1.0 \times 10^{-3})$	3.00	
1.0×10^{-4}	$-\log (1.0 \times 10^{-4})$	4.00	
1.0×10^{-5}	$-\log (1.0 \times 10^{-5})$	5.00	
1.0×10^{-6}	$-\log (1.0 \times 10^{-6})$	6.00	Acidic
1.0×10^{-7}	$-\log (1.0 \times 10^{-7})$	7.00	Neutral
1.0×10^{-8}	$-\log (1.0 \times 10^{-8})$	8.00	Basic
1.0×10^{-9}	$-\log (1.0 \times 10^{-9})$	9.00	
1.0×10^{-10}	$-\log (1.0 \times 10^{-10})$	10.00	
1.0×10^{-11}	$-\log (1.0 \times 10^{-11})$	11.00	
1.0×10^{-12}	$-\log (1.0 \times 10^{-12})$	12.00	
1.0×10^{-13}	$-\log (1.0 \times 10^{-13})$	13.00	
1.0×10^{-14}	$-\log (1.0 \times 10^{-14})$	14.00	

TABLE 16.5	Typical pH Values of Some Common Fluids		
Fluid	**pH**	**Fluid**	**pH**
Stomach acid	1.0	Saliva	6.4–6.9
Lemon juice	2.0	Milk	6.5
Vinegar	3.0	Pure water	7.0
Grapefruit juice	3.2	Blood	7.35–7.45
Orange juice	3.5	Tears	7.4
Urine	4.8–7.5	Milk of magnesia	10.6
Rainwater (in clean air)	5.5	Household ammonia	11.5

Worked Examples 16.5 and 16.6 illustrate calculations involving pH.

Worked Example 16.5

Determine the pH of a solution at 25°C in which the hydronium ion concentration is (a) 3.5×10^{-4} M, (b) 1.7×10^{-7} M, and (c) 8.8×10^{-11} M.

Strategy Given [H₃O⁺], use Equation 16.2 to solve for pH.

Setup

(a) pH = $-\log (3.5 \times 10^{-4})$

(b) pH = $-\log (1.7 \times 10^{-7})$

(c) pH = $-\log (8.8 \times 10^{-11})$

Solution

(a) pH = 3.46

(b) pH = 6.77

(c) pH = 10.06

Think About It

When a hydronium ion concentration falls between two "benchmark" concentrations in Table 16.4, the pH falls between the two corresponding pH values. In part (c), for example, the hydronium ion concentration (8.8×10^{-11} M) is greater than 1.0×10^{-11} M but less than 1.0×10^{-10} M. Therefore, we expect the pH to be between 11.00 and 10.00.

$[H_3O^+]$ (M)	$-\log [H_3O^+]$	pH
1.0×10^{-10}	$-\log (1.0 \times 10^{-10})$	10.00
$8.8 \times 10^{-11*}$	$-\log (8.8 \times 10^{-11})$	10.06[†]
1.0×10^{-11}	$-\log (1.0 \times 10^{-11})$	11.00

[*]$[H_3O^+]$ between two benchmark values
[†]pH between two benchmark values

Recognizing the benchmark concentrations and corresponding pH values is a good way to determine whether or not your calculated result is reasonable.

Practice Problem A Determine the pH of a solution at 25°C in which the hydronium ion concentration is (a) 3.2×10^{-9} M, (b) 4.0×10^{-8} M, and (c) 5.6×10^{-2} M.

Practice Problem B Determine the pH of a solution at 25°C in which the hydronium ion concentration is (a) 1.2 M, (b) 3.0×10^{-11} M, and (c) 8.6×10^{-12} M.

Worked Example 16.6

Calculate the hydronium ion concentration in a solution at 25°C in which the pH is (a) 4.76, (b) 11.95, and (c) 8.01.

Strategy Given pH, use Equation 16.3 to calculate $[H_3O^+]$.

Setup

(a) $[H_3O^+] = 10^{-4.76}$

(b) $[H_3O^+] = 10^{-11.95}$

(c) $[H_3O^+] = 10^{-8.01}$

Solution

(a) $[H_3O^+] = 1.7 \times 10^{-5}$ M

(b) $[H_3O^+] = 1.1 \times 10^{-12}$ M

(c) $[H_3O^+] = 9.8 \times 10^{-9}$ M

Think About It

If you use the calculated hydronium ion concentrations to recalculate pH, you will get numbers slightly different from those given in the problem. In part (a), for example, $-\log (1.7 \times 10^{-5}) = 4.77$. The small difference between this and 4.76 (the pH given in the problem) is due to a rounding error. Remember that a concentration derived from a pH with two digits to the right of the decimal point can have only two significant figures. Note also that the benchmarks can be used equally well in this circumstance. A pH between 4 and 5 corresponds to a hydronium ion concentration between 1×10^{-4} M and 1×10^{-5} M.

Practice Problem A Calculate the hydronium ion concentration in a solution at 25°C in which the pH is (a) 9.90, (b) 1.45, and (c) 7.01.

Practice Problem B Calculate the hydronium ion concentration in a solution at 25°C in which the pH is (a) 2.11, (b) 11.59, and (c) 6.87.

A *pOH* scale analogous to the pH scale can be defined using the negative base-10 logarithm of the *hydroxide* ion concentration of a solution, [OH⁻].

Equation 16.4	$\text{pOH} = -\log\,[\text{OH}^-]$

Rearranging Equation 16.4 to solve for hydroxide ion concentration gives

Equation 16.5	$[\text{OH}^-] = 10^{-\text{pOH}}$

Now consider again the K_w equilibrium expression for water at 25°C:

$$[\text{H}_3\text{O}^+][\text{OH}^-] = 1.0 \times 10^{-14}$$

Taking the negative logarithm of both sides, we obtain

$$-\log([\text{H}_3\text{O}^+][\text{OH}^-]) = -\log(1.0 \times 10^{-14})$$

$$-(\log[\text{H}_3\text{O}^+] + \log[\text{OH}^-]) = 14.00$$

$$-\log[\text{H}_3\text{O}^+] - \log[\text{OH}^-] = 14.00$$

$$(-\log[\text{H}_3\text{O}^+]) + (-\log[\text{OH}^-]) = 14.00$$

And from the definitions of pH and pOH, we see that at 25°C

Equation 16.6	$\text{pH} + \text{pOH} = 14.00$

Equation 16.6 provides another way to express the relationship between the hydronium ion concentration and the hydroxide ion concentration. On the pOH scale, 7.00 is neutral, numbers greater than 7.00 indicate that a solution is acidic, and numbers less than 7.00 indicate that a solution is basic. Table 16.6 lists pOH values for a range of hydroxide ion concentrations at 25°C.

Worked Examples 16.7 and 16.8 illustrate calculations involving pOH.

TABLE 16.6	Benchmark pOH Values for a Range of Hydroxide Ion Concentrations at 25°C	
[OH⁻] (M)	**pOH**	
0.10	1.00	↑
1.0×10^{-3}	3.00	
1.0×10^{-5}	5.00	Basic
1.0×10^{-7}	7.00	Neutral
1.0×10^{-9}	9.00	Acidic
1.0×10^{-11}	11.00	
1.0×10^{-13}	13.00	↓

Worked Example 16.7

Determine the pOH of a solution at 25°C in which the hydroxide ion concentration is (a) 3.7×10^{-5} *M*, (b) 4.1×10^{-7} *M*, and (c) 8.3×10^{-2} *M*.

Strategy Given [OH⁻], use Equation 16.4 to calculate pOH.

Setup

(a) $\text{pOH} = -\log\,(3.7 \times 10^{-5})$

(b) $\text{pOH} = -\log\,(4.1 \times 10^{-7})$

(c) $\text{pOH} = -\log\,(8.3 \times 10^{-2})$

Solution

(a) $\text{pOH} = 4.43$

(b) $\text{pOH} = 6.39$

(c) $\text{pOH} = 1.08$

Think About It
Remember that the pOH scale is, in essence, the *reverse* of the pH scale. On the pOH scale, numbers below 7 indicate a basic solution, whereas numbers above 7 indicate an acidic solution. The pOH benchmarks (abbreviated in Table 16.6) work the same way the pH benchmarks do. In part (a), for example, a hydroxide ion concentration between 1×10^{-4} M and 1×10^{-5} M corresponds to a pOH between 4 and 5:

$[OH^-]$ (M)	pOH
1.0×10^{-4}	4.00
$3.7 \times 10^{-5*}$	4.43†
1.0×10^{-5}	5.00

*$[OH^-]$ between two benchmark values
†pOH between two benchmark values

Practice Problem A Determine the pOH of a solution at 25°C in which the hydroxide ion concentration is (a) 5.7×10^{-12} M, (b) 7.3×10^{-3} M, and (c) 8.5×10^{-6} M.

Practice Problem B Determine the pOH of a solution at 25°C in which the hydroxide ion concentration is (a) 2.8×10^{-8} M, (b) 9.9×10^{-9} M, and (c) 1.0×10^{-11} M.

Worked Example 16.8

Calculate the hydroxide ion concentration in a solution at 25°C in which the pOH is (a) 4.91, (b) 9.03, and (c) 10.55.

Strategy Given pOH, use Equation 16.5 to calculate $[OH^-]$.

Setup	**Solution**
(a) $[OH^-] = 10^{-4.91}$	(a) $[OH^-] = 1.2 \times 10^{-5}$ M
(b) $[OH^-] = 10^{-9.03}$	(b) $[OH^-] = 9.3 \times 10^{-10}$ M
(c) $[OH^-] = 10^{-10.55}$	(c) $[OH^-] = 2.8 \times 10^{-11}$ M

Think About It
Use the benchmark pOH values to determine whether these solutions are reasonable. In part (a), for example, the pOH between 4 and 5 corresponds to $[OH^-]$ between 1×10^{-4} M and 1×10^{-5} M.

Practice Problem A Calculate the hydroxide ion concentration in a solution at 25°C in which the pOH is (a) 13.02, (b) 5.14, and (c) 6.98.

Practice Problem B Calculate the hydroxide ion concentration in a solution at 25°C in which the pOH is (a) 11.26, (b) 3.69, and (c) 1.60.

SECTION 16.4 REVIEW

The pH Scale

16.4.1 Determine the pH of a solution at 25°C in which $[H^+] = 6.35 \times 10^{-8}$ M.

16.4.2 Determine $[H^+]$ in a solution at 25°C if pH = 5.75.

16.4.3 Determine the pOH of a solution at 25°C in which $[OH^-] = 4.65 \times 10^{-3}$ M.

16.4.4 Determine $[OH^-]$ in a solution at 25°C if pH = 10.50.

16.5 STRONG ACIDS AND BASES

Most of this chapter and Chapter 17 deal with equilibrium and the application of the principles of equilibrium to a variety of reaction types. In the context of our discussion of acids and bases, however, it is necessary to review the ionization of strong acids and the dissociation of strong bases. These reactions generally are not treated as *equilibria* but rather as processes that go to completion. This makes the determination of pH for a solution of strong acid or strong base relatively simple.

Student Annotation: We indicate that ionization of a strong acid is *complete* by using a single arrow ($\longrightarrow$) instead of the double, equilibrium arrow ($\rightleftharpoons$) in the equation.

Strong Acids

There are many different acids, but as we learned in Chapter 9, relatively few qualify as *strong*.

Strong acid	Ionization reaction
Hydrochloric acid	$HCl(aq) + H_2O(l) \longrightarrow H_3O^+(aq) + Cl^-(aq)$
Hydrobromic acid	$HBr(aq) + H_2O(l) \longrightarrow H_3O^+(aq) + Br^-(aq)$
Hydroiodic acid	$HI(aq) + H_2O(l) \longrightarrow H_3O^+(aq) + I^-(aq)$
Nitric acid	$HNO_3(aq) + H_2O(l) \longrightarrow H_3O^+(aq) + NO_3^-(aq)$
Chloric acid	$HClO_3(aq) + H_2O(l) \longrightarrow H_3O^+(aq) + ClO_3^-(aq)$
Perchloric acid	$HClO_4(aq) + H_2O(l) \longrightarrow H_3O^+(aq) + ClO_4^-(aq)$
Sulfuric acid	$H_2SO_4(aq) + H_2O(l) \longrightarrow H_3O^+(aq) + HSO_4^-(aq)$

Multi 16.2
Acids and bases—the dissociation of strong and weak acids (interactive)

Student Annotation: Remember that although sulfuric acid has two ionizable protons, only the first ionization is complete.

It is a good idea to commit this short list of strong acids to memory.

Because the ionization of a strong acid is complete, the concentration of hydronium ion at equilibrium is equal to the starting concentration of the strong acid. For instance, if we prepare a 0.10-M solution of HCl, the concentration of hydronium ion in the solution is 0.10 M. All the HCl ionizes, and no HCl molecules remain. Thus, at equilibrium (when the ionization is complete), [HCl] = 0 M and [H_3O^+] = [Cl^-] = 0.10 M. Therefore, the pH of the solution (at 25°C) is

$$\text{pH} = -\log(0.10) = 1.00$$

Student Annotation: As we will see in Section 16.8, a solution of equal concentration but containing a weak acid has a higher pH.

This is a very low pH, which is consistent with a relatively concentrated solution of a strong acid.

Worked Examples 16.9 and 16.10 let you practice relating the concentration of a strong acid to the pH of an aqueous solution.

Worked Example 16.9

Calculate the pH of an aqueous solution at 25°C that is (a) 0.035 M in HI, (b) 1.2×10^{-4} M in HNO_3, and (c) 6.7×10^{-5} M in $HClO_4$.

Strategy HI, HNO_3, and $HClO_4$ are all strong acids, so the concentration of hydronium ion in each solution is the same as the stated concentration of the acid. Use Equation 16.2 to calculate pH.

Setup

(a) [H_3O^+] = 0.035 M

(b) [H_3O^+] = 1.2×10^{-4} M

(c) [H_3O^+] = 6.7×10^{-5} M

Solution

(a) pH = $-\log(0.035)$ = 1.46

(b) pH = $-\log(1.2 \times 10^{-4})$ = 3.92

(c) pH = $-\log(6.7 \times 10^{-5})$ = 4.17

Think About It
Again, note that when a hydronium ion concentration falls between two of the benchmark concentrations in Table 16.4, the pH falls between the two corresponding pH values. In part (b), for example, the hydronium ion concentration of 1.2×10^{-4} M is greater than 1.0×10^{-4} M and less than 1.0×10^{-3} M. Therefore, we expect the pH to be between 4.00 and 3.00.

$[H_3O^+]$ (M)	$-\log [H_3O^+]$	pH
1.0×10^{-3}	$-\log (1.0 \times 10^{-3})$	3.00
$1.2 \times 10^{-4*}$	$-\log (1.2 \times 10^{-3})$	3.92†
1.0×10^{-4}	$-\log (1.0 \times 10^{-4})$	4.00

$^*[H_3O^+]$ between two benchmark values
†pH between two benchmark values

Being comfortable with the benchmark hydronium ion concentrations and the corresponding pH values will help you avoid some of the common errors in pH calculations.

Practice Problem A Calculate the pH of an aqueous solution at 25°C that is (a) 0.081 M in HI, (b) 8.2×10^{-6} M in HNO_3, and (c) 5.4×10^{-3} M in $HClO_4$.

Practice Problem B Calculate the pH of an aqueous solution at 25°C that is (a) 0.011 M in HNO_3, (b) 3.5×10^{-3} M in HBr, and (c) 9.3×10^{-10} M in HCl.

Worked Example 16.10

Calculate the concentration of HCl in a solution at 25°C that has pH (a) 4.95, (b) 3.45, and (c) 2.78.

Strategy Use Equation 16.3 to convert from pH to the molar concentration of hydronium ion. In a strong acid solution, the molar concentration of hydronium ion is equal to the acid concentration.

Setup

(a) $[HCl] = [H_3O^+] = 10^{-4.95}$

(b) $[HCl] = [H_3O^+] = 10^{-3.45}$

(c) $[HCl] = [H_3O^+] = 10^{-2.78}$

Solution

(a) 1.1×10^{-5} M

(b) 3.5×10^{-4} M

(c) 1.7×10^{-3} M

Student Annotation: When we take the inverse log of a number with two digits to the right of the decimal point, the result has two significant figures.

Think About It
As pH decreases, acid concentration increases.

Practice Problem A Calculate the concentration of HNO_3 in a solution at 25°C that has pH (a) 2.06, (b) 1.77, and (c) 6.01.

Practice Problem B Calculate the concentration of HBr in a solution at 25°C that has pH (a) 4.81, (b) 1.82, and (c) 3.04.

Strong Bases

The list of strong bases is also fairly short. It consists of the hydroxides of alkali metals (Group 1A) and the hydroxides of the heaviest alkaline earth metals (Group 2A). The dissociation of a strong base is, for practical purposes, complete. Equations representing dissociations of the strong bases are as follows:

Multi 16.3
Acids and bases—ionization of a strong base and weak base (interactive)

Group 1A hydroxides

$LiOH(aq) \longrightarrow Li^+(aq) + OH^-(aq)$

$NaOH(aq) \longrightarrow Na^+(aq) + OH^-(aq)$

$KOH(aq) \longrightarrow K^+(aq) + OH^-(aq)$

$RbOH(aq) \longrightarrow Rb^+(aq) + OH^-(aq)$

$CsOH(aq) \longrightarrow Cs^+(aq) + OH^-(aq)$

Group 2A hydroxides

$Ca(OH)_2(aq) \longrightarrow Ca^{2+}(aq) + 2OH^-(aq)$

$Sr(OH)_2(aq) \longrightarrow Sr^{2+}(aq) + 2OH^-(aq)$

$Ba(OH)_2(aq) \longrightarrow Ba^{2+}(aq) + 2OH^-(aq)$

Student Annotation: Recall that $Ca(OH)_2$ and $Sr(OH)_2$ are not very soluble, but what *does* dissolve dissociates completely [◄◄ Section 9.3, Table 9.4].

Again, because the reaction goes to completion, the pH of such a solution is relatively easy to calculate. In the case of a Group 1A hydroxide, the hydroxide ion concentration is simply the starting concentration of the strong base. In a solution that is 0.018 M in NaOH, for example, $[OH^-] = 0.018\ M$. Its pH can be calculated in two ways. We can either use Equation 16.1 to determine hydronium ion concentration,

$$[H_3O^+][OH^-] = 1.0 \times 10^{-14}$$

$$[H_3O^+] = \frac{1.0 \times 10^{-14}}{[OH^-]} = \frac{1.0 \times 10^{-14}}{0.018} = 5.56 \times 10^{-13}\ M$$

and then Equation 16.2 to determine pH:

$$pH = -\log (5.56 \times 10^{-13}\ M) = 12.25$$

or we can calculate the pOH with Equation 16.3,

$$pOH = -\log (0.018) = 1.75$$

and use Equation 16.6 to convert to pH:

$$pH + pOH = 14.00$$

$$pH = 14.00 - 1.75 = 12.25$$

Both methods give the same result.

In the case of a Group 2A metal hydroxide, we must be careful to account for the reaction stoichiometry. For instance, if we prepare a solution that is $1.9 \times 10^{-4}\ M$ in barium hydroxide, the concentration of hydroxide ion at equilibrium (after complete dissociation) is $2(1.9 \times 10^{-4}\ M)$ or $3.8 \times 10^{-4}\ M$—twice the original concentration of $Ba(OH)_2$. Once we have determined the hydroxide ion concentration, we can determine pH as before:

$$[H_3O^+] = \frac{1.0 \times 10^{-14}}{[OH^-]} = \frac{1.0 \times 10^{-14}}{3.8 \times 10^{-4}} = 2.63 \times 10^{-11}\ M$$

and

$$pH = -\log (2.63 \times 10^{-11}\ M) = 10.58$$

or

$$pOH = -\log (3.8 \times 10^{-4}) = 3.42$$

$$pH + pOH = 14.00$$

$$pH = 14.00 - 3.42 = 10.58$$

Worked Examples 16.11 and 16.12 illustrate calculations involving hydroxide ion concentration, pOH, and pH.

Worked Example 16.11

Calculate the pOH of the following aqueous solutions at 25°C: (a) 0.013 M LiOH, (b) 0.013 M $Ba(OH)_2$, (c) $9.2 \times 10^{-5}\ M$ KOH.

Strategy LiOH, $Ba(OH)_2$, and KOH are all strong bases. Use reaction stoichiometry to determine hydroxide ion concentration and Equation 16.4 to determine pOH.

Setup

(a) The hydroxide ion concentration is simply equal to the concentration of the base. Therefore, $[OH^-] = [LiOH]\ 0.013\ M$.

(b) The hydroxide ion concentration is twice that of the base:

$$Ba(OH)_2(aq) \longrightarrow Ba^{2+}(aq) + 2OH^-(aq)$$

Therefore, $[OH^-] = 2 \times [Ba(OH)_2] = 2(0.013\ M) = 0.026\ M$.

(c) The hydroxide ion concentration is equal to the concentration of the base. Therefore, $[OH^-] = [KOH] = 9.2 \times 10^{-5}\ M$.

Solution

(a) pOH = −log (0.013) = 1.89

(b) pOH = −log (0.026) = 1.59

(c) pOH = −log (9.2×10^{-5}) = 4.04

> **Think About It**
> These are basic pOH values, which is what we should expect for the solutions described in the problem. Note that while the solutions in parts (a) and (b) have the same base concentration, they do not have the same hydroxide concentration and therefore do not have the same pOH.

Practice Problem A Calculate the pOH of the following aqueous solutions at 25°C:

(a) 0.15 M NaOH, (b) 8.4×10^{-3} M RbOH, (c) 1.7×10^{-5} M CsOH.

Practice Problem B Calculate the pOH of the following aqueous solutions at 25°C:

(a) 9.5×10^{-8} M NaOH, (b) 6.1×10^{-2} M LiOH, (c) 6.1×10^{-2} M Ba(OH)$_2$.

Worked Example 16.12

An aqueous solution of a strong base has pH 8.15 at 25°C. Calculate the original concentration of base in the solution (a) if the base is NaOH and (b) if the base is Ba(OH)$_2$.

Strategy Use Equation 16.6 to convert from pH to pOH and Equation 16.5 to determine the hydroxide ion concentration. Consider the stoichiometry of dissociation in each case to determine the concentration of the base itself.

Setup

$$pOH = 14.00 - 8.15 = 5.85$$

(a) The dissociation of 1 mole of NaOH produces 1 mole of OH⁻. Therefore, the concentration of the base is *equal* to the concentration of hydroxide ion.

(b) The dissociation of 1 mole of Ba(OH)$_2$ produces 2 moles of OH⁻. Therefore, the concentration of the base is only one-half the concentration of hydroxide ion.

Solution

$$[OH^-] = 10^{-5.85} = 1.41 \times 10^{-6}\ M$$

(a) [NaOH] = [OH⁻] = 1.4×10^{-6} M

(b) [Ba(OH)$_2$] = $\frac{1}{2}$[OH⁻] = 7.1×10^{-7} M

> **Student Annotation:** Remember to keep an additional significant figure or two until the end of the problem—to avoid *rounding error* [◀ Section 1.5].

> **Think About It**
> Alternatively, we could determine the hydroxide ion concentration using Equation 16.3, [H$_3$O⁺] = $10^{-8.15}$ = 7.1×10^{-9} M and Equation 16.1,
>
> $$[OH^-] = \frac{1.0 \times 10^{-14}}{7.1 \times 10^{-9}\ M}$$
>
> $$= 1.4 \times 10^{-6}\ M$$
>
> Once [OH⁻] is known, the solution is the same as shown previously.

Practice Problem A An aqueous solution of a strong base has pH 8.98 at 25°C. Calculate the concentration of base in the solution (a) if the base is LiOH and (b) if the base is Ba(OH)$_2$.

Practice Problem B An aqueous solution of a strong base has pH 12.24 at 25°C. Calculate the concentration of base in the solution (a) if the base is NaOH and (b) if the base is Ba(OH)$_2$.

Strong Acids and Bases

16.5.1   Calculate the pH of a 0.075 M solution of perchloric acid ($HClO_4$) at 25°C.

16.5.2   What is the concentration of HBr in a solution with pH 5.89 at 25°C?

16.5.3   What is the pOH of a solution at 25°C that is 1.3×10^{-3} M in $Ba(OH)_2$?

16.5.4   What is the concentration of KOH in a solution at 25°C that has pOH 3.31?

16.5.5   What is the pH of a solution at 25°C that is 0.0095 M in LiOH?

16.5.6   What is the concentration of $Ca(OH)_2$ in a solution at 25°C if the pH is 9.01?

16.5.7   Which diagram best represents a solution of sulfuric acid (H_2SO_4)?

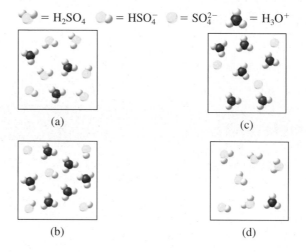

= H_2SO_4 = HSO_4^- = SO_4^{2-} = H_3O^+

(a)

(c)

(b)

(d)

16.6   WEAK ACIDS AND ACID IONIZATION CONSTANTS

Most acids are **weak acids,** which ionize only to a limited extent in water. At equilibrium, an aqueous solution of a weak acid contains a mixture of aqueous acid molecules, hydronium ions, and the corresponding conjugate base. The degree to which a weak acid ionizes depends on the *concentration* of the acid and the *equilibrium constant* for the ionization.

The Ionization Constant, K_a

Consider a weak monoprotic acid HA. Its ionization in water is represented by

$$HA(aq) + H_2O(l) \rightleftharpoons H_3O^+(aq) + A^-(aq)$$

or by

$$HA(aq) \rightleftharpoons H^+(aq) + A^-(aq)$$

Student Annotation: Remember that H_3O^+ and H^+ are used interchangeably.

The equilibrium expression for this reaction is

$$K_a = \frac{[H_3O^+][A^-]}{[HA]} \quad \text{or} \quad K_a = \frac{[H^+][A^-]}{[HA]}$$

Student Annotation: Remember that a K_a is a K_c. The subscript "a" simply stands for "acid."

where K_a is the equilibrium constant for the reaction. More specifically, K_a is called the **acid ionization constant.** Although all weak acids ionize less than 100 percent, they vary in strength.

TABLE 16.7	Ionization Constants of Some Weak Acids at 25°C		
Name of acid	**Formula**	**Structure**	**K_a**
Chloroacetic acid	$CH_2ClCOOH$	$CH_2Cl-\overset{\overset{\displaystyle O}{\|\|}}{C}-O-H$	5.6×10^{-2}
Hydrofluoric acid	HF	H—F	7.1×10^{-4}
Nitrous acid	HNO_2	O=N—O—H	4.5×10^{-4}
Formic acid	HCOOH	$H-\overset{\overset{\displaystyle O}{\|\|}}{C}-O-H$	1.7×10^{-4}
Benzoic acid	C_6H_5COOH	$\langle\bigcirc\rangle-\overset{\overset{\displaystyle O}{\|\|}}{C}-O-H$	6.5×10^{-5}
Acetic acid	CH_3COOH	$CH_3-\overset{\overset{\displaystyle O}{\|\|}}{C}-O-H$	1.8×10^{-5}
Hydrocyanic acid	HCN	H—C≡N	4.9×10^{-10}
Phenol	C_6H_5OH	$\langle\bigcirc\rangle-O-H$	1.3×10^{-10}

The magnitude of K_a indicates how strong a weak acid is. A large K_a value indicates a stronger acid, whereas a small K_a value indicates a weaker acid. For example, acetic acid (CH_3COOH) and hydrofluoric acid (HF) are both weak acids, but HF is the stronger acid of the two, as evidenced by its larger K_a value. Solutions of equal concentration of the two acids do *not* have the same pH. The pH of the HF solution is lower.

> **Student Annotation:** For comparison, the pH of a 0.1 M solution of a strong acid such as HCl or HNO_3 is 1.0.

Solution (at 25°C)	K_a	pH
0.10 M HF	7.1×10^{-4}	2.09
0.10 M CH_3COOH	1.8×10^{-5}	2.87

Table 16.7 lists a number of weak acids and their K_a values at 25°C in order of decreasing acid strength.

Calculating pH from K_a

Calculating the pH of a weak acid solution is an equilibrium problem, which we solve using the methods introduced in Chapter 15. Figure 16.4 on pages 674 and 675 shows in detail how an equilibrium table is used to determine the pH of a weak acid. Suppose we want to determine the pH of a 0.50 M HF solution at 25°C. The ionization of HF is represented by

Multi 16.4
Using Equilibrium Tables to Solve Problems (Figure 16.4)

$$HF(aq) + H_2O(l) \rightleftharpoons H_3O^+(aq) + F^-(aq)$$

The equilibrium expression for this reaction is

$$K_a = \frac{[H_3O^+][F^-]}{[HF]} = 7.1 \times 10^{-4}$$

(Continued on page 676)

Figure 16.4

Using Equilibrium Tables to Solve Problems

Using K_a and Concentration to Determine pH of a Weak Acid

Determine the pH of a weak acid with a concentration of 0.10 M and a K_a of 2.5×10^{-5}.

HA	$\rightleftharpoons$ H^+	$+$ A^-
i	0.10	0	0
c			
e			

The concentrations will change by an unknown amount, x.
- [HA] will decrease by x
- [H^+] and [A^-] will increase by x

We enter the anticipated changes in concentrations in the middle row of the table.

HA	$\rightleftharpoons$ H^+	$+$ A^-
i	0.10	0	0
c	$-x$	$+x$	$+x$
e			

HA	$\rightleftharpoons$ H^+	$+$ A^-
i			
c			
e			

Many equilibrium problems can be solved using an equilibrium table. The table is constructed with a column under each species in the equilibrium equation, and three rows labeled i (initial), c (change), and e (equilibrium). (This is why such a table is sometimes referred to as an "ice" table.)

HA

Using pH and Concentration to Determine K_a of a Weak Acid

We use pH to determine the equilibrium concentration of H^+:

$$[H^+] = 10^{-pH} = 10^{-3.82} = 1.5 \times 10^{-4} \, M$$

Because the ionization of HA produces equal amounts of H^+ and A^-, the equilibrium concentration of A^- is also $1.5 \times 10^{-4} \, M$. We enter these concentrations in the bottom row of the table.

Determine the K_a of a weak acid if a 0.12-M solution has a pH of 3.82.

HA	$\rightleftharpoons$ H^+	$+$ A^-
i			
c			
e		1.5×10^{-4}	1.5×10^{-4}

The equilibrium concentrations, which we enter in the last row of the table, are expressed in terms of the unknown x. We write the equilibrium expression for the reaction,

$$K_a = \frac{[H^+][A^-]}{[HA]}$$

and enter the K_a value and the equilibrium concentrations from the last row in the table:

$$2.5 \times 10^{-5} = \frac{(x)(x)}{(0.10 - x)} = \frac{x^2}{(0.10 - x)}$$

Because the magnitude of K_a is small, we expect the amount of HA ionized (x) to be small compared to 0.10. Therefore, we can assume that $0.10 - x \approx 0.10$. This simplifies the solution to

$$2.5 \times 10^{-5} = \frac{x^2}{0.10}$$

Solving for x gives

$$(2.5 \times 10^{-5})(0.10) = x^2$$

$$2.5 \times 10^{-6} = x^2$$

$$\sqrt{2.5 \times 10^{-6}} = x$$

$$x = 1.6 \times 10^{-3}\ M$$

We used x to represent $[H^+]$ at equilibrium. (x is also equal to $[A^-]$ at equilibrium and to the change in $[HA]$.) Therefore, we determine pH by taking the negative log of x.

$$pH = -\log [H^+] = -\log (1.6 \times 10^{-3}) = 2.80$$

CHECK Verify that $\dfrac{1.6 \times 10^{-3}\ M}{0.10\ M} \times 100\% < 5\%$

and that $\dfrac{(1.6 \times 10^{-3})^2}{(0.10 - 1.6 \times 10^{-3})} \approx K_a$

To complete the last row of the table, we also need the equilibrium value of [HA]. The amount of weak acid that ionized is equal to the amount of H^+ produced by the ionization. Therefore, at equilibrium,

$$[HA] = 0.12\ M - 1.5 \times 10^{-4}\ M \approx 0.12\ M$$

With the bottom row of the table complete, we can use these equilibrium concentrations to calculate the value of K_a.

$$K_a = \frac{[H^+][A^-]}{[HA]} = \frac{(1.5 \times 10^{-4})(1.5 \times 10^{-4})}{(0.12)} = 1.9 \times 10^{-7}$$

CHECK Verify that when $[HA] = 0.12\ M$ and $K_a = 1.9 \times 10^{-7}$, $[H^+] = \sqrt{(1.9 \times 10^{-7})(0.12)} = 1.5 \times 10^{-4}\ M$ and pH = 3.82.

What's the point?

- Starting with the molar concentration and K_a of a weak monoprotic acid, we can use an equilibrium table to determine pH.
- Starting with pH and molar concentration, we can use an equilibrium table to determine the K_a of a weak monoprotic acid.

$$HA \rightleftharpoons H^+ + A^-$$

We construct an equilibrium table and enter the starting concentrations of all species in the equilibrium expression.

$$HF(aq) + H_2O(l) \rightleftharpoons H_3O^+(aq) + F^-(aq)$$

	HF	H₂O	H₃O⁺	F⁻
Initial concentration (M):	0.50		0	0
Change in concentration (M):				
Equilibrium concentration (M):				

Using the reaction stoichiometry, we determine the changes in all species:

$$HF(aq) + H_2O(l) \rightleftharpoons H_3O^+(aq) + F^-(aq)$$

	HF	H₂O	H₃O⁺	F⁻
Initial concentration (M):	0.50		0	0
Change in concentration (M):	$-x$		$+x$	$+x$
Equilibrium concentration (M):				

Finally, we express the equilibrium concentration of each species in terms of x.

$$HF(aq) + H_2O(l) \rightleftharpoons H_3O^+(aq) + F^-(aq)$$

	HF	H₂O	H₃O⁺	F⁻
Initial concentration (M):	0.50		0	0
Change in concentration (M):	$-x$		$+x$	$+x$
Equilibrium concentration (M):	$0.50 - x$		x	x

These equilibrium concentrations are then entered into the equilibrium expression to give

$$K_a = \frac{(x)(x)}{0.50 - x} = 7.1 \times 10^{-4}$$

Rearranging this expression, we get

$$x^2 + 7.1 \times 10^{-4}x - 3.55 \times 10^{-4} = 0$$

This is a quadratic equation, which we can solve using the quadratic formula given in Appendix 1. In the case of a weak acid, however, often we can use a shortcut to simplify the calculation. Because HF is a weak acid, and weak acids ionize only to a slight extent, x must be small compared to 0.50. Therefore, we can make the following approximation:

$$0.50 - x \approx 0.50$$

Now the equilibrium expression becomes

$$\frac{x^2}{0.50 - x} \approx \frac{x^2}{0.50} = 7.1 \times 10^{-4}$$

Rearranging, we get

$$x^2 = (0.50)(7.1 \times 10^{-4}) = 3.55 \times 10^{-4}$$

$$x = \sqrt{3.55 \times 10^{-4}} = 1.9 \times 10^{-2}$$

Thus, we have solved for x without having to use the quadratic equation. At equilibrium we have

$$[HF] = (0.50 - 0.019) \, M = 0.48 \, M$$

$$[H_3O^+] = 0.019 \, M$$

$$[F^-] = 0.019 \, M$$

and the pH of the solution is

$$pH = -\log(0.019) = 1.72$$

This shortcut gives a good approximation as long as the magnitude of x is significantly smaller than the initial acid concentration. As a rule, it is acceptable to use this shortcut if the calculated value of x is less than 5 percent of the initial acid concentration. In this case, the approximation is acceptable because

$$\frac{0.019\ M}{0.50\ M} \times 100\% = 3.8\%$$

This is the formula for the *percent ionization* of the acid [◄◄ Section 13.6]. Recall that the percent ionization of a weak electrolyte, such as a weak acid, depends on concentration. Consider a more dilute solution of HF, one that is 0.050 M. Using the preceding procedure to solve for x, we would get 6.0×10^{-3} M. The following test shows, however, that this answer is *not* a valid approximation because it is greater than 5 percent of 0.050 M:

$$\frac{6.0 \times 10^{-3}\ M}{0.050\ M} \times 100\% = 12\%$$

In this case, we must solve for x using the quadratic equation [◄◄ Worked Example 15.9].
  Worked Example 16.13 shows how to use K_a to determine the pH of a weak acid solution.

> **Student Annotation:** In many cases, use of the quadratic equation can be avoided with a method called *successive approximation*, which is presented in Appendix 1.

Worked Example 16.13

The K_a of hypochlorous acid (HClO) is 3.5×10^{-8}. Calculate the pH of a solution at 25°C that is 0.0075 M in HClO.

Strategy Construct an equilibrium table, and express the equilibrium concentration of each species in terms of x. Solve for x using the approximation shortcut, and evaluate whether or not the approximation is valid. Use Equation 16.2 to determine pH.

Setup $HClO(aq) + H_2O(l) \rightleftharpoons H_3O^+(aq) + ClO^-(aq)$

Initial concentration (M):	0.0075	0	0
Change in concentration (M):	$-x$	$+x$	$+x$
Equilibrium concentration (M):	$0.0075 - x$	x	x

Solution These equilibrium concentrations are then substituted into the equilibrium expression to give

$$K_a = \frac{(x)(x)}{0.0075 - x} = 3.5 \times 10^{-8}$$

Assuming that $0.0075 - x \approx 0.0075$,

$$\frac{x^2}{0.0075} = 3.5 \times 10^{-8} \qquad\qquad x^2 = (3.5 \times 10^{-8})(0.0075)$$

Solving for x, we get

$$x = \sqrt{2.625 \times 10^{-10}} = 1.62 \times 10^{-5}\ M$$

According to the equilibrium table, $x = [H_3O^+]$. Therefore,

$$pH = -\log(1.62 \times 10^{-5}) = 4.79$$

> **Student Annotation:** Applying the 5 percent test indicates that the approximation shortcut is valid in this case: $(1.62 \times 10^{-5}/0.0075) \times 100\% < 5\%$.

Think About It
We learned in Section 16.3 that the concentration of hydronium ion in pure water at 25°C is 1.0×10^{-7} M, yet we use 0 M as the starting concentration to solve for the pH of a solution of weak acid:

$$HA(aq) \rightleftharpoons H^+(aq) + A^-(aq)$$

Initial concentration (M):	0	0
Change in concentration (M):		
Equilibrium concentration (M):		

The reason for this is that the *actual* concentration of hydronium ion in pure water is insignificant compared to the amount produced by the ionization of the weak acid. We could use the actual concentration of hydronium as the initial concentration, but doing so would not change the result because $(x + 1.0 \times 10^{-7})\ M \approx x\ M$. In solving problems of this type, we neglect the small concentration of H^+ due to the autoionization of water.

Practice Problem A Calculate the pH at 25°C of a 0.18-M solution of a weak acid that has $K_a = 9.2 \times 10^{-6}$.

Practice Problem B Calculate the pH at 25°C of a 0.065-M solution of a weak acid that has $K_a = 1.2 \times 10^{-5}$.

Thinking Outside the Box

Acid Rain

Rainwater in unpolluted areas is slightly acidic. The cause is carbon dioxide in the air, which dissolves in raindrops and reacts to form the weak acid, *carbonic* acid (H_2CO_3). In areas where the air is polluted by the burning of fossil fuels, rain can be very acidic. This phenomenon, known as *acid rain,* was first discovered in 1852 by Scottish chemist Robert Angus Smith (1817–1884) in Manchester, England. At that time, the industrial revolution was well under way and the British economy relied heavily on the use of coal to generate steam. The two main atmospheric contributors to the acidity of acid rain are sulfur dioxide (SO_2) and the oxides of nitrogen, NO and NO_2 (collectively referred to as NO_x), which react to produce sulfuric acid (H_2SO_4) and nitric acid (HNO_3)—both *strong* acids. SO_2 and NO_x are both produced by the burning of sulfur-bearing coal.

Although acid rain was first discovered in 1852, scientific and societal efforts to understand and remedy its causes did not emerge for another century. U.S. scientists began to study the causes and effects of acid rain extensively only in the late 1960s. Public awareness of the phenomenon was heightened in the 1970s when results of studies at the Hubbard Brook Experimental Forest in New Hampshire were published, detailing the devastating impact of acid rain on the ecology of the region.

Despite the dire circumstance described by atmospheric scientists and ecologists in the last half of the twentieth century, there appears to be reason for optimism with regard to acid rain. The Acid Rain Program, part of the 1990 amendment to the Clean Air Act (originally enacted in 1963), has contributed to reducing the acidity of rainwater in industrial areas of the United States to levels below those seen in the 1960s. Reducing sulfur emissions from coal-burning power plants has involved using coal containing less sulfur, fitting smokestacks with chemical scrubbers to remove SO_2, and developing alternative sources of energy. Significant reductions in NO_x emissions have been achieved through the use of catalytic converters, which have been standard equipment on automobiles in the United States since the mid 1970s.

Percent Ionization

When we encountered acids earlier [◄◄ Section 9.3], we learned that a strong acid is one that ionizes completely. Weak acids ionize only partially. The degree to which a weak acid ionizes is a measure of its strength, just as the magnitude of its ionization constant (K_a) is a measure of its strength. A quantitative measure of the degree of ionization is *percent ionization*, which, for a weak, monoprotic acid (HA) is calculated as follows:

Equation 16.7 $$\text{percent ionization} = \frac{[H^+]_{eq}}{[HA]_0} \times 100\%$$

in which the hydrogen ion concentration, $[H^+]_{eq}$, is the concentration at equilibrium and the weak acid concentration, $[HA]_0$, is the *original* concentration of the acid, which is not necessarily the same as the concentration at equilibrium.

Student Annotation: In fact, a weak acid's original concentration is never *exactly* equal to its equilibrium concentration. However, sometimes the amount that ionizes is so small compared to the original concentration that, to an appropriate number of significant figures, the weak acid concentration does not change and $[HA]_0 \approx [HA]_{eq}$.

Consider a 0.10-*M* solution of benzoic acid, for which the ionization constant (K_a) is 6.5×10^{-5}. Using the procedure described in Worked Example 16.13, we can determine the equilibrium concentrations of benzoic acid, H^+, and the benzoate ion.

$$C_6H_5COOH(aq) + H_2O(l) \rightleftharpoons H_3O^+(aq) + C_6H_5COO^-(aq)$$

	C_6H_5COOH	H_2O	H_3O^+	$C_6H_5COO^-$
Initial concentration (M):	0.100		0	0
Change in concentration (M):	$-x$		$+x$	$+x$
Equilibrium concentration (M):	$0.100 - x$		x	x

Solving for x gives 0.0025 *M*. Therefore, at equilibrium, $[C_6H_5COOH] = 0.097$ *M* and $[H^+] = [C_6H_5COO^-] = 0.0025$ *M*. The percent ionization of benzoic acid at this concentration is

$$\frac{0.0025\ M}{0.100\ M} \times 100\% = 2.5\%$$

Now consider what happens when we dilute this equilibrium mixture by adding enough water to double the volume. The concentrations of all three species are cut in half; $[C_6H_5COOH] = 0.049$ *M*,

Figure 16.5 Percent ionization of a weak acid depends on the original acid concentration. As concentration approaches zero, ionization approaches 100 percent. The dashed grey line represents 100 percent ionization, which is characteristic of a strong acid.

$[H^+] = 0.0013\ M$, and $[C_6H_5COO^-] = 0.0013\ M$. If we plug these new concentrations into the equilibrium expression and calculate the reaction quotient (Q), we get a number different from K_a. In fact, we get $(0.0013^2/0.049) = 3.4 \times 10^{-5}$, which is *smaller* than K_a. When Q is smaller than K, the reaction must proceed to the right to reestablish equilibrium [◄◄ Section 15.4]. Proceeding to the right, in the case of weak acid ionization, corresponds to more of the acid ionizing—meaning that its percent ionization increases.

> **Student Annotation:** According to Le Châtelier's principle [◄◄ Section 15.5], the reduction in particle concentration caused by dilution stresses the equilibrium. The equilibrium shifts to minimize the effects of the stress by shifting toward the side with more dissolved particles, causing more of the weak acid to ionize.

We can solve again for percent ionization starting with half the original concentration of benzoic acid.

$$C_6H_5COOH(aq) + H_2O(l) \rightleftharpoons H_3O^+(aq) + C_6H_5COO^-(aq)$$

	C_6H_5COOH	H_2O	H_3O^+	$C_6H_5COO^-$
Initial concentration (M):	0.050		0	0
Change in concentration (M):	$-x$		$+x$	$+x$
Equilibrium concentration (M):	$0.050 - x$		x	x

This time, solving for x gives $0.0018\ M$. Therefore, at equilibrium, $[C_6H_5COOH] = 0.048\ M$, and $[H^+] = [C_6H_5COO^-] = 0.0018\ M$. The percent ionization of benzoic acid at this concentration is

$$\frac{0.0018\ M}{0.0050\ M} \times 100\% = 3.6\%$$

Figure 16.5 shows the dependence of percent ionization of a weak acid on concentration. Note that as concentration approaches zero, percent ionization approaches 100.

Worked Example 16.14 lets you practice calculating percent ionization of weak acid solutions.

Worked Example 16.14

Determine the pH and percent ionization for acetic acid solutions at 25°C with concentrations (a) $0.15\ M$, (b) $0.015\ M$, and (c) $0.0015\ M$.

Strategy Using the procedure described in Worked Example 16.13, we construct an equilibrium table and for each concentration of acetic acid, we solve for the equilibrium concentration of H^+. We use equation 16.2 to find pH, and Equation 16.7 to find percent ionization.

Setup From Table 16.7, the ionization constant, K_a, for acetic acid is 1.8×10^{-5}.

Solution

(a)

$$CH_3COOH(aq) + H_2O(l) \rightleftharpoons H_3O^+(aq) + CH_3COO^-(aq)$$

	CH_3COOH	H_2O	H_3O^+	CH_3COO^-
Initial concentration (M):	0.15		0	0
Change in concentration (M):	$-x$		$+x$	$+x$
Equilibrium concentration (M):	$0.15 - x$		x	x

Solving for x gives $[H_3O^+] = 0.0016\ M$ and pH $= -\log(0.0016) = 2.78$.

$$\text{percent ionization} = \frac{0.0016\ M}{0.15\ M} \times 100\% = 1.1\%$$

(Continued on next page)

(b) Solving in the same way as part (a) gives $[H_3O^+] = 5.2 \times 10^{-4}\ M$ and pH = 3.28.

$$\text{percent ionization} = \frac{5.2 \times 10^{-4}\ M}{0.015\ M} \times 100\% = 3.5\%$$

(c) Solving the quadratic equation, or using successive approximation [▶▶ Appendix 1] gives $[H_3O^+] = 1.6 \times 10^{-4}\ M$ and pH = 3.78.

$$\text{percent ionization} = \frac{1.6 \times 10^{-4}\ M}{0.0015\ M} \times 100\% = 11\%$$

> **Think About It**
> Percent ionization also increases as concentration decreases for weak bases. [▶▶ Section 16.7]

Practice Problem A Determine the pH and percent ionization for hydrocyanic acid (HCN) solutions of concentration (a) 0.25 M, (b) 0.0075 M, and (c) $8.3 \times 10^{-5}\ M$.

Practice Problem B At what concentration does hydrocyanic acid exhibit (a) 0.05 percent ionization, (b) 0.10 percent ionization, and (c) 0.15 percent ionization?

Using pH to Determine K_a

In Chapter 15 we learned that we can determine the value of an equilibrium constant using equilibrium concentrations [◀◀ Section 15.2]. Using a similar approach, we can use the pH of a weak acid solution to determine the value of K_a. Suppose we want to determine the K_a of a weak acid (HA) and we know that a 0.25 M solution of the acid has a pH of 3.47 at 25°C. The first step is to use pH to determine the equilibrium hydronium ion concentration. Using Equation 16.3, we get

> **Student Annotation:** Remember that we keep extra significant figures until the end of a multistep problem to minimize rounding error [◀◀ Section 1.5].

$$[H_3O^+] = 10^{-3.47} = 3.39 \times 10^{-4}\ M$$

We use the starting concentration of the weak acid and the equilibrium concentration of the hydronium ion to construct an equilibrium table and determine the equilibrium concentrations of all three species.

	HA(aq)	+ H$_2$O(l)	⇌ H$_3$O$^+$(aq)	+ A$^-$(aq)
Initial concentration (M):	0.25		0	0
Change in concentration (M):	-3.39×10^{-4}		$+3.39 \times 10^{-4}$	$+3.39 \times 10^{-4}$
Equilibrium concentration (M):	0.2497		3.39×10^{-4}	3.39×10^{-4}

These equilibrium concentrations are substituted into the equilibrium expression to give

$$K_a = \frac{(3.39 \times 10^{-4})^2}{0.2497} = 4.6 \times 10^{-7}$$

Therefore, the K_a of this weak acid is 4.6×10^{-7}.

Worked Example 16.15 shows how to determine K_a using pH.

Worked Example 16.15

Aspirin (acetylsalicylic acid, HC$_9$H$_7$O$_4$) is a weak acid. It ionizes in water according to the equation

$$HC_9H_7O_4(aq) + H_2O(l) \rightleftharpoons H_3O^+(aq) + C_9H_7O_4^-(aq)$$

A 0.10-M aqueous solution of aspirin has a pH of 2.27 at 25°C. Determine the K_a of aspirin.

Strategy Determine the hydronium ion concentration from the pH. Use the hydronium ion concentration to determine the equilibrium concentrations of the other species, and plug the equilibrium concentrations into the equilibrium expression to evaluate K_a.

Aspirin

Setup Using Equation 16.3, we have

$$[H_3O^+] = 10^{-2.27} = 5.37 \times 10^{-3}\ M$$

To calculate K_a, though, we also need the equilibrium concentrations of $C_9H_7O_4^-$ and $HC_9H_7O_4$. The stoichiometry of the reaction tells us that $[C_9H_7O_4^-] = [H_3O^+]$. Furthermore, the amount of aspirin that has *ionized* is equal to the amount of hydronium ion in solution. Therefore, the equilibrium concentration of aspirin is $(0.10 - 5.37 \times 10^{-3})\ M = 0.095\ M$.

$$HC_9H_7O_4(aq) + H_2O(l) \rightleftharpoons H_3O^+(aq) + C_9H_7O_4^-(aq)$$

	$HC_9H_7O_4(aq) + H_2O(l)$	$H_3O^+(aq)$	$C_9H_7O_4^-(aq)$
Initial concentration (M):	0.10	0	0
Change in concentration (M):	−0.005	$+5.37 \times 10^{-3}$	$+5.37 \times 10^{-3}$
Equilibrium concentration (M):	0.095	5.37×10^{-3}	5.37×10^{-3}

Solution Substitute the equilibrium concentrations into the equilibrium expression as follows:

$$K_a = \frac{[H_3O^+][C_9H_7O_4^-]}{[HC_9H_7O_4]} = \frac{(5.37 \times 10^{-3})^2}{0.095} = 3.0 \times 10^{-4}$$

The K_a of aspirin is 3.0×10^{-4}.

Think About It

Check your work by using the calculated value of K_a to solve for the pH of a 0.10-M solution of aspirin.

Practice Problem A Calculate the K_a of a weak acid if a 0.065-M solution of the acid has a pH of 2.96 at 25°C.

Practice Problem B Calculate the K_a of a weak acid if a 0.015-M solution of the acid has a pH of 5.03 at 25°C.

SECTION 16.6 REVIEW

Weak Acids and Acid Ionization Constants

16.6.1 The K_a of a weak acid is 5.5×10^{-4}. What is the pH of a 0.63-M solution of this acid at 25°C?

16.6.2 A 0.042-M solution of a weak acid has pH 4.01 at 25°C. What is the K_a of this acid?

16.6.3 The diagrams show solutions of three different weak acids with the general formula HA. List the acids in order of increasing K_a value.

(i)	(ii)	(iii)

16.7 WEAK BASES AND BASE IONIZATION CONSTANTS

Just as most acids are weak, most bases are also weak. The ionization of a *weak base* is incomplete and is treated in the same way as the ionization of a weak acid. In this section, we will see how the ionization constant for a weak base, K_b, is related to the pH of an aqueous solution.

The Ionization Constant, K_b

The ionization of a weak base can be represented by the equation

$$B(aq) + H_2O(l) \rightleftharpoons HB^+(aq) + OH^-(aq)$$

where B is the weak base and HB^+ is its conjugate acid. The equilibrium expression for the ionization is

$$K_b = \frac{[HB^+][OH^-]}{[B]}$$

where K_b is the equilibrium constant—specifically known as the ***base ionization constant.*** Like weak acids, weak bases vary in strength. Table 16.8 lists a number of common weak bases and their ionization constants. The ability of any one of these substances to act as a base is the result of the lone pair of electrons on the nitrogen atom. The presence of this lone pair is what enables a compound to accept a proton, which is what makes a compound a Brønsted base.

Calculating pH from K_b

Solving problems involving weak bases requires the same approach we used for weak acids. It is important to remember, though, that solving for x in a typical weak base problem gives us the hydroxide ion concentration rather than the hydronium ion concentration.

Worked Example 16.16 shows how to use K_b to calculate the pH of a weak base solution.

Worked Example 16.16

What is the pH of a 0.040 M ammonia solution at 25°C?

Strategy Construct an equilibrium table, and express equilibrium concentrations in terms of the unknown x. Plug these equilibrium concentrations into the equilibrium expression, and solve for x. From the value of x, determine the pH.

Setup

	$NH_3(aq)$ +	$H_2O(l) \rightleftharpoons$	$NH_4^+(aq)$ +	$OH^-(aq)$
Initial concentration (M):	0.040		0	0
Change in concentration (M):	$-x$		$+x$	$+x$
Equilibrium concentration (M):	$0.040 - x$		x	x

Solution The equilibrium concentrations are substituted into the equilibrium expression to give

$$K_b = \frac{[NH_4^+][OH^-]}{[NH_3]} = \frac{(x)(x)}{0.040 - x} = 1.8 \times 10^{-5}$$

Assuming that $0.040 - x \approx 0.040$ and solving for x gives

$$\frac{(x)(x)}{0.040 - x} \approx \frac{(x)(x)}{0.040} = 1.8 \times 10^{-5}$$

$$x^2 = (1.8 \times 10^{-5})(0.040) = 7.2 \times 10^{-7}$$

$$x = \sqrt{7.2 \times 10^{-7}} = 8.5 \times 10^{-4}\ M$$

According to the equilibrium table, $x = [OH^-]$. Therefore, pOH $= -\log(x)$:

$$-\log(8.5 \times 10^{-4}) = 3.07$$

and pH $= 14.00 -$ pOH $= 14.00 - 3.07 = 10.93$. The pH of a 0.040-M solution of NH_3 at 25°C is 10.93.

Student Annotation: Applying the 5 percent test indicates that the approximation shortcut is valid in this case: $(8.5 \times 10^{-4}/0.040) \times 100\% \approx 2\%$.

Think About It
It is a common error in K_b problems to forget that x is the *hydroxide* ion concentration rather than the *hydronium* ion concentration. Always make sure that the pH you calculate for a solution of base is a basic pH, that is, a pH greater than 7.

Practice Problem A Calculate the pH at 25°C of a 0.0028-M solution of a weak base with a K_b of 6.8×10^{-8}.

Practice Problem B Calculate the pH at 25°C of a 0.16-M solution of a weak base with a K_b of 2.9×10^{-11}.

TABLE 16.8	Ionization Constants of Some Weak Bases at 25°C		
Name of base	**Formula**	**Structure**	K_b
Ethylamine	$C_2H_5NH_2$	CH₃—CH₂—N̈—H | H	5.6×10^{-4}
Methylamine	CH_3NH_2	CH₃—N̈—H | H	4.4×10^{-4}
Ammonia	NH_3	H—N̈—H | H	1.8×10^{-5}
Pyridine	C_5H_5N	N:	1.7×10^{-9}
Aniline	$C_6H_5NH_2$	N̈—H | H	3.8×10^{-10}
Urea	H_2NCONH_2	H—N̈—C—N̈—H (with C=O) | | H H	1.5×10^{-14}

Using pH to Determine K_b

Just as we can use pH to determine the K_a of a weak acid, we can also use it to determine the K_b of a weak base. Worked Example 16.17 demonstrates this procedure.

Worked Example 16.17

Caffeine, the stimulant in coffee and tea, is a weak base that ionizes in water according to the equation

$$C_8H_{10}N_4O_2(aq) + H_2O(l) \rightleftharpoons HC_8H_{10}N_4O_2^+(aq) + OH^-(aq)$$

A 0.15-M solution of caffeine at 25°C has a pH of 8.45. Determine the K_b of caffeine.

Caffeine

Strategy Use pH to determine pOH, and pOH to determine the hydroxide ion concentration. From the hydroxide ion concentration, use reaction stoichiometry to determine the other equilibrium concentrations and plug those concentrations into the equilibrium expression to evaluate K_b.

Setup

$$pOH = 14.00 - 8.45 = 5.55$$

$$[OH^-] = 10^{-5.55} = 2.82 \times 10^{-6} \ M$$

(Continued on next page)

Based on the reaction stoichiometry, $[HC_8H_{10}N_4O_2^+] = [OH^-]$, and the amount of hydroxide ion in solution at equilibrium is equal to the amount of caffeine that has ionized. At equilibrium, therefore,

$$[C_8H_{10}N_4O_2] = (0.15 - 2.82 \times 10^{-6}) \, M \approx 0.15 \, M$$

	$C_8H_{10}N_4O_2(aq)$ + $H_2O(l)$	$\rightleftharpoons$ $HC_8H_{10}N_4O_2^+(aq)$ +	$OH^-(aq)$
Initial concentration (M):	0.15	0	0
Change in concentration (M):	-2.82×10^{-6}	$+2.82 \times 10^{-6}$	$+2.82 \times 10^{-6}$
Equilibrium concentration (M):	0.15	2.82×10^{-6}	2.82×10^{-6}

Solution Plugging the equilibrium concentrations into the equilibrium expression gives

$$K_b = \frac{[HC_8H_{10}N_4O_2^+][OH^-]}{[C_8H_{10}N_4O_2]} = \frac{(2.82 \times 10^{-6})^2}{0.15} = 5.3 \times 10^{-11}$$

Think About It
Check your answer by using the calculated K_b to determine the pH of a 0.15-M solution.

Practice Problem A Determine the K_b of a weak base if a 0.50-M solution of the base has a pH of 9.59 at 25°C.

Practice Problem B Determine the K_b of a weak base if a 0.35-M solution of the base has a pH of 11.84 at 25°C.

SECTION 16.7 REVIEW

Weak Bases and Base Ionization Constants

16.7.1   What is the pH of a 0.63-M solution of weak base at 25°C if $K_b = 9.5 \times 10^{-7}$?

16.7.2   A 0.12-M solution of a weak base has a pH of 10.76 at 25°C. Determine K_b.

16.7.3   The diagrams show solutions of three different weak bases. List the bases in order of increasing K_b value.

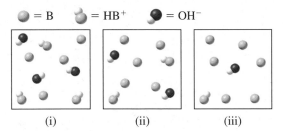

(i)	(ii)	(iii)

16.8   CONJUGATE ACID-BASE PAIRS

At the beginning of this chapter, we introduced the concept of conjugate acids and conjugate bases. In this section, we examine the properties of conjugate acids and bases, independent of their parent compounds.

The Strength of a Conjugate Acid or Base

When a strong acid such as HCl dissolves in water, it ionizes completely because its conjugate base (Cl⁻) has essentially *no* affinity for the H⁺ ion in solution.

$$HCl(aq) \longrightarrow H^+(aq) + Cl^-(aq)$$

Because the chloride ion has no affinity for the H^+ ion, it does not act as a Brønsted base in water. If we dissolve a chloride salt such as NaCl in water, for example, the Cl^- ions in solution would not accept protons from the water:

$$Cl^-(aq) + H_2O(l) \not\longrightarrow HCl(aq) + OH^-(aq)$$

> **Student Annotation:** The products HCl and OH⁻ do *not* actually form when Cl⁻ and H₂O are combined.

The chloride ion, which is the conjugate base of a strong acid, is an example of a *weak conjugate base.*

Now consider the case of a weak acid. When HF dissolves in water, the ionization happens only to a *limited* degree because the conjugate base, F^-, has a strong affinity for the H^+ ion:

$$HF(aq) \rightleftharpoons H^+(aq) + F^-(aq)$$

This equilibrium lies far to the left ($K_a = 7.1 \times 10^{-4}$). Because the fluoride ion has a strong affinity for the H^+ ion, it acts as a Brønsted base in water. If we were to dissolve a fluoride salt, such as NaF in water, the F^- ions in solution would, to some extent, accept protons from water:

$$F^-(aq) + H_2O(l) \rightleftharpoons HF(aq) + OH^-(aq)$$

> **Student Annotation:** Note that one of the products of the reaction of a conjugate base with water is always the corresponding weak acid.

The fluoride ion, which is the conjugate base of a weak acid, is an example of a *strong conjugate base.*

Conversely, a strong base has a *weak conjugate acid* and a weak base has a *strong conjugate acid.* For example, H_2O is the weak conjugate acid of the strong base OH^-, whereas the ammonium ion (NH_4^+) is the strong conjugate acid of the weak base ammonia (NH_3). When an ammonium salt is dissolved in water, the ammonium ions donate protons to the water molecules:

$$NH_4^+(aq) + H_2O(l) \rightleftharpoons NH_3(aq) + H_3O^+(aq)$$

In general, there is a reciprocal relationship between the strength of an acid or base and the strength of its conjugate.

> **Student Annotation:** The Group 1A and heavy Group 2A metal hydroxides are classified as *strong bases.* It is the hydroxide ion itself, however, that accepts a proton and is therefore the Brønsted base. Soluble metal hydroxides are simply sources of the hydroxide ion.

Acid	Example	Conjugate base	Formula		Base	Example	Conjugate acid	Formula
strong	HNO_3	weak conjugate	NO_3^-		strong	OH^-	weak conjugate	H_2O
weak	HCN	strong conjugate	CN^-		weak	NH_3	strong conjugate	NH_4^+

It is important to recognize that the words *strong* and *weak* do not mean the same thing in the context of conjugate acids and conjugate bases as they do in the context of acids and bases in general. A strong conjugate reacts with water—either accepting a proton from it or donating a proton to it—to a small but measurable extent. A strong conjugate acid acts as a weak Brønsted acid in water; and a strong conjugate base acts as a weak Brønsted base in water. A *weak* conjugate does not react with water to any measurable extent.

> **Student Annotation:**
> • A strong *conjugate* acid is a *weak* Brønsted acid.
> • A strong *conjugate* base is a *weak* Brønsted base.

The Relationship Between K_a and K_b of a Conjugate Acid-Base Pair

Because it accepts a proton from water to a small extent, what we refer to as a "strong *conjugate* base" is actually a *weak* Brønsted base. Therefore, every strong conjugate base has an ionization constant, K_b. Likewise, every strong conjugate acid, because it acts as a weak Brønsted acid, has an ionization constant, K_a.

A simple relationship between the ionization constant of a weak acid (K_a) and the ionization constant of its conjugate base (K_b) can be derived as follows, using acetic acid as an example:

$$CH_3COOH(aq) \rightleftharpoons H^+(aq) + CH_3COO^-(aq)$$
$$\text{acid} \qquad\qquad\qquad \text{conjugate base}$$

$$K_a = \frac{[H^+][CH_3COO^-]}{[CH_3COOH]}$$

The conjugate base, CH_3COO^-, reacts with water according to the equation

$$CH_3COO^-(aq) + H_2O(l) \rightleftharpoons CH_3COOH(aq) + OH^-(aq)$$

and the base ionization equilibrium expression is written as

$$K_b = \frac{[CH_3COOH][OH^-]}{[CH_3COO^-]}$$

As for any chemical equations, we can add these two equilibria and cancel identical terms:

$$\cancel{CH_3COOH(aq)} \rightleftharpoons H^+(aq) + \cancel{CH_3COO^-(aq)}$$

$$\underline{+ \cancel{CH_3COO^-(aq)} + H_2O(l) \rightleftharpoons \cancel{CH_3COOH(aq)} + OH^-(aq)}$$

$$H_2O(l) \rightleftharpoons H^+(aq) + OH^-(aq)$$

The sum is the autoionization of water. In fact, this is the case for any weak acid and its conjugate base:

$$\cancel{HA} \rightleftharpoons H^+ + \cancel{A^-}$$

$$\underline{+ \cancel{A^-} + H_2O \rightleftharpoons \cancel{HA} + OH^-}$$

$$H_2O \rightleftharpoons H^+ + OH^-$$

or for any weak base and its conjugate acid.

$$\cancel{B} + H_2O \rightleftharpoons \cancel{HB^+} + OH^-$$

$$\underline{+ \cancel{HB^+} + H_2O \rightleftharpoons \cancel{B} + H_3O^+}$$

$$2H_2O \rightleftharpoons H_3O^+ + OH^-$$

Recall that when we add two equilibria, the equilibrium constant for the *net* reaction is the product of the equilibrium constants for the individual equations [◄◄ Section 15.3]. Thus, for any conjugate acid-base pair,

Equation 16.8 $K_a \times K_b = K_w$

Equation 16.8 gives the quantitative basis for the reciprocal relationship between the strength of an acid and that of its conjugate base (or between the strength of a base and that of its conjugate acid). Because K_w is a constant, K_b must decrease if K_a increases, and vice versa.

Worked Example 16.18 shows how to determine ionization constants for conjugates.

Worked Example 16.18

Determine (a) K_b of the acetate ion (CH_3COO^-), (b) K_a of the methylammonium ion ($CH_3NH_3^+$), (c) K_b of the fluoride ion (F^-), and (d) K_a of the ammonium ion (NH_4^+).

Strategy Each species listed is either a conjugate base or a conjugate acid. Determine the identity of the acid corresponding to each conjugate base and the identity of the base corresponding to each conjugate acid; then, consult Tables 16.7 and 16.8 for their ionization constants. Use the tabulated ionization constants and Equation 16.8 to calculate each indicated K value.

Setup

(a) A K_b value is requested, indicating that the acetate ion is a conjugate base. To identify the corresponding Brønsted acid, add a proton to the formula to get CH_3COOH (acetic acid). The K_a of acetic acid (from Table 16.7) is 1.8×10^{-5}.

(b) A K_a value is requested, indicating that the methylammonium ion is a conjugate acid. Determine the identity of the corresponding Brønsted base by removing a proton from the formula to get CH_3NH_2 (methylamine). The K_b of methylamine (from Table 16.8) is 4.4×10^{-4}.

(c) F^- is the conjugate base of HF; $K_a = 7.1 \times 10^{-4}$.

(d) NH_4^+ is the conjugate acid of NH_3; $K_b = 1.8 \times 10^{-5}$. Solving Equation 16.8 separately for K_a and K_b gives, respectively,

$$K_a = \frac{K_w}{K_b} \quad \text{and} \quad K_b = \frac{K_w}{K_a}$$

Solution

(a) Conjugate base CH_3COO^-: $K_b = \dfrac{1.0 \times 10^{-14}}{1.8 \times 10^{-5}} = 5.6 \times 10^{-10}$

(b) Conjugate acid $CH_3NH_3^+$: $K_a = \dfrac{1.0 \times 10^{-14}}{4.4 \times 10^{-4}} = 2.3 \times 10^{-11}$

(c) Conjugate base F^-: $K_b = \dfrac{1.0 \times 10^{-14}}{7.1 \times 10^{-4}} = 1.4 \times 10^{-11}$

(d) Conjugate acid NH_4^+: $K_a = \dfrac{1.0 \times 10^{-14}}{1.8 \times 10^{-5}} = 5.6 \times 10^{-10}$

Think About It
Because the conjugates of weak acids and bases have ionization constants, salts containing these ions have an effect on the pH of a solution. In Section 16.10 we will use the ionization constants of conjugate acids and conjugate bases to calculate pH for solutions containing dissolved salts.

Practice Problem A Determine (a) K_b of the benzoate ion ($C_6H_5COO^-$), (b) K_b of the chloroacetate ion (CH_2ClCOO^-), and (c) K_a of the ethylammonium ion ($C_2H_5NH_3^+$).

Practice Problem B Determine (a) K_b of the weak base B whose conjugate acid HB^+ has $K_a = 8.9 \times 10^{-4}$ and (b) K_a of the weak acid HA whose conjugate base has $K_b = 2.1 \times 10^{-8}$.

SECTION 16.8 REVIEW

Conjugate Acid-Base Pairs

16.8.1 Calculate the K_b of the cyanide ion (CN^-).

16.8.2 Which of the following anions is the strongest base? (See Table 16.8.) formate ion ($HCOO^-$), benzoate ion ($C_6H_5COO^-$), phenolate ion ($C_6H_5O^-$)

16.8.3 The diagrams show solutions of three different weak acids with formulas HX, HY, and HZ. List the anions X^-, Y^-, and Z^- in order of increasing K_b value.

16.9   DIPROTIC AND POLYPROTIC ACIDS

Diprotic and polyprotic acids undergo successive ionizations, losing one proton at a time [◄◄ Section 9.3], and each ionization has a K_a associated with it. Ionization constants for a diprotic acid are designated K_{a_1} and K_{a_2}. A triprotic acid has K_{a_1}, K_{a_2}, and K_{a_3}. We write a separate equilibrium expression for each ionization, and we may need two or more equilibrium expressions to calculate the concentrations of species in solution at equilibrium. For carbonic acid (H_2CO_3), for example, we write

$$H_2CO_3(aq) \rightleftharpoons H^+(aq) + HCO_3^-(aq) \qquad K_{a_1} = \frac{[H^+][HCO_3^-]}{[H_2CO_3]}$$

$$HCO_3^-(aq) \rightleftharpoons H^+(aq) + CO_3^{2-}(aq) \qquad K_{a_2} = \frac{[H^+][CO_3^{2-}]}{[HCO_3^-]}$$

Note that the conjugate base in the first ionization is the acid in the second ionization. Table 16.9 shows the ionization constants of several diprotic acids and one polyprotic acid. For a given acid, the first ionization constant is much larger than the second ionization constant, and so on. This trend makes sense because it is easier to remove a proton from a neutral species than from one that is negatively charged, and it is easier to remove a proton from a species with a single negative charge than from one with a double negative charge.

TABLE 16.9	Ionization Constants of Some Diprotic and Polyprotic Acids at 25°C				
Name of acid	Formula	Structure	K_{a_1}	K_{a_2}	K_{a_3}
Sulfuric acid	H_2SO_4	H—O—S—O—H (with two =O on S)	Very large	1.3×10^{-2}	
Oxalic acid	$H_2C_2O_4$	H—O—C—C—O—H (with two =O)	6.5×10^{-2}	6.1×10^{-5}	
Sulfurous acid	H_2SO_3	H—O—S—O—H (with =O)	1.3×10^{-2}	6.3×10^{-8}	
Ascorbic acid (vitamin C)	$H_2C_6H_6O_6$	(ring structure)	8.0×10^{-5}	1.6×10^{-12}	
Carbonic acid	H_2CO_3	H—O—C—O—H (with =O)	4.2×10^{-7}	4.8×10^{-11}	
Hydrosulfuric acid*	H_2S	H—S—H	9.5×10^{-8}	1×10^{-19}	
Phosphoric acid	H_3PO_4	H—O—P—O—H (with =O and O—H)	7.5×10^{-3}	6.2×10^{-8}	4.8×10^{-13}

*The second ionization constant of H_2S is very low and difficult to measure. The value in this table is an estimate.

Worked Example 16.19 shows how to calculate equilibrium concentrations of all species in solution for an aqueous solution of a diprotic acid.

Worked Example 16.19

Oxalic acid ($H_2C_2O_4$) is a poisonous substance used mainly as a bleaching agent. Calculate the concentrations of all species present at equilibrium in a 0.10-M solution at 25°C.

Strategy Follow the same procedure for each ionization as for the determination of equilibrium concentrations for a monoprotic acid. The conjugate base resulting from the first ionization is the acid for the second ionization, and its starting concentration is the equilibrium concentration from the first ionization.

Setup The ionizations of oxalic acid and the corresponding ionization constants are

$$H_2C_2O_4(aq) \rightleftharpoons H^+(aq) + HC_2O_4^-(aq) \qquad K_{a_1} = 6.5 \times 10^{-2}$$

$$HC_2O_4^-(aq) \rightleftharpoons H^+(aq) + C_2O_4^{2-}(aq) \qquad K_{a_2} = 6.1 \times 10^{-5}$$

Construct an equilibrium table for each ionization, using x as the unknown in the first ionization and y as the unknown in the second ionization.

$$H_2C_2O_4(aq) \rightleftharpoons H^+(aq) + HC_2O_4^-(aq)$$

	$H_2C_2O_4$	H^+	$HC_2O_4^-$
Initial concentration (M):	0.10	0	0
Change in concentration (M):	$-x$	$+x$	$+x$
Equilibrium concentration (M):	$0.10 - x$	x	x

The equilibrium concentration of the hydrogen oxalate ion ($HC_2O_4^-$) after the first ionization becomes the starting concentration for the second ionization. Additionally, the equilibrium concentration of H^+ is the starting concentration for the second ionization.

$$HC_2O_4^-(aq) \rightleftharpoons H^+(aq) + C_2O_4^{2-}(aq)$$

	$HC_2O_4^-$	H^+	$C_2O_4^{2-}$
Initial concentration (M):	x	x	0
Change in concentration (M):	$-y$	$+y$	$+y$
Equilibrium concentration (M):	$x - y$	$x + y$	y

Solution

$$K_{a_1} = \frac{[H^+][HC_2O_4^-]}{[H_2C_2O_4]}$$

$$6.5 \times 10^{-2} = \frac{x^2}{0.10 - x}$$

Applying the approximation and neglecting x in the denominator of the expression gives

$$6.5 \times 10^{-2} \approx \frac{x^2}{0.10}$$

$$x^2 = 6.5 \times 10^{-3}$$

$$x = 8.1 \times 10^{-2} \, M$$

Testing the approximation,

$$\frac{8.1 \times 10^{-2} \, M}{0.10 \, M} \times 100\% = 81\%$$

Clearly the approximation is not valid, so we must solve the following quadratic equation:

$$x^2 + 6.5 \times 10^{-2} \, x - 6.5 \times 10^{-3} = 0$$

The result is $x = 0.054 \, M$. Thus, after the first ionization, the concentrations of species in solution are

$$[H^+] = 0.054 \, M$$

$$[HC_2O_4^-] = 0.054 \, M$$

$$[H_2C_2O_4] = (0.10 - 0.054) \, M = 0.046 \, M$$

(Continued on next page)

Rewriting the equilibrium table for the second ionization, using the calculated value of x, gives the following:

$$HC_2O_4^-(aq) \rightleftharpoons H^+(aq) + C_2O_4^{2-}(aq)$$

Initial concentration (M):	0.054	0.054	0
Change in concentration (M):	$-y$	$+y$	$+y$
Equilibrium concentration (M):	$0.054 - y$	$0.054 + y$	y

$$K_{a_2} = \frac{[H^+][C_2O_4^{2-}]}{[HC_2O_4^-]}$$

$$6.1 \times 10^{-5} = \frac{(0.054 + y)(y)}{0.054 - y}$$

Assuming that y is very small and applying the approximations $0.054 + y \approx 0.054$ and $0.054 - y \approx 0.054$ gives

$$\frac{(0.054)(y)}{0.054} = y = 6.1 \times 10^{-5}$$

We must test the approximation as follows to see if it is valid:

$$\frac{6.1 \times 10^{-5}\,M}{0.054\,M} \times 100\% = 0.11\%$$

This time, because the ionization constant is much smaller, the approximation is valid. At equilibrium, the concentrations of all species are

$$[H_2C_2O_4] = 0.046\,M$$

$$[HC_2O_4^-] = (0.054 - 6.1 \times 10^{-5})\,M = 0.054\,M$$

$$[H^+] = (0.054 + 6.1 \times 10^{-5})\,M = 0.054\,M$$

$$[C_2O_4^{2-}] = 6.1 \times 10^{-5}\,M$$

Think About It

Note that the second ionization did not contribute significantly to the H^+ concentration. Therefore, we could determine the pH of this solution by considering only the first ionization. This is true in general for polyprotic acids where K_{a_1} is at least $1000 \times K_{a_2}$. [Note that it is necessary to consider the second ionization to determine the concentration of oxalate ion ($C_2O_4^{2-}$).]

Practice Problem A Calculate the concentrations of $H_2C_2O_4$, $HC_2O_4^-$, $C_2O_4^{2-}$, and H^+ ions in a 0.20 M oxalic acid solution at 25°C.

Practice Problem B Calculate the concentrations of H_2SO_4, HSO_4^-, SO_4^{2-}, and H^+ ions in a 0.14 M sulfuric acid solution at 25°C.

SECTION 16.9 REVIEW

Diprotic and Polyprotic Acids

16.9.1   Calculate the equilibrium concentration of CO_3^{2-} in a 0.050-M solution of carbonic acid at 25°C.

16.9.2   What is the pH of a 0.40-M solution of phosphoric acid at 25°C?

16.9.3   List the molecular and ionic species in order of increasing concentration in a solution of ascorbic acid ($H_2C_6H_6O_6$).

Student Annotation: Recall that a *salt* is an ionic compound formed by the reaction between an acid and a base [◀◀ Section 9.3]. Salts are strong electrolytes that dissociate completely into ions.

16.10   ACID-BASE PROPERTIES OF SALT SOLUTIONS

In Section 16.8, we saw that the conjugate base of a weak acid acts as a weak Brønsted base in water. Consider a solution of the salt sodium fluoride (NaF). Because NaF is a strong electrolyte, it dissociates completely in water to give a solution of sodium cations (Na^+) and fluoride anions (F^-).

The fluoride ion, which is the conjugate base of hydrofluoric acid, reacts with water to produce hydrofluoric acid and hydroxide ion:

$$F^-(aq) + H_2O(l) \rightleftharpoons HF(aq) + OH^-(aq)$$

This is a specific example of **salt hydrolysis**, in which ions produced by the dissociation of a salt react with water to produce either hydroxide ions or hydronium ions—thus impacting pH. Using our knowledge of how ions from a dissolved salt interact with water, we can determine (based on the identity of the dissolved salt) whether a solution will be neutral, basic, or acidic. Note in the preceding example that sodium ions (Na^+) do not hydrolyze and thus have no impact on the pH of the solution.

Basic Salt Solutions

Sodium fluoride is a salt that dissolves to give a basic solution. In general, an anion that is the conjugate base of a weak acid reacts with water to produce hydroxide ion. Other examples include the acetate ion (CH_3COO^-), the nitrite ion (NO_2^-), the sulfite ion (SO_3^{2-}), and the hydrogen carbonate ion (HCO_3^-). Each of these anions undergoes hydrolysis to produce the corresponding weak acid and hydroxide ion:

$$A^-(aq) + H_2O(l) \rightleftharpoons HA(aq) + OH^-(aq)$$

We can therefore make the qualitative prediction that a solution of a salt in which the anion is the conjugate base of a weak acid will be basic. We calculate the pH of a basic salt solution the same way we calculate the pH of any weak base solution, using the K_b value for the anion. The necessary K_b value is calculated using the tabulated K_a value of the corresponding weak acid (see Table 16.7).
Worked Example 16.20 shows how to calculate the pH of a basic salt solution.

> **Student Annotation:** HCO_3^- has an ionizable proton and can also act as a Brønsted acid. However, its tendency to *accept* a proton is stronger than its tendency to *donate* a proton:
> $$HCO_3^- + H_2O \rightleftharpoons H_2CO_3 + OH^-$$
> $$K_b \approx 10^{-8}$$
> $$HCO_3^- + H_2O \rightleftharpoons CO_3^{2-} + H_3O^+$$
> $$K_a \approx 10^{-11}$$

> **Student Annotation:** Remember that for any conjugate acid-base pair (Equation 16.8):
> $$K_a \times K_b = K_w$$

Worked Example 16.20

Calculate the pH of a 0.10-*M* solution of sodium fluoride (NaF) at 25°C.

Strategy A solution of NaF contains Na^+ ions and F^- ions. The F^- ion is the conjugate base of the weak acid, HF. Use the K_a value for HF (7.1×10^{-4}, from Table 16.7) and Equation 16.8 to determine K_b for F^-:

$$K_b = \frac{K_w}{K_a} = \frac{1.0 \times 10^{-14}}{7.1 \times 10^{-4}} = 1.4 \times 10^{-11}$$

Then, solve this pH problem like any equilibrium problem, using an equilibrium table.

Setup It's always a good idea to write the equation corresponding to the reaction that takes place along with the equilibrium expression:

$$F^-(aq) + H_2O(l) \rightleftharpoons HF(aq) + OH^-(aq) \qquad K_b = \frac{[HF][OH^-]}{[F^-]}$$

Construct an equilibrium table, and determine, in terms of the unknown *x*, the equilibrium concentrations of the species in the equilibrium expression:

	$F^-(aq)$ +	$H_2O(l)$ $\rightleftharpoons$	$HF(aq)$ +	$OH^-(aq)$
Initial concentration (M):	0.10		0	0
Change in concentration (M):	−*x*		+*x*	+*x*
Equilibrium concentration (M):	0.10 − *x*		*x*	*x*

Solution Substituting the equilibrium concentrations into the equilibrium expression and using the shortcut to solve for *x*, we get

$$1.4 \times 10^{-11} = \frac{x^2}{0.10 - x} \approx \frac{x^2}{0.10}$$

$$x = \sqrt{(1.4 \times 10^{-11})(0.10)} = 1.2 \times 10^{-6} \, M$$

According to our equilibrium table, $x = [OH^-]$. In this case, the autoionization of water makes a significant contribution to the hydroxide ion concentration so the total concentration will be the sum

(Continued on next page)

of 1.2×10^{-6} M (from the ionization of F^-) and 1.0×10^{-7} M (from the autoionization of water). Therefore, we calculate the pOH first as

$$pOH = -\log (1.2 \times 10^{-6} + 1.0 \times 10^{-7}) = 5.95$$

and then the pH,

$$pH = 14.00 - pOH = 14.00 - 5.95 = 8.05$$

The pH of a 0.10-M solution of NaF at 25°C is 8.05.

Think About It

It's easy to mix up pH and pOH in this type of problem. Always make a qualitative prediction regarding the pH of a salt solution first, and then check to make sure that your calculated pH agrees with your prediction. In this case, we would predict a basic pH because the anion in the salt (F^-) is the conjugate base of a weak acid (HF). The calculated pH, 8.05, is indeed basic.

Practice Problem A Determine the pH of a 0.15-M solution of sodium acetate (CH_3COONa) at 25°C.

Practice Problem B Determine the concentration of a solution of sodium fluoride (NaF) that has pH 8.51 at 25°C.

Acidic Salt Solutions

When the cation of a salt is the conjugate acid of a weak base, a solution of the salt will be acidic. For example, when ammonium chloride dissolves in water, it dissociates to give a solution of ammonium ions and chloride ions:

$$NH_4Cl(s) \xrightarrow{H_2O} NH_4^+(aq) + Cl^-(aq)$$

The ammonium ion is the conjugate acid of the weak base ammonia (NH_3). It acts as a weak Brønsted acid, reacting with water to produce hydronium ion:

$$NH_4^+(aq) + H_2O(l) \rightleftharpoons NH_3(aq) + H_3O^+(aq)$$

We would therefore predict that a solution containing the ammonium ion is acidic. To calculate the pH, we must determine the K_a for NH_4^+ using the tabulated K_b value for NH_3 and Equation 16.8. Because Cl^- is the weak conjugate base of the strong acid HCl, Cl^- does not hydrolyze and therefore has no impact on the pH of the solution.

Worked Example 16.21 shows how to calculate the pH of an acidic salt solution.

Worked Example 16.21

Calculate the pH of a 0.10-M solution of ammonium chloride (NH_4Cl) at 25°C.

Strategy A solution of NH_4Cl contains NH_4^+ cations and Cl^- anions. The NH_4^+ ion is the conjugate acid of the weak base NH_3. Use the K_b value for NH_3 (1.8×10^{-5} from Table 16.8) and Equation 16.8 to determine K_a for NH_4^+.

$$K_a = \frac{K_w}{K_b} = \frac{1.0 \times 10^{-14}}{1.8 \times 10^{-5}} = 5.6 \times 10^{-10}$$

Setup Again, we write the balanced chemical equation and the equilibrium expression:

$$NH_4^+(aq) + H_2O(l) \rightleftharpoons NH_3(aq) + H_3O^+(aq) \qquad K_a = \frac{[NH_3][H_3O^+]}{[NH_4^+]}$$

Next, construct a table to determine the equilibrium concentrations of the species in the equilibrium expression:

	$NH_4^+(aq)$ + $H_2O(l)$ $\rightleftharpoons$	$NH_3(aq)$ +	$H_3O^+(aq)$
Initial concentration (M):	0.10	0	0
Change in concentration (M):	$-x$	$+x$	$+x$
Equilibrium concentration (M):	$0.10 - x$	x	x

Solution Substituting the equilibrium concentrations into the equilibrium expression and using the shortcut to solve for x, we get

$$5.6 \times 10^{-10} = \frac{x^2}{0.10 - x} \approx \frac{x^2}{0.10}$$

$$x = \sqrt{(5.6 \times 10^{-10})(0.10)} = 7.5 \times 10^{-6} \, M$$

According to the equilibrium table, $x = [H_3O^+]$. The pH can be calculated as follows:

$$pH = -\log (7.5 \times 10^{-6}) = 5.12$$

The pH of a 0.10-M solution of ammonium chloride (at 25°C) is 5.12.

Think About It

In this case, we would predict an acidic pH because the cation in the salt (NH_4^+) is the conjugate acid of a weak base (NH_3). The calculated pH is acidic.

Practice Problem A Determine the pH of a 0.25-M solution of pyridinium nitrate ($C_5H_6NNO_3$) at 25°C. [Pyridinium nitrate dissociates in water to give pyridinium ions ($C_5H_6N^+$), the conjugate acid of *pyridinium* (see Table 16.8), and nitrate ions (NO_3^-).]

Practice Problem B Determine the concentration of a solution of ammonium chloride (NH_4Cl) that has pH 5.37 at 25°C.

The metal ion in a dissolved salt can also react with water to produce an acidic solution. The extent of hydrolysis is greatest for the small and highly charged metal cations such as Al^{3+}, Cr^{3+}, Fe^{3+}, Bi^{3+}, and Be^{2+}. For example, when aluminum chloride dissolves in water, each Al^{3+} ion becomes associated with six water molecules (Figure 16.6).

Consider one of the bonds that forms between the metal ion and an oxygen atom from one of the six water molecules in $Al(H_2O)_6^{3+}$:

$$Al \rightleftharpoons O \underset{H}{\overset{H}{<}}$$

The positively charged Al^{3+} ion draws electron density toward itself, increasing the polarity of the O—H bonds. Consequently, the H atoms have a greater tendency to ionize than those in water molecules not associated with the Al^{3+} ion. The resulting ionization process can be written as

$$Al(H_2O)_6^{3+}(aq) + H_2O(l) \rightleftharpoons Al(OH)(H_2O)_5^{2+}(aq) + H_3O^+(aq)$$

or as

$$Al(H_2O)_6^{3+}(aq) \rightleftharpoons Al(OH)(H_2O)_5^{2+}(aq) + H^+(aq)$$

The equilibrium constant for the metal cation hydrolysis is given by

$$K_a = \frac{[Al(OH)(H_2O)_5^{2+}][H^+]}{[Al(H_2O)_6^{3+}]} = 1.3 \times 10^{-5}$$

$$Al(H_2O)_6^{3+} \quad + \quad H_2O \quad \longrightarrow \quad Al(OH)(H_2O)_5^{2+} \quad + \quad H_3O^+$$

Figure 16.6 The six H_2O molecules surround the Al^{3+} ion in an octahedral arrangement. The attraction of the small Al^{3+} ion for the lone pairs on the oxygen atoms is so great that the O—H bonds in an H_2O molecule attached to the metal cation are weakened, allowing the loss of a proton (H^+) to an incoming H_2O molecule. This hydrolysis of the metal cation makes the solution acidic.

Al(OH)(H$_2$O)$_5^{2+}$ can undergo further ionization:

$$Al(OH)(H_2O)_5^{2+}(aq) \rightleftharpoons Al(OH)_2(H_2O)_4^+(aq) + H^+(aq)$$

and so on. It is generally sufficient, however, to take into account only the first stage of hydrolysis when determining the pH of a solution that contains metal ions.

Neutral Salt Solutions

The extent of hydrolysis is greatest for the smallest and most highly charged metal ions because a compact, highly charged ion is more effective in polarizing the O—H bond and facilitating ionization. This is why relatively large ions of low charge, including the metal cations of Groups 1A and 2A (the cations of the strong bases), do not undergo significant hydrolysis (Be^{2+} is an exception). Thus, most metal cations of Groups 1A and 2A do not impact the pH of a solution.

Similarly, anions that are conjugate bases of strong acids do not hydrolyze to any significant degree. Consequently, a salt composed of the cation of a strong base and the anion of a strong acid, such as NaCl, produces a neutral solution.

To summarize, the pH of a salt solution can be predicted qualitatively by identifying the ions in solution and determining which of them, if any, undergoes significant hydrolysis.

> **Student Annotation:** The metal cations of the strong bases are those of the alkali metals: (Li$^+$, Na$^+$, K$^+$, Rb$^+$, and Cs$^+$) and those of the heavy alkaline earth metals (Sr^{2+} and Ba^{2+}).

	Examples
A cation that will make a solution acidic is • The conjugate acid of a weak base • A small, highly charged metal ion (other than from Group 1A or 2A)	NH$_4^+$, CH$_3$NH$_3^+$, C$_2$H$_5$NH$_3^+$ Al^{3+}, Cr^{3+}, Fe^{3+}, Bi^{3+}
An anion that will make a solution basic is • The conjugate base of a weak acid	CN$^-$, NO$_2^-$, CH$_3$COO$^-$
A cation that will not affect the pH of a solution is • A Group 1A or heavy Group 2A cation (except Be^{2+})	Li$^+$, Na$^+$, Ba^{2+}
An anion that will not affect the pH of a solution is • The conjugate base of a strong acid	Cl$^-$, NO$_3^-$, ClO$_4^-$

Worked Example 16.22 lets you practice predicting the pH of salt solutions.

Worked Example 16.22

Predict whether a 0.10-M solution of each of the following salts will be basic, acidic, or neutral:
(a) LiI, (b) NH$_4$NO$_3$, (c) Sr(NO$_3$)$_2$, (d) KNO$_2$, (e) NaCN.

Strategy Identify the ions present in each solution, and determine which, if any, will impact the pH of the solution.

Setup

(a) Ions in solution: Li$^+$ and I$^-$. Li$^+$ is a Group 1A cation; I$^-$ is the conjugate base of the strong acid HI. Therefore, neither ion hydrolyzes to any significant degree.

(b) Ions in solution: NH$_4^+$ and NO$_3^-$. NH$_4^+$ is the conjugate acid of the weak base NH$_3$; NO$_3^-$ is the conjugate base of the strong acid HNO$_3$. In this case, the cation will hydrolyze, making the pH acidic:

$$NH_4^+(aq) + H_2O(l) \rightleftharpoons NH_3(aq) + H_3O^+(aq)$$

(c) Ions in solution: Sr^{2+} and NO$_3^-$. Sr^{2+} is a heavy Group 2A cation; NO$_3^-$ is the conjugate base of the strong acid HNO$_3$. Neither ion hydrolyzes to any significant degree.

(d) Ions in solution: K$^+$ and NO$_2^-$. K$^+$ is a Group 1A cation; NO$_2^-$ is the conjugate base of the weak acid HNO$_2$. In this case, the anion hydrolyzes, thus making the pH basic:

$$NO_2^-(aq) + H_2O(l) \rightleftharpoons HNO_2(aq) + OH^-(aq)$$

(e) Ions in solution: Na$^+$ and CN$^-$. Na$^+$ is a Group 1A cation; CN$^-$ is the conjugate base of the weak acid HCN. In this case, too, the anion hydrolyzes, thus making the pH basic:

$$CN^-(aq) + H_2O(l) \rightleftharpoons HCN(aq) + OH^-(aq)$$

Solution

(a) Neutral

(b) Acidic

(c) Neutral

(d) Basic

(e) Basic

Think About It
It's very important that you be able to identify the ions in solution correctly. If necessary, review the formulas and charges of the common polyatomic ions [◄◄ Section 5.7, Table 5.10].

Practice Problem A Predict whether a 0.10-*M* solution of each of the following salts will be basic, acidic, or neutral:

(a) CH_3COOLi (b) C_5H_5NHCl (c) KF (d) KNO_3 (e) $KClO_4$

Practice Problem B In addition to those given in Worked Example 16.22 and Practice Problem A, identify two salts that will dissolve to give (a) an acidic solution, (b) a basic solution, and (c) a neutral solution.

Salts in Which Both the Cation and the Anion Hydrolyze

So far, we have considered salts in which only one ion undergoes hydrolysis. In some salts, both the cation and the anion hydrolyze. Whether a solution of such a salt is basic, acidic, or neutral depends on the relative strengths of the weak acid and the weak base. Although the process of calculating the pH in these cases is more complex than in cases where only one ion hydrolyzes, we can make qualitative predictions regarding pH using the values of K_b (of the salt's anion) and K_a (of the salt's cation):

- When $K_b > K_a$, the solution is basic.
- When $K_b < K_a$, the solution is acidic.
- When $K_b \approx K_a$, the solution is neutral or nearly neutral.

The salt NH_4NO_2, for example, dissociates in solution to give NH_4^+ ($K_a = 5.6 \times 10^{-10}$) and NO_2^- ($K_b = 2.2 \times 10^{-11}$). Because K_a for the ammonium ion is larger than K_b for the nitrite ion, we would expect the pH of an ammonium nitrite solution to be slightly acidic.

SECTION 16.10 REVIEW

Acid-Base Properties of Salt Solutions

16.10.1 Calculate the pH of a 0.075-*M* solution of NH_4NO_3 at 25°C.

16.10.2 Calculate the pH of a 0.082-*M* solution of NaCN at 25°C.

16.10.3 When sodium hypochlorite is dissolved in water is the resulting solution acidic, basic, or neutral?

16.10.4 When lithium nitrate is dissolved in water is the resulting solution acidic, basic, or neutral?

16.10.5 The diagrams represent solutions of three salts NaX (X = A, B, or C). Arrange the three X⁻ anions in order of increasing base strength. (The Na⁺ ions are not shown.)

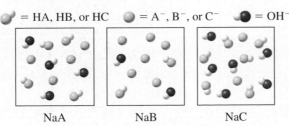

●‿ = HA, HB, or HC   ● = A⁻, B⁻, or C⁻   ● = OH⁻

NaA   NaB   NaC

16.11   ACID-BASE PROPERTIES OF OXIDES AND HYDROXIDES

Oxides of Metals and Nonmetals

Figure 16.7 shows the formulas of a number of oxides of the main group elements in their highest oxidation states. All alkali metal oxides and all alkaline earth metal oxides except BeO are basic. Beryllium oxide and several metallic oxides in Groups 3A and 4A are amphoteric. Nonmetallic oxides in which the oxidation number of the main group element is high are acidic (e.g., N_2O_5, SO_3, and Cl_2O_7), but those in which the oxidation number of the main group element is low (e.g., CO and NO) show no measurable acidic properties. No nonmetallic oxides are known to have basic properties.

The basic metallic oxides react with water to form metal hydroxides:

$$Na_2O(s) + H_2O(l) \longrightarrow 2NaOH(aq)$$

$$BaO(s) + H_2O(l) \longrightarrow Ba(OH)_2(aq)$$

The reactions between acidic oxides and water are as follows:

$$CO_2(g) + H_2O(l) \rightleftharpoons H_2CO_3(aq)$$

$$SO_3(g) + H_2O(l) \rightleftharpoons H_2SO_4(aq)$$

$$N_2O_5(g) + H_2O(l) \rightleftharpoons 2HNO_3(aq)$$

$$P_4O_{10}(g) + 6H_2O(l) \rightleftharpoons 4H_3PO_4(aq)$$

$$Cl_2O_7(g) + H_2O(l) \rightleftharpoons 2HClO_4(aq)$$

The reaction between CO_2 and H_2O explains why pure water gradually becomes acidic when it is exposed to air, which contains CO_2. The pH of rainwater exposed only to unpolluted air is about 5.5. The reaction between SO_3 and H_2O is largely responsible for acid rain.

Reactions between acidic oxides and bases and those between basic oxides and acids resemble normal acid-base reactions in that the products are a salt and water:

$$CO_2(g) + 2NaOH(aq) \longrightarrow Na_2CO_3(aq) + H_2O(l)$$

$$BaO(s) + 2HNO_3(aq) \longrightarrow Ba(NO_3)_2(aq) + H_2O(l)$$

Figure 16.7 Oxides of the main group elements in their highest oxidation states.

Aluminum oxide (Al_2O_3) is amphoteric. Depending on the reaction conditions, it can behave either as an acidic oxide or as a basic oxide. For example, Al_2O_3 acts as a base with hydrochloric acid to produce a salt ($AlCl_3$) and water:

$$Al_2O_3(s) + 6HCl(aq) \longrightarrow 2AlCl_3(aq) + 3H_2O(l)$$

and acts as an acid with sodium hydroxide:

$$Al_2O_3(s) + 2NaOH(aq) + 3H_2O(l) \longrightarrow 2NaAl(OH)_4(aq)$$

Only a salt, sodium aluminum hydroxide [$NaAl(OH)_4$, which contains the Na^+ and $Al(OH)_4^-$ ions] is formed in the reaction with sodium hydroxide—no water is produced. Nevertheless, the reaction is still classified as an acid-base reaction because Al_2O_3 neutralizes NaOH. Other amphoteric oxides are ZnO, BeO, and Bi_2O_3.

Silicon dioxide is insoluble and does not react with water. It has acidic properties, however, because it reacts with a very concentrated aqueous base:

$$SiO_2(s) + 2OH^-(aq) \longrightarrow SiO_3^{2-}(aq) + H_2O(l)$$

For this reason, concentrated aqueous, strong bases such as sodium hydroxide (NaOH) should *not* be stored in Pyrex glassware, which is made of SiO_2.

Some transition metal oxides in which the metal has a high oxidation number act as acidic oxides. Two examples are manganese(VII) oxide (Mn_2O_7) and chromium(VI) oxide (CrO_3), both of which react with water to produce acids:

$$Mn_2O_7(s) + H_2O(l) \longrightarrow 2HMnO_4(aq)$$
$$\text{permanganic acid}$$

$$CrO_3(s) + H_2O(l) \longrightarrow H_2CrO_4(aq)$$
$$\text{chromic acid}$$

Basic and Amphoteric Hydroxides

All the alkali and alkaline earth metal hydroxides, except $Be(OH)_2$, are basic. $Be(OH)_2$, as well as $Al(OH)_3$, $Sn(OH)_2$, $Pb(OH)_2$, $Cr(OH)_3$, $Cu(OH)_2$, $Zn(OH)_2$, and $Cd(OH)_2$, is amphoteric. All amphoteric hydroxides are insoluble, but beryllium hydroxide reacts with both acids and bases as follows:

$$Be(OH)_2(s) + 2H^+(aq) \longrightarrow Be^{2+}(aq) + 2H_2O(l)$$

$$Be(OH)_2(s) + 2OH^-(aq) \longrightarrow Be(OH)_4^{2-}(aq)$$

Aluminum hydroxide reacts with both acids and bases in a similar fashion:

$$Al(OH)_3(s) + 3H^+(aq) \longrightarrow Al^{3+}(aq) + 3H_2O(l)$$

$$Al(OH)_3(s) + OH^-(aq) \longrightarrow Al(OH)_4^-(aq)$$

Student Annotation: The similarity in behavior of aluminum hydroxide to that of beryllium hydroxide is a result of the diagonal relationship [◄◄ Section 8.5].

16.12 LEWIS ACIDS AND BASES

So far, we have discussed acid-base properties in terms of the Brønsted theory. For example, a Brønsted base is a substance that must be able to accept protons. By this definition, both the hydroxide ion and ammonia are bases:

In each case, the atom to which the proton becomes attached possesses at least one unshared pair of electrons. This characteristic property of OH⁻, NH₃, and other Brønsted bases suggests a more general definition of acids and bases.

In 1932, G. N. Lewis defined what we now call a ***Lewis base*** as a substance that can donate a pair of electrons. A ***Lewis acid*** is a substance that can accept a pair of electrons. In the protonation of ammonia, for example, NH_3 acts as a Lewis base because it donates a pair of electrons to the proton H^+, which acts as a Lewis acid by accepting the pair of electrons. A Lewis acid-base reaction, therefore, is one that involves the donation of a pair of electrons from one species to another.

The significance of the Lewis concept is that it is more general than other definitions. Lewis acid-base reactions include many reactions that do not involve Brønsted acids. Consider, for example, the reaction between boron trifluoride (BF_3) and ammonia to form an adduct compound:

$$
\begin{array}{ccccc}
& F & & H & \\
& | & & | & \\
F\!-\!B & + & :N\!-\!H & \longrightarrow & F\!-\!B\!-\!N\!-\!H \\
& | & & | & \\
& F & & H & \\
\text{acid} & & \text{base} & &
\end{array}
$$

The B atom in BF_3 is sp^2-hybridized [◄◄ Section 7.4]. The vacant, unhybridized $2p_z$ orbital accepts the pair of electrons from NH_3. Thus, BF_3 functions as an acid according to the Lewis definition, even though it does not contain an ionizable proton. A *coordinate covalent* bond [◄◄ Section 6.6] is formed between the B and N atoms. In fact, every Lewis acid-base reaction results in the formation of a coordinate covalent bond.

Boric acid is another Lewis acid containing boron. Boric acid (a weak acid used in eyewash) is an oxoacid with the following structure:

$$
\begin{array}{c}
H \\
| \\
:O: \\
| \\
H\!-\!\ddot{O}\!-\!B\!-\!\ddot{O}\!-\!H
\end{array}
$$

Boric acid does not ionize in water to produce H^+. Instead, it produces H^+ in solution by taking a hydroxide ion away from water.

$$B(OH)_3(aq) + H_2O(l) \rightleftharpoons B(OH)_4^-(aq) + H^+(aq)$$

In this Lewis acid-base reaction, boric acid accepts a pair of electrons from the hydroxide ion that is derived from the water molecule, leaving behind the hydrogen ion.

The hydration of carbon dioxide to produce carbonic acid,

$$CO_2(g) + H_2O(l) \rightleftharpoons H_2CO_3(aq)$$

can be explained in terms of Lewis acid-base theory as well. The first step involves the donation of a lone pair on the O atom in H_2O to the C atom in CO_2. An orbital is vacated on the C atom to accommodate the lone pair by relocation of the electron pair in one of the C–O pi bonds, changing the hybridization of the oxygen atom from sp^2 to sp^3:

As a result, H_2O is a Lewis base and CO_2 is a Lewis acid. Finally, a proton is transferred onto the O atom bearing the negative charge to form H_2CO_3:

Other examples of Lewis acid-base reactions are

$$Ag^+(aq) + 2NH_3(aq) \rightleftharpoons Ag(NH_3)_2^+(aq)$$

$$Cd^{2+}(aq) + 4I^-(aq) \rightleftharpoons CdI_4^{2-}(aq)$$

$$Ni(s) + 4CO(g) \rightleftharpoons Ni(CO)_4(g)$$

The hydration of metal ions is in itself a Lewis acid-base reaction. When copper(II) sulfate ($CuSO_4$) dissolves in water, each Cu^{2+} ion becomes associated with six water molecules as $Cu(H_2O)_6^{2+}$. In this case, Cu^{2+} acts as the acid, accepting electrons, whereas H_2O acts as the base, donating electrons.

Worked Example 16.23 shows how to classify Lewis acids and bases.

Worked Example 16.23

Identify the Lewis acid and Lewis base in each of the following reactions:

(a) $C_2H_5OC_2H_5 + AlCl_3 \rightleftharpoons (C_2H_5)_2OAlCl_3$

(b) $Hg^{2+}(aq) + 4CN^-(aq) \rightleftharpoons Hg(CN)_4^{2-}(aq)$

Strategy Determine which species in each reaction accepts a pair of electrons (Lewis acid) and which species donates a pair of electrons (Lewis base).

Setup

(a) It can be helpful to draw Lewis structures of the species involved:

(b) Metal ions act as Lewis acids, accepting electron pairs from anions or molecules with lone pairs.

Solution

(a) The Al is sp^2-hybridized in $AlCl_3$ with an empty $2p_z$ orbital. It is electron deficient, sharing only six electrons. Therefore, the Al atom has the capacity to gain two electrons to complete its octet. This property makes $AlCl_3$ a Lewis acid. On the other hand, the lone pairs on the oxygen atom in $C_2H_5OC_2H_5$ make the compound a Lewis base:

> **Student Annotation:** An electron-deficient molecule is one with less than a complete octet around the central atom.

(b) Hg^{2+} accepts four pairs of electrons from the CN^- ions. Therefore, Hg^{2+} is the Lewis acid and CN^- is the Lewis base.

Think About It
In Lewis acid-base reactions, the acid is usually a cation or an electron-deficient molecule, whereas the base is an anion or a molecule containing an atom with lone pairs.

Practice Problem A Identify the Lewis acid and Lewis base in the following reaction:

$$Co^{3+}(aq) + 6NH_3(aq) \rightleftharpoons Co(NH_3)_6^{3+}$$

Practice Problem B Write formulas for the Lewis acid and Lewis base that react to form H_3NAlBr_3.

SECTION 16.12 REVIEW

Lewis Acids and Bases

16.12.1 Which of the following cannot act as a Lewis base? NH_3, H_2O, or CH_4

16.12.2 Which of the following is a Lewis acid but not a Brønsted acid? H_2O, BCl_3, or NH_3

Learning Outcomes

- Define conjugate acid and conjugate base and cite examples of conjugate pairs.
- Give in your own words definitions of acids/bases: Brønsted and Lewis.
- Define amphoteric.
- Rank species of each of the following acids based upon relative strength: hydrohalic, oxoacids, and carboxylic.
- Use the equilibrium expression for water and its value to perform calculations and determine whether a solution is acidic, basic, or neutral.
- Use the pH scale to classify a solution as being acidic, basic, or neutral.
- Use pH, pOH, concentration of hydroxide ion, or concentration of protons to conduct calculations asking for one of these terms.
- Identify an acid or base as being strong or weak.

- Use the value of the acid-dissociation constant (K_a) in equilibrium calculations.
- Understand the relationship between K_a, K_b, and K_w.
- Calculate the percent ionization of a weak acid or base.
- Use the pH of a weak acid or base solution to calculate the K_a or K_b, respectively.
- Use K_w to determine the relative strength of conjugate pairs.
- Identify polyprotic acids and explain why the initial ionization is easier than subsequent ones.
- Classify a salt as being basic, acidic, or neutral based upon the acid and base used to form the salt.
- Calculate the pH of a salt solution.
- Classify an oxide as being acidic, basic, or amphoteric.
- Identify a species as a Lewis acid or Lewis base.

Chapter Summary

SECTION 16.1

- A Brønsted acid donates a proton; a Brønsted base accepts a proton.
- When a Brønsted acid donates a proton, the anion that remains is a *conjugate base.*
- When a Brønsted base accepts a proton, the resulting cation is a *conjugate acid.*
- The combination of a Brønsted acid and its conjugate base (or the combination of a Brønsted base and its conjugate acid) is called a *conjugate pair.*

SECTION 16.2

- The strength of an acid is affected by molecular structure.
- Polar and weak bonds to the ionizable hydrogen lead to a stronger acid.
- Resonance stabilization of the conjugate base favors the ionization process, resulting in a stronger acid.

SECTION 16.3

- Water is *amphoteric,* meaning it can act both as a Brønsted acid and a Brønsted base.
- Pure water undergoes *autoionization* (to a very small extent), resulting in concentrations of H^+ and OH^- of 1.0×10^{-7} M at 25°C.
- K_w is the equilibrium constant for the autoionization of water, also called the *ion-product constant.*
  $K_w = [H^+][OH^-] = 1.0 \times 10^{-14}$ at 25°C.

SECTION 16.4

- The *pH* scale measures acidity: pH = $-\log [H^+]$.
- pH = 7.00 is neutral, pH < 7.00 is acidic, and pH > 7.00 is basic.
- The *pOH* scale is analogous to the pH scale, but it measures *basicity:* pOH = $-\log [OH^-]$.
- pOH = 7.00 is neutral, pOH < 7.00 is basic, and pOH > 7.00 is acidic.
- pH + pOH = 14.00 (at 25°C).

SECTION 16.5

- There are seven strong acids: HCl, HBr, HI, HNO_3, $HClO_3$, $HClO_4$, and H_2SO_4.
- Strong acids ionize completely in aqueous solution. (Only the first ionization of the diprotic acid H_2SO_4 is complete.)
- The strong bases are the Group 1A and the heaviest Group 2A hydroxides: LiOH, NaOH, KOH, RbOH, CsOH, $Ca(OH)_2$, $Sr(OH)_2$, and $Ba(OH)_2$.

SECTION 16.6

- A *weak acid* ionizes only partially. The *acid ionization constant,* K_a, is the equilibrium constant that indicates to what extent a weak acid ionizes.
- We solve for the pH of a solution of weak acid using the concentration of the acid, the K_a value, and an equilibrium table.
- We can also determine the K_a of a weak acid if we know the initial acid concentration and the pH at equilibrium.

SECTION 16.7

- A *weak base* ionizes only partially. The *base ionization constant*, K_b, is the equilibrium constant that indicates to what extent a weak base ionizes.
- We solve for the pH of a solution of weak base using the concentration of the base, the K_b value, and an equilibrium table.
- We can also determine the K_b of a weak base if we know the concentration and the pH at equilibrium.

SECTION 16.8

- The conjugate base of a strong acid is a *weak conjugate base*, meaning that it does not react with water.
- The conjugate base of a weak acid is a *strong conjugate base*, meaning that it acts as a weak Brønsted base in water.
- The conjugate acid of a strong base is a *weak conjugate acid*, meaning that it does not react with water.
- The conjugate acid of a weak base is a *strong conjugate acid*, meaning that it acts as a weak Brønsted acid in water.
- For any conjugate acid-base pair, $K_a \times K_b = K_w$.

SECTION 16.9

- Diprotic and polyprotic acids have more than one proton to donate. They undergo stepwise ionizations. Each ionization has a K_a value associated with it.
- The K_a values for stepwise ionizations become progressively smaller.
- In most cases, it is only necessary to consider the first ionization of an acid to determine pH. To determine the concentrations of other species at equilibrium, it may be necessary to consider subsequent ionizations.

SECTION 16.10

- Salts dissolve in water to give neutral, acidic, or basic solutions depending on their constituent ions. *Salt hydrolysis* is the reaction of an ion with water to produce hydronium or hydroxide ions.
- Cations that are strong conjugate acids such as NH_4^+ make a solution more acidic.
- Anions that are strong conjugate bases such as F^- make a solution more basic. Anions that are conjugate bases of strong acids have no effect on pH.
- Small, highly charged metal ions hydrolyze to give acidic solutions.

SECTION 16.11

- Oxides of metals generally are basic; oxides of nonmetals generally are acidic.
- Metal hydroxides may be basic or amphoteric.

SECTION 16.12

- Lewis theory provides more general definitions of acids and bases.
- A *Lewis acid* accepts a pair of electrons; a *Lewis base* donates a pair of electrons.
- A Lewis acid is generally electron-poor and need not have a hydrogen atom.
- A Lewis base is an anion or a molecule with one or more lone pairs of electrons.

Key Words

Acid ionization constant (K_a), 672	Conjugate acid, 657	Lewis base, 698	Strong conjugate base, 685
Amphoteric, 662	Conjugate base, 657	pH, 663	Weak acid, 672
Autoionization of water, 662	Conjugate pair, 657	pOH, 666	Weak base, 681
Base ionization constant (K_b), 682	Ion-product constant, 662	Salt hydrolysis, 691	Weak conjugate acid, 685
	Lewis acid, 698	Strong conjugate acid, 685	Weak conjugate base, 685

Key Equations

16.1 $K_w = [H_3O^+][OH^-] = 1.0 \times 10^{-14}$ (at 25°C)

16.2 $pH = -\log [H_3O^+]$ or $pH = -\log [H^+]$

16.3 $[H_3O^+] = 10^{-pH}$

16.4 $pOH = -\log [OH^-]$

16.5 $[OH^-] = 10^{-pOH}$

16.6 $pH + pOH = 14.00$

16.7 $\text{percent ionization} = \dfrac{[H^+]_{eq}}{[HA]_0} \times 100\%$

16.8 $K_a \times K_b = K_w$

Questions and Problems

SECTION 16.1:   BRØNSTED ACIDS AND BASES

Review Questions

16.1   For a species to act as a Brønsted base, an atom in the species must possess a lone pair of electrons. Explain why this is so.

Problems

16.2   Identify the acid-base conjugate pairs in each of the following reactions:
(a) $CH_3COO^- + HCN \rightleftharpoons CH_3COOH + CN^-$
(b) $HCO_3^- + HCO_3^- \rightleftharpoons H_2CO_3 + CO_3^{2-}$
(c) $H_2PO_4^- + NH_3 \rightleftharpoons HPO_4^{2-} + NH_4^+$
(d) $HClO + CH_3NH_2 \rightleftharpoons CH_3NH_3^+ + ClO^-$
(e) $CO_3^{2-} + H_2O \rightleftharpoons HCO_3^- + OH^-$

16.3   Classify each of the following species as a Brønsted acid or base, or both: (a) H_2O, (b) OH^-, (c) H_3O^+, (d) NH_3, (e) NH_4^+, (f) NH_2^-, (g) NO_3^-, (h) CO_3^{2-}, (i) HBr, (j) HCN.

16.4   Write the formula for the conjugate acid of each of the following bases: (a) HS^-, (b) HCO_3^-, (c) CO_3^{2-}, (d) $H_2PO_4^-$, (e) HPO_4^{2-}, (f) PO_4^{3-}, (g) HSO_4^-, (h) SO_4^{2-}, (i) SO_3^{2-}

16.5   Write the formulas of the conjugate bases of the following acids: (a) HNO_2, (b) H_2SO_4, (c) H_2S, (d) HCN, (e) $HCOOH$ (formic acid).

16.6   Oxalic acid ($H_2C_2O_4$) has the following structure:

O=C—OH
|
O=C—OH

An oxalic acid solution contains the following species in varying concentrations: $H_2C_2O_4$, $HC_2O_4^-$, $C_2O_4^{2-}$, and H^+.
(a) Draw Lewis structures of $HC_2O_4^-$ and $C_2O_4^{2-}$.
(b) Which of the four species can act only as acids, which can act only as bases, and which can act as both acids and bases?

16.7   Write the formula for the conjugate base of each of the following acids: (a) $CH_2ClCOOH$, (b) HIO_4, (c) H_3PO_4, (d) $H_2PO_4^-$, (e) HPO_4^{2-}, (f) H_2SO_4, (g) HSO_4^-, (h) HIO_3, (i) HSO_3^-, (j) NH_4^+, (k) H_2S, (l) HS^-, (m) $HClO$.

SECTION 16.2:   MOLECULAR STRUCTURE AND ACID STRENGTH

Review Questions

16.8   List four factors that affect the strength of an acid.

16.9   How does the strength of an oxoacid depend on the electronegativity and oxidation number of the central atom?

Problems

16.10   Predict the relative acid strengths of the following compounds: H_2O, H_2S, and H_2Se.

16.11   Compare the strengths of the following pairs of acids: (a) H_2SO_4 and H_2SeO_4, (b) H_3PO_4 and H_3AsO_4.

16.12   Which of the following is the stronger acid: $CH_2ClCOOH$ or $CHCl_2COOH$? Explain your choice.

16.13   Consider the following compounds: Experimentally, phenol is found to be a stronger acid than methanol. Explain this difference in terms of the structures of the conjugate bases. (*Hint:* A more stable conjugate base favors ionization. Only one of the conjugate bases can be stabilized by resonance.)

Phenol   Methanol

SECTION 16.3:   THE ACID-BASE PROPERTIES OF WATER

Review Questions

16.14   Write the equilibrium expression for the autoionization of water.

16.15   Write an equation relating $[H^+]$ and $[OH^-]$ in solution at 25°C.

16.16   The equilibrium constant for the autoionization of water

$$H_2O(l) \rightleftharpoons H^+(aq) + OH^-(aq)$$

is 1.0×10^{-14} at 25°C and 3.8×10^{-14} at 40°C. Is the forward process endothermic or exothermic?

16.17   Compare the magnitudes of $[H^+]$ and $[OH^-]$ in aqueous solutions that are acidic, basic, and neutral.

Problems

16.18   Calculate the OH^- concentration in an aqueous solution at 25°C with each of the following H_3O^+ concentrations: (a) 1.13×10^{-4} M, (b) 4.55×10^{-8} M, (c) 7.05×10^{-11} M, (d) 3.13×10^{-2} M.

16.19   Calculate the H_3O^+ concentration in an aqueous solution at 25°C with each of the following OH^- concentrations: (a) 2.50×10^{-2} M, (b) 1.67×10^{-5} M, (c) 8.62×10^{-3} M, (d) 1.75×10^{-12} M.

16.20   The value of K_w at 50°C is 5.48×10^{-14}. Calculate the OH^- concentration in each of the aqueous solutions from Problem 16.18 at 50°C.

16.21   The value of K_w at 100°C is 5.13×10^{-13}. Calculate the H_3O^+ concentration in each of the aqueous solutions from Problem 16.19 at 100°C.

SECTION 16.4:   THE pH SCALE

Review Questions

16.22   Define pH. Why do chemists normally choose to discuss the acidity of a solution in terms of pH rather than hydrogen ion concentration $[H^+]$? Define pOH. Write the equation relating pH and pOH.

16.23   The pH of a solution is 6.7. From this statement alone, can you conclude that the solution is acidic? If not, what additional information would you need? Can the pH of a solution be zero or negative? If so, give examples to illustrate these values.

Problems

16.24 Calculate the concentration of H^+ ions in a 0.62 M NaOH solution.

16.25 Calculate the concentration of OH^- ions in a 1.4×10^{-3} M HCl solution.

16.26 Calculate the pH of each of the following solutions: (a) 2.8×10^{-4} M $Ba(OH)_2$, (b) 5.2×10^{-4} M HNO_3.

16.27 Calculate the pH of each of the following solutions: (a) 0.0010 M HCl, (b) 0.76 M KOH.

16.28 Calculate the hydrogen ion concentration in mol/L for each of the following solutions: (a) a solution whose pH is 5.20, (b) a solution whose pH is 16.00, (c) a solution whose hydroxide concentration is 3.7×10^{-9} M.

16.29 Calculate the hydrogen ion concentration in mol/L for solutions with the following pH values: (a) 2.42, (b) 11.21, (c) 6.96, (d) 15.00.

16.30 Fill in the word *acidic, basic,* or *neutral* for the following solutions at 25°C:
(a) pOH > 7; solution is _____.
(b) pOH = 7; solution is _____.
(c) pOH < 7; solution is _____.

16.31 Complete the following table for a solution at 25°C:

pH	[H^+]	Solution is
<7		
	<1.0×10^{-7} M	
		Neutral

16.32 Calculate the number of moles of KOH in 5.50 mL of a 0.360 M KOH solution. What is the pOH of the solution at 25°C?

16.33 The pOH of a solution is 9.40 at 25°C. Calculate the hydrogen ion concentration of the solution.

16.34 A solution is made by dissolving 18.4 g of HCl in enough water to make 662 mL of solution. Calculate the pH of the solution at 25°C.

16.35 How much NaOH (in grams) is needed to prepare 546 mL of solution with a pH of 10.00 at 25°C?

SECTION 16.5: STRONG ACIDS AND BASES

Review Questions

16.36 Which of the following statements are true regarding a 1.0-M solution of a strong acid HA at 25°C? (Choose all that apply.)
(a) $[A^-] > [H^+]$
(b) The pH is 0.00.
(c) $[H^+] = 1.0$ M
(d) $[HA] = 1.0$ M

16.37 Why are ionizations of strong acids and strong bases generally not treated as equilibria?

Problems

16.38 Calculate the pH of an aqueous solution at 25°C that is (a) 0.12 M in HCl, (b) 2.4 M in HNO_3, and (c) 3.2×10^{-4} M in $HClO_4$.

16.39 Calculate the pH of an aqueous solution at 25°C that is (a) 1.02 M in HI, (b) 0.035 M in $HClO_4$, and (c) 1.5×10^{-6} M in HCl.

16.40 Calculate the concentration of HBr in a solution at 25°C that has a pH of (a) 0.12, (b) 2.46, and (c) 6.27.

16.41 Calculate the concentration of HNO_3 in a solution at 25°C that has a pH of (a) 4.21, (b) 3.55, and (c) 0.98.

16.42 Calculate the pOH and pH of the following aqueous solutions at 25°C: (a) 0.066 M KOH, (b) 5.43 M NaOH, (c) 0.74 M $Ba(OH)_2$.

16.43 Calculate the pOH and pH of the following aqueous solutions at 25°C: (a) 1.24 M LiOH, (b) 0.22 M $Ba(OH)_2$, (c) 0.085 M NaOH.

16.44 An aqueous solution of a strong base has a pH of 9.78 at 25°C. Calculate the concentration of the base if the base is (a) LiOH and (b) $Ba(OH)_2$.

16.45 An aqueous solution of a strong base has a pH of 11.04 at 25°C. Calculate the concentration of the base if the base is (a) KOH and (b) $Ba(OH)_2$.

16.46 Determine [H^+] and pH for a raindrop in which the carbonic acid concentration is 1.8×10^{-5} M. Assume that carbonic acid is the only acid in the raindrop and that the second ionization is negligible.

16.47 A sample of acid rain collected from a pond was shown to have a pH = 4.65. What concentration of HNO_3 does this pH correspond to?

SECTION 16.6: WEAK ACIDS AND ACID IONIZATION CONSTANTS

Visualizing Chemistry
Figure 16.4

Three weak acid solutions are shown here.

(i)   (ii)   (iii)

VC 16.1 Which weak acid has the largest K_a value?
(a) i
(b) ii
(c) iii

VC 16.2 Which weak acid has the highest pH?
(a) i
(b) ii
(c) iii

VC 16.3 For which weak acid solution can we most likely neglect x in the denominator of the equilibrium expression in the determination of pH?
(a) i
(b) ii
(c) iii

VC 16.4 In the event that we cannot neglect x in the denominator of the equilibrium expression, _____ to solve for pH.
(a) we cannot use an equilibrium table
(b) we must use the quadratic equation
(c) it is unnecessary

Review Questions

16.48   Explain what is meant by the strength of an acid.

16.49   What does the ionization constant tell us about the strength of an acid?

16.50   List the factors on which the K_a of a weak acid depends.

16.51   Why do we normally not quote K_a values for strong acids such as HCl and HNO_3?

16.52   Why is it necessary to specify temperature when giving K_a values?

16.53   Which of the following solutions has the highest pH: (a) 0.40 M HCOOH, (b) 0.40 M $HClO_4$, (c) 0.40 M CH_3COOH?

Problems

16.54   Classify each of the following species as a weak or strong acid: (a) HNO_3, (b) HF, (c) H_2SO_4, (d) HSO_4^-, (e) H_2CO_3, (f) HCO_3^-, (g) HCl, (h) HCN, (i) HNO_2.

16.55   Classify each of the following species as a weak or strong base: (a) LiOH, (b) CN^-, (c) H_2O, (d) ClO_4^-, (e) NH_2^-.

16.56   Which of the following statements are true for a 0.10-M solution of a weak acid HA? (Choose all that apply.)
(a) The pH is 1.00.
(b) $[H^+] \gg [A^-]$
(c) $[H^+] = [A^-]$
(d) The pH is less than 1.

16.57   The K_a for benzoic acid is 6.5×10^{-5}. Calculate the pH of a 0.10-M aqueous solution of benzoic acid at 25°C.

16.58   The K_a for hydrofluoric acid is 7.1×10^{-4}. Calculate the pH of a 0.15-M aqueous solution of hydrofluoric acid at 25°C.

16.59   Calculate the pH of an aqueous solution at 25°C that is 0.095 M in hydrocyanic acid (HCN). (K_a for hydrocyanic acid = 4.9×10^{-10}.)

16.60   Calculate the pH of an aqueous solution at 25°C that is 0.34 M in phenol (C_6H_5OH). (K_a for phenol = 1.3×10^{-10}.)

16.61   Determine the percent ionization of the following solutions of formic acid at 25°C: (a) 0.016 M, (b) 5.7×10^{-4} M, (c) 1.75 M.

16.62   Determine the percent ionization of the following solutions of phenol: (a) 0.56 M, (b) 0.25 M, (c) 1.8×10^{-6} M.

16.63   A 0.015-M solution of a monoprotic acid is 0.92 percent ionized. Calculate the ionization constant for the acid.

16.64   Calculate the concentration at which a monoprotic acid with $K_a = 4.5 \times 10^{-5}$ will be 2.5 percent ionized.

16.65   Calculate the K_a of a weak acid if a 0.19-M aqueous solution of the acid has a pH of 4.52 at 25°C.

16.66   The pH of an aqueous acid solution is 6.20 at 25°C. Calculate the K_a for the acid. The initial acid concentration is 0.010 M.

16.67   What is the original molarity of a solution of formic acid (HCOOH) whose pH is 3.26 at 25°C? (K_a for formic acid = 1.7×10^{-4}.)

16.68   What is the original molarity of a solution of a weak acid whose K_a is 3.5×10^{-5} and whose pH is 5.26 at 25°C?

16.69   In biological and medical applications, it is often necessary to study the autoionization of water at 37°C instead of 25°C. Given that K_w for water is 2.5×10^{-14} at 37°C, calculate the pH of pure water at this temperature.

SECTION 16.7:   WEAK BASES AND BASE IONIZATION CONSTANTS

Review Questions

16.70   Compare the pH values for 0.10-M solutions of NaOH and of NH_3 to illustrate the difference between a strong base and a weak base.

16.71   Which of the following has a higher pH: (a) 1.0 M NH_3, (b) 0.20 M NaOH (K_b for $NH_3 = 1.8 \times 10^{-5}$)?

Problems

16.72   Calculate the pH for each of the following solutions at 25°C: (a) 0.10 M NH_3, (b) 0.050 M C_5H_5N (pyridine). (K_b for pyridine = 1.7×10^{-9}.)

16.73   The pH of a 0.30-M solution of a weak base is 10.66 at 25°C. What is the K_b of the base?

16.74   What is the original molarity of an aqueous solution of ammonia (NH_3) whose pH is 11.22 at 25°C? (Use the K_b for ammonia provided in Problem 16.71.)

16.75   Calculate the pH at 25°C of a 0.61-M aqueous solution of a weak base B with a K_b of 1.5×10^{-4}.

16.76   Determine the K_b of a weak base if a 0.19-M aqueous solution of the base at 25°C has a pH of 10.88.

16.77   The following diagrams represent aqueous solutions of three different monoprotic acids: HA, HB, and HC. (a) Which conjugate base (A^-, B^-, or C^-) has the smallest K_b value? (b) Which anion is the strongest base? The water molecules have been omitted for clarity.

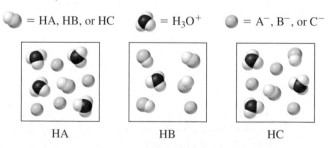

SECTION 16.8:   CONJUGATE ACID-BASE PAIRS

Review Questions

16.78   Write the equation relating K_a for a weak acid and K_b for its conjugate base. Use NH_3 and its conjugate acid NH_4^+ to derive the relationship between K_a and K_b.

16.79   From the relationship $K_aK_b = K_w$, what can you deduce about the relative strengths of a weak acid and its conjugate base?

Problems

16.80 The following diagrams represent solutions of three salts NaX (X = A, B, or C). (a) Which X⁻ has the weakest conjugate acid? (b) Arrange the three X⁻ anions in order of decreasing base strength. The Na⁺ ion and water molecules have been omitted for clarity.

● = A⁻, B⁻, or C⁻   ◐ = OH⁻   ○ = HA, HB, or HC

NaA   NaB   NaC

16.81 Calculate K_b for each of the following ions: CN⁻, F⁻, CH₃COO⁻, HCO₃⁻.

SECTION 16.9: DIPROTIC AND POLYPROTIC ACIDS

Review Questions

16.82 Write all the species (except water) that are present in a phosphoric acid solution. Indicate which species can act as a Brønsted acid, which as a Brønsted base, and which as both a Brønsted acid and a Brønsted base.

16.83 Write the K_{a_1} and K_{a_2} expressions for sulfurous acid, H_2SO_3.

Problems

16.84 The first and second ionization constants of a diprotic acid H_2A are K_{a_1} and K_{a_2} at a certain temperature. Under what conditions will $[A^{2-}] = K_{a_2}$?

16.85 Compare the pH of a 0.040 M HCl solution with that of a 0.040 M H_2SO_4 solution. (*Hint:* H_2SO_4 is a strong acid; K_a for $HSO_4^- = 1.3 \times 10^{-2}$.)

16.86 What are the concentrations of HSO_4^-, SO_4^{2-}, and H^+ in a 0.20 M KHSO₄ solution? (*Hint:* H_2SO_4 is a strong acid; K_a for $HSO_4^- = 1.3 \times 10^{-2}$.)

16.87 Calculate the concentrations of H^+, HCO_3^-, and CO_3^{2-} in a 0.025 M H_2CO_3 solution.

16.88 Calculate the pH at 25°C of a 0.25-M aqueous solution of phosphoric acid (H_3PO_4). (K_{a_1}, K_{a_2}, and K_{a_3} for phosphoric acid are 7.5×10^{-3}, 6.25×10^{-8}, and 4.8×10^{-13}, respectively.)

16.89 Calculate the pH at 25°C of a 0.25-M aqueous solution of oxalic acid ($H_2C_2O_4$). (K_{a_1} and K_{a_2} for oxalic acid are 6.5×10^{-2} and 6.1×10^{-5}, respectively.)

16.90 (1) Which of the following diagrams represents a solution of a weak diprotic acid? (2) Which diagrams represent chemically implausible situations? (The hydrated proton is shown as a hydronium ion. Water molecules are omitted for clarity.)

   (a)   (b)   (c)   (d)

SECTION 16.10: ACID-BASE PROPERTIES OF SALT SOLUTIONS

Review Questions

16.91 Define salt hydrolysis. Categorize salts according to how they affect the pH of a solution.

16.92 Al^{3+} is not a Brønsted acid, but $Al(H_2O)_6^{3+}$ is. Explain.

16.93 Specify which of the following salts will undergo hydrolysis: KF, NaNO₃, NH₄NO₂, MgSO₄, KCN, C₆H₅COONa, RbI, Na₂CO₃, CaCl₂, HCOOK.

Problems

16.94 Predict the pH (>7, <7, or ≈7) of aqueous solutions containing the following salts: (a) KBr, (b) Al(NO₃)₃, (c) BaCl₂, (d) Bi(NO₃)₃.

16.95 Predict whether the following solutions are acidic, basic, or nearly neutral: (a) NaBr, (b) K₂SO₃, (c) NH₄NO₂, (d) Cr(NO₃)₃.

16.96 A certain salt, MX (containing the M⁺ and X⁻ ions), is dissolved in water, and the pH of the resulting solution is 7.0. What can you say about the strengths of the acid and the base from which the salt is derived?

16.97 In a certain experiment, a student finds that the pHs of 0.10-M solutions of three potassium salts KX, KY, and KZ are 7.0, 9.0, and 11.0, respectively. Arrange the acids HX, HY, and HZ in order of increasing acid strength.

16.98 Predict whether a solution containing the salt K_2HPO_4 will be acidic, neutral, or basic.

16.99 Predict the pH (>7, <7, or ≈7) of a NaHCO₃ solution.

16.100 Calculate the pH of a 0.36 M CH₃COONa solution. (K_a for acetic acid = 1.8×10^{-5}.)

16.101 Calculate the pH of a 0.42 M NH₄Cl solution. (K_b for ammonia = 1.8×10^{-5}.)

16.102 Calculate the pH of a 0.082 M NaF solution. (K_a for HF = 7.1×10^{-4}.)

16.103 Calculate the pH of a 0.91 M C₂H₅NH₃I solution. (K_b for C₂H₅NH₂ = 5.6×10^{-4}.)

SECTION 16.11: ACID-BASE PROPERTIES OF OXIDES AND HYDROXIDES

Review Questions

16.104 Classify the following oxides as acidic, basic, amphoteric, or neutral: (a) CO₂, (b) K₂O, (c) CaO, (d) N₂O₅, (e) CO, (f) NO, (g) SnO₂, (h) SO₃, (i) Al₂O₃, (j) BaO.

16.105 Write equations for the reactions between (a) CO₂ and NaOH(*aq*), (b) Na₂O and HNO₃(*aq*).

Problems

16.106 Explain why metal oxides tend to be basic if the oxidation number of the metal is low and tend to be acidic if the oxidation number of the metal is high. (*Hint:* Metallic compounds in which the oxidation numbers of the metals are low are more ionic than those in which the oxidation numbers of the metals are high.)

16.107 Arrange the oxides in each of the following groups in order of increasing basicity: (a) K_2O, Al_2O_3, BaO, (b) CrO_3, CrO, Cr_2O_3.

16.108 $Zn(OH)_2$ is an amphoteric hydroxide. Write balanced ionic equations to show its reaction with (a) HCl, (b) NaOH [the product is $Zn(OH)_4^{2-}$].

16.109 $Al(OH)_3$ is insoluble in water. It dissolves in concentrated NaOH solution. Write a balanced ionic equation for this reaction. What type of reaction is this?

16.110 How do the chemical properties of oxides change from left to right across a period? How do they change from top to bottom within a particular group?

16.111 Write balanced equations for the reactions between each of the following oxides and water: (a) Li_2O, (b) CaO, (c) SO_3.

SECTION 16.12:   LEWIS ACIDS AND BASES

Review Questions

16.112 What are the Lewis definitions of an acid and a base? In what way are they more general than the Brønsted definitions?

16.113 In terms of orbitals and electron arrangements, what must be present for a molecule or an ion to act as a Lewis acid (use H^+ and BF_3 as examples)? What must be present for a molecule or ion to act as a Lewis base (use OH^- and NH_3 as examples)?

Problems

16.114 Classify each of the following species as a Lewis acid or a Lewis base: (a) CO_2, (b) H_2O, (c) I^-, (d) SO_2, (e) NH_3, (f) OH^-, (g) H^+, (h) BCl_3.

16.115 Describe the following reaction in terms of the Lewis theory of acids and bases:

$$AlCl_3(s) + Cl^-(aq) \longrightarrow AlCl_4^-(aq)$$

16.116 Which would be considered a stronger Lewis acid: (a) BF_3 or BCl_3, (b) Fe^{2+} or Fe^{3+}? Explain.

16.117 All Brønsted acids are Lewis acids, but the reverse is not true. Give two examples of Lewis acids that are not Brønsted acids.

16.118 Identify the Lewis acid and the Lewis base in the following reactions:
(a) $Fe(s) + 5CO(g) \longrightarrow Fe(CO)_5(l)$
(b) $BCl_3(g) + NH_3(g) \longrightarrow Cl_3BNH_3(s)$
(c) $Hg^{2+}(aq) + 4I^-(aq) \longrightarrow HgI_4^{2-}(aq)$

16.119 Identify the Lewis acid and the Lewis base in the following reactions:
(a) $AlBr_3(s) + Br^-(aq) \longrightarrow AlBr_4^-(aq)$
(b) $Cr(s) + 6CO(g) \longrightarrow Cr(CO)_6(s)$
(c) $Cu^{2+}(aq) + 4CN^-(aq) \longrightarrow Cu(CN)_4^{2-}(aq)$

ADDITIONAL PROBLEMS

16.120 H_2SO_4 is a strong acid, but HSO_4^- is a weak acid. Account for the difference in strength of these two related species.

16.121 Which of the following diagrams best represents a strong acid, such as HCl, dissolved in water? Which represents a weak acid? Which represents a very weak

acid? (The hydrated proton is shown as a hydronium ion. Water molecules are omitted for clarity.)

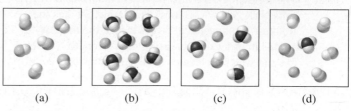

(a)   (b)   (c)   (d)

16.122 Predict the direction that predominates in this reaction:

$$F^-(aq) + H_2O(l) \rightleftharpoons HF(aq) + OH^-(aq)$$

16.123 Predict the products and tell whether the following reaction will occur to any measurable extent:

$$CH_3COOH(aq) + Cl^-(aq) \longrightarrow$$

16.124 In a 0.080 M NH_3 solution, what percent of the NH_3 is present as NH_4^+?

16.125 Calculate the pH and percent ionization of a 0.88 M HNO_2 solution at 25°C.

16.126 A typical reaction between an antacid and the hydrochloric acid in gastric juice is

$$NaHCO_3(s) + HCl(aq) \rightleftharpoons NaCl(aq) + H_2O(l) + CO_2(g)$$

Calculate the volume (in liters) of CO_2 generated from 0.350 g of $NaHCO_3$ and excess gastric juice at 1.00 atm and 37.0°C.

16.127 To which of the following would the addition of an equal volume of 0.60 M NaOH lead to a solution having a lower pH: (a) water, (b) 0.30 M HCl, (c) 0.70 M KOH, (d) 0.40 M $NaNO_3$?

16.128 The pH of a 0.0642-M solution of a monoprotic acid is 3.86. Is this a strong acid?

16.129 Like water, liquid ammonia undergoes autoionization:

$$NH_3 + NH_3 \rightleftharpoons NH_4^+ + NH_2^-$$

(a) Identify the Brønsted acids and Brønsted bases in this reaction. (b) What species correspond to H^+ and OH^-, and what is the condition for a neutral solution?

16.130 HA and HB are both weak acids although HB is the stronger of the two. Will it take a larger volume of a 0.10 M NaOH solution to neutralize 50.0 mL of 0.10 M HB than would be needed to neutralize 50.0 mL of 0.10 M HA?

16.131 A solution contains a weak monoprotic acid HA and its sodium salt NaA both at 0.1 M concentration. Show that $[OH^-] = K_w/K_a$.

16.132 The three common chromium oxides are CrO, Cr_2O_3, and CrO_3. If Cr_2O_3 is amphoteric, what can you say about the acid-base properties of CrO and CrO_3?

16.133 Use the data in Table 16.7 to calculate the equilibrium constant for the following reaction:

$$HCOOH(aq) + OH^-(aq) \rightleftharpoons HCOO^-(aq) + H_2O(l)$$

16.134 Use the data in Table 16.7 to calculate the equilibrium constant for the following reaction:

$$CH_3COOH(aq) + NO_2^- \rightleftharpoons CH_3COO^-(aq) + HNO_2(aq)$$

16.135 Most of the hydrides of Group 1A and Group 2A metals are ionic (the exceptions are BeH_2 and MgH_2, which are covalent compounds). (a) Describe the reaction between the hydride ion (H^-) and water in terms of a Brønsted acid-base reaction. (b) The same reaction can also be classified as a redox reaction. Identify the oxidizing and reducing agents.

16.136 Calculate the pH of a 0.20 M ammonium acetate (CH_3COONH_4) solution.

16.137 Novocaine, used as a local anesthetic by dentists, is a weak base ($K_b = 8.91 \times 10^{-6}$). What is the ratio of the concentration of the base to that of its acid in the blood plasma (pH = 7.40) of a patient? (As an approximation, use the K_a values at 25°C.)

16.138 Which of the following is the stronger base: NF_3 or NH_3? (*Hint:* F is more electronegative than H.)

16.139 Which of the following is a stronger base: NH_3 or PH_3? (*Hint:* The N—H bond is stronger than the P—H bond.)

16.140 The ion product of D_2O is 1.35×10^{-15} at 25°C. (a) Calculate pD where pD $= -\log [D^+]$. (b) For what values of pD will a solution be acidic in D_2O? (c) Derive a relation between pD and pOD.

16.141 Give an example of (a) a weak acid that contains oxygen atoms, (b) a weak acid that does not contain oxygen atoms, (c) a neutral molecule that acts as a Lewis acid, (d) a neutral molecule that acts as a Lewis base, (e) a weak acid that contains two ionizable H atoms, (f) a conjugate acid-base pair, both of which react with HCl to give carbon dioxide gas.

16.142 What is the pH of 250.0 mL of an aqueous solution containing 0.616 g of a strong acid?

16.143 (a) Use VSEPR to predict the geometry of the hydronium ion (H_3O^+). (b) The O atom in H_2O has two lone pairs and in principle can accept two H^+ ions. Explain why the species H_4O^{2+} does not exist. What would be its geometry if it did exist?

16.144 HF is a weak acid, but its strength increases with concentration. Explain. (*Hint:* F^- reacts with HF to form HF_2^-. The equilibrium constant for this reaction is 5.2 at 25°C.)

16.145 When chlorine reacts with water, the resulting solution is weakly acidic and reacts with $AgNO_3$ to give a white precipitate. Write balanced equations to represent these reactions. Explain why manufacturers of household bleaches add bases such as NaOH to their products to increase their effectiveness.

16.146 When the concentration of a strong acid is not substantially higher than 1.0×10^{-7} M, the ionization of water must be taken into account in the calculation of the solution's pH. (a) Derive an expression for the pH of a strong acid solution, including the contribution to [H^+] from H_2O. (b) Calculate the pH of a 1.0×10^{-7} M HCl solution.

16.147 Calculate the pH of a 2.00 M NH_4CN solution.

16.148 Calculate the concentrations of all species in a 0.100 M H_3PO_4 solution.

16.149 In the vapor phase, acetic acid molecules associate to a certain extent to form dimers:

$$2CH_3COOH(g) \rightleftharpoons (CH_3COOH)_2(g)$$

At 51°C, the pressure of a certain acetic acid vapor system is 0.0342 atm in a 360-mL flask. The vapor is condensed and neutralized with 13.8 mL of 0.0568 M NaOH. (a) Calculate the degree of dissociation (α) of the dimer under these conditions:

$$(CH_3COOH)_2 \rightleftharpoons 2CH_3COOH$$

(b) Calculate the equilibrium constant K_p for the reaction in part (a).

16.150 Calculate the concentrations of all the species in a 0.100 M Na_2CO_3 solution.

16.151 Henry's law constant for CO_2 at 38°C is 2.28×10^{-3} mol/L atm. Calculate the pH of a solution of CO_2 at 38°C in equilibrium with the gas at a partial pressure of 3.20 atm.

16.152 Hydrocyanic acid (HCN) is a weak acid and a deadly poisonous compound—in the gaseous form (hydrogen cyanide), it is used in gas chambers. Why is it dangerous to treat sodium cyanide with acids (such as HCl) without proper ventilation?

16.153 How many grams of NaCN would you need to dissolve in enough water to make exactly 250 mL of solution with a pH of 10.00?

16.154 A solution of formic acid (HCOOH) has a pH of 2.53. How many grams of formic acid are there in 100.0 mL of the solution?

16.155 Calculate the pH of a 1-L solution containing 0.150 mole of CH_3COOH and 0.100 mole of HCl.

16.156 Predict the products of the following oxides with water: Na_2O, BaO, CO_2, N_2O_5, P_4O_{10}, SO_3. Write an equation for each of the reactions. Specify whether the oxides are acidic, basic, or amphoteric.

16.157 You are given two beakers, one containing an aqueous solution of strong acid (HA) and the other an aqueous solution of weak acid (HB) of the same concentration. Describe how you would compare the strengths of these two acids by (a) measuring the pH, (b) measuring electrical conductance, and (c) studying the rate of hydrogen gas evolution when these solutions are combined with an active metal such as Mg or Zn.

16.158 Use Le Châtelier's principle to predict the effect of the following changes on the extent of hydrolysis of sodium nitrite ($NaNO_2$) solution: (a) HCl is added, (b) NaOH is added, (c) NaCl is added, (d) the solution is diluted.

16.159 A 0.400 M formic acid (HCOOH) solution freezes at −0.758°C. Calculate the K_a of the acid at that temperature. (*Hint:* Assume that molarity is equal to molality. Carry out your calculations to three significant figures and round off to two for K_a.)

16.160 The disagreeable odor of fish is mainly due to organic compounds (RNH_2) containing an amino group, $−NH_2$, where R is the rest of the molecule. Amines are bases just like ammonia. Explain why putting some lemon juice on fish can greatly reduce the odor.

16.161 A solution of methylamine (CH_3NH_2) has a pH of 10.64. How many grams of methylamine are there in 100.0 mL of the solution?

16.162 Describe the hydration of SO_2 as a Lewis acid-base reaction.

16.163 Both the amide ion (NH_2^-) and the nitride ion (N^{3-}) are stronger bases than the hydroxide ion and hence do not exist in aqueous solutions. (a) Write equations showing the reactions of these ions with water, and identify the Brønsted acid and base in each case. (b) Which of the two is the stronger base?

16.164 When carbon dioxide is bubbled through a clear calcium hydroxide solution, the solution appears milky. Write an equation for the reaction, and explain how this reaction illustrates that CO_2 is an acidic oxide.

16.165 Explain the action of smelling salt, which is ammonium carbonate [$(NH_4)_2CO_3$]. (*Hint:* The thin film of aqueous solution that lines the nasal passage is slightly basic.)

16.166 About half of the hydrochloric acid produced annually in the United States (3.0 billion pounds) is used in metal pickling. This process involves the removal of metal oxide layers from metal surfaces to prepare them for coating. (a) Write the overall and net ionic equations for the reaction between iron(III) oxide, which represents the rust layer over iron, and HCl. Identify the Brønsted acid and base. (b) Hydrochloric acid is also used to remove scale (which is mostly $CaCO_3$) from water pipes. Hydrochloric acid reacts with calcium carbonate in two stages; the first stage forms the bicarbonate ion, which then reacts further to form carbon dioxide. Write equations for these two stages and for the overall reaction. (c) Hydrochloric acid is used to recover oil from the ground. It dissolves rocks (often $CaCO_3$) so that the oil can flow more easily. In one process, a 15 percent (by mass) HCl solution is injected into an oil well to dissolve the rocks. If the density of the acid solution is 1.073 g/mL, what is the pH of the solution?

16.167 Which of the following does not represent a Lewis acid-base reaction?
(a) $H_2O + H^+ \longrightarrow H_3O^+$
(b) $NH_3 + BF_3 \longrightarrow H_3NBF_3$
(c) $PF_3 + F_2 \longrightarrow PF_5$
(d) $Al(OH)_3 + OH^- \longrightarrow Al(OH)_4^-$

16.168 Determine whether each of the following statements is true or false. If false, explain why the statement is wrong.
(a) All Lewis acids are Brønsted acids.
(b) The conjugate base of an acid always carries a negative charge.
(c) The percent ionization of a base increases with its concentration in solution.
(d) A solution of barium fluoride is acidic.

16.169 How many milliliters of a strong monoprotic acid solution at pH = 4.12 must be added to 528 mL of the same acid solution at pH = 5.76 to change its pH to 5.34? Assume that the volumes are additive.

16.170 Hemoglobin (Hb) is a blood protein that is responsible for transporting oxygen. It can exist in the protonated form as HbH^+. The binding of oxygen can be represented by the simplified equation

$$HbH^+ + O_2 \rightleftharpoons HbO_2 + H^+$$

(a) What form of hemoglobin is favored in the lungs where oxygen concentration is highest? (b) In body tissues, where the cells release carbon dioxide produced by metabolism, the blood is more acidic due to the formation of carbonic acid. What form of hemoglobin is favored under this condition? (c) When a person hyperventilates, the concentration of CO_2 in his or her blood decreases. How does this action affect the given equilibrium? Frequently a person who is hyperventilating is advised to breathe into a paper bag. Why does this action help the individual?

16.171 A 20.27-g sample of a metal carbonate (MCO_3) is combined with 500 mL of a 1.00 M HCl solution. The excess HCl acid is then neutralized by 32.80 mL of 0.588 M NaOH. Identify M.

16.172 Calculate the pH of a solution that is 1.00 M HCN and 1.00 M HF. Compare the concentration (in molarity) of the CN^- ion in this solution with that in a 1.00 M HCN solution. Comment on the difference.

16.173 Tooth enamel is largely hydroxyapatite [$Ca_3(PO_4)_3OH$]. When it dissolves in water (a process called *demineralization*), it dissociates as follows:

$$Ca_5(PO_4)_3OH \longrightarrow 5Ca^{2+} + 3PO_4^{3-} + OH^-$$

The reverse process, called *remineralization,* is the body's natural defense against tooth decay. Acids produced from food remove the OH^- ions and thereby weaken the enamel layer. Most toothpastes contain a fluoride compound such as NaF or SnF_2. What is the function of these compounds in preventing tooth decay?

16.174 Use the van't Hoff equation (see Problem 15.120) and the data in Appendix 2 to calculate the pH of water at its normal boiling point.

16.175 Write the formulas and names of the oxides of the second period elements (Li to N). Identify the oxides as acidic, basic, or amphoteric. Use the highest oxidation state of each element.

16.176 The atmospheric sulfur dioxide (SO_2) concentration over a certain region is 0.12 ppm by volume. Calculate the pH of the rainwater due to this pollutant. Assume that the dissolution of SO_2 does not affect its pressure. (K_a for $H_2SO_3 = 1.3 \times 10^{-2}$.)

16.177 Sulfuric acid (H_2SO_4) accounts for as much as 80 percent of the acid in acid rain. Its first ionization is complete, producing H^+ and the hydrogen sulfate ion:

$$H_2SO_4(aq) \rightleftharpoons H^+(aq) + HSO_4^-(aq)$$

Its second ionization, which produces additional H^+ and the sulfate ion, has an ionization constant (K_{a_2}) of 1.3×10^{-2}.

$$HSO_4^-(aq) \rightleftharpoons H^+(aq) + SO_4^{2-}(aq)$$

Calculate the concentration of all species in a raindrop in which the sulfuric acid concentration is 4.00×10^{-5} M. Assume that sulfuric acid is the only acid present.

16.178 A 1.87-g sample of Mg reacts with 80.0 mL of a HCl solution whose pH is −0.544. What is the pH of the solution after all the Mg has reacted? Assume constant volume.

Answers to In-Chapter Materials

PRACTICE PROBLEMS

16.1A (a) $HClO_4$, (b) HS^-, (c) HS^-, (d) $HC_2O_4^-$. **16.1B** SO_3^{2-}, H_2SO_3.
16.2A (a) NH_4^+ acid, H_2O base, NH_3 conjugate base, H_3O^+ conjugate
acid; (b) CN^- base, H_2O acid, HCN conjugate acid, OH^- conjugate base.
16.2B (a) $HSO_4^- + H_2O \longrightarrow H_3O^+ + SO_4^{2-}$, (b) $HSO_4^- + H_2O \longrightarrow$
$H_2SO_4 + OH^-$. **16.3A** (a) $HBrO_4$, (b) H_2SO_4. **16.3B** Electronegativity.
The greater difference in electronegativities of two elements in a bond
leads to a weaker bond and thus acidity increases. **16.4A** 2.0×10^{-11} M.
16.4B 2.8×10^{-13} M. **16.5A** (a) 8.49, (b) 7.40, (c) 1.25. **16.5B** (a) -0.08,
(b) 10.52, (c) 11.07. **16.6A** (a) 1.3×10^{-10} M, (b) 3.5×10^{-2} M,
(c) 9.8×10^{-8} M. **16.6B** (a) 7.8×10^{-3} M, (b) 2.6×10^{-12} M,
(c) 1.3×10^{-7} M. **16.7A** (a) 11.24, (b) 2.14, (c) 5.07. **16.7B** (a) 7.55,
(b) 8.00, (c) 11.00. **16.8A** (a) 9.5×10^{-14} M, (b) 7.2×10^{-6} M,
(c) 1.0×10^{-7} M. **16.8B** (a) 5.5×10^{-12} M, (b) 2.0×10^{-4} M,
(c) 2.5×10^{-2} M. **16.9A** (a) 1.09, (b) 5.09, (c) 2.27. **16.9B** (a) 1.96, (b) 2.46,
(c) 7.00. **16.10A** (a) 8.7×10^{-3} M, (b) 1.7×10^{-2} M, (c) 9.8×10^{-7} M.
16.10B (a) 1.5×10^{-5} M, (b) 1.5×10^{-2} M, (c) 9.1×10^{-4} M.
16.11A (a) 0.82, (b) 2.08, (c) 4.77. **16.11B** (a) 6.71, (b) 1.21, (c) 0.91.
16.12A (a) 9.5×10^{-6} M, (b) 4.8×10^{-6} M. **16.12B** (a) 1.7×10^{-2} M,
(b) 8.7×10^{-3} M. **16.13A** 2.89. **16.13B** 3.05. **16.14A** (a) 4.96, 0.0044%,
(b) 5.72, 0.026%, (c) 6.70, 0.24%. **16.14B** (a) 2.0×10^{-3} M,
(b) 4.9×10^{-4} M, (c) 2.2×10^{-4} M. **16.15A** 1.9×10^{-5}.
16.15B 5.8×10^{-9}. **16.16A** 9.14. **16.16B** 8.33. **16.17A** 3.0×10^{-9}.
16.17B 1.4×10^{-4}. **16.18A** (a) 1.5×10^{-10}, (b) 1.8×10^{-13}, (c) 1.8×10^{-11}.
16.18B (a) 1.1×10^{-11}, (b) 4.8×10^{-7}. **16.19A** $[H_2C_2O_4] = 0.11$ M,
$[HC_2O_4^-] = 0.086$ M, $[C_2O_4^{2-}] = 6.1 \times 10^{-5}$ M, $[H^+] = 0.086$ M.
16.19B $[H_2SO_4] = 0$ M, $[HSO_4^-] = 0.13$ M, $[SO_4^{2-}] = 0.011$ M,
$[H^+] = 0.15$ M. **16.20A** 8.96. **16.20B** 0.75 M. **16.21A** 2.92.
16.21B 0.032 M. **16.22A** (a) basic, (b) acidic, (c) basic, (d) neutral,
(e) neutral. **16.22B** (a) NH_4Br and CH_3NH_3I, (b) $NaHPO_4$ and $KOBr$,
(c) NaI and KBr. **16.23A** Lewis acid: Co^{3+}, Lewis base: NH_3.
16.23B NH_3 and $AlBr_3$.

SECTION REVIEW

16.1.1 HS^-, Br^-, HSO_4^-. **16.1.2** H_2O, HCO_3^-, $H_2C_2O_4$.
16.2.1 $CH_2ICOOH < CH_2BrCOOH < CH_2ClCOOH < CH_2FCOOH$.
16.2.2 $HBrO < HBrO_3 < HBrO_4$. **16.2.3** H_2A, strongest; H_2B, weakest.
16.3.1 8.3×10^{-12} M. **16.3.2** 4.0×10^{-14} M. **16.4.1** 7.20. **16.4.2** 1.8×10^{-6} M.
16.4.3 2.33. **16.4.4** 3.2×10^{-4} M. **16.5.1** 1.12. **16.5.2** 1.3×10^{-6} M.
16.5.3 2.59. **16.5.4** 4.9×10^{-4} M. **16.5.5** 11.98. **16.5.6** 5.1×10^{-6} M.
16.5.7 b. **16.6.1** 1.73. **16.6.2** 2.3×10^{-7}. **16.6.3** i $<$ iii $<$ ii. **16.7.1** 10.89.
16.7.2 2.8×10^{-6}. **16.7.3** iii $<$ ii $<$ i. **16.8.1** 2.0×10^{-5}. **16.8.2** phenolate
ion ($C_6H_5O^-$). **16.8.3** $Z^- < Y^- < X^-$. **16.9.1** 4.8×10^{-11} M. **16.9.2** 1.29.
16.9.3 $[C_6H_6O_6^{2-}] < [HC_6H_6O_6^-] = [H^+] < [H_2C_6H_6O_6]$. **16.10.1** 5.19.
16.10.2 11.11. **16.10.3** basic. **16.10.4** neutral. **16.10.5** $B^- < A^- < C^-$.
16.12.1 CH_4. **16.12.2** BCl_3.

KEY SKILLS

Salt Hydrolysis

Salt hydrolysis is critical to the understanding of certain acid-base titrations. When a weak acid is titrated with a strong base, the product of the neutralization is the weak acid's conjugate base.

$$HA(aq) + OH^-(aq) \longrightarrow A^-(aq) + H_2O(l)$$

The conjugate base of a weak acid behaves as a weak Brønsted base in water.

$$A^-(aq) + H_2O(l) \rightleftharpoons HA(aq) + OH^-(aq)$$

If we know the concentrations of the weak acid and the strong base, we can determine pH at the equivalence point of a weak acid–strong base titration as follows:

In the case of a monoprotic weak acid such as acetic acid ($HC_2H_3O_2$) and a monobasic strong base such as NaOH, the number of millimoles of base is equal to the number of millimoles of acid at the equivalence point.

This enables us to determine the volume of strong base necessary to reach the equivalence point.

The combination of the original weak acid volume and the volume of base added to reach the equivalence point gives the total volume at the equivalence point. Further, the number of millimoles of conjugate base produced is equal to the number of millimoles of weak acid present at the start of the titration.

Using this information, we find the concentration of conjugate base; and to get K_b, we use the tabulated K_a for the weak acid and Equation 16.8.

Once we have both the concentration and the ionization constant for the conjugate base, we construct an ice table and solve for the equilibrium concentration of hydroxide—and for pH. To illustrate the process, let's determine the pH at the equivalence point of the titration of 30.0 mL 0.15 M acetic acid ($HC_2H_3O_2$, $K_a = 1.8 \times 10^{-5}$) with 0.12 M NaOH at 25°C.

The neutralization net ionic equation is: $HC_2H_3O_2(aq) + OH^-(aq) \longrightarrow C_2H_3O_2^-(aq) + H_2O(l)$

We now construct an equilibrium table and solve for [OH⁻]. The reaction of acetate ion with water is:

$$C_2H_3O_2^-(aq) + H_2O(l) \rightleftharpoons HC_2H_3O_2(aq) + OH^-(aq)$$

i	0.0667	0	0
c	$-x$	$+x$	$+x$
e	$0.0667 - x$	x	x

$$5.56 \times 10^{-10} = \frac{[HC_2H_3O_2][OH^-]}{[C_2H_3O_2^-]}$$

Solving for x gives 6.09×10^{-6} M. This is the concentration of the OH⁻ ion.

$$pOH = -\log [OH^-] = -\log (6.09 \times 10^{-6}) = 5.22$$

and pH = 14.00 − pOH, which gives

$$pH = 8.78$$

Key Skills Problems

16.1
Calculate the pH of a solution that is 0.22 M in nitrite ion (NO_2^-) at 25°C. K_a for nitrous acid (HNO_2) is 4.5×10^{-4}.

(a) 11.79　(b) 8.34　(c) 5.65　(d) 7.00　(e) 2.21

16.2
Determine pH at the equivalence point in the titration of 41.0 mL 0.096 M formic acid with 0.108 M NaOH at 25°C.

(a) 12.94　(b) 7.00　(c) 5.76　(d) 8.24　(e) 1.06

16.3
Calculate the pH of a solution that is 0.22 M in pyridinium ion ($C_5H_5NH^+$) at 25°C. K_b for pyridine (C_5H_5N) is 1.7×10^{-9}.

(a) 11.06　(b) 7.00　(c) 7.51　(d) 2.94　(e) 4.19

16.4
Determine pH at the equivalence point in the titration of 26.0 mL 1.12 M pyridine with 0.93 M HCl at 25°C.

(a) 7.00　(b) 2.76　(c) 11.24　(d) 1.73　(e) 12.27

CHAPTER 17

Acid-Base Equilibria and Solubility Equilibria

17.1 **The Common Ion Effect**

17.2 **Buffer Solutions**
• Calculating the pH of a Buffer • Preparing a Buffer Solution with a Specific pH

17.3 **Acid-Base Titrations**
• Strong Acid–Strong Base Titrations • Weak Acid–Strong Base Titrations • Strong Acid–Weak Base Titrations • Acid-Base Indicators

17.4 **Solubility Equilibria**
• Solubility Product Expression and K_{sp}
• Calculations Involving K_{sp} and Solubility
• Predicting Precipitation Reactions

17.5 **Factors Affecting Solubility**
• The Common Ion Effect • pH • Complex Ion Formation

17.6 **Separation of Ions Using Differences in Solubility**
• Fractional Precipitation • Qualitative Analysis of Metal Ions in Solution

A buffer solution is an aqueous mixture of a weak acid and a weak base that is used to maintain the pH of a solution within a desired range. The ability of buffers to minimize the effect of added strong acid or strong base makes them useful in a variety of chemical and biochemical processes. Chemists have developed methods for buffering foods, cosmetics, drugs and drug-delivery systems, and many other familiar products to optimize their performance. One such application of buffers is in the preparation of standard ophthalmic solutions, for which a narrow pH is necessary to make their use in eyedrops safe and effective.

17.1 THE COMMON ION EFFECT

Up until now, we have discussed the properties of solutions containing a single solute. In this section, we will examine how the properties of a solution change when a second solute is introduced.

Recall that a system at equilibrium will shift in response to being stressed and that stress can be applied in a variety of ways, including the addition of a reactant or a product [◄◄ Section 15.5]. Consider a liter of solution containing 0.10 mole of acetic acid. Using the K_a for acetic acid (1.8×10^{-5}) and an equilibrium table [◄◄ Section 16.6], the pH of this solution at 25°C can be determined:

$$CH_3COOH(aq) \rightleftharpoons H^+(aq) + CH_3COO^-(aq)$$

	CH_3COOH	H^+	CH_3COO^-
Initial concentration (M):	0.10	0	0
Change in concentration (M):	$-x$	$+x$	$+x$
Equilibrium concentration (M):	$0.10 - x$	x	x

Assuming that $(0.10 - x)\ M \approx 0.10\ M$ and solving for x, we get 1.34×10^{-3}. Therefore, $[CH_3COOH] = 0.09866\ M$, $[H^+] = [CH_3COO^-] = 1.34 \times 10^{-3}\ M$ and pH = 2.87.

Now consider what happens when we add 0.050 mole of sodium acetate (CH_3COONa) to the solution. Sodium acetate dissociates completely in aqueous solution to give sodium ions and acetate ions:

$$CH_3COONa(aq) \xrightarrow{H_2O} Na^+(aq) + CH_3COO^-(aq)$$

Thus, by adding sodium acetate, we have increased the concentration of acetate ion. Because acetate ion is a product in the ionization of acetic acid, the addition of acetate ion causes the equilibrium to shift to the left. The net result is a reduction in the percent ionization of acetic acid.

addition

$$CH_3COOH(aq) \longleftarrow H^+(aq) + CH_3COO^-(aq)$$

Equilibrium is driven toward reactant.

Shifting the equilibrium to the left consumes not only some of the added acetate ion, but also some of the hydrogen ion. This causes the pH to change (in this case the pH increases).

Student Annotation: The percent ionization of acetic acid is

$$\frac{1.34 \times 10^{-3}\ M}{0.10\ M} \times 100\% = 1.3\%$$

Student Annotation: By adding sodium acetate, we also add sodium ions to the solution. However, sodium ions do not interact with water or with any of the other species present [◄◄ Section 16.10].

Worked Example 17.1 shows how an equilibrium table can be used to calculate the pH of a solution of acetic acid after the addition of sodium acetate.

Worked Example 17.1

Determine the pH at 25°C of a solution prepared by adding 0.050 mole of sodium acetate to 1.0 L of 0.10-M acetic acid. (Assume that the addition of sodium acetate does not change the volume of the solution.)

Strategy Construct a new equilibrium table to solve for the hydrogen ion concentration.

Setup We use the stated concentration of acetic acid, 0.10 M, and [H^+] ≈ 0 M as the initial concentrations in the table:

Student Annotation: Remember that prior to the ionization of a weak acid, the concentration of hydrogen ion in water at 25°C is 1.0×10^{-7} M. However, because this concentration is insignificant compared to the concentration resulting from the ionization, we can neglect it in our equilibrium table.

$$CH_3COOH(aq) \rightleftharpoons H^+(aq) + CH_3COO^-(aq)$$

	CH_3COOH	H^+	CH_3COO^-
Initial concentration (M):	0.10	0	0.050
Change in concentration (M):	$-x$	$+x$	$+x$
Equilibrium concentration (M):	$0.10 - x$	x	$0.050 + x$

Solution Substituting the equilibrium concentrations, in terms of the unknown x, into the equilibrium expression gives

$$1.8 \times 10^{-5} = \frac{(x)(0.050 + x)}{0.10 - x}$$

Because we expect x to be very small (even smaller than 1.34×10^{-3} M—see above), because the ionization of CH_3COOH is suppressed by the presence of CH_3COO^-, we assume

$$(0.10 - x) M \approx 0.10 M \qquad \text{and} \qquad (0.050 + x) M \approx 0.050 M$$

Therefore, the equilibrium expression simplifies to

$$1.8 \times 10^{-5} = \frac{(x)(0.050)}{0.10}$$

Student Annotation: In this case, the percent ionization of acetic acid is

$\frac{3.6 \times 10^{-5} M}{0.10 M} \times 100\% = 0.036\%$

This is considerably smaller than the percent ionization prior to the addition of sodium acetate.

and $x = 3.6 \times 10^{-5}$ M. According to the equilibrium table, [H^+] = x, so pH = $-\log (3.6 \times 10^{-5})$ = 4.44.

Think About It

The equilibrium concentrations of CH_3COOH, CH_3COO^-, and H^+ are the same regardless of whether we add sodium acetate to a solution of acetic acid, add acetic acid to a solution of sodium acetate, or dissolve both species at the same time. We could have constructed an equilibrium table starting with the equilibrium concentrations in the 0.10 M acetic acid solution:

Student Annotation: This is the sum of the equilibrium concentration of acetate ion in a 0.10-M solution of acetic acid (1.34×10^{-3} M) and the added acetate ion (0.050 M).

	$CH_3COOH(aq)$	$H^+(aq)$	$CH_3COO^-(aq)$
Initial concentration (M):	0.09866	1.34×10^{-3}	5.134×10^{-2}
Change in concentration (M):	$+y$	$-y$	$-y$
Equilibrium concentration (M):	$0.09866 + y$	$1.34 \times 10^{-3} - y$	$5.134 \times 10^{-2} - y$

Student Annotation: Treating the problem as though both CH_3COOH and CH_3COO^- are added at the same time and the reaction proceeds to the right simplifies the solution.

In this case, the reaction proceeds to the left. (The acetic acid concentration increases, and the concentrations of hydrogen and acetate ions decrease.) Solving for y gives 1.304×10^{-3} M. [H^+] = $1.34 \times 10^{-3} - y = 3.6 \times 10^{-5}$ M and pH = 4.44. We get the same pH either way.

Practice Problem A Determine the pH at 25°C of a solution prepared by dissolving 0.075 mole of sodium acetate in 1.0 L of 0.25 M acetic acid. (Assume that the addition of sodium acetate does not change the volume of the solution.)

Practice Problem B Determine the pH at 25°C of a solution prepared by dissolving 0.35 mole of ammonium chloride in 1.0 L of 0.25 M aqueous ammonia.

Student Annotation: The *common ion* can also be H^+ or OH^-. For example, addition of a strong acid to a solution of a weak acid suppresses ionization of the weak acid. Similarly, addition of a strong base to a solution of weak base suppresses ionization of the weak base.

An aqueous solution of a weak electrolyte contains both the weak electrolyte and its ionization products, which are ions. If a soluble salt that contains one of those ions is added, the equilibrium shifts to the left, thereby *suppressing* the ionization of the weak electrolyte. In general, when a compound containing an ion in common with a dissolved substance is added to a solution at equilibrium, the equilibrium shifts to the left. This phenomenon is known as the ***common ion effect.***

The Common Ion Effect

17.1.1 For each of the following substances, indicate if addition would cause an increase, a decrease, or no change in the percent ionization of a solution of nitrous acid (HNO_2) initially at equilibrium.
(a) $NaNO_2$
(b) H_2O
(c) $Ca(NO_2)_2$
(d) HNO_3
(e) $NaNO_3$

17.1.2 What is the pH of a solution prepared by adding 0.05 mole of NaF to 1.0 L of 0.1 M HF at 25°C? (Assume that the addition of NaF does not change the volume of the solution.) (K_a for HF = 7.1×10^{-4}.)

17.2 BUFFER SOLUTIONS

A solution that contains a weak acid and its conjugate base (or a weak base and its conjugate acid) is a *buffer solution* or simply a **buffer**. Buffer solutions, by virtue of their composition, *resist* changes in pH upon addition of small amounts of either an acid or a base. The ability to resist pH change is very important to chemical and biological systems, including the human body. The pH of blood is about 7.4, whereas that of gastric juices is about 1.5. Each of these pH values is crucial for proper enzyme function and the balance of osmotic pressure, and each is maintained within a very narrow pH range by a buffer.

> **Student Annotation:** Any solution of a weak acid contains some conjugate base. In a buffer solution, though, the amounts of weak acid and conjugate base must be *comparable*, meaning that the conjugate base must be supplied by a dissolved salt.

Calculating the pH of a Buffer

Consider a solution that is 1.0 M in acetic acid and 1.0 M sodium acetate. If a small amount of acid is added to this solution, it is consumed completely by the acetate ion,

$$H^+(aq) + CH_3COO^-(aq) \longrightarrow CH_3COOH(aq)$$

thus converting a strong acid (H^+) to a weak acid (CH_3COOH). Addition of a strong acid lowers the pH of a solution. However, a buffer's ability to convert a strong acid to a weak acid minimizes the effect of the addition on the pH.

Similarly, if a small amount of a base is added, it is consumed completely by the acetic acid,

$$CH_3COOH(aq) + OH^-(aq) \longrightarrow CH_3COO^-(aq) + H_2O(l)$$

thus converting a strong base (OH^-) to a weak base (CH_3COO^-). Addition of a strong base increases the pH of a solution. Again, however, a buffer's ability to convert a strong base to a weak base minimizes the effect of the addition on pH.

To illustrate the function of a buffer, suppose that we have 1 L of the acetic acid–sodium acetate solution described previously. We can calculate the pH of the buffer using the procedure in Section 17.1:

> **Student Annotation:** Remember that sodium acetate is a strong electrolyte [◀◀ Section 9.1], so it dissociates completely in water to give sodium ions and acetate ions:
>
> $CH_3COONa(s) \longrightarrow Na^+(aq) + CH_3COO^-(aq)$

$$CH_3COOH(aq) \rightleftharpoons H^+(aq) + CH_3COO^-(aq)$$

	CH_3COOH	H^+	CH_3COO^-
Initial concentration (M):	1.0	0	1.0
Change in concentration (M):	$-x$	$+x$	$+x$
Equilibrium concentration (M):	$1.0 - x$	x	$1.0 + x$

The equilibrium expression is

$$K_a = \frac{(x)(1.0 + x)}{1.0 - x}$$

Multi 17.1
Acids and bases—effect of addition of a strong acid and a strong base on a buffer

Because it is reasonable to assume that x will be very small,

$$(1.0 - x)\,M \approx 1.0\,M \qquad \text{and} \qquad (1.0 + x)\,M \approx 1.0\,M$$

Thus, the equilibrium expression simplifies to

$$1.8 \times 10^{-5} = \frac{(x)(1.0)}{1.0} = x$$

At equilibrium, therefore, $[H^+] = 1.8 \times 10^{-5}\,M$ and pH = 4.74.

Now consider what happens when we add 0.10 mole of HCl to the buffer. (We assume that the addition of HCl causes no change in the volume of the solution.) The reaction that takes place when we add a strong acid is the conversion of H^+ to CH_3COOH. The added acid is all consumed, along with an equal amount of acetate ion. We keep track of the amounts of acetic acid and acetate ion when a strong acid (or base) is added by writing the starting amounts above the equation and the final amounts (after the added substance has been consumed) below the equation:

Upon addition of H^+:	1.0 mol	0.1 mol	1.0 mol
	$CH_3COO^-(aq) + H^+(aq) \longrightarrow CH_3COOH(aq)$		
After H^+ has been consumed:	0.9 mol	0 mol	1.1 mol

We can use the resulting amounts of acetic acid and acetate ion to construct a new equilibrium table:

$$CH_3COOH(aq) \rightleftharpoons H^+(aq) + CH_3COO^-(aq)$$

Initial concentration (M):	1.1	0	0.9
Change in concentration (M):	$-x$	$+x$	$+x$
Equilibrium concentration (M):	$1.1 - x$	x	$0.9 + x$

We can solve for pH as we have done before, assuming that x is small enough to be neglected,

$$1.8 \times 10^{-5} = \frac{(x)(0.9 + x)}{1.1 - x} \approx \frac{(x)(0.9)}{1.1}$$

$$x = 2.2 \times 10^{-5}\,M$$

Thus, when equilibrium is reestablished, $[H^+] = 2.2 \times 10^{-5}\,M$ and pH = 4.66—a change of only 0.08 pH unit.

In the determination of the pH of a buffer such as the one just described, we always neglect the small amount of weak acid that ionizes (x) because ionization is suppressed by the presence of a common ion. Similarly, we ignore the hydrolysis of the acetate ion because of the presence of acetic acid. This enables us to derive an expression for determining the pH of a buffer. We begin with the equilibrium expression

$$K_a = \frac{[H^+][A^-]}{[HA]}$$

Rearranging to solve for $[H^+]$ gives

$$[H^+] = \frac{K_a[HA]}{[A^-]}$$

Taking the negative logarithm of both sides, we obtain

$$-\log\,[H^+] = -\log K_a - \log \frac{[HA]}{[A^-]}$$

or

$$-\log\,[H^+] = -\log K_a + \log \frac{[A^-]}{[HA]}$$

Thus,

$$pH = pK_a + \log \frac{[A^-]}{[HA]} \qquad \textbf{Equation 17.1}$$

where

$$pK_a = -\log K_a \qquad \textbf{Equation 17.2}$$

Equation 17.1 is known as the ***Henderson-Hasselbalch equation.*** Its more general form is

$$pH = pK_a + \log \frac{[\text{conjugate base}]}{[\text{weak acid}]} \qquad \textbf{Equation 17.3}$$

In the case of our acetic acid (1.0 M) and sodium acetate (1.0 M) buffer, the concentrations of weak acid and conjugate base are *equal*. When this is true, the log term in the Henderson-Hasselbalch equation is zero and the pH is numerically equal to the pK_a. In the case of an acetic acid–acetate ion buffer, p$K_a = -\log 1.8 \times 10^{-5} = 4.74$.

After the addition of 0.10 mole of HCl, we determined that the concentrations of acetic acid and acetate ion were 1.1 M and 0.9 M, respectively. Using these concentrations in the Henderson-Hasselbalch equation gives

$$pH = 4.74 + \log \frac{[CH_3COO^-]}{[CH_3COOH]}$$

$$= 4.74 + \log \frac{0.9\ M}{1.1\ M}$$

$$= 4.74 + (-0.087) = 4.65$$

The small difference between this pH and the 4.66 calculated using an equilibrium table is due to differences in rounding. Figure 17.1 illustrates how a buffer solution resists drastic changes in pH.

Worked Example 17.2 shows how the Henderson-Hasselbalch equation is used to determine the pH of a buffer after the addition of a strong base.

Multi 17.2
Buffer solutions

Worked Example 17.2

Starting with 1.00 L of a buffer that is 1.00 M in acetic acid and 1.00 M in sodium acetate, calculate the pH after the addition of 0.100 mole of NaOH. (Assume that the addition does not change the volume of the solution.)

Strategy Added base will react with the acetic acid component of the buffer, converting OH⁻ to CH₃COO⁻:

$$CH_3COOH(aq) + OH^-(aq) \longrightarrow H_2O(l) + CH_3COO^-(aq)$$

Write the starting amount of each species above the equation and the final amount of each species below the equation. Use the final amounts as concentrations in Equation 17.1.

Setup

Upon addition of OH⁻:	1.00 mol	0.10 mol		1.00 mol
	$CH_3COOH(aq)$ +	$OH^-(aq)$	$\longrightarrow H_2O(l)$ +	$CH_3COO^-(aq)$
After OH⁻ has been consumed:	0.90 mol	0 mol		1.10 mol

Solution

$$pH = 4.74 + \log \frac{1.10\ M}{0.90\ M}$$

$$= 4.74 + \log \frac{1.10\ M}{0.90\ M} = 4.83$$

Thus, the pH of the buffer after addition of 0.10 mole of NaOH is 4.83.

Student Annotation: The volume of the buffer is 1 L in this example, so the number of moles of a substance is equal to the molar concentration. In cases where the buffer volume is something other than 1 L, however, we can still use molar amounts in the Henderson-Hasselbalch equation because the volume would cancel in the top and bottom of the log term.

(Continued on page 720)

Figure 17.1

Buffer Solutions

When we add 0.001 mol of strong acid, it is completely consumed by the acetate ion in the buffer.

Before reaction: 0.001 mol   0.010 mol   0.010 mol

$$H^+(aq) + CH_3COO^-(aq) \longrightarrow CH_3COOH(aq)$$

After reaction: 0 mol   0.009 mol   0.011 mol

START

0.100 M CH$_3$COOH
0.100 M CH$_3$COO$^-$

$$pH = 4.74 + \log\frac{[CH_3COO^-]}{[CH_3COOH]} = 4.74$$

Water
pH = 7.00

The buffer solution is 0.100 M in acetic acid and 0.100 M in sodium acetate. 100 mL of this buffer contains (0.100 mol/L)(0.10 L) = 0.010 mol each acetic acid and acetate ion.

START

When we add 0.001 mol of strong base, it is completely consumed by the acetic acid in the buffer.

Before reaction: 0.001 mol   0.010 mol   0.010 mol

$$OH^-(aq) + CH_3COOH(aq) \longrightarrow H_2O(l) + CH_3COO^-(aq)$$

After reaction: 0 mol   0.009 mol   0.011 mol

We can calculate the new pH using the Henderson-Hasselbalch equation:

$$pH = 4.74 + \log \frac{0.009}{0.011} = 4.65$$

There is nothing in pure water to consume strong acid. Therefore, its pH drops drastically.

$$pH = -\log \frac{0.001 \text{ mol}}{0.10 \text{ L}} = 2.00$$

We can calculate the new pH using the Henderson-Hasselbalch equation:

$$pH = 4.74 + \log \frac{0.011}{0.009} = 4.83$$

There is nothing in pure water to consume strong base. Therefore, its pH rises drastically.

$$pOH = -\log \frac{0.001 \text{ mol}}{0.10 \text{ L}} = 2.00, pH = 12.00$$

What's the point?

A buffer contains both a weak acid and its conjugate base.* Small amounts of strong acid or strong base are consumed by the buffer components, thereby preventing drastic pH changes. Pure water does not contain species that can consume acid or base. Even a very small addition of either acid or base causes a large change in pH.

*A buffer could also be prepared using a weak base and its conjugate acid.

Think About It

Always do a "reality check" on a calculated pH. Although a buffer does minimize the effect of added base, the pH does increase. If you find that you've calculated a lower pH after the addition of a base, check for errors like mixing up the weak acid and conjugate base concentrations or losing track of a minus sign.

Practice Problem A Calculate the pH of 1 L of a buffer that is 1.0 M in acetic acid and 1.0 M in sodium acetate after the addition of 0.25 mole of NaOH.

Practice Problem B How much HCl must be added to a liter of buffer that is 1.5 M in acetic acid and 0.75 M in sodium acetate to result in a buffer pH of 4.10?

Preparing a Buffer Solution with a Specific pH

A solution is only a buffer if it has the capacity to resist pH change when either an acid or a base is added. If the concentrations of a weak acid and conjugate base differ by more than a factor of 10, the solution does not have this capacity. Therefore, we consider a solution a buffer, and can use Equation 17.1 to calculate its pH, only if the following condition is met:

$$10 \geq \frac{[\text{conjugate base}]}{[\text{weak acid}]} \geq 0.1$$

Consequently, the log term in Equation 17.1 can only have values from −1 to 1, and the pH of a buffer cannot be more than one pH unit different from the pK_a of the weak acid it contains. This is known as the *range* of the buffer, where pH = $pK_a \pm 1$. This enables us to select the appropriate conjugate pair to prepare a buffer with a specific, desired pH.

First, we choose a weak acid whose pK_a is close to the desired pH. Next, we substitute the pH and pK_a values into Equation 17.1 to obtain the necessary ratio of [conjugate base]/[weak acid]. This ratio can then be converted to molar quantities for the preparation of the buffer.

Worked Example 17.3 demonstrates this procedure.

Worked Example 17.3

Weak Acid	K_a	pK_a
HF	7.1×10^{-4}	3.15
HNO$_2$	4.5×10^{-4}	3.35
HCOOH	1.7×10^{-4}	3.77
C$_6$H$_5$COOH	6.5×10^{-5}	4.19
CH$_3$COOH	1.8×10^{-5}	4.74
HCN	4.9×10^{-10}	9.31
C$_6$H$_5$OH	1.3×10^{-10}	9.89

Select an appropriate weak acid from the table in the margin, and describe how you would prepare a buffer with a pH of 9.50.

Strategy Select an acid with a pK_a within one pH unit of 9.50. Use the pK_a of the acid and Equation 17.1 to calculate the necessary ratio of [conjugate base]/[weak acid]. Select concentrations of the buffer components that yield the calculated ratio.

Setup Two of the acids listed in the margin have pK_a values in the desired range: hydrocyanic acid (HCN, $pK_a = 9.31$) and phenol (C$_6$H$_5$OH, $pK_a = 9.89$).

Solution Plugging the values for phenol into Equation 17.1 gives

$$9.50 = 9.89 + \log \frac{[\text{C}_6\text{H}_5\text{O}^-]}{[\text{C}_6\text{H}_5\text{OH}]}$$

$$9.50 - 9.89 = \log \frac{[\text{C}_6\text{H}_5\text{O}^-]}{[\text{C}_6\text{H}_5\text{OH}]} = -0.39$$

$$\frac{[\text{C}_6\text{H}_5\text{O}^-]}{[\text{C}_6\text{H}_5\text{OH}]} = 10^{-0.39} = 0.41$$

Therefore, the ratio of [C$_6$H$_5$O$^-$] to [C$_6$H$_5$OH] must be 0.41 to 1. One way to achieve this would be to dissolve 0.41 mole of C$_6$H$_5$ONa and 1.00 mole of C$_6$H$_5$OH in 1 L of water.

Think About It

There is an infinite number of combinations of [conjugate base] and [weak acid] that will give the necessary ratio. Note that this pH could also be achieved using HCN and a cyanide salt. For most purposes, it is best to use the least toxic compounds available.

Practice Problem A Select an appropriate acid from the table in the margin on page 720, and describe how you would prepare a buffer with pH = 4.5.

Practice Problem B What range of pH values could be achieved with a buffer consisting of nitrous acid (HNO_2) and sodium nitrite (NO_2^-)?

SECTION 17.2 REVIEW

Buffer Solutions

17.2.1 What is the pH of a buffer that is 0.76 M in HF and 0.98 M in NaF?

17.2.2 Consider 1 L of a buffer that is 0.85 M in formic acid (HCOOH) and 1.4 M in sodium formate (HCOONa). Calculate the pH after the addition of 0.15 mol HCl. (Assume the addition causes no volume change.)

17.2.3 Consider 1 L of a buffer that is 1.5 M in hydrocyanic acid (HCN) and 1.2 M in sodium cyanide (NaCN). Calculate the pH after the addition of 0.25 mol NaOH. (Assume the addition causes no volume change.)

17.2.4 The solutions shown contain a combination of the weak acid HA and its sodium salt NaA. (For clarity, the sodium ions and water molecules are not shown.) Arrange the solutions in order of increasing pH.

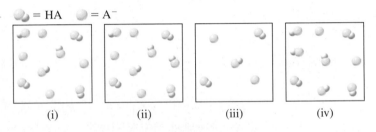

| (i) | (ii) | (iii) | (iv) |

17.3 ACID-BASE TITRATIONS

In Section 9.6 we introduced acid-base titrations as a form of chemical analysis. Having discussed buffer solutions, we can now look in more detail at the quantitative aspects of acid-base titrations. We will consider three types of reactions: (1) titrations involving a strong acid and a strong base, (2) titrations involving a weak acid and a strong base, and (3) titrations involving a strong acid and a weak base. Titrations involving a weak acid and a weak base are complicated by the hydrolysis of both the cation and the anion of the salt formed. These titrations will not be discussed here. Figure 17.2 shows the experimental setup for monitoring the pH over the course of an acid-base titration.

Multi 17.3
Acids and bases—titration of HCl with NaOH

Strong Acid–Strong Base Titrations

The reaction between the strong acid HCl and the strong base NaOH can be represented by

$$NaOH(aq) + HCl(aq) \longrightarrow NaCl(aq) + H_2O(l)$$

or by the net ionic equation,

$$OH^-(aq) + H^+(aq) \longrightarrow H_2O(l)$$

Consider the addition of a 0.100 M NaOH solution (from a burette) to a vessel containing 25.0 mL of 0.100 M HCl. For convenience, we will use only three significant figures for volume and concentration and two significant figures for pH. Figure 17.3 shows the titration curve—the plot of pH as a function of titrant volume added.

Student Annotation: Recall that only the digits to the right of the decimal point are significant in a pH value.

Student Annotation: The *titrant* is the solution that is added from the burette.

Figure 17.2 A pH meter is used to monitor an acid-base titration.

Figure 17.3 Titration curve (pH as a function of volume titrant added) of a strong acid–strong base titration. A 0.100 *M* NaOH solution, the titrant, is added from a burette to 25.0 mL of a 0.100 *M* HCl solution in an Erlenmeyer flask.

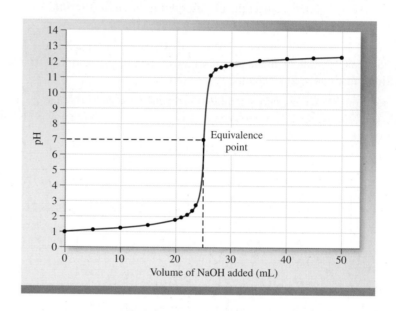

Student Annotation: Recall that for an acid and base that combine in a 1:1 ratio, the equivalence point is where equal molar amounts of acid and base have been combined [◄◄ Section 9.6].

Before the addition of NaOH begins, the pH of the acid is given by −log (0.100), or 1.00. When NaOH is added, the pH of the solution increases slowly at first. Near the equivalence point, the pH begins to rise steeply, and at the equivalence point, when equimolar amounts of acid and base have reacted, the curve rises almost vertically. In a strong acid–strong base titration, both the hydrogen ion and hydroxide ion concentrations are very small at the equivalence point (roughly $1 \times 10^{-7}\,M$); consequently, the addition of a single drop of the base causes a large increase in [OH⁻] and a steep rise in the pH of the solution. Beyond the equivalence point, the pH again increases slowly with the continued addition of NaOH.

It is possible to calculate the pH of the solution at every stage of titration. Here are three sample calculations.

Student Annotation: These calculations could also be done using *moles*, but using millimoles simplifies the calculations. Remember that millimoles = *M* × mL [◄◄ Section 9.5].

1. Consider the addition of 10.0 mL of 0.100 *M* NaOH to 25.0 mL of 0.100 *M* HCl: The total volume of the solution is 35.0 mL. The number of millimoles of NaOH in 10.0 mL is

$$10.0\text{ mL} \times \frac{0.100\text{ mmol NaOH}}{1\text{ mL}} = 1.00\text{ mmol}$$

The number of millimoles of HCl originally present in 25.0 mL of solution is

$$25.0\text{ mL} \times \frac{0.100\text{ mmol HCl}}{1\text{ mL}} = 2.50\text{ mmol}$$

Thus, the amount of HCl left after partial neutralization is 2.50 − 1.00, or 1.50 mmol. Next, we determine the resulting concentration of H⁺. We have 1.50 mmol in 35.0 mL:

$$\frac{1.50\text{ mmol HCl}}{35.0\text{ mL}} = 0.0429\ M$$

Thus $[H^+] = 0.0429\ M$, and the pH of the solution is

$$pH = -\log(0.04289) = 1.37$$

2. Consider the addition of 25.0 mL of 0.100 M NaOH to 25.0 mL of 0.100 M HCl: This is a straightforward calculation, because it involves a complete neutralization reaction and neither ion in the salt (NaCl) undergoes hydrolysis [◄◄ Section 16.10]. At the equivalence point, $[H^+] = [OH^-] = 1.00 \times 10^{-7}\ M$ and the pH of the solution is 7.000.

3. Consider the addition of 35.0 mL of 0.100 M NaOH to 25.0 mL of 0.100 M HCl: The total volume of the solution is now 60.0 mL. The number of millimoles of NaOH added is

$$35.0\ \text{mL} \times \frac{0.100\ \text{mmol NaOH}}{1\ \text{mL}} = 3.50\ \text{mmol}$$

There are 2.50 mmol of HCl in 25.0 mL of solution. After complete neutralization of HCl, 2.50 mmol of NaOH have been consumed, and the number of millimoles of NaOH remaining is $3.5 - 2.5$ or 1.00 mmol. The concentration of NaOH in 60.0 mL of solution is

$$\frac{1.00\ \text{mmol NaOH}}{60.0\ \text{mL}} = 0.0167\ M$$

Thus $[OH^-] = 0.0167\ M$ and $pOH = -\log(0.0167) = 1.78$. The pH of the solution is $14.00 - 1.78$ or 12.22.

Table 17.1 lists the data at nine different points during a strong acid–strong base titration along with the calculated pH at each point.

Weak Acid–Strong Base Titrations

Consider the neutralization reaction between acetic acid (a weak acid) and sodium hydroxide (a strong base):

$$CH_3COOH(aq) + NaOH(aq) \longrightarrow CH_3COONa(aq) + H_2O(l)$$

This equation can be simplified to

$$CH_3COOH(aq) + OH^-(aq) \longrightarrow CH_3COO^-(aq) + H_2O(l)$$

The acetate ion that results from this neutralization undergoes hydrolysis [◄◄ Section 16.10] as follows:

$$CH_3COO^-(aq) + H_2O(l) \rightleftharpoons CH_3COOH(aq) + OH^-(aq)$$

At the equivalence point, therefore, when we only have sodium acetate in solution, the pH will be greater than 7 as a result of the OH^- formed by hydrolysis of the acetate ion.

TABLE 17.1	Determination of pH at Several Different Points in a Strong Acid–Strong Base Titration					
Volume OH⁻ added (mL)	**OH⁻ added (mmol)**	**H⁺ remaining (mmol)**	**Total volume (mL)**	**[H⁺] (mol/L)**		**pH**
0	0	2.5	25.0	0.100		1.000
5.0	0.50	2.0	30.0	0.0667		1.176
10.0	1.0	1.5	35.0	0.0429		1.364
15.0	1.5	1.0	40.0	0.0250		1.602
20.0	2.0	0.5	45.0	0.0111		1.955
25.0	2.5	0	50.0	1.00×10^{-7}		7.000
Volume OH⁻ added (mL)	**OH⁻ added (mmol)**	**Excess OH⁻ (mmol)**	**Total volume (mL)**	**[OH⁻] (mol/L)**	**pOH**	**pH**
30.0	3.0	0.5	55.0	0.0091	2.04	11.96
35.0	3.5	1.0	60.0	0.0167	1.78	12.223

Figure 17.4 Titration curve of a weak acid–strong base titration. A 0.100 M NaOH solution is added from a burette to 25.0 mL of a 0.100 M CH_3COOH solution in an Erlenmeyer flask. Because of the hydrolysis of the salt formed, the pH at the equivalence point is greater than 7.

The curve for titration of 25.0 mL of 0.1 M acetic acid with 0.10 M sodium hydroxide is shown in Figure 17.4. Note how the shape of the curve differs from the one in Figure 17.3. Compared to the curve for titration of a strong acid with a strong base, the curve for titration of a weak acid with a strong base has a higher initial pH, a more gradual change in pH as base is added, and a shorter vertical region near the equivalence point.

Again, it is possible to calculate the pH at every stage of the titration. Here are four sample calculations.

1. Prior to the addition of any base, the pH is determined by the ionization of acetic acid. We use its concentration (0.10 M) and its K_a (1.8 × 10⁻⁵) to calculate the H⁺ concentration using an equilibrium table:

$$CH_3COOH(aq) \rightleftharpoons H^+(aq) + CH_3COO^-(aq)$$

Initial concentration (M):	0.10	0	0
Change in concentration (M):	$-x$	$+x$	$+x$
Equilibrium concentration (M):	$0.10 - x$	x	x

$$K_a = \frac{[H^+][CH_3COO^-]}{[CH_3COOH]} = \frac{x^2}{0.10 - x} = 1.8 \times 10^{-5}$$

We can neglect x on the bottom of the equation [◄◄ Section 16.6]. Solving for x,

$$\frac{x^2}{0.10} = 1.8 \times 10^{-5}$$

$$x^2 = (1.8 \times 10^{-5})(0.10) = 1.8 \times 10^{-6}$$

$$x = \sqrt{1.8 \times 10^{-6}} = 1.34 \times 10^{-3} M$$

gives [H⁺] = 1.34 × 10⁻³ M and pH = 2.87.

2. After the first addition of base, some of the acetic acid has been converted to acetate ion via the reaction

$$CH_3COOH(aq) + OH^-(aq) \longrightarrow CH_3COO^-(aq) + H_2O(l)$$

With significant amounts of both acetic acid and acetate ion in solution, we now treat the solution as a buffer and use the Henderson-Hasselbalch equation to calculate the pH.

After the addition of 10.0 mL of base, the solution contains 1.5 mmol of acetic acid and 1.0 mmol of acetate ion (see Table 17.2).

Student Annotation: Remember that we can use mol or mmol amounts in place of concentrations in the Henderson-Hasselbalch equation.

$$pH = 4.74 + \log \frac{1.0 \text{ mmol}}{1.5 \text{ mmol}} = 4.56$$

Each of the points between the beginning of the titration and the equivalence point can be calculated in this way.

3. At the equivalence point, all the acetic acid has been neutralized and we are left with acetate ion in solution. (There is also sodium ion, which does not undergo hydrolysis and therefore does not impact the pH of the solution.) At this point, pH is determined by the concentration and the K_b of acetate ion. The equivalence point occurs when 25.0 mL of base has been added, making the total volume 50.0 mL. The 2.5 mmol of acetic acid (see Table 17.2) has all been converted to acetate ion. Therefore, the concentration of acetate ion is

$$[CH_3COO^-] = \frac{2.5 \text{ mmol}}{50.0 \text{ mL}} = 0.050 \ M$$

As we did at the beginning of the titration, we construct an equilibrium table:

$$CH_3COO^-(aq) + H_2O(l) \rightleftharpoons OH^-(aq) + CH_3COOH(aq)$$

Initial concentration (M):	0.050		0	0
Change in concentration (M):	$-x$		$+x$	$+x$
Equilibrium concentration (M):	$0.050 - x$		x	x

The K_b for acetate ion is 5.6×10^{-10}.

Student Annotation: $K_a \times K_b = K_w$ [◀◀ Section 16.8].

$$K_b = \frac{[OH^-][CH_3COOH]}{[CH_3COO^-]} = \frac{x^2}{0.050 - x} = 5.6 \times 10^{-10}$$

As before, we can neglect x in the denominator of the equation. Solving for x,

$$\frac{x^2}{0.050} = 5.6 \times 10^{-10}$$

$$x^2 = (5.6 \times 10^{-10})(0.050) = 2.8 \times 10^{-11}$$

$$x = \sqrt{2.8 \times 10^{-11}} = 5.3 \times 10^{-6} \ M$$

gives $[OH^-] = 5.3 \times 10^{-6} \ M$, pOH = 5.28, and pH = 8.72.

4. After the equivalence point, the curve for titration of a weak acid with a strong base is identical to the curve for titration of a strong acid with a strong base. Because all the acetic acid has been consumed, there is nothing in solution to consume the additional added OH^-, and the pH levels off between 12 and 13.

Table 17.2 lists the data for the titration of 25.0 mL of 0.10 M acetic acid with 0.10 M NaOH.

TABLE 17.2	Determination of pH at Several Different Points in a CH_3COOH-NaOH Titration

Student Annotation: Prior to the addition of any base, *and* at the equivalence point, this is an *equilibrium* problem that is solved using a *concentration*, an *ionization constant*, and an *equilibrium table*.

Volume OH^- added (mL)	OH^- added (mmol)	CH_3COOH remaining	CH_3COO^- produced	pH
0	0	2.5	0.0	2.87*
5.0	0.50	2.0	0.50	4.14
10.0	1.0	1.5	1.0	4.56
15.0	1.5	1.0	1.5	4.92
20.0	2.0	0.5	2.0	5.34
25.0	2.5	0.0	2.5	8.72†

Student Annotation: *Prior* to the equivalence point, pH is determined using the Henderson-Hasselbalch equation:

$$pH = pK_a + \log \frac{[\text{conjugate base}]}{[\text{weak acid}]}$$

Volume OH^- added (mL)	OH^- added (mmol)	Excess OH^- (mmol)	Total volume (mL)	$[OH^-]$ (mol/L)	pOH	pH
30.0	3.0	0.5	55.0	0.0091	2.04	11.96
35.0	3.5	1.0	60.0	0.017	1.78	12.22

*$[CH_3COOH] = 0.10 \ M$, $K_a = 1.8 \times 10^{-5}$.

†$[CH_3COO^-] = 0.050 \ M$, $K_b = 5.6 \times 10^{-10}$.

Student Annotation: After the equivalence point, the titration curve of a weak acid is identical to that of a strong acid.

Worked Example 17.4 shows how to calculate the pH for the titration of a weak acid with a strong base.

Worked Example 17.4

Calculate the pH in the titration of 50.0 mL of 0.120 M acetic acid by 0.240 M sodium hydroxide after the addition of (a) 10.0 mL of base, (b) 25.0 mL of base, and (c) 35.0 mL of base.

Strategy The reaction between acetic acid and sodium hydroxide is

$$CH_3COOH(aq) + OH^-(aq) \longrightarrow H_2O(l) + CH_3COO^-(aq)$$

Prior to the equivalence point [part (a)], the solution contains both acetic acid and acetate ion, making the solution a buffer. We can solve part (a) using Equation 17.1, the Henderson-Hasselbalch equation. At the equivalence point [part (b)], all the acetic acid has been neutralized and we have only acetate ion in solution. We must determine the concentration of acetate ion and solve part (b) as an equilibrium problem, using the K_b for acetate ion. After the equivalence point [part (c)], all the acetic acid has been neutralized and there is nothing to consume the additional added base. We must determine the concentration of excess hydroxide ion in the solution and solve for pH using Equations 16.4 and 16.6.

Setup Remember that M can be defined as either mol/L or mmol/mL [◀◀ Section 9.5]. For this type of problem, it simplifies the calculations to use millimoles rather than moles. K_a for acetic acid is 1.8×10^{-5}, so $pK_a = 4.74$. K_b for acetate ion is 5.6×10^{-10}.

(a) The solution originally contains (0.120 mmol/mL)(50.0 mL) = 6.00 mmol of acetic acid. A 10.0-mL amount of base contains (0.240 mmol/mL)(10.0 mL) = 2.40 mmol of base. After the addition of 10.0 mL of base, 2.40 mmol of OH^- has neutralized 2.40 mmol of acetic acid, leaving 3.60 mmol of acetic acid and 2.40 mmol acetate ion in solution:

Upon addition of OH^-:	6.00 mmol	2.40 mmol	0 mmol
	$CH_3COOH(aq)$ +	$OH^-(aq) \rightleftharpoons$	$H_2O(l)$ + $CH_3COO^-(aq)$
After OH^- has been consumed:	3.60 mmol	0 mmol	2.40 mmol

(b) After the addition of 25.0 mL of base, the titration is at the equivalence point. We calculate the pH using the concentration and the K_b of acetate ion.

(c) After the addition of 35.0 mL of base, the titration is past the equivalence point and we solve for pH by determining the concentration of excess hydroxide ion.

Solution (a) $pH = pK_a + \log \dfrac{2.40}{3.60} = 4.74 - 0.18 = 4.56$

(b) At the equivalence point, we have 6.0 mmol of acetate ion in the total volume. We determine the total volume by calculating what volume of 0.24 M base contains 6.0 mmol:

$$(\text{volume})(0.240 \text{ mmol/mL}) = 6.00 \text{ mmol}$$

$$\text{volume} = \frac{6.00 \text{ mmol}}{0.240 \text{ mmol/mL}} = 25.0 \text{ mL}$$

Therefore, the equivalence point occurs when 25.0 mL of base has been added, making the total volume 50.0 mL + 25.0 mL = 75.0 mL. The concentration of acetate ion at the equivalence point is therefore

$$\frac{6.00 \text{ mmol } CH_3COO^-}{75.0 \text{ mL}} = 0.0800 \, M$$

We can construct an equilibrium table using this concentration and solve for pH using the ionization constant for CH_3COO^- ($K_b = 5.6 \times 10^{-10}$):

	$CH_3COO^-(aq)$ + $H_2O(l)$ $\rightleftharpoons$		$OH^-(aq)$ +	$CH_3COOH(aq)$
Initial concentration (M):	0.0800		0	0
Change in concentration (M):	$-x$		$+x$	$+x$
Equilibrium concentration (M):	$0.0800 - x$		x	x

Using the equilibrium expression and assuming that x is small enough to be neglected,

$$K_b = \frac{[CH_3COOH][OH^-]}{[CH_3COO^-]} = \frac{(x)(x)}{0.0800 - x} \approx \frac{x^2}{0.0800} = 5.6 \times 10^{-10}$$

$$x = \sqrt{4.48 \times 10^{-11}} = 6.7 \times 10^{-6} \, M$$

According to the equilibrium table, $x = [OH^-]$, so $[OH^-] = 6.7 \times 10^{-6}$ M. At equilibrium, therefore, $pOH = -\log(6.7 \times 10^{-6}) = 5.17$ and $pH = 14.00 - 5.17 = 8.83$.

(c) After the equivalence point, we must determine the concentration of excess base and calculate pOH and pH using Equations 16.4 and 16.6. A 35.0-mL amount of the base contains $(0.240 \text{ mmol/mL})(35.0 \text{ mL}) = 8.40$ mmol of OH^-. After neutralizing the 6.00 mmol of acetic acid originally present in the solution, this leaves $8.40 - 6.00 = 2.40$ mmol of excess OH^-. The total volume is $50.0 + 35.0 = 85.0$ mL. Therefore, $[OH^-] = 2.40 \text{ mmol}/85.0 \text{ mL} = 0.0280$ M, $pOH = -\log(0.0280) = 1.553$, and $pH = 14.000 - 1.553 = 12.447$.

In summary, (a) pH = 4.56, (b) pH = 8.83, and (c) pH = 12.447.

Think About It

For each point in a titration, decide first what species are in solution and what *type* of problem it is. If the solution contains only a weak acid (or weak base), as is the case before any titrant is added, or if it contains only a conjugate base (or conjugate acid), as is the case at the equivalence point, when pH is determined by salt hydrolysis, it is an *equilibrium* problem that requires a concentration, an ionization constant, and an equilibrium table. If the solution contains comparable concentrations of both members of a conjugate pair, which is the case at points prior to the equivalence point, it is a *buffer* problem and is solved using the Henderson-Hasselbalch equation. If the solution contains excess titrant, either a strong base or strong acid, it is simply a pH problem requiring only a concentration.

Practice Problem A For the titration of 10.0 mL of 0.15 M acetic acid with 0.10 M sodium hydroxide, determine the pH when (a) 10.0 mL of base has been added, (b) 15.0 mL of base has been added, and (c) 20.0 mL of base has been added.

Practice Problem B For the titration of 25.0 mL of 0.20 M hydrofluoric acid with 0.20 M sodium hydroxide, determine the volume of base added when pH is (a) 2.85, (b) 3.15, and (c) 11.89. [To solve part (c), you may want to review the approach in Worked Example 9.9 (page 336).]

Strong Acid–Weak Base Titrations

Consider the titration of HCl, a strong acid, with NH_3, a weak base:

$$HCl(aq) + NH_3(aq) \longrightarrow NH_4Cl(aq)$$

or simply

$$H^+(aq) + NH_3(aq) \longrightarrow NH_4^+(aq)$$

The pH at the equivalence point is less than 7 because the ammonium ion acts as a weak Brønsted acid:

$$NH_4^+(aq) + H_2O(l) \rightleftharpoons NH_3(aq) + H_3O^+(aq)$$

or simply

$$NH_4^+(aq) \rightleftharpoons NH_3(aq) + H^+(aq)$$

Because of the volatility of an aqueous ammonia solution, it is more convenient to use hydrochloric acid as the titrant (i.e., to add HCl solution from the burette). Figure 17.5 shows the titration curve for this experiment.

Analogous to the titration of a weak acid with a strong base, the initial pH is determined by the concentration and the K_b of ammonia:

$$NH_3(aq) + H_2O(l) \rightleftharpoons NH_4^+(aq) + OH^-(aq)$$

Consider the titration of 25.0 mL of 0.10 M NH_3 with 0.10 M HCl. We calculate the initial pH by constructing an equilibrium table and solving for x:

	$NH_3(aq)$ +	$H_2O(l)$ $\rightleftharpoons$	$NH_4^+(aq)$ +	$OH^-(aq)$
Initial concentration (*M*):	0.10		0	0
Change in concentration (*M*):	$-x$		$+x$	$+x$
Equilibrium concentration (*M*):	$0.10 - x$		x	x

Figure 17.5 Titration curve of a strong acid–weak base titration. A 0.100 *M* HCl solution is added from a burette to 25.0 mL of a 0.100 *M* NH₃ solution in an Erlenmeyer flask. As a result of salt hydrolysis, the pH at the equivalence point is lower than 7.

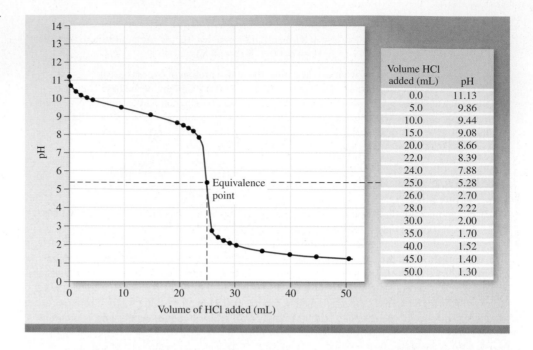

Volume HCl added (mL)	pH
0.0	11.13
5.0	9.86
10.0	9.44
15.0	9.08
20.0	8.66
22.0	8.39
24.0	7.88
25.0	5.28
26.0	2.70
28.0	2.22
30.0	2.00
35.0	1.70
40.0	1.52
45.0	1.40
50.0	1.30

Using the equilibrium expression and assuming that x is small enough to be neglected,

$$K_b = \frac{[NH_4^+][OH^-]}{[NH_3]} = \frac{(x)(x)}{0.10 - x} \approx \frac{x^2}{0.10} = 1.8 \times 10^{-5}$$

$$x^2 = 1.8 \times 10^{-6}$$

$$x = \sqrt{1.8 \times 10^{-6}} = 1.3 \times 10^{-3}$$

$$pH = 11.11$$

The pH at the equivalence point is calculated using the concentration and K_a of the conjugate base of NH_3, the NH_4^+ ion, and an equilibrium table.

Worked Example 17.5 shows how this is done.

Worked Example 17.5

Calculate the pH at the equivalence point when 25.0 mL of 0.100 *M* NH₃ is titrated with 0.100 *M* HCl.

Strategy The reaction between NH_3 and HCl is

$$NH_3(aq) + H^+(aq) \longrightarrow NH_4^+(aq)$$

At the equivalence point, all the NH_3 has been converted to NH_4^+. Therefore, we must determine the concentration of NH_4^+ at the equivalence point and use the K_a for NH_4^+ to solve for pH using an equilibrium table.

Setup The solution originally contains (0.100 mmol/mL)(25.0 mL) = 2.50 mmol NH_4^+. At the equivalence point, 2.50 mmol of HCl has been added. The volume of 0.100 *M* HCl that contains 2.50 mmol is

$$(volume)(0.100 \text{ mmol/mL}) = 2.50 \text{ mmol}$$

$$volume = \frac{2.50 \text{ mmol}}{0.100 \text{ mmol/mL}} = 25.0 \text{ mL}$$

It takes 25.0 mL of titrant to reach the equivalence point, so the total solution volume is 25.0 + 25.0 = 50.0 mL. At the equivalence point, all the NH_3 originally present has been converted to NH_4^+. The concentration of NH_4^+ is (2.50 mmol)/(50.0 mL) = 0.0500 *M*. We must use this concentration as the starting concentration of ammonium ion in our equilibrium table.

Solution

	$NH_4^+(aq) + H_2O(l) \rightleftharpoons$		$NH_3(aq) +$	$H_3O^+(aq)$
Initial concentration (M):	0.0500		0	0
Change in concentration (M):	$-x$		$+x$	$+x$
Equilibrium concentration (M):	$0.0500 - x$		x	x

The equilibrium expression is

$$K_a = \frac{[NH_3][H^+]}{[NH_4^+]} = \frac{(x)(x)}{0.0500 - x} \approx \frac{x^2}{0.0500} = 5.6 \times 10^{-10}$$

$$x^2 = 2.8 \times 10^{-11}$$

$$x = \sqrt{2.8 \times 10^{-11}} = 5.3 \times 10^{-6} \, M$$

$[H^+] = x = 5.3 \times 10^{-6} \, M$. At equilibrium, therefore, pH $= -\log (5.3 \times 10^{-6}) = 5.28$.

Think About It

In the titration of a weak base with a strong acid, the species in solution at the equivalence point is the conjugate acid. Therefore, we should expect an *acidic* pH. Once all the NH_3 has been converted to NH_4^+, there is no longer anything in the solution to consume added acid. Thus, the pH after the equivalence point depends on the number of millimoles of H^+ added and not consumed divided by the new total volume.

Practice Problem A Calculate the pH at the equivalence point in the titration of 50.0 mL of 0.10 *M* methylamine (see Table 16.8 on page 683) with 0.20 *M* HCl.

Practice Problem B A 50.0-mL quantity of a 0.20-*M* solution of one of the weak bases in Table 16.8 is titrated with 0.050 *M* HCl. At the equivalence point, the pH is 2.99. Identify the weak base.

Acid-Base Indicators

The equivalence point is the point at which the acid has been neutralized completely by the added base. The equivalence point in a titration can be determined by monitoring the pH over the course of the titration, or it can be determined using an *acid-base indicator*. An acid-base indicator is usually a weak organic acid or base for which the ionized and un-ionized forms are different colors.

Consider a weak organic acid that we will refer to as HIn. To be an effective acid-base indicator, HIn and its conjugate base, In^-, must have distinctly different colors. In solution, the acid ionizes to a small extent:

$$HIn(aq) \rightleftharpoons H^+(aq) + In^-(aq)$$

In a sufficiently acidic medium, the ionization of HIn is suppressed according to Le Châtelier's principle, and the preceding equilibrium shifts to the left. In this case, the color of the solution will be that of HIn. In a basic medium, on the other hand, the equilibrium shifts to the right and the color of the solution will be that of the conjugate base, In^-.

The **endpoint** of a titration is the point at which the color of the indicator changes. Not all indicators change color at the same pH, however, so the choice of indicator for a particular titration depends on the strength of the acid (and the base) used in the titration. To use the endpoint to determine the equivalence point of a titration, we must select an appropriate indicator.

The endpoint of an indicator does not occur at a specific pH; rather, there is a range of pH over which the color change occurs. In practice, we select an indicator whose color change occurs over a pH range that coincides with the steepest part of the titration curve. Consider the information in Figure 17.6, which shows the titration curves for hydrochloric acid and acetic acid—each being titrated with sodium hydroxide. Either of the indicators shown can be used for the titration of a strong acid with a strong base because both endpoints coincide with the steepest part of the HCl-NaOH titration curve. However, methyl red changes from red to yellow over the pH range of 4.2 to 6.3. This endpoint occurs significantly *before* the equivalence point in the titration of acetic acid, which occurs at about pH 8.7. Therefore, methyl red is *not* a suitable indicator for use in the titration of acetic acid with sodium hydroxide. Phenolphthalein, on the other hand, *is* a suitable indicator for the CH_3COOH-NaOH titration.

Student Annotation: The *endpoint* is where the color changes. The *equivalence point* is where neutralization is complete. Experimentally, we use the endpoint to estimate the equivalence point.

Many acid-base indicators are plant pigments. For example, boiling red cabbage in water extracts pigments that exhibit a variety of colors at different pH values (Figure 17.7).

Table 17.3 lists a number of indicators commonly used in acid-base titrations. The choice of indicator for a particular titration depends on the strength of the acid and base to be titrated.

Figure 17.6 Titration curve of a strong acid with a strong base (blue) and titration curve of a weak acid with a strong base (red). The indicator phenolphthalein can be used to determine the equivalence point of either titration. Methyl red can be used for the strong acid–strong base titration but cannot be used for the weak acid–strong base titration because its color change does not coincide with the steepest part of the curve.

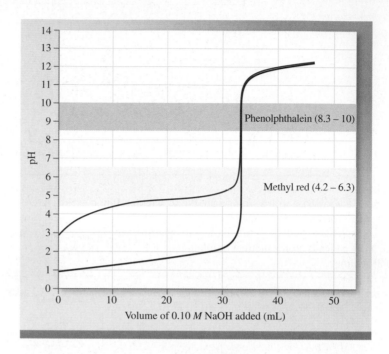

Figure 17.7 Solutions containing extracts of red cabbage (obtained by boiling the cabbage in water) produce different colors when treated with an acid and a base. The pH of the solutions increases from left to right.

TABLE 17.3	Some Common Acid-Base Indicators		
	Color		
Indicator	**In acid**	**In base**	**pH range**
Thymol blue	Red	Yellow	1.2–2.8
Bromophenol blue	Yellow	Bluish purple	3.0–4.6
Methyl orange	Orange	Yellow	3.1–4.4
Methyl red	Red	Yellow	4.2–6.3
Chlorophenol blue	Yellow	Red	4.8–6.4
Bromothymol blue	Yellow	Blue	6.0–7.6
Cresol red	Yellow	Red	7.2–8.8
Phenolphthalein	Colorless	Reddish pink	8.3–10.0

Worked Example 17.6 illustrates this point.

Worked Example 17.6

Which indicator (or indicators) listed in Table 17.3 would you use for the acid-base titrations shown in (a) Figure 17.3, (b) Figure 17.4, and (c) Figure 17.5?

Strategy Determine the pH range that corresponds to the steepest part of each titration curve and select an indicator (or indicators) that changes color within that range.

Setup (a) The titration curve in Figure 17.3 is for the titration of a strong acid with a strong base. The steep part of the curve spans a pH range of about 4 to 10.

(b) Figure 17.4 shows the curve for the titration of a weak acid with a strong base. The steep part of the curve spans a pH range of about 7 to 10.

(c) Figure 17.5 shows the titration of a weak base with a strong acid. The steep part of the curve spans a pH range of about 7 to 3.

Solution (a) Most of the indicators listed in Table 17.3, with the exceptions of thymol blue, bromophenol blue, and methyl orange, would work for the titration of a strong acid with a strong base.

(b) Cresol red and phenolphthalein are suitable indicators.

(c) Bromophenol blue, methyl orange, methyl red, and chlorophenol blue are all suitable indicators.

> **Think About It**
> If we don't select an appropriate indicator, the endpoint (color change) will not coincide with the equivalence point.

Practice Problem A Referring to Table 17.3, specify at least one indicator that would be suitable for the following titrations: (a) CH_3NH_2 with HBr, (b) HNO_3 with NaOH, (c) HNO_2 with KOH.

Practice Problem B For which of the bases in Table 16.8 (page 683) could you titrate a 0.1-M solution of base with 0.1 M nitric acid using the indicator thymol blue?

SECTION 17.3 REVIEW

Acid-Base Titrations

17.3.1   Calculate the pH at the equivalence point in the titration of 30 mL of 0.25 M CH_3COOH with 0.25 M KOH.

17.3.2   Calculate the pH after the addition of 25 mL of 0.10 M NaOH to 50 mL of 0.10 M HF.

17.3.3   Calculate the pH after the addition of 35 mL of 0.10 M NaOH to 30 mL of 0.10 M HCN.

17.4   SOLUBILITY EQUILIBRIA

The solubility of ionic compounds is important in industry, medicine, and everyday life. For example, barium sulfate ($BaSO_4$), an insoluble compound that is opaque to X rays, is used to diagnose ailments of the digestive tract. Tooth decay begins when tooth enamel, which is mainly made of hydroxyapatite [$Ca_5(PO_4)_3OH$], is made more soluble in saliva by the presence of acid.

The general rules for predicting the solubility of ionic compounds in water were introduced in Section 9.2. While these rules are useful, they do not allow us to make quantitative predictions about how much of a given ionic compound will dissolve in water. To develop a quantitative approach, we must start with the principles of chemical equilibrium. Unless otherwise stated, the solvent is water in the following discussion and the temperature is 25°C.

> **Student Annotation:** The compounds described as "insoluble" in Chapter 9 [◄◄ Section 9.2, Table 9.3] are actually very *slightly* soluble—each to a different degree.

Solubility Product Expression and K_{sp}

Consider a saturated solution of silver chloride that is in contact with undissolved solid silver chloride. The equilibrium can be represented as

$$AgCl(s) \rightleftharpoons Ag^+(aq) + Cl^-(aq)$$

Although AgCl is not very soluble, *all* the AgCl that does dissolve in water dissociates completely into Ag^+ and Cl^- ions. We can write the equilibrium expression for the dissociation of AgCl as

$$K_{sp} = [Ag^+][Cl^-]$$

where K_{sp} is called the *solubility product constant*. (K_{sp} is just another specially subscripted K_c, where "sp" stands for "solubility product.")

Because each AgCl unit contains only one Ag^+ and one Cl^- ion, its solubility product expression is particularly simple to write. Many ionic compounds dissociate into more than two ions. Table 17.4 and Appendix 4 list a number of slightly soluble ionic compounds along with equations representing their dissolution equilibria and their solubility product constants. (Compounds deemed "soluble" by the solubility rules in Chapter 9 are not listed for the same reason we did not list K_a values for the strong acids in Table 16.7.) In general, the magnitude of K_{sp} indicates the solubility of an ionic compound—the smaller the K_{sp} value, the less soluble the compound. To make a direct comparison of K_{sp} values, however, we must compare salts with similar formulas, such as AgCl with ZnS (one cation, one anion) or CaF_2 with $Fe(OH)_2$ (one cation, two anions).

Calculations Involving K_{sp} and Solubility

There are two ways to express the solubility of a substance: *molar solubility,* which is the number of moles of solute in 1 L of a saturated solution (mol/L), and *solubility,* which is the number of grams of solute in 1 L of a saturated solution (g/L). Both of these expressions refer to concentrations of saturated solutions at a particular temperature (usually 25°C).

Often we know the value of K_{sp} for a compound and are asked to calculate the compound's molar solubility. The procedure for solving such a problem is essentially identical to the procedure for solving weak acid or weak base equilibrium problems:

1. Construct an equilibrium table.
2. Fill in what we know.
3. Figure out what we don't know.

For example, the K_{sp} of silver bromide (AgBr) is 7.7×10^{-13}. We can construct an equilibrium table and fill in the starting concentrations of Ag^+ and Br^- ions:

$AgBr(s) \rightleftharpoons$	$Ag^+(aq) +$	$Br^-(aq)$
Initial concentration (M):	0	0
Change in concentration (M):		
Equilibrium concentration (M):		

Let s be the molar solubility (in mol/L) of AgBr. Because one unit of AgBr yields one Ag^+ cation and one Br^- anion, both $[Ag^+]$ and $[Br^-]$ are equal to s at equilibrium:

$AgBr(s) \rightleftharpoons$	$Ag^+(aq) +$	$Br^-(aq)$
Initial concentration (M):	0	0
Change in concentration (M):	$+s$	$+s$
Equilibrium concentration (M):	s	s

The equilibrium expression is

$$K_{sp} = [Ag^+][Br^-]$$

Therefore,

$$7.7 \times 10^{-13} = (s)(s)$$

TABLE 17.4	Solubility Products of Some Slightly Soluble Ionic Compounds at 25°C	
Compound	**Dissolution equilibrium**	K_{sp}
Aluminum hydroxide	$Al(OH)_3(s) \rightleftharpoons Al^{3+}(aq) + 3OH^-(aq)$	1.8×10^{-33}
Barium carbonate	$BaCO_3(s) \rightleftharpoons Ba^{2+}(aq) + CO_3^{2-}(aq)$	8.1×10^{-9}
Barium fluoride	$BaF_2(s) \rightleftharpoons Ba^{2+}(aq) + 2F^-(aq)$	1.7×10^{-6}
Barium sulfate	$BaSO_4(s) \rightleftharpoons Ba^{2+}(aq) + SO_4^{2-}(aq)$	1.1×10^{-10}
Bismuth sulfide	$Bi_2S_3(s) \rightleftharpoons 2Bi^{3+}(aq) + 3S^{2-}(aq)$	1.6×10^{-72}
Cadmium sulfide	$CdS(s) \rightleftharpoons Cd^{2+}(aq) + S^{2-}(aq)$	8.0×10^{-28}
Calcium carbonate	$CaCO_3(s) \rightleftharpoons Ca^{2+}(aq) + CO_3^{2-}(aq)$	8.7×10^{-9}
Calcium fluoride	$CaF_2(s) \rightleftharpoons Ca^{2+}(aq) + 2F^-(aq)$	4.0×10^{-11}
Calcium hydroxide	$Ca(OH)_2(s) \rightleftharpoons Ca^{2+}(aq) + 2OH^-(aq)$	8.0×10^{-6}
Calcium phosphate	$Ca_3(PO_4)_2(s) \rightleftharpoons 3Ca^{2+}(aq) + 2PO_4^{3+}(aq)$	1.2×10^{-26}
Calcium sulfate	$CaSO_4(s) \rightleftharpoons Ca^{2+}(aq) + SO_4^{2-}(aq)$	2.4×10^{-5}
Chromium(III) hydroxide	$Cr(OH)_3(s) \rightleftharpoons Cr^{3+}(aq) + 3OH^-(aq)$	3.0×10^{-29}
Cobalt(II) sulfide	$CoS(s) \rightleftharpoons Co^{2+}(aq) + S^{2-}(aq)$	4.0×10^{-21}
Copper(I) bromide	$CuBr(s) \rightleftharpoons Cu^+(aq) + Br^-(aq)$	4.2×10^{-8}
Copper(I) iodide	$CuI(s) \rightleftharpoons Cu^+(aq) + I^-(aq)$	5.1×10^{-12}
Copper(II) hydroxide	$Cu(OH)_2(s) \rightleftharpoons Cu^{2+}(aq) + 2OH^-(aq)$	2.2×10^{-20}
Copper(II) sulfide	$CuS(s) \rightleftharpoons Cu^{2+}(aq) + S^{2-}(aq)$	6.0×10^{-37}
Iron(II) hydroxide	$Fe(OH)_2(s) \rightleftharpoons Fe^{2+}(aq) + 2OH^-(aq)$	1.6×10^{-14}
Iron(III) hydroxide	$Fe(OH)_3(s) \rightleftharpoons Fe^{3+}(aq) + 3OH^-(aq)$	1.1×10^{-36}
Iron(III) phosphate	$FePO_4(s) \rightleftharpoons Fe^{3+}(aq) + PO_4^{3+}(aq)$	1.3×10^{-22}
Iron(II) sulfide	$FeS(s) \rightleftharpoons Fe^{2+}(aq) + S^{2-}(aq)$	6.0×10^{-19}
Lead(II) bromide	$PbBr_2(s) \rightleftharpoons Pb^{2+}(aq) + 2Br^-(aq)$	6.6×10^{-6}
Lead(II) carbonate	$PbCO_3(s) \rightleftharpoons Pb^{2+}(aq) + CO_3^{2-}(aq)$	3.3×10^{-14}
Lead(II) chloride	$PbCl_2(s) \rightleftharpoons Pb^{2+}(aq) + 2Cl^-(aq)$	2.4×10^{-4}
Lead(II) chromate	$PbCrO_4(s) \rightleftharpoons Pb^{2+}(aq) + CrO_4^{2-}(aq)$	2.0×10^{-14}
Lead(II) fluoride	$PbF_2(s) \rightleftharpoons Pb^{2+}(aq) + 2F^-(aq)$	4.0×10^{-8}
Lead(II) iodide	$PbI_2(s) \rightleftharpoons Pb^{2+}(aq) + 2I^-(aq)$	1.4×10^{-8}
Lead(II) sulfate	$PbSO_4(s) \rightleftharpoons Pb^{2+}(aq) + SO_4^{2-}(aq)$	1.8×10^{-8}
Lead(II) sulfide	$PbS(s) \rightleftharpoons Pb^{2+}(aq) + S^{2-}(aq)$	3.4×10^{-28}
Magnesium carbonate	$MgCO_3(s) \rightleftharpoons Mg^{2+}(aq) + CO_3^{2-}(aq)$	4.0×10^{-5}
Magnesium hydroxide	$Mg(OH)_2(s) \rightleftharpoons Mg^{2+}(aq) + 2OH^-(aq)$	1.2×10^{-11}
Manganese(II) sulfide	$MnS(s) \rightleftharpoons Mn^{2+}(aq) + S^{2-}(aq)$	3.0×10^{-14}
Mercury(I) bromide	$Hg_2Br_2(s) \rightleftharpoons Hg_2^{2+}(aq) + 2Br^-(aq)$	6.4×10^{-23}
Mercury(I) chloride	$Hg_2Cl_2(s) \rightleftharpoons Hg_2^{2+}(aq) + 2Cl^-(aq)$	3.5×10^{-18}
Mercury(I) sulfate	$Hg_2SO_4(s) \rightleftharpoons Hg_2^{2+}(aq) + SO_4^{2-}(aq)$	6.5×10^{-7}
Mercury(II) sulfide	$HgS(s) \rightleftharpoons Hg^{2+}(aq) + S^{2-}(aq)$	4.0×10^{-54}
Nickel(II) sulfide	$NiS(s) \rightleftharpoons Ni^{2+}(aq) + S^{2-}(aq)$	1.4×10^{-24}
Silver bromide	$AgBr(s) \rightleftharpoons Ag^+(aq) + Br^-(aq)$	7.7×10^{-13}
Silver carbonate	$Ag_2CO_3(s) \rightleftharpoons 2Ag^+(aq) + CO_3^{2-}(aq)$	8.1×10^{-12}
Silver chloride	$AgCl(s) \rightleftharpoons Ag^+(aq) + Cl^-(aq)$	1.6×10^{-10}
Silver chromate	$Ag_2CrO_4(s) \rightleftharpoons 2Ag^+(aq) + CrO_4^{2-}(aq)$	1.2×10^{-12}
Silver iodide	$AgI(s) \rightleftharpoons Ag^+(aq) + I^-(aq)$	8.3×10^{-17}
Silver sulfate	$Ag_2SO_4(s) \rightleftharpoons 2Ag^+(aq) + SO_4^{2-}(aq)$	1.5×10^{-5}
Silver sulfide	$Ag_2S(s) \rightleftharpoons 2Ag^+(aq) + S^{2-}(aq)$	6.0×10^{-51}
Strontium carbonate	$SrCO_3(s) \rightleftharpoons Sr^{2+}(aq) + CO_3^{2-}(aq)$	1.6×10^{-9}
Strontium hydroxide	$Sr(OH)_2(s) \rightleftharpoons Sr^{2+}(aq) + 2OH^-(aq)$	3.2×10^{-4}
Strontium sulfate	$SrSO_4(s) \rightleftharpoons Sr^{2+}(aq) + SO_4^{2-}(aq)$	3.8×10^{-7}
Tin(II) sulfide	$SnS(s) \rightleftharpoons Sn^{2+}(aq) + S^{2-}(aq)$	1.0×10^{-26}
Zinc hydroxide	$Zn(OH)_2(s) \rightleftharpoons Zn^{2+}(aq) + 2OH^-(aq)$	1.8×10^{-14}
Zinc sulfide	$ZnS(s) \rightleftharpoons Zn^{2+}(aq) + S^{2-}(aq)$	3.0×10^{-23}

and

$$s = \sqrt{7.7 \times 10^{-13}} = 8.8 \times 10^{-7} \ M$$

Thus, the molar solubility of AgBr is $8.8 \times 10^{-7} \ M$. Furthermore, we can express this solubility in g/L by multiplying the molar solubility by the molar mass of AgBr:

$$\frac{8.8 \times 10^{-7} \ \text{mol AgBr}}{1 \ \text{L}} \times \frac{187.8 \ \text{g}}{1 \ \text{mol AgBr}} = 1.7 \times 10^{-4} \ \text{g/L}$$

Worked Example 17.7 demonstrates this approach.

Worked Example 17.7

Calculate the solubility of copper(II) hydroxide [$Cu(OH)_2$] in g/L.

Strategy Write the dissociation equation for $Cu(OH)_2$, and look up its K_{sp} value in Table 17.4. Solve for molar solubility using the equilibrium expression. Convert molar solubility to solubility in g/L using the molar mass of $Cu(OH)_2$.

Setup The equation for the dissociation of $Cu(OH)_2$ is

$$Cu(OH)_2(s) \rightleftharpoons Cu^{2+}(aq) + 2OH^-(aq)$$

and the equilibrium expression is $K_{sp} = [Cu^{2+}][OH^-]^2$. According to Table 17.4, K_{sp} for $Cu(OH)_2$ is 2.2×10^{-20}. The molar mass of $Cu(OH)_2$ is 97.57 g/mol.

Solution

	$Cu(OH)_2(s) \rightleftharpoons$	$Cu^{2+}(aq)$ +	$2OH^-(aq)$
Initial concentration (*M*):		0	0
Change in concentration (*M*):		+s	+2s
Equilibrium concentration (*M*):		s	2s

> **Student Annotation:** The stoichiometry of the balanced dissociation equation indicates that the concentration of OH⁻ increases by twice as much as that of Cu^{2+}.

Therefore,

$$2.2 \times 10^{-20} = (s)(2s)^2 = 4s^3$$

$$s = \sqrt[3]{\frac{2.2 \times 10^{-20}}{4}} = 1.8 \times 10^{-7} \ M$$

The molar solubility of $Cu(OH)_2$ is $1.8 \times 10^{-7} \ M$. Multiplying by its molar mass gives

$$\text{solubility of } Cu(OH)_2 = \frac{1.8 \times 10^{-7} \ \text{mol } Cu(OH)_2}{1 \ \text{L}} \times \frac{97.57 \ \text{g } Cu(OH)_2}{1 \ \text{mol } Cu(OH)_2}$$

$$= 1.7 \times 10^{-5} \ \text{g/L}$$

> **Think About It**
> Common errors arise in this type of problem when students neglect to raise an entire term to the appropriate power. For example, $(2s)^2$ is equal to $4s^2$ (not $2s^2$).

Practice Problem A Calculate the molar solubility and the solubility in g/L of each salt at 25°C: (a) AgCl, (b) SnS, (c) $SrCO_3$.

Practice Problem B Calculate the molar solubility and the solubility in g/L of each salt at 25°C: (a) PbF_2, (b) Ag_2CO_3, (c) Bi_2S_3.

We can also use molar solubility to determine the value of K_{sp}. Worked Example 17.8 illustrates this procedure.

Worked Example 17.8

The solubility of calcium sulfate ($CaSO_4$) is measured experimentally and found to be 0.67 g/L. Calculate the value of K_{sp} for calcium sulfate.

Strategy Convert solubility to molar solubility using the molar mass of $CaSO_4$, and substitute the molar solubility into the equilibrium expression to determine K_{sp}.

Setup The molar mass of $CaSO_4$ is 136.2 g/mol. The molar solubility of $CaSO_4$ is

$$\text{molar solubility of } CaSO_4 = \frac{0.67 \text{ g } CaSO_4}{1 \text{ L}} \times \frac{1 \text{ mol } CaSO_4}{136.2 \text{ g } CaSO_4}$$

$$s = 4.9 \times 10^{-3} \text{ mol/L}$$

The equation and the equilibrium expression for the dissociation of $CaSO_4$ are

$$CaSO_4(s) \rightleftharpoons Ca^{2+}(aq) + SO_4^{2-}(aq) \quad \text{and} \quad K_{sp} = [Ca^{2+}][SO_4^{2-}]$$

Solution Substituting the molar solubility into the equilibrium expression gives

$$K_{sp} = (s)(s) = (4.9 \times 10^{-3})^2 = 2.4 \times 10^{-5}$$

Think About It
The K_{sp} for $CaSO_4$ is relatively large (compared to many of the K_{sp} values in Table 17.4). In fact, sulfates are listed as soluble compounds in Table 9.2, but calcium sulfate is listed as an insoluble exception. Remember that the term *insoluble* really refers to compounds that are *slightly* soluble, and that different sources may differ with regard to how soluble a compound must be to be considered "soluble."

Practice Problem A Given the solubility, calculate the solubility product constant (K_{sp}) of each salt at 25°C: (a) $PbCrO_4$, $s = 4.0 \times 10^{-5}$ g/L; (b) BaC_2O_4, $s = 0.29$ g/L; (c) $MnCO_3$, $s = 4.2 \times 10^{-6}$ g/L.

Practice Problem B Given the solubility, calculate the solubility product constant (K_{sp}) of each salt at 25°C: (a) Ag_2SO_3, $s = 4.6 \times 10^{-3}$ g/L; (b) Hg_2I_2, $s = 1.5 \times 10^{-7}$ g/L; (c) $Zn_3(PO_4)_2$, $s = 5.9 \times 10^{-5}$ g/L.

Predicting Precipitation Reactions

For the dissociation of an ionic solid in water, any one of the following conditions may exist: (1) the solution is unsaturated, (2) the solution is saturated, or (3) the solution is supersaturated. For concentrations of ions that do not correspond to equilibrium conditions, we use the reaction quotient (Q) [◄◄ Section 15.2] to predict when a precipitate will form. Note that Q has the same form as K_{sp} except that the concentrations of ions are not equilibrium concentrations. For example, if we mix a solution containing Ag^+ ions with one containing Cl^- ions, we write

$$Q = [Ag^+]_i[Cl^-]_i$$

The subscript "i" denotes that these are *initial* concentrations and do not necessarily correspond to those at equilibrium. If Q is less than or equal to K_{sp}, no precipitate will form. If Q is greater than K_{sp}, AgCl will precipitate out. (Precipitation will continue until the product of the ion concentrations is equal to K_{sp}.)

The ability to predict whether precipitation will occur often has practical value. In industrial and laboratory preparations, we can adjust the concentrations of ions until the ion product exceeds K_{sp} to obtain a desired ionic compound (in the form of a precipitate). The ability to predict precipitation reactions is also useful in medicine. Kidney stones, which can be extremely painful, consist largely of calcium oxalate (CaC_2O_4, $K_{sp} = 2.3 \times 10^{-9}$). The normal physiological concentration of calcium ions in blood plasma is about 5×10^{-3} M. Oxalate ions ($C_2O_4^{2-}$), derived from oxalic acid present in vegetables such as rhubarb and spinach, react with the calcium ions to form insoluble calcium oxalate, which can gradually build up in the kidneys. Proper adjustment of a patient's diet can help to reduce precipitate formation.

Worked Example 17.9 demonstrates the steps involved in predicting precipitation reactions.

Worked Example 17.9

Predict whether a precipitate will form when each of the following is added to 650 mL of 0.0080 M K_2SO_4: (a) 250 mL of 0.0040 M $BaCl_2$; (b) 175 mL of 0.15 M $AgNO_3$; (c) 325 mL of 0.25 M $Sr(NO_3)_2$. (Assume volumes are additive.)

Strategy For each part, identify the compound that might precipitate and look up its K_{sp} value in Table 17.4 or Appendix 4. Determine the concentrations of each compound's constituent ions, and use them to determine the value of the reaction quotient, Q_{sp}; then compare each reaction quotient with the value of the corresponding K_{sp}. If the reaction quotient is greater than K_{sp}, a precipitate will form.

Setup The compounds that might precipitate and their K_{sp} values are (a) $BaSO_4$, $K_{sp} = 1.1 \times 10^{-10}$; (b) Ag_2SO_4, $K_{sp} = 1.5 \times 10^{-5}$; (c) $SrSO_4$, $K_{sp} = 3.8 \times 10^{-7}$.

Solution (a) Concentrations of the constituent ions of $BaSO_4$ are:

$$[Ba^{2+}] = \frac{250 \text{ mL} \times 0.0040 \text{ } M}{650 \text{ mL} + 250 \text{ mL}} = 0.0011 \text{ } M \quad \text{and} \quad [SO_4^{2-}] = \frac{650 \text{ mL} \times 0.0080 \text{ } M}{650 \text{ mL} + 250 \text{ mL}} = 0.0058 \text{ } M$$

Using these concentrations in the equilibrium expression, $[Ba^{2+}][SO_4^{2-}]$, gives a reaction quotient of $(0.0011)(0.0058) = 6.4 \times 10^{-6}$, which is greater than the K_{sp} of $BaSO_4$ (1.1×10^{-10}). Therefore, $BaSO_4$ will precipitate.

(b) Concentrations of the constituent ions of Ag_2SO_4 are:

$$[Ag^+] = \frac{175 \text{ mL} \times 0.15 \text{ } M}{650 \text{ mL} + 175 \text{ mL}} = 0.0032 \text{ } M \quad \text{and} \quad [SO_4^{2-}] = \frac{650 \text{ mL} \times 0.0080 \text{ } M}{650 \text{ mL} + 175 \text{ mL}} = 0.0063 \text{ } M$$

Using these concentrations in the equilibrium expression, $[Ag^+]^2[SO_4^{2-}]$, gives a reaction quotient of $(0.032)^2(0.0063) = 6.5 \times 10^{-6}$, which is less than the K_{sp} of Ag_2SO_4 (1.5×10^{-5}). Therefore, Ag_2SO_4 will not precipitate.

(c) Concentrations of the constituent ions of $SrSO_4$ are:

$$[Sr^{2+}] = \frac{325 \text{ mL} \times 0.25 \text{ } M}{650 \text{ mL} + 325 \text{ mL}} = 0.083 \text{ } M \quad \text{and} \quad [SO_4^{2-}] = \frac{650 \text{ mL} \times 0.0080 \text{ } M}{650 \text{ mL} + 325 \text{ mL}} = 0.0053 \text{ } M$$

Using these concentrations in the equilibrium expression, $[Sr^{2+}][SO_4^{2-}]$, gives a reaction quotient of $(0.083)(0.0053) = 4.4 \times 10^{-4}$, which is greater than the K_{sp} of $SrSO_4$ (3.8×10^{-7}). Therefore, $SrSO_4$ will precipitate.

Think About It

Students sometimes have difficulty deciding what compound might precipitate. Begin by writing down the constituent ions in the two solutions before they are combined. Consider the two possible combinations: the cation from the first solution and the anion from the second, or vice versa. You can consult the information in Tables 9.2 and 9.3 to determine whether one of the combinations is insoluble. Also keep in mind that only an *insoluble* salt will have a tabulated K_{sp} value.

Practice Problem A Predict whether a precipitate will form from each of the following combinations: (a) 25 mL of 1×10^{-5} M $Co(NO_3)_2$ and 75 mL of 5×10^{-4} M Na_2S; (b) 500 mL of 7.5×10^{-4} M $AlCl_3$ and 100 mL of 1.7×10^{-5} M $Hg_2(NO_3)_2$; (c) 1.5 L of 0.025 M $BaCl_2$ and 1.25 L of 0.014 M $Pb(NO_3)_2$.

Practice Problem B What is the maximum mass (in grams) of each of the following soluble salts that can be added to 150 mL of 0.050 M $BaCl_2$ without causing a precipitate to form: (a) $(NH_4)_2SO_4$, (b) $Pb(NO_3)_2$, (c) NaF? (Assume that the addition of solid causes no change in volume.)

Solubility Equilibria

17.4.1 Using the K_{sp} for aluminum hydroxide [$Al(OH)_3$], calculate its molar solubility.

17.4.2 What precipitate if any will form if 0.10 M solutions of $Pb(NO_3)_2$ and NaI are mixed?

17.4.3 The diagrams represent saturated solutions of MX, MY, and MZ, each in equilibrium with its solid. Each solution also contains the soluble nitrate salt of M^{n+}. Arrange the solutions in order of increasing K_{sp}. (For clarity, the water molecules and nitrate ions are not shown.)

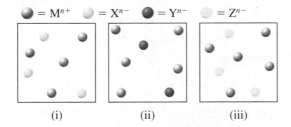

$\bullet = M^{n+}$ $\circ = X^{n-}$ $\bullet = Y^{n-}$ $\circ = Z^{n-}$

(i)　　　　(ii)　　　　(iii)

17.5 FACTORS AFFECTING SOLUBILITY

In this section we will examine the effect of several factors on solubility including the common ion effect, pH, and the formation of complex ions.

The Common Ion Effect

The solubility product is an equilibrium constant, and precipitation of an ionic compound from solution occurs whenever the ion product exceeds the K_{sp} for that substance. In a saturated solution of AgCl, for example, the ion product $[Ag^+][Cl^-]$ is equal to K_{sp}. The solubility of AgCl in water can be calculated as follows, using the procedure introduced in Section 17.4:

$$1.6 \times 10^{-10} = [Ag^+][Cl^-]$$

In a solution in which AgCl is the only solute, $[Ag^+] = [Cl^-]$. Therefore,

$$1.6 \times 10^{-10} = s^2$$

and $s = 1.3 \times 10^{-5}$ M. Thus, the solubility of AgCl in water at 25°C is 1.3×10^{-5} M.

Now suppose we want to determine the solubility of AgCl in a solution already containing a solute that has an ion in common with AgCl. For example, consider dissolving AgCl in a 0.10-M solution of $AgNO_3$. In this case, the Ag^+ and Cl^- concentrations at equilibrium will not be equal. In fact, the Ag^+ ion concentration will be equal to 0.10 M *plus* the concentration contributed by AgCl. The equilibrium expression is

$$1.6 \times 10^{-10} = [Ag^+][Cl^-] = (0.10 + s)(s)$$

Student Annotation: *s* still represents the concentration of Cl⁻ at equilibrium and the *solubility* of AgCl.

Because we expect s to be very small, we can simplify this calculation as follows:

$$(0.10 + s)\ M \approx 0.10\ M$$

Therefore,

$$1.6 \times 10^{-10} = 0.10s$$

Student Annotation: The common ion effect is an example of Le Châtelier's principle [◄◄ Section 15.5].

and $s = 1.6 \times 10^{-9}$ M. Thus, AgCl is *significantly* less soluble in 0.10 M $AgNO_3$ than in pure water—due to the common ion effect. Figure 17.8 (pages 738–739) illustrates the common ion effect.

Figure 17.8

Common Ion Effect

We prepare a saturated solution by adding AgCl to water and stirring.

In the resulting saturated solution, the concentrations of Ag^+ and Cl^- are equal, and the product of their concentrations is equal to K_{sp}.

$$[Ag^+][Cl^-] = 1.6 \times 10^{-10}$$

Therefore, the concentrations are

$$[Ag^+] = 1.3 \times 10^{-5}\ M$$

$$\text{and } [Cl^-] = 1.3 \times 10^{-5}\ M$$

Neither AgCl nor a saturated solution of AgCl is purple. The color has been used in this illustration to clarify the process.

START

After filtering off the solid AgCl, we dissolve enough NaCl to make the concentration of Cl$^-$ = 1.0 M.

Because the concentration of Cl$^-$ is now larger, the product of Ag$^+$ and Cl$^-$ concentrations is no longer equal to K_{sp}.

$$[Ag^+][Cl^-] = (1.3 \times 10^{-5}\,M)(1.0\,M) > 1.6 \times 10^{-10}$$

In any solution saturated with AgCl at 25°C, the product of [Ag$^+$] and [Cl$^-$] must equal the K_{sp} of AgCl. Therefore, AgCl will precipitate until the product of ion concentrations is again 1.6×10^{-10}.

Note that this causes nearly all the dissolved AgCl to precipitate. With a Cl$^-$ concentration of 1.0 M, the highest possible concentration of Ag$^+$ is $1.6 \times 10^{-10}\,M$.

$$[Ag^+](1.0\,M) = 1.6 \times 10^{-10}$$

therefore, $[Ag^+] = 1.6 \times 10^{-10}\,M$

The amount of AgCl precipitated is exaggerated for emphasis. The actual amount of AgCl would be extremely small.

What's the point?

When two salts contain the same ion, the ion they both contain is called the "common ion." The solubility of a slightly soluble salt such as AgCl can be decreased by the addition of a *soluble* salt with a common ion. In this example, AgCl is precipitated by adding NaCl. AgCl could also be precipitated by adding a soluble salt containing the Ag$^+$ ion, such as AgNO$_3$.

Worked Example 17.10 shows how the common ion effect affects solubility.

Multi 17.4
Common ion effect

Worked Example 17.10

Calculate the molar solubility of silver chloride in a solution that is 6.5×10^{-3} M in silver nitrate.

Strategy Silver nitrate is a strong electrolyte that dissociates completely in water. Therefore, the concentration of Ag^+ before any AgCl dissolves is 6.5×10^{-3} M. Use the equilibrium expression, the K_{sp} for AgCl, and an equilibrium table to determine how much AgCl will dissolve.

Setup The dissolution equilibrium and the equilibrium expression are

$$AgCl(s) \rightleftharpoons Ag^+(aq) + Cl^-(aq) \qquad 1.6 \times 10^{-10} = [Ag^+][Cl^-]$$

Solution

$AgCl(s) \rightleftharpoons$	$Ag^+(aq)$	$+$	$Cl^-(aq)$
Initial concentration (M):	6.5×10^{-3}		0
Change in concentration (M):	$+s$		$+s$
Equilibrium concentration (M):	$6.5 \times 10^{-3} + s$		s

Substituting these concentrations into the equilibrium expression gives

$$1.6 \times 10^{-10} = (6.5 \times 10^{-3} + s)(s)$$

We expect s to be very small, so

$$6.5 \times 10^{-3} + s \approx 6.5 \times 10^{-3}$$

and

$$1.6 \times 10^{-10} = (6.5 \times 10^{-3})(s)$$

Thus

$$s = \frac{1.6 \times 10^{-10}}{6.5 \times 10^{-3}} = 2.5 \times 10^{-8} \ M$$

Therefore, the molar solubility of AgCl in 6.5×10^{-3} M $AgNO_3$ is 2.5×10^{-8} M.

Think About It
The molar solubility of AgCl in water is $\sqrt{1.6 \times 10^{-10}} = 1.3 \times 10^{-5}$ M. The presence of 6.5×10^{-3} M $AgNO_3$ reduces the solubility of AgCl by a factor of ~500.

Practice Problem A Calculate the molar solubility of AgI in (a) pure water and (b) 0.0010 M NaI.

Practice Problem B Arrange the following salts in order of increasing molar solubility in 0.0010 M $AgNO_3$: AgBr, Ag_2CO_3, AgCl, AgI, Ag_2S.

pH

The solubility of a substance can also depend on the pH of the solution. Consider the solubility equilibrium of magnesium hydroxide:

$$Mg(OH)_2(s) \rightleftharpoons Mg^{2+}(aq) + 2OH^-(aq)$$

According to Le Châtelier's principle, adding OH^- ions (increasing the pH) shifts the equilibrium from right to left, thereby decreasing the solubility of $Mg(OH)_2$. (This is actually another example of the common ion effect.) On the other hand, adding H^+ ions (decreasing the pH) shifts the equilibrium from left to right, and the solubility of $Mg(OH)_2$ *increases*. Thus, insoluble bases tend to dissolve in acidic solutions. Similarly, insoluble acids tend to dissolve in basic solutions.

To examine the effect of pH on the solubility of $Mg(OH)_2$, we first calculate the pH of a saturated $Mg(OH)_2$ solution:

$$K_{sp} = (s)(2s)^2 = 4s^3$$

$$4s^3 = 1.2 \times 10^{-11}$$

$$s^3 = 3.0 \times 10^{-12}$$

$$s = 1.4 \times 10^{-4} \ M$$

At equilibrium, therefore,

$$[OH^-] = 2(1.4 \times 10^{-4}\,M) = 2.8 \times 10^{-4}\,M$$

$$pOH = -\log(2.8 \times 10^{-4}) = 3.55$$

$$pH = 14.00 - 3.55 = 10.45$$

In a solution with a pH of *less* than 10.45, the solubility of $Mg(OH)_2$ would increase. The dissolution process and the effect of additional H^+ ions are summarized as follows:

$$Mg(OH)_2(s) \rightleftharpoons Mg^{2+}(aq) + 2\cancel{OH^-}(aq)$$

$$2H^+(aq) + 2\cancel{OH^-}(aq) \longrightarrow 2H_2O(l)$$

Overall: $Mg(OH)_2(s) + 2H^+(aq) \rightleftharpoons Mg^{2+}(aq) + 2H_2O(l)$

If the pH of the medium were higher than 10.45, $[OH^-]$ would be higher and the solubility of $Mg(OH)_2$ would decrease because of the common ion (OH^-) effect.

The pH also influences the solubility of salts that contain a basic anion. For example, the solubility equilibrium for BaF_2 is

$$BaF_2(s) \rightleftharpoons Ba^{2+}(aq) + 2F^-(aq)$$

and

$$K_{sp} = [Ba^{2+}][F^-]^2$$

In an acidic medium, the high $[H^+]$ will shift the following equilibrium to the left, consuming F^-:

$$HF(aq) \rightleftharpoons H^+(aq) + F^-(aq)$$

As the concentration of F^- decreases, the concentration of Ba^{2+} must increase to satisfy the equality $K_{sp} = [Ba^{2+}][F^-]^2$ and maintain the state of equilibrium. Thus, more BaF_2 dissolves. The process and the effect of pH on the solubility of BaF_2 can be summarized as follows:

$$BaF_2(s) \rightleftharpoons Ba^{2+}(aq) + 2\cancel{F^-}(aq)$$

$$2H^+(aq) + 2\cancel{F^-}(aq) \longrightarrow 2HF(aq)$$

Overall: $BaF_2(s) + 2H^+(aq) \rightleftharpoons Ba^{2+}(aq) + 2HF(aq)$

The solubilities of salts containing anions that do *not* hydrolyze, such as Cl^-, Br^-, and NO_3^-, are unaffected by pH.

Worked Example 17.11 demonstrates the effect of pH on solubility.

Worked Example 17.11

Which of the following compounds will be more soluble in acidic solution than in water: (a) CuS, (b) AgCl, (c) $PbSO_4$?

Strategy For each salt, write the dissociation equilibrium equation and determine whether it produces an anion that will react with H^+. Only an anion that is the conjugate base of a weak acid will react with H^+.

Setup

(a) $CuS(s) \rightleftharpoons Cu^{2+}(aq) + S^{2-}(aq)$
  S^{2-} is the conjugate base of the weak acid HS^-. S^{2-} reacts with H^+ as follows:

$$S^{2-}(aq) + H^+(aq) \longrightarrow HS^-(aq)$$

(b) $AgCl(s) \rightleftharpoons Ag^+(aq) + Cl^-(aq)$
  Cl^- is the conjugate base of the strong acid HCl. Cl^- does not react with H^+.

(Continued on next page)

(c) $PbSO_4(s) \rightleftharpoons Pb^{2+}(aq) + SO_4^{2-}(aq)$

SO_4^{2-} is the conjugate base of the weak acid HSO_4^-. It reacts with H^+ as follows:

$$SO_4^{2-}(aq) + H^+(aq) \longrightarrow HSO_4^-(aq)$$

A salt that produces an anion that reacts with H^+ will be more soluble in acid than in water.

Solution CuS and $PbSO_4$ are more soluble in acid than in water. (AgCl is no more or less soluble in acid than in water.)

Think About It

When a salt dissociates to give the conjugate base of a weak acid, H^+ ions in an acidic solution *consume* a product (base) of the dissolution. This drives the equilibrium to the right (more solid dissolves) according to Le Châtelier's principle.

Practice Problem A Determine if the following compounds are more soluble in acidic solution than in pure water: (a) $Ca(OH)_2$, (b) $Mg_3(PO_4)_2$, (c) $PbBr_2$.

Practice Problem B Other than those in Worked Example 17.11 and those in Practice Problem A, list three salts that are more soluble in acidic solution than in pure water.

Complex Ion Formation

A ***complex ion*** is an ion containing a central metal cation bonded to one or more molecules or ions. Complex ions are crucial to many chemical and biological processes. Here we will consider the effect of complex ion formation on solubility. In Chapter 22 we will discuss the chemistry of complex ions in more detail.

Transition metals have a particular tendency to form complex ions. For example, a solution of cobalt(II) chloride ($CoCl_2$) is pink because of the presence of the $Co(H_2O)_6^{2+}$ ions (Figure 17.9). When HCl is added, the solution turns blue because the complex ion $CoCl_4^{2-}$ forms:

$$Co^{2+}(aq) + 4Cl^-(aq) \rightleftharpoons CoCl_4^{2-}(aq)$$

Figure 17.9 (Left) An aqueous cobalt(II) chloride solution. The pink color is due to the presence of $Co(H_2O)_6^{2+}$ ions. (Right) After the addition of HCl solution, the solution turns blue because of the formation of the complex $CoCl_4^{2-}$ ions.

Thinking Outside the Box

Equilibrium and Tooth Decay

Teeth are protected by a hard enamel layer about 2 mm thick that is composed of a mineral called *hydroxyapatite* [$Ca_5(PO_4)_3OH$]. *Demineralization* is the process by which hydroxyapatite dissolves in the saliva. Because phosphates of alkaline earth metals such as calcium are insoluble [◄◄ Section 9.2, Table 9.3], this process happens only to a very small extent:

$$Ca_5(PO_4)_3OH(s) \rightleftharpoons 5Ca^{2+}(aq) + 3PO_4^{3-}(aq) + OH^-(aq)$$

The reverse process, called *remineralization*, is the body's natural defense against tooth decay:

$$5Ca^{2+}(aq) + 3PO_4^{3-}(aq) + OH^-(aq) \rightleftharpoons Ca_5(PO_4)_3OH(s)$$

Bacteria in the mouth break down some of the food we eat to produce organic acids such as acetic acid and lactic acid. Acid production is greatest from foods that are high in sugar. Thus, after a sugary snack, the H^+ concentration in the mouth increases, causing OH^- ions in the saliva to be consumed.

$$H^+(aq) + OH^-(aq) \longrightarrow H_2O(l)$$

Removal of OH^- from the saliva draws the $Ca_5(PO_4)_3OH$ dissolution equilibrium to the right, promoting demineralization. Once the protective enamel layer is weakened, tooth decay begins. The best way to prevent tooth decay is to eat a diet low in sugar and brush immediately after every meal.

Most toothpastes contain fluoride, which helps to reduce tooth decay. The F^- ions in toothpaste replace some of the OH^- ions during the remineralization process:

$$5Ca^{2+}(aq) + 3PO_4^{3-}(aq) + F^-(aq) \rightleftharpoons Ca_5(PO_4)_3F(s)$$

Because F^- is a weaker base than OH^-, the modified enamel, called *fluoroapatite*, is more resistant to the acid produced by bacteria.

> **Student Annotation:** In children, the growth of the enamel layer (mineralization) occurs faster than demineralization; in adults, demineralization and remineralization occur at roughly equal rates.

Copper(II) sulfate ($CuSO_4$) dissolves in water to produce a blue solution. The hydrated copper(II) ions are responsible for this color; many other sulfates (e.g., Na_2SO_4) are colorless. Adding a few drops of concentrated ammonia solution to a $CuSO_4$ solution causes the formation of a light-blue precipitate, copper(II) hydroxide:

$$Cu^{2+}(aq) + 2OH^-(aq) \longrightarrow Cu(OH)_2(s)$$

The OH^- ions are supplied by the ammonia solution. If more NH_3 is added, the blue precipitate redissolves to produce a beautiful dark-blue solution, this time due to the formation of the complex ion $Cu(NH_3)_4^{2+}$ (Figure 17.10):

$$Cu(OH)_2(s) + 4NH_3(aq) \rightleftharpoons Cu(NH_3)_4^{2+}(aq) + 2OH^-(aq)$$

Thus, the formation of the complex ion $Cu(NH_3)_4^{2+}$ increases the solubility of $Cu(OH)_2$.

A measure of the tendency of a metal ion to form a particular complex ion is given by the *formation constant* (K_f) (also called the stability constant), which is the equilibrium constant for the complex ion formation. The larger K_f is, the more stable the complex ion is. Table 17.5 (page 744) lists the formation constants of a number of complex ions.

The formation of the $Cu(NH_3)_4^{2+}$ ion can be expressed as

$$Cu^{2+}(aq) + 4NH_3(aq) \rightleftharpoons Cu(NH_3)_4^{2+}(aq)$$

The corresponding formation constant is

$$K_f = \frac{[Cu(NH_3)_4^{2+}]}{[Cu^{2+}][NH_3]^4} = 5.0 \times 10^{13}$$

The large value of K_f in this case indicates that the complex ion is very stable in solution and accounts for the very low concentration of copper(II) ions at equilibrium.

Figure 17.10 (Left) An aqueous solution of copper(II) sulfate. (Center) After the addition of a few drops of concentrated aqueous ammonia solution, a light-blue precipitate of $Cu(OH)_2$ is formed. (Right) When more concentrated aqueous ammonia solution is added, the $Cu(OH)_2$ precipitate dissolves to form the dark-blue complex ion $Cu(NH_3)_4^{2+}$.

TABLE 17.5	Formation Constants of Selected Complex Ions in Water at 25°C	
Complex ion	Equilibrium expression	Formation constant (K_f)
$Ag(NH_3)_2^+$	$Ag^+ + 2NH_3 \rightleftharpoons Ag(NH_3)_2^+$	1.5×10^7
$Ag(CN)_2^-$	$Ag^+ + 2CN^- \rightleftharpoons Ag(CN)_2^-$	1.0×10^{21}
$Cu(CN)_4^{2-}$	$Cu^{2+} + 4CN^- \rightleftharpoons Cu(CN)_4^{2-}$	1.0×10^{25}
$Cu(NH_3)_4^{2+}$	$Cu^{2+} + 4NH_3 \rightleftharpoons Cu(NH_3)_4^{2+}$	5.0×10^{13}
$Cd(CN)_4^{2-}$	$Cd^{2+} + 4CN^- \rightleftharpoons Cd(CN)_4^{2-}$	7.1×10^{16}
CdI_4^{2-}	$Cd^{2+} + 4I^- \rightleftharpoons CdI_4^{2-}$	2.0×10^6
$HgCl_4^{2-}$	$Hg^{2+} + 4Cl^- \rightleftharpoons HgCl_4^{2-}$	1.7×10^{16}
HgI_4^{2-}	$Hg^{2+} + 4I^- \rightleftharpoons HgI_4^{2-}$	2.0×10^{30}
$Hg(CN)_4^{2-}$	$Hg^{2+} + 4CN^- \rightleftharpoons Hg(CN)_4^{2-}$	2.5×10^{41}
$Co(NH_3)_6^{3+}$	$Co^{3+} + 6NH_3 \rightleftharpoons Co(NH_3)_6^{3+}$	5.0×10^{31}
$Zn(NH_3)_4^{2+}$	$Zn^{2+} + 4NH_3 \rightleftharpoons Zn(NH_3)_4^{2+}$	2.9×10^9
$Cr(OH)_4^-$	$Cr^{3+} + 4OH^- \rightleftharpoons Cr(OH)_4^-$	8×10^{29}

Recall that K for the sum of two reactions is the product of the individual K values [◄◄ Section 15.3]. The dissolution of silver chloride is represented by the equation

$$AgCl(s) \rightleftharpoons Ag^+(aq) + Cl^-(aq)$$

The sum of this equation and the one representing the formation of $Ag(NH_3)_2^+$ is

$$AgCl(s) \rightleftharpoons Ag^+(aq) + Cl^-(aq) \qquad K_{sp} = 1.6 \times 10^{-10}$$

$$\underline{Ag^+(aq) + 2NH_3(aq) \rightleftharpoons Ag(NH_3)_2^+(aq) \qquad K_f = 1.5 \times 10^7}$$

$$AgCl(s) + 2NH_3(aq) \rightleftharpoons Ag(NH_3)_2^+(aq) + Cl^-(aq)$$

Student Annotation: Formation of a complex ion *consumes* the metal ion produced by the dissociation of a salt, increasing the salt's solubility simply due to Le Châtelier's principle [◄◄ Section 15.5].

and the corresponding equilibrium constant is $(1.6 \times 10^{-10})(1.5 \times 10^7) = 2.4 \times 10^{-3}$. This is significantly larger than the K_{sp} value, indicating that much more AgCl will dissolve in the presence of aqueous ammonia than in pure water. In general, the effect of complex ion formation generally is to *increase* the solubility of a substance.

The solution of an equilibrium problem involving complex ion formation is complicated both by the magnitude of K_f and by the stoichiometry of the reaction. Consider the combination of aqueous copper(II) ions and ammonia to form the complex ion $Cu(NH_3)_4^{2+}$:

$$Cu^{2+}(aq) + 4NH_3(aq) \rightleftharpoons Cu(NH_3)_4^{2+}(aq) \qquad K_f = 5.0 \times 10^{14}$$

Let's say we wish to determine the molar concentration of free copper(II) ion in solution when 0.10 mole of $Cu(NO_3)_2$ is dissolved in a liter of 3.0 M NH_3. We cannot solve this with the same approach we used to determine the pH of a weak acid solution. Not only can we not neglect x, the amount of copper(II) ion consumed in the reaction, but having to raise the ammonia concentration to the fourth power in the equilibrium expression results in an equation that is not easily solved. Another approach is needed.

Student Annotation: The term *free* is used to refer to a metal ion that is *not* part of a complex ion.

Because the magnitude of K_f is so large, we begin by assuming that *all* the copper(II) ion is consumed to form the complex ion. Then we consider the equilibrium in terms of the *reverse* reaction; that is, the dissociation of $Cu(NH_3)_4^{2+}$, for which the equilibrium constant is the reciprocal of K_f.

$$Cu(NH_3)_4^{2+}(aq) \rightleftharpoons Cu^{2+}(aq) + 4NH_3(aq) \qquad K = 2.0 \times 10^{-15}$$

Now we construct an equilibrium table and, because this K is so small, we can expect x (the amount of complex ion that dissociates) to be insignificant compared to the concentration of the complex ion and the concentration of ammonia. [Note that the concentration of ammonia, which had been 3.0 M, has been diminished by 4×0.10 M due to the amount required to complex 0.10 mole of copper(II) ion.]

$$Cu(NH_3)_4^{2+}(aq) \rightleftharpoons Cu^{2+}(aq) + 4NH_3(aq)$$

Initial concentration (M):	0.10	0	2.6
Change in concentration (M):	$-x$	$+x$	$+4x$
Equilibrium concentration (M):	$0.10 - x$	x	$2.6 + 4x$

We can neglect x with respect to the concentrations of $Cu(NH_3)_4^{2+}$ and NH_3 ($0.10 - x \approx 0.10$ and $2.6 + 4x \approx 2.6$), and the solution becomes

$$\frac{[Cu^{2+}][NH_3]^4}{[Cu(NH_3)_4^{2+}]} = \frac{x(2.6)^4}{0.10} = 2.0 \times 10^{-15}$$

and $x = 4.4 \times 10^{-18}$ M. Note that because the formation constant is so large, the amount of copper that remains uncomplexed is extremely small. As always, it is a good idea to check the answer by plugging it into the equilibrium expression:

$$\frac{(4.4 \times 10^{-18})[2.6 + 4(4.4 \times 10^{-18})]^4}{0.10 - 4.4 \times 10^{-18}} = 2.0 \times 10^{-15}$$

Worked Example 17.12 lets you practice applying this approach to a complex ion formation equilibrium problem.

Worked Example 17.12

In the presence of aqueous cyanide, cadmium(II) forms the complex ion $Cd(CN)_4^{2-}$. Determine the molar concentration of free (uncomplexed) cadmium(II) ion in solution when 0.20 mole of $Cd(NO_3)_2$ is dissolved in a liter of 2.0 M sodium cyanide (NaCN).

Strategy Because formation constants are typically very large, we begin by assuming that all the Cd^{2+} ion is consumed and converted to complex ion. We then determine how much Cd^{2+} is produced by the subsequent dissociation of the complex ion, a process for which the equilibrium constant is the reciprocal of K_f.

Setup From Table 17.5, the formation constant (K_f) for the complex ion $Cd(CN)_4^{2-}$ is 7.1×10^{16}. The reverse process,

$$Cd(CN)_4^{2-}(aq) \rightleftharpoons Cd^{2+}(aq) + 4CN^-(aq)$$

(Continued on next page)

has an equilibrium constant of $1/K_f = 1.4 \times 10^{-17}$. The equilibrium expression for the dissociation is

$$1.4 \times 10^{-17} = \frac{[Cd^{2+}][CN^-]^4}{[Cd(CN)_4^{2-}]}$$

The formation of complex ion will consume some of the cyanide originally present. Stoichiometry indicates that four CN^- ions are required to react with one Cd^{2+} ion. Therefore, the concentration of CN^- that we enter in the top row of the equilibrium table will be $[2.0\ M - 4(0.20\ M)] = 1.2\ M$.

Solution We construct an equilibrium table:

$$Cd(CN)_4^{2-}(aq) \rightleftharpoons Cd^{2+}(aq) + 4CN^-(aq)$$

	$Cd(CN)_4^{2-}$	Cd^{2+}	$4CN^-$
Initial concentration (M):	0.20	0	1.2
Change in concentration (M):	$-x$	$+x$	$+4x$
Equilibrium concentration (M):	$0.20 - x$	x	$1.2 + 4x$

and, because the magnitude of K is so *small*, we can neglect x with respect to the initial concentrations of $Cd(CN)_4^{2-}$ and CN^- ($0.20 - x \approx 0.20$ and $1.2 + 4x \approx 1.2$), so the solution becomes

$$\frac{[Cd^{2+}][CN^-]^4}{[Cd(CN)_4^{2-}]} = \frac{x(1.2)^4}{0.20} = 1.4 \times 10^{-17}$$

and $x = 1.4 \times 10^{-18}\ M$.

Think About It

When you assume that all the metal ion is consumed and converted to complex ion, it's important to remember that some of the complexing agent (in this case, CN^- ion) is consumed in the process. Don't forget to adjust its concentration accordingly before entering it in the top row of the equilibrium table.

Practice Problem A In the presence of aqueous ammonia, cobalt(III) forms the complex ion $Co(NH_3)_6^{3+}$. Determine the molar concentration of free cobalt(III) ion in solution when 0.15 mole of $Co(NO_3)_3$ is dissolved in a liter of 2.5 M aqueous ammonia.

Practice Problem B Use information from Tables 17.4 and 17.5 to determine the molar solubility of chromium(III) hydroxide in a buffered solution with pH = 11.45.

Finally, there is a class of hydroxides, called amphoteric hydroxides, which can react with both acids and bases. Examples are $Al(OH)_3$, $Pb(OH)_2$, $Cr(OH)_3$, $Zn(OH)_2$, and $Cd(OH)_2$. $Al(OH)_3$ reacts with acids and bases as follows:

$$Al(OH)_3(s) + 3H^+(aq) \longrightarrow Al^{3+}(aq) + 3H_2O(l)$$

$$Al(OH)_3(s) + OH^-(aq) \rightleftharpoons Al(OH)_4^-(aq)$$

The increase in solubility of $Al(OH)_3$ in a basic medium is the result of the formation of the complex ion $Al(OH)_4^-$ in which $Al(OH)_3$ acts as the Lewis acid and OH^- acts as the Lewis base. Other amphoteric hydroxides react similarly with acids and bases.

SECTION 17.5 REVIEW

Factors Affecting Solubility

17.5.1 Calculate the molar solubility of AgCl in 0.10 M $CaCl_2$.

17.5.2 In which of the solutions would the slightly soluble salt MC_2 be *most* soluble, and in which would it be *least* soluble? (For clarity, water molecules and counter ions in soluble salts are not shown.)

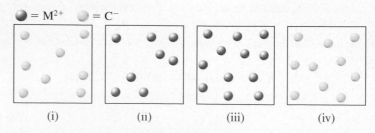

| (i) | (ii) | (iii) | (iv) |

17.6 SEPARATION OF IONS USING DIFFERENCES IN SOLUBILITY

In chemical analysis, it sometimes is necessary to remove one type of ion from solution by precipitation while leaving other ions in solution. For instance, the addition of sulfate ions to a solution containing both potassium and barium ions causes $BaSO_4$ to precipitate out, thereby removing most of the Ba^{2+} ions from the solution. The other "product," K_2SO_4, is soluble and will remain in solution. The $BaSO_4$ precipitate can be separated from the solution by filtration.

Fractional Precipitation

Even when both products are insoluble, we can still achieve some degree of separation by choosing the proper reagent to bring about precipitation. Consider a solution that contains Cl^-, Br^-, and I^- ions. One way to separate these ions is to convert them to insoluble silver halides. As the K_{sp} values in the margin show, the solubility of the silver halides decreases from AgCl to AgI. Thus, when a soluble compound such as silver nitrate is slowly added to this solution, AgI begins to precipitate first, followed by AgBr, and then AgCl. This practice is known as *fractional precipitation.*

  Worked Example 17.13 describes the separation of only two ions (Cl^- and Br^-), but the procedure can be applied to a solution containing more than two different types of ions.

Compound	K_{sp}
AgCl	1.6×10^{-10}
AgBr	7.7×10^{-13}
AgI	8.3×10^{-17}

Multi 17.5
Solutions precipitation—fractional crystallization

Worked Example 17.13

Silver nitrate is added slowly to a solution that is 0.020 M in Cl^- ions and 0.020 M in Br^- ions. Calculate the concentration of Ag^+ ions (in mol/L) required to initiate the precipitation of AgBr without precipitating AgCl.

Strategy Silver nitrate dissociates in solution to give Ag^+ and NO_3^- ions. Adding Ag^+ ions in sufficient amount will cause the slightly soluble ionic compounds AgCl and AgBr to precipitate from solution. Knowing the K_{sp} values for AgCl and AgBr (and the concentrations of Cl^- and Br^- already in solution), we can use the equilibrium expressions to calculate the maximum concentration of Ag^+ that can exist in solution without exceeding K_{sp} for each compound.

Setup The solubility equilibria, K_{sp} values, and equilibrium expressions for AgCl and AgBr are

$$AgCl(s) \rightleftharpoons Ag^+(aq) + Cl^-(aq) \qquad K_{sp} = 1.6 \times 10^{-10} = [Ag^+][Cl^-]$$

$$AgBr(s) \rightleftharpoons Ag^+(aq) + Br^-(aq) \qquad K_{sp} = 7.7 \times 10^{-13} = [Ag^+][Br^-]$$

Because the K_{sp} for AgBr is smaller (by a factor of more than 200), AgBr should precipitate first; that is, it will require a lower concentration of added Ag^+ to begin precipitation. Therefore, we first solve for $[Ag^+]$ using the equilibrium expression for AgBr to determine the minimum Ag^+ concentration necessary to initiate precipitation of AgBr. We then solve for $[Ag^+]$ again, using the equilibrium expression for AgCl to determine the *maximum* Ag^+ concentration that can exist in the solution without initiating the precipitation of AgCl.

Solution Solving the AgBr equilibrium expression for Ag^+ concentration, we have

$$[Ag^+] = \frac{K_{sp}}{[Br^-]}$$

and

$$[Ag^+] = \frac{7.7 \times 10^{-13}}{0.020} = 3.9 \times 10^{-11} \, M$$

For AgBr to precipitate from solution, the silver ion concentration must exceed $3.9 \times 10^{-11} \, M$. Solving the AgCl equilibrium expression for the Ag^+ concentration, we have

$$[Ag^+] = \frac{K_{sp}}{[Cl^-]}$$

(Continued on next page)

and

$$[Ag^+] = \frac{1.6 \times 10^{-10}}{0.020} = 8.0 \times 10^{-9}\ M$$

For AgCl *not* to precipitate from solution, the silver ion concentration must stay below $8.0 \times 10^{-9}\ M$. Therefore, to precipitate the Br^- ions without precipitating the Cl^- from this solution, the Ag^+ concentration must be greater than $3.9 \times 10^{-11}\ M$ and less than $8.0 \times 10^{-9}\ M$.

Think About It

If we continue adding $AgNO_3$ until the Ag^+ concentration is high enough to begin the precipitation of AgCl, the concentration of Br^- remaining in solution can also be determined using the K_{sp} expression:

$$[Br^-] = \frac{K_{sp}}{[Ag^+]} = \frac{7.7 \times 10^{-13}}{8.0 \times 10^{-9}}$$

$$= 9.6 \times 10^{-5}\ M$$

Thus, by the time AgCl begins to precipitate, $(9.6 \times 10^{-5}\ M) \div (0.020\ M) = 0.0048$, so less than 0.5 percent of the original bromide ion remains in the solution.

Practice Problem A Lead(II) nitrate is added slowly to a solution that is $0.020\ M$ in Cl^- ions. Calculate the concentration of Pb^{2+} ions (in mol/L) required to initiate the precipitation of $PbCl_2$. (K_{sp} for $PbCl_2$ is 2.4×10^{-4}.)

Practice Problem B Calculate the concentration of Ag^+ (in mol/L) necessary to initiate the precipitation of (a) AgCl and (b) Ag_3PO_4 from a solution in which $[Cl^-]$ and $[PO_4^{3-}]$ are each $0.10\ M$. (K_{sp} for Ag_3PO_4 is 1.8×10^{-18}.)

Qualitative Analysis of Metal Ions in Solution

The principle of selective precipitation can be used to identify the types of ions present in a solution. This practice is called *qualitative analysis.* There are about 20 common cations that can be analyzed readily in aqueous solution. These cations can be divided into five groups according to the solubility products of their insoluble salts (Table 17.4). Because an unknown solution may contain from 1 to all 20 ions, any analysis must be carried out systematically from group 1 through group 5. The general procedure for separating these 20 ions is as follows:

> **Student Annotation:** Note that these group numbers do *not* correspond to groups in the periodic table.

- *Group 1 cations.* When dilute HCl is added to the unknown solution, only the Ag^+, Hg_2^{2+}, and Pb^{2+} ions precipitate as insoluble chlorides. The other ions, whose chlorides are soluble, remain in solution.

- *Group 2 cations.* After the chloride precipitates have been removed by filtration, hydrogen sulfide is added to the unknown solution, which is acidic due to the addition of HCl. Metal ions from group 2 react to produce metal sulfides:

$$M^{2+}(aq) + H_2S(aq) \rightleftharpoons MS(s) + 2H^+(aq)$$

In the presence of H^+, this equilibrium shifts to the *left.* Therefore, only the metal sulfides with the *smallest* K_{sp} values precipitate under acidic conditions. These are Bi_2S_3, CdS, CuS, and SnS (see Table 17.4). The solution is then filtered to remove the insoluble sulfides.

- *Group 3 cations.* At this stage, sodium hydroxide is added to the solution to make it basic. In a basic solution, the metal sulfide equilibrium shifts to the right and the more soluble sulfides (CoS, FeS, MnS, NiS, ZnS) now precipitate out of solution. The Al^{3+} and Cr^{3+} ions actually precipitate as the hydroxides $Al(OH)_3$ and $Cr(OH)_3$, rather than as the sulfides, because the hydroxides are less soluble. The solution is filtered again to remove the insoluble sulfides and hydroxides.

- *Group 4 cations.* After all the group 1, 2, and 3 cations have been removed from solution, sodium carbonate is added to the basic solution to precipitate Ba^{2+}, Ca^{2+}, and Sr^{2+} ions as $BaCO_3$, $CaCO_3$, and $SrCO_3$. These precipitates, too, are removed from solution by filtration.

- *Group 5 cations.* At this stage, the only cations possibly remaining in solution are Na^+, K^+, and NH_4^+. The presence of NH_4^+ ions can be determined by adding sodium hydroxide:

$$NaOH(aq) + NH_4^+(aq) \longrightarrow Na^+(aq) + H_2O(l) + NH_3(g)$$

The ammonia gas is detected either by its characteristic odor or by observing a wet piece of red litmus paper turning blue when placed above (not in contact with) the solution. To confirm the presence of Na^+ and K^+ ions, a flame test is usually used in which a piece of platinum wire (chosen because platinum is inert) is dipped into the original solution and then held over a Bunsen burner flame. Na^+ ions emit a yellow flame when heated in this manner, whereas K^+ ions emit a violet flame (Figure 17.11). Figure 17.12 summarizes this scheme for separating metal ions.

Multi 17.6
Chemical analysis—flame tests of metals

SECTION 17.6 REVIEW

Separation of Ions Using Differences in Solubility

17.6.1   A solution is 0.10 M in Br^-, CO_3^{2-}, Cl^-, I^-, and SO_4^{2-} ions. Which compound will precipitate first as silver nitrate is added to the solution?

17.6.2   Barium nitrate is added slowly to a solution that is 0.10 M in SO_4^{2-} ions and 0.10 M in F^- ions. Calculate the concentration of Ba^{2+} ions (in mol/L) required to initiate the precipitation of $BaSO_4$ without precipitating BaF_2.

Figure 17.11 Flame tests for sodium (yellow flame) and potassium (violet flame).

Figure 17.12 A flowchart for the separation of cations in qualitative analysis.

Learning Outcomes

- Describe the common ion effect.
- Calculate equilibrium concentrations or pH of a solution involving a common ion.
- Calculate the pH of a buffer using equilibrium calculations and the Henderson-Hasselbalch equation.
- Describe how to prepare a buffer with a given pH.
- Select the appropriate weak acid (or weak base) to make a buffer of given pH.
- Predict the pH of a titration given the type of acid and base (strong or weak).
- Calculate the pH throughout a titration between acids and bases: strong plus strong or strong plus weak.
- Use a titration curve to identify what type of titration was employed (e.g., weak acid plus strong base).

- Distinguish between endpoint and equivalence point.
- Select an indicator given the acid and base species used in a titration.
- Define solubility product constant (K_{sp}).
- Use K_{sp} to determine molar solubility and vice versa.
- Use K_{sp} to predict whether a precipitation will occur.
- Cite examples of how the following can affect solubility: common ions, pH, or complex ion formation.
- Use K_f, the formation constant, in equilibrium calculations.
- Explain fractional precipitation.
- Give, in your own words, the meaning and primary basis of qualitative analysis.

Chapter Summary

SECTION 17.1

- The presence of a common ion suppresses the ionization of a weak acid or weak base. This is known as the **common ion effect.**
- A common ion is added to a solution in the form of a *salt*.

SECTION 17.2

- A solution that contains significant concentrations of both members of a conjugate acid-base pair (weak acid–conjugate base or weak base–conjugate acid) is a *buffer solution* or simply a **buffer.**
- Buffer solutions resist pH change upon addition of small amounts of strong acid or strong base. Buffers are important to biological systems.
- The pH of a buffer can be calculated using an equilibrium table or with the **Henderson-Hasselbalch equation.**
- The pK_a of a weak acid is $-\log K_a$. When the weak acid and conjugate base concentrations in a buffer solution are equal, pH = pK_a.
- We can prepare a buffer with a specific pH by choosing a weak acid with a pK_a close to the desired pH.

SECTION 17.3

- The titration curve of a strong acid–strong base titration has a long, steep region near the equivalence point.
- Titration curves for weak acid–strong base or weak base–strong acid titrations have a significantly shorter steep region.
- The pH at the equivalence point of a strong acid–strong base titration is 7.00.
- The pH at the equivalence point of a weak acid–strong base titration is above 7.00.
- The pH at the equivalence point of a weak base–strong acid titration is below 7.00.
- Acid-base indicators are usually weak organic acids that exhibit two different colors depending on the pH of the solution. The

endpoint of a titration is the point at which the color of the indicator changes. It is used to estimate the *equivalence point* of a titration.
- The indicator used for a particular titration should exhibit a color change in the pH range corresponding to the steep region of the titration curve.

SECTION 17.4

- The *solubility product constant* (K_{sp}) is the equilibrium constant that indicates to what extent a slightly soluble ionic compound dissociates in water.
- K_{sp} can be used to determine *molar solubility* or *solubility* in g/L, and vice versa.
- K_{sp} can also be used to predict whether or not a precipitate will form when two solutions are mixed.

SECTION 17.5

- Solubility is affected by common ions, pH, and complex ion formation. The *formation constant* (K_f) indicates to what extent complex ions form.
- A salt that dissociates to give a strong conjugate base such as fluoride ion will be more soluble in acidic solution than in pure water.
- A salt that dissociates to give hydroxide ion will be more soluble at lower pH and less soluble at higher pH.
- The solubility of an ionic compound increases when the formation of a *complex ion* consumes one of the products of dissociation.

SECTION 17.6

- Ions can be separated using *fractional precipitation.*
- Fractional precipitation schemes can be designed based on K_{sp} values.
- Groups of cations can be identified through the use of selective precipitation. This is the basis of *qualitative analysis.*

Key Words

Buffer, 715
Common ion effect, 714
Complex ion, 742

Endpoint, 729
Formation constant (K_f), 743
Fractional precipitation, 747

Henderson-Hasselbalch
  equation, 717
Molar solubility, 732

Qualitative analysis, 748
Solubility, 732
Solubility product constant
  (K_{sp}), 732

Key Equations

17.1 $pH = pK_a + \log \dfrac{[A^-]}{[HA]}$

17.2 $pK_a = -\log K_a$

17.3 $pH = pK_a + \log \dfrac{[\text{conjugate base}]}{[\text{weak acid}]}$

Questions and Problems

SECTION 17.1:   THE COMMON ION EFFECT

Review Questions

17.1   Use Le Châtelier's principle to explain how the common ion effect affects the pH of a weak acid solution.

17.2   Describe the effect on pH (increase, decrease, or no change) that results from each of the following additions: (a) potassium acetate to an acetic acid solution, (b) ammonium nitrate to an ammonia solution, (c) sodium formate (HCOONa) to a formic acid (HCOOH) solution, (d) potassium chloride to a hydrochloric acid solution, (e) barium iodide to a hydroiodic acid solution.

17.3   Define pK_a for a weak acid. What is the relationship between the value of the pK_a and the strength of the acid?

17.4   The pK_a's of two monoprotic acids HA and HB are 5.9 and 8.1, respectively. Which of the two is the stronger acid?

Problems

17.5   Determine the pH of (a) a 0.40 M CH$_3$COOH solution and (b) a solution that is 0.40 M CH$_3$COOH and 0.20 M CH$_3$COONa.

17.6   Determine the pH of (a) a 0.20 M NH$_3$ solution, and (b) a solution that is 0.20 M NH$_3$ and 0.30 M NH$_4$Cl.

SECTION 17.2:   BUFFER SOLUTIONS

Visualizing Chemistry
Figure 17.1

VC 17.1   Which pair of substances can be dissolved together to prepare a buffer solution?

CH$_3$COOH	CH$_3$COONa	NaOH	HCl	NaCl
(i)	(ii)	(iii)	(iv)	(v)

(a) i/ii
(b) i/ii, i/iii, ii/iv
(c) i/ii, i/iii, ii/iii, iv/v

VC 17.2   Consider the buffer shown in Figure 17.1, in which [CH$_3$COOH] = 0.10 M, [CH$_3$COO$^-$] = 0.10 M, and pH = 4.74. How would the pH of the buffer change if we doubled the volume by adding 100 mL of water?
(a) The pH would increase.
(b) The pH would decrease.
(c) The pH would not change.

VC 17.3   Consider a buffer similar to the one shown in Figure 17.1, in which [CH$_3$COOH] = 0.50 M and [CH$_3$COO$^-$] = 0.75 M. Which substance can we add more of without causing a drastic change in pH?
(a) HCl
(b) NaOH
(c) Neither

VC 17.4   According to Figure 17.1, the reaction that occurs when strong acid is added to the buffer is

$$H^+(aq) + CH_3COO^-(aq) \longrightarrow CH_3COOH(aq)$$

Estimate the value of K for this reaction.
(a) 1×10^{14}
(b) 6×10^{-10}
(c) 6×10^4

Review Questions

17.7   What is a buffer solution? What must a solution contain to be a buffer?

17.8   Using only a pH meter, water, and a graduated cylinder, how would you distinguish between an acid solution and a buffer solution at the same pH?

Problems

17.9   Which of the following solutions can act as a buffer: (a) KCl/HCl, (b) KHSO$_4$/H$_2$SO$_4$, (c) Na$_2$HPO$_4$/NaH$_2$PO$_4$, (d) KNO$_2$/HNO$_2$?

17.10   Which of the following solutions can act as a buffer: (a) KCN/HCN, (b) Na$_2$SO$_4$/NaHSO$_4$, (c) NH$_3$/NH$_4$NO$_3$, (d) NaI/HI?

17.11 Calculate the pH of the buffer system made up of 0.15 M NH_3/0.35 M NH_4Cl.

17.12 Calculate the pH of the following two buffer solutions: (a) 2.0 M CH_3COONa/2.0 M CH_3COOH, (b) 0.20 M CH_3COONa/0.20 M CH_3COOH. Which is the more effective buffer? Why?

17.13 The pH of a bicarbonate–carbonic acid buffer is 8.00. Calculate the ratio of the concentration of carbonic acid (H_2CO_3) to that of the bicarbonate ion (HCO_3^-).

17.14 What is the pH of the buffer 0.10 M Na_2HPO_4/0.15 M KH_2PO_4?

17.15 The pH of a sodium acetate–acetic acid buffer is 4.50. Calculate the ratio $[CH_3COO^-]/[CH_3COOH]$.

17.16 The pH of blood plasma is 7.40. Assuming the principal buffer system is HCO_3^-/H_2CO_3, calculate the ratio $[HCO_3^-]/[H_2CO_3]$. Is this buffer more effective against an added acid or an added base?

17.17 Calculate the pH of the 0.20 M NH_3/0.20 M NH_4Cl buffer. What is the pH of the buffer after the addition of 10.0 mL of 0.10 M HCl to 65.0 mL of the buffer?

17.18 Calculate the pH of 1.00 L of the buffer 1.00 M CH_3COONa/1.00 M CH_3COOH before and after the addition of (a) 0.080 mol NaOH and (b) 0.12 mol HCl. (Assume that there is no change in volume.)

17.19 A diprotic acid, H_2A, has the following ionization constants: $K_{a_1} = 1.1 \times 10^{-3}$ and $K_{a_2} = 2.5 \times 10^{-6}$. To make up a buffer solution of pH 5.80, which combination would you choose: $NaHA/H_2A$ or $Na_2A/NaHA$?

17.20 A student is asked to prepare a buffer solution at pH 8.60, using one of the following weak acids: HA ($K_a = 2.7 \times 10^{-3}$), HB ($K_a = 4.4 \times 10^{-6}$), HC ($K_a = 2.6 \times 10^{-9}$). Which acid should the student choose? Why?

17.21 The following diagrams contain one or more of the compounds: H_2A, NaHA, and Na_2A, where H_2A is a weak diprotic acid. (1) Which of the solutions can act as buffer solutions? (2) Which solution is the most effective buffer solution? Water molecules and Na^+ ions have been omitted for clarity.

◕ = H_2A ◕ = HA^- ● = A^{2-}

    (a)   (b)   (c)   (d)

17.22 The following diagrams represent solutions containing a weak acid HA ($pK_a = 5.0$) and its sodium salt NaA. (1) Which solution has the lowest pH? Which has the highest pH? (2) How many different species are present after the addition of two H^+ ions to solution (a)? (3) How many different species are present after the addition of two OH^- ions to solution (b)?

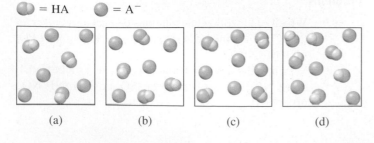

◕ = HA   ● = A^-

    (a)   (b)   (c)   (d)

SECTION 17.3: ACID-BASE TITRATIONS

Review Questions

17.23 Briefly describe what happens in an acid-base titration.

17.24 Sketch titration curves for the following acid-base titrations: (a) HCl versus NaOH, (b) HCl versus CH_3NH_2, (c) CH_3COOH versus NaOH. In each case, the base is added to the acid in an Erlenmeyer flask. Your graphs should show the pH on the y axis and the volume of base added on the x axis.

17.25 Explain how an acid-base indicator works in a titration. What are the criteria for choosing an indicator for a particular acid-base titration?

17.26 The amount of indicator used in an acid-base titration must be small. Why?

Problems

17.27 A 0.2688-g sample of a monoprotic acid neutralizes 16.4 mL of 0.08133 M KOH solution. Calculate the molar mass of the acid.

17.28 A 5.00-g quantity of a diprotic acid was dissolved in water and made up to exactly 250 mL. Calculate the molar mass of the acid if 25.0 mL of this solution required 11.1 mL of 1.00 M KOH for neutralization. Assume that both protons of the acid were titrated.

17.29 In a titration experiment, 12.5 mL of 0.500 M H_2SO_4 neutralizes 50.0 mL of NaOH. What is the concentration of the NaOH solution?

17.30 In a titration experiment, 20.4 mL of 0.883 M HCOOH neutralizes 19.3 mL of $Ba(OH)_2$. What is the concentration of the $Ba(OH)_2$ solution?

17.31 A 0.1276-g sample of an unknown monoprotic acid was dissolved in 25.0 mL of water and titrated with a 0.0633 M NaOH solution. The volume of base required to bring the solution to the equivalence point was 18.4 mL. (a) Calculate the molar mass of the acid. (b) After 10.0 mL of base had been added during the titration, the pH was determined to be 5.87. What is the K_a of the unknown acid?

17.32 A solution is made by mixing exactly 500 mL of 0.167 M NaOH with exactly 500 mL of 0.100 M CH_3COOH. Calculate the equilibrium concentrations of H^+, CH_3COOH, CH_3COO^-, OH^-, and Na^+.

17.33 Calculate the pH at the equivalence point for the following titration: 0.20 M HCl versus 0.20 M methylamine (CH_3NH_2).

17.34 Calculate the pH at the equivalence point for the following titration: 0.10 M HCOOH versus 0.10 M NaOH.

17.35 A 25.0-mL solution of 0.100 M CH_3COOH is titrated with a 0.200 M KOH solution. Calculate the pH after the following additions of the KOH solution: (a) 0.0 mL, (b) 5.0 mL, (c) 10.0 mL, (d) 12.5 mL, (e) 15.0 mL.

17.36 A 10.0-mL solution of 0.300 M NH_3 is titrated with a 0.100 M HCl solution. Calculate the pH after the following additions of the HCl solution: (a) 0.0 mL, (b) 10.0 mL, (c) 20.0 mL, (d) 30.0 mL, (e) 40.0 mL.

17.37 Referring to Table 17.3, specify which indicator or indicators you would use for the following titrations: (a) HCOOH versus NaOH, (b) HCl versus KOH, (c) HNO_3 versus CH_3NH_2.

17.38 A student carried out an acid-base titration by adding NaOH solution from a burette to an Erlenmeyer flask containing an HCl solution and using phenolphthalein as the indicator. At the equivalence point, she observed a faint reddish-pink color. However, after a few minutes, the solution gradually turned colorless. What do you suppose happened?

17.39 The ionization constant K_a of an indicator HIn is 1.0×10^{-6}. The color of the nonionized form is red and that of the ionized form is yellow. What is the color of this indicator in a solution whose pH is 4.00?

17.40 The K_a of a certain indicator is 2.0×10^{-6}. The color of HIn is green and that of In⁻ is red. A few drops of the indicator are added to an HCl solution, which is then titrated against an NaOH solution. At what pH will the indicator change color?

17.41 The following diagrams represent solutions at various stages in the titration of a weak base B (such as NH_3) with HCl. Identify the solution that corresponds to (1) the initial stage before the addition of HCl, (2) halfway to the equivalence point, (3) the equivalence point, (4) beyond the equivalence point. Is the pH greater than, less than, or equal to 7 at the equivalence point? Water and Cl⁻ ions have been omitted for clarity.

● = B   ◖ = BH⁺   ◓ = H_3O^+

(a)   (b)   (c)   (d)

17.42 The following diagrams represent solutions at various stages in the titration of a weak acid HA with NaOH. Identify the solution that corresponds to (1) the initial stage before the addition of NaOH, (2) halfway to the equivalence point, (3) the equivalence point, (4) beyond the equivalence point. Is the pH greater than, less than, or equal to 7 at the equivalence point? Water and Na⁺ ions have been omitted for clarity.

◖ = HA   ◓ = A⁻   ◑ = OH⁻

(a)   (b)   (c)   (d)

SECTION 17.4: SOLUBILITY EQUILIBRIA

Review Questions

17.43 Use $BaSO_4$ to distinguish between the terms *solubility* and *solubility product*.

17.44 Why do we usually not quote the K_{sp} values for soluble ionic compounds?

17.45 Write balanced equations and solubility product expressions for the solubility equilibria of the following compounds: (a) CuBr, (b) ZnC_2O_4, (c) Ag_2CrO_4, (d) Hg_2Cl_2, (e) $AuCl_3$, (f) $Mn_3(PO_4)_2$.

17.46 Write the solubility product expression for the ionic compound A_xB_y.

17.47 How can we predict whether a precipitate will form when two solutions are mixed?

17.48 Silver chloride has a larger K_{sp} than silver carbonate (see Table 17.4). Does this mean that AgCl also has a larger molar solubility than Ag_2CO_3?

Problems

17.49 Calculate the concentration of ions in the following saturated solutions: (a) [I⁻] in AgI solution with $[Ag^+] = 9.1 \times 10^{-9}$ M, (b) $[Al^{3+}]$ in $Al(OH)_3$ solution with [OH⁻] = 2.9×10^{-9} M.

17.50 From the solubility data given, calculate the solubility products for the following compounds: (a) SrF_2, 7.3×10^{-2} g/L, (b) Ag_3PO_4, 6.7×10^{-3} g/L.

17.51 The molar solubility of $MnCO_3$ is 4.2×10^{-6} M. What is K_{sp} for this compound?

17.52 The solubility of an ionic compound MX (molar mass = 346 g) is 4.63×10^{-3} g/L. What is K_{sp} for this compound?

17.53 The solubility of an ionic compound M_2X_3 (molar mass = 288 g) is 3.6×10^{-17} g/L. What is K_{sp} for this compound?

17.54 Using data from Table 17.4, calculate the molar solubility of CaF_2.

17.55 What is the pH of a saturated zinc hydroxide solution?

17.56 The pH of a saturated solution of a metal hydroxide MOH is 9.68. Calculate the K_{sp} for this compound.

17.57 If 20.0 mL of 0.10 M $Ba(NO_3)_2$ is added to 50.0 mL of 0.10 M Na_2CO_3, will $BaCO_3$ precipitate?

17.58 A volume of 75 mL of 0.060 M NaF is mixed with 25 mL of 0.15 M $Sr(NO_3)_2$. Calculate the concentrations in the final solution of NO_3^-, Na⁺, Sr^{2+}, and F⁻. (K_{sp} for $SrF_2 = 2.0 \times 10^{-10}$.)

17.59 The diagram represents a saturated solution of the salt MA_2. Which soluble salt will cause the precipitation of the greatest quantity of MA_2 when 0.1 mole is dissolved in the saturated solution? (For clarity, the water molecules are not shown.)

(a) NaA
(b) BaA_2
(c) AlA_3
(d) $M(NO_3)_2$
(e) $M_3(PO_4)_2$

◖ = M^{2+} ● = A⁻

17.60 Diagrams 1 and 2 represent a saturated solution of the slightly soluble salt M_2B and a solution of the soluble salt MNO_3, respectively. Which of the solutions of the soluble salt Na_2B can be added to the solution of MNO_3 without causing a precipitate to form? Select all that apply. Assume that the solution volumes are equal, and that they are additive when combined. (For clarity, the water molecules, nitrate ions, and sodium ions are not shown.)

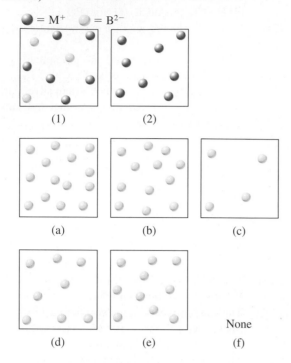

= M⁺   = B²⁻

(1)   (2)

(a)   (b)   (c)

(d)   (e)   (f)
                              None

SECTION 17.5:   FACTORS AFFECTING SOLUBILITY

 Visualizing Chemistry
Figure 17.8

VC 17.5   Which of the following would cause precipitation of the largest amount of AgCl when 0.1 mole is dissolved in the saturated solution shown in Figure 17.8?
(a) NaCl
(b) CsCl
(c) Both would cause precipitation of the same amount.

VC 17.6   Which of the following would cause precipitation of the largest amount of AgCl when 0.1 g is dissolved in the saturated solution shown in Figure 17.8?
(a) NaCl
(b) CsCl
(c) Both would cause precipitation of the same amount.

VC 17.7   How would the concentration of silver ion in the last view of Figure 17.8 be different if we dissolved the sodium chloride *before* dissolving the silver chloride?
(a) It would be higher.
(b) It would be lower.
(c) It would not change.

VC 17.8   How would the concentration of silver ion in the last view of Figure 17.8 be different if we added silver nitrate to the saturated solution of AgCl instead of sodium chloride?
(a) It would be higher.
(b) It would be lower.
(c) It would not change.

Review Questions

17.61   How does the common ion effect influence solubility equilibria? Use Le Châtelier's principle to explain the decrease in solubility of $CaCO_3$ in an Na_2CO_3 solution.

17.62   The molar solubility of AgCl in 6.5×10^{-3} M AgNO₃ is 2.5×10^{-8} M. In deriving K_{sp} from these data, which of the following assumptions are reasonable? (a) K_{sp} is the same as solubility. (b) K_{sp} of AgCl is the same in 6.5×10^{-3} M AgNO₃ as in pure water. (c) Solubility of AgCl is independent of the concentration of AgNO₃. (d) [Ag⁺] in solution does not change significantly upon the addition of AgCl to 6.5×10^{-3} M AgNO₃. (e) [Ag⁺] in solution after the addition of AgCl to 6.5×10^{-3} M AgNO₃ is the same as it would be in pure water.

17.63   Give an example to illustrate the general effect of complex ion formation on solubility.

Problems

17.64   How many grams of $CaCO_3$ will dissolve in 3.0×10^2 mL of 0.050 M $Ca(NO_3)_2$?

17.65   The solubility product of $PbBr_2$ is 8.9×10^{-6}. Determine the molar solubility in (a) pure water, (b) 0.20 M KBr solution, and (c) 0.20 M $Pb(NO_3)_2$ solution.

17.66   Calculate the molar solubility of AgCl in a 1.00-L solution containing 10.0 g of dissolved $CaCl_2$.

17.67   Calculate the molar solubility of $BaSO_4$ in (a) water and (b) a solution containing 1.0 M SO_4^{2-} ions.

17.68   Which of the following ionic compounds will be more soluble in acid solution than in water: (a) $BaSO_4$, (b) $PbCl_2$, (c) $Fe(OH)_3$, (d) $CaCO_3$?

17.69   Which of the following will be more soluble in acid solution than in pure water: (a) CuI, (b) Ag_2SO_4, (c) $Zn(OH)_2$, (d) BaC_2O_4, (e) $Ca_3(PO_4)_2$?

17.70   Compare the molar solubility of $Mg(OH)_2$ in water and in a solution buffered at a pH of 9.0.

17.71   Calculate the molar solubility of $Fe(OH)_2$ in a solution buffered at (a) a pH of 8.00 and (b) a pH of 10.00.

17.72   The solubility product of $Mg(OH)_2$ is 1.2×10^{-11}. What minimum OH⁻ concentration must be attained (for example, by adding NaOH) to decrease the Mg concentration in a solution of $Mg(NO_3)_2$ to less than 1.0×10^{-10} M?

17.73   Calculate whether or not a precipitate will form if 2.00 mL of 0.60 M NH_3 is added to 1.0 L of 1.0×10^{-3} M $FeSO_4$.

17.74   If 2.50 g of $CuSO_4$ is dissolved in 9.0×10^2 mL of 0.30 M NH_3, what are the concentrations of Cu^{2+}, $Cu(NH_3)_4^{2+}$, and NH_3 at equilibrium?

17.75   Calculate the concentrations of Cd^{2+}, $Cd(CN)_4^{2-}$, and CN⁻ at equilibrium when 0.50 g of $Cd(NO_3)_2$ dissolves in 5.0×10^2 mL of 0.50 M NaCN.

17.76   If NaOH is added to 0.010 M Al^{3+}, which will be the predominant species at equilibrium: $Al(OH)_3$ or $Al(OH)_4^-$? The pH of the solution is 14.00. [K_f for $Al(OH)_4^- = 2.0 \times 10^{33}$.]

17.77   Calculate the molar solubility of AgI in a 1.0 M NH_3 solution.

17.78   (a) Calculate the molar solubility of hydroxyapatite given that its K_{sp} is 2×10^{-59}.
(b) Calculate the molar solubility of hydroxyapatite in a buffered aqueous solution with pH = 4.0.

17.79   (a) Calculate the K_{sp} of fluoroapatite given that its molar solubility is 7×10^{-8} M.
(b) Calculate the molar solubility of fluoroapatite in an aqueous solution in which the concentration of fluoride ion is 0.10 M.

SECTION 17.6: SEPARATION OF IONS USING DIFFERENCES IN SOLUBILITY

Review Questions

17.80   Outline the general procedure of qualitative analysis.

17.81   Give two examples of metal ions in each group (1 through 5) in the qualitative analysis scheme.

Problems

17.82   Solid NaI is slowly added to a solution that is 0.010 M in Cu^+ and 0.010 M in Ag^+. (a) Which compound will begin to precipitate first? (b) Calculate $[Ag^+]$ when CuI just begins to precipitate. (c) What percent of Ag^+ remains in solution at this point?

17.83   Find the approximate pH range suitable for the separation of Fe^{3+} and Zn^{2+} ions by precipitation of $Fe(OH)_3$ from a solution that is initially 0.010 M in both Fe^{3+} and Zn^{2+}.

17.84   In a group 1 analysis, a student obtained a precipitate containing both AgCl and $PbCl_2$. Suggest one reagent that would enable the student to separate $AgCl(s)$ from $PbCl_2(s)$.

17.85   In a group 1 analysis, a student adds HCl acid to the unknown solution to make $[Cl^-] = 0.15\ M$. Some $PbCl_2$ precipitates. Calculate the concentration of Pb^{2+} remaining in solution.

ADDITIONAL PROBLEMS

17.86   The buffer range is defined by the equation $pH = pK_a \pm 1$. Calculate the range of the ratio [conjugate base]/[acid] that corresponds to this equation.

17.87   The pK_a of the indicator methyl orange is 3.46. Over what pH range does this indicator change from 90 percent HIn to 90 percent In^-?

17.88   Sketch the titration curve of a weak acid with a strong base like the one shown in Figure 17.4. On your graph, indicate the volume of base used at the equivalence point and also at the half-equivalence point, that is, the point at which half of the acid has been neutralized. Explain how the measured pH at the half-equivalence point can be used to determine K_a of the acid.

17.89   A 200-mL volume of NaOH solution was added to 400 mL of a 2.00 M HNO_2 solution. The pH of the mixed solution was 1.50 units greater than that of the original acid solution. Calculate the molarity of the NaOH solution.

17.90   The pK_a of butyric acid (HBut) is 4.7. Calculate K_b for the butyrate ion (But^-).

17.91   A solution is made by mixing exactly 500 mL of 0.167 M NaOH with exactly 500 mL 0.100 M HCOOH. Calculate the equilibrium concentrations of H^+, HCOOH, $HCOO^-$, OH^-, and Na^+.

17.92   Tris [tris(hydroxymethyl)aminomethane] is a common buffer for studying biological systems: (a) Calculate the pH of the tris buffer after mixing 15.0 mL of 0.10 M HCl solution with 25.0 mL of 0.10 M tris. (b) This buffer was used to study an enzyme-catalyzed reaction. As a result of the reaction, 0.00015 mole of H^+ was consumed. What is the pH of the buffer at the end

of the reaction? (c) What would be the final pH if no buffer were present?

$$HOCH_2-\underset{\underset{HOCH_2}{|}}{\overset{\overset{HOCH_2}{|}}{C}}-\overset{+}{N}H_3 \quad \underset{\rightleftharpoons}{\overset{pK_a = 8.1}{}} \quad HOCH_2-\underset{\underset{HOCH_2}{|}}{\overset{\overset{HOCH_2}{|}}{C}}-NH_2 + H^+$$

17.93 $Cd(OH)_2$ is an insoluble compound. It dissolves in excess NaOH in solution. Write a balanced ionic equation for this reaction. What type of reaction is this?

17.94   A student mixes 50.0 mL of 1.00 M $Ba(OH)_2$ with 86.4 mL of 0.494 M H_2SO_4. Calculate the mass of $BaSO_4$ formed and the pH of the mixed solution.

17.95   For which of the following reactions is the equilibrium constant called a solubility product?

(a) $Zn(OH)_2(s) + 2OH^-(aq) \rightleftharpoons Zn(OH)_4^{2-}(aq)$
(b) $3Ca^{2+}(aq) + 2PO_4^{3-}(aq) \rightleftharpoons Ca_3(PO_4)_2(s)$
(c) $CaCO_3(s) + 2H^+(aq) \rightleftharpoons Ca^{2+}(aq) + H_2O(l) + CO_2(g)$
(d) $PbI_2(s) \rightleftharpoons Pb^{2+}(aq) + 2I^-(aq)$

17.96   A 2.0-L kettle contains 116 g of boiler scale ($CaCO_3$). How many times would the kettle have to be completely filled with distilled water to remove all the deposit at 25°C?

17.97   Equal volumes of 0.12 M $AgNO_3$ and 0.14 M $ZnCl_2$ solution are mixed. Calculate the equilibrium concentrations of Ag^+, Cl^-, Zn^{2+}, and NO_3^-.

17.98   Find the approximate pH range suitable for separating Mg^{2+} and Zn^{2+} by the precipitation of $Zn(OH)_2$ from a solution that is initially 0.010 M in Mg^{2+} and Zn^{2+}.

17.99   Calculate the solubility (in g/L) of Ag_2CO_3.

17.100   A volume of 25.0 mL of 0.100 M HCl is titrated against a 0.100 M CH_3NH_2 solution added to it from a burette. Calculate the pH values of the solution after (a) 10.0 mL of CH_3NH_2 solution has been added, (b) 25.0 mL of CH_3NH_2 solution has been added, (c) 35.0 mL of CH_3NH_2 solution has been added.

17.101   The molar solubility of $Pb(IO_3)_2$ in a 0.10 M $NaIO_3$ solution is 2.4×10^{-11} mol/L. What is K_{sp} for $Pb(IO_3)_2$?

17.102   When a KI solution was added to a solution of mercury(II) chloride, a precipitate [mercury(II) iodide] formed. A student plotted the mass of the precipitate versus the volume of the KI solution added and obtained the following graph. Explain the shape of the graph.

17.103   Barium is a toxic substance that can seriously impair heart function. For an X ray of the gastrointestinal tract, a patient drinks an aqueous suspension of 20 g $BaSO_4$. If this substance were to equilibrate with the 5.0 L of the blood in the patient's body, what would be $[Ba^{2+}]$? For a good estimate, we may assume that the K_{sp} of $BaSO_4$ at body temperature is the same as at 25°C. Why is $Ba(NO_3)_2$ not chosen for this procedure?

17.104   The pK_a of phenolphthalein is 9.10. Over what pH range does this indicator change from 95 percent HIn to 95 percent In⁻?

17.105   Solid NaBr is slowly added to a solution that is 0.010 M in Cu^+ and 0.010 M in Ag^+. (a) Which compound will begin to precipitate first? (b) Calculate $[Ag^+]$ when CuBr just begins to precipitate. (c) What percent of Ag^+ remains in solution at this point?

17.106   Cacodylic acid is $(CH_3)_2AsO_2H$. Its ionization constant is 6.4×10^{-7}. (a) Calculate the pH of 50.0 mL of a 0.10 M solution of the acid. (b) Calculate the pH of 25.0 mL of 0.15 M $(CH_3)_2AsO_2Na$. (c) Mix the solutions in parts (a) and (b). Calculate the pH of the resulting solution.

17.107   Radiochemical techniques are useful in estimating the solubility product of many compounds. In one experiment, 50.0 mL of a 0.010 M $AgNO_3$ solution containing a silver isotope with a radioactivity of 74,025 counts per min per mL was mixed with 100 mL of a 0.030 M $NaIO_3$ solution. The mixed solution was diluted to 500 mL and filtered to remove all the $AgIO_3$ precipitate. The remaining solution was found to have a radioactivity of 44.4 counts per min per mL. What is the K_{sp} of $AgIO_3$?

17.108   The molar mass of a certain metal carbonate, MCO_3, can be determined by adding an excess of HCl acid to react with all the carbonate and then "back-titrating" the remaining acid with NaOH. (a) Write an equation for these reactions. (b) In a certain experiment, 20.00 mL of 0.0800 M HCl was added to a 0.1022-g sample of MCO_3. The excess HCl required 5.64 mL of 0.1000 M NaOH for neutralization. Calculate the molar mass of the carbonate and identify M.

17.109   Acid-base reactions usually go to completion. Confirm this statement by calculating the equilibrium constant for each of the following cases: (a) A strong acid reacting with a strong base. (b) A strong acid reacting with a weak base (NH_3). (c) A weak acid (CH_3COOH) reacting with a strong base. (d) A weak acid (CH_3COOH) reacting with a weak base (NH_3). (*Hint:* Strong acids exist as H^+ ions and strong bases exist as OH^- ions in solution. You need to look up K_a, K_b, and K_w.)

17.110   Calculate x, the number of molecules of water in oxalic acid hydrate ($H_2C_2O_4 \cdot xH_2O$), from the following data: 5.00 g of the compound is made up to exactly 250 mL solution, and 25.0 mL of this solution requires 15.9 mL of 0.500 M NaOH solution for neutralization.

17.111   Describe how you would prepare a 1-L 0.20 M $CH_3COONa/0.20$ M CH_3COOH buffer system by (a) mixing a solution of CH_3COOH with a solution of CH_3COONa, (b) mixing a solution of CH_3COOH with a solution of NaOH, and (c) mixing a solution of CH_3COONa with a solution of HCl.

17.112   Phenolphthalein is the common indicator for the titration of a strong acid with a strong base. (a) If the pK_a of phenolphthalein is 9.10, what is the ratio of the nonionized form of the indicator (colorless) to the ionized form (reddish pink) at pH 8.00? (b) If 2 drops of 0.060 M phenolphthalein are used in a titration involving a

50.0-mL volume, what is the concentration of the ionized form at pH 8.00? (Assume that 1 drop = 0.050 mL.)

17.113   Of the reactions depicted, which best represents (a) what occurs when strong acid is added to a buffer solution, and (b) what occurs when strong base is added to a buffer solution?

$\bullet\!\!\!\bullet$ = HA $\bullet$ = A⁻ $\bigcirc\!\!\!\bullet$ = H_3O^+ $\bullet\!\!\!\bullet$ = OH⁻ $\bigcirc\!\!\!\bullet$ = H_2O

(a) $\bullet\!\!\!\bullet$ + $\bullet\!\!\!\bullet$ $\longrightarrow$ $\bigcirc\!\!\!\bullet$ + $\bullet$

(b) $\bullet\!\!\!\bullet$ + $\bigcirc\!\!\!\bullet$ $\longrightarrow$ $\bullet\!\!\!\bullet$ + $\bigcirc\!\!\!\bullet$

(c) $\bullet\!\!\!\bullet$ + $\bigcirc\!\!\!\bullet$ $\rightleftharpoons$ $\bullet$ + $\bigcirc\!\!\!\bullet$

(d) $\bullet\!\!\!\bullet$ + $\bigcirc\!\!\!\bullet$ $\rightleftharpoons$ $\bullet\!\!\!\bullet$ + $\bullet\!\!\!\bullet$

(e) $\bigcirc\!\!\!\bullet$ + $\bullet\!\!\!\bullet$ $\longrightarrow$ $\bullet\!\!\!\bullet$ + $\bigcirc\!\!\!\bullet$

17.114   Oil paintings containing lead(II) compounds as constituents of their pigments darken over the years. Suggest a chemical reason for the color change.

17.115   What reagents would you employ to separate the following pairs of ions in solution: (a) Na^+ and Ba^{2+}, (b) K^+ and Pb^{2+}, (c) Zn^{2+} and Hg^{2+}?

17.116   Look up the K_{sp} values for $BaSO_4$ and $SrSO_4$ in Table 17.4. Calculate the concentrations of Ba^{2+}, Sr^{2+}, and SO_4^{2-} in a solution that is saturated with both compounds.

17.117   In principle, amphoteric oxides, such as Al_2O_3 and BeO, can be used to prepare buffer solutions because they possess both acidic and basic properties (see Section 16.11). Explain why these compounds are of little practical use as buffer components.

17.118 $CaSO_4$ ($K_{sp} = 2.4 \times 10^{-5}$) has a larger K_{sp} value than that of Ag_2SO_4 ($K_{sp} = 1.4 \times 10^{-5}$). Does it necessarily follow that $CaSO_4$ also has greater solubility (g/L)? Explain.

17.119   When lemon juice is added to tea, the color becomes lighter. In part, the color change is due to dilution, but the main reason for the change is an acid-base reaction. What is the reaction? (*Hint:* Tea contains "polyphenols," which are weak acids, and lemon juice contains citric acid.)

17.120   How many milliliters of 1.0 M NaOH must be added to 200 mL of 0.10 M NaH_2PO_4 to make a buffer solution with a pH of 7.50?

17.121   The maximum allowable concentration of Pb^{2+} ions in drinking water is 0.05 ppm (that is, 0.05 g of Pb^{2+} in 1 million grams of water). Is this guideline exceeded if an underground water supply is at equilibrium with the mineral anglesite ($PbSO_4$) ($K_{sp} = 1.6 \times 10^{-8}$)?

17.122   The solutions shown contain one or more of the following compounds: H_2A (a weak diprotic acid), NaHA, and Na_2A (the sodium salts of HA^- and A^{2-}). (For clarity, the sodium ions and water molecules are not shown.) Which solutions are buffers? (Select all that apply.)

$\bullet\!\!\!\bullet$ = H_2A $\bullet\!\!\!\bullet$ = HA^- $\bullet$ = A^{2-}

(a)   (b)   (c)   (d)

17.123 Which of the following solutions has the highest $[H^+]$: (a) 0.10 M HF, (b) 0.10 M HF in 0.10 M NaF, (c) 0.10 M HF in 0.10 M SbF$_5$? (*Hint:* SbF$_5$ reacts with F$^-$ to form the complex ion SbF$_6^-$.)

17.124 Distribution curves show how the fractions of a nonionized acid and its conjugate base vary as a function of the pH of the medium. Plot distribution curves for CH$_3$COOH and its conjugate base CH$_3$COO$^-$ in solution. Your graph should show fraction as the y axis and pH as the x axis. What are the fractions and pH at the point where these two curves intersect?

17.125 Calcium oxalate is a major component of kidney stones. Predict whether the formation of kidney stones can be minimized by increasing or decreasing the pH of the fluid present in the kidney. The pH of normal kidney fluid is about 8.2. [The first and second acid ionization constants of oxalic acid (H$_2$C$_2$O$_4$) are 6.5×10^{-2} and 6.1×10^{-5}, respectively. The solubility product of calcium oxalate is 3.0×10^{-9}.]

17.126 Water containing Ca^{2+} and Mg^{2+} ions is called *hard water* and is unsuitable for some household and industrial use because these ions react with soap to form insoluble salts, or curds. One way to remove the Ca^{2+} ions from hard water is by adding washing soda (Na$_2$CO$_3 \cdot$ 10H$_2$O). (a) The molar solubility of CaCO$_3$ is 9.3×10^{-5} M. What is its molar solubility in a 0.050 M Na$_2$CO$_3$ solution? (b) Why are Mg^{2+} ions not removed by this procedure? (c) The Mg^{2+} ions are removed as Mg(OH)$_2$ by adding slaked lime [Ca(OH)$_2$] to the water to produce a saturated solution. Calculate the pH of a saturated Ca(OH)$_2$ solution. (d) What is the concentration of Mg^{2+} ions at this pH? (e) In general, which ion (Ca^{2+} or Mg^{2+}) would you remove first? Why?

17.127 Amino acids are building blocks of proteins. These compounds contain at least one amino group ($-$NH$_2$) and one carboxyl group ($-$COOH). Consider glycine (NH$_2$CH$_2$COOH). Depending on the pH of the solution, glycine can exist in one of three possible forms:

Fully protonated: $^+$NH$_3$$-CH_2$$-$COOH
Dipolar ion: $^+$NH$_3$$-CH_2$$-COO^-$
Fully ionized: NH$_2$$-CH_2$$-COO^-$

Predict the predominant form of glycine at pH 1.0, 7.0, and 12.0. The pK_a of the carboxyl group is 2.3 and that of the ammonium group ($-$NH$_3^+$) is 9.6.

17.128 Consider the ionization of the following acid-base indicator:

$$\text{HIn}(aq) \rightleftharpoons \text{H}^+(aq) + \text{In}^-(aq)$$

The indicator changes color according to the ratios of the concentrations of the acid to its conjugate base. When [HIn]/[In$^-$] $\geq$ 10, color of acid (HIn) predominates. When [HIn]/[In$^-$] $\leq$ 0.1, color of conjugate base (In$^-$) predominates. Show that the pH range over which the indicator changes from the acid color to the base color is pH $=$ p$K_a \pm 1$, where K_a is the ionization constant of the acid HIn.

17.129 One way to distinguish a buffer solution from an acid solution is by dilution. (a) Consider a buffer solution made of 0.500 M CH$_3$COOH and 0.500 M CH$_3$COONa. Calculate its pH and the pH after it has been diluted 10-fold. (b) Compare the result in part (a) with the pHs of a 0.500 M CH$_3$COOH solution before and after it has been diluted 10-fold.

17.130 (a) Referring to Figure 17.4, describe how you would determine the pK_b of the base. (b) Derive an analogous Henderson-Hasselbalch equation relating pOH to pK_b of a weak base B and its conjugate acid HB$^+$. Sketch a titration curve showing the variation of the pOH of the base solution versus the volume of a strong acid added from a burette. Describe how you would determine the pK_b from this curve.

17.131 AgNO$_3$ is added slowly to a solution that contains 0.1 M each of Br$^-$, CO$_3^{2-}$, and SO$_4^{2-}$ ions. What compound will precipitate first and what compound will precipitate last?

17.132 The diagrams represent solutions of MX, which may also contain one or both of the soluble salts, MNO$_3$ and NaX. (Na$^+$ and NO$_3^-$ ions are not shown.) If (a) represents a saturated solution of MX, classify each of the other solutions as unsaturated, saturated, or supersaturated.

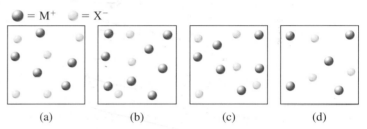

●$= M^+$ ○$= X^-$

(a)   (b)   (c)   (d)

17.133 Which of the following compounds, when added to water, will increase the solubility of CdS: (a) LiNO$_3$, (b) Na$_2$SO$_4$, (c) KCN, (d) NaClO$_3$?

17.134 The titration curve shown here represents the titration of a weak diprotic acid (H$_2$A) versus NaOH. (a) Label the major species present at the marked points. (b) Estimate the pK_{a_1} and pK_{a_2} values of the acid. Assume that any salt hydrolysis is negligible.

Volume of NaOH added

17.135 A 1.0-L saturated silver carbonate solution at 5°C is filtered to remove undissolved solid and treated with enough hydrochloric acid to decompose the dissolved compound. The carbon dioxide generated is collected in a 19-mL vial and exerts a pressure of 114 mmHg at 25°C. What is the K_{sp} of silver carbonate at 5°C?

17.136 Draw distribution curves for an aqueous carbonic acid solution. Your graph should show fraction of species present as the y axis and pH as the x axis. Note that at any pH, only two of the three species (H$_2$CO$_3$, HCO$_3^-$, and CO$_3^{2-}$) are present in appreciable concentrations. Use the K_a values in Table 16.9.

17.137   A sample of 0.96 L of HCl gas at 372 mmHg and 22°C is bubbled into 0.034 L of 0.57 *M* NH$_3$. What is the pH of the resulting solution? Assume the volume of solution remains constant and that the HCl is totally dissolved in the solution.

17.138   Histidine is one of the 20 amino acids found in proteins. Shown here is a fully protonated histidine molecule, where the numbers denote the pK_a values of the acidic groups:

$$
\begin{array}{c}
\overset{9.17}{\underset{\overset{+}{H_3N}}{}}-CH-\overset{\overset{\displaystyle O}{\|}}{C}-OH \quad 1.82 \\
| \\
CH_2 \\
\overset{6.00}{\underset{\overset{+}{HN}}{}} \\
\diagdown\hspace{-0.3em}=\hspace{-0.3em}\diagup \\
NH
\end{array}
$$

(a) Show stepwise ionization of histidine in solution. (*Hint:* The H$^+$ ion will first come off from the strongest acid group followed by the next strongest acid group and so on.) (b) A dipolar ion is one in which the species has an equal number of positive and negative charges. Identify the dipolar ion in part (a). (c) The pH at which the dipolar ion predominates is called the isoelectric point, denoted by p*I*. The isoelectric point is the average of the pK_a values leading to and following the formation of the dipolar ion. Calculate the p*I* of histidine. (d) The histidine group plays an important role in buffering blood (the pH of blood is about 7.4).

Which conjugate acid-base pair shown in part (a) is responsible for maintaining the pH of blood?

17.139   The solutions shown represent various points in the titration of the weak acid HA with NaOH. (For clarity, the sodium ions and water molecules are not shown.)
(a) Which diagram corresponds to the beginning of the titration, prior to the addition of any NaOH?
(b) Which diagram corresponds to the equivalence point of the titration? (Ignore salt hydrolysis.)
(c) Which diagram illustrates the solution *after* the equivalence point, when excess NaOH has been added?
(d) Which diagram corresponds to the point at which the pH is equal to the pK_a of the weak acid?

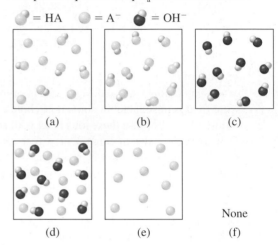

Answers to In-Chapter Materials

PRACTICE PROBLEMS

17.1A 4.22. **17.1B** 9.11. **17.2A** 5.0. **17.2B** 0.33 mol. **17.3A** Dissolve 0.6 mol CH_3COONa and 1 mol CH_3COOH in enough water to make 1 L of solution. **17.3B** 2.35–4.35. **17.4A** (a) 5.04, (b) 8.76, (c) 12.2. **17.4B** (a) 8.3 mL, (b) 12.5 mL, (c) 27.0 mL. **17.5A** 5.91. **17.5B** aniline. **17.6A** (a) bromophenol blue, methyl orange, methyl red, or chlorophenol, (b) any but thymol blue, bromophenol blue, or methyl orange, (c) cresol red or phenolphthalein. **17.6B** pyridine or aniline. **17.7A** (a) 1.3×10^{-5} M, 1.8×10^{-3} g/L; (b) 1.0×10^{-3} M, 1.5×10^{-11} g/L; (c) 4.0×10^{-5} M, 5.9×10^{-3} g/L. **17.7B** (a) 2.2×10^{-3} M, 0.53 g/L; (b) 1.3×10^{-4} M, 3.5×10^{-2} g/L; (c) 1.7×10^{-15} M, 8.8×10^{-13} g/L. **17.8A** (a) 1.5×10^{-14}, (b) 1.7×10^{-6}, (c) 1.3×10^{-15}. **17.8B** (a) 1.5×10^{-14}, (b) 4.8×10^{-29}, (c) 9.0×10^{-33}. **17.9A** (a) yes, (b) yes, (c) no. **17.9B** (a) 4.4×10^{-8} g, (b) 1.2 g, (c) 0.037 g. **17.10A** (a) 9.1×10^{-9} M, (b) 8.3×10^{-14} M. **17.10B** $Ag_2S < AgI < AgBr < AgCl < Ag_2CO_3$. **17.11A** (a) yes, (b) yes, (c) no. **17.11B** Any salts containing the CO_3^{2-} ion, the OH^- ion, the S^{2-} ion, or any anion of a weak acid such as the SO_3^{2-} ion or the F^- ion. **17.12A** 1.8×10^{-34} M. **17.12B** 6.8×10^{-2} M. **17.13A** 0.60 M. **17.13B** (a) 1.6×10^{-9} M, (b) 2.6×10^{-6} M.

SECTION REVIEW

17.1.1 (a) decrease, (b) increase, (c) decrease, (d) decrease, (e) no effect. **17.1.2** 2.8. **17.2.1** 3.26. **17.2.2** 3.87. **17.2.3** 9.37. **17.2.4** iv < ii < i = iii. **17.3.1** 8.92. **17.3.2** 3.15. **17.3.3** 11.89. **17.4.1** 2.9×10^{-9} M. **17.4.2** PbI_2. **17.4.3** ii < i < iii. **17.5.1** 8.0×10^{-10} M. **17.5.2** ii, iv. **17.6.1** AgI. **17.6.2** 1.1×10^{-9} M.

KEY SKILLS

Buffers

The Henderson-Hasselbalch equation (Equation 17.3) enables us to calculate the pH of a buffer if we know the concentrations of the weak acid and conjugate base (or of the weak base and conjugate acid); and to determine the pH of a buffer after the addition of strong acid or base. It can also be used to determine the amounts or *relative* amounts of both members of a conjugate pair necessary to prepare a buffer of specified pH.

The most familiar form of the Henderson-Hasselbalch equation is

$$\text{pH} = \text{p}K_a + \log \frac{[\text{conjugate base}]}{[\text{weak acid}]}$$

Although the equation contains the ratio of *molar concentrations* of conjugate base and weak acid, because both are contained within the same volume, volume cancels in the numerator and denominator of the log term. Therefore, we can also use *moles* or *millimoles* of conjugate base and weak acid, which is more convenient in many cases.

$$\text{pH} = \text{p}K_a + \log \frac{\text{mol conjugate base}}{\text{mol weak acid}} \quad \text{or} \quad \text{pH} = \text{p}K_a + \log \frac{\text{mmol conjugate base}}{\text{mmol weak acid}}$$

If we wish to prepare a buffer in a specific pH range, we must first select a suitable conjugate pair. Because the concentrations of weak acid and conjugate base cannot differ by more than a factor of 10, the log term in the Henderson-Hasselbalch equation can have values only from −1 through 1.

$$\text{pH} = \text{p}K_a \pm 1$$

Therefore, we must select a weak acid with a pK_a within one pH unit of the desired buffer pH. For example, to prepare a buffer with a pH between 4 and 5, we could use acetic acid ($HC_2H_3O_2$). [From Table 16.7, K_a for acetic acid is 1.8×10^{-5}, therefore its pK_a is $-\log (1.8 \times 10^{-5}) = 4.74$.]

To prepare a buffer with a specific pH, we solve the Henderson-Hasselbalch equation to determine the relative amounts of weak acid and conjugate base. The following flowchart illustrates this process for preparation of a buffer with pH = 4.15 using acetic acid (pK_a = 4.74) and sodium acetate ($NaC_2H_3O_2$).

$$4.15 \;=\; 4.74 \;+\; \log\left(\frac{[NaC_2H_3O_2]}{[HC_2H_3O_2]}\right)$$

$$-0.59 \;=\; \log\left(\frac{[NaC_2H_3O_2]}{[HC_2H_3O_2]}\right)$$

To eliminate the log term, we must take the antilog (10^x) of both sides of the equation.

$$10^{-0.59} \;=\; \frac{[NaC_2H_3O_2]}{[HC_2H_3O_2]}$$

This gives

This means that we need 0.257 mole of sodium acetate for every mole of acetic acid. If the amount of one member of the conjugate pair is specified, this ratio enables us to calculate the amount of the other member. For instance, if we know that the buffer must contain 25.0 g acetic acid, we can determine the amount of sodium acetate necessary to achieve the desired pH. We will need the molar masses of both members of the conjugate pair [◀◀ Key Skills Chapter 5].

Therefore, we would need 8.78 g sodium acetate. Because the pH of a buffer does not depend on volume, we could combine these amounts of acetic acid and sodium acetate in any volume that is convenient.

Key Skills Problems

17.1
Which of the acids in Table 16.7 (page 673) can be used to prepare a buffer of pH 6.5? (Select all that apply.)

(a) hydrofluoric acid   (b) benzoic acid   (c) hydrocyanic acid   (d) phenol   (e) none

17.2
What molar ratio of sodium cyanide to hydrocyanic acid is necessary to prepare a buffer with pH = 9.72?

(a) 0.39:1   (b) 0.41:1   (c) 2.3:1   (d) 2.6:1   (e) 1:1

17.3
How many moles of sodium benzoate must be added to 175 mL of 0.955 M benzoic acid to prepare a buffer with pH = 5.05?

(a) 0.18   (b) 0.15   (c) 6.8   (d) 7.2   (e) 1.2

17.4
How much sodium fluoride must be dissolved in 250 mL of 0.98 M HF to prepare a buffer with pH 3.50?

(a) 23 g   (b) 2.2 g   (c) 15 g   (d) 92 g   (e) 0.98 g

CHAPTER 18

Entropy, Free Energy, and Equilibrium

18.1 Spontaneous Processes

18.2 Entropy
• A Qualitative Description of Entropy
• A Quantitative Definition of Entropy

18.3 Entropy Changes in a System
• Calculating ΔS_{sys} • Standard Entropy, $S°$
• Qualitatively Predicting the Sign of $\Delta S°_{sys}$

18.4 Entropy Changes in the Universe
• Calculating ΔS_{surr} • The Second Law of Thermodynamics • The Third Law of Thermodynamics

18.5 Predicting Spontaneity
• Gibbs Free-Energy Change, ΔG • Standard Free-Energy Changes, $\Delta G°$ • Using ΔG and $\Delta G°$ to Solve Problems

18.6 Free Energy and Chemical Equilibrium
• Relationship Between ΔG and $\Delta G°$
• Relationship Between $\Delta G°$ and K

18.7 Thermodynamics in Living Systems

Many chemical processes are not spontaneous—meaning that obtaining useful product is not feasible. However, with an understanding of thermodynamics, chemists can combine or "couple" two chemical processes, one spontaneous and one nonspontaneous, that result in an overall spontaneous reaction. For example, the extractive metallurgy or "smelting" of copper (shown here) requires a coupled reaction system to produce copper metal from copper ore.

Before You Begin, Review These Skills

- System and surroundings [◀◀ Section 10.1]
- Hess's law [◀◀ Section 10.5]
- Equilibrium expressions [◀◀ Section 15.3]

18.1 SPONTANEOUS PROCESSES

An understanding of thermodynamics enables us to predict whether or not a reaction will occur when reactants are combined. This is important in the synthesis of new compounds in the laboratory, the manufacturing of chemicals on an industrial scale, and the understanding of natural processes such as cell function. A process that *does* occur under a specific set of conditions is called a ***spontaneous process.*** One that does *not* occur under a specific set of conditions is called ***nonspontaneous.*** Table 18.1 lists examples of familiar spontaneous processes and their nonspontaneous counterparts. These examples illustrate what we know intuitively: Under a given set of conditions, a process that occurs spontaneously in one direction does not also occur spontaneously in the opposite direction.

> **Student Annotation:** The conditions that most often are specified are *temperature, pressure,* and in the case of a solution, *concentration.*

Processes that result in a decrease in the energy of a system often are spontaneous. For example, the combustion of methane is exothermic:

$$CH_4(g) + 2O_2(g) \longrightarrow CO_2(g) + 2H_2O(l) \qquad \Delta H° - -890.4 \text{ kJ/mol}$$

Thus, the energy of the system is lowered because heat is given off during the course of the reaction. Likewise, in the acid-base neutralization reaction,

$$H^+(aq) + OH^-(aq) \longrightarrow H_2O(l) \qquad \Delta H° = -56.2 \text{ kJ/mol}$$

heat is given off, lowering the energy of the system. Each of these processes is spontaneous, and each results in a lowering of the system's energy.

Now consider the melting of ice:

$$H_2O(s) \longrightarrow H_2O(l) \qquad \Delta H° = 6.01 \text{ kJ/mol}$$

In this case, the process is endothermic and yet it is also spontaneous at temperatures above 0°C. Conversely, the freezing of water is an *exothermic* process:

$$H_2O(l) \longrightarrow H_2O(s) \qquad \Delta H° = -6.01 \text{ kJ/mol}$$

Yet it is *not* spontaneous at temperatures above 0°C.

TABLE 18.1	Familiar Spontaneous and Nonspontaneous Processes
Spontaneous	**Nonspontaneous**
Ice melting at room temperature	Water freezing at room temperature
Sodium metal reacting violently with water to produce sodium hydroxide and hydrogen gas [◀◀ Section 8.5]	Sodium hydroxide reacting with hydrogen gas to produce sodium metal and water
A ball rolling downhill	A ball rolling uphill
The rusting of iron at room temperature	The conversion of rust back to iron metal at room temperature
Water freezing at −10°C	Ice melting at −10°C

Based on the first two examples, and many others like them, we might conclude that exothermic processes tend to be spontaneous and, indeed, a negative ΔH does *favor* spontaneity. The last two examples, however, make it clear that the sign of ΔH *alone* is insufficient to predict spontaneity in every circumstance. For the remainder of this chapter, we will examine the *two* factors that determine whether or not a process is spontaneous under a given set of conditions.

18.2   ENTROPY

To predict the spontaneity of a chemical or physical process, we need to know both the change in *enthalpy* [◄◄ Section 10.3] and the change in *entropy* associated with the process. We first encountered the concept of entropy in our discussion of solution formation [◄◄ Section 13.2]. We will now look in more detail at what entropy is, and why it matters.

A Qualitative Description of Entropy

Qualitatively, the **entropy (S)** of a system is a measure of how *spread out* or how *dispersed* the system's energy is. The simplest interpretation of this is how spread out a system's energy is in *space*. In other words, for a given system, the greater the volume it occupies, the greater its entropy. This interpretation explains how the process in Figure 18.1 occurs spontaneously despite there being no enthalpy change. Because they are moving, the gas molecules that were originally confined to one side of the container possess *motional energy*. In the absence of a barrier preventing it, the motional energy of molecules will spread out to occupy a larger volume. The dispersal of a system's motional energy to occupy a larger volume when the barrier is removed constitutes an *increase* in the system's entropy. Just as spontaneity is favored by a process being exothermic, spontaneity is also favored by an increase in the system's entropy. Whether it is the enthalpy change, the entropy change, or both, for a process to be spontaneous, *something* must favor spontaneity.

Student Annotation: Motional energy includes *translational* energy, in which the entire molecule moves through space [◄◄ Section 3.1]; *rotational* energy, in which the molecule spins about an axis running through its center of mass; and *vibrational* energy, in which atoms of a molecule move relative to one another.

A Quantitative Definition of Entropy

At this point, it is useful to introduce the mathematical definition of entropy proposed by Ludwig Boltzmann:

Equation 18.1	$S = k \ln W$

Student Annotation: The Boltzmann constant is equal to the gas constant, R (in J/K · mol), divided by Avogadro's constant, N_A.

where k is the Boltzmann constant (1.38×10^{-23} J/K) and W is the number of energetically equivalent different ways the molecules in a system can be arranged. To illustrate what this means, let's consider a simplified version of the process shown in Figure 18.1. Prior to the removal of the barrier between the left and right sides of the container, at any given instant, each molecule has a particular location, somewhere in the left side of the container. To narrow down the possible locations of the molecules, we imagine that each side of the container is divided into a number of equal smaller volumes called *cells*. In the simplest scenario, with just one molecule in the system, the number of possible locations of the molecule is equal to the number of cells. If the system contains

Figure 18.1 A spontaneous process. The rapidly moving gas molecules originally confined to one side of a container spread out to fill the whole container when the barrier is removed.

two molecules, the number of possible arrangements is equal to the number of cells *squared*. (Note that a cell may contain more than one molecule.) Each time we increase the number of molecules by one, the number of possible arrangements increases by a factor equal to the number of cells. In general, for a volume consisting of X cells, and containing N molecules, the number of possible arrangements, W, is given by the equation

Student Annotation: The number of possible arrangements is sometimes called the number of *microstates*.

$$W = X^N \qquad \textbf{Equation 18.2}$$

Figure 18.2 illustrates this for a simple case involving just two molecules. We imagine the container is divided into four cells each with volume v. Initially, both molecules are confined to the left side, which consists of two cells. With two molecules in two cells, there are $2^2 = 4$ possible arrangements of the molecules [Figure 18.2(a)]. When the barrier is removed, doubling the volume available to the molecules, the number of cells also doubles. With four cells available, there are $4^2 = 16$ possible arrangements of the molecules. Eight of the sixteen arrangements have the molecules on opposite sides of the container [Figure 18.2(b)]. Of the other eight arrangements, four have both molecules on the left side [as shown in Figure 18.2(a)], and four have both molecules on the right side (not shown). There are three different states possible for this system.

1. One molecule on each side (eight possible arrangements)
2. Both molecules on the left (four possible arrangements)
3. Both molecules on the right (four possible arrangements)

Student Annotation: The state with the largest number of possible arrangements has the greatest entropy.

The most *probable* state is the one with the *largest* number of possible arrangements. In this case, the most probable state is the one with one molecule on each side of the container. The same principle applies to systems with larger numbers of molecules. Increasing the number of molecules increases the number of possible arrangements, but the most probable state will be the one in which the gas molecules are divided evenly between the two sides of the container.

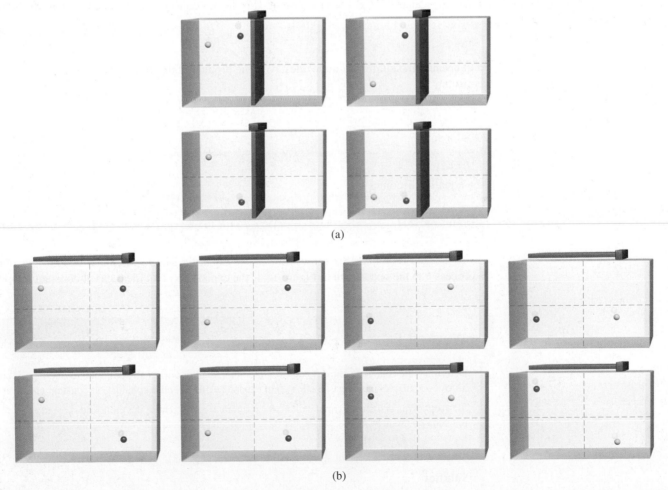

(a)

(b)

Figure 18.2 (a) Before the barrier is removed, the molecules are both in the left side of the container, which we imagine is divided into two cells of equal volume. There are four possible arrangements of two molecules in two cells. (b) When the barrier between the two sides of the container is removed, the volume (and the number of cells) available to the molecules doubles. The new number of possible arrangements is $4^2 = 16$, eight of which have the molecules in opposite sides of the container—the most probable outcome.

18.3 ENTROPY CHANGES IN A SYSTEM

Calculating ΔS_{sys}

The change in entropy of a system is the difference between the entropy of the final state and the entropy of the initial state.

Equation 18.3	$\Delta S_{sys} = S_{final} - S_{initial}$

Using Equation 18.1, we can write an expression for the entropy of each state,

$$\Delta S_{sys} = k \ln W_{final} - k \ln W_{initial} = k \ln \frac{W_{final}}{W_{initial}}$$

Student Annotation: Remember that the difference between two logs is equal to the log of the corresponding quotient:

$$\ln A - \ln B = \ln \frac{A}{B}$$

and that $\ln A^x = x \ln A$ [▶▶ Appendix 1].

Combining this result with Equation 18.2 gives

$$\Delta S_{sys} = k \ln \frac{(X_{final})^N}{(X_{initial})^N} = k \ln \left(\frac{X_{final}}{X_{initial}}\right)^N = k N \ln \left(\frac{X_{final}}{X_{initial}}\right)$$

Because X is the number of cells, and the volume of each cell is v, the total volume is related to the number of cells by

$$V = Xv \qquad \text{or} \qquad X = \frac{V}{v}$$

We substitute V_{final}/v for X_{final} and $V_{initial}/v$ for $X_{initial}$ to get

$$\Delta S_{sys} = k N \ln \frac{V_{final}/v}{V_{initial}/v} = k N \ln \frac{V_{final}}{V_{initial}}$$

Finally, because the Boltzmann constant, k, is the gas constant, R, divided by Avogadro's constant,

$$k = \frac{R}{N_A}$$

and because the number of molecules, N, is the product of the number of moles, n, and Avogadro's constant, N_A;

$$N = n \times N_A$$

$$kN = \left(\frac{R}{N_A} \times n \times N_A\right) = nR$$

the equation becomes

Equation 18.4	$\Delta S_{sys} = nR \ln \dfrac{V_{final}}{V_{initial}}$

Worked Example 18.1 shows how to use Equation 18.4 to calculate the entropy change for a process like the one shown in Figure 18.1, the expansion of an ideal gas at constant temperature.

Worked Example 18.1

Determine the change in entropy for 1.0 mole of an ideal gas originally confined to one-half of a 5.0-L container when the gas is allowed to expand to fill the entire container at constant temperature.

Strategy This is the isothermal expansion of an ideal gas. Because the molecules spread out to occupy a greater volume, we expect there to be an increase in the entropy of the system. Use Equation 18.3 to solve for ΔS_{sys}.

Setup $R = 8.314$ J/K · mol, $n = 1.0$ mole, $V_{final} = 5.0$ L, and $V_{initial} = 2.5$ L.

Solution

$$\Delta S_{sys} = nR \ln \frac{V_{final}}{V_{initial}} = 1.0 \text{ mol} \times \frac{8.314 \text{ J}}{\text{K} \cdot \text{mol}} \times \ln \frac{5.0 \text{ L}}{2.5 \text{ L}} = 5.8 \text{ J/K}$$

Think About It
Remember that for a process to be spontaneous, *something* must favor spontaneity. If the process is spontaneous but not exothermic (in this case, there is no enthalpy change), then we should expect ΔS_{sys} to be positive.

Practice Problem A Determine the change in entropy (ΔS_{sys}), for the expansion of 0.10 mole of an ideal gas from 2.0 L to 3.0 L at constant temperature.

Practice Problem B To what fraction of its original volume must a 0.50-mole sample of ideal gas be compressed at constant temperature for ΔS_{sys} to be −6.7 J/K?

Standard Entropy, $S°$

Although Equation 18.1 provides a quantitative definition of entropy, we seldom use it or Equation 18.3 to calculate the entropy change for a real process because of the difficulty involved in determining W, the number of different possible arrangements (Equation 18.2) in a macroscopic system. Instead, for processes other than isothermal expansion or compression of an ideal gas (for which we can use Equation 18.4), we routinely determine entropy changes using tabulated values.

Using calorimetry [◄◄ Section 10.4], it is possible to determine the *absolute* value of the entropy of a substance, S; something we cannot do with either energy or enthalpy. (Recall that while we can determine ΔU and ΔH for a process that a system undergoes, we cannot determine the absolute values of either U or H for a system [◄◄ Sections 10.2 and 10.3].) *Standard entropy* is the absolute entropy of a substance at 1 atm. (Tables of standard entropy values typically are the values at 25°C because so many processes are carried out at room temperature—although temperature is *not* part of the standard state definition and therefore must be specified.) Table 18.2 lists standard entropies of a few elements and compounds. Appendix 2 provides a more extensive listing. The units of entropy are J/K · mol. We use joules rather than kilojoules because entropy values typically are quite small. The entropies of substances (elements and compounds) are always positive (i.e., $S > 0$), even for elements in their standard states. (Recall that the standard *enthalpy* of formation, $\Delta H_f°$, for elements in their standard states is arbitrarily defined as zero, and for compounds it may be either positive or negative [◄◄ Section 10.6].)

Referring to Table 18.2, we can identify several important trends:

- For a given substance, the standard entropy is greater in the liquid phase than in the solid phase. [Compare the standard entropies of Na(s) and Na(l).] This results from there being greater molecular motion in a liquid, resulting in many possible arrangements of atoms in the liquid phase; whereas the positions of atoms in the solid are fixed.
- For a given substance, the standard entropy is greater in the gas phase than in the liquid phase. [Compare the standard entropies of Na(l) and Na(g) and those of H₂O(l) and H₂O(g).] This results from there being much greater molecular motion in a gas, resulting in many more possible arrangements of atoms in the gas phase than in the liquid phase—in part because the gas phase occupies a much greater volume than either of the condensed phases.
- For two monatomic species, the one with the larger molar mass has the greater standard entropy. [Compare the standard entropies of He(g) and Ne(g).]

Student Annotation: For even the simplest of hypothetical systems, where there are only two possible positions for molecules ($X = 2$), most calculators cannot display a number as large as the result of Equation 18.2 for even as few as 500 molecules—much less for the *enormous* number of molecules present in any *real* sample. (If your calculator is like most, with $X = 2$, you can calculate the number of possible arrangements for $N \le 332$ molecules. Try it: 2 ^ 332 = ? and 2 ^ 333 = ?)

Student Annotation: You will find that tables, including Appendix 2, contain *negative* absolute entropies for some aqueous ions. Unlike a substance, an individual ion cannot be studied experimentally. Therefore, standard entropies of ions are actually *relative* values, where a standard entropy of zero is arbitrarily assigned to the hydrated hydrogen ion. Depending on an ion's extent of hydration, its standard entropy may be positive or negative, relative to that of hydrogen ion.

TABLE 18.2	Standard Entropy Values ($S°$) for Some Substances at 25°C		
Substance	**$S°$ (J/K · mol)**	**Substance**	**$S°$ (J/K · mol)**
H₂O(l)	69.9	C(diamond)	2.4
H₂O(g)	188.7	C(graphite)	5.69
Na(s)	51.05	O₂(g)	205.0
Na(l)	57.56	O₃(g)	237.6
Na(g)	153.7	F₂(g)	203.34
He(g)	126.1	Au(s)	47.7
Ne(g)	146.2	Hg(l)	77.4

- For two substances in the same phase, and with similar molar masses, the substance with the more complex molecular structure has the greater standard entropy. [Compare the standard entropies of $O_3(g)$ and $F_2(g)$.] The more complex a molecular structure, the more different types of motion the molecule can exhibit. A diatomic molecule such as F_2, for example, exhibits only one type of vibration, whereas a bent triatomic molecule such as O_3 exhibits three different types of vibrations. Each mode of motion contributes to the total number of available energy levels within which a system's energy can be dispersed. Figure 18.3 illustrates the ways in which the F_2 and O_3 molecules can rotate and vibrate.

- In cases where an element exists in two or more allotropic forms, the form in which the atoms are more mobile has the greater entropy. [Compare the standard entropies of C(diamond) and C(graphite). In diamond, the carbon atoms occupy fixed positions in a three-dimensional array. In graphite, although the carbon atoms occupy fixed positions within the two-dimensional sheets (see Figure 12.25, page 485), the sheets are free to move with respect to one another, which increases the mobility and, therefore, total number of possible arrangements of atoms within the solid.]

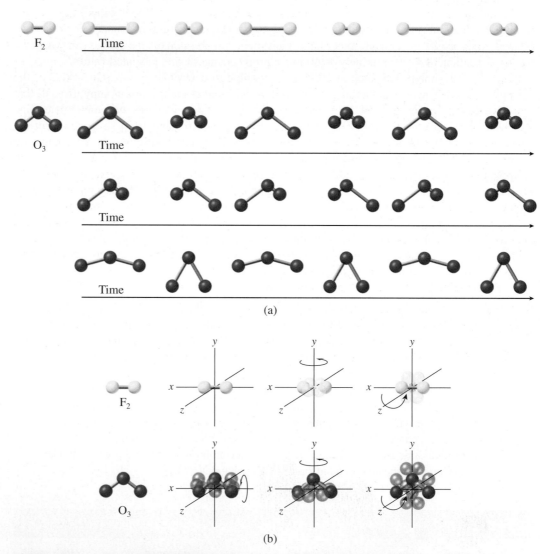

Figure 18.3 In addition to translational motion, molecules exhibit both *vibrations,* in which the atoms' positions relative to one another change, and *rotations,* in which the molecule rotates about its center of mass. (a) A diatomic molecule such as fluorine only exhibits one type of vibration. A bent, triatomic molecule such as ozone exhibits three types of vibration. (b) A diatomic molecule exhibits two different rotations, whereas a bent, triatomic molecule exhibits three different rotations. (Note that rotation of F_2 about the x axis would cause no change in the positions of either atom in the molecule.)

Now let's consider a process represented by the following chemical equation:

$$aA + bB \longrightarrow cC + dD$$

Just as the enthalpy change of a reaction is the difference between the enthalpies of the products and reactants (Equation 10.10), the entropy change is the difference between the entropies of the products and reactants:

$$\Delta S^\circ_{rxn} = [cS^\circ(C) + dS^\circ(D)] - [aS^\circ(A) + bS^\circ(B)] \qquad \textbf{Equation 18.5}$$

Or, using Σ to represent summation and m and n to represent the stoichiometric coefficients of the reactants and products, respectively, Equation 18.5 can be generalized as follows:

$$\Delta S^\circ_{rxn} = \Sigma nS^\circ(\text{products}) - \Sigma mS^\circ(\text{reactants}) \qquad \textbf{Equation 18.6}$$

The standard entropy values of a large number of substances have been measured in J/K · mol. To calculate the standard entropy change for a reaction (ΔS°_{rxn}), we look up the standard entropies of the products and reactants and use Equation 18.5.

Worked Example 18.2 demonstrates this approach.

Student Annotation: The *reaction* generally is the *system*. Therefore, ΔS°_{rxn} is ΔS°_{sys}.

Worked Example 18.2

From the standard entropy values in Appendix 2, calculate the standard entropy changes for the following reactions at 25°C:

(a) $CaCO_3(s) \longrightarrow CaO(s) + CO_2(g)$ (b) $N_2(g) + 3H_2(g) \longrightarrow 2NH_3(g)$

(c) $H_2(g) + Cl_2(g) \longrightarrow 2HCl(g)$

Strategy Look up standard entropy values and use Equation 18.5 to calculate ΔS°_{rxn}. Just as we did when we calculated standard enthalpies of reaction, we consider stoichiometric coefficients to be dimensionless—giving ΔS°_{rxn} units of J/K · mol.

Student Annotation: Recall that here *per mole* means per mole of reaction as written [◄◄ Section 10.3].

Setup From Appendix 2, $S^\circ[CaCO_3(s)] = 92.9$ J/K · mol, $S^\circ[CaO(s)] = 39.8$ J/K · mol, $S^\circ[CO_2(g)] = 213.6$ J/K · mol, $S^\circ[N_2(g)] = 191.5$ J/K · mol, $S^\circ[H_2(g)] = 131.0$ J/K · mol, $S^\circ[NH_3(g)] = 193.0$ J/K · mol, $S^\circ[Cl_2(g)] = 223.0$ J/K · mol, and $S^\circ[HCl(g)] = 187.0$ J/K · mol.

Solution

(a) $\Delta S^\circ_{rxn} = [S^\circ(CaO) + S^\circ(CO_2)] - [S^\circ(CaCO_3)]$

$= [(39.8 \text{ J/K} \cdot \text{mol}) + (213.6 \text{ J/K} \cdot \text{mol})] - (92.9 \text{ J/K} \cdot \text{mol})$

$= 160.5$ J/K · mol

(b) $\Delta S^\circ_{rxn} = [2S^\circ(NH_3)] - [S^\circ(N_2) + 3S^\circ(H_2)]$

$= (2)(193.0 \text{ J/K} \cdot \text{mol}) - [(191.5 \text{ J/K} \cdot \text{mol}) + (3)(131.0 \text{ J/K} \cdot \text{mol})]$

$= -198.5$ J/K · mol

(c) $\Delta S^\circ_{rxn} = [2S^\circ(HCl)] - [S^\circ(H_2) + S^\circ(Cl_2)]$

$= (2)(187.0 \text{ J/K} \cdot \text{mol}) - [(131.0 \text{ J/K} \cdot \text{mol}) + (223.0 \text{ J/K} \cdot \text{mol})]$

$= 20.0$ J/K · mol

Think About It
Remember to multiply each standard entropy value by the correct stoichiometric coefficient. Like Equation 10.18, Equation 18.5 can only be used with a *balanced* chemical equation.

Practice Problem A Calculate the standard entropy change for the following reactions at 25°C. Predict first whether each one will be positive, negative, or too close to call.

(a) $2CO_2(g) \longrightarrow 2CO(g) + O_2(g)$ (b) $3O_2(g) \longrightarrow 2O_3(g)$

(c) $2NaHCO_3(s) \longrightarrow Na_2CO_3(s) + H_2O(l) + CO_2(g)$

Practice Problem B In each of the following reactions, there is one species for which the standard entropy is not listed in Appendix 2. In each case, using the values that *are* in Appendix 2 and the ΔS°_{rxn} that is given, determine the value of the missing standard entropy at 25°C: (a) $K(s) \longrightarrow K(l)$, $\Delta S^\circ_{rxn} = 7.9$ J/K · mol, (b) $2S(\text{rhombic}) + Cl_2(g) \longrightarrow S_2Cl_2(g)$, $\Delta S^\circ_{rxn} = 44.74$ J/K · mol, (c) $O_2(g) + 2MgF_2(s) \longrightarrow 2MgO(s) + 2F_2(g)$, $\Delta S^\circ_{rxn} = 140.76$ J/K · mol.

Qualitatively Predicting the Sign of ΔS°_{sys}

Equation 18.5 enables us to calculate ΔS°_{rxn} for a process when the standard entropies of the products and reactants are known. However, sometimes it's useful just to know the *sign* of ΔS°_{rxn}. Although multiple factors can influence the sign of ΔS°_{rxn}, the outcome is often dominated by a single factor, which can be used to make a qualitative prediction. Several processes that lead to an increase in entropy are

- Melting
- Vaporization or sublimation
- Temperature increase
- Reaction resulting in a greater number of gas molecules

When a solid is melted, the molecules have greater energy and are more mobile. They go from being in fixed positions in the solid, to being free to move about in the liquid. As we saw in the discussion of standard entropy, this leads to many more possible arrangements of the molecules and, therefore, greater entropy. The same rationale holds for the vaporization or sublimation of a substance. There is a dramatic increase in energy/mobility, and in the number of possible arrangements of a system's molecules when the molecules go from a condensed phase to the gas phase. Therefore, there is a much larger increase in the system's entropy, relative to the solid-to-liquid transition.

When the temperature of a system is increased, the energy of the system's molecules increases. To visualize this, recall from the discussion of kinetic molecular theory that increasing the temperature of a gas increases its average kinetic energy. This corresponds to an increase in the average speed of the gas molecules and a spreading out of the range of molecular speeds. [See Figure 11.4(a).] If we think of each of the possible molecular speeds within the range as a discrete energy level, we can see that at higher temperatures, there is a greater number of possible molecular speeds and, therefore, a greater number of energy states available to the molecules in the system. With a greater number of available energy states, there is a greater number of possible arrangements of molecules *within* those states and, therefore, a greater entropy.

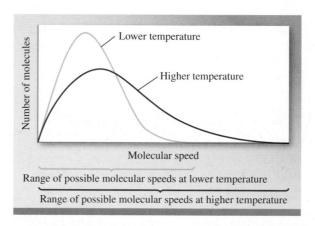

Because the entropy of a substance in the gas phase is always significantly greater than its entropy in either the liquid or solid phase, a reaction that results in an increase in the number of gas molecules causes an increase in the system's entropy. For reactions that do not involve gases, an increase in the number of solid, liquid, or aqueous molecules also usually causes an entropy increase.

By considering these factors, we can usually make a reasonably good prediction of the sign of ΔS°_{rxn} for a physical or chemical process, without having to look up the absolute entropy values for the species involved. Figure 18.4 (pages 772–773) summarizes the factors that can be used to compare entropies and illustrates several comparisons.

In addition to melting, vaporization/sublimation, temperature increase, and reactions that increase the number of gas molecules, which can always be counted upon to result in an entropy increase, the process of *dissolving* a substance often leads to an increase in entropy. In the case of a molecular solute, such as sucrose (sugar), dissolving causes dispersal of the molecules (and consequently, of the system's *energy*) into a larger volume—resulting in an increase in entropy.

Multi 18.1
Animation: Factors that influence the entropy of a system

TABLE 18.3	Entropy Changes for the Dissolution (ΔS°_{soln}) of Some Ionic Solids at 25°C	
Dissolution equation		ΔS°_{soln} (J/K · mol)
$NH_4NO_3(s) \longrightarrow NH_4^+(aq) + NO_3^-(aq)$		108.1
$AlCl_3(s) \longrightarrow Al^{3+}(aq) + 3Cl^-(aq)$		−253.2
$FeCl_3(s) \longrightarrow Fe^{3+}(aq) + 3Cl^-(aq)$		−266.1

Student Annotation: Note that the subscript "rxn" in ΔS°_{rxn} changes to "soln" to refer specifically to the *solution* process.

In the case of an ionic solute, the analysis is slightly more complicated. We saw in our discussion of solution formation [◄◄ Section 13.2] that the dissolution of ammonium nitrate (NH_4NO_3) is spontaneous, even though it is endothermic, because the system's entropy increases when the ionic solid dissociates and is dispersed throughout the solution. In general, this is the case for ionic solutes in which the charges on ions are small. (In the case of NH_4NO_3, they are +1 and −1.) However, when ions are dispersed in water, they become hydrated (surrounded by water molecules in a specific arrangement [◄◄ Figure 9.4 page 313]). This leads to a *decrease* in the entropy of the *water*, as hydration reduces the mobility of some of the water molecules by fixing them in positions around the dissolved ions. When the charges on ions are low, the increase in entropy of the solute typically outweighs the decrease in entropy of the water—resulting in an overall *increase* in the entropy of the system—as is the case with NH_4NO_3. By contrast, when highly charged ions such as Al^{3+} and Fe^{3+} are hydrated, the decrease in entropy of the water can actually outweigh the increase in entropy of the solute, leading to an overall *decrease* in entropy of the system. Table 18.3 lists the changes in entropy associated with the spontaneous dissolution of several ionic solids.

Worked Example 18.3 lets you practice making qualitative predictions of the sign of ΔS°_{rxn}.

Worked Example 18.3

For each process, determine the sign of ΔS for the system: (a) decomposition of $CaCO_3(s)$ to give $CaO(s)$ and $CO_2(g)$, (b) heating bromine vapor from 45°C to 80°C, (c) condensation of water vapor on a cold surface, (d) reaction of $NH_3(g)$ and $HCl(g)$ to give $NH_4Cl(s)$, and (e) dissolution of sugar in water.

Strategy Consider the change in energy/mobility of atoms and the resulting change in number of possible positions that each particle can occupy in each case. An increase in the number of arrangements corresponds to an increase in entropy and therefore a positive ΔS.

Setup Increases in entropy generally accompany solid-to-liquid, liquid-to-gas, and solid-to-gas transitions; the dissolving of one substance in another; a temperature increase; and reactions that increase the net number of moles of gas.

Solution ΔS is (a) positive, (b) positive, (c) negative, (d) negative, and (e) positive.

Think About It
For reactions involving only liquids and solids, predicting the sign of ΔS° can be more difficult, but in many such cases an increase in the total number of molecules and/or ions is accompanied by an increase in entropy.

Practice Problem A For each of the following processes, determine the sign of ΔS: (a) crystallization of sucrose from a supersaturated solution, (b) cooling water vapor from 150°C to 110°C, (c) sublimation of dry ice.

Practice Problem B Make a qualitative prediction of the sign of ΔH°_{soln} for $AlCl_3(s)$ and the dissolution of $FeCl_3(s)$. See Table 18.3. Explain your reasoning.

Figure 18.4

Factors That Influence the Entropy of a System

Volume Change

Quantum mechanical analysis shows that the spacing between translational energy levels is inversely proportional to the volume of the container. Thus, when the volume is increased, more energy levels become available within which the system's energy can be dispersed.

Temperature Change

At higher temperatures, molecules have greater kinetic energy—making more energy levels accessible. This increases the number of energy levels within which the system's energy can be dispersed, causing entropy to increase.

Molecular Complexity

Unlike atoms, which exhibit only translational motion, molecules can also exhibit rotational and vibrational motions. The greater a molecule's complexity, the greater the number of possible ways it can rotate and vibrate. The ozone molecule (O_3), for example, is more complex than the fluorine molecule (F_2) and exhibits more different kinds of vibrations and rotations. (See Figure 18.3.) This results in more energy levels within which the system's energy can be dispersed. The number and spacing of additional energy levels have been simplified to keep the illustration clear.

Molar Mass

The energy levels for a substance with a larger molar mass are more closely spaced. Kr, for example, has roughly twice the molar mass of Ar. Thus, Kr has roughly twice as many energy levels within which the system's energy can be dispersed.

Phase Change

Because of greater mobility, there are many more different possible arrangements (W) of molecules in the liquid phase than there are in the solid phase; and there are many, *many* more different possible arrangements of molecules in the gas phase than there are in the liquid phase. Entropy of a substance increases when it is melted ($s \rightarrow l$), vaporized ($l \rightarrow g$), or sublimed ($s \rightarrow g$).

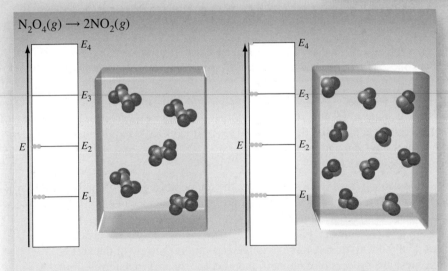

Chemical Reaction

When a chemical reaction produces more gas molecules than it consumes, the number of different possible arrangements of molecules (W) increases and entropy increases.

What's the point?

Although several factors can influence the entropy of a system or the entropy change associated with a process, often one factor dominates the outcome. Each of these comparisons shows a qualitative illustration of one of the important factors.

SECTION 18.3 REVIEW

Entropy Changes in a System

18.3.1   Determine the sign of ΔS for each of the following processes.

(a) Freezing ethanol

(b) Evaporating water

(c) Mixing carbon tetrachloride and benzene

(d) Heating water

(e) Condensing bromine vapor

18.3.2   Determine the sign of ΔS for each of the following reactions.

(a) $2O_3(g) \longrightarrow 3O_2(g)$

(b) $4Fe(s) + 3O_2(g) \longrightarrow 2Fe_2O_3(s)$

(c) $2H_2O_2(aq) \longrightarrow 2H_2O(l) + O_2(g)$

(d) $2Li(s) + 2H_2O(l) \longrightarrow 2LiOH(aq) + H_2(g)$

(e) $2NH_3(g) \longrightarrow N_2(g) + 3H_2(g)$

18.3.3   Consider the gas-phase reaction of A_2 (blue) and B_2 (orange) to form AB_3. Write the correct balanced equation and determine the sign of ΔS for the reaction.

18.4   ENTROPY CHANGES IN THE UNIVERSE

Recall that the *system* typically is the part of the universe we are investigating (e.g., the reactants and products in a chemical reaction). The *surroundings* are everything else [◄◄ Section 10.1]. Together, the system and surroundings make up the *universe*. We have seen that the *dispersal* or *spreading out* of a system's energy corresponds to an increase in the system's entropy. Moreover, an increase in the system's entropy is one of the factors that determines whether or not a process is spontaneous. However, correctly predicting the spontaneity of a process requires us to consider entropy changes in both the system and the surroundings.

Consider the following processes:

- An ice cube spontaneously melts in a room where the temperature is 25°C. In this case, the motional energy of the air molecules at 25°C is transferred to the ice cube (at 0°C), causing the ice to melt. There is no temperature change during a phase change. However, because the molecules are more mobile and there are many more different possible arrangements in *liquid* water than there are in ice, there is an increase in the entropy of the system. In this case, because the process of melting is endothermic, heat is transferred *from* the surroundings *to* the system and the temperature of the surroundings decreases. The slight decrease in temperature causes a small decrease in molecular motion and a decrease in the entropy of the surroundings.

  ΔS_{sys} is positive.

  ΔS_{surr} is negative.

- A cup of hot water spontaneously cools to room temperature as the motional energy of the water molecules spreads out to the cooler surrounding air. Although the loss of energy from the system and corresponding temperature decrease cause a *decrease* in the entropy of the *system*, the increased temperature of the surrounding air causes an *increase* in the entropy of the *surroundings*.

ΔS_{sys} is negative.

ΔS_{surr} is positive.

Thus, it is not just the entropy of the *system* that determines if a process is spontaneous, the entropy of the *surroundings* is also important. There are also examples of spontaneous processes in which ΔS_{sys} and ΔS_{surr} are *both* positive. The decomposition of hydrogen peroxide produces water and oxygen gas, $2H_2O_2(l) \longrightarrow 2H_2O(l) + O_2(g)$. Because the reaction results in an increase in the number of gas molecules, we know that there is an increase in the entropy of the system. However, this is an exothermic reaction, meaning that it also gives off heat to the surroundings. An increase in temperature of the surroundings causes an increase in the entropy of the surroundings as well. (Note that there are no spontaneous processes in which ΔS_{sys} and ΔS_{surr} are both negative, which will become clear shortly.)

Calculating ΔS_{surr}

When an exothermic process takes place, the heat transferred from the system to the surroundings increases the temperature of the molecules in the surroundings. Consequently, there is an increase in the number of energy levels accessible to the molecules in the surroundings and the entropy of the surroundings increases. Conversely, in an endothermic process, heat is transferred from the surroundings to the system, decreasing the entropy of the surroundings. Remember that for constant-pressure processes, the heat released or absorbed, q, is equal to the enthalpy change of the system, ΔH_{sys} [◄◄ Section 10.3]. The change in entropy for the surroundings, ΔS_{surr}, is directly proportional to ΔH_{sys}:

$$\Delta S_{surr} \propto -\Delta H_{sys}$$

The minus sign indicates that a negative enthalpy change in the system (an *exothermic* process) corresponds to a positive entropy change in the surroundings. For an *endothermic* process, the enthalpy change in the system is a positive number and corresponds to a negative entropy change in the surroundings.

In addition to being directly proportional to ΔH_{sys}, ΔS_{surr} is inversely proportional to temperature:

$$\Delta S_{surr} \propto \frac{1}{T}$$

Combining the two expressions gives

$$\Delta S_{surr} = \frac{-\Delta H_{sys}}{T} \qquad \textbf{Equation 18.7}$$

The Second Law of Thermodynamics

We have seen that both the system and surroundings can undergo changes in entropy during a process. The sum of the entropy changes for the system and the surroundings is the entropy change for the universe overall:

$$\Delta S_{univ} = \Delta S_{sys} + \Delta S_{surr} \qquad \textbf{Equation 18.8}$$

The *second law of thermodynamics* says that for a process to be spontaneous as written (in the forward direction), ΔS_{univ} must be positive. Therefore, the system may undergo a *decrease* in entropy, as long as the surroundings undergoes a larger *increase* in entropy, and vice versa. A process for which ΔS_{univ} is *negative* is not spontaneous as written.

In some cases, ΔS_{univ} is neither positive nor negative but is equal to zero. This happens when the entropy changes of the system and surroundings are equal in magnitude and opposite in sign and describes a specific type of process known as an *equilibrium* process. An ***equilibrium process*** is one that does not occur spontaneously in either the net forward or net reverse direction but can be made to occur by the addition or removal of energy to a system at equilibrium. An example of an equilibrium process is the melting of ice at 0°C. (Remember that at 0°C, ice and liquid water are in equilibrium with each other [◄◄ Section 12.6].)

> **Student Annotation:** Most of the equilibrium processes that we will encounter are phase changes.

With Equations 18.6 and 18.7, we can calculate the entropy changes for both the system and surroundings in a process. We can then use the second law of thermodynamics (Equation 18.8) to determine if the process is spontaneous or nonspontaneous as written or if it is an equilibrium process.

Consider the synthesis of ammonia at 25°C:

$$N_2(g) + 3H_2(g) \longrightarrow 2NH_3(g) \qquad \Delta H^{\circ}_{rxn} = -92.6 \text{ kJ/mol}$$

From Worked Example 18.2(b), we have $\Delta S^{\circ}_{sys} = -199 \text{ J/K} \cdot \text{mol}$, and substituting ΔH°_{sys} (−92.6 kJ/mol) into Equation 18.7, we get

$$\Delta S_{surr} = \frac{-(-92.6 \times 1000) \text{ J/mol}}{298 \text{ K}} = 311 \text{ J/K} \cdot \text{mol}$$

The entropy change for the universe is

$$\Delta S^{\circ}_{univ} = \Delta S^{\circ}_{sys} + \Delta S^{\circ}_{surr}$$

$$= -199 \text{ J/K} \cdot \text{mol} + 311 \text{ J/K} \cdot \text{mol}$$

$$= 112 \text{ J/K} \cdot \text{mol}$$

> **Student Annotation:** The spontaneity that we have seen as favored by a process being exothermic is due to the spreading out of energy from the system to the surroundings; thus, the negative ΔH_{sys} corresponds to a positive ΔS_{surr}. It is this positive contribution to the overall ΔS_{univ} that actually favors spontaneity.

Because ΔS°_{univ} is positive, the reaction will be spontaneous at 25°C. Keep in mind, though, that just because a reaction is spontaneous does not mean that it will occur at an observable rate. The synthesis of ammonia is, in fact, extremely slow at room temperature. Thermodynamics can tell us whether or not a reaction will occur spontaneously under specific conditions, but it does not tell us how fast it will occur.

Worked Example 18.4 lets you practice identifying spontaneous, nonspontaneous, and equilibrium processes.

Worked Example 18.4

Determine if each of the following is a spontaneous process, a nonspontaneous process, or an equilibrium process at the specified temperature: (a) $H_2(g) + I_2(g) \longrightarrow 2HI(g)$ at 0°C, (b) $CaCO_3(s) \longrightarrow CaO(s) + CO_2(g)$ at 200°C, (c) $CaCO_3(s) \longrightarrow CaO(s) + CO_2(g)$ at 1000°C, (d) $Na(s) \longrightarrow Na(l)$ at 98°C. (Assume that the thermodynamic data in Appendix 2 do not vary with temperature.)

Strategy For each process, use Equation 18.6 to determine ΔS°_{sys} and Equations 10.18 and 18.7 to determine ΔH°_{sys} and ΔS°_{surr}. At the specified temperature, the process is *spontaneous* if ΔS_{sys} and ΔS_{surr} sum to a positive number, *nonspontaneous* if they sum to a negative number, and an *equilibrium process* if they sum to zero. Note that because the *reaction* is the *system*, ΔS_{rxn} and ΔS_{sys} are used interchangeably.

Setup From Appendix 2,

(a) $S^{\circ}[H_2(g)] = 131.0 \text{ J/K} \cdot \text{mol}$, $S^{\circ}[I_2(g)] = 260.57 \text{ J/K} \cdot \text{mol}$, $S^{\circ}[HI(g)] = 206.3 \text{ J/K} \cdot \text{mol}$; $\Delta H^{\circ}_f[H_2(g)] = 0 \text{ kJ/mol}$, $\Delta H^{\circ}_f[I_2(g)] = 62.25 \text{ kJ/mol}$, $\Delta H^{\circ}_f[HI(g)] = 25.9 \text{ kJ/mol}$.

(b), (c) In Worked Example 18.2(a), we determined that for this reaction, $\Delta S^{\circ}_{rxn} = 160.5 \text{ J/K} \cdot \text{mol}$, $\Delta H^{\circ}_f[CaCO_3(s)] = -1206.9 \text{ kJ/mol}$, $\Delta H^{\circ}_f[CaO(s)] = -635.6 \text{ kJ/mol}$, $\Delta H^{\circ}_f[CO_2(g)] = -393.5 \text{ kJ/mol}$.

(d) $S^{\circ}[Na(s)] = 51.05 \text{ J/K} \cdot \text{mol}$, $S^{\circ}[Na(l)] = 57.56 \text{ J/K} \cdot \text{mol}$; $\Delta H^{\circ}_f[Na(s)] = 0 \text{ kJ/mol}$, $\Delta H^{\circ}_f[Na(l)] = 2.41 \text{ kJ/mol}$.

Solution

(a) $\Delta S^\circ_{rxn} = [2S^\circ(HI)] - [S^\circ(H_2) + S^\circ(I_2)]$

$= (2)(206.3 \text{ J/K} \cdot \text{mol}) - [131.0 \text{ J/K} \cdot \text{mol} + 260.57 \text{ J/K} \cdot \text{mol}] = 21.03 \text{ J/K} \cdot \text{mol}$

$\Delta H^\circ_{rxn} = [2\Delta H^\circ_f(HI)] - [\Delta H^\circ_f(H_2) + \Delta H^\circ_f(I_2)]$

$= (2)(25.9 \text{ kJ/mol}) - [0 \text{ kJ/mol} + 62.25 \text{ kJ/mol}] = -10.5 \text{ kJ/mol}$

$\Delta S_{surr} = \dfrac{-\Delta H_{rxn}}{T} = \dfrac{-(-10.5 \text{ kJ/mol})}{273 \text{ K}} = 0.0385 \text{ kJ/K} \cdot \text{mol} = 38.5 \text{ J/K} \cdot \text{mol}$

$\Delta S_{univ} = \Delta S_{sys} + \Delta S_{surr} = 21.03 \text{ J/K} \cdot \text{mol} + 38.5 \text{ J/K} \cdot \text{mol} = 59.5 \text{ J/K} \cdot \text{mol}$

ΔS_{univ} is positive; therefore the reaction is spontaneous at 0°C.

(b), (c) $\Delta S^\circ_{rxn} = 160.5 \text{ J/K} \cdot \text{mol}$

$\Delta H^\circ_{rxn} = [\Delta H^\circ_f(CaO) + \Delta H^\circ_f(CO_2)] - [\Delta H^\circ_f(CaCO_3)]$

$= [-635.6 \text{ kJ/mol} + (-393.5 \text{ kJ/mol})] - (-1206.9 \text{ kJ/mol}) = 177.8 \text{ kJ/mol}$

(b) $T = 200°C$ and

$\Delta S_{surr} = \dfrac{-\Delta H_{sys}}{T} = \dfrac{-(177.8 \text{ kJ/mol})}{473 \text{ K}} = -0.376 \text{ kJ/K} \cdot \text{mol} = -376 \text{ J/K} \cdot \text{mol}$

$\Delta S_{univ} = \Delta S_{sys} + \Delta S_{surr} = 160.5 \text{ J/K} \cdot \text{mol} + (-376 \text{ J/K} \cdot \text{mol}) = -216 \text{ J/K} \cdot \text{mol}$

ΔS_{univ} is negative, therefore the reaction is nonspontaneous at 200°C.

(c) $T = 1000°C$ and

$\Delta S_{surr} = \dfrac{-\Delta H_{sys}}{T} = \dfrac{-(177.8 \text{ kJ/mol})}{1273 \text{ K}} = -0.1397 \text{ kJ/K} \cdot \text{mol} = -139.7 \text{ J/K} \cdot \text{mol}$

$\Delta S_{univ} = \Delta S_{sys} + \Delta S_{surr} = 160.5 \text{ J/K} \cdot \text{mol} + (-139.7 \text{ J/K} \cdot \text{mol}) = 20.8 \text{ J/K} \cdot \text{mol}$

In this case, ΔS_{univ} is positive; therefore, the reaction is spontaneous at 1000°C.

(d) $\Delta S^\circ_{rxn} = S^\circ[Na(l)] - S^\circ[Na(s)] = 57.56 \text{ J/K} \cdot \text{mol} - 51.05 \text{ J/K} \cdot \text{mol} = 6.51 \text{ J/K} \cdot \text{mol}$

$\Delta H^\circ_{rxn} = \Delta H^\circ_f[Na(l)] - \Delta H^\circ_f[Na(s)] = 2.41 \text{ kJ/mol} - 0 \text{ kJ/mol} = 2.41 \text{ kJ/mol}$

$\Delta S_{surr} = \dfrac{-\Delta H_{rxn}}{T} = \dfrac{-(2.41 \text{ kJ/mol})}{371 \text{ K}} = -0.0650 \text{ kJ/K} \cdot \text{mol} = -6.50 \text{ J/K} \cdot \text{mol}$

$\Delta S_{univ} = \Delta S_{sys} + \Delta S_{surr} = 6.51 \text{ J/K} \cdot \text{mol} + (-6.50 \text{ J/K} \cdot \text{mol}) = 0.01 \text{ J/K} \cdot \text{mol} \approx 0$

ΔS_{univ} is zero; therefore, the reaction is an equilibrium process at 98°C. In fact, this is the melting point of sodium.

> **Student Annotation:** The small difference between the magnitudes of ΔS_{sys} and ΔS_{surr} results from thermodynamic values not being entirely independent of temperature. The tabulated values of S° and ΔH°_f are for 25°C.

Think About It

Remember that standard enthalpies of formation have units of kJ/mol, whereas standard absolute entropies have units of J/K · mol. Make sure that you convert kilojoules to joules, or vice versa, before combining the terms.

Practice Problem A For each of the following, calculate ΔS_{univ} and identify the process as a spontaneous process, a nonspontaneous process, or an equilibrium process at the specified temperature: (a) $CO_2(g) \longrightarrow CO_2(aq)$ at 25°C, (b) $N_2O_4(g) \longrightarrow 2NO_2(g)$ at 10.4°C, (c) $PCl_3(l) \longrightarrow PCl_3(g)$ at 61.2°C. (Assume that the thermodynamic data in Appendix 2 do not vary with temperature.)

Practice Problem B (a) Calculate ΔS_{univ} and determine if the reaction $H_2O_2(l) \longrightarrow H_2O_2(g)$ is spontaneous, nonspontaneous, or an equilibrium process at 163°C. (b) The reaction $NH_3(g) + HCl(g) \longrightarrow NH_4Cl(s)$ is spontaneous in the forward direction at room temperature but, because it is exothermic, becomes less spontaneous with increasing temperature. Determine the temperature at which it is no longer spontaneous in the forward direction. (c) Determine the boiling point of Br_2. (Assume that the thermodynamic data in Appendix 2 do not vary with temperature.)

Thinking Outside the Box

Thermodynamics and Living Systems

Under normal physiological conditions, polypeptides spontaneously fold into unique three-dimensional structures called native proteins, which can perform various functions. Because the original chain can assume many possible configurations while the native protein can have only one specific arrangement, the folding process is accompanied by a decrease in entropy of the system. (Note that solvent molecules, water in this case, can also play a role in affecting the entropy change.) In accord with the second law of thermodynamics, any spontaneous process must result in an increase in the entropy of the universe. It follows, therefore, that there must be an increase in the entropy of the surroundings that outweighs the decrease in the entropy of the system. The intramolecular attractions between amino acid residues cause the folding of the polypeptide chain to be exothermic. The energy produced by the process spreads out, increasing molecular motion in the surroundings—thereby increasing the entropy of the surroundings.

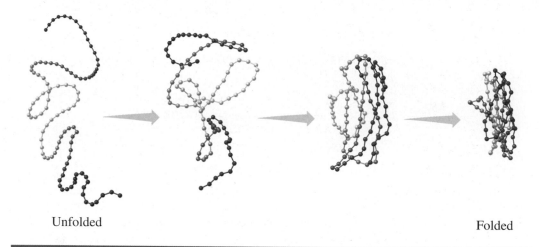

Unfolded   Folded

The Third Law of Thermodynamics

Finally, we consider the third law of thermodynamics briefly in connection with the determination of standard entropy. We have related the entropy of a system to the number of possible arrangements of the system's molecules. The larger the number of possible arrangements, the larger the entropy. Imagine a pure, perfect crystalline substance at absolute zero (0 K). Under these conditions, there is essentially no molecular motion and, because the molecules occupy fixed positions in the solid, there is only one way to arrange the molecules. From Equation 18.1, we write

$$S = k \ln W = k \ln 1 = 0$$

According to the ***third law of thermodynamics,*** the entropy of a perfect crystalline substance is *zero* at absolute zero. As temperature increases, molecular motion increases, causing an increase in the number of possible arrangements of the molecules and in the number of accessible energy states, among which the system's energy can be dispersed. (See Figure 18.4.) This results in an increase in the system's entropy. Thus, the entropy of any substance at any temperature above 0 K is greater than zero. If the crystalline substance is impure or imperfect in any way, then its entropy is greater than zero even at 0 K because without perfect crystalline order, there is more than one possible arrangement of molecules.

The significance of the third law of thermodynamics is that it enables us to determine experimentally the *absolute* entropies of substances. Starting with the knowledge that the entropy of a pure crystalline substance is zero at 0 K, we can measure the increase in entropy of the substance as it is heated. The change in entropy of a substance, ΔS, is the difference between the final and initial entropy values:

$$\Delta S = S_{final} - S_{initial}$$

where $S_{initial}$ is zero if the substance starts at 0 K. Therefore, the measured *change* in entropy is equal to the *absolute* entropy of the substance at the final temperature.

$$\Delta S = S_{final}$$

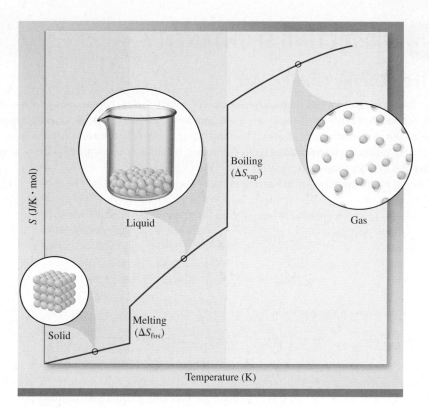

The entropy values arrived at in this way are called *absolute* entropies because they are *true* values—unlike standard enthalpies of formation, which are derived using an arbitrary reference. Because the tabulated values are determined at 1 atm, we usually refer to absolute entropies as *standard* entropies, $S°$. Figure 18.5 shows the increase in entropy of a substance as temperature increases from absolute zero. At 0 K, it has a zero entropy value (assuming that it is a perfect crystalline substance). As it is heated, its entropy increases gradually at first because of greater molecular motion within the crystal. At the melting point, there is a large increase in entropy as the solid is transformed into the liquid. Further heating increases the entropy of the liquid again due to increased molecular motion. At the boiling point, there is a large increase in entropy as a result of the liquid-to-vapor transition. Beyond that temperature, the entropy of the gas continues to increase with increasing temperature.

SECTION 18.4 REVIEW

Entropy Changes in the Universe

18.4.1   Using data from Appendix 2, calculate $\Delta S°$ (in J/K · mol) for the following reaction:

$$2NO(g) + O_2(g) \longrightarrow 2NO_2(g)$$

18.4.2   Using data from Appendix 2, calculate $\Delta S°$ (in J/K · mol) for the following reaction:

$$CH_4(g) + 2O_2(g) \longrightarrow CO_2(g) + 2H_2O(l)$$

18.4.3   For each of the processes shown, state whether ΔS_{surr} is positive, negative, or if there is not enough information to determine the sign of ΔS_{surr}.

(a)   (b)   (c)

18.5 PREDICTING SPONTANEITY

Gibbs Free-Energy Change, ∆G

According to the second law of thermodynamics, $\Delta S_{univ} > 0$ for a spontaneous process. What we are usually concerned with and usually *measure,* however, are the properties of the *system* rather than those of the surroundings or those of the universe overall. Therefore, it is convenient to have a thermodynamic function that enables us to determine whether or not a process is spontaneous by considering the system alone.

We begin with Equation 18.8. For a spontaneous process,

$$\Delta S_{univ} = \Delta S_{sys} + \Delta S_{surr} > 0$$

Substituting $-\Delta H_{sys}/T$ for ΔS_{surr}, we write

$$\Delta S_{univ} = \Delta S_{sys} + \left(-\frac{\Delta H_{sys}}{T} \right) > 0$$

Multiplying both sides of the equation by T gives

$$T\Delta S_{univ} = T\Delta S_{sys} - \Delta H_{sys} > 0$$

Now we have an equation that expresses the second law of thermodynamics (and predicts whether or not a process is spontaneous) in terms of only the *system.* We no longer need to consider the surroundings. For convenience, we can rearrange the preceding equation, multiply through by −1, and replace the > sign with a < sign:

$$-T\Delta S_{univ} = \Delta H_{sys} - T\Delta S_{sys} < 0$$

According to this equation, a process carried out at constant pressure and temperature is spontaneous if the changes in enthalpy and entropy of the system are such that $\Delta H_{sys} - T\Delta S_{sys}$ is less than zero.

To express the spontaneity of a process more directly, we introduce another thermodynamic function called the **Gibbs**[1] *free energy (G),* or simply *free energy.*

Equation 18.9	$G = H - TS$

Each of the terms in Equation 18.9 pertains to the system. G has units of energy just as H and TS do. Furthermore, like enthalpy and entropy, free energy is a state function. The change in free energy, ΔG, of a system for a process that occurs at constant temperature is

Equation 18.10	$\Delta G = \Delta H - T\Delta S$

Equation 18.10 enables us to predict the spontaneity of a process using the change in enthalpy, the change in entropy, and the absolute temperature. At constant temperature and pressure, for processes that are spontaneous as written (in the forward direction), ΔG is negative. For processes that are not spontaneous as written but that are spontaneous in the reverse direction, ΔG is positive. For systems at equilibrium, ΔG is zero.

> **Student Annotation:** In this context, *free energy* is the energy available to do work. Thus, if a particular process is accompanied by a release of usable energy (i.e., if ∆G is negative), this fact alone guarantees that it is spontaneous, and there is no need to consider what happens to the rest of the universe.

- $\Delta G < 0$ The reaction is spontaneous in the forward direction (and nonspontaneous in the reverse direction).
- $\Delta G > 0$ The reaction is nonspontaneous in the forward direction (and spontaneous in the reverse direction).
- $\Delta G = 0$ The system is at equilibrium.

Often we can predict the sign of ΔG for a process if we know the signs of ΔH and ΔS. Table 18.4 shows how we can use Equation 18.10 to make such predictions.

---

[1]Josiah Willard Gibbs (1839–1903), an American physicist, was one of the founders of thermodynamics. Gibbs was a modest and private individual who spent almost all his professional life at Yale University. Because he published most of his work in obscure journals, Gibbs never gained the eminence that his contemporary and admirer James Maxwell did. Even today, very few people outside of chemistry and physics have ever heard of Gibbs.

TABLE 18.4	Predicting the Sign of ΔG Using Equation 18.10 and the Signs of ΔH and ΔS			
When ΔH is	**And ΔS is**	**ΔG will be**	**And the process is**	**Example**
Negative	Positive	Negative	Always spontaneous	$2H_2O_2(aq) \longrightarrow 2H_2O(l) + O_2(g)$
Positive	Negative	Positive	Always nonspontaneous	$3O_2(g) \longrightarrow 2O_3(g)$
Negative	Negative	Negative when $T\Delta S < \Delta H$ Positive when $T\Delta S > \Delta H$	Spontaneous at low T Nonspontaneous at high T	$H_2O(l) \longrightarrow H_2O(s)$ (freezing of water)
Positive	Positive	Negative when $T\Delta S > \Delta H$ Positive when $T\Delta S < \Delta H$	Spontaneous at high T Nonspontaneous at low T	$2HgO(s) \longrightarrow 2Hg(l) + O_2(g)$

Based on the information in Table 18.4, you may wonder what constitutes a "low" or a "high" temperature. For the freezing of water, 0°C is the temperature that divides high from low. Water freezes spontaneously at temperatures below 0°C, and ice melts spontaneously at temperatures above 0°C. At 0°C, a system of ice and water is at equilibrium. The temperature that divides "high" from "low" depends, though, on the individual reaction. To determine that temperature, we must set ΔG equal to 0 in Equation 18.10 (i.e., the equilibrium condition):

$$0 = \Delta H - T\Delta S$$

Rearranging to solve for T yields

$$T = \frac{\Delta H}{\Delta S}$$

The temperature that divides high from low for a particular reaction can now be calculated if the values of ΔH and ΔS are known.

Worked Example 18.5 demonstrates the use of this approach.

Worked Example 18.5

According to Table 18.4, a reaction will be spontaneous only at high temperatures if both ΔH and ΔS are positive. For a reaction in which $\Delta H = 199.5$ kJ/mol and $\Delta S = 476$ J/K · mol, determine the temperature (in °C) above which the reaction is spontaneous.

Strategy The temperature that divides high from low is the temperature at which $\Delta H = T\Delta S$ ($\Delta G = 0$). Therefore, we use Equation 18.10, substituting 0 for ΔG and solving for T to determine temperature in kelvins; we then convert to degrees Celsius.

Setup

$$\Delta S = \left(\frac{476 \text{ J}}{\text{K} \cdot \text{mol}}\right)\left(\frac{1 \text{ kJ}}{1000 \text{ J}}\right) = 0.476 \text{ kJ/K} \cdot \text{mol}$$

Solution

$$T = \frac{\Delta H}{\Delta S} = \frac{199.5 \text{ kJ/mol}}{0.476 \text{ kJ/K} \cdot \text{mol}} = 419 \text{ K}$$

$$= (419 - 273) = 146°\text{C}$$

Think About It
Spontaneity is favored by a release of energy (ΔH being negative) and by an increase in entropy (ΔS being positive). When both quantities are positive, as in this case, only the entropy change favors spontaneity. For an endothermic process such as this, which requires the input of heat, it should make sense that adding more heat by increasing the temperature will shift the equilibrium to the right, thus making it "more spontaneous."

Practice Problem A A reaction will be spontaneous only at low temperatures if both ΔH and ΔS are negative. For a reaction in which $\Delta H = -380.1$ kJ/mol and $\Delta S = -95.00$ J/K · mol, determine the temperature (in °C) below which the reaction is spontaneous.

Practice Problem B Given that the reaction $4Fe(s) + 3O_2(g) + 6H_2O(l) \longrightarrow 4Fe(OH)_3(s)$ is spontaneous at temperatures below 1950°C, estimate the standard entropy of $Fe(OH)_3(s)$.

Student Annotation: The introduction of the term $\Delta G°$ enables us to write Equation 18.10 as

$$\Delta G° = \Delta H° - T\Delta S°$$

Standard Free-Energy Changes, $\Delta G°$

The ***standard free energy of reaction*** $(\Delta G°_{rxn})$ is the free-energy change for a reaction when it occurs under standard-state conditions—that is, when reactants in their standard states are converted to products in *their* standard states. The conventions used by chemists to define the standard states of pure substances and solutions are

- Gases   1 atm pressure
- Liquids   Pure liquid
- Solids   Pure solid
- Elements   The most stable allotropic form at 1 atm and 25°C
- Solutions   1 molar concentration

To calculate $\Delta G°_{rxn}$, we start with the general equation

$$aA + bB \longrightarrow cC + dD$$

The standard free-energy change for this reaction is given by

Equation 18.11 $\Delta G°_{rxn} = [c\Delta G°_f(C) + d\Delta G°_f(D)] - [a\Delta G°_f(A) + b\Delta G°_f(B)]$

Equation 18.11 can be generalized as follows:

Equation 18.12 $\Delta G°_{rxn} = \Sigma n\Delta G°_f \text{ (products)} - \Sigma m\Delta G°_f \text{ (reactants)}$

where m and n are stoichiometric coefficients. The term $\Delta G°_f$ is the ***standard free energy of formation*** of a compound—that is, the free-energy change that occurs when 1 mole of the compound is synthesized from its constituent elements, each in its standard state. For the combustion of graphite,

$$C(graphite) + O_2(g) \longrightarrow CO_2(g)$$

the standard free-energy change (from Equation 18.12) is

$$\Delta G°_{rxn} = [\Delta G°_f(CO_2)] - [\Delta G°_f(C, graphite) + \Delta G°_f(O_2)]$$

As with standard enthalpy of formation, the standard free energy of formation of any element (in its most stable allotropic form at 1 atm) is defined as zero. Thus,

$$\Delta G°_f(C, graphite) = 0 \quad \text{and} \quad \Delta G°_f(O_2) = 0$$

Therefore, the standard free-energy change for the reaction in this case is equal to the standard free energy of formation of CO_2:

$$\Delta G°_{rxn} = \Delta G°_f(CO_2)$$

Appendix 2 lists the values of $\Delta G°_f$ at 25°C for a number of compounds.

Worked Example 18.6 demonstrates the calculation of standard free-energy changes.

Worked Example 18.6

Calculate the standard free-energy changes for the following reactions at 25°C:

(a) $CH_4(g) + 2O_2(g) \longrightarrow CO_2(g) + 2H_2O(l)$

(b) $2MgO(s) \longrightarrow 2Mg(s) + O_2(g)$

Strategy Look up the $\Delta G°_f$ values for the reactants and products in each equation, and use Equation 18.12 to solve for $\Delta G°_{rxn}$.

Setup From Appendix 2, we have the following values: $\Delta G°_f[CH_4(g)] = -50.8$ kJ/mol, $\Delta G°_f[CO_2(g)] = -394.4$ kJ/mol, $\Delta G°_f[H_2O(l)] = -237.2$ kJ/mol, and $\Delta G°_f[MgO(s)] = -569.6$ kJ/mol. All the other substances are elements in their standard states and have, by definition, $\Delta G°_f = 0$.

Solution

(a) $\Delta G^{\circ}_{\text{rxn}} = (\Delta G^{\circ}_{\text{f}}[CO_2(g)] + 2\Delta G^{\circ}_{\text{f}}[H_2O(l)]) - (\Delta G^{\circ}_{\text{f}}[CH_4(g)] + 2\Delta G^{\circ}_{\text{f}}[O_2(g)])$

$= [(-394.4 \text{ kJ/mol}) + (2)(-237.2 \text{ kJ/mol})] - [(-50.8 \text{ kJ/mol}) + (2)(0 \text{ kJ/mol})]$

$= -818.0 \text{ kJ/mol}$

(b) $\Delta G^{\circ}_{\text{rxn}} = (2\Delta G^{\circ}_{\text{f}}[Mg(s)] + \Delta G^{\circ}_{\text{f}}[O_2(g)]) - (2\Delta G^{\circ}_{\text{f}}[MgO(s)])$

$= [(2)(0 \text{ kJ/mol}) + (0 \text{ kJ/mol})] - [(2)(-569.6 \text{ kJ/mol})]$

$= 1139 \text{ kJ/mol}$

Think About It

Note that, like standard enthalpies of formation ($\Delta H^{\circ}_{\text{f}}$), standard free energies of formation ($\Delta G^{\circ}_{\text{f}}$) depend on the *state* of matter. Using water as an example, $\Delta G^{\circ}_{\text{f}}[H_2O(l)] = -237.2 \text{ kJ/mol}$ and $\Delta G^{\circ}_{\text{f}}[H_2O(g)] = -228.6 \text{ kJ/mol}$. Always double-check to make sure you have selected the right value from the table.

Practice Problem A Calculate the standard free-energy changes for the following reactions at 25°C:

(a) $H_2(g) + Br_2(l) \longrightarrow 2HBr(g)$

(b) $2C_2H_6(g) + 7O_2(g) \longrightarrow 4CO_2(g) + 6H_2O(l)$

Practice Problem B For each reaction, determine the value of $\Delta G^{\circ}_{\text{f}}$ that is not listed in Appendix 2:

(a) $Li_2O(s) + 2HCl(g) \longrightarrow 2LiCl(s) + H_2O(g)$ $\Delta G^{\circ}_{\text{rxn}} = -244.88 \text{ kJ/mol}$

(b) $Na_2O(s) + 2HI(g) \longrightarrow 2NaI(s) + H_2O(l)$ $\Delta G^{\circ}_{\text{rxn}} = -435.44 \text{ kJ/mol}$

Using ΔG and ΔG° to Solve Problems

It is the sign of ΔG, the free-energy change, *not* the sign of ΔG°, the standard free-energy change, that indicates whether or not a process will occur spontaneously under a given set of conditions. What the *sign* of ΔG° tells us is the same thing that the magnitude of the equilibrium constant (K) tells us [◄◄ Section 15.2]. A negative ΔG° value corresponds to a large K value (products favored at equilibrium), whereas a positive ΔG° value corresponds to a small K value (reactants favored at equilibrium).

Like equilibrium constants, ΔG° values change with temperature. One of the uses of Equation 18.10 is to determine the temperature at which a particular equilibrium will begin to favor a desired product. For example, calcium oxide (CaO), also called quicklime, is an extremely valuable inorganic substance with a variety of industrial uses, including water treatment and pollution control. It is prepared by heating limestone ($CaCO_3$), which decomposes at a high temperature:

$$CaCO_3(s) \rightleftharpoons CaO(s) + CO_2(g)$$

The reaction is reversible, and under the right conditions, CaO and CO_2 readily recombine to form $CaCO_3$ again. To prevent this from happening in the industrial preparation, the system is never maintained at equilibrium; rather, CO_2 is constantly removed as it forms, shifting the equilibrium from left to right, thus promoting the formation of calcium oxide.

An important piece of information for the chemist responsible for maximizing CaO production is the temperature at which the decomposition equilibrium of $CaCO_3$ begins to favor products. We can make a reliable estimate of that temperature as follows. First we calculate ΔH° and ΔS° for the reaction at 25°C, using the data in Appendix 2. To determine ΔH°, we apply Equation 10.18:

$$\Delta H^{\circ} = [\Delta H^{\circ}_{\text{f}}(CaO) + \Delta H^{\circ}_{\text{f}}(CO_2)] - [\Delta H^{\circ}_{\text{f}}(CaCO_3)]$$

$$= [(-635.6 \text{ kJ/mol}) + (-393.5 \text{ kJ/mol})] - (-1206.9 \text{ kJ/mol})$$

$$= 177.8 \text{ kJ/mol}$$

Next we apply Equation 18.6 to find ΔS°:

$$\Delta S^{\circ} = [S^{\circ}(CaO) + S^{\circ}(CO_2)] - S^{\circ}(CaCO_3)$$

$$= [(39.8 \text{ J/K} \cdot \text{mol}) + (213.6 \text{ J/K} \cdot \text{mol})] - (92.9 \text{ J/K} \cdot \text{mol})$$

$$= 160.5 \text{ J/K} \cdot \text{mol}$$

Student Annotation: The sign of ΔG° does indicate whether or not a process is spontaneous when *all* reactants and products are in their standard states, but this is very seldom the case.

From Equation 18.10, we can write

$$\Delta G° = \Delta H° - T\Delta S°$$

and we obtain

$$\Delta G° = (177.8 \text{ kJ/mol}) - (298 \text{ K})(0.1605 \text{ kJ/K} \cdot \text{mol})$$

$$= 130.0 \text{ kJ/mol}$$

Because $\Delta G°$ is a large positive number, the reaction does *not* favor product formation at 25°C (298 K). And, because $\Delta H°$ and $\Delta S°$ are both positive, we know that $\Delta G°$ will be negative (product formation will be favored) at high temperatures. We can determine what constitutes a high temperature for this reaction by calculating the temperature at which $\Delta G°$ is zero.

$$0 = \Delta H° - T\Delta S°$$

or

$$T = \frac{\Delta H°}{\Delta S°}$$

$$= \frac{(177.8 \text{ kJ/mol})(1000 \text{ J/kJ})}{0.1605 \text{ kJ/K} \cdot \text{mol}}$$

$$= 1108 \text{ K } (835°\text{C})$$

At temperatures higher than 835°C, $\Delta G°$ becomes negative, indicating that the reaction would then favor the formation of CaO and CO_2. At 840°C (1113 K), for example,

$$\Delta G° = \Delta H° - T\Delta S°$$

$$= 177.8 \text{ kJ/mol} - (1113 \text{ K})(0.1605 \text{ kJ/K} \cdot \text{mol})\left(\frac{1 \text{ kJ}}{1000 \text{ J}}\right)$$

$$= -0.8 \text{ kJ/mol}$$

At still higher temperatures, $\Delta G°$ becomes increasingly negative, thus favoring product formation even more. Note that in this example we used the $\Delta H°$ and $\Delta S°$ values at 25°C to calculate changes to $\Delta G°$ at much higher temperatures. Because both $\Delta H°$ and $\Delta S°$ actually change with temperature, this approach does not give us a truly accurate value for $\Delta G°$, but it does give us a reasonably good estimate.

Equation 18.10 can also be used to calculate the change in entropy that accompanies a phase change. At the temperature at which a phase change occurs (i.e., the melting point or boiling point of a substance), the system is at equilibrium ($\Delta G = 0$). Therefore, Equation 18.10 becomes

$$0 = \Delta H - T\Delta S$$

or

$$\Delta S = \frac{\Delta H}{T}$$

Consider the ice-water equilibrium. For the ice-to-water transition, ΔH is the molar heat of fusion (see Table 12.8) and T is the melting point. The entropy change is therefore

$$\Delta S_{\text{ice} \longrightarrow \text{water}} = \frac{6010 \text{ J/mol}}{273 \text{ K}} = 22.0 \text{ J/K} \cdot \text{mol}$$

Thus, when 1 mole of ice melts at 0°C, there is an increase in entropy of 22.0 J/K · mol. The increase in entropy is consistent with the increase in the number of possible arrangements of molecules from solid to liquid. Conversely, for the water-to-ice transition, the decrease in entropy is given by

$$\Delta S_{\text{water} \longrightarrow \text{ice}} = \frac{-6010 \text{ J/mol}}{273 \text{ K}} = -22.0 \text{ J/K} \cdot \text{mol}$$

The same approach can be applied to the water-to-steam transition. In this case, ΔH is the heat of vaporization and T is the boiling point of water.

Worked Example 18.7 examines the phase transitions in benzene.

Worked Example 18.7

The molar heats of fusion and vaporization of benzene are 10.9 and 31.0 kJ/mol, respectively. Calculate the entropy changes for the solid-to-liquid and liquid-to-vapor transitions for benzene. At 1 atm pressure, benzene melts at 5.5°C and boils at 80.1°C.

Strategy The solid-liquid transition at the melting point and the liquid-vapor transition at the boiling point are *equilibrium* processes. Therefore, because ΔG is zero at equilibrium, in each case we can use Equation 18.10, substituting 0 for ΔG and solving for ΔS, to determine the entropy change associated with the process.

Setup The melting point of benzene is $5.5 + 273.15 = 278.7$ K and the boiling point is $80.1 + 273.15 = 353.3$ K.

Solution

$$\Delta S_{fus} = \frac{\Delta H_{fus}}{T_{melting}} = \frac{10.9 \text{ kJ/mol}}{278.7 \text{ K}}$$

$$= 0.0391 \text{ kJ/K} \cdot \text{mol} \quad \text{or} \quad 39.1 \text{ J/K} \cdot \text{mol}$$

$$\Delta S_{vap} = \frac{\Delta H_{vap}}{T_{boiling}} = \frac{31.0 \text{ kJ/mol}}{353.3 \text{ K}}$$

$$= 0.0877 \text{ kJ/K} \cdot \text{mol} \quad \text{or} \quad 87.7 \text{ J/K} \cdot \text{mol}$$

Think About It
For the same substance, ΔS_{vap} is always significantly larger than ΔS_{fus}. The change in number of arrangements is always bigger in a liquid-to-gas transition than in a solid-to-liquid transition.

Practice Problem A The molar heats of fusion and vaporization of argon are 1.3 and 6.3 kJ/mol, respectively, and argon's melting point and boiling point are −190°C and −186°C, respectively. Calculate the entropy changes for the fusion and vaporization of argon.

Practice Problem B Using data from Appendix 2 and assuming that the tabulated values do not change with temperature, (a) calculate ΔH°_{fus} and ΔS°_{fus} for sodium metal and determine the melting temperature of sodium, and (b) calculate ΔH°_{vap} and ΔS°_{vap} for sodium metal and determine the boiling temperature of sodium.

SECTION 18.5 REVIEW

Predicting Spontaneity

18.5.1   Using data from Appendix 2, calculate ΔG° (in kJ/mol) at 25°C for the reaction:

$$CH_4(g) + 2O_2(g) \longrightarrow CO_2(g) + 2H_2O(g)$$

18.5.2   Calculate ΔS_{sub} (in J/K · mol) for the sublimation of iodine in a closed flask at 45°C.

$$I_2(s) \longrightarrow I_2(g) \qquad \Delta H_{sub} = 62.4 \text{ kJ/mol}$$

18.5.3   At what temperature (in °C) does a reaction go from being nonspontaneous to spontaneous if it has $\Delta H = 171$ kJ/mol and $\Delta S = 161$ J/K · mol?

18.6 FREE ENERGY AND CHEMICAL EQUILIBRIUM

Reactants and products in a chemical reaction are almost always in something *other* than their standard states—that is, solutions usually have concentrations other than 1 M and gases usually have pressures other than 1 atm. To determine whether or not a reaction is spontaneous, therefore, we must take into account the actual concentrations and/or pressures of the species involved. And although we can determine $\Delta G°$ from tabulated values, we need to know ΔG to determine spontaneity.

Relationship Between ΔG and $\Delta G°$

The relationship between ΔG and $\Delta G°$, which is derived from thermodynamics, is

Equation 18.13	$\Delta G = \Delta G° + RT \ln Q$

where R is the gas constant (8.314 J/K · mol or 8.314×10^{-3} kJ/K · mol), T is the absolute temperature at which the reaction takes place, and Q is the reaction quotient [◄◄ Section 15.2]. Thus, ΔG depends on two terms: $\Delta G°$ and $RT \ln Q$. For a given reaction at temperature T, the value of $\Delta G°$ is fixed but that of $RT \ln Q$ can vary because Q varies according to the composition of the reaction mixture.

Consider the following equilibrium:

$$H_2(g) + I_2(g) \rightleftharpoons 2HI(g)$$

Using Equation 18.12 and information from Appendix 2, we find that $\Delta G°$ for this reaction at 25°C is 2.60 kJ/mol. The value of ΔG, however, depends on the pressures of all three gaseous species. If we start with a mixture of gases in which $P_{H_2} = 2.0$ atm, $P_{I_2} = 2.0$ atm, and $P_{HI} = 3.0$ atm, the reaction quotient, Q_P, is

$$Q_P = \frac{(P_{HI})^2}{(P_{H_2})(P_{I_2})} = \frac{(3.0)^2}{(2.0)(2.0)} = \frac{9.0}{4.0}$$

$$= 2.25$$

Using this value in Equation 18.13 gives

$$\Delta G = \frac{2.60 \text{ kJ}}{\text{mol}} + \left(\frac{8.314 \times 10^{-3} \text{ kJ}}{\text{K} \cdot \text{mol}}\right)(298 \text{ K})(\ln 2.25)$$

$$= 4.3 \text{ kJ/mol}$$

Because ΔG is positive, we conclude that, starting with these concentrations, the forward reaction will not occur spontaneously as written. Instead, the *reverse* reaction will occur spontaneously and the system will reach equilibrium by consuming part of the HI initially present and producing more H_2 and I_2.

If, on the other hand, we start with a mixture of gases in which $P_{H_2} = 2.0$ atm, $P_{I_2} = 2.0$ atm, and $P_{HI} = 1.0$ atm, the reaction quotient, Q_P, is

$$Q_P = \frac{(P_{HI})^2}{(P_{H_2})(P_{I_2})} = \frac{(1.0)^2}{(2.0)(2.0)} = \frac{1}{4}$$

$$= 0.25$$

Using this value in Equation 18.13 gives

$$\Delta G = \frac{2.6 \text{ kJ}}{\text{mol}} + \left(\frac{8.314 \times 10^{-3} \text{ kJ}}{\text{K} \cdot \text{mol}}\right)(298 \text{ K})(\ln 0.25)$$

$$= -0.8 \text{ kJ/mol}$$

With a negative value for ΔG, the reaction will be spontaneous as written—in the forward direction. In this case, the system will achieve equilibrium by consuming some of the H_2 and I_2 to produce more HI.

Worked Example 18.8 uses $\Delta G°$ and the reaction quotient to determine in which direction a reaction is spontaneous.

Worked Example 18.8

The equilibrium constant, K_p, for the reaction

$$N_2O_4(g) \rightleftharpoons 2NO_2(g)$$

is 0.113 at 298 K, which corresponds to a standard free-energy change of 5.4 kJ/mol. In a certain experiment, the initial pressures are $P_{N_2O_4} = 0.453$ atm and $P_{NO_2} = 0.122$ atm. Calculate ΔG for the reaction at these pressures, and predict the direction in which the reaction will proceed spontaneously to establish equilibrium.

Strategy Use the partial pressures of N_2O_4 and NO_2 to calculate the reaction quotient Q_p, and then use Equation 18.13 to calculate ΔG.

Setup The reaction quotient expression is

$$Q_P = \frac{(P_{NO_2})^2}{P_{N_2O_4}} = \frac{(0.122)^2}{0.453} = 0.0329$$

Solution

$$\Delta G = \Delta G° + RT \ln Q_P$$

$$= \frac{5.4 \text{ kJ}}{\text{mol}} + \left(\frac{8.314 \times 10^{-3} \text{ kJ}}{\text{K} \cdot \text{mol}}\right)(298 \text{ K})(\ln 0.0329)$$

$$= 5.4 \text{ kJ/mol} - 8.46 \text{ kJ/mol}$$

$$= -3.1 \text{ kJ/mol}$$

Because ΔG is negative, the reaction proceeds spontaneously from left to right to reach equilibrium.

Think About It
Remember, a reaction with a positive $\Delta G°$ value can be spontaneous if the starting concentrations of reactants and products are such that $Q < K$.

Practice Problem A $\Delta G°$ for the reaction

$$H_2(g) + I_2(g) \rightleftharpoons 2HI(g)$$

is 2.60 kJ/mol at 25°C. Calculate ΔG, and predict the direction in which the reaction is spontaneous if the starting concentrations are $P_{H_2} = 3.5$ atm, $P_{I_2} = 1.5$ atm, and $P_{HI} = 1.75$ atm.

Practice Problem B What is the minimum partial pressure of I_2 required for the preceding reaction to be spontaneous in the forward direction at 25°C if the partial pressures of H_2 and HI are 3.5 and 1.75 atm, respectively?

Relationship Between $\Delta G°$ and K

By definition, $\Delta G = 0$ and $Q = K$ at equilibrium, where K is the equilibrium constant. Thus, $\Delta G = \Delta G° + RT \ln Q$ (Equation 18.13) becomes

$$0 = \Delta G° + RT \ln K$$

or

$$\Delta G° = -RT \ln K \qquad \textbf{Equation 18.14}$$

According to Equation 18.14, then, the larger K is, the more negative $\Delta G°$ is. For chemists, Equation 18.14 is one of the most important equations in thermodynamics because it enables us to find the equilibrium constant of a reaction if we know the change in standard free energy, and vice versa.

Student Annotation: In this equation and in Equation 18.14, K is K_c for reactions that take place in solution and K_p for reactions that take place in the gas phase.

Multi 18.2
Chemical equilibrium—equilibrium

Multi 18.3
Chemical kinetics—interactive reaction
coordinate diagram

Student Annotation: The sign of
$\Delta G°$ tells us the same thing that the
magnitude of K tells us. The sign of ΔG
tells us the same thing as the comparison
of Q and K values [◄◄ Section 15.4].

It is significant that Equation 18.14 relates the equilibrium constant to the standard free-energy change, $\Delta G°$, rather than to the actual free-energy change, ΔG. The actual free-energy change of the system varies as the reaction progresses and becomes zero at equilibrium. On the other hand, $\Delta G°$, like K, is a constant for a particular reaction at a given temperature. Figure 18.6 shows plots of the free energy of a reacting system versus the extent of the reaction for two reactions. Table 18.5 summarizes the relationship between the *magnitude* of an equilibrium constant and the *sign* of the corresponding $\Delta G°$. Remember this important distinction: It is the sign of ΔG and not that of $\Delta G°$ that determines the direction of reaction spontaneity. The sign of $\Delta G°$ only tells us the relative amounts of products and reactants when equilibrium is reached, *not* the direction the reaction must go to reach equilibrium.

For reactions with very large or very small equilibrium constants, it can be very difficult—sometimes impossible—to determine K values by measuring the concentrations of the reactants

Figure 18.6 (a) $\Delta G° < 0$. At equilibrium, there is a significant conversion of reactants to products. (b) $\Delta G° > 0$. At equilibrium, reactants are favored over products. In both cases, the net reaction toward equilibrium is from left to right (reactants to products) if $Q < K$ and right to left (products to reactants) if $Q > K$. At equilibrium, $Q = K$.

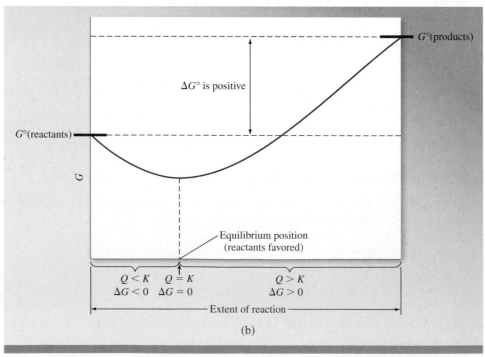

TABLE 18.5		Relationship Between K and $\Delta G°$ as Predicted by Equation 18.14	
K	ln K	$\Delta G°$	Result at equilibrium
> 1	Positive	Negative	Products are favored.
= 1	0	0	Neither products nor reactants are favored.
< 1	Negative	Positive	Reactants are favored.

and products. Consider, for example, the formation of nitric oxide from molecular nitrogen and molecular oxygen:

$$N_2(g) + O_2(g) \rightleftharpoons 2NO(g)$$

At 25°C, the equilibrium constant, K_P, is

$$K_P = \frac{(P_{NO})^2}{(P_{N_2})(P_{O_2})} = 4.0 \times 10^{-31}$$

The very small value of K_P means that the concentration of NO at equilibrium will be exceedingly low and, for all intents and purposes, impossible to measure directly. In such a case, the equilibrium constant is more conveniently determined using $\Delta G°$, which can be calculated either from tabulated $\Delta G_f°$ values or from $\Delta H°$ and $\Delta S°$.

Worked Examples 18.9 and 18.10 show how to use $\Delta G°$ to calculate K and how to use K to calculate $\Delta G°$, respectively.

Worked Example 18.9

Using data from Appendix 2, calculate the equilibrium constant, K_P, for the following reaction at 25°C:

$$2H_2O(l) \rightleftharpoons 2H_2(g) + O_2(g)$$

Strategy Use data from Appendix 2 and Equation 18.12 to calculate $\Delta G°$ for the reaction. Then use Equation 18.14 to solve for K_P.

Setup

$$\Delta G° = (2\Delta G_f°[H_2(g)] + \Delta G_f°[O_2(g)]) - (2\Delta G_f°[H_2O(l)])$$

$$= [(2)(0 \text{ kJ/mol}) + (0 \text{ kJ/mol})] - [(2)(-237.2 \text{ kJ/mol})]$$

$$= 474.4 \text{ kJ/mol}$$

Solution

$$\Delta G° = -RT \ln K_P$$

$$\frac{474.4 \text{ kJ}}{\text{mol}} = -\left(\frac{8.314 \times 10^{-3} \text{ kJ}}{\text{K} \cdot \text{mol}}\right)(298 \text{ K}) \ln K_P$$

$$-191.5 = \ln K_P$$

$$K_P = e^{-191.5}$$

$$= 7 \times 10^{-84}$$

Think About It
This is an extremely small equilibrium constant, which is consistent with the large, positive value of $\Delta G°$. We know from everyday experience that water does not decompose spontaneously into its constituent elements at 25°C.

Practice Problem A Using data from Appendix 2, calculate the equilibrium constant, K_P, for the following reaction at 25°C:

$$2O_3(g) \rightleftharpoons 3O_2(g)$$

Practice Problem B K_f for the complex ion $Ag(NH_3)_2^+$ is 1.5×10^7 at 25°C. Using this and data from Appendix 2, calculate the value of $\Delta G_f°$ for $Ag(NH_3)_2^+(aq)$.

Worked Example 18.10

The equilibrium constant, K_{sp}, for the dissolution of silver chloride in water at 25°C,

$$AgCl(s) \rightleftharpoons Ag^+(aq) + Cl^-(aq)$$

is 1.6×10^{-10}. Calculate $\Delta G°$ for the process.

Strategy Use Equation 18.14 to calculate $\Delta G°$.

Setup $R = 8.314 \times 10^{-3}$ kJ/K · mol and $T = (25 + 273) = 298$ K.

Solution

$$\Delta G° = -RT \ln K_{sp}$$

$$= -\left(\frac{8.314 \times 10^{-3} \text{ kJ}}{\text{K} \cdot \text{mol}}\right)(298 \text{ K}) \ln (1.6 \times 10^{-10})$$

$$= 55.9 \text{ kJ/mol}$$

Think About It
The relatively large, positive $\Delta G°$, like the very small K value, corresponds to a process that lies very far to the left. Note that the K in Equation 18.14 can be any type of K_c (K_a, K_b, K_{sp}, etc.) or K_P.

Practice Problem A Calculate $\Delta G°$ for the process:

$$BaF_2(s) \rightleftharpoons Ba^{2+}(aq) + 2F^-(aq)$$

The K_{sp} of BaF_2 at 25°C is 1.7×10^{-6}.

Practice Problem B K_{sp} for $Co(OH)_2$ at 25°C is 3.3×10^{-16}. Using this and data from Appendix 2, calculate the value of $\Delta G_f°$ for $Co(OH)_2(s)$.

SECTION 18.6 REVIEW

Free Energy and Chemical Equilibrium

18.6.1   For the reaction

$$A(aq) + B(aq) \rightleftharpoons C(aq)$$

$\Delta G° = -1.95$ kJ/mol at 25°C. What is ΔG (in kJ/mol) at 25°C when the concentrations are [A] = [B] = 0.315 M and [C] = 0.405 M?

18.6.2   The K_{sp} for iron(III) hydroxide [$Fe(OH)_3$] is 1.1×10^{-36} at 25°C. For the process

$$Fe(OH)_3(s) \rightleftharpoons Fe^{3+}(aq) + 3OH^-(aq)$$

determine $\Delta G°$ (in kJ/mol) at 25°C.

18.6.3   The $\Delta G°$ for the reaction

$$N_2(g) + 3H_2(g) \rightleftharpoons 2NH_3(g)$$

is −33.3 kJ/mol at 25°C. What is the value of K_P?

18.7   THERMODYNAMICS IN LIVING SYSTEMS

Many biochemical reactions have a positive $\Delta G°$ value, yet they are essential to the maintenance of life. In living systems, these reactions are coupled to an energetically favorable process, one that has a negative $\Delta G°$ value. The principle of coupled reactions is based on a simple concept: we can use a thermodynamically favorable reaction to drive an unfavorable one. Suppose, for example, that we want to extract zinc from a zinc sulfide (ZnS). The following reaction will not work because it has a large positive $\Delta G°$ value:

$$ZnS(s) \longrightarrow Zn(s) + S(s) \qquad \Delta G° = 198.3 \text{ kJ/mol}$$

On the other hand, the combustion of sulfur to form sulfur dioxide is favored because of its large negative $\Delta G°$ value:

$$S(s) + O_2(g) \longrightarrow SO_2(g) \qquad \Delta G° = -300.1 \text{ kJ/mol}$$

By coupling the two processes, we can bring about the separation of zinc from zinc sulfide. In practice, this means heating ZnS in air so that the tendency of S to form SO_2 will promote the decomposition of ZnS:

$$ZnS(s) \longrightarrow Zn(s) + \cancel{S(s)} \qquad \Delta G° = 198.3 \text{ kJ/mol}$$
$$\cancel{S(s)} + O_2(g) \longrightarrow SO_2(g) \qquad \Delta G° = -300.1 \text{ kJ/mol}$$
$$\overline{ZnS(s) + O_2(g) \longrightarrow Zn(s) + SO_2(g)} \qquad \Delta G° = -101.8 \text{ kJ/mol}$$

Coupled reactions play a crucial role in our survival. In biological systems, enzymes facilitate a wide variety of nonspontaneous reactions. In the human body, for example, food molecules, represented by glucose ($C_6H_{12}O_6$), are converted to carbon dioxide and water during metabolism, resulting in a substantial release of free energy:

$$C_6H_{12}O_6(s) + 6O_2(g) \longrightarrow 6CO_2(g) + 6H_2O(l) \qquad \Delta G° = -2880 \text{ kJ/mol}$$

In a living cell, this reaction does not take place in a single step; rather, the glucose molecule is broken down with the aid of enzymes in a series of steps. Much of the free energy released along the way is used to synthesize adenosine triphosphate (ATP) from adenosine diphosphate (ADP) and phosphoric acid (Figure 18.7):

$$ADP + H_3PO_4 \longrightarrow ATP + H_2O \qquad \Delta G° = 31 \text{ kJ/mol}$$

The function of ATP is to store free energy until it is needed by cells. Under appropriate conditions, ATP undergoes hydrolysis to give ADP and phosphoric acid, with a release of 31 kJ/mol of free energy, which can be used to drive energetically unfavorable reactions, such as protein synthesis.

Proteins are polymers made of amino acids. The stepwise synthesis of a protein molecule involves the joining of individual amino acids. Consider the formation of the dipeptide (a unit composed of two amino acids) alanylglycine from alanine and glycine. This reaction represents the first step in the synthesis of a protein molecule:

$$\text{alanine} + \text{glycine} \longrightarrow \text{alanylglycine} \qquad \Delta G° = 29 \text{ kJ/mol}$$

The positive $\Delta G°$ value means this reaction does not favor the formation of product, so only a little of the dipeptide would be formed at equilibrium. With the aid of an enzyme, however, the reaction is coupled to the hydrolysis of ATP as follows:

$$ATP + H_2O + \text{alanine} + \text{glycine} \longrightarrow ADP + H_3PO_4 + \text{alanylglycine}$$

Adenosine triphosphate
(ATP)

Adenosine diphosphate
(ADP)

Figure 18.7 Structures of ATP and ADP.

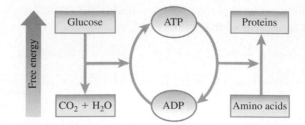

Figure 18.8 Schematic representation of ATP synthesis and coupled reactions in living systems. The conversion of glucose to carbon dioxide and water during metabolism releases free energy. The released free energy is used to convert ADP to ATP. The ATP molecules are then used as an energy source to drive unfavorable reactions such as protein synthesis from amino acids.

The overall free-energy change is given by $\Delta G° = -31$ kJ/mol $+ 29$ kJ/mol $= -2$ kJ/mol, which means that the coupled reaction now favors the formation of product and an appreciable amount of alanylglycine will be formed under these conditions. Figure 18.8 shows the ATP-ADP interconversions that act as energy storage (from metabolism) and free-energy release (from ATP hydrolysis) to drive essential reactions.

Learning Outcomes

- Distinguish between a spontaneous and nonspontaneous process and cite examples of each.
- Define entropy.
- Calculate the change in entropy of a system given the moles of ideal gas, initial and final volumes of the gas.
- Describe the conditions for standard entropy.
- Calculate the standard entropy change for a given reaction.
- List key trends in standard entropy of atoms and molecules.
- Predict the sign of ΔS for a process and use the sign to indicate whether the system has undergone an increase or decrease in entropy.
- Calculate ΔS_{surr} given ΔS_{sys} and temperature.
- Give in your own words the second law of thermodynamics.

- Determine whether a process is spontaneous given ΔS_{surr} and ΔS_{sys}.
- Give in your own words the third law of thermodynamics.
- Define Gibbs free energy.
- Use ΔH and ΔS to calculate ΔG and, in turn, determine whether a process is spontaneous.
- Predict the sign of ΔG given ΔH and ΔS.
- Define standard free energy of formation.
- Calculate the standard free energy of a given reaction.
- Calculate ΔG and $\Delta G°$ of a reaction at a specified temperature given Q or K.
- Explain, using thermodynamic terms, why energetically unfavored metabolic reactions can occur.

Chapter Summary

SECTION 18.1
- A **spontaneous process** is one that occurs under a specified set of conditions.
- A **nonspontaneous process** is one that does *not* occur under a specified set of conditions.
- Spontaneous processes do not necessarily happen quickly.

SECTION 18.2
- *Entropy* is a thermodynamic state function that measures how dispersed or spread out a system's energy is.

SECTION 18.3
- Entropy change for a process can be calculated using standard entropy values or can be predicted qualitatively based on factors such as temperature, phase, and number of molecules.
- Whether or not a process is spontaneous depends on the change in *enthalpy* and the change in *entropy* of the system.
- Tabulated **standard entropy** values are absolute values.

SECTION 18.4

- According to the *second law of thermodynamics,* the entropy change for the universe is positive for a *spontaneous* process and zero for an *equilibrium process.*
- According to the *third law of thermodynamics,* the entropy of a perfectly crystalline substance at 0 K is zero.

SECTION 18.5

- The *Gibbs free energy (G)* or simply the *free energy* of a system is the energy available to do work.
- The *standard free energy of reaction* (ΔG_{rxn}°) for a reaction tells us whether the equilibrium lies to the right (negative ΔG_{rxn}°) or to the left (positive ΔG_{rxn}°).
- *Standard free energies of formation* (ΔG_{f}°) can be used to calculate standard free energies of reaction.

SECTION 18.6

- The free-energy change (ΔG) is determined using the standard free-energy change (ΔG°) and the reaction quotient (Q).
- The sign of ΔG tells us whether the reaction is spontaneous under the conditions described.
- ΔG° is related to the equilibrium constant, K. A negative ΔG° corresponds to a large K; a positive ΔG° corresponds to a small K.

SECTION 18.7

- In living systems, thermodynamically favorable reactions provide the free energy needed to drive necessary but thermodynamically unfavorable reactions.

Key Words

Entropy (S), 764
Equilibrium process, 776
Free energy, 780
Gibbs free energy (G), 780

Nonspontaneous process, 763
Second law of thermodynamics, 775
Spontaneous process, 763

Standard entropy, 767
Standard free energy of formation (ΔG_{f}°), 782

Standard free energy of reaction (ΔG_{rxn}°), 782
Third law of thermodynamics, 778

Key Equations

18.1 $S = k \ln W$

18.2 $W = X^{N}$

18.3 $\Delta S_{sys} = S_{final} - S_{initial}$

18.4 $\Delta S_{sys} = nR \ln \dfrac{V_{final}}{V_{initial}}$

18.5 $\Delta S_{rxn}^{\circ} = [cS^{\circ}(C) + dS^{\circ}(D)] - [aS^{\circ}(A) + bS^{\circ}(B)]$

18.6 $\Delta S_{rxn}^{\circ} = \Sigma nS^{\circ}(\text{products}) - \Sigma mS^{\circ}(\text{reactants})$

18.7 $\Delta S_{surr} = \dfrac{-\Delta H_{sys}}{T}$

18.8 $\Delta S_{univ} = \Delta S_{sys} + \Delta S_{surr}$

18.9 $G = H - TS$

18.10 $\Delta G = \Delta H - T\Delta S$

18.11 $\Delta G_{rxn}^{\circ} = [c\Delta G_{f}^{\circ}(C) + d\Delta G_{f}^{\circ}(D)] - [a\Delta G_{f}^{\circ}(A) + b\Delta G_{f}^{\circ}(B)]$

18.12 $\Delta G_{rxn}^{\circ} = \Sigma n\Delta G_{f}^{\circ}(\text{products}) - \Sigma m\Delta G_{f}^{\circ}(\text{reactants})$

18.13 $\Delta G = \Delta G^{\circ} + RT \ln Q$

18.14 $\Delta G^{\circ} = -RT \ln K$

Questions and Problems

SECTION 18.1: SPONTANEOUS PROCESSES

Review Questions

18.1   Explain what is meant by a *spontaneous process.* Give two examples each of spontaneous and nonspontaneous processes.

18.2   Which of the following processes are spontaneous and which are nonspontaneous: (a) dissolving table salt (NaCl) in hot soup, (b) climbing Mt. Everest, (c) spreading fragrance in a room by removing the cap from a perfume bottle, (d) separating helium and neon from a mixture of the gases?

18.3 Which of the following processes are spontaneous and which are nonspontaneous at a given temperature?

(a) $NaNO_3(s) \xrightarrow{H_2O} NaNO_3(aq)$ saturated soln

(b) $NaNO_3(s) \xrightarrow{H_2O} NaNO_3(aq)$ unsaturated soln

(c) $NaNO_3(s) \xrightarrow{H_2O} NaNO_3(aq)$ supersaturated soln

SECTION 18.2: ENTROPY

Review Questions

18.4 Describe what is meant by the term *entropy*. What are the units of entropy?

18.5 What is the relationship between entropy and the number of possible arrangements of molecules in a system?

Problems

18.6 Referring to the setup in Figure 18.2, determine the number of possible arrangements, *W*, and calculate the entropy before and after removal of the barrier if the number of molecules is (a) 10, (b) 50, (c) 100.

18.7 In the setup shown, a container is divided into eight cells and contains two molecules. Initially, both molecules are confined to the left side of the container. (a) Determine the number of possible arrangements before and after removal of the central barrier. (b) After the removal of the barrier, how many of the arrangements correspond to the state in which both molecules are in the left side of the container? How many correspond to the state in which both molecules are in the right side of the container? How many correspond to the state in which the molecules are in opposite sides of the container? Calculate the entropy for each state and comment on the most probable state of the system after removal of the barrier.

SECTION 18.3: ENTROPY CHANGES IN A SYSTEM

 Visualizing Chemistry
Figure 18.4

VC 18.1 Consider two gas samples at STP: one consisting of a mole of F_2 gas ($S° = 203.34$ J/K · mol) and one consisting of a mole of F gas ($S° = 158.7$ J/K · mol). What factors account for the difference in standard entropies of these two species?

Volume increase (i)	Molar mass increase (ii)	Increased number of molecules (iii)	Phase change (iv)	Increase in molecular complexity (v)

(a) i, ii, iii, and iv

(b) ii and v

(c) ii, iv, and v

VC 18.2 Now consider the reaction $F_2(g) \longrightarrow 2F(g)$ at constant temperature and pressure. What factors contribute to the entropy increase associated with the reaction?

Volume increase (i)	Molar mass increase (ii)	Increased number of molecules (iii)	Phase change (iv)	Increase in molecular complexity (v)

(a) i and iii

(b) i, ii, and iii

(c) i, iv, and v

VC 18.3 Which of the following best describes why entropy always increases with temperature?

(a) As temperature increases, the number of molecules increases.

(b) As temperature increases, energy levels become more closely spaced.

(c) As temperature increases, the molecules become more energetic and can access more energy levels.

VC 18.4 Which of the following best explains why entropy typically increases with molar mass?

(a) As molar mass increases, the number of molecules increases.

(b) As molar mass increases, energy levels become more closely spaced.

(c) As molar mass increases, the molecules become more energetic and can access more energy levels.

Review Questions

18.8 How does the entropy of a system change for each of the following processes?

(a) A solid melts.

(b) A liquid freezes.

(c) A liquid boils.

(d) A vapor is converted to a solid.

(e) A vapor condenses to a liquid.

(f) A solid sublimes.

(g) A solid dissolves in water.

18.9 How does the entropy of a system change for each of the following processes?

(a) Bromine liquid vaporizes.

(b) Water freezes to form ice.

(c) Naphthalene, the key component of mothballs, sublimes.

(d) Sugar crystals form from a supersaturated solution.

(e) A block of lead melts.

(f) Iodine vapor condenses to form solid iodine.

(g) Carbon tetrachloride dissolves in liquid benzene.

18.10 Predict whether the entropy change is positive or negative for each of the following reactions. Give reasons for your predictions.

(a) $2KClO_4(s) \longrightarrow 2KClO_3(s) + O_2(g)$

(b) $H_2O(g) \longrightarrow H_2O(l)$

(c) $2Na(s) + 2H_2O(l) \longrightarrow 2NaOH(aq) + H_2(g)$

(d) $N_2(g) \longrightarrow 2N(g)$

18.11 State whether the sign of the entropy change expected for each of the following processes will be positive or negative, and explain your predictions.

(a) $PCl_3(g) + Cl_2(g) \longrightarrow PCl_5(g)$
(b) $2HgO(s) \longrightarrow 2Hg(l) + O_2(g)$
(c) $H_2(g) \longrightarrow 2H(g)$
(d) $U(s) + 3F_2(g) \longrightarrow UF_6(s)$

Problems

18.12 Calculate ΔS_{sys} for (a) the isothermal expansion of 2.0 moles of an ideal gas from 10.0 L to 15.0 L, (b) the isothermal expansion of 1.5 moles of an ideal gas from 20.0 L to 22.5 L, and (c) the isothermal compression of 5.0 moles of an ideal gas from 100.0 L to 75.0 L.

18.13 Calculate ΔS_{sys} for (a) the isothermal compression of 0.0050 mole of an ideal gas from 112 mL to 52.5 mL, (b) the isothermal compression of 0.015 mole of an ideal gas from 225 mL to 22.5 mL, and (c) the isothermal expansion of 22.1 moles of an ideal gas from 122 L to 275 L.

18.14 For each pair of substances listed here, choose the one having the larger standard entropy value at 25°C. The same molar amount is used in the comparison. Explain the basis for your choice. (a) Li(s) or Li(l), (b) $C_2H_5OH(l)$ or $CH_3OCH_3(l)$ (*Hint:* Which molecule can hydrogen bond?), (c) Ar(g) or Xe(g), (d) CO(g) or $CO_2(g)$, (e) $O_2(g)$ or $O_3(g)$, (f) $NO_2(g)$ or $N_2O_4(g)$.

18.15 Arrange the following substances (1 mole each) in order of increasing entropy at 25°C: (a) Ne(g), (b) $SO_2(g)$, (c) Na(s), (d) NaCl(s), (e) $H_2(g)$. Give the reasons for your arrangement.

18.16 Using the data in Appendix 2, calculate the standard entropy changes for the following reactions at 25°C:
(a) $S(rhombic) + O_2(g) \longrightarrow SO_2(g)$
(b) $MgCO_3(s) \longrightarrow MgO(s) + CO_2(g)$
(c) $2C_2H_6(g) + 7O_2(g) \longrightarrow 4CO_2(g) + 6H_2O(l)$

18.17 Using the data in Appendix 2, calculate the standard entropy changes for the following reactions at 25°C:
(a) $H_2(g) + CuO(s) \longrightarrow Cu(s) + H_2O(g)$
(b) $2Al(s) + 3ZnO(s) \longrightarrow Al_2O_3(s) + 3Zn(s)$
(c) $CH_4(g) + 2O_2(g) \longrightarrow CO_2(g) + 2H_2O(l)$

SECTION 18.4:   ENTROPY CHANGES IN THE UNIVERSE

Review Questions

18.18 State the second law of thermodynamics in words, and express it mathematically.

18.19 State the third law of thermodynamics in words, and explain its usefulness in calculating entropy values.

Problems

18.20 Calculate ΔS_{surr} for each of the reactions in Problem 18.16 and determine if each reaction is spontaneous at 25°C.

18.21 Calculate ΔS_{surr} for each of the reactions in Problem 18.17 and determine if each reaction is spontaneous at 25°C.

18.22 Using data from Appendix 2, calculate ΔS°_{rxn} and ΔS_{surr} for each of the reactions in Problem 18.10 and determine if each reaction is spontaneous at 25°C.

18.23 Using data from Appendix 2, calculate ΔS°_{rxn} and ΔS_{surr} for each of the reactions in Problem 18.11 and determine if each reaction is spontaneous at 25°C.

18.24 When a folded protein in solution is heated to a high enough temperature, its polypeptide chain will unfold to become the denatured protein—a process known as "denaturation." The temperature at which most of the protein unfolds is called the "melting" temperature. The melting temperature of a certain protein is found to be 63°C, and the enthalpy of denaturation is 510 kJ/mol. Estimate the entropy of denaturation, assuming that the denaturation is a single-step equilibrium process; that is, folded protein $\rightleftharpoons$ denatured protein. The single polypeptide protein chain has 98 amino acids. Calculate the entropy of denaturation per amino acid.

SECTION 18.5:   PREDICTING SPONTANEITY

Review Questions

18.25 Define *free energy*. What are its units?

18.26 Why is it more convenient to predict the direction of a reaction in terms of ΔG_{sys} instead of ΔS_{univ}? Under what conditions can ΔG_{sys} be used to predict the spontaneity of a reaction?

18.27 What is the significance of the sign of ΔG_{sys}?

18.28 From the following combinations of ΔH and ΔS, predict if a process will be spontaneous at a high or low temperature: (a) both ΔH and ΔS are negative, (b) ΔH is negative and ΔS is positive, (c) both ΔH and ΔS are positive, (d) ΔH is positive and ΔS is negative.

Problems

18.29 Assuming that ΔH and ΔS do not change with temperature, determine ΔG for the denaturation in Problem 18.24 at 20°C.

18.30 Calculate ΔG° for the following reactions at 25°C:
(a) $N_2(g) + O_2(g) \longrightarrow 2NO(g)$
(b) $H_2O(l) \longrightarrow H_2O(g)$
(c) $2C_2H_2(g) + 5O_2(g) \longrightarrow 4CO_2(g) + 2H_2O(l)$
(*Hint:* Look up the standard free energies of formation of the reactants and products in Appendix 2.)

18.31 Calculate ΔG° for the following reactions at 25°C:
(a) $2Mg(s) + O_2(g) \longrightarrow 2MgO(s)$
(b) $2SO_2(g) + O_2(g) \longrightarrow 2SO_3(g)$
(c) $2C_2H_6(g) + 7O_2(g) \longrightarrow 4CO_2(g) + 6H_2O(l)$
(See Appendix 2 for thermodynamic data.)

18.32 From the values of ΔH and ΔS, predict which of the following reactions would be spontaneous at 25°C: reaction A: $\Delta H = 10.5$ kJ/mol, $\Delta S = 30$ J/K · mol; reaction B: $\Delta H = 1.8$ kJ/mol, $\Delta S = -113$ J/K · mol. If either of the reactions is nonspontaneous at 25°C, at what temperature might it become spontaneous?

18.33 Find the temperatures at which reactions with the following ΔH and ΔS values would become spontaneous: (a) $\Delta H = -126$ kJ/mol, $\Delta S = 84$ J/K · mol; (b) $\Delta H = -11.7$ kJ/mol, $\Delta S = -105$ J/K · mol.

18.34 The molar heats of fusion and vaporization of ethanol are 7.61 and 26.0 kJ/mol, respectively. Calculate the molar entropy changes for the solid-liquid and liquid-vapor transitions for ethanol. At 1 atm pressure, ethanol melts at −117.3°C and boils at 78.3°C.

18.35   The molar heats of fusion and vaporization of mercury are 23.4 and 59.0 kJ/mol, respectively. Calculate the molar entropy changes for the solid-liquid and liquid-vapor transitions for mercury. At 1 atm pressure, mercury melts at −38.9°C and boils at 357°C.

18.36   Use the values listed in Appendix 2 to calculate $\Delta G°$ for the following alcohol fermentation:

$$C_6H_{12}O_6(s) \longrightarrow 2C_2H_5OH(l) + 2CO_2(g)$$

18.37   Certain bacteria in the soil obtain the necessary energy for growth by oxidizing nitrites to nitrates:

$$2NO_2^- + O_2 \longrightarrow 2NO_3^-$$

Given that the standard Gibbs free energies of formation of NO_2^- and NO_3^- are −34.6 and −110.5 kJ/mol, respectively, calculate the amount of Gibbs free energy released when 1 mole of NO_2^- is oxidized to 1 mole of NO_3^-.

SECTION 18.6:   FREE ENERGY AND CHEMICAL EQUILIBRIUM

Review Questions

18.38   Explain the difference between ΔG and $\Delta G°$.
18.39   Explain why Equation 18.14 is of great importance in chemistry.
18.40   Fill in the missing entries in the following table:

K	$\ln K$	$\Delta G°$	Result at equilibrium
< 1			
		0	
			Products are favored

Problems

18.41   Calculate K_P for the following reaction at 25°C:

$$H_2(g) + I_2(g) \rightleftharpoons 2HI(g) \qquad \Delta G° = 2.60 \text{ kJ/mol}$$

18.42   For the autoionization of water at 25°C,

$$H_2O(l) \rightleftharpoons H^+(aq) + OH^-(aq)$$

K_w is 1.0×10^{-14}. What is $\Delta G°$ for the process?

18.43   Consider the following reaction at 25°C:

$$Fe(OH)_2(s) \rightleftharpoons Fe^{2+}(aq) + 2OH^-(aq)$$

Calculate $\Delta G°$ for the reaction. K_{sp} for $Fe(OH)_2$ is 1.6×10^{-14}.

18.44   Calculate $\Delta G°$ and K_P for the following equilibrium reaction at 25°C:

$$2H_2O(g) \rightleftharpoons 2H_2(g) + O_2(g)$$

18.45   (a) Calculate $\Delta G°$ and K_P for the following equilibrium reaction at 25°C.

$$PCl_5(g) \rightleftharpoons PCl_3(g) + Cl_2(g)$$

(b) Calculate ΔG for the reaction if the partial pressures of the initial mixture are $P_{PCl_5} = 0.0029$ atm, $P_{PCl_3} = 0.27$ atm, and $P_{Cl_2} = 0.40$ atm.

18.46   The equilibrium constant (K_P) for the reaction

$$H_2(g) + CO_2(g) \rightleftharpoons H_2O(g) + CO(g)$$

is 4.40 at 2000 K. (a) Calculate $\Delta G°$ for the reaction. (b) Calculate ΔG for the reaction when the partial pressures are $P_{H_2} = 0.25$ atm, $P_{CO_2} = 0.78$ atm, $P_{H_2O} = 0.66$ atm, and $P_{CO} = 1.20$ atm.

18.47   Consider the decomposition of calcium carbonate:

$$CaCO_3(s) \rightleftharpoons CaO(s) + CO_2(g)$$

Calculate the pressure in atm of CO_2 in an equilibrium process (a) at 25°C and (b) at 800°C. Assume that $\Delta H° = 177.8$ kJ/mol and $\Delta S° = 160.5$ J/K · mol for the temperature range.

18.48   The equilibrium constant K_P for the reaction

$$CO(g) + Cl_2(g) \rightleftharpoons COCl_2(g)$$

is 5.62×10^{35} at 25°C. Calculate $\Delta G_f°$ for $COCl_2$ at 25°C.

18.49   At 25°C, $\Delta G°$ for the process

$$H_2O(l) \rightleftharpoons H_2O(g)$$

is 8.6 kJ/mol. Calculate the vapor pressure of water at this temperature.

18.50   Calculate $\Delta G°$ for the process

$$C(\text{diamond}) \rightleftharpoons C(\text{graphite})$$

Is the formation of graphite from diamond favored at 25°C? If so, why is it that diamonds do not become graphite on standing?

SECTION 18.7:   THERMODYNAMICS IN LIVING SYSTEMS

Review Questions

18.51   What is a coupled reaction? What is its importance in biological reactions?
18.52   What is the role of ATP in biological reactions?

Problems

18.53   Referring to the metabolic process involving glucose in Figure 18.8, calculate the maximum number of moles of ATP that can be synthesized from ADP from the breakdown of 1 mole of glucose.

18.54   In the metabolism of glucose, the first step is the conversion of glucose to glucose 6-phosphate:

$$\text{glucose} + H_3PO_4 \longrightarrow \text{glucose 6-phosphate} + H_2O$$

$$\Delta G° = 13.4 \text{ kJ/mol}$$

Because $\Delta G°$ is positive, this reaction does not favor the formation of products. Show how this reaction can be made to proceed by coupling it with the hydrolysis of ATP. Write an equation for the coupled reaction, and estimate the equilibrium constant for the coupled process.

ADDITIONAL PROBLEMS

18.55   Predict the signs of ΔH, ΔS, and ΔG of the system for the following processes at 1 atm: (a) ammonia melts at −60°C, (b) ammonia melts at −77.7°C, (c) ammonia melts at −100°C. (The normal melting point of ammonia is −77.7°C.)

18.56 Calculate ΔG for the reaction

$$H_2O(l) \rightleftharpoons H^+(aq) + OH^-(aq)$$

at 25°C for the following initial concentrations:
(a) $[H^+] = 1.0 \times 10^{-7} M$, $[OH^-] = 1.0 \times 10^{-7} M$
(b) $[H^+] = 1.0 \times 10^{-3} M$, $[OH^-] = 1.0 \times 10^{-4} M$
(c) $[H^+] = 1.0 \times 10^{-12} M$, $[OH^-] = 2.0 \times 10^{-8} M$
(d) $[H^+] = 3.5 M$, $[OH^-] = 4.8 \times 10^{-4} M$

18.57 Which of the following thermodynamic functions are associated only with the first law of thermodynamics: S, U, G, and H?

18.58 A student placed 1 g of each of three compounds A, B, and C in a container and found that after 1 week no change had occurred. Offer some possible explanations for the fact that no reactions took place. Assume that A, B, and C are totally miscible liquids.

18.59 The enthalpy change in the denaturation of a certain protein is 125 kJ/mol. If the entropy change is 397 J/K · mol, calculate the minimum temperature at which the protein would denature spontaneously.

18.60 Consider the following facts: Water freezes spontaneously at −5°C and 1 atm, and ice has a lower entropy than liquid water. Explain how a spontaneous process can lead to a decrease in entropy.

18.61 Ammonium nitrate (NH_4NO_3) dissolves spontaneously and endothermically in water. What can you deduce about the sign of ΔS for the solution process?

18.62 Calculate the equilibrium pressure of CO_2 due to the decomposition of barium carbonate ($BaCO_3$) at 25°C.

18.63 (a) Trouton's rule states that the ratio of the molar heat of vaporization of a liquid (ΔH_{vap}) to its boiling point in kelvins is approximately 90 J/K · mol. Use the following data to show that this is the case and explain why Trouton's rule holds true:

	T_{bp} (°C)	ΔH_{vap}(kJ/mol)
Benzene	80.1	31.0
Hexane	68.7	30.8
Mercury	357	59.0
Toluene	110.6	35.2

(b) Use the values in Table 12.6 to calculate the same ratio for ethanol and water. Explain why Trouton's rule does not apply to these two substances as well as it does to other liquids.

18.64 Referring to Problem 18.63, explain why the ratio is considerably smaller than 90 J/K · mol for liquid HF.

18.65 Carbon monoxide (CO) and nitric oxide (NO) are polluting gases contained in automobile exhaust. Under suitable conditions, these gases can be made to react to form nitrogen (N_2) and the less harmful carbon dioxide (CO_2). (a) Write an equation for this reaction. (b) Identify the oxidizing and reducing agents. (c) Calculate the K_P for the reaction at 25°C. (d) Under normal atmospheric conditions, the partial pressures are $P_{N_2} = 0.80$ atm, $P_{CO_2} = 3.0 \times 10^{-4}$ atm, $P_{CO} = 5.0 \times 10^{-5}$ atm, and $P_{NO} = 5.0 \times 10^{-7}$ atm. Calculate Q_P, and predict the direction toward which the reaction will proceed. (e) Will raising the temperature favor the formation of N_2 and CO_2?

18.66 For reactions carried out under standard-state conditions, Equation 18.10 takes the form $\Delta G° = \Delta H° - T\Delta S°$. (a) Assuming $\Delta H°$ and $\Delta S°$ are independent of temperature, derive the equation

$$\ln \frac{K_2}{K_1} = \frac{\Delta H°}{R}\left(\frac{T_2 - T_1}{T_1 T_2}\right)$$

where K_1 and K_2 are the equilibrium constants at T_1 and T_2, respectively. (b) Given that at 25°C K_c is 4.63×10^{-3} for the reaction

$$N_2O_4(g) \rightleftharpoons 2NO_2(g) \qquad \Delta H° = 58.0 \text{ kJ/mol}$$

calculate the equilibrium constant at 65°C.

18.67 The K_{sp} of AgCl is given in Table 17.4. What is its value at 60°C? [Hint: You need the result of Problem 18.66(a) and the data in Appendix 2 to calculate $\Delta H°$.]

18.68 Under what conditions does a substance have a standard entropy of zero? Can an element or a compound ever have a negative standard entropy?

18.69 Water gas, a mixture of H_2 and CO, is a fuel made by combining steam with red-hot coke (a by-product of coal distillation):

$$H_2O(g) + C(s) \rightleftharpoons CO(g) + H_2(g)$$

From the data in Appendix 2, estimate the temperature at which the reaction begins to favor the formation of products.

18.70 Consider the following Brønsted acid-base reaction at 25°C:

$$HF(aq) + Cl^-(aq) \rightleftharpoons HCl(aq) + F^-(aq)$$

(a) Predict whether K will be greater or smaller than 1. (b) Does $\Delta S°$ or $\Delta H°$ make a greater contribution to $\Delta G°$? (c) Is $\Delta H°$ likely to be positive or negative?

18.71 The pH of gastric juice is about 1.00 and that of blood plasma is 7.40. Calculate the Gibbs free energy required to secrete a mole of H^+ ions from blood plasma to the stomach at 37°C.

18.72 Crystallization of sodium acetate from a supersaturated solution occurs spontaneously (see page 511). Based on this, what can you deduce about the signs of ΔS and ΔH?

18.73 Consider the thermal decomposition of $CaCO_3$:

$$CaCO_3(s) \rightleftharpoons CaO(s) + CO_2(g)$$

The equilibrium vapor pressures of CO_2 are 22.6 mmHg at 700°C and 1829 mmHg at 950°C. Calculate the standard enthalpy of the reaction. [Hint: See Problem 18.66(a).]

18.74 A certain reaction is spontaneous at 72°C. If the enthalpy change for the reaction is 19 kJ/mol, what is the minimum value of ΔS (in J/K · mol) for the reaction?

18.75 Predict whether the entropy change is positive or negative for each of these reactions:
(a) $Zn(s) + 2HCl(aq) \rightleftharpoons ZnCl_2(aq) + H_2(g)$
(b) $O(g) + O(g) \rightleftharpoons O_2(g)$
(c) $NH_4NO_3(s) \rightleftharpoons N_2O(g) + 2H_2O(g)$
(d) $2H_2O_2(l) \rightleftharpoons 2H_2O(l) + O_2(g)$

18.76 The reaction $NH_3(g) + HCl(g) \longrightarrow NH_4Cl(s)$ proceeds spontaneously at 25°C even though there is a decrease in entropy in the system (gases are converted to a solid). Explain.

18.77   Use the following data to determine the normal boiling point, in kelvins, of mercury. What assumptions must you make to do the calculation?

$Hg(l)$: $\Delta H_f^{\circ} = 0$ (by definition)
$\quad\quad\quad\quad S^{\circ} = 77.4$ J/K · mol

$Hg(g)$: $\Delta H_f^{\circ} = 60.78$ kJ/mol
$\quad\quad\quad\quad S^{\circ} = 174.7$ J/K · mol

18.78   The molar heat of vaporization of ethanol is 39.3 kJ/mol, and the boiling point of ethanol is 78.3°C. Calculate ΔS for the vaporization of 0.50 mole of ethanol.

18.79   A certain reaction is known to have a ΔG° value of -122 kJ/mol. Will the reaction necessarily occur if the reactants are mixed together?

18.80   In the Mond process for the purification of nickel, carbon monoxide is combined with heated nickel to produce $Ni(CO)_4$, which is a gas and can therefore be separated from solid impurities:

$$Ni(s) + 4CO(g) \rightleftharpoons Ni(CO)_4(g)$$

Given that the standard free energies of formation of $CO(g)$ and $Ni(CO)_4(g)$ are -137.3 and -587.4 kJ/mol, respectively, calculate the equilibrium constant of the reaction at 80°C. Assume that ΔG_f° is temperature independent.

18.81   Calculate ΔG° and K_P for the following processes at 25°C:
(a) $H_2(g) + Br_2(l) \rightleftharpoons 2HBr(g)$
(b) $\frac{1}{2}H_2(g) + \frac{1}{2}Br_2(l) \rightleftharpoons HBr(g)$
Account for the differences in ΔG° and K_P obtained for parts (a) and (b).

18.82   Calculate the pressure of O_2 (in atm) over a sample of NiO at 25°C if $\Delta G^{\circ} = 212$ kJ/mol for the reaction

$$NiO(s) \rightleftharpoons Ni(s) + \tfrac{1}{2}O_2(g)$$

18.83   As an approximation, we can assume that proteins exist either in the native (physiologically functioning) state or the denatured state. The standard molar enthalpy and entropy of the denaturation of a certain protein are 512 kJ/mol and 1.60 kJ/K · mol, respectively. Comment on the signs and magnitudes of these quantities, and calculate the temperature at which the denaturation becomes spontaneous.

18.84   For a reaction with a negative ΔG° value, which of the following statements is false? (a) The equilibrium constant K is greater than one. (b) The reaction is spontaneous when all the reactants and products are in their standard states. (c) The reaction is always exothermic.

18.85   Consider the reaction

$$N_2(g) + O_2(g) \rightleftharpoons 2NO(g)$$

Given that ΔG° for the reaction at 25°C is 173.4 kJ/mol, (a) calculate the standard free energy of formation of NO and (b) calculate K_P of the reaction. (c) One of the starting substances in smog formation is NO. Assuming that the temperature in a running automobile engine is 1100°C, estimate K_P for the given reaction.

(d) As farmers know, lightning helps to produce a better crop. Why?

18.86   Heating copper(II) oxide at 400°C does not produce any appreciable amount of Cu:

$$CuO(s) \rightleftharpoons Cu(s) + \tfrac{1}{2}O_2(g) \quad \Delta G^{\circ} = 127.2 \text{ kJ/mol}$$

However, if this reaction is coupled to the conversion of graphite to carbon monoxide, it becomes spontaneous. Write an equation for the coupled process, and calculate the equilibrium constant for the coupled reaction.

18.87   Consider the decomposition of magnesium carbonate:

$$MgCO_3(s) \rightleftharpoons MgO(s) + CO_2(g)$$

Calculate the temperature at which the decomposition begins to favor products. Assume that both ΔH° and ΔS° are independent of temperature.

18.88   A reaction for which ΔH and ΔS are both negative is
(a) nonspontaneous at all temperatures.
(b) spontaneous at all temperatures.
(c) spontaneous at high temperatures.
(d) spontaneous at low temperatures.
(e) at equilibrium.

18.89   The activity series in Table 9.6 shows that reaction (a) is spontaneous whereas reaction (b) is nonspontaneous at 25°C:
(a) $Fe(s) + 2H^+(aq) \longrightarrow Fe^{2+}(aq) + H_2(g)$
(b) $Cu(s) + 2H^+(aq) \longrightarrow Cu^{2+}(aq) + H_2(g)$
Use the data in Appendix 2 to calculate the equilibrium constant for these reactions and hence confirm that the activity series is correct.

18.90   The rate constant for the elementary reaction

$$2NO(g) + O_2(g) \longrightarrow 2NO_2(g)$$

is $7.1 \times 10^9/M^2 \cdot$ s at 25°C. What is the rate constant for the reverse reaction at the same temperature?

18.91   The following reaction was described as the cause of sulfur deposits formed at volcanic sites.

$$2H_2S(g) + SO_2(g) \rightleftharpoons 3S(s) + 2H_2O(g)$$

It may also be used to remove SO_2 from power plant stack gases. (a) Identify the type of redox reaction it is. (b) Calculate the equilibrium constant (K_P) at 25°C, and comment on whether this method is feasible for removing SO_2. (c) Would this procedure become more effective or less effective at a higher temperature?

18.92   Describe two ways that you could determine ΔG° of a reaction.

18.93   The following reaction represents the removal of ozone in the stratosphere:

$$2O_3(g) \rightleftharpoons 3O_2(g)$$

Calculate the equilibrium constant (K_P) for this reaction. In view of the magnitude of the equilibrium constant, explain why this reaction is not considered a major cause of ozone depletion in the absence of human-made pollutants such as the nitrogen oxides and CFCs. Assume the temperature of the stratosphere is -30°C and ΔG_f° is temperature independent.

18.94   When a native protein in solution is heated to a high enough temperature, its polypeptide chain will unfold to become the denatured protein. The temperature at which a large portion of the protein unfolds is called the melting temperature. The melting temperature of a certain protein is found to be 46°C, and the enthalpy of denaturation is 382 kJ/mol. Estimate the entropy of denaturation, assuming that the denaturation is a two-state process; that is, native protein ⟶ denatured protein. The single polypeptide protein chain has 122 amino acids. Calculate the entropy of denaturation per amino acid. Comment on your result.

18.95 A 74.6-g ice cube floats in the Arctic Sea. The pressure and temperature of the system and surroundings are at 1 atm and 0°C, respectively. Calculate ΔS_{sys}, ΔS_{surr}, and ΔS_{univ} for the melting of the ice cube. What can you conclude about the nature of the process from the value of ΔS_{univ}? (The molar heat of fusion of water is 6.01 kJ/mol.)

18.96 Comment on the feasibility of extracting copper from its ore chalcocite (Cu_2S) by heating:

$$Cu_2S(s) \longrightarrow 2Cu(s) + S(s)$$

Calculate the $\Delta G°$ for the overall reaction if this process is coupled to the conversion of sulfur to sulfur dioxide and $\Delta G_f°(Cu_2S) = -86.1$ kJ/mol.

18.97 Active transport is the process in which a substance is transferred from a region of lower concentration to one of higher concentration. This is a nonspontaneous process and must be coupled to a spontaneous process, such as the hydrolysis of ATP. The concentrations of K^+ ions in the blood plasma and in nerve cells are 15 mM and 400 mM, respectively (1 mM = 1×10^{-3} M). Use Equation 18.13 to calculate ΔG for the process at the physiological temperature of 37°C:

$$K^+(15 \text{ m}M) \longrightarrow K^+(400 \text{ m}M)$$

In this calculation, the $\Delta G°$ term can be set to zero. What is the justification for this step?

18.98 Large quantities of hydrogen are needed for the synthesis of ammonia. One preparation of hydrogen involves the reaction between carbon monoxide and steam at 300°C in the presence of a copper-zinc catalyst:

$$CO(g) + H_2O(g) \rightleftharpoons CO_2(g) + H_2(g)$$

Calculate the equilibrium constant (K_P) for the reaction and the temperature at which the reaction favors the formation of CO and H_2O. Will a larger K_P be attained at the same temperature if a more efficient catalyst is used?

18.99 Consider two carboxylic acids (acids that contain the —COOH group): CH_3COOH (acetic acid, $K_a = 1.8 \times 10^{-5}$) and $CH_2ClCOOH$ (chloroacetic acid, $K_a = 1.4 \times 10^{-3}$). (a) Calculate $\Delta G°$ for the ionization of these acids at 25°C. (b) From the equation $\Delta G° = \Delta H° - T\Delta S°$, we see that the contributions to the $\Delta G°$ term are an enthalpy term ($\Delta H°$) and a temperature times entropy term ($T\Delta S°$). These contributions are listed here for the two acids:

	$\Delta H°$ (kJ/mol)	$T\Delta S°$ (kJ/mol)
CH_3COOH	−0.57	−27.6
$CH_2ClCOOH$	−4.7	−21.1

Which is the dominant term in determining the value of $\Delta G°$ (and hence K_a of the acid)? (c) What processes contribute to $\Delta H°$? (Consider the ionization of the acids as a Brønsted acid-base reaction.) (d) Explain why the $T\Delta S°$ term is more negative for CH_3COOH.

18.100 Many hydrocarbons exist as structural isomers, which are compounds that have the same molecular formula but different structures. For example, both butane and isobutane have the same molecular formula of C_4H_{10} (see Problem 12.20 on page 499). Calculate the mole percent of these molecules in an equilibrium mixture at 25°C, given that the standard free energy of formation of butane is −15.9 kJ/mol and that of isobutane is −18.0 kJ/mol. Does your result support the notion that straight-chain hydrocarbons (that is, hydrocarbons in which the C atoms are joined along a line) are less stable than branch-chain hydrocarbons?

18.101 One of the steps in the extraction of iron from its ore (FeO) is the reduction of iron(II) oxide by carbon monoxide at 900°C:

$$FeO(s) + CO(g) \rightleftharpoons Fe(s) + CO_2(g)$$

If CO is allowed to react with an excess of FeO, calculate the mole fractions of CO and CO_2 at equilibrium. State any assumptions.

18.102 Derive the equation

$$\Delta G = RT \ln \frac{Q}{K}$$

where Q is the reaction quotient, and describe how you would use it to predict the spontaneity of a reaction.

18.103 The sublimation of carbon dioxide at −78°C is given by

$$CO_2(s) \longrightarrow CO_2(g) \qquad \Delta H_{sub} = 25.2 \text{ kJ/mol}$$

Calculate ΔS_{sub} when 84.8 g of CO_2 sublimes at this temperature.

18.104 A student looked up the $\Delta G_f°$, $\Delta H_f°$, and $\Delta S°$ values for CO_2 in Appendix 2. Plugging these values into Equation 18.10, the student found that $\Delta G_f° \neq \Delta H_f° - T\Delta S°$ at 298 K. What is wrong with this approach?

18.105 Consider the following reaction at 298 K:

$$2H_2(g) + O_2(g) \longrightarrow 2H_2O(l) \quad \Delta H° = -571.6 \text{ kJ/mol}$$

Calculate ΔS_{sys}, ΔS_{surr}, and ΔS_{univ} for the reaction.

18.106 The concentration of glucose inside a cell is 0.12 mM and that outside a cell is 12.3 mM. Calculate the Gibbs free-energy change for the transport of 3 moles of glucose into the cell at 37°C.

18.107 Which of the following are not state functions: S, H, q, w, T?

18.108 Which of the following is not accompanied by an increase in the entropy of the system: (a) mixing of two gases at the same temperature and pressure, (b) mixing of ethanol and water, (c) discharging a battery, (d) expansion of a gas followed by compression to its original temperature, pressure, and volume?

18.109 Hydrogenation reactions (for example, the process of converting C=C bonds to C—C bonds in the food industry) are facilitated by the use of a transition metal catalyst, such as Ni or Pt. The initial step is the adsorption, or binding, of hydrogen gas onto the metal surface. Predict the signs of ΔH, ΔS, and ΔG when hydrogen gas is adsorbed onto the surface of Ni metal.

18.110 Give a detailed example of each of the following, with an explanation: (a) a thermodynamically spontaneous process, (b) a process that would violate the first law of thermodynamics, (c) a process that would violate the second law of thermodynamics, (d) an irreversible process, (e) an equilibrium process.

18.111 At 0 K, the entropy of carbon monoxide crystal is not zero but has a value of 4.2 J/K · mol, called the residual entropy. According to the third law of thermodynamics, this means that the crystal does not have a perfect arrangement of the CO molecules. (a) What would be the residual entropy if the arrangement were totally random? (b) Comment on the difference between the result in part (a) and 4.2 J/K · mol. (*Hint:* Assume that each CO molecule has two choices for orientation, and use Equation 18.1 to calculate the residual entropy.)

18.112 The following diagram shows the variation of the equilibrium constant with temperature for the reaction

$$I_2(g) \rightleftharpoons 2I(g)$$

Calculate $\Delta G°$, $\Delta H°$, and $\Delta S°$ for the reaction at 872 K. (*Hint:* See Problem 18.66.)

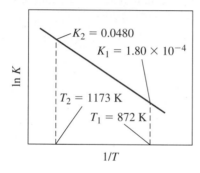

18.113 The standard enthalpy of formation and the standard entropy of gaseous benzene are 82.93 kJ/mol and 269.2 J/K · mol, respectively. Calculate $\Delta H°$, $\Delta S°$, and $\Delta G°$ for the given process at 25°C. Comment on your answers.

$$C_6H_6(l) \longrightarrow C_6H_6(g)$$

18.114 Consider the gas-phase reaction between A_2 (green) and B_2 (red) to form AB at 298 K:

$$A_2(g) + B_2(g) \rightleftharpoons 2AB(g) \qquad \Delta G° = -3.4 \text{ kJ/mol}$$

(a) Which of the following reaction mixtures is at equilibrium?
(b) Which of the following reaction mixtures has a negative ΔG value?
(c) Which of the following reaction mixtures has a positive ΔG value?

The partial pressures of the gases in each frame are equal to the number of A_2, B_2, and AB molecules times 0.10 atm. Round your results to two significant figures.

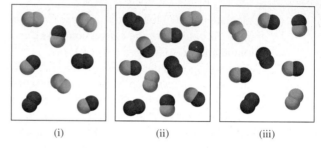

(i)   (ii)   (iii)

18.115 Assuming that this ΔG value from Problem 18.29 is $\Delta G°$ for the denaturation, determine the value of equilibrium constant for the process at 20°C.

Answers to In-Chapter Materials

PRACTICE PROBLEMS

18.1A 0.34 J/K. **18.1B** $\frac{1}{5}$. **18.2A** (a) 173.6 J/K · mol, (b) −139.8 J/K · mol, (c) 215.3 J/K · mol. **18.2B** (a) $S°[K(l)]$ = 71.5 J/K · mol, (b) $S°[S_2Cl_2(g)]$ = 331.5 J/K · mol, (c) $S°[MgF_2(s)]$ = 57.24 J/K · mol. **18.3A** (a) negative, (b) negative, (c) positive. **18.3B** The sign of $\Delta H°$ for both dissolution processes is negative. Something must favor spontaneity; if not entropy change, then enthalpy change. Because these processes both involve decreases in the system's entropy, they must be exothermic, or they could not be spontaneous. **18.4A** (a) ΔS_{univ} = −27.2 J/K · mol, nonspontaneous, (b) ΔS_{univ} = −28.1 J/K · mol, nonspontaneous, (c) ΔS_{univ} = 0 J/K · mol, equilibrium. **18.4B** (a) ΔS_{univ} = 5.2 J/K · mol, spontaneous, (b) 346°C, (c) 58°C. **18.5A** 3728°C. **18.5B** 108 J/K · mol. **18.6A** (a) −106 kJ/mol, (b) −2935 kJ/mol. **18.6B** (a) $\Delta G°_f[Li_2O(s)]$ = −561.2 kJ/mol, (b) $\Delta G°_f[NaI(s)]$ = −286.1 kJ/mol. **18.7A** ΔS_{fus} = 16 J/K · mol, ΔS_{vap} = 72 J/K · mol. **18.7B** (a) $\Delta H°_{fus}$ = 2.41 kJ/mol, $\Delta S°_{fus}$ = 6.51 J/K · mol, $T_{melting}$ = 97°C. (b) $\Delta H°_{vap}$ = 105.3 kJ/mol, $\Delta S°_{vap}$ = 96.1 J/K · mol, $T_{boiling}$ = 823°C. **18.8A** 1.3 kJ/mol, reverse reaction is spontaneous. **18.8B** 2.5 atm. **18.9A** 2×10^{57}. **18.9B** −16.8 kJ/mol. **18.10A** 32.9 kJ/mol. **18.10B** −454.4 kJ/mol.

SECTION REVIEW

18.3.1 (a) negative, (b) positive, (c) positive, (d) positive, (e) negative. **18.3.2** (a) positive, (b) negative, (c) positive, (d) positive, (e) positive. **18.3.3** $A_2 + 3B_2 \longrightarrow 2AB_3$, negative. **18.4.1** −145.3 J/K · mol. **18.4.2** −242.8 J/K · mol. **18.4.3** (a) negative, (b) positive, (c) not enough information to determine. **18.5.1** −800.8 kJ/mol. **18.5.2** 196 J/K · mol. **18.5.3** 790°C. **18.6.1** 1.53 kJ/mol. **18.6.2** 205 kJ/mol. **18.6.3** 7×10^5.

KEY SKILLS

Free Energy and Equilibrium

In Chapter 15, you learned how to calculate reaction quotient (Q), and that by comparing its magnitude to that of the equilibrium constant (K), you can determine whether a reaction must proceed to the right or to the left in order to reach equilibrium. In Chapter 18, you learned how to calculate free-energy change (ΔG) and standard free-energy change ($\Delta G°$), and that the sign of ΔG indicates whether or not a process is spontaneous. It is useful to consider how these parameters are related, and that they give us essentially the same information. Equation 18.14 relates K and $\Delta G°$:

$$\Delta G° = -RT \ln K$$

According to this equation, if $\Delta G°$ is negative, the value of K is geater than 1. Recall that $K > 1$ tells us the equilibrium *lies to the right*. This is different from saying that it will *proceed* to the right. A reaction may have a large equilibrium constant and yet proceed to the *left* in order to reach equilibrium—if the starting conditions are such that Q is greater than K. For example, $K = 54.3$ for the following reaction at 430°C.

$$H_2(g) + I_2(g) \rightleftharpoons 2HI(g)$$

Because K is greater than 1, we would say that this equilibrium lies to the right. However, if we initially have only HI and no H_2 or I_2, clearly the reaction must *proceed* to the *left* in order for equilibrium to be established.

So what does it mean for an equilibrium to *lie* to the right? It means that if the starting conditions are *standard* conditions (the concentrations of all aqueous species are 1 M and the pressures of all gaseous species are 1 atm), products will predominate at equilibrium. This corresponds to the reaction proceeding to the right from *standard* initial conditions. Likewise, for an equilibrium that lies to the *left,* if the starting conditions are standard conditions, reactants will predominate at equilibrium—the reaction will proceed to the *left* from standard initial conditions.

We can also describe this in terms of spontaneity. The sign of $\Delta G°$ tells us whether or not a process or reaction is *spontaneous* under *standard* conditions. This is simply another way to say that the equilibrium lies to the right. ΔG, on the other hand, tells us whether or not a process is spontaneous under *actual* conditions—which usually are not standard. ΔG and $\Delta G°$ are related by Equation 18.13.

$$\Delta G = \Delta G° + RT \ln Q$$

The sign of ΔG depends not only on the sign of $\Delta G°$, but also on the value of Q. The information provided by the sign of ΔG is the same as that provided by the *comparison* of Q and K.

By combining Equations 18.13 and 18.14, we can write an expression that indicates at a glance the relationship between the sign of ΔG and the relative magnitudes of Q and K.

Substituting the right side of Equation 18.14 for the $\Delta G°$ term in Equation 18.13 gives

$$\Delta G = -RT \ln K + RT \ln Q$$

or

$$\Delta G = -RT \ln Q - RT \ln K$$

And because $\ln A - \ln B = \ln \dfrac{A}{B}$ [▶▶ Appendix 1], we get

$$\Delta G = RT \ln \frac{Q}{K}$$

This enables us to simply compare Q and K. When Q is greater than K, the log term in our final equation will be positive and ΔG will be positive—meaning that the reaction must proceed to the left to establish equilibrium. When Q is *less* than K, the log term and ΔG will both be *negative*—meaning that the reaction will proceed to the *right*.

Key Skills Problems

18.1
Which of the following must be negative for a process to be spontaneous as written?

(a) $\Delta G°$ (b) ΔG (c) K (d) Q (e) R

18.2
ΔG for a reaction is always negative when

(a) $\Delta G°$ is negative   (b) $K < 1$ (c) $K > 1$
(d) $Q < K$ (e) $Q > K$

18.3
The figure shown here depicts a system at equilibrium for the reaction $A_2 + B_2 \rightleftharpoons 2AB$.

 = A, = B

$\Delta G°$ for the reaction is −4.8 kJ/mol. Which of the following figures depicts starting conditions for the reaction where ΔG is negative? Select all that apply.

(a)

(b)

(c)

(d)

18.4
The reaction shown here has $\Delta G° = -1.83$ kJ/mol at 25°C. Under the starting conditions shown in the picture, the reaction will proceed to the right. Which of the following could be the reaction depicted in the figure? Select all that apply.

● = A, ● = B, ● = C

(a) $C \rightleftharpoons A + B$
(b) $2C \rightleftharpoons A + B$
(c) $2C \rightleftharpoons 2A + B$
(d) $2C \rightleftharpoons A + 2B$

803

CHAPTER 19

Electrochemistry

19.1   Balancing Redox Reactions

19.2   Galvanic Cells

19.3   Standard Reduction Potentials

19.4   Spontaneity of Redox Reactions Under Standard-State Conditions

19.5   Spontaneity of Redox Reactions Under Conditions Other Than Standard State
  • The Nernst Equation • Concentration Cells

19.6   Batteries
  • Dry Cells and Alkaline Batteries • Lead Storage Batteries • Lithium-Ion Batteries • Fuel Cells

19.7   Electrolysis
  • Electrolysis of Molten Sodium Chloride • Electrolysis of Water • Electrolysis of an Aqueous Sodium Chloride Solution • Quantitative Applications of Electrolysis

19.8   Corrosion

Chemical reactions can be harnessed to release electrical energy; and the resulting energy can be stored in a battery for later use. Eventually, when the stored energy is used up, a battery "runs down," whereas a fuel cell (shown here) operates and produces energy continuously as long as the necessary reactants are supplied. Known in principle since 1838, fuel cells provided both electrical energy and potable water aboard the Apollo space missions. Now fuel cell technology is being used to power automobiles and provide a cleaner alternative to internal combustion engines.

19.1 BALANCING REDOX REACTIONS

In Chapter 9 we briefly discussed oxidation-reduction or "redox" reactions, those in which electrons are transferred from one species to another. In this section we review how to identify a reaction as a redox reaction and look more closely at how such reactions are balanced.

A redox reaction is one in which there are *changes* in oxidation states, which we identify using the rules introduced in Chapter 9. The following are examples of redox reactions:

$$2KClO_3(s) \longrightarrow 2KCl(s) + 3O_2(g)$$
$$+1 +5 -2 \qquad +1 -1 \qquad 0$$

$$CH_4(g) + 2O_2(g) \longrightarrow CO_2(g) + 2H_2O(l)$$
$$-4 +1 \qquad 0 \qquad +4 -2 \qquad +1 -2$$

$$Sn(s) + Cu^{2+}(aq) \longrightarrow Cu(s) + Sn^{2+}(aq)$$
$$0 \qquad +2 \qquad 0 \qquad +2$$

Equations for redox reactions, such as those shown here, can be balanced by inspection, the method of balancing introduced in Chapter 8 [◄◄ Section 8.1], but remember that redox equations must be balanced for mass (number of atoms) *and* for charge (number of electrons) [◄◄ Section 9.4]. In this section we introduce the *half-reaction method* to balance equations that cannot be balanced simply by inspection.

Consider the aqueous reaction of the iron(II) ion (Fe^{2+}) with the dichromate ion ($Cr_2O_7^{2-}$):

$$Fe^{2+} + Cr_2O_7^{2-} \longrightarrow Fe^{3+} + Cr^{3+}$$

Because there is no species containing oxygen on the product side of the equation, it would not be possible to balance this equation simply by adjusting the coefficients of reactants and products. However, there are two things about the reaction that make it possible to *add* species to the equation to balance it—without changing the chemical reaction it represents:

- The reaction takes place in aqueous solution, so we can add H_2O as needed to balance the equation.
- This particular reaction takes place in acidic solution, so we can add H^+ as needed to balance the equation. (Some reactions take place in basic solution, enabling us to add OH^- as needed for balancing. We will learn more about this shortly.)

After writing the unbalanced equation, we balance it stepwise as follows:

1. Separate the unbalanced reaction into ***half-reactions.*** A half-reaction is an oxidation or a reduction that occurs as part of the overall redox reaction.

$$Oxidation: \qquad Fe^{2+} \longrightarrow Fe^{3+}$$

$$Reduction: \qquad Cr_2O_7^{2-} \longrightarrow Cr^{3+}$$

Multi 19.1
Electrochemistry—oxidation-reduction reactions

Student Annotation: Now is a good time to review how oxidation numbers are assigned [◄◄ Section 9.4].

2. Balance each of the half-reactions with regard to atoms other than O and H. In this case, no change is required for the oxidation half-reaction. We adjust the coefficient of the chromium(III) ion to balance the reduction half-reaction.

$$Oxidation: \qquad Fe^{2+} \longrightarrow Fe^{3+}$$

$$Reduction: \qquad Cr_2O_7^{2-} \longrightarrow 2Cr^{3+}$$

3. Balance both half-reactions for O by adding H_2O. Again, the oxidation in this case requires no change, but we must add seven water molecules to the product side of the reduction.

$$Oxidation: \qquad Fe^{2+} \longrightarrow Fe^{3+}$$

$$Reduction: \qquad Cr_2O_7^{2-} \longrightarrow 2Cr^{3+} + 7H_2O$$

4. Balance both half-reactions for H by adding H^+. Once again, the oxidation in this case requires no change, but we must add 14 hydrogen ions to the reactant side of the reduction.

$$Oxidation: \qquad Fe^{2+} \longrightarrow Fe^{3+}$$

$$Reduction:\ 14H^+ + Cr_2O_7^{2-} \longrightarrow 2Cr^{3+} + 7H_2O$$

5. Balance both half-reactions for charge by adding electrons. To do this, we determine the total charge on each side and add electrons to make the total charges equal. In the case of the oxidation, there is a charge of $+2$ on the reactant side and a charge of $+3$ on the product side. Adding one electron to the product side makes the charges equal.

$$Oxidation: \qquad \underbrace{Fe^{2+}}\ \longrightarrow\ \underbrace{Fe^{3+} + e^-}$$
$$Total\ charge: \qquad\ \ +2 \qquad\qquad\quad +2$$

In the case of the reduction, there is a total charge of $[(14)(+1) + (1)(-2)] = +12$ on the reactant side and a total charge of $[(2)(+3)] = +6$ on the product side. Adding six electrons to the reactant side makes the charges equal.

$$Reduction: \qquad \underbrace{6e^- + 14H^+ + Cr_2O_7^{2-}}\ \longrightarrow\ \underbrace{2Cr^{3+} + 7H_2O}$$
$$Total\ charge: \qquad\qquad\quad +6 \qquad\qquad\qquad\qquad +6$$

6. If the number of electrons in the balanced oxidation half-reaction is not the same as the number of electrons in the balanced reduction half-reaction, multiply one or both of the half-reactions by the number(s) required to make the number of electrons the same in both. In this case, with one electron in the oxidation and six in the reduction, multiplying the oxidation by 6 accomplishes this.

$$Oxidation: \qquad\qquad\qquad 6(Fe^{2+} \longrightarrow Fe^{3+} + e^-)$$

$$6Fe^{2+} \longrightarrow 6Fe^{3+} + \boxed{6e^-}$$

$$Reduction: \quad \boxed{6e^-} + 14H^+ + Cr_2O_7^{2-} \longrightarrow 2Cr^{3+} + 7H_2O$$

7. Finally, add the balanced half-reactions back together and cancel the electrons, in addition to any other identical terms that appear on both sides.

$$6Fe^{2+} \longrightarrow 6Fe^{3+} + \cancel{6e^-}$$

$$\underline{\cancel{6e^-} + 14H^+ + Cr_2O_7^{2-} \longrightarrow 2Cr^{3+} + 7H_2O}$$

$$6Fe^{2+} + 14H^+ + Cr_2O_7^{2-} \longrightarrow 6Fe^{3+} + 2Cr^{3+} + 7H_2O$$

A final check shows that the resulting equation is balanced both for mass and for charge.

Some redox reactions occur in basic solution. When this is the case, balancing by the half-reaction method is done exactly as described for reactions in acidic solution, but it requires two additional steps:

8. For each H^+ ion in the final equation, add one OH^- ion to each side of the equation, combining the H^+ and OH^- ions to produce H_2O.

9. Make any additional cancellations made necessary by the new H_2O molecules.

Worked Example 19.1 shows how to use the half-reaction method to balance a reaction that takes place in basic solution.

Worked Example 19.1

Permanganate ion and iodide ion react in basic solution to produce manganese(IV) oxide and molecular iodine. Use the half-reaction method to balance the equation:

$$MnO_4^- + I^- \longrightarrow MnO_2 + I_2$$

Strategy The reaction takes place in basic solution, so apply steps 1 through 9 to balance for mass and for charge.

Setup Identify the oxidation and reduction half-reactions by assigning oxidation numbers.

$$MnO_4^- + I^- \longrightarrow MnO_2 + I_2$$
$$\text{(+7)(-2)} \quad \text{(-1)} \qquad \text{(+4)(-2)} \quad \text{(0)}$$

Solution

Step 1. Separate the unbalanced reaction into half-reactions.

Oxidation: $I^- \longrightarrow I_2$

Reduction: $MnO_4^- \longrightarrow MnO_2$

Step 2. Balance each half-reaction for mass, excluding O and H.

$$2I^- \longrightarrow I_2$$

$$MnO_4^- \longrightarrow MnO_2$$

Step 3. Balance both half-reactions for O by adding H_2O.

$$2I^- \longrightarrow I_2$$

$$MnO_4^- \longrightarrow MnO_2 + 2H_2O$$

Step 4. Balance both half-reactions for H by adding H^+.

$$2I^- \longrightarrow I_2$$

$$4H^+ + MnO_4^- \longrightarrow MnO_2 + 2H_2O$$

Step 5. Balance the total charge of both half-reactions by adding electrons.

$$2I^- \longrightarrow I_2 + 2e^-$$

$$3e^- + 4H^+ + MnO_4^- \longrightarrow MnO_2 + 2H_2O$$

Step 6. Multiply the half-reactions to make the numbers of electrons the same in both.

$$3(2I^- \longrightarrow I_2 + 2e^-)$$

$$2(3e^- + 4H^+ + MnO_4^- \longrightarrow MnO_2 + 2H_2O)$$

Step 7. Add the half-reactions back together, canceling electrons.

$$6I^- \longrightarrow 3I_2 + \cancel{6e^-}$$

$$\underline{\cancel{6e^-} + 8H^+ + 2MnO_4^- \longrightarrow 2MnO_2 + 4H_2O}$$

$$8H^+ + 2MnO_4^- + 6I^- \longrightarrow 2MnO_2 + 3I_2 + 4H_2O$$

(Continued on next page)

Step 8.   For each H^+ ion in the final equation, add one OH^- ion to each side of the equation, combining the H^+ and OH^- ions to produce H_2O.

$$8H^+ + 2MnO_4^- + 6I^- \longrightarrow 2MnO_2 + 3I_2 + 4H_2O$$

$$+\ 8OH^- \qquad\qquad\qquad\qquad\qquad\qquad\qquad +\ 8OH^-$$

$$\overline{\textcircled{8H_2O} + 2MnO_4^- + 6I^- \longrightarrow 2MnO_2 + 3I_2 + \textcircled{4H_2O} + 8OH^-}$$

Step 9.   Carry out any cancellations made necessary by the additional H_2O molecules.

$$4H_2O + 2MnO_4^- + 6I^- \longrightarrow 2MnO_2 + 3I_2 + 8OH^-$$

> **Think About It**
> Verify that the final equation is balanced for mass and for charge. Remember that electrons cannot appear in the overall balanced equation.

Practice Problem A Use the half-reaction method to balance the following equation in basic solution:

$$CN^- + MnO_4^- \longrightarrow CNO^- + MnO_2$$

Practice Problem B Use the half-reaction method to balance the following equation in acidic solution:

$$Fe^{2+} + MnO_4^- \longrightarrow Fe^{3+} + Mn^{2+}$$

SECTION 19.1 REVIEW

Balancing Redox Reactions

19.1.1   Determine whether or not each of the following equations represents a redox reaction.

(a) $NH_3 + HCl \longrightarrow NH_4Cl$

(b) $2H_2O_2 \longrightarrow 2H_2O + O_2$

(c) $2O_3 \longrightarrow 3O_2$

(d) $3NO_2 + H_2O \longrightarrow NO + 2HNO_3$

(e) $LiCl \longrightarrow Li^+ + Cl^-$

19.1.2 MnO_4^- and $C_2O_4^{2-}$ react in basic solution to form MnO_2 and CO_3^{2-}. Write and balance the equation for this reaction.

19.2 GALVANIC CELLS

When zinc metal is placed in a solution containing copper(II) ions, Zn is oxidized to Zn^{2+} ions whereas Cu^{2+} ions are reduced to Cu [◄◄ Section 9.4]:

$$Zn(s) + Cu^{2+}(aq) \longrightarrow Zn^{2+}(aq) + Cu(s)$$

Student Annotation: This reaction is shown in Figure 9.6.

The electrons are transferred directly from the reducing agent, Zn, to the oxidizing agent, Cu^{2+}, in solution. However, if we physically separate two half-reactions from each other, we can arrange it such that the electrons must travel through a wire to pass from the Zn atoms to the Cu^{2+} ions. As the reaction progresses, it generates a flow of electrons through the wire and thereby generates electricity.

The experimental apparatus for generating electricity through the use of a spontaneous reaction is called a **galvanic cell.** Figure 19.1 shows the essential components of a galvanic cell. A zinc bar is immersed in an aqueous $ZnSO_4$ solution in one container, and a copper bar is immersed in an aqueous $CuSO_4$ solution in another container. The cell operates on the principle that the oxidation of Zn to Zn^{2+} and the reduction of Cu^{2+} to Cu can be made to take place simultaneously in separate locations with the transfer of electrons between them occurring through an external wire. The zinc and copper bars are called **electrodes.** By definition, the **anode** in a galvanic cell is the electrode at which *oxidation* occurs and the **cathode** is the electrode at which *reduction* occurs. (Each combination of container, electrode, and solution is called a **half-cell.**) This particular arrangement of electrodes and electrolytes is called a Daniell cell.

Student Annotation: A *galvanic* cell can also be called a *voltaic* cell. Both terms refer to a cell in which a spontaneous chemical reaction generates a flow of electrons.

The half-reactions for the galvanic cell shown in Figure 19.1 are

Oxidation: $\qquad$ $Zn(s) \longrightarrow Zn^{2+}(aq) + 2e^-$

Reduction: $Cu^{2+}(aq) + 2e^- \longrightarrow Cu(s)$

To complete the electric circuit, and allow electrons to flow through the external wire, the solutions must be connected by a conducting medium through which the cations and anions can move from one half-cell to the other. This requirement is satisfied by a **salt bridge,** which, in its simplest form, is an inverted U tube containing an inert electrolyte solution, such as KCl or NH_4NO_3. The ions in the salt bridge must not react with the other ions in solution or with the electrodes (see Figure 19.1). During the course of the redox reaction, electrons flow through the external wire from the anode (Zn electrode) to the cathode (Cu electrode). In the solution, the cations (Zn^{2+}, Cu^{2+}, and K^+) move toward the cathode, while the anions (SO_4^{2-} and Cl^-) move toward the anode. Without the salt bridge connecting the two solutions, the buildup of positive charge in the anode compartment (due to the departure of electrons and the resulting formation of Zn^{2+}) and the buildup of negative charge in the cathode compartment (created by the arrival of electrons and the reduction of Cu^{2+} ions to Cu) would quickly prevent the cell from operating.

Student Annotation: This is the origin of the terms *cathode* and *anode:*
• Cations move toward the cathode.
• Anions move toward the anode.

An electric current flows from the anode to the cathode because there is a difference in electrical potential energy between the electrodes. This flow of electric current is analogous to the flow of water down a waterfall, which occurs because there is a difference in the gravitational potential energy, or the flow of gas from a high-pressure region to a low-pressure region. Experimentally the difference in electrical potential between the anode and the cathode is measured by a voltmeter (Figure 19.2, page 812) and the reading (in volts) is called the **cell potential** (E_{cell}). The potential of a cell depends not only on the nature of the electrodes and the ions in solution, but also on the concentrations of the ions and the temperature at which the cell is operated.

Student Annotation: The volt is a derived SI unit: 1 V = 1 J/1 C.

The conventional notation for representing galvanic cells is the cell diagram. For the cell shown in Figure 19.1, if we assume that the concentrations of Zn^{2+} and Cu^{2+} ions are 1 M, the cell diagram is

$$Zn(s) \,|\, Zn^{2+}(1 \ M) \,\|\, Cu^{2+}(1 \ M) \,|\, Cu(s)$$

Student Annotation: The terms *cell potential, cell voltage, cell electromotive force,* and *cell emf* are used interchangeably and are all symbolized the same way with E_{cell}.

The single vertical line represents a phase boundary. For example, the zinc electrode is a solid and the Zn^{2+} ions are in solution. Thus, we draw a line between Zn and Zn^{2+} to show the phase boundary. The double vertical lines denote the salt bridge. By convention, the anode is written first, to the left of the double lines, and the other components appear in the order in which we would encounter them in moving from the anode to the cathode (from left to right in the cell diagram).

Multi 19.2
Electrochemistry—operation of voltaic cell

Figure 19.1

Construction of a Galvanic Cell

We add a salt bridge, a tube containing a solution of a strong electrolyte—in this case Na$_2$SO$_4$. Having this solution in electrical contact with the two solutions in the beakers allows ions to migrate toward the electrodes, ensuring that the two compartments remain electrically neutral.

The two metal pieces are the electrodes in the galvanic cell. We connect the electrodes with a length of wire routed through a voltmeter and a switch so that we can complete the circuit when we have completed construction of the cell.

To make the reaction between zinc and copper more useful, we can construct a galvanic cell. In one beaker, we place a piece of zinc metal in a 1.00-M solution of Zn^{2+} ions. In the other, we place a piece of copper metal in a 1.00-M solution of Cu^{2+} ions.

START

As shown in Figure 9.6, when zinc metal (Zn) is immersed in a solution containing copper ions (Cu^{2+}), the zinc is oxidized to zinc ions (Zn^{2+}), and copper ions are reduced to copper metal (Cu).

$$Zn(s) + Cu^{2+}(aq) \longrightarrow Zn^{2+}(aq) + Cu(s)$$

This is an oxidation-reduction reaction in which electrons flow spontaneously from zinc metal to the copper ions in solution. The lightening of the blue color indicates that the concentration of Cu^{2+} has decreased. Copper metal is deposited on the solid zinc surface. Some of the zinc metal has gone into solution as Zn^{2+} ions, which do not impart any color in the solution.

before   after

When we close the switch, we complete the circuit; the voltmeter indicates the initial potential of the cell: 1.10 V.

When we replace the voltmeter with a lightbulb, electrons flow from the zinc electrode (the anode) to the copper electrode (the cathode). The flow of electrons lights the bulb. Anions in the salt bridge migrate toward the anode; cations migrate toward the cathode.

As the reaction proceeds, zinc metal from the anode is oxidized, increasing the Zn^{2+} concentration in the beaker on the left; and additional copper metal is deposited on the cathode, decreasing the Cu^{2+} concentration in the beaker on the right. As the concentrations of both ions change, the potential of the cell decreases. After allowing the reaction to proceed for a time, we can reinsert the voltmeter to measure the decreased voltage.

What's the point?

Zinc is a stronger reducing agent than copper, so there is a natural tendency for electrons to flow from zinc metal to copper ions. We can harness this flow of electrons by forcing the half-reactions to occur in separate compartments. Electrons still flow from Zn to Cu^{2+}, but they must flow through the wire connecting the two electrodes. The potential of the cell decreases as the reaction proceeds, as the reading on the voltmeter shows.

Multi 19.3
Electrochemistry—an interactive voltaic
cell

Student Annotation: A cell in which
different half-reactions take place will have
a different emf.

19.3 STANDARD REDUCTION POTENTIALS

When the concentrations of the Cu^{2+} and Zn^{2+} ions are both 1.0 *M*, the cell potential of the cell
described in Section 19.2 is 1.10 V at 25°C (see Figure 19.2). This measured potential is related to
the half-reactions that take place in the anode and cathode compartments. The overall cell potential
is the difference between the electric potentials at the Zn and Cu electrodes—known as the *half-cell
potentials*. Just as it is impossible for only one of the half-reactions to occur independently, it is
impossible to measure the potential of just a single half-cell. However, if we arbitrarily define the
potential value of a particular half-cell as zero, we can use it to determine the *relative* potentials of
other half-cells. Then we can use these relative potentials to determine overall *cell* potentials. The
hydrogen electrode, shown in Figure 19.3, serves as the reference for this purpose. Hydrogen gas is
bubbled into a hydrochloric acid solution at 25°C. The platinum electrode has two functions. First, it
provides a surface on which the dissociation (and oxidation) of hydrogen molecules can take place:

$$H_2 \longrightarrow 2H^+ + 2e^-$$

Second, it serves as an electrical conductor to the external circuit.

Under standard-state conditions [◀◀ Section 18.5], when the pressure of H_2 is 1 atm and the
concentration of HCl solution is 1 *M*, the potential for the reduction of H^+ at 25°C is defined as
exactly zero:

$$2H^+(1\ M) + 2e^- \longrightarrow H_2(1\ atm) \qquad E° = 0\ V$$

Figure 19.2 The galvanic cell
described in Figure 19.1. Note the
U tube (salt bridge) connecting the two
beakers. When the concentrations of
Zn^{2+} and Cu^{2+} are 1 molar (1 *M*) at
25°C, the cell voltage is 1.10 V.

Figure 19.3 A hydrogen electrode
operating under standard-state
conditions. Hydrogen gas at 1 atm is
bubbled through a 1 *M* HCl solution.
The electrode itself is made of
platinum.

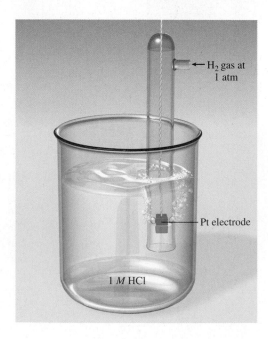

As before, the ° superscript denotes standard-state conditions, and $E°$ is the **standard reduction potential;** that is, $E°$ is the potential associated with a reduction half-reaction at an electrode when the ion concentration is 1 M and the gas pressure is 1 atm. Because the hydrogen electrode is used to determine all other electrode potentials, it is called the **standard hydrogen electrode (SHE).**

A half-cell potential is measured by constructing a galvanic cell in which one of the electrodes is the SHE. The measured voltage is then used to determine the potential for the other half-cell. Figure 19.4(a) shows a galvanic cell with a zinc electrode and a SHE. When the circuit is completed in this cell, electrons flow from the zinc electrode to the SHE, thereby oxidizing Zn to Zn^{2+} and reducing H^+ ions to H_2. In this case, therefore, the zinc electrode is the anode (where oxidation takes place) and the SHE is the cathode (where reduction takes place). The cell diagram is

$$Zn(s) \,|\, Zn^{2+}(1\ M) \,\|\, H^+(1\ M) \,|\, H_2(1\ atm) \,|\, Pt(s)$$

The measured potential for this cell is 0.76 V at 25°C. We can write the half-cell reactions as follows:

Anode (oxidation): $\qquad\qquad\qquad Zn(s) \longrightarrow Zn^{2+}(1\ M) + 2e^-$

Cathode (reduction): $\qquad 2H^+(1\ M) + 2e^- \longrightarrow H_2(1\ atm)$

Overall: $\qquad\qquad\qquad Zn(s) + 2H^+(1\ M) \longrightarrow Zn^{2+}(1\ M) + H_2(1\ atm)$

By convention, the standard cell potential, $E°_{cell}$, which is composed of a contribution from the anode and a contribution from the cathode, is given by

$$E°_{cell} = E°_{cathode} - E°_{anode} \qquad\qquad \textbf{Equation 19.1}$$

where $E°_{cathode}$ and $E°_{anode}$ are the standard reduction potentials of the cathode and anode, respectively. For the Zn-SHE cell, we write

$$E°_{cell} = E°_{H^+/H_2} - E°_{Zn^{2+}/Zn}$$

$$0.76\ V = 0 - E°_{Zn^{2+}/Zn}$$

where the subscript "H^+/H_2" means "$2H^+ + 2e^- \longrightarrow H_2$" and the subscript "$Zn^{2+}/Zn$" means "$Zn^{2+} + 2e^- \longrightarrow Zn$". Thus, the standard reduction potential of zinc, $E_{Zn^{2+}/Zn}$ is -0.76 V.

The standard reduction potential of copper can be determined in a similar fashion, by using a cell with a copper electrode and a SHE [Figure 19.4(b)]. In this case, electrons flow from the SHE to the copper electrode when the circuit is completed; that is, the *copper* electrode is the cathode and the SHE is the *anode.*

The cell diagram is

$$Pt(s) \,|\, H_2(1\ atm) \,|\, H^+(1\ M) \,\|\, Cu^{2+}(1\ M) \,|\, Cu(s)$$

> **Student Annotation:** One indication of the direction of electron flow is the fact that as the reaction proceeds, the mass of the zinc electrode decreases as a result of the oxidation half-reaction:
>
> $$Zn(s) \longrightarrow Zn^{2+}(aq) + 2e^-$$

> **Student Annotation:** Reduction of Cu^{2+} ions causes the mass of the Cu electrode to increase.

Figure 19.4 (a) A cell consisting of a zinc electrode and a hydrogen electrode. (b) A cell consisting of a copper electrode and a hydrogen electrode. Both cells are operating under standard-state conditions. Note that in (a) the SHE is the cathode, but in (b) it is the anode.

and the half-cell reactions are

Anode (oxidation):		$H_2(1\ atm) \longrightarrow 2H^+(1\ M) + 2e^-$
Cathode (reduction):		$\underline{Cu^{2+}(1\ M) + 2e^- \longrightarrow Cu(s)}$
Overall:		$H_2(1\ atm) + Cu^{2+}(1\ M) \longrightarrow 2H^+(1\ M) + Cu(s)$

Under standard-state conditions and at 25°C, the measured potential for the cell is 0.34 V, so we write

$$E^\circ_{cell} = E^\circ_{cathode} - E^\circ_{anode}$$

$$= E^\circ_{Cu^{2+}/Cu} - E^\circ_{H^+/H_2}$$

$$0.34\ V = E^\circ_{Cu^{2+}/Cu} - 0$$

Thus, the standard reduction potential of copper, $E^\circ_{Cu^{2+}/Cu}$, is 0.34 V, where the subscript "Cu^{2+}/Cu" means "$Cu^{2+} + 2e^- \longrightarrow Cu$."

Having determined the standard reduction potentials of Zn and Cu, we can use Equation 19.1 to calculate the cell potential for the Daniell cell described in Section 19.2:

$$E^\circ_{cell} = E^\circ_{cathode} - E^\circ_{anode}$$

$$= E^\circ_{Cu^{2+}/Cu} - E^\circ_{Zn^{2+}/Zn}$$

$$= 0.34\ V - (-0.76\ V)$$

$$= 1.10\ V$$

As in the case of ΔG° [◀◀ Section 18.5], we can use the sign of E° to predict whether a reaction lies to the right or to the left. A positive E° means that the redox reaction will favor the formation of products at equilibrium. Conversely, a negative E° indicates that reactants will be favored at equilibrium. We will examine how E°_{cell}, ΔG°, and K are related in Section 19.4.

Table 19.1 lists standard reduction potentials, in order of decreasing reduction potential, for a number of half-cell reactions. To avoid ambiguity, all half-cell reactions are shown as reductions. A galvanic cell is composed of two half-cells, and therefore two half-cell reactions. Whether or not a particular half-cell reaction occurs as a reduction in a galvanic cell depends on how its reduction potential compares to that of the other half-cell reaction. If it has the greater (or more *positive*) reduction potential of the two, it will occur as a reduction. If it has the smaller (or more *negative*) reduction potential of the two, it will occur in the reverse direction, as an oxidation.

Student Annotation: The half-reaction with the greater reduction potential has the greater potential to occur as a reduction.

Consider the example of the cell described in Section 19.2. The two half-cell reactions and their standard reduction potentials are

$$Cu^{2+} + 2e^- \longrightarrow Cu \qquad E^\circ = 0.34\ V$$

$$Zn^{2+} + 2e^- \longrightarrow Zn \qquad E^\circ = -0.76\ V$$

Student Annotation: The electrode where reduction occurs is the cathode. Therefore, $E^\circ_{cathode} = 0.34$ V.

The Cu half-reaction, having a greater (more positive) reduction potential, is the half-reaction that will occur as a reduction:

$$Cu^{2+} + 2e^- \longrightarrow Cu$$

Student Annotation: The electrode where oxidation occurs is the anode. Therefore, $E^\circ_{anode} = -0.76$ V.

The Zn half-reaction has a smaller (less positive) reduction potential and will occur, instead, as an oxidation:

$$Zn \longrightarrow Zn^{2+} + 2e^-$$

Adding the two half-reactions gives the overall cell reaction:

$$Zn + Cu^{2+} \longrightarrow Zn^{2+} + Cu$$

TABLE 19.1   Standard Reduction Potentials at 25°C[*]

Half-Reaction	$E°$(V)
$F_2(g) + 2e^- \longrightarrow 2F^-(aq)$	+2.87
$O_3(g) + 2H^+(aq) + 2e^- \longrightarrow O_2(g) + H_2O(l)$	+2.07
$Co^{3+}(aq) + e^- \longrightarrow Co^{2+}(aq)$	+1.82
$H_2O_2(aq) + 2H^+(aq) + 2e^- \longrightarrow 2H_2O(l)$	+1.77
$PbO_2(s) + 4H^+(aq) + SO_4^{2-}(aq) + 2e^- \longrightarrow PbSO_4(s) + 2H_2O(l)$	+1.70
$Ce^{4+}(aq) + e^- \longrightarrow Ce^{3+}(aq)$	+1.61
$MnO_4^-(aq) + 8H^+(aq) + 5e^- \longrightarrow Mn^{2+}(aq) + 4H_2O(l)$	+1.51
$Au^{3+}(aq) + 3e^- \longrightarrow Au(s)$	+1.50
$Cl_2(g) + 2e^- \longrightarrow 2Cl^-(aq)$	+1.36
$Cr_2O_7^{2-}(aq) + 14H^+(aq) + 6e^- \longrightarrow 2Cr^{3+}(aq) + 7H_2O(l)$	+1.33
$MnO_2(s) + 4H^+(aq) + 2e^- \longrightarrow Mn^{2+}(aq) + 2H_2O(l)$	+1.23
$O_2(g) + 4H^+(aq) + 4e^- \longrightarrow 2H_2O(l)$	+1.23
$Br_2(l) + 2e^- \longrightarrow 2Br^-(aq)$	+1.07
$NO_3^-(aq) + 4H^+(aq) + 3e^- \longrightarrow NO(g) + 2H_2O(l)$	+0.96
$2Hg^{2+}(aq) + 2e^- \longrightarrow Hg_2^{2+}(aq)$	+0.92
$Hg_2^{2+}(aq) + 2e^- \longrightarrow 2Hg(l)$	+0.85
$Ag^+(aq) + e^- \longrightarrow Ag(s)$	+0.80
$Fe^{3+}(aq) + e^- \longrightarrow Fe^{2+}(aq)$	+0.77
$O_2(g) + 2H^+(aq) + 2e^- \longrightarrow H_2O_2(aq)$	+0.68
$MnO_4^-(aq) + 2H_2O(l) + 3e^- \longrightarrow MnO_2(s) + 4OH^-(aq)$	+0.59
$I_2(s) + 2e^- \longrightarrow 2I^-(aq)$	+0.53
$O_2(g) + 2H_2O(l) + 4e^- \longrightarrow 4OH^-(aq)$	+0.40
$Cu^{2+}(aq) + 2e^- \longrightarrow Cu(s)$	+0.34
$AgCl(s) + e^- \longrightarrow Ag(s) + Cl^-(aq)$	+0.22
$SO_4^{2-}(aq) + 4H^+(aq) + 2e^- \longrightarrow SO_2(g) + 2H_2O(l)$	+0.20
$Cu^{2+}(aq) + e^- \longrightarrow Cu^+(aq)$	+0.15
$Sn^{4+}(aq) + 2e^- \longrightarrow Sn^{2+}(aq)$	+0.13
$2H^+(aq) + 2e^- \longrightarrow H_2(g)$	0.00
$Pb^{2+}(aq) + 2e^- \longrightarrow Pb(s)$	−0.13
$Sn^{2+}(aq) + 2e^- \longrightarrow Sn(s)$	−0.14
$Ni^{2+}(aq) + 2e^- \longrightarrow Ni(s)$	−0.25
$Co^{2+}(aq) + 2e^- \longrightarrow Co(s)$	−0.28
$PbSO_4(s) + 2e^- \longrightarrow Pb(s) + SO_4^{2-}(aq)$	−0.31
$Cd^{2+}(aq) + 2e^- \longrightarrow Cd(s)$	−0.40
$Fe^{2+}(aq) + 2e^- \longrightarrow Fe(s)$	−0.44
$Cr^{3+}(aq) + 3e^- \longrightarrow Cr(s)$	−0.74
$Zn^{2+}(aq) + 2e^- \longrightarrow Zn(s)$	−0.76
$2H_2O(l) + 2e^- \longrightarrow H_2(g) + 2OH^-(aq)$	−0.83
$Mn^{2+}(aq) + 2e^- \longrightarrow Mn(s)$	−1.18
$Al^{3+}(aq) + 3e^- \longrightarrow Al(s)$	−1.66
$Be^{2+}(aq) + 2e^- \longrightarrow Be(s)$	−1.85
$Mg^{2+}(aq) + 2e^- \longrightarrow Mg(s)$	−2.37
$Na^+(aq) + e^- \longrightarrow Na(s)$	−2.71
$Ca^{2+}(aq) + 2e^- \longrightarrow Ca(s)$	−2.87
$Sr^{2+}(aq) + 2e^- \longrightarrow Sr(s)$	−2.89
$Ba^{2+}(aq) + 2e^- \longrightarrow Ba(s)$	−2.90
$K^+(aq) + e^- \longrightarrow K(s)$	−2.93
$Li^+(aq) + e^- \longrightarrow Li(s)$	−3.05

Increasing strength as oxidizing agent (left margin, upward arrow)

Increasing strength as reducing agent (right margin, downward arrow)

[*]For all half-reactions the concentration is 1 M for dissolved species and the pressure is 1 atm for gases. These are the standard-state values.

Consider, however, what would happen if we were to construct a galvanic cell combining the Zn half-cell with an Mn half-cell. The reduction potential of Mn is −1.18 V.

$$Zn^{2+} + 2e^- \longrightarrow Zn \qquad E° = -0.76 \text{ V}$$

$$Mn^{2+} + 2e^- \longrightarrow Mn \qquad E° = -1.18 \text{ V}$$

In this case, the greater (less negative) reduction potential is that of Zn, so the Zn half-reaction will occur as a reduction and the Zn electrode will be the cathode. The Mn electrode will be the anode. The cell potential is therefore

$$E°_{cell} = E°_{cathode} - E°_{anode}$$

$$= E°_{Zn^{2+}/Zn} - E°_{Mn^{2+}/Mn}$$

$$= (-0.76 \text{ V}) - (-1.18 \text{ V})$$

$$= 0.42 \text{ V}$$

The overall cell reaction is

$$Mn + Zn^{2+} \longrightarrow Mn^{2+} + Zn$$

By using Equation 19.1, we can predict the direction of an overall cell reaction.

It is important to understand that the standard reduction potential is an *intensive* property (like temperature and density), not an *extensive* property (like mass and volume) [◄◄ Section 1.3]. This means that the value of the standard reduction potential does *not* depend on the amount of a substance involved. Therefore, when it is necessary to multiply one of the half-reactions by a coefficient to balance the overall equation, the value of $E°$ for the half-reaction remains the same. Consider a galvanic cell made up of a Zn half-cell and an Ag half-cell:

$$Zn(s) \,|\, Zn^{2+}(1 \, M) \,\|\, Ag^+(1 \, M) \,|\, Ag(s)$$

The half-cell reactions are

$$Ag^+ + e^- \longrightarrow Ag \qquad E° = 0.80 \text{ V}$$

$$Zn^{2+} + 2e^- \longrightarrow Zn \qquad E° = -0.76 \text{ V}$$

The Ag half-reaction, with the more positive standard reduction potential, will occur as a reduction, and the Zn half-reaction will occur as an oxidation. Balancing the equation for the overall cell reaction requires multiplying the reduction (the Ag half-reaction) by 2:

$$2(Ag^+ + e^- \longrightarrow Ag)$$

We can then add the two half-reactions and cancel the electrons to get the overall, balanced equation:

$$2Ag^+ + \cancel{2e^-} \longrightarrow 2Ag$$

$$\underline{ + Zn \longrightarrow Zn^{2+} + \cancel{2e^-}}$$

$$2Ag^+ + Zn \longrightarrow 2Ag + Zn^{2+}$$

The standard cell potential can be calculated using Equation 19.1:

$$E°_{cell} = E°_{cathode} - E°_{anode}$$

$$= E°_{Ag^+/Ag} - E°_{Zn^{2+}/Zn}$$

$$= 0.80 \text{ V} - (-0.76 \text{ V})$$

$$= 1.56 \text{ V}$$

Although we multiplied the Ag half-reaction by 2, we did not multiply its standard reduction potential by 2.

Student Annotation: It is a common error to multiply $E°$ values by the same number as the half-cell equation. Think of the reduction potential as the height of a waterfall. Just as water falls from a higher elevation to a lower elevation, electrons move from an electrode with a higher potential toward one with a lower potential. The amount of water falling does not affect the net change in its elevation. Likewise, the number of electrons moving from higher potential to lower potential does not affect the size of the change in potential.

Table 19.1 is essentially an extended version of the activity series [◀◀ Section 9.4]. Worked Example 19.2 illustrates how to use standard reduction potentials to predict the direction of the overall reaction in a galvanic cell.

Worked Example 19.2

A galvanic cell consists of an Mg electrode in a 1.0 M Mg(NO$_3$)$_2$ solution and a Cd electrode in a 1.0 M Cd(NO$_3$)$_2$ solution. Determine the overall cell reaction, and calculate the standard cell potential at 25°C.

Strategy Use the tabulated values of $E°$ to determine which electrode is the cathode and which is the anode, combine cathode and anode half-cell reactions to get the overall cell reaction, and use Equation 19.1 to calculate $E°_{cell}$.

Setup The half-cell reactions and their standard reduction potentials are

$$Mg^{2+} + 2e^- \longrightarrow Mg \qquad E° = -2.37 \text{ V}$$

$$Cd^{2+} + 2e^- \longrightarrow Cd \qquad E° = -0.40 \text{ V}$$

Because the Cd half-cell reaction has the greater (less negative) standard reduction potential, it will occur as the reduction. The Mg half-cell reaction will occur as the oxidation. Therefore, $E°_{cathode} = -0.40$ V and $E°_{anode} = -2.37$ V.

Solution Adding the two half-cell reactions together gives the overall cell reaction:

$$Mg \longrightarrow Mg^{2+} + 2e^-$$

$$\underline{Cd^{2+} + 2e^- \longrightarrow Cd}$$

$$Overall: \quad Mg + Cd^{2+} \longrightarrow Mg^{2+} + Cd$$

The standard cell potential is

$$E°_{cell} = E°_{cathode} - E°_{anode}$$
$$= E°_{Cd^{2+}/Cd} - E°_{Mg^{2+}/Mg}$$
$$= (-0.40 \text{ V}) - (-2.37 \text{ V})$$
$$= 1.97 \text{ V}$$

Think About It
If you ever calculate a negative voltage for a galvanic cell potential, you have done something wrong—check your work. Under standard-state conditions, the overall cell reaction will proceed in the direction that gives a positive $E°_{cell}$.

Practice Problem A Determine the overall cell reaction and $E°_{cell}$ (at 25°C) of a galvanic cell made of a Cd electrode in a 1.0 M Cd(NO$_3$)$_2$ solution and a Pb electrode in a 1.0 M Pb(NO$_3$)$_2$ solution.

Practice Problem B A galvanic cell with $E°_{cell} = 0.30$ V can be constructed using an iron electrode in a 1.0 M Fe(NO$_3$)$_2$ solution, and either a tin electrode in a 1.0 M Sn(NO$_3$)$_2$ solution, or a chromium electrode in a 1.0 M Cr(NO$_3$)$_3$ solution—even though Sn^{2+}/Sn and Cr^{3+}/Cr have different standard reduction potentials. Explain and give the overall balanced reaction for each cell.

Standard reduction potentials can also be used to determine what, if any, redox reaction will take place when reactants are combined in the same beaker—rather than divided into half-cells. Unlike a galvanic cell, in which we use reduction potentials to determine if the reaction proceeds in the *forward* or *reverse* direction, when the reaction is not divided into half-cells, we use reduction potentials to determine *if* the reaction will occur as written—or *not*.

Worked Example 19.3 illustrates this technique.

Worked Example 19.3

Predict what redox reaction will take place, if any, when molecular bromine (Br_2) is added to (a) a 1-M solution of NaI and (b) a 1-M solution of NaCl. (Assume a temperature of 25°C.)

Strategy In each case, write the equation for the redox reaction that *might* take place and use $E°$ values to determine whether or not the proposed reaction will actually occur.

Setup From Table 19.1:

$$Br_2(l) + 2e^- \longrightarrow 2Br^-(aq) \qquad E° = 1.07 \text{ V}$$

$$I_2(s) + 2e^- \longrightarrow 2I^-(aq) \qquad E° = 0.53 \text{ V}$$

$$Cl_2(g) + 2e^- \longrightarrow 2Cl^-(aq) \qquad E° = 1.36 \text{ V}$$

Solution (a) If a redox reaction is to occur, it will be the oxidation of I^- ions by Br_2:

$$Br_2(l) + 2I^-(aq) \longrightarrow 2Br^-(aq) + I_2(s)$$

Because the reduction potential of Br_2 is greater than that of I_2, Br_2 will be reduced to Br^- and I^- will be oxidized to I_2. Thus, the preceding reaction *will* occur.

(b) In this case, the proposed reaction is the reduction of Br_2 by Cl^- ions:

$$Br_2(l) + 2Cl^-(aq) \longrightarrow 2Br^-(aq) + Cl_2(g)$$

However, because the reduction potential of Br_2 is smaller than that of Cl_2, this reaction will *not* occur. Cl_2 is more readily reduced than Br_2, so Br_2 is not reduced by Cl^-.

Think About It
We can use Equation 19.1 and treat problems of this type like galvanic cell problems. Write the proposed redox reaction, and identify the "cathode" and the "anode." If the calculated $E°_{cell}$ is positive, the reaction will occur. If the calculated $E°_{cell}$ is negative, the reaction will not occur.

Practice Problem A Determine what redox reaction, if any, occurs (at 25°C) when lead metal (Pb) is added to (a) a 1.0-M solution of $NiCl_2$ and (b) a 1.0-M solution of HCl.

Practice Problem B Would it be safer to store a cobalt(II) chloride solution in a tin container or an iron container? Explain.

SECTION 19.3 REVIEW

Standard Reduction Potentials

19.3.1 Calculate $E°_{cell}$ at 25°C for a galvanic cell made of a Cr electrode in a solution that is 1.0 M in Cr^{3+} and an Au electrode in a solution that is 1.0 M in Au^{3+}.

19.3.2 Calculate $E°_{cell}$ at 25°C for a galvanic cell made of a Cr electrode in a solution that is 1.0 M in Cr^{3+} and an Ag electrode in a solution that is 1.0 M in Ag^+.

19.3.3 What redox reaction, if any, will occur at 25°C when Al metal is placed in a solution that is 1.0 M in Cr^{3+}?

19.3.4 What redox reaction, if any, will occur at 25°C when Zn metal is placed in a solution that is 1.0 M in Sr^{2+}?

19.4 SPONTANEITY OF REDOX REACTIONS UNDER STANDARD-STATE CONDITIONS

We now look at how E_{cell}° is related to thermodynamic quantities such as ΔG° and K. In a galvanic cell, chemical energy is converted to electric energy. The electric energy produced in a galvanic cell is the product of the cell potential and the total electric charge (in coulombs) that passes through the cell:

$$\text{electric energy} = \text{volts} \times \text{coulombs}$$
$$= \text{joules}$$

The total charge is determined by the number of moles of electrons (n) that pass through the circuit. By definition,

$$\text{total charge} = nF$$

where F, the Faraday[1] constant, is the electric charge contained in 1 mole of electrons. One faraday is equivalent to 96,485.3 C, although we usually round the number to three significant figures. Thus,

$$1\ F = 96,500\ \text{C/mol } e^-$$

Because

$$1\ \text{J} = 1\ \text{C} \times 1\ \text{V}$$

we can also express the units of faraday as

$$1\ F = 96,500\ \text{J/V} \cdot \text{mol } e^-$$

The measured cell potential is the maximum voltage that the cell can produce. This value is used to calculate the maximum amount of electric energy that can be obtained from the chemical reaction. This energy is used to do electrical work ($w_{electrical}$), so

$$w_{max} = w_{electrical}$$
$$= -nFE_{cell}$$

where w_{max} is the maximum amount of work that can be done. The negative sign on the right-hand side indicates that the electrical work is done *by* the system *on* the surroundings. In Chapter 18 we defined *free energy* as the energy available to do *work*. Specifically, the change in free energy, ΔG, represents the maximum amount of useful work that can be obtained from a reaction:

$$\Delta G = w_{max}$$

Therefore, we can write

$$\Delta G = -nFE_{cell} \qquad \qquad \textbf{Equation 19.2}$$

Both n and F are positive quantities and ΔG is negative for a spontaneous process, so E_{cell} must be positive for a spontaneous process. For reactions in which reactants and products are in their standard states, Equation 19.2 becomes

$$\Delta G^{\circ} = -nFE_{cell}^{\circ} \qquad \qquad \textbf{Equation 19.3}$$

Equation 19.3 makes it possible to relate E_{cell}° to the equilibrium constant, K, of a redox reaction. In Section 18.6 we saw that the standard free-energy change, ΔG°, for a reaction is related to its equilibrium constant as follows [◄◄ Section 18.6, Equation 18.14]:

$$\Delta G^{\circ} = -RT \ln K$$

---

[1]Michael Faraday (1791–1867), an English chemist and physicist, is regarded by many as the greatest experimental scientist of the nineteenth century. He started as an apprentice to a bookbinder at the age of 13, but became interested in science after reading a book on chemistry. Faraday invented the electric motor and was the first person to demonstrate the principle governing electric generators. Besides making notable contributions to the fields of electricity and magnetism, Faraday also worked on optical activity and discovered and named benzene.

Therefore, if we combine Equations 18.14 and 19.3, we get

$$-nFE°_{cell} = -RT \ln K$$

Solving for $E°_{cell}$ gives

Equation 19.4	$E°_{cell} = \dfrac{RT}{nF} \ln K$

When $T = 298$ K and n moles of electrons are transferred per mole of reaction, Equation 19.4 can be simplified by inserting the values for R and F:

$$E°_{cell} = \dfrac{\left(8.314 \dfrac{J}{K \cdot mol}\right)(298\ K)}{(n)\left(96{,}500 \dfrac{J}{V \cdot mol}\right)}$$

$$= \dfrac{0.0257\ V}{n} \ln K$$

And, by converting to the base-10 logarithm of K, we get

Equation 19.5	$E°_{cell} = \dfrac{0.0592\ V}{n} \log K$	(at 25°C)

Thus, if we know any one of the three quantities $\Delta G°$, K, or $E°_{cell}$, we can convert to the others by using Equations 18.14, 19.3, and 19.5.

Worked Examples 19.4 and 19.5 demonstrate the interconversions among $\Delta G°$, K, and $E°_{cell}$. For simplicity, the subscript "cell" is not shown.

Worked Example 19.4

Calculate the standard free-energy change for the following reaction at 25°C:

$$2Au(s) + 3Ca^{2+}(1.0\ M) \rightleftharpoons 2Au^{3+}(1.0\ M) + 3Ca(s)$$

Strategy Use $E°$ values from Table 19.1 to calculate $E°$ for the reaction, and then use Equation 19.3 to calculate the standard free-energy change.

Setup The half-cell reactions are

$$\textit{Cathode (reduction):}\quad 3Ca^{2+}(aq) + 6e^- \longrightarrow 3Ca(s)$$

$$\textit{Anode (oxidation):}\qquad\qquad 2Au(s) \longrightarrow 2Au^{3+}(aq) + 6e^-$$

From Table 19.1, $E°_{Ca^{2+}/Ca} = -2.87$ V and $E°_{Au^{3+}/Au} = 1.50$ V.

Solution

$$E°_{cell} = E°_{cathode} - E°_{anode}$$

$$= E°_{Ca^{2+}/Ca} - E°_{Au^{3+}/Au}$$

$$= -2.87\ V - 1.50\ V$$

$$= -4.37\ V$$

Next, substitute this value of $E°$ into Equation 19.3 to obtain $\Delta G°$:

$$\Delta G° = -nFE°$$

The overall reaction shows that $n = 6$, so

$$\Delta G° = -(6\ mol\ e^-)(96{,}500\ J/V \cdot mol\ e^-)(-4.37\ V)$$

$$= 2.53 \times 10^6\ J/mol$$

$$= 2.53 \times 10^3\ kJ/mol$$

Think About It
The large positive value of $\Delta G°$ indicates that reactants are favored at equilibrium, which is consistent with the fact that $E°$ for the reaction is negative.

Practice Problem A Calculate $\Delta G°$ for the following reaction at 25°C:

$$3Mg(s) + 2Al^{3+}(aq) \rightleftharpoons 3Mg^{2+}(aq) + 2Al(s)$$

Practice Problem B Calculate $\Delta G°$ for the following reaction at 25°C:

$$Pb(s) + Ni^{2+}(aq) \rightleftharpoons Pb^{2+}(aq) + Ni(s)$$

Worked Example 19.5

Calculate the equilibrium constant for the following reaction at 25°C:

$$Sn(s) + 2Cu^{2+}(aq) \rightleftharpoons Sn^{2+}(aq) + 2Cu^+(aq)$$

Strategy Use $E°$ values from Table 19.1 to calculate $E°$ for the reaction, and then calculate the equilibrium constant using Equation 19.5 (rearranged to solve for K).

Setup The half-cell reactions are

$$\text{Cathode (reduction):} \quad 2Cu^{2+}(aq) + 2e^- \longrightarrow 2Cu^+(aq)$$

$$\text{Anode (oxidation):} \quad Sn(s) \longrightarrow Sn^{2+}(aq) + 2e^-$$

From Table 19.1, $E°_{Cu^{2+}/Cu^+} = 0.15$ V and $E°_{Sn^{2+}/Sn} = -0.14$ V.

Solution

$$E°_{cell} = E°_{cathode} - E°_{anode}$$

$$= E°_{Cu^{2+}/Cu^+} - E°_{Sn^{2+}/Sn}$$

$$= 0.15 \text{ V} - (-0.14 \text{ V})$$

$$= 0.29 \text{ V}$$

Solving Equation 19.5 for K gives

$$K = 10^{nE°/0.0592 \text{ V}}$$

$$= 10^{(2)(0.29 \text{ V})/0.0592 \text{ V}}$$

$$= 6 \times 10^9$$

Think About It
A positive standard cell potential corresponds to a large equilibrium constant.

Practice Problem A Calculate the equilibrium constant for the following reaction at 25°C:

$$2Ag(s) + Fe^{2+}(aq) \rightleftharpoons 2Ag^+(aq) + Fe(s)$$

Practice Problem B Like equilibrium constants, $E°_{cell}$ values are temperature dependent. At 80°C, $E°_{cell}$ for the cell diagram shown is 0.18 V.

$$Pt \mid H_2(g) \mid HCl(aq) \parallel AgCl(s) \mid Ag(s)$$

The corresponding cell reaction is

$$H_2(g) + 2AgCl(s) \rightleftharpoons 2Ag(s) + 2H^+(aq) + 2Cl^-(aq)$$

Calculate the equilibrium constant for this reaction at 80°C.

Thinking Outside the Box

Amalgam Fillings and Dental Pain

The pain caused by having aluminum foil contact an amalgam filling is the result of electrical stimulation of the nerve of a tooth caused by a current flowing between the aluminum foil and the metal in the filling. Historically, the material most commonly used to fill cavities is known as *dental amalgam*. (An *amalgam* is a substance made by combining mercury with one or more other metals.) Dental amalgam consists of liquid mercury mixed in roughly equal parts with an alloy powder containing silver, tin, copper, and sometimes smaller amounts of other metals such as zinc.

What happens is this: the aluminum and the dental filling act as *electrodes* in a galvanic cell. Aluminum acts as the anode, and the amalgam acts as the cathode. In effect, when the aluminum comes into contact with the amalgam, an electrochemical cell is established in the mouth, causing a current to flow. This current stimulates the nerve of the tooth, causing a *very* unpleasant sensation.

Another type of discomfort can result from the filling being made the anode in an electrochemical cell. This occurs when the filling touches a metal with a greater reduction potential than the components of the amalgam, such as gold. When an amalgam filling comes into contact with a gold inlay, the tin in the filling (the most easily oxidized of the major amalgam components) is *oxidized*—creating an unpleasant metallic taste in the mouth. A simplified, unbalanced equation for the redox reaction that takes place is

$$Sn(s) + O_2(g) \longrightarrow Sn^{2+}(aq) + H_2O(l)$$

Gold inlay touching amalgam dental filling.

SECTION 19.4 REVIEW

Spontaneity of Redox Reactions Under Standard-State Conditions

19.4.1   Calculate K at 25°C for the following reaction:
$$Fe^{2+}(aq) + Ni(s) \rightleftharpoons Fe(s) + Ni^{2+}(aq)$$

19.4.2   Calculate $\Delta G°$ at 25°C for the following reaction:
$$3Cu^{2+}(aq) + Cr(s) \rightleftharpoons 3Cu^{+}(aq) + Cr^{3+}(aq)$$

19.5 SPONTANEITY OF REDOX REACTIONS UNDER CONDITIONS OTHER THAN STANDARD STATE

So far we have focused on redox reactions in which the reactants and products are in their standard states. Standard-state conditions, though, are difficult to come by and usually impossible to maintain. Just as there is an equation that relates ΔG to $\Delta G°$ [◄◄ Section 18.6, Equation 18.13], there is an equation that relates E to $E°$. We will now derive this equation.

The Nernst Equation

Consider a redox reaction of the type

$$a\text{A} + b\text{B} \longrightarrow c\text{C} + d\text{D}$$

From Equation 18.13,

$$\Delta G = \Delta G^\circ + RT \ln Q$$

Because $\Delta G = -nFE$ and $\Delta G^\circ = -nFE^\circ$, the equation can be expressed as

$$-nFE = -nFE^\circ + RT \ln Q$$

Dividing the equation through by $-nF$, we get

$$E = E^\circ - \frac{RT}{nF} \ln Q \qquad \textbf{Equation 19.6}$$

where Q is the reaction quotient [◀◀ Section 15.2]. Equation 19.6 is known as the **Nernst**[2] **equation.** At 298 K, Equation 19.6 can be rewritten as

$$E = E^\circ - \frac{0.0257 \text{ V}}{n} \ln Q$$

or using the base-10 logarithm of Q as

$$E = E^\circ - \frac{0.0592 \text{ V}}{n} \log Q \qquad \textbf{Equation 19.7}$$

During the operation of a galvanic cell, electrons flow from the anode to the cathode, resulting in product formation and a decrease in reactant concentration. Thus, Q increases, which means that E decreases. Eventually, the cell reaches equilibrium. At equilibrium, there is no net transfer of electrons, so $E = 0$ and $Q = K$, where K is the equilibrium constant.

The Nernst equation enables us to calculate E as a function of reactant and product concentrations in a redox reaction. For example, for the cell pictured in Figure 19.1,

$$\text{Zn}(s) + \text{Cu}^{2+}(aq) \longrightarrow \text{Zn}^{2+}(aq) + \text{Cu}(s)$$

The Nernst equation for this cell at 25°C can be written as

$$E = 1.10 \text{ V} - \frac{0.0592 \text{ V}}{2} \log \frac{[\text{Zn}^{2+}]}{[\text{Cu}^{2+}]}$$

If the ratio $[\text{Zn}^{2+}]/[\text{Cu}^{2+}]$ is less than 1, $\log ([\text{Zn}^{2+}]/[\text{Cu}^{2+}])$ is a negative number, making the second term on the right-hand side of the preceding equation a positive quantity. Under this condition, E is *greater* than the standard potential E°. If the ratio is greater than 1, E is *smaller* than E°.

Worked Example 19.6 shows how to use the Nernst equation.

Worked Example 19.6

Predict whether the following reaction will occur spontaneously as written at 298 K:

$$\text{Co}(s) + \text{Fe}^{2+}(aq) \longrightarrow \text{Co}^{2+}(aq) + \text{Fe}(s)$$

assuming $[\text{Co}^{2+}] = 0.15 \ M$ and $[\text{Fe}^{2+}] = 0.68 \ M$.

Strategy Use E° values from Table 19.1 to determine E° for the reaction, and use Equation 19.7 to calculate E. If E is positive, the reaction will occur spontaneously.

(Continued on next page)

---

[2]Walther Hermann Nernst (1864–1941), a German chemist and physicist, worked mainly on electrolyte solutions and thermodynamics. He also invented an electric piano. Nernst was awarded the Nobel Prize in Chemistry in 1920 for his contribution to thermodynamics.

Setup From Table 19.1,

$$\textit{Cathode (reduction):}\ \ Fe^{2+}(aq) + 2e^- \longrightarrow Fe(s)$$

$$\textit{Anode (oxidation):}\ \ \ \ \ \ \ \ \ \ \ \ \ Co(s) \longrightarrow Co^{2+}(aq) + 2e^-$$

$$E^\circ_{cell} = E^\circ_{cathode} - E^\circ_{anode}$$

$$= E^\circ_{Fe^{2+}/Fe} - E^\circ_{Co^{2+}/Co}$$

$$= -0.44\ V - (-0.28\ V)$$

$$= -0.16\ V$$

The reaction quotient, Q, for the reaction is $[Co^{2+}]/[Fe^{2+}]$. Therefore, $Q = (0.15/0.68) = 0.22$.

Solution From Equation 19.7,

$$E = E^\circ - \frac{0.0592\ V}{n} \log Q$$

$$= -0.16\ V - \frac{0.0592\ V}{2} \log 0.22$$

$$= -0.14\ V$$

The negative E value indicates that the reaction is *not* spontaneous as written under the conditions described.

Think About It

For this reaction to be spontaneous as written, the ratio of $[Fe^{2+}]$ to $[Co^{2+}]$ would have to be enormous. We can determine the required ratio by first setting E equal to zero:

$$0\ V = -0.16\ V - \frac{0.0592\ V}{2} \log Q$$

$$-\frac{(0.16\ V)(2)}{0.0592\ V} = \log Q$$

$$\log Q = -5.4$$

$$Q = 10^{-5.4} = \frac{[Co^{2+}]}{[Fe^{2+}]} = 4 \times 10^{-6}$$

For E to be positive, therefore, the ratio of $[Fe^{2+}]$ to $[Co^{2+}]$, the reciprocal of Q, would have to be greater than 3×10^5 to 1.

Practice Problem A Will the following reaction occur spontaneously at 298 K if $[Fe^{2+}] = 0.60\ M$ and $[Cd^{2+}] = 0.010\ M$?

$$Cd(s) + Fe^{2+}(aq) \longrightarrow Cd^{2+}(aq) + Fe(s)$$

Practice Problem B Consider the electrochemical cell in Practice Problem 19.5B (page 821), for which $E^\circ_{cell} = 0.18\ V$ at 80°C.

$$H_2(g) + 2AgCl(s) \rightleftharpoons 2Ag(s) + 2H^+(aq) + 2Cl^-(aq)$$

If pH $= 1.05$ in the anode compartment, and $[Cl^-] = 2.5\ M$ in the cathode compartment, determine the partial pressure of H_2 necessary in the anode compartment for the cell potential to be 0.27 V at 80°C.

Concentration Cells

Because electrode potential depends on ion concentrations, it is possible to construct a galvanic cell from two half-cells composed of the same material but differing in ion concentrations. Such a cell is called a *concentration cell.*

Consider a galvanic cell consisting of a zinc electrode in 0.10 *M* zinc sulfate in one compartment and a zinc electrode in 1.0 *M* zinc sulfate in the other compartment (Figure 19.5). According to Le Châtelier's principle, the tendency for the reduction

$$Zn^{2+}(aq) + 2e^- \longrightarrow Zn(s)$$

Figure 19.5 A concentration cell. Oxidation will occur in the container with the lower Zn^{2+} concentration. Reduction will occur in the container with the higher Zn^{2+} concentration.

to occur increases with increasing concentration of Zn^{2+} ions. Therefore, reduction should occur in the more concentrated compartment and oxidation should take place on the more dilute side. The cell diagram is

$$Zn(s) \mid Zn^{2+}(0.10\ M) \parallel Zn^{2+}(1.0\ M) \mid Zn(s)$$

and the half-cell reactions are

Oxidation: $Zn(s) \longrightarrow Zn^{2+}(0.10\ M) + 2e^-$

Reduction: $Zn^{2+}(1.0\ M) + 2e^- \longrightarrow Zn(s)$

Overall: $Zn^{2+}(1.0\ M) \longrightarrow Zn^{2+}(0.10\ M)$

The cell potential is

$$E = E^\circ - \frac{0.0592\ \text{V}}{2} \log \frac{[Zn^{2+}]_{\text{dilute}}}{[Zn^{2+}]_{\text{concentrated}}}$$

where the subscripts "dilute" and "concentrated" refer to the $0.10\ M$ and $1.0\ M$ concentrations, respectively. The E° for this cell is zero (because the same electrode-ion combination is used in both half-cells; i.e., $E^\circ_{\text{cathode}} = E^\circ_{\text{anode}}$), so

$$E = 0 - \frac{0.0592\ \text{V}}{2} \log \frac{0.10}{1.0}$$

$$= 0.030\ \text{V}$$

The cell potential for a concentration cell is typically *small* and decreases continually during the operation of the cell as the concentrations in the two compartments approach each other. When the concentrations of the ions in the two compartments are equal, E becomes zero and no further change occurs.

In Chapter 17, we studied solubility equilibria and learned how to use tabulated K_{sp} values to determine solubilities of ionic compounds that are only very slightly soluble. The tabulated K_{sp}

values are determined by measuring the concentration of one of a compound's constituent ions in a saturated solution of the compound. For example, to determine the K_{sp} of silver bromide (AgBr), we must measure the concentration of Ag^+, or the concentration of Br^-. Because the K_{sp} of silver bromide is 7.7×10^{-13}, the concentration of either ion in a saturated solution is 8.8×10^{-7} M. You may have wondered how such a small concentration is measured. It cannot be done using visible spectrophotometry, the method described in Chapter 9; not only because the concentration is so low, but also because a solution AgBr is colorless—meaning that it does not absorb visible light. In fact, concentrations of ions in these cases are measured using concentration cells.

Worked Example 19.7 illustrates this process.

Worked Example 19.7

An electrochemical cell is constructed for the purpose of determining the K_{sp} of silver cyanide (AgCN) at 25°C. One half-cell consists of a silver electrode in a 1.00-M solution of silver nitrate. The other half-cell consists of a silver electrode in a saturated solution of silver cyanide. The cell potential is measured and found to be 0.470 V. Determine the concentration of silver ion in the saturated silver cyanide solution and the value of K_{sp} for AgCN.

Strategy Use Equation 19.7 to solve for the unknown concentration of silver ion. The half-cell with the higher Ag^+ (1.0 M $AgNO_3$) concentration will be the cathode; the half-cell with the lower, unknown Ag^+ concentration (saturated AgCN solution) will be the anode. The overall reaction is $Ag^+(1.0\ M) \longrightarrow Ag^+(x\ M)$.

Setup Because this is a concentration cell, $E°_{cell} = 0$ V. The reaction quotient, Q, is $(x\ M)/(1.00\ M)$; and the value of n is 1.

Solution

$$E_{cell} = E°_{cell} - \frac{0.0592\ V}{n} \log Q$$

$$0.470\ V = 0 - \frac{0.0592\ V}{1} \log \frac{x}{1.00}$$

$$-7.939 = \log \frac{x}{1.00}$$

$$10^{-7.939} = 1.15 \times 10^{-8} = \log \frac{x}{1.00}$$

$$x = 1.15 \times 10^{-8}$$

Therefore, $[Ag^+] = 1.15 \times 10^{-8}\ M$ and K_{sp} for AgCN $= x^2 = 1.3 \times 10^{-16}$.

> **Think About It**
> Remember that in a saturated solution of a salt that dissociates into two ions, the ion concentrations are equal to each other and each ion concentration is equal to the square root of K_{sp} [◀◀ Section 17.4].

Practice Problem A An electrochemical cell is constructed for the purpose of determining the K_{sp} of copper(I) chloride, CuCl, at 25°C. One half-cell consists of a copper electrode in a 1.00-M solution of copper(I) nitrate. The other half-cell consists of a copper electrode in a saturated solution of copper(I) chloride. The measured cell potential is 0.175 V. Determine the concentration of copper(I) ion in the saturated copper(I) chloride solution and the value of K_{sp} for CuCl.

Practice Problem B The K_{sp} of copper(II) ferrocyanide ($Cu_2[Fe(CN)_6]$) is 1.3×10^{-16} at 25°C. Determine the potential of a concentration cell in which one half-cell consists of a copper electrode in 1.00 M copper(II) nitrate, and the other consists of a copper electrode in a saturated solution of $Cu_2[Fe(CN)_6]$. Ferrocyanide, ($[Fe(CN)_6]^{4-}$), is a *complex ion* [◀◀ Section 17.5].

Spontaneity of Redox Reactions Under Conditions Other Than Standard State

19.5.1 Calculate E at 25°C for a galvanic cell based on the reaction,

$$Zn(s) + Cu^{2+}(aq) \longrightarrow Zn^{2+}(aq) + Cu(s),$$

in which $[Zn^{2+}] = 0.55\ M$ and $[Cu^{2+}] = 1.02\ M$.

19.5.2 Calculate the cell potential at 25°C of a galvanic cell consisting of an Ag electrode in 0.15 M AgNO$_3$ and an Ag electrode in 1.0 M AgNO$_3$.

19.5.3 For each of the following, determine whether the action would cause an increase, a decrease, or no change in the cell potential of the electrochemical cell in Question 19.5.2. (a) Adding AgNO$_3$ to the cathode compartment; (b) adding saturated AgCl solution to the anode compartment; (c) adding NaCl to the anode compartment.

19.5.4 Calculate E°_{cell} at 80°C for a galvanic cell based on the reaction

$$H_2(g) + 2AgCl(s) \rightleftharpoons 2Ag(s) + 2H^+(aq) + 2Cl^-(aq)$$

in which $[H^+] = 0.10\ M$, $[Cl^-] = 1.5\ M$, and $P = 1.25$ atm. ($E^\circ_{cell} = 0.18$ V at 80°C.)

19.6 BATTERIES

A *battery* is a galvanic cell, or a series of connected galvanic cells, that can be used as a portable, self-contained source of direct electric current. In this section we examine several types of batteries.

Figure 19.6 Interior view of the type of dry cell used in flashlights and other small devices.

Dry Cells and Alkaline Batteries

The most common batteries, *dry cells* and *alkaline batteries,* are those used in flashlights, toys, and certain portable electronics such as CD players. The two are similar in appearance, but differ in the spontaneous chemical reaction responsible for producing a voltage. Although the reactions that take place in these batteries are somewhat complex, the reactions shown here approximate the overall processes.

A dry cell, so named because it has no fluid component, consists of a zinc container (the anode) in contact with manganese dioxide and an electrolyte (Figure 19.6). The electrolyte consists of ammonium chloride and zinc chloride in water, to which starch is added to thicken the solution to a paste so that it is less likely to leak. A carbon rod, immersed in the electrolyte in the center of the cell, serves as the cathode. The cell reactions are:

Anode: $Zn(s) \longrightarrow Zn^{2+}(aq) + 2e^-$

Cathode: $2NH_4^+(aq) + 2MnO_2(s) + 2e^- \longrightarrow Mn_2O_3(s) + 2NH_3(aq) + H_2O(l)$

Overall: $Zn(s) + 2NH_4^+(aq) + 2MnO_2(s) \longrightarrow Zn^{2+}(aq) + Mn_2O_3(s) + 2NH_3(aq) + H_2O(l)$

The voltage produced by a dry cell is about 1.5 V.

An alkaline battery is also based on the reduction of manganese dioxide and the oxidation of zinc. However, the reactions take place in a *basic* medium, hence the name *alkaline* battery. The anode consists of powdered zinc suspended in a gel, which is in contact with a concentrated solution of KOH. The cathode is a mixture of manganese dioxide and graphite. The anode and cathode are separated by a porous barrier (Figure 19.7).

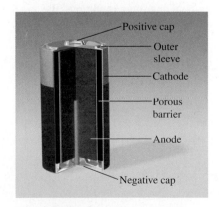

Figure 19.7 Interior view of an alkaline battery.

Anode:	$Zn(s) + 2OH^-(aq) \longrightarrow Zn(OH)_2(s) + 2e^-$
Cathode:	$2MnO_2(s) + 2H_2O(l) + 2e^- \longrightarrow 2MnO(OH)(s) + 2OH^-(aq)$
Overall:	$Zn(s) + 2MnO_2(s) + 2H_2O(l) \longrightarrow Zn(OH)_2(s) + 2MnO(OH)(s)$

Alkaline batteries are more expensive than dry cells and offer superior performance and shelf life.

Lead Storage Batteries

The lead storage battery commonly used in automobiles consists of six identical cells joined together in series. Each cell has a lead anode and a cathode made of lead dioxide (PbO_2) packed on a metal plate (Figure 19.8). Both the cathode and the anode are immersed in an aqueous solution of sulfuric acid, which acts as the electrolyte. The cell reactions are

Anode:	$Pb(s) + SO_4^{2-}(aq) \longrightarrow PbSO_4(s) + 2e^-$
Cathode:	$PbO_2(s) + 4H^+(aq) + SO_4^{2-}(aq) + 2e^- \longrightarrow PbSO_4(s) + 2H_2O(l)$
Overall:	$Pb(s) + PbO_2(s) + 4H^+(aq) + 2SO_4^{2-}(aq) \longrightarrow 2PbSO_4(s) + 2H_2O(l)$

Under normal operating conditions, each cell produces 2 V. A total of 12 V from the six cells is used to power the ignition circuit of the automobile and its other electric systems. The lead storage battery can deliver large amounts of current for a short time, such as the time it takes to start the engine.

Unlike dry cells and alkaline batteries, the lead storage battery is rechargeable. Recharging the battery means reversing the normal electrochemical reaction by applying an external voltage at the cathode and the anode. (This kind of process is called *electrolysis,* which we discuss in Section 19.7.)

Lithium-Ion Batteries

Sometimes called "the battery of the future," lithium-ion batteries have several advantages over other battery types. The overall reaction that takes place in the lithium-ion battery is

Anode:	$Li(s) \longrightarrow Li^+ + e^-$
Cathode:	$Li^+ + CoO_2 + e^- \longrightarrow LiCoO_2(s)$
Overall:	$Li(s) + CoO_2 \longrightarrow LiCoO_2(s)$

Student Annotation: Lithium has the largest negative reduction potential of all the metals, making it a powerful reducing agent.

The overall cell potential is 3.4 V, which is relatively large. Lithium is also the lightest metal— only 6.941 g of Li (its molar mass) are needed to produce 1 mole of electrons. Furthermore, a

Figure 19.8 Interior view of a lead storage battery. Under normal operating conditions, the concentration of the sulfuric acid solution is about 38 percent by mass.

lithium-ion battery can be recharged hundreds of times. These qualities make lithium batteries suitable for use in portable devices such as cell phones, digital cameras, and laptop computers.

Fuel Cells

Fossil fuels are a major source of energy, but the conversion of fossil fuel into electric energy is a highly inefficient process. Consider the combustion of methane:

$$CH_4(g) + 2O_2(g) \longrightarrow CO_2(g) + 2H_2O(l) + \text{energy}$$

To generate electricity, heat produced by the reaction is first used to convert water to steam, which then drives a turbine, which then drives a generator. A significant fraction of the energy released in the form of heat is lost to the surroundings at each step (even the most efficient power plant converts only about 40 percent of the original chemical energy into electricity). Because combustion reactions are redox reactions, it is more desirable to carry them out directly by electrochemical means, thereby greatly increasing the efficiency of power production. This objective can be accomplished by a device known as a *fuel cell,* a galvanic cell that requires a continuous supply of reactants to keep functioning.

> **Student Annotation:** Strictly speaking, a fuel cell is not a battery because it is not self-contained.

In its simplest form, a hydrogen-oxygen fuel cell consists of an electrolyte solution, such as a potassium hydroxide solution, and two inert electrodes. Hydrogen and oxygen gases are bubbled through the anode and cathode compartments (Figure 19.9), where the following reactions take place:

Anode: $2H_2(g) + 4OH^-(aq) \longrightarrow 4H_2O(l) + 4e^-$

Cathode: $O_2(g) + 2H_2O(l) + 4e^- \longrightarrow 4OH^-(aq)$

_____

Overall: $2H_2(g) + O_2(g) \longrightarrow 2H_2O(l)$

Using $E°$ values from Table 19.1, the standard cell potential is calculated as follows:

$$E°_{cell} = E°_{cathode} - E°_{anode}$$

$$= 0.40 \text{ V} - (-0.83 \text{ V})$$

$$= 1.23 \text{ V}$$

Thus, the cell reaction is spontaneous under standard-state conditions. Note that the reaction is the same as the hydrogen combustion reaction, but the oxidation and reduction are carried out

Oxidation
$2H_2(g) + 4OH^-(aq) \longrightarrow 4H_2O(l) + 4e^-$

Reduction
$O_2(g) + 2H_2O(l) + 4e^- \longrightarrow 4OH^-(aq)$

Figure 19.9 A hydrogen-oxygen fuel cell. The Ni and NiO embedded in the porous carbon electrodes are catalysts.

separately at the anode and the cathode. Like platinum in the standard hydrogen electrode, the electrodes serve two purposes. They serve as electrical conductors, and they provide the necessary surfaces for the initial decomposition of the molecules into atomic species, which must take place before electrons can be transferred. Electrodes that serve this particular purpose are called "electrocatalysts." Metals such as platinum, nickel, and rhodium also make good electrocatalysts.

In addition to the H_2-O_2 system, a number of other fuel cells have been developed. Among these is the propane-oxygen fuel cell. The corresponding half-cell reactions are

$$\textit{Anode:} \qquad C_3H_8(g) + 6H_2O(l) \longrightarrow 3CO_2(g) + 20H^+(aq) + 20e^-$$

$$\textit{Cathode:} \quad 5O_2(g) + 20H^+(aq) + 20e^- \longrightarrow 10H_2O(l)$$

$$\textit{Overall:} \qquad C_3H_8(g) + 5O_2(g) \longrightarrow 3CO_2(g) + 4H_2O(l)$$

The overall reaction is identical to the burning of propane in oxygen.

Unlike batteries, fuel cells do not store chemical energy. Reactants must be constantly resupplied as they are consumed, and products must be removed as they form. However, properly designed fuel cells may be as much as 70 percent efficient, which is about twice as efficient as an internal combustion engine. In addition, fuel-cell generators are free of the noise, vibration, heat transfer, thermal pollution, and other problems normally associated with conventional power plants. Nevertheless, fuel cells are not yet in widespread use. One major problem is the expense of electrocatalysts that can function efficiently for long periods of time without contamination. One notable application of fuel cells is their use in space vehicles. Hydrogen-oxygen fuel cells provide electric power (and drinking water!) for space flight.

Multi 19.4
Electrochemistry—the electrolysis of potassium iodide

Student Annotation:

Cell type	Chemical reaction	Electric energy
Galvanic	Spontaneous	Produced
Electrolytic	Nonspontaneous	Consumed

19.7 ELECTROLYSIS

In Section 19.6, we mentioned that lead storage batteries are rechargeable and that recharging means reversing the electrochemical processes by which the battery ordinarily operates through the application of an external voltage. This process, the use of electric energy to drive a nonspontaneous chemical reaction, is called ***electrolysis.*** An ***electrolytic cell*** is one used to carry out electrolysis. The same principles apply to the processes in both galvanic and electrolytic cells. In this section, we discuss three examples of electrolysis based on those principles. We then examine some of the quantitative aspects of electrolysis.

Electrolysis of Molten Sodium Chloride

In its molten (melted) state, sodium chloride, an ionic compound, can be electrolyzed to separate it into its constituent elements, sodium and chlorine. Figure 19.10(a) is a diagram of a Downs cell, which is used for the large-scale electrolysis of NaCl. In molten NaCl, the cations and anions are the Na^+ and Cl^- ions, respectively. Figure 19.10(b) is a simplified diagram showing the reactions that occur at the electrodes. The electrolytic cell contains a pair of electrodes connected to the battery. The battery serves to push electrons in the direction they would not flow spontaneously. The electrode toward which the electrons are pushed is the cathode, where reduction takes place. The electrode away from which electrons are drawn is the anode, where oxidation takes place. The reactions at the electrodes are

$$\textit{Anode (oxidation):} \qquad 2Cl^-(l) \longrightarrow Cl_2(g) + 2e^-$$

$$\textit{Cathode (reduction):} \quad 2Na^+(l) + 2e^- \longrightarrow 2Na(l)$$

$$\textit{Overall:} \qquad 2Na^+(l) + 2Cl^-(l) \longrightarrow 2Na(l) + Cl_2(g)$$

This process is a major industrial source of pure sodium metal and chlorine gas.

Student Annotation: We can only estimate the value of $E°_{cell}$ because the values in Table 19.1 refer to the species in aqueous solution.

Using data from Table 19.1, we estimate $E°_{cell}$ to be −4 V for this process. The negative standard reduction potential indicates that for the process to occur as written, a minimum of approximately 4 V must be supplied by the battery to drive the reaction in the desired direction. In practice, an even higher voltage is required because of inefficiencies in the electrolytic process and because of overvoltage, a phenomenon we will discuss later in this section.

Figure 19.10 (a) A practical arrangement called a Downs cell for the electrolysis of molten NaCl (m.p. = 801°C). The sodium metal formed at the cathodes is in the liquid state. Because liquid sodium metal is lighter than molten NaCl, the sodium floats to the surface, as shown, and is collected. Chlorine gas forms at the anode and is collected at the top. (b) A simplified diagram showing the electrode reactions during the electrolysis of molten NaCl. The battery is needed to drive the nonspontaneous reaction.

Electrolysis of Water

Under ordinary atmospheric conditions (1 atm and 25°C), water will not spontaneously decompose to form hydrogen and oxygen gas because the standard free-energy change for the reaction is a large positive quantity:

$$2H_2O(l) \longrightarrow 2H_2(g) + O_2(g) \qquad \Delta G° = 474.4 \text{ kJ/mol}$$

However, this reaction can be made to occur in an electrolytic cell like the one shown in Figure 19.11. This cell consists of a pair of electrodes made of a nonreactive metal, such as platinum, immersed in water. When the electrodes are connected to the battery, nothing happens because there are not enough ions in pure water to carry much of an electric current. The reaction occurs readily in a 0.1 M H_2SO_4 solution, however, because there is a sufficient ion concentration to conduct electricity. Immediately, gas bubbles begin to appear at both electrodes.

> **Student Annotation:** Remember that at 25°C pure water has only a very low concentration of ions [◀◀ Section 16.3]:
>
> $[H^+] = [OH^-] = 1 \times 10^{-7} M$

Figure 19.11 Apparatus for small-scale electrolysis of water. The volume of hydrogen gas generated at the cathode is twice that of oxygen gas generated at the anode.

The processes at the electrodes are

Anode: $2H_2O(l) \longrightarrow O_2(g) + 4H^+(aq) + 4e^-$

Cathode: $4H^+(aq) + 4e^- \longrightarrow 2H_2(g)$

Overall: $2H_2O(l) \longrightarrow O_2(g) + 2H_2(g)$

Note that there is no net consumption of the acid.

Electrolysis of an Aqueous Sodium Chloride Solution

An aqueous sodium chloride solution is the most complicated of the three examples of electrolysis considered here because $NaCl(aq)$ contains several species that could be oxidized and reduced. The reductions that might occur at the cathode are

$$2H^+(aq) + 2e^- \longrightarrow H_2(g) \qquad\qquad E^\circ = 0.00 \text{ V}$$

$$2H_2O(l) + 2e^- \longrightarrow H_2(g) + 2OH^-(aq) \qquad\qquad E^\circ = -0.83 \text{ V}$$

or

$$Na^+(aq) + e^- \longrightarrow Na(s) \qquad\qquad E^\circ = -2.71 \text{ V}$$

We can rule out the reduction of Na^+ ion because of the large negative E° value. Under standard-state conditions, the reduction of H^+ is more apt to occur than the reduction of H_2O. However, in a solution of NaCl, the H^+ concentration is very low, making the reduction of H_2O the more probable reaction at the cathode.

The oxidation reactions that might occur at the anode are

$$2Cl^-(aq) \longrightarrow Cl_2(g) + 2e^-$$

or

$$2H_2O(l) \longrightarrow O_2(g) + 4H^+(aq) + 4e^-$$

Referring to Table 19.1, we find

$$Cl_2(g) + 2e^- \longrightarrow 2Cl^-(aq) \qquad E^\circ = 1.36 \text{ V}$$

$$O_2(g) + 4H^+(aq) + 4e^- \longrightarrow 2H_2O(l) \qquad E^\circ = 1.23 \text{ V}$$

The standard reduction potentials of the two reactions are not very different, but the values do suggest that the oxidation of H_2O *should* occur more readily. However, by experiment we find that the gas produced at the anode is Cl_2, not O_2. In the study of electrolytic processes, we sometimes find that the voltage required for a reaction is considerably higher than the electrode potentials would indicate. The ***overvoltage*** is the difference between the calculated voltage and the actual voltage required to cause electrolysis. The overvoltage for O_2 formation is quite high. Under normal operating conditions, therefore, Cl_2 gas forms at the anode instead of O_2.

Thus, the half-cell reactions in the electrolysis of aqueous sodium chloride are

Anode (oxidation): $2Cl^-(aq) \longrightarrow Cl_2(g) + 2e^-$

Cathode (reduction): $2H_2O(l) + 2e^- \longrightarrow H_2(g) + 2OH^-(aq)$

Overall: $2H_2O(l) + 2Cl^-(aq) \longrightarrow H_2(g) + Cl_2(g) + 2OH^-(aq)$

Student Annotation: Keep in mind that in the electrolysis of aqueous solutions, the water itself may be oxidized and/or reduced.

As the overall reaction shows, the concentration of the Cl^- ions decreases during electrolysis and that of the OH^- ions increases. Therefore, in addition to H_2 and Cl_2, the useful by-product NaOH can be obtained by evaporating the aqueous solution at the end of the electrolysis.

Electrolysis has many important applications in industry, mainly in the extraction and puri-fication of metals. We discuss some of these applications in Chapter 21.

Quantitative Applications of Electrolysis

The quantitative treatment of electrolysis was developed primarily by Faraday. He observed that the mass of product formed (or reactant consumed) at an electrode was proportional to both the amount of electricity transferred at the electrode and the molar mass of the substance being pro-duced (or consumed). In the electrolysis of molten NaCl, for example, the cathode reaction tells us that one Na atom is produced when one Na^+ ion accepts an electron from the electrode. To reduce 1 mole of Na^+ ions, we must supply an Avogadro's number (6.02×10^{23}) of electrons to the cath-ode. On the other hand, stoichiometry tells us that it takes 2 moles of electrons to reduce 1 mole of Mg^{2+} ions and 3 moles of electrons to reduce 1 mole of Al^{3+} ions:

$$Na^+ + e^- \longrightarrow Na$$

$$Mg^{2+} + 2e^- \longrightarrow Mg$$

$$Al^{3+} + 3e^- \longrightarrow Al$$

In an electrolysis experiment, we generally measure the current (in amperes) that passes through an electrolytic cell in a given period of time. The relationship between charge (in coulombs) and the current is

$$1 \text{ C} = 1 \text{ A} \times 1 \text{ s}$$

That is, a coulomb is the quantity of electric charge passing any point in the circuit in 1 s when the current is 1 A. Therefore, if we know the current (in amperes) and how long it is applied (in seconds), we can calculate the charge (in coulombs). Knowing the charge enables us to determine the number of moles of electrons. And knowing the number of moles of electrons allows us to use stoichiometry to determine the number of moles of product. Figure 19.12 shows the steps involved in calculating the quantities of substances produced in electrolysis.

To illustrate this approach, consider an electrolytic cell in which molten $CaCl_2$ is separated into its constituent elements, Ca and Cl_2. Suppose a current of 0.452 A is passed through the cell for 1.50 h. How much product will be formed at each electrode? The first step is to determine which species will be oxidized at the anode and which species will be reduced at the cathode. Here the choice is straightforward because we have only Ca^{2+} and Cl^- ions. The cell reactions are

Anode (oxidation): $2Cl^-(l) \longrightarrow Cl_2(g) + 2e^-$

Cathode (reduction): $Ca^{2+}(l) + 2e^- \longrightarrow Ca(l)$
_____

Overall: $Ca^{2+}(l) + 2Cl^-(l) \longrightarrow Ca(l) + Cl_2(g)$

The quantities of calcium metal and chlorine gas formed depend on the number of electrons that pass through the electrolytic cell, which in turn depends on *charge*, or current × time:

$$\text{coulombs} = 0.452 \, \cancel{A} \times 1.50 \, \cancel{h} \times \frac{3600 \, \cancel{s}}{1 \, \cancel{h}} \times \frac{1 \text{ C}}{1 \, \cancel{A} \cdot \cancel{s}} = 2.441 \times 10^3 \text{ C}$$

Because 1 mol $e^- = 96,500$ C and 2 mol e^- are required to reduce 1 mole of Ca^{2+} ions, the mass of Ca metal formed at the cathode is calculated as follows:

$$\text{grams Ca} = (2.441 \times 10^3 \, \cancel{C})\left(\frac{1 \, \cancel{\text{mol } e^-}}{96,500 \, \cancel{C}}\right)\left(\frac{1 \, \cancel{\text{mol Ca}}}{2 \, \cancel{\text{mol } e^-}}\right)\left(\frac{40.08 \text{ g Ca}}{1 \, \cancel{\text{mol Ca}}}\right) = 0.507 \text{ g Ca}$$

The anode reaction indicates that 1 mole of chlorine is produced per 2 mol e^- of electricity. Hence, the mass of chlorine gas formed is

$$\text{grams } Cl_2 = (2.441 \times 10^3 \, \cancel{C})\left(\frac{1 \, \cancel{\text{mol } e^-}}{96,500 \, \cancel{C}}\right)\left(\frac{1 \, \cancel{\text{mol } Cl_2}}{2 \, \cancel{\text{mol } e^-}}\right)\left(\frac{70.90 \text{ g } Cl_2}{1 \, \cancel{\text{mol } Cl_2}}\right) = 0.897 \text{ g } Cl_2$$

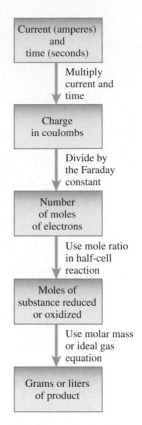

Figure 19.12 Steps involved in calculating amounts of substances reduced or oxidized in electrolysis.

Worked Example 19.8 applies this approach to electrolysis in an aqueous solution.

Worked Example 19.8

A current of 1.26 A is passed through an electrolytic cell containing a dilute sulfuric acid solution for 7.44 h. Write the half-cell reactions, and calculate the volume of gases generated at STP.

Strategy As shown in Figure 19.12, we can use current and time to determine charge. We can then convert charge to moles of electrons, and use the balanced half-reactions to determine how many moles of product form at each electrode. Finally, we can convert moles to volume.

Setup The half-cell reactions for the electrolysis of water are

$$
\begin{array}{lll}
\textit{Anode:} & 2H_2O(l) \longrightarrow O_2(g) + 4H^+(aq) + 4e^- \\
\textit{Cathode:} & \underline{4H^+(aq) + 4e^- \longrightarrow 2H_2(g)} \\
\textit{Overall:} & 2H_2O(l) \longrightarrow O_2(g) + 2H_2(g)
\end{array}
$$

Remember that STP for gases means 273 K and 1 atm.

Solution

$$
\text{coulombs} = (1.26\ A)(7.44\ h)\left(\frac{3600\ s}{1\ h}\right)\left(\frac{1\ C}{1\ A \cdot s}\right) = 3.375 \times 10^4\ C
$$

At the anode:

$$
\text{moles O}_2 = (3.375 \times 10^4\ C)\left(\frac{1\ mol\ e^-}{96{,}500\ C}\right)\left(\frac{1\ mol\ O_2}{4\ mol\ e^-}\right) = 0.0874\ \text{mol O}_2
$$

The volume of 0.0874 mol O_2 at STP is given by

$$
V = \frac{nRT}{P}
$$

$$
= \frac{(0.0874\ \text{mol})(0.08206\ \text{L} \cdot \text{atm/K} \cdot \text{mol})(273.15\ \text{K})}{1\ \text{atm}} = 1.96\ \text{L O}_2
$$

Similarly, for hydrogen we write

$$
\text{moles H}_2 = (3.375 \times 10^4\ C)\left(\frac{1\ mol\ e^-}{96{,}500\ C}\right)\left(\frac{1\ mol\ H_2}{2\ mol\ e^-}\right) = 0.175\ \text{mol H}_2
$$

The volume of 0.175 mol H_2 at STP is given by

$$
V = \frac{nRT}{P}
$$

$$
= \frac{(0.175\ \text{mol})(0.08206\ \text{L} \cdot \text{atm/K} \cdot \text{mol})(273.15\ \text{K})}{1\ \text{atm}} = 3.92\ \text{L H}_2
$$

Think About It
The volume of H_2 is twice that of O_2 (see Figure 19.11), which is what we would expect based on Avogadro's law (at the same temperature and pressure, volume is directly proportional to the number of moles of gas: $V \propto n$) [◄◄ Section 11.4].

Practice Problem A A constant current of 0.912 A is passed through an electrolytic cell containing molten $MgCl_2$ for 18 h. What mass of Mg is produced?

Practice Problem B A constant current is passed through an electrolytic cell containing molten $MgCl_2$ for 12 h. If 4.83 L of Cl_2 (at STP) is produced at the anode, what is the current in amperes?

Electrolysis

19.7.1   In the electrolysis of molten $CaCl_2$, a current of 1.12 A is passed through the cell for 3.0 h. What is the mass of Ca produced at the cathode?

19.7.2   How long will a current of 0.995 A need to be passed through water (containing H_2SO_4) for 5.00 L of O_2 to be produced at STP?

19.7.3   The diagram shows an electrolytic cell being powered by a galvanic cell. Identify each of the electrodes from left to right as an anode or a cathode.

19.8   CORROSION

The term *corrosion* generally refers to the deterioration of a metal by an electrochemical process. There are many examples of corrosion, including rust on iron, tarnish on silver, and the green layer that forms on copper and brass. In this section we discuss the processes involved in corrosion and some of the measures taken to prevent it.

The formation of rust on iron requires oxygen and water. Although the reactions involved are quite complex and not completely understood, the main steps are believed to be as follows. A region of the metal's surface serves as the anode, where the following oxidation occurs:

$$Fe(s) \longrightarrow Fe^{2+}(aq) + 2e^-$$

The electrons given up by iron reduce atmospheric oxygen to water at the cathode, which is another region of the same metal's surface:

$$O_2(g) + 4H^+(aq) + 4e^- \longrightarrow 2H_2O(l)$$

The overall redox reaction is

$$2Fe(s) + O_2(g) + 4H^+(aq) \longrightarrow 2Fe^{2+}(g) + 2H_2O(l)$$

With data from Table 19.1, the standard potential for this process can be calculated as follows:

$$E°_{cell} = E°_{cathode} - E°_{anode}$$

$$= 1.23 \text{ V} - (-0.44 \text{ V})$$

$$= 1.67 \text{ V}$$

Multi 19.5
Electrochemistry—the production of aluminum

Note that this reaction occurs in an *acidic* medium; the H^+ ions are supplied in part by the reaction of atmospheric carbon dioxide with water to form the weak acid, carbonic acid (H_2CO_3).

The Fe^{2+} ions formed at the anode are further oxidized by oxygen as follows:

$$4Fe^{2+}(aq) + O_2(g) + (4 + 2x)H_2O(l) \longrightarrow 2Fe_2O_3 \cdot xH_2O(s) + 8H^+(aq)$$

This hydrated form of iron(III) oxide is known as rust. The amount of water associated with the iron(III) oxide varies, so we represent the formula as $Fe_2O_3 \cdot xH_2O$.

Figure 19.13 shows the mechanism of rust formation. The electric circuit is completed by the migration of electrons and ions; this is why rusting occurs so rapidly in saltwater. In cold climates, salts (NaCl or $CaCl_2$) spread on roadways to melt ice and snow are a major cause of rust formation on automobiles.

Other metals also undergo oxidation. Aluminum, for example, which is used to make airplanes, beverage cans, and aluminum foil, has a much greater tendency to oxidize than does iron. Unlike the corrosion of iron, though, corrosion of aluminum produces an insoluble layer of protective coating (Al_2O_3) that prevents the underlying metal from additional corrosion.

Coinage metals such as copper and silver also corrode, but much more slowly than either iron or aluminum:

$$Cu(s) \longrightarrow Cu^{2+}(aq) + 2e^-$$

$$Ag(s) \longrightarrow Ag^+(aq) + e^-$$

In ordinary atmospheric exposure, copper forms a layer of copper carbonate ($CuCO_3$), a green substance referred to as *patina*, that protects the metal underneath from further corrosion. Likewise, silverware that comes into contact with foodstuffs develops a layer of silver sulfide (Ag_2S).

A number of methods have been devised to protect metals from corrosion. Most of these methods are aimed at preventing rust formation. The most obvious approach is to coat the metal surface with paint to prevent exposure to the substances necessary for corrosion. If the paint is scratched or otherwise damaged, however, thus exposing even the smallest area of bare metal, rust will form under the paint layer. The surface of iron metal can be made inactive by a process called *passivation*. A thin oxide layer is formed when the metal is treated with a strong oxidizing agent such as concentrated nitric acid. A solution of sodium chromate is often added to cooling systems and radiators to prevent rust formation.

The tendency for iron to oxidize is greatly reduced when it is alloyed with certain other metals. For example, in stainless steel, an alloy of iron and chromium, a layer of chromium oxide forms that protects the iron from corrosion.

An iron container can be covered with a layer of another metal such as tin or zinc. A "tin" can is made by applying a thin layer of tin over iron. Rust formation is prevented as long as the tin layer remains intact. However, once the surface has been breached by a scratch or a dent, rusting

> **Student Annotation:** From Table 19.1:
>
> $Fe^{2+}(aq) + 2e^- \longrightarrow Fe(s)$ $E° = -0.44$ V
>
> $Al^{3+}(aq) + 3e^- \longrightarrow Al(s)$ $E° = -1.66$ V
>
> Al, with the more negative reduction potential, is less likely to be reduced (more likely to be oxidized) than Fe.

Multi 19.6
Electrochemistry—chrome plating

Figure 19.13 The electrochemical process involved in rust formation. The H^+ ions are supplied by H_2CO_3, which forms when CO_2 from air dissolves in water.

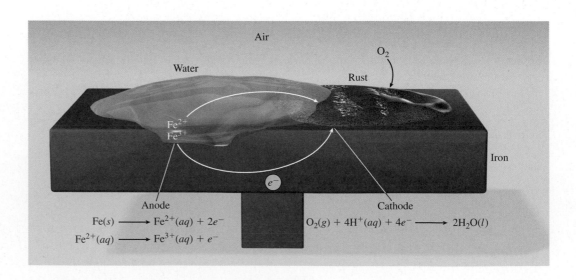

occurs rapidly. If we look up the standard reduction potentials in Table 19.1, we find that when tin and iron are in contact with each other, tin, with its greater reduction potential, acts as a cathode. Iron acts as an anode and is therefore oxidized.

$$Sn^{2+}(aq) + 2e^- \longrightarrow Sn(s) \qquad E° = -0.14 \text{ V}$$

$$Fe^{2+}(aq) + 2e^- \longrightarrow Fe(s) \qquad E° = -0.44 \text{ V}$$

Zinc-plating, or *galvanization,* protects iron from corrosion by a different mechanism. According to Table 19.1,

$$Zn^{2+}(aq) + 2e^- \longrightarrow Zn(s) \qquad E° = -0.76 \text{ V}$$

so zinc is *more* easily oxidized than iron. Like aluminum, zinc oxidizes to form a protective coating. Even when the zinc layer is compromised, though, and the underlying iron is exposed, zinc is still the more easily oxidized of the two metals and will act as the anode. Iron will be the cathode, thereby remaining reduced.

Galvanization is one example of *cathodic protection,* the process by which a metal is protected by being made the cathode in what amounts to a galvanic cell. Another example is the use of zinc or magnesium bars to protect underground storage tanks and ships. When a steel tank or hull is connected to a more easily oxidized metal, corrosion of the steel is prevented.

Learning Outcomes

- Use the half-reaction method to balance equations of oxidation-reduction reactions.
- Define key electrochemical terms: galvanic cell, anode, cathode, and salt bridge.
- Describe the conditions used to calculate the standard reduction potential for a reaction.
- Explain the importance of the standard hydrogen electrode.
- Determine the standard cell potential and the spontaneous cell reaction for a given chemical combination.
- Calculate $E°_{cell}$ of a reaction given the value of ΔG and K and interconvert between these three.

- Use the Nernst equation to calculate the E_{cell} of a cell under non-standard conditions.
- Define concentration cell.
- Distinguish between different types of batteries including: dry cell, alkaline, lead storage, lithium, and fuel cells.
- Describe in your own words the construction and operation of an electrolytic cell.
- Calculate the $E°$ of a given electrolytic cell.
- Cite examples of electrolytic cells.
- Explain overvoltage.
- Describe in your own words the basis of corrosion and galvanization.

Chapter Summary

SECTION 19.1

- Redox reactions are those in which oxidation numbers change. **Half-reactions** are the separated oxidation and reduction reactions that make up the overall redox reaction.
- Redox equations can be balanced via the half-reaction method, which allows for the addition of H_2O to balance O, H^+ to balance H, and OH^- for reactions taking place in basic solution.

SECTION 19.2

- An electrochemical cell in which a spontaneous chemical reaction generates a flow of electrons through a wire is called a **galvanic cell.**
- Half-reactions in a galvanic cell take place in separate compartments called **half-cells.** Half-cells contain **electrodes** in solutions and are connected via an external wire and by a **salt bridge.**

- The electrode at which reduction occurs is called the **cathode;** the electrode at which oxidation occurs is called the **anode.**
- The difference in electric potential between the cathode and the anode is the **cell potential** (E_{cell}).

SECTION 19.3

- We use **standard reduction potentials** ($E°$) to calculate the standard cell voltage or *standard cell potential* ($E°_{cell}$).
- Half-cell potentials are measured relative to the **standard hydrogen electrode (SHE),** the half-reaction for which has an arbitrarily defined standard reduction potential of zero.

SECTION 19.4

- $E°_{cell}$ is related to the standard free-energy change ($\Delta G°$) and to the equilibrium constant, K. A positive $E°_{cell}$ corresponds to a negative ($\Delta G°$) value and a large K value.

SECTION 19.5

- E_{cell} under other than standard-state conditions is determined from $E°_{cell}$ and the reaction quotient, Q, using the **Nernst equation.**
- A **concentration cell** has the same type of electrode and the same ion in solution (at different concentrations) in the anode and cathode compartments.

SECTION 19.6

- **Batteries** are portable, self-contained sources of electric energy consisting of galvanic cells—or a series of galvanic cells.

- **Fuel cells** are not really batteries but also supply electric energy via a spontaneous redox reaction. Reactants must be supplied constantly for a fuel cell to operate.

SECTION 19.7

- **Electrolysis** is the use of electric energy to drive a nonspontaneous redox reaction. An electrochemical cell used for this purpose is called an **electrolytic cell.**
- The voltage that must actually be supplied to drive a nonspontaneous redox reaction is greater than the calculated amount because of **overvoltage.**
- Electrolysis is used to recharge lead storage batteries, separate compounds into their constituent elements, and separate and purify metals.
- We can calculate the amount of a substance produced in electrolysis if we know the current applied to the cell and the length of time for which it is applied.

SECTION 19.8

- **Corrosion** is the undesirable oxidation of metals.
- Corrosion can be prevented by coating the metal surface with paint, a less easily oxidized metal, or a more easily oxidized metal such as zinc.
- The use of a more easily oxidized metal is known as *cathodic protection,* wherein the metal being protected is made the cathode in a galvanic cell. **Galvanization** is the cathodic protection of iron or steel using zinc.

Key Words

Anode, 809
Battery, 827
Cathode, 809
Cell potential (E_{cell}), 809
Concentration cell, 824
Corrosion, 835

Electrode, 809
Electrolysis, 830
Electrolytic cell, 830
Fuel cell, 829
Galvanic cell, 809

Galvanization, 837
Half-cell, 809
Half-reaction, 805
Nernst equation, 823
Overvoltage, 832

Salt bridge, 809
Standard hydrogen electrode (SHE), 813
Standard reduction potential ($E°$), 813

Key Equations

19.1 $E°_{cell} = E°_{cathode} - E°_{anode}$

19.2 $\Delta G = -nFE_{cell}$

19.3 $\Delta G° = -nFE°_{cell}$

19.4 $E°_{cell} = \dfrac{RT}{nF} \ln K$

19.5 $E°_{cell} = \dfrac{0.0592 \text{ V}}{n} \log K$ (at 25°C)

19.6 $E = E° - \dfrac{RT}{nF} \ln Q$

19.7 $E = E° - \dfrac{0.0592 \text{ V}}{n} \log Q$

Questions and Problems

SECTION 19.1:   BALANCING REDOX REACTIONS

Problems

19.1 Balance the following redox equations by the half-reaction method:
(a) $H_2O_2 + Fe^{2+} \longrightarrow Fe^{3+} + H_2O$ (in acidic solution)
(b) $Cu + HNO_3 \longrightarrow Cu^{2+} + NO + H_2O$ (in acidic solution)
(c) $CN^- + MnO_4^- \longrightarrow CNO^- + MnO_2$ (in basic solution)
(d) $Br_2 \longrightarrow BrO_3^- + Br^-$ (in basic solution)
(e) $S_2O_3^{2-} + I_2 \longrightarrow I^- + S_4O_6^{2-}$ (in acidic solution)

19.2 Balance the following redox equations by the half-reaction method:
(a) $Mn^{2+} + H_2O_2 \longrightarrow MnO_2 + H_2O$ (in basic solution)
(b) $Bi(OH)_3 + SnO_2^{2-} \longrightarrow SnO_3^{2-} + Bi$ (in basic solution)
(c) $Cr_2O_7^{2-} + C_2O_4^{2-} \longrightarrow Cr^{3+} + CO_2$ (in acidic solution)
(d) $ClO_3^- + Cl^- \longrightarrow Cl_2 + ClO_2$ (in acidic solution)
(e) $Mn^{2+} + BiO_3^- \longrightarrow Bi^{3+} + MnO_4^-$ (in acidic solution)

SECTION 19.2:   GALVANIC CELLS

Visualizing Chemistry
Figure 19.1

VC 19.1 In the first scene of the animation, when a zinc bar is immersed in an aqueous copper sulfate solution, solid copper deposits on the bar. What reaction would take place if a *copper* bar were immersed in an aqueous *zinc* sulfate solution?
(a) No reaction would take place.
(b) Solid copper would still deposit on the bar.
(c) Solid zinc would deposit on the bar.

VC 19.2 What causes the change in the potential of the galvanic cell in Figure 19.1 as the cell operates?
(a) Changes in the sizes of the zinc and copper electrodes.
(b) Changes in the concentrations of zinc and copper ions.
(c) Changes in the volumes of solutions in the half-cells.

VC 19.3 Why does the color of the blue solution in the galvanic cell (Figure 19.1) fade as the cell operates?
(a) Blue Cu^{2+} ions are replaced by colorless Zn^{2+} ions solution.
(b) Blue Cu^{2+} ions are removed from solution by reduction.
(c) Blue Cu^{2+} ions are removed from solution by oxidation.

VC 19.4 What happens to the mass of the copper electrode in the galvanic cell in Figure 19.1 as the cell operates?
(a) It increases.
(b) It decreases.
(c) It does not change.

Review Questions

19.3 Define the following terms: *anode, cathode, cell voltage, electromotive force, standard reduction potential.*

19.4 Describe the basic features of a galvanic cell. Why are the two components of the cell separated from each other?

19.5 What is the function of a salt bridge? What kind of electrolyte should be used in a salt bridge?

19.6 What is a cell diagram? Write the cell diagram for a galvanic cell consisting of an Al electrode placed in a $1\ M$ $Al(NO_3)_3$ solution and an Ag electrode placed in a $1\ M$ $AgNO_3$ solution.

19.7 What is the difference between the half-reactions discussed in redox processes in Chapter 4 and the half-cell reactions discussed in Section 19.2?

SECTION 19.3:   STANDARD REDUCTION POTENTIALS

Review Questions

19.8 Discuss the spontaneity of an electrochemical reaction in terms of its standard emf (E_{cell}°).

19.9 After operating a Daniell cell (see Figure 19.1) for a few minutes, the cell emf begins to drop. Explain.

Problems

19.10 Calculate the standard emf of a cell that uses the Mg/Mg^{2+} and Cu/Cu^{2+} half-cell reactions at 25°C. Write the equation for the cell reaction that occurs under standard-state conditions.

19.11 Calculate the standard emf of a cell that uses Ag/Ag^+ and Al/Al^{3+} half-cell reactions. Write the cell reaction that occurs under standard-state conditions.

19.12 Predict whether Fe^{3+} can oxidize I^- to I_2 under standard-state conditions.

19.13 Which of the following reagents can oxidize H_2O to $O_2(g)$ under standard-state conditions: $H^+(aq)$, $Cl^-(aq)$, $Cl_2(g)$, $Cu^{2+}(aq)$, $Pb^{2+}(aq)$, $MnO_4^-(aq)$ (in acid)?

19.14 Consider the following half-reactions:

$$MnO_4^-(aq) + 8H^+(aq) + 5e^- \longrightarrow Mn^{2+}(aq) + 4H_2O(l)$$

$$NO_3^-(aq) + 4H^+(aq) + 3e^- \longrightarrow NO(g) + 2H_2O(l)$$

Predict whether NO_3^- ions will oxidize Mn^{2+} to MnO_4^- under standard-state conditions.

19.15 Predict whether the following reactions would occur spontaneously in aqueous solution at 25°C. Assume that the initial concentrations of dissolved species are all 1.0 M.
(a) $Ca(s) + Cd^{2+}(aq) \longrightarrow Ca^{2+}(aq) + Cd(s)$
(b) $2Br^-(aq) + Sn^{2+}(aq) \longrightarrow Br_2(l) + Sn(s)$
(c) $2Ag(s) + Ni^{2+}(aq) \longrightarrow 2Ag^+(aq) + Ni(s)$
(d) $Cu^+(aq) + Fe^{3+}(aq) \longrightarrow Cu^{2+}(aq) + Fe^{2+}(aq)$

19.16 Which species in each pair is a better oxidizing agent under standard-state conditions: (a) Br_2 or Au^{3+}, (b) H_2 or Ag^+, (c) Cd^{2+} or Cr^{3+}, (d) O_2 in acidic media or O_2 in basic media?

19.17   Which species in each pair is a better reducing agent under standard-state conditions: (a) Na or Li, (b) H_2 or I_2, (c) Fe^{2+} or Ag, (d) Br^- or Co^{2+}?

SECTION 19.4:   SPONTANEITY OF REDOX REACTIONS UNDER STANDARD-STATE CONDITIONS

Review Questions

19.18   Write the equations relating $\Delta G°$ and K to the standard emf of a cell. Define all the terms.

19.19   Compare the ease of measuring the equilibrium constant electrochemically with that by chemical means (see Equation 18.14).

Problems

19.20   Use the information in Table 2.1, and calculate the Faraday constant.

19.21   What is the equilibrium constant for the following reaction at 25°C?

$$Mg(s) + Zn^{2+}(aq) \rightleftharpoons Mg^{2+}(aq) + Zn(s)$$

19.22   The equilibrium constant for the reaction

$$Sr(s) + Mg^{2+}(aq) \rightleftharpoons Sr^{2+}(aq) + Mg(s)$$

is 2.69×10^{12} at 25°C. Calculate $E°$ for a cell made up of Sr/Sr^{2+} and Mg/Mg^{2+} half-cells.

19.23   Use the standard reduction potentials to find the equilibrium constant for each of the following reactions at 25°C:
(a) $Br_2(l) + 2I^-(aq) \rightleftharpoons 2Br^-(aq) + I_2(s)$
(b) $2Ce^{4+}(aq) + 2Cl^-(aq) \rightleftharpoons Cl_2(g) + 2Ce^{3+}(aq)$
(c) $5Fe^{2+}(aq) + MnO_4^-(aq) + 8H^+(aq) \rightleftharpoons$
$Mn^{2+}(aq) + 4H_2O + 5Fe^{3+}(aq)$

19.24   Calculate $\Delta G°$ and K_c for the following reactions at 25°C:
(a) $Mg(s) + Pb^{2+}(aq) \rightleftharpoons Mg^{2+}(aq) + Pb(s)$
(b) $O_2(g) + 4H^+(aq) + 4Fe^{2+}(aq) \rightleftharpoons$
$2H_2O(l) + 4Fe^{3+}(aq)$
(c) $2Al(s) + 3I_2(s) \rightleftharpoons 2Al^{3+}(aq) + 6I^-(aq)$

19.25   Under standard-state conditions, what spontaneous reaction will occur in aqueous solution among the ions Ce^{4+}, Ce^{3+}, Fe^{3+}, and Fe^{2+}? Calculate $\Delta G°$ and K_c for the reaction.

19.26   Given that $E° = 0.52$ V for the reduction $Cu^+(aq) + e^- \longrightarrow Cu(s)$, calculate $E°$, $\Delta G°$, and K for the following reaction at 25°C:

$$2Cu^+(aq) \rightleftharpoons Cu^{2+}(aq) + Cu(s)$$

19.27   Balance (in acidic medium) the equation for the oxidation of tin from an amalgam filling when it comes into contact with aluminum foil, and calculate the standard cell potential for the reaction.

19.28   Calculate the standard free-energy change and the equilibrium constant at 25°C for the reaction in Problem 19.27.

SECTION 19.5:   SPONTANEITY OF REDOX REACTIONS UNDER CONDITIONS OTHER THAN STANDARD STATE

Review Question

19.29   Write the Nernst equation, and explain all the terms.

Problems

19.30   Write the Nernst equation for the following processes at some temperature T:
(a) $Mg(s) + Sn^{2+}(aq) \rightleftharpoons Mg^{2+}(aq) + Sn(s)$
(b) $2Cr(s) + 3Pb^{2+}(aq) \rightleftharpoons 2Cr^{3+}(aq) + 3Pb(s)$

19.31   What is the potential of a cell made up of Zn/Zn^{2+} and Cu/Cu^{2+} half-cells at 25°C if $[Zn^{2+}] = 0.25$ M and $[Cu^{2+}] = 0.15$ M?

19.32   Calculate $E°$, E, and ΔG for the following cell reactions.
(a) $Mg(s) + Sn^{2+}(aq) \rightleftharpoons Mg^{2+}(aq) + Sn(s)$
$[Mg^{2+}] = 0.045$ M, $[Sn^{2+}] = 0.035$ M
(b) $3Zn(s) + 2Cr^{3+}(aq) \rightleftharpoons 3Zn^{2+}(aq) + 2Cr(s)$
$[Cr^{3+}] = 0.010$ M, $[Zn^{2+}] = 0.0085$ M

19.33   Calculate the standard potential of the cell consisting of the Zn/Zn^{2+} half-cell and the SHE. What will the emf of the cell be if $[Zn^{2+}] = 0.45$ M, $P_{H_2} = 2.0$ atm, and $[H^+] = 1.8$ M?

19.34   What is the emf of a cell consisting of a Pb^{2+}/Pb half-cell and a $Pt/H^+/H_2$ half-cell if $[Pb^{2+}] = 0.10$ M, $[H] = 0.050$ M, and $P_{H_2} = 1.0$ atm?

19.35   Referring to the arrangement in Figure 19.1, calculate the $[Cu^{2+}]/[Zn^{2+}]$ ratio at which the following reaction is spontaneous at 25°C:

$$Cu(s) + Zn^{2+}(aq) \longrightarrow Cu^{2+}(aq) + Zn(s)$$

19.36   Calculate the emf of the following concentration cell:

$$Mg(s) \,|\, Mg^{2+}(0.24\ M) \,\|\, Mg^{2+}(0.53\ M) \,|\, Mg(s)$$

SECTION 19.6:   BATTERIES

Review Questions

19.37   What is a battery? Describe several types of batteries.

19.38   Explain the differences between a primary galvanic cell—one that is not rechargeable—and a storage cell (for example, the lead storage battery), which is rechargeable.

19.39   Discuss the advantages and disadvantages of fuel cells over conventional power plants in producing electricity.

Problems

19.40   The hydrogen-oxygen fuel cell is described in Section 19.6. (a) What volume of $H_2(g)$, stored at 25°C at a pressure of 155 atm, would be needed to run an electric motor drawing a current of 8.5 A for 3.0 h? (b) What volume (in liters) of air at 25°C and 1.00 atm will have to pass into the cell per minute to run the motor? Assume that air is 20 percent O_2 by volume and that all the O_2 is consumed in the cell. The other components of air do not affect the fuel-cell reactions. Assume ideal gas behavior.

19.41 Calculate the standard emf of the propane fuel cell discussed on page 830 at 25°C, given that ΔG_f° for propane is −23.5 kJ/mol.

SECTION 19.7: ELECTROLYSIS

Review Questions

19.42 What is the difference between a galvanic cell (such as a Daniell cell) and an electrolytic cell?

19.43 Define the term *overvoltage*. How does overvoltage affect electrolytic processes?

Problems

19.44 Calculate the number of grams of copper metal that can be produced by supplying 1.00 F to a solution of Cu^{2+} ions.

19.45 The half-reaction at an electrode is

$$Mg^{2+}(molten) + 2e^- \longrightarrow Mg(s)$$

Calculate the number of grams of magnesium that can be produced by supplying 1.00 F to the electrode.

19.46 Consider the electrolysis of molten barium chloride ($BaCl_2$). (a) Write the half-reactions. (b) How many grams of barium metal can be produced by supplying 0.50 A for 30 min?

19.47 Considering only the cost of electricity, would it be cheaper to produce a ton of sodium or a ton of aluminum by electrolysis?

19.48 If the cost of electricity to produce magnesium by the electrolysis of molten magnesium chloride is $155 per ton of metal, what is the cost (in dollars) of the electricity necessary to produce (a) 10.0 tons of aluminum, (b) 30.0 tons of sodium, and (c) 50.0 tons of calcium?

19.49 One of the half-reactions for the electrolysis of water is

$$2H_2O(l) \longrightarrow O_2(g) + 4H^+(aq) + 4e^-$$

If 0.076 L of O_2 is collected at 25°C and 755 mmHg, how many faradays of electricity had to pass through the solution?

19.50 How many faradays of electricity are required to produce (a) 0.84 L of O_2 at exactly 1 atm and 25°C from aqueous H_2SO_4 solution, (b) 1.50 L of Cl_2 at 750 mmHg and 20°C from molten NaCl, and (c) 6.0 g of Sn from molten $SnCl_2$?

19.51 Calculate the amounts of Cu and Br_2 produced in 1.0 h at inert electrodes in a solution of $CuBr_2$ by a current of 4.50 A.

19.52 In the electrolysis of an aqueous $AgNO_3$ solution, 0.67 g of Ag is deposited after a certain period of time. (a) Write the half-reaction for the reduction of Ag^+. (b) What is the probable oxidation half-reaction? (c) Calculate the quantity of electricity used (in coulombs).

19.53 A steady current was passed through molten $CoSO_4$ until 2.35 g of metallic cobalt was produced. Calculate the number of coulombs of electricity used.

19.54 A constant electric current flows for 3.75 h through two electrolytic cells connected in series. One contains a solution of $AgNO_3$ and the second a solution of $CuCl_2$. During this time, 2.00 g of silver is deposited in the first cell. (a) How many grams of copper are deposited in the second cell? (b) What is the current flowing (in amperes)?

19.55 What is the hourly production rate of chlorine gas (in kg) from an electrolytic cell using aqueous NaCl electrolyte and carrying a current of 1.500×10^3 A? The anode efficiency for the oxidation of Cl^- is 93.0 percent.

19.56 Chromium plating is applied by electrolysis to objects suspended in a dichromate solution, according to the following (unbalanced) half-reaction:

$$Cr_2O_7^{2-}(aq) + e^- + H^+(aq) \longrightarrow Cr(s) + H_2O(l)$$

How long (in hours) would it take to apply a chromium plating 1.0×10^{-2} mm thick to a car bumper with a surface area of 0.25 m² in an electrolytic cell carrying a current of 25.0 A? (The density of chromium is 7.19 g/cm³.)

19.57 The passage of a current of 0.750 A for 25.0 min deposited 0.369 g of copper from a $CuSO_4$ solution. From this information, calculate the molar mass of copper.

19.58 A quantity of 0.300 g of copper was deposited from a $CuSO_4$ solution by passing a current of 3.00 A through the solution for 304 s. Calculate the value of the Faraday constant.

19.59 In a certain electrolysis experiment, 1.44 g of Ag were deposited in one cell (containing an aqueous $AgNO_3$ solution), while 0.120 g of an unknown metal X was deposited in another cell (containing an aqueous XCl_3 solution) in series with the $AgNO_3$ cell. Calculate the molar mass of X.

19.60 One of the half-reactions for the electrolysis of water is

$$2H^+(aq) + 2e^- \longrightarrow H_2(g)$$

If 0.845 L of H_2 is collected at 25°C and 782 mmHg, how many faradays of electricity had to pass through the solution?

SECTION 19.8: CORROSION

Review Questions

19.61 Steel hardware, including nuts and bolts, is often coated with a thin plating of cadmium. Explain the function of the cadmium layer.

19.62 "Galvanized iron" is steel sheet that has been coated with zinc; "tin" cans are made of steel sheet coated with tin. Discuss the functions of these coatings and the electrochemistry of the corrosion reactions that occur if an electrolyte contacts the scratched surface of a galvanized iron sheet or a tin can.

19.63 Tarnished silver contains Ag_2S. The tarnish can be removed by placing silverware in an aluminum pan containing an inert electrolyte solution, such as NaCl. Explain the electrochemical principle for this procedure. [The standard reduction potential for the half-cell reaction $Ag_2S(s) + 2e^- \longrightarrow 2Ag(s) + S^{2-}(aq)$ is -0.71 V.]

19.64 How does the tendency of iron to rust depend on the pH of the solution?

ADDITIONAL PROBLEMS

19.65 For each of the following redox reactions, (i) write the half-reactions, (ii) write a balanced equation for the whole reaction, (iii) determine in which direction the reaction will proceed spontaneously under standard-state conditions:
   (a) $H_2(g) + Ni^{2+}(aq) \longrightarrow H^+(aq) + Ni(s)$
   (b) $MnO_4^-(aq) + Cl^-(aq) \longrightarrow Mn^{2+}(aq) + Cl_2(g)$ (in acid solution)
   (c) $Cr(s) + Zn^{2+}(aq) \longrightarrow Cr^{3+}(aq) + Zn(s)$

19.66 The oxidation of 25.0 mL of a solution containing Fe^{2+} requires 26.0 mL of 0.0250 M $K_2Cr_2O_7$ in acidic solution. Balance the following equation, and calculate the molar concentration of Fe^{2+}:

$$Cr_2O_7^{2-} + Fe^{2+} + H^+ \longrightarrow Cr^{3+} + Fe^{3+}$$

19.67 The SO_2 present in air is mainly responsible for the phenomenon of acid rain. The concentration of SO_2 can be determined by titrating against a standard permanganate solution as follows:

$$5SO_2 + 2MnO_4^- + 2H_2O \longrightarrow 5SO_4^{2-} + 2Mn^{2+} + 4H^+$$

Calculate the number of grams of SO_2 in a sample of air if 7.37 mL of 0.00800 M $KMnO_4$ solution is required for the titration.

19.68 A sample of iron ore weighing 0.2792 g was dissolved in an excess of a dilute acid solution. All the iron was first converted to Fe(II) ions. The solution then required 23.30 mL of 0.0194 M $KMnO_4$ for oxidation to Fe(III) ions. Calculate the percent by mass of iron in the ore.

19.69 The concentration of a hydrogen peroxide solution can be conveniently determined by titration against a standardized potassium permanganate solution in an acidic medium according to the following unbalanced equation:

$$MnO_4^- + H_2O_2 \longrightarrow O_2 + Mn^{2+}$$

(a) Balance this equation. (b) If 36.44 mL of a 0.01652 M $KMnO_4$ solution is required to completely oxidize 25.00 mL of an H_2O_2 solution, calculate the molarity of the H_2O_2 solution.

19.70 Oxalic acid ($H_2C_2O_4$) is present in many plants and vegetables. (a) Balance the following equation in acid solution:

$$MnO_4^- + C_2O_4^{2-} \longrightarrow Mn^{2+} + CO_2$$

(b) If a 1.00-g sample of plant matter requires 24.0 mL of 0.0100 M $KMnO_4$ solution to reach the equivalence point, what is the percent by mass of $H_2C_2O_4$ in the sample?

19.71 Calcium oxalate (CaC_2O_4) is insoluble in water. This property has been used to determine the amount of Ca^{2+} ions in blood. The calcium oxalate isolated from blood is dissolved in acid and titrated against a standardized

$KMnO_4$ solution as described in Problem 19.70. In one test it is found that the calcium oxalate isolated from a 10.0-mL sample of blood requires 24.2 mL of 9.56×10^{-4} M $KMnO_4$ for titration. Calculate the number of milligrams of calcium per milliliter of blood.

19.72 Complete the following table. State whether the cell reaction is spontaneous, nonspontaneous, or at equilibrium.

E	ΔG	**Cell Reaction**
>0		
	>0	
$=0$		

19.73 From the following information, calculate the solubility product of AgBr:

$$Ag^+(aq) + e^- \longrightarrow Ag(s) \qquad E° = 0.80 \text{ V}$$

$$AgBr(s) + e^- \longrightarrow Ag(s) + Br^-(aq) \qquad E° = 0.07 \text{ V}$$

19.74 Consider a galvanic cell composed of the SHE and a half-cell using the reaction $Ag^+(aq) + e^- \longrightarrow Ag(s)$. (a) Calculate the standard cell potential. (b) What is the spontaneous cell reaction under standard-state conditions? (c) Calculate the cell potential when $[H^+]$ in the hydrogen electrode is changed to (i) 1.0×10^{-2} M and (ii) 1.0×10^{-5} M, all other reagents being held at standard-state conditions. (d) Based on this cell arrangement, suggest a design for a pH meter.

19.75 A galvanic cell consists of a silver electrode in contact with 346 mL of 0.100 M $AgNO_3$ solution and a magnesium electrode in contact with 288 mL of 0.100 M $Mg(NO_3)_2$ solution. (a) Calculate E for the cell at 25°C. (b) A current is drawn from the cell until 1.20 g of silver has been deposited at the silver electrode. Calculate E for the cell at this stage of operation.

19.76 Explain why chlorine gas can be prepared by electrolyzing an aqueous solution of NaCl but fluorine gas cannot be prepared by electrolyzing an aqueous solution of NaF.

19.77 Calculate the emf of the following concentration cell at 25°C:

$$Cu(s) \,|\, Cu^{2+}(0.080 \, M) \,\|\, Cu^{2+}(1.2 \, M) \,|\, Cu(s)$$

19.78 The cathode reaction in the Leclanché cell is given by

$$2MnO_2(s) + Zn^{2+}(aq) + 2e^- \longrightarrow ZnMn_2O_4(s)$$

If a Leclanché cell produces a current of 0.0050 A, calculate how many hours this current supply will last if there is initially 4.0 g of MnO_2 present in the cell. Assume that there is an excess of Zn^{2+} ions.

19.79 For a number of years, it was not clear whether mercury(I) ions existed in solution as Hg^+ or as Hg_2^{2+}. To distinguish between these two possibilities, we could set up the following system:

$$Hg(l) \,|\, \text{soln A} \,\|\, \text{soln B} \,|\, Hg(l)$$

where soln A contained 0.263 g mercury(I) nitrate per liter and soln B contained 2.63 g mercury(I) nitrate per liter. If the measured emf of such a cell is 0.0289 V at 18°C, what can you deduce about the nature of the mercury(I) ions?

19.80 An aqueous KI solution to which a few drops of phenolphthalein have been added is electrolyzed using an apparatus like the one shown here:

Describe what you would observe at the anode and the cathode. (*Hint:* Molecular iodine is only slightly soluble in water, but in the presence of I^- ions, it forms the brown color of I_3^- ions. See Problem 13.114.)

19.81 A piece of magnesium metal weighing 1.56 g is placed in 100.0 mL of 0.100 M AgNO$_3$ at 25°C. Calculate [Mg^{2+}] and [Ag$^+$] in solution at equilibrium. What is the mass of the magnesium left? The volume remains constant.

19.82 Describe an experiment that would enable you to determine which is the cathode and which is the anode in a galvanic cell using copper and zinc electrodes.

19.83 An acidified solution was electrolyzed using copper electrodes. A constant current of 1.18 A caused the anode to lose 0.584 g after 1.52×10^3 s. (a) What is the gas produced at the cathode, and what is its volume at STP? (b) Given that the charge of an electron is 1.6022×10^{-19} C, calculate Avogadro's number. Assume that copper is oxidized to Cu^{2+} ions.

19.84 In a certain electrolysis experiment involving Al^{3+} ions, 60.2 g of Al is recovered when a current of 0.352 A is used. How many minutes did the electrolysis last?

19.85 Consider the oxidation of ammonia:

$$4NH_3(g) + 3O_2(g) \longrightarrow 2N_2(g) + 6H_2O(l)$$

(a) Calculate the $\Delta G°$ for the reaction. (b) If this reaction were used in a fuel cell, what would the standard cell potential be?

19.86 When an aqueous solution containing gold(III) salt is electrolyzed, metallic gold is deposited at the cathode and oxygen gas is generated at the anode. (a) If 9.26 g of Au is deposited at the cathode, calculate the volume (in liters) of O$_2$ generated at 23°C and 747 mmHg. (b) What is the current used if the electrolytic process took 2.00 h?

19.87 In an electrolysis experiment, a student passes the same quantity of electricity through two electrolytic cells, one containing a silver salt and the other a gold salt. Over a certain period of time, the student finds that 2.64 g of Ag and 1.61 g of Au are deposited at the cathodes. What is the oxidation state of gold in the gold salt?

19.88 Consider the electrochemical cell represented by the following diagram:

$$Pb(s) \,|\, Pb(NO_3)_2 \,(0.60\,M) \,\|\, AgNO_3 \,(0.40\,M) \,|\, Ag(s)$$

Determine the initial value of E_{cell} under the conditions shown in the cell diagram; and determine the initial value of E_{cell} if [Ag$^+$] were increased by a factor of 4 at 25°C.

19.89 Given that

$$2Hg^{2+}(aq) + 2e^- \longrightarrow Hg_2^{2+}(aq) \qquad E° = 0.92 \text{ V}$$

$$Hg_2^{2+}(aq) + 2e^- \longrightarrow 2Hg(l) \qquad E° = 0.85 \text{ V}$$

calculate $\Delta G°$ and K for the following process at 25°C:

$$Hg_2^{2+}(aq) \longrightarrow Hg^{2+}(aq) + Hg(l)$$

(The preceding reaction is an example of a *disproportionation reaction* in which an element in one oxidation state is both oxidized and reduced.)

19.90 Fluorine (F$_2$) is obtained by the electrolysis of liquid hydrogen fluoride (HF) containing potassium fluoride (KF). (a) Write the half-cell reactions and the overall reaction for the process. (b) What is the purpose of KF? (c) Calculate the volume of F$_2$ (in liters) collected at 24.0°C and 1.2 atm after electrolyzing the solution for 15 h at a current of 502 A.

19.91 A 300-mL solution of NaCl was electrolyzed for 6.00 min. If the pH of the final solution was 12.24, calculate the average current used.

19.92 Industrially, copper is purified by electrolysis. The impure copper acts as the anode, and the cathode is made of pure copper. The electrodes are immersed in a CuSO$_4$ solution. During electrolysis, copper at the anode enters the solution as Cu^{2+} while Cu^{2+} ions are reduced at the cathode. (a) Write half-cell reactions and the overall reaction for the electrolytic process. (b) Suppose the anode was contaminated with Zn and Ag. Explain what happens to these impurities during electrolysis. (c) How many hours will it take to obtain 1.00 kg of Cu at a current of 18.9 A?

19.93 An aqueous solution of a platinum salt is electrolyzed at a current of 2.50 A for 2.00 h. As a result, 9.09 g of metallic Pt is formed at the cathode. Calculate the charge on the Pt ions in this solution.

19.94 Consider a galvanic cell consisting of a magnesium electrode in contact with 1.0 M Mg(NO$_3$)$_2$ and a cadmium electrode in contact with 1.0 M Cd(NO$_3$)$_2$. Calculate $E°$ for the cell, and draw a diagram showing the cathode, anode, and direction of electron flow.

19.95 A current of 6.00 A passes through an electrolytic cell containing dilute sulfuric acid for 3.40 h. If the volume of O$_2$ gas generated at the anode is 4.26 L (at STP), calculate the charge (in coulombs) on an electron.

19.96 Gold will not dissolve in either concentrated nitric acid or concentrated hydrochloric acid. However, the metal does dissolve in a mixture of the acids (one part HNO$_3$ and three parts HCl by volume), called *aqua regia*. (a) Write a balanced equation for this reaction.

(*Hint:* Among the products are $HAuCl_4$ and NO_2.)
(b) What is the function of HCl?

19.97 Explain why most useful galvanic cells give voltages of no more than 1.5 to 2.5 V. What are the prospects for developing practical galvanic cells with voltages of 5 V or more?

19.98 A silver rod and a SHE are dipped into a saturated aqueous solution of silver oxalate ($Ag_2C_2O_4$), at 25°C. The measured potential difference between the rod and the SHE is 0.589 V, the rod being positive. Calculate the solubility product constant for silver oxalate.

19.99 Zinc is an amphoteric metal; that is, it reacts with both acids and bases. The standard reduction potential is −1.36 V for the reaction

$$Zn(OH)_4^{2-}(aq) + 2e^- \longrightarrow Zn(s) + 4OH^-(aq)$$

Calculate the formation constant (K_f) for the reaction

$$Zn^{2+}(aq) + 4OH^-(aq) \rightleftharpoons Zn(OH)_4^{2-}(aq)$$

19.100 Use the data in Table 19.1 to determine whether or not hydrogen peroxide will undergo disproportionation in an acid medium: $2H_2O_2 \longrightarrow 2H_2O + O_2$.

19.101 The magnitudes (but *not* the signs) of the standard reduction potentials of two metals X and Y are

$$Y^{2+} + 2e^- \longrightarrow Y \qquad |E^\circ| = 0.34 \text{ V}$$

$$X^{2+} + 2e^- \longrightarrow X \qquad |E^\circ| = 0.25 \text{ V}$$

where the $\|$ notation denotes that only the magnitude (but not the sign) of the E° value is shown. When the half-cells of X and Y are connected, electrons flow from X to Y. When X is connected to a SHE, electrons flow from X to SHE. (a) Are the E° values of the half-reactions positive or negative? (b) What is the standard emf of a cell made up of X and Y?

19.102 A galvanic cell is constructed as follows. One half-cell consists of a platinum wire immersed in a solution containing 1.0 M Sn^{2+} and 1.0 M Sn^{4+}; the other half-cell has a thallium rod immersed in a solution of 1.0 M Tl^+. (a) Write the half-cell reactions and the overall reaction. (b) What is the equilibrium constant at 25°C? (c) What is the cell voltage if the Tl^+ concentration is increased 10-fold? ($E^\circ_{Tl^+/Tl} = -0.34$ V.)

19.103 Given the standard reduction potential for Au^{3+} in Table 19.1 and

$$Au^+(aq) + e^- \longrightarrow Au(s) \qquad E^\circ = 1.69 \text{ V}$$

answer the following questions. (a) Why does gold not tarnish in air? (b) Will the following disproportionation occur spontaneously?

$$3Au^+(aq) \longrightarrow Au^{3+}(aq) + 2Au(s)$$

(c) Predict the reaction between gold and fluorine gas.

19.104 The ingestion of a very small quantity of mercury is not considered too harmful. Would this statement still hold if the gastric juice in your stomach were mostly nitric acid instead of hydrochloric acid?

19.105 When 25.0 mL of a solution containing both Fe^{2+} and Fe^{3+} ions is titrated with 23.0 mL of 0.0200 M $KMnO_4$

(in dilute sulfuric acid), all the Fe^{2+} ions are oxidized to Fe^{3+} ions. Next, the solution is treated with Zn metal to convert all the Fe^{3+} ions to Fe^{2+} ions. Finally, 40.0 mL of the same $KMnO_4$ solution is added to the solution to oxidize the Fe^{2+} ions to Fe^{3+}. Calculate the molar concentrations of Fe^{2+} and Fe^{3+} in the original solution.

19.106 Consider the Daniell cell in Figure 19.1. When viewed externally, the anode appears negative and the cathode positive (electrons are flowing from the anode to the cathode). Yet in solution anions are moving toward the anode, which means that it must appear positive to the anions. Because the anode cannot simultaneously be negative and positive, give an explanation for this apparently contradictory situation.

19.107 Use the data in Table 19.1 to show that the decomposition of H_2O_2 (a disproportionation reaction) is spontaneous at 25°C:

$$2H_2O_2(aq) \longrightarrow 2H_2O(l) + O_2(g)$$

19.108 The concentration of sulfuric acid in the lead-storage battery of an automobile over a period of time has decreased from 38.0 percent by mass (density = 1.29 g/mL) to 26.0 percent by mass (1.19 g/mL). Assume the volume of the acid remains constant at 724 mL. (a) Calculate the total charge in coulombs supplied by the battery. (b) How long (in hours) will it take to recharge the battery back to the original sulfuric acid concentration using a current of 22.4 A?

19.109 Consider a Daniell cell operating under nonstandard-state conditions. Suppose that the cell's reaction is multiplied by 2. What effect does this have on each of the following quantities in the Nernst equation: (a) E, (b) E°, (c) Q, (d) $\ln Q$, (e) n?

19.110 A spoon was silver-plated electrolytically in an $AgNO_3$ solution. (a) Sketch a diagram for the process. (b) If 0.884 g of Ag was deposited on the spoon at a constant current of 18.5 mA, how long (in min) did the electrolysis take?

19.111 Comment on whether F_2 will become a stronger oxidizing agent with increasing H^+ concentration.

19.112 In recent years there has been much interest in electric cars. List some advantages and disadvantages of electric cars compared to automobiles with internal combustion engines.

19.113 Calculate the pressure of H_2 (in atm) required to maintain equilibrium with respect to the following reaction at 25°C,

$$Pb(s) + 2H^+(aq) \rightleftharpoons Pb^{2+}(aq) + H_2(g)$$

given that [Pb^{2+}] = 0.035 M and the solution is buffered at pH 1.60.

19.114 A piece of magnesium ribbon and a copper wire are partially immersed in a 0.1 M HCl solution in a beaker. The metals are joined externally by another piece of metal wire. Bubbles are seen to evolve at both the Mg and Cu surfaces. (a) Write equations representing the reactions occurring at the metals. (b) What visual evidence would you seek to show that Cu is not oxidized to Cu^{2+}? (c) At some stage, NaOH solution is added to the beaker to neutralize the HCl acid. Upon further addition of NaOH, a white precipitate forms. What is it?

19.115 The zinc-air battery shows much promise for electric cars because it is lightweight and rechargeable:

The net transformation is $Zn(s) + \frac{1}{2}O_2(g) \longrightarrow ZnO(s)$. (a) Write the half-reactions at the zinc-air electrodes, and calculate the standard emf of the battery at 25°C. (b) Calculate the emf under actual operating conditions when the partial pressure of oxygen is 0.21 atm. (c) What is the energy density (measured as the energy in kilojoules that can be obtained from 1 kg of the metal) of the zinc electrode? (d) If a current of 2.1×10^5 A is to be drawn from a zinc-air battery system, what volume of air (in liters) would need to be supplied to the battery every second? Assume that the temperature is 25°C and the partial pressure of oxygen is 0.21 atm.

19.116 Calculate $E°$ for the reactions of mercury with (a) 1 *M* HCl and (b) 1 *M* HNO$_3$. Which acid will oxidize Hg to Hg_2^{2+} under standard-state conditions? Can you identify which pictured test tube contains HNO$_3$ and Hg and which contains HCl and Hg?

19.117 Because all alkali metals react with water, it is not possible to measure the standard reduction potentials of these metals directly as in the case of, say, zinc. An indirect method is to consider the following hypothetical reaction:

$$Li^+(aq) + \frac{1}{2}H_2(g) \longrightarrow Li(s) + H^+(aq)$$

Using the appropriate equation presented in this chapter and the thermodynamic data in Appendix 2, calculate $E°$ for $Li^+(aq) + e^- \longrightarrow Li(s)$ at 298 K. Use 96,485.338 C/mol e^- for the Faraday constant. Compare your result with that listed in Table 19.1.

19.118 A galvanic cell using Mg/Mg^{2+} and Cu/Cu^{2+} half-cells operates under standard-state conditions at 25°C, and each compartment has a volume of 218 mL. The cell delivers 0.22 A for 31.6 h. (a) How many grams of Cu are deposited? (b) What is the [Cu^{2+}] remaining?

19.119 Given the following standard reduction potentials, calculate the ion-product, K_w, for water at 25°C:

$$2H^+(aq) + 2e^- \longrightarrow H_2(g) \qquad E° = 0.00 \text{ V}$$

$$2H_2O(l) + 2e^- \longrightarrow H_2(g) + 2OH^-(aq) \quad E° = -0.83 \text{ V}$$

19.120 Compare the pros and cons of a fuel cell, such as the hydrogen-oxygen fuel cell, and a coal-fired power station for generating electricity.

19.121 Lead storage batteries are rated by ampere-hours, that is, the number of amperes they can deliver in an hour. (a) Show that 1 Ah = 3600 C. (b) The lead anodes of a certain lead storage battery have a total mass of 406 g. Calculate the maximum theoretical capacity of the battery in ampere-hours. Explain why in practice we can never extract this much energy from the battery. (*Hint:* Assume all the lead will be used up in the electrochemical reaction, and refer to the electrode reactions on page 828.) (c) Calculate $E°_{cell}$ and $\Delta G°$ for the battery.

19.122 Use Equations 18.10 and 19.3 to calculate the emf values of the Daniell cell at 25°C and 80°C. Comment on your results. What assumptions are used in the derivation? (*Hint:* You need the thermodynamic data in Appendix 2.)

19.123 A construction company is installing an iron culvert (a long cylindrical tube) that is 40.0 m long with a radius of 0.900 m. To prevent corrosion, the culvert must be galvanized. This process is carried out by first passing an iron sheet of appropriate dimensions through an electrolytic cell containing Zn^{2+} ions, using graphite as the anode and the iron sheet as the cathode. If the voltage is 3.26 V, what is the cost of electricity for depositing a layer 0.200 mm thick if the efficiency of the process is 95 percent? The electricity rate is $0.12 per kilowatt hour (kWh), where 1 W = 1 J/s and the density of Zn is 7.14 g/cm^3.

19.124 A 9.00×10^2 mL amount of 0.200 *M* MgI$_2$ solution was electrolyzed. As a result, hydrogen gas was generated at the cathode and iodine was formed at the anode. The volume of hydrogen collected at 26°C and 779 mmHg was 1.22×10^3 mL. (a) Calculate the charge in coulombs consumed in the process. (b) How long (in min) did the electrolysis last if a current of 7.55 A was used? (c) A white precipitate was formed in the process. What was it, and what was its mass in grams? Assume the volume of the solution was constant.

19.125 Based on the following standard reduction potentials,

$$Fe^{2+}(aq) + 2e^- \longrightarrow Fe(s) \qquad E°_1 = -0.44 \text{ V}$$

$$Fe^{3+}(aq) + e^- \longrightarrow Fe^{2+}(aq) \qquad E°_2 = 0.77 \text{ V}$$

calculate the standard reduction potential for the half-reaction

$$Fe^{3+}(aq) + 3e^- \longrightarrow Fe(s) \qquad E°_3 = ?$$

19.126 Which of the components of dental amalgam (mercury, silver, tin, copper, or zinc) would be oxidized when a filling is brought into contact with lead?

19.127 Calculate the equilibrium constant for the following reaction at 298 K:

$$Zn(s) + Cu^{2+}(aq) \rightleftharpoons Zn^{2+}(aq) + Cu(s)$$

19.128 Cytochrome-c is a protein involved in biological electron transfer processes. The redox half-reaction is shown by the reduction of the Fe^{3+} ion to the Fe^{2+} ion:

$$\text{cyt } c(Fe^{3+}) + e^- \longrightarrow \text{cyt } c(Fe^{2+}) \qquad E° = 0.254 \text{ V}$$

Calculate the number of moles of cyt c(Fe^{3+}) formed from cyt c(Fe^{2+}) with the Gibbs free energy derived from the oxidation of 1 mole of glucose.

19.129 The nitrite ion (NO_2^-) in soil is oxidized to the nitrate ion (NO_3^-) by the bacterium *Nitrobacter agilis* in the presence of oxygen. The half-reactions are

$$NO_3^- + 2H^+ + 2e^- \longrightarrow NO_2^- + H_2O \qquad E° = 0.42 \text{ V}$$

$$O_2 + 4H^+ + 4e^- \longrightarrow 2H_2O \qquad E° = 1.23 \text{ V}$$

Calculate the yield of ATP synthesis per mole of nitrite oxidized. (*Hint:* Refer to Section 18.7.)

19.130 Fluorine is a highly reactive gas that attacks water to form HF and other products. Follow the procedure in Problem 19.117 to show how you can determine indirectly the standard reduction potential for fluorine. Compare your result with the value in Table 19.1.

19.131 As discussed in Section 19.5, the potential of a concentration cell diminishes as the cell operates and the concentrations in the two compartments approach each other. When the concentrations in both compartments are the same, the cell ceases to operate. At this stage, is it possible to generate a cell potential by adjusting a parameter other than concentration? Explain.

Answers to In-Chapter Materials

PRACTICE PROBLEMS

19.1A $2MnO_4^- + H_2O + 3CN^- \longrightarrow 2MnO_2 + 2OH^- + 3CNO^-$.

19.1B $MnO_4^- + 5Fe^{2+} + 8H^+ \longrightarrow Mn^{2+} + 5Fe^{3+} + 4H_2O$.

19.2A $Cd + Pb^{2+} \longrightarrow Cd^{2+} + Pb$, $E_{cell}^\circ = 0.27$ V. **19.2B** In one cell, the iron electrode is the anode and the overall reaction is

$Fe(s) + Sn^{2+}(aq) \longrightarrow Fe^{2+}(aq) + Sn(s)$. $E_{cell}^\circ = E_{Sn^{2+}/Sn}^\circ - E_{Fe^{2+}/Fe}^\circ$

$= (-0.14$ V$) - (-0.44$ V$) = 0.30$ V. In the other cell, the iron electrode is the cathode and the overall reaction is $3Fe^{2+}(aq) + 2Cr(s) \longrightarrow$

$3Fe(s) + 2Cr^{3+}(aq)$. $E_{cell}^\circ = E_{Fe^{2+}/Fe}^\circ - E_{Cr^{3+}/Cr}^\circ = (-0.44$ V$) - (-0.74$ V$)$

$= 0.30$ V. **19.3A** (a) no reaction, (b) $2H^+ + Pb \longrightarrow H_2 + Pb^{2+}$.

19.3B Cobalt has a more positive reduction potential than iron. Cobalt ion would, therefore, be *reduced* in the presence of iron metal; and the iron in an iron container would oxidize to Fe^{2+}. Metal that is oxidized goes from the solid phase to the aqueous phase, meaning that the container would effectively *dissolve*. Cobalt has a less positive reduction potential than tin. Tin metal would not be oxidized by Co^{2+} ion, and the container would remain intact. A cobalt(II) chloride solution would be more safely stored in a tin container than in an iron container. **19.4A** -411 kJ/mol. **19.4B** 23.2 kJ/mol. **19.5A** 1×10^{-42}.

19.5B 1.4×10^5. **19.6A** Yes, the reaction is spontaneous. **19.6B** 18 atm.

19.7A $[Cu^+] = 1.11 \times 10^{-3}$ M, $K_{sp} = 1.2 \times 10^{-6}$. **19.7B** 0.16 V.

19.8A 7.44 g Mg. **19.8B** 0.96 A.

SECTION REVIEW

19.1.1 (a) not redox, (b) redox, (c) not redox, (d) redox, (e) not redox.

19.1.2 $2MnO_4^- + 3C_2O_4^{2-} + 4OH^- \longrightarrow 2MnO_2 + 6CO_3^{2-} + 2H_2O$.

19.3.1 2.24 V. **19.3.2** 1.54 V. **19.3.3** $Cr^{3+} + Al \longrightarrow Cr + Al^{3+}$.

19.3.4 No redox reaction will occur. **19.4.1** 4×10^{-7}.

19.4.2 -2.6×10^2 kJ/mol. **19.5.1** 1.11 V. **19.5.2** 0.049 V.

19.5.3 (a) increase, (b) increase, (c) increase. **19.5.4** 0.24 V. **19.7.1** 2.51 g.

19.7.2 24.0 h. **19.7.3** right to left: Anode, cathode, anode, cathode.

KEY SKILLS

Electrolysis of Metals

Electrolysis is used extensively in the processing and refining of metals. Converting between the current (and the time over which it is applied), and the amount of metal produced requires application of dimensional analysis [◄◄ Key Skills Chapter 1]. When we are given the current in amperes (A) and the time in seconds (s), we first convert to charge in coulombs (C):

$$\text{Current (A)} \times \text{Time (s)} \Rightarrow \text{Charge (C)}$$

We then divide by Faraday's constant to get the number of moles of electrons:

$$\frac{\text{Charge (C)}}{96{,}500 \text{ C/mol } e^-} \Rightarrow \text{mol } e^-$$

Using the reduction half-reaction, we can determine the number of moles of electrons needed to reduce a mole of metal:

$$M^{n+} + ne^- \longrightarrow M \qquad \frac{1 \text{ mol metal}}{n \text{ mol } e^-}$$

Finally, we convert moles electrons to moles metal:

$$\text{mol } e^- \times \frac{1 \text{ mol metal}}{n \text{ mol } e^-} \Rightarrow \text{mol metal}$$

Consider the following example. A current of 2.09 A is applied to a solution containing chromium(III) nitrate for 2.10 h. We determine the number of moles of Cr deposited as follows:

$$2.09 \text{ A} \times 2.10 \text{ h} \times \frac{60 \text{ min}}{1 \text{ h}} \times \frac{60 \text{ s}}{1 \text{ min}} \Rightarrow 1.58 \times 10^4 \text{ C}$$

$$\frac{1.58 \times 10^4 \text{ C}}{96{,}500 \text{ C/mol } e^-} \Rightarrow 0.1637 \text{ mol } e^-$$

$$Cr^{3+} + 3e^- \longrightarrow Cr \qquad \frac{1 \text{ mol Cr}}{3 \text{ mol } e^-}$$

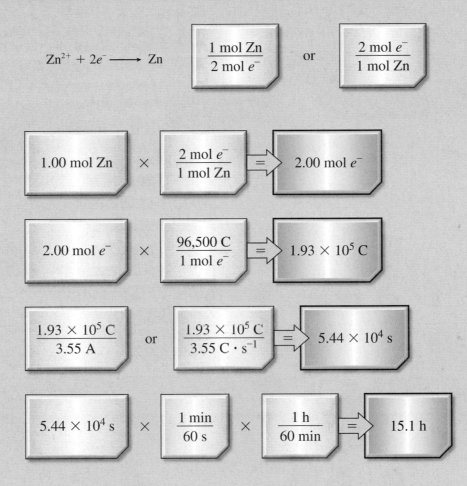

$$0.1637 \text{ mol } e^- \quad \times \quad \frac{1 \text{ mol Cr}}{3 \text{ mol } e^-} \quad = \quad 0.0546 \text{ mol Cr}$$

Conversely, we may know both the amount of metal to be produced and the current to be applied, and have to determine the amount of time required. If the goal is to produce 1.00 mole of zinc by electrolysis of a solution containing Zn^{2+} ions, and we will apply a current of 3.55 A, we determine the time over which the current must be applied as follows.

The reduction half-reaction indicates that 2 moles of electrons are needed to reduce a mole of zinc:

$$Zn^{2+} + 2e^- \longrightarrow Zn \qquad \frac{1 \text{ mol Zn}}{2 \text{ mol } e^-} \quad \text{or} \quad \frac{2 \text{ mol } e^-}{1 \text{ mol Zn}}$$

$$1.00 \text{ mol Zn} \quad \times \quad \frac{2 \text{ mol } e^-}{1 \text{ mol Zn}} \quad = \quad 2.00 \text{ mol } e^-$$

$$2.00 \text{ mol } e^- \quad \times \quad \frac{96,500 \text{ C}}{1 \text{ mol } e^-} \quad = \quad 1.93 \times 10^5 \text{ C}$$

$$\frac{1.93 \times 10^5 \text{ C}}{3.55 \text{ A}} \quad \text{or} \quad \frac{1.93 \times 10^5 \text{ C}}{3.55 \text{ C} \cdot \text{s}^{-1}} \quad = \quad 5.44 \times 10^4 \text{ s}$$

$$5.44 \times 10^4 \text{ s} \quad \times \quad \frac{1 \text{ min}}{60 \text{ s}} \quad \times \quad \frac{1 \text{ h}}{60 \text{ min}} \quad = \quad 15.1 \text{ h}$$

Key Skills Problems

19.1
How much copper metal can be produced by electrolysis of a solution containing Cu^{2+} ions by a current of 1.85 A applied for exactly four hours?

(a) 0.276 mol (b) 0.138 mol (c) 0.552 mol (d) 5.14×10^9 mol
(e) 2.00 mol

19.2
What mass of cadmium will be produced by electrolysis of a solution of $Cd(NO_3)_2$ when a current of 4.83 A is applied for six hours and 15 minutes?

(a) 63.3 g   (b) 127 g   (c) 253 g   (d) 31.6 g   (e) 57.2 g

19.3
Of the following aqueous solutions, identify the one that would yield the *smallest* mass of metal and the one that would yield the *largest* mass of metal when it is electrolyzed with a current of 2.00 A for 25 minutes.

$\quad$ $CuSO_4$ $\quad$ $AgNO_3$ $\quad$ $AuCl_3$ $\quad$ $ZnSO_4$ $\quad$ $Cr(NO_3)_3$

(a) $ZnSO_4$, $CuSO_4$ (b) $CuSO_4$, $ZnSO_4$ (c) $AgNO_3$, $Cr(NO_3)_3$
(d) $Cr(NO_3)_3$, $AuCl_3$ (e) $AuCl_3$, $AgNO_3$

19.4
When a current of 5.22 A is applied over 3.50 hours to a solution containing metal ions, 20.00 grams of metal are produced. Which of the following could be the metal ion in the solution?

(a) Zn^{2+} (b) Au^{3+} (c) Ag^+ (d) Ni^{2+} (e) Cu^{2+}

CHAPTER 20

Nuclear Chemistry

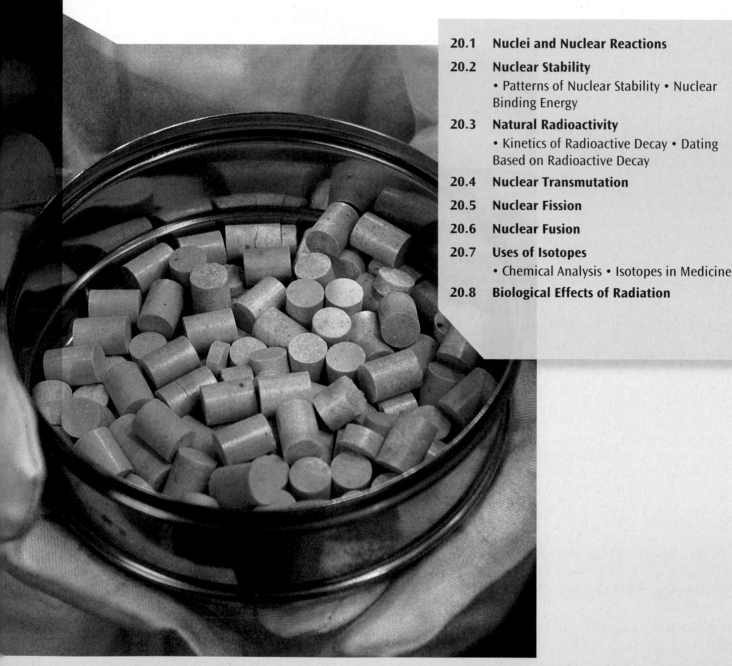

20.1 Nuclei and Nuclear Reactions

20.2 Nuclear Stability
• Patterns of Nuclear Stability • Nuclear Binding Energy

20.3 Natural Radioactivity
• Kinetics of Radioactive Decay • Dating Based on Radioactive Decay

20.4 Nuclear Transmutation

20.5 Nuclear Fission

20.6 Nuclear Fusion

20.7 Uses of Isotopes
• Chemical Analysis • Isotopes in Medicine

20.8 Biological Effects of Radiation

Nuclear reactors have been employed for the production of electricity for a number of decades but there are significant issues facing their continued use. These include nuclear waste production, handling, and storage; as well as fears of limited worldwide uranium sources. Thus, nuclear chemists are now reinvestigating the extended use of thorium as reactor fuel. Shown here are thorium pellets which can be used in a nuclear reactor to produce fissile materials. Some of the advantages of a thorium fuel cycle include safer reactor conditions, better waste management options, and prevention of nuclear proliferation.

Before You Begin, Review These Skills

- Radioactivity [◄◄ Section 2.2]
- Atomic number, mass number, and isotopes [◄◄ Section 2.3]
- First-order kinetics [◄◄ Section 14.5]

20.1 NUCLEI AND NUCLEAR REACTIONS

With the exception of hydrogen (^1_1H), all nuclei contain protons and neutrons. Some nuclei are unstable and undergo *radioactive decay,* emitting particles and/or electromagnetic radiation [◄◄ Section 2.2]. Spontaneous emission of particles or electromagnetic radiation is known as ***radioactivity.*** All elements having an atomic number greater than 83 are unstable and are therefore radioactive. Polonium-210 ($^{210}_{84}Po$), for example, decays spontaneously to Pb by emitting an α particle.

Another type of nuclear process, known as ***nuclear transmutation,*** results from the bombardment of nuclei by neutrons, protons, or other nuclei. An example of a nuclear transmutation is the conversion of atmospheric $^{14}_7N$ to $^{14}_6C$ and ^1_1H, which results when the nitrogen isotope is bombarded by neutrons (from the sun). In some cases, heavier elements are synthesized from lighter elements. This type of transmutation occurs naturally in outer space, but it can also be achieved artificially, as we will see in Section 20.4.

Radioactive decay and nuclear transmutation are *nuclear reactions,* which differ significantly from ordinary chemical reactions. Table 20.1 summarizes the differences.

To discuss nuclear reactions in any depth, we must understand how to write and balance nuclear equations. Writing a nuclear equation differs somewhat from writing equations for chemical reactions. In addition to writing the symbols for the various chemical elements, we must also explicitly indicate the number of subatomic particles in *every* species involved in the reaction.

The symbols for subatomic particles are as follows:

$$\underset{\text{proton}}{^1_1H \text{ or } ^1_1p} \quad \underset{\text{neutron}}{^1_0n} \quad \underset{\text{electron}}{^{\ 0}_{-1}e \text{ or } ^{\ 0}_{-1}\beta} \quad \underset{\text{positron}}{^{\ 0}_{+1}e \text{ or } ^{\ 0}_{+1}\beta} \quad \underset{\alpha \text{ particle}}{^4_2\alpha \text{ or } ^4_2He}$$

In accordance with the notation introduced in Section 2.3, the superscript in each case denotes the mass number (the total number of neutrons and protons present) and the subscript is the atomic number (the number of protons). Thus, the "atomic number" of a proton is 1, because there is one proton present, and the "mass number" is also 1, because there is one proton but no neutrons

TABLE 20.1	Comparison of Chemical Reactions and Nuclear Reactions	
Chemical reactions	**Nuclear reactions**
1. Atoms are rearranged by the breaking and forming of chemical bonds.	1. Elements are converted to other elements (or isotopes).
2. Only electrons in atomic or molecular orbitals are involved in the reaction.	2. Protons, neutrons, electrons, and other subatomic particles such as α particles may be involved.
3. Reactions are accompanied by the absorption or release of relatively small amounts of energy.	3. Reactions are accompanied by the absorption or release of tremendous amounts of energy.
4. Rates of reaction are influenced by temperature, pressure, concentration, and catalysts.	4. Rates of reaction normally are not affected by temperature, pressure, or catalysts.

present. On the other hand, the mass number of a neutron is 1, but its atomic number is zero, because there are no protons present. For the electron, the mass number is zero (there are neither protons nor neutrons present), but the atomic number is −1, because the electron possesses a unit negative charge.

The symbol $_{-1}^{0}e$ represents an electron in or from an atomic orbital. The symbol $_{-1}^{0}\beta$, on the other hand, represents an electron that, although physically identical to any other electron, comes from a nucleus (in a decay process in which a neutron is converted to a proton and an electron) and not from an atomic orbital. The ***positron*** has the same mass as the electron, but bears a charge of +1. The α particle has two protons and two neutrons, so its atomic number is 2 and its mass number is 4.

In balancing any nuclear equation, we must balance the total of all atomic numbers and the total of all mass numbers for the products and reactants. If we know the atomic numbers and mass numbers of all but one of the species in a nuclear equation, we can identify the *unknown* species by applying these rules, as shown in Worked Example 20.1.

Student Annotation: An α particle is identical to a helium-4 nucleus and can be represented either as $_{2}^{4}\alpha$ or $_{2}^{4}$He.

Worked Example 20.1

Identify the missing species X in each of the following nuclear equations:

(a) $_{84}^{212}\text{Po} \longrightarrow _{82}^{208}\text{Pb} + \text{X}$

(b) $_{38}^{90}\text{Sr} \longrightarrow \text{X} + _{-1}^{0}\beta$

(c) $\text{X} \longrightarrow _{8}^{18}\text{O} + _{+1}^{0}\beta$

Strategy Determine the mass number for the unknown species, X, by summing the mass numbers on both sides of the equation:

$$\Sigma \text{ reactant mass numbers} = \Sigma \text{ product mass numbers}$$

Similarly, determine the atomic number for the unknown species:

$$\Sigma \text{ reactant atomic numbers} = \Sigma \text{ product atomic numbers}$$

Use the mass number and atomic number to determine the identity of the unknown species.

Setup (a) 212 = (208 + mass number of X); mass number of X = 4. 84 = (82 + atomic number of X); atomic number of X = 2.

(b) 90 = (mass number of X + 0); mass number of X = 90. 38 = [atomic number of X + (−1)]; atomic number of X = 39.

(c) Mass number of X = (18 + 0); mass number of X = 18. Atomic number of X = (8 + 1); atomic number of X = 9.

Solution (a) $\text{X} = _{2}^{4}\alpha$: $_{84}^{212}\text{Po} \longrightarrow _{82}^{208}\text{Pb} + _{2}^{4}\alpha$

(b) $\text{X} = _{39}^{90}\text{Y}$: $_{38}^{90}\text{Sr} \longrightarrow _{39}^{90}\text{Y} + _{-1}^{0}\beta$

(c) $\text{X} = _{9}^{18}\text{F}$: $_{9}^{18}\text{F} \longrightarrow _{8}^{18}\text{O} + _{+1}^{0}\beta$

Think About It
The rules of summation that we apply to balance nuclear equations can be thought of as the *conservation of mass number* and the *conservation of atomic number*.

Practice Problem A Identify X in each of the following nuclear equations:

(a) $_{33}^{78}\text{As} \longrightarrow \text{X} + _{-1}^{0}\beta$

(b) $_{1}^{1}\text{H} + _{2}^{4}\text{He} \longrightarrow \text{X}$

(c) $_{100}^{258}\text{Fm} \longrightarrow _{100}^{257}\text{Fm} + \text{X}$

Practice Problem B Identify X in each of the following nuclear equations:

(a) $\text{X} + _{-1}^{0}\beta \longrightarrow _{94}^{244}\text{Pu}$

(b) $_{92}^{238}\text{U} \longrightarrow \text{X} + _{2}^{4}\text{He}$

(c) $\text{X} \longrightarrow _{7}^{14}\text{N} + _{-1}^{0}e$

Nuclei and Nuclear Reactions

20.1.1 Identify the species X in the following nuclear equation:

$$^{222}_{86}\text{Rn} \longrightarrow \text{X} + {}^{4}_{2}\alpha$$

20.1.2 Identify the species X in the following nuclear equation:

$$^{15}_{8}\text{O} \longrightarrow \text{X} + {}^{0}_{-1}\beta$$

20.2 NUCLEAR STABILITY

The nucleus occupies a very small portion of the total volume of an atom, but it contains most of the atom's mass because both the protons and the neutrons reside there. In studying the stability of the atomic nucleus, it is helpful to know something about its density, because it tells us how tightly the particles are packed together. As a sample calculation, let us assume that a nucleus has a radius of 5×10^{-3} pm and a mass of 1×10^{-22} g. These figures correspond roughly to a nucleus containing 30 protons and 30 neutrons. Density is mass/volume, and we can calculate the volume from the known radius (the volume of a sphere is $\frac{4}{3}\pi r^3$, where r is the radius of the sphere). First we convert the picometer units to centimeters. Then, we calculate the density in g/cm^3:

$$r = (5 \times 10^{-3}\text{ pm})\left(\frac{1 \times 10^{-12}\text{ m}}{1\text{ pm}}\right)\left(\frac{100\text{ cm}}{1\text{ m}}\right) = 5 \times 10^{-13}\text{ cm}$$

$$\text{density} = \frac{\text{mass}}{\text{volume}} = \frac{1 \times 10^{-22}\text{ g}}{\frac{4}{3}\pi r^3} = \frac{1 \times 10^{-22}\text{ g}}{\frac{4}{3}\pi(5 \times 10^{-13}\text{ cm})^3}$$

$$= 2 \times 10^{14}\text{ g/cm}^3$$

This is an exceedingly high density. The highest density known for an element is 22.6 g/cm^3, for osmium (Os). Thus, the average atomic nucleus is roughly 9×10^{12} (or 9 *trillion*) times as dense as the densest element known!

The enormously high density of the nucleus means that some very strong force is needed to hold the particles together so tightly. From *Coulomb's law* we know that like charges repel and unlike charges attract one another. We would thus expect the protons to repel one another strongly, particularly when we consider how close they must be to each other. This indeed is so. However, in addition to the repulsion, there are also short-range attractions between proton and proton, proton and neutron, and neutron and neutron. The stability of any nucleus is determined by the difference between coulombic repulsion and the short-range attraction. If repulsion outweighs attraction, the nucleus disintegrates, emitting particles and/or radiation. If attractive forces prevail, the nucleus is stable.

Patterns of Nuclear Stability

The principal factor that determines whether a nucleus is stable is the *neutron-to-proton ratio* (*n/p*). For stable atoms of elements having low atomic number ($\leq$20), the n/p value is close to 1. As the atomic number increases, the neutron-to-proton ratios of the stable nuclei also increase. This deviation at higher atomic numbers arises because more neutrons are needed to counteract the strong repulsion among the protons and stabilize the nucleus. The following rules are useful in gauging whether or not a particular nucleus is expected to be stable:

1. There are more stable nuclei containing 2, 8, 20, 50, 82, or 126 protons or neutrons than there are containing other numbers of protons or neutrons. For example, there are 10 stable isotopes of tin (Sn) with the atomic number 50 and only 2 stable isotopes of antimony (Sb) with the atomic number 51. The numbers 2, 8, 20, 50, 82, and 126 are called *magic numbers*.

Student Annotation: The significance of these numbers for nuclear stability is similar to the numbers of electrons associated with the very stable noble gases (i.e., 2, 10, 18, 36, 54, and 86 electrons).

TABLE 20.2	Number of Stable Isotopes with Even and Odd Numbers of Protons and Neutrons		
Protons	**Neutrons**	**Number of stable isotopes**	
Odd	Odd	4	
Odd	Even	50	
Even	Odd	53	
Even	Even	164	

Student Annotation: Of the two stable isotopes of antimony mentioned in rule 1, both have even numbers of neutrons: $^{121}_{51}$Sb and $^{123}_{51}$Sb.

2. There are many more stable nuclei with even numbers of both protons and neutrons than with odd numbers of these particles (Table 20.2).
3. All isotopes of the elements with atomic numbers higher than 83 are radioactive.
4. All isotopes of technetium (Tc, $Z = 43$) and promethium (Pm, $Z = 61$) are radioactive.

Figure 20.1 shows a plot of the number of neutrons versus the number of protons in various isotopes. The stable nuclei are located in an area of the graph known as the *belt of stability*. Most radioactive nuclei lie outside this belt. Above the belt of stability, the nuclei have higher neutron-to-proton ratios than those within the belt (for the same number of protons). To lower this ratio (and hence move down toward the belt of stability), these nuclei undergo the following process, called *β-particle emission:*

$$^1_0\text{n} \longrightarrow ^1_1\text{p} + ^{\ 0}_{-1}\beta$$

Beta-particle emission leads to an increase in the number of protons in the nucleus and a simultaneous decrease in the number of neutrons. Some examples are

$$^{14}_6\text{C} \longrightarrow ^{14}_7\text{N} + ^{\ 0}_{-1}\beta$$

$$^{40}_{19}\text{K} \longrightarrow ^{40}_{20}\text{Ca} + ^{\ 0}_{-1}\beta$$

$$^{97}_{40}\text{Zr} \longrightarrow ^{97}_{41}\text{Nb} + ^{\ 0}_{-1}\beta$$

Figure 20.1 Plot of neutrons versus protons for various stable isotopes, represented by dots. The straight line represents the points at which the neutron-to-proton ratio is 1. The shaded area represents the belt of stability.

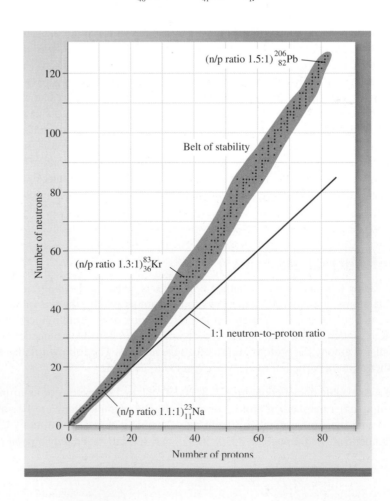

Below the belt of stability, the nuclei have lower neutron-to-proton ratios than those in the belt (for the same number of protons). To increase this ratio (and hence move up toward the belt of stability), these nuclei may emit a positron,

$$^{1}_{1}\text{p} \longrightarrow {}^{1}_{0}\text{n} + {}^{0}_{+1}\beta$$

An example of positron emission is

$$^{38}_{19}\text{K} \longrightarrow {}^{38}_{18}\text{Ar} + {}^{0}_{+1}\beta$$

Alternatively, a nucleus may undergo electron capture,

$$^{1}_{1}\text{p} + {}^{0}_{-1}e \longrightarrow {}^{1}_{0}\text{n}$$

Electron capture is the capture of an electron—usually a $1s$ electron—by the nucleus. The captured electron combines with a proton in the nucleus to form a *neutron* so that the atomic number decreases by 1 while the mass number remains the same. Electron capture has the same net effect on the nucleus as positron emission. Examples of electron capture are

$$^{37}_{18}\text{Ar} + {}^{0}_{-1}e \longrightarrow {}^{37}_{17}\text{Cl}$$

$$^{55}_{26}\text{Fe} + {}^{0}_{-1}e \longrightarrow {}^{55}_{25}\text{Mn}$$

Nuclear Binding Energy

A quantitative measure of nuclear stability is the **nuclear binding energy**, which is the energy required to break up a nucleus into its component protons and neutrons. This quantity represents the conversion of mass to energy that occurs during an exothermic nuclear reaction.

The concept of nuclear binding energy evolved from studies of nuclear properties showing that the masses of nuclei are always less than the sum of the masses of the *nucleons,* which is a general term for the protons and neutrons in a nucleus. For example, the $^{19}_{9}\text{F}$ isotope has an atomic mass of 18.99840 amu. The nucleus has 9 protons and 10 neutrons and therefore a total of 19 nucleons. Using the known masses of the $^{1}_{1}\text{H}$ atom (1.007825 amu) and the neutron (1.008665 amu), we can carry out the following analysis. The mass of 9 $^{1}_{1}\text{H}$ atoms (i.e., the mass of 9 protons and 9 electrons) is

$$9 \times 1.007825 \text{ amu} = 9.070425 \text{ amu}$$

and the mass of 10 neutrons is

$$10 \times 1.008665 \text{ amu} = 10.08665 \text{ amu}$$

Therefore, the atomic mass of an $^{19}_{9}\text{F}$ atom calculated from the known numbers of electrons, protons, and neutrons is

$$9.070425 \text{ amu} + 10.08665 \text{ amu} = 19.15708 \text{ amu}$$

This value is larger than 18.99840 amu (the measured mass of $^{19}_{9}\text{F}$) by 0.15868 amu.

The difference between the mass of an atom and the sum of the masses of its protons, neutrons, and electrons is called the **mass defect.** According to relativity theory, the loss in mass shows up as energy (heat) given off to the surroundings. Thus, the formation of $^{19}_{9}\text{F}$ is *exothermic.* According to *Einstein's mass-energy equivalence relationship* ($E = mc^2$, where E is energy, m is mass, and c is the velocity of light), we can calculate the amount of energy released. We start by writing

$$\Delta E = (\Delta m)c^2 \qquad \text{\textbf{Equation 20.1}}$$

where ΔE and Δm are defined as follows:

$$\Delta E = \text{energy of product} - \text{energy of reactants}$$

$$\Delta m = \text{mass of product} - \text{mass of reactants}$$

Thus, the change in mass is

$$\Delta m = 18.99840 \text{ amu} - 19.15708 \text{ amu}$$

$$= -0.15868 \text{ amu}$$

or

$$\Delta m = (-0.15868 \text{ amu})\left(\frac{1 \text{ kg}}{6.0221418 \times 10^{26} \text{ amu}}\right)$$

$$= -2.6349 \times 10^{-28} \text{ kg}$$

Because $^{19}_{9}F$ has a mass that is less than the mass calculated from the number of electrons and nucleons present, Δm is a negative quantity. Consequently, ΔE is also a negative quantity; that is, energy is released to the surroundings as a result of the formation of the fluorine-19 nucleus. We calculate ΔE as follows:

$$\Delta E = (-2.6349 \times 10^{-28} \text{ kg})(2.99792458 \times 10^8 \text{ m/s})^2$$

$$= -2.3681 \times 10^{-11} \text{ kg} \cdot \text{m}^2/\text{s}^2$$

$$= -2.3681 \times 10^{-11} \text{ J}$$

This is the amount of energy released when one fluorine-19 nucleus is formed from 9 protons and 10 neutrons. The nuclear binding energy of the nucleus is 2.3682×10^{-11} J, which is the amount of energy needed to decompose the nucleus into separate protons and neutrons. In the formation of 1 mole of fluorine nuclei, for instance, the energy released is

$$\Delta E = (-2.3681 \times 10^{-11} \text{ J})(6.0221418 \times 10^{23}/\text{mol})$$

$$= -1.4261 \times 10^{13} \text{ J/mol}$$

$$= -1.4261 \times 10^{10} \text{ kJ/mol}$$

The nuclear binding energy, therefore, is 1.4261×10^{10} kJ for 1 mole of fluorine-19 nuclei, which is a tremendously large quantity when we consider that the enthalpies of ordinary chemical reactions are on the order of only 200 kJ. The procedure we have followed can be used to calculate the nuclear binding energy of any nucleus.

As we have noted, nuclear binding energy is an indication of the stability of a nucleus. When comparing the stability of any two nuclei, however, we must account for the fact that they have different numbers of nucleons. It makes more sense, therefore, to compare nuclei using the *nuclear binding energy per nucleon:*

$$\text{nuclear binding energy per nucleon} = \frac{\text{nuclear binding energy}}{\text{number of nucleons}}$$

For the fluorine-19 nucleus,

$$\text{nuclear binding energy per nucleon} = \frac{2.3681 \times 10^{-11} \text{ J}}{19 \text{ nucleons}}$$

$$= 1.2464 \times 10^{-12} \text{ J/nucleon}$$

The nuclear binding energy per nucleon makes it possible to compare the stability of all nuclei on a common basis. Figure 20.2 shows the variation of nuclear binding energy per nucleon plotted

Figure 20.2 Plot of nuclear binding energy per nucleon versus mass number.

against mass number. As you can see, the curve rises rather steeply. The highest binding energies per nucleon belong to elements with intermediate mass numbers—between 40 and 100—and are greatest for elements in the iron, cobalt, and nickel region (the Group 8B elements) of the periodic table. This means that the net attractive forces among the particles (protons and neutrons) are greatest for the nuclei of these elements.

Nuclear binding energy and nuclear binding energy per nucleon are calculated for an iodine nucleus in Worked Example 20.2.

Worked Example 20.2

The atomic mass of $^{127}_{53}\text{I}$ is 126.904473 amu. Calculate the nuclear binding energy of this nucleus and the corresponding nuclear binding energy per nucleon.

Strategy To calculate the nuclear binding energy, we first determine the difference between the mass of the nucleus and the mass of all the protons and neutrons, which yields the mass defect. Next, we must apply Einstein's mass-energy relationship [$\Delta E = (\Delta m)c^2$].

Solution There are 53 protons and 74 neutrons in the iodine nucleus. The mass of 53 ^1_1H atoms is

$$53 \times 1.007825 \text{ amu} = 53.41473 \text{ amu}$$

and the mass of 74 neutrons is

$$74 \times 1.008665 \text{ amu} = 74.64121 \text{ amu}$$

Therefore, the predicted mass for $^{127}_{53}\text{I}$ is 53.41473 + 74.64121 = 128.05594 amu, and the mass defect is

$$\Delta m = 126.904473 \text{ amu} - 128.05594 \text{ amu}$$

$$= -1.15147 \text{ amu}$$

$$= (-1.15147 \text{ amu})\left(\frac{1 \text{ kg}}{6.0221418 \times 10^{26} \text{ amu}}\right)$$

$$= -1.91206 \times 10^{-27} \text{ kg}$$

The energy released is

$$\Delta E = (\Delta m)c^2$$

$$= (-1.91206 \times 10^{-27} \text{ kg})(2.99792458 \times 10^8 \text{ m/s})^2$$

$$= 1.71847 \times 10^{-10} \text{ kg} \cdot \text{m}^2/\text{s}^2$$

$$= 1.71847 \times 10^{-10} \text{ J}$$

Thus the nuclear binding energy is 1.71847×10^{-10} J. The nuclear binding energy per nucleon is obtained as follows:

$$\frac{1.71847 \times 10^{-10} \text{ J}}{127 \text{ nucleons}} = 1.35313 \times 10^{-12} \text{ J/nucleon}$$

Practice Problem A Calculate the nuclear binding energy (in joules) and the nuclear binding energy per nucleon of $^{209}_{83}\text{Bi}$ (208.980374 amu).

Practice Problem B The nuclear binding energy for $^{197}_{79}\text{Au}$ is 1.2683×10^{-12} J/nucleon. Determine the mass of a $^{197}_{79}\text{Au}$ atom.

Nuclear Stability

20.2.1   Determine the binding energy per nucleon in a ^{238}U nucleus (238.0507847 amu).

20.2.2   What is the energy associated with a mass defect of 2.000 amu?

20.2.3   What is the change in mass (in kg) for the following reaction? $\Delta H°$ for the reaction is −890.4 kJ/mol.

20.2.4   What type of radioactive decay will the isotopes ^{13}B and ^{188}Au most likely undergo?

20.3   NATURAL RADIOACTIVITY

Nuclei that do not lie within the belt of stability, as well as nuclei with more than 83 protons, tend to be unstable. The spontaneous emission by unstable nuclei of particles or electromagnetic radiation, or both, is known as radioactivity. The main types of radioactivity are the emission of α particles (doubly charged helium nuclei, He^{2+}); the emission of β particles (electrons of nuclear origin); the emission of γ rays, which are very-short-wavelength (0.1 nm to 104 nm) electromagnetic waves; the emission of positrons; and electron capture.

The disintegration of a radioactive nucleus often is the beginning of a ***radioactive decay series,*** which is a *sequence* of nuclear reactions that ultimately result in the formation of a stable isotope. Figure 20.3 shows the decay series of naturally occurring uranium-238, which involves 14 steps. This decay scheme, known as the *uranium decay series,* also shows the half-lives of all the nuclei involved.

It is important to be able to balance the nuclear reaction for each of the steps in a radioactive decay series. For example, the first step in the uranium decay series is the decay of uranium-238 to thorium-234, with the emission of an α particle. Hence, the reaction is represented by

$$^{238}_{92}\text{U} \longrightarrow \, ^{234}_{90}\text{Th} + \, ^{4}_{2}\alpha$$

The next step is represented by

$$^{234}_{90}\text{Th} \longrightarrow \, ^{234}_{91}\text{Pa} + \, ^{0}_{-1}\beta$$

and so on. In a discussion of radioactive decay steps, the beginning radioactive isotope is called the *parent* and the product isotope is called the *daughter.* Thus, $^{238}_{92}$U is the parent in the first step of the uranium decay series, and $^{234}_{90}$Th is the daughter.

Kinetics of Radioactive Decay

Student Annotation: Most nuclear scientists (and some general chemistry books) use the symbol λ instead of k for the rate constant of nuclear reactions.

All radioactive decays obey first-order kinetics. Therefore, the rate of radioactive decay at any time t is given by

$$\text{rate of decay at time } t = kN$$

where k is the first-order rate constant and N is the number of radioactive nuclei present at time t. According to Equation 14.3, the number of radioactive nuclei at time zero (N_0) and time t (N_t) is

Student Annotation: Although Equation 14.3 uses concentrations of a reactant at times t and 0, it is the *ratio* of the two that is important, so we can also use the *number* of radioactive nuclei in this equation. [◄◄ Key Skills Chapter 14]

$$\ln \frac{N_t}{N_0} = -kt$$

and the corresponding half-life of the reaction is given by Equation 14.5:

$$t_{1/2} = \frac{0.693}{k}$$

$$^{238}_{92}\text{U} \longrightarrow \alpha$$
$$4.51 \times 10^9 \text{ yr}$$

$$^{234}_{90}\text{Th} \longrightarrow \beta$$
$$24.1 \text{ days}$$

$$^{234}_{91}\text{Pa} \longrightarrow \beta$$
$$1.17 \text{ min}$$

$$^{234}_{92}\text{U} \longrightarrow \alpha$$
$$2.47 \times 10^5 \text{ yr}$$

$$^{230}_{90}\text{Th} \longrightarrow \alpha$$
$$7.5 \times 10^4 \text{ yr}$$

$$^{226}_{88}\text{Ra} \longrightarrow \alpha$$
$$1.60 \times 10^3 \text{ yr}$$

$$^{222}_{86}\text{Rn} \longrightarrow \alpha$$
$$3.82 \text{ days}$$

$$\beta \longleftarrow {}^{218}_{84}\text{Po} \longrightarrow \alpha$$
$$0.04\% \qquad\qquad 3.05 \text{ min}$$

$$\alpha \longleftarrow {}^{218}_{85}\text{At} \qquad {}^{214}_{82}\text{Pb} \longrightarrow \beta$$
$$2 \text{ s} \qquad\qquad\qquad 26.8 \text{ min}$$

$$\beta \longleftarrow {}^{214}_{83}\text{Bi} \longrightarrow \alpha$$
$$99.96\% \qquad\qquad 19.7 \text{ min}$$

$$\alpha \longleftarrow {}^{214}_{84}\text{Po} \qquad {}^{210}_{81}\text{Tl} \longrightarrow \beta$$
$$1.6 \times 10^{-4} \text{ s} \qquad\qquad 1.32 \text{ min}$$

$$^{210}_{82}\text{Pb} \longrightarrow \beta$$
$$20.4 \text{ yr}$$

$$\beta \longleftarrow {}^{210}_{83}\text{Bi} \longrightarrow \alpha$$
$$\sim 100\% \qquad\qquad 5.01 \text{ days}$$

$$\alpha \longleftarrow {}^{210}_{84}\text{Po} \qquad {}^{206}_{81}\text{Tl} \longrightarrow \beta$$
$$138 \text{ days} \qquad\qquad 4.20 \text{ min}$$

$$^{206}_{82}\text{Pb}$$

Figure 20.3 Decay series for uranium-238. (Times shown are half-lives.)

The half-lives and, therefore, the rate constants of radioactive isotopes vary greatly from nucleus to nucleus. Looking at Figure 20.3, for example, we find that $^{238}_{92}\text{U}$ and $^{214}_{84}\text{Po}$ are two extreme cases:

$$^{238}_{92}\text{U} \longrightarrow {}^{234}_{90}\text{Th} + {}^{4}_{2}\alpha \qquad\qquad t_{1/2} = 4.51 \times 10^9 \text{ yr}$$

$$^{214}_{84}\text{Po} \longrightarrow {}^{210}_{82}\text{Pb} + {}^{4}_{2}\alpha \qquad\qquad t_{1/2} = 1.6 \times 10^{-4} \text{ s}$$

These two rate constants, after conversion to the same time unit, differ by many orders of magnitude. Furthermore, the rate constants are unaffected by changes in environmental conditions such as temperature and pressure. These highly unusual features are not seen in ordinary chemical reactions (see Table 20.1).

Multi 20.1
Nuclear chemistry—radioactive half-life

Dating Based on Radioactive Decay

The half-lives of radioactive isotopes have been used as "atomic clocks" to determine the ages of certain objects. Some examples of dating by radioactive decay measurements will be described here.

The carbon-14 isotope is produced when atmospheric nitrogen is bombarded by cosmic rays:

$$^{14}_{7}\text{N} + {}^{1}_{0}\text{n} \longrightarrow {}^{14}_{6}\text{C} + {}^{1}_{1}\text{H}$$

The radioactive carbon-14 isotope decays according to the equation

$$^{14}_{6}\text{C} \longrightarrow {}^{14}_{7}\text{N} + {}^{0}_{-1}\beta$$

This reaction is the basis of radiocarbon or "carbon-14" dating. To determine the age of an object, we measure the *activity* (disintegrations per second) of ^{14}C and compare it to the activity of ^{14}C in living matter.

Worked Example 20.3 shows how to use radiocarbon dating to determine the age of an artifact.

Worked Example 20.3

A wooden artifact is found to have a ^{14}C activity of 9.1 disintegrations per second. Given that the ^{14}C activity of an equal mass of fresh-cut wood has a constant value of 15.2 disintegrations per second, determine the age of the artifact. The half-life of carbon-14 is 5715 years.

Strategy The activity of a radioactive sample is proportional to the number of radioactive nuclei. Thus, we can use Equation 14.3 with activity in place of concentration:

$$\ln \frac{^{14}C \text{ activity in artifact}}{^{14}C \text{ activity in fresh-cut wood}} = -kt$$

To determine k, though, we must solve Equation 14.5, using the value of $t_{1/2}$ for carbon-14 (5715 years) given in the problem statement.

Setup Solving Equation 14.5 for k gives

$$k = \frac{0.693}{5715 \text{ yr}} = 1.21 \times 10^{-4} \text{ yr}^{-1}$$

Solution

$$\ln \frac{9.1 \text{ disintegrations per second}}{15.2 \text{ disintegrations per second}} = -1.21 \times 10^{-4} \text{ yr}^{-1} (t)$$

$$t = \frac{-0.513}{-1.21 \times 10^{-4} \text{ yr}^{-1}} = 4240 \text{ yr}$$

Therefore, the age of the artifact is 4.2×10^3 years.

Think About It
Carbon dating cannot be used for objects older than about 60,000 years (about 10 half-lives). After that much time has passed, the activity of carbon-14 has fallen to a level too low to be measured reliably.

Practice Problem A A piece of linen cloth found at an ancient burial site is found to have a ^{14}C activity of 4.8 disintegrations per minute. Determine the age of the cloth. Assume that the carbon-14 activity of an equal mass of living flax (the plant from which linen is made) is 14.8 disintegrations per minute.

Practice Problem B What would be the ^{14}C activity in a 2500-year-old wooden object? Assume that the ^{14}C activity of an equal mass of fresh-cut wood is 13.9 disintegrations per second.

Because some of the intermediate products in the uranium decay series have very long half-lives (see Figure 20.3), this series is particularly suitable for estimating the age of rocks found on Earth and of extraterrestrial objects. The half-life for the first step ($^{238}_{92}U$ to $^{234}_{90}Th$) is 4.51×10^9 years. This is about 20,000 times the second largest value (i.e., 2.47×10^5 years), which is the half-life for $^{234}_{92}U$ to $^{230}_{90}Th$. As a good approximation, therefore, we can assume that the half-life for the *overall* process (i.e., from $^{238}_{92}U$ to $^{206}_{82}Pb$) is equal to the half-life of the first step:

$$^{238}_{92}U \longrightarrow \; ^{206}_{82}Pb + 8^4_2\alpha + 6^{\;0}_{-1}\beta \qquad t_{1/2} = 4.51 \times 10^9 \text{ yr}$$

In naturally occurring uranium minerals, we should and do find some lead-206 formed by radioactive decay. Assuming that no lead was present when the mineral was formed and that the mineral has not undergone chemical changes that would allow the lead-206 isotope to be separated from the parent uranium-238, it is possible to estimate the age of the rocks from the mass ratio of $^{206}_{82}Pb$

to $^{238}_{92}$U. According to the preceding nuclear equation, 1 mol (206 g) of lead is formed for every 1 mol (238 g) of uranium that undergoes complete decay. If only half a mole of uranium-238 has undergone decay, the mass ratio ^{206}Pb/^{238}U becomes

$$\frac{206 \text{ g}/2}{238 \text{ g}/2} = 0.866$$

and the process would have taken a half-life of 4.51×10^9 years to complete (Figure 20.4). Ratios lower than 0.866 mean that the rocks are less than 4.51×10^9 years old, and higher ratios suggest a greater age. Interestingly, studies based on the uranium series, as well as other decay series, put the age of the oldest rocks and, therefore, probably the age of Earth itself, at 4.5×10^9, or 4.5 billion years.

One of the most important dating techniques in geochemistry is based on the radioactive decay of potassium-40. Radioactive potassium-40 decays by several different modes, but the one relevant for dating is that of electron capture:

$$^{40}_{19}\text{K} + ^{0}_{-1}e \longrightarrow ^{40}_{18}\text{Ar} \qquad t_{1/2} = 1.2 \times 10^9 \text{ yr}$$

The accumulation of gaseous argon-40 is used to gauge the age of a specimen. When a potassium-40 atom in a mineral decays, argon-40 is trapped in the lattice of the mineral and can escape only if the material is melted. Melting, therefore, is the procedure for analyzing a mineral sample in the laboratory. The amount of argon-40 present can be conveniently measured with a mass spectrometer (see page 42). Knowing the ratio of argon-40 to potassium-40 in the mineral and the half-life of decay makes it possible to establish the ages of rocks ranging from millions to billions of years old.

Worked Example 20.4 shows how to use radioisotopes to determine the age of a specimen.

Figure 20.4 After one half-life, half of the original uranium-238 has been converted to lead-206.

Worked Example 20.4

A rock is found to contain 5.51 mg of ^{238}U and 1.63 mg of ^{206}Pb. Determine the age of the rock ($t_{1/2}$ of ^{238}U = 4.51×10^9 yr).

Strategy We must first determine what mass of ^{238}U decayed to produce the measured amount of ^{206}Pb and then use it to determine the original mass of ^{238}U. Knowing the initial and final masses of ^{238}U, we can use Equation 14.3 to solve for t.

Setup

$$1.63 \text{ mg } ^{206}\text{Pb} \times \frac{238 \text{ mg } ^{238}\text{U}}{206 \text{ mg } ^{206}\text{Pb}} = 1.88 \text{ mg } ^{238}\text{U}$$

Thus, the original mass of ^{238}U was 5.51 mg + 1.88 mg = 7.39 mg. The rate constant, k, is determined using Equation 14.5 and $t_{1/2}$ for ^{238}U:

$$k = \frac{0.693}{4.51 \times 10^9} = 1.54 \times 10^{-10} \text{ yr}^{-1}$$

Solution

$$\ln \frac{5.51 \text{ mg}}{7.39 \text{ mg}} = -1.54 \times 10^{-10} \text{ yr}^{-1} \, (t)$$

$$t = \frac{-0.294}{-1.54 \times 10^{-10} \text{ yr}^{-1}} = 1.91 \times 10^9 \text{ yr}$$

The rock is 1.9 billion years old.

Think About It
This is slightly more complicated than the radiocarbon problem. We cannot use the measured masses of the two isotopes in Equation 14.3 because they are masses of different elements.

Practice Problem A Determine the age of a rock that contains 12.75 mg of ^{238}U and 1.19 mg of ^{206}Pb.

Practice Problem B How much ^{206}Pb will be in a rock sample that is 1.3×10^8 years old and that contains 3.25 mg of ^{238}U?

SECTION 20.3 REVIEW

Natural Radioactivity

20.3.1   Determine the age of a rock found to contain 4.31 mg ^{238}U and 2.47 mg of ^{206}Pb.

20.3.2   Determine the ^{14}C activity in disintegrations per second (dps) of a wooden artifact that is 23,000 years old. (Assume that fresh-cut wood of equal mass has an activity of 15.2 dps.)

20.3.3   Iron-59 decays to cobalt via beta emission with a half-life of 45.1 days. From the diagram, determine how many half-lives have elapsed since the sample was pure iron-59.

$\bigcirc$ = Cobalt $\bullet$ = Iron-59

20.4 NUCLEAR TRANSMUTATION

The scope of nuclear chemistry would be rather narrow if study were limited to natural radioactive elements. An experiment performed by Rutherford in 1919, however, suggested the possibility of producing radioactivity artificially. When he bombarded a sample of nitrogen with α particles, the following reaction took place:

$$^{14}_{7}\text{N} + ^{4}_{2}\alpha \longrightarrow ^{17}_{8}\text{O} + ^{1}_{1}\text{p}$$

An oxygen-17 isotope was produced with the emission of a proton. This reaction demonstrated for the first time the feasibility of converting one element into another, by the process of nuclear transmutation. Nuclear transmutation differs from radioactive decay in that transmutation is brought about by the *collision* of two particles.

The preceding reaction can be abbreviated as $^{14}_{7}\text{N}(\alpha,\text{p})^{17}_{8}\text{O}$. In the parentheses the bombarding particle is written first, followed by the emitted particle.

Worked Example 20.5 shows how to use this notation to represent nuclear transmutations.

Worked Example 20.5

Write the balanced nuclear equation for the reaction represented by $^{56}_{26}\text{Fe}(\text{d},\alpha)^{54}_{25}\text{Mn}$, where d represents a deuterium nucleus.

Strategy   The species written first is a reactant. The species written last is a product. Within the parentheses, the bombarding particle (a reactant) is written first, followed by the emitted particle (a product).

Setup   The bombarding and emitted particles are represented by $^{2}_{1}\text{H}$ and $^{4}_{2}\alpha$, respectively.

Solution $^{56}_{26}\text{Fe} + ^{2}_{1}\text{H} \longrightarrow ^{54}_{25}\text{Mn} + ^{4}_{2}\alpha$

Think About It
Check your work by summing the mass numbers and the atomic numbers on both sides of the equation.

Practice Problem A   Write an equation for the process represented by $^{106}_{46}\text{Pd}(\alpha,\text{p})^{109}_{47}\text{Ag}$.

Practice Problem B   Write the abbreviated form of the following process:

$$^{33}_{17}\text{Cl} + ^{1}_{0}\text{n} \longrightarrow ^{31}_{15}\text{P} + ^{3}_{2}\text{He}$$

Particle accelerators made it possible to synthesize the so-called ***transuranium elements,*** with atomic numbers greater than 92. Neptunium ($Z = 93$) was first prepared in 1940. Since then, 26 other transuranium elements have been synthesized. All isotopes of these elements are radioactive. Table 20.3 lists the transuranium elements that have been reported and some of the reactions by which they have been produced.

Although light elements are generally not radioactive, they can be made so by bombarding their nuclei with appropriate particles. As we saw in the previous section, the radioactive carbon-14 isotope can be prepared by bombarding nitrogen-14 with neutrons. Tritium (^3_1H) is prepared according to the following bombardment:

$$^6_3Li + {}^1_0n \longrightarrow {}^3_1H + {}^4_2\alpha$$

Tritium decays with the emission of β particles:

$$^3_1H \longrightarrow {}^3_2He + {}^0_{-1}\beta \qquad t_{1/2} = 12.5 \text{ yr}$$

TABLE 20.3	Preparation of the Transuranium Elements		
Atomic number	**Name**	**Symbol**	**Preparation***
93	Neptunium	Np	$^{238}_{92}U + {}^1_0n \longrightarrow {}^{239}_{93}Np + {}^0_{-1}\beta$
94	Plutonium	Pu	$^{239}_{93}Np \longrightarrow {}^{239}_{94}Pu + {}^0_{-1}\beta$
95	Americium	Am	$^{239}_{94}Pu + {}^1_0n \longrightarrow {}^{240}_{95}Am + {}^0_{-1}\beta$
96	Curium	Cm	$^{239}_{94}Pu + {}^4_2\alpha \longrightarrow {}^{242}_{96}Cm + {}^1_0n$
97	Berkelium	Bk	$^{241}_{95}Am + {}^4_2\alpha \longrightarrow {}^{243}_{97}Bk + 2{}^1_0n$
98	Californium	Cf	$^{242}_{96}Cm + {}^4_2\alpha \longrightarrow {}^{245}_{98}Cf + {}^1_0n$
99	Einsteinium	Es	$^{238}_{92}U + 15{}^1_0n \longrightarrow {}^{253}_{99}Es + 7{}^0_{-1}\beta$
100	Fermium	Fm	$^{238}_{92}U + 17{}^1_0n \longrightarrow {}^{255}_{100}Fm + 8{}^0_{-1}\beta$
101	Mendelevium	Md	$^{253}_{99}Es + {}^4_2\alpha \longrightarrow {}^{256}_{101}Md + {}^1_0n$
102	Nobelium	No	$^{246}_{96}Cm + {}^{12}_6C \longrightarrow {}^{254}_{102}No + 4{}^1_0n$
103	Lawrencium	Lr	$^{252}_{98}Cf + {}^{10}_5B \longrightarrow {}^{257}_{103}Lr + 5{}^1_0n$
104	Rutherfordium	Rf	$^{249}_{98}Cf + {}^{12}_6C \longrightarrow {}^{257}_{104}Rf + 4{}^1_0n$
105	Dubnium	Db	$^{249}_{98}Cf + {}^{15}_7N \longrightarrow {}^{260}_{105}Db + 4{}^1_0n$
106	Seaborgium	Sg	$^{249}_{98}Cf + {}^{18}_8O \longrightarrow {}^{263}_{106}Sg + 4{}^1_0n$
107	Bohrium	Bh	$^{209}_{83}Bi + {}^{54}_{24}Cr \longrightarrow {}^{262}_{107}Bh + {}^1_0n$
108	Hassium	Hs	$^{208}_{82}Pb + {}^{58}_{26}Fe \longrightarrow {}^{265}_{108}Hs + {}^1_0n$
109	Meitnerium	Mt	$^{209}_{83}Bi + {}^{58}_{26}Fe \longrightarrow {}^{266}_{109}Mt + {}^1_0n$
110	Darmstadtium	Ds	$^{208}_{82}Pb + {}^{62}_{28}Ni \longrightarrow {}^{269}_{110}Ds + {}^1_0n$
111	Roentgenium	Rg	$^{209}_{83}Bi + {}^{64}_{28}Ni \longrightarrow {}^{272}_{111}Rg + {}^1_0n$
112	Copernicium	Cn	$^{208}_{82}Pb + {}^{70}_{30}Zn \longrightarrow {}^{277}_{112}Uub + {}^1_0n$
113	Ununtrium	Uut	$^{288}_{115}Uup \longrightarrow {}^{284}_{113}Uut + {}^4_2\alpha$
114	Ununquadium	Uuq	$^{244}_{94}Pu + {}^{48}_{20}Ca \longrightarrow {}^{289}_{114}Uuq + 3{}^1_0n$
115	Ununpentium	Uup	$^{243}_{95}Am + {}^{48}_{20}Ca \longrightarrow {}^{288}_{115}Uup + 3{}^1_0n$
116	Ununhexium	Uuh	$^{248}_{96}Cm + {}^{48}_{20}Ca \longrightarrow {}^{292}_{116}Uuh + 4{}^1_0n$
117	Ununseptium	Uus	$^{48}_{20}Ca + {}^{249}_{97}Bk \longrightarrow {}^{297}_{117}Uus + 4{}^1_0n$
118	Ununoctium	Uuo	$^{249}_{98}Cf + {}^{48}_{20}Ca \longrightarrow {}^{294}_{118}Uuo + 3{}^1_0n$

*Some of the transuranium elements have been prepared by more than one method.

Many synthetic isotopes are prepared by using neutrons as projectiles. This approach is particularly convenient because neutrons carry no charges and therefore are not repelled by the targets—the nuclei. In contrast, when the projectiles are positively charged particles (e.g., protons or α particles), they must have considerable kinetic energy to overcome the electrostatic repulsion between themselves and the target nuclei. The synthesis of phosphorus from aluminum is one example:

$$\,^{27}_{13}\text{Al} + \,^{4}_{2}\alpha \longrightarrow \,^{30}_{15}\text{P} + \,^{1}_{0}\text{n}$$

A *particle accelerator* uses electric and magnetic fields to increase the kinetic energy of charged species so that a reaction will occur (Figure 20.5). Alternating the polarity (i.e., $+$ and $-$) on specially constructed plates causes the particles to accelerate along a spiral path. When they have the energy necessary to initiate the desired nuclear reaction, they are guided out of the accelerator into a collision with a target substance.

Various designs have been developed for particle accelerators, one of which accelerates particles along a linear path of about 3 km (Figure 20.6). It is now possible to accelerate particles to

Figure 20.5 Schematic diagram of a cyclotron particle accelerator. The particle (an ion) to be accelerated starts at the center and is forced to move in a spiral path through the influence of electric and magnetic fields until it emerges at a high velocity. The magnetic fields are perpendicular to the plane of the dees (so-called because of their shape), which are hollow and serve as electrodes.

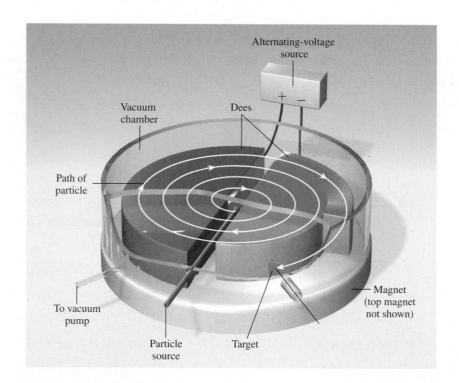

Figure 20.6 Section of a particle accelerator.

a speed well above 90 percent of the speed of light. (According to Einstein's theory of relativity, it is impossible for a particle to move *at* the speed of light. The only exception is the photon, which has a zero rest mass.) The extremely energetic particles produced in accelerators are employed by physicists to smash atomic nuclei to fragments. Studying the debris from such disintegrations provides valuable information about nuclear structure and binding forces.

SECTION 20.4 REVIEW

Nuclear Transmutation

20.4.1   Write the balanced nuclear equation for the reaction represented by $^{98}_{42}\text{Mo}(d,n)^{99}_{43}\text{Tc}$.

20.4.2   Write the correct abbreviated form of the equation

$$^{125}_{53}\text{I} + ^{0}_{-1}\beta \longrightarrow ^{125}_{52}\text{Te} + \gamma$$

20.5   NUCLEAR FISSION

Nuclear fission is the process in which a heavy nucleus (mass number > 200) divides to form smaller nuclei of intermediate mass and one or more neutrons. Because the heavy nucleus is less stable than its products (see Figure 20.2), this process releases a large amount of energy.

The first nuclear fission reaction to be studied was that of uranium-235 bombarded with slow neutrons, whose speed is comparable to that of air molecules at room temperature. Under these conditions, uranium-235 undergoes fission, as shown in Figure 20.7. Actually, this reaction is very complex: more than 30 different elements have been found among the fission products (Figure 20.8, page 868). A representative reaction is

$$^{235}_{92}\text{U} + ^{1}_{0}\text{n} \longrightarrow ^{90}_{38}\text{Sr} + ^{143}_{54}\text{Xe} + 3^{1}_{0}\text{n}$$

Although many heavy nuclei can be made to undergo fission, only the fission of naturally occurring uranium-235 and of the artificial isotope plutonium-239 has any practical importance. Table 20.4 lists the nuclear binding energies of uranium-235 and its fission products. As the table shows, the binding energy per nucleon for uranium-235 is less than the sum of the binding energies for strontium-90 and xenon-143. Therefore, when a uranium-235 nucleus is split into two smaller nuclei, a certain amount of energy is released.

Let's estimate the magnitude of this energy. The difference between the binding energies of the reactants and products is $(1.23 \times 10^{-10} + 1.92 \times 10^{-10})$ J $- (2.82 \times 10^{-10})$ J, or 3.3×10^{-11} J per uranium-235 nucleus. For 1 mole of uranium-235, the energy released would be (3.3×10^{-11}) (6.02×10^{23}), or 2.0×10^{13} J. This is an *extremely* exothermic reaction, considering that the heat of combustion of 1 ton of coal is only about 5×10^{7} J.

The significant feature of uranium-235 fission is not just the enormous amount of energy released, but the fact that more neutrons are produced than are originally captured in the process. This property makes possible a *nuclear chain reaction,* which is a self-sustaining sequence of nuclear fission reactions. The neutrons generated during the initial stages of fission can induce fission in other uranium-235 nuclei, which in turn produce more neutrons, and so on.

Multi 20.2
Nuclear chemistry—nuclear chain reaction

TABLE 20.4	Nuclear Binding Energies of ^{235}U and Its Fission Products
	Nuclear binding energy
^{235}U	2.82×10^{-10} J
^{90}Sr	1.23×10^{-10} J
^{143}Xe	1.92×10^{-10} J

Figure 20.7

Nuclear Fission and Fusion

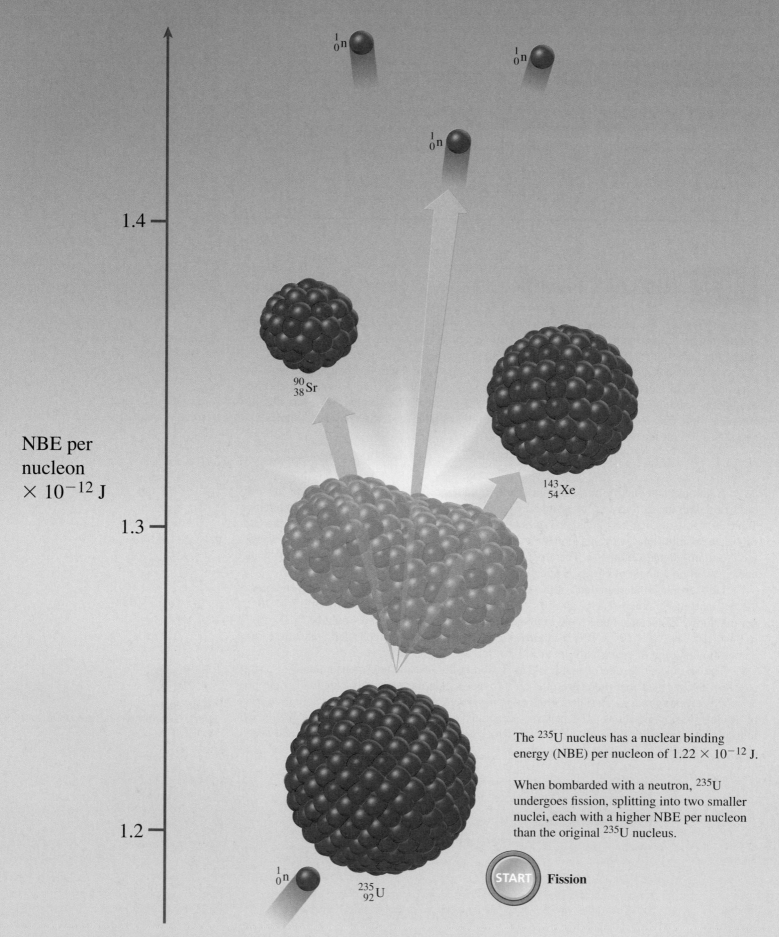

${}^{1}_{0}n$

${}^{1}_{0}n$

${}^{1}_{0}n$

NBE per
nucleon
$\times 10^{-12}$ J

1.4 —

${}^{90}_{38}Sr$

${}^{143}_{54}Xe$

1.3 —

The ${}^{235}U$ nucleus has a nuclear binding energy (NBE) per nucleon of 1.22×10^{-12} J.

When bombarded with a neutron, ${}^{235}U$ undergoes fission, splitting into two smaller nuclei, each with a higher NBE per nucleon than the original ${}^{235}U$ nucleus.

1.2 —

${}^{1}_{0}n$

${}^{235}_{92}U$

START **Fission**

$\frac{1}{0}n$

$\frac{4}{2}He$

NBE per
nucleon
$\times 10^{-12}$ J

1.2

1.0

0.8

0.6

0.4

0.2

0.0

$\frac{2}{1}H$ $\frac{3}{1}H$

(START) **Fusion**

The ^2H and ^3H nuclei have the following
nuclear binding energies per nucleon:

^2H: 0.185×10^{-12} J
^3H: 0.451×10^{-12} J

At very high temperatures, the ^2H and ^3H nuclei
undergo fusion to produce a ^4He nucleus and a
neutron. The ^4He nucleus has a significantly
higher NBE per nucleon: 1.13×10^{-12} J.

What's the point?

Large nuclei, such as ^{235}U, can achieve greater nuclear stability
by splitting into smaller nuclei with greater NBE per nucleon.
Small nuclei achieve stability by undergoing fusion to produce
a larger nucleus with a greater NBE per nucleon. Note that
different scales are used to show the change in NBE per nucleon
for the two processes. There is a much greater change in NBE
per nucleon in the fusion process than in the fission process. As
with chemical reactions, nuclear reactions are favored when the
products are more stable than the reactants.

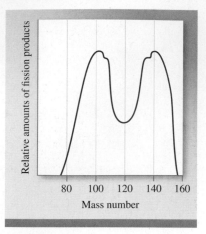

Figure 20.8 Relative yields of the products resulting from the fission of ^{235}U as a function of mass number.

Multi 20.3
Nuclear chemistry—nuclear fission

In less than a second, the reaction can become uncontrollable, liberating a tremendous amount of heat to the surroundings. Figure 20.9 shows two types of fission reactions. For a chain reaction to occur, enough uranium-235 must be present in the sample to capture the neutrons. Otherwise, many of the neutrons will escape from the sample and the chain reaction will not occur. In this situation the mass of the sample is said to be *subcritical*. Figure 20.9 shows what happens when the amount of the fissionable material is equal to or greater than the **critical mass,** the minimum mass of fissionable material required to generate a self-sustaining nuclear chain reaction. In this case, most of the neutrons will be captured by uranium-235 nuclei, and a chain reaction will occur.

The first application of nuclear fission was in the development of the atomic bomb. How is such a bomb made and detonated? The crucial factor in the bomb's design is the determination of the critical mass for the bomb. A small atomic bomb is equivalent to 20,000 tons of TNT (trinitrotoluene). Because 1 ton of TNT releases about 4×10^9 J of energy, 20,000 tons would produce 8×10^{13} J. Recall that 1 mole, or 235 g, of uranium-235 liberates 2.0×10^{13} J of energy when it undergoes fission. Thus, the mass of the isotope present in a small bomb must be at least

$$(235 \text{ g}) \left(\frac{8 \times 10^{13} \text{ J}}{2.0 \times 10^{13} \text{ J}} \right) \approx 1 \text{ kg}$$

An atomic bomb is never assembled with the critical mass already present. Instead, the critical mass is formed by using a conventional explosive, such as TNT, to force the fissionable sections together, as shown in Figure 20.10. Neutrons from a source at the center of the device trigger the nuclear chain reaction. Uranium-235 was the fissionable material in the bomb dropped on Hiroshima, Japan, on August 6, 1945. Plutonium-239 was used in the bomb exploded over Nagasaki three days later. The fission reactions generated were similar in these two cases, as was the extent of the destruction.

A peaceful but controversial application of nuclear fission is the generation of electricity using heat from a controlled chain reaction in a nuclear reactor. Currently, nuclear reactors provide about 20 percent of the electric energy in the United States. This is a small but by no means negligible contribution to the nation's energy production. Several different types of nuclear reactors are in operation; we will briefly discuss the main features of three of them, along with their advantages and disadvantages.

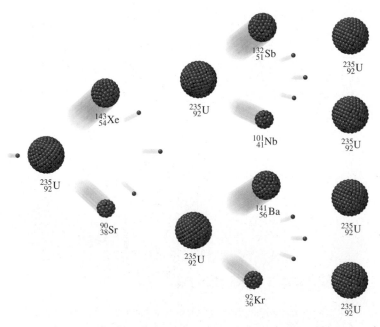

Figure 20.9 If a critical mass is present, many of the neutrons emitted during the fission process will be captured by other ^{235}U nuclei and a chain reaction will occur.

Figure 20.10 Schematic diagram of an atomic bomb. The TNT explosives are set off first. The explosion forces the sections of fissionable material together to form an amount considerably larger than the critical mass.

Most of the nuclear reactors in the United States are *light water reactors.* Figure 20.11 is a schematic diagram of such a reactor, and Figure 20.12 shows the refueling process in the core of a nuclear reactor.

An important aspect of the fission process is the speed of the neutrons. Slow neutrons split uranium-235 nuclei more efficiently than do fast ones. Because fission reactions are highly exothermic, the neutrons produced usually move at high velocities. For greater efficiency, they must be slowed down before they can be used to induce nuclear disintegration. To accomplish this goal, scientists use **moderators,** which are substances that can reduce the kinetic energy of neutrons. A good moderator must satisfy several requirements: It should be nontoxic and inexpensive (as very large quantities of it are necessary), and it should resist conversion into a radioactive substance by neutron bombardment. Furthermore, it is advantageous for the moderator to be a fluid so that it can also be used as a coolant. No substance fulfills all these requirements, although water comes

Figure 20.11 Schematic diagram of a nuclear fission reactor. The fission process is controlled by cadmium or boron rods. The heat generated by the process is used to produce steam for the generation of electricity via a heat exchange system.

Figure 20.12 Refueling the core of a nuclear reactor.

Multi 20.4
Nuclear chemistry—operation of a nuclear power plant

Figure 20.13 Uranium oxide (U_3O_8).

closer than many others that have been considered. Nuclear reactors that use light water (H_2O) as a moderator are called *light* water reactors because ^1_1H is the lightest isotope of the element hydrogen.

The nuclear fuel consists of uranium, usually in the form of its oxide, U_3O_8 (Figure 20.13). Naturally occurring uranium contains about 0.7 percent of the uranium-235 isotope, which is too low a concentration to sustain a small-scale chain reaction. For effective operation of a light water reactor, uranium-235 must be enriched to a concentration of 3 or 4 percent. In principle, the main difference between an atomic bomb and a nuclear reactor is that the chain reaction that takes place in a nuclear reactor is kept under control at all times. The factor limiting the rate of the reaction is the number of neutrons present. This can be controlled by lowering cadmium or boron *control rods* between the fuel elements. These rods capture neutrons according to the equations

$$^{113}_{48}Cd + {}^1_0n \longrightarrow {}^{114}_{48}Cd + \gamma$$

$$^{10}_{5}B + {}^1_0n \longrightarrow {}^7_3Li + {}^4_2\alpha$$

where γ denotes gamma rays. Without the control rods, the reactor core would melt from the heat generated and release radioactive materials into the environment. Nuclear reactors have rather elaborate cooling systems that absorb the heat given off by the nuclear reaction and transfer it outside the reactor core, where it is used to produce enough steam to drive an electric generator. In this respect, a nuclear power plant is similar to a conventional power plant that burns fossil fuel. In both cases, large quantities of cooling water are needed to condense steam for reuse. Thus, most nuclear power plants are built near a river or a lake. Unfortunately, this method of cooling causes thermal pollution.

Another type of nuclear reactor uses D_2O, or *heavy* water, as the moderator, rather than H_2O. Deuterium absorbs neutrons much less efficiently than does ordinary hydrogen. Because fewer neutrons are absorbed, the reactor is more efficient and does not require enriched uranium. More neutrons leak out of the reactor, too, though this is not a serious disadvantage.

The main advantage of a heavy water reactor is that it eliminates the need for building expensive uranium enrichment facilities. However, D_2O must be prepared by either fractional distillation or electrolysis of ordinary water, which can be very expensive considering the amount of water used in a nuclear reactor. In countries where hydroelectric power is abundant, the cost of producing D_2O by electrolysis can be reasonably low. At present, Canada is the only nation successfully using heavy water nuclear reactors. The fact that no enriched uranium is required in a heavy water reactor allows a country to enjoy the benefits of nuclear power without undertaking work that is closely associated with weapons technology.

A **breeder reactor** uses uranium fuel, but unlike a conventional nuclear reactor, it produces more fissionable materials than it uses.

When uranium-238 is bombarded with fast neutrons, the following reactions take place:

$$^{238}_{92}U + {}^1_0n \longrightarrow {}^{239}_{92}U$$

$$^{239}_{92}U \longrightarrow {}^{239}_{93}Np + {}^{0}_{-1}\beta \qquad t_{1/2} = 23.4 \text{ min}$$

$$^{239}_{93}Np \longrightarrow {}^{239}_{94}Pu + {}^{0}_{-1}\beta \qquad t_{1/2} = 2.35 \text{ days}$$

In this manner, the nonfissionable uranium-238 is transmuted into the fissionable isotope plutonium-239 (Figure 20.14).

In a typical breeder reactor, nuclear fuel containing uranium-235 or plutonium-239 is mixed with uranium-238 so that breeding takes place within the core. For every uranium-235 (or plutonium-239) nucleus undergoing fission, more than one neutron is captured by uranium-238 to generate plutonium-239. Thus, the stockpile of fissionable material can be steadily increased as the starting nuclear fuels are consumed. It takes about 7 to 10 years to regenerate the sizable amount of material needed to refuel the original reactor and to fuel another reactor of comparable size. This interval is called the *doubling time.*

Another *fertile* isotope is $^{232}_{90}Th$. Upon capturing slow neutrons, thorium is transmuted to uranium-233, which, like uranium-235, is a fissionable isotope:

$$^{232}_{90}Th + {}^1_0n \longrightarrow {}^{233}_{90}Th$$

$$^{233}_{90}Th \longrightarrow {}^{233}_{91}Pa + {}^{0}_{-1}\beta \qquad t_{1/2} = 22 \text{ min}$$

$$^{233}_{91}Pa \longrightarrow {}^{233}_{92}U + {}^{0}_{-1}\beta \qquad t_{1/2} = 27.4 \text{ days}$$

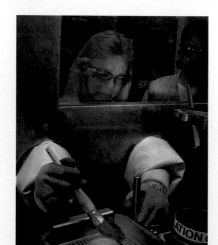

Figure 20.14 Radioactive plutonium oxide (PuO_2) has a red glow.

Uranium-233 ($t_{1/2} = 1.6 \times 10^5$ years) is stable enough for long-term storage.

Although the amounts of uranium-238 and thorium-232 in Earth's crust are relatively plentiful (4 ppm and 12 ppm by mass, respectively), the development of breeder reactors has been very slow. To date, the United States does not have a single operating breeder reactor, and only a few have been built in other countries, such as France and Russia. One problem is economics; breeder reactors are more expensive to build than conventional reactors. There are also more technical difficulties associated with the construction of such reactors. As a result, the future of breeder reactors, in the United States at least, is rather uncertain.

Many people, including environmentalists, regard nuclear fission as a highly undesirable method of energy production. Many fission products such as strontium-90 are dangerous radioactive isotopes with long half-lives. Plutonium-239, used as a nuclear fuel and produced in breeder reactors, is one of the most toxic substances known. It is an α-emitter with a half-life of 24,400 years.

Accidents, too, present many dangers. An accident at the Three Mile Island reactor in Pennsylvania in 1979 first brought the potential hazards of nuclear plants to public attention. In this instance, very little radiation escaped the reactor, but the plant remained closed for more than a decade while repairs were made and safety issues addressed. Only a few years later, on April 26, 1986, a reactor at the Chernobyl nuclear plant in Ukraine surged out of control. The fire and explosion that followed released much radioactive material into the environment. People working near the plant died within weeks as a result of the exposure to the intense radiation. The long-term effect of the radioactive fallout from this incident has not yet been clearly assessed, although agriculture and dairy farming were affected by the fallout. The number of potential cancer deaths attributable to the radiation contamination is estimated to be between a few thousand and more than 100,000.

In addition to the risk of accidents, the problem of radioactive waste disposal has not been satisfactorily resolved even for safely operated nuclear plants. Many suggestions have been made as to where to store or dispose of nuclear waste, including burial underground, burial beneath the ocean floor, and storage in deep geologic formations. But none of these sites has proved absolutely safe in the long run. Leakage of radioactive wastes into underground water, for example, can endanger nearby communities. The ideal disposal site would seem to be the sun, where a bit more radiation would make little difference, but this kind of operation requires space technology that is 100 percent reliable.

Because of the hazards, the future of nuclear reactors is clouded. What was once hailed as the ultimate solution to our energy needs in the twenty-first century is now being debated and questioned by both the scientific community and the general public. It seems likely that the controversy will continue for some time.

20.6 NUCLEAR FUSION

In contrast to the nuclear fission process, **nuclear fusion,** the combining of small nuclei into larger ones, is largely exempt from the waste disposal problem.

Figure 20.2 showed that for the lightest elements, nuclear stability increases with increasing mass number. This behavior suggests that if two light nuclei combine or fuse together to form a larger, more stable nucleus, an appreciable amount of energy will be released in the process. This is the basis for ongoing research into the harnessing of nuclear fusion for the production of energy.

Nuclear fusion occurs constantly in the sun. The sun is made up mostly of hydrogen and helium. In its interior, where temperatures reach about 15 million degrees Celsius, the following fusion reactions are believed to take place:

$$^{1}_{1}\text{H} + ^{2}_{1}\text{H} \longrightarrow ^{3}_{2}\text{He}$$

$$^{3}_{2}\text{He} + ^{3}_{2}\text{He} \longrightarrow ^{4}_{2}\text{He} + 2^{1}_{1}\text{H}$$

$$^{1}_{1}\text{H} + ^{1}_{1}\text{H} \longrightarrow ^{2}_{1}\text{H} + ^{0}_{-1}\beta$$

Because fusion reactions take place only at very high temperatures, they are often called **thermonuclear reactions.**

A major concern in choosing the proper nuclear fusion process for energy production is the temperature necessary to carry out the process. Some promising reactions are listed here:

Reaction	Energy released
$^{2}_{1}\text{H} + ^{2}_{1}\text{H} \longrightarrow ^{3}_{1}\text{H} + ^{1}_{1}\text{H}$	6.3×10^{-13} J
$^{2}_{1}\text{H} + ^{3}_{1}\text{H} \longrightarrow ^{3}_{2}\text{He} + 2^{1}_{0}\text{n}$	2.8×10^{-12} J
$^{6}_{3}\text{Li} + ^{2}_{1}\text{H} \longrightarrow 2^{4}_{2}\text{He}$	3.6×10^{-12} J

Figure 20.15 A magnetic plasma confinement design called a tokamak.

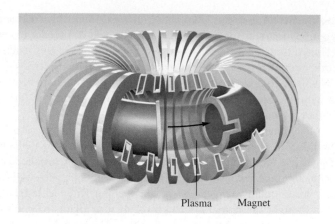

Plasma   Magnet

These reactions must take place at extremely high temperatures, on the order of 100 million degrees Celsius, to overcome the repulsive forces between the nuclei. The first reaction is particularly attractive because the world's supply of deuterium is virtually inexhaustible. The total volume of water on Earth is about 1.5×10^{21} L. Because the natural abundance of deuterium is 0.015 percent, the total amount of deuterium present is roughly 4.5×10^{21} g, or 5.0×10^{15} tons. Although it is expensive to prepare deuterium, the cost is minimal compared to the value of the energy released by the reaction.

In contrast to the fission process, nuclear fusion looks like a very promising energy source, at least on paper. Although thermal pollution would be a problem, fusion has the following advantages: (1) the fuels are cheap and almost inexhaustible and (2) the process produces little radioactive waste. If a fusion machine were turned off, it would shut down completely and instantly, without any danger of a meltdown.

If nuclear fusion is so great, why isn't there even one fusion reactor producing energy? Although we possess the scientific knowledge to design such a reactor, the technical difficulties have not yet been solved. The basic problem is finding a way to hold the nuclei together long enough, and at the appropriate temperature, for fusion to occur. At temperatures of about 100 million degrees Celsius, molecules cannot exist, and most or all of the atoms are stripped of their electrons. This state of matter, a gaseous mixture of positive ions and electrons, is called *plasma*. The problem of containing this plasma is a formidable one. No solid container can exist at such temperatures, unless the amount of plasma is small, but then the solid surface would immediately cool the sample and quench the fusion reaction. One approach to solving this problem is to use *magnetic confinement*. Because plasma consists of charged particles moving at high speeds, a magnetic field will exert a force on it. As Figure 20.15 shows, the plasma moves through a doughnut-shaped tunnel, confined by a complex magnetic field. Thus, the plasma never comes in contact with the walls of the container.

Another promising design employs high-power lasers to initiate the fusion reaction. In test runs, a number of laser beams transfer energy to a small fuel pellet, heating it and causing it to *implode*—that is, to collapse inward from all sides and compress into a small volume (Figure 20.16). Consequently, fusion occurs. Like the magnetic confinement approach, laser fusion presents a number of technical difficulties that still need to be overcome before it can be put to practical use on a large scale.

Figure 20.16 This small-scale fusion reaction was carried out at the Lawrence Livermore National Laboratory using one of the world's most powerful lasers, Nova.

The technical problems inherent in the design of a nuclear fusion reactor do not affect the production of a *hydrogen bomb*, also called a *thermonuclear* bomb. In this case, the objective is all power and no control. Hydrogen bombs do not contain gaseous hydrogen or gaseous deuterium; they contain solid lithium deuteride (LiD), which can be packed very tightly. The detonation of a hydrogen bomb occurs in two stages—first a fission reaction and then a fusion reaction. The required temperature for fusion is achieved with an atomic bomb. Immediately after the atomic bomb explodes, the following fusion reactions occur, releasing vast amounts of energy (Figure 20.17):

$$_{3}^{6}\text{Li} + {}_{1}^{2}\text{H} \longrightarrow 2\,_{2}^{4}\alpha$$

$$_{1}^{2}\text{H} + {}_{1}^{2}\text{H} \longrightarrow {}_{1}^{3}\text{H} + {}_{1}^{1}\text{H}$$

Figure 20.17 Explosion of a thermonuclear bomb.

There is no critical mass in a fusion bomb, and the force of the explosion is limited only by the quantity of reactants present. Thermonuclear bombs are described as being "cleaner" than atomic bombs because the only radioactive isotopes they produce are tritium, which is a weak β-particle emitter ($t_{\frac{1}{2}} = 12.5$ years), and the products of the fission starter. Their damaging effects on the environment can be aggravated, however, by incorporating in the construction some nonfissionable material such as cobalt. Upon bombardment by neutrons, cobalt-59 is converted to cobalt-60, which is a very strong γ-ray emitter with a half-life of 5.2 years. The presence of radioactive cobalt isotopes in the debris or fallout from a thermonuclear explosion would be fatal to those who survived the initial blast.

20.7 USES OF ISOTOPES

Radioactive and stable isotopes alike have many applications in science and medicine. We have previously described the use of isotopes in the study of reaction mechanisms [◄◄ Section 14.7] and in determining the age of rocks [◄◄ Key Skills Chapter 14]. In this section we will discuss a few more examples.

Chemical Analysis

The formula of the thiosulfate ion is $S_2O_3^{2-}$. For some years, chemists were uncertain as to whether the two sulfur atoms occupied equivalent positions in the ion. The thiosulfate ion is prepared by treating the sulfite ion with elemental sulfur:

$$SO_3^{2-}(aq) + S(s) \longrightarrow S_2O_3^{2-}(aq)$$

When thiosulfate is treated with dilute acid, the reaction is reversed. The sulfite ion is re-formed, and elemental sulfur precipitates:

$$S_2O_3^{2-}(aq) \xrightarrow{H^+} SO_3^{2-}(aq) + S(s)$$

Multi 20.5
Nuclear chemistry—nuclear medical techniques

If this sequence is started with elemental sulfur enriched with the radioactive sulfur-35 isotope, the isotope acts as a "label" for S atoms. All the labels are found in the sulfur precipitate; none of them appears in the final sulfite ions. As a result, the two atoms of sulfur in $S_2O_3^2$ are not structurally equivalent, as would be the case if the structure were

$$\left[\ddot{\underset{..}{O}} - \underset{..}{\ddot{S}} - \ddot{\underset{..}{O}} - \underset{..}{\ddot{S}} - \ddot{\underset{..}{O}} \right]^{2-}$$

If the sulfur atoms were equivalent, the radioactive isotope would be present in both the elemental sulfur precipitate and the sulfite ion. Based on spectroscopic studies, we now know that the structure of the thiosulfate ion is

$$\left[\begin{array}{c} \ddot{S} \\ \| \\ \ddot{O} - S - \ddot{O} \\ \| \\ \underset{..}{O} \end{array} \right]^{2-}$$

The study of photosynthesis is also rich with isotope applications. The overall photosynthesis reaction can be represented as

$$6CO_2 + 6H_2O \longrightarrow C_6H_{12}O_6 + 6O_2$$

In Section 14.5 we learned that the ^{18}O isotope was used to determine the source of O_2. The radioactive ^{14}C isotope helped to determine the path of carbon in photosynthesis. Starting with $^{14}CO_2$, it was possible to isolate the intermediate products during photosynthesis and measure the amount of radioactivity of each carbon-containing compound. In this manner the path from CO_2 through various intermediate compounds to carbohydrate could be clearly charted. Isotopes, especially radioactive isotopes that are used to trace the path of the atoms of an element in a chemical or biological process, are called *tracers.*

Isotopes in Medicine

Tracers are also used for diagnosis in medicine. Sodium-24 (a β-emitter with a half-life of 14.8 h) injected into the bloodstream as a salt solution can be monitored to trace the flow of blood and detect possible constrictions or obstructions in the circulatory system. Iodine-131 (a β-emitter with a half-life of 8 days) has been used to test the activity of the thyroid gland. A malfunctioning thyroid can be detected by giving the patient a drink of a solution containing a known amount of $Na^{131}I$ and measuring the radioactivity just above the thyroid to see if the iodine is absorbed at the

Thinking Outside the Box

Nuclear Medicine

Brain tumors are some of the most difficult cancers to treat because the site of the malignant growth makes surgical excision difficult or impossible. Likewise, conventional radiation therapy using X rays or γ rays from outside the skull is usually not effective. An ingenious approach to this problem is *boron neutron capture therapy* (BNCT). This technique involves first administering a boron-10 compound that is selectively taken up by tumor cells and then applying a beam of low-energy neutrons to the tumor site. ^{10}B captures a neutron to produce ^{11}B, which disintegrates via the following nuclear reaction:

$$^{10}_{5}B + ^{1}_{0}n \longrightarrow ^{7}_{3}Li + ^{4}_{2}\alpha$$

The highly energetic particles produced by this reaction destroy the tumor cells in which the ^{10}B is concentrated. Because the particles are confined to just a few micrometers, they preferentially destroy tumor cells without damaging neighboring normal cells.

BNCT is a highly promising treatment and is an active area of research. One of the major goals of the research is to develop suitable compounds to deliver ^{10}B to the desired site. For such a compound to be effective, it must meet several criteria. It must have a high affinity for tumor cells, be able to pass through membrane barriers to reach the tumor site, and have minimal toxic effects on the human body.

In addition to BNCT, another promising treatment for brain tumors is brachytherapy using iodine-125. In brachytherapy, "seeds" containing ^{125}I are implanted directly into the tumor. As the radioisotope decays, γ rays destroy the tumor cells. Careful implantation prevents the radiation from harming nearby healthy cells.

Brachytherapy seeds (shown with a penny to illustrate their size.)

Figure 20.18 ^{123}I image of a normal brain (left) and the brain of an Alzheimer's victim (right).

normal rate. Another radioactive isotope of iodine, iodine-123 (a γ-ray emitter), is used to image the brain (Figure 20.18). In each of these cases, though, the amount of radioisotope used must be kept small to prevent the patient from suffering permanent damage from the high-energy radiation.

Technetium, the first artificially prepared element, is one of the most useful elements in nuclear medicine. Although technetium is a transition metal, all its isotopes are radioactive. In the laboratory it is prepared by the nuclear reactions

$$^{98}_{42}Mo + ^{1}_{0}n \longrightarrow ^{99}_{42}Mo$$

$$^{99}_{42}Mo \longrightarrow ^{99m}_{43}Tc + ^{0}_{-1}\beta$$

where the superscript "m" denotes that the technetium-99 isotope is produced in its *excited* nuclear state. This isotope has a half-life of about 6 hours, decaying by γ radiation to technetium-99 in its nuclear *ground* state. Thus, it is a valuable diagnostic tool. The patient either drinks or is injected with a solution containing ^{99m}Tc. By detecting the γ rays emitted by ^{99m}Tc, doctors can obtain images of organs such as the heart, liver, and lungs.

A major advantage of using radioactive isotopes as tracers is that they are easy to detect. Their presence even in very small amounts can be detected by photographic techniques or by devices known as counters. Figure 20.19 is a diagram of a Geiger counter, an instrument widely used in scientific work and medical laboratories to detect radiation.

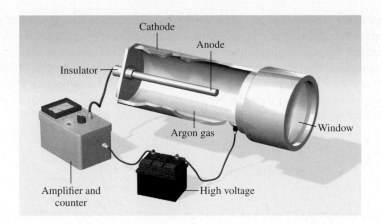

Figure 20.19 Schematic diagram of a Geiger counter. Radiation (α, β, or γ rays) entering through the window ionizes the argon gas to generate a small current flow between the electrodes. This current is amplified and is used to flash a light or operate a counter with a clicking sound.

20.8 BIOLOGICAL EFFECTS OF RADIATION

In this section we will examine briefly the effects of radiation on biological systems. But first we must define the quantitative measures of radiation. The fundamental unit of radioactivity is the *curie* (Ci); 1 Ci corresponds to exactly 3.70×10^{10} nuclear disintegrations per second. This decay rate is equivalent to that of 1 g of radium. A *millicurie* (mCi) is one-thousandth of a curie. Thus, 10 mCi of a carbon-14 sample is the quantity that undergoes $(10 \times 10^{-3})(3.70 \times 10^{10}) = 3.70 \times 10^8$ disintegrations per second.

The intensity of radiation depends on the number of disintegrations as well as on the energy and type of radiation emitted. One common unit for the absorbed dose of radiation is the *rad* (radiation *absorbed dose*), which is the amount of radiation that results in the absorption of 1×10^{-5} J per gram of irradiated material. The biological effect of radiation depends on the part of the body irradiated and the type of radiation. For this reason, the rad is often multiplied by a factor called the *RBE* (*r*elative *b*iological *e*ffectiveness). The product is called a *rem* (*r*oentgen *e*quivalent for *m*an):

$$\text{number of rems} = \text{number of rads} \times 1 \text{ RBE}$$

Of the three types of nuclear radiation, α particles usually have the least-penetrating power. Beta particles are more penetrating than α particles, but less so than γ rays.

Gamma rays have very short wavelengths and high energies. Furthermore, because they carry no charge, they cannot be stopped by shielding materials as easily as α and β particles. If α- or β-emitters are ingested or inhaled, however, their damaging effects are greatly aggravated because the organs will be constantly subject to damaging radiation at close range. For example, strontium-90, a β-emitter, can replace calcium in bones, where it does the greatest damage.

Table 20.5 lists the average amounts of radiation an American receives every year. For short-term exposures to radiation, a dosage of 50 to 200 rems will cause a decrease in white blood cell counts and other complications, while a dosage of 500 rems or greater may result in death within

Multi 20.6
Nuclear chemistry—alpha, beta, and gamma emission (interactive)

TABLE 20.5	Average Yearly Radiation Doses for Americans
Source	**Dose (mrem/yr)***
Cosmic rays	20–50
Ground and surroundings	25
Human body†	26
Medical and dental X rays	50–75
Air travel	5
Fallout from weapons tests	5
Nuclear waste	2
Total	133–188

*1 mrem = millirem = 1×10^{-3} rem.
†The radioactivity in the body comes from food and air.

weeks. Current safety standards permit nuclear workers to be exposed to no more than 5 rems per year and specify a maximum of 0.5 rem of human-made radiation per year for the general public.

The chemical basis of radiation damage is that of ionizing radiation. Radiation (of either particles or γ rays) can remove electrons from atoms and molecules in its path, leading to the formation of ions and radicals. **_Radicals_** (also called _free radicals_) are molecular fragments having one or more unpaired electrons; they are usually short lived and highly reactive. When water is irradiated with γ rays, for example, the following reactions take place:

$$\text{H}_2\text{O} \xrightarrow{\text{radiation}} \text{H}_2\text{O}^+ + e^-$$

$$\text{H}_2\text{O}^+ + \text{H}_2\text{O} \longrightarrow \text{H}_3\text{O}^+ + \bullet\text{OH}$$
$$\text{hydroxyl radical}$$

The electron (in the hydrated form) can subsequently react with water or with a hydrogen ion to form atomic hydrogen, and with oxygen to produce the superoxide ion (O_2^-) (a radical):

$$e^- + \text{O}_2 \longrightarrow \bullet\text{O}_2^-$$

In the tissues, the superoxide ions and other free radicals attack cell membranes and a host of organic compounds, such as enzymes and DNA molecules. Organic compounds can themselves be directly ionized and destroyed by high-energy radiation.

It has long been known that exposure to high-energy radiation can induce cancer in humans and other animals. Cancer is characterized by uncontrolled cellular growth. On the other hand, it is also well established that cancer cells can be destroyed by proper radiation treatment. In radiation therapy, a compromise is sought. The radiation to which the patient is exposed must be sufficient to destroy cancer cells without killing too many normal cells and, it is hoped, without inducing another form of cancer.

Radiation damage to living systems is generally classified as _somatic_ or _genetic_. Somatic injuries are those that affect the organism during its own lifetime. Sunburn, skin rash, cancer, and cataracts are examples of somatic damage. Genetic damage means inheritable changes or gene mutations. For example, a person whose chromosomes have been damaged or altered by radiation may have deformed offspring.

Learning Outcomes

- List the particles or types of radiation that an unstable nucleus can produce.
- Identify a subatomic particle in a nuclear equation.
- Distinguish between chemical and nuclear reactions.
- Demonstrate use of subatomic particles in balancing nuclear reactions.
- List the rules for nuclear stability and use them to predict whether a particular nucleus is stable.
- Define nuclear binding energy.
- Calculate the nuclear binding energy of a nucleus.

- Use the half-life of a radioactive decay in calculations.
- Produce the balanced nuclear reaction for a nuclear transmutation.
- Distinguish between fusion and fission.
- Define critical mass and nuclear chain reaction.
- Describe the basis of a nuclear reactor.
- Provide examples of the uses of isotopes in science and medicine.
- Explain why high-energy radiation is biologically harmful.

Chapter Summary

SECTION 20.1

- Spontaneous emission of particles or radiation from unstable nuclei is known as **radioactivity.** Unstable nuclei emit α particles, β particles, **positrons,** or γ rays.
- **Nuclear transmutation** is the conversion of one nucleus to another. Nuclear reactions are balanced by summing the mass numbers and the atomic numbers.

SECTION 20.2

- Stable nuclei with low atomic numbers have neutron-to-proton ratios close to 1. Heavier stable nuclei have higher ratios. Nuclear stability is favored by certain numbers of nucleons including even numbers and "magic" numbers.
- The difference between the actual mass of a nucleus and the mass calculated by summing the masses of the individual nucleons is the **mass defect.**
- **Nuclear binding energy,** determined by using Einstein's equation $E = mc^2$, is a measure of nuclear stability.

SECTION 20.3

- Uranium-238 is the parent of a natural **radioactive decay series** that can be used to determine the ages of rocks. Radiocarbon dating is done using carbon-14.

SECTION 20.4

- **Transuranium elements** are created by bombarding other elements with accelerated neutrons, protons, α particles, or other nuclei.

SECTION 20.5

- **Nuclear fission** is the splitting of a large nucleus into two smaller nuclei and one or more neutrons. When the free neutrons are captured efficiently by other nuclei, a **nuclear chain reaction** can occur in which the fission process is sustained. The minimum amount of fissionable material required to sustain the reaction is known as the **critical mass.**
- Nuclear reactors use the heat from a controlled nuclear fission reaction to produce power. Fission is controlled, in part, by **moderators**—materials that limit the speed of liberated neutrons but that do not themselves undergo fission when bombarded with neutrons. The three important types of reactors are light water reactors, heavy water reactors, and **breeder reactors.** Breeder reactors produce more fissionable material than they consume.

SECTION 20.6

- **Nuclear fusion,** the type of reaction that occurs in the sun, is the combination of two light nuclei to form one heavier nucleus. Fusion reactions are sometimes referred to as **thermonuclear reactions** because they take place only at very high temperatures.

SECTION 20.7

- Radioactive isotopes are easy to detect and thus make excellent **tracers** in chemical reactions and in medical procedures.

SECTION 20.8

- High-energy radiation damages living systems by causing ionization and the formation of **radicals,** or *free radicals,* which are chemical species with unpaired electrons.

Key Words

Breeder reactor, 870	Nuclear binding energy, 855	Nuclear transmutation, 851	Radioactivity, 851
Critical mass, 868	Nuclear chain reaction, 865	Positron, 852	Thermonuclear reaction, 871
Mass defect, 855	Nuclear fission, 865	Radical, 876	Tracers, 873
Moderator, 869	Nuclear fusion, 871	Radioactive decay series, 858	Transuranium elements, 863

Key Equation

20.1 $\Delta E = (\Delta m)c^2$

Questions and Problems

SECTION 20.1:   NUCLEI AND NUCLEAR REACTIONS

Review Questions

20.1   How do nuclear reactions differ from ordinary chemical reactions?

20.2   What are the steps in balancing nuclear equations?

20.3   What is the difference between $_{-1}^{0}e$ and $_{-1}^{0}\beta$?

20.4   What is the difference between an electron and a positron?

Problems

20.5   Complete the following nuclear equations, and identify X in each case:
(a) $_{12}^{26}\text{Mg} + _{1}^{1}\text{p} \longrightarrow \alpha + X$
(b) $_{27}^{59}\text{Co} + _{1}^{2}\text{H} \longrightarrow _{27}^{60}\text{Co} + X$
(c) $_{92}^{235}\text{U} + _{0}^{1}\text{n} \longrightarrow _{36}^{94}\text{Kr} + _{56}^{139}\text{Ba} + 3X$
(d) $_{24}^{53}\text{Cr} + _{2}^{4}\alpha \longrightarrow _{0}^{1}\text{n} + X$
(e) $_{8}^{20}\text{O} \longrightarrow _{9}^{20}\text{F} + X$

20.6   Complete the following nuclear equations, and identify X in each case:
(a) $_{53}^{135}\text{I} \longrightarrow _{54}^{135}\text{Xe} + X$
(b) $_{19}^{40}\text{K} \longrightarrow _{-1}^{0}\beta + X$
(c) $_{27}^{59}\text{Co} + _{0}^{1}\text{n} \longrightarrow _{25}^{56}\text{Mn} + X$
(d) $_{92}^{235}\text{U} + _{0}^{1}\text{n} \longrightarrow _{40}^{99}\text{Zr} + _{52}^{135}\text{Te} + 2X$

SECTION 20.2:   NUCLEAR STABILITY

Review Questions

20.7   State the general rules for predicting nuclear stability.

20.8   What is the belt of stability?

20.9   Why is it impossible for the isotope $_{2}^{2}\text{He}$ to exist?

20.10   Define *nuclear binding energy, mass defect,* and *nucleon.*

20.11   How does Einstein's equation, $E = mc^2$, enable us to calculate nuclear binding energy?

20.12   Why is it preferable to use nuclear binding energy per nucleon for a comparison of the stabilities of different nuclei?

Problems

20.13   The radius of a uranium-235 nucleus is about 7.0×10^{-3} pm. Calculate the density of the nucleus in g/cm³. (Assume the atomic mass is 235 amu.)

20.14   For each pair of isotopes listed, predict which one is less stable: (a) $_{3}^{6}\text{Li}$ or $_{3}^{9}\text{Li}$, (b) $_{11}^{23}\text{Na}$ or $_{11}^{25}\text{Na}$, (c) $_{20}^{48}\text{Ca}$ or $_{21}^{48}\text{Sc}$.

20.15   For each pair of elements listed, predict which one has more stable isotopes: (a) Co or Ni, (b) F or Se, (c) Ag or Cd.

20.16   In each pair of isotopes shown, indicate which one you would expect to be radioactive: (a) $_{10}^{20}\text{Ne}$ or $_{10}^{17}\text{Ne}$, (b) $_{20}^{40}\text{Ca}$ or $_{20}^{45}\text{Ca}$, (c) $_{42}^{95}\text{Mo}$ or $_{43}^{92}\text{Tc}$, (d) $_{80}^{195}\text{Hg}$ or $_{80}^{196}\text{Hg}$, (e) $_{83}^{209}\text{Bi}$ or $_{96}^{242}\text{Cm}$.

20.17   Given that

$$\text{H}(g) + \text{H}(g) \longrightarrow \text{H}_2(g) \qquad \Delta H° = -436.4 \text{ kJ/mol}$$

calculate the change in mass (in kg) per mole of H_2 formed.

20.18   Estimates show that the total energy output of the sun is 5×10^{26} J/s. What is the corresponding mass loss in kg/s of the sun?

20.19   Calculate the nuclear binding energy (in joules) and the binding energy per nucleon of the following isotopes: (a) $_{3}^{7}\text{Li}$ (7.01600 amu) and (b) $_{17}^{35}\text{Cl}$ (34.96885 amu).

20.20   Calculate the nuclear binding energy (in joules) and the binding energy per nucleon of the following isotopes: (a) $_{2}^{4}\text{He}$ (4.002603 amu) and (b) $_{74}^{184}\text{W}$ (183.950928 amu).

20.21   Given that the nuclear binding energy of ^{48}Cr is 1.37340×10^{-12} J/nucleon, calculate the mass of a single ^{48}Cr atom.

20.22   Given that the nuclear binding energy of ^{192}Ir is 1.27198×10^{-12} J/nucleon, calculate the mass of a single ^{192}Ir atom.

SECTION 20.3:   NATURAL RADIOACTIVITY

Review Questions

20.23   Discuss factors that lead to nuclear decay.

20.24   Outline the principle for dating materials using radioactive isotopes.

Problems

20.25   Fill in the blanks in the following radioactive decay series:

(a) $^{232}\text{Th} \xrightarrow{\ \alpha\ } \underline{\hspace{1.2cm}} \xrightarrow{\ \beta\ } \underline{\hspace{1.2cm}} \xrightarrow{\ \beta\ } {}^{228}\text{Th}$

(b) $^{235}\text{U} \xrightarrow{\ \alpha\ } \underline{\hspace{1.2cm}} \xrightarrow{\ \beta\ } \underline{\hspace{1.2cm}} \xrightarrow{\ \alpha\ } {}^{227}\text{Ac}$

(c) $\underline{\hspace{1.2cm}} \xrightarrow{\ \alpha\ } {}^{233}\text{Pa} \xrightarrow{\ \beta\ } \underline{\hspace{1.2cm}} \xrightarrow{\ \alpha\ } \underline{\hspace{1.2cm}}$

20.26   A radioactive substance undergoes decay as follows:

Time (days)	Mass (g)
0	500
1	389
2	303
3	236
4	184
5	143
6	112

Calculate the first-order decay constant and the half-life of the reaction.

20.27   The radioactive decay of Tl-206 to Pb-206 has a half-life of 4.20 min. Starting with 5.00×10^{22} atoms of Tl-206, calculate the number of such atoms left after 42.0 min.

20.28   A freshly isolated sample of ^{90}Y was found to have an activity of 9.8×10^5 disintegrations per minute at 1:00 P.M. on December 3, 2010. At 2:15 P.M. on December 17, 2010, its activity was measured again and found to be 2.6×10^4 disintegrations per minute. Calculate the half-life of ^{90}Y.

20.29   A wooden artifact has a ^{14}C activity of 18.9 disintegrations per minute, compared to 27.5 disintegrations per minute for live wood. Given that the half-life of ^{14}C is 5715 years, determine the age of the artifact.

20.30 In the thorium decay series, thorium-232 loses a total of six α particles and four β particles in a 10-stage process. What is the final isotope produced?

20.31 Consider the decay series A $\longrightarrow$ B $\longrightarrow$ C $\longrightarrow$ D where A, B, and C are radioactive isotopes with half-lives of 4.50 s, 15.0 days, and 1.00 s, respectively, and D is nonradioactive. Starting with 1.00 mole of A, and none of B, C, or D, calculate the number of moles of A, B, C, and D left after 30 days.

20.32 The activity of radioactive carbon-14 decay of a piece of charcoal found at a volcanic site is 11.2 disintegrations per second. If the activity of carbon-14 decay in an equal mass of living matter is 18.3 disintegrations per second, what is the age of the charcoal? (See Problem 20.29 for the half-life of carbon-14.)

20.33 The age of some animal bones was determined by carbon-14 dating to be 8.4×10^3 years old. Calculate the activity of the carbon-14 in the bones in disintegrations per minute per gram, given that the original activity was 15.3 disintegrations per minute per gram. (See Problem 20.29 for the half-life of carbon-14.)

20.34 Given that the half-life of ^{238}U is 4.51×10^9 years, determine the age of a rock found to contain 1.09 mg ^{238}U and 0.08 mg ^{206}Pb.

20.35 Determine the ratio of ^{238}U to ^{206}Pb in a rock that is 1.7×10^8 years old. (See Problem 20.34 for the half-life of ^{238}U.)

SECTION 20.4: NUCLEAR TRANSMUTATION

Review Questions

20.36 What is the difference between radioactive decay and nuclear transmutation?

20.37 How is nuclear transmutation achieved in practice?

Problems

20.38 Write balanced nuclear equations for the following reactions, and identify X: (a) X(p,α)$^{12}_{6}$C, (b) $^{27}_{13}$Al(d,α)X, (c) $^{55}_{25}$Mn(n,γ)X.

20.39 Write the abbreviated forms for the following reactions:
(a) $^{14}_{7}$N + $^{4}_{2}\alpha \longrightarrow$ $^{17}_{8}$O + $^{1}_{1}$p
(b) $^{9}_{4}$Be + $^{4}_{2}\alpha \longrightarrow$ $^{12}_{6}$C + $^{1}_{0}$n
(c) $^{238}_{92}$U + $^{2}_{1}$H $\longrightarrow$ $^{238}_{93}$Np + 2^{1}_{0}n

20.40 Write balanced nuclear equations for the following reactions, and identify X: (a) $^{80}_{34}$Se(d,p)X, (b) X(d,2p)$^{9}_{3}$Li, (c) $^{10}_{5}$B(n,α)X.

20.41 Write the abbreviated forms for the following reactions:
(a) $^{40}_{20}$Ca + $^{2}_{1}$H $\longrightarrow$ $^{41}_{20}$Ca + $^{1}_{1}$p
(b) $^{32}_{16}$S + $^{1}_{0}$n $\longrightarrow$ $^{32}_{15}$P + $^{1}_{1}$p
(c) $^{239}_{94}$Pu + $^{4}_{2}\alpha \longrightarrow$ $^{242}_{96}$Cm + $^{1}_{0}$n

20.42 Describe how you would prepare astatine-211, starting with bismuth-209.

20.43 A long-cherished dream of alchemists was to produce gold from cheaper and more abundant elements. This dream was finally realized when $^{198}_{80}$Hg was converted into gold by neutron bombardment. Write a balanced equation for this reaction.

SECTION 20.5: NUCLEAR FISSION

Visualizing Chemistry
Figure 20.7

VC 20.1 The fission of ^{235}U can result in a variety of products, including those shown in Figure 20.7. Which of the following equations does *not* represent another possible fission process?
(a) $^{1}_{0}$n + $^{235}_{92}$U $\longrightarrow$ $^{137}_{52}$Te + $^{97}_{40}$Zr + 2^{1}_{0}n
(b) $^{1}_{0}$n + $^{235}_{92}$U $\longrightarrow$ $^{142}_{56}$Ba + $^{91}_{36}$Kr + 3^{1}_{0}n
(c) $^{1}_{0}$n + $^{235}_{92}$U $\longrightarrow$ $^{137}_{55}$Cs + $^{90}_{37}$Rb + 3^{1}_{0}n

VC 20.2 How many neutrons are produced in the fission reaction shown?

$$^{1}_{0}\text{n} + ^{239}_{94}\text{Pu} \longrightarrow ^{109}_{44}\text{Ru} + ^{129}_{50}\text{Sn} + \underline{\quad} ^{1}_{0}\text{n}$$

(a) 1
(b) 2
(c) 3

VC 20.3 The fission of ^{235}U shown in Figure 20.7 is represented by the equation

$$^{1}_{0}\text{n} + ^{235}_{92}\text{U} \longrightarrow ^{143}_{54}\text{Xe} + ^{90}_{38}\text{Sr} + 3^{1}_{0}\text{n}$$

How does the combined mass of products compare to the combined mass of reactants for this process?
(a) The combined mass of products is smaller than the combined mass of reactants.
(b) The combined mass of products is larger than the combined mass of reactants.
(c) The combined mass of products is equal to the combined mass of reactants.

VC 20.4 The fusion of $^{2}_{1}$H and $^{3}_{1}$H shown in Figure 20.7 is represented by the equation

$$^{2}_{1}\text{H} + ^{3}_{1}\text{H} \longrightarrow ^{4}_{2}\text{He} + ^{1}_{0}\text{n}$$

How does the combined mass of products compare to the combined mass of reactants for this process?
(a) The combined mass of products is smaller than the combined mass of reactants.
(b) The combined mass of products is larger than the combined mass of reactants.
(c) The combined mass of products is equal to the combined mass of reactants.

Review Questions

20.44 Define *nuclear fission, nuclear chain reaction,* and *critical mass.*

20.45 Which isotopes can undergo nuclear fission?

20.46 Explain how an atomic bomb works.

20.47 Explain the functions of a moderator and a control rod in a nuclear reactor.

20.48 Discuss the differences between a light water and a heavy water nuclear fission reactor. What are the advantages of a breeder reactor over a conventional nuclear fission reactor?

20.49 No form of energy production is without risk. Make a list of the risks to society involved in fueling and operating a conventional coal-fired electric power plant, and compare them with the risks of fueling and operating a nuclear fission-powered electric plant.

SECTION 20.6: NUCLEAR FUSION

Review Questions

20.50 Define *nuclear fusion, thermonuclear reaction,* and *plasma.*

20.51 Why do heavy elements such as uranium undergo fission whereas light elements such as hydrogen and lithium undergo fusion?

20.52 How does a hydrogen bomb work?

20.53 What are the advantages of a fusion reactor over a fission reactor? What are the practical difficulties in operating a large-scale fusion reactor?

SECTION 20.7: USES OF ISOTOPES

Problems

20.54 Describe how you would use a radioactive iodine isotope to demonstrate that the following process is in dynamic equilibrium:

$$PbI_2(s) \rightleftharpoons Pb^{2+}(aq) + 2I^-(aq)$$

20.55 Consider the following redox reaction:

$$IO_4^-(aq) + 2I^-(aq) + H_2O(l) \longrightarrow$$
$$I_2(s) + IO_3^-(aq) + 2OH^-(aq)$$

When KIO_4 is added to a solution containing iodide ions labeled with radioactive iodine-128, all the radioactivity appears in I_2 and none in the IO_3^- ion. What can you deduce about the mechanism for the redox process?

20.56 Explain how you might use a radioactive tracer to show that ions are not completely motionless in crystals.

20.57 Each molecule of hemoglobin, the oxygen carrier in blood, contains four Fe atoms. Explain how you would use the radioactive $^{59}_{26}Fe$ ($t_{1/2} = 46$ days) to show that the iron in a certain food is converted into hemoglobin.

20.58 ^{125}I is produced by a two-step process in which ^{124}Xe nuclei are bombarded with neutrons to produce ^{125}Xe— a process called *neutron activation.* ^{125}Xe then decays by electron capture to produce ^{125}I, which also decays by electron capture. Write nuclear equations for the two steps that produce ^{125}I from ^{124}Xe, and identify the product of the electron capture decay of ^{125}I.

20.59 The half-life of ^{125}I is 59.4 days. How long will it take for the activity of implanted ^{125}I seeds to fall to 5.00 percent of their original value?

SECTION 20.8: BIOLOGICAL EFFECTS OF RADIATION

Review Questions

20.60 List the factors that affect the intensity of radiation from a radioactive element.

20.61 What are *rad* and *rem,* and how are they related?

20.62 Explain, with examples, the difference between somatic and genetic radiation damage.

20.63 Compare the extent of radiation damage done by α, β, and γ sources.

ADDITIONAL PROBLEMS

20.64 How does a Geiger counter work?

20.65 Strontium-90 is one of the products of the fission of uranium-235. This strontium isotope is radioactive, with a half-life of 28.1 years. Calculate how long (in years) it will take for 1.00 g of the isotope to be reduced to 0.200 g by decay.

20.66 Nuclei with an even number of protons and an even number of neutrons are more stable than those with an odd number of protons and/or an odd number of neutrons. What is the significance of the even numbers of protons and neutrons in this case?

20.67 Tritium (^3H) is radioactive and decays by electron emission. Its half-life is 12.5 years. In ordinary water the ratio of ^1H to ^3H atoms is 1.0×10^{17} to 1. (a) Write a balanced nuclear equation for tritium decay. (b) How many disintegrations will be observed per minute in a 1.00-kg sample of water?

20.68 (a) What is the activity, in millicuries, of a 0.500-g sample of $^{237}_{93}Np$? (This isotope decays by α-particle emission and has a half-life of 2.20×10^6 years.) (b) Write a balanced nuclear equation for the decay of $^{237}_{93}Np$.

20.69 The following equations are for nuclear reactions that are known to occur in the explosion of an atomic bomb. Identify X.

(a) $^{235}_{92}U + ^1_0n \longrightarrow ^{140}_{56}Ba + 3^1_0n + X$

(b) $^{235}_{92}U + ^1_0n \longrightarrow ^{144}_{55}Cs + ^{90}_{37}Rb + 2X$

(c) $^{235}_{92}U + ^1_0n \longrightarrow ^{87}_{35}Br + 3^1_0n + X$

(d) $^{235}_{92}U + ^1_0n \longrightarrow ^{160}_{62}Sm + ^{72}_{30}Zn + 4X$

20.70 Calculate the nuclear binding energies (in J/nucleon) for the following species: (a) ^{10}B (10.0129 amu), (b) ^{11}B (11.009305 amu), (c) ^{14}N (14.003074 amu), (d) ^{56}Fe (55.93494 amu).

20.71 Write complete nuclear equations for the following processes: (a) tritium (^3H) undergoes β decay, (b) ^{242}Pu undergoes α-particle emission, (c) ^{131}I undergoes β decay, (d) ^{251}Cf emits an α particle.

20.72 The nucleus of nitrogen-18 lies above the stability belt. Write the equation for a nuclear reaction by which nitrogen-18 can achieve stability.

20.73 Why is strontium-90 a particularly dangerous isotope for humans? The half-life of strontium-90 is 29.1 years. Calculate the radioactivity in millicuries of 15.6 mg of ^{90}Sr.

20.74 How are scientists able to tell the age of a fossil?

20.75 After the Chernobyl accident, people living close to the nuclear reactor site were urged to take large amounts of potassium iodide as a safety precaution. What is the chemical basis for this action?

20.76 To detect bombs that may be smuggled onto airplanes, the Federal Aviation Administration (FAA) will soon require all major airports in the United States to install thermal neutron analyzers. The thermal neutron analyzer will bombard baggage with low-energy neutrons, converting some of the nitrogen-14 nuclei to nitrogen-15, with simultaneous emission of γ rays. Because nitrogen content is usually high in explosives, detection of a high dosage of γ rays will suggest that a bomb may be present. (a) Write an equation for the nuclear process. (b) Compare this technique with the conventional X-ray detection method.

20.77 Astatine, the last member of Group 7A, can be prepared by bombarding bismuth-209 with α particles. (a) Write an equation for the reaction. (b) Represent the equation in the abbreviated form as discussed in Section 20.4.

20.78 Explain why achievement of nuclear fusion in the laboratory requires a temperature of about 100 million degrees Celsius, which is much higher than that in the interior of the sun (15 million degrees Celsius).

20.79 The carbon-14 decay rate of a sample obtained from a young tree is 0.260 disintegration per second per gram of the sample. Another wood sample prepared from an object recovered at an archaeological excavation gives a decay rate of 0.186 disintegration per second per gram of the sample. What is the age of the object?

20.80 Tritium contains one proton and two neutrons. There is no significant proton-proton repulsion present in the nucleus. Why, then, is tritium radioactive?

20.81 The usefulness of radiocarbon dating is limited to objects no older than 60,000 years. What percent of the carbon-14, originally present in the sample, remains after this period of time?

20.82 The radioactive potassium-40 isotope decays to argon-40 with a half-life of 1.2×10^9 years. (a) Write a balanced equation for the reaction. (b) A sample of moon rock is found to contain 18 percent potassium-40 and 82 percent argon by mass. Calculate the age of the rock in years. (Assume that all the argon in the sample is the result of potassium decay.)

20.83 Nuclear waste disposal is one of the major concerns of the nuclear industry. In choosing a safe and stable environment to store nuclear wastes, consideration must be given to the heat released during nuclear decay. As an example, consider the β decay of ^{90}Sr (89.907738 amu):

$$^{90}_{38}\text{Sr} \longrightarrow {}^{90}_{39}\text{Y} + {}^{0}_{-1}\beta \qquad t_{1/2} = 28.1 \text{ yr}$$

The ^{90}Y (89.907152 amu) further decays as follows:

$$^{90}_{39}\text{Y} \longrightarrow {}^{90}_{40}\text{Zr} + {}^{0}_{-1}\beta \qquad t_{1/2} = 64 \text{ h}$$

Zirconium-90 (89.904703 amu) is a stable isotope. (a) Use the mass defect to calculate the energy released (in joules) in each of the preceding two decays. (The mass of the electron is 5.4857×10^{-4} amu.) (b) Starting with 1 mole of ^{90}Sr, calculate the number of moles of ^{90}Sr that will decay in a year. (c) Calculate the amount of heat released (in kJ) corresponding to the number of moles of ^{90}Sr decayed to ^{90}Zr in part (b).

20.84 Which of the following poses a greater health hazard: a radioactive isotope with a short half-life or a radioactive isotope with a long half-life? Explain. [Assume the same type of radiation (α or β) and comparable energetics per particle emitted.]

20.85 From the definition of curie, calculate Avogadro's number, given that the molar mass of ^{226}Ra is 226.03 g/mol and that it decays with a half-life of 1.6×10^3 years.

20.86 As a result of being exposed to the radiation released during the Chernobyl nuclear accident, the dose of iodine-131 in a person's body is 7.4 mC ($1 \text{ mC} = 1 \times 10^{-3}$ Ci). Use the relationship rate $= \lambda N$ to calculate the number of atoms of iodine-131 to which this radioactivity corresponds. (The half-life of ^{131}I is 8.1 days.)

20.87 (a) Calculate the energy released when a U-238 isotope decays to Th-234. The atomic masses are as follows: U-238: 238.05078 amu; Th-234: 234.03596 amu; and He-4: 4.002603 amu. (b) The energy released in part (a) is transformed into the kinetic energy of the recoiling Th-234 nucleus and the α particle. Which of the two will move away faster? Explain.

20.88 A person received an anonymous gift of a decorative cube, which he placed on his desk. A few months later he became ill and died shortly afterward. After investigation, the cause of his death was linked to the box. The box was airtight and had no toxic chemicals on it. What might have killed the man?

20.89 Identify two of the most abundant radioactive elements that exist on Earth. Explain why they are still present. (You may wish to consult a website such as that of the University of Sheffield and WebElements Ltd, UK, webelements.com.)

20.90 Sources of energy on Earth include fossil fuels, geothermal power, gravity, hydroelectric power, nuclear fission, nuclear fusion, the sun, and wind. Which of these have a "nuclear origin," either directly or indirectly?

20.91 Cobalt-60 is an isotope used in diagnostic medicine and cancer treatment. It decays with γ-ray emission. Calculate the wavelength of the radiation in nanometers if the energy of the γ ray is 2.4×10^{-13} J/photon.

20.92 Americium-241 is used in smoke detectors because it has a long half-life (458 years) and its emitted α particles are energetic enough to ionize air molecules. Using the given schematic diagram of a smoke detector, explain how it works.

20.93 The constituents of wine contain, among others, carbon, hydrogen, and oxygen atoms. A bottle of wine was sealed about 6 years ago. To confirm its age, which of the isotopes would you choose in a radioactive dating study? The half-lives of the isotopes are: ^{13}C: 5715 years; ^{15}O: 124 s; ^{3}H: 12.5 years. Assume that the activities of the isotopes were known at the time the bottle was sealed.

20.94 Name two advantages of a nuclear-powered submarine over a conventional submarine.

20.95 In 1997 a scientist at a nuclear research center in Russia placed a thin shell of copper on a sphere of highly enriched uranium-235. Suddenly, there was a huge burst of radiation, which turned the air blue. Three days later, the scientist died of radiation exposure. Explain what caused the accident. (*Hint:* Copper is an effective metal for reflecting neutrons.)

20.96 A radioactive isotope of copper decays as follows:

$$^{64}\text{Cu} \longrightarrow {}^{64}\text{Zn} + {}_{-1}^{0}\beta \qquad t_{\frac{1}{2}} = 12.8 \text{ h}$$

Starting with 84.0 g of ^{64}Cu, calculate the quantity of ^{64}Zn produced after 18.4 h.

20.97 A 0.0100-g sample of a radioactive isotope with a half-life of 1.3×10^9 years decays at the rate of 2.9×10^4 disintegrations per minute. Calculate the molar mass of the isotope.

20.98 The half-life of ^{27}Mg is 9.50 min. (a) Initially there were 4.20×10^{12} ^{27}Mg nuclei present. How many ^{27}Mg nuclei are left 30.0 min later? (b) Calculate the ^{27}Mg activities (in Ci) at $t = 0$ and $t = 30.0$ min. (c) What is the probability that any one ^{27}Mg nucleus decays during a 1-s interval? What assumption is made in this calculation?

20.99 (a) Assuming nuclei are spherical in shape, show that the radius (r) of a nucleus is proportional to the cube root of mass number (A). (b) In general, the radius of a nucleus is given by $r = r_0 A^{1/3}$, where r_0, the proportionality constant, is given by 1.2×10^{-15} m. Calculate the volume of the ^{238}U nucleus.

20.100 Modern designs of atomic bombs contain, in addition to uranium or plutonium, small amounts of tritium and deuterium to boost the power of explosion. What is the role of tritium and deuterium in these bombs?

20.101 Isotope X decays to isotope Y with a half-life of 45 days. Which diagram most closely represents the sample of X after 105 days?

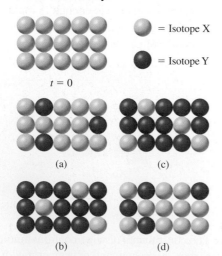

t = 0

(a)   (c)

(b)   (d)

20.102 In 2006, an ex-KGB agent was murdered in London. The investigation following the agent's death revealed that he was poisoned with the radioactive isotope ^{210}Po, which had apparently been added to his food. (a) ^{210}Po is prepared by bombarding ^{209}Bi with neutrons. Write an equation for the reaction. (b) The half-life of ^{210}Po is 138 days. It decays by α-particle emission. Write the equation for the decay process. (c) Calculate the energy of an emitted α particle. Assume both the parent and daughter nuclei have zero kinetic energy. The atomic masses of ^{210}Po, ^{206}Pb, and $_2^4\alpha$ are 209.98286, 205.97444, and 4.00150 amu, respectively. (d) Ingestion of 1 μg of ^{210}Po could prove fatal. What is the total energy released by this quantity of ^{210}Po over the course of 138 days?

20.103 Alpha particles produced by radioactive decay eventually pick up electrons from their surroundings to form helium atoms. Calculate the volume (in mL) of He collected at STP when 1.00 g of pure ^{226}Ra is stored in a closed container for 125 years. (Assume that there are five α particles generated per ^{226}Ra as it decays to ^{206}Pb.)

20.104 An electron and a positron are accelerated to nearly the speed of light before colliding in a particle accelerator. The resulting collision produces an exotic particle having a mass many times that of a proton. Does this result violate the law of conservation of mass? Explain.

20.105 Iridium-192 can be used in brachytherapy. It is produced by a nuclear transmutation. (a) Identify the target nucleus X, and write the balanced nuclear equation for the reaction represented by ^{191}X(n,γ)^{192}Ir. (b) The mass of an ^{125}I nucleus is 124.904624 amu. Calculate the nuclear binding energy and the nuclear binding energy per nucleon.

Answers to In-Chapter Materials

PRACTICE PROBLEMS

20.1A (a) $^{78}_{34}\text{Se}$, (b) $^{5}_{3}\text{Li}$, (c) $^{1}_{0}\text{n}$. **20.1B** (a) $^{244}_{95}\text{Am}$, (b) $^{234}_{90}\text{Th}$, (c) $^{14}_{6}\text{C}$.
20.2A 2.6280×10^{-10} J; 1.2574×10^{-12} J/nucleon. **20.2B** 196.9665 amu.
20.3A 9.3×10^{3} yr. **20.3B** 1.0×10^{1} dps. **20.4A** 6.6×10^{8} yr.
20.4B 5.7×10^{-2} mg. **20.5A** $^{106}_{46}\text{Pd} + ^{4}_{2}\text{He} \longrightarrow ^{1}_{1}\text{H} + ^{109}_{47}\text{Ag}$.
20.5B $^{33}_{17}\text{Cl}(\text{n},^{3}_{2}\text{He})^{31}_{15}\text{P}$.

SECTION REVIEW

20.1.1 $^{218}_{84}\text{Po}$. **20.1.2** $^{15}_{9}\text{F}$. **20.2.1** 1.215×10^{-12} J/nucleon.
20.2.2 2.989×10^{-10} J. **20.2.3** 1.645×10^{-35} kg. **20.2.4** beta emission,
positron emission. **20.3.1** 3.30×10^{9} years. **20.3.2** 0.935 dps. **20.3.3** 3.
20.4.1 $^{98}_{42}\text{Mo} + ^{2}_{1}\text{H} \longrightarrow ^{99}_{43}\text{Tc} + ^{1}_{0}\text{n}$. **20.4.2** $^{125}_{53}\text{I}(\beta,\gamma)\,^{125}_{52}\text{Te}$.

CHAPTER 21

Metallurgy and the Chemistry of Metals

21.1 Occurrence of Metals

21.2 Metallurgical Processes
• Preparation of the Ore • Production of Metals
• The Metallurgy of Iron • Steelmaking •
Purification of Metals

21.3 Band Theory of Conductivity
• Conductors • Semiconductors

21.4 Periodic Trends in Metallic Properties

21.5 The Alkali Metals

21.6 The Alkaline Earth Metals
• Magnesium • Calcium

21.7 Aluminum

Devices such as transistors and solar cells made from semiconducting materials are the foundation of modern electronics. The bonding in semiconducting materials allows electricity to be conducted with relatively low resistance, making semiconductors, such as silicon and germanium, of paramount importance in electronics. Chemists and materials scientists have exploited the chemical and physical properties of semiconducting materials to design such devices as the high resolution image sensor shown here.

21.1 OCCURRENCE OF METALS

Most metals come from minerals. A ***mineral*** is a naturally occurring substance with a range of chemical composition. A mineral deposit concentrated enough to allow economical recovery of a desired metal is known as ***ore***. Table 21.1 lists the principal types of minerals, and Figure 21.1 shows a classification of metals according to their minerals.

The most abundant metals, which exist as minerals in Earth's crust, are aluminum, iron, calcium, magnesium, sodium, potassium, titanium, and manganese. Seawater is a rich source

TABLE 21.1	Natural Sources of Common Metals
Type	**Minerals**
Uncombined metals	Ag, Au, Bi, Cu, Pd, Pt
Carbonates	$BaCO_3$ (witherite), $CaCO_3$ (calcite, limestone), $MgCO_3$ (magnesite), $CaCO_3 \cdot MgCO_3$ (dolomite), $PbCO_3$ (cerussite), $ZnCO_3$ (smithsonite)
Halides	CaF_2 (fluorite), NaCl (halite), KCl (sylvite), Na_3AlF_6 (cryolite)
Oxides	$Al_2O_3 \cdot 2H_2O$ (bauxite), Al_2O_3 (corundum), Fe_2O_3 (hematite), Fe_3O_4 (magnetite), Cu_2O (cuprite), MnO_2 (pyrolusite), SnO_2 (cassiterite), TiO_2 (rutile), ZnO (zincite)
Phosphates	$Ca_3(PO_4)_2$ (phosphate rock), $Ca_5(PO_4)_3OH$ (hydroxyapatite)
Silicates	$Be_3Al_2Si_6O_{18}$ (beryl), $ZrSiO_4$ (zircon), $NaAlSi_3O_8$ (albite), $Mg_3(Si_4O_{10})(OH)_2$ (talc)
Sulfides	Ag_2S (argentite), CdS (greenockite), Cu_2S (chalcocite), FeS_2 (pyrite), HgS (cinnabar), PbS (galena), ZnS (sphalerite)
Sulfates	$BaSO_4$ (barite), $CaSO_4$ (anhydrite), $PbSO_4$ (anglesite), $SrSO_4$ (celestite), $MgSO_4 \cdot 7H_2O$ (epsomite)

Figure 21.1 Metals and their best-known minerals. Lithium is found in spodumene ($LiAlSi_2O_6$), and beryllium in beryl (see Table 21.1). The rest of the alkaline earth metals are found in minerals that are carbonates and sulfates. The minerals for Sc, Y, and La are the phosphates. Some metals have more than one type of important mineral. For example, in addition to the sulfide, iron is found as the oxides hematite (Fe_2O_3) and magnetite (Fe_3O_4); and aluminum, in addition to the oxide, is found in beryl ($Be_3Al_2Si_6O_{18}$). Technetium (Tc) is a synthetic element.

Figure 21.2 Magnesium nodules on the ocean floor.

of some metal ions, including Na^+, Mg^{2+}, and Ca^{2+}. Furthermore, vast areas of the ocean floor are covered with *manganese nodules,* which are made up mostly of manganese, along with iron, nickel, copper, and cobalt in a chemically combined state (Figure 21.2).

21.2 METALLURGICAL PROCESSES

Metallurgy is the science and technology of separating metals from their ores and of compounding alloys. An **alloy** is a solid solution either of two or more metals, or of a metal or metals with one or more *nonmetals.* The three principal steps in the recovery of a metal from its ore are (1) preparation of the ore, (2) production of the metal, and (3) purification of the metal.

Preparation of the Ore

In the preliminary treatment of an ore, the desired mineral is separated from waste materials—usually clay and silicate minerals—which are collectively called the *gangue.* One very useful method for carrying out such a separation is called *flotation.*

In this process, the ore is finely ground and added to water containing oil and detergent. The liquid mixture is then beaten or blown to form a froth. The oil preferentially wets the mineral particles, which are then carried to the top in the froth, while the gangue settles to the bottom. The froth is skimmed off, allowed to collapse, and dried to recover the mineral particles.

Another physical separation process makes use of the magnetic properties of certain minerals. *Ferromagnetic* metals are strongly attracted to magnets. The mineral magnetite (Fe_3O_4), in particular, can be separated from the gangue by using a strong electromagnet. Cobalt is another ferromagnetic metal.

Mercury forms amalgams with a number of metals. An **amalgam** is an alloy of mercury with another metal or metals [◂◂ Chapter 19]. Mercury can therefore be used to extract metal from ore. Mercury dissolves the silver and gold in an ore to form a liquid amalgam, which is easily separated from the remaining ore. The gold or silver is recovered by distilling off the mercury.

Production of Metals

Because metals in their combined forms always have positive oxidation numbers, the production of a free metal is a reduction process. Preliminary operations may be necessary to convert the ore to a chemical state more suitable for reduction. For example, an ore may be *roasted* to drive off volatile impurities and at the same time to convert the carbonates and sulfides to the corresponding oxides, which can be reduced more conveniently to yield the pure metals:

$$CaCO_3(s) \longrightarrow CaO(s) + CO_2(g)$$

$$2PbS(s) + 3O_2(g) \longrightarrow 2PbO(s) + 2SO_2(g)$$

This last equation demonstrates that the conversion of sulfides to oxides is a major source of sulfur dioxide, a notorious air pollutant.

How a pure metal is obtained by reduction from its combined form depends on the standard reduction potential of the metal. Table 21.2 outlines the reduction processes for several metals. Most major metallurgical processes now in use involve **pyrometallurgy,** procedures carried out at high temperatures. The reduction in these procedures may be accomplished either chemically or electrolytically.

Chemical Reduction

A more electropositive metal can be used as a reducing agent to separate a less electropositive metal from its compound at high temperatures:

$$V_2O_5(s) + 5Ca(l) \longrightarrow 2V(l) + 5CaO(s)$$

$$TiCl_4(g) + 2Mg(l) \longrightarrow Ti(s) + 2MgCl_2(l)$$

$$Cr_2O_3(s) + 2Al(s) \longrightarrow 2Cr(l) + Al_2O_3(s)$$

$$3Mn_3O_4(s) + 8Al(s) \longrightarrow 9Mn(l) + 4Al_2O_3(s)$$

TABLE 21.2	Reduction Processes for Some Common Metals	
	Metal	**Reduction process**
Decreasing activity of metals ↓	Lithium, sodium, magnesium, calcium	Electrolytic reduction of the molten chloride
	Aluminum	Electrolytic reduction of anhydrous oxide (in molten cryolite)
	Chromium, manganese, titanium, vanadium, iron, zinc	Reduction of the metal oxide with a more electropositive metal, or reduction with coke and carbon monoxide
	Mercury, silver, platinum, copper, gold	These metals occur in the free (uncombined) state, or they can be obtained by roasting their sulfides

In some cases, even molecular hydrogen can be used as a reducing agent, as in the preparation of tungsten (used as filaments in lightbulbs) from tungsten(VI) oxide:

$$WO_3(s) + 3H_2(g) \longrightarrow W(s) + 3H_2O(g)$$

Electrolytic Reduction

Electrolytic reduction is suitable for very electropositive metals, such as sodium, magnesium, and aluminum. The process is usually carried out on the anhydrous molten oxide or halide of the metal:

$$2MO(l) \longrightarrow 2M \text{ (at cathode)} + O_2 \text{ (at anode)}$$

$$2MCl(l) \longrightarrow 2M \text{ (at cathode)} + Cl_2 \text{ (at anode)}$$

We will describe the specific procedures later in this section.

The Metallurgy of Iron

Iron exists in Earth's crust in many different minerals, such as iron pyrite (FeS_2), siderite ($FeCO_3$), hematite (Fe_2O_3), and magnetite (Fe_3O_4, often represented as $FeO \cdot Fe_2O_3$). Of these, hematite and magnetite are particularly suitable for the extraction of iron. The metallurgical processing of iron involves the chemical reduction of the minerals by carbon (in the form of coke) in a blast furnace (Figure 21.3). The concentrated iron ore, limestone ($CaCO_3$), and coke are introduced into the furnace from the top. A blast of hot air is forced up the furnace from the bottom—hence, the name *blast furnace*. The oxygen gas reacts with the carbon in the coke to form mostly carbon monoxide and some carbon dioxide. These reactions are highly exothermic, and as the hot CO and CO_2 gases rise, they react with the iron oxides in different temperature zones as shown in Figure 21.3. The key steps in the extraction of iron are

$$3Fe_2O_3(s) + CO(g) \longrightarrow 2Fe_3O_4(s) + CO_2(g)$$

$$Fe_3O_4(s) + CO(g) \longrightarrow 3FeO(s) + CO_2(g)$$

$$FeO(s) + CO(g) \longrightarrow Fe(l) + CO_2(g)$$

The limestone decomposes in the furnace as follows:

$$CaCO_3(s) \longrightarrow CaO(s) + CO_2(g)$$

The calcium oxide then reacts with the impurities in the iron, which are mostly sand (SiO_2) and aluminum oxide (Al_2O_3):

$$CaO(s) + SiO_2(s) \longrightarrow CaSiO_3(l)$$

$$CaO(s) + Al_2O_3(s) \longrightarrow Ca(AlO_2)_2(l)$$

The mixture of calcium silicate and calcium aluminate that remains molten at the furnace temperature is known as *slag*.

Multi 21.1
Chemical reactions—smelting of iron

Figure 21.3 A blast furnace. Iron ore, limestone, and coke are introduced at the top of the furnace. Iron is obtained from the ore by reduction with carbon.

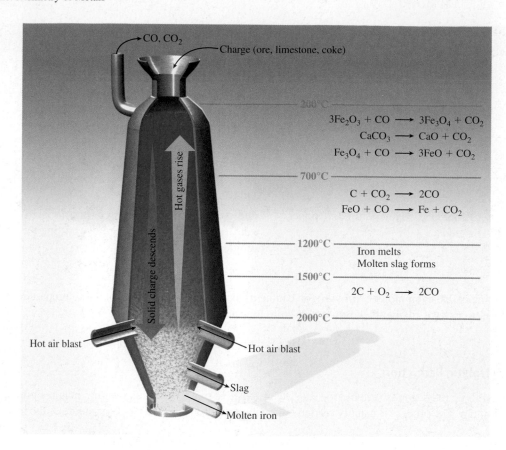

By the time the ore works its way down to the bottom of the furnace, most of it has already been reduced to iron. The temperature of the lower part of the furnace is above the melting point of impure iron, and so the molten iron at the lower level can be run off to a receiver. The slag, because it is less dense, forms the top layer above the molten iron and can be run off at that level, as shown in Figure 21.3.

Iron extracted in this way contains many impurities and is called *pig iron;* it may contain up to 5 percent carbon and some silicon, phosphorus, manganese, and sulfur. Some of the impurities stem from the silicate and phosphate minerals, while carbon and sulfur come from coke. Pig iron is granular and brittle. It has a relatively low melting point (about 1180°C), so it can be cast in various forms; for this reason it is also called *cast iron.*

Steelmaking

Steel manufacturing is one of the most important metal industries. In the United States, the annual consumption of steel is well above 100 million tons. Steel is an iron alloy that contains from 0.03 to 1.4 percent carbon plus various amounts of other elements. The wide range of useful mechanical properties associated with steel is primarily a function of the chemical composition and heat treatment of a particular type of steel.

Whereas the production of iron is basically a reduction process (converting iron oxides to metallic iron), the conversion of iron to steel is essentially an oxidation process in which the unwanted impurities are removed from the iron by reaction with oxygen gas. One of several methods used in steelmaking is the *basic oxygen process.* Because of its ease of operation and the relatively short time (about 20 minutes) required for each large-scale (hundreds of tons) conversion, the basic oxygen process is by far the most common means of producing steel today.

Figure 21.4 shows the basic oxygen process. Molten iron from the blast furnace is poured into an upright cylindrical vessel. Pressurized oxygen gas is introduced via a water-cooled tube above the molten metal. Under these conditions, manganese, phosphorus, and silicon, as well as excess carbon, react with oxygen to form oxides. These oxides are then reacted with the appropriate fluxes (e.g., CaO or SiO_2) to form slag. The type of flux chosen depends on the composition of the iron. If the main impurities are silicon and phosphorus, a basic flux such as CaO is added to the iron:

$$SiO_2(s) + CaO(s) \longrightarrow CaSiO_3(l)$$

$$P_4O_{10}(l) + 6CaO(s) \longrightarrow 2Ca_3(PO_4)_2(l)$$

Figure 21.4 The basic oxygen process of steelmaking. The capacity of a typical vessel is 100 tons of cast iron.

On the other hand, if manganese is the main impurity, then an acidic flux such as SiO_2 is needed to form the slag:

$$MnO(s) + SiO_2(s) \longrightarrow MnSiO_3(l)$$

The molten steel is sampled at intervals. When the desired blend of carbon and other impurities has been reached, the vessel is rotated to a horizontal position so that the molten steel can be tapped off (Figure 21.5).

The properties of steel depend not only on its chemical composition but also on the heat treatment. At high temperatures, iron and carbon in steel combine to form iron carbide (Fe_3C), called *cementite:*

$$3Fe(s) + C(s) \longrightarrow Fe_3C(s)$$

The forward reaction is endothermic, so the formation of cementite is favored at high temperatures. When steel containing cementite is cooled slowly, the preceding equilibrium shifts to the left and the carbon separates as small particles of graphite, which give the steel a grey color. (Very slow decomposition of cementite also takes place at room temperature.) If the steel is cooled rapidly, equilibrium is not attained and the carbon remains largely in the form of cementite (Fe_3C). Steel containing cementite is light in color, and it is harder and more brittle than that containing graphite.

Heating the steel to some appropriate temperature for a short time and then cooling it rapidly to give it the desired mechanical properties is known as "tempering." In this way, the ratio of carbon present as graphite and as cementite can be varied within rather wide limits. Table 21.3 lists the composition, properties, and uses of various types of steel.

Figure 21.5 Steelmaking.

TABLE 21.3	Types of Steel								
	Composition (percent by mass)*								
Type	C	Mn	P	S	Si	Ni	Cr	Others	Uses
Plain	1.35	1.65	0.04	0.05	0.06	—	—	Cu (0.2–0.6)	Sheet products, tools
High-strength	0.25	1.65	0.04	0.05	0.15–0.9	0.4–1.0	0.3–1.3	Cu (0.01–0.08)	Construction, steam turbines
Stainless	0.03–1.2	1.0–10	0.04–0.06	0.03	1–3	1–22	4.0–27	—	Kitchen utensils, razor blades

*A single number indicates the maximum amount of the substance present.

Purification of Metals

Metals prepared by reduction usually need further treatment to remove impurities. The extent of purification depends on how the metal will be used. Three common purification procedures are distillation, electrolysis, and zone refining.

Distillation

Metals that have low boiling points, such as mercury, magnesium, and zinc, can be separated from other metals by fractional distillation. One well-known method of fractional distillation is the *Mond*[1] *process* for the purification of nickel. Carbon monoxide gas is passed over the impure nickel metal at about 70°C to form the volatile tetracarbonylnickel (b.p. 43°C), a highly toxic substance, which is separated from the less volatile impurities by distillation:

$$Ni(s) + 4CO(g) \longrightarrow Ni(CO)_4(g)$$

Pure metallic nickel is recovered from $Ni(CO)_4$ by heating the gas at 200°C:

$$Ni(CO)_4(g) \longrightarrow Ni(s) + 4CO(g)$$

The carbon monoxide that is released is recycled back into the process.

Electrolysis

Electrolysis is another important purification technique. The copper metal obtained by roasting copper sulfide usually contains impurities such as zinc, iron, silver, and gold. The more electropositive metals are removed by an electrolysis process in which the impure copper acts as the anode and *pure* copper acts as the cathode in a sulfuric acid solution containing Cu^{2+} ions (Figure 21.6). The reactions are

Anode (oxidation): $\qquad\qquad$ $Cu(s) \longrightarrow Cu^{2+}(aq) + 2e^-$

Cathode (reduction): $\quad$ $Cu^{2+}(aq) + 2e^- \longrightarrow Cu(s)$

Reactive metals in the copper anode, such as iron and zinc, are also oxidized at the anode and enter the solution as Fe^{2+} and Zn^{2+} ions. They are not reduced at the cathode, however. The less electropositive metals, such as gold and silver, are not oxidized at the anode. Eventually, as the copper anode dissolves, these metals fall to the bottom of the cell. Thus, the net result of this electrolysis process is the transfer of copper from the anode to the cathode. Copper prepared this way has a purity greater than 99.5 percent (Figure 21.7).

Zone Refining

Another often-used method of obtaining extremely pure metals is zone refining. In this process, a metal rod containing a few impurities is drawn through an electric heating coil that melts the metal (Figure 21.8). Most impurities dissolve in the molten metal. As the metal rod emerges from the heating coil, it cools and the pure metal crystallizes, leaving the impurities in the molten metal portion

Figure 21.6 Electrolytic purification of copper.

Figure 21.7 Copper cathodes used in the electrorefining process.

---

[1]Ludwig Mond (1839–1909), a British chemist of German origin, made many important contributions to industrial chemistry. His method for purifying nickel by converting it to the volatile $Ni(CO)_4$ compound has been described as having given "wings" to the metal.

Thinking Outside the Box

Copper

Calcium, potassium, and sodium are the three most abundant metals in the human body. Present in a much smaller amount, copper is nonetheless vitally important to human health. Copper-dependent enzymes known as *cuproenzymes* play a critical role in a host of biochemical processes, including cellular energy production, connective tissue formation, and reactions essential to normal functioning of the brain and central nervous system. Two hereditary diseases that involve errors of copper metabolism are Menkes disease and Wilson's disease.

In Menkes disease, copper is not absorbed in the intestine and is not available for distribution throughout the body. Consequently, cuproenzymes such as *cytochrome c oxidase, lysyl oxidase,* and *dopamine beta hydroxylase* cannot function normally. Sufferers exhibit severe developmental delay; subnormal body temperature; kinky, steel-colored hair; seizures; and ultimately the degeneration of muscle, bone, and organs. Baby boys born with the most severe form of Menkes disease typically do not live beyond their third year of life.

Wilson's disease causes the body to *retain* copper. Although people with Wilson's disease are able to absorb copper in the intestine, the liver of a person with Wilson's disease does not release copper into the bile as it should. Eventually, damaged by the buildup of copper, the liver releases copper directly into the blood, where it is carried throughout the body. Excess copper causes damage to the kidneys, brain, and eyes. Unlike Menkes disease, Wilson's disease can be managed and treated. Sufferers must follow a strict low-copper diet, avoiding such foods as mushrooms, nuts, and chocolate. In addition, they must undergo lifelong periodic chelation therapy.

Most health problems related to copper are the result of errors in copper metabolism. However, although it is rare, copper deficiency can result from a diet that is poor in copper. Symptoms of dietary copper deficiency include anemia (a deficiency of red blood cells) and neutropenia (a deficiency of a particular type of white blood cell).

The fact that copper is essential to human health was first demonstrated with a group of children in Peru. One patient's ordeal was detailed by Cordano and Graham in the journal *Pediatrics* in 1966. During her first few years of life, the patient was hospitalized several times with anemia, neutropenia, osteoporosis, and multiple fractures. At age 6, over a period of 3 months, she received 20 blood transfusions for her severe anemia, which had not responded to treatment. When Dr. Cordano became aware of the patient's history, he initiated treatment with copper supplementation. The patient never required another transfusion and after 6 months on copper supplements, at age 7, she walked for the first time in her life.

> **Student Annotation:** Menkes disease is an X-linked recessive condition and nearly all victims are male.

that is still in the heating coil. (This is analogous to the freezing of seawater, in which the solid that separates is mostly pure solvent—water. In zone refining, the liquid metal acts as the solvent and the impurities act as the solutes.) When the molten zone carrying the impurities, now at increased concentration, reaches the end of the rod, it is allowed to cool and is then cut off. Repeating this procedure a number of times results in metal with a purity greater than 99.99 percent.

Figure 21.8 Zone-refining technique for purifying metals. Top to bottom: An impure metal rod is moved slowly through a heating coil. As the metal rod moves forward, the impurities dissolve in the molten portion of the metal while pure metal crystallizes out in front of the molten zone.

21.3 BAND THEORY OF CONDUCTIVITY

To gain a better understanding of the conductivity properties of metals, we must also apply our knowledge of quantum mechanics. The model we will use to study metallic bonding is **band theory,** so called because it states that delocalized electrons move freely through "bands" formed by overlapping molecular orbitals. We will also apply band theory to certain elements that are semiconductors.

Conductors

Metals are characterized by high electrical conductivity. Consider magnesium, for example. The electron configuration of Mg is $[Ne]3s^2$, so each atom has two valence electrons in the $3s$ orbital. In a metallic crystal, the atoms are packed closely together, so the energy levels of each magnesium atom are affected by the immediate neighbors of the atom as a result of orbital overlaps. According to molecular orbital theory [◄◄ Section 7.6], the interaction between two atomic orbitals leads to the formation of a bonding and an antibonding molecular orbital. Because the number of atoms in even a small piece of magnesium is enormously large (on the order of 10^{20} atoms), the number of molecular orbitals they form is also very large. These molecular orbitals are so closely spaced on the energy scale that they are more appropriately described as a "band" (Figure 21.9). The closely spaced *filled* energy levels make up the *valence band.* The upper half of the energy levels corresponds to the empty, delocalized molecular orbitals formed by the overlap of the $3p$ orbitals. This set of closely spaced *empty* levels is called the *conduction band.*

We can imagine a metallic crystal as an array of positive ions immersed in a sea of delocalized valence electrons. The great cohesive force resulting from the delocalization is partly responsible for the strength noted in most metals. Because the valence band and the conduction band are adjacent to each other, the amount of energy needed to promote a valence electron to the conduction band is negligible. There the electron can travel freely through the metal, because the conduction band is void of electrons. This freedom of movement explains why metals are good *conductors*—that is, they are capable of conducting an electric current.

Why don't substances like wood and glass conduct electricity as metals do? Figure 21.10 provides an answer to this question. Basically, the electrical conductivity of a solid depends on the spacing of the energy bands and the extent to which they are occupied. In magnesium and other metals, the valence bands are adjacent to the conduction bands, so these metals readily act as conductors. In wood and glass, on the other hand, the gap between the valence band and the conduction band is considerably greater than it is in a metal. Consequently, much more energy is needed to excite an electron into the conduction band. Lacking this energy, electrons cannot move freely. Therefore, glass and wood are **insulators,** ineffective conductors of electricity.

Semiconductors

Semiconductors are elements that normally are *not* conductors, but will conduct electricity at elevated temperatures or when combined with a small amount of certain other elements. The Group 4A elements silicon and germanium are especially suited for this purpose. The use of semiconductors

Figure 21.9 Formation of conduction bands in magnesium. The electrons in the 1s, 2s, and 2p orbitals are localized on each Mg atom. However, the 3s and 3p orbitals overlap to form delocalized molecular orbitals. Electrons in these orbitals can travel throughout the metal, and this accounts for the electrical conductivity of the metal.

Figure 21.10 Comparison of the energy gaps between the valence band and the conduction band in a metal, a semiconductor, and an insulator. In a metal the energy gap is virtually nonexistent; in a semiconductor the energy gap is small; and in an insulator the energy gap is very large, thus making the promotion of an electron from the valence band to the conduction band difficult.

in transistors and solar cells, to name two applications, has revolutionized the electronic industry in recent decades, leading to the increased miniaturization of electronic equipment.

The energy gap between the filled and empty bands of these solids is much smaller than it is for insulators (see Figure 21.10). If the energy needed to excite electrons from the valence band into the conduction band is provided, the solid becomes a conductor. This behavior is opposite that of the metals. A metal's ability to conduct electricity decreases with increasing temperature, because the enhanced vibration of atoms at higher temperatures tends to disrupt the flow of electrons.

The ability of a semiconductor to conduct electricity can also be enhanced by adding small amounts of certain impurities to the element, a process called *doping*. Consider what happens, for example, when a trace amount of boron or phosphorus is added to solid silicon. (Only about five out of every million Si atoms are replaced by B or P atoms.) The structure of solid silicon is similar to that of diamond; that is, each Si atom is covalently bonded to four other Si atoms. Phosphorus ($[Ne]3s^23p^3$) has one more valence electron than silicon ($[Ne]3s^23p^2$), so there is a valence electron left over after four of them are used to form covalent bonds with silicon (Figure 21.11).

This extra electron can be removed from the phosphorus atom by applying a voltage across the solid. The free electron can move through the structure and function as a conduction electron. Impurities of this type are known as *donor impurities,* because they provide conduction electrons. Solids containing donor impurities are called ***n-type semiconductors,*** where n stands for negative (the charge of the "extra" electron).

The opposite effect occurs if boron is added to silicon. A boron atom has three valence electrons ($1s^22s^22p^1$), one less than silicon. Thus, for every boron atom in the silicon crystal, there is a single *vacancy* in a bonding orbital. It is possible, though, to excite a valence electron from a nearby Si into this vacant orbital. A vacancy created at that Si atom can then be filled by an electron from a neighboring Si atom, and so on. In this manner, electrons can move through the crystal in one direction while the vacancies, or "positive holes," move in the opposite direction, and the solid becomes an electrical conductor. Impurities that are electron deficient are called *acceptor impurities.* Semiconductors that contain acceptor impurities are called ***p-type semiconductors,*** where p stands for positive.

In both the p-type and n-type semiconductors, the energy gap between the valence band and the conduction band is effectively reduced, so only a small amount of energy is needed to excite the electrons. Typically, the conductivity of a semiconductor is increased by a factor of 100,000 or so by the presence of impurity atoms.

The growth of the semiconductor industry since the early 1960s has been truly remarkable. Today semiconductors are essential components of nearly all electronic equipment, ranging from radios and television sets to pocket calculators and computers. One of the main advantages of solid-state devices over vacuum-tube electronics is that the former can be made on a single "chip" of silicon no larger than the cross section of a pencil eraser. Consequently, much more equipment can be packed into a small volume—a point of particular importance in space travel, as well as in handheld calculators and microprocessors (computers-on-a-chip).

(a)   (b)

Figure 21.11 (a) Silicon crystal doped with phosphorus. (b) Silicon crystal doped with boron. Note the formation of a negative center in (a) and a positive center in (b).

Figure 21.12 Main group metals (green) and Group 2B metals (blue) according to their positions in the periodic table.

Figure 21.12 Main group metals (green) and Group 2B metals (blue) according to their positions in the periodic table.

21.4 PERIODIC TRENDS IN METALLIC PROPERTIES

Metals are lustrous in appearance, solid at room temperature (with the exception of mercury), good conductors of heat and electricity, malleable (can be hammered flat), and ductile (can be drawn into wires). Figure 21.12 shows the positions of the representative metals and the Group 2B metals in the periodic table. (The transition metals are discussed in Chapter 22.) As we saw in Chapter 6, the electronegativity of elements increases from left to right across a period and from bottom to top in a group [◄◄ Section 6.2]. The metallic character of metals increases in just the opposite directions— that is, from right to left across a period and from top to bottom in a group. Because metals generally have low electronegativities, they tend to form cations and almost always have positive oxidation numbers in their compounds. However, beryllium and magnesium in Group 2A and the metals in Group 3A and beyond also form covalent compounds.

In Sections 21.5 through 21.7 we will study the chemistry of selected metals from Group 1A (the alkali metals), Group 2A (the alkaline earth metals), and Group 3A (aluminum).

21.5 THE ALKALI METALS

As a group, the alkali metals (the Group 1A elements) are the most electropositive (or the least electronegative) elements known. They exhibit many similar properties, some of which are listed in Table 21.4. Based on their electron configurations, we expect the oxidation number of these elements in their compounds to be +1 because the cations would be isoelectronic with the preceding noble gases. This is indeed the case.

The alkali metals have low melting points and are soft enough to be sliced with a knife. These metals all possess a body-centered crystal structure with low packing efficiency. This accounts for their low densities among metals. In fact, lithium is the lightest metal known. Because of their great

TABLE 21.4	Properties of Alkali Metals				
	Li	**Na**	**K**	**Rb**	**Cs**
Valence electron configuration	$2s^1$	$3s^1$	$4s^1$	$5s^1$	$6s^1$
Density (g/cm^3)	0.534	0.97	0.86	1.53	1.87
Melting point (°C)	179	97.6	63	39	28
Boiling point (°C)	1317	892	770	688	678
Atomic radius (pm)	155	190	235	248	267
Ionic radius (pm)*	60	95	133	148	169
Ionization energy (kJ/mol)	520	496	419	403	375
Electronegativity	1.0	0.9	0.8	0.8	0.7
Standard reduction potential (V)†	−3.05	−2.71	−2.93	−2.93	−2.92

* Refers to the cation M$^+$, where M denotes an alkali metal atom.

† The half-reaction is M$^+(aq) + e^- \longrightarrow$ M(s).

chemical reactivity, the alkali metals never occur naturally in elemental form; instead, they are found combined with halide, sulfate, carbonate, and silicate ions. In this section we will describe the chemistry of two members of Group 1A—sodium and potassium. The chemistry of lithium, rubidium, and cesium is less important; all isotopes of francium, the last member of the group, are radioactive.

Sodium and potassium are about equally abundant in nature. They occur in silicate minerals such as albite ($NaAlSi_3O_8$) and orthoclase ($KAlSi_3O_8$). Over long periods of time (on a geologic scale), silicate minerals are slowly decomposed by wind and rain, and their sodium and potassium ions are converted to more soluble compounds. Eventually rain leaches these compounds out of the soil and carries them to the sea. Yet when we look at the composition of seawater, we find that the concentration ratio of sodium to potassium is about 28 to 1. The reason for this uneven distribution is that potassium is essential to plant growth, while sodium is not. Thus, plants take up many of the potassium ions along the way, while sodium ions are free to move on to the sea. Other minerals that contain sodium or potassium are halite ($NaCl$), shown in Figure 21.13, Chile saltpeter ($NaNO_3$), and sylvite (KCl). Sodium chloride is also obtained from rock salt.

Figure 21.13 Halite ($NaCl$).

Metallic sodium is most conveniently obtained from *molten* sodium chloride by electrolysis in the Downs cell (review Figure 19.10). The melting point of sodium chloride is rather high (801°C), and much energy is needed to keep large amounts of the substance molten. Adding a suitable substance, such as $CaCl_2$, lowers the melting point to about 600°C—a more convenient temperature for the electrolysis process.

Metallic potassium cannot be easily prepared by the electrolysis of molten KCl because it is too soluble in the molten KCl to float to the top of the cell for collection. Moreover, it vaporizes readily at the operating temperatures, creating hazardous conditions. Instead, it is usually obtained by the distillation of molten KCl in the presence of sodium vapor at 892°C. The reaction that takes place at this temperature is

$$Na(g) + KCl(l) \longrightarrow NaCl(l) + K(g)$$

This reaction may seem strange given that potassium is a stronger reducing agent than sodium (see Table 21.4). Potassium has a lower boiling point (770°C) than sodium (892°C), however, so it is more volatile at 892°C and distills off more easily. According to Le Châtelier's principle, constantly removing the potassium vapor drives the reaction to the right, ensuring metallic potassium is recovered.

Sodium and potassium are both extremely reactive, but potassium is the more reactive of the two. Both react with water to form the corresponding hydroxides. In a limited supply of oxygen, sodium burns to form sodium oxide (Na_2O). In the presence of excess oxygen, however, sodium forms the pale-yellow peroxide:

$$2Na(s) + O_2(g) \longrightarrow Na_2O_2(s)$$

Sodium peroxide reacts with water to give an alkaline solution and hydrogen peroxide:

$$Na_2O_2(s) + 2H_2O(l) \longrightarrow 2NaOH(aq) + H_2O_2(aq)$$

Like sodium, potassium forms the peroxide. In addition, potassium also forms the superoxide when it burns in air:

$$K(s) + O_2(g) \longrightarrow KO_2(s)$$

When potassium superoxide reacts with water, oxygen gas is evolved:

$$2KO_2(s) + 2H_2O(l) \longrightarrow 2KOH(aq) + O_2(g) + H_2O_2(aq)$$

This reaction is utilized in breathing equipment (Figure 21.14). Exhaled air contains both moisture and carbon dioxide. The moisture reacts with KO_2 in the apparatus to generate oxygen gas as shown in the preceding reaction. Furthermore, KO_2 also reacts with exhaled CO_2, which produces more oxygen gas:

$$4KO_2(s) + 2CO_2(g) \longrightarrow 2K_2CO_3(s) + 3O_2(g)$$

Thus, a person using the apparatus can continue to breathe oxygen without being exposed to toxic fumes outside.

Sodium and potassium metals dissolve in liquid ammonia to produce beautiful blue solutions:

$$Na \xrightarrow{\text{NH}_3} Na^+ + e^-$$

$$K \xrightarrow{\text{NH}_3} K^+ + e^-$$

Multi 21.2
Periodic table—properties of the alkali and alkaline earth metals

Figure 21.14 Self-contained breathing apparatus.

Both the cation and the electron exist in the solvated form, and the solvated electrons are responsible for the characteristic blue color of such solutions. Metal-ammonia solutions are powerful reducing agents (because they contain free electrons); they are useful in synthesizing both organic and inorganic compounds. It was discovered that the hitherto unknown alkali metal *anions,* M^-, are also formed in such solutions. This means that an ammonia solution of an alkali metal contains ion pairs such as Na^+Na^- and K^+K^-! (In each case, the metal cation exists as a complex ion with *crown ether,* an organic compound with a high affinity for cations.) In fact, these "salts" are so stable that they can be isolated in crystalline form. This finding is of considerable theoretical interest, because it shows clearly that the alkali metals can have an oxidation number of -1, although -1 is not found in ordinary compounds.

Sodium and potassium are essential elements of living matter. Sodium ions and potassium ions are present in intracellular and extracellular fluids, and they are essential for osmotic balance and enzyme functions. We now describe the preparations and uses of several of the important compounds of sodium and potassium.

Sodium Carbonate

Sodium carbonate (called soda ash) is used in all kinds of industrial processes, including water treatment and the manufacture of soaps, detergents, medicines, and food additives. Today about half of all Na_2CO_3 produced is used in the glass industry. Sodium carbonate ranks eleventh among the chemicals produced in the United States. For many years, Na_2CO_3 was produced by the *Solvay*[2] *process,* in which ammonia is first dissolved in a saturated solution of sodium chloride. Bubbling carbon dioxide into the solution precipitates sodium bicarbonate as follows:

$$NH_3(aq) + NaCl(aq) + H_2CO_3(aq) \longrightarrow NaHCO_3(s) + NH_4Cl(aq)$$

Sodium bicarbonate is then separated from the solution and heated to give sodium carbonate:

$$2NaHCO_3(s) \longrightarrow Na_2CO_3(s) + CO_2(g) + H_2O(g)$$

However, the rising cost of ammonia and the pollution problem resulting from the by-products have prompted chemists to look for other sources of sodium carbonate. One is the mineral *trona* $[Na_5(CO_3)_2(HCO_3) \cdot 2H_2O]$, large deposits of which have been found in Wyoming. When trona is crushed and heated, it decomposes as follows:

$$2Na_5(CO_3)_2(HCO_3) + 2H_2O(s) \longrightarrow 5Na_2CO_3(s) + CO_2(g) + 3H_2O(g)$$

The sodium carbonate obtained this way is dissolved in water, the solution is filtered to remove the insoluble impurities, and the sodium carbonate is crystallized as $Na_2CO_3 \cdot 10H_2O$. Finally, the hydrate is heated to give pure, anhydrous sodium carbonate.

Sodium Hydroxide and Potassium Hydroxide

The properties of sodium hydroxide and potassium hydroxide are very similar. These hydroxides are prepared by the electrolysis of aqueous NaCl and KCl solutions; both hydroxides are strong bases and very soluble in water. Sodium hydroxide is used in the manufacture of soap and many organic and inorganic compounds. Potassium hydroxide is used as an electrolyte in some storage batteries, and aqueous potassium hydroxide is used to remove carbon dioxide and sulfur dioxide from air.

Sodium Nitrate and Potassium Nitrate

Large deposits of sodium nitrate (*Chile saltpeter*) are found in Chile. It decomposes with the evolution of oxygen at about 500°C:

$$2NaNO_3(s) \longrightarrow 2NaNO_2(s) + O_2(g)$$

Potassium nitrate (*saltpeter*) is prepared beginning with the "reaction"

$$KCl(aq) + NaNO_3(aq) \longrightarrow KNO_3(aq) + NaCl(aq)$$

---

[2]Ernest Solvay (1838–1922) was a Belgian chemist. Solvay's main contribution to industrial chemistry was the development of the process for the production of sodium carbonate that now bears his name.

This process is carried out just below 100°C. Because KNO_3 is the least soluble salt at room temperature, it is separated from the solution by fractional crystallization. Like $NaNO_3$, KNO_3 decomposes when heated.

Gunpowder consists of potassium nitrate, wood charcoal, and sulfur in the approximate proportions of 6:1:1 by mass. When gunpowder is heated, the reaction is

$$2KNO_3(s) + S(l) + 3C(s) \longrightarrow K_2S(s) + N_2(g) + 3CO_2(g)$$

The sudden formation of hot nitrogen and carbon dioxide gases causes an explosion.

21.6 THE ALKALINE EARTH METALS

The alkaline earth metals are somewhat less electropositive and less reactive than the alkali metals. Except for the first member of the family, beryllium, which resembles aluminum (a Group 3A metal) in some respects, the alkaline earth metals have similar chemical properties. Because their M^{2+} ions attain the stable electron configuration of the preceding noble gas, the oxidation number of alkaline earth metals in the combined form is almost always +2. Table 21.5 lists some common properties of these metals. Radium is not included in the table because all radium isotopes are radioactive and it is difficult and expensive to study the chemistry of this Group 2A element.

Magnesium

Magnesium is the sixth most plentiful element in Earth's crust (about 2.5 percent by mass). Among the principal magnesium ores are brucite [$Mg(OH)_2$], dolomite ($CaCO_3 \cdot MgCO_3$) (Figure 21.15), and epsomite ($MgSO_4 \cdot 7H_2O$). Seawater is a good source of magnesium—there are about 1.3 g of magnesium in each kilogram of seawater. As is the case with most alkali and alkaline earth metals, metallic magnesium is obtained by electrolysis, in this case from its molten chloride, $MgCl_2$ (obtained from seawater).

The chemistry of magnesium is intermediate between that of beryllium and the heavier Group 2A elements. Magnesium does not react with cold water but does react slowly with steam:

$$Mg(s) + H_2O(g) \longrightarrow MgO(s) + H_2(g)$$

It burns brilliantly in air to produce magnesium oxide and magnesium nitride:

$$2Mg(s) + O_2(g) \longrightarrow 2MgO(s)$$

$$3Mg(s) + N_2(g) \longrightarrow Mg_3N_2(s)$$

Figure 21.15 Dolomite ($CaCO_3 \cdot MgCO_3$).

TABLE 21.5	Properties of Alkaline Earth Metals				
	Be	**Mg**	**Ca**	**Sr**	**Ba**
Valence electron configuration	$2s^2$	$3s^2$	$4s^2$	$5s^2$	$6s^2$
Density (g/cm³)	1.86	1.74	1.55	2.6	3.5
Melting point (°C)	1280	650	838	770	714
Boiling point (°C)	2770	1107	1484	1380	1640
Atomic radius (pm)	112	160	197	215	222
Ionic radius (pm)*	31	65	99	113	135
First ionization energy (kJ/mol)	899	738	590	548	502
Second ionization energy (kJ/mol)	1757	1450	1145	1058	958
Electronegativity	1.5	1.2	1.0	1.0	0.9
Standard reduction potential (V)†	−1.85	−2.37	−2.87	−2.89	−2.90

* Refers to the cation M^{2+}, where M denotes an alkali earth metal atom.

† The half-reaction is $M^{2+}(aq) + 2e^- \longrightarrow M(s)$.

This property makes magnesium (in the form of thin ribbons or fibers) useful in flash photography and flares.

Magnesium oxide reacts very slowly with water to form magnesium hydroxide, a white solid suspension called *milk of magnesia,* which is used to treat acid indigestion:

$$MgO(s) + H_2O(l) \longrightarrow Mg(OH)_2(s)$$

Magnesium is a typical alkaline earth metal in that its hydroxide is a strong base. [The only alkaline earth hydroxide that is not a strong base is $Be(OH)_2$, which is amphoteric.]

The major uses of magnesium are in lightweight structural alloys, for cathodic protection; in organic synthesis; and in batteries. Magnesium is essential to plant and animal life, and Mg^{2+} ions are not toxic. It is estimated that the average adult ingests about 0.3 g of magnesium ions daily. Magnesium plays several important biological roles. It is present, for instance, in intracellular and extracellular fluids, and magnesium ions are essential for the proper functioning of a number of enzymes. Magnesium is also present in the green plant pigment chlorophyll, which plays an important part in photosynthesis.

Calcium

Figure 21.16 Fluorite (CaF_2).

Earth's crust contains about 3.4 percent calcium by mass. Calcium occurs in limestone, calcite, chalk, and marble as $CaCO_3$; in dolomite as $CaCO_3 \cdot MgCO_3$ (see Figure 21.15); in gypsum as $CaSO_4 \cdot 2H_2O$; and in fluorite as CaF_2 (Figure 21.16). Metallic calcium is best prepared by the electrolysis of molten calcium chloride ($CaCl_2$).

As we read down Group 2A from beryllium to barium, metallic properties increase. Unlike beryllium and magnesium, calcium (like strontium and barium) reacts with cold water to yield the corresponding hydroxide, although the rate of reaction is much slower than those involving the alkali metals:

$$Ca(s) + 2H_2O(l) \longrightarrow Ca(OH)_2(aq) + H_2(g)$$

Calcium hydroxide [$Ca(OH)_2$] is commonly known as slaked lime or hydrated lime. Lime (CaO), which is also referred to as quicklime, is one of the oldest materials known to humankind. Quicklime is produced by the thermal decomposition of calcium carbonate:

$$CaCO_3(s) \longrightarrow CaO(s) + CO_2(g)$$

whereas slaked lime is produced by the reaction between quicklime and water:

$$CaO(s) + H_2O(l) \longrightarrow Ca(OH)_2(aq)$$

Quicklime is used in metallurgy (see Section 21.2) and in the removal of SO_2 when fossil fuel is burned. Slaked lime is used in water treatment. For many years, farmers have used lime to lower the acidity of the soil for their crops (a process called *liming*). Nowadays lime is also applied to lakes affected by acid rain.

Metallic calcium has rather limited uses. It serves mainly as an alloying agent for metals like aluminum and copper and in the preparation of beryllium metal from its compounds. It is also used as a dehydrating agent for organic solvents.

Calcium is an essential element in living matter. It is the major component of bones and teeth; the calcium ion is present in a complex phosphate salt called hydroxyapatite [$Ca_5(PO_4)_3OH$]. A characteristic function of Ca^{2+} ions in living systems is the activation of a variety of metabolic processes, including a vital role in heart action, blood clotting, muscle contraction, and nerve impulse transmission.

Figure 21.17 Corundum (Al_2O_3).

21.7 ALUMINUM

Aluminum is the most abundant metal and the third most plentiful element in Earth's crust (7.5 percent by mass). The elemental form does not occur in nature; instead, its principal ore is bauxite ($Al_2O_3 \cdot 2H_2O$). Other minerals containing aluminum are orthoclase ($KAlSi_3O_8$), beryl ($Be_3Al_2Si_6O_{18}$), cryolite (Na_3AlF_6), and corundum (Al_2O_3) (Figure 21.17).

Aluminum is usually prepared from bauxite, which is frequently contaminated with silica (SiO_2), iron oxides, and titanium(IV) oxide. The ore is first heated in sodium hydroxide solution to convert the silica into soluble silicates:

$$SiO_2(s) + 2OH^-(aq) \longrightarrow SiO_3^{2-}(aq) + H_2O(l)$$

At the same time, aluminum oxide is converted to the aluminate ion (AlO_2^-):

$$Al_2O_3(s) + 2OH^-(aq) \longrightarrow 2AlO_2^-(aq) + H_2O(l)$$

Iron oxide and titanium oxide are unaffected by this treatment and are filtered off. Next, the solution is treated with acid to precipitate the insoluble aluminum hydroxide:

$$AlO_2^-(aq) + H_3O^+(aq) \longrightarrow Al(OH)_3(s)$$

After filtration, the aluminum hydroxide is heated to obtain aluminum oxide:

$$2Al(OH)_3(s) \longrightarrow Al_2O_3(s) + 3H_2O(g)$$

Anhydrous aluminum oxide, or *corundum,* is reduced to aluminum by the **Hall[3] process.** Figure 21.18 shows a Hall electrolytic cell, which contains a series of carbon anodes. The cathode is also made of carbon and constitutes the lining inside the cell. The key to the Hall process is the use of cryolite (Na_3AlF_6; m.p. 1000°C) as the solvent for aluminum oxide (m.p. 2045°C). The mixture is electrolyzed to produce aluminum and oxygen gas:

Anode (oxidation): $\qquad\qquad 3[2O^{2-} \longrightarrow O_2(g) + 4e^-]$

Cathode (reduction): $\quad 4[Al^{3+} + 3e^- \longrightarrow Al(l)]$

Overall: $\qquad\qquad\qquad 2Al_2O_3 \longrightarrow 4Al(l) + 3O_2(g)$

Oxygen gas reacts with the carbon anodes (at elevated temperatures) to form carbon monoxide, which escapes as a gas. The liquid aluminum metal (m.p. 660.2°C) sinks to the bottom of the vessel, from which it can be drained from time to time during the procedure.

Aluminum is one of the most versatile metals known. It has a low density (2.7 g/cm³) and high tensile strength (i.e., it can be stretched or drawn out). Aluminum is malleable, it can be rolled into thin foils, and it is an excellent electrical conductor. Its conductivity is about 65 percent that of

Figure 21.18 Electrolytic production of aluminum based on the Hall process.

---

[3]Charles Martin Hall (1863–1914). While Hall, an American inventor, was an undergraduate at Oberlin College, he became interested in finding an inexpensive way to extract aluminum. Shortly after graduation, when he was only 22 years old, Hall succeeded in obtaining aluminum from aluminum oxide in a backyard woodshed. Amazingly, the same discovery was made at almost the same moment in France by Paul Héroult, another 22-year-old inventor working in a similar makeshift laboratory.

copper. However, because aluminum is cheaper and lighter than copper, it is widely used in high-voltage transmission lines. Although aluminum's chief use is in aircraft construction, the pure metal itself is too soft and weak to withstand much strain. Its mechanical properties are greatly improved by alloying it with small amounts of metals such as copper, magnesium, and manganese, as well as silicon. Aluminum is not used by living systems and is generally considered to be nontoxic.

As we read across the periodic table from left to right in a given period, metallic properties gradually decrease. Thus, although aluminum is considered an active metal, it does not react with water as do sodium and calcium. Aluminum reacts with hydrochloric acid and with strong bases as follows:

$$2Al(s) + 6HCl(aq) \longrightarrow 2AlCl_3(aq) + 3H_2(g)$$

$$2Al(s) + 2NaOH(aq) + 2H_2O(l) \longrightarrow 2NaAlO_2(aq) + 3H_2(g)$$

Aluminum readily forms the oxide Al_2O_3 when exposed to air:

$$4Al(s) + 3O_2(g) \longrightarrow 2Al_2O_3(s)$$

A tenacious film of this oxide protects metallic aluminum from further corrosion and accounts for some of the unexpected inertness of aluminum. Aluminum oxide has a very large exothermic enthalpy of formation ($\Delta H_f^\circ = -1670$ kJ/mol). This property makes aluminum suitable for use in solid propellants for rockets such as those used for some space shuttles. When a mixture of aluminum and ammonium perchlorate (NH_4ClO_4) is ignited, aluminum is oxidized to Al_2O_3, and the heat liberated in the reaction causes the gases that are formed to expand with great force. This action lifts the rocket.

The great affinity of aluminum for oxygen is illustrated nicely by the reaction of aluminum powder with a variety of metal oxides, particularly the transition metal oxides, to produce the corresponding metals. A typical reaction is

$$2Al(s) + Fe_2O_3(s) \longrightarrow Al_2O_3(l) + 2Fe(l) \qquad \Delta H^\circ = -852 \text{ kJ/mol}$$

which can result in temperatures approaching 3000°C. This transformation, which is used in the welding of steel and iron, is called the *thermite reaction* (Figure 21.19).

Figure 21.19 The temperature of a thermite reaction can reach 3000°C.

Aluminum chloride exists as a dimer:

$$
\begin{array}{ccccc}
\text{Cl} & & \text{Cl} & & \text{Cl} \\
 & \text{Al} & & \text{Al} & \\
\text{Cl} & & \text{Cl} & & \text{Cl}
\end{array}
$$

Each of the bridging chlorine atoms forms a normal covalent bond and a *coordinate* covalent bond (each indicated by an arrow) with two aluminum atoms. Each aluminum atom is assumed to be sp^3-hybridized, so the vacant sp^3 hybrid orbital can accept a lone pair from the chlorine atom (Figure 21.20). Aluminum chloride undergoes hydrolysis as follows:

$$\text{AlCl}_3(s) + 3\text{H}_2\text{O}(l) \longrightarrow \text{Al(OH)}_3(s) + 3\text{HCl}(aq)$$

Aluminum hydroxide, like Be(OH)_2, is amphoteric:

$$\text{Al(OH)}_3(s) + 3\text{H}^+(aq) \longrightarrow \text{Al}^{3+}(aq) + 3\text{H}_2\text{O}(l)$$

$$\text{Al(OH)}_3(s) + \text{OH}^-(aq) \longrightarrow \text{Al(OH)}_4^-(aq)$$

In contrast to the boron hydrides, which are a well-defined series of compounds, aluminum hydride is a polymer in which each aluminum atom is surrounded octahedrally by bridging hydrogen atoms (Figure 21.21).

When an aqueous mixture of aluminum sulfate and potassium sulfate is evaporated slowly, crystals of $\text{KAl(SO}_4)_2 \cdot 12\text{H}_2\text{O}$ are formed. Similar crystals can be formed by substituting Na^+ or NH_4^+ for K^+, and Cr^{3+} or Fe^{3+} for Al^{3+}. These compounds are called *alums,* and they have the general formula

$$\text{M}^+\text{M}^{3+}(\text{SO}_4)_2 \cdot 12\text{H}_2\text{O} \qquad \text{M}^+: \text{K}^+, \text{Na}^+, \text{NH}_4^+$$

$$\text{M}^{3+}: \text{Al}^{3+}, \text{Cr}^{3+}, \text{Fe}^{3+}$$

Alums are examples of double salts—that is, salts that contain two different cations.

Figure 21.20 The sp^3 hybridization of an Al atom in Al_2Cl_6. Each Al atom has one vacant sp^3 hybrid orbital that can accept a lone pair from the bridging Cl atom.

Figure 21.21 Structure of aluminum hydride. Note that this compound is a polymer. Each Al atom is surrounded in an octahedral arrangement by six bridging H atoms.

Learning Outcomes

- Define key metallurgy terms including: mineral, ore, alloy, and amalgam.
- Describe the three steps involved in obtaining a metal from its ore.
- List the three common methods used for purifying metals.
- Give in your own words the relevance of band theory to metallic bonding.
- Distinguish between conductors and semiconductors.
- Use the periodic table to predict the metallic character of a series of metals.
- Describe some of the common characteristics of the Group 1A and 2A metals as well as aluminum. Include properties such as melting point, density, and relative reactivity.
- Describe the Hall process.

Chapter Summary

SECTION 21.1
- Depending on their reactivities, metals exist in nature in either the free or combined state. (More reactive metals are found combined with other elements.) Most metals are found in *minerals*. Minerals with high metal content are called *ores*.

SECTION 21.2
- *Metallurgy* involves recovering metal from ores. The three stages of metal recovery are *preparation, separation,* and *purification.* An *alloy* is a solid mixture of one or more metals, sometimes also containing one or more *nonmetals.* An *amalgam* is a mixture of mercury and one or more other metals.
- The methods commonly used for purifying metals are distillation, electrolysis, and zone refining. *Pyrometallurgy* refers to metallurgical processes carried out at high temperatures.

SECTION 21.3
- Metallic bonds can be thought of as the force between positive ions immersed in a sea of electrons. In terms of *band theory,* the atomic orbitals merge to form energy bands.
- A substance is a *conductor* when electrons can be readily promoted to the conduction band, where they are free to move through the substance. In an *insulator,* the energy gap between the valence band and the conduction band is so large that electrons cannot be promoted into the conduction band.
- *Semiconductors* are substances that normally are not conductors but will conduct electricity at elevated temperatures or when combined with a small amount of certain other elements.

Semiconductors in which an electron-rich impurity is added to enhance conduction are known as *n-type semiconductors.* Semiconductors in which an electron-poor impurity is added to enhance conduction are known as *p-type semiconductors.*

SECTION 21.4
- Metals typically are good conductors and are malleable and ductile. Metallic character increases from top to bottom in a group and decreases from left to right across a period.

SECTION 21.5
- The alkali metals are the most reactive of all the metallic elements. They have an oxidation state of $+1$ in their compounds. Under special conditions, some of them can form anions with an oxidation state of -1.

SECTION 21.6
- The alkaline earth metals are somewhat less reactive than the alkali metals. They almost always have an oxidation number of $+2$ in their compounds. The properties of the alkaline earth elements become increasingly metallic from top to bottom in their group.

SECTION 21.7
- Aluminum ordinarily does not react with water due to a protective coating of aluminum oxide; its hydroxide is amphoteric. The *Hall process* is used to reduce aluminum oxide to aluminum.

Key Words

Alloy, 886
Amalgam, 886
Band theory, 892
Conductor, 892

Hall process, 899
Insulator, 892
Metallurgy, 886

Mineral, 885
n-type semiconductor, 893
Ore, 885

p-type semiconductor, 893
Pyrometallurgy, 886
Semiconductor, 892

Questions and Problems

SECTION 21.1:   OCCURRENCE OF METALS

Review Questions

21.1   Define the terms *mineral* and *ore*.
21.2   List three metals that are usually found in an uncombined state in nature and three metals that are always found in a combined state in nature.

Problems

21.3   Write chemical formulas for the following minerals: (a) calcite, (b) dolomite, (c) fluorite, (d) halite, (e) corundum, (f) magnetite, (g) beryl, (h) galena, (i) epsomite, (j) anhydrite.

21.4   Name the following minerals: (a) $MgCO_3$, (b) Na_3AlF_6, (c) Al_2O_3, (d) Ag_2S, (e) HgS, (f) ZnS, (g) $SrSO_4$, (h) $PbCO_3$, (i) MnO_2, (j) TiO_2.

SECTION 21.2:   METALLURGICAL PROCESSES

Review Questions

21.5   Define the terms *metallurgy, alloy,* and *amalgam.*
21.6   Describe the main steps involved in the preparation of an ore.
21.7   What does *roasting* mean in metallurgy? Why is roasting a major source of air pollution and acid rain?

21.8 Describe with examples the chemical and electrolytic reduction processes used in the production of metals.

21.9 Describe the main steps used to purify metals.

21.10 Describe the extraction of iron in a blast furnace.

21.11 Briefly discuss the steelmaking process.

21.12 Briefly describe the zone refining process.

Problems

21.13 In the Mond process for the purification of nickel, CO is passed over metallic nickel to give $Ni(CO)_4$:

$$Ni(s) + 4CO(g) \rightleftharpoons Ni(CO)_4(g)$$

Given that the standard free energies of formation of $CO(g)$ and $Ni(CO)_4(g)$ are −137.3 and −587.4 kJ/mol, respectively, calculate the equilibrium constant of the reaction at 80°C. (Assume ΔG_f° to be independent of temperature.)

21.14 Copper is purified by electrolysis (see Figure 21.6). A 5.00-kg anode is used in a cell where the current is 37.8 A. How long (in hours) must the current run to dissolve this anode and electroplate it onto the cathode?

21.15 Consider the electrolytic procedure for purifying copper described in Figure 21.6. Suppose that a sample of copper contains the following impurities: Fe, Ag, Zn, Au, Co, Pt, and Pb. Which of the metals will be oxidized and dissolved in solution and which will be unaffected and simply form the sludge that accumulates at the bottom of the cell?

21.16 How would you obtain zinc from sphalerite (ZnS)?

21.17 A certain mine produces 2.0×10^8 kg of copper from chalcopyrite ($CuFeS_2$) each year. The ore contains only 0.80 percent Cu by mass. (a) If the density of the ore is 2.8 g/cm³, calculate the volume (in cm³) of ore removed each year. (b) Calculate the mass (in kg) of SO_2 produced by roasting (assume chalcopyrite to be the only source of sulfur).

21.18 Starting with rutile (TiO_2), explain how you would obtain pure titanium metal. (*Hint:* First convert TiO_2 to $TiCl_4$. Next, reduce $TiCl_4$ with Mg. Look up physical properties of $TiCl_4$, Mg, and $MgCl_2$ in a chemistry handbook.)

21.19 Which of the following compounds would require electrolysis to yield the free metals: Ag_2S, $CaCl_2$, NaCl, Fe_2O_3, Al_2O_3, $TiCl_4$?

21.20 Although iron is only about two-thirds as abundant as aluminum in Earth's crust, mass for mass it costs only about one-quarter as much to produce. Why?

SECTION 21.3: BAND THEORY OF CONDUCTIVITY

Review Questions

21.21 Define the following terms: *conductor, insulator, semiconducting elements, donor impurities, acceptor impurities, n-type semiconductors, p-type semiconductors.*

21.22 Briefly discuss the nature of bonding in metals, insulators, and semiconducting elements.

21.23 Describe the general characteristics of *n*-type and *p*-type semiconductors.

Problems

21.24 State whether silicon would form *n*-type or *p*-type semiconductors with the following elements: Ga, Sb, Al, As.

SECTION 21.4: PERIODIC TRENDS IN METALLIC PROPERTIES

Review Questions

21.25 Discuss the general properties of metals.

21.26 Use periodic trends in ionization energy and electronegativity to show how the metallic character changes within a group.

21.27 Use periodic trends in ionization energy and electronegativity to show how the metallic character changes across a period.

SECTION 21.5: THE ALKALI METALS

Review Questions

21.28 How is sodium prepared commercially?

21.29 Why is potassium usually not prepared electrolytically from one of its salts?

21.30 Describe the uses of the following compounds: NaCl, Na_2CO_3, NaOH, KOH, KO_2.

21.31 Under what conditions do sodium and potassium form Na^- and K^- ions?

Problems

21.32 Complete and balance the following equations:
(a) $K(s) + H_2O(l) \longrightarrow$
(b) $NaH(s) + H_2O(l) \longrightarrow$
(c) $Na(s) + O_2(g) \longrightarrow$
(d) $K(s) + O_2(g) \longrightarrow$

21.33 Write a balanced equation for each of the following reactions: (a) sodium reacts with water, (b) an aqueous solution of NaOH reacts with CO_2, (c) solid Na_2CO_3 reacts with an HCl solution, (d) solid $NaHCO_3$ reacts with an HCl solution, (e) solid $NaHCO_3$ is heated, (f) solid Na_2CO_3 is heated.

21.34 Sodium hydride (NaH) can be used as a drying agent for many organic solvents. Explain how it works.

21.35 Calculate the volume of CO_2 at 10.0°C and 746 mmHg pressure obtained by treating 25.0 g of Na_2CO_3 with an excess of hydrochloric acid.

SECTION 21.6: THE ALKALINE EARTH METALS

Review Questions

21.36 List the common ores of magnesium and calcium.

21.37 How are magnesium and calcium obtained commercially?

Problems

21.38 From the thermodynamic data in Appendix 2, calculate the ΔH° values for the following decompositions:
(a) $MgCO_3(s) \longrightarrow MgO(s) + CO_2(g)$
(b) $CaCO_3(s) \longrightarrow CaO(s) + CO_2(g)$
Which of the two compounds is more easily decomposed by heat?

21.39   Starting with magnesium and concentrated nitric acid, describe how you would prepare magnesium oxide. [*Hint:* First convert Mg to $Mg(NO_3)_2$. Next, MgO can be obtained by heating $Mg(NO_3)_2$.]

21.40   Describe two ways of preparing magnesium chloride.

21.41   The second ionization energy of magnesium is only about twice as great as the first, but the third ionization energy is 10 times as great. Why does it take so much more energy to remove the third electron?

21.42   List the sulfates of the Group 2A metals in order of increasing solubility in water. Explain the trend. (*Hint:* You need to consult a chemistry handbook.)

21.43   Helium contains the same number of electrons in its outer shell as do the alkaline earth metals. Explain why helium is inert whereas the Group 2A metals are not.

21.44   When exposed to air, calcium first forms calcium oxide, which is then converted to calcium hydroxide, and finally to calcium carbonate. Write a balanced equation for each step.

21.45   Write chemical formulas for (a) quicklime and (b) slaked lime.

SECTION 21.7:   ALUMINUM

Review Questions

21.46   Describe the Hall process for preparing aluminum.

21.47   What action renders aluminum inert?

Problems

21.48   Before Hall invented his electrolytic process, aluminum was produced by the reduction of its chloride with an active metal. Which metals would you use for the production of aluminum in that way?

21.49   With the Hall process, how many hours will it take to deposit 664 g of Al at a current of 32.6 A?

21.50   Aluminum forms the complex ions $AlCl_4^-$ and AlF_6^{3-}. Describe the shapes of these ions. $AlCl_6^{3-}$ does not form. Why? (*Hint:* Consider the relative sizes of Al^{3+}, F^-, and Cl^- ions.)

21.51   The overall reaction for the electrolytic production of aluminum by means of the Hall process may be represented as

$$Al_2O_3(s) + 3C(s) \longrightarrow 2Al(l) + 3CO(g)$$

At 1000°C, the standard free-energy change for this process is 594 kJ/mol. (a) Calculate the minimum voltage required to produce 1 mole of aluminum at this temperature. (b) If the actual voltage applied is exactly three times the ideal value, calculate the energy required to produce 1.00 kg of the metal.

21.52   In basic solution, aluminum metal is a strong reducing agent and is oxidized to AlO_2^-. Give balanced equations for the reaction of Al in basic solution with the following: (a) $NaNO_3$, to give ammonia; (b) water, to give hydrogen; (c) Na_2SnO_3, to give metallic tin.

21.53   Write a balanced equation for the thermal decomposition of aluminum nitrate to form aluminum oxide, nitrogen dioxide, and oxygen gas.

21.54   Describe some of the properties of aluminum that make it one of the most versatile metals known.

21.55   The pressure of gaseous Al_2Cl_6 increases more rapidly with temperature than predicted by the ideal gas equation even though Al_2Cl_6 behaves like an ideal gas. Explain.

21.56   Starting with aluminum, describe with balanced equations how you would prepare (a) Al_2Cl_6, (b) Al_2O_3, (c) $Al_2(SO_4)_3$, (d) $NH_4Al(SO_4)_2 \cdot 12H_2O$.

21.57   Explain the change in bonding when Al_2Cl_6 dissociates to form $AlCl_3$ in the gas phase.

ADDITIONAL PROBLEMS

21.58   In steelmaking, nonmetallic impurities such as P, S, and Si are removed as the corresponding oxides. The inside of the furnace is usually lined with $CaCO_3$ and $MgCO_3$, which decompose at high temperatures to yield CaO and MgO. How do CaO and MgO help in the removal of the nonmetallic oxides?

21.59   When 1.164 g of a certain metal sulfide was roasted in air, 0.972 g of the metal oxide was formed. If the oxidation number of the metal is +2, calculate the molar mass of the metal.

21.60   An early view of metallic bonding assumed that bonding in metals consisted of localized, shared electron-pair bonds between metal atoms. What evidence would help you to argue against this viewpoint?

21.61   Referring to Figure 21.6, would you expect H_2O and H to be reduced at the cathode and H_2O oxidized at the anode?

21.62   A 0.450-g sample of steel contains manganese as an impurity. The sample is dissolved in acidic solution and the manganese is oxidized to the permanganate ion MnO_4^-. The MnO_4^- ion is reduced to Mn^{2+} by reacting with 50.0 mL of 0.0800 M $FeSO_4$ solution. The excess Fe^{2+} ions are then oxidized to Fe^{3+} by 22.4 mL of 0.0100 M $K_2Cr_2O_7$. Calculate the percent by mass of manganese in the sample.

21.63   Given that $\Delta G_f^\circ(Fe_2O_3) = -741.0$ kJ/mol and that $\Delta G_f^\circ(Al_2O_3) = -1576.4$ kJ/mol, calculate ΔG° for the following reactions at 25°C:
(a) $2Fe_2O_3(s) \longrightarrow 4Fe(s) + 3O_2(g)$
(b) $2Al_2O_3(s) \longrightarrow 4Al(s) + 3O_2(g)$

21.64   Use compounds of aluminum as examples to explain what is meant by amphoterism.

21.65   When an inert atmosphere is needed for a metallurgical process, nitrogen is frequently used. However, in the reduction of $TiCl_4$ by magnesium, helium is used. Explain why nitrogen is not suitable for this process.

21.66   It has been shown that Na_2 species form in the vapor phase. Describe the formation of the "disodium molecule" in terms of a molecular orbital energy level diagram. Would you expect the alkaline earth metals to exhibit a similar property?

21.67   Explain each of the following statements: (a) An aqueous solution of $AlCl_3$ is acidic. (b) $Al(OH)_3$ is soluble in NaOH solution but not in NH_3 solution.

21.68   Write balanced equations for the following reactions: (a) the heating of aluminum carbonate, (b) the reaction between $AlCl_3$ and K, (c) the reaction between solutions of Na_2CO_3 and $Ca(OH)_2$.

21.69 Write a balanced equation for the reaction between calcium oxide and dilute HCl solution.

21.70 What is wrong with the following procedure for obtaining magnesium?

$$MgCO_3(s) \longrightarrow MgO(s) + CO_2(g)$$

$$MgO(s) + CO(g) \longrightarrow Mg(s) + CO_2(g)$$

21.71 Explain why most metals have a flickering appearance.

21.72 Predict the chemical properties of francium, the last member of Group 1A.

21.73 Describe a medicinal or health-related application for each of the following compounds: NaF, Li_2CO_3, $Mg(OH)_2$, $CaCO_3$, $BaSO_4$.

21.74 The following are two reaction schemes involving magnesium. *Scheme I:* When magnesium burns in oxygen, a white solid (A) is formed. A dissolves in 1 *M* HCl to give a colorless solution (B). Upon addition of Na_2CO_3 to B, a white precipitate is formed (C). On heating, C decomposes to D and a colorless gas is generated (E). When E is passed through limewater [an aqueous suspension of $Ca(OH)_2$], a white precipitate appears (F). *Scheme II:* Magnesium reacts with 1 *M* H_2SO_4 to produce a colorless solution (G). Treating G with an excess of NaOH produces a white precipitate (H). H dissolves in 1 *M* HNO_3 to form a colorless solution. When the solution is slowly evaporated, a white solid (I) appears. On heating I, a brown gas is given off. Identify A–I, and write equations representing the reactions involved.

21.75 Lithium and magnesium exhibit a diagonal relationship in some chemical properties. How does lithium resemble magnesium in its reaction with oxygen

and nitrogen? Consult a handbook of chemistry and compare the solubilities of carbonates, fluorides, and phosphates of these metals.

21.76 To prevent the formation of oxides, peroxides, and superoxides, alkali metals are sometimes stored in an inert atmosphere. Which of the following gases should not be used for lithium: Ne, Ar, N_2, Kr? Why?

21.77 Which of the following metals is not found in the free state in nature: Ag, Cu, Zn, Au, Pt?

21.78 After heating, a metal surface (such as that of a cooking pan or skillet) develops a color pattern like an oil slick on water. Explain.

21.79 A sample of 10.00 g of sodium reacts with oxygen to form 13.83 g of sodium oxide (Na_2O) and sodium peroxide (Na_2O_2). Calculate the percent composition of the mixture.

21.80 The electrical conductance of copper metal decreases with temperature, but that of a $CuSO_4$ solution increases with temperature. Explain.

21.81 As stated in the chapter, potassium superoxide (KO_2) is a useful source of oxygen employed in breathing equipment. Calculate the pressure at which oxygen gas stored at 20°C would have the same density as the oxygen gas provided by KO_2. The density of KO_2 at 20°C is 2.15 g/cm^3.

21.82 Chemical tests of four metals A, B, C, and D show the following results: (a) Only B and C react with 0.5 *M* HCl to give H_2 gas. (b) When B is added to a solution containing the ions of the other metals, metallic A, C, and D are formed. (c) A reacts with 6 *M* HNO_3, but D does not. Arrange the metals in the increasing order as reducing agents. Suggest four metals that fit these descriptions.

CHAPTER 22

Coordination Chemistry

22.1 **Coordination Compounds**
- Properties of Transition Metals • Ligands
- Nomenclature of Coordination Compounds

22.2 **Structure of Coordination Compounds**

22.3 **Bonding in Coordination Compounds: Crystal Field Theory**
- Crystal Field Splitting in Octahedral Complexes
- Color • Magnetic Properties • Tetrahedral and Square-Planar Complexes

22.4 **Reactions of Coordination Compounds**

22.5 **Applications of Coordination Compounds**

Because they contain unpaired electrons, transition metals and their compounds are attractive for use in magnetic applications. Chemists can manipulate the magnetic states in transition-metal compounds and alloys, tailoring them for a variety of specific uses. These powerful magnets can be incorporated into appplications such as electric motors and generators, magnetic resonance imaging (MRI) instruments, and magnetic levitation transportation (maglev) (shown here) which operates by suspending, guiding, and propelling vehicles using electromagnetic forces.

22.1 COORDINATION COMPOUNDS

Coordination compounds contain *coordinate covalent* bonds [◀◀ Section 6.6] formed by the reactions of metal ions with groups of *anions* or *polar molecules*. The metal ion in these kinds of reactions acts as a Lewis acid, accepting electrons, whereas the anions or polar molecules act as Lewis bases, donating pairs of electrons to form bonds to the metal ion. Thus, a coordinate covalent bond is a covalent bond in which one of the atoms donates *both* of the electrons that constitute the bond. Often a coordination compound consists of a *complex* ion and one or more *counter* ions. In writing formulas for such coordination compounds, we use square brackets to separate the complex ion from the counter ion.

> **Student Annotation:** A complex ion is one in which a metal cation is covalently bound to one or more molecules or ions [◀◀ Section 17.5].

$$\underline{K_2[PtCl_6]}$$

This compound consists of the complex ion $PtCl_6^{2-}$ and two K^+ counter ions.

Some coordination compounds, such as $Fe(CO)_5$, do not contain complex ions. Most but not all of the metals in coordination compounds are transition metals. Our understanding of the nature of coordination compounds stems from the classic work of Alfred Werner,[1] who prepared and characterized many coordination compounds. In 1893, at the age of 26, Werner proposed what is now commonly referred to as Werner's coordination theory.

> **Student Annotation:** We can use the term *coordination complex* to refer to a compound, such as $Fe(CO)_5$, or to a complex ion.

Nineteenth-century chemists were puzzled by a certain class of reactions that seemed to violate valence theory. For example, the valences of the elements in cobalt(III) chloride and those in ammonia seem to be completely satisfied, and yet these two substances react to form a stable compound having the formula $CoCl_3 \cdot 6NH_3$. To explain this behavior, Werner postulated that most elements exhibit two types of valence: *primary valence* and *secondary valence*. In modern terminology, primary valence corresponds to the oxidation number and secondary valence to the coordination number of the element. In $CoCl_3 \cdot 6NH_3$, according to Werner, cobalt has a primary valence of 3 and a secondary valence of 6.

Today we use the formula $[Co(NH_3)_6]Cl_3$ to indicate that the ammonia molecules and the cobalt atom form a complex ion; the chloride ions are not part of the complex but are counter ions, held to the complex ion by coulombic attraction.

Properties of Transition Metals

Transition metals are those that either have incompletely filled *d* subshells or form ions with incompletely filled *d* subshells (Figure 22.1). Incompletely filled *d* subshells give rise to several notable properties, including distinctive colors, the formation of paramagnetic compounds, catalytic activity, and the tendency to form complex ions. The most common transition metals are scandium through copper, which occupy the fourth row of the periodic table. Table 22.1 lists the electron configurations and some of the properties of these metals.

> **Student Annotation:** The Group 2B metals—Zn, Cd, and Hg—do not fit either of these criteria. As a result, they are *d*-block metals, but they are not actually transition metals.

Most of the transition metals exhibit a close-packed structure in which each atom has a coordination number of 12. Furthermore, these elements have relatively small atomic radii. The combined effect of closest packing and small atomic size results in strong metallic bonds. Therefore, transition metals have higher densities, higher melting points and boiling points, and higher heats of fusion and vaporization than the main group and Group 2B metals (Table 22.2).

Multi 22.1
Chemical reactions—oxidation states of vanadium

---

[1]Alfred Werner (1866–1919). Swiss chemist. Werner started as an organic chemist but did his most notable work in coordination chemistry. For his theory of coordination compounds, Werner was awarded the Nobel Prize in Chemistry in 1913.

Figure 22.1 The transition metals (shown in green). Note that although the Group 2B elements (Zn, Cd, Hg) are described as transition metals by some chemists, neither the metals nor their ions possess incompletely filled *d* subshells.

Student Annotation: The trends in radii, electronegativity, and ionization energy for the first row of transition metals are somewhat different from those for main group elements. This is largely the effect of *shielding* of the 4*s* electrons by the 3*d* electrons.

Student Annotation: The electron configurations of the first row transition metals and their ions were discussed in Section 3.10 and Section 4.5, respectively.

TABLE 22.1	Electron Configurations and Other Properties of the Fourth Period Transition Metals								
	Sc	Ti	V	Cr	Mn	Fe	Co	Ni	Cu
Electron configuration									
M	$4s^2 3d^1$	$4s^2 3d^2$	$4s^2 3d^3$	$4s^1 3d^5$	$4s^2 3d^5$	$4s^2 3d^6$	$4s^2 3d^7$	$4s^2 3d^8$	$4s^1 3d^{10}$
M^{2+}	—	$3d^2$	$3d^3$	$3d^4$	$3d^5$	$3d^6$	$3d^7$	$3d^8$	$3d^9$
M^{3+}	[Ar]	$3d^1$	$3d^2$	$3d^3$	$3d^4$	$3d^5$	$3d^6$	$3d^7$	$3d^8$
Electronegativity									
	1.3	1.5	1.6	1.6	1.5	1.8	1.9	1.9	1.9
Ionization energy (kJ/mol)									
First	631	658	650	652	717	759	760	736	745
Second	1235	1309	1413	1591	1509	1561	1645	1751	1958
Third	2389	2650	2828	2986	3250	2956	3231	3393	3578
Radius (pm)									
M	162	147	134	130	135	126	125	124	128
M^{2+}	—	90	88	85	80	77	75	69	72
M^{3+}	81	77	74	64	66	60	64		

TABLE 22.2	Physical Properties of Elements K to Zn										
	1A	2A				Transition metals					2B
	K	Ca	Sc	Ti	V	Cr	Mn	Fe	Co	Ni	Cu	Zn
Atomic radius (pm)	235	197	162	147	134	130	135	126	125	124	128	138
Melting point (°C)	63.7	838	1539	1668	1900	1875	1245	1536	1495	1453	1083	419.5
Boiling point (°C)	760	1440	2730	3260	3450	2665	2150	3000	2900	2730	2595	906
Density (g/cm³)	0.86	4.51	3.0	4.51	6.1	7.19	7.43	7.86	8.9	8.9	8.96	7.14

Student Annotation: The oxidation state of O in each of these compounds is −2, making those of V, Cr, and Mn +5, +6, and +7, respectively [◄◄ Section 9.4].

Transition metals exhibit variable oxidation states in their compounds. Figure 22.2 shows the oxidation states of the first row of transition metals. Note that all these metals can exhibit the oxidation state +3 and *nearly* all can exhibit the oxidation state +2. Of these two, the +2 oxidation state is somewhat more common for the heavier elements. The highest oxidation state for a transition metal is +7, exhibited by manganese ($4s^2 3d^5$). Transition metals exhibit their highest oxidation states in compounds that contain highly electronegative elements such as oxygen and fluorine—for example, V_2O_5, CrO_3, and Mn_2O_7.

Ligands

The molecules or ions that surround the metal in a complex ion are called **ligands** (Table 22.3). The formation of covalent bonds between ligands and a metal can be thought of as a Lewis acid-base reaction. (Recall that a Lewis base is a species that donates a pair of electrons [◄◄ Section 16.12].) To be a ligand, a molecule or ion must have at least one unshared pair of valence electrons, as these examples illustrate:

Therefore, ligands play the role of Lewis bases. The transition metal, on the other hand, acts as a Lewis acid, accepting (and sharing) pairs of electrons from the Lewis bases.

The atom in a ligand that is bound directly to the metal atom is known as the **donor atom.** For example, *nitrogen* is the donor atom in the $[Cu(NH_3)_4]^{2+}$ complex ion:

				+7				
			+6	+6	+6			
		+5	+5	+5	+5			
	+4	+4	+4	+4	+4	+4		
+3	+3	+3	+3	+3	+3	+3	+3	+3
	+2	+2	+2	+2	+2	+2	+2	+2
								+1
Sc	Ti	V	Cr	Mn	Fe	Co	Ni	Cu

Figure 22.2 Oxidation states of the first row transition metals. The most stable oxidation numbers are shown in red. The zero oxidation state is encountered in some compounds, such as $Ni(CO)_4$ and $Fe(CO)_5$.

TABLE 22.3	Common Ligands
Name	**Structure**
Monodentate	
Ammonia	H—N̈—H with H below
Carbon monoxide	:C≡O:
Chloride ion	:C̈l:⁻
Cyanide ion	[:C≡N:]⁻
Thiocyanate ion	[:S̈—C≡N:]⁻
Water	H—Ö—H
Bidentate	
Ethylenediamine	$H_2\ddot{N}—CH_2—CH_2—\ddot{N}H_2$
Oxalate ion	
Polydentate	
Ethylenediaminetetraacetate ion (EDTA)	

(a)

(b)

Figure 22.3 (a) Structure of a metal-ethylenediamine complex cation, such as $[Co(en)_3]^{2+}$. Each ethylenediamine molecule provides two N donor atoms and is therefore a bidentate ligand. (b) Simplified structure of the same complex cation.

(a)   (b)

Figure 22.4 (a) EDTA complex of lead. The complex bears a net charge of 2− because each O donor atom has one negative charge and the lead ion carries two positive charges. Only the lone pairs that participate in bonding are shown. Note the octahedral geometry about the Pb^{2+} ion. (b) Molecular model of the Pb^{2+}-EDTA complex. The light green sphere is the Pb^{2+} ion.

The ***coordination number*** in a coordination compound refers to the number of donor atoms surrounding the central metal atom in a complex ion. The coordination number of Cu^{2+} in $[Cu(NH_3)_4]^{2+}$ is 4. The most common coordination numbers are 4 and 6, although coordination numbers of 2 and 5 are also known.

Depending on the number of donor atoms a ligand possesses, it is classified as monodentate (1 donor atom), bidentate (2 donor atoms), or polydentate (> 2 donor atoms). Table 22.3 lists some common ligands. Figure 22.3 shows how ethylenediamine, sometimes abbreviated "en," forms two bonds to a metal atom.

Bidentate and polydentate ligands are also called ***chelating agents*** because of their ability to hold the metal atom like a claw (from the Greek *chele,* meaning "claw"). One example is EDTA (Figure 22.4), a polydentate ligand used to treat metal poisoning. Six donor atoms enable EDTA to form a very stable complex ion with lead. This stable complex enables the body to remove lead from the blood.

The oxidation state of a transition metal in a complex ion is determined using the known charges of the *ligands* and the known *overall* charge of the complex ion. In the complex ion $[PtCl_6]^{2-}$, for example, each chloride ion ligand has an oxidation number of −1. For the overall charge of the ion to be −2, the Pt must have an oxidation number of +4.

Worked Example 22.1 shows how to determine transition metal oxidation states in coordination compounds.

Student Annotation: Remember that the oxidation number of a monoatomic ion is equal to the charge [◄◄ Section 9.4].

Worked Example 22.1

Determine the oxidation state of the central metal atom in each of the following compounds:
(a) $[Ru(NH_3)_5(H_2O)]Cl_2$, (b) $[Cr(NH_3)_6](NO_3)_3$, and (c) $Fe(CO)_5$.

Strategy Identify the components of each compound, and use known oxidation states and charges to determine the oxidation state of the metal.

Setup (a) $[Ru(NH_3)_5(H_2O)]Cl_2$ consists of a complex ion (the part of the formula enclosed in square brackets) and two Cl^- counter ions. Because the overall charge on the compound is zero, the complex ion is $[Ru(NH_3)_5(H_2O)]^{2+}$. There are six ligands: five ammonia molecules and one water molecule. Each molecule has a zero charge (i.e., each ligand is neutral), so the charge on the metal is equal to the overall charge on the complex ion.

(b) $[Cr(NH_3)_6](NO_3)_3$ consists of a complex ion and three NO_3^- ions, making the complex ion $[Cr(NH_3)_6]^{3+}$. Each of the six ammonia molecule ligands is neutral (i.e., each has a zero charge), making the charge on the metal equal to the overall charge on the complex ion.

(c) $Fe(CO)_5$ does not contain a complex ion. The ligands are CO molecules, which have a zero charge, so the central metal also has a zero charge.

Solution (a) +2 (b) +3 (c) 0

Think About It
To solve a problem like this, you must be able to recognize the common polyatomic ions and you must know their charges.

Practice Problem A Give oxidation numbers for the metals in (a) $K[Au(OH)_4]$ and (b) $K_4[Fe(CN)_6]$.

Practice Problem B The oxidation state of cobalt in each of the following species is +3. Determine the overall charge on each complex: $[Co(NH_3)_4Cl_2]^?$, $[Co(CN)_6]^?$, $[Co(NH_3)_3Br_3]^?$, $[Co(en)_2Cl_2]^?$, $[Co(en)_3]^?$, $[Co(NH_3)_6]^?$, $[Co(NH_3)_5Cl]^?$.

Nomenclature of Coordination Compounds

Now that we have discussed the various types of ligands and the oxidation numbers of metals, our next step is to learn how to name coordination compounds. The rules for naming ionic coordination compounds are as follows:

1. The cation is named before the anion, as in other ionic compounds. The rule holds regardless of whether the complex ion bears a net positive or a net negative charge. In the compounds $K_2[Fe(CN)_6]$ and $[Co(NH_3)_4]Cl$, for example, we name the K^+ and $[Co(NH_3)_4]^+$ cations first, respectively.
2. Within a complex ion, the ligands are named first, in alphabetical order, and the metal ion is named last.
3. The names of anionic ligands end with the letter *o*, whereas neutral ligands are usually called by the names of the molecules. The exceptions are H_2O (aqua), CO (carbonyl), and NH_3 (ammine). Table 22.4 lists some common ligands and their nomenclature.
4. When two or more of the same ligand are present, use Greek prefixes *di*, *tri*, *tetra*, *penta*, and *hexa*, to specify their number. Thus, the ligands in the cation $[Co(NH_3)_4Cl_2]^+$ are "tetra-amminedichloro." (Note that prefixes are *not* used for the purpose of *alphabetizing* the ligands.)

Student Annotation: When the name of a ligand already contains a Greek prefix, a different set of prefixes is used to denote the number of the ligand:

2	bis
3	tris
4	tetrakis

Two ethylenediamine ligands, for example, would be specified by *bis*(ethylenediamine).

TABLE 22.4	Names of Common Ligands in Coordination Compounds
Ligand	**Name of ligand in coordination compound**
Bromide (Br^-)	Bromo
Chloride (Cl^-)	Chloro
Cyanide (CN^-)	Cyano
Hydroxide (OH^-)	Hydroxo
Oxide (O^{2-})	Oxo
Carbonate (CO_3^{2-})	Carbonato
Nitrite (NO_2^-)	Nitro
Oxalate ($C_2O_4^{2-}$)	Oxalato
Ammonia (NH_3)	Ammine
Carbon monoxide (CO)	Carbonyl
Water (H_2O)	Aqua
Ethylenediamine	Ethylenediamine
Ethylenediaminetetraacetate	Ethylenediaminetetraacetate

TABLE 22.5	Names of Anions Containing Metal Atoms
Metal	**Name of metal in anionic complex**
Aluminum	Aluminate
Chromium	Chromate
Cobalt	Cobaltate
Copper	Cuprate
Gold	Aurate
Iron	Ferrate
Lead	Plumbate
Manganese	Manganate
Molybdenum	Molybdate
Nickel	Nickelate
Silver	Argentate
Tin	Stannate
Tungsten	Tungstate
Zinc	Zincate

5. The oxidation number of the metal is indicated in Roman numerals immediately following the name of the metal. For example, the Roman numeral III is used to indicate the +3 oxidation state of chromium in $[Cr(NH_3)_4Cl_2]^+$, which is called tetraamminedichlorochromium(III) ion.

6. If the complex is an anion, its name ends in *–ate*. In $K_4[Fe(CN)_6]$, for example, the anion $[Fe(CN)_6]^{4-}$ is called hexacyanoferrate(II) ion. Note that the Roman numeral indicating the oxidation state of the metal *follows* the suffix *–ate*. Table 22.5 lists the names of anions containing metal atoms.

> **Student Annotation:** Note that there is no space between the compound name and the parenthetical Roman numeral.

Worked Examples 22.2 and 22.3 apply these rules to the nomenclature of coordination compounds.

Worked Example 22.2

Write the names of the following coordination compounds: (a) $[Co(NH_3)_4Cl_2]Cl$ and (b) $K_3[Fe(CN)_6]$.

Strategy For each compound, name the cation first and the anion second. Refer to Tables 22.4 and 22.5 for the names of ligands and anions containing metal atoms.

Setup (a) The cation is a complex ion containing four ammonia molecules and two chloride ions. The counter ion is chloride (Cl^-), so the charge on the complex cation is +1, making the oxidation state of cobalt +3.

(b) The cation is K^+, and the anion is a complex ion containing six cyanide ions. The charge on the complex ion is −3, making the oxidation state of iron +3.

Solution (a) Tetraamminedichlorocobalt(III) chloride

(b) Potassium hexacyanoferrate(III)

> **Think About It**
> When the anion is a *complex* ion, its name must end in *–ate*, followed by the metal's oxidation state in Roman numerals. Also, do not use prefixes to denote numbers of counter ions.

Practice Problem A Give the correct name for (a) $[Co(NH_3)_4Br_2]Cl$, (b) $[Cr(H_2O)_4Cl_2]Cl$, and (c) $K_2[CuCl_4]$.

Practice Problem B Give the correct name for (a) $Na_3[Fe(CN)_6]$, (b) $[Cr(en)_2Cl_2]Br$, and (c) $[Co(en)_3]Cl_3$. [*Hint:* For parts (b) and (c), read the Student Annotation on page 911 regarding the use of prefixes.]

Worked Example 22.3

Write formulas for the following compounds: (a) pentaamminechlorocobalt(III) chloride and (b) dichloro*bis*(ethylenediamine)platinum(IV) nitrate.

Strategy If you can't remember them yet, refer to Tables 22.4 and 22.5 for the names of ligands and anions containing metal atoms.

Setup (a) There are six ligands: five NH_3 molecules and one Cl^- ion. The oxidation state of cobalt is $+3$, making the overall charge on the complex ion $+2$. Therefore, there are two chloride ions as counter ions.

(b) There are four ligands: two bidentate ethylenediamines and two Cl^- ions. The oxidation state of platinum is $+4$, making the overall charge on the complex ion $+2$. Therefore, there are two nitrate ions as counter ions.

Solution (a) $[Co(NH_3)_5Cl]Cl_2$

(b) $[Pt(en)_2Cl_2](NO_3)_2$

> **Think About It**
> Although ligands are alphabetized in a compound's name, they do not necessarily appear in alphabetical order in the compound's formula.

Practice Problem A Write the formulas for (a) pentaaquabromoruthenium(II) nitrate, (b) potassium tetrabromodichloroplatinate(IV), and (c) sodium hexanitrocobaltate(III).

Practice Problem B Write the formulas for (a) *bis*(ethylenediamine)oxalatovanadium(IV) chloride, (b) dibromo*bis*(ethylenediamine)chromium(III) nitrate, and (c) *tris*(ethylenediamine)platinum(IV) sulfate. (*Hint:* Read the Student Annotation on page 911.)

Thinking Outside the Box

Chelation Therapy

Although the Consumer Product Safety Commission (CPSC) banned the residential use of lead-based paint in 1978, millions of children remain at risk for exposure to lead from deteriorating paint in older homes. Lead poisoning is especially harmful to children under the age of 5 years because it interferes with growth and development and it has been shown to lower IQ. Symptoms of chronic exposure to lead include diminished appetite, nausea, malaise, and convulsions. *Blood lead level* (BLL), expressed as micrograms per deciliter ($\mu g/dL$), is used to monitor the effect of chronic exposure. A BLL $\leq 10\ \mu g/dL$ is considered normal; a BLL $> 45\ \mu g/dL$ requires medical and environmental intervention. At high levels ($>70\ \mu g/dL$), lead can cause seizures, coma, and death.

Treatment for lead poisoning involves *chelation therapy*, in which a chelating agent is administered orally, intravenously, or intramuscularly. Chelating agents form strong coordinate-covalent bonds to metal ions, forming stable, water-soluble complex ions that are easily removed from the body via the urine.

Elevated BLL and other heavy metal poisoning can be treated with one of several chelating agents, including DMSA and EDTA. EDTA is administered intravenously as either the sodium salt (Endrate) or as the calcium disodium salt (Versenate). Endrate is not approved for the treatment of lead poisoning because of its high affinity for calcium. It is approved, however, for treating *hypercalcemia*, a condition in which there is excess calcium in the blood—usually as a result of bone cancer. The accidental use of Endrate during treatment for lead poisoning resulted in the death of a 2-year-old girl in February of 2005. The girl's death was attributed to sudden cardiac arrest caused by the removal of too much calcium from her blood.

Coordination Compounds

22.1.1   Write the correct name for the compound $[Cu(NH_3)_4]Cl_2$.

22.1.2   Write the correct name for the compound $K_3[FeF_6]$.

22.1.3   Write the correct formula for pentaamminenitrocobalt(III).

22.1.4   Write the correct formula for tetraaquadichlorochromium(III) chloride.

22.2 STRUCTURE OF COORDINATION COMPOUNDS

The geometry of a coordination compound often plays a significant role in determining its properties. Figure 22.5 shows four different geometric arrangements for metal atoms with monodentate ligands. In these diagrams we see that structure and the coordination number of the metal relate to each other as follows:

Coordination number	Structure
2	Linear
4	Tetrahedral or square planar
6	Octahedral

> **Student Annotation:** In general, stereoisomers are compounds that are made up of the same types and numbers of atoms, bonded together in the same sequence, but with different spatial arrangements.

In studying the geometry of coordination compounds, we sometimes find that there is more than one way to arrange the ligands around the central atom. Such compounds in which ligands are arranged differently, known as **stereoisomers**, have distinctly different physical and chemical properties. Coordination compounds may exhibit two types of stereoisomerism: *geometric* and *optical*.

Geometrical isomers are stereoisomers that cannot be interconverted without breaking chemical bonds. Geometric isomers come in pairs. We use the terms *cis* and *trans* to distinguish one geometric isomer of a compound from the other. *Cis* means that two particular atoms (or groups of atoms) are adjacent to each other, and *trans* means that the atoms (or groups of atoms) are on opposite sides in the structural formula. The *cis* and *trans* isomers of coordination compounds generally have quite different colors, melting points, dipole moments, and chemical reactivities. Figure 22.6 shows the *cis* and *trans* isomers of diamminedichloroplatinum(II). Note that although the types of bonds are the same in both isomers (two Pt—N and two Pt—Cl bonds), the spatial arrangements are different. Another example is the tetraamminedichlorocobalt(III) ion, shown in Figure 22.7.

Optical isomers are nonsuperimposable mirror images. (*Superimposable* means that if one structure is laid over the other, the positions of all the atoms will match.) Like geometric isomers,

Figure 22.5 Common geometries of complex ions. In each case M is a metal and L is a monodentate ligand.

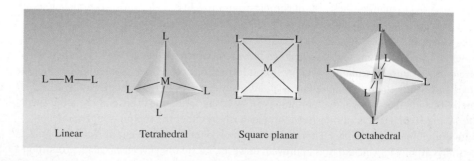

Linear   Tetrahedral   Square planar   Octahedral

Figure 22.6 The (a) *cis* and (b) *trans* isomers of diamminedichloroplatinum(II). Note that the two Cl atoms are adjacent to each other in the *cis* isomer and diagonally across from each other in the *trans* isomer.

(a)   (b)

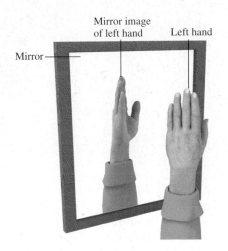

Figure 22.8 A left hand and its mirror image.

optical isomers come in pairs. However, the optical isomers of a compound have *identical* physical and chemical properties, such as melting point, boiling point, dipole moment, and chemical reactivity toward molecules that are not *themselves* optical isomers. Optical isomers differ from each other, though, in their interactions with plane-polarized light, as we will see.

The structural relationship between two optical isomers is analogous to the relationship between your left and right hands. If you place your left hand in front of a mirror, the image you see will look like your right hand (Figure 22.8). Your left hand and right hand are mirror images of each other. They are nonsuperimposable, however, because when you place your left hand over your right hand (with both palms facing down), they do not match. This is why a right-handed glove will not fit comfortably on your left hand.

Figure 22.9 shows the *cis* and *trans* isomers of dichloro*bis*(ethylenediamine)cobalt(III) ion and the mirror image of each. Careful examination reveals that the *trans* isomer and its mirror image are superimposable, but the *cis* isomer and its mirror image are not. Thus, the *cis* isomer and its mirror image are *optical isomers.*

Optical isomers are described as *chiral* (from the Greek word for "hand") because, like your left and right hands, chiral molecules are nonsuperimposable. Isomers that are superimposable with their mirror images are said to be *achiral.* Chiral molecules play a vital role in enzyme reactions in biological systems. Many drug molecules are chiral, although only one of a pair of chiral isomers is biologically effective.

Chiral molecules are said to be optically active because of their ability to rotate the plane of polarization of polarized light as it passes through them. Unlike ordinary light, which vibrates in all directions, plane-polarized light vibrates only in a single plane. We use a ***polarimeter*** to measure the rotation of polarized light by optical isomers (Figure 22.10). A beam of unpolarized light first passes through a Polaroid sheet, called the polarizer, and then through a sample tube containing a solution of an optically active, chiral compound. As the polarized light passes through the sample tube, its plane of polarization is rotated either to the right (clockwise) or to the left (counterclockwise). This rotation can be measured directly by turning the analyzer in the appropriate direction until minimal light transmission is achieved (Figure 22.11). If the plane of polarization is rotated to the right, the isomer is said to be ***dextrorotatory*** and the isomer is labeled *d;* if the rotation is to the left, the isomer is ***levorotatory*** and the isomer is labeled *l.* The *d* and *l* isomers of a chiral substance, called ***enantiomers,*** always rotate the plane of polarization by the same amount, but in opposite directions. Thus, in an equimolar mixture of two enantiomers, called a ***racemic mixture,*** the net rotation is zero.

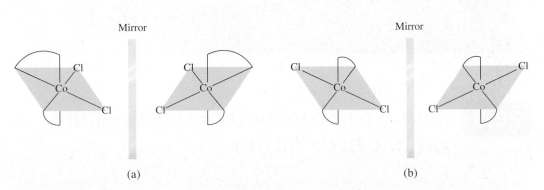

(a) (b)

Figure 22.9 The (a) *cis* and (b) *trans* isomers of dichlorobis(ethylenediamine)cobalt(III) ion and their mirror images. If you could rotate the mirror image in (b) 90° clockwise about the vertical position and place the ion over the *trans* isomer, you would find that the two are superimposable. No matter how you rotate the *cis* isomer and its mirror image in (a), however, you cannot superimpose one on the other.

Figure 22.10 Operation of a polarimeter. Initially, the tube is filled with an achiral compound. The analyzer is rotated so that its plane of polarization is perpendicular to that of the polarizer. Under this condition, no light reaches the observer. Next, a chiral compound is placed in the tube as shown. The plane of polarization of the polarized light is rotated as it travels through the tube so that some light reaches the observer. Rotating the analyzer (either to the left or to the right) until no light reaches the observer again allows the angle of optical rotation to be measured.

Figure 22.11 Polarized lenses. No light passes through the lenses when they are rotated so that their planes of polarization are perpendicular.

22.3 BONDING IN COORDINATION COMPOUNDS: CRYSTAL FIELD THEORY

A satisfactory theory of bonding in coordination compounds must account for properties such as color and magnetism, as well as stereochemistry and bond strength. No single theory as yet does all this for us. Rather, several different approaches have been applied to transition metal complexes. We will consider only one of them here—crystal field theory—because it accounts for both the color and magnetic properties of many coordination compounds.

We will begin our discussion of crystal field theory with the most straightforward case—namely, complex ions with octahedral geometry. Then we will see how it is applied to tetrahedral and square-planar complexes.

Crystal Field Splitting in Octahedral Complexes

Crystal field theory explains the bonding in complex ions purely in terms of electrostatic forces. In a complex ion, two types of electrostatic interaction come into play. One is the attraction between the positive metal ion and the negatively charged ligand or the negatively charged end of a polar ligand. This is the force that binds the ligands to the metal. The second type of interaction is the electrostatic repulsion between the lone pairs on the ligands and the electrons in the d orbitals of the metals.

The d orbitals have different orientations [◀◀ Section 3.8], but in the absence of an external disturbance, they all have the same energy. In an octahedral complex, a central metal atom is surrounded by six lone pairs of electrons (on the six ligands), so all five d orbitals experience electrostatic repulsion. The magnitude of this repulsion depends on the orientation of the d orbital that is involved. Take the $d_{x^2-y^2}$ orbital as an example. In Figure 22.12, we see that the lobes of this orbital point toward the corners of the octahedron along the x and y axes, where the lone-pair electrons are positioned. Thus, an electron residing in this orbital would experience a greater repulsion from the ligands than an electron would in the d_{xy}, d_{yz}, or d_{xz} orbitals. For this reason, the energy of the $d_{x^2-y^2}$ orbital is increased relative to the d_{xy}, d_{yz}, and d_{xz} orbitals. The d_{z^2} orbital's energy is also greater, because its lobes are pointed at the ligands along the z axis. As a result of these metal-ligand interactions, the five d orbitals in an octahedral complex are split between two sets of energy levels: a higher level with two orbitals ($d_{x^2-y^2}$ and d_{z^2}) having the same energy, and a lower level with three equal-energy orbitals (d_{xy}, d_{yz}, and d_{xz}), as shown in Figure 22.13. The ***crystal field splitting*** (Δ) is the energy difference between two sets of d orbitals in a metal atom when ligands are present. The magnitude of Δ depends on the metal and the nature of the ligands; it has a direct effect on the color and magnetic properties of complex ions.

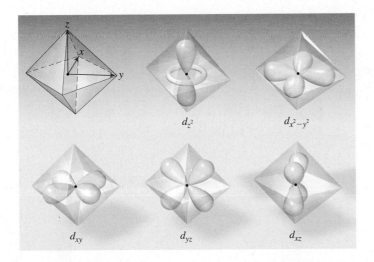

Figure 22.12 The five d orbitals in an octahedral environment. The metal atom (or ion) is at the center of the octahedron, and the six lone pairs on the donor atoms of the ligands are at the corners.

d_{z^2} $d_{x^2-y^2}$

d_{xy} d_{yz} d_{xz}

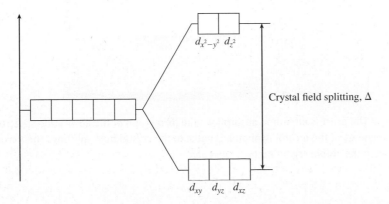

$d_{x^2-y^2}$ d_{z^2}

Crystal field splitting, Δ

d_{xy} d_{yz} d_{xz}

Figure 22.13 Crystal field splitting between d orbitals in an octahedral complex.

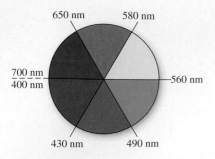

650 nm   580 nm

$\dfrac{700\ nm}{400\ nm}$ 560 nm

430 nm   490 nm

Figure 22.14 A color wheel with appropriate wavelengths. Complementary colors, such as red and green, are on opposite sides of the wheel.

Color

In Chapter 3 we learned that white light, such as sunlight, is a combination of all colors. A substance appears black if it absorbs all the visible light that strikes it. If it absorbs no visible light, it is white or colorless. An object appears green if it absorbs all light but reflects the green component. An object also looks green if it reflects all colors except red, the *complementary* color of green (Figure 22.14).

What has been said of reflected light also applies to *transmitted* light (i.e., the light that passes *through* the medium, such as a solution). Consider the hydrated cupric ion ($[Cu(H_2O)_6]^{2+}$); it absorbs light in the orange region of the spectrum, so a solution of $CuSO_4$ appears blue to us. Recall from Chapter 3 that when the energy of a photon is equal to the difference between the ground state and an excited state, absorption occurs as the photon strikes the atom (or ion or compound), and an electron is promoted to a higher level. Using these concepts, we can calculate the energy change involved in the electron transition. The energy of a photon is given by

$$E = h\nu$$

where h represents Planck's constant (6.63×10^{-34} J · s) and ν is the frequency of the radiation, which is 5.00×10^{14} s^{-1} for a wavelength of 600 nm. Here $E = \Delta$, so we have

$$\Delta = h\nu$$

$$= (6.63 \times 10^{-34}\ \text{J · s})(5.00 \times 10^{14}\ \text{s}^{-1})$$

$$= 3.32 \times 10^{-19}\ \text{J}$$

This value is very small, but it is the energy absorbed by only *one* ion. If the wavelength of the photon absorbed by an ion lies outside the visible region, then the transmitted light looks the same (to us) as the incident light—white—and the ion appears colorless.

The best way to measure crystal field splitting is to use spectroscopy to determine the wavelength at which light is absorbed. The $[Ti(H_2O)_6]^{3+}$ ion provides a straightforward example, because Ti^{3+} has only one $3d$ electron (Figure 22.15). The $[Ti(H_2O)_6]^{3+}$ ion absorbs light in

Figure 22.15 (a) The process of photon absorption, and (b) a graph of the absorption spectrum of $[Ti(H_2O)_6]^{3+}$. The energy of the incoming photon is equal to the crystal field splitting. The maximum absorption peak in the visible region occurs at 498 nm.

the visible region of the spectrum (Figure 22.16). The wavelength corresponding to maximum absorption is 498 nm [Figure 22.15(b)]. To calculate the crystal field splitting energy, we start by writing

$$\Delta = h\nu$$

Next, recall that

$$\nu = \frac{c}{\lambda}$$

where c is the speed of light and λ is the wavelength. Therefore,

$$\Delta = \frac{hc}{\lambda} = \frac{(6.63 \times 10^{-34} \text{ J} \cdot \text{s})(3.00 \times 10^8 \text{ m/s})}{(498 \text{ nm})(1 \times 10^{-9} \text{ m/nm})} = 3.99 \times 10^{-19} \text{ J}$$

This is the energy required to excite *one* $[Ti(H_2O)_6]^{3+}$ ion. To express this energy difference in the more convenient units of kJ/mol, we write

$$\Delta = (3.99 \times 10^{-19} \text{ J/ion})(6.02 \times 10^{23} \text{ ions/mol})$$

$$= 240,000 \text{ J/mol}$$

$$= 240 \text{ kJ/mol}$$

Aided by spectroscopic data for a number of complexes, all having the same metal ion but different ligands, chemists calculated the crystal field splitting for each ligand and established the following *spectrochemical series,* which is a list of ligands arranged in increasing order of their abilities to split the d orbital energy levels:

$$I^- < Br^- < Cl^- < OH^- < F^- < H_2O < NH_3 < en < CN^- < CO$$

These ligands are arranged in the order of increasing value of Δ. CO and CN^- are called *strong-field ligands,* because they cause a large splitting of the d orbital energy levels. The halide ions and hydroxide ion are *weak-field ligands,* because they split the d orbitals to a lesser extent.

Magnetic Properties

The magnitude of the crystal field splitting also determines the magnetic properties of a complex ion. The $[Ti(H_2O)_6]^{3+}$ ion, having only one d electron, is always paramagnetic. However, for an ion with several d electrons, the situation is less immediately clear. Consider, for example, the octahedral complexes $[FeF_6]^{3-}$ and $[Fe(CN)_6]^{3-}$ (Figure 22.17). The electron configuration of Fe^{3+} is $[Ar]3d^5$, and there are two possible ways to distribute the five d electrons among the d orbitals. According to Hund's rule [◄◄ Section 3.9], maximum stability is reached when the electrons are placed in five separate orbitals with parallel spins. This arrangement can be achieved only at a cost, however, because two of the five electrons must be promoted to the higher-energy $d_{x^2-y^2}$ and d_{z^2} orbitals. No such energy investment is needed if all five electrons enter the d_{xy}, d_{yz}, and d_{xz} orbitals.

Figure 22.16 Colors of some of the first row transition metal ions in solution. From left to right: Ti^{3+}, Cr^{3+}, Mn^{2+}, Fe^{3+}, Co^{2+}, Ni^{2+}, Cu^{2+}. The Sc^{3+} and V^{5+} ions are colorless.

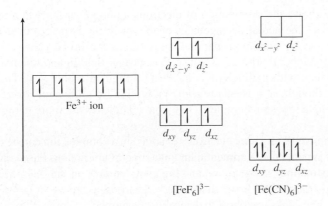

Figure 22.17 Energy-level diagrams for the Fe^{3+} ion and for the $[FeF_6]^{3-}$ and $[Fe(CN)_6]^{3-}$ complex ions.

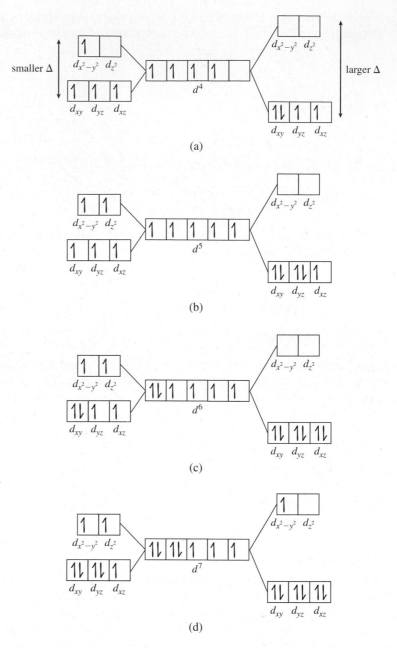

Figure 22.18 Orbital diagrams for the high-spin and low-spin octahedral complexes corresponding to the electron configurations of (a) d^4, (b) d^5, (c) d^6, and (d) d^7.

According to Pauli's exclusion principle [◄◄ Section 3.9], there will be only one unpaired electron present in this case.

Figure 22.18 shows the distribution of electrons among d orbitals that results in low- and high-spin complexes. The actual arrangement of the electrons is determined by the amount of stability gained by having maximum parallel spins versus the investment in energy required to promote electrons to higher d orbitals. Because F^- is a weak-field ligand, the five d electrons enter five separate d orbitals with parallel spins to create a high-spin complex. The cyanide ion is a strong-field ligand, though, so it is energetically preferable for all five electrons to be in the lower orbitals, thus forming a low-spin complex. High-spin complexes are more paramagnetic than low-spin complexes.

The actual number of unpaired electrons (or spins) in a complex ion can be found by magnetic measurements, and in general, experimental findings support predictions based on crystal field splitting. However, a distinction between low- and high-spin complexes can be made only if the metal ion contains more than three and fewer than eight d electrons, as shown in Figure 22.18.

Worked Example 22.4 shows how to determine the number of spins in an octahedral complex.

Worked Example 22.4

Predict the number of unpaired spins in the $[Cr(en)_3]^{2+}$ ion.

Strategy The magnetic properties of a complex ion depend on the strength of the ligands. Strong-field ligands, which cause a high degree of splitting among the d orbital energy levels, result in low-spin complexes. Weak-field ligands, which cause only a small degree of splitting among the d orbital energy levels, result in high-spin complexes.

Setup The electron configuration of Cr^{2+} is $[Ar]3d^4$; and en is a strong-field ligand.

Solution Because en is a *strong*-field ligand, we expect $[Cr(en)_3]^{2+}$ to be a low-spin complex. According to Figure 22.18, all four electrons will be placed in the lower-energy d orbitals (d_{xy}, d_{yz}, and d_{xz}) and there will be a total of two unpaired spins.

> **Think About It**
> It is easy to draw the wrong conclusion regarding high- and low-spin complexes. Remember that the term *high spin* refers to the number of spins (*unpaired electrons*), not to the energy levels of the d orbitals. The greater the energy gap between the lower-energy and higher-energy d orbitals, the greater the chance that the complex will be *low* spin.

Practice Problem A How many unpaired spins are in $[Mn(H_2O)_6]^{2+}$? (*Hint:* H_2O is a weak-field ligand.)

Practice Problem B Visible transitions can occur in metal ions having as few as one d electron or as many as nine d electrons. Which numbers of d electrons (1–9) would result in the same number of unpaired spins in both the high-spin and low-spin states?

Tetrahedral and Square-Planar Complexes

So far we have concentrated on octahedral complexes. The splitting of the d orbital energy levels in tetrahedral and square-planar complexes, though, can also be accounted for satisfactorily by the crystal field theory. In fact, the splitting pattern for a tetrahedral ion is just the reverse of that for octahedral complexes. In this case, the d_{xy}, d_{yz}, and d_{xz} orbitals are more closely directed at the ligands and therefore have more energy than the $d_{x^2-y^2}$ and d_{z^2} orbitals (Figure 22.19). Most tetrahedral complexes are high-spin complexes. Presumably, the tetrahedral arrangement reduces the magnitude of the metal-ligand interactions, resulting in a smaller Δ value. This is a reasonable assumption because the number of ligands is smaller in a tetrahedral complex.

As Figure 22.20 shows, the splitting pattern for square-planar complexes is the most complicated. The $d_{x^2-y^2}$ orbital possesses the highest energy (as in the octahedral case), and the d_{xy} orbital is the next highest. However, the relative placement of the d_{z^2} and the d_{xz} and d_{yz} orbitals cannot be determined simply by inspection and must be calculated.

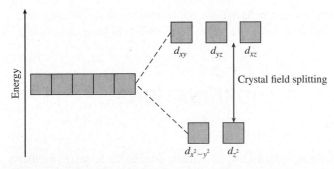

Figure 22.19 Crystal field splitting between d orbitals in a tetrahedral complex.

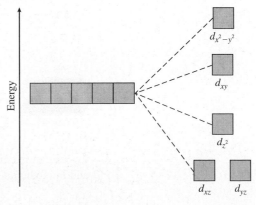

Figure 22.20 Energy-level diagram for a square-planar complex. Because there are more than two energy levels, we cannot define crystal field splitting as we can for octahedral and tetrahedral complexes.

Bonding in Coordination Compounds: Crystal Field Theory

22.3.1   How many unpaired spins would you expect the $[Mn(CO)_6]^{2+}$ ion to have?

22.3.2   Which of the following metal ions can potentially form both low-spin and high-spin complexes: Ti^{2+}, Cu^+, Fe^{2+}, Ni^{2+}, Cr^{3+}?

22.4   REACTIONS OF COORDINATION COMPOUNDS

Complex ions undergo *ligand exchange* (or *substitution*) reactions in solution. The rates of these reactions vary widely, depending on the nature of the metal ion and the ligands.

In studying ligand exchange reactions, it is often useful to distinguish between the stability of a complex ion and its tendency to react, which we call *kinetic lability*. Stability in this context is a thermodynamic property, which is measured in terms of the species' formation constant K_f [◄◄ Section 17.5]. For example, we say that the complex ion tetracyanonickelate(II) is *stable* because it has a large formation constant ($K_f = 1 \times 10^{30}$):

$$Ni^{2+} + 4CN^- \rightleftharpoons [Ni(CN)_4]^{2-}$$

By using cyanide ions labeled with the radioactive isotope carbon-14, chemists have shown that $[Ni(CN)_4]^{2-}$ undergoes ligand exchange very rapidly in solution. The following equilibrium is established almost as soon as the species are mixed:

$$[Ni(CN)_4]^{2-} + 4*CN^- \rightleftharpoons [Ni(*CN)_4]^{2-} + 4CN^-$$

where the asterisk denotes a ^{14}C atom. Complexes like the tetracyanonickelate(II) ion are termed *labile complexes* because they undergo *rapid* ligand exchange reactions. Thus, a thermodynamically *stable* species (i.e., one that has a *large* formation constant) is not necessarily unreactive.

A complex that is thermodynamically *unstable* in acidic solution is $[Co(NH_3)_6]^{3+}$. The equilibrium constant for the following reaction is about 1×10^{20}:

$$[Co(NH_3)_6]^{3+} + 6H^+ + 6H_2O \rightleftharpoons [Co(H_2O)_6]^{3+} + 6NH_4^+$$

When equilibrium is reached, the concentration of the $[Co(NH_3)_6]^{3+}$ ion is very low. This reaction requires several days to complete, however, because the $[Co(NH_3)_6]^{3+}$ ion is so inert. This is an example of an *inert complex*—a complex ion that undergoes very slow exchange reactions (on the order of hours or even days). It shows that a thermodynamically unstable species is not necessarily chemically reactive. The rate of reaction is determined by the energy of activation, which is high in this case.

Most complex ions containing Co^{3+}, Cr^{3+}, and Pt^{2+} are kinetically inert. Because they exchange ligands very slowly, they are easy to study in solution. As a result, our knowledge of the bonding, structure, and isomerism of coordination compounds has come largely from studies of these compounds.

22.5   APPLICATIONS OF COORDINATION COMPOUNDS

Coordination compounds are found in living systems and have many uses in the home, in industry, and in medicine. We briefly describe a few examples in this section.

Metallurgy

The extraction of silver and gold by the formation of cyanide complexes and the purification of nickel by converting the metal to the gaseous compound $Ni(CO)_4$ are typical examples of the use of coordination compounds in metallurgical processes.

Chelation Therapy

Earlier we mentioned that chelation therapy is used in the treatment of lead poisoning. Other metals, such as arsenic and mercury, can also be removed using chelating agents.

Chemotherapy

Several platinum-containing coordination compounds, including cisplatin $[Pt(NH_3)_2Cl_2]$ and carboplatin $[Pt(NH_3)_2(OCO)_2C_4H_6]$, can effectively inhibit the growth of cancerous cells. The mechanism for the action of cisplatin is the *chelation* of DNA, the molecule that contains the genetic code. During cell division, the double-stranded DNA unwinds into two single strands, which must be accurately copied for the new cells to be identical to their parent cell. X-ray studies show that cisplatin binds to DNA by forming cross-links in which the two chlorides on cisplatin are replaced by nitrogen atoms in the adjacent guanine bases on the same strand of the DNA. (Guanine is one of the four bases in DNA.) This causes a bend in the double-stranded structure at the binding site. It is believed that this structural distortion is a key factor in inhibiting replication. The damaged cell is then destroyed by the body's immune system. Because the binding of cisplatin to DNA requires both Cl atoms to be on the same side of the complex, the *trans* isomer of the compound is totally ineffective as an anticancer drug.

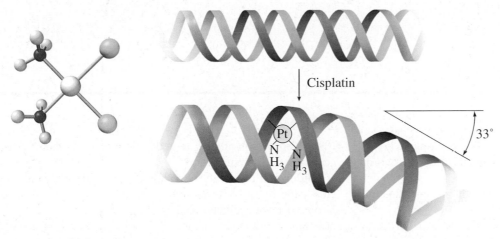

Chemical Analysis

Although EDTA has a great affinity for a large number of metal ions (especially 2+ and 3+ ions), other chelates are more selective in binding. Dimethylglyoxime, for example, forms an insoluble brick-red solid with Ni^{2+} and an insoluble bright-yellow solid with Pd^{2+}. These characteristic colors are used in qualitative analysis to identify nickel and palladium. Furthermore, the quantities of ions present can be determined by gravimetric analysis [◂◂ Section 9.6] as follows: To a solution containing Ni^{2+} ions, say, we add an excess of dimethylglyoxime reagent, and a brick-red precipitate forms. The precipitate is then filtered, dried, and weighed. Knowing the formula of the complex (Figure 22.21), we can readily calculate the amount of nickel in the original solution.

Figure 22.21 Structure of nickel dimethylglyoxime. Note that the overall structure is stabilized by hydrogen bonds.

Detergents

The cleansing action of soap in hard water is hampered by the reaction of the Ca^{2+} ions in the water with the soap molecules to form insoluble salts or curds. In the late 1940s the detergent industry introduced a "builder," usually sodium tripolyphosphate, to circumvent this problem. The tripolyphosphate ion is an effective chelating agent that forms stable, soluble complexes with Ca^{2+} ions. Sodium tripolyphosphate revolutionized the detergent industry. Because phosphates are plant nutrients, however, wastewater containing phosphates discharged into rivers and lakes causes algae to grow, resulting in oxygen depletion. Under these conditions, most or all aquatic life eventually succumbs. This process is called *eutrophication*. Consequently, many states have banned phosphate detergents since the 1970s, and manufacturers have reformulated their products to eliminate phosphates.

Sequestrants

In addition to its use in medicine and chemical analysis, EDTA is used as a food additive to sequester metal ions. EDTA sequesters copper, iron, and nickel ions that would otherwise catalyze the oxidation reactions that cause food to spoil. EDTA is a common preservative in a wide variety of consumer products.

INGREDIENTS: Water, Butylene Glycol, Mineral Oil Alcohol, Propylene Glycol Dicaprylate/Dicaprate, Isoparaffin, Glyceryl Stearate, Tri-PPG-3 Myristyl Ether Citrate, Cetearyl Alcohol, Dimethicone, Methylparaben, Polysorbate 60, DMDM Hydantoin, Carbomer, Ethylparaben, Propylparaben, Disodium EDTA, Sodium Hydroxide, Xanthan Gum, Butylparaben, Titanium Dioxide

QUESTIONS? Call **1-877-543-8477**,

Learning Outcomes

- Define coordination compound.
- Describe some of the properties of transition metals.
- List some common ligands found in transition metal complexes.
- Define coordination number.
- Explain what a chelating agent does.
- Name a coordination compound using nomenclature rules.
- Determine the structure of a coordination compound.

- Distinguish between geometric and optical isomers.
- Define the following stereochemical terms: *chiral, dextrorotatory, levorotatory,* and *enantiomer.*
- Use concepts of crystal field theory to explain properties of coordination compounds (e.g., color and magnetic properties).
- Describe the nature of ligand exchange reactions including an explanation of kinetic lability.
- Provide examples of common applications of coordination compounds.

Chapter Summary

SECTION 22.1

- *Coordination compounds* contain coordinate covalent bonds between a metal ion (often a transition metal ion) and two or more polar molecules or ions.
- The molecules or anions that surround a metal in a coordination complex are called **ligands.**
- Many coordination compounds consist of a *complex ion* and a *counter* ion.
- Transition metals are those that have incompletely filled *d* subshells—or that *give rise* to ions with incompletely filled *d* subshells.
- Transition metals exhibit variable oxidation states ranging from +1 to +7.
- To act as a ligand, a molecule or ion must have at least one unshared pair of electrons. The atom that bears the unshared pair of electrons is the **donor atom.**
- Ligands are classified as *monodentate, bidentate,* or *polydentate,* based on the number of donor atoms they contain. Bidentate and polydentate ions are also known as **chelating agents.**
- The **coordination number** is the number of donor atoms surrounding a metal in a complex.
- Ionic coordination compounds are named by first naming the cation and then the anion. Complex ions are named by listing the ligands in alphabetical order, followed by the metal and its oxidation state (as a Roman numeral). When the complex ion is the anion, the anion's name ends in *–ate.*

SECTION 22.2

- The coordination number largely determines the geometry of a coordination complex.
- Coordination compounds containing different arrangements of the same ligands are **stereoisomers.** The two types of stereo-isomerism are geometric and optical.
- *Geometrical isomers* contain the same atoms and bonds arranged differently in space.
- *Optical isomers* are nonsuperimposable mirror images. We call a *pair* of optical isomers **enantiomers.** The rotation of polarized light is measured with a **polarimeter.**
- Enantiomers rotate the plane of plane-polarized light in opposite directions. The enantiomer that rotates it to the right is called **dextrorotatory** and is labeled *d.* The enantiomer that rotates it to the left is called **levorotatory** and is labeled *l.* An equal mixture of a pair of enantiomers, called a **racemic mixture,** does not cause any net rotation of plane-polarized light.

SECTION 22.3

- Ligands in a coordination complex cause the energy levels of the *d* orbitals on a metal to split. The difference in energy between the lower and higher *d* orbital energy levels is called the **crystal field splitting (Δ).**
- The magnitude of Δ depends on the nature of the ligands in the complex. The **spectrochemical series** orders some common ligands in order of increasing *field strength.*

- *Strong*-field ligands give rise to a larger Δ value; *weak*-field ligands yield a smaller Δ value.
- Crystal field splitting sometimes changes the number of unpaired electrons, and therefore the magnetic properties, of a metal.
- Complexes containing transition metals with d^4, d^5, d^6, or d^7 configurations may be *high spin* or *low spin*. In high-spin complexes, the number of unpaired electrons is maximized because Δ is small; in low-spin complexes, the number of unpaired electrons is minimized because Δ is large.

SECTION 22.4

- Complex ions undergo ligand exchange in solution. The rate at which ligand exchange occurs is a measure of a complex's *kinetic lability* and does not necessarily correspond directly to the complex's *thermodynamic stability*.

SECTION 22.5

- Coordination chemistry is important in many biological, medical, and industrial processes.

Key Words

Chelating agent, 910
Coordination compound, 907
Coordination number, 910
Crystal field splitting (Δ), 917

Dextrorotatory, 915
Donor atom, 909
Enantiomers, 915
Geometrical isomers, 914

Levorotatory, 915
Ligand, 909
Optical isomers, 914
Polarimeter, 915

Racemic mixture, 915
Spectrochemical series, 919
Stereoisomers, 914

Questions and Problems

SECTION 22.1: COORDINATION COMPOUNDS

Review Questions

22.1 What distinguishes a transition metal from a main group metal?

22.2 Why is zinc not considered a transition metal?

22.3 Explain why atomic radii decrease very gradually from scandium to copper.

22.4 Without referring to the text, write the ground-state electron configurations of the first row transition metals. Explain any irregularities.

22.5 Write the electron configurations of the following ions: V^{5+}, Cr^{3+}, Mn^{2+}, Fe^{3+}, Cu^{2+}, Sc^{3+}, Ti^{4+}.

22.6 Why do transition metals have more oxidation states than other elements?

22.7 Give the highest oxidation states for scandium to copper.

22.8 Define the following terms: *coordination compound, ligand, donor atom, coordination number, chelating agent.*

22.9 Describe the interaction between a donor atom and a metal atom in terms of a Lewis acid-base reaction.

Problems

22.10 Complete the following statements for the complex ion $[Co(en)_2(H_2O)CN]^{2+}$. (a) en is the abbreviation for _____. (b) The oxidation number of Co is _____. (c) The coordination number of Co is _____. (d) _____ is a bidentate ligand.

22.11 Complete the following statements for the complex ion $[Cr(C_2O_4)_2(H_2O)_2]^-$. (a) The oxidation number of Cr is _____. (b) The coordination number of Cr is _____. (c) _____ is a bidentate ligand.

22.12 Give the oxidation numbers of the metals in the following species: (a) $K_3[Fe(CN)_6]$, (b) $K_3[Cr(C_2O_4)_3]$, (c) $[Ni(CN)_4]^{2-}$.

22.13 Give the oxidation numbers of the metals in the following species: (a) Na_2MoO_4, (b) $MgWO_4$, (c) $Fe(CO)_5$.

22.14 What are the systematic names for the following ions and compounds?
(a) $[Co(NH_3)_4Cl_2]^+$ (c) $[Co(en)_2Br_2]^+$
(b) $[Cr(NH_3)_3Cl_3]$ (d) $[Co(NH_3)_6]Cl_3$

22.15 What are the systematic names for the following ions and compounds?
(a) $[cis\text{-}Co(en)_2Cl_2]^+$ (c) $[Co(NH_3)_5Cl]Cl_2$
(b) $[Pt(NH_3)_5Cl]Cl_3$

22.16 Write the formulas for each of the following ions and compounds: (a) tetrahydroxozincate(II), (b) penta-aquachlorochromium(III) chloride, (c) tetrabromo-cuprate(II), (d) ethylenediaminetetraacetatoferrate(II).

22.17 One of the drugs commonly used for chelation therapy is dimercaptosuccinic acid (DMSA), marketed under the name Chemet. How many donor atoms does DMSA have?

Dimercaptosuccinic acid (DMSA)

SECTION 22.2:   STRUCTURE OF COORDINATION COMPOUNDS

Review Questions

22.18   Define the following terms: *stereoisomers, geometric isomers, optical isomers, plane-polarized light.*

22.19   Specify which of the following structures can exhibit geometric isomerism: (a) linear, (b) square planar, (c) tetrahedral, (d) octahedral.

22.20   What determines whether a molecule is chiral? How does a polarimeter measure the chirality of a molecule?

22.21   Explain the following terms: *enantiomers, racemic mixtures.*

Problems

22.22   The complex ion $[Ni(CN)_2Br_2]^{2-}$ has a square-planar geometry. Draw the structures of the geometric isomers of this complex.

22.23   How many geometric isomers are in the following species: (a) $[Co(NH_3)_2Cl_4]^-$, (b) $[Co(NH_3)_3Cl_3]$?

22.24   Draw structures of all the geometric and optical isomers of each of the following cobalt complexes:
(a) $[Co(NH_3)_6]^{3+}$
(b) $[Co(NH_3)_5Cl]^{2+}$
(c) $[Co(C_2O_4)_3]^{3-}$

22.25   Draw structures of all the geometric and optical isomers of each of the following cobalt complexes:
(a) $[Co(NH_3)_4Cl_2]^+$, (b) $[Co(en)_3]^{3+}$.

SECTION 22.3:   BONDING IN COORDINATION COMPOUNDS: CRYSTAL FIELD THEORY

Review Questions

22.26   Briefly describe crystal field theory.

22.27   Define the following terms: *crystal field splitting, high-spin complex, low-spin complex, spectrochemical series.*

22.28   What is the origin of color in a coordination compound?

22.29   Compounds containing the Sc^{3+} ion are colorless, whereas those containing the Ti^{3+} ion are colored. Explain.

22.30   For the same type of ligands, explain why the crystal field splitting for an octahedral complex is always greater than that for a tetrahedral complex.

Problems

22.31   Transition metal complexes containing CN^- ligands are often yellow in color, whereas those containing H_2O ligands are often green or blue. Explain.

22.32   Predict the number of unpaired electrons in the following complex ions: (a) $[Cr(CN)_6]^{4-}$, (b) $[Cr(H_2O)_6]^{2+}$.

22.33   The absorption maximum for the complex ion $[Co(NH_3)_6]^{3+}$ occurs at 470 nm. (a) Predict the color of the complex, and (b) calculate the crystal field splitting in kJ/mol.

22.34   From each of the following pairs, choose the complex that absorbs light at a longer wavelength:
(a) $[Co(NH_3)_6]^{2+}$, $[Co(H_2O)_6]^{2+}$; (b) $[FeF_6]^{3-}$, $[Fe(CN)_6]^{3-}$;
(c) $[Cu(NH_3)_4]^{2+}$, $[CuCl_4]^{2-}$.

22.35   A solution made by dissolving 0.875 g of $Co(NH_3)_4Cl_3$ in 25.0 g of water freezes at $-0.56°C$. Calculate the number of moles of ions produced when 1 mole of $Co(NH_3)_4Cl_3$ is dissolved in water, and suggest a structure for the complex ion present in this compound.

22.36   In biological systems, the Cu^{2+} ions coordinated with S atoms tend to form tetrahedral complexes, whereas those coordinated with N atoms tend to form octahedral complexes. Explain.

22.37   Plastocyanin, a copper-containing protein found in photosynthetic systems, is involved in electron transport, with the copper ion switching between the $+1$ and $+2$ oxidation states. The copper ion is coordinated with two histidine residues, a cysteine residue, and a methionine residue in a tetrahedral configuration. How does the crystal field splitting (Δ) change between these two oxidation states?

SECTION 22.4:   REACTIONS OF COORDINATION COMPOUNDS

Review Questions

22.38   Define the terms *labile complex* and *inert complex.*

22.39   Explain why a thermodynamically stable species may be chemically reactive and a thermodynamically unstable species may be unreactive.

Problems

22.40   Oxalic acid ($H_2C_2O_4$) is sometimes used to clean rust stains from sinks and bathtubs. Explain the chemistry underlying this cleaning action.

22.41   The $[Fe(CN)_6]^{3-}$ complex is more labile than the $[Fe(CN)_6]^{4-}$ complex. Suggest an experiment that would prove that $[Fe(CN)_6]^{3-}$ is a labile complex.

22.42   Aqueous copper(II) sulfate solution is blue in color. When aqueous potassium fluoride is added, a green precipitate is formed. When aqueous potassium chloride is added instead, a bright-green solution is formed. Explain what is happening in these two cases.

22.43   When aqueous potassium cyanide is added to a solution of copper(II) sulfate, a white precipitate, soluble in an excess of potassium cyanide, is formed. No precipitate is formed when hydrogen sulfide is bubbled through the solution at this point. Explain.

22.44   A concentrated aqueous copper(II) chloride solution is bright green in color. When diluted with water, the solution becomes light blue. Explain.

22.45   In a dilute nitric acid solution, Fe^{3+} reacts with thiocyanate ion (SCN^-) to form a dark-red complex:

$$[Fe(H_2O)_6]^{3+} + SCN^- \rightleftharpoons H_2O + [Fe(H_2O)_5NCS]^{2+}$$

The equilibrium concentration of $[Fe(H_2O)_5NCS]^{2+}$ may be determined by how darkly colored the solution is (measured by a spectrometer). In one such experiment, 1.0 mL of 0.20 M $Fe(NO_3)_3$ was mixed with 1.0 mL of 1.0×10^{-3} M KSCN and 8.0 mL of dilute HNO_3. The color of the solution quantitatively indicated that the $[Fe(H_2O)_5NCS]^{2+}$ concentration was 7.3×10^{-5} M. Calculate the formation constant for $[Fe(H_2O)_5NCS]^{2+}$.

SECTION 22.5:   APPLICATIONS OF COORDINATION COMPOUNDS

Review Question

22.46   Describe and give examples of the applications of coordination compounds.

ADDITIONAL PROBLEMS

22.47   Suffocation victims usually look purple, but a person poisoned by carbon monoxide often has rosy cheeks. Explain.

22.48   As we read across the first row transition metals from left to right, the +2 oxidation state becomes more stable in comparison with the +3 state. Why is this so?

22.49   Which is a stronger oxidizing agent in aqueous solution, Mn^{3+} or Cr^{3+}? Explain your choice.

22.50   Carbon monoxide binds to Fe in hemoglobin some 200 times more strongly than oxygen. This is the reason why CO is a toxic substance. The metal-to-ligand sigma bond is formed by donating a lone pair from the donor atom to an empty sp^3d^2 orbital on Fe. (a) On the basis of electronegativities, would you expect the C or O atom to form the bond to Fe? (b) Draw a diagram illustrating the overlap of the orbitals involved in the bonding.

22.51   What are the oxidation states of Fe and Ti in the ore ilmenite ($FeTiO_3$)? (*Hint:* Look up the ionization energies of Fe and Ti in Table 22.1; the fourth ionization energy of Ti is 4180 kJ/mol.)

22.52   A student has prepared a cobalt complex that has one of the following three structures: $[Co(NH_3)_6]Cl_3$, $[Co(NH_3)_5Cl]Cl_2$, or $[Co(NH_3)_4Cl_2]Cl$. Explain how the student would distinguish between these possibilities by an electrical conductance experiment. At the student's disposal are three strong electrolytes—$NaCl$, $MgCl_2$, and $FeCl_3$—which may be used for comparison purposes.

22.53   Chemical analysis shows that hemoglobin contains 0.34 percent of Fe by mass. What is the minimum possible molar mass of hemoglobin? The actual molar mass of hemoglobin is about 65,000 g. How do you account for the discrepancy between your minimum value and the actual value?

22.54   Explain the following facts: (a) Copper and iron have several oxidation states, whereas zinc has only one. (b) Copper and iron form colored ions, whereas zinc does not.

22.55   A student in 1895 prepared three coordination compounds containing chromium, with the following properties:

Formula	Color	Cl⁻ Ions in solution per formula unit
(a) $CrCl_3 \cdot 6H_2O$	Violet	3
(b) $CrCl_3 \cdot 6H_2O$	Light green	2
(c) $CrCl_3 \cdot 6H_2O$	Dark green	1

Write modern formulas for these compounds, and suggest a method for confirming the number of Cl⁻ ions present in solution in each case. (*Hint:* Some of the compounds may exist as hydrates.)

22.56   The formation constant for the reaction $Ag^+ + 2NH_3 \rightleftharpoons [Ag(NH_3)_2]^+$ is 1.5×10^7, and that for the reaction $Ag^+ + 2CN^- \rightleftharpoons [Ag(CN)_2]^-$ is 1.0×10^{21} at 25°C (see Table 17.5). Calculate the equilibrium constant and $\Delta G°$ at 25°C for the reaction

$$[Ag(NH_3)_2]^+ + 2CN^- \rightleftharpoons [Ag(CN)_2]^- + 2NH_3$$

22.57   From the standard reduction potentials listed in Table 19.1 for Zn/Zn^{2+} and Cu/Cu^{2+}, calculate $\Delta G°$ and the equilibrium constant for the reaction

$$Zn(s) + 2Cu^{2+}(aq) \longrightarrow Zn^{2+}(aq) + 2Cu^+(aq)$$

22.58   Using the standard reduction potentials listed in Table 19.1 and the *Handbook of Chemistry and Physics,* show that the following reaction is favorable under standard-state conditions:

$$2Ag(s) + Pt^{2+}(aq) \longrightarrow 2Ag^+(aq) + Pt(s)$$

What is the equilibrium constant of this reaction at 25°C?

22.59   The Co^{2+}-porphyrin complex is more stable than the Fe^{2+}-porphyrin complex. Why, then, is iron the metal ion in hemoglobin (and other heme-containing proteins)?

22.60   What are the differences between geometric isomers and optical isomers?

22.61   Oxyhemoglobin is bright red, whereas deoxyhemoglobin is purple. Show that the difference in color can be accounted for qualitatively on the basis of high-spin and low-spin complexes. (*Hint:* O_2 is a strong-field ligand.)

22.62   Hydrated Mn^{2+} ions are practically colorless (see Figure 22.16) even though they possess five $3d$ electrons. Explain. (*Hint:* Electronic transitions in which there is a change in the number of unpaired electrons do not occur readily.)

22.63   Which of the following hydrated cations are colorless: $Fe^{2+}(aq)$, $Zn^{2+}(aq)$, $Cu^+(aq)$, $Cu^{2+}(aq)$, $V^{5+}(aq)$, $Ca^{2+}(aq)$, $Co^{2+}(aq)$, $Sc^{3+}(aq)$, $Pb^{2+}(aq)$? Explain your choice.

22.64   Aqueous solutions of $CoCl_2$ are generally either light pink or blue. Low concentrations and low temperatures favor the pink form, whereas high concentrations and high temperatures favor the blue form. Adding hydrochloric acid to a pink solution of $CoCl_2$ causes the solution to turn blue; the pink color is restored by the addition of $HgCl_2$. Account for these observations.

22.65   Suggest a method that would allow you to distinguish between *cis*-Pt(NH$_3$)$_2$Cl$_2$ and *trans*-Pt(NH$_3$)$_2$Cl$_2$.

22.66   You are given two solutions containing FeCl$_2$ and FeCl$_3$ at the same concentration. One solution is light yellow, and the other one is brown. Identify these solutions based only on color.

22.67   The label of a certain brand of mayonnaise lists EDTA as a food preservative. How does EDTA prevent the spoilage of mayonnaise?

22.68   The compound 1,1,1-trifluoroacetylacetone (tfa) is a bidentate ligand:

$$\overset{O}{\overset{\|}{}}\quad\overset{O}{\overset{\|}{}}$$
$$CF_3CCH_2CCH_3$$

It forms a tetrahedral complex with Be^{2+} and a square-planar complex with Cu^{2+}. Draw structures of these complex ions, and identify the type of isomerism exhibited by these ions.

22.69   How many geometric isomers can the following square-planar complex have?

$$\begin{array}{ccc} a & & b \\ & \diagdown\; \diagup & \\ & Pt & \\ & \diagup\; \diagdown & \\ d & & c \end{array}$$

22.70   [Pt(NH$_3$)$_2$Cl$_2$] is found to exist in two geometric isomers designated I and II, which react with oxalic acid as follows:

$$I + H_2C_2O_4 \longrightarrow [Pt(NH_3)_2C_2O_4]$$
$$II + H_2C_2O_4 \longrightarrow [Pt(NH_3)_2(HC_2O_4)_2]$$

Comment on the structures of I and II.

22.71   Commercial silver-plating operations frequently use a solution containing the complex Ag(CN)$_2^-$ ion. Because the formation constant (K_f) is quite large, this procedure ensures that the free Ag$^+$ concentration in solution is low for uniform electrodeposition. In one process, a chemist added 9.0 L of 5.0 *M* NaCN to 90.0 L of 0.20 *M* AgNO$_3$. Calculate the concentration of free Ag$^+$ ions at equilibrium. See Table 17.5 for K_f value.

22.72   Draw qualitative diagrams for the crystal field splittings in (a) a linear complex ion ML$_2$, (b) a trigonal-planar complex ion ML$_3$, and (c) a trigonal-bipyramidal complex ion ML$_5$.

22.73   (a) The free Cu(I) ion is unstable in solution and has a tendency to disproportionate:

$$2Cu^+(aq) \rightleftharpoons Cu^{2+}(aq) + Cu(s)$$

Use the information in Table 19.1 (page 815) to calculate the equilibrium constant for the reaction. (b) Based on your results in part (a), explain why most Cu(I) compounds are insoluble.

22.74   Consider the following two ligand exchange reactions:

$$[Co(H_2O)_6]^{3+} + 6NH_3 \rightleftharpoons [Co(NH_3)_6]^{3+} + 6H_2O$$
$$[Co(H_2O)_6]^{3+} + 3en \rightleftharpoons [Co(en)_3]^{3+} + 6H_2O$$

(a) Which of the reactions should have a larger $\Delta S°$?
(b) Given that the Co−N bond strength is approximately the same in both complexes, which reaction will have a larger equilibrium constant? Explain your choices.

22.75   The Cr^{3+} ion forms octahedral complexes with two neutral ligands X and Y. The color of CrX$_6^{3+}$ is blue while that of CrY$_6^{3+}$ is yellow. Which is a stronger field ligand, X or Y?

22.76   Explain the difference between these two compounds: CrCl$_3$ · 6H$_2$O and [Cr(H$_2$O)$_6$]Cl$_3$.

22.77   The K_f for the formation of the complex ion between Pb^{2+} and EDTA^{4-},

$$Pb^{2+} + EDTA^{4-} \rightleftharpoons [Pb(EDTA)]^{2-}$$

is 1.0×10^{18} at 25°C. Calculate [Pb^{2+}] at equilibrium in a solution containing 1.0×10^{-3} *M* Pb^{2+} and 2.0×10^{-3} *M* EDTA^{4-}.

22.78   Locate the transition metal atoms and ions in the periodic table shown here. Atoms: (a) [Kr]5s^{2}4d^5. (b) [Xe]6s^{2}4f^{14}5d^4. Ions: (c) [Ar]3d^3 (ion with charge 4+). (d) [Xe]4f^{14}5d^8 (ion with charge 3+).

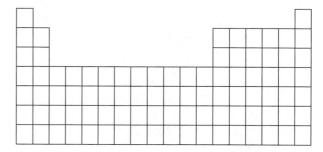

22.79   Manganese forms three low-spin complex ions with the cyanide ion with the formulas [Mn(CN)$_6$]$^{5-}$, [Mn(CN)$_6$]$^{4-}$, and [Mn(CN)$_6$]$^{3-}$. For each complex ion, determine the oxidation number of Mn and the number of unpaired *d* electrons.

22.80   Copper is known to exist in the +3 oxidation state, which is believed to be involved in some biological electron-transfer reactions. (a) Would you expect this oxidation state of copper to be stable? Explain. (b) Name the compound K$_3$CuF$_6$ and predict the geometry and magnetic properties of the complex ion. (c) Most of the known Cu(III) compounds have square-planar geometry. Are these compounds diamagnetic or paramagnetic?

Answers to In-Chapter Materials

PRACTICE PROBLEMS

22.1A (a) K: +1, Au: +3, (b) K: +1, Fe: +2. **22.1B** (a) +1, −3, 0, +1, +3, +3, +2. **22.2A** (a) tetraamminedibromocobalt(III) chloride, (b) tetraaquadichlorochromium(III) chloride, (c) potassium tetrachlorocuprate(II). **22.2B** (a) sodium hexacyanoferrate(III), (b) dichlorobis(ethylenediamine)chromium(III) chloride, (c) tris(ethylenediamine)cobalt(III) chloride. **22.3A** (a) [Ru(H$_2$O)$_5$Br] NO$_3$, (b) K$_2$[PtBr$_4$Cl$_2$], (c) Na$_3$[Co(NO$_2$)$_6$]. **22.3B** (a) [V(en)$_2$C$_2$O$_4$]Cl$_2$, (b) [Cr(en)$_2$Br$_2$]NO$_3$, (c) [Pt(en)$_3$](SO$_4$)$_2$. **22.4A** 5. **22.4B** 1, 2, 3, 8, and 9.

SECTION REVIEW

22.1.1 Tetraamminecopper(II) chloride. **22.1.2** Potassium hexafluoroferrate(III). **22.1.3** [Co(NH$_3$)$_5$NO$_2$]$^{2+}$. **22.1.4** [Cr(H$_2$O)$_4$Cl$_2$]Cl. **22.3.1** 1. **22.3.2** Fe^{2+}.

CHAPTER 23

Nonmetallic Elements and Their Compounds

23.1 General Properties of Nonmetals

23.2 Hydrogen
- Binary Hydrides • Isotopes of Hydrogen
- Hydrogenation • The Hydrogen Economy

23.3 Carbon

23.4 Nitrogen and Phosphorus
- Nitrogen • Phosphorus

23.5 Oxygen and Sulfur
- Oxygen • Sulfur

23.6 The Halogens
- Preparation and General Properties of the Halogens • Compounds of the Halogens
- Uses of the Halogens

The fossil fuels that have for many years sustained our culture and industry are a finite, nonrenewable resource. Ultimately, we will need to transition to new sources of energy. One such alternative energy opportunity may exist in the form of the "hydrogen economy." Coined in 1970, the term *hydrogen economy* refers to the use of hydrogen gas $H_2(g)$ as a more environmentally clean energy source to power everything from portable electronics to automobiles (shown here). Obstacles to full-scale implementation of the hydrogen economy include the high purity of hydrogen required for fuel cell operation and the technical difficulties associated with storing and delivering a gaseous, potentially explosive fuel. Chemists are working to develop methods for efficient and safe production, storage, and utilization of hydrogen gas.

23.1 GENERAL PROPERTIES OF NONMETALS

Properties of nonmetals are more varied than those of metals. Hydrogen, oxygen, nitrogen, fluorine, chlorine, and the noble gases are all gases in the elemental state, whereas only bromine is a liquid. All the remaining nonmetals are solids at room temperature. Unlike metals, nonmetals are poor conductors of heat and electricity, and when they form compounds, nonmetals can exhibit either positive or negative oxidation numbers.

A small group of elements, called *metalloids,* have properties characteristic of both metals and nonmetals. The metalloids boron, silicon, germanium, and arsenic are semiconducting elements.

Nonmetals are more electronegative than metals [◀◀ Section 6.2]. The electronegativity of elements increases from left to right across any period and from bottom to top in any group in the periodic table [◀◀ Key Skills Chapter 4]. With the exception of hydrogen, the nonmetals are concentrated in the upper right-hand corner of the periodic table (Figure 23.1). Compounds formed by a combination of metals with nonmetals tend to be *ionic,* having a metallic cation and a nonmetallic anion.

In this chapter we will discuss the chemistry of a number of common and important nonmetallic elements—namely, hydrogen; carbon (Group 4A); nitrogen and phosphorus (Group 5A); oxygen and sulfur (Group 6A); and the halogens: fluorine, chlorine, bromine, and iodine (Group 7A).

1A 1																	8A 18
1 H	2A 2											3A 13	4A 14	5A 15	6A 16	7A 17	2 He
3 Li	4 Be											5 B	6 C	7 N	8 O	9 F	10 Ne
11 Na	12 Mg	3B 3	4B 4	5B 5	6B 6	7B 7	8	8B 9	10	1B 11	2B 12	13 Al	14 Si	15 P	16 S	17 Cl	18 Ar
19 K	20 Ca	21 Sc	22 Ti	23 V	24 Cr	25 Mn	26 Fe	27 Co	28 Ni	29 Cu	30 Zn	31 Ga	32 Ge	33 As	34 Se	35 Br	36 Kr
37 Rb	38 Sr	39 Y	40 Zr	41 Nb	42 Mo	43 Tc	44 Ru	45 Rh	46 Pd	47 Ag	48 Cd	49 In	50 Sn	51 Sb	52 Te	53 I	54 Xe
55 Cs	56 Ba	57 La	72 Hf	73 Ta	74 W	75 Re	76 Os	77 Ir	78 Pt	79 Au	80 Hg	81 Tl	82 Pb	83 Bi	84 Po	85 At	86 Rn
87 Fr	88 Ra	89 Ac	104 Rf	105 Db	106 Sg	107 Bh	108 Hs	109 Mt	110 Ds	111 Rg	112 Cn	113 –	114 –	115 –	116 –	117 –	118 –

Figure 23.1 Main group nonmetallic elements (in blue) and metalloids (in orange).

23.2   HYDROGEN

Hydrogen is the simplest element known—its most common atomic form contains only one proton and one electron. The atomic form of hydrogen exists only at very high temperatures, however. Normally, elemental hydrogen is a diatomic molecule, the product of an exothermic reaction between H atoms:

$$H(g) + H(g) \longrightarrow H_2(g) \qquad \Delta H° = -436.4 \text{ kJ/mol}$$

Molecular hydrogen is a colorless, odorless, and nonpoisonous gas. At 1 atm, liquid hydrogen has a boiling point of −252.9°C (20.3 K).

Hydrogen is the most abundant element in the universe, accounting for about 70 percent of the universe's total mass. It is the tenth most abundant element in Earth's crust, where it is found in combination with other elements. Unlike Jupiter and Saturn, Earth does not have a strong enough gravitational pull to retain the lightweight H_2 molecules, so hydrogen is not found in our atmosphere.

The ground-state electron configuration of H is $1s^1$. It resembles the alkali metals (Group 1A) in that it can be oxidized to the H^+ ion, which exists in aqueous solutions in the hydrated form. On the other hand, hydrogen resembles the *halogens* (Group 7A) in that it forms the hydride ion (H^-), which is isoelectronic with *helium* ($1s^2$). Hydrogen is found in a large number of covalent compounds. It also has the unique capacity, when bonded to small, electronegative atoms, for hydrogen-bond formation [◄◄ Section 12.1].

Student Annotation: Remember that the halogens also form anions that are isoelectronic with the noble gases [◄◄ Section 4.5].

Hydrogen gas plays an important role in industrial processes. About 95 percent of the hydrogen produced is produced at or near the plant where it is used for industrial processes, such as the synthesis of ammonia. The large-scale industrial preparation is the reaction between propane (from natural gas and also as a product of oil refineries) and steam in the presence of a catalyst at 900°C:

$$C_3H_8(g) + 3H_2O(g) \longrightarrow 3CO(g) + 7H_2(g)$$

In another process, steam is passed over a bed of red-hot coke:

$$C(s) + H_2O(g) \longrightarrow CO(g) + H_2(g)$$

The mixture of carbon monoxide and hydrogen gas produced in this reaction is commonly known as *water gas*. Because both CO and H_2 burn in air, water gas was used as a fuel for many years. But because CO is poisonous, water gas has been replaced by natural gases, such as methane and propane.

Small quantities of hydrogen gas can be prepared conveniently in the laboratory by combining zinc with dilute hydrochloric acid (Figure 23.2):

$$Zn(s) + 2HCl(aq) \longrightarrow ZnCl_2(aq) + H_2(g)$$

Figure 23.2 Apparatus for the laboratory preparation of hydrogen gas. The gas is collected over water.

Hydrogen gas can also be produced by the reaction between an alkali metal or an alkaline earth metal (Ca or Ba) and water, but these reactions are too violent to be suitable for the laboratory preparation of hydrogen gas. Very pure hydrogen gas can be obtained by the electrolysis of water, but this method consumes too much energy to be practical on a large scale.

Binary Hydrides

Binary hydrides are compounds containing hydrogen and another element, either a metal or a nonmetal. Depending on the structure and properties, these hydrides are broadly divided into three types: (1) ionic hydrides, (2) covalent hydrides, and (3) interstitial hydrides.

Ionic hydrides are formed when molecular hydrogen combines directly with any alkali metal or with the alkaline earth metals Ca, Sr, or Ba:

$$2Li(s) + H_2(g) \longrightarrow 2LiH(s)$$

$$Ca(s) + H_2(g) \longrightarrow CaH_2(s)$$

All ionic hydrides are solids that have the high melting points characteristic of ionic compounds. The anion in these compounds is the hydride ion (H^-), which is a very strong Brønsted base. It readily accepts a proton from a proton donor such as water:

$$H^-(aq) + H_2O(l) \longrightarrow OH^-(aq) + H_2(g)$$

Because of their high reactivity with water, ionic hydrides are frequently used to remove traces of water from organic solvents.

In *covalent hydrides,* the hydrogen atom is covalently bonded to the atom of another element. There are two types of covalent hydrides—those containing discrete molecular units, such as CH_4 and NH_3, and those having complex polymeric structures, such as $(BeH_2)_x$ and $(AlH_3)_x$, where x is a very large number.

Figure 23.3 shows the binary ionic and covalent hydrides of the main group elements. The physical and chemical properties of these compounds change from *ionic* to *covalent* across a given period. Consider, for example, the hydrides of the second period elements: LiH, BeH_2, B_2H_6, CH_4, NH_3, H_2O, and HF. LiH is an ionic compound with a high melting point (680°C). The structure of BeH_2 (in the solid state) is polymeric; it is a covalent compound. The molecules B_2H_6 and CH_4 are nonpolar. In contrast, NH_3, H_2O, and HF are all polar molecules in which the hydrogen atom is the *positive* end of the polar bond. Of this group of hydrides (NH_3, H_2O, and HF), only HF is acidic in water.

As we move down any group in Figure 23.3, the compounds change from *covalent* to *ionic.* In Group 2A, for example, BeH_2 and MgH_2 are covalent, but CaH_2, SrH_2, and BaH_2 are ionic.

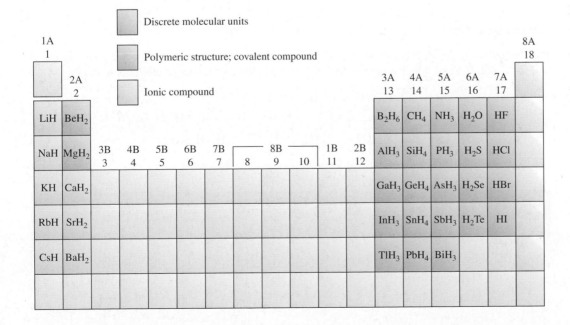

Figure 23.3 Binary hydrides of the representative elements. In cases in which hydrogen forms more than one compound with the same element, only the formula of the simplest hydride is shown. The properties of many of the transition metal hydrides are not well characterized.

Molecular hydrogen forms a number of hydrides with transition metals. In some of these compounds, the ratio of hydrogen atoms to metal atoms is *not* a constant. Such compounds are called *interstitial hydrides*. Depending on conditions, for example, the formula for titanium hydride can vary between $TiH_{1.8}$ and TiH_2.

Many of the interstitial hydrides have metallic properties such as electrical conductivity. It is known, however, that hydrogen is definitely bonded to the metal in these compounds, although the exact nature of the bonding is often unclear.

Molecular hydrogen interacts in a unique way with palladium (Pd). Hydrogen gas is readily adsorbed onto the surface of the palladium metal, where it dissociates into atomic hydrogen. The H atoms then "dissolve" into the metal. On heating and under the pressure of H_2 gas on one side of the metal, these atoms diffuse through the metal and recombine to form molecular hydrogen, which emerges as the gas from the other side. Because no other gas behaves in this way with palladium, this process has been used to separate hydrogen gas from other gases on a small scale.

Isotopes of Hydrogen

Hydrogen has three isotopes: $_1^1H$ (hydrogen), $_1^2H$ (deuterium, symbol D), and $_1^3H$ (tritium, symbol T). The natural abundances of the stable hydrogen isotopes are hydrogen, 99.985 percent; and deuterium, 0.015 percent. Tritium is a radioactive isotope with a half-life of about 12.5 years.

Table 23.1 compares some of the common properties of H_2O with those of D_2O. Deuterium oxide, or *heavy water* as it is commonly called, is used in some nuclear reactors as a coolant and a moderator of nuclear reactions [◄◄ Section 20.5]. D_2O can be separated from H_2O by fractional distillation because H_2O boils at a lower temperature, as Table 23.1 shows. Another technique for separating D_2O is the electrolysis of water. Because H_2 gas is formed about eight times as fast as D_2 during electrolysis, the water remaining in the electrolytic cell becomes progressively enriched with D_2O. Interestingly, the Dead Sea, which for thousands of years has entrapped water that has no outlet other than through evaporation, has a higher $[D_2O]/[H_2O]$ ratio than water found elsewhere.

Although D_2O resembles H_2O chemically in most respects, it is still a toxic substance. The reason is that deuterium is heavier than hydrogen, so its compounds often react more slowly than those of the lighter isotope. Drinking D_2O instead of H_2O on a regular basis could prove fatal because of the slower rate of transfer of D compared with that of H in the acid-base reactions involved in enzyme catalysis. This *kinetic isotope effect* is also manifest in acid ionization constants. For example, the ionization constant of acetic acid

$$CH_3COOH(aq) \rightleftharpoons CH_3COO(aq) + H^+(aq) \qquad K_a = 1.8 \times 10^{-5}$$

is about three times as large as that of *deuterated* acetic acid, in which the ionizable hydrogen atom is replaced by a deuterium atom:

$$CH_3COOD(aq) \rightleftharpoons CH_3COO(aq) + D^+(aq) \qquad K_a = 6 \times 10^{-6}$$

Hydrogenation

Hydrogenation is the addition of hydrogen to compounds containing multiple bonds, usually C=C and C≡C bonds. A simple example of hydrogenation is the conversion of ethylene to ethane:

Ethylene   Ethane

TABLE 23.1	Properties of H_2O and D_2O		
Property		**H_2O**	**D_2O**
Molar mass (g/mol)		18.02	20.03
Melting point (°C)		0	3.8
Boiling point (°C)		100	101.4
Density at 4°C (g/cm³)		1.000	1.108

This reaction is quite slow under normal conditions, but the rate can be greatly increased by the presence of a catalyst such as nickel or platinum.

Hydrogenation is an extremely important process in the food industry. Vegetable oils have considerable nutritional value, but some oils must be hydrogenated before we can use them because of their unsavory flavor and their inappropriate molecular structures (i.e., there are too many C=C bonds present). Upon exposure to air, these *polyunsaturated* molecules (i.e., molecules with many C=C bonds) undergo oxidation to yield unpleasant-tasting products (oil that has oxidized is said to be *rancid*). In the hydrogenation process, a small amount of nickel (about 0.1 percent by mass) is added to the oil and the mixture is exposed to hydrogen gas at high temperature and pressure. Afterward, the nickel is removed by filtration. Hydrogenation reduces the number of double bonds in the molecule but does not completely eliminate them. If all the double bonds are eliminated, the oil becomes hard and brittle. Under controlled conditions, suitable cooking oils and margarine may be prepared by the hydrogenation of vegetable oils extracted from cottonseed, corn, and soybeans.

The Hydrogen Economy

The world's fossil fuel reserves are being depleted at an alarmingly fast rate. Faced with this dilemma, scientists have made intensive efforts in recent years to develop a method of obtaining hydrogen gas as an alternative energy source. Hydrogen gas could replace gasoline to power automobiles (after considerable modification of the engine) or be used with oxygen gas in fuel cells to generate electricity (see page 829). One major advantage of using hydrogen gas in these ways is that the reactions are essentially free of pollutants; the end product formed in a hydrogen-powered engine or in a fuel cell would be water, just as in the burning of hydrogen gas in air:

$$2H_2(g) + O_2(g) \longrightarrow 2H_2O(l)$$

Despite these attractive features, though, the success of a hydrogen economy would depend on how cheaply we could produce hydrogen gas and how easily we could store it.

Although electrolysis of water consumes too much energy for large-scale application, if scientists can devise a more practical method of "splitting" water molecules, we could obtain vast amounts of hydrogen from seawater. One approach that is currently in the early stages of development would use solar energy. In this scheme, a catalyst (a complex molecule containing one or more transition metal atoms, such as ruthenium) absorbs a photon from solar radiation and becomes energetically excited. In its excited state, the catalyst is capable of reducing water to molecular hydrogen.

Some of the interstitial hydrides we have discussed would make suitable storage compounds for hydrogen. The reactions that form these hydrides are usually reversible, so hydrogen gas can be obtained simply by reducing the pressure of the hydrogen gas above the metal. The advantages of using interstitial hydrides are as follows: (1) many metals have a high capacity to take up hydrogen gas—sometimes up to three times as many hydrogen atoms as there are metal atoms; and (2) because these hydrides are solids, they can be stored and transported more easily than gases or liquids.

23.3 CARBON

Although it constitutes only about 0.09 percent by mass of Earth's crust, carbon is an essential element of living matter. It is found free in the form of diamond and graphite, and it is also a component of natural gas, petroleum, and coal. (Coal is a natural dark-brown to black solid used as a fuel; it is formed from fossilized plants and consists of amorphous carbon with various organic and some inorganic compounds.) Carbon combines with oxygen to form carbon dioxide in the atmosphere and occurs as carbonate in limestone and chalk.

Diamond and graphite are *allotropes* of carbon. Figure 23.4 shows the phase diagram of carbon. Although graphite is the stable form of carbon at 1 atm and 25°C, owners of diamond jewelry need not be alarmed, because the rate of the spontaneous process

$$C(diamond) \longrightarrow C(graphite) \qquad \Delta G° = -2.87 \text{ kJ/mol}$$

is extremely slow. In fact, millions of years may pass before a diamond turns to graphite.

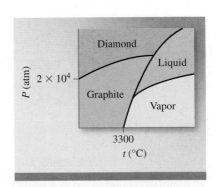

Figure 23.4 Phase diagram of carbon. Note that under atmospheric conditions, graphite is the stable form of carbon.

Figure 23.5 A synthetic diamond and the starting material—graphite.

Synthetic diamond can be prepared from graphite by applying very high pressures and temperatures. Figure 23.5 shows a synthetic diamond and its starting material, graphite. Synthetic diamonds generally lack the optical properties of natural diamonds. They are useful, however, as abrasives and in cutting concrete and many other hard substances, including metals and alloys. Graphite is used as a lubricant and as the "lead" in pencils.

Carbon has the unique ability to form long chains (consisting of more than 50 C atoms) and stable rings with five or six members. This phenomenon is called *catenation,* the linking of like atoms. Carbon's versatility is responsible for the millions of organic compounds (made up of carbon and hydrogen and other elements such as oxygen, nitrogen, and the halogens) found on Earth.

Carbon combines with metals to form ionic compounds called *carbides,* such as CaC_2 and Be_2C, in which carbon is in the form of C_2^{2-} or C^{4-} ions. These ions are strong Brønsted bases and react with water as follows:

$$C_2^{2-}(aq) + 2H_2O(l) \longrightarrow 2OH^-(aq) + C_2H_2(g)$$

$$C^{4-}(aq) + 4H_2O(l) \longrightarrow 4OH^-(aq) + CH_4(g)$$

Carbon also forms a covalent compound with silicon. Silicon carbide (SiC) is called *carborundum* and is prepared as follows:

$$SiO_2(s) + 3C(s) \longrightarrow SiC(s) + 2CO(g)$$

Carborundum is also formed by heating silicon with carbon at 1500°C. Carborundum is almost as hard as diamond, and it has the diamond structure; that is, each carbon atom is bonded tetrahedrally to four Si atoms, and vice versa. It is used mainly for cutting, grinding, and polishing metals and glasses.

Another important class of carbon compounds, the *cyanides,* contain the anion group $:C{\equiv}N:^-$. Cyanide ions are *extremely* toxic because they bind almost irreversibly to the Fe(III) ion in cytochrome oxidase, a key enzyme in metabolic processes. Hydrogen cyanide, which has the aroma of bitter almonds, is even more dangerous because of its volatility (b.p. 26°C). A few tenths of 1 percent by volume of HCN in air can cause death within minutes. Hydrogen cyanide can be prepared by treating sodium cyanide or potassium cyanide with acid:

$$NaCN(s) + HCl(aq) \longrightarrow NaCl(aq) + HCN(aq)$$

Student Annotation: Hydrogen cyanide (HCN) is the gas used in gas-chamber executions.

Because HCN (in solution it is called *hydrocyanic acid*) is a very weak acid ($K_a = 4.9 \times 10^{-10}$), most of the HCN produced in this reaction is in the nonionized form and leaves the solution as hydrogen cyanide gas. For this reason, acids should never be mixed with metal cyanides in the laboratory without proper ventilation.

Cyanide ions are used to extract gold and silver. Although these metals are usually found in the uncombined state in nature, in other metal ores they may be present in relatively small concentrations and are more difficult to extract. In a typical process, the crushed ore is treated with an aqueous cyanide solution in the presence of air to dissolve the gold by forming the soluble complex ion $[Au(CN)_2]^-$:

$$4Au(s) + 8CN^-(aq) + O_2(g) + 2H_2O(l) \longrightarrow 4[Au(CN)_2]^-(aq) + 4OH^-(aq)$$

The complex ion $[Au(CN)_2]^-$ (along with some cation, such as Na^+) is separated from other insoluble materials by filtration and treated with an electropositive metal such as zinc to recover the gold:

$$Zn(s) + 2[Au(CN)_2]^-(aq) \longrightarrow [Zn(CN)_4]^{2-}(aq) + 2Au(s)$$

Figure 23.6 shows an aerial view of a "cyanide pond" used for the extraction of gold.

Of the several oxides of carbon, the most important are carbon monoxide (CO) and carbon dioxide (CO_2). Carbon monoxide is a colorless, odorless gas formed by the incomplete combustion of carbon or carbon-containing compounds:

$$2C(s) + O_2(g) \longrightarrow 2CO(g)$$

Figure 23.6 A cyanide pond for extracting gold from metal ore.

Carbon monoxide is used in metallurgical processes for extracting nickel in organic synthesis and in the production of hydrocarbon fuels with hydrogen. Industrially, it is prepared by passing steam over heated coke. Carbon monoxide burns readily in oxygen to form carbon dioxide:

$$2CO(g) + O_2(g) \longrightarrow 2CO_2(g) \qquad \Delta H° = -566 \text{ kJ/mol}$$

Carbon monoxide is *not* an acidic oxide (it differs from carbon dioxide in that regard), and it is only slightly soluble in water.

Carbon dioxide is a colorless and odorless gas. Unlike carbon monoxide, CO_2 is nontoxic—although it is a simple asphyxiant. It is an acidic oxide. Carbon dioxide is used in beverages, in fire extinguishers, and in the manufacture of baking soda ($NaHCO_3$) and soda ash (Na_2CO_3). Solid carbon dioxide, called *dry ice,* is used as a refrigerant.

23.4 NITROGEN AND PHOSPHORUS

Nitrogen

About 78 percent of air by volume is nitrogen. The most important mineral sources of nitrogen are saltpeter (KNO_3) and Chile saltpeter ($NaNO_3$). Nitrogen is an essential element of life because it is a component of proteins and nucleic acids.

Molecular nitrogen is obtained by the fractional distillation of air (the boiling points of liquid nitrogen and liquid oxygen are $-196°C$ and $-183°C$, respectively). In the laboratory, very pure nitrogen gas can be prepared by the thermal decomposition of ammonium nitrite:

$$NH_4NO_2(s) \longrightarrow 2H_2O(g) + N_2(g)$$

The N_2 molecule contains a triple bond and is very stable with respect to dissociation into atomic species. However, nitrogen forms a large number of compounds with hydrogen and oxygen in which the oxidation number of nitrogen varies from -3 to $+5$ (Table 23.2). Most nitrogen compounds are covalent; when heated with certain metals, however, nitrogen forms ionic nitrides containing the N^{3-} ion:

$$6Li(s) + N_2(g) \longrightarrow 2Li_3N(s)$$

The nitride ion is a very strong Brønsted base and reacts with water to produce ammonia and hydroxide ions:

$$N^{3-}(aq) + 3H_2O(l) \longrightarrow NH_3(g) + 3OH^-(aq)$$

TABLE 23.2	Common Compounds of Nitrogen		
Oxidation number	**Compound**	**Formula**	**Structure**
-3	Ammonia	NH_3	H—N̈—H with H below
-2	Hydrazine	N_2H_4	H—N̈—N̈—H with H H below
-1	Hydroxylamine	NH_2OH	H—N̈—O—H with H below
0	Nitrogen (for reference)	N_2	:N≡N:
$+1$	Nitrous oxide	N_2O	:N≡N—Ö:
$+2$	Nitric oxide	NO	:Ṅ=Ö:
$+3$	Nitrous acid	HNO_2	:O=N̈—Ö—H
$+4$	Nitrogen dioxide	NO_2	:Ö—Ṅ=Ö:
$+5$	Nitric acid	HNO_3	:O=N—Ö—H with :O: below

Ammonia is one of the best-known nitrogen compounds. It is prepared industrially from nitrogen and hydrogen by the Haber process. It can be prepared in the laboratory by treating ammonium chloride with sodium hydroxide:

$$NH_4Cl(aq) + NaOH(aq) \longrightarrow NaCl(aq) + H_2O(l) + NH_3(g)$$

Ammonia is a colorless gas (b.p. $-33.4°C$) with an irritating odor. Most of the ammonia produced annually in the United States is used in fertilizers.

Liquid ammonia, like water, undergoes autoionization:

$$2NH_3(l) \rightleftharpoons NH_4^+ + NH_2^-$$

or simply

$$NH_3(l) \rightleftharpoons H^+ + NH_2^-$$

where NH_2^- is called the *amide ion*. Both the H^+ and NH_2^- ions are solvated with NH_3 molecules—an example of an ion-dipole interaction [◀◀ Section 12.1]. At 50°C, the ion product $[H^+][NH_2^-]$ is about 1×10^{-33}, considerably smaller than the 1×10^{-14} for water at 25°C. Nevertheless, liquid ammonia is a suitable solvent for many electrolytes, especially when a more basic medium is required or if the solutes react with water.

Another important hydride of nitrogen is hydrazine:

$$\begin{array}{ccc} H & & H \\ \diagdown & & \diagup \\ & \ddot{N}-\ddot{N} & \\ \diagup & & \diagdown \\ H & & H \end{array}$$

Each N atom is sp^3-hybridized. Hydrazine is a colorless liquid that smells like ammonia. It melts at 2°C and boils at 114°C.

Hydrazine is a base that can be protonated to give the $N_2H_5^+$ and $N_2H_6^{2+}$ ions. A reducing agent, it can reduce Fe^{3+} to Fe^{2+}, MnO_4^- to Mn^{2+}, and I_2 to I^-. Its reaction with oxygen is highly exothermic:

$$N_2H_4(l) + O_2(g) \longrightarrow N_2(g) + 2H_2O(l) \qquad \Delta H° = -666.6 \text{ kJ/mol}$$

Hydrazine and its derivative methylhydrazine [$N_2H_3(CH_3)$], together with the oxidizer dinitrogen tetroxide (N_2O_4), are used as rocket fuels. Hydrazine also plays a role in polymer synthesis and in the manufacture of pesticides.

There are many nitrogen oxides, but the three particularly important ones are nitrous oxide, nitric oxide, and nitrogen dioxide. Nitrous oxide (N_2O) is a colorless gas with a pleasing odor and sweet taste. It is prepared by heating ammonium nitrate to about 270°C:

$$NH_4NO_3(s) \longrightarrow N_2O(g) + 2H_2O(g)$$

Nitrous oxide resembles molecular oxygen in that it supports combustion. It does so because it decomposes when heated to form molecular nitrogen and molecular oxygen:

$$2N_2O(g) \longrightarrow 2N_2(g) + O_2(g)$$

It is chiefly used as an anesthetic in dental procedures and other minor surgery. Nitrous oxide is also called "laughing gas" because a person inhaling the gas becomes somewhat giddy. No satisfactory explanation has yet been proposed for this unusual physiological response.

Nitric oxide (NO) is a colorless gas. The reaction of N_2 and O_2 in the atmosphere,

$$N_2(g) + O_2(g) \rightleftharpoons 2NO(g) \qquad \Delta G° = 173.4 \text{ kJ/mol}$$

is a form of *nitrogen fixation*. The equilibrium constant for the preceding reaction is very small at room temperature: K_p is only 4.0×10^{-31} at 25°C, so very little NO will form at that temperature. However, the equilibrium constant increases rapidly with temperature, such as in a running auto engine. An appreciable amount of nitric oxide is formed in the atmosphere by the action of lightning. In the laboratory, the gas can be prepared by the reduction of dilute nitric acid with copper:

$$3Cu(s) + 8HNO_3(aq) \longrightarrow 3Cu(NO_3)_2(aq) + 4H_2O(l) + 2NO(g)$$

The nitric oxide molecule is paramagnetic, containing one unpaired electron. It can be represented by the following resonance structures:

$$\ddot{\cdot N}=\ddot{O} \cdot \longleftrightarrow \quad ^{-}\ddot{\cdot N}=\ddot{O} \cdot ^{+}$$

Student Annotation: The NO molecule does not obey the octet rule [◄◄ Section 6.6].

Unlike nitrous oxide and nitric oxide, nitrogen dioxide is a highly toxic, yellow-brown gas with a choking odor. In the laboratory, nitrogen dioxide is prepared by the action of concentrated nitric acid on copper (Figure 23.7):

$$Cu(s) + 4HNO_3(aq) \longrightarrow Cu(NO_3)_2(aq) + 2H_2O(l) + 2NO_2(g)$$

Nitrogen dioxide is paramagnetic, and it has a strong tendency to dimerize to dinitrogen tetroxide, which is diamagnetic:

$$2NO_2 \rightleftharpoons N_2O_4$$

This reaction occurs in both the gas phase and the liquid phase.

Nitrogen dioxide is an *acidic* oxide; it reacts rapidly with cold water to form both nitrous acid (HNO_2) and nitric acid (HNO_3):

$$2NO_2(g) + H_2O(l) \longrightarrow HNO_2(aq) + HNO_3(aq)$$

This is a disproportionation reaction in which the oxidation number of nitrogen changes from +4 (in NO_2) to +3 (in HNO_2) and +5 (in HNO_3). This reaction is quite different from that between CO_2 and H_2O, in which only one acid (carbonic acid) is formed.

Nitric acid is one of the most important inorganic acids. It is a liquid (b.p. 82.6°C), but it does not exist as a pure liquid because it decomposes spontaneously to some extent as follows:

$$4HNO_3(l) \longrightarrow 4NO_2(g) + 2H_2O(l) + O_2(g)$$

Figure 23.7 The production of NO_2 gas when copper reacts with concentrated nitric acid.

The concentrated nitric acid used in the laboratory is 68 percent HNO_3 by mass (density 1.42 g/cm³), which corresponds to 15.7 M.

Nitric acid is a powerful oxidizing agent. The oxidation number of N in HNO_3 is +5. The most common reduction products of nitric acid are NO_2 (oxidation number of N = +4), NO (oxidation number of N = +2), and NH_4^+ (oxidation number of N = −3). Nitric acid can oxidize metals both above and below hydrogen in the activity series. Copper, for example, is oxidized by concentrated nitric acid.

In the presence of a strong reducing agent, such as zinc metal, nitric acid can be reduced all the way to the ammonium ion:

$$4Zn(s) + 10H^+(aq) + NO_3^-(aq) \longrightarrow 4Zn^{2+}(aq) + NH_4^+(aq) + 3H_2O(l)$$

Concentrated nitric acid does not oxidize gold. However, when the acid is added to concentrated hydrochloric acid in a 1:3 ratio by volume (one part HNO_3 to three parts HCl), the resulting solution, called *aqua regia,* can oxidize gold as follows:

$$Au(s) + 3HNO_3(aq) + 4HCl(aq) \longrightarrow HAuCl_4(aq) + 3H_2O(l) + 3NO_2(g)$$

The oxidation of Au is promoted by the complexing ability of the Cl⁻ ion (to form the $AuCl_4^-$ ion).

Concentrated nitric acid also oxidizes a number of nonmetals to their corresponding oxoacids:

$$P_4(s) + 20HNO_3(aq) \longrightarrow 4H_3PO_4(aq) + 20NO_2(g) + 4H_2O(l)$$

$$S(s) + 6HNO_3(aq) \longrightarrow H_2SO_4(aq) + 6NO_2(g) + 2H_2O(l)$$

Nitric acid is used in the manufacture of fertilizers, dyes, drugs, and explosives.

Phosphorus

Like nitrogen, phosphorus is a member of the Group 5A family, and in some respects the chemistry of phosphorus resembles that of nitrogen. Phosphorus occurs most commonly in nature as *phosphate rocks,* which are mostly calcium phosphate [$Ca_3(PO_4)_2$] and fluoroapatite [$Ca_5(PO_4)_3F$]

Figure 23.8 Fluoroapatite [$Ca_5(PO_4)_3F$].

(Figure 23.8). Elemental phosphorus can be obtained by heating calcium phosphate with coke and silica sand:

$$2Ca_3(PO_4)_2(s) + 10C(s) + 6SiO_2(s) \longrightarrow 6CaSiO_3(s) + 10CO(g) + P_4(s)$$

There are several allotropic forms of phosphorus, but only white phosphorus and red phosphorus are of importance. White phosphorus consists of discrete tetrahedral P_4 molecules (Figure 23.9). A solid (m.p. 44.2°C), white phosphorus is insoluble in water but quite soluble in carbon disulfide (CS_2) and organic solvents such as chloroform ($CHCl_3$). White phosphorus is a highly toxic substance. It bursts into flames spontaneously when exposed to air; hence, it is used in incendiary bombs and grenades:

$$P_4(s) + 5O_2(g) \longrightarrow P_4O_{10}(s)$$

The high reactivity of white phosphorus is attributed to structural strain: the P—P bonds are compressed in the tetrahedral P_4 molecule. White phosphorus was once used in matches, but because of its toxicity it has been replaced by tetraphosphorus trisulfide (P_4S_3).

When heated in the absence of air, white phosphorus is slowly converted to red phosphorus at about 300°C:

$$nP_4(\text{white phosphorus}) \longrightarrow (P_4)_n(\text{red phosphorus})$$

Red phosphorus has a polymeric structure (see Figure 23.9) and is more stable and less volatile than white phosphorus.

The most important hydride of phosphorus is phosphine (PH_3), a colorless, very poisonous gas formed by heating white phosphorus in concentrated sodium hydroxide:

$$P_4(s) + 3NaOH(aq) + 3H_2O(l) \longrightarrow 3NaH_2PO_2(aq) + PH_3(g)$$

Phosphine is moderately soluble in water and more soluble in carbon disulfide and organic solvents. Its aqueous solution is neutral, unlike that of ammonia. In liquid ammonia, phosphine dissolves to give $NH_4^+PH_2^-$. Phosphine is a strong reducing agent; it reduces many metal salts to the corresponding metals. The gas burns in air:

$$PH_3(g) + 2O_2(g) \longrightarrow H_3PO_4(s)$$

Phosphorus forms binary compounds with halogens—namely, the trihalides (PX_3) and the pentahalides (PX_5), where X denotes a halogen atom. In contrast, nitrogen can form only trihalides (NX_3). Unlike nitrogen, phosphorus has a $3d$ subshell, which can be used for valence-shell expansion. We can explain the bonding in PCl_5 by assuming that phosphorus undergoes sp^3d hybridization of its $3s$, $3p$, and $3d$ orbitals [◄◄ Section 7.4]. The five sp^3d hybrid orbitals also account for the trigonal bipyramidal geometry of the PCl_5 molecule (see Table 7.4).

Phosphorus trichloride is prepared by heating white phosphorus in chlorine:

$$P_4(l) + 6Cl_2(g) \longrightarrow 4PCl_3(g)$$

Figure 23.9 The structures of white and red phosphorus. Red phosphorus is believed to have a chain structure, as shown.

White phosphorus

Red phosphorus

A colorless liquid (b.p. 76°C), PCl_3 is hydrolyzed according to the following equation:

$$PCl_3(l) + 3H_2O(l) \longrightarrow H_3PO_3(aq) + 3HCl(g)$$

In the presence of an excess of chlorine gas, PCl_3 is converted to phosphorus pentachloride, which is a light-yellow solid:

$$PCl_3(l) + Cl_2(g) \longrightarrow PCl_5(s)$$

X-ray studies indicate that solid phosphorus pentachloride exists as $[PCl_4^+][PCl_6^-]$, in which the PCl_4^+ ion has a *tetrahedral* geometry and the PCl_6^- ion has an *octahedral* geometry. In the gas phase, PCl_5 (which has trigonal bipyramidal geometry) is in equilibrium with PCl_3 and Cl_2:

$$PCl_5(g) \rightleftharpoons PCl_3(g) + Cl_2(g)$$

Phosphorus pentachloride reacts with water as follows:

$$PCl_5(s) + 4H_2O(l) \longrightarrow H_3PO_4(aq) + 5HCl(aq)$$

The two important oxides of phosphorus are tetraphosphorus hexaoxide (P_4O_6) and tetraphosphorus decaoxide (P_4O_{10}), shown in Figure 23.10. The oxides are obtained by burning white phosphorus in limited and excess amounts of oxygen gas, respectively:

$$P_4(s) + 3O_2(g) \longrightarrow P_4O_6(s)$$
$$P_4(s) + 5O_2(g) \longrightarrow P_4O_{10}(s)$$

Both oxides are acidic; that is, they are converted to acids in water. The compound P_4O_{10} is a white flocculent powder (m.p. 420°C) that has a great affinity for water:

$$P_4O_{10}(s) + 6H_2O(l) \longrightarrow 4H_3PO_4(aq)$$

For this reason, it is often used for drying gases and for removing water from solvents.

There are many oxoacids containing phosphorus. Some examples are phosphorous acid (H_3PO_3), phosphoric acid (H_3PO_4), hypophosphorous acid (H_3PO_2), and triphosphoric acid ($H_5P_3O_{10}$) (the structures of which are shown in Figure 23.11). Phosphoric acid, also called ortho-phosphoric acid, is a weak triprotic acid. It is prepared industrially by the reaction of calcium phosphate with sulfuric acid:

$$Ca_3(PO_4)_2(s) + 3H_2SO_4(aq) \longrightarrow 2H_3PO_4(aq) + 3CaSO_4(s)$$

Phosphorous acid (H_3PO_3)

Hypophosphorous acid (H_3PO_2)

Phosphoric acid (H_3PO_4)

Triphosphoric acid ($H_5P_3O_{10}$)

Figure 23.11 Structures of some common phosphorus-containing oxoacids.

In the pure form, phosphoric acid is a colorless solid (m.p. 42.2°C). The phosphoric acid we use in the laboratory is usually an 82 percent H_3PO_4 solution (by mass). Phosphoric acid and phosphates have many commercial applications in detergents, fertilizers, flame retardants, and toothpastes, and as buffers in carbonated beverages.

Like nitrogen, phosphorus is an element that is essential to life. It constitutes only about 1 percent by mass of the human body, but it is a very important 1 percent. About 23 percent of the human skeleton is mineral matter. The phosphorus content of this mineral matter, calcium phosphate $[Ca_3(PO_4)_2]$, is 20 percent. Our teeth are basically $Ca_3(PO_4)_2$ and $Ca_5(PO_4)_3OH$. Phosphates are also important components of the genetic materials deoxyribonucleic acid (DNA) and ribonucleic acid (RNA).

23.5 OXYGEN AND SULFUR

Oxygen

Oxygen is by far the most abundant element in Earth's crust, constituting about 46 percent of its mass. In addition, the atmosphere contains about 21 percent molecular oxygen by volume (23 percent by mass). Like nitrogen, oxygen in the free state is a diatomic molecule (O_2). In the laboratory, oxygen gas can be obtained by heating potassium chlorate:

$$2KClO_3(s) \longrightarrow 2KCl(s) + 3O_2(g)$$

The reaction is usually catalyzed by manganese(IV) dioxide (MnO_2). Pure oxygen gas can be prepared by electrolyzing water (page 831). Industrially, oxygen gas is prepared by the fractional distillation of liquefied air. Oxygen gas is colorless and odorless.

Oxygen is a building block of practically all biomolecules, accounting for about a fourth of the atoms in living matter. Molecular oxygen is the essential oxidant in the metabolic breakdown of food molecules. Without it, a human being cannot survive for more than a few minutes.

Although oxygen has two allotropes, O_2 and O_3, when we speak of molecular oxygen, we normally mean O_2. Ozone (O_3) is less stable than O_2. The O_2 molecule is paramagnetic because it contains two unpaired electrons.

A strong oxidizing agent, molecular oxygen is one of the most widely used industrial chemicals. Its main uses are in the steel industry and in sewage treatment. Oxygen is also used as a bleaching agent for pulp and paper, in medicine to ease breathing difficulties, in oxyacetylene torches, and as an oxidizing agent in many inorganic and organic reactions.

Oxygen forms three types of oxides: the normal oxide (or simply the *oxide*), which contains the O^{2-} ion; the peroxide, which contains the O_2^{2-} ion; and the superoxide, which contains the O_2^- ion:

$$:\ddot{O}:^{2-} \qquad :\ddot{O}:\ddot{O}:^{2-} \qquad :\ddot{O}:\ddot{O}:^-$$

$$\text{Oxide} \qquad \text{Peroxide} \qquad \text{Superoxide}$$

The ions are all strong Brønsted bases and react with water as follows:

Oxide: $O^{2-}(aq) + H_2O(l) \longrightarrow 2OH^-(aq)$

Peroxide: $2O_2^{2-}(aq) + 2H_2O(l) \longrightarrow O_2(g) + 4OH^-(aq)$

Superoxide: $4O_2^-(aq) + 2H_2O(l) \longrightarrow 3O_2(g) + 4OH^-(aq)$

The reaction of O^{2-} with water is a *hydrolysis* reaction, but those involving O_2^{2-} and O_2^- are *redox* processes.

The nature of bonding in oxides changes across any period in the periodic table. Oxides of elements on the left side of the periodic table, such as those of the alkali metals and alkaline earth metals, are generally ionic solids with high melting points. Oxides of the metalloids and of the metallic elements toward the middle of the periodic table are also solids, but they have much less ionic character. Oxides of nonmetals are covalent compounds that generally exist as liquids or gases at room temperature. The acidic character of the oxides increases from left to right. Consider the oxides of the third period elements:

$$\underbrace{Na_2O \qquad MgO}_{\text{Basic}} \qquad \underbrace{Al_2O_3}_{\text{Amphoteric}} \qquad \underbrace{SiO_2 \qquad P_4O_{10} \qquad SO_3 \qquad Cl_2O_7}_{\text{Acidic}}$$

The basicity of the oxides increases as we move down a particular group. MgO does not react with water, for example, but reacts with acid as follows:

$$MgO(s) + 2H^+(aq) \longrightarrow Mg^{2+}(aq) + H_2O(l)$$

On the other hand, BaO, which is more basic, undergoes hydrolysis to yield the corresponding hydroxide:

$$BaO(s) + H_2O(l) \longrightarrow Ba(OH)_2(aq)$$

The best-known peroxide is hydrogen peroxide (H_2O_2). It is a colorless, syrupy liquid (m.p. $-0.9°C$), prepared in the laboratory by the action of cold dilute sulfuric acid on barium peroxide octahydrate:

$$BaO_2(s) + 8H_2O(s) + H_2SO_4(aq) \longrightarrow BaSO_4(s) + H_2O_2(aq) + 8H_2O(l)$$

The structure of hydrogen peroxide is shown in Figure 23.12. Using the VSEPR method, we see that the H—O and O—O bonds are bent about each oxygen atom in a configuration similar to the structure of water. The lone-pair–bonding-pair repulsion is greater in H_2O_2 than in H_2O, so the H—O—O angle is only 97° (compared with 104.5° for H—O—H in H_2O). Hydrogen peroxide is a polar molecule ($\mu = 2.16$ D). Hydrogen peroxide readily decomposes when heated or exposed to sunlight or even in the presence of dust particles or certain metals, including iron and copper:

$$2H_2O_2(l) \longrightarrow 2H_2O(l) + O_2(g) \qquad \Delta H° = -196.4 \text{ kJ/mol}$$

This is a *disproportionation* reaction. The oxidation number of oxygen changes from -1 to -2 and 0.

Hydrogen peroxide is miscible with water in all proportions due to its ability to hydrogen bond with water. Dilute hydrogen peroxide solutions (3 percent by mass), available in drugstores, are used as mild antiseptics; more concentrated H_2O_2 solutions are employed as bleaching agents for textiles, fur, and hair. The high heat of decomposition of hydrogen peroxide also makes it a suitable component in rocket fuel.

Hydrogen peroxide is a strong oxidizing agent; it can oxidize Fe^{2+} ions to Fe^{3+} ions in an acidic solution:

$$H_2O_2(aq) + 2Fe^{2+}(aq) + 2H^+(aq) \longrightarrow 2Fe^{3+}(aq) + 2H_2O(l)$$

It also oxidizes SO_3^{2-} ions to SO_4^{2-} ions:

$$H_2O_2(aq) + SO_3^{2-}(aq) \longrightarrow SO_4^{2-}(aq) + H_2O(l)$$

In addition, hydrogen peroxide can act as a reducing agent toward substances that are stronger oxidizing agents than itself. For example, hydrogen peroxide reduces silver oxide to metallic silver,

$$H_2O_2(aq) + Ag_2O(s) \longrightarrow 2Ag(s) + H_2O(l) + O_2(g)$$

and permanganate (MnO_4^-) to manganese(II) in an acidic solution,

$$5H_2O_2(aq) + 2MnO_4^-(aq) + 6H^+(aq) \longrightarrow 2Mn^{2+}(aq) + 5O_2(g) + 8H_2O(l)$$

If we want to determine hydrogen peroxide concentration, this reaction can be carried out as a redox titration, using a standard permanganate solution.

There are relatively few known superoxides (i.e., compounds containing the O_2^- ion). In general, only the most reactive alkali metals (K, Rb, and Cs) form superoxides.

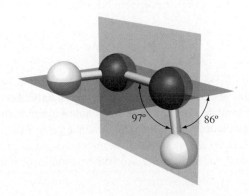

Figure 23.12 The structure of H_2O_2.

Figure 23.13 The preparation of O_3 from O_2 by electrical discharge. The outside of the outer tube and the inside of the inner tube are coated with metal foils that are connected to a high-voltage source. (The metal foil on the inside of the inner tube is not shown.) During the electrical discharge, O_2 gas is passed through the tube. The O_3 gas formed exits from the upper right-hand tube, along with some unreacted O_2 gas.

Both the peroxide ion and the superoxide ion are by-products of metabolism. Because these ions are highly reactive, they can inflict great damage on living cells. Fortunately, our bodies are equipped with the enzymes catalase, peroxidase, and superoxide dismutase, which convert these toxic substances to water and molecular oxygen.

Ozone is a rather toxic, light-blue gas (b.p. $-111.3°C$). Its pungent odor is noticeable around sources of significant electrical discharges (such as a subway train). Ozone can be prepared from molecular oxygen, either photochemically or by subjecting O_2 to an electrical discharge (Figure 23.13):

$$3O_2(g) \longrightarrow 2O_3(g) \qquad \Delta G° = 326.8 \text{ kJ/mol}$$

Because the standard free energy of formation of ozone is a large positive quantity ($\Delta G°_f = 163.4$ kJ/mol), ozone is less stable than molecular oxygen. The ozone molecule has a bent structure in which the bond angle is $116.5°$:

Ozone is mainly used to purify drinking water; to deodorize air and sewage gases; and to bleach waxes, oils, and textiles.

Ozone is a very powerful oxidizing agent—its oxidizing power is exceeded only by that of molecular fluorine (see Table 19.1). For example, ozone can oxidize sulfides of many metals to the corresponding sulfates:

$$4O_3(g) + PbS(s) \longrightarrow PbSO_4(s) + 4O_2(g)$$

Ozone oxidizes all the common metals except gold and platinum. In fact, a convenient test for ozone is based on its action on mercury. When exposed to ozone, mercury loses its metallic luster and sticks to glass tubing (instead of flowing freely through it). This behavior is attributed to the change in surface tension caused by the formation of mercury(II) oxide:

$$O_3(g) + 3Hg(l) \longrightarrow 3HgO(s)$$

The effect of ozone is beneficial in the stratosphere but it has an undesirable role in smog formation at ground level.

Sulfur

Although sulfur is not a very abundant element (it constitutes only about 0.06 percent of Earth's crust by mass), it is readily available because it occurs commonly in nature in the elemental form. The largest known reserves of sulfur are found in sedimentary deposits. In addition, sulfur occurs widely in gypsum ($CaSO_4 \cdot 2H_2O$) and various sulfide minerals such as pyrite (FeS_2) (Figure 23.14). Sulfur is also present in natural gas as H_2S, SO_2, and other sulfur-containing compounds.

Figure 23.14 Pyrite (FeS_2).

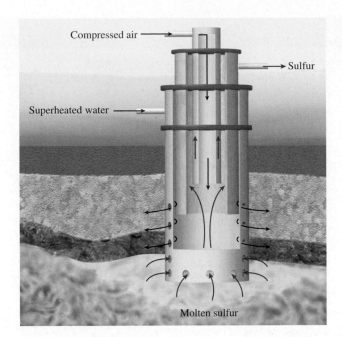

Compressed air

Sulfur

Superheated water

Molten sulfur

Figure 23.15 The Frasch process. Three concentric pipes are inserted into a hole drilled down to the sulfur deposit. Superheated water is forced down the outer pipe into the sulfur, causing it to melt. Molten sulfur is then forced up the middle pipe by compressed air.

Sulfur is extracted from underground deposits by the *Frasch*[1] *process,* shown in Figure 23.15. In this process, superheated water (liquid water heated to about 160°C under high pressure to prevent it from boiling) is pumped down the outermost pipe to melt the sulfur. Next, compressed air is forced down the innermost pipe. Liquid sulfur mixed with air forms an emulsion that is less dense than water and therefore rises to the surface as it is forced up the middle pipe. Sulfur produced in this manner, which amounts to about 10 million tons per year, has a purity of about 99.5 percent.

There are several allotropic forms of sulfur, the most important being the rhombic and monoclinic forms. Rhombic sulfur is thermodynamically the most stable form; it has a puckered S_8 ring structure:

S_8

It is a yellow, tasteless, and odorless solid (m.p. 112°C) that is insoluble in water but soluble in carbon disulfide. When heated, it is slowly converted to monoclinic sulfur (m.p. 119°C), which also consists of the S_8 units. When liquid sulfur is heated above 150°C, the rings begin to break up, and the entangling of the sulfur chains results in a sharp increase in the liquid's viscosity. Further heating tends to rupture the chains, so the viscosity decreases.

Like nitrogen, sulfur shows a wide variety of oxidation numbers in its compounds (Table 23.3). The best-known hydrogen compound of sulfur is hydrogen sulfide, which is prepared by the action of an acid on a sulfide; for example,

$$FeS(s) + H_2SO_4(aq) \longrightarrow FeSO_4(aq) + H_2S(g)$$

Multi 23.1
Nonmetallic elements—the extraction of sulfur

---

[1]Herman Frasch (1851–1914) was a German chemical engineer. Besides inventing the process for obtaining pure sulfur, Frasch developed methods for refining petroleum.

TABLE 23.3	Common Compounds of Sulfur		
Oxidation number	**Compound**	**Formula**	**Structure**
−2	Hydrogen sulfide	H_2S	
0	Sulfur (for reference)	S_8	
+1	Disulfur dichloride	S_2Cl_2	
+2	Sulfur dichloride	SCl_2	
+4	Sulfur dioxide	SO_2	
+6	Sulfur trioxide	SO_3	

Nowadays, hydrogen sulfide used in qualitative analysis is prepared by the hydrolysis of thioacetamide:

Hydrogen sulfide is a colorless gas (b.p. −60.2°C) that smells like rotten eggs. (The odor of rotten eggs actually does come from hydrogen sulfide, which is formed by the bacterial decomposition of sulfur-containing proteins.) Hydrogen sulfide is a highly toxic substance that, like hydrogen cyanide, attacks respiratory enzymes. It is a very weak diprotic acid (see Table 16.9). In basic solution, H_2S is a reducing agent. For example, it is oxidized by permanganate to elemental sulfur:

$$3H_2S(aq) + 2MnO_4^-(aq) \longrightarrow 3S(s) + 2MnO_2(s) + 2H_2O(l) + 2OH^-(aq)$$

Sulfur has two important oxides: sulfur dioxide (SO_2) and sulfur trioxide (SO_3). Sulfur dioxide is formed when sulfur burns in air:

$$S(s) + O_2(g) \longrightarrow SO_2(g)$$

In the laboratory, it can be prepared by the action of an acid on a sulfite; for example,

$$2HCl(aq) + Na_2SO_3(aq) \longrightarrow 2NaCl(aq) + H_2O(l) + SO_2(g)$$

or by the action of concentrated sulfuric acid on copper:

$$Cu(s) + 2H_2SO_4(aq) \longrightarrow CuSO_4(aq) + 2H_2O(l) + SO_2(g)$$

Sulfur dioxide (b.p. −10°C) is a pungent, colorless gas that is quite toxic. An acidic oxide, it reacts with water as follows:

$$SO_2(g) + H_2O(l) \rightleftharpoons H^+(aq) + HSO_3^-(aq)$$

Sulfur dioxide is slowly oxidized to sulfur trioxide, but the reaction rate can be greatly enhanced by a platinum or vanadium oxide catalyst:

$$2SO_2(g) + O_2(g) \longrightarrow 2SO_3(g)$$

Sulfur trioxide dissolves in water to form sulfuric acid:

$$SO_3(g) + H_2O(l) \longrightarrow H_2SO_4(aq)$$

The contributing role of sulfur dioxide to acid rain is discussed on page 678.

Sulfuric acid is the world's most important industrial chemical. It is prepared industrially by first burning sulfur in air:

$$S(s) + O_2(g) \longrightarrow SO_2(g)$$

Next is the key step of converting sulfur dioxide to sulfur trioxide:

$$2SO_2(g) + O_2(g) \longrightarrow 2SO_3(g)$$

Vanadium(V) oxide (V_2O_5) is the catalyst used for the second step. Because the sulfur dioxide and oxygen molecules react in contact with the surface of solid V_2O_5, the process is referred to as the *contact process*.

Sulfuric acid is a diprotic acid. It is a colorless, viscous liquid (m.p. 10.4°C). The concentrated sulfuric acid we use in the laboratory is 98 percent H_2SO_4 by mass (density = 1.84 g/cm^3), which corresponds to a concentration of 18 M. The oxidizing strength of sulfuric acid depends on its temperature and concentration. A cold, dilute sulfuric acid solution reacts with metals above hydrogen in the activity series, thereby liberating molecular hydrogen in a displacement reaction:

$$Mg(s) + H_2SO_4(aq) \longrightarrow MgSO_4(aq) + H_2(g)$$

This is a typical reaction of an active metal with an acid. The strength of sulfuric acid as an oxidizing agent is greatly enhanced when it is both hot and concentrated. In such a solution, the oxidizing agent is actually the sulfate ion rather than the hydrated proton, $H^+(aq)$. Thus, copper reacts with concentrated sulfuric acid as follows:

$$Cu(s) + 2H_2SO_4(aq) \longrightarrow CuSO_4(aq) + SO_2(g) + 2H_2O(l)$$

Depending on the nature of the reducing agents, the sulfate ion may be further reduced to elemental sulfur or the sulfide ion. For example, the reduction of H_2SO_4 by HI yields H_2S and I_2:

$$8HI(aq) + H_2SO_4(aq) \longrightarrow H_2S(aq) + 4I_2(s) + 4H_2O(l)$$

Concentrated sulfuric acid oxidizes nonmetals. For example, it oxidizes carbon to carbon dioxide and sulfur to sulfur dioxide:

$$C(s) + 2H_2SO_4(aq) \longrightarrow CO_2(g) + 2SO_2(g) + 2H_2O(l)$$

$$S(s) + 2H_2SO_4(aq) \longrightarrow 3SO_2(g) + 2H_2O(l)$$

Carbon disulfide, a colorless, flammable liquid (b.p. 46°C), is formed by heating carbon and sulfur to a high temperature:

$$C(s) + 2S(l) \longrightarrow CS_2(l)$$

It is only slightly soluble in water. Carbon disulfide is a good solvent for sulfur, phosphorus, iodine, and nonpolar substances such as waxes and rubber.

Another interesting compound of sulfur is sulfur hexafluoride (SF_6), which is prepared by heating sulfur in an atmosphere of fluorine:

$$S(l) + 3F_2(g) \longrightarrow SF_6(g)$$

Sulfur hexafluoride is a nontoxic, colorless gas (b.p. 63.8°C). It is the most inert of all sulfur compounds; it resists attack even by molten KOH. The structure and bonding of SF_6 were discussed in Chapters 6 and 7.

Thinking Outside the Box

Arsenic

Arsenic has always been the poison of choice for murder mysteries. In the 1960s, samples of Napoleon's hair were analyzed and found to contain a high level of arsenic. It was naturally concluded that he was intentionally poisoned. Studies in recent years, however, have shown that Napoleon's exposure to arsenic may have been environmental. The wallpaper in his drawing room was found to contain the green pigment copper arsenite ($CuHAsO_4$). The mold growing on the papers could have converted the compound to the volatile, toxic trimethylarsine [$(CH_3)_3As$], which Napoleon then ingested.

Unlike the first two elements in Group 5A, nitrogen and phosphorus, arsenic is not an essential element in the human body. Moreover, elemental arsenic itself is not all that harmful. The commonly used poison is actually arsenic(III) oxide (As_2O_3), a white compound that dissolves in water, has no taste, and if administered over a period of time, is hard to detect. The toxicity of As(III) inorganic compounds lies in their ability to bind to the sulfhydryl group ($-SH$) of proteins and enzymes, thus impairing their normal functions. Arsenite also inhibits enzyme activities in the mitochondria and uncouples oxidative phosphorylation. This results in a decrease in ATP production and an increase in harmful reactive oxygen species (ROS) such as hydrogen peroxide and superoxide ion. The accumulation of ROS can lead to DNA damage and initiate carcinogenic processes.

King George III of Britain (1738–1820) suffered from periodic physical and mental illness throughout his adult life. Several of the episodes were severe enough to render the king temporarily unable to rule. Although most of the king's symptoms are now attributed to *porphyria,* a hereditary metabolic disorder, a 2004 analysis of samples of the king's hair revealed high levels of arsenic. One possibility that has been raised regarding the source of the arsenic is the *antimony* used in the king's treatment for chronic illness. Antimony is an element known since ancient times and used in cosmetics (stibnite, the most common antimony ore was used as eye liner during biblical times) and in medicine.

23.6 THE HALOGENS

The halogens—fluorine, chlorine, bromine, and iodine—are reactive nonmetals. Table 23.4 lists some of the properties of these elements. Although all halogens are highly reactive and toxic, the magnitude of reactivity and toxicity generally decreases from fluorine to iodine. The chemistry of fluorine differs from that of the rest of the halogens in the following ways:

1. Fluorine is the most reactive of all the halogens. The difference in reactivity between fluorine and chlorine is greater than that between chlorine and bromine. Table 23.4 shows that the F—F bond is considerably weaker than the Cl—Cl bond. The weak bond in F_2 can be explained in terms of the lone pairs on the F atoms:

$$:\ddot{F}-\ddot{F}:$$

The small size of the F atoms (see Table 23.4) allows a close approach of the three lone pairs on each of the F atoms, resulting in a greater repulsion than that found in Cl_2, which consists of larger atoms.

2. Hydrogen fluoride (HF) has a relatively high boiling point (19.5°C) as a result of strong intermolecular hydrogen bonding, whereas all other hydrogen halides have much lower boiling points.

3. Hydrofluoric acid is a weak acid, whereas all other hydrohalic acids (HCl, HBr, and HI) are strong acids.

4. Fluorine reacts with cold sodium hydroxide solution to produce oxygen difluoride as follows:

$$2F_2(g) + 2NaOH(aq) \longrightarrow 2NaF(aq) + H_2O(l) + OF_2(g)$$

The same reaction with chlorine or bromine, on the other hand, produces a halide and a hypohalite:

$$X_2(g) + 2NaOH(aq) \longrightarrow NaX(aq) + NaXO(aq) + H_2O(l)$$

where X stands for Cl or Br. Iodine does not react under the same conditions.

5. Silver fluoride (AgF) is soluble. All other silver halides (AgCl, AgBr, and AgI) are insoluble.

TABLE 23.4	Properties of the Halogens			
Property	**F**	**Cl**	**Br**	**I**
Valence electron configuration	$2s^2 2p^5$	$3s^2 3p^5$	$4s^2 4p^5$	$5s^2 5p^5$
Melting point (°C)	−223	−102	−7	114
Boiling point (°C)	−187	−35	59	183
Appearance*	Pale-yellow gas	Yellow-green gas	Red-brown liquid	Dark-violet vapor Dark metallic-looking solid
Atomic radius (pm)	72	99	114	133
Ionic radius (pm)†	136	181	195	216
Ionization energy (kJ/mol)	1680	1251	1139	1003
Electronegativity	4.0	3.0	2.8	2.5
Standard reduction potential (V)*	2.87	1.36	1.07	0.53
Bond enthalpy (kJ/mol)*	150.6	242.7	192.5	151.0

* These values and descriptions apply to the diatomic species X_2, where X represents a halogen atom. The half-reaction is $X_2(g) + 2e^- \longrightarrow 2X^-(aq)$.

† Refers to the anion X^-.

The element astatine also belongs to the Group 7A family. However, all isotopes of astatine are radioactive; its longest-lived isotope is astatine-210, which has a half-life of 8.3 h. As a result, it is both difficult and expensive to study astatine in the laboratory.

The halogens form a very large number of compounds. In the elemental state, they form diatomic molecules (X_2). In nature, however, because of their high reactivity, halogens are always found combined with other elements. Chlorine, bromine, and iodine occur as halides in seawater, and fluorine occurs in the minerals fluorite (CaF_2) and cryolite (Na_3AlF_6).

Preparation and General Properties of the Halogens

Because fluorine and chlorine are strong oxidizing agents, they must be prepared by electrolysis rather than by chemical oxidation of the fluoride and chloride ions. Electrolysis does not work for aqueous solutions of fluorides, however, because fluorine is a stronger oxidizing agent than oxygen. From Table 19.1 (page 815), we find that

$$F_2(g) + 2e^- \longrightarrow 2F^-(aq) \qquad E° = 2.87 \text{ V}$$

$$O_2(g) + 4H^+(aq) + 4e^- \longrightarrow 2H_2O(l) \qquad E° = 1.23 \text{ V}$$

If F_2 were formed by the electrolysis of an aqueous fluoride solution, it would immediately oxidize water to oxygen. For this reason, fluorine is prepared by electrolyzing liquid hydrogen fluoride containing potassium fluoride to increase its conductivity, at about 70°C (Figure 23.16):

Anode (oxidation): $\qquad\qquad 2F^- \longrightarrow F_2(g) + 2e^-$

Cathode (reduction): $\quad 2H^+ + 2e^- \longrightarrow H_2(g)$

Overall reaction: $\qquad\quad 2HF(l) \longrightarrow H_2(g) + F_2(g)$

Chlorine gas (Cl_2) is prepared industrially by the electrolysis of molten NaCl or by the *chlor-alkali process,* the electrolysis of a concentrated aqueous NaCl solution (called brine). (*Chlor* denotes chlorine, and *alkali* denotes an alkali metal, such as sodium.) Two of the common cells used in the chlor-alkali process are the mercury cell and the diaphragm cell. In both cells, the overall reaction is

$$2NaCl(aq) + 2H_2O(l) \xrightarrow{\text{electrolysis}} 2NaOH(aq) + H_2(g) + Cl_2(g)$$

Figure 23.16 Electrolytic cell for the preparation of fluorine gas. Note that because H_2 and F_2 form an explosive mixture, these gases must be separated from each other.

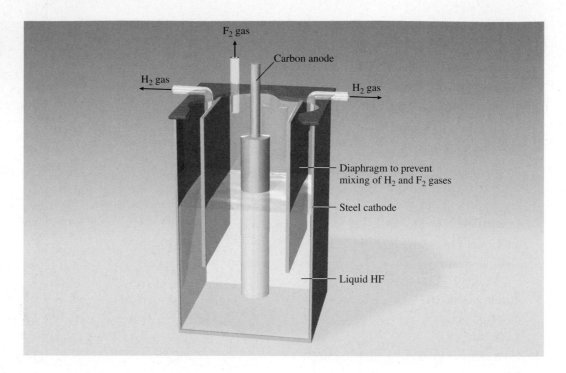

As you can see, this reaction yields two useful by-products, NaOH and H_2. The cells are designed to separate the molecular chlorine from the sodium hydroxide solution and the molecular hydrogen to prevent side reactions such as

$$2NaOH(aq) + Cl_2(g) \longrightarrow NaOCl(aq) + NaCl(aq) + H_2O(l)$$

and

$$H_2(g) + Cl_2(g) \longrightarrow 2HCl(g)$$

These reactions must be prevented because they consume the desired products and can be dangerous because a mixture of H_2 and Cl_2 is explosive.

Figure 23.17 shows the mercury cell used in the chlor-alkali process. The cathode is a liquid mercury pool at the bottom of the cell, and the anode is made of either graphite or titanium coated with platinum. Brine is continuously passed through the cell as shown in the diagram. The electrode reactions are

Anode (oxidation): $2Cl^-(aq) \longrightarrow Cl_2(g) + 2e^-$

Cathode (reduction): $\underline{2Na(aq) + 2e^- \xrightarrow{Hg(l)} 2NaHg}$

Overall reaction: $2NaCl(aq) \longrightarrow 2Na/Hg + Cl_2(g)$

Figure 23.17 Mercury cell used in the chlor-alkali process. The cathode contains mercury. The sodium-mercury amalgam is treated with water outside the cell to produce sodium hydroxide and hydrogen gas.

where Na/Hg denotes the formation of sodium amalgam. The chlorine gas generated this way is very pure. The sodium amalgam does not react with the brine solution but decomposes as follows when treated with pure water outside the cell:

$$2Na/Hg + 2H_2O(l) \longrightarrow 2NaOH(aq) + H_2(g) + 2Hg(l)$$

The by-products are sodium hydroxide and hydrogen gas. Although the mercury is cycled back into the cell for reuse, some of it is always discharged with waste solutions into the environment, resulting in mercury pollution. This is a major drawback of the mercury cell. Figure 23.18 shows the industrial manufacture of chlorine gas.

The half-cell reactions in a diaphragm cell are shown in Figure 23.19. The asbestos diaphragm is permeable to the ions but not to the hydrogen and chlorine gases and so prevents the gases from mixing. During electrolysis, a positive pressure is applied on the anode side of the compartment to prevent the migration of the OH$^-$ ions from the cathode compartment. Periodically, fresh brine solution is added to the cell and the sodium hydroxide solution is run off as shown. The diaphragm cell presents no pollution problems. Its main disadvantage is that the sodium hydroxide solution is contaminated with unreacted sodium chloride.

In the laboratory, chlorine, bromine, and iodine can be prepared by heating the alkali halides (NaCl, KBr, or KI) in concentrated sulfuric acid in the presence of manganese(IV) oxide. A representative reaction is

$$MnO_2(s) + 2H_2SO_4(aq) + 2NaCl(aq) \longrightarrow MnSO_4(aq) + Na_2SO_4(aq) + 2H_2O(l) + Cl_2(g)$$

Figure 23.18 The industrial manufacture of chlorine gas.

Compounds of the Halogens

Most of the halides can be categorized as either ionic or covalent. The fluorides and chlorides of many metallic elements, especially those belonging to the alkali metal and alkaline earth metal (except beryllium) families, are *ionic* compounds. Most of the halides of *nonmetals* such as sulfur and phosphorus are *covalent* compounds. The oxidation numbers of the halogens can vary from -1 to $+7$. The only exception is fluorine. Because it is the most electronegative element, fluorine can have only two oxidation numbers, 0 (as in F$_2$) and -1, in all its compounds.

The hydrogen halides, an important class of halogen compounds, can be formed by the direct combination of the elements:

$$H_2(g) + X_2(g) \rightleftharpoons 2HX(g)$$

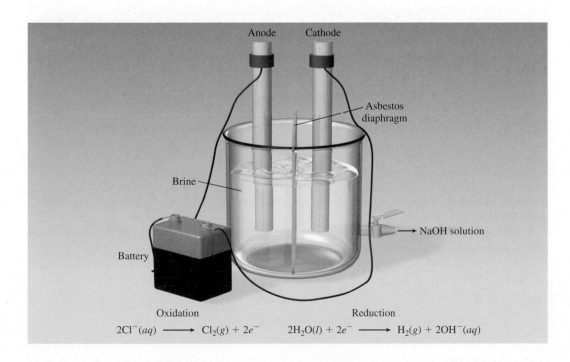

Anode Cathode

Asbestos diaphragm

Brine

NaOH solution

Battery

Oxidation

$$2Cl^-(aq) \longrightarrow Cl_2(g) + 2e^-$$

Reduction

$$2H_2O(l) + 2e^- \longrightarrow H_2(g) + 2OH^-(aq)$$

Figure 23.19 Diaphragm cell used in the chlor-alkali process.

where X denotes a halogen atom. These reactions (especially the ones involving F_2 and Cl_2) can occur with explosive violence. Industrially, hydrogen chloride is produced as a by-product in the manufacture of chlorinated hydrocarbons:

$$C_2H_6(g) + Cl_2(g) \longrightarrow C_2H_5Cl(g) + HCl(g)$$

In the laboratory, hydrogen fluoride and hydrogen chloride can be prepared by combining the metal halides with concentrated sulfuric acid:

$$CaF_2(s) + H_2SO_4(aq) \longrightarrow 2HF(g) + CaSO_4(s)$$

$$2NaCl(s) + H_2SO_4(aq) \longrightarrow 2HCl(g) + Na_2SO_4(aq)$$

Hydrogen bromide and hydrogen iodide cannot be prepared this way because they are oxidized to elemental bromine and iodine. For example, the reaction between NaBr and H_2SO_4 is

$$2NaBr(s) + 2H_2SO_4(aq) \longrightarrow Br_2(l) + SO_2(g) + Na_2SO_4(aq) + 2H_2O(l)$$

Instead, hydrogen bromide is prepared by first reacting bromine with phosphorus to form phosphorus tribromide:

$$P_4(s) + 6Br_2(l) \longrightarrow 4PBr_3(l)$$

Next, PBr_3 is treated with water to yield HBr:

$$PBr_3(l) + 3H_2O(l) \longrightarrow 3HBr(g) + H_3PO_3(aq)$$

Hydrogen iodide can be prepared in a similar manner.

HF is so highly reactive that it attacks silica and silicates:

$$6HF(aq) + SiO_2(g) \longrightarrow H_2SiF_6(aq) + 2H_2O(l)$$

This property makes HF suitable for etching glass and is the reason that hydrogen fluoride must be kept in plastic or inert metal (e.g., Pt) containers. Hydrogen fluoride is used in the manufacture of Freons; for example,

$$CCl_4(l) + HF(g) \longrightarrow CFCl_3(g) + HCl(g)$$

$$CFCl_3(g) + HF(g) \longrightarrow CF_2Cl_2(g) + HCl(g)$$

It is also important in the production of aluminum. Hydrogen chloride is used in the preparation of hydrochloric acid, inorganic chlorides, and in various metallurgical processes. Hydrogen bromide and hydrogen iodide do not have any major industrial uses.

Aqueous solutions of hydrogen halides are acidic. The strength of the acids increases as follows:

$$HF \ll HCl < HBr < HI$$

The halogens also form a series of oxoacids with the following general formulas:

HXO	HXO_2	HXO_3	HXO_4
Hypohalous acid	Halous acid	Halic acid	Perhalic acid

(for example, HClO, hypochlorous acid; $HClO_2$, chlorous acid; $HClO_3$, chloric acid; and $HClO_4$, perchloric acid).

Chlorous acid ($HClO_2$) is the only known *halous* acid. All the halogens except fluorine form halic and perhalic acids. The Lewis structures of the chlorine oxoacids are

Hypochlorous acid	Chlorous acid	Chloric acid	Perchloric acid

For a given halogen, the acid strength decreases from perhalic acid to hypohalous acid [◄◄ Section 16.2].

TABLE 23.5	Common Compounds of Halogens*			
Compound	**F**	**Cl**	**Br**	**I**
Hydrogen halide	HF (−1)	HCl (−1)	HBr (−1)	HI (−1)
Oxides	OF_2 (−1)	Cl_2O (+1)	Br_2O (+1)	I_2O_5 (+5)
		ClO_2 (+4)	BrO_2 (+4)	
		Cl_2O_7 (+7)		
Oxoacids	HFO (−1)	HClO (+1)	HBrO (+1)	HIO (+1)
		$HClO_2$ (+3)		
		$HClO_3$ (+5)	$HBrO_3$ (+5)	HIO_3 (+5)
		$HClO_4$ (+7)	$HBrO_4$ (+7)	H_5IO_6 (+7)

* The number in parentheses indicates the oxidation number of the halogen.

Table 23.5 lists some of the halogen compounds. Periodic acid (HIO_4) does not appear because this compound cannot be isolated in the pure form. Instead the formula H_5IO_6 is often used to represent periodic acid.

Uses of the Halogens

Applications of the halogens and their compounds are widespread in industry, health care, and other areas. One such application is fluoridation, the practice of adding small quantities of fluorides (about 1 ppm by mass) such as NaF to drinking water to reduce dental caries.

One of the most important inorganic fluorides is uranium hexafluoride (UF_6), which is essential to the gaseous diffusion process for separating isotopes of uranium (U 235 and U 238). Industrially, fluorine is used to produce polytetrafluoroethylene, a material better known as Teflon:

$$-(CF_2-CF_2)_n$$

where n is a large number. Teflon is used in electrical insulators, high-temperature plastics, cooking utensils, and so on.

Chlorine plays an important biological role in the human body, where the chloride ion is the principal anion in intracellular and extracellular fluids. Chlorine is widely used as an industrial bleaching agent for paper and textiles. Ordinary household laundry bleach contains the active ingredient sodium hypochlorite (about 5 percent by mass), which is prepared by combining chlorine gas with a cold solution of sodium hydroxide:

$$Cl_2(g) + 2NaOH(aq) \longrightarrow NaCl(aq) + NaClO(aq) + H_2O(l)$$

Chlorine is also used to purify water and disinfect swimming pools. When chlorine dissolves in water, it undergoes the following reaction:

$$Cl_2(g) + H_2O(l) \longrightarrow HCl(aq) + HClO(aq)$$

It is thought that the ClO^- ions destroy bacteria by oxidizing life-sustaining compounds within them.

Chlorinated methanes, such as carbon tetrachloride and chloroform, are useful organic solvents. Large quantities of chlorine are used to produce insecticides, such as DDT. However, in view of the damage they inflict on the environment, the use of many of these compounds is either totally banned or greatly restricted in the United States. Chlorine is also used to produce polymers such as poly(vinyl chloride).

So far as we know, bromine compounds occur naturally only in some marine organisms. Seawater is about 1×10^{-3} M Br^-, so it is the main source of bromine. Bromine is used to prepare ethylene dibromide ($BrCH_2CH_2Br$), which is used as an insecticide and as a scavenger for lead (i.e., to combine with lead) in gasoline to keep lead deposits from clogging engines. Studies have shown that ethylene dibromide is a very potent carcinogen.

Bromine combines directly with silver to form silver bromide (AgBr), which is used in photographic films.

Iodine is not used as widely as the other halogens. A 50 percent (by mass) alcohol solution of iodine, known as *tincture of iodine,* is used medicinally as an antiseptic. Iodine is an essential constituent of the thyroid hormone thyroxine:

Figure 23.20 Cloud seeding using AgI particles.

Iodine deficiency in the diet may result in enlargement of the thyroid gland (known as goiter). Iodized table salt sold in the United States usually contains 0.01 percent KI or NaI, which is more than sufficient to satisfy the 1 mg of iodine per week required for the formation of thyroxine in the human body.

Silver iodide (AgI) is a pale-yellow solid that darkens when exposed to light. In this respect, it is similar to silver bromide. Silver iodide is sometimes used in cloud seeding, a process for inducing rainfall on a small scale (Figure 23.20). The advantage of using silver iodide is that enormous numbers of nuclei (i.e., small particles of silver iodide on which ice crystals can form) become available. About 10^{15} nuclei are produced from 1 g of AgI by vaporizing an acetone solution of silver iodide in a hot flame. The nuclei are then dispersed into the clouds from an airplane.

Learning Outcomes

- Describe properties of nonmetals.
- Describe the two types of hydrides that can form.
- List the three isotopes of hydrogen.
- Give in your own words the relevance of the hydrogen economy.
- List some of the major compounds that are formed from carbon.
- List some of the common compounds of nitrogen.

- Provide some of the common applications of phosphorus in industry.
- List the common compounds formed by oxygen.
- Describe the Frasch process.
- Explain why the chemistry of fluorine is different than the other halogens.
- Describe processes used to prepare halogens.
- List some of the common uses of halogens.

Chapter Summary

SECTION 23.1

- Properties of nonmetals vary more than properties of metals.
- Nonmetal elements may be solid, liquid, or gaseous and may exhibit both positive and negative oxidation numbers in their compounds.

SECTION 23.2

- Hydrogen atoms contain one proton and one electron. They are the simplest atoms.
- Hydrogen combines with many metals and nonmetals to form hydrides; some hydrides are ionic and some are covalent.
- There are three isotopes of hydrogen: $_1^1H$, $_1^2H$ (deuterium), and $_1^3H$ (tritium).
- "Heavy water" (D_2O) contains deuterium.

SECTION 23.3

- The important inorganic compounds of carbon are the *carbides;* the *cyanides,* most of which are extremely toxic; *carbon monoxide,* also toxic and a major air pollutant; the *carbonates* and *bicarbonates;* and *carbon dioxide,* an end product of metabolism and a component of the global carbon cycle.

SECTION 23.4

- Elemental nitrogen (N_2) contains a triple bond and is very stable.
- Compounds in which nitrogen has oxidation numbers from -3 to $+5$ are formed between nitrogen and hydrogen and/or oxygen atoms.
- Ammonia (NH_3) is widely used in fertilizers.

- White phosphorus (P_4) is highly toxic, very reactive, and flammable; the polymeric red phosphorus [$(P_4)_n$] is more stable.
- Phosphorus forms oxides and halides with oxidation numbers of $+3$ and $+5$ and several oxoacids. The phosphates are the most important phosphorus compounds.

SECTION 23.5

- Elemental oxygen (O_2) is paramagnetic and contains two unpaired electrons.
- Oxygen forms ozone (O_3), oxides (O^{2-}), peroxides (O_2^{2-}), and superoxides (O_2^-).
- The most abundant element in Earth's crust, oxygen is essential for life on Earth.
- Sulfur is obtained from Earth's crust as a molten liquid via the Frasch process.
- Sulfur exists in a number of allotropic forms and has a variety of oxidation numbers in its compounds.
- Sulfuric acid is the cornerstone of the chemical industry. It is produced from sulfur via sulfur dioxide and sulfur trioxide by means of the contact process.

SECTION 23.6

- The halogens are toxic and reactive elements that are found only in compounds with other elements.
- Fluorine and chlorine are strong oxidizing agents and are prepared by electrolysis.
- With the exception of fluorine, the halogens may have both negative and positive oxidation states.
- Fluorine's oxidation state in its compounds is always -1.

Questions and Problems

SECTION 23.1: GENERAL PROPERTIES OF NONMETALS

Review Questions

23.1   Without referring to Figure 23.1, state whether each of the following elements are metals, metalloids, or nonmetals:
(a) Cs, (b) Ge, (c) I, (d) Kr, (e) W, (f) Ga, (g) Te, (h) Bi.

23.2   List two chemical and two physical properties that distinguish a metal from a nonmetal.

23.3   Make a list of physical and chemical properties of chlorine (Cl_2) and magnesium. Comment on their differences with reference to the fact that one is a metal and the other is a nonmetal.

23.4   Carbon is usually classified as a nonmetal. However, the graphite used in "lead" pencils conducts electricity. Look at a pencil, and list two nonmetallic properties of graphite.

SECTION 23.2: HYDROGEN

Review Questions

23.5   Explain why hydrogen has a unique position in the periodic table.

23.6   Describe two laboratory and two industrial preparations for hydrogen.

23.7   Hydrogen exhibits three types of bonding in its compounds. Describe each type of bonding with an example.

23.8   What are interstitial hydrides?

23.9   Give the name of (a) an ionic hydride and (b) a covalent hydride. In each case describe the preparation and give the structure of the compound.

23.10 Describe what is meant by the "hydrogen economy."

Problems

23.11 Elements 17 and 20 form compounds with hydrogen. Write the formulas for these two compounds, and compare their chemical behavior in water.

23.12 Give an example of hydrogen as (a) an oxidizing agent and (b) a reducing agent.

23.13 Compare the physical and chemical properties of the hydrides of each of the following elements: Na, Ca, C, N, O, Cl.

23.14 Suggest a physical method that would enable you to separate hydrogen gas from neon gas.

23.15 Write a balanced equation to show the reaction between CaH_2 and H_2O. How many grams of CaH_2 are needed to produce 26.4 L of H_2 gas at 20°C and 746 mmHg?

23.16 How many kilograms of water must be processed to obtain 2.0 L of D_2 at 25°C and 0.90 atm pressure? Assume that deuterium abundance is 0.015 percent and that recovery is 80 percent.

23.17 Predict the outcome of the following reactions:
(a) $CuO(s) + H_2(g) \longrightarrow$
(b) $Na_2O(s) + H_2(g) \longrightarrow$

23.18 Starting with H_2, describe how you would prepare (a) HCl, (b) NH_3, and (c) LiOH.

SECTION 23.3: CARBON

Review Questions

23.19 Give an example of a carbide and a cyanide.

23.20 How are cyanide ions used in metallurgy?

23.21 Briefly discuss the preparation and properties of carbon monoxide and carbon dioxide.

23.22 What is coal?

23.23 Describe two chemical differences between CO and CO_2.

23.24 Describe the reaction between CO_2 and OH^- in terms of a Lewis acid-base reaction.

Problems

23.25 Draw a Lewis structure for the C_2^{2-} ion.

23.26 Balance the following equations:
(a) $Be_2C(s) + H_2O(l) \longrightarrow$
(b) $CaC_2(s) + H_2O(l) \longrightarrow$

23.27 Unlike $CaCO_3$, Na_2CO_3 does not readily yield CO_2 when heated. On the other hand, $NaHCO_3$ undergoes thermal decomposition to produce CO_2 and Na_2CO_3. (a) Write a balanced equation for the reaction. (b) How would you test for the CO_2 evolved? [*Hint:* Treat the gas with limewater, an aqueous solution of $Ca(OH)_2$.]

23.28 Two solutions are labeled A and B. Solution A contains Na_2CO_3, and solution B contains $NaHCO_3$. Describe how you would distinguish between the two solutions if you were provided with an $MgCl_2$ solution. (*Hint:* You need to know the solubilities of $MgCO_3$ and $MgHCO_3$.)

23.29 Magnesium chloride is dissolved in a solution containing sodium bicarbonate. On heating, a white precipitate is formed. Explain what causes the precipitation.

23.30 A few drops of concentrated ammonia solution added to a calcium bicarbonate solution cause a white precipitate to form. Write a balanced equation for the reaction.

23.31 Sodium hydroxide is hygroscopic—that is, it absorbs moisture when exposed to the atmosphere. A student placed a pellet of NaOH on a watch glass. A few days later, she noticed that the pellet was covered with a white solid. What is the identity of this solid? (*Hint:* Air contains CO_2.)

23.32 A piece of red-hot magnesium ribbon will continue to burn in an atmosphere of CO_2 even though CO_2 does not support combustion. Explain.

23.33 Is carbon monoxide isoelectronic with nitrogen (N_2)?

SECTION 23.4:   NITROGEN AND PHOSPHORUS

Review Questions

23.34   Describe a laboratory and an industrial preparation of nitrogen gas.

23.35   What is meant by *nitrogen fixation*? Describe a process for fixation of nitrogen on an industrial scale.

23.36   Describe an industrial preparation of phosphorus.

23.37   Why is the P_4 molecule unstable?

Problems

23.38   Nitrogen can be obtained by (a) passing ammonia over red-hot copper(II) oxide and (b) heating ammonium dichromate [one of the products is Cr(III) oxide]. Write a balanced equation for each preparation.

23.39   Write balanced equations for the preparation of sodium nitrite by (a) heating sodium nitrate and (b) heating sodium nitrate with carbon.

23.40   Sodium amide ($NaNH_2$) reacts with water to produce sodium hydroxide and ammonia. Describe this reaction as a Brønsted acid-base reaction.

23.41   Write a balanced equation for the formation of urea, $[(NH_2)_2CO]$, from carbon dioxide and ammonia. Should the reaction be run at a high or low pressure to maximize the yield?

23.42   Some farmers feel that lightning helps produce a better crop. What is the scientific basis for this belief?

23.43   Explain why nitric acid can be reduced but not oxidized.

23.44   At 620 K, the vapor density of ammonium chloride relative to hydrogen (H_2) under the same conditions of temperature and pressure is 14.5, although, according to its formula mass, it should have a vapor density of 26.8. How would you account for this discrepancy?

23.45   Write a balanced equation for each of the following processes: (a) On heating, ammonium nitrate produces nitrous oxide. (b) On heating, potassium nitrate produces potassium nitrite and oxygen gas. (c) On heating, lead nitrate produces lead(II) oxide, nitrogen dioxide (NO_2), and oxygen gas.

23.46   Explain why, under normal conditions, the reaction of zinc with nitric acid does not produce hydrogen.

23.47   Potassium nitrite can be produced by heating a mixture of potassium nitrate and carbon. Write a balanced equation for this reaction. Calculate the theoretical yield of KNO_2 produced by heating 57.0 g of KNO_3 with an excess of carbon.

23.48   Predict the geometry of nitrous oxide (N_2O), by the VSEPR method, and draw resonance structures for the molecule. (*Hint:* The atoms are arranged as NNO.)

23.49   Consider the reaction

$$N_2(g) + O_2(g) \rightleftharpoons 2NO(g)$$

Given that the $\Delta G°$ for the reaction at 298 K is 173.4 kJ/mol, calculate (a) the standard free energy of formation of NO, (b) K_P for the reaction, and (c) K_c for the reaction.

23.50   From the data in Appendix 2, calculate $\Delta H°$ for the synthesis of NO (which is the first step in the manufacture of nitric acid) at 25°C:

$$4NH_3(g) + 5O_2(g) \longrightarrow 4NO(g) + 6H_2O(l)$$

23.51   When 1.645 g of white phosphorus is dissolved in 75.5 g of CS_2, the solution boils at 46.709°C, whereas pure CS_2 boils at 46.300°C. The molal boiling-point elevation constant for CS_2 is 2.34°C/*m*. Calculate the molar mass of white phosphorus, and give the molecular formula.

23.52   Explain why two N atoms can form a double bond or a triple bond, whereas two P atoms normally can form only a single bond.

23.53   Dinitrogen pentoxide is a product of the reaction between P_4O_{10} and HNO_3. Write a balanced equation for this reaction. Calculate the theoretical yield of N_2O_5 if 79.4 g of P_4O_{10} is combined with an excess of HNO_3. (*Hint:* One of the products is HPO_3.)

23.54   Starting with elemental phosphorus (P_4), show how you would prepare phosphoric acid.

23.55   What is the hybridization of phosphorus in the phosphonium ion (PH_4^+)?

23.56   Explain why (a) NH_3 is more basic than PH_3, (b) NH_3 has a higher boiling point than PH_3, (c) PCl_5 exists but NCl_5 does not, and (d) N_2 is more inert than P_4.

SECTION 23.5:   OXYGEN AND SULFUR

Review Questions

23.57   Describe one industrial and one laboratory preparation of O_2.

23.58   Give an account of the various kinds of oxides that exist, and illustrate each type by two examples.

23.59   Hydrogen peroxide can be prepared by treating barium peroxide with sulfuric acid. Write a balanced equation for this reaction.

23.60   Describe the Frasch process for obtaining sulfur.

23.61   Describe the contact process for the production of sulfuric acid.

23.62   How is hydrogen sulfide generated in the laboratory?

Problems

23.63   One of the steps involved in the depletion of ozone in the stratosphere by nitric oxide may be represented as

$$NO(g) + O_3(g) \longrightarrow NO_2(g) + O_2(g)$$

From the data in Appendix 2, calculate $\Delta G°$, K_P, and K_c for the reaction at 25°C.

23.64   Draw molecular orbital energy level diagrams for O_2, O_2^-, and O_2^{2-}.

23.65   Hydrogen peroxide is unstable and decomposes readily:

$$2H_2O_2(aq) \longrightarrow 2H_2O(l) + O_2(g)$$

This reaction is accelerated by light, heat, or a catalyst. (a) Explain why hydrogen peroxide sold in drugstores comes in dark bottles. (b) The concentrations of aqueous hydrogen peroxide solutions are normally expressed as percent by mass. In the decomposition of hydrogen peroxide, how many liters of oxygen gas can be produced at STP from 15.0 g of a 7.50 percent hydrogen peroxide solution?

23.66 Oxygen forms double bonds in O_2, but sulfur forms single bonds in S_8. Explain.

23.67 What are the oxidation numbers of O and F in HFO?

23.68 In 2004 about 48 million tons of sulfuric acid was produced in the United States. Calculate the amount of sulfur (in grams and moles) used to produce that amount of sulfuric acid.

23.69 Sulfuric acid is a dehydrating agent. Write balanced equations for the reactions between sulfuric acid and the following substances: (a) HCOOH, (b) H_3PO_4, (c) HNO_3, (d) $HClO_3$. (*Hint:* Sulfuric acid is not decomposed by the dehydrating action.)

23.70 Calculate the amount of $CaCO_3$ (in grams) that would be required to react with 50.6 g of SO_2 emitted by a power plant.

23.71 SF_6 exists, but OF_6 does not. Explain.

23.72 Explain why SCl_6, SBr_6, and SI_6 cannot be prepared.

23.73 The bad smell of water containing hydrogen sulfide can be removed by the action of chlorine. The reaction is

$$H_2S(aq) + Cl_2(aq) \longrightarrow 2HCl(aq) + S(s)$$

If the hydrogen sulfide content of contaminated water is 22 ppm by mass, calculate the amount of Cl_2 (in grams) required to remove all the H_2S from 2.0×10^2 gal of water. (1 gallon = 3.785 L.)

23.74 Compare the physical and chemical properties of H_2O and H_2S.

23.75 Concentrated sulfuric acid reacts with sodium iodide to produce molecular iodine, hydrogen sulfide, and sodium hydrogen sulfate. Write a balanced equation for the reaction.

23.76 Describe two reactions in which sulfuric acid acts as an oxidizing agent.

SECTION 23.6: THE HALOGENS

Review Questions

23.77 Describe an industrial method for preparing each of the halogens.

23.78 Name the major uses of the halogens.

Problems

23.79 Draw structures for (a) $(HF)_2$ and (b) HF_2^-.

23.80 Sulfuric acid is a weaker acid than hydrochloric acid. Yet hydrogen chloride is evolved when concentrated sulfuric acid is added to sodium chloride. Explain.

23.81 Use the VSEPR method to predict the geometries of the following species: (a) I_3^-, (b) $SiCl_4$, (c) PF_5, (d) SF_4.

23.82 Metal chlorides can be prepared in a number of ways: (a) direct combination of metal and molecular chlorine, (b) reaction between metal and hydrochloric acid, (c) acid-base neutralization, (d) metal carbonate treated with hydrochloric acid, (e) precipitation reaction. Give an example for each type of preparation.

23.83 A 375-gal tank is filled with water containing 167 g of bromine in the form of Br^- ions. How many liters of Cl_2 gas at 1.00 atm and 20°C will be required to oxidize all the bromide to molecular bromine?

23.84 Hydrogen fluoride can be prepared by the action of sulfuric acid on sodium fluoride. Explain why hydrogen bromide cannot be prepared by the action of the same acid on sodium bromide.

23.85 What volume of bromine (Br_2) vapor measured at 100°C and 700 mmHg pressure would be obtained if 2.00 L of dry chlorine (Cl_2), measured at 15°C and 760 mmHg, was absorbed by a potassium bromide solution?

23.86 Aqueous copper(II) sulfate solution is blue. When aqueous potassium fluoride is added to the $CuSO_4$ solution, a green precipitate is formed. If aqueous potassium chloride is added instead, a bright-green solution is formed. Explain what happens in each case.

23.87 Iodine pentoxide (I_2O_5) is sometimes used to remove carbon monoxide from the air by forming carbon dioxide and iodine. Write a balanced equation for this reaction, and identify species that are oxidized and reduced.

23.88 Show that chlorine, bromine, and iodine are very much alike by giving an account of their behavior (a) with hydrogen, (b) in producing silver salts, (c) as oxidizing agents, and (d) with sodium hydroxide. (e) In what respects is fluorine not a typical halogen element?

ADDITIONAL PROBLEMS

23.89 Write a balanced equation for each of the following reactions: (a) Heating phosphorous acid yields phosphoric acid and phosphine (PH_3). (b) Lithium carbide reacts with hydrochloric acid to give lithium chloride and methane. (c) Bubbling HI gas through an aqueous solution of HNO_2 yields molecular iodine and nitric oxide. (d) Hydrogen sulfide is oxidized by chlorine to give HCl and SCl_2.

23.90 Both N_2O and O_2 support combustion. Suggest one physical and one chemical test to distinguish between the two gases.

23.91 (a) Which of the following compounds has the greatest ionic character: PCl_5, $SiCl_4$, CCl_4, BCl_3? (b) Which of the following ions has the smallest ionic radius: F^-, C^{4-}, N^{3-}, O^{2-}? (c) Which of the following atoms has the highest ionization energy: F, Cl, Br, I? (d) Which of the following oxides is most acidic: H_2O, SiO_2, CO_2?

23.92 Describe the bonding in the C_2^{2-} ion in terms of the molecular orbital theory.

23.93 What is the change in oxidation number for the following reaction?

$$3O_2 \longrightarrow 2O_3$$

23.94 Starting with deuterium oxide (D_2O), describe how you would prepare (a) NaOD, (b) DCl, (c) ND_3, (d) C_2D_2, (e) CD_4, and (f) D_2SO_4.

23.95 Solid PCl_5 exists as $[PCl_4^+][PCl_6^-]$. Draw Lewis structures for these ions. Describe the hybridization state of the P atoms.

23.96   Consider the Frasch process. (a) How is it possible to heat water well above 100°C without turning it into steam? (b) Why is water sent down the outermost pipe? (c) Why would excavating a mine and digging for sulfur be a dangerous procedure for obtaining the element?

23.97   As we saw in Section 21.2, the reduction of iron oxides is accomplished by using carbon monoxide as a reducing agent. Starting with coke in a blast furnace, the following equilibrium plays a key role in the extraction of iron:

$$C(s) + CO_2(g) \longrightarrow 2CO(g)$$

Use the data in Appendix 2 to calculate the equilibrium constant at 25°C and 100°C. Assume $\Delta H°$ and $\Delta S°$ to be independent of temperature.

23.98   Lubricants used in watches usually consist of long-chain hydrocarbons. Oxidation by air forms solid polymers that eventually destroy the effectiveness of the lubricants. It is believed that one of the initial steps in the oxidation is removal of a hydrogen atom (hydrogen abstraction). By replacing the hydrogen atoms at reactive sites with deuterium atoms, it is possible to substantially slow down the overall oxidation rate. Why? (*Hint:* Consider the kinetic isotope effect.)

23.99   How are lightbulbs frosted? (*Hint:* Consider the action of hydrofluoric acid on glass, which is made of silicon dioxide.)

23.100   Life evolves to adapt to its environment. In this respect, explain why life most frequently needs oxygen for survival, rather than the more abundant nitrogen.

23.101   A 10.0-g sample of white phosphorus was burned in an excess of oxygen. The product was dissolved in enough water to make 500 mL of solution. Calculate the pH of the solution at 25°C.

23.102   Predict the physical and chemical properties of astatine, a radioactive element and the last member of Group 7A.

23.103   Assuming ideal behavior, calculate the density of gaseous HF at its normal boiling point (19.5°C). The experimentally measured density under the same conditions is 3.10 g/L. Account for the discrepancy between your calculated value and the experimental result.

23.104   Ammonium nitrate is the most important nitrogen-containing fertilizer in the world. Given only air and water as starting materials and any equipment and catalyst at your disposal, describe how you would prepare ammonium nitrate. State conditions under which you can increase the yield in each step.

CHAPTER 24

Organic Chemistry

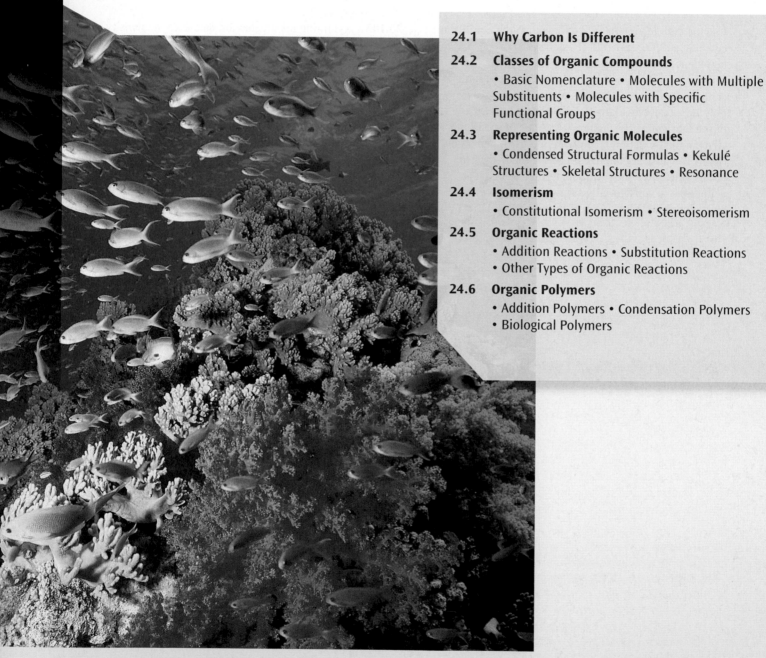

24.1 Why Carbon Is Different

24.2 Classes of Organic Compounds
• Basic Nomenclature • Molecules with Multiple Substituents • Molecules with Specific Functional Groups

24.3 Representing Organic Molecules
• Condensed Structural Formulas • Kekulé Structures • Skeletal Structures • Resonance

24.4 Isomerism
• Constitutional Isomerism • Stereoisomerism

24.5 Organic Reactions
• Addition Reactions • Substitution Reactions • Other Types of Organic Reactions

24.6 Organic Polymers
• Addition Polymers • Condensation Polymers • Biological Polymers

Earth's oceans, which cover 79 percent of our planet, are a rich and fertile source for bioprospecting—the effort to find new and useful natural products. Corals, sponges, fish, and even marine microorganisms produce a bounty of biologically potent organic compounds with significant anti-inflammatory, antiviral, and anticancer properties. A natural product found to be of major importance is known as a *lead* (lēd) compound. Chemists may devise a way to synthesize a lead compound, or to use it as a precursor for synthesis or other useful compounds. This work can provide chemists a template for synthesizing structurally different, yet chemically related compounds to develop new drugs.

Before You Begin, Review These Skills

• Lewis structures and formal charge [◄◄ Sections 6.3 and 6.4]
• Resonance [◄◄ Section 6.5]
• Molecular geometry and polarity [◄◄ Sections 7.1 and 7.2]

24.1 WHY CARBON IS DIFFERENT

Organic chemistry is usually defined as the study of compounds that contain carbon. This definition is not entirely satisfactory, though, because it would include such things as cyanide and cyanate complexes and metal carbonates, which are considered to be *inorganic*. A somewhat more useful definition of organic chemistry is the study of compounds that contain carbon and hydrogen, although many organic compounds also contain other elements, such as oxygen, sulfur, nitrogen, phosphorus, or the halogens, and many do not contain hydrogen. Examples of organic compounds include the following:

CH_4	C_2H_5OH	$C_5H_7O_4COOH$	CH_3NH_2	CCl_4
Methane	Ethanol	Ascorbic acid	Methylamine	Carbon tetrachloride

> **Student Annotation:** Carbon-containing compounds that are considered *inorganic* are generally those that are obtained from minerals.

Early in the study of organic chemistry there was thought to be some fundamental difference between compounds that came from living things, such as plants and animals, and those that came from nonliving things, such as rocks. Compounds obtained from plants or animals were called *organic,* whereas compounds obtained from nonliving sources were called *inorganic.* In fact, until early in the nineteenth century, scientists believed that only nature could produce organic compounds. In 1829, however, Friedrich Wöhler prepared urea, a well-known organic compound, by combining the inorganic substances lead cyanate and aqueous ammonia:

$$Pb(OCN)_2 + 2NH_3 + 2H_2O \xrightarrow{\Delta} 2NH_2CONH_2 + Pb(OH)_2$$

Urea

Wöhler's synthesis of urea dispelled the notion that organic compounds were fundamentally different from inorganic compounds—and that they could only be produced by nature. We now know that it is possible to synthesize a wide variety of organic compounds in the laboratory; in fact, many thousands of new organic compounds are produced in research laboratories each year. In this chapter, we will consider several types of organic compounds that are important biologically.

> **Student Annotation:** By contrast, there are only about 100,000 known *inorganic* compounds.

Because of its unique nature, carbon is capable of forming millions of different compounds. Carbon's position in the periodic table (Group 4A, period 2) gives it the following set of unique characteristics:

• The electron configuration of carbon ($[He]2s^2 2p^2$) effectively prohibits ion formation. This and carbon's electronegativity, which is intermediate between those of metals and nonmetals, cause carbon to complete its octet by sharing electrons. In nearly all its compounds, carbon forms four covalent bonds, which can be oriented in as many as four different directions:

> **Student Annotation:** To form an ion that is isoelectronic with a noble gas, a C atom would have to either gain or lose *four* electrons [◄◄ Section 4.5]—something that is energetically impossible under ordinary conditions. This is not to say that carbon *cannot* form ions. But in the vast majority of its compounds, carbon acquires a complete octet by *sharing* electrons—rather than by gaining or losing them.

Methane	Formaldehyde	Carbon dioxide
(4 σ bonds)	(3 σ bonds & 1 π bond)	(2 σ bonds & 2 π bonds)

Boron and nitrogen, carbon's neighbors in Groups 3A and 5A, respectively, usually form covalent compounds, too, but B and N form ions more readily than C.

Ethane

Disilane

- Carbon's small atomic radius allows the atoms to approach one another closely, giving rise to short, *strong*, carbon-carbon bonds and *stable* carbon compounds. In addition, carbon atoms that are *sp*- or *sp²*-hybridized approach one another closely enough for their singly occupied, unhybridized *p* orbitals to overlap effectively—giving rise to relatively strong π bonds [◄◄ Section 7.5]. Recall that elements in the same group generally exhibit similar chemical behavior. Silicon atoms, however, are bigger than carbon atoms, so silicon atoms generally cannot approach one another closely enough for their unhybridized *p* orbitals to overlap significantly. As a result, very few compounds exhibit significant π bonding between Si atoms:

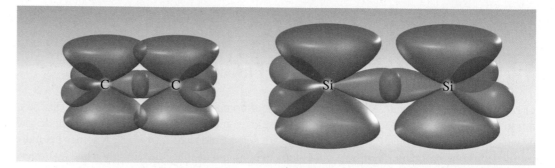

- Carbon's valence electrons are in the second shell ($n = 2$), where there are no *d* orbitals. The valence electrons of silicon, on the other hand, are in the third shell ($n = 3$) where there are *d* orbitals, which can be occupied or attacked by lone pairs on another substance—resulting in a reaction. This reactivity makes silicon compounds far less stable than the analogous carbon compounds. Ethane (CH_3-CH_3), for example, is stable in both water and air, whereas disilane (SiH_3-SiH_3) is unstable—breaking down in water and combusting spontaneously in air.

Student Annotation: Carbon's formation of chains is called *catenation*.

These attributes enable carbon to form chains (straight, branched, and cyclic) containing single, double, and triple carbon-carbon bonds, This, in turn, results in an endless array of organic compounds containing any number and arrangement of carbon atoms. Each carbon atom in a compound can be classified by the number of other carbon atoms to which it is bonded. A carbon atom that is bonded to just one other carbon atom is called a *primary* carbon; one that is bonded to two other carbon atoms is called a *secondary* carbon; one that is bonded to three other carbon atoms is called a *tertiary* carbon; and one that is bonded to four other carbon atoms is called a *quaternary* carbon. These four types of carbon atoms are identified with the labels 1°, 2°, 3°, and 4°, respectively. Each of the four carbon types is labeled in the following structure.

One of the important organic molecules that we encountered in Chapter 7 is benzene (C_6H_6). Organic compounds that are related to benzene, or that contain one or more benzene rings, are called *aromatic* compounds. Organic molecules that do not contain the benzene ring are called *aliphatic* compounds.

Benzene   Phenol   Cinnamic aldehyde

Aromatic compounds

Ethanol   Butyric acid   Acetone

Aliphatic compounds

24.2 CLASSES OF ORGANIC COMPOUNDS

Organic molecules occur in seemingly limitless variety. Different types of organic compounds, each with their own characteristic properties, result from the following:

1. Carbon's ability to form chains by bonding with itself
2. The presence of elements other than carbon and hydrogen
3. Functional groups
4. Multiple bonds

In this section, we will discuss several types of organic compounds and how we represent them. Consider two isomers of C_3H_6O:

$$\underset{\text{Propanal}}{\overset{\displaystyle \text{O} \atop \displaystyle \|}{CH_3CH_2CH}} \qquad \underset{\text{Acetone}}{\overset{\displaystyle \text{O} \atop \displaystyle \|}{CH_3CCH_3}}$$

> **Student Annotation:** A functional group is a group of atoms that determines many of a molecule's properties.

> **Student Annotation:** *Isomers* are different compounds with the same chemical formula.

Although the two isomers contain exactly the same atoms, their different arrangements of atoms result in two very different compounds. The first is an *aldehyde* called propanal. The second is a *ketone* called acetone. Aldehydes and ketones are two classes of organic compounds. The classes of organic compounds that we will discuss in this chapter are alcohols, carboxylic acids, aldehydes, ketones, esters, amines, and amides.

A class of organic compounds often is represented with a general formula that shows the atoms of the functional group(s) explicitly, and the remainder of the molecule using one or more R's, where R represents an alkyl group. An *alkyl group* is a portion of a molecule that resembles an alkane. In fact, an alkyl group is formed by removing one hydrogen atom from the corresponding alkane. The *methyl group* ($-CH_3$), for example, is formed by removing a hydrogen atom from methane (CH_4), the simplest alkane. Methyl groups are found in many organic molecules. Table 24.1 lists some of the simplest alkyl groups. Table 24.2 (page 965) gives the general formula for each of the classes of organic compounds discussed in this chapter and the Lewis structure of each functional group.

Acetone

Methylamine

Toluene

The functional groups in the types of compounds shown in Table 24.2 are the *hydroxy* group (in *alcohols*), the *carboxy* group (in *carboxylic acids*), the $-COOR$ group (in *esters*), the *carbonyl* group (in *aldehydes* and *ketones*), the *amino* group (in *amines*), and the *amide* group (in *amides*). Functional groups determine many of the properties of a compound, including what types of reactions it is likely to undergo. Figure 24.1 shows ball-and-stick models and electrostatic potential maps of the hydroxy, carboxy, carbonyl, amino, and amide functional groups.

TABLE 24.1	Alkyl Groups	
Name	**Formula**	**Model**
Methyl	$-CH_3$	
Ethyl	$-CH_2CH_3$	
Propyl	$-CH_2CH_2CH_3$	
Isopropyl	$-CH(CH_3)_2$	
Butyl	$-CH_2CH_2CH_2CH_3$	
tert-Butyl	$-CH(CH_3)_3$	
Pentyl	$-CH_2CH_2CH_2CH_2CH_3$	
Isopentyl	$-CH_2CH_2CH(CH_3)_2$	
Hexyl	$-CH_2CH_2CH_2CH_2CH_2CH_3$	
Heptyl	$-CH_2CH_2CH_2CH_2CH_2CH_2CH_3$	
Octyl	$-CH_2CH_2CH_2CH_2CH_2CH_2CH_2CH_3$	

sp^3	sp^2 sp^3	sp^2	sp^3	sp^2 sp^3
Hydroxy group	Carboxy group	Carbonyl group	Amino group	Amide group

Figure 24.1 Models and electrostatic potential maps of the hydroxy, carboxy, carbonyl, amino, and amide functional groups.

TABLE 24.2	General Formulas for Select Classes of Organic Compounds		
Class	**General formula**	**Structure**	**Functional group**
Alcohol	ROH	—Ö—H	Hydroxy group
Carboxylic acid	RCOOH	$\overset{\overset{\ddot{O}}{\|\|}}{-C}-\ddot{O}-H$	Carboxy group
Ester*	RCOOR′	$\overset{\overset{\ddot{O}}{\|\|}}{-C}-\ddot{O}-R'$	Ester group
Aldehyde	RCHO	$\overset{\overset{\ddot{O}}{\|\|}}{-C}-H$	Carbonyl group
Ketone	RCOR′	$\overset{\overset{\ddot{O}}{\|\|}}{-C}-R'$	Carbonyl group
Amine†	RNH₂	$\overset{-\ddot{N}-H}{\underset{H}{\|}}$	Amino group (primary, 1°)
Amine	RNR′H	$\overset{-\ddot{N}-R'}{\underset{H}{\|}}$	Amino group (secondary, 2°)
Amine	RNR′R″	$\overset{-\ddot{N}-R'}{\underset{R''}{\|}}$	Amino group (tertiary, 3°)
Amide	RCONH₂	$\overset{\overset{\ddot{O}}{\|\|}}{-C}-\overset{\ddot{N}-H}{\underset{H}{\|}}$	Amide group (primary, 1°)
Amide	RCONR′H	$\overset{\overset{\ddot{O}}{\|\|}}{-C}-\overset{\ddot{N}-R'}{\underset{H}{\|}}$	Amide group (secondary, 2°)
Amide	RCONR′R″	$\overset{\overset{\ddot{O}}{\|\|}}{-C}-\overset{\ddot{N}-R'}{\underset{R''}{\|}}$	Amide group (tertiary, 3°)

Student Annotation: Some functional groups have special names and some do not.

*R′ represents a second alkyl group that may or may not be identical to the first alkyl group R. Likewise, R″ represents a third alkyl group that may or may not be identical to R or R′.

†The designations 1°, 2°, and 3° refer to how many R groups are bonded to the N atom.

A compound consisting of an alkyl group and the functional group —OH is an *alcohol*. The identity of an individual alcohol depends on the identity of R, the alkyl group. For example, when R is the *methyl* group, we have CH₃OH. This is methyl alcohol or methanol, also known as wood alcohol. It is highly toxic and can cause blindness or even death in relatively small doses. When R is the *ethyl* group, we have CH₃CH₂OH. This is ethyl alcohol or ethanol. Ethanol is the alcohol in alcoholic beverages. When R is the *isopropyl* group, we have (CH₃)₂CHOH. This is isopropyl alcohol. Isopropyl alcohol, what we commonly call "rubbing alcohol," is widely used as a disinfectant.

Methanol

Ethanol

Isopropyl alcohol

Many compounds contain more than one functional group. An *amino acid,* for example, contains both the amine group and the carboxy group.

$$\text{H-C-C-C-OH}$$

Alanine

Worked Example 24.1 lets you practice identifying functional groups in molecules.

Worked Example 24.1

Many familiar substances are organic compounds. Some examples include aspartame, the artificial sweetener in the sugar substitute Equal and in many diet sodas; salicylic acid, found in some acne medicines and wart-removal treatments; and amphetamine, a stimulant used to treat narcolepsy, attention-deficit hyperactivity disorder (ADHD), and obesity. Identify the functional group(s) in each molecule:

Aspartame
(a)

Salicylic acid
(b)

Amphetamine
(c)

Strategy Look for and identify the combinations of atoms shown in Table 24.2.

Setup (a) From right to left, aspartame contains a —COOH group, an —NH$_2$ group, a —CONHR group, and a —COOR group:

(b) Salicylic acid contains an —OH group and a —COOH group:

(c) Amphetamine contains an —NH$_2$ group:

Solution (a) From right to left, aspartame contains a *carboxy* group, an *amino* group, an *amide* group, and a —COOR (ester) group.

(b) Salicylic acid contains a *hydroxy* group and a *carboxy* group.

(c) Amphetamine contains an *amino* group.

Think About It

In part (b), the salicylic acid molecule contains a benzene ring and is therefore *aromatic*. When the hydroxy group is attached to a benzene ring, the resulting aromatic compound is a *phenol*, not an alcohol. Amphetamine has several legitimate medicinal uses, but it is also one of the most commonly misused drugs in the United States. Because it frequently is prescribed to adolescents for ADHD, much of it finds its way into high schools, where its misuse is a serious problem. A closely related compound that frequently makes headlines is *methamphetamine*:

In August of 2005, an issue of *Newsweek* magazine devoted a cover story to methamphetamine and its abuse.

Practice Problem A Identify the functional groups in each of the following molecules:

(a) Ethyl butyrate   (b) Aspirin

(c) Tartaric acid

Practice Problem B Identify the functional groups in each of the following cyclic compounds:

Basic Nomenclature

Organic compounds are named systematically using International Union of Pure and Applied Chemistry (IUPAC) rules.

Root Names for Alkanes and Alkyl Groups

Number of carbons	Name	Number of carbons	Name
1	Meth-	6	Hex-
2	Eth-	7	Hept-
3	Prop-	8	Oct-
4	But-	9	Non-
5	Pent-	10	Dec-

Prefixes for Halogen Substituents

—F	Fluoro
—Cl	Chloro
—Br	Bromo
—I	Iodo

Alkanes

In Chapter 5, we encountered the names of some simple, straight-chain alkanes such as pentane:

$$
\begin{array}{c}
\text{H} \quad \text{H} \quad \text{H} \quad \text{H} \quad \text{H} \\
| \quad\; | \quad\; | \quad\; | \quad\; | \\
\text{H—C—C—C—C—C—H} \\
| \quad\; | \quad\; | \quad\; | \quad\; | \\
\text{H} \quad \text{H} \quad \text{H} \quad \text{H} \quad \text{H}
\end{array}
$$

To name substituted alkanes (i.e., those that have **substituents**, which are groups other than —H bonded to the carbons of the chain), we follow a series of steps:

1. Identify the longest continuous carbon chain to get the *parent name.*
2. Number the carbons in the continuous chain, beginning at the end closest to the substituent. Commonly encountered substituents include alkyl groups and halogens.
3. Identify the substituent and use a *number* followed by a dash and a *prefix* to specify its *location* and *identity,* respectively.

Step 1:   The longest continuous carbon chain contains five C atoms.

2-Methylpentane

(We could also identify the carbon chain as

but the number of C atoms in the chain is the same either way.) The parent name of a five-carbon chain is *pentane.* (See root names.)

Step 2:   We number the carbon atoms beginning at the end nearest the substituent (shaded in green):

Step 3:   The substituent is a methyl group, —CH$_3$. It is attached to carbon 2. Therefore, the name is 2-methylpentane.

Worked Example 24.2 lets you practice naming some simple organic compounds.

Worked Example 24.2

Give names for the following compounds:

(a)

(b)

(c)

Strategy Use the three-step procedure for naming substituted alkanes: (1) name the parent alkane, (2) number the carbons, and (3) name and number the substituent. (Consult Table 5.8 for parent alkane names.)

Setup (a) This is a five-carbon chain. We can number the carbons starting at either end because the Cl substituent will be located on carbon 3 either way:

(b) This may look like a substituted pentane, too, but the longest carbon chain in this molecule is seven carbons long.

Although Lewis structures appear to be flat and to contain 90° angles, the C atoms in this molecule are all sp^3-hybridized (four electron domains around each) and there is free rotation about the C—C bonds [◄◄ Section 7.5]. Thus, the molecule can also be drawn as

The substituent is a methyl group on carbon 4.

(c) This is a substituted *hexane*.

Solution (a) 3-chloropentane, (b) 4-methylheptane, (c) 2-methylhexane

(Continued on next page)

Think About It

A common error is to misidentify the parent alkane. Double-check to be sure you have identified the *longest* continuous carbon chain in the molecule. Also be sure to number the carbon atoms so as to give the substituent the *lowest* possible number.

Practice Problem A Give the systematic IUPAC name for each of the following:

(a)   (b)   (c)

Practice Problem B Draw structures for (a) 4-ethyloctane, (b) 2-fluoropentane, and (c) 3-methyldecane.

Molecules with Multiple Substituents

A systematic name must identify a compound unambiguously. Therefore, a special system of rules must be followed to name molecules that contain more than one substituent.

In molecules that contain two or more identical substituents, the prefixes *di, tri, tetra, penta,* and so forth, are used to denote the number of substituents. Numbers are then used to denote their positions. (Note that two substituents may be bonded to the same carbon atom. In this case, the carbon's number is repeated with a comma between the numbers.)

2,3-Dimethylpentane   2,2-Dichlorohexanoic acid

In the case where two or more different substituents are present, the substituent names are alphabetized in the systematic name of the compound. Numbers are used to indicate the positions of the alphabetized substituents. If a prefix is used to denote two or more identical substituents, the prefix is *not* used to determine the alphabetization—only the substituent name is used.

4-Ethyl-2-methylhexane   4-Ethyl-2,2-dimethylhexane

Molecules with Specific Functional Groups
Alcohols

Identify the longest continuous carbon chain that includes the carbon to which the −OH group is attached. This is the parent alkyl group. Name it according to the number of carbons it contains, and change the –*e* ending to –*ol*. Number the C atoms such that the —OH group has the lowest possible number, and, when necessary, use a number to indicate the position of the —OH group:

Ethanol   1-Propanol   2-Butanol

When the chain that bears the —OH group also bears an alkyl substituent, the chain is numbered in the direction that gives the lowest possible number to the carbon attached to —OH.

5-Methyl-3-hexanol

Carboxylic Acids

Identify the longest continuous carbon chain that includes the carboxy group. Name it according to the number of carbons it contains, and change the –*e* ending to –*oic* acid. Number the C atoms starting with the carbonyl carbon. Use numbers and prefixes to indicate the position and the identity of any substituents.

> **Student Annotation:** The carbonyl carbon is the one that is doubly bonded to oxygen.

   Many organic compounds have common names in addition to their systematic names. Common names for some of the carboxylic acids shown here are given in parentheses:

Ethanoic acid   Propanoic acid   Butanoic acid   5-Methylhexanoic acid
(acetic acid)   (propionic acid)   (butyric acid)

Esters

Name esters as derivatives of carboxylic acids by replacing the –*ic* acid ending with –*ate:*

Ethyl acetate   Methyl propionate
Based on acetic acid   Based on propionic acid

(The first part of an ester's name specifies the substituent that replaces the ionizable hydrogen of the corresponding carboxylic acid.)

Aldehydes

> **Student Annotation:** With carboxylic acids and aldehydes, because we always begin numbering the carbons at the carbonyl, it is not necessary to include the number of the carbonyl carbon (1) in the name.

Identify the longest continuous carbon chain that includes the carbonyl group. Name it according to the number of carbons it contains, and change the –*e* ending to –*al*. Number the C atoms starting with the carbonyl carbon. Use numbers and prefixes to indicate the position and the identity of any substituents:

Ethanal   Propanal   Butanal   5-Methylhexanal
(acetaldehyde)   (propionaldehyde)

Ketones

Identify the longest continuous carbon chain that includes the carbonyl group. Name it according to the number of carbons it contains, and change the –e ending to –one. If necessary, number the C atoms to give the carbonyl carbon the lowest possible number. Use numbers and prefixes to indicate the position and the identity of any substituents:

> **Student Annotation:** Note that there is only one possible location for the carbonyl carbon in propanone (the middle carbon), making a number in the name unnecessary. If the carbonyl occurred on either of the other carbons, the compound would be an *aldehyde,* not a ketone.

Propanone
(acetone)

2-Butanone
(ethyl methyl ketone)

5-Methyl-3-hexanone

Primary Amines

Identify the longest continuous carbon chain that includes the carbon to which the $-NH_2$ group is bonded. Name it according to the number of carbons it contains, and change the –e ending to –amine. Number the C atoms starting with the carbon to which the $-NH_2$ group is bonded. Use numbers and prefixes to indicate the position and the identity of any substituents:

Ethanamine
(ethylamine)

1-Propanamine
(propylamine)

1-Butanamine
(butylamine)

5-Methyl-1-hexanamine
(5-methylhexylamine)

Primary Amides

> **Student Annotation:** We will not introduce the nomenclature for secondary and tertiary amines and amides in this text.

Primary amides are named as derivatives of carboxylic acids, but they can also be named by replacing the –e ending of the corresponding alkane with –amide.

Propanamide
(propionamide)

Butanamide
(butyramide)

SECTION 24.2 REVIEW

Classes of Organic Compounds

24.2.1   Write the name of the following compound:

24.2.2   Write the name of the following compound:

24.2.3 Write the name of the following compound:

$$CH_3-CH_2-\overset{\overset{\displaystyle O}{\|}}{C}-CH_3$$

(with CH_2 between)

24.2.4 Write the name of the following compound:

$$CH_3-\overset{\overset{\displaystyle CH_3}{|}}{CH}-CH_2-CH_2-NH_2$$

24.2.5 Identify the functional group(s) in the following molecule:

24.2.6 Identify the functional group(s) in the following molecule:

$$CH_3-\overset{\underset{\displaystyle OH}{|}}{CH}-\overset{\overset{\displaystyle O}{\|}}{C}-OH$$

24.3 REPRESENTING ORGANIC MOLECULES

You've learned previously how to represent molecules using *molecular* and *structural* formulas [◄◄ Section 5.5], as well as using Lewis structures [◄◄ Section 6.3]. In this section, we will learn several additional ways to represent molecules—ways that are particularly useful in the study of organic chemistry.

The representation of organic molecules is especially important because the atoms in an organic molecule, unlike those in inorganic compounds, may be arranged in an enormous variety of different ways. For example, there are literally dozens of different ways that a compound containing five carbon atoms, one oxygen atom, and the necessary number of hydrogen atoms can be arranged, with each arrangement representing a unique organic compound. Here are ten possibilities:

Student Annotation: The "necessary" number of H atoms is the number necessary to *complete the octet* of each C and O atom [◄◄ Section 6.3].

Condensed Structural Formulas

A *condensed structural formula,* or simply a *condensed structure,* shows the same information as a *structural formula,* but in a *condensed* form. For instance, the molecular formula, structural formula, and condensed structural formula of octane are as follows:

$$C_8H_{18}$$
Molecular formula

$$CH_3CH_2CH_2CH_2CH_2CH_2CH_2CH_3$$
Structural formula

$$CH_3(CH_2)_6CH_3$$
Condensed structural formula

Octane

In the condensed structural formula, the identical adjacent groups of atoms (in this case $-CH_2-$ groups) are enclosed in parentheses and subscripted to denote their number.

In molecules where the carbon atoms do not form a single, unbranched chain, branches are indicated using additional parentheses in the condensed structural formula. For example, 2-methylheptane has the same molecular formula (C_8H_{18}) as octane. In effect, the chain is one C atom *shorter* than in octane and one of the hydrogen atoms on the second C atom has been replaced by a methyl group. The molecular formula, structural formula, and condensed structural formula of 2-methylheptane are as follows:

$$C_8H_{18}$$
Molecular formula

$$\overset{\displaystyle CH_3}{\underset{\textstyle}{|}}$$
$$CH_3CHCH_2CH_2CH_2CH_2CH_3$$
Structural formula

$$CH_3CH(CH_3)(CH_2)_4CH_3$$
Condensed structural formula

2-Methylheptane

Kekulé Structures

Kekulé structures are similar to Lewis structures except that they do not show lone pairs. For molecules that contain no lone pairs, such as octane, the Lewis and Kekulé structures are identical:

$$H-\overset{H}{\underset{H}{C}}-\overset{H}{\underset{H}{C}}-\overset{H}{\underset{H}{C}}-\overset{H}{\underset{H}{C}}-\overset{H}{\underset{H}{C}}-\overset{H}{\underset{H}{C}}-\overset{H}{\underset{H}{C}}-\overset{H}{\underset{H}{C}}-H$$

Octane

(Many of the structures already shown in this chapter are Kekulé structures.) The Kekulé structures for several familiar organic molecules are as follows:

$$H-\overset{H}{\underset{H}{C}}-\overset{H}{\underset{H}{C}}-O-H$$

Ethanol

$$H-\overset{O}{\overset{\|}{C}}-H$$

Formaldehyde

$$H-\overset{H}{\underset{H}{C}}-\overset{O}{\overset{\|}{C}}-O-H$$

Acetic acid

Skeletal Structures

Skeletal structures are especially useful for representing complex organic molecules. A *skeletal structure* consists of straight lines that represent carbon-carbon bonds. The carbon atoms themselves (and the attached hydrogen atoms) are not shown, but you need to know that they are there. The structural formulas and skeletal structures for several hydrocarbons [◀◀ Section 5.6] are as follows:

Name	Structural formula	Skeletal structure
Pentane	$CH_3CH_2CH_2CH_2CH_3$	
Isopentane	CH$_3$ | $CH_3CHCH_2CH_3$	
Neopentane	CH$_3$ | CH_3CCH_3 | CH$_3$	

The end of each straight line in a skeletal structure corresponds to a carbon atom (unless another atom of a different type is explicitly shown at the end of the line). Additionally, there are as many hydrogen atoms attached to each carbon atom as are necessary to give each carbon atom a total of four bonds.

When a molecule contains an element *other* than carbon or hydrogen, those atoms, called **heteroatoms,** are shown explicitly in the skeletal structure. Furthermore, while the hydrogens attached to carbon atoms typically are not shown, hydrogens attached to heteroatoms *are* shown, as illustrated by the molecule ethylamine in the following:

Name	Structural formula	Skeletal structure
Propanone (acetone)	O || CH_3CCH_3	
Ethylamine	$CH_3CH_2NH_2$	
Tetrahydrofuran	H$_2$C$\overset{O}{\diagup\diagdown}CH_2$ H$_2$C—CH$_2$	

Student Annotation: Study these structural formulas and skeletal structures, and those shown earlier, and make sure you understand how to interpret the skeletal structures.

Although carbon and hydrogen atoms need not be shown in a skeletal structure, some of the C and H atoms *can* be shown for the purpose of emphasizing a particular part of a molecule. Often when we show a molecule, we choose to emphasize the *functional group(s),* which are largely responsible for the properties and reactivity of the compound [◀◀ Section 5.6].

Worked Example 24.3 shows how to interpret skeletal structures.

Worked Example 24.3

Write a molecular formula and a structural formula (or *condensed* structural formula) for the following:

(a)   (b)

Strategy Count the C atoms represented and the heteroatoms shown. Determine how many H atoms are present using the octet rule.

(Continued on next page)

Setup Each line represents a bond. (Double lines represent double bonds.) Count one C atom at the end of each line unless another atom is shown there. Count the number of H atoms necessary to complete the octet of each C atom.

C atom + 1 H atom   C atom + 3 H atoms   C atom + 3 H atoms

C atom + 3 H atoms   C atom + 1 H atom   C atom (no H atoms)

Solution (a) Molecular formula: C_4H_8; structural formula: $CH_3(CH)_2CH_3$.

(b) Molecular formula: C_2H_5NO; structural formula: CH_3CONH_2.

> **Think About It**
> Make sure that each C atom is surrounded by four electron pairs: four single bonds, two single bonds and a double bond, or two double bonds. Remember that the single bonds to H typically are not shown in a skeletal structure—you have to remember that they are there and account for the H atoms when you deduce the formula.

Practice Problem A Write a structural formula for the compound represented by the following skeletal structure:

Practice Problem B Draw the skeletal structure for $(CH_3)_2C=CHNH_2$.

Resonance

Recall from Chapter 6 that many molecules and ions can be represented by more than one Lewis structure [◄◄ Section 6.5]. Furthermore, two or more equally valid Lewis structures that differ only in the position of their electrons are called *resonance structures*. For example, SO_3 can be represented by three different Lewis structures [◄◄ Worked Example 6.7].

None of these Lewis structures represents the SO_3 molecule accurately. The bonds in SO_3 are actually *equivalent*—equal in length and strength, which we would not expect if two were single bonds and one were a double bond. Each individual resonance structure implies that electron pairs are *localized* in specific bonds or on specific atoms. The concept of resonance allows us to envision certain electron pairs as *delocalized* over several atoms [◄◄ Section 7.7]. Delocalization of electron pairs imparts additional stability to a molecule (or polyatomic ion), and a species that can be represented by two or more resonance structures is said to be *resonance stabilized*.

Student Annotation: Remember that the real structure of the molecule is neither the first structure nor the second, but rather something in between that cannot be represented by a single structure [◄◄ Section 6.5].

Chemists sometimes use curved arrows to specify the differences in positions of electrons in resonance structures. In SO_3, for example, the "repositioning" of electrons in the resonance structures can be indicated as follows:

Resonance stabilization is observed in many organic species as well and affects chemical properties such as in the acidic behavior of ethanol (CH_3CH_2OH) and ethanoic acid (CH_3COOH), also commonly known as *acetic* acid. Each of these molecules has one *ionizable hydrogen atom* [◄◄ Section 5.6], enabling it to behave as a Brønsted acid [◄◄ Section 9.3]. However, the concentration of hydronium ions in a solution of ethanoic acid is hundreds of thousands of times higher than that in a comparable solution of ethanol. The reason for this large discrepancy is that the hydrogen atom on ethanoic acid is far more *easily* ionized than the one on ethanol. *Resonance* helps us explain why.

When a species loses its ionizable hydrogen atom, what remains is an anion. In the case of ethanoic acid and ethanol, the anions are

$$\left[\begin{array}{c} H \quad \overset{\displaystyle ..}{\underset{\displaystyle ..}{O}} \\ | \quad \parallel \\ H-C-C-\overset{..}{\underset{..}{O}}: \\ | \\ H \end{array} \right]^{-} \quad \text{and} \quad \left[\begin{array}{c} H \quad H \\ | \quad | \\ H-C-C-\overset{..}{\underset{..}{O}}: \\ | \quad | \\ H \quad H \end{array} \right]^{-}$$

We can draw a second resonance structure for the anion produced by the ionization of ethanoic acid by repositioning the electron pairs as follows:

$$\left[\begin{array}{c} H \quad \overset{\displaystyle ..}{O} \\ | \quad \parallel \\ H-C-C-\overset{..}{\underset{..}{O}}: \\ | \\ H \end{array} \right]^{-} \longleftrightarrow \left[\begin{array}{c} H \quad :\overset{..}{O}: \\ | \quad | \\ H-C-C=\overset{..}{O}: \\ | \\ H \end{array} \right]^{-}$$

The negative charge on the anion resides on an oxygen atom. Which oxygen atom bears the charge depends on which resonance structure we look at. In essence, the greater the number of possible locations for the negative charge, the more stable the anion. And the more stable the anion, the more easily the ionizable hydrogen atom is lost, resulting in the production of more hydronium ions in solution.

It is not possible to draw additional resonance structures for the anion produced by the ionization of ethanol because there is nowhere else to put the lone pairs that reside on the O atom. They cannot be moved in between the O and C atoms because C can only have four electron pairs around it. (We were able to do this with CH_3COO^- because we could also move one of the pairs already around C to the other O atom. See the curved arrows in the preceding resonance structure.)

Worked Examples 24.4 and 24.5 illustrate the use of curved arrow notation and the determination of resonance structures.

> **Student Annotation:** We determine where a charge resides in a polyatomic anion by calculating the *formal charge* on each atom [◄◄ Section 6.4].

Worked Example 24.4

Following the curved arrows, draw a resonance structure for the HCONH⁻ ion.

$$\begin{array}{c} \overset{\displaystyle ..}{\underset{\displaystyle }{O}}: \\ \parallel \\ H-C-\overset{..}{\underset{..}{N}}-H \end{array}$$

Strategy Move electron pairs as indicated by the curved arrows, and calculate formal charges to reposition the negative charge.

Setup To determine the formal charge, we must first calculate the number of valence electrons on the atoms in question. The O and N atoms have *six* and *five* valence electrons, respectively.

Solution Repositioning electron pairs as directed by the curved arrows gives

$$\begin{array}{c} \overset{\displaystyle ..}{\underset{\displaystyle }{O}}: \\ \parallel \\ H-C-\overset{..}{\underset{..}{N}}-H \end{array} \longleftrightarrow \begin{array}{c} :\overset{..}{O}:^{-} \\ | \\ H-C=\overset{..}{N}-H \end{array}$$

The formal charge on N, which had been -1, is now $[5 - (3 + 2)] = 0$. The formal charge on O, which had been 0, is now $[6 - (1 + 6)] = -1$. Thus, the negative charge now resides on the oxygen atom.

> **Student Annotation:** Recall that formal charge is equal to *valence* electrons − *associated* electrons [◄◄ Section 6.4].

Think About It
Count the number of electron pairs around each atom. Remember that the C and N atoms can have no more than four electron pairs. The H atom can have no more than one electron pair.

Practice Problem A Follow the curved arrows to draw a second resonance structure for the HCOO⁻ ion.

$$\begin{array}{c} \overset{\displaystyle ..}{\underset{\displaystyle }{O}}: \\ \parallel \\ H-C-\overset{..}{\underset{..}{O}}:^{-} \end{array}$$

Practice Problem B Given the following two resonance structures, draw the curved arrows on the first structure that will give rise to the second structure.

$$\left[\begin{array}{c} :\overset{..}{O}: \\ | \\ :\overset{..}{O}-S-\overset{..}{O}: \\ | \\ :\overset{..}{O}: \end{array} \right]^{2-} \longleftrightarrow \left[\begin{array}{c} \overset{\displaystyle ..}{O} \\ \parallel \\ :\overset{..}{O}-S-\overset{..}{O}: \\ \parallel \\ \overset{..}{O}. \end{array} \right]^{2-}$$

Worked Example 24.5

Adenosine triphosphate (ATP) is sometimes called the "universal energy carrier" or "molecular energy currency." It contains two high-energy bonds (shown in red) that, when *hydrolyzed* (broken by the addition of water), release the energy necessary for cell function. Resonance stabilization of the hydrogen phosphate ion is one of the reasons the breakdown of ATP releases energy.

Student Annotation: The hydrogen phosphate ion that results from the breakdown of ATP is commonly referred to in biology textbooks as *phosphate* or as *inorganic phosphate*.

Inorganic phosphate

Adenosine triphosphate   Adenosine diphosphate

Draw all the possible resonance structures for the hydrogen phosphate ion (HPO_4^{2-}). Use curved arrows to indicate how electrons are repositioned, and determine the position(s) of the negative charges.

Strategy Draw a valid Lewis structure for HPO_4^{2-}, and determine whether and where electrons can be repositioned to produce one or more additional structures. Indicate the movement of electrons with curved arrows, and draw all possible resonance structures. Calculate the formal charge on each atom to determine the placement of charges.

Setup A valid Lewis structure for the hydrogen phosphate ion is

For the purpose of determining formal charges, P and O have five and six valence electrons, respectively.

Solution A lone pair can be moved from one of the oxygen atoms to create a double bond to the phosphorus, and a pair of electrons from the *original* double bond can be moved onto *that* oxygen atom. The net result is simply a repositioning of the double bond by moving two electron pairs. This can be done once more, giving a total of three resonance structures for HPO_4^{2-}. In each of the resonance structures, the formal charge on phosphorus is $[5 - (5)] = 0$. The formal charge on each singly bonded oxygen is $[6 - (1 + 6)] = -1$, and the formal charge on the doubly bonded oxygen is $[6 - (2 + 4)] = 0$.

Think About It

ATP can also be hydrolyzed to give AMP (adenosine *mono*phosphate) and *pyrophosphate* ($P_2O_7^{4-}$). Pyrophosphate hydrolyzes, in turn, to give two hydrogen phosphate ions. The oxygen atoms that can help delocalize the negative charges are highlighted:

These structures can also be drawn with one double bond to each phosphorus atom, to minimize formal charges [◀◀ Section 6.4].

Practice Problem A Draw a valid Lewis structure for the carbonate ion (CO_3^{2-}), and use curved arrows to generate all possible resonance structures.

Practice Problem B In which of the following examples do the curved arrows *not* correspond correctly to the repositioning of electrons needed to arrive at the resonance structure shown?

$$\left[:\ddot{O}-\ddot{N}=\ddot{O}:\right]^{-} \longleftrightarrow \left[:O=\ddot{N}-\ddot{O}:\right]^{-}$$

(a)

$$\left[:\ddot{O}-\ddot{N}=\ddot{O}:\right]^{-} \longleftrightarrow \left[:O=\ddot{N}-\ddot{O}:\right]^{-}$$

(b)

$$\left[:\ddot{O}-\ddot{N}=\ddot{O}:\right]^{-} \longleftrightarrow \left[:O=\ddot{N}-\ddot{O}:\right]^{-}$$

(c)

SECTION 24.3 REVIEW

Representing Organic Molecules

24.3.1 Give the molecular formula of the compound represented by

24.3.2 Give the molecular formula of the compound represented by

24.3.3 Which of the following pairs of species are resonance structures?

(a)

(b)

(c)

(d)

(e)

24.3.4 Which of the following structural formulas represents a species that has two or more resonance structures: $HCOOH$, $HCOO^{-}$, CH_2CH_2, O_3, CO_2?

24.4 ISOMERISM

We first encountered the term *isomer* in the context of molecular geometry and molecular polarity [◄◄ Section 7.2]. Isomers are different compounds that have the same chemical formula. In this section, we will discuss the different types of isomerism (namely, constitutional isomerism and stereoisomerism) and their importance to organic chemistry.

Constitutional Isomerism

Also known as *structural* isomerism, **constitutional isomerism** occurs when the same atoms can be connected in two or more different ways. For example, there are three different ways to arrange the atoms in a compound with the chemical formula C_5H_{12}. Constitutional isomers have distinct names and generally have different physical and chemical properties. Table 24.3 lists the three constitutional isomers of C_5H_{12} along with their boiling points for comparison.

Multi 24.1
Organic and biochemistry—structural isomers of hexane

Stereoisomerism

Stereoisomers are those that contain identical bonds but differ in the orientation of those bonds in space. Two types of stereoisomers exist: geometrical isomers and optical isomers. *Geometrical isomers* occur in compounds that have restricted rotation around a bond. For instance, compounds that contain carbon-carbon double bonds can form geometrical isomers. Individual geometrical isomers have the same names but are distinguished by a prefix such as *cis* or *trans*. Dichloroethylene, ethylene in which two of the H atoms (one on each C atom) have been replaced by Cl atoms, exists as two geometrical isomers. The isomer in which the Cl atoms both lie on the same side (above or below, in this example) of the double bond is called the **cis** isomer. The isomer in which the Cl atoms lie on opposite sides of the double bond is called the **trans** isomer. (The compound in which both Cl atoms are attached to the same C atom is a *constitutional* isomer rather than a stereoisomer.) Figure 24.2 depicts the isomers of $C_2H_2Cl_2$.

Figure 24.2 Three isomers of dichloroethylene.

cis-Dichloroethylene	*trans*-Dichloroethylene	1,1-Dichloroethylene

TABLE 24.3	Constitutional Isomers of C_5H_{12}				
Name	**Structural formula**	**Skeletal structure**	**Ball-and-stick model**		**BP (°C)**
Pentane (*n*-pentane)					36.1
Methylbutane (isopentane)					27.8
2,2-Dimethylpropane (neopentane)					9.5

(a)

(b)

Figure 24.3 (a) Nonsuperimposable mirror images. (b) Despite being mirror images of each other, enantiomers are different compounds.

Geometrical isomers usually have different physical and chemical properties. *Trans* isomers tend to be more stable and are generally easier to synthesize than their *cis* counterparts. The existence of *cis* isomers in living systems is a testament to how much better nature is at chemical synthesis than we are. As the information in the box on page 984 demonstrates, geometrical isomerism is sometimes of tremendous biological significance.

Stereoisomers that are mirror images of each other, but are not superimposable, are called *optical isomers.* Consider the hypothetical organic molecule shown in Figure 24.3. It consists of an sp^3-hybridized carbon atom that is bonded to four different groups. Its mirror image appears identical to it, just as your right and left hands appear identical to each other. But, if you have ever tried to put a right-handed glove on your left hand, or vice versa, you know that your hands are not identical. Imagine rotating the molecule on the right so that its green and red spheres coincide with those of the molecule on the left. Doing so results in the yellow sphere of one molecule coinciding with the blue sphere on the other. These two molecules are mirror images of each other, but they are not identical.

Molecules with nonsuperimposable mirror images are called *chiral;* and a pair of such mirror-image molecules are called *enantiomers.* Most of the chemical properties of enantiomers and all their physical properties are identical. Their chemical properties differ only in reactions that involve another chiral species, such as a chiral molecule or a receptor site that is shaped to fit only one enantiomer. Most biochemical processes consist of a series of chemically specific reactions that use chiral receptor sites to facilitate reaction by allowing only the specific reactants to fit (and thus react).

In organic chemistry, it often is necessary to represent tetrahedral molecules (three-dimensional objects) on paper (a two-dimensional surface). By convention, this is done using solid lines to represent bonds that lie in the plane of the page, dashes to represent bonds that point behind the page, and wedges to represent bonds that point in front of the page:

Multi 24.2
Organic and biochemistry—chiral molecules

Student Annotation: The word *chiral* comes from the Greek word *cheir* for "hand." Chiral molecules may be right-handed or left-handed.

Methane   1,2-Dichloroethane

One property of chiral molecules is that the two enantiomers rotate the plane of plane-polarized light in opposite directions; that is, they are *optically active.* Unlike ordinary light, which

Figure 24.4 Schematic of a polarimeter.

oscillates in all directions, plane-polarized light oscillates only in a single plane. We use a polarimeter, shown schematically in Figure 24.4, to measure the rotation of polarized light by optical isomers. A beam of unpolarized light first passes through a Polaroid sheet, called the *polarizer*, and then through a sample tube containing a solution of an optically active, chiral species. As the polarized light passes through the sample tube, its plane of polarization is rotated either to the right or to the left. The amount of rotation can be measured by turning the analyzer in the appropriate direction until minimal light transmission is achieved.

Minimal transmission occurs when the plane of polarization of the light is perpendicular to that of the analyzer through which it is viewed. This effect can be demonstrated using two pairs of polarized sunglasses as shown in Figure 24.5. If the plane of polarization is rotated to the right, the isomer is said to be *dextrorotatory* and is labeled *d*; if it is rotated to the left, the isomer is called *levorotatory* and labeled *l*. Enantiomers always rotate the light by the same amount, but in opposite directions. Thus, in an equimolar mixture of both enantiomers, called a ***racemic mixture,*** the net rotation is zero.

A fascinating use of plane-polarized light is in 3-D movies. We see in three dimensions because our eyes view the world from slightly different positions. Our brains synthesize a three-dimensional (3-D) picture based on the two different pictures sent to it by our eyes. Modern 3-D movies make use of this phenomenon to make it seem as though objects on the screen are actually moving toward the viewer.

> **Student Annotation:** There are several conventions used to designate specific enantiomers. *Dextro-* and *levo-* prefixes refer to the direction of rotation of polarized light. *R* and *S,* the most commonly used designations, are assigned based on the "priority" assigned to each of the four groups attached to the chiral carbon—something that is beyond the scope of this text.

Figure 24.5 Two pairs of polarized sunglasses. (a) When two polarized lenses overlap with their planes of polarization parallel to each other, light is transmitted. (b) When one pair is rotated so that its plane of polarization is perpendicular to the other, no light is transmitted through the overlapped lenses.

(a)

(b)

Polarized glasses

Figure 24.6 Two different versions of the same movie are projected onto the screen. Polarized lenses make it so that each eye sees only one version. The result is the perception of three-dimensional action.

Three-dimensional movies are filmed using two different cameras at slightly different angles to the action. Thus, there are actually *two* movies that must be shown to us simultaneously. To make sure that our two eyes receive two different perspectives, each movie is projected through a polarizer, which polarizes the two projections in directions perpendicular to each other (Figure 24.6).

If we were to watch the movie without the special glasses provided by the movie house, we would see the blurry combination of the two movies. However, the 3-D glasses consist of polarized lenses, with planes of polarization that are mutually perpendicular. The left lens, polarized in one direction, blocks the image that is polarized perpendicular to it. The right lens, polarized in the other direction, blocks the other image. Our eyes are "tricked" into seeing two different movies, which our brain combines to form one 3-D image. The results of this process can be quite impressive!

Numerous processes important to biological function involve one enantiomer of a chiral compound. Many drugs, including thalidomide (page 984), are chiral with only one enantiomer having the desired properties. Some such drugs have been manufactured and marketed as racemic mixtures. It has become common, though, for drug companies to invest in *chiral switching,* the preparation of single-isomer versions of drugs originally marketed as racemic mixtures, in an effort to improve on existing therapies and to combat the revenue losses caused by generic drugs. A fairly high-profile example of this is the single-isomer drug Nexium, the so-called purple pill. AstraZeneca, makers of Nexium, held a patent for the drug Prilosec, originally a prescription heartburn medication that is now available over the counter. Prilosec is a racemic mixture of the chiral compound omeprazole. Prior to the 2002 expiration of its patent on Prilosec, AstraZeneca began producing and marketing Nexium, which contains only the therapeutically effective enantiomer (S)-omeprazole or *esomeprazole.*

Another example of chiral switching is that of the selective serotonin reuptake inhibitor (SSRI) antidepressant Celexa, which was introduced to the market in 1998 by Forest Laboratories. Celexa is a racemic mixture of (R)-citalopram oxalate and (S)-citalopram oxalate. While only the (S) enantiomer has therapeutic antidepressant properties, both enantiomers contribute to the side effects of the drug and therefore limit effectiveness and patient tolerance. In 2002, the FDA approved Lexapro, a new antidepressant derived from Celexa but from which the therapeutically ineffective (R) enantiomer has been removed. The benefits of isolating the active isomer include smaller required dosages, reduced side effects, and a faster and better patient response to the drug.

Although the intellectual property laws regarding single-isomer drug patents are somewhat ambiguous, chiral switching has enabled some pharmaceutical companies to extend the time that they are able to market their popular prescriptions exclusively. Strictly speaking, the FDA does not consider a single enantiomer of an already approved chiral drug to be a "new chemical entity," which is a requirement for obtaining a patent on a compound. Early in the history of chiral switching, however, there was some disagreement among patent examiners regarding what constituted a new chemical entity, and patents were granted on single-isomer drugs that might not be granted today.

Student Annotation: In some cases, the other enantiomer has no biological activity; in other cases, the other enantiomer has a different type of activity, making it detrimental or even deadly—as in the case of thalidomide.

Thinking Outside the Box

Thalidomide Analogues

Beginning in 1957, the drug thalidomide was marketed in 48 countries around the world as a sleeping pill and as an antinausea medicine for pregnant women suffering from morning sickness. By 1962, the drug was shown to have caused horrific birth defects and an untold number of fetal deaths. Thalidomide interferes with spinal cord and limb development, and more than 10,000 babies had been born with severe spinal cord abnormalities and malformed or absent limbs. Many of the victims were born to mothers who reportedly had taken just *one* thalidomide pill early in their pregnancies. At the time, thalidomide was not approved for use in the United States, but the otherwise worldwide tragedy did prompt the U.S. Congress to enact a new law to give the FDA more control over the testing and approval of new drugs.

In August of 1998, the FDA approved thalidomide for the treatment of *erythema nodosum leprosum* (ENL), a painful inflammatory skin condition associated with leprosy. This approval is controversial because of the drug's infamous history, but thalidomide has shown tremendous promise in the treatment of a wide variety of painful and debilitating conditions, including complications from certain cancers, AIDS, and some autoimmune disorders such as lupus and rheumatoid arthritis. Because of the dangers known to be associated with thalidomide, researchers are working on developing *analogues*—drugs that are chemically similar enough to have the same therapeutic benefits but chemically *different* enough *not* to have the undesirable and/or dangerous properties. Two such analogues that are currently being investigated are lenalidomide and CC-4047, shown here:

Thalidomide   Lenalidomide   CC-4047

Although it was approved by the FDA in 1998, thalidomide is the most regulated prescription drug in history, because it is known to harm developing fetuses. The drug's manufacturer, Celgene Corporation, has developed the *System for Thalidomide Education and Prescribing Safety* (STEPS) program. In order for physicians to prescribe thalidomide to their patients, they must be registered in the STEPS program. Female patients must have a negative pregnancy test within 24 hours of beginning treatment and must undergo periodic pregnancy testing throughout treatment. Both female and male patients must comply with mandatory contraceptive measures, patient registration, and patient surveys. Moreover, new patients must view an informational video in which a thalidomide victim explains the potential dangers of the drug.

Student Annotation: Thalidomide was not approved for use in the United States thanks in large part to the vigilance of one doctor at the FDA. She was troubled by inadequate research into the safety of the drug and steadfastly refused to approve the drug-maker's application.

24.5 ORGANIC REACTIONS

Coulomb's law, which we first encountered in the box in Section 4.3, measures the force of the attraction between opposite charges. The attraction between regions of opposite charge on neighboring species and the resulting movement of electrons are the basis for our understanding of many organic reactions. We begin by defining what *electrophiles* and *nucleophiles* are, two terms used frequently in organic chemistry.

An **electrophile** is a species with a positive or partial positive charge. Literally, an electrophile "loves electrons." Thus, an electrophile is attracted to a region of negative or partial negative charge. An electrophile may be a cation, such as H^+, or the positive portion of a polar molecule, such as the H atom in HCl. Electrophiles are *electron-poor*.

A **nucleophile** is a species with a negative or partial negative charge. Literally, a nucleophile "loves a nucleus." A nucleophile is attracted to a region of positive or partial positive charge (i.e., an electrophile). A nucleophile may be an anion, such as Cl^-, or the negative portion of a polar molecule, such as the Cl atom in HCl. Nucleophiles are *electron-rich*. Electron-rich sites and electron-poor sites are attracted to one another.

Addition Reactions

The electrostatic potential maps of HCl and C_2H_4 shown in Figure 24.7 demonstrate that both molecules have regions of partial positive charge and partial negative charge. For example, HCl is a polar molecule, with H bearing a partial positive charge, due to the large difference in electronegativity between hydrogen and chlorine. Moreover, the carbon-carbon double bond in C_2H_4 consists of two pairs of shared electrons, one pair in a sigma bond and one pair in a pi bond [◄◄ Section 7.5], making the double bond a region of partial negative charge. The partial positive charge on the H in the HCl molecule is an electrophile. The double bond in ethylene, a region of relatively high electron density, is a nucleophile.

A reaction takes place when the positive end of the HCl molecule approaches the double bond in ethylene. The pi bond breaks, and the electrons it contained move as indicated by the curved arrows shown in the following equation, forming a sigma bond between the H atom of the HCl molecule and one of the C atoms. As this new bond forms, two things happen:

1. Because there cannot be more than one bond to the H atom, the original bond between H and Cl breaks. Both of the electrons originally shared by H and Cl go with the Cl atom. The resulting intermediate species are shown in square brackets in the following equation (dashed lines represent bonds that are being formed):

Student Annotation: Although it ionizes completely in aqueous solution [◄◄ Section 9.1], HCl exists as *molecules* in the gas phase.

Student Annotation: When an electrophile approaches another species and accepts electrons from it to form a bond, this is called *electrophilic attack*.

Student Annotation: Curved arrows are used to illustrate the mechanism by which an organic reaction occurs. Unlike their use in resonance structures, curved arrows in a reaction mechanism correspond to the actual *movement* of electrons.

The C atom on the right bears a positive charge after the valence electron it originally shared (in the pi bond with the other C atom) is removed from it completely. A species such as this, in which one of the carbons is surrounded by only six electrons, is called a ***carbocation.*** Although carbon must obey the octet in any stable compound, some reactions involve transient, *intermediate* species in which a carbon atom may be electron deficient—having only three electron pairs around it.

2. The C atom forming the new sigma bond to the H atom changes from sp^2-hybridized to sp^3-hybridized:

Figure 24.7 The partial positive charge on H in HCl is attracted to the region of electron density in ethylene's double bond.

The carbon atom bearing the positive charge is still sp^2-hybridized at this point.

The chloride ion produced when both of the electrons originally shared by H and Cl go with Cl is a *nucleophile.* It is attracted to the newly formed positive charge and two of its electrons form a bond to the positively charged C atom as shown by the curved arrows.

The formation of a new sigma bond between the Cl and C atoms causes the hybridization of the second C to change from sp^2 to sp^3:

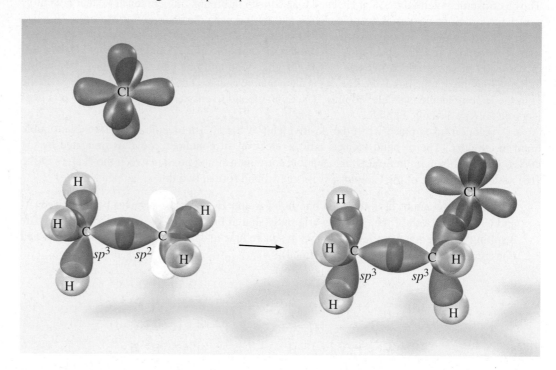

The overall reaction is called an *addition reaction*. Specifically, this is an ***electrophilic addition*** reaction because it begins with the electrophilic attack by HCl on the region of electron density in the double bond.

Addition reactions can also begin with nucleophilic attack, in which case the reaction is called a ***nucleophilic addition.*** In a nucleophilic addition reaction, a bond forms when a nucleophile donates a pair of electrons to an electron-deficient atom. Water, for example, reacts with carbon dioxide to produce carbonic acid. Although the addition reaction happens essentially all at once, it is helpful to think of the movement of electrons as the following stepwise process:

1.

One of the lone pairs on the O atom in water attacks the C atom, which is electron deficient because of the highly electronegative O atoms bonded to it. As the new bond forms, one of the original C—O pi bonds breaks. The electron pair from the broken pi bond is repositioned on the corresponding O atom, leaving the atom with a negative charge.

Student Annotation: Nucleophilic attack in which only one electron is donated by the attacking species can also occur. These are called *radical* reactions.

2.

One of the O—H bonds in water breaks, with both electrons remaining with the O atom. The H atom separates from the water molecule as a proton.

3.

Finally, the negatively charged O atom acquires the proton lost by the water molecule that served as the nucleophile.

(a)

(b)

Figure 24.8 (a) Electrophilic addition reaction. (b) Nucleophilic addition reaction. Curved arrows indicate movement of electrons. (Nu represents a nucleophile.)

A summary of the mechanisms of electrophilic and nucleophilic addition reactions is given in Figure 24.8.

Substitution Reactions

Electrophilic and nucleophilic attack can also lead to **substitution reactions** in which one group is replaced by another group. Electrophilic substitution occurs when an electrophile attacks an aromatic molecule and replaces a hydrogen atom. Nucleophilic substitution occurs when a nucleophile replaces another group on a carbon atom. Figure 24.9 shows the general mechanisms for substitution reactions.

The nitration of benzene is an example of an electrophilic substitution reaction:

Student Annotation: Specifically, this type of reaction is called an *electrophilic aromatic substitution* reaction.

Nitric acid and sulfuric acid react to produce the nitronium ion ($^+NO_2$), which acts as the electrophile:

The positively charged nitronium ion is attracted to the electron-rich pi bonds of the benzene ring. A bond forms between one of the carbon atoms and the nitronium ion, breaking one of benzene's pi bonds:

(a)   (b)

Figure 24.9 (a) Electrophilic substitution. Benzene is attacked by an electrophile (E^+). (b) Nucleophilic substitution reaction.

The resulting carbocation is stabilized by resonance:

Finally, the electrons in the C—H bond move to the ring, restoring the original pi bond, and the hydrogen atom leaves as a proton, H$^+$:

When necessary, one additional step can convert the —NO$_2$ group into the —NH$_2$ group:

Student Annotation: The C atom in methyl bromide bears a partial positive charge because it is bonded to the somewhat more electronegative bromine atom [◄◄ Section 6.2].

A simple example of nucleophilic substitution is the reaction of an alkyl halide such as methyl bromide with a nucleophile such as the chloride ion. The chloride ion is attracted to the partial positive charge on the C atom in methyl bromide. A lone pair on the chloride ion moves to form a sigma bond between the Cl atom and the C atom. And, because there can be no more than four electron pairs around the C atom, the original C—Br bond breaks, with both of the electrons originally shared by C and Br going to the Br atom. The result is a methyl chloride molecule and a bromide ion:

Student Annotation: Digestion of proteins also begins with a nucleophilic substitution reaction.

Nucleophilic substitutions are particularly important in living systems. The hydrolysis of ATP (adenosine triphosphate), which was described in Section 24.3, is an example of nucleophilic substitution. In hydrolysis, the oxygen atom in water acts as the nucleophile, attacking the electron-deficient phosphorus atom. A similar reaction happens between glucose and ATP, as shown in Figure 24.10. The P atom that is attacked is electron deficient because of the four highly electronegative O atoms bonded to it. As a bond forms between the attacking O and the P, one of the original P—O bonds breaks. The net result is the replacement of the original —H group on glucose with a —PO$_4^{3-}$ group to give glucose-6-phosphate and ADP (adenosine diphosphate).

Figure 24.10 Reaction of glucose and ATP to produce glucose-6-phosphate and ADP.

Nucleophilic substitution reactions fall into two categories, called S_N1 reactions and S_N2 reactions. (The numbers 1 and 2 refer to a specific aspect of the *kinetics* of the reactions [◄◄ Chapter 14].) The nucleophilic substitution that converts one enantiomer to a mixture of both is an S_N1 reaction. An S_N1 reaction begins when one of the groups bonded to a carbon "leaves," leaving behind a carbocation [Figure 24.9(b)]. The hybridization of the carbon atom changes from sp^3 to sp^2 when the carbocation forms.

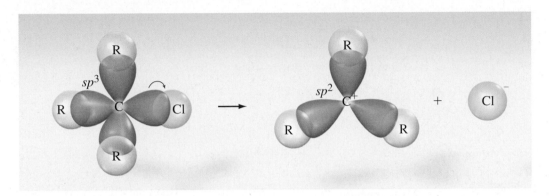

Commonly encountered "leaving groups" include Cl^-, Br^-, and I^-. A carbocation is an unstable species and, being positively charged, is prone to nucleophilic attack. Because the carbocation is *planar* about the carbon that bears the positive charge, it is equally likely that a nucleophile will attack from either side.

In the reaction of $(CH_3)_3CBr$ with H_2O, the product is the same regardless of whether the nucleophile (water) attacks from the front or from the back. When a molecule loses a leaving group from a chiral carbon, however, as would be the case with the thalidomide molecule, attack from one side of the carbocation will yield one enantiomer whereas attack from the other side will yield the other enantiomer. The result is a racemic mixture. The conversion of a single enantiomer to a racemic mixture of both enantiomers is called ***racemization.***

Nucleophilic attack on opposite sides of the carbocation leads to two different products, which are mirror images of each other.

Worked Examples 24.6 and 24.7 show how to draw mechanisms for addition and substitution reactions.

Worked Example 24.6

The electrophilic addition of water to a molecule containing a double bond, known as *hydration,* is a reaction that is important biologically. One example is the enzyme-catalyzed hydration of fumarate to form malate, one of the steps in the citric acid cycle (also known as the Krebs cycle).

Using curved arrows to indicate the movement of electrons, draw the mechanism for the electrophilic addition of water to fumarate to yield malate.

Strategy For electrophilic addition, draw Lewis structures with the electrophile close to the region of electron density where attack will occur.

Setup The electrophile is one of the H atoms in H_2O. The site of attack is the pi bond between the C atoms in fumarate:

Solution

Think About It

This time the product is the same regardless of which C atom forms the C—O bond and which forms the C—H bond, but this is not always the case. If CH_2CHCH_3 undergoes hydration, for instance, there are two possible products:

n-Propanol   2-Propanol

In this case, for reasons beyond the scope of this book, the product that forms is 2-propanol. If you take organic chemistry, you will learn what factors determine which C atom gets the —OH group and which gets the —H.

Practice Problem A Using curved arrows to indicate the movement of electrons, draw the mechanism for the electrophilic addition of HI to C_2H_4.

Practice Problem B In which of the following examples do the curved arrows correspond correctly to the proper movement of electrons in the mechanism of electrophilic addition?

Worked Example 24.7

Using curved arrows to indicate the movement of electrons, draw the mechanism for each of the following reactions: (a) nucleophilic addition of CN^- to CH_3CHO and (b) electrophilic substitution of benzene with $^+SO_3H$. (Draw all resonance structures for the carbocation intermediate.)

Strategy For nucleophilic addition, draw Lewis structures with the nucleophile close to the electron-poor atom where attack will occur (in this case, the carbonyl carbon). For electrophilic substitution, draw Lewis structures with the electrophile close to the site of attack on the benzene ring. Remember that nucleophiles are attracted to and react with electron-poor atoms whereas electrophiles are attracted to and react with electron-rich areas of the molecule. Using this information, and the octet rule, determine which electrons are likely to be involved in the reaction and indicate their repositioning with curved arrows.

Setup (a) The nucleophile is CN^-. The site of attack is the carbonyl C in CH_3CHO, which is electron-poor because it is bonded to the more electronegative O atom.

(b) The electrophile is $^+SO_3H$. The site of attack is the electron-rich, delocalized pi bonds of the benzene ring.

(Continued on next page)

Solution

(a)

(b)

Think About It

Additions such as the one in part (a) are carried out in acidic solution. The availability of protons in solution makes the final step the protonation of the negatively charged O atom:

Also, the C atoms in benzene are all equivalent, so the choice of which C will bear the substituent in part (b) is arbitrary. All the following represent the same product:

Practice Problem A Draw mechanisms for (a) nucleophilic addition of H^- to CH_3COCH_3 and (b) electrophilic substitution of benzene with Cl^+.

Practice Problem B Draw all the possible products that could result from the following electrophilic substitution reaction:

Figure 24.11 The highlighted atoms are those that constitute the eliminated water molecule.

Other Types of Organic Reactions

Other important organic reaction types are elimination, oxidation-reduction, and isomerization. An *elimination reaction* is one in which a double bond forms and a molecule such as water is removed. The dehydration of 2-phosphoglycerate to form phosphoenolpyruvate (Figure 24.11), one of the steps in carbohydrate metabolism, is an example of an elimination reaction.

Oxidation-reduction reactions, as we learned previously [◀◀ Section 9.4], involve the *loss* and *gain* of electrons, respectively. Determining which species have lost or gained electrons may seem less straightforward with organic reactions than with the inorganic reactions we have encountered, but the following guidelines can help you decide when an organic molecule has been oxidized or reduced:

1. When a molecule gains O or loses H, it is *oxidized.*
2. When a molecule loses O or gains H, it is *reduced.*

An important biological example of oxidation is the enzyme-catalyzed reaction by which ethanol is converted to acetaldehyde in the liver:

$$CH_3CH_2OH \longrightarrow CH_3CHO$$

The ethanol molecule loses two H atoms in this reaction, so it is *oxidized.*

Isomerization reactions are those in which one isomer is converted to another. The interconversion between the sugars aldose and ketose is an example:

Aldose   Ketose

Vision, our ability to perceive light, is the result of an isomerization reaction. Our eyes contain millions of cells called rods that are packed with *rhodopsin,* an 11-*cis*-retinal molecule

11-*cis*-retinal

bonded to a large protein. When visible light strikes rhodopsin, the retinal molecule isomerizes to the all-*trans* isomer:

All-*trans*-retinal

Student Annotation: Many of the organic reactions in living systems require *enzymes,* natural *catalysts,* in order to occur rapidly enough to be useful [◀◀ Chapter 14].

This isomerization causes such a significant change in the structure of retinal that it separates from the protein. These events trigger the electrical impulses that stimulate the optic nerve and result in the brain receiving the signals that we know as vision. The all-*trans*-retinal diffuses away from the protein and is converted back to 11-*cis*-retinal. The regenerated 11-*cis*-retinal can then rebind with the protein. Interestingly, the conversion of the all-*trans* isomer back to the 11-*cis* isomer, which is necessary for us to perceive light, is much slower than the light-induced conversion from *cis* to *trans*. This is why after looking at a bright light, you have a "blind spot" for a period of time.

SECTION 24.5 REVIEW

Organic Reactions

24.5.1　Identify each species as a nucleophile or an electrophile.

$$CH_3-\ddot{O}\colon^- \qquad H-\ddot{S}\colon^- \qquad H_3C-\overset{\overset{\displaystyle CH_3}{|}}{\underset{\underset{\displaystyle CH_3}{|}}{C}}{}^+$$

　　　(i)　　　　(ii)　　　　(iii)

24.5.2　Identify each reaction as addition, substitution, elimination, or isomerization.

(i) $H_2C=CHCH_2CH_2CH_3 + Br_2 \longrightarrow BrCH_2-\underset{\underset{\displaystyle Br}{|}}{C}HCH_2CH_2CH_3$

(ii) $CH_3Br + OH^- \longrightarrow CH_3OH + Br^-$

(iii) $\underset{H}{\overset{H_3C}{}}\!C\!=\!C\underset{CH_3}{\overset{H}{}} \longrightarrow \underset{H}{\overset{H_3C}{}}\!C\!=\!C\underset{H}{\overset{CH_3}{}}$

24.6 ORGANIC POLYMERS

Multi 24.3
Organic and biochemistry—natural and synthetic polymers

Polymers are molecular compounds, either natural or synthetic, that are made up of many *repeating units* called **monomers**. The physical properties of these so-called macromolecules differ greatly from those of small, ordinary molecules.

The development of polymer chemistry began in the 1920s with the investigation of the puzzling behavior of some materials including wood, gelatin, cotton, and rubber. For example, when rubber, with the known empirical formula of C_5H_8, was dissolved in an organic solvent, the solution displayed several properties, including a higher than expected viscosity, which suggested that the dissolved compound had a very high molar mass. Despite the experimental evidence, though, scientists at the time were not ready to accept the idea that such giant molecules could exist. Instead, they postulated that materials such as rubber consisted of aggregates of small molecular units, like C_5H_8 or $C_{10}H_{16}$, held together by intermolecular forces. This misconception persisted for a number of years, until Hermann Staudinger[1] clearly showed that these so-called aggregates were, in fact, enormously large molecules, each of which contained many thousands of atoms held together by covalent bonds.

Once the *structures* of these macromolecules were understood, the way was open for the synthesis of polymers, which now pervade almost every aspect of our daily lives. About 90 percent of today's chemists, including biochemists, work with polymers. In this section, we will discuss the reactions that result in polymer formation and some of the natural polymers that are important to biology.

---

[1]Hermann Staudinger (1881–1963), a German chemist, was one of the pioneers in polymer chemistry. Staudinger was awarded the Nobel Prize in Chemistry in 1953.

Addition Polymers

Addition polymers form when monomers such as ethylene join end to end to make polyethylene. Reactions of this type can be initiated by a *radical*—a species that contains an unpaired electron [◄◄ Section 6.6]. The mechanism of addition polymerization is as follows:

1. The radical, which is unstable because of its unpaired electron, attacks a carbon atom on an ethylene molecule. This is the *initiation* of the reaction.
2. This attack would result in the carbon atom in question having more than eight electrons around it. To keep the carbon atom from having too many electrons around it, the double bond breaks.
3. One of the electrons in the double bond, together with the electron from the radical, becomes a new bond between the ethylene molecule and the radical.
4. The other electron remains with the other carbon atom, generating a new radical species.
5. The new radical species, also unstable, attacks another ethylene molecule, causing the same sequence of events to happen again. The generation of a new, highly reactive radical species at each step is known as *propagation* of the reaction.
6. Each step lengthens the chain of carbon atoms and results in the formation of a new radical, continuing the propagation of the reaction. Reactions such as this are known as *chain* reactions. They continue until the system runs out of ethylene molecules or until the radical species encounters another radical species—resulting in *termination* of the reaction.

Initiation step

Propagation step

Termination step

Some familiar and important addition polymers are listed in Table 24.4.

Condensation Polymers

Reactions in which two or more molecules become connected with the elimination of a small molecule, often water, are called *condensation reactions* (Figure 24.12). *Condensation polymers* form when molecules with two different functional groups combine, with the elimination of a small molecule, often water. Many condensation polymers are *copolymers,* meaning that they are made up of two or more *different* monomers.

(a)

(b)

Figure 24.12 (a) Condensation reaction between an alcohol and a carboxylic acid to form an ester. (b) Condensation of two alcohol molecules in the presence of sulfuric acid to form an ether.

Name	Monomer unit	Structure	Uses
Polytetrafluoroethylene (Teflon)		$\left[\begin{array}{cc} F & F \\ C & \\ & C \\ F & F \end{array}\right]_n$	Nonstick coatings
Polyethylene		$\left[\begin{array}{cc} H & H \\ C & \\ & C \\ H & H \end{array}\right]_n$	Plastic bags, bottles, toys
Polypropylene		$\left[\begin{array}{cc} H & H \\ C & \\ & C \\ H & CH_3 \end{array}\right]_n$	Carpeting, bottles
Polyvinylchloride (PVC)		$\left[\begin{array}{cc} H & H \\ C & \\ & C \\ H & Cl \end{array}\right]_n$	Water pipes, garden hoses, plastic wrap
Polystyrene			Packing material, insulation, furniture

TABLE 24.4   Addition Polymers

The first synthetic fiber, nylon 66, is a condensation copolymer of two molecules: one with carboxy groups at each end (adipic acid) and one with amine groups at both ends (hexamethylenediamine):

$$H_2N-(CH_2)_6-NH_2 \quad + \quad HOOC-(CH_2)_4-COOH$$

Hexamethylenediamine   Adipic acid

↓ Condensation

$$H_2N-(CH_2)_6-N-\overset{O}{\underset{H}{C}}-(CH_2)_4-COOH \quad + \quad H_2O$$

↓ Further condensation reactions

$$-(CH_2)_4-\overset{O}{C}-N-(CH_2)_6-N-\overset{O}{C}-(CH_2)_4-\overset{O}{C}-N-(CH_2)_6-$$

Nylon was first made by Wallace Carothers[2] at DuPont in 1931. The versatility of nylons is so great that the annual production of nylons and related substances now amounts to several billion pounds.

[2]Wallace H. Carothers (1896–1937) was an American chemist. Besides its enormous commercial success, Carothers's work on nylon is ranked with that of Staudinger in clearly elucidating macromolecular structure and properties. Depressed by the death of his sister and wrongly believing that his life's work had been a failure, Carothers committed suicide at the age of 41.

Figure 24.13 Formation of a peptide bond with elimination of water.

Peptide bond
(amide linkage)

Biological Polymers

Naturally occurring polymers include *proteins, polysaccharides,* and *nucleic acids.*

   Proteins, polymers of amino acids, play an important role in nearly all biological processes. The human body contains an estimated 100,000 different kinds of proteins, each of which has a specific physiological function. An amino acid has both the carboxylic acid functional group and the amino functional group. Amino acids are joined together into chains when a condensation reaction occurs between a carboxy group on one molecule and an amino group on another molecule (Figure 24.13).

   The bonds that form between amino acids are called ***peptide bonds.*** Very long chains of amino acids assembled in this way are called *proteins,* while shorter chains are called ***polypeptides.***

   Amino acids consist of a central carbon atom bonded to four different groups: an amino group, a carboxy group, a hydrogen atom, and an additional group (highlighted in Figure 24.14) consisting of carbon, hydrogen, and sometimes other elements such as nitrogen or sulfur. Proteins are made essentially from the 20 different amino acids shown in Figure 24.14. The identity of a protein depends on which of the 20 amino acids it contains and on the order in which the amino acids are assembled.

   Polysaccharides are polymers of sugars such as glucose and fructose. Starch and cellulose are two polymers of glucose with slightly different linkages—and very different properties. In starch, glucose molecules are connected by what biochemists call α linkages. This enables animals, including humans, to digest the starch in such foods as corn, wheat, potatoes, and rice.

> **Student Annotation:** Peptide bonds are also called *amide bonds* or *amide linkages* because they contain the amide functional group.

Starch

In cellulose, the glucose molecules are connected by β linkages. Digestion of cellulose requires enzymes that most animals do not have. Species that *do* digest cellulose, such as termites and ruminants (including cattle, sheep, and llamas), do so with the help of enzyme-producing symbiotic bacteria in the gut.

Cellulose

   Nucleic acids, which are polymers of *nucleotides,* play an important role in protein synthesis. There are two types of nucleic acids: ***deoxyribonucleic acid (DNA)*** and ***ribonucleic acid (RNA).*** Each ***nucleotide*** in a nucleic acid consists of a purine or pyrimidine *base,* a furanose sugar (*deoxyribose* for DNA; *ribose* for RNA), and a phosphate group. Figure 24.15 (page 1000) shows the building blocks of DNA and RNA. The components of a nucleotide are linked together as shown in Figure 24.16 (page 1000). These molecules are among the largest known—they can have molar masses of up to tens of billions of grams. RNA molecules, on the other hand, typically have molar masses on the order of tens of thousands of grams. Despite their sizes, the composition of nucleic acids is relatively simple compared with proteins. Proteins consist of up to 20 different amino acids, whereas DNA and RNA consist of only four different nucleotides each.

Multi 24.4
Organic and biochemistry—molecular structure in DNA

Figure 24.14 The 20 amino acids essential to living organisms. The shaded area represents the R group.

Name	Abbreviation	Structure
Alanine	Ala	
Arginine	Arg	
Asparagine	Asn	
Aspartic acid	Asp	
Cysteine	Cys	
Glutamic acid	Glu	
Glutamine	Gln	
Glycine	Gly	
Histidine	His	
Isoleucine	Ile	

Name	Abbreviation	Structure
Leucine	Leu	H_3C–CH–CH$_2$–C(H)(NH$_3^+$)–COO$^-$; H_3C
Lysine	Lys	H_2N–CH$_2$–CH$_2$–CH$_2$–CH$_2$–C(H)(NH$_3^+$)–COO$^-$
Methionine	Met	H_3C–S–CH$_2$–CH$_2$–C(H)(NH$_3^+$)–COO$^-$
Phenylalanine	Phe	C$_6$H$_5$–CH$_2$–C(H)(NH$_3^+$)–COO$^-$
Proline	Pro	H_2N^+—C(H)—COO$^-$; H_2C, CH$_2$, CH$_2$ ring
Serine	Ser	HO–CH$_2$–C(H)(NH$_3^+$)–COO$^-$
Threonine	Thr	H_3C–C(OH)(H)–C(H)(NH$_3^+$)–COO$^-$
Tryptophan	Trp	indole–C–CH$_2$–C(H)(NH$_3^+$)–COO$^-$
Tyrosine	Tyr	HO–C$_6$H$_4$–CH$_2$–C(H)(NH$_3^+$)–COO$^-$
Valine	Val	H_3C–CH–C(H)(NH$_3^+$)–COO$^-$; H_3C

Found only in DNA	Found in both DNA and RNA	Found only in RNA
Purines	Adenine Guanine	
Pyrimidines Thymine	Cytosine	Uracil
Sugars Deoxyribose		Ribose
Phosphate	Phosphate	

Figure 24.15 The components of the nucleic acids DNA and RNA.

Adenine unit

Phosphate unit

Deoxyribose unit

Figure 24.16 Structure of a nucleotide, one of the repeating units in DNA.

Learning Outcomes

- Give in your own words a workable definition of organic chemistry and provide examples of organic and inorganic compounds.
- Describe the significance of Friedrich Wöhler's experiment to contemporary understanding of organic chemistry.
- List characteristics of carbon that allow it to form so many different compounds.
- Classify and name organic compounds based upon carbon number, structural characteristics, functional group, and constituents.
- Construct molecular formulas, structural formulas, and skeletal structures of organic compounds.
- Define resonance.

- Produce all of the resonance structures of a given organic compound.
- Define, identify, and provide examples of the various types of isomers including: constitutional, stereo, geometrical, and optical isomers.
- Produce all of the isomers of a given compound.
- Define chiral and identify chiral carbons in a given structure.
- Differentiate between nucleophiles and electrophiles.
- Describe a carbocation.
- Categorize organic reactions as addition, substitution (S_N1 or S_N2), elimination, hydration, oxidation-reduction, or isomerization.
- Produce the mechanism of a simple organic reaction.

Chapter Summary

SECTION 24.1

- Organic chemistry is the study of carbon-based substances. Although it was once thought that organic compounds could only be produced by nature, thousands of new organic compounds are now synthesized each year by scientists.
- Carbon's position in the periodic table makes it uniquely able to form long, stable chains—a process called *catenation.*
- *Aromatic* compounds contain one or more benzene rings. *Aliphatic* compounds are organic compounds that do not contain benzene rings.

SECTION 24.2

- *Alkyl groups* consist of just carbon and hydrogen. They are derived from the corresponding alkane by removing one hydrogen atom and are represented generically in the formulas of organic compounds with the letter R.
- Functional groups are specific arrangements of atoms that are responsible for the properties and reactivity of organic compounds. Common functional groups and their formulas include

Alcohol	ROH
Carboxylic acid	RCOOH
Aldehyde	RCHO
Ketone	RCOR′
Ester	RCOOR′
Amine	RNH_2, RNHR′, or RNR′R″
Amide	$RCONH_2$, RCONHR′, or RCONR′R″

- Many organic compounds contain more than one functional group. A *substituent* in an alkane is a group other than hydrogen that is bonded to the carbon chain.
- An *amino acid* contains both the carboxy group and the amino group.

SECTION 24.3

- *Condensed structural formulas* or *condensed structures* abbreviate a series of repeating units, such as $-CH_2CH_2CH_2CH_2-$, into a more compact form, such as $(CH_2)_4$. *Kekulé structures* are similar to Lewis structures but do not show the lone pairs on a molecule. *Skeletal structures* use straight lines to represent C—C bonds. They typically do not show the C atoms explicitly except for the purpose of emphasizing a particular functional group. H atoms are not shown in skeletal structures—again, except to emphasize a functional group. The number of H atoms bonded to a C atom must be inferred from the number of C—C bonds in the structure. *Heteroatoms,* atoms other than C and H, are always shown explicitly in a skeletal structure.

SECTION 24.4

- *Constitutional isomers* are molecules in which the same atoms are connected differently. *Stereoisomers* are molecules in which the same atoms are connected by the same bonds but the bonds are oriented differently. *Geometrical isomers* arise due to restricted rotation about a carbon-carbon double bond. *Cis* and *trans* isomers are geometrical isomers.
- Molecules that are nonsuperimposable mirror images of each other are *optical isomers.* They are also referred to as *chiral,* and each of the mirror images is called an *enantiomer.* Optical isomers are so called because they rotate the plane of plane-polarized light. The degree of rotation is the same for both enantiomers, but the directions of rotation are opposite each other. An equal mixture of both enantiomers is called a *racemic mixture.* A racemic mixture does not rotate the plane of plane-polarized light.

SECTION 24.5

- An *electrophile* generally is a positively charged ion that is attracted to electrons. A *nucleophile* is a negatively charged ion or a partially negatively charged atom in a polar molecule. Nucleophiles and electrophiles are attracted to each other.
- A *carbocation* is an intermediate species in which one of the carbon atoms is surrounded by only six electrons and bears a positive charge.
- *Electrophilic addition* reactions and *nucleophilic addition* reactions involve the addition of a molecule or an ion to another molecule.
- *Substitution reactions* occur when an electrophile replaces a hydrogen on an aromatic ring or when a nucleophile replaces a leaving group on a carbon atom.
- Carbocations are the intermediate species in *racemization,* a nucleophilic substitution reaction in which a single enantiomer is converted into a racemic mixture.
- *Hydration* is the addition of a water molecule across a double bond.
- An *elimination reaction* is one in which a double bond forms and a small molecule, such as water, is eliminated.
- *Isomerization reactions* convert one isomer into another.

SECTION 24.6

- *Polymers* are long chains of repeating molecular units called *monomers. Polysaccharides* are polymers of sugars. *Addition polymers* form when a radical species attacks a double bond, forming a new, longer radical species that attacks another double bond, and so on.
- An elimination reaction that joins two molecules is a *condensation reaction. Condensation polymers* form when molecules with two different functional groups undergo a condensation reaction.
- *Copolymers* are polymers that contain more than one type of monomer.
- *Proteins* and *polypeptides* are biological polymers in which the monomers are amino acids. Amino acids are joined by *peptide bonds,* which result from the condensation reaction between the amino group of one amino acid and the carboxyl group of another amino acid.
- *Nucleic acids* are polymers of *nucleotides.* The two types of nucleic acid are *deoxyribonucleic acid (DNA)* and *ribonucleic acid (RNA).* Each nucleotide in a nucleic acid consists of a purine or pyrimidine base, a furanose sugar (deoxyribose for DNA; ribose for RNA), and a phosphate group linked together.

Key Words

Addition polymer, 995	Condensation polymer, 995	Geometrical isomer, 980	Polypeptide, 997
Alcohol, 963	Condensation reaction, 995	Heteroatom, 975	Polysaccharides, 997
Aldehyde, 963	Condensed structural	Hydration, 990	Protein, 997
Aliphatic, 962	formula, 974	Isomerization reaction, 993	Racemic mixture, 982
Alkyl group, 963	Condensed structure, 974	Kekulé structure, 974	Racemization, 989
Amide, 963	Constitutional isomerism, 980	Ketone, 963	Ribonucleic acid (RNA), 997
Amine, 963	Copolymer, 995	Monomer, 994	Skeletal structure, 974
Amino acid, 970	Deoxyribonucleic acid	Nucleic acid, 997	Stereoisomers, 980
Aromatic, 962	(DNA), 997	Nucleophile, 984	Substituent, 968
Carbocation, 985	Electrophile, 984	Nucleophilic addition, 986	Substitution reaction, 987
Carboxylic acid, 963	Electrophilic addition, 986	Nucleotide, 997	*Trans,* 980
Catenation, 962	Elimination reaction, 993	Optical isomers, 981	
Chiral, 981	Enantiomer, 981	Peptide bond, 997	
Cis, 980	Ester, 963	Polymer, 994	

Questions and Problems

SECTION 24.1:   WHY CARBON IS DIFFERENT

Review Questions

24.1   Explain why carbon is able to form so many more compounds than any other element.

24.2   Why was Wöhler's synthesis of urea so important for the development of organic chemistry?

24.3   What are aromatic organic compounds? What are aliphatic organic compounds?

SECTION 24.2:   CLASSES OF ORGANIC COMPOUNDS

Review Questions

24.4   What are functional groups? Why is it logical and useful to classify organic compounds according to their functional groups?

24.5   Draw the Lewis structure for each of the following functional groups: alcohol, aldehyde, ketone, carboxylic acid, amine.

24.6 Name the classes to which the following compounds belong:
(a) C_4H_9OH
(b) C_2H_5CHO
(c) C_6H_5COOH
(d) CH_3NH_2

Problems

24.7 Classify each of the following molecules as alcohol, aldehyde, ketone, carboxylic acid, or amine:
(a) $CH_3—CH_2—NH_2$

(b) $CH_3—CH_2—\overset{\displaystyle O}{\underset{\displaystyle H}{C}}$

(c) $CH_3—\overset{\displaystyle }{\underset{\displaystyle \underset{O}{\|}}{C}}—CH_2—CH_3$

(d) $H—\overset{\displaystyle \overset{O}{\|}}{C}—OH$

(e) $CH_3—CH_2CH_2—OH$

24.8 Draw structures for molecules with the following formulas:
(a) CH_4O
(b) C_2H_6O
(c) $C_3H_6O_2$
(d) C_3H_8O

24.9 Name each of the following compounds:

(a)

(b) $\underset{\underset{\displaystyle CH_3}{|}}{CH_3}\overset{\overset{\displaystyle CH_3}{|}}{C}CH_2CH_2CH_2\overset{\overset{\displaystyle OH}{|}}{C}HCH_3$

(c) $Cl\overset{\displaystyle }{\underset{\displaystyle \underset{CH_2CH_3}{|}}{C}}HCH_2CH_2\overset{\displaystyle \overset{O}{\|}}{C}H$

24.10 Name each of the following compounds:
(a)

(b)

(c)

24.11 Give the name of the alkane represented by the model shown.

24.12 The molecular formula corresponding to the model is $C_5H_9ClO_2$. What is the name of the compound?

24.13 Write structural formulas for each of the following based on their systematic names. The names quoted in parentheses are so-called common names. Common names are not systematic and are more difficult, sometimes impossible, to connect with a unique structure.
(a) 2,2,4-trimethylpentane ("isooctane")
(b) 3-methyl-1-butanol ("isoamyl alcohol")
(c) hexanamide ("caproamide")
(d) 2,2,2-trichloroethanal ("chloral")

24.14 Write structural formulas for each of the following:
(a) 3,3-dimethyl-2-butanone ("pinacolone")
(b) 3-hydroxybutanal ("acetaldol")
(c) ethyl pentanoate ("ethyl valerate")
(d) 6-methyl-2-heptanamine ("isooctylamine")

24.15 Classify the oxygen-containing groups in the plant hormone abscisic acid.

24.16 Identify the functional groups in the antipsychotic drug haloperidol.

24.17 PABA was the active UV-absorbing compound in earlier versions of sunblock creams. What functional groups are present in PABA?

24.18 Lidocaine ($C_{14}H_{22}N_2O$) is a widely used local anesthetic. Classify its nitrogen-containing functional groups.

SECTION 24.3: REPRESENTING ORGANIC MOLECULES

Problems

24.19 Write structural formulas for the following organic compounds: (a) 3-methylhexane, (b) 2,3-dimethylpentane, (c) 2-bromo-4-phenylpentane, (d) 3,4,5-trimethyloctane.

24.20 Write structural formulas for the following compounds: (a) 1,1,3-trichloro-2-propanol, (b) 3-methyl-3-pentanamine, (c) 3-bromo-1-chloro-2-butanone, (d) propyl-4-bromobutanoate.

24.21 (a) Convert $CH_3(CH_2)_4C(O)CH_2CO_2H$ to a Kekulé structure and to a skeletal (line) structure.
(b) Convert the following to a condensed structure and to a skeletal (line) structure:

$$CH_3CH_2CHCH_2COCCH_3$$

with O (double bond) above the second C from right, CH₃ above; CH₃CH₂ below the CHCH₂ carbon; CH₃ below.

(c) Convert the following to a condensed structure and to a Kekulé structure:

24.22 (a) Convert $(CH_3)_2C=CHCO_2H$ to a Kekulé structure and to a skeletal (line) structure.
(b) Convert the following to a condensed structure and to a skeletal (line) structure:

$$CH_3CH_2NCH_2CH_3$$
$$\hspace{1.2em}|$$
$$\hspace{1.2em}CH_3$$

(c) Convert the skeletal structure of the general anesthetic isoflurane to a condensed structure and to a Kekulé structure:

24.23 Convert each of the molecular models to a condensed structural formula, a Kekulé structure, and a skeletal (line) structure.

(a) C_3H_7NO: DMF, a widely used organic solvent.

(b) $C_6H_8O_7$: Citric acid, which contributes to the tart taste of citrus fruits.

(c) $C_6H_8O_6$: Commonly known as "isoamyl acetate," this ester is largely responsible for the characteristic odor of bananas.

24.24 Convert each of the molecular models to a condensed structural formula, a Kekulé structure, and a skeletal (line) structure.

(a) $C_3H_6O_3$: Dihydroxyacetone, an intermediate in glycolysis, the process by which glucose is converted to energy.

(b) C_4H_5Cl: Chloroprene, which gives neoprene on polymerization.

(c) $C_6H_{13}NO_2$: Isoleucine, one of the 20 amino acids that occur in proteins.

24.25 Given a structural formula or skeletal (line) structure, rewrite it in the other style.

(a) $CH_3CH_2CHCH_2CH_2CH_2CH_3$
$$\hspace{3em}|$$
$$\hspace{3em}OH$$

(b) skeletal structure with Br and H labels and C=O

(c) skeletal ring structure with CH(CH₃)₂, H₂C, H₂C, O, and C=O

24.26 Given a structural formula or skeletal (line) structure, rewrite it in the other style.
(a) $ClCH_2CH_2CH_2CH=CH_2$

(b) skeletal structure with N and H

(c) skeletal structure with two C=O and O

24.27 Using the curved arrows as a guide to placing the electrons, write a resonance structure for each of the compounds shown. The resonance structure should include formal charges where appropriate.

(a) $CH_3-C≡N:$

(b)
$$CH_3$$
$$\hspace{1em}|$$
$$:\ddot{O}\overset{+}{}C-CH_3$$
$$\hspace{1em}|$$
$$\hspace{1em}H$$

(c)
$$CH_3$$
$$\hspace{1em}|$$
$$^-:\ddot{O}-C-CH_2$$

24.28 Using the curved arrows as a guide to placing the electrons, write a resonance structure for each of the compounds shown. The resonance structure should include formal charges where appropriate.

(a)

(b)

(c)

24.29 Use curved arrows to show how the resonance structure on the left can be transformed to the one on the right.

(a)

(b)

(c)

24.30 Use curved arrows to show how the resonance structure on the left can be transformed to the one on the right.

(a)

(b)

(c)

SECTION 24.4: ISOMERISM

Review Questions

24.31 Alkenes exhibit geometrical isomerism because rotation about the C=C bond is restricted. Explain.

24.32 Why is it that alkanes and alkynes, unlike alkenes, have no geometrical isomers?

24.33 Define the term *chiral*. What are enantiomers?

24.34 What factor determines whether a carbon atom in a compound is chiral?

24.35 Fill in the blanks in the given paragraph with the most appropriate term from the following: chiral, *cis,* constitutional isomers, enantiomers, resonance structures, stereoisomers, *trans.*

Isomers are different compounds that have the *same molecular formula.* Isomers that have their atoms connected in a different order (branched versus unbranched chain, for example) or a different sequence of bond types (C=CCC versus CC=CC, for example) are termed _____. Isomers with the same order of connections and sequence of bond types, but which differ in the spatial arrangement of the atoms are called _____. This is often seen in compounds where substituents may be on the same or opposite sides of a carbon-carbon double bond. Substituents on the same side are described as _____; those on opposite sides are _____. A different kind of isomerism characterizes a _____ molecule, that is, a molecule with a structure that allows for two nonsuperimposable mirror-image forms. Two nonsuperimposable mirror images are _____ of the other.

Problems

24.36 Write structural formulas for all the C_5H_{10} alkenes, and identify the relationship (constitutional isomer or stereoisomer) of each one to the others. Are any chiral?

24.37 Draw all possible structural isomers for the following alkane: C_7H_{16}.

24.38 Draw all possible isomers for the molecule C_4H_8.

24.39 Draw all possible isomers for the molecule C_3H_5Br.

24.40 Which of the following amino acids are chiral: (a) $CH_3CH(NH_2)COOH$, (b) $CH_2(NH_2)COOH$, (c) $CH_2(OH)CH(NH_2)COOH$?

24.41 Draw all the possible structural isomers for the molecule having the formula C_7H_7Cl. All isomers contain one benzene ring.

24.42 Draw all the structural isomers of compounds with the formula $C_4H_8Cl_2$. Indicate which isomers are chiral, and give them systematic names.

24.43 Indicate the asymmetric carbon atoms in the following compounds:

(a)

(b)

24.44 Suppose benzene contained three distinct single bonds and three distinct double bonds. How many different isomers would there be for dichlorobenzene ($C_6H_4Cl_2$)? Draw all your proposed structures.

24.45 Write the structural formula of an aldehyde that is a structural isomer of acetone.

24.46 How many asymmetric carbon atoms are present in each of the following compounds?

(a)
$$\text{H}-\overset{\overset{\displaystyle H}{|}}{\text{C}}-\overset{\overset{\displaystyle H}{|}}{\underset{\underset{\displaystyle Cl}{|}}{\text{C}}}-\overset{\overset{\displaystyle H}{|}}{\underset{\underset{\displaystyle H}{|}}{\text{C}}}-\text{Cl}$$

(b)
$$\text{H}_3\text{C}-\overset{\overset{\displaystyle OH}{|}}{\underset{\underset{\displaystyle H}{|}}{\text{C}}}-\overset{\overset{\displaystyle CH_3}{|}}{\underset{\underset{\displaystyle H}{|}}{\text{C}}}-\text{CH}_2\text{OH}$$

(c)

24.47 Draw structures of each of the compounds shown, using wedges and dashes to show stereochemistry.

(a) (C_4H_9Br)

(b) ($C_3H_7NO_3$)

(c) ($C_6H_{14}O$)

(d) ($C_4H_7BrO_2$)

24.48 Write the structural formulas of the alcohols with the formula $C_6H_{14}O$ and indicate those that are chiral. Show only the C atoms and the −OH groups.

SECTION 24.5:   ORGANIC REACTIONS

Review Questions

24.49 What property distinguishes an electrophile from a nucleophile? Of the two, which would you expect to be more reactive toward a cation? Toward an anion? Give a specific example of an electrophile and a nucleophile.

24.50 Classify each of the following according to whether you think it reacts as an electrophile or a nucleophile.

(a)
$$\text{CH}_3-\overset{\overset{\displaystyle CH_3}{|}}{\underset{\underset{\displaystyle CH_3}{|}}{\text{C}}}-\ddot{\text{O}}\text{:}^-$$

(b) $\text{CH}_3\text{CH}_2\ddot{\text{N}}\text{H}_2$

(c)
$$\underset{\text{H}_3\text{C}}{\overset{\overset{\displaystyle CH_3}{|}}{\text{C}^+}}{}^{\diagdown}\text{CH}_3$$

(d) $\text{CH}_3-\text{C}\equiv\overset{+}{\text{O}}\text{:}$

24.51 (a) The compound 2-bromopropane [$(CH_3)_2CHBr$] can undergo both substitution and elimination when treated with $CH_3CH_2O^-$, which is a strong base. Predict the organic product in each case, and write a separate chemical equation for each reaction.

(b) The compound 1,2-dibromoethane ($BrCH_2CH_2Br$) was formerly used in large amounts as an agricultural chemical. Write a chemical equation showing how this compound could be prepared from ethylene by an addition reaction.

(c) Certain reactions of aldehydes and ketones begin with isomerization of the aldehyde or ketone to an *enol* isomer. Enols contain an −OH group attached to a carbon-carbon double bond. Write a chemical equation for the isomerization of acetone [$(CH_3)_2C=O$] to its enol isomer.

24.52 Classify the following reactions according to whether they are addition, substitution, elimination, or isomerization.

(a)
$$\text{(structure)} \xrightarrow{\text{Enzyme}} \text{(structure)}$$

(b) $\text{CH}_3\text{CH}=\text{CH}_2 + \text{Cl}_2 \xrightarrow{\text{heat}} \text{ClCH}_2\text{CH}=\text{CH}_2 + \text{HCl}$

(c) $\text{CH}_3\text{CH}=\text{CH}_2 + \text{Cl}_2 \longrightarrow \text{CH}_3\overset{\overset{\displaystyle }{}}{\underset{\underset{\displaystyle Cl}{|}}{\text{C}}}\text{HCH}_2\text{Cl}$

(d) $\text{CH}_3\underset{\underset{\displaystyle Cl}{|}}{\text{C}}\text{HCH}_2\text{Cl} + \text{NaSH} \longrightarrow \text{CH}_3\underset{\underset{\displaystyle Cl}{|}}{\text{C}}\text{HCH}_2\text{SH} + \text{NaCl}$

(e) $\text{(cyclohexanone)}=\text{O} + \text{H}-\text{C}\equiv\text{N} \longrightarrow \text{(structure with OH and C}\equiv\text{N)}$

(f) $\text{(cyclohexane with OH and C}\equiv\text{N)} \xrightarrow[\text{heat}]{\text{H}_2\text{SO}_4} \text{(cyclohexene)}-\text{C}\equiv\text{N} + \text{H}_2\text{O}$

24.53 (a) Define *carbocation*.

(b) Which of the following are carbocations?

$$\text{CH}_3\text{CH}_2-\overset{+}{\underset{\underset{\displaystyle H}{|}}{\overset{\overset{\displaystyle H}{\diagup}}{\text{O}}}}\text{:} \qquad \text{CH}_3-\overset{+}{\ddot{\text{O}}}-\text{CH}_2 \qquad \text{H}_2\overset{+}{\text{C}}-\text{CH}=\text{CH}_2$$

(i)   (ii)   (iii)

$$\text{CH}_3\text{CH}_2\overset{+}{\text{CH}}_2 \qquad \text{CH}_3-\overset{\overset{\displaystyle CH_3}{|}}{\underset{\underset{\displaystyle CH_3}{|}}{\overset{+}{\text{N}}}}-\text{CH}_3$$

(iv)   (v)

Problems

24.54 Halogenated hydrocarbons are biodegraded in the natural environment by reactions catalyzed by dehalogenase enzymes. The reaction that takes place with 1,2-dichloroethane begins with nucleophilic substitution involving a carboxylate site of the enzyme.

Expand this equation by adding curved arrows to show the movement of electrons.

24.55 A common reaction in carbohydrate biochemistry is the conversion of an aldose to a ketose. The glucose to fructose isomerization is a specific example; the equation illustrates the general case:

The first stage in the reaction is shown in the following equation. Enzymes facilitate the reaction, but for simplicity the overall change can be approximated with water molecules. Use curved arrows to show the flow of electrons in the equation.

24.56 (a) Benzene reacts with *tert*-butyl cation [(CH₃)₃C⁺] by a two-step electrophilic aromatic substitution mechanism to yield *tert*-butylbenzene [C₆H₅C(CH₃)₃]. Write a chemical equation for each step in the mechanism and use curved arrows to track electron flow.
(b) Electrophilic addition of hydrogen chloride to styrene gives the product shown. Write the mechanism for this reaction including curved arrows.

24.57 (a) Acetylide ion undergoes nucleophilic addition to aldehydes and ketones to give the species shown. Subsequent addition of water yields an acetylenic alcohol. Add curved arrows to the equations to show how the reaction occurs.

(b) A nucleophilic site on a molecule can substitute for a halogen elsewhere in the same molecule to form a ring. Use curved arrows to show how the following *cyclization* is related to a conventional nucleophilic substitution.

24.58 Complete the following reaction by including essential unshared electron pairs and formal charges. Use curved arrows to show electron flow.

24.59 The product of the reaction of chlorobenzene with NaNH₂ is a very reactive species called *benzyne*. Add necessary electron pairs and formal charges to the net ionic equation, and use curved arrows to show how benzyne is formed. To what general type of reaction does this belong?

24.60 Consider the following reactions of butanal:

In which reaction is butanal oxidized? In which reaction is it reduced?

24.61 Esters can be prepared by the acid-catalyzed condensation of a carboxylic acid and an alcohol:

Is this an oxidation-reduction reaction? If so, identify the species being oxidized and the species being reduced.

24.62 A compound has the empirical formula C₅H₁₂O. Upon controlled oxidation, it is converted into a compound of empirical formula C₅H₁₀O, which behaves as a ketone. Draw possible structures for the original compound and the final compound.

24.63 Isopropanol is prepared by reacting propylene (CH₃CHCH₂) with sulfuric acid, followed by treatment with water. (a) Show the sequence of steps leading to the product. What is the role of sulfuric acid? (b) Draw the structure of an alcohol that is an isomer of isopropanol. (c) Is isopropanol a chiral molecule?

24.64   From the structures given in the box on page 984, identify the functional groups in thalidomide.

24.65   Write molecular formulas for thalidomide, lenalidomide, and CC-4047.

SECTION 24.6:   ORGANIC POLYMERS

Review Questions

24.66   Define the following terms: *monomer, polymer, copolymer.*

24.67   Name 10 objects that contain synthetic organic polymers.

24.68   Calculate the molar mass of a particular polyethylene sample, $+CH_2-CH_2\frac{}{}_n$, where $n = 4600$.

24.69   Describe the two major mechanisms of organic polymer synthesis.

24.70   What are the steps involved in polymer formation by chain reaction?

24.71   Polysaccharides, proteins, and nucleic acids comprise the three main classes of biopolymers. Compare and contrast them with respect to structure and function. What are the building block units for each? What are the key functional groups involved in linking the units together? In which biopolymer is there the greatest variety of building block structure? In which is there the least?

Problems

24.72   Teflon is formed by a radical addition reaction involving the monomer tetrafluoroethylene. Show the mechanism for this reaction.

24.73   Vinyl chloride ($H_2C=CHCl$), undergoes copolymerization with 1,1-dichloroethylene, ($H_2C=CCl_2$), to form a polymer commercially known as Saran. Draw the structure of the polymer, showing the repeating monomer units.

24.74   Deduce plausible monomers for polymers with the following repeating units:
(a) $+CH_2-CF_2\frac{}{}_n$

(b) $\left[-CO-\bigcirc-CONH-\bigcirc-NH-\right]_n$

24.75   Deduce plausible monomers for polymers with the following repeating units:
(a) $+CH_2-CH=CH-CH_2\frac{}{}_n$
(b) $+CO+CH_2\frac{}{}_6NH\frac{}{}_n$

24.76   Draw the structures of the dipeptides that can be formed from the reaction between the amino acids glycine and alanine.

24.77   Draw the structures of the dipeptides that can be formed from the reaction between the amino acids glycine and lysine.

24.78   From among the given nucleotides, identify those that occur naturally in RNA and those that occur in DNA. Do any not occur in either RNA or DNA?

(a)

(b)

(c)

(d)

ADDITIONAL PROBLEMS

24.79   Write structural formulas for all the constitutionally isomeric C_4H_9 alkyl groups. Check your answers with Table 24.1, and note the names of these groups.

24.80   *Ethers* are compounds (excluding esters) that contain the C—O—C functional group. An acceptable way to name them is to list the two groups attached to oxygen in alphabetical order as separate words, followed by the word *ether*. If the two groups are the same, add the prefix *di* to the name of the alkyl group. Thus, $CH_3OCH_2CH_3$ is "ethyl methyl ether" and $CH_3CH_2OCH_2CH_3$ is "diethyl ether."

Write structural formulas and provide names for all the constitutionally isomeric ethers in which only the C_4H_9 alkyl groups from Problem 24.79 are attached to oxygen. Which of these ethers is potentially chiral?

24.81   The α-amino acids found in proteins are based on the structural formula:

$$\begin{array}{c} RCHCO_2H \\ | \\ NH_2 \end{array}$$

From the C_4H_9 alkyl groups in Problem 24.79, find the ones that correspond to "R" among the amino acids listed in Figure 24.14. Match the name of the amino acid with the name of the group.

24.82 *Alkynes* are hydrocarbons that contain a carbon-carbon triple bond.

(a) Write structural formulas for all the isomeric alkynes of molecular formula C_5H_8.

(b) Are any of the alkynes chiral?

(c) Are any of the alkynes stereoisomeric?

24.83 Among the many alkenes of molecular formula C_6H_{12}, only one is chiral.

(a) Write a structural formula for this alkene.

(b) Place substituents on the tetrahedral carbons so as to represent the two enantiomers of this alkene.

24.84 (a) Use VSEPR to predict the geometry at the carbon shown in bold in the carbocation, radical, and anion derived from the *tert*-butyl group. Is the arrangement of bonds to this carbon linear, tetrahedral, trigonal planar, or trigonal pyramidal?

$^+C(CH_3)_3$	$\cdot C(CH_3)_3$	$:\bar{C}(CH_3)_3$
tert-Butyl	Cation	Radical	Anion

(b) Which of these species is the most nucleophilic? Which is the most electrophilic?

(c) Predict which species reacts with water to give $HC(CH_3)_3$.

(d) Write a chemical equation for the reaction in part (c), and use curved arrows to show the flow of electrons.

24.85 In each of the following pairs, specify whether the two structural formulas represent constitutional isomers, *cis,trans*-stereoisomers, enantiomers, resonance structures, or are simply a different representation of the same structure.

(a) and

(b) and

(c) and

(d) and

24.86 In each of the following pairs, specify whether the two structural formulas represent constitutional isomers, *cis,trans*-stereoisomers, enantiomers, resonance structures, or are simply a different representation of the same structure.

(a) HÖ⋯ ÖH and HÖ⋯ ÖH
$H_2N: H$ $H :NH_2$

(b) and

(c) and

(d) and

24.87 The electrophile in the following aromatic substitution is $(CH_3)_2CH^+$, and the mechanism involves the intermediate shown. Write two other resonance structures for this intermediate.

24.88 Two isomeric alkenes are formed in the dehydration of 2-methyl-2-butanol. What are these two alkenes? Are they constitutional isomers or stereoisomers?

24.89 Electrophilic addition of HCl to *cis*-2-butene gave 2-chlorobutane, which was determined *not* to be optically active when examined with a polarimeter.

Which of the following is the better explanation for the lack of optical activity in the 2-chlorobutane formed in this reaction?

(a) 2-Chlorobutane is not chiral.

(b) Two enantiomers of 2-chlorobutane were formed in equal amounts.

24.90 Reactions such as the following have been used in carbohydrate synthesis since the nineteenth century.

Classify this procedure according to reaction type.
(a) electrophilic addition
(b) electrophilic substitution
(c) nucleophilic addition
(d) nucleophilic substitution

24.91 Excluding compounds that have rings, there are three hydrocarbons that have the molecular formula C_4H_6. Write their structural formulas, and specify the hybridization of each carbon in these isomers.

24.92 Give the structures of the two tertiary amines that are isomers of $CH_3CH_2CH_2CH_2CH_2NH_2$.

24.93 In which class of compounds, esters or amides, do you think electron donation into the carbonyl group is more pronounced? Explain.

Ester   Amide

24.94 (a) A plane of symmetry in a molecule is a plane passing through the middle of the molecule that bisects the molecule into two mirror-image halves. If a molecule has a plane of symmetry, it cannot be chiral and cannot be optically active. Which of the following have at least one plane of symmetry? Do any have more than one?

1,1-Dichlorocyclopropane

cis-1,2-Dichlorocyclopropane

trans-1,2-Dichlorocyclopropane

(b) Specify the relationships (constitutionally isomeric or stereoisomeric) among these compounds.

24.95 All alkanes give off heat when burned in air. Such *combustion* of alkanes is exothermic, and the sign of $\Delta H°$ is negative. The general equation for the combustion of the alkanes of molecular formula C_5H_{12} is

$$C_5H_{12} + 8O_2 \longrightarrow 5CO_2 + 6H_2O$$

The values of $\Delta H°$ for the combustion of the three pentane isomers are

$CH_3CH_2CH_2CH_2CH_3 = -3536$ kJ/mol
$(CH_3)_2CHCH_2CH_3 \quad = -3529$ kJ/mol
$(CH_3)_4C \qquad\qquad = -3515$ kJ/mol

(a) What do these data tell you about the effect of chain branching on the relative potential energies and stabilities of these isomers?
(b) Assume this effect is general to predict which one of the 18 C_8H_{18} isomers should be the most stable.

24.96 Carbon dioxide reacts with sodium hydroxide according to the following equation:

$$CO_2 + 2NaOH \longrightarrow Na_2CO_3 + H_2O$$

The overall reaction is the result of two separate reactions.

Reaction I: $H-\ddot{O}\!\!:^- + \;:\!\ddot{O}\!=\!C\!=\!\ddot{O}\!: \longrightarrow$

Reaction II:

(a) Use curved arrows to track the flow of electrons in reaction I.
(b) Use curved arrows to track the flow of electrons in reaction II.
(c) Classify reaction I as electrophilic addition, nucleophilic addition, electrophilic substitution, or acid-base.
(d) Classify reaction II according to the choices in part (c).

24.97 The combustion of 20.63 mg of compound Y, which contains only C, H, and O, with excess oxygen gave 57.94 mg of CO_2 and 11.85 mg of H_2O. (a) Calculate how many milligrams of C, H, and O were present in the original sample of Y. (b) Derive the empirical formula of Y. (c) Suggest a plausible structure for Y if the empirical formula is the same as the molecular formula.

24.98 Match each molecular model with the correct line-wedge-dash structure.

(d)

24.99 Kevlar is a copolymer used in bulletproof vests. It is formed in a condensation reaction between the following two monomers:

H₂N—⟨ ⟩—NH₂   HO—C(=O)—⟨ ⟩—C(=O)—OH

Sketch a portion of the polymer chain showing several monomer units. Write the overall equation for the condensation reaction.

24.100 Describe the formation of polystyrene.

24.101 The amino acid glycine can be condensed to form a polymer called polyglycine. Draw the repeating monomer unit.

24.102 Nylon can be destroyed easily by strong acids. Explain the chemical basis for the destruction. (*Hint:* The products are the starting materials of the polymerization reaction.)

24.103 How many different tripeptides can be formed by lysine and alanine?

24.104 Nylon was designed to be a synthetic silk. (a) The average molar mass of a batch of nylon 66 is 12,000 g/mol. How many monomer units are there in this sample? (b) Which part of nylon's structure is similar to a polypeptide's structure? (c) How many different tripeptides (made up of three amino acids) can be formed from the amino acids alanine (Ala), glycine (Gly), and serine (Ser), which account for most of the amino acids in silk?

24.105 Thalidomide is converted to the drug CC-4047 by substitution of an amino group for one of the H atoms on the aromatic portion of the molecule. Using curved arrows, and starting with the structure on page 984, draw the mechanism for this reaction and all the resonance structures for the carbocation intermediate.

Answers to In-Chapter Materials

PRACTICE PROBLEMS

24.1A (a) 3-ethylpentane, (b) 2-bromohexane, (c) 2-chlorobutane.

24.1B (a) CH₃CH₂CH₂CHCH₂CH₂CH₂CH₃, (b) CH₃CHCH₂CH₂CH₃,
$\quad$ with CH₂/CH₃ branch; with F branch

(c) CH₃CH₂CHCH₂CH₂CH₂CH₂CH₂CH₃ with CH₃ branch. **24.2A** (a) ester,

(b) carboxy group; ester, (c) 2 hydroxy groups, 2 carboxy groups.

24.2B (a) ketone, (b) 3° amide, (c) ester.

24.3A CH₂BrCH₂COOH. **24.3B** (structure with NH₂, :Ö:⁻)

24.4A H—C=O:

24.4B [:Ö—S—Ö: resonance structures]²⁻

24.5A [:Ö—C—Ö: resonance structures]²⁻

24.5B c. **24.6A** (H₂C=CH₂ → H—C—C⁺ → H—C—C—H mechanism with HI)

24.6B b. **24.7A** (a) (acetone with ⁻H: → H₃C—C—CH₃ with :Ö:⁻)

(b) (benzene + Cl⁺ → carbocation intermediate → chlorobenzene + H⁺)

24.7B (ortho, meta, para chlorobenzenesulfonic acid structures: Cl/SO₃H ortho; Cl/SO₃H meta; Cl/SO₃H para)

SECTION REVIEW

24.2.1 2-methylbutane. **24.2.2** 2-chloropropane. **24.2.3** 2-pentanone.
24.2.4 3-methyl-1-butanamine. **24.2.5** carboxy and carbonyl.
24.2.6 Hydroxy and carboxy. **24.3.1** C₆H₈O. **24.3.2** C₆H₁₄O.
24.3.3 e. **24.3.4** HCOO⁻ and O₃. **24.5.1** (i) nucleophile, (ii) nucleophile, (iii) electrophile. **24.5.2** (i) addition, (ii) substitution, (iii) isomerization.

CHAPTER 25

Modern Materials

25.1 Polymers
• Addition Polymers • Condensation Polymers

25.2 Ceramics and Composite Materials
• Ceramics • Composite Materials

25.3 Liquid Crystals

25.4 Biomedical Materials
• Dental Implants • Soft Tissue Materials
• Artificial Joints

25.5 Nanotechnology
• Graphite, Buckyballs, and Nanotubes

25.6 Semiconductors

25.7 Superconductors

Modern electronic devices heavily rely on semiconducting materials but heretofore existing engineering technologies have imposed a limit on how small such devices can be built. With nanotechnology, chemists and materials scientists are able to build working devices that are just *tens* of atoms wide. Shown here is a nanowire, the world's smallest electrical wire, a mere 10 atoms wide (1.5 nanometers across). Devices fabricated at this tiny scale possess properties so different from their predecessors, that they may ultimately lead to an entirely new era in electronics.

25.1 POLYMERS

Many biological molecules, such as DNA, starch, and proteins, have very large molecular masses. These molecules are **polymers** because they are made up of many smaller parts linked together [◀◀ Section 24.6]. The prefix *poly* comes from a Greek root meaning "many," and the small molecules that make up the individual building blocks of polymers are called **monomers.** Many natural polymers, such as silk and rubber, now have synthetic analogues that are manufactured by the chemical industry.

Polymers are used in many medical applications, such as flexible wound dressings, surgical implants, and prosthetics. Some of these polymers are **thermoplastic,** which means that they can be melted and reshaped, or heated and bent. Others are **thermosetting,** which means that their shape is determined as part of the chemical process that formed the polymer. Thermosetting polymers cannot be reshaped easily and are not easily recycled, whereas thermoplastic polymers can be melted down and cast into new shapes in different products.

Bottles that can be recycled are made of thermoplastic polymers.

Addition Polymers

The simplest type of polymerization reaction involves the bonding of monomer molecules by movement of electrons from a multiple bond into new single bonds between molecules. This type of polymerization is called **addition polymerization** [◀◀ Section 24.6]. A molecule with a carbon-carbon double bond is called an *alkene,* and a molecule with a carbon-carbon triple bond is called an *alkyne.* The synthesis of polyethylene from ethylene (C_2H_4) illustrates an addition polymerization. The arrows with half-pointed heads show movement of a single electron. The process of "splitting open" the double bond is initiated by a molecule with a single O—O bond that can be broken in half by heating. The free radical initiator molecule attaches to one of the ethylene carbon atoms and breaks the pi bond between the two carbon atoms in ethylene. Figure 25.1 shows the scheme of addition polymerization with respect to the double bonds opening up to form single bonds between monomer units to form polyethylene from ethylene.

The structure of polyethylene can be represented as $-(CH_2-CH_2)_n$, where *n* is the number of ethylene monomer molecules that reacted (which could be hundreds, thousands, or more). The end of the chain contains a carbon atom with an unpaired electron (i.e., $-CH_2CH_2\cdot$), though, so it must be closed by bonding with another atom. This might be a hydrogen atom (e.g., $-CH_2CH_2-H$), but it might also be part of the initiator molecule (e.g., $-CH_2CH_2-OR$). Although the residue of the initiator molecule has very different chemical properties than the main polymer chain, it will not significantly affect the polymer's properties because the polyethylene chain is so long.

Student Annotation: The systematic name of C_2H_4 is *ethene,* but the common name *ethylene* is still widely used.

Student Annotation: Recall that species with an unpaired electron are called *free radicals* [◀◀ Section 6.6].

Multi 25.1
Organic and biochemistry—natural and synthetic polymers

Figure 25.1 Addition polymerization to form polyethylene from ethylene. Each curved, single-headed arrow represents the movement of one electron.

Figure 25.2 Linear polyethylene is used to make plastic milk bottles. Plastic bags and wrap like Glad Cling Wrap are made from branched polyethylene.

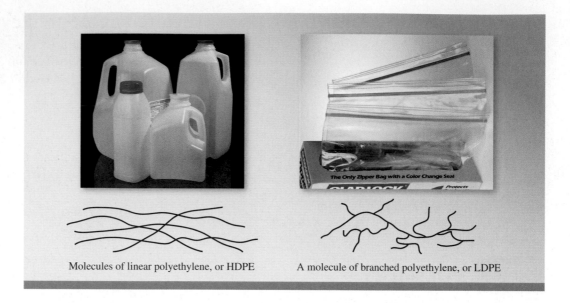

Molecules of linear polyethylene, or HDPE   A molecule of branched polyethylene, or LDPE

Although the structure of a polyethylene chain is drawn in Figure 25.1 as a straight line, the bond angles around a central carbon atom with four bonds are approximately 109.5° each [◄◄ Section 7.1]. Thus, the "straight" chain really zigzags, instead. The polymer chain bends, too, because there is free rotation about carbon-carbon single bonds. These molecular-level features manifest themselves in such macroscopic properties as flexibility.

It is possible, depending on the reaction conditions, for branches to form off the main polyethylene chain during polymerization. Polymer chains with many branches cannot pack together as efficiently as "straight" or unbranched chains, so branched-chain polyethylene is more flexible and lower in density than straight-chain polyethylene. The difference between branched and unbranched polyethylene is shown schematically in Figure 25.2.

Polyethylene consisting primarily of unbranched chains is known as high-density polyethylene (HDPE), whereas polyethylene that consists primarily of branched chains is known as low-density polyethylene (LDPE). HDPE is used in plastic bottles and containers where it is important to maintain shape, whereas LDPE is used in plastic food bags and wraps.

Natural rubber formed from latex is an addition polymer. The monomer unit is isoprene, a molecule with two C=C double bonds. In the reaction that forms *polyisoprene,* a pair of electrons moves from one double bond to form a new double bond between the middle two carbon atoms, and the other double bond opens up to form a carbon-carbon single bond to the next monomer unit.

$$H_2C \qquad CH_2$$
$$\backslash \qquad /$$
$$C-C$$
$$/ \qquad \backslash$$
$$H_3C \qquad H$$

Isoprene

cis-Polyisoprene

Natural rubber is not very durable—it only retains its useful properties in a relatively narrow temperature range. To address this problem, Charles Goodyear[1] developed industrial *vulcanization*

---

[1]Charles Goodyear (1800–1860), an American chemist, was the first person to realize the potential of natural rubber. His vulcanization process made the use of rubber practical, contributing greatly to the development of the automobile industry.

Figure 25.3 Vulcanization.

in 1839, a process in which sulfur is used to create linkages between individual polymer chains in the rubber. By heating the rubber with sulfur (S_8) under carefully controlled conditions, some of the carbon-hydrogen bonds are broken and replaced with carbon-sulfur bonds. The sulfur atoms are bonded to one or more additional sulfur atoms and then to another polymer chain through another sulfur-carbon bond (Figure 25.3). These linkages, called **cross-links,** make the rubber much stronger and more rigid than natural polyisoprene. Rubber is an **elastomer,** a material that can stretch or bend and then return to its original shape as long as the limits of its elasticity are not exceeded. The cross-linking of the polyisoprene chains plays an important role in maintaining rubber's elastomer properties.

Goodyear, the current supplier of tires to NASCAR teams, varies the composition of the rubber in its tires for each race depending on the expected tire wear and banking of the track. The left- and right-side tires can even be of different compositions depending on the track layout and conditions. Softer tire compounds offer more grip but wear out faster, whereas harder compounds last longer but grip less.

Many other molecules containing carbon-carbon double bonds can form addition polymers. Styrene [Figure 25.4(a)] is an analogue of ethylene in which a hydrogen atom has been replaced with a C_6H_5 (a *phenyl*) group. The polymerization of styrene forms *polystyrene* (Figure 25.5). As a foam (with air or some other gas blown into the solid), polystyrene is used in disposable cups and plates as well as Styrofoam insulation and craft materials. Vinyl chloride [Figure 25.4(b)], an analogue of ethylene in which one of the hydrogen atoms has been replaced by a chlorine atom, is another monomer that can be used to form a polymer with many common uses. Poly(vinyl chloride) (PVC) is used in pipes and fittings, some plastic wraps, and the classic "vinyl" records that were the predecessors to musical recordings on cassettes and CDs.

Polytetrafluoroethylene, more commonly known as the trademarked brand name Teflon, is formed from the addition polymerization of tetrafluoroethylene. Tetrafluoroethylene, shown in Figure 25.4(c), is an analogue of ethylene in which fluorine atoms have replaced all four of the hydrogen atoms. Teflon is a very good electrical insulator, so it is commonly used to coat wires. It is probably best known, though, as a nonstick substance used to coat bakeware, frying pans, and pots. It is also used in films that can be inserted into threaded joints between metal pipes to make it easier to unscrew the connection when necessary. Because Teflon is chemically inert, it is not possible to cross-link the chains like an elastomer. The structures of some addition polymers, including the structures of their respective monomers and what they are typically used for, are summarized in Table 25.1.

Figure 25.4 (a) Styrene, (b) vinyl chloride, and (c) tetrafluoroethylene (the monomer of Teflon).

Student Annotation: Each tire used in the NASCAR race series costs approximately $400. A single race car can go through as many as 32 tires in one 500-mile race, depending on track conditions. There are dozens of races throughout the year, and even more tires are used up during practices and prerace qualifying. It takes a lot of tires to compete in NASCAR!

Student Annotation: This figure shows the structure of a general "vinyl" compound. Styrene and vinyl chloride are vinyl compounds in which R is a phenyl group and a chlorine atom, respectively.

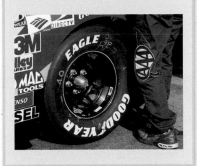

Student Annotation: Traditional record albums are made of PVC mixed with carbon.

Figure 25.5 Structure of polystyrene.

TABLE 25.1	Some Common Addition Polymers		
Polymer	**Structure**	**Monomer**	**Uses**
Polyethylene	$-(CH_2-CH_2)_n-$	$H_2C=CH_2$	Plastic bags and wraps, bottles, toys, Tyvek wrap
Polystyrene			Disposable cups and plates, insulation, packing materials
Poly(vinyl chloride)			Pipes and fittings, plastic wraps, records
Polyacrylonitrile			Fibers for carpeting and clothing (Orlon)
Polybutadiene		$HC=CH_2$ $H_2C=CH$	Synthetic rubber

The diversity of polymers increases greatly when different monomers are used in the same polymer chain. *Copolymers* are polymers made from two or more different monomers [◂◂ Section 24.6]. Different combinations of the two or more monomers give rise to different types of copolymers. These different copolymers are summarized in Table 25.2.

TABLE 25.2	Types of Copolymers
Copolymer type	**Representation***
Random	... −A−A−B−A−B−B−B−A−A−B−A−B−A−B−A−B−B−A− ...
Alternating	... −A−B−A−B−A−B−A−B−A−B−A−B−A−B−A−B− ...
Block	... −A−A−A−A−A−A−B−B−B−B−B−B−A−A−A−A−A−A− ...
Graft	... −A−A−A−A−A−A−A−A−A−A−A−A−A−A−A−A−A− ... | B−B−B−B−B−B−B−B−B ...

*A and B represent different monomers (e.g., ethylene and styrene).

Worked Example 25.1 lets you practice deducing the structure of an addition polymer based on the structure of its monomer.

Worked Example 25.1

Student Annotation: An Australian bank note issued in 1988 is printed on polypropylene for increased durability and security.

Polypropylene is used in applications that range from indoor-outdoor carpeting to soda bottles to bank notes. It is produced by the addition polymerization of propylene, $H_2C=CH-CH_3$. Draw the structure of polypropylene, showing at least two repeating monomer units, and write its general formula.

Strategy Addition polymers form via a free-radical reaction in which the pi electrons in the carbon-carbon double bond of a monomer molecule are used to form carbon-carbon single bonds to other monomer molecules. Draw the structural formula of propylene such that the double bond can be "opened up" to form single bonds between consecutive monomer units.

Setup The structural formula of propylene is

$$
\begin{array}{ccc}
H & & H \\
\diagdown & & \diagup \\
& C = C \\
\diagup & & \diagdown \\
H & & CH_3
\end{array}
$$

By drawing three adjacent propylene molecules, we can rearrange the bonds to show three repeating units.

$$
\begin{array}{ccc}
H & & H \\
\diagdown & & \diagup \\
& C = C \\
\diagup & & \diagdown \\
H & & CH_3
\end{array}
\quad
\begin{array}{ccc}
H & & H \\
\diagdown & & \diagup \\
& C = C \\
\diagup & & \diagdown \\
H & & CH_3
\end{array}
\quad
\begin{array}{ccc}
H & & H \\
\diagdown & & \diagup \\
& C = C \\
\diagup & & \diagdown \\
H & & CH_3
\end{array}
$$

Solution The structure of polypropylene showing three monomer units is

$$
\begin{array}{cccccc}
H & H & H & H & H & H \\
| & | & | & | & | & | \\
-C & -C & -C & -C & -C & -C- \\
| & | & | & | & | & | \\
H & CH_3 & H & CH_3 & H & CH_3
\end{array}
$$

Thus, the general formula of polypropylene is

$$
\left(
\begin{array}{cc}
H & H \\
| & | \\
C & -C \\
| & | \\
H & CH_3
\end{array}
\right)_n
$$

Think About It
The general formula looks like the structure of the monomer, except that the carbon-carbon double bond has been opened up to form bonds to monomer units on each side. This means the answer is reasonable. In fact, the opposite process (i.e., restoring the carbon-carbon double bond) can be used to determine the structure of the monomer used to create an addition polymer.

(Continued on next page)

Practice Problem A Saran Wrap, the original plastic film, is polyvinylidene chloride, which is formed by the addition polymerization of vinylidene chloride, $H_2C=CCl_2$. Draw the structure of polyvinylidene chloride, showing at least two repeating units, and write its general structure.

Practice Problem B The general structure of polymethyl methacrylate, an addition polymer used in Plexiglas and Lucite, is as follows:

$$\left(\begin{array}{ccc} H & CH_3 \\ | & | \\ C - C & \\ | & | \\ H & C-OCH_3 \\ & \| \\ & O \end{array}\right)_n$$

Draw the structure of the monomer used to make this polymer.

Butadiene ($CH_2=CH-CH=CH_2$) and styrene, two monomers listed in Table 25.1, can form a block copolymer called poly(styrene-butadiene-styrene) or SBS rubber [Figure 25.6(a)], in which there are alternating blocks of polybutadiene and polystyrene. They also form a graft polymer known as high-impact polystyrene (HIPS) [Figure 25.6(b)], in which chains of polybutadiene branch off of the main polystyrene chain.

Polymers containing a vinyl group ($-CH_2-CHR-$) can exist as optical isomers because the carbon atom bonded to the R group is tetrahedral and bonded to four *different* groups [◄◄ Section 24.4]. ***Tacticity*** is the term that describes the relative arrangements of such chiral carbon atoms within a polymer. Polymers in which all the substituents (i.e., the R groups) are in the same relative orientation (i.e., on the same side of the polymer chain) are said to be ***isotactic***. Polymers in which the substituents alternate positions along the polymer chain are said to be ***syndiotactic***. Finally, polymers in which the substituents are oriented randomly along the polymer chain are said to be ***atactic***. The tacticity of polystyrene is shown in Figure 25.7. Polymers that are formed by free-radical polymerization processes, such as polystyrene and PVC, are usually atactic. Special catalysts have been developed, though, that can be used to synthesize isotactic and syndiotactic polymers.

Condensation Polymers

Condensation polymers form when monomers with two different functional groups combine, resulting in the elimination of a small molecule (usually water) [◄◄ Section 24.6]. Proteins are biological condensation polymers that can have molecular weights in the thousands or millions of

Figure 25.6 Structures of (a) SBS rubber and (b) HIPS. SBS consists of alternating blocks of polybutadiene and polystyrene, whereas HIPS consists of a polystyrene backbone with polybutadiene branches.

(a)

(b)

Figure 25.7 Structures of (a) isotactic, (b) syndiotactic, and (c) atactic polymers.

(a) (b) (c)

grams per mole. Proteins form between amino acid monomers. Each amino acid contains an amino group ($-NH_2$) and a carboxy group ($-COOH$), and the condensation reaction occurs between the amino group of one amino acid and the carboxy group of another. (See Figure 24.13.) One water molecule is produced as each new $C-N$ bond is formed.

The $C-N$ bond formed between an amino group and a carboxy group is called an amide bond because $RCONR'R''$ is the general form of an amide [◄◄ Section 24.2, Table 24.2]. Polymers in which the monomers are connected by amide linkages are called **polyamides.** The amide bond between amino acids is more specifically called a peptide bond, and proteins are routinely referred to as polypeptides. Although polypeptides can form from a single amino acid (e.g., polyvaline), most proteins in organisms consist of chains of different amino acids. As a result, most proteins are random copolymers (Table 25.2).

Nylon 6,6 is a synthetic condensation polymer formed from hexamethylenediamine, a molecule with two amino groups, and adipic acid, which has two carboxy groups. Water is the small molecule eliminated in this condensation reaction.

$$+ 2nH_2O$$

Both hexamethylenediamine and adipic acid contain six carbon atoms, which is why the resulting polymer is called nylon 6,6. Like proteins, nylon 6,6 contains amide linkages between monomers, so nylon 6,6 is a polyamide, too. Also like proteins, nylon 6,6 is a copolymer, although nylon 6,6 is an *alternating* copolymer (Table 25.2), not a *random* copolymer.

Dacron is the trade name for the condensation copolymer formed from ethylene glycol (a diol—a molecule with two alcohol groups) and *para*-terephthalic acid (a diacid—a molecule with two carboxy groups). The condensation reaction removes the hydrogen atom from the alcohol on one monomer and the OH group from the carboxy group on a second monomer, producing water.

$$+ 2nH_2O$$

The bond that forms between each ethylene glycol monomer and each *para*-terephthalic acid monomer is called an ester linkage because $RCOOR'$ is the general form of an ester [◄◄ Section 24.2, Table 24.2]. Polymers in which the monomers are connected by ester linkages are called **polyesters.**

Deoxyribonucleic acid (DNA; see Figure 25.8), which stores the genetic information for every known organism and has a molecular weight as large as billions of grams per mole, is a biological condensation copolymer. If your body contained anything but a tiny fraction of a mole

Repeating unit along DNA chain

Figure 25.8 Structure of DNA.

of DNA, you would be extremely heavy! DNA is a copolymer of a five-carbon sugar called deoxy-ribose, four different molecular bases (adenine, thymine, guanine, and cytosine), and phosphoric acid (H_3PO_4). Ribonucleic acid (RNA) is a biological condensation copolymer analogous to DNA, except that RNA is made from a five-carbon sugar called ribose and the four different molecular bases are adenine, uracil, guanine, and cytosine. RNA molecules vary greatly in size. They are large molecules, but still much smaller than DNA molecules.

Worked Example 25.2 shows how to determine the monomers in a copolymer.

Worked Example 25.2

Kevlar, a condensation polymer used in bulletproof vests, has the following general structure:

Write the structure of the two monomers that form Kevlar.

Strategy Identify the condensation linkages, split them apart, and then add H to one of the resulting exposed bonds and OH to the other.

Setup Kevlar contains an *amide* (linkage between C and N). We split the C—N bond, adding an H to the exposed N and an OH to the exposed C to produce an amine and a carboxylic acid, respectively.

Solution To determine what the monomers are, first remove the C—N bond:

Next, add H_2O as H to the N and OH to the C:

Finally, add the components of another water molecule to the open ends of the molecules—H to N and OH to C, as before:

Think About It
To determine whether the monomers in the final answer are reasonable, recombine them in a condensation reaction to see if they re-form Kevlar, the polymer in the problem.

Practice Problem A Nylon 6, like nylon 6,6, is a condensation polymer (a polyamide). Unlike nylon 6,6, however, nylon 6 is *not* a copolymer because it is synthesized from a single monomer called 6-aminohexanoic acid:

$$H_2NCH_2(CH_2)_3CH_2\overset{O}{\overset{\|}{C}}OH$$

Draw the structure of at least three repeating units of nylon 6.

Practice Problem B Kodel is a polymer used to make stain-resistant carpets.

Draw the structure of the monomer. Is this an additional polymer or a condensation polymer?

Thinking Outside the Box

Electrically Conducting Polymers

You have seen so far that it is possible to polymerize organic compounds with carbon-carbon double bonds (alkenes). The resulting addition polymers (e.g., polyethylene) have carbon-carbon single bonds. It is also possible, though, to polymerize organic compounds with carbon-carbon triple bonds. The simplest of these compounds (known collectively as *alkynes*) is acetylene (C_2H_2), which is commonly used in welding torches. The polymerization of acetylene is very similar to the addition polymerization of ethylene. That is, a free-radical initiator molecule attaches to one of the carbon atoms and breaks one of the pi bonds between the two carbon atoms in acetylene. The resulting polymer, polyacetylene, thus retains a carbon-carbon double bond:

Student Annotation: The systematic name of acetylene is ethyne, but the common name *acetylene* is far more commonly used, which is somewhat unfortunate since the *–ene* ending makes it sound like it is an alkene with a double bond instead of an alkyne with a triple bond!

$$H-C\equiv C-H \quad H-C\equiv C-H \quad H-C\equiv C-H \quad \longrightarrow \quad -\overset{\overset{\displaystyle H}{|}}{C}=\overset{\overset{\displaystyle H}{|}}{C}-\overset{\overset{\displaystyle H}{|}}{C}=\overset{\overset{\displaystyle H}{|}}{C}-\overset{\overset{\displaystyle H}{|}}{C}=\overset{\overset{\displaystyle H}{|}}{C}-$$

The generalized form of the reaction can be represented as follows:

$$n\,H-C\equiv C-H \quad \longrightarrow \quad \left(\!\!\begin{array}{c} H \\ | \\ C=C \\ | \\ H \end{array}\!\!\right)_n$$

The structure of polyacetylene contains alternating carbon-carbon single and carbon-carbon double bonds. Recall from Chapter 7 that the carbon atoms in a C=C double bond are sp^2-hybridized and that it is the leftover *p* orbital on each carbon atom that overlaps to form the pi bond. Each carbon atom in polyacetylene is identical (structurally and electronically), so there is extended overlap of the *p* orbitals throughout the polymer chain. The *p* electrons are *delocalized*—that is, they can move throughout the network of overlapping orbitals that extend the length of the polymer chain. By being able to move electrons from one end of the polymer chain to the other, polyacetylene can conduct electricity much like a wire. That is, polyacetylene is a plastic that conducts electricity!

For comparison, consider polyethylene and Teflon. Both are polyalkenes in which the polymer chain contains only carbon-carbon single bonds. Since all the electrons are localized in sigma bonds between the carbon atoms, there are no delocalized electrons available to carry charge throughout the polymer chain. The presence of electrons in *delocalized* orbitals, such as those in polyacetylene, is the key to electrical conductivity.

SECTION 25.1 REVIEW

Polymers

25.1.1   Classify the following copolymer:

   −B−B−B−B−B−A−A−A−A−A−B−B−B−B−B−A−A−A−A−A−

25.1.2   What feature is common to molecules that can undergo polymerization?

25.2   CERAMICS AND COMPOSITE MATERIALS

Ceramics

The use of ceramics in the form of pottery dates back to antiquity. Along with common ceramic substances like brick and cement, modern advanced ceramics are found in electronic devices and on the exterior of spaceships. All these *ceramics* are polymeric inorganic compounds that share the properties of hardness, strength, and high melting points. Ceramics are usually formed by melting and then solidifying inorganic substances (including clays).

Student Annotation: The larger the lattice energy of an ionic compound, the higher the melting point. Ceramics all have large lattice energies.

Figure 25.9 Captain Wendy Lawrence inspects the ceramic tiles on the exterior of the space shuttle.

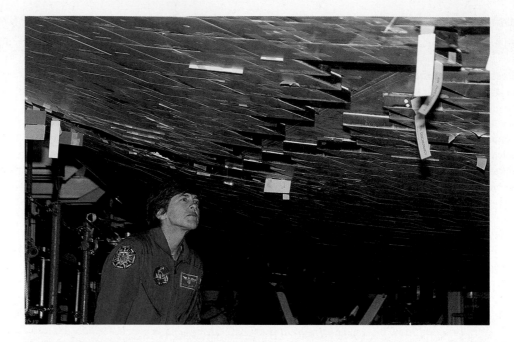

Student Annotation: The sintering of bronze in the manufacture of bearings takes advantage of the inherent imperfections produced by the process. Porous bearings are sometimes preferred because the porosity allows a lubricant to flow throughout the material.

Student Annotation: The "sol" in sol-gel refers to a colloidal suspension of individual particles. The "gel" refers to the suspension of the resulting polymer.

Multi 25.2
Chemical reactions—thermite reaction

Most ceramic materials are electrical insulators, but some conduct electricity very well at very cold temperatures. Ceramics are also good heat insulators, which is why the outer layer of the space shuttle (shown in Figure 25.9) is made of ceramic tiles. These ceramic tiles can withstand the very hot temperatures of reentry into the atmosphere (where temperatures can reach 1650°C), while keeping the underlying metal structural body of the orbiter (and the astronauts within) relatively cool.

Ceramics can be prepared by heating a slurry of a powder of the inorganic substance in water to a very high temperature under high pressure. This process, called *sintering,* bonds the particles to each other, thus producing the finished ceramic. Sintering is a relatively easy process to perform, but the resulting particle size is irregular, so the solid may contain cracks, spaces, and imperfections. Imperfections in the interior of a solid ceramic can be impossible to detect, but they make weak spots in the substance that can cause the ceramic piece to fail. To avoid these problems, the *sol-gel process* is frequently employed for modern ceramics that are used in structural applications. The sol-gel process produces particles of nearly uniform size that are much more likely to produce a solid ceramic without gaps or cracks.

The first step in the sol-gel process is the preparation of an alkoxide of the metal or metalloid that is going to be made into the ceramic. This can be illustrated with the yttrium(III) ion, which is used to prepare a yttrium-oxygen ceramic:

$$Y + 3CH_3CH_2OH \longrightarrow \underset{\text{yttrium alkoxide}}{Y(OCH_3CH_2)_3} + 3H^+$$

The resulting metal alkoxide is dissolved in alcohol. Water is then added to generate the metal hydroxide and regenerate the alcohol:

$$\underset{\text{yttrium alkoxide}}{Y(OCH_3CH_2)_3} + 3H_2O \longrightarrow \underset{\text{yttrium hydroxide}}{Y(OH)_3} + \underset{\text{ethanol}}{3CH_3CH_2OH}$$

The metal hydroxide, once formed, undergoes condensation polymerization to form a chain with bridging oxygen atoms between the metal atoms:

$$\overset{\displaystyle OH}{\underset{\displaystyle |}{HO-Y-OH}} \quad \overset{\displaystyle OH}{\underset{\displaystyle |}{HO-Y-OH}} \longrightarrow \overset{\displaystyle OH \quad\ OH}{\underset{\displaystyle |\qquad |}{HO-Y-O-Y-OH}} + H_2O \text{ (water)}$$

Just as in condensation polymerization between organic molecules, a small molecule (water, in this case) is produced by the combination of atoms from the two monomers. Repeated condensation produces an insoluble chain of metal atoms connected by oxygen atoms. The polymer chain may contain branches (i.e., it may be three dimensional) because all three of the hydroxide groups attached to the central metal ion are identical (and are thus equally likely to react). The suspension of the metal oxide-hydroxide polymer is called a *gel.* The gel is carefully heated to remove the liquid, and what remains is a collection of tiny, remarkably uniformly sized particles. Sintering of material produced by the sol-gel process produces a ceramic with relatively few imperfections.

Composite Materials

A *composite material* is made from two or more substances with different properties that remain separate in the bulk material. Each contributes properties to the overall material, though, such that the composite exhibits the best properties of each of its components. One of the oldest examples of a human-made composite material is the formation of bricks from mud and straw, a process that dates back to biblical times.

Modern composite materials commonly include reinforcing fibers, analogous to the straw in mud bricks, in a polymer matrix called a resin. Fiberglass, Kevlar, or carbon fibers can be used to give strength to the composite, whereas polyester, polyamide, or epoxy forms the matrix that holds the fibers together. These types of composites are called *polymer matrix composites.* Composites made from a metal and a ceramic, organic polymer, or another metal are called *metal matrix composites.* Carbide drill tips are made with a combination of softer cobalt and tougher tungsten carbide. Toyota has used a metal matrix composite in the engine block of some of its cars, and some bicycles are made with aluminum metal matrix composites. Composites made of a ceramic as the primary reinforcing material accompanied by organic polymers are called *ceramic matrix composites.* A common biological ceramic matrix composite is bone. Bones consist of reinforcing fibers made of collagen (a protein) surrounded by a matrix of hydroxyapatite [$Ca_5(PO_4)_3OH$].

Another type of composite material that does not fit neatly into one of these categories is a reinforced carbon-carbon composite (RCC), which consists of carbon fibers in a graphite matrix. To prevent oxidation, a silicon carbide coating is applied. RCC is used on the nose cones of missiles, but it is most commonly known as the coating on the nose of the space shuttle. It is believed that the Space Shuttle *Columbia* disaster in 2003 occurred because the ceramic tiles and RCC panel material were both damaged on liftoff by the impact of falling foam insulation. The extreme heat of reentry into the atmosphere damaged the orbiter's structure through the breaches in the ceramic tiles and the RCC panel, and the orbiter and all seven astronauts on board were lost.

Carbon fibers can be woven into fabrics and threads to be used as the structural components of vehicles and for sporting equipment such as bicycles, tennis rackets, and skateboards.

25.3 LIQUID CRYSTALS

Liquid crystals are substances that exhibit properties of both liquids, such as the ability to flow and to take on the shape of a container, and those of crystals, such as a regular arrangement of particles in a lattice. Some substances exhibit liquid crystal behavior when they are melted from a solid. As the temperature increases, the solid liquefies but retains some order in one or two dimensions. At a higher temperature, the ordered liquid becomes a more conventional liquid in which there is no consistent orientation of the molecules.

Liquids are *isotropic,* because their properties are independent of the direction of testing. Because particles in a liquid are free to rotate, there are molecules present in every possible orientation, so the bulk sample gives the same measurements regardless of the direction in which the measurements are taken or observations are made. Liquid crystals are *anisotropic* because the properties they display depend on the direction (orientation) of the measurement. A box full of pencils, all neatly aligned, is an analogy for anisotropy, because the pencils are long and narrow. Looking at the pencils end on is different than looking at them from the side. What you see depends on the direction from which you view the pencils. Similarly, what you see when you look at anisotropic molecules depends on the direction from which you view them.

Frederick Reinitzer discovered the first compound to exhibit liquid crystal behavior in 1888. Cholesteryl benzoate was observed to form an ordered liquid crystalline phase when melted, and this liquid crystalline phase became an ordinary liquid at higher temperatures:

Cholesteryl benzoate

The structure of cholesteryl benzoate is fairly rigid due to the presence of the fused rings and sp^2-hybridized carbon atoms. The molecule is relatively long compared to its width, too. Rigidity and

Student Annotation: Recall from Chapter 7 that there is free rotation about carbon-carbon single bonds (i.e., bonds between sp^3-hybridized carbon atoms), but not about carbon-carbon double bonds (i.e., bonds between sp^2-hybridized carbon atoms).

Figure 25.10 (a) Nematic, (b) cholesteric, and (c) smectic liquid crystals.

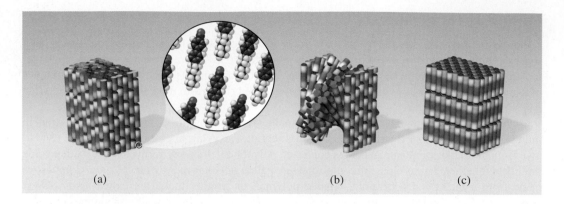

(a)   (b)   (c)

this particular shape makes it possible for the cholesteryl benzoate molecules to arrange themselves in an orderly manner, in much the way that pencils, chopsticks, or tongue depressors can be arranged.

There are three different types of ordering (called nematic, smectic, and cholesteric) that a liquid crystal can adopt (see Figure 25.10). A *nematic* liquid crystal contains molecules ordered in one dimension only. Nematic molecules are all aligned parallel to one another, but there is no organization into layers or rows. A *smectic* liquid crystal is ordered in two dimensions. Smectic molecules are aligned parallel to one other and are further arranged in layers that are parallel to one another. *Cholesteric* liquid crystal molecules are parallel to each other within each layer, but each layer is rotated with respect to the layers above and below it. The layers are rotated because there are repulsive intermolecular forces between layers.

Liquid crystalline substances were curiosities for many years but have found applications in many fields. Liquid crystal displays (LCDs) in calculators, watches, and laptop computers are possible, for example, because polarized light can be transmitted through liquid crystals in one phase

Figure 25.11 Liquid crystal display. When the current is on, the liquid crystal molecules are aligned and polarized light cannot pass through. When the current is off, the molecules are not aligned and light can pass through.

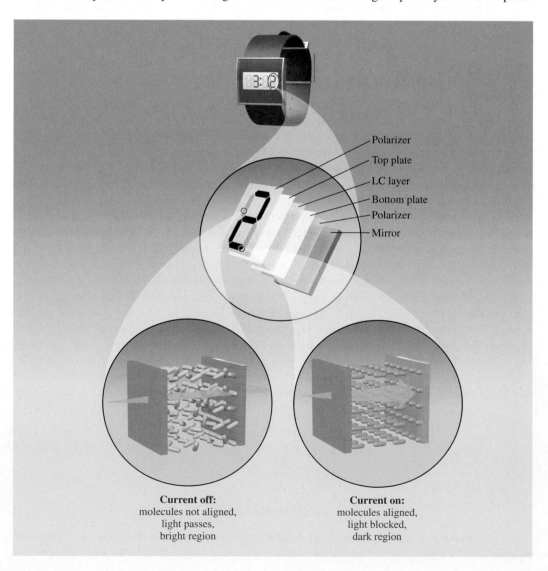

Polarizer
Top plate
LC layer
Bottom plate
Polarizer
Mirror

Current off:
molecules not aligned,
light passes,
bright region

Current on:
molecules aligned,
light blocked,
dark region

but not transmitted through another (Figure 25.11). Polarized light is produced by passing ordinary light (which oscillates in all directions perpendicular to the beam) through a filter that allows only the light waves oscillating in one particular plane to pass through. This plane-polarized light can be rotated by a twisted liquid crystal such that it is allowed to pass through another filter when a voltage is applied to the liquid. If the light passes through the liquid when the voltage is off, though, the light will *not* pass through. This principle can be used in calculator and watch displays because each digit is made up of no more than the seven segments shown in Figure 25.11, and the specific digit depends on which segments are bright and which are dark. LCDs in laptop computers and televisions are more sophisticated, but still operate on the same basic principle.

Liquid crystals can also be used in thermometers (Figure 25.12). The spacing between crystal layers depends on temperature, and the wavelength of light reflected by the crystal depends on this spacing. Thus, the color reflected by the liquid crystal will change with temperature, and this color can be used to indicate the temperature to which the liquid crystal is exposed.

Worked Example 25.3 lets you practice determining whether or not a molecule might exhibit liquid crystal properties.

Figure 25.12 LCD thermometer.

Worked Example 25.3

Would the following molecule make a good liquid crystal? Why or why not?

Strategy Cholesteryl benzoate exhibits liquid crystal properties because it has structurally rigid regions (fused rings and sp^2-hybridized carbon atoms) and because it is relatively long compared to its width. Examine the structure in question to see if it has rigid regions and to see if it is longer in one dimension than in another.

Setup Carbon atoms that are sp^2-hybridized contribute to the rigidity of a molecule's shape.

Solution The left-hand portion of the molecule contains an sp^2-hybridized carbon atom, a benzene ring, another sp^2-hybridized carbon atom, and another benzene ring. These features are relatively rigid and should allow the molecule to maintain its shape when heated. The chain of CH_2 groups ending in a CH_3 group is not rigid due to free rotation about the carbon-carbon single bonds (i.e., sp^3-hybridized carbon atoms). The overall shape of the molecule is longer than it is wide, though, which combined with a large portion that is rigid should make the molecule a good candidate for liquid crystal behavior.

Think About It
Double bonds in a molecular structure indicate the presence of pi bonds. Recall that it is the pi bonds that restrict rotation about bonds in a molecule [◄◄ Section 7.5] and lend rigidity to the structure.

Practice Problem A Which compound would you expect to exhibit liquid crystal behavior, and why?

Practice Problem B This compound does not possess liquid crystal properties. What changes are needed (for example, addition of a group) to convert it to a liquid crystal?

Liquid Crystals

25.3.1   Which is a better analogy for anisotropy: a box of spaghetti or a box of elbow macaroni?

25.3.2   What characteristics make a molecule likely to exhibit liquid crystal properties?

25.4 BIOMEDICAL MATERIALS

Many modern materials are finding uses in medical applications. Replacement joints, dental implants, and artificial organs all contain modern polymers, composites, and ceramics. To function successfully in a biomedical application, though, a material must first be compatible with the living system. The human body very easily recognizes foreign substances and attacks them in an effort to rid them from the body. Thus, a biomaterial must be designed with enough similarity to the body's own systems that the body will accept the material as its own. Additionally, if the polymer, ceramic, or composite contains leftover chemicals from its manufacture, these contaminants may lead to adverse reactions with the body over the lifetime of the medical implant. It is important, therefore, that the substance be as pure as possible.

The physical properties of a biomedical material are important, too, because the longer the material lasts, the less often the medical device has to be replaced during the lifetime of the patient. Most biomedical materials must possess great strength and flexibility to perform in the body. For example, the materials in artificial joints and heart valves must be able to flex many times without breaking. Materials used in dental implants must show great hardness, moreover, so as not to crack during biting and chewing. It takes years of research to develop successful biomedical materials that meet these needs.

Dental Implants

Dental implant materials have been used for many years. The oldest dental fillings were made of various materials including lead (which fell out of favor due to its softness—the danger of lead poisoning was as yet unknown), tin, platinum, gold, and aluminum. The remains of Confederate soldiers have been shown to include fillings made of a lead-tungsten mixture, probably from shot-gun pellets; tin-iron; a mercury amalgam; gold; and even radioactive thorium. (The dentist probably thought he was using tin, which is similar in appearance.) Many modern fillings are made of dental *amalgam* [◄◄ Chapter 19], a solution of several metals in mercury. Modern dental amalgam consists of 50 percent mercury and 50 percent of an alloy powder that usually contains (in order of abundance) silver, tin, copper, and zinc. These metals tend to expand slightly with age, causing fissures and cracks in the tooth that may require further intervention (e.g., crowns, root canals, or tooth replacement). Some people consider amalgam fillings to be unsightly, too.

Dental composite materials are now used that have several advantages over traditional amalgams. The composites can be made in a wide range of colors, for example, to match the color of the other teeth. The existing healthy portion of the tooth can be etched with acid, moreover, to create pores into which the composite material can bond. With traditional dental amalgam, the dentist must create indentations in the healthy tooth to hold the amalgam in place. Destroying a portion of the healthy tooth is undesirable and can be avoided with the use of the composite.

The dental composite consists of a matrix (made from a methacrylate resin) and a silica filler. The composite material is applied to the cavity in a putty-like consistency and then is dried and polymerized by a photochemical reaction initiated by light of a particular wavelength. Because the light does not penetrate very far into the composite, the thickness of the applied composite is critical. If the layer of composite is too thick, some of the composite will remain soft. A properly constructed dental composite filling will last more than 10 years. Over time, though, composite fillings tend to shrink, leaving breaches that can cause leakage, a situation that must be addressed to prevent further tooth decay.

Porcelain ceramic fillings and crowns are very common, but the ceramic has two disadvantages: it is very hard and can wear on the opposing teeth, and it is brittle and may crack if subjected to great force. Most dentists, therefore, do not recommend porcelain ceramic crowns and fillings for the molar teeth, which do the bulk of the grinding work during chewing.

A material used in dentistry must have properties that maximize both patient comfort and the lifetime of the implant. Dental fillings and tooth replacements must be resistant to acids, for example, because many foods (such as citrus fruits and soft drinks) contain acids directly. Any food containing carbohydrates can produce acids, though, if traces are left in the mouth because the bacteria that reside there consume carbohydrates, producing acids in the process. These acids eat away at the natural hydroxyapatite in teeth, creating caries (cavities). Materials like dental amalgam, gold, and dental composite resist attack by acids in the mouth.

A dental material should also have low thermal conductivity; that is, it should conduct heat poorly. This is especially important in applications where the implant material is in contact with the nerve inside the tooth. If the implant material conducts heat well, then whenever hot or cold foods come in contact with the implant, the hot or cold will be transmitted through the material to the nerve, causing pain. Metals are good thermal conductors, so dental amalgams must not touch nerves.

Finally, dental materials should resist wear (so they last a long time) and they should resist expansion and contraction as the temperature fluctuates. The close spacing and precision fits involved in dental fillings and implants would result in discomfort and possibly failure of the implant if the material expanded or contracted appreciably with changes in temperature.

Soft Tissue Materials

Burn victims who have lost large amounts of skin do not have enough cells to grow new skin, so a synthetic substitute must be used. The most promising artificial skin material is based on a polymer of lactic acid and glycolic acid. Both of these compounds contain an alcohol group ($-OH$) and a carboxy group ($-COOH$), so they can form a polyester copolymer in a condensation reaction that mirrors the formation of Dacron polyester (Section 25.1):

glycolic acid   lactic acid

This copolymer forms the structural mesh that supports the growth of skin tissue cells from a source other than the patient. Once the skin cells grow on the structural mesh, the artificial skin is applied to the patient, and the copolymer mesh eventually disappears as the ester linkages are hydrolyzed. During this treatment, the patients must take drugs that will suppress their immune systems, which ordinarily would attack these substances as foreign to prevent their bodies from rejecting the new skin.

Sutures, commonly known as stitches, are now made of the same lactic acid–glycolic acid copolymer as the structural mesh of artificial skin. Before, sutures were made of materials that did not degrade so they eventually had to be removed again. This type of suture is still used in cases where the degrading suture is deemed a risk or there might be a need to reopen the incision at a later time. Biodegradable sutures are routinely used during operations on animals, too, which decreases the number of trips to the veterinarian, thereby reducing the stress on the pet and its owner.

When portions of blood vessels need to be replaced or circumvented in the body, it may or may not be possible to obtain a suitable vascular graft from another part of the patient's body. Dacron polyester (Section 25.1) can be woven into a tubular shape for this purpose, and pores can be worked into the material so that the graft can integrate itself into the tissue around it, as well as to allow capillaries to connect. Unfortunately, the body's immune system recognizes this as a foreign substance and blood platelets stick to the walls of the Dacron graft, causing clotting.

Artificial hearts and heart valves are potential solutions to the shortage of donor organs. Artificial hearts have not yet been perfected to the point that they can work on a permanent basis, but valve replacement is a common procedure that can successfully prolong a patient's life. The most common replacement heart valve is fixed in position by surrounding the valve with lactic acid–glycolic acid copolymer, the same polyester that is used in skin grafts and biodegradable sutures. The polymer is woven into a mesh ring that allows the body tissue to grow into the ring and hold it in place.

Researchers today are using *electrospinning* to place nanofibers directly onto wounds. (Nanofibers are products of nanotechnology; see Section 25.5.) Electrospinning uses a high-voltage

Student Annotation: Hydrolysis is essentially the opposite of a condensation reaction.

electric field to create a jet of polymer solution that transforms into a spiraling dry fiber only nanometers in diameter. The wound dressings applied by direct electrospinning have high rates of moisture transmission and bacterial resistance. Enzymes can be added to the solution containing the nanofiber polymer, and these enzymes can be released into the skin after the dressing is applied. Proteins can also be cross-linked onto the nanofiber, making possible many applications of the nanofiber wound dressing.

Artificial Joints

Joint replacements, such as artificial knees, elbows, and hips, require major surgery but have become relatively commonplace because suitable materials have become available for not only the bone replacement but also the contact surfaces. In knee replacement, for example, the goal is usually to replace worn-out cartilage surfaces (which may have resulted from arthritis or injury). It is possible to replace shattered bones that cannot heal back to their original state as well.

The materials originally used in joint replacements were ivory, metals, and glass, but they are fast being replaced by polymeric plastics and ceramics. Polymethyl methacrylate (PMMA), which was the subject of Practice Problem 25.1B in Section 25.1, and polyethylene have been used in many total joint replacements. However, these joints tend to fail over time when they are implanted in younger, more active patients, so efforts are under way to improve the wear quality of the PMMA and polyethylene parts.

Although metallurgical research provided new substances that were much stronger and less likely to break, including titanium-based alloys, total joint replacements were predicted to last no more than 20 years in a patient before needing to be replaced again. Ultrahigh-molecular-weight polyethylene, treated with radiation to initiate cross-linking of the polymer chains and stored under inert nitrogen gas to stop free-radical damage to the chain from the radiation, is now commonly used in many replacement joints, with the expectation of improved wear. It remains to be seen whether ultrahigh-molecular-weight polyethylene will prolong the life of these devices, since many of the joints have been in service in patients for less than a decade.

Other surfaces have also been researched to reduce wear. Metal-on-metal bearing surfaces suffered early setbacks due to the manufacturing tolerances of the cobalt-based alloy used. As the bearing surfaces wore, they produced metal sludge, and high friction between components caused loosening of the joint. Modern metal-on-metal bearing surfaces have improved as the manufacturing has become more consistent and produced components lower in friction.

Ceramic-on-ceramic bearing surfaces have also been developed. Some ceramics have been prone to cracking, but many have shown great promise for long-lasting use. When a ceramic component in a replacement joint does crack, however, it can be disastrous because the entire joint may need to be replaced and further healthy bone may need to be sacrificed to install the new replacement joint.

Despite the progress made so far on developing safe, durable, and useful artificial joints, much work remains to be done. One long-term issue that has yet to be researched extensively, for example, is the effect of the release of metal cations from the joint into the body over the lifetime of the joint replacement. This may become a more urgent health issue as the lifetimes of the artificial joints increases and the ages at which patients get the replacements decreases.

NANOTECHNOLOGY

Atoms and molecules have sizes on the order of a tenth of a nanometer (where 1 nm = 10^{-9} m) [◄◄ Section 1.4]. *Nanotechnology* is the development and study of such small-scale materials and objects. An atomic force microscope [Figure 25.13(a)] is one way to image the surface of a material at the atomic or molecular level.

A sharp-pointed stylus is moved over the surface of the substance under study, and the intermolecular forces between the material and the stylus force the stylus up and down. The stylus is mounted on a probe that reflects a laser beam into a detector. From the differences in deflection of the laser beam, the electronics attached to the probe can create an image of the surface of the object [Figure 25.13(b)].

(a)   (b)   (c)

Figure 25.13 (a) Atomic force microscope (AFM). (b) AFM image of a yeast cell. (c) STM image of iron atoms arranged to display the Chinese characters for *atom* on a copper surface.

The scanning tunneling microscope (STM) works on a similar principle but only for samples that conduct electricity. The STM measures the peak and valley heights of the sample from the flow of electric current. The tip of the STM must move up and down to keep the current constant, and the up-and-down movements are translated into an image of the atomic and molecular structure of the substance [Figure 25.13(c)].

Graphite, Buckyballs, and Nanotubes

Carbon exists as several allotropes, one of which is graphite. Graphite consists of sheets of carbon atoms that are all sp^2-hybridized [◀◀ Section 7.4]:

> **Student Annotation:** Recall that *allotropes* are different forms of the same element [◀◀ Section 5.5].

Intermolecular forces [◀◀ Chapter 12] hold the sheets together. Because of the delocalization of the electrons in the extended network of *p* orbitals perpendicular to the graphite sheet, graphite is an electrical conductor within its sheets, but not between them. Electrical conductivity is much more common for metals than it is for nonmetals like graphite.

Graphite and diamond were long thought to be the only two allotropes of carbon. In 1985, though, a compound consisting of 60 carbon atoms was isolated from graphite rods that had been vaporized with an intense pulse of laser light. The structure of the compound (C_{60}) was identical to that of a soccer ball, with 12 pentagonal and 20 hexagonal faces and carbon atoms at the corners of each face:

This pattern also resembles an architectural structure called a geodesic dome, so the C_{60} molecule was named *buckminsterfullerene* in honor of R. Buckminster Fuller, the designer of the geodesic dome. The nickname for C_{60} is the *buckyball*.

Figure 25.14 Carbon nanotubes.

Since the discovery of C$_{60}$, elongated and elliptical cages of 70 and 80 carbon atoms have also been discovered. These molecules, called *fullerenes* as a group, have been proposed to exist in such exotic places as stars and interstellar media and have been observed in such mundane places as deposits of chimney soot.

A single sheet of graphite is known as *graphene.* A graphene is essentially a two-dimensional carbon crystal consisting of an array of six-membered rings. Graphenes are extraordinarily strong (hundreds of times stronger than steel), they conduct electricity, and their shapes can be customized by the introduction of five-membered and seven-membered rings at specific locations. Because of their unique combination of properties, graphenes currently are the subject of a great deal of research. Proposed uses of graphenes include replacement of copper interconnects in integrated circuits, production of transparent conduction electrodes—useful for touchscreens and liquid crystal displays—and ultrahigh-sensitivity detection devices.

Student Annotation: The 2010 Nobel Prize in Physics was awarded to Andre Geim and Konstantin Novoselov for their work with graphene.

Unless otherwise constrained, graphene sheets will wrap around on themselves forming cylinders with diameters on the scale of nanometers. Such cylinders are called *carbon nanotubes.* Two types of nanotube structures are known, as shown in Figure 25.14. The differences in arrangement of hexagons give the two kinds of nanotubes different electrical conductivities.

Student Annotation: An analogy is to take a piece of paper and roll it so that you have a tube.

Carbon nanotubes of different diameters can nest inside each other, producing multiple-walled nanotubes. Most nanotubes are single-walled, though, and they can be as narrow as 1 nm in diameter. These nanotubes are remarkably strong—stronger, in fact, than a comparably sized piece of *steel*! Because nanotubes consist only of carbon atoms, they can come into close contact, thereby allowing intermolecular forces to hold large numbers of tubes together. This, in turn, makes it possible to align groups of tubes, potentially forming long strands and fibers. Lightweight fibers and strands with tremendous strength have many applications in such things as auto parts, medical implants, and sports equipment.

Besides carbon, other elements have been fashioned into nanotubes, too. Molybdenum sulfide nanotubes have been synthesized, for example, with openings between atoms that are just the right size to permit some gas molecules to pass through, but not others. This may have potential for the nanoscale storage of gases for fuel cells.

Many universities have developed large-scale facilities for nanotechnology research in collaboration with industrial partners. Since the lower limits of size have been reached in the production of silicon chip-based electronic circuits, nanotechnology may provide the pathway to circuits that are much smaller than have ever been imagined.

25.6 SEMICONDUCTORS

Recall from Section 7.6 that bonds between atoms can be described as resulting from the combination of *atomic* orbitals to form *molecular* orbitals. In a bulk sample of metal containing many, many atoms, there are many, many molecular orbitals. These molecular orbitals are so close in energy that instead of forming individual bonding and antibonding orbitals for each pair of atomic

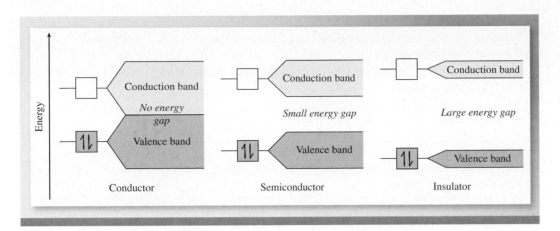

orbitals that combine, they form a band of bonding levels and a band of antibonding levels. The energies of the bonding and antibonding bands depend on the energies of the atomic orbitals that combined to form them in the first place. As a result, the band structure of a bulk sample depends on the original atoms' energy levels. The band energies and the gaps (or lack of gaps) between the bonding band (called the **valence band**) and the antibonding band (called the **conduction band**) make it possible to classify a substance as an electrical conductor, a semiconductor, or an electrical insulator based on the behavior of the electrons in the bands (Figure 25.15).

The valence band is filled with the valence (bonding) electrons, whereas the conduction band is empty or only partially filled with electrons. It is the conduction band that allows electrons to move between atoms. The gap between the valence band and the conduction band can vary from nothing (for an electrical conductor) to a small amount (for a semiconductor) to a very large amount (for an electrical insulator). Thus, the size of the band gap determines the conduction behavior of the material.

Metals have no band gap, so they are good conductors of electricity. The valence band and conduction band actually overlap or are one and the same in metallic conductors, so there is no energy barrier to the movement of electrons from one atom to another in a metal. **Semiconductors** have a band gap, but it is relatively small, so there is limited movement of electrons from the valence band to the conduction band. **Nonconductors** (electrical insulators) have large band gaps, so it is nearly impossible to promote electrons from the valence band to the conduction band.

Silicon, germanium, and carbon in the form of graphite are the only elemental semiconductors at room temperature. All three of these elements are in Group 4A and have four valence electrons. (Tin and lead are also in Group 4A, but they are metals, not semiconductors.) Other semiconductors consist of combinations of elements whose valence electron count totals 8. For example, gallium (Group 3A) and phosphorus (Group 5A) form a semiconductor because gallium contributes three valence electrons and phosphorus contributes five, giving a total of eight valence electrons. Semiconductors have also been formed between Group 2B elements (particularly Zn and Cd) and Group 6A elements.

Worked Example 25.4 lets you practice identifying combinations of elements that can exhibit semiconductor properties.

Student Annotation: The group number for a main group element corresponds to the number of valence electrons that the atom has.

Worked Example 25.4

State whether each of the following combinations of elements could form a semiconductor:
(a) Ga-Se, (b) In-P, (c) Cd-Te.

Strategy Count the valence electrons in each type of atom. If they total eight for the two elements, then the combination will probably form a semiconductor.

Setup Locate each element in the periodic table. All of them are main group elements, so we can use their group numbers to directly determine the number of valence electrons each element contributes: (a) Ga is in Group 3A, and Se is in Group 6A. (b) In is in Group 3A, and P is in Group 5A. (c) Cd is in Group 2B, and Te is in Group 6A.

(Continued on next page)

Solution (a) Ga has three valence electrons, and Se has six. This gives a total of nine, which is too many to form a semiconductor.

(b) In (three valence electrons) and P (five valence electrons) combine for a total of eight, so In-P should be a semiconductor.

(c) Cd (two valence electrons) and Te (six valence electrons) also combine for a total of eight, so Cd-Te should be a semiconductor, too.

Think About It

Semiconductors consisting of Group 3 and Group 5 elements are used in the contact layers of light-emitting diodes (LEDs).

Practice Problem A Name an element in each case that could be combined with each of the following elements to form a semiconductor: (a) O, (b) Sb, (c) Zn.

Practice Problem B For each of the elements C, As, and Ga, indicate which can be combined with silicon to produce a semiconductor, which can be added to silicon as a dopant to produce a *p*-type semiconductor, and which can be added to silicon as a dopant to produce an *n*-type semiconductor.

The conductivity of a semiconductor can be enhanced greatly by ***doping,*** the addition of very small quantities of an element with one more or one fewer valence electron than the natural semiconductor. For the purpose of simplicity, we will consider a pure silicon semiconductor. Silicon is a Group 4A element, so it has four valence electrons per atom. A small (parts per million) amount of phosphorus (Group 5A, five valence electrons) can be added, thus doping the silicon with phosphorus. Since each phosphorus atom has an "extra" electron relative to the pure semiconductor, these extra electrons must reside in the conduction band, where they increase its conductivity. This type of doped semiconductor is called an ***n-type semiconductor*** because the semiconductivity has been enhanced by the addition of negative particles, the extra electrons.

It is also possible to dope a semiconductor with an element that has fewer valence electrons than the semiconductor itself. For example, a silicon semiconductor could be doped with small amounts (again, parts per million) of gallium (Group 3A, three valence electrons). Now, instead of an "extra" electron, there is a "hole" (one less electron) in every place that a gallium atom has replaced a silicon atom. These holes are effectively positive charges (because each is the absence of an electron), so this type of material is called a ***p-type semiconductor.*** A *p*-type semiconductor has increased conductivity because the holes (which are in the valence band) move through the silicon rather than electrons. The energy required to move an electron from the valence band into a hole (also in the valence band) is considerably less than the energy needed to promote an electron from the valence band to the conduction band of a semiconductor (Figure 25.16). Thus, the movement of the holes results from the movement of charge, and conductivity is the movement of charge.

A combination of *p*-type and *n*-type semiconductors can be used to create a solar cell in which the holes and extra electrons in the semiconductors are at equilibrium in the dark. At equilibrium, the positive holes in the *n*-type layer have offset the movement of electrons into the *p*-type layer. Light falling on the solar cell causes the electrons that have entered the *p*-type layer to go back to the *n*-type layer, and other electrons to pass through a wire from the *n*-type layer to the *p*-type layer. This movement of electrons constitutes an electric current.

Figure 25.16 The effects of doping on the conduction of semiconductors.

Diodes, which are electronic devices that restrict the flow of electrons in a circuit to one direction, work in essentially the opposite direction from solar cells. A light-emitting diode (LED) consists of *n*-type and *p*-type semiconductor layers placed in contact. When a small voltage is applied, the "extra" electrons from the *n*-type side combine with the holes in the *p*-type side, thus emitting energy (light) whose wavelength depends on the band gap. The band gap is different for different semiconductors (e.g., Ga-As versus Ga-P), so the specific combination of semiconductor materials can be chosen to make the band gap correspond to a desired color of light. LEDs are finding increasing use in applications previously dominated by traditional incandescent lightbulbs such as emergency exit signs, car tail lights, and traffic signals (Figure 25.17).

Figure 25.17 LED arrays in traffic signals. Many communities have replaced the red and green signals with LED arrays that are much more energy efficient than the incandescent bulbs used previously. The yellow lights are being replaced more slowly, however, because LED arrays are expensive and the short duration of yellow lights would not necessarily allow an overall cost saving when the energy efficiency is factored in.

SECTION 25.6 REVIEW

Semiconductors

25.6.1 Which group of the periodic table contains elements that are semiconductors at room temperature?

25.7 SUPERCONDUCTORS

No ordinary electrical conductor is perfect. Even metals have some resistance to the flow of electrons, which wastes energy in the form of heat. ***Superconductors*** have no resistance to the flow of electrons and thus could be very useful for the transmission of electricity over the long distances between power plants and cities and towns. The first superconductor was discovered in 1911 by the Dutch physicist H. Kamerlingh-Onnes. He received the 1913 Nobel Prize in Physics for showing that mercury was a superconductor at 4 K, the temperature of liquid helium. Liquid helium is very expensive, however, so there were few feasible applications of a mercury superconductor.

Since that time, more superconductors have been discovered including a lanthanum-, barium-, copper-, and oxygen-containing *ceramic* compound, and a series of copper oxides ("cuprates"), all of which become superconducting below 77 K, the temperature of liquid nitrogen (a much more common and less expensive refrigerant than liquid helium). The temperature below which an element, compound, or material becomes superconducting is called the ***superconducting transition temperature, T_c.*** The higher the T_c, the more useful the superconductor.

By 1987, superconductivity was observed in another ceramic, yttrium barium copper oxide (YBCO) ($YBa_2Cu_3O_7$). Commonly called a "1-2-3 compound" because of the 1:2:3 ratio of yttrium to barium to copper, YBCO has a T_c of 93 K (above the temperature of liquid nitrogen). Although 93 K is still cold, it qualifies as quite warm in the world of superconductors, so YBCO is considered to be the first ***high-temperature superconductor.*** YBCO was first prepared by combining the three metal carbonates at high temperature (1000 to 1300 K). The copper ions are present in a mixture of +2 and +3 oxidation states:

$$4BaCO_3 + Y_2(CO_3)_3 + 4CuCO_3 + Cu_2(CO_3)_3 \longrightarrow 2YBa_2Cu_3O_7 + 14CO_2$$

YBCO must be sintered carefully to obtain the optimal superconductivity.

Superconducting wires were first made from $Bi_2Sr_2CaCu_2O_8$, known as BSCCO-2212, a high-temperature superconductor with $T_c = 95$ K. It can be prepared in wire forms because it has layers of bismuth and oxygen atoms that YBCO does not have. BSCCO-2212 is so named because its formula consists of two bismuth, two strontium, one calcium, and two copper atoms. Other BSCCO compounds exist, too, and they all have a general formula of $Bi_2Sr_2Ca_nCu_{n+1}O_{2n+6}$. BSCCO-2223, for example, which has the formula $Bi_2Sr_2Ca_2Cu_3O_{10}$ (where $n = 2$), is a superconductor with $T_c = 107$ K.

Superconductors at or below T_c exhibit the ***Meissner effect,*** the exclusion of magnetic fields. In Figure 25.18, for example, a magnet is shown levitating above a YBCO pellet, a superconductor at or below −180°C, its T_c.

Magnetic levitation is being researched for use in trains, because the amount of friction between the train and the tracks would be drastically reduced in a magnetically levitated ("maglev") train versus one running on ordinary tracks and wheels. The engineering challenge to a

Student Annotation: Allex Müller and Georg Bednorz were awarded the 1987 Nobel Prize in Physics "for their important breakthrough in the discovery of superconductivity in ceramic materials."

Student Annotation: The decomposition of a metal carbonate to the metal oxide and carbon dioxide gas is a very common reaction.

Figure 25.18 The Meissner effect. A magnet levitates above a YBCO pellet at the temperature of liquid nitrogen (−196°C).

Student Annotation: Many a Nobel Prize has been won by scientists who research and develop modern materials!

Student Annotation: You might be skeptical that two negatively charged electrons would attract each other, but there is evidence that all subatomic particles do exert some attractive forces on each other.

maglev train is that the superconductor must be kept at or below its T_c for the magnetic levitation to occur, and the highest temperatures obtained for superconducting substances are approximately 140 K—warm on the superconductivity scale but still very cold by ordinary standards.

Superconductivity in metals can be explained satisfactorily by BCS theory, first proposed by John Bardeen, Leon Neil Cooper, and John Robert Schrieffer in 1957. They received the Nobel Prize in Physics in 1972 for their work. BCS theory treats superconductivity using quantum mechanical effects, proposing that electrons with opposite spin can pair due to fundamental attractive forces between the electrons. At temperatures below T_c, the paired electrons resist energetic interference from other atoms and experience no resistance to flow. Superconductivity in ceramics has yet to be satisfactorily explained.

Learning Outcomes

- Define polymer and monomer.
- Describe the mechanism of addition polymerization.
- Differentiate between thermoplastic and thermosetting polymers.
- Distinguish between addition and condensation polymers.
- Cite examples of polymers: addition, condensation, biological (nucleic acid, protein, polysaccharide), and copolymer.
- List some of the common characteristics of ceramics.
- Describe how ceramics are produced.

- Give examples of composite materials.
- Describe the characteristics of a liquid crystal.
- Define isotropic and anisotropic.
- Discriminate between the different types of liquid crystals.
- List biomedical applications associated with modern materials.
- Differentiate between graphite, buckyballs, and nanotubes.
- Define semiconductor.
- Define superconductor.

Chapter Summary

SECTION 25.1

- *Polymers* are made up of many repeating units, called *monomers,* that are linked together by covalent bonds.
- *Thermoplastic* polymers can be melted and reshaped, whereas *thermosetting* polymers assume their final shape as part of the chemical reaction that forms them in the first place.
- *Addition polymers* are formed via a radical reaction in which a pi bond in an alkene or alkyne is opened up to form new bonds to adjacent monomers.
- Polymer chains can be *cross-linked* to provide added durability and flexibility.
- *Elastomers,* such as natural rubber, can stretch and bend and then return to their original shape.
- *Copolymers* contain more than one type of monomer. Copolymers can be random, alternating, block, or graft, depending on the sequence of the different monomers and the way that the monomers are attached in the polymer.
- *Tacticity* describes the relative geometric arrangements of the groups attached to the chiral carbon atoms in vinyl polymers. In *isotactic* polymers, all the groups attached to the chiral carbon atoms have identical arrangements. In *syndiotactic* polymers, they alternate positions along the polymer chain. In *atactic* polymers, they have random arrangements.
- *Condensation polymers* form when two different groups on monomers react, thus producing a covalent bond between monomers and a small molecule (usually water) that is expelled. The two reacting groups may be on the same monomer (as in the amino acids that form polypeptides and proteins), or they may be on two different monomers (as in hexamethylenediamine and adipic acid, which form nylon 6,6). Most condensation polymers are really copolymers.
- Amines and organic acids form condensation polymers known as *polyamides.* Alcohols and organic acids form condensation polymers known as *polyesters.* Amino acids form polyamide polymers known as polypeptides. Long, straight-chain polypeptides are known as proteins.
- DNA and RNA are condensation polymers consisting of sugars, organic bases, and phosphate ions.

SECTION 25.2

- *Ceramics* are polymeric inorganic compounds that are hard and strong and have high melting points.
- Ceramics are *sintered* to bond the particles to each other and to close any gaps that may exist in the material.
- The sol-gel process is used to prepare ceramics for structural applications because it produces particles of nearly uniform size that are much more likely to produce a solid ceramic without gaps or cracks.
- *Composite materials* contain several components each of which contributes properties to the overall material. Modern composites include reinforcing fibers and a surrounding matrix. The reinforcing fibers may be made of polymers, metals, or ceramics.

SECTION 25.3

- *Liquid crystals* are substances that maintain an ordered arrangement in the liquid phase. Molecules containing structurally rigid regions (e.g., rings and multiple bonds) and molecules that are longer in one dimension than in another seem to form the best liquid crystals. Although ordinary liquids are *isotropic,* liquid crystals are *anisotropic,* meaning that their apparent properties depend on the direction from which we view them.
- Liquid crystals may be *nematic, smectic,* or *cholesteric,* depending on the type of ordering the molecules can adopt. Nematic liquid crystals contain order in only one dimension (parallel molecules), smectic liquid crystals contain order in two dimensions (parallel molecules in parallel layers), and cholesteric liquid crystals contain layers that are rotated with respect to one another. Within each cholesteric layer, the molecules are parallel.

SECTION 25.4

- Dental amalgam consists of several metals dissolved in an alloy with mercury. Dental composite materials consist of a methacrylate polymer in a silica matrix. The composite can be varied in color to match existing teeth, making the repair more aesthetically pleasing than metallic amalgam.
- Biodegradable *sutures* and artificial skin are made of synthetic polyesters that support the growth of tissue around the polymer and then hydrolyze into the body.
- Artificial joint replacements can be made of metal, ceramics, and organic polymers.

SECTION 25.5

- *Nanotechnology* is the study and development of objects with sizes on the order of a nanometer (one billionth of a meter).
- Pure carbon exists as diamond, graphite, *fullerenes,* and *carbon nanotubes.*
- Two-dimensional sheets of sp^2-hybridized carbon atoms are called *graphenes.*

SECTION 25.6

- Electrical conductors (e.g., metals) have no gap between their *valence band* and *conduction band,* so electrons are easily promoted from the valence to the conduction band. Semiconductors, which conduct electricity more than nonconductors (insulators) but less than metallic conductors, have a small gap. The gap in *nonconductors* is too large for electrons to be promoted from the valence to the conduction band.
- *Semiconductors* generally have a total of eight valence electrons per formula unit. Thus, they typically form between two Group 4A elements, one Group 3A element and one Group 5A element, or one Group 2B element and one Group 6A element.
- Semiconductors can be *doped* with an element with fewer valence electrons to produce a *p-type semiconductor,* or with an element with more valence electrons to produce an *n-type semiconductor.*
- p-Type and n-type semiconductors can be used together in solar cells and *diodes.*

SECTION 25.7

- **Superconductors** offer no resistance to the flow of electrons. The earliest known superconductors only exhibited the behavior at liquid helium temperature (4 K), but modern **high-temperature superconductors** conduct at temperatures as high as 140 K.

- The highest temperature at which a superconductor exhibits superconductivity is called the **superconducting transition temperature (T_c).**

- Superconducting substances exhibit the **Meissner effect,** the exclusion of magnetic fields in the substance's volume. This can be demonstrated by levitating a magnet above a superconductor.

Key Words

Addition polymerization, 1013	Diode, 1033	Monomer, 1013	Smectic, 1024
Anisotropic, 1023	Doping, 1032	Nanotechnology, 1028	Superconducting transition
Atactic, 1018	Elastomer, 1015	Nematic, 1024	temperature (T_c), 1033
Carbon nanotube, 1030	Fullerene, 1030	Nonconductor, 1031	Superconductor, 1033
Ceramic, 1021	Graphene, 1030	n-Type semiconductor, 1032	Suture, 1027
Cholesteric, 1024	High-temperature	Polyamide, 1019	Syndiotactic, 1018
Composite material, 1023	superconductor, 1033	Polyester, 1019	Tacticity, 1018
Condensation polymer, 1018	Isotactic, 1018	Polymer, 1013	Thermoplastic, 1013
Conduction band, 1031	Isotropic, 1023	p-Type semiconductor, 1032	Thermosetting, 1013
Copolymer, 1016	Liquid crystal, 1023	Semiconductor, 1031	Valence band, 1031
Cross-link, 1015	Meissner effect, 1033	Sintering, 1022	

Questions and Problems

SECTION 25.1:   POLYMERS

Review Questions

25.1   Bakelite, the first commercially produced polymer, contains monomer units of phenol and formaldehyde. If an item made of Bakelite were broken, it could not be melted down and re-formed. Is Bakelite a thermoplastic or thermosetting polymer? Can Bakelite be recycled?

25.2   How are SBS rubber [Figure 25.6(a)] and nylon 6,6 similar? How are they different?

Problems

 25.3   What type of monomer unit is needed to make an electrically conducting organic polymer?

25.4   Draw the structure of the addition polymer formed by 1-butene:

$$H_2C \overset{\displaystyle H}{\underset{\displaystyle H_2}{=C}} \overset{\displaystyle }{\underset{\displaystyle C}{}} CH_3$$

Show at least two repeating units.

25.5   Draw the structure of the alternating copolymer of these two compounds, showing at least two repeating units.

$$\underset{H_3C}{\overset{H_3C}{>}}C=C\underset{CH_3}{\overset{CH_2}{<}}\qquad H-C\equiv C-H$$

25.6   Draw the structure of an alternating copolymer of these two amino acids, showing at least two repeating units:

$$H_2N-CH-\overset{\displaystyle O}{\overset{\displaystyle \|}{C}}-OH \qquad H_2N-CH-\overset{\displaystyle O}{\overset{\displaystyle \|}{C}}-OH$$
$$\qquad\underset{SH}{\overset{|}{CH_2}} \qquad\qquad\qquad \underset{CH_3}{\overset{|}{CH-OH}}$$

SECTION 25.2:   CERAMICS AND COMPOSITE MATERIALS

Review Questions

25.7   What types of atoms and bonds are present in the polymer "backbone" in a ceramic containing a transition metal?

25.8   Describe two natural types of composite materials and the substances that they contain.

Problems

25.9   What steps would be used to form a ceramic material from scandium and ethanol (CH_3CH_2OH) using the sol-gel process?

25.10   Amorphous silica (SiO_2) can be formed in uniform spheres from a sol-gel process using methanol (CH_3OH) solvent. List the chemical reactions involved in this process.

25.11   Bakelite, described in Review Question 25.1, is manufactured using materials like cellulose paper or glass fibers that are compressed and heated among the monomer units. Is Bakelite a simple polymer? If not, what classification best fits Bakelite?

SECTION 25.3:   LIQUID CRYSTALS

Review Questions

25.12   Is a normal liquid isotropic or anisotropic? How is an anisotropic material different from an isotropic material?

25.13   Describe how nematic, smectic, and cholesteric liquid crystals are similar and different.

Problems

25.14   Would each of these molecules be likely to form a liquid crystal? If not, why not?

(a)

(b)

(c) $H_2C{=}C{=}C$

25.15   Would long-chain hydrocarbons or addition polymers of alkene molecules form liquid crystals? Why or why not?

25.16   Would an ionic compound form a liquid crystal? Why or why not?

SECTION 25.4:   BIOMEDICAL MATERIALS

Review Questions

25.17   Name three major concerns that must be addressed when proposing any material to be used in medical applications inside the body.

25.18   Name a necessary chemical property and a necessary physical property of dental materials.

Problems

25.19   Is the polymer commonly used in artificial skin material (shown here) an addition polymer or a condensation polymer? Is it a block, alternating, graft, or random copolymer?

25.20   What are some advantages and disadvantages of the use of ceramics in replacement joint bearing surfaces relative to metals?

25.21   How do amalgam and composite tooth fillings differ in the ways they fail over time?

SECTION 25.5:   NANOTECHNOLOGY

Review Questions

25.22   How does an STM measure the peak and valley heights along the surface of a sample?

25.23   Name four allotropic forms of carbon.

Problems

25.24   How does an AFM differ from an STM? Why can graphite possibly be investigated with either instrument whereas diamond can only be investigated with an AFM?

25.25   What is the hybridization of the carbon atoms in a single-walled nanotube?

25.26   What structural or bonding aspect of graphite and carbon nanotubes allows their use as semiconductors, whereas diamond is an electrical insulator?

25.27   What type of intermolecular forces holds the sheets of carbon atoms together in graphite? What type of intermolecular forces hold carbon nanotubes together in strands and fibers?

SECTION 25.6:   SEMICONDUCTORS

Review Questions

25.28   How do the band gaps differ among conductors, semiconductors, and insulators?

25.29   The only elemental semiconductors (Si, Ge, and graphite) are members of Group 4A. Why are Sn and Pb, which are also in Group 4A, not classified as semiconductors?

Problems

25.30   State whether each combination of elements would be expected to produce a semiconductor: (a) Ga and Sb, (b) As and N, (c) B and P, (d) Zn and Sb, (e) Cd and S.

25.31   What type of semiconductor would be formed (a) if Si were doped with Sb and (b) if Ge were doped with B?

25.32   Describe the movement of electrons in a solar battery that uses *p*-type and *n*-type semiconductors when light shines on the solar cell.

SECTION 25.7:   SUPERCONDUCTORS

Review Questions

25.33   Why is YBCO called a "high-temperature" semiconductor when it exhibits superconductivity only below −180°C, which is very cold?

25.34   How might the Meissner effect be used in a real-world application? What are the engineering challenges to this application with the current superconductors?

Problems

25.35   What is the molecular formula of BSCCO-2201?

25.36   Superconductivity at room temperature is sometimes a subject of science fiction or fantasy. For example, in the movie *Terminator 2: Judgment Day,* a cyborg has a CPU that contains a room-temperature superconductor. How might a computer with such a CPU differ in design from current computers?

25.37   What are the electron configurations of the copper ions in YBCO? Are both ions expected oxidation states for copper?

ADDITIONAL PROBLEMS

25.38 Draw representations of block copolymers and graft copolymers using the symbols A and B for two types of monomer units. Are the categories exclusive? Using a third monomer type, see if you can draw a representation of a polymer that is both a block and a graft copolymer.

25.39 Draw the structures of the two monomer units in this polymer:

$$\left[NH-(CH_2)_8-NH-\overset{\overset{O}{\|}}{C}-(CH_2)_4-\overset{\overset{O}{\|}}{C} \right]_n$$

25.40 Is the polymer in Problem 25.39 a condensation polymer or an addition polymer? Is it a polyester, a polyamide, or something else?

25.41 What types of bonding (covalent, ionic, network, metallic) are present in a plastic polymer? In a ceramic material?

25.42 Draw representations of isotactic, syndiotactic, and atactic polyacrylonitrile (for the monomer unit, see Table 25.1).

25.43 Fluoride ion is commonly used in drinking water supplies and in toothpaste (in the form of sodium fluoride) to prevent tooth decay. The fluoride ions replace hydroxide ions in the enamel mineral hydroxyapatite [$Ca_5(PO_4)_3OH$, the same mineral as in bone], forming fluoroapatite [$Ca_5(PO_4)_3F$]. Why does replacing the hydroxide ion with fluoride ion prevent tooth decay? How does this relate to the properties of materials used in artificial fillings?

25.44 Would the metal alkoxide in the sol-gel process be acidic or basic?

25.45 Would the compound shown form a liquid crystal? Why or why not?

25.46 The semiconductor band gap energy determines the color of an LED. Knowing what you learned in Chapter 6 about the energies of photons of different colors of light, which semiconductor would have the larger band gap: the one in a green exit sign's LEDs, or the one in a red traffic signal?

25.47 Draw the structures of poly(1-butyne) and poly(1-butene), showing three or more repeating units. How are they different? How are they similar? Which of them, if any, do you think will conduct electricity?

$$H-C\equiv C-CH_2CH_3 \qquad H_2C=CH-CH_2CH_3$$
$$\text{1-butyne} \qquad\qquad \text{1-butene}$$

25.48 Propyne ($HC\equiv CCH_3$) can be used to form an electrically conducting polymer. Draw the structure of polypropyne, showing at least three repeating units, and write the general formula for the polymer.

Answers to In-Chapter Materials

PRACTICE PROBLEMS

25.1A 25.1B

$$-(CH_2CCl_2)-$$

25.2A

$$-NHCH_2(CH_2)_3CH_2\overset{\overset{O}{\|}}{C}NHCH_2(CH_2)_3CH_2\overset{\overset{O}{\|}}{C}NHCH_2(CH_2)_3CH_2\overset{\overset{O}{\|}}{C}-$$

25.2B condensation.

25.3A The top molecule would be more likely to exhibit liquid crystal behavior because it is long, thin, and has conjugated rings that limit free rotation. **25.3B** Addition of an alkyl chain makes the molecule longer, contributing to its ability to exhibit liquid crystal behavior.

25.5A (a) elements with two valence electrons, e.g., Be, Sr, Cd, (b) elements with three valence electrons, e.g., B, Ga, In, (c) elements with six valence electrons, e.g., O, Se, Te. **25.5B** Carbon can be combined with silicon to produce a semiconductor. Arsenic can be used to dope silicon to produce an n-type semiconductor; and gallium can be used to dope silicon to produce a p-type semiconductor.

SECTION REVIEW

25.1.1 block. **25.1.2** multiple bonds. **25.3.1** a box of spaghetti. **25.3.2** long narrow shape. **25.6.1** Group 4A.

Appendix 1

Scientific Notation

Chemists often deal with numbers that are either extremely large or extremely small. For example, in 1 g of the element hydrogen there are roughly

$$602{,}200{,}000{,}000{,}000{,}000{,}000{,}000$$

hydrogen atoms. Each hydrogen atom has a mass of only

$$0.00000000000000000000000166 \text{ g}$$

These numbers are cumbersome to handle, and it is easy to make mistakes when using them in arithmetic computations. Consider the following multiplication:

$$0.0000000056 \times 0.00000000048 = 0.000000000000000002688$$

It would be easy for us to miss one zero or add one more zero after the decimal point. Consequently, when working with very large and very small numbers, we use a system called *scientific notation*. Regardless of their magnitude, all numbers can be expressed in the form

$$N \times 10^n$$

where N is a number between 1 and 10 and n, the exponent, is a positive or negative integer (whole number). Any number expressed in this way is said to be written in scientific notation.

Suppose that we are given a certain number and asked to express it in scientific notation. Basically, this assignment calls for us to find n. We count the number of places that the decimal point must be moved to give the number N (which is between 1 and 10). If the decimal point has to be moved to the left, then n is a positive integer; if it has to be moved to the right, n is a negative integer. The following examples illustrate the use of scientific notation:

1. Express 568.762 in scientific notation:

$$568.762 = 5.68762 \times 10^2$$

   Note that the decimal point is moved to the left by two places and $n = 2$.

2. Express 0.00000772 in scientific notation:

$$0.00000772 = 7.72 \times 10^{-6}$$

   Here the decimal point is moved to the right by six places and $n = -6$.

   Keep in mind the following two points. First, $n = 0$ is used for numbers that are not expressed in scientific notation. For example, 74.6×10^0 ($n = 0$) is equivalent to 74.6. Second, the usual practice is to omit the superscript when $n = 1$. Thus the scientific notation for 74.6 is 7.46×10 and not 7.46×10^1

Next, we consider how scientific notation is handled in arithmetic operations.

Addition and Subtraction

To add or subtract using scientific notation, we first write each quantity—say N_1 and N_2—with the same exponent n. Then we combine N_1 and N_2; the exponents remain the same. Consider the following examples:

$$(7.4 \times 10^3) + (2.1 \times 10^3) = 9.5 \times 10^3$$

$$(4.31 \times 10^4) + (3.9 \times 10^3) = (4.31 \times 10^4) + (0.39 \times 10^4)$$

$$= 4.70 \times 10^4$$

$$(2.22 \times 10^{-2}) - (4.10 \times 10^{-3}) = (2.22 \times 10^{-2}) - (0.41 \times 10^{-2})$$

$$= 1.81 \times 10^{-2}$$

Multiplication and Division

To multiply numbers expressed in scientific notation, we multiply N_1 and N_2 in the usual way, but *add* the exponents together. To divide using scientific notation, we divide N_1 and N_2 as usual and subtract the exponents. The following examples show how these operations are performed:

$$(8.0 \times 10^4) \times (5.0 \times 10^2) = (8.0 \times 5.0)(10^{4 + 2})$$

$$= 40 \times 10^6$$

$$= 4.0 \times 10^7$$

$$(4.0 \times 10^{-5}) \times (7.0 \times 10^3) = (4.0 \times 7.0)(10^{-5 + 3})$$

$$= 28 \times 10^{-2}$$

$$= 2.8 \times 10^{-1}$$

$$\frac{6.9 \times 10^7}{3.0 \times 10^{-5}} = \frac{6.9}{3.0} \times 10^{7-(-5)}$$

$$= 2.3 \times 10^{12}$$

$$\frac{8.5 \times 10^4}{5.0 \times 10^9} = \frac{8.5}{5.0} \times 10^{4-9}$$

$$= 1.7 \times 10^{-5}$$

Basic Trigonometry

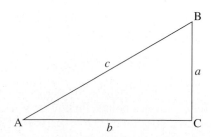

In the triangle shown, A, B, and C are angles ($C = 90°$) and a, b, and c are side lengths. To calculate unknown angles or sides, we use the following relationships:

$$a^2 + b^2 = c^2$$

$$\sin A = \frac{a}{c}$$

$$\cos A = \frac{b}{c}$$

$$\tan A = \frac{a}{b}$$

Logarithms

Common Logarithms

The concept of logarithms is an extension of the concept of exponents, which is discussed on page A-1. The common, or base-10, logarithm of any number is the power to which 10 must be raised to equal the number. The following examples illustrate this relationship:

Logarithm	Exponent
$\log 1 = 0$	$10^0 = 1$
$\log 10 = 1$	$10^1 = 10$
$\log 100 = 2$	$10^2 = 100$
$\log 10^{-1} = -1$	$10^{-1} = 0.1$
$\log 10^{-2} = -2$	$10^{-2} = 0.01$

In each case the logarithm of the number can be obtained by inspection.

Because the logarithms of numbers are exponents, they have the same properties as exponents. Thus, we have

Logarithm	Exponent
$\log AB = \log A + \log B$	$10^A \times 10^B = 10^{A+B}$
$\log \dfrac{A}{B} = \log A - \log B$	$\dfrac{10^A}{10^B} = 10^{A-B}$

Furthermore, $\log A^n = n \log A$.

Now suppose we want to find the common logarithm of 6.7×10^{-4}. On most electronic calculators, the number is entered first and then the log key is pressed. This operation gives us

$$\log 6.7 \times 10^{-4} = -3.17$$

Note that there are as many digits *after* the decimal point as there are significant figures in the original number. The original number has two significant figures, and the "17" in −3.17 tells us that the log has two significant figures. The "3" in −3.17 serves only to locate the decimal point in the number 6.7×10^{-4}. Other examples are

Number	Common Logarithm
62	1.79
0.872	−0.0595
1.0×10^{-7}	−7.00

Sometimes (as in the case of pH calculations) it is necessary to obtain the number whose logarithm is known. This procedure is known as taking the antilogarithm; it is simply the reverse of taking the logarithm of a number. Suppose in a certain calculation we have pH = 1.46 and are asked to calculate [H$^+$]. From the definition of pH (pH = −log [H$^+$]) we can write

$$[H^+] = 10^{-1.46}$$

Many calculators have a key labeled $\log^{-1}$ or INV log to obtain antilogs. Other calculators have a 10^x or y^x key (where x corresponds to −1.46 in our example and y is 10 for base-10 logarithm). Therefore, we find that $[H^+] = 0.035\ M$.

Natural Logarithms

Logarithms taken to the base e instead of 10 are known as natural logarithms (denoted by ln or $\log_e$); e is equal to 2.7183. The relationship between common logarithms and natural logarithms is as follows:

$$\log 10 = 1 \qquad\qquad 10^1 = 10$$

$$\ln 10 = 2.303 \qquad\qquad e^{2.303} = 10$$

Thus,

$$\ln x = 2.303 \log x$$

To find the natural logarithm of 2.27, say, we first enter the number on the electronic calculator and then press the ln key to get

$$\ln 2.27 = 0.820$$

If no ln key is provided, we can proceed as follows:

$$2.303 \log 2.27 = 2.303 \times 0.356$$

$$= 0.820$$

Sometimes we may be given the natural logarithm and asked to find the number it represents. For example,

$$\ln x = 59.7$$

On many calculators, we simply enter the number and press the e key:

$$e^{59.7} = 8 \times 10^{25}$$

The Quadratic Equation

A quadratic equation takes the form

$$ax^2 + bx + c = 0$$

If coefficients a, b, and c are known, then x is given by

$$x = \frac{-b \pm \sqrt{b^2 - 4ac}}{2a}$$

Suppose we have the following quadratic equation:

$$2x^2 + 5x - 12 = 0$$

Solving for x, we write

$$x = \frac{-5 \pm \sqrt{(5)^2 - 4(2)(-12)}}{2(2)}$$

$$= \frac{-5 \pm \sqrt{25 + 96}}{4}$$

Therefore,

$$x = \frac{-5 + 11}{4} = \frac{3}{2}$$

and

$$x = \frac{-5 - 11}{4} = -4$$

Successive Approximation

In the determination of hydrogen ion concentration in a weak acid solution, use of the quadratic equation can sometimes be avoided using a method known as *successive approximation*. Consider the example of a 0.0150 M solution of hydrofluoric acid (HF). The K_a for HF is 7.10×10^{-4}. To determine the hydrogen ion concentration in this solution, we construct an equilibrium table and enter the initial concentrations, the expected change in concentrations, and the equilibrium concentrations of all species:

$$HF(aq) \rightleftharpoons H^+(aq) + F^-(aq)$$

	HF	H⁺	F⁻
Initial concentration (M):	0.0150	0	0
Change in concentration (M):	$-x$	$+x$	$+x$
Equilibrium concentration (M):	$0.0150 - x$	x	x

Using the rule that x can be neglected if the initial acid concentration divided by the K_a is greater than 100, we find that in this case x cannot be neglected ($0.0150/7.1 \times 10^{-4} \approx 21$). Successive approximation involves first neglecting x with respect to initial acid concentration

$$\frac{x^2}{0.0150 - x} \approx \frac{x^2}{0.0150} = 7.10 \times 10^{-4}$$

and solving for x:

$$x^2 = (0.0150)(7.10 \times 10^{-4}) = 1.07 \times 10^{-5}$$

$$x = \sqrt{1.07 \times 10^{-5}} = 0.00326 \ M$$

We then solve for x again, this time using the calculated value of x on the bottom of the fraction:

$$\frac{x^2}{0.0150 - x} = \frac{x^2}{0.0150 - 0.00326} = 7.10 \times 10^{-4}$$

$$x^2 = (0.0150 - 0.00326)(7.10 \times 10^{-4}) = 8.33 \times 10^{-6}$$

$$x = \sqrt{8.33 \times 10^{-6}} = 0.00289 \ M$$

Note that the calculated value of x decreased from 0.00326 to 0.00289. We now use the new calculated value of x on the bottom of the fraction and solve for x again:

$$\frac{x^2}{0.0150 - x} = \frac{x^2}{0.0150 - 0.00289} = 7.10 \times 10^{-4}$$

$$x^2 = (0.0150 - 0.00289)(7.10 \times 10^{-4}) = 8.60 \times 10^{-6}$$

$$x = \sqrt{8.60 \times 10^{-6}} = 0.00293 \ M$$

This time the value of x increased slightly. We use the new calculated value and solve for x again.

$$\frac{x^2}{0.0150 - x} = \frac{x^2}{0.0150 - 0.00293} = 7.10 \times 10^{-4}$$

$$x^2 = (0.0150 - 0.00293)(7.10 \times 10^{-4}) = 8.57 \times 10^{-6}$$

$$x = \sqrt{8.57 \times 10^{-6}} = 0.00293 \ M$$

This time we find that the answer is still 0.00293 M, so there is no need to repeat the process. In general, we apply the method of successive approximation until the value of x obtained does not differ from the value obtained in the previous step. The value of x determined using successive approximation is the same value we would get if we were to use the quadratic equation.

Appendix 2

Inorganic Substances

Substance	ΔH_f° (kJ/mol)	ΔG_f° (kJ/mol)	S° (J/K · mol)
Ag(s)	0	0	42.7
Ag$^+$(aq)	105.9	77.1	73.9
AgCl(s)	−127.0	−109.7	96.1
AgBr(s)	−99.5	−95.9	107.1
AgI(s)	−62.4	−66.3	114.2
AgNO$_3$(s)	−123.1	−32.2	140.9
AI(s)	0	0	28.3
Al^{3+}(aq)	−524.7	−481.2	−313.38
Al$_2$O$_3$(s)	−1669.8	−1576.4	50.99
As(s)	0	0	35.15
AsO$_4^{3-}$(aq)	−870.3	−635.97	−144.77
AsH$_3$(g)	171.5		
H$_3$AsO$_4$(s)	−900.4		
Au(s)	0	0	47.7
Au$_2$O$_3$(s)	80.8	163.2	125.5
AuCl(s)	−35.2		
AuCl$_3$(s)	−118.4		
B(s)	0	0	6.5
B$_2$O$_3$(s)	−1263.6	−1184.1	54.0
H$_3$BO$_3$(s)	−1087.9	−963.16	89.58
H$_3$BO$_3$(aq)	−1067.8	−963.3	159.8
Ba(s)	0	0	66.9
Ba^{2+}(aq)	−538.4	−560.66	12.55
BaO(s)	−558.2	−528.4	70.3
BaCl$_2$(s)	−860.1	−810.66	125.5
BaSO$_4$(s)	−1464.4	−1353.1	132.2
BaCO$_3$(s)	−1218.8	−1138.9	112.1
Be(s)	0	0	9.5
BeO(s)	−610.9	−581.58	14.1

*The thermodynamic quantities of ions are based on the reference states that $\Delta H_f^\circ[\text{H}^+(aq)] = 0$, $\Delta G_f^\circ[\text{H}^+(aq)] = 0$, and $S^\circ[\text{II}^+(aq)] = 0$.

Substance	ΔH_f° (kJ/mol)	ΔG_f° (kJ/mol)	S° (J/K · mol)
$Br_2(l)$	0	0	152.3
$Br_2(g)$	30.7	3.14	245.13
$Br^-(aq)$	−120.9	−102.8	80.7
$HBr(g)$	−36.2	−53.2	198.48
$C(graphite)$	0	0	5.69
$C(diamond)$	1.90	2.87	2.4
$CO(g)$	−110.5	−137.3	197.9
$CO_2(g)$	−393.5	−394.4	213.6
$CO_2(aq)$	−412.9	−386.2	121.3
$CO_3^{2-}(aq)$	−676.3	−528.1	−53.1
$HCO_3^-(aq)$	−691.1	−587.1	94.98
$H_2CO_3(aq)$	−699.7	−623.2	187.4
$CS_2(g)$	115.3	65.1	237.8
$CS_2(l)$	87.3	63.6	151.0
$HCN(aq)$	105.4	112.1	128.9
$CN^-(aq)$	151.0	165.69	117.99
$(NH_2)_2CO(s)$	−333.19	−197.15	104.6
$(NH_2)_2CO(aq)$	−319.2	−203.84	173.85
$Ca(s)$	0	0	41.6
$Ca(g)$	179.3	145.5	154.8
$Ca^{2+}(aq)$	−542.96	−553.0	−55.2
$CaO(s)$	−635.6	−604.2	39.8
$Ca(OH)_2(s)$	−986.6	−896.8	83.4
$CaF_2(s)$	−1214.6	−1161.9	68.87
$CaCl_2(s)$	−794.96	−750.19	113.8
$CaSO_4(s)$	−1432.69	−1320.3	106.69
$CaCO_3(s)$	−1206.9	−1128.8	92.9
$Cd(s)$	0	0	51.46
$Cd^{2+}(aq)$	−72.38	−77.7	−61.09
$CdO(s)$	−254.6	−225.06	54.8
$CdCl_2(s)$	−389.1	−342.59	118.4
$CdSO_4(s)$	−926.17	−820.2	137.2
$Cl_2(g)$	0	0	223.0
$Cl(g)$	121.7	105.7	165.2
$Cl^-(aq)$	−167.2	−131.2	56.5
$HCl(g)$	−92.3	−95.27	187.0
$Co(s)$	0	0	28.45
$Co^{2+}(aq)$	−67.36	−51.46	155.2
$CoO(s)$	−239.3	−213.38	43.9

(Continued)

Substance	ΔH°_f (kJ/mol)	ΔG°_f (kJ/mol)	S° (J/K · mol)
$Cr(s)$	0	0	23.77
$Cr^{2+}(aq)$	−138.9		
$Cr_2O_3(s)$	−1128.4	−1046.8	81.17
$CrO_4^{2-}(aq)$	−863.16	−706.26	38.49
$Cr_2O_7^{2-}(aq)$	−1460.6	−1257.29	213.8
$Cs(s)$	0	0	82.8
$Cs(g)$	76.50	49.53	175.6
$Cs^+(aq)$	−247.69	−282.0	133.05
$CsCl(s)$	−442.8	−414.4	101.2
$Cu(s)$	0	0	33.3
$Cu^+(aq)$	51.88	50.2	−26.4
$Cu^{2+}(aq)$	64.39	64.98	−99.6
$CuO(s)$	−155.2	−127.2	43.5
$Cu_2O(s)$	−166.69	−146.36	100.8
$CuCl(s)$	−134.7	−118.8	91.6
$CuCl_2(s)$	−205.85	?	?
$CuS(s)$	−48.5	−49.0	66.5
$CuSO_4(s)$	−769.86	−661.9	113.39
$F_2(g)$	0	0	203.34
$F(g)$	80.0	61.9	158.7
$F^-(aq)$	−329.1	−276.48	−9.6
$HF(g)$	−271.6	−270.7	173.5
$Fe(s)$	0	0	27.2
$Fe^{2+}(aq)$	−87.86	−84.9	−113.39
$Fe^{3+}(aq)$	−47.7	−10.5	−293.3
$FeO(s)$	−272.0	−255.2	60.8
$Fe_2O_3(s)$	−822.2	−741.0	90.0
$Fe(OH)_2(s)$	−568.19	−483.55	79.5
$Fe(OH)_3(s)$	−824.25	?	?
$H(g)$	218.2	203.2	114.6
$H_2(g)$	0	0	131.0
$H^+(aq)$	0	0	0
$OH^-(aq)$	−229.94	−157.30	−10.5
$H_2O(g)$	−241.8	−228.6	188.7
$H_2O(l)$	−285.8	−237.2	69.9
$H_2O_2(g)$	−136.1	−105.5	232.9
$H_2O_2(l)$	−187.6	−118.1	109.6
$Hg(l)$	0	0	77.4
$Hg^{2+}(aq)$		−164.38	

Substance	ΔH_f° (kJ/mol)	ΔG_f° (kJ/mol)	S° (J/K · mol)
$HgO(s)$	−90.7	−58.5	72.0
$HgCl_2(s)$	−230.1		
$Hg_2Cl_2(s)$	−264.9	−210.66	196.2
$HgS(s)$	−58.16	−48.8	77.8
$HgSO_4(s)$	−704.17		
$Hg_2SO_4(s)$	−741.99	−623.92	200.75
$I_2(g)$	62.25	19.37	260.57
$I_2(s)$	0	0	116.7
$I(g)$	106.8	70.21	180.67
$I^-(aq)$	−55.9	−51.67	109.37
$HI(g)$	25.9	1.30	206.3
$K(s)$	0	0	63.6
$K^+(aq)$	−251.2	−282.28	102.5
$KOH(s)$	−425.85		
$KCl(s)$	−435.87	−408.3	82.68
$KClO_3(s)$	−391.20	−289.9	142.97
$KClO_4(s)$	−433.46	−304.18	151.0
$KBr(s)$	−392.17	−379.2	96.4
$KI(s)$	−327.65	−322.29	104.35
$KNO_3(s)$	−492.7	−393.1	132.9
$Li(s)$	0	0	28.0
$Li(g)$	159.3	126.6	138.8
$Li^+(aq)$	−278.46	−293.8	14.2
$LiCl(s)$	−408.3	−384.0	59.30
$Li_2O(s)$	−595.8	?	?
$LiOH(s)$	−487.2	−443.9	50.2
$Mg(s)$	0	0	32.5
$Mg(g)$	150	115	148.55
$Mg^{2+}(aq)$	−461.96	−456.0	−117.99
$MgO(s)$	−601.8	−569.6	26.78
$Mg(OH)_2(s)$	−924.66	−833.75	63.1
$MgCl_2(s)$	−641.8	−592.3	89.5
$MgSO_4(s)$	−1278.2	−1173.6	91.6
$MgCO_3(s)$	−1112.9	−1029.3	65.69
$Mn(s)$	0	0	31.76
$Mn^{2+}(aq)$	−218.8	−223.4	−83.68
$MnO_2(s)$	−520.9	−466.1	53.1
$N(g)$	470.4	455.5	153.3
$N_2(g)$	0	0	191.5

(Continued)

Substance	ΔH_f° (kJ/mol)	ΔG_f° (kJ/mol)	S° (J/K · mol)
$N_3^-(aq)$	245.18	?	?
$NH_3(g)$	−46.3	−16.6	193.0
$NH_4^+(aq)$	−132.80	−79.5	112.8
$NH_4Cl(s)$	−315.39	−203.89	94.56
$NH_3(aq)$	−80.3	−26.5	111.3
$N_2H_4(l)$	50.4		
$NO(g)$	90.4	86.7	210.6
$NO_2(g)$	33.85	51.8	240.46
$N_2O_4(g)$	9.66	98.29	304.3
$N_2O(g)$	81.56	103.6	219.99
$HNO_2(aq)$	−118.8	−53.6	
$HNO_3(l)$	−173.2	−79.9	155.6
$NO_3^-(aq)$	−206.57	−110.5	146.4
$Na(s)$	0	0	51.05
$Na(l)$	2.41	0.50	57.56
$Na(g)$	107.7	77.3	153.7
$Na^+(aq)$	−239.66	−261.87	60.25
$NaOH(aq)$	−469.6	−419.2	49.8
$Na_2O(s)$	−415.9	−376.56	72.8
$NaCl(s)$	−410.9	−384.0	72.38
$NaI(s)$	−288.0		
$Na_2SO_4(s)$	−1384.49	−1266.8	149.49
$NaNO_3(s)$	−466.68	−365.89	116.3
$Na_2CO_3(s)$	−1130.9	−1047.67	135.98
$NaHCO_3(s)$	−947.68	−851.86	102.09
$Ni(s)$	0	0	30.1
$Ni^{2+}(aq)$	−64.0	−46.4	−159.4
$NiO(s)$	−244.35	−216.3	38.58
$Ni(OH)_2(s)$	−538.06	−453.1	79.5
$O(g)$	249.4	230.1	160.95
$O_2(g)$	0	0	205.0
$O_3(aq)$	−12.09	16.3	110.88
$O_3(g)$	142.2	163.4	237.6
$P(white)$	0	0	44.0
$P(red)$	−18.4	13.8	29.3
$PCl_3(l)$	−319.7	−272.3	217.1
$PCl_3(g)$	−288.07	−269.6	311.7
$PCl_5(g)$	−374.9	−305.0	364.5
$PO_4^{3-}(aq)$	−1284.07	−1025.59	−217.57

Substance	ΔH_f° (kJ/mol)	ΔG_f° (kJ/mol)	S° (J/K · mol)
$P_4O_{10}(s)$	−3012.48		
$PH_3(g)$	9.25	18.2	210.0
$HPO_4^{2-}(aq)$	−1298.7	−1094.1	−35.98
$H_2PO_4^-(aq)$	−1302.48	−1135.1	89.1
$Pb(s)$	0	0	64.89
$Pb^{2+}(aq)$	1.6	−24.3	21.3
$PbO(s)$	−217.86	−188.49	69.45
$PbO_2(s)$	−276.65	−218.99	76.57
$PbCl_2(s)$	−359.2	−313.97	136.4
$PbS(s)$	−94.3	−92.68	91.2
$PbSO_4(s)$	−918.4	−811.2	147.28
$Pt(s)$	0	0	41.84
$PtCl_4^{2-}(aq)$	−516.3	−384.5	175.7
$Rb(s)$	0	0	69.45
$Rb(g)$	85.8	55.8	170.0
$Rb^+(aq)$	−246.4	−282.2	124.27
$RbBr(s)$	−389.2	−378.1	108.3
$RbCl(s)$	−435.35	−407.8	95.90
$RbI(s)$	−328	−326	118.0
$S(rhombic)$	0	0	31.88
$S(monoclinic)$	0.30	0.10	32.55
$SO(g)$	5.01	−19.9	221.8
$SO_2(g)$	−296.4	−300.4	248.5
$SO_3(g)$	−395.2	−370.4	256.2
$SO_3^{2-}(aq)$	−624.25	−497.06	43.5
$SO_4^{2-}(aq)$	−907.5	−741.99	17.15
$H_2S(g)$	−20.15	−33.0	205.64
$HSO_3^-(aq)$	−627.98	−527.3	132.38
$HSO_4^-(aq)$	−885.75	−752.87	126.86
$H_2SO_4(l)$	−811.3	?	?
$SF_6(g)$	−1096.2	?	?
$Si(s)$	0	0	18.70
$SiO_2(s)$	−859.3	−805.0	41.84
$Sr(s)$	0	0	54.39
$Sr^{2+}(aq)$	−545.5	−557.3	−39.33
$SrCl_2(s)$	−828.4	−781.15	117.15
$SrSO_4(s)$	−1444.74	−1334.28	121.75
$SrCO_3(s)$	−1218.38	−1137.6	97.07
$U(s)$	0	0	50.21

(Continued)

Substance	ΔH_f° (kJ/mol)	ΔG_f° (kJ/mol)	S° (J/K · mol)
$UF_6(g)$	−2147	−2064	378
$Zn(s)$	0	0	41.6
$Zn^{2+}(aq)$	−152.4	−147.2	−106.48
$ZnO(s)$	−348.0	−318.2	43.9
$ZnCl_2(s)$	−415.89	−369.26	108.37
$ZnS(s)$	−202.9	−198.3	57.7
$ZnSO_4(s)$	−978.6	−871.6	124.7

Organic Substances

Substance	Formula	ΔH_f° (kJ/mol)	ΔG_f° (kJ/mol)	S° (J/K · mol)
Acetic acid(l)	CH_3COOH	−484.2	−389.45	159.8
Acetaldehyde(g)	CH_3CHO	−166.35	−139.08	264.2
Acetone(l)	CH_3COCH_3	−246.8	−153.55	198.7
Acetylene(g)	C_2H_2	226.6	209.2	200.8
Benzene(l)	C_6H_6	49.04	124.5	172.8
Butane(g)	C_4H_{10}	−124.7	−15.7	310.0
Ethanol(l)	C_2H_5OH	−276.98	−174.18	161.0
Ethane(g)	C_2H_6	−84.7	−32.89	229.5
Ethylene(g)	C_2H_4	52.3	68.1	219.5
Formic acid(l)	$HCOOH$	−409.2	−346.0	129.0
Glucose(s)	$C_6H_{12}O_6$	−1274.5	−910.56	212.1
Methane(g)	CH_4	−74.85	−50.8	186.2
Methanol(l)	CH_3OH	−238.7	−166.3	126.8
Propane(g)	C_3H_8	−103.9	−23.5	269.9
Sucrose(s)	$C_{12}H_{22}O_{11}$	−2221.7	−1544.3	360.2

Appendix 3

Name of acid	Formula	K_{a_1}	K_{a_2}	K_{a_3}
Acetic acid	CH_3COOH	1.8×10^{-5}		
Acetylsalicylic acid	$HC_9H_7O_4$	3.3×10^{-4}		
Arsenic acid	H_3AsO_4	5.6×10^{-3}	1.0×10^{-7}	3.0×10^{-12}
Arsenous acid	H_3AsO_3	5.1×10^{-10}		
Ascorbic acid	$H_2C_6H_6O_6$	8.0×10^{-5}	1.6×10^{-12}	
Benzoic acid	C_6H_5COOH	6.5×10^{-5}		
Bromoacetic acid	$CH_2BrCOOH$	1.3×10^{-3}		
Carbonic acid	H_2CO_3	4.2×10^{-7}	4.8×10^{-11}	
Chloroacetic acid	$CH_2ClCOOH$	1.4×10^{-3}		
Chlorous acid	$HClO_2$	1.1×10^{-2}		
Cyanic acid	$HCNO$	3.5×10^{-4}		
Formic acid	$HCOOH$	1.7×10^{-4}		
Hydrocyanic acid	HCN	4.9×10^{-10}		
Hydrofluoric acid	HF	7.1×10^{-4}		
Hydrosulfuric acid*	H_2S	9.5×10^{-8}	1×10^{-19}	
Hypobromous acid	$HBrO$	2.5×10^{-9}		
Hypochlorous acid	$HClO$	3.5×10^{-8}		
Hypoiodous acid	HIO	2.3×10^{-11}		
Iodic acid	HIO_3	1.7×10^{-1}		
Iodoacetic acid	CH_2ICOOH	7.6×10^{-4}		
Nitrous acid	HNO_2	4.5×10^{-4}		
Oxalic acid	$H_2C_2O_4$	6.5×10^{-2}	6.1×10^{-5}	
Phenol	C_6H_5OH	1.3×10^{-10}		
Phosphoric acid	H_3PO_4	7.5×10^{-3}	6.2×10^{-8}	4.8×10^{-13}
Sulfuric acid	H_2SO_4	Very large	1.3×10^{-2}	
Sulfurous acid	H_2SO_3	1.3×10^{-2}	6.3×10^{-8}	
Trichloroacetic acid	CCl_3COOH	2.2×10^{-1}		
Trifluoroacetic acid	CF_3COOH	3.0×10^{-1}		

*The second ionization constant of H_2S is very low and difficult to measure. The value in this table is an estimate.

Name of base	Formula	K_b
Ammonia	NH_3	1.8×10^{-5}
Aniline	$C_6H_5NH_2$	3.8×10^{-10}
Diethylamine	$(C_2H_5)_2NH$	5.4×10^{-4}
Dimethylamine	$(CH_3)_2NH$	6.9×10^{-4}
Ethylamine	$C_2H_5NH_2$	5.6×10^{-4}
Methylamine	CH_3NH_2	4.4×10^{-4}
Pyridine	C_5H_5N	1.7×10^{-9}
Triethylamine	$(C_2H_5)_3N$	5.6×10^{-4}
Trimethylamine	$(CH_3)_3N$	6.4×10^{-5}
Urea	H_2NCONH_2	1.5×10^{-14}

Appendix 4

SOLUBILITY PRODUCT CONSTANTS AT 25°C

Compound	Dissolution equilibrium	K_{sp}
Bromides		
Copper(I) bromide	$CuBr(s) \rightleftharpoons Cu^+(aq) + Br^-(aq)$	4.2×10^{-8}
Lead(II) bromide	$PbBr_2(s) \rightleftharpoons Pb^{2+}(aq) + 2Br^-(aq)$	6.6×10^{-6}
Mercury(I) bromide	$Hg_2Br_2(s) \rightleftharpoons Hg_2^{2+}(aq) + 2Br^-(aq)$	6.4×10^{-23}
Silver bromide	$AgBr(s) \rightleftharpoons Ag^+(aq) + Br^-(aq)$	7.7×10^{-13}
Carbonates		
Barium carbonate	$BaCO_3(s) \rightleftharpoons Ba^{2+}(aq) + CO_3^{2}(aq)$	8.1×10^{-9}
Calcium carbonate	$CaCO_3(s) \rightleftharpoons Ca^{2+}(aq) + CO_3^{2-}(aq)$	8.7×10^{-9}
Lead(II) carbonate	$PbCO_3(s) \rightleftharpoons Pb^{2+}(aq) + CO_3^{2-}(aq)$	3.3×10^{-14}
Magnesium carbonate	$MgCO_3(s) \rightleftharpoons Mg^{2+}(aq) + CO_3^{2-}(aq)$	4.0×10^{-5}
Silver carbonate	$Ag_2CO_3(s) \rightleftharpoons 2Ag^+(aq) + CO_3^{2-}(aq)$	8.1×10^{-12}
Strontium carbonate	$SrCO_3(s) \rightleftharpoons Sr^{2+}(aq) + CO_3^{2-}(aq)$	1.6×10^{-9}
Chlorides		
Lead(II) chloride	$PbCl_2(s) \rightleftharpoons Pb^{2+}(aq) + 2Cl^-(aq)$	2.4×10^{-4}
Mercury(I) chloride	$Hg_2Cl_2(s) \rightleftharpoons Hg_2^{2+}(aq) + 2Cl^-(aq)$	3.5×10^{-18}
Silver chloride	$AgCl(s) \rightleftharpoons Ag^+(aq) + Cl^-(aq)$	1.6×10^{-10}
Chromates		
Lead(II) chromate	$PbCrO_4(s) \rightleftharpoons Pb^{2+}(aq) + CrO_4^{2-}(aq)$	2.0×10^{-14}
Silver(I) chromate	$Ag_2CrO_4(s) \rightleftharpoons 2Ag^+(aq) + CrO_4^{2-}(aq)$	1.2×10^{-12}
Fluorides		
Barium fluoride	$BaF_2(s) \rightleftharpoons Ba^{2+}(aq) + 2F^-(aq)$	1.7×10^{-6}
Calcium fluoride	$CaF_2(s) \rightleftharpoons Ca^{2+}(aq) + 2F^-(aq)$	4.0×10^{-11}
Lead(II) fluoride	$PbF_2(s) \rightleftharpoons Pb^{2+}(aq) + 2F^-(aq)$	4.0×10^{-8}
Hydroxides		
Aluminum hydroxide	$Al(OH)_3(s) \rightleftharpoons Al^{3+}(aq) + 3OH^-(aq)$	1.8×10^{-33}
Calcium hydroxide	$Ca(OH)_2(s) \rightleftharpoons Ca^{2+}(aq) + 2OH^-(aq)$	8.0×10^{-6}
Chromium(III) hydroxide	$Cr(OH)_3(s) \rightleftharpoons Cr^{3+}(aq) + 3OH^-(aq)$	3.0×10^{-29}
Copper(II) hydroxide	$Cu(OH)_2(s) \rightleftharpoons Cu^{2+}(aq) + 2OH^-(aq)$	2.2×10^{-20}
Iron(II) hydroxide	$Fe(OH)_2(s) \rightleftharpoons Fe^{2+}(aq) + 2OH^-(aq)$	1.6×10^{-14}
Iron(III) hydroxide	$Fe(OH)_3(s) \rightleftharpoons Fe^{3+}(aq) + 3OH^-(aq)$	1.1×10^{-36}
Magnesium hydroxide	$Mg(OH)_2(s) \rightleftharpoons Mg^{2+}(aq) + 2OH^-(aq)$	1.2×10^{-11}
Strontium hydroxide	$Sr(OH)_2(s) \rightleftharpoons Sr^{2+}(aq) + 2OH^-(aq)$	3.2×10^{-4}
Zinc hydroxide	$Zn(OH)_2(s) \rightleftharpoons Zn^{2+}(aq) + 2OH^-(aq)$	1.8×10^{-14}

Compound	Dissolution equilibrium	K_{sp}
Iodides		
Copper(I) iodide	$CuI(s) \rightleftharpoons Cu^+(aq) + I^-(aq)$	5.1×10^{-12}
Lead(II) iodide	$PbI_2(s) \rightleftharpoons Cu^{2+}(aq) + 2I^-(aq)$	1.4×10^{-8}
Silver iodide	$AgI(s) \rightleftharpoons Ag^+(aq) + I^-(aq)$	8.3×10^{-17}
Phosphates		
Calcium phosphate	$Ca_3(PO_4)_2(s) \rightleftharpoons 3Ca^{2+}(aq) + 2PO_4^{3-}(aq)$	1.2×10^{-26}
Iron(III) phosphate	$FePO_4(s) \rightleftharpoons Fe^{3+}(aq) + PO_4^{3-}(aq)$	1.3×10^{-22}
Sulfates		
Barium sulfate	$BaSO_4(s) \rightleftharpoons Ba^{2+}(aq) + SO_4^{2-}(aq)$	1.1×10^{-10}
Calcium sulfate	$CaSO_4(s) \rightleftharpoons Ca^{2+}(aq) + SO_4^{2-}(aq)$	2.4×10^{-5}
Lead(II) sulfate	$PbSO_4(s) \rightleftharpoons Pb^{2+}(aq) + SO_4^{2-}(aq)$	1.8×10^{-8}
Mercury(I) sulfate	$Hg_2SO_4(s) \rightleftharpoons Hg_2^{2+}(aq) + SO_4^{2-}(aq)$	6.5×10^{-7}
Silver sulfate	$Ag_2SO_4(s) \rightleftharpoons 2Ag^+(aq) + SO_4^{2-}(aq)$	1.5×10^{-5}
Strontium sulfate	$SrSO_4(s) \rightleftharpoons Sr^{2+}(aq) + SO_4^{2-}(aq)$	3.8×10^{-7}
Sulfides		
Bismuth sulfide	$Bi_2S_3(s) \rightleftharpoons 2Bi^{3+}(aq) + 3S^{2-}(aq)$	1.6×10^{-72}
Cadmium sulfide	$CdS(s) \rightleftharpoons Cd^{2+}(aq) + S^{2-}(aq)$	8.0×10^{-28}
Cobalt(II) sulfide	$CoS(s) \rightleftharpoons Co^{2+}(aq) + S^{2-}(aq)$	4.0×10^{-21}
Copper(II) sulfide	$CuS(s) \rightleftharpoons Cu^{2+}(aq) + S^{2-}(aq)$	6.0×10^{-37}
Iron(II) sulfide	$FeS(s) \rightleftharpoons Fe^{2+}(aq) + S^{2-}(aq)$	6.0×10^{-19}
Lead(II) sulfide	$PbS(s) \rightleftharpoons Pb^{2+}(aq) + S^{2-}(aq)$	3.4×10^{-28}
Manganese(II) sulfide	$MnS(s) \rightleftharpoons Mn^{2+}(aq) + S^{2-}(aq)$	3.0×10^{-14}
Mercury(II) sulfide	$HgS(s) \rightleftharpoons Hg^{2+}(aq) + S^{2-}(aq)$	4.0×10^{-54}
Nickel(II) sulfide	$NiS(s) \rightleftharpoons Ni^{2+}(aq) + S^{2-}(aq)$	1.4×10^{-24}
Silver sulfide	$Ag_2S(s) \rightleftharpoons 2Ag^+(aq) + S^{2-}(aq)$	6.0×10^{-51}
Tin(II) sulfide	$SnS(s) \rightleftharpoons Sn^{2+}(aq) + S^{2-}(aq)$	1.0×10^{-26}
Zinc sulfide	$ZnS(s) \rightleftharpoons Zn^{2+}(aq) + S^{2-}(aq)$	3.0×10^{-23}

Glossary

A

absolute temperature scale. A scale based on −273.15°C (absolute zero) being the lowest point. (11.4)

absolute zero. Theoretically the lowest obtainable temperature: −273.15°C or 0 K. (11.4)

absorbance. Negative base ten logarithm of transmittance. (9.5)

absorption spectrum. Plot of absorbance as a function of wavelength of incident light. (9.5)

accuracy. The closeness of a measurement to the true or accepted value. (1.5)

acid. See *Arrhenius acid*, *Brønsted acid*, and *Lewis acid*.

acid ionization constant (K_a). The equilibrium constant that indicates to what extent a weak acid ionizes. (16.6)

actinide series. Series of elements that has partially filled $5f$ and/or $6d$ subshells. (3.10)

activated complex. A transient species that forms when molecules collide in an effective collision. (14.2)

activation energy (E_a). The minimum amount of energy to begin a chemical reaction. (14.2)

activity series. A list of metals arranged from top to bottom in order of decreasing ease of oxidation. (9.4)

actual yield. The amount of product actually obtained from a reaction. (8.4)

addition polymer. A large molecule that forms when small molecules known as monomers join together. (24.6)

addition polymerization. Process by which monomers combine to form polymers without the elimination of small molecules, such as water. (25.1)

adhesion. The attractions between unlike molecules. (12.2)

alcohol. A compound consisting of an alkyl group and the functional group −OH. (24.2)

aldehyde. A compound containing a hydrogen atom bonded to a carbonyl group. (24.2)

aliphatic. Describes organic molecules that do not contain the benzene ring. (24.1)

alkali metal. An element from Group 1A, with the exception of H (i.e., Li, Na, K, Rb, Cs, and Fr). (2.5)

alkaline earth metal. An element from Group 2A (Be, Mg, Ca, Sr, Ba, and Ra). (2.5)

alkane. Hydrocarbons having the general formula C_nH_{2n+2}, where $n = 1, 2, \ldots$ (2.5)

alkyl group. A portion of a molecule that resembles an alkane. (24.2)

allotrope. One of two or more distinct forms of an element. (5.5)

alloy. Homogeneous mixture of two or more metals. (21.2)

alpha particle. A helium ion with a positive charge of +2. (2.2)

alpha ray. See *alpha particle*.

amalgam. A substance made by combining mercury with one or more other metals. (Chapter 19, Opening Essay; 21.2)

amide. An organic molecule that contains an amide group. (24.2)

amine. An organic molecule that contains an amino group. (24.2)

amino acid. A compound that contains both an amino group and a carboxy group. (24.2)

amorphous solid. A solid that lacks a regular three-dimensional arrangement of atoms. (12.5)

amphoteric. Describes an oxide that displays both acidic and basic properties. (16.3, 16.11)

amplitude. The vertical distance from the midline of a wave to the top of the peak or the bottom of the trough. (3.2)

angular momentum quantum number (ℓ). Describes the shape of the atomic orbital. (3.7)

anion. An ion with a negative charge. (4.4)

anisotropic. Dependent upon the axis of measurement. (25.3)

anode. The electrode at which oxidation occurs. (19.2)

antibonding molecular orbital. A molecular orbital that is higher in energy than the atomic orbitals that combined to produce it. (7.6)

aqueous. Dissolved in water. (8.1)

aromatic. Describes organic compounds that are related to benzene or that contain one or more benzene rings. (24.1)

Arrhenius acid. Substance that increases H^+ concentration when added to water. (2.6, 9.3)

Arrhenius base. Substance that increases OH^- concentration when added to water. (4.1, 9.3)

Arrhenius equation. An equation that gives the dependence of the rate constant of a reaction on temperature: $k = Ae^{-E_a/RT}$. (14.6)

atactic. Describes polymers in which the substituents are oriented randomly along the polymer chain. (25.1)

atom. The basic unit of an element that can enter into chemical combination. (2.1)

atomic ion. Atom that has lost or gained one or more electrons, giving it a positive or negative charge. (see *monatomic ion*)

atomic mass. The mass of the atom given in atomic mass units (amu). (2.4)

atomic mass unit (amu). A mass exactly equal to one-twelfth the mass of one carbon-12 atom. (1.4)

atomic number (Z). The number of protons in the nucleus of each atom of an element. (2.3)

atomic orbital. The wave function of an electron in an atom. (3.6)

atomic radius. Metallic: One-half the distance between the nuclei in the two adjacent atoms of the same element in a metal. Covalent: One-half the distance between the nuclei of the two identical atoms in a diatomic molecule. (4.4)

atomic weight. The average atomic mass. (2.4)

Aufbau principle. The process by which the periodic table can be built up by successively adding one proton to the nucleus and one electron to the appropriate atomic orbital. (3.9)

autoionization of water. Ionization of water molecules to give H^+ and OH^- ions. (16.3)

Avogadro's law. The volume of a sample of gas (V) is directly proportional to the number of moles (n) in the sample at constant temperature and pressure: $V \propto n$. (11.4)

Avogadro's number (N_A). The number of atoms in exactly 12 g of carbon-12: 6.022×10^{23}. (2.6)

axial. Describes the two bonds that form an axis perpendicular to the trigonal plane. (7.1)

B

band theory. A theory wherein atomic orbitals merge to form energy bands. (21.3)

barometer. An instrument used to measure atmospheric pressure. (11.3)

base. See *Arrhenius base*, *Brønsted base*, and *Lewis base*.

base ionization constant (K_b). The equilibrium constant that indicates to what extent a weak base ionizes. (16.7)

battery. A portable, self-contained source of electric energy consisting of galvanic cells or a series of galvanic cells. (19.6)

Beer-Lambert law. Equation relating absorbance to molar absorptivity, solution concentration, and distance that light travels through a solution. (9.5)

beta particle. An electron. (2.2)

beta ray. See *beta particle*.

bimolecular. Describes a reaction in which two reactant molecules collide. (14.7)

binary compound. A substance that consists of just two different elements. (5.5, 5.6)

blackbody radiation. The electromagnetic radiation emitted from a heated solid. (3.3)

body-centered cubic cell. A unit cell with one atom at the center of the cube and one atom at each of the eight corners. (12.3)

boiling point. The temperature at which vapor pressure equals atmospheric pressure. (12.6)

bond angle. The angle between two adjacent A—B bonds. (7.1)

bond enthalpy. The enthalpy change associated with breaking a particular bond in 1 mole of gaseous molecules. (10.7)

bonding molecular orbital. A molecular orbital that is lower in energy than the atomic orbitals that combined to produce it. (7.6)

bond order. A number based on the number of electrons in bonding and antibonding molecular orbitals that indicates, qualitatively, how stable a bond is. (7.6)

Born-Haber cycle. The cycle that relates the lattice energy of an ionic compound to quantities that can be measured. (10.8)

Boyle's law. The pressure of a fixed amount of gas at a constant temperature is inversely proportional to the volume of the gas: $P \propto 1/V$. (11.4)

Bragg equation. An equation relating the wavelength of X rays, the angle of diffraction, and the spacing between atoms in a lattice. (12.3)

breeder reactor. A nuclear reactor that produces more fissionable material than it consumes. (20.5)

Brønsted acid. A substance that donates a proton (H^+). (9.3, 16.1)

Brønsted base. A substance that accepts a proton (H^+). (9.3, 16.1)

buffer. A solution that contains significant concentrations of both members of a conjugate pair (weak acid/conjugate base or weak base/conjugate acid). (17.2)

C

calorimetry. The measurement of heat changes. (10.4)

capillary action. The movement of liquid up a narrow tube as the result of adhesive forces. (12.2)

carbocation. A species in which one of the carbons is surrounded by only six electrons. (24.5)

carbon nanotube. A tube made of carbon atoms with dimensions on the order of nanometers. (25.5)

carboxylic acid. An organic acid that contains a carboxy group. (24.2)

catalyst. A substance that increases the rate of a chemical reaction without itself being consumed. (14.8)

catenation. The formation of long carbon chains. (24.1)

cathode. The electrode at which reduction occurs. (19.2)

cation. An ion with a positive charge. (4.4)

cell potential (E_{cell}). The difference in electric potential between the cathode and the anode. (19.2)

ceramics. Polymeric inorganic compounds that share the properties of hardness, strength, and high melting points. (25.2)

chalcogens. Elements in Group 6A (O, S, Se, Te, and Po). (2.5)

Charles and Gay-Lussac's law. See *Charles's law*.

Charles's law. The volume of a fixed amount of gas (V) maintained at constant pressure is directly proportional to absolute temperature (T): $V \propto T$. (11.4)

chelating agent. A polydentate ligand that forms complex ions with metal ions in solution. (22.1)

chemical change. A process in which one or more substances are changed into one or more new substances. (1.3)

chemical energy. Energy stored within the structural units (molecules or polyatomic ions) of chemical substances. (3.1)

chemical equation. Chemical symbols used to represent a chemical reaction. (8.1)

chemical formula. Chemical symbols and numerical subscripts used to denote the composition of the substance. (5.3)

chemical property. Any property of a substance that cannot be studied without converting the substance into some other substance. (1.3)

chemistry. The study of matter and the changes it undergoes. (1.1)

chiral. Describes molecules with nonsuperimposable mirror images. (24.4)

cholesteric. Describes molecules that are parallel to each other within each layer, but where each layer is rotated with respect to the layers above and below it. (25.3)

cis. Describes the isomer in which two substituents both lie on the same side of a double bond. (24.4)

Clausius-Clapeyron equation. A linear relationship that exists between the natural log of vapor pressure and the reciprocal of absolute temperature. (12.2)

closed system. A system that can exchange energy (but not mass) with the surroundings. (10.2)

cohesion. The attraction between like molecules. (12.2)

colligative properties. Properties that depend on the number of solute particles in solution but do not depend on the nature of the solute particles. (13.5)

collision theory. The reaction rate is directly proportional to the number of molecular collisions per second. (14.2)

colloid. A dispersion of particles of one substance throughout another substance. (13.7)

combination reaction. A reaction in which two or more reactants combine to form a single product. (8.1)

combustion. Burning in air. (8.1)

combustion analysis. An experimental determination of an empirical formula by a reaction with oxygen to produce carbon dioxide and water. (8.2)

combustion reaction. A reaction in which a substance burns in the presence of oxygen. (8.1)

common ion effect. The presence of a common ion suppresses the ionization of a weak acid or weak base. (17.1)

complex ion. Charged species consisting of a central metal cation bonded to two or more anions or polar molecules. (17.5)

composite material. A material made from two or more substances with different properties that remain separate in the bulk material. (25.2)

compound. A substance composed of atoms of two or more elements chemically united in fixed proportions. (5.1)

concentration. Amount of solute relative to the volume of a solution or to the amount of solvent in a solution. (9.5)

concentration cell. A cell that has the same type of electrode and the same ion in solution (at different concentrations) in the anode and cathode compartments. (19.5)

condensation. The phase transition from gas to liquid. (12.2)

condensation polymer. A large molecule that forms when small molecules undergo condensation reactions. (24.6, 25.1)

condensation reaction. An elimination reaction in which two or more molecules become connected with the elimination of a small molecule, often water. (24.6)

condensed structural formula. Shows the same information as a structural formula, but in a condensed form. (24.3)

condensed structure. Chemical structure simplified by using abbreviations for repeating structural units. (24.3)

conduction band. The antibonding band. (25.6)

conductor. A substance through which electrons move freely. (21.3)

conjugate acid. The cation that remains when a Brønsted base accepts a proton. (16.1)

conjugate base. The anion that remains when a Brønsted acid donates a proton. (16.1)

conjugate pair. The combination of a Brønsted acid and its conjugate base (or the combination of a Brønsted base and its conjugate acid). (16.1)

constitutional isomers. Compounds with the same chemical formula but different structures. (24.4)

conversion factor. A fraction in which the same quantity is expressed one way in the numerator and another way in the denominator. (1.6)

coordinate covalent bond. A covalent bond in which one of the atoms donates both electrons. (6.6)

coordination compound. A compound that contains coordinate covalent bonds between a metal ion (often a transition metal ion) and two or more polar molecules or ions. (22.1)

coordination number. The number of atoms surrounding an atom in a crystal lattice. (12.3) The number of donor atoms surrounding a metal in a complex. (22.1)

copolymer. A polymer made of two or more different monomers. (24.6, 25.1)

corrosion. The undesirable oxidation of metals. (19.8)

Coulomb's law. The force (F) between two charged objects (Q_1 and Q_2) is directly proportional to the product of the two charges and inversely proportional to the distance (d) between the objects squared. (4.4)

covalent bond. A shared pair of electrons. (5.5)

covalent bonding. Two atoms sharing a pair of electrons. (8.3)

covalent radius. Half the distance between adjacent, identical nuclei in a molecule. (5.5)

critical mass. The minimum amount of fissionable material required to sustain a reaction. (20.5)

critical pressure (P_c). The minimum pressure that must be applied to liquefy a substance at its critical temperature. (12.6)

critical temperature (T_c). The temperature at which the gas phase cannot be liquefied, no matter how great the applied pressure. (12.6)

cross-link. A bond that forms between a functional group off the backbone of the polymer chain that interacts with another functional group of a second polymer strand creating a new covalent bond and causing the polymer to be stronger and more rigid. (25.1)

crystal field splitting (Δ). The difference in energy between the lower and higher d-orbital energy levels. (22.3)

crystalline solid. A solid that possesses rigid and long-range order; its atoms, molecules, or ions occupy specific positions. (12.3)

D

Dalton's law of partial pressures. The total pressure exerted by a gas mixture is the sum of the partial pressures exerted by each component of the mixture. (11.7)

dative bond. A covalent bond in which one of the atoms donates both electrons. (see *coordinate covalent bond*)

de Broglie wavelength. A wavelength calculated using the following equation: $\lambda = h/mu$. (3.5)

decomposition reaction. A reaction in which one reactant forms two or more products. (8.1)

degenerate. Having an equal energy. (3.9)

delocalized. Spread out over the molecule or part of the molecule, rather than confined between two specific atoms. (7.7)

density. The ratio of mass to volume. (1.4)

deoxyribonucleic acid (DNA). Biological polymer arranged in a double-helix shape, consisting of two long chains of nucleotides in which the sugar is deoxyribose. (24.6)

deposition. The phase change from gas to solid. (12.6)

dextrorotatory. The term used to describe the enantiomer that rotates the plane-polarized light to the right. (22.2)

diagonal relationships. Similarities in chemical properties of elements that are in different groups but that are positioned diagonally to one another in the periodic table. (4.4)

diamagnetic. A species without unpaired electrons that is weakly repelled by magnetic fields. (3.9)

diatomic molecule. A molecule that contains two atoms. (5.5)

diffusion. The mixing of gases. (11.2)

dilution. The process of preparing a less concentrated solution from a more concentrated one. (9.5)

dimensional analysis. The use of conversion factors in problem solving. (1.6)

diode. An electronic device that restricts the flow of electrons in a circuit to one direction. (25.6)

dipole moment (μ). A quantitative measure of the polarity of a bond. (6.2)

dipole-dipole interactions. Attractive forces that act between polar molecules. (12.1)

diprotic acid. An acid with two ionizable protons. (9.3)

dispersion forces. See *London dispersion forces.*

displacement. An atom or ion in a compound is replaced by an atom of another element. (9.4)

displacement reaction. Reaction in which two reactants trade components (double displacement) or where a component of a reactant is removed (single displacement). (9.4)

disproportionation. When an element undergoes both oxidation and reduction in the same reaction. (9.4)

dissociation. The process by which an ionic compound, upon dissolution, breaks apart into its constituent ions. (9.1)

donor atom. The atom that bears the unshared pair of electrons. (22.1)

doping. The addition of very small quantities of an element with one more or one fewer valence electron than the natural semiconductor. (25.6)

d orbital. Atomic orbital in which the angular momentum quantum number (ℓ) is 2. (6.6)

double bond. A multiple bond in which the atoms share two pairs of electrons. (8.3)

dynamic equilibrium. Occurs when a forward process and reverse process are occurring at the same rate. (9.1, 12.2, 15.1)

E

effective collision. A collision that results in a reaction. (14.2)

effective nuclear charge (Z_{eff}). The actual magnitude of positive charge that is "experienced" by an electron in the atom. (4.3)

effusion. The escape of a gas from a container into a vacuum. (11.2)

elastomer. A material that can stretch or bend and then return to its original shape as long as the limits of its elasticity are not exceeded. (25.1)

electricity. The movement of electrons. (9.1)

electrode. A piece of conducting metal in an electrochemical cell at which either oxidation or reduction takes place. (19.2)

electrolysis. The use of electric energy to drive a nonspontaneous redox reaction. (19.7)

electrolyte. A substance that dissolves in water to yield a solution that conducts electricity. (9.1)

electrolytic cell. An electrochemical cell used for electrolysis. (19.7)

electromagnetic spectrum. Consists of radio waves, microwave radiation, infrared radiation, visible light, ultraviolet radiation, X rays, and gamma rays. (3.2)

electromagnetic wave. A wave that has an electric field component and a magnetic field component. (3.2)

electron. A negatively charged subatomic particle found outside the nucleus of all atoms. (2.2)

electron affinity (EA). The energy released (the negative of the enthalpy change, $-\Delta H$) when an atom in the gas phase accepts an electron. (4.4)

electron configuration. The distribution of electrons in the atomic orbitals of an atom. (3.9)

electron density. The probability that an electron will be found in a particular region of an atom. (3.6)

electron domain. A lone pair or a bond, regardless of whether the bond is single, double, or triple. (7.1)

electron-domain geometry. The arrangement of electron domains (bonds and lone pairs) around a central atom. (7.1)

electron spin quantum number (m_s). The fourth quantum number that differentiates two electrons in the same orbital. (3.7)

electronegativity. The ability of an atom in a compound to draw electrons to itself. (6.2)

electrophile. A region of positive or partial positive charge. (24.5)

electrophilic addition. An addition reaction that begins when an electrophile approaches a region of electron density. (24.5)

electrostatic energy. The potential energy that results from the interaction of charged particles. (3.1)

element. A substance that cannot be separated into simpler substances by chemical means. (2.1)

elementary reaction. A reaction that occurs in a single collision of the reactant molecules. (14.7)

elimination reaction. A reaction in which a double bond forms and a molecule such as water is removed. (24.5)

emission spectrum. The light emitted, either as a continuum or in discrete lines, by a substance in an excited electronic state. (3.4)

empirical formula. The chemical formula that conveys with the smallest possible whole numbers the ratio of combination of elements in a compound. (5.5)

enantiomers. Molecules that are mirror images of each other but cannot be superimposed. (22.2, 24.4)

endothermic process. A process that absorbs heat. (10.1)

endpoint. The point at which the color of the indicator changes. (9.6, 17.3)

energy. The capacity to do work or transfer heat. (3.1)

enthalpy (H). A thermodynamic quantity defined by the equation $H = U + PV$. The change in enthalpy, ΔH, is equal to the heat exchanged between the system and surroundings at constant pressure q_P. (10.3)

enthalpy of reaction (ΔH_{rxn}). The difference between the enthalpy of the products and the enthalpy of the reactants. (10.3)

entropy (S). A thermodynamic state function that describes how dispersed a system's energy is. (13.2, 18.2)

enzymes. Biological catalysts. (14.8)

equatorial. The three bonds that are arranged in a trigonal plane in a trigonal bipyramidal geometry. (7.1)

equilibrium. A state in which forward and reverse processes are occurring at the same rate. (15.1)

equilibrium constant (K). A number equal to the ratio of the equilibrium concentrations of products to the equilibrium concentrations of reactants, with each concentration raised to the power of its stoichiometric coefficient. (15.2)

equilibrium expression. The quotient of product concentrations and reactant concentrations, each raised to the power of its stoichiometric coefficient. (15.2)

equilibrium process. A process that can be made to occur by the addition or removal of energy but does not happen on its own. (18.4)

equilibrium vapor pressure. The pressure exerted by the molecules that have escaped to the gas phase, once the pressure has stopped increasing. (12.2)

equivalence point. The point in a titration where the reaction (e.g., neutralization) is complete. (9.6)

ester. An organic molecule containing a —COOR group. (24.2)

evaporation. The phase change from liquid to solid at a temperature below the boiling point. (12.2)

excess reactant. The reactant present in a greater amount than necessary to react with all the limiting reactant. (8.4)

excited state. A state that is higher in energy than the ground state. (3.7)

exothermic process. A process that gives off heat. (10.1)

extensive property. A property that depends on the amount of matter involved. (1.3)

F

face-centered cubic cell. A cubic unit cell with one atom on each of the six faces and one atom at each of the eight corners. (12.3)

family. The elements in a vertical column of the periodic table. (2.5)

first law of thermodynamics. Energy can be converted from one form to another, but cannot be created or destroyed. (10.2)

first-order reaction. A reaction whose rate depends on the reactant concentration raised to the first power. (14.5)

f orbital. Atomic orbital in which the angular momentum quantum number (ℓ) is 3. (3.7)

formal charge. Method of electron "bookkeeping" in which shared electrons are divided equally between the atoms that share them. (6.4)

formation constant (K_f). The equilibrium constant that indicates to what extent complex-ion formation reactions occur. (17.5)

formula mass. The mass of a formula unit. (5.8)

formula weight. See *formula mass*.

fractional precipitation. The separation of a mixture based upon the components' solubilities. (17.6)

free energy. The energy available to do work. (18.5)

free radical. A molecule with an odd number of electrons. (6.6)

freezing point. The temperature at which a liquid undergoes the phase transition to solid. (12.6)

frequency (ν). The number of waves that pass through a particular point in 1 s. (3.2)

fuel cell. A voltaic cell in which reactants must be continually supplied. (19.6)

fullerenes. Molecules with elongated and elliptical cages of 70 and 80 carbon atoms. (25.5)

functional group. The part of a molecule characterized by a special arrangement of atoms that is largely responsible for the chemical behavior of the parent molecule. (5.6)

fusion. The phase transition from solid to liquid (melting) (12.6) or the combination of light nuclei to form heavier nuclei. (20.5)

G

galvanic cell. An electrochemical cell in which a spontaneous chemical reaction generates a flow of electrons. (19.2)

galvanization. The cathodic protection of iron or steel using zinc. (19.8)

gamma rays. High-energy radiation. (2.2)

gas constant (R). The proportionality constant that appears in the ideal gas equation. (11.2)

gas laws. Equations that relate the volume of a gas sample to its other parameters: temperature (T), pressure (P), and number of moles (n). (11.4)

geometrical isomers. Molecules that contain the same atoms and bonds arranged differently in space. (22.2, 24.4)

Gibbs free energy. The energy available to do work. (18.5)

glass. Commonly refers to an optically transparent fusion product of inorganic materials that has cooled to a rigid state without crystallizing. (12.5)

Graham's law. The rates of diffusion and effusion are inversely proportional to the square root of the molar mass of the gas. (11.2)

graphene. Two-dimensional sheet of sp^2-hybridized carbon atoms. (25.5)

gravimetric analysis. An analytical technique based on the measurement of mass. (9.6)

ground state. The lowest energy state of an atom. (3.4)

group. The elements in a vertical column of the periodic table. (2.5)

H

half-cell. One compartment of an electrochemical cell containing an electrode immersed in a solution. (19.2)

half-life ($t_{1/2}$). The time required for the reactant concentration to drop to half its original value. (14.5)

half-reaction. The separated oxidation and reduction reactions that make up the overall redox reaction. (9.4, 19.1)

half-reaction method. Balancing an oxidation-reduction equation by separating the oxidation and the reduction, balancing them separately, and adding them back together. (9.4, 19.1)

Hall process. Electrolytic reduction of aluminum from anhydrous aluminum oxide (corundum). (21.7)

halogens. The elements in Group 7A (F, Cl, Br, I, and At). (2.5)

heat. The transfer of thermal energy between two bodies that are at different temperatures. (10.1)

heat capacity (*C*). The amount of heat required to raise the temperature of an object by 1°C. (10.4)

Heisenberg uncertainty principle. It is impossible to know simultaneously both the momentum (*p*) (defined as mass times velocity, $m \times u$) and the position (*x*) of a particle with certainty. (3.6)

Henderson-Hasselbalch equation. pH = pK_a + log ([conjugate base]/[weak acid]). (17.2)

Henry's law. The solubility of a gas in a liquid is proportional to the pressure of the gas over the solution. (13.4)

Henry's law constant (*k*). The proportionality constant that is specific to the gas-solvent combination and varies with temperature. (13.4)

Hess's law. The change in enthalpy that occurs when reactants are converted to products in a reaction is the same whether the reaction takes place in one step or in a series of steps. (10.5)

heteroatom. Any atom in an organic molecule other than carbon or hydrogen. (24.3)

heterogeneous catalysis. A catalysis in which the reactants and the catalyst are in different phases. (14.8)

heterogeneous mixture. A mixture in which the composition varies. (1.2)

heteronuclear. Containing two or more different elements. (5.5)

high-temperature superconductor. A material that shows no resistance to the flow of electrons at an unusually high temperature. (25.7)

homogeneous catalysis. A catalysis in which the reactants and the catalyst are in the same phase. (14.8)

homogeneous mixture. A mixture in which the composition is uniform. Also called a solution. (1.2)

homonuclear. Containing atoms of only one element. (5.5)

Hund's rule. The most stable arrangement of electrons in orbitals of equal energy is the one in which the number of electrons with the same spin is maximized. (3.9)

hybridization. The mixing of atomic orbitals. (7.4)

hydrate. A compound with a specific number of water molecules within its solid structure. (5.7)

hydration. The process by which water molecules surround solute particles in an aqueous solution. (9.2)

hydrocarbon. A compound containing only carbon and hydrogen. (5.6)

hydrogen bonding. A special type of dipole-dipole interaction that occurs only in molecules that contain H bonded to a small, highly electronegative atom, such as N, O, or F. (12.1)

hydronium ion. A hydrated proton (H_3O^+). (9.3)

hydrophilic. Water-loving. (13.7)

hydrophobic. Water-fearing. (13.7)

hypertonic. Describes a solution with a higher concentration of dissolved substances than plasma. (13.5)

hypothesis. A tentative explanation for a set of observations. (1.1)

hypotonic. Describes a solution that has a lower concentration of dissolved substances than plasma. (13.5)

I

ideal gas. A hypothetical sample of gas whose pressure-volume-temperature behavior is predicted accurately by the ideal gas equation. (11.5)

ideal gas equation. An equation that describes the relationship among the four variables *P*, *V*, *n*, and *T*. (11.5)

ideal solution. A solution that obeys Raoult's law. (13.5)

indicator. A substance that has a distinctly different color in acidic and basic media. (9.6)

initial rate. The instantaneous rate at the beginning of a reaction. (14.4)

inorganic compounds. Compounds that do not contain carbon or that are derived from nonliving sources. (5.6)

instantaneous dipole. A fleeting nonuniform distribution of electron density in a molecule without a permanent dipole. (12.1)

instantaneous rate. The reaction rate at a specific time. (14.3)

insulator. A substance that does not conduct electricity. (21.3)

integrated rate law. ln $([A]_t/[A]_0) = -kt$. (14.5)

intensive property. A property that does not depend on the amount of matter involved. (1.3)

intermediate. A chemical species that is produced in one step of a reaction mechanism and consumed in a subsequent step. (14.7)

intermolecular forces. The attractive forces that hold particles together in the condensed phases. (7.2, 12.1)

International System of Units. See *SI units*. (1.4)

ion. Atom or molecule that has lost or gained one or more electrons giving it a positive or negative charge. (4.4)

ion-dipole interactions. Coulombic attractions between ions and polar molecules. (12.1)

ionic bonding. An electrostatic attraction that holds oppositely charged ions together in an ionic compound. (5.3)

ionic compound. Substance consisting of ions held together by electrostatic attraction. (5.3)

ionic equation. Chemical equation in which all strong electrolytes are shown as ions. (9.2)

ionic radius. The radius of a cation or an anion. (4.6)

ionizable hydrogen atom. A hydrogen atom that can be lost as a hydrogen ion, (H^+). (5.6)

ionization. The process by which a molecular compound forms ions when it dissolves. (9.1)

ionization energy (*IE*). The minimum energy required to remove an electron from an atom in the gas phase. (4.4)

ion pair. Ions in solution that are held together by electrostatic forces. (13.5)

isoelectronic. Describes two or more species with identical electron configurations. (7.5)

isoelectronic series. A series of two or more species that have identical electron configurations but different nuclear charges. (4.5)

isolated system. A system that can exchange neither energy nor mass with the surroundings. (10.2)

isomerization reaction. A reaction in which one isomer is converted to another. (24.5)

isotactic. Polymers in which all the substituents (i.e., the R groups) are in the same relative orientation (i.e., on the same side of the polymer chain). (25.1)

isotonic. Equal in concentration and osmotic pressure. (13.5)

isotope. Atoms that have the same atomic number (Z) but different mass numbers (A). (2.3)

isotropic. Independent of the axis of measurement. (25.3)

J

joule. SI unit of energy, 1 kg · m²/s². (3.1)

K

Kekulé structure. A structure similar to a Lewis structure in which the lone pairs may not be shown. (24.3)

kelvin. The SI base unit of temperature. (1.4)

Kelvin temperature scale. A temperature scale offset from the Celsius scale by 273.15. One kelvin (1 K) is equal in magnitude to one degree Celsius (1°C). (1.4, 11.4)

ketone. An organic compound consisting of two R groups bonded to a carbonyl. (24.2)

kinetic energy. The energy that results from motion. (3.1)

kinetic molecular theory. A theory that explains how the molecular nature of gases gives rise to their macroscopic properties. (11.2)

L

Lanthanide (rare earth) series. A series of 14 elements that have incompletely filled 4f subshells or that readily give rise to cations that have incompletely filled 4f subshells. (3.10)

lattice. A three-dimensional array of cations and anions. (5.3)

lattice energy. The amount of energy required to convert a mole of ionic solid to its constituent ions in the gas phase. (5.3, 10.8)

lattice points. Positions occupied by atoms, ions, or molecules in a unit cell. (12.3)

lattice structure. The arrangement of the particles in a crystalline solid. (12.3)

law. A concise verbal or mathematical statement of a reliable relationship between phenomena. (1.1)

law of conservation of energy. First law of thermodynamics stating that energy can be neither created nor destroyed. (10.1)

law of conservation of mass. An alternate statement of the first law of thermodynamics stating that matter can be neither created nor destroyed. (8.1)

law of definite proportions. Different samples of a given compound always contain the same elements in the same mass ratio. (5.5)

law of mass action. For a reversible reaction at equilibrium and a constant temperature, the reaction quotient, Q, has a constant value, K (the equilibrium constant). (15.2)

law of multiple proportions. Different compounds made up of the same elements differ in the number of atoms of each kind that combine. (5.5)

Le Châtelier's principle. When a stress is applied to a system at equilibrium, the system will respond by shifting in the direction that minimizes the effect of the stress. (15.5)

levorotatory. The term used to describe the enantiomer that rotates the plane-polarized light to the left. (22.2)

Lewis acid. A species that can accept a pair of electrons. (16.12)

Lewis base. A species that can donate a pair of electrons. (16.12)

Lewis dot symbol. An elemental symbol surrounded by dots, where each dot represents a valence electron. (5.2)

Lewis structure. A representation of covalent bonding in which shared electron pairs are shown either as dashes or as pairs of dots between two atoms, and lone pairs are shown as pairs of dots on individual atoms. (6.1)

Lewis theory of bonding. A chemical bond involves atoms sharing electrons. (5.5)

ligand. A molecule or anion that can form coordinate bonds to a metal to form a coordination complex. (22.1)

limiting reactant. The reactant that is completely consumed and determines the amount of product formed. (8.4)

line spectra. The emission or absorption of light only at discrete wavelengths. (3.4)

liquid crystal. A substance that exhibits properties of both a liquid, such as the ability to flow and to take on the shape of a container, and those of a crystal, such as a regular arrangement of particles in a lattice. (25.3)

localized. Describes electrons that are shared between two specific atoms and that cannot be repositioned to generate additional resonance structures. (7.7)

London dispersion forces. Attractive forces that act between all molecules, including nonpolar molecules, resulting from the formation of instantaneous dipoles and induced dipoles. (12.1)

lone pair. A pair of valence electrons that are not involved in covalent bond formation. (6.1)

M

magnetic quantum number (m_ℓ). Describes the orientation of an orbital in space. (3.7)

main group elements. Elements in the s and p blocks of the periodic table. (4.2)

manometer. A device used to measure the pressure of gases relative to atmospheric pressure. (11.3)

mass. A measure of the amount of matter in an object or sample. (1.4)

mass defect. The difference between the actual mass of a nucleus and the mass calculated by summing the masses of the individual nucleons. (20.2)

mass number (A). The number of neutrons and protons present in the nucleus of an atom of an element. (2.3)

matter. Anything that occupies space and has mass. (1.1)

Meissner effect. The exclusion of magnetic fields. (25.7)

melting point. The temperature at which solid and liquid phases are in equilibrium. (12.6)

metal. Element with a tendency to lose electrons, located left of the zigzag line on the periodic table. (2.5)

metallic radius. Half the distance between the nuclei of two adjacent, identical metal atoms. (4.4)

metalloid. Elements with properties intermediate between metals and nonmetals. (4.4)

metallurgy. The preparation, separation, and purification of metals. (21.2)

microstate. A specific microscopic configuration of a system. (18.2)

mineral. A naturally occurring substance with a characteristic chemical composition and specific physical properties. (21.1)

miscible. Mutually soluble in any proportions. (13.1)

mixture. A combination of two or more substances in which the substances retain their distinct identities. (1.2)

moderator. A material that limits the speed of liberated neutrons but does not itself undergo fission when bombarded with neutrons. (20.5)

molality (m). The number of moles of solute dissolved in 1 kg (1000 g) of solvent. (13.3)

molar absorptivity. Proportionality constant relating absorbance to solution concentration and distance that light travels through a solution. (9.5)

molar concentration. See *molarity (M)*.

molar heat (enthalpy) of fusion (ΔH_{fus}). The energy, usually expressed in kJ/mol, required to melt 1 mole of a solid. (12.6)

molar heat (enthalpy) of sublimation (ΔH_{sub}). The energy, usually expressed in kilojoules, required to sublime 1 mole of a solid. (12.6)

molar heat of vaporization (ΔH_{vap}). The amount of heat required to vaporize a mole of substance at its boiling point. (12.6)

molarity (M). The number of moles of solute per liter of solution. (9.5)

molar mass. The mass in grams of 1 mole of the substance. (2.6)

molar solubility. The number of moles of solute in 1 liter of saturated solution (mol/L). (17.4)

mole (mol). The amount of a substance that contains as many elementary entities (atoms, molecules, formula units, etc.) as there are atoms in exactly 0.012 kg (12 g) of carbon-12. (2.6)

molecular equation. A chemical equation written with all compounds represented by their chemical formulas. (9.2)

molecular formula. A chemical formula that gives the number of atoms of each element in a molecule. (5.5)

molecular geometry. The arrangement of bonded atoms. (7.1)

molecularity. The number of molecules involved in a specific step in a reaction mechanism. (14.7)

molecular mass. The sum of the atomic masses (in amu) of the atoms that make up a molecule. (5.8)

molecular orbital. An orbital that results from the interaction of the atomic orbitals of the bonding atoms. (7.6)

molecular orbital theory. A theory that describes the orbitals in a molecule as bonding and antibonding combinations of atomic orbitals. (7.6)

molecular weight. Average molecular mass. (5.8)

molecule. A combination of two or more atoms in a specific arrangement held together by chemical bonds. (5.5)

mole fraction (χ_i). The number of moles of a component divided by the total number of moles in a mixture. (11.7)

monatomic ion. An ion that contains only one atom. (4.5)

monomer. A small molecule that can be linked in large numbers to form a large molecule (polymer). (24.6, 25.1)

monoprotic acid. An acid with one ionizable proton. (9.3)

multiple bond. A chemical bond in which two atoms share two or more pairs of electrons. (6.1)

N

nanotechnology. The development and study of extremely small-scale materials and objects. (25.5)

nematic. Describes an arrangement in which molecules are all aligned parallel to one another but with no organization into layers or rows. (25.3)

Nernst equation. An equation relating the emf of a galvanic cell with the standard emf and the concentrations of reactants and products. (19.5)

net ionic equation. Chemical equation from which spectator ions have been removed. (9.2)

neutralization reaction. A reaction between an acid and a base. (9.3)

neutron. An electrically neutral subatomic particle with a mass slightly greater than that of a proton. (2.2)

newton (N). The SI unit of force. (11.3)

nitrogen fixation. The conversion of molecular nitrogen into nitrogen compounds. (21.1)

noble gas core. A representation in an electron configuration that shows in brackets the most recently completed noble gas. (3.10)

noble gases. Elements in Group 8A (He, Ne, Ar, Kr, Xe, and Rn). (2.5)

node. A collection of points at which electron density in an atom is zero. (3.5)

nonconductor. A substance that does not conduct electricity. (25.6)

nonelectrolyte. A substance that dissolves in water to yield a solution that does not conduct electricity. (9.1)

nonmetal. Element with a tendency to gain electrons, located in the upper right portion of the periodic table. (2.5)

nonpolar. Having a uniform distribution of electron density. (6.2)

nonspontaneous process. A process that does not occur under a specified set of conditions. (18.1)

nonvolatile. Having no measurable vapor pressure. (13.5)

normal boiling point. Temperature at which a substance boils at 1 atm pressure. (12.6)

***n*-type semiconductor.** Semiconductors in which an electron-rich impurity is added to enhance conduction. (21.3, 25.6)

nuclear binding energy. The energy required to separate the nucleons in a nucleus. (20.2)

nuclear chain reaction. A self-sustaining reaction sequence of fission reactions. (20.5)

nuclear fission. The splitting of a large nucleus into smaller nuclei and one or more neutrons. (20.5)

nuclear fusion. The combination of two light nuclei to form one heavier nucleus. (20.6)

nuclear transmutation. The conversion of one nucleus to another. (20.1)

nucleic acid. Macromolecule formed by polymerization of nucleotides. (24.6)

nucleons. Protons, neutrons, and electrons. (2.2)

nucleophile. A region of negative or partial negative charge. (24.5)

nucleophilic addition. An addition reaction that begins when a nucleophile donates a pair of electrons to an electron-deficient atom. (24.5)

nucleotide. A structural unit consisting of a sugar (ribose or deoxyribose) bonded to both a cyclic-amine base and a phosphate group. (24.6)

nucleus. The central core of the atom that contains the protons and neutrons. (2.2)

O

octet rule. Atoms will lose, gain, or share electrons to achieve a noble gas electron configuration. (6.1)

open system. A system that can exchange mass and energy with its surroundings. (10.2)

optical isomers. Nonsuperimposable mirror images. (22.2, 24.4)

ore. A mineral deposit concentrated enough to allow economical recovery of a desired metal. (21.1)

organic compounds. Compounds containing carbon and hydrogen, sometimes in combination with other elements such as oxygen, nitrogen, sulfur, and the halogens. (5.5)

osmosis. The selective passage of solvent molecules through a porous membrane from a more dilute solution to a more concentrated one. (13.5)

osmotic pressure (π). The pressure required to stop osmosis. (13.5)

overvoltage. The difference between the electrode potential and the actual voltage required to cause electrolysis. (19.7)

oxidation. Loss of electrons. (9.4)

oxidation number. See *oxidation state*.

oxidation-reduction reaction. See *redox reaction*.

oxidation state. The charge an atom would have if electrons were transferred completely. (9.4)

oxidizing agent. A species that accepts electrons. (9.4)

oxoacid. An acid consisting of one or more ionizable protons and an oxoanion. (5.7)

oxoanion. A polyatomic anion that contains one or more oxygen atoms bonded to a central atom. (5.7)

P

paramagnetic. A species with unpaired electrons that are attracted by magnetic fields. (3.9)

partial pressure (P_i). The pressure exerted by a component in a gas mixture. (11.7)

pascal (Pa). The SI unit of pressure. (11.3)

Pauli exclusion principle. No two electrons in an atom can have the same four quantum numbers. (3.9)

peptide bond. The bond that forms between amino acids. (24.6)

percent by mass. The ratio of the mass of an individual component to the total mass, multiplied by 100 percent. (13.3)

percent composition by mass. The percent of the total mass contributed by each element in a compound. (5.9)

percent dissociation. The percentage of dissolved molecules (or formula units, in the case of an ionic compound) that separate into ions in solution. (13.6)

percent ionization. Quantitative description of the degree to which an electrolyte exists as ions in solution. (13.6)

percent yield. The ratio of actual yield to theoretical yield, multiplied by 100 percent. (8.4)

period. A horizontal row of the periodic table. (2.5)

periodic table. A chart in which elements having similar chemical and physical properties are grouped together. (2.5)

pH. A scale used to measure acidity. $pH = -\log [H^+]$. (16.4)

phase. The sign of a wake's amplitude. (7.6)

phase change. When a substance goes from one phase to another phase. (12.6)

phase diagram. Summarizes the conditions (temperature and pressure) at which a substance exists as a solid, a liquid, or a gas. (12.7)

photoelectric effect. A phenomenon in which electrons are ejected from the surface of a metal exposed to light of at least a certain minimum frequency. (3.3)

photon. A particle of light. (3.3)

physical change. A process in which the state of matter changes but the identity of the matter does not change. (1.3)

physical property. A property that can be observed and measured without changing the identity of a substance. (1.3)

pi (π) bond. Bonds that form from the interaction of parallel p orbitals. (7.5)

pOH. A scale used to measure basicity. $pOH = -\log [OH^-]$. (16.4)

polar. Having a nonuniform electron density. (6.2)

polar covalent bond. Bonds in which electrons are unequally shared. (6.2)

polarimeter. Device used to measure the angle of rotation of plane-polarized light caused by an optically active compound. (22.2)

polarized. A molecule in which a dipole moment has been induced. (12.1)

polyamide. Polymers in which the monomers are connected by amide linkages. (25.1)

polyatomic. Molecules containing more than two atoms. (5.5)

polyatomic ion. Molecule that has lost or gained one or more electrons giving it a positive or negative charge. (5.7)

polyester. Polymers in which the monomers are connected by ester linkages. (25.1)

polymer. Molecular compounds, either natural or synthetic, that are made up of many repeating units called monomers. (24.6, 25.1)

polypeptide. Short chains of amino acids. (24.6)

polyprotic acid. An acid with more than two ionizable protons. (9.3)

polysaccharides. Biological polymer consisting of sugars. (24.6)

p orbital. Atomic orbital in which the angular momentum quantum number (ℓ) is 1. (3.7)

positron. A subatomic particle with the same mass as an electron, but with a positive charge. (20.1)

potential energy. The energy possessed by an object by virtue of its position. (3.1)

precipitate. An insoluble solid product that separates from a solution. (9.2)

precipitation reaction. A chemical reaction in which a precipitate forms. (9.2)

precision. The closeness of agreement of two or more measurements of the same quantity. (1.5)

pressure. The force applied per unit area. (11.3)

principal quantum number (n). Designates the size of the orbital. (3.7)

product. A substance that forms in a chemical reaction. (8.1)

protein. A polymer of amino acids. (24.6)

proton. A positively charged particle in the nucleus of an atom. (2.2)

p-type semiconductor. A semiconductor in which an electron-poor impurity is added to enhance conduction. (21.3, 25.6)

pyrometallurgy. Metallurgic processes carried out at high temperatures. (21.2)

Q

qualitative analysis. The determination of the types of ions present in a solution. (17.6)

qualitative property. A property of a system that can be determined by general observation. (1.3)

quantitative property. A property of a system that can be measured and expressed with a number. (1.3)

quantum. The smallest quantity of energy that can be emitted (or absorbed) in the form of electromagnetic radiation. (3.6)

quantum numbers. Numbers required to describe the arrangement of electrons in an atom. (3.7)

R

racemic mixture. An equimolar mixture of enantiomers that does not rotate the plane of plane-polarized light. (22.2, 24.4)

racemization. The conversion of a single enantiomer to a racemic mixture of both enantiomers. (24.5)

radiation. The emission and transmission of energy through space in the form of waves. (2.2)

radical. A chemical species with an odd number of electrons. (8.8, 20.8)

radioactive decay series. A sequence of nuclear reactions that ultimately result in the formation of a stable isotope. (20.3)

radioactivity. The spontaneous emission of particles or radiation from unstable nuclei. (2.2, 20.1)

Raoult's law. The partial pressure of a solvent over a solution, P_i, is given by the vapor pressure of the pure solvent, $P°$, times the mole fraction of the solvent in the solution, χ_i. (13.5)

rate constant (k). The proportionality constant in a rate law. (14.3)

rate-determining step. The slowest step in a reaction mechanism. (14.7)

rate law. An equation relating the rate of reaction to the concentrations of reactants. (14.2)

rate of reaction. The change in concentration of reactants or products per unit time. (14.1)

reactant. A substance that is consumed in a chemical reaction. (8.1)

reaction mechanism. Series of steps by which a chemical reaction occurs. (14.7)

reaction order. The sum of the powers to which all reactant concentrations appearing in the rate law are raised. (14.4)

reaction quotient (Q). A fraction with product concentrations in the numerator and reactant concentrations in the denominator, each raised to its stoichiometric coefficient. (15.2)

redox reaction. A chemical reaction in which electrons are transferred from one reactant to another. (9.4)

reducing agent. A species that can donate electrons. (4.4)

reduction. A gain of electrons. (9.4)

resonance structures. Two or more equally valid Lewis structures for a single molecule that differ only in the positions of electrons. (6.5)

reversible process. A process in which the products can react to form reactants. (15.1)

ribonucleic acid (RNA). Biological polymer consisting of nucleotides in which the sugar is ribose. (24.6)

root-mean-square speed (μ_{rms})**.** The molecular speed that is inversely proportional to the molecular mass. (11.2)

S

salt. An ionic compound made up of the cation from a base and the anion from an acid. (9.3)

salt bridge. An inverted U tube containing an inert electrolyte solution, such as KCl or NH_4NO_3, that maintains electrical neutrality in an electrochemical cell. (19.2)

salt hydrolysis. The reaction of a salt's constituent ions with water to produce either hydroxide ions or hydronium ions. (16.10)

saturated solution. A solution that contains the maximum amount of a solute that will dissolve in a solvent at a specific temperature. (13.1)

scientific method. A systematic approach to experimentation. (1.1)

second law of thermodynamics. The entropy of the universe increases in a spontaneous process and remains unchanged in an equilibrium process. (18.4)

second-order reaction. A reaction whose rate depends on the concentration of one reactant raised to the second power or on the product of the concentrations of two different reactants each raised to the first power. (14.5)

semiconductor. A substance that normally does not conduct electricity but that will conduct at elevated temperatures or when combined with a small amount of certain other elements. (21.3, 25.6)

semipermeable membrane. A membrane that allows the passage of solvent molecules but blocks the passage of solute molecules. (13.5)

shielding. The partial obstruction of nuclear charge by core electrons. (4.3)

sigma (σ) bond. A bond in which the shared electron density is concentrated directly along the internuclear axis. (7.5)

significant figures. Meaningful digits in a measured or calculated value. (1.5)

simple cubic cell. The basic repeating unit in which there is one atom at each of the eight corners in a cube. (12.3)

single bond. A pair of electrons shared by two atoms. (6.1)

sintering. A method used to form objects by heating a finely divided substance. (25.2)

SI units. International System of Units. A system of units based on metric units. (1.4)

skeletal structure. A structure in which straight lines represent carbon-carbon bonds. (24.3)

smectic. Containing molecules ordered in two dimensions. The molecules are aligned parallel to one other and are further arranged in layers that are parallel to one another. (25.3)

solubility. The maximum amount of solute that will dissolve in a given quantity of solvent at a specific temperature. (9.2, 13.1, 17.4)

solubility product constant (K_{sp}). The equilibrium constant that indicates to what extent a slightly soluble ionic compound dissolves in water. (17.4)

solute. The dissolved substance in a solution. (9.1)

solution. A homogeneous mixture consisting of a solvent and one or more solutes. (9.1)

solvent. A substance in a solution that is present in the largest amount. (9.1)

s orbital. Atomic orbital in which the angular momentum quantum number (ℓ) is 0. (3.7)

specific heat (s). The amount of heat required to raise the temperature of 1 g of a substance by 1°C. (10.4)

spectator ion. An ion that does not participate in the reaction and appears on both the reactant and product side in the ionic equation. (9.2)

spectrochemical series. A list of ligands arranged in increasing order of their abilities to split the d orbital energy levels. (22.3)

spontaneous process. A process that occurs under a specified set of conditions. (18.1)

standard atmospheric pressure. The pressure that would support a column of mercury exactly 760 mm high at 0°C. (11.3)

standard enthalpy of formation (ΔH_f°). The heat change that results when 1 mole of a compound is formed from its constituent elements in their standard states. (10.6)

standard enthalpy of reaction (ΔH_{rxn}°). The enthalpy of a reaction carried out under standard conditions. (10.6)

standard entropy (S°). The absolute entropy of a substance at 1 atm. (18.3)

standard free energy of formation (ΔG_f°). The free-energy change that occurs when 1 mole of the compound forms from its constituent elements in their standard states. (18.5)

standard free energy of reaction (ΔG_{rxn}°). The free-energy change for a reaction when it occurs under standard-state conditions. (18.5)

standard hydrogen electrode (SHE). A half-cell based on the half-reaction $2H^+(1\ M) + 2e^- \longrightarrow H_2(1\ \text{atm})$, which has an arbitrarily defined standard reduction potential of zero. (19.3)

standard reduction potential (E_{red}). The potential associated with a reduction half-reaction at an electrode when the ion concentration is 1 M and the gas pressure is 1 atm. (19.3)

standard solution. A solution of precisely known concentration. (9.6)

standard temperature and pressure (STP). 0°C and 1 atm. (11.5)

state function. Properties that are determined by the state of the system, independent of how the state was achieved. (10.2)

state of a system. The values of all relevant macroscopic properties, such as composition, energy, temperature, pressure, and volume. (10.2)

stereoisomers. Molecules that contain identical bonds but differ in the orientation of those bonds in space. (22.2, 24.4)

stoichiometric amounts. Quantities of reactants in the same relative amounts as those represented in the balanced chemical equation. (8.3)

stoichiometric coefficients. The numeric values written to the left of each species in a chemical equation to balance the equation. (8.1)

strong conjugate acid. The conjugate acid of a weak base. Acts as a weak Brønsted acid in water. (16.8)

strong conjugate base. The conjugate base of a weak acid. Acts as a weak Brønsted base in water. (16.8)

strong electrolyte. An electrolyte that ionizes or dissociates completely. (9.1)

structural formula. A chemical formula that shows the general arrangement of atoms within the molecule. (5.5)

structural isomer. Molecules that have the same chemical formula but different arrangements of atoms. (7.2)

sublimation. The phase change from solid to gas. (12.6)

substance. Matter with a definite (constant) composition and distinct properties. (1.2)

substituent. A group other than $-H$ bonded to the carbons of an organic molecule. (24.2)

substitution reaction. One group is replaced by another group by electrophilic or nucleophilic attack. (24.5)

superconducting transition temperature (T_c). The temperature below which an element, compound, or material becomes superconducting. (25.7)

superconductor. A substance with no resistance to the flow of electrons. (25.7)

supercooling. A phenomenon in which a liquid can be temporarily cooled to below its freezing point. (12.6)

supercritical fluid. A fluid at a temperature and pressure that exceed T_c and P_c. (12.6)

supersaturated solution. A solution that contains more dissolved solute than is present in a saturated solution. (13.1)

surface tension. The amount of energy required to stretch or increase the surface of a liquid by a unit area. (12.2)

surroundings. The part of the universe not included in the system. (10.1)

suture. Thread used by physicians to close wounds and/or incisions. (25.4)

syndiotactic. Polymers in which the substituents alternate positions along the polymer chain. (25.1)

system. The specific part of the universe that is of interest to us. (10.1)

T

tacticity. Describes the relative arrangements of chiral carbon atoms within a polymer. (25.1)

termolecular. Involving three reactant molecules. (14.7)

theoretical yield. The maximum amount of product that can be obtained from a reaction. (8.4)

theory. A unifying principle that explains a body of experimental observations and the laws that are based on them. (1.1)

thermal energy. The energy associated with the random motion of atoms and molecules. (3.1)

thermochemical equation. A chemical equation that includes the enthalpy change. (10.3)

thermochemistry. The study of the heat associated with chemical reactions and physical processes. (10.1)

thermodynamics. The scientific study of the interconversion of heat and other kinds of energy. (10.1)

thermonuclear reaction. Generally refers to a fusion reaction. (20.6)

thermoplastic. Polymers that can be melted and reshaped. (25.1)

thermosetting. Polymers that assume their final shape as part of the chemical reaction that forms them. (25.1)

third law of thermodynamics. The entropy of a pure crystalline solid is zero at absolute zero (0 K). (18.4)

titration. The gradual addition of a solution of known concentration to another solution of unknown concentration until the chemical reaction between the two solutions is complete. (9.6)

tracers. Radioactive isotopes that are used to trace the path of the atoms of an element in a chemical or biological process. (20.7)

trans. The isomer in which two substituents lie on opposite sides of a double bond. (24.4)

transition element. An element that has—or readily forms one or more ions that have—an incompletely filled *d* subshell (Groups 3B to 8B or Group 1B). (2.5)

transition metals. The elements in Group 1B and Groups 3B to 8B. (2.5)

transition state. See *activated complex.*

transmittance. Ratio of the intensity of light transmitted through a sample (I) to the intensity of the incident light (I_0). (9.5)

transuranium elements. Elements with atomic numbers greater than 92, created by bombarding other elements with accelerated neutrons, protons, alpha particles, or other nuclei. (20.4)

triple bond. A multiple bond in which the atoms share three pairs of electrons. (6.1)

triple point. The point at which all three phase boundary lines meet. (12.7)

triprotic acid. An acid molecule with three ionizable protons. (9.3)

Tyndall effect. The scattering of visible light by colloidal particles. (13.7)

U

unimolecular. Describes a reaction involving one reactant molecule. (14.7)

unit cell. The basic repeating structural unit of a crystalline solid. (12.3)

unsaturated solution. A solution that contains less solute than it has the capacity to dissolve. (13.1)

V

valence band. The bonding band. (25.6)

valence bond theory. Atoms share electrons when an atomic orbital on one atom overlaps with an atomic orbital on the other. (7.3)

valence electrons. The outermost electrons of an atom. (4.2)

valence-shell electron-pair repulsion (VSEPR). A model that accounts for electron pairs in the valence shell of an atom repelling one another. (7.1)

van der Waal's equation. An equation relating the volume of a real gas to the other parameters, P, T, and n. (11.6)

van der Waal's forces. The attractive forces that hold particles together in the condensed phases that include dipole-dipole interactions (including hydrogen bonding) and dispersion forces. (12.1)

van't Hoff factor (i). The ratio of the actual number of particles in solution after dissociation to the number of formula units initially dissolved in solution. (13.5)

vaporization. The phase change from liquid to gas at the boiling point. (12.2)

vapor pressure. See *equilibrium vapor pressure.*

viscosity. A measure of a fluid's resistance to flow. (12.2)

visible spectrophotometry. Measurement of absorption of visible light for qualitative and quantitative analysis. (9.5)

volatile. Describes a substance that has a high vapor pressure. (12.2, 13.5)

W

wavelength (λ). The distance between identical points on successive waves. (3.2)

weak acid. An acid that ionizes only partially. (16.6)

weak base. A base that ionizes only partially. (16.7)

weak conjugate acid. A conjugate acid of a strong base. Does not react with water. (16.8)

weak conjugate base. A conjugate base of a strong acid. Does not react with water. (16.8)

weak electrolyte. A compound that produces ions upon dissolving but exists in solution predominantly as molecules that are not ionized. (9.1)

X

X-ray diffraction. A method of using X rays to bombard a crystalline sample to determine the structure of the crystal. (12.3)

Z

zeroth-order reaction. A constant rate, independent of reactant concentration. (14.5)

Chapter 1

1.5 (a) Law. (b) Theory. (c) Hypothesis. **1.9** (a) Homogeneous mixture. (b) Pure substance. (c) Pure substance. (d) Homogeneous mixture. (e) Homogeneous mixture. (f) Pure substance. (g) Heterogeneous mixture. (h) Pure substance. (i) Pure substance. **1.15** (a) Quantitative. (b) Qualitative. (c) Qualitative. (d) Qualitative. (e) Qualitative. **1.17** (a) Physical change. (b) Chemical change. (c) Physical change. (d) Chemical change. (e) Physical change. **1.23** 3.12 g/mL. **1.25** (a) 35°C. (b) −11°C. (c) 39°C. (d) 1011°C. (e) −459.67°F. **1.27** 2.52 mL. **1.29** (a) 386 K. (b) 3.10×10^2 K. (c) 6.30×10^2 K. **1.31** 99.9 g; 20°C; 11.35 g/cm^3. **1.37** (a) 0.0152. (b) 0.0000000778. (c) 0.00000329. (d) 0.841. **1.39** (a) 1.8×10^{-2}. (b) 1.14×10^{10}. (c) -5×10^4. (d) 1.3×10^3. **1.41** Upper thermometer: 41.85°; Lower thermometer: 41.85°. **1.43** (a) One. (b) Three. (c) Three. (d) Four. (e) Three. (f) One. (g) One or two. (h) Three. **1.45** (a) 1.28. (b) 3.18×10^{-3} mg. (c) 8.14×10^7 dm. **1.47** Carpenter Z's measurements are the most accurate. Carpenter Y's measurements are the least accurate. Carpenter X's measurements are the most precise. Carpenter Y's measurements are the least precise. **1.49** 1.3 g/L. **1.51** (a) 1.10×10^8 mg. (b) 6.83×10^{-5} m^3. (c) 7.2×10^3 L. (d) 6.24×10^{-8} lb. **1.53** (a) 66 amu. (b) 6.50×10^{-3} amu. (c) 83 Å. (d) 1.32 Å. **1.55** 3.1557×10^7 s. **1.57** (a) 81 in/s. (b) 1.2×10^7 m/min. (c) 7.4 km/h. **1.59** 1.0×10^2 km/h. **1.61** 3.7×10^3 g Pb. **1.63** (a) 1.85×10^{-7} m. (b) 1.4×10^{17} s. (c) 7.12×10^{-5} m^3. (d) 8.86×10^4 L. **1.65** 6.25×10^4 g/cm^3. **1.67** (a) 2.5 cm. (b) 2.55 cm. **1.69** (a) Chemical. (b) Chemical. (c) Physical. (d) Physical. (e) Chemical. **1.71** 4.75×10^7 tons. **1.73** (a) 8.08×10^4 g. (b) 1.4×10^{-6} g. (c) 39.9 g. **1.75** 31.35 cm^3. **1.77** 10.50 g/cm^3. **1.79** 11.4 g/cm^3. **1.81** %Error(°F) = 0.1%; %Error(°C) = 0.3%. **1.83** 72.8°S. **1.85** 5×10^2 mL/breath. **1.87** 4.8×10^{19} kg NaCl = 5.3×10^{16} tons NaCl. **1.89** (a) 75.0 g Au. (b) A troy ounce is heavier than an ounce. **1.91** (a) 0.5%. (b) 3.1%. **1.93** 1.77×10^6 g Cu. **1.95** 9.5×10^{10} kg CO$_2$. **1.97** 1.1×10^2 yr. **1.99** 4.0×10^{-19} g/L. **1.101** Density = 7.20 g/cm^3; r = 0.853 cm. **1.103** It would be more difficult to prove that it was a pure substance. Most mixtures can be separated into two or more different substances. **1.105** Gently heat the liquid to see if any solid remains after the liquid evaporates. Also, collect the vapor and then compare the densities of the condensed liquid with the original liquid. **1.107** The volume occupied by the ice is larger than the volume of the glass bottle. The glass bottle would break. **1.109** (a) Yes. (b) No. (c) No. **1.111** (a) 527°C; 1227°C; 800K; 1500K; the range of 700°C is equal to the range of 700K. (b) 5.883×10^{-2}°F/s; 3.241×10^{-2}°C/s; 3.241×10^{-2}K/s. **1.113** (a) −40°. (b) 574.59. (c) No. Since the value of Kelvin is always equal to a value that is 273.15 greater than the Celsius value, there is no temperature at which the values can be numerically equal. **1.115** (a) 20°C – 25°C. (b) 1.18 g/mL. (c) 1180 g/L; 1180 kg/m^3. (d) 420 mg.

Chapter 2

2.9 1.0×10^2 m; 6.2×10^{-2} mi. **2.15** 149. **2.17** $^{17}_{8}$O: protons = 8, neutrons = 8, electrons = 7; $^{29}_{14}$Si: protons = 14, neutrons = 15, electrons = 14; $^{58}_{28}$Ni: protons = 28, neutrons = 30, electrons = 28; $^{89}_{39}$Y: protons = 39, neutrons = 50, electrons = 39; $^{180}_{73}$Ta: protons = 73,

neutrons = 107, electrons = 73; $^{203}_{81}$Tl: protons = 81, neutrons = 122, electrons = 81. **2.19** (a) $^{187}_{75}$Re. (b) $^{209}_{83}$Bi. (c) $^{75}_{33}$As. (d) $^{236}_{93}$Np. **2.21** (a) 35. (b) 32. (c) 121. (d) 105. **2.27** 207.2 amu. **2.29** ^{6}Li = 7.5%, ^{7}Li = 92.5%. **2.31** 23.98 amu. **2.37** Metallic character (a) increases as you progress down a group of the periodic table and (b) decreases from the left to right across the periodic table. **2.39** Na and K; N and P; F and Cl. **2.41** Iron: Fe, period 4, upper-left square of Group 8B; Iodine: I, period 5, Group 7A; Sodium: Na, period 3, Group 1A; Phosphorus: P, period 3, Group 5A; Sulfur: S, period 3, Group 6A; Magnesium: Mg, period 3, Group 2A. **2.45** 2.10×10^5 atoms. **2.47** 8.30×10^{-15} mol Ni. **2.49** 5.15×10^3 g Pt. **2.51** (a) 2.023×10^{-22} g/Sb atom. (b) 1.767×10^{-22} g/Pd atom. **2.53** 5.48×10^{22} Sc atoms. **2.55** 7.5×10^{-22} mole of silver. **2.57** 8.1×10^{22} atoms. **2.59** $^{131}_{54}$Xe. **2.61** Atom A: $^{22}_{10}$Ne; Atom B: $^{185}_{75}$Re; Atom C: $^{42}_{21}$Sc; Atom D: need the number of neutrons to write the symbol. **2.63** It establishes a standard mass unit that permits the measurement of masses of all other isotopes relative to cabon-12. **2.65** (a) $^4_2$He: protons = 2, neutrons = 2; $^{20}_{10}$Ne: protons = 10, neutrons = 10; $^{40}_{18}$Ar: protons = 18, neutrons = 22; $^{84}_{36}$Kr: protons = 36, neutrons = 48; $^{132}_{54}$Xe: protons = 54, neutrons = 78. (b) $^4_2$He: neutrons/protons = 1.00; $^{20}_{10}$Ne: neutrons/protons = 1.00; $^{40}_{18}$Ar: neutrons/protons = 1.22; $^{84}_{36}$Kr: neutrons/protons = 1.33; $^{132}_{54}$Xe: neutrons/protons = 1.44; the neutron/proton ratio increases with increasing atomic number. **2.67** 192 amu; this is the atomic mass that appears in the periodic table. **2.69** (a) Iodine. (b) Radon. (c) Selenium. (d) Sodium. (e) Lead. **2.71** (a) 28. (b) 30. (c) 28. (d) 30. **2.73** Symbol: ^{101}Ru, ^{181}Ta, ^{150}Sm; Protons: 44, 73, 62; Neutrons: 57, 108, 88; Electrons: 44, 73, 62. **2.75** (a) 6.6×10^{22} Pt atoms. (b) 1.4×10^2 pm.

Chapter 3

3.5 (a) 2.3×10^2 J. (b) 4.5×10^5 J. (c) 4.52×10^{-26} J. (d) 2.51×10^{-22} J. **3.7** (a) 817 m/s. (b) 401 m/s. (c) 44.9 amu; scandium. **3.9** (a) 1.5. (b) $\frac{2}{3}d$. **3.15** (a) 3.5×10^3 nm. (b) 5.30×10^{14} Hz. **6.7** 7.0×10^2 s. **3.19** 3.26×10^7 nm, microwave. **3.25** 2.82×10^{-19} J. **3.27** (a) 4.6×10^7 nm; not in the visible region. (b) 4.3×10^{-24} J/photon. (c) 2.6 J/mol. **3.29** 1.57×10^{-19} J. **3.31** 1.29×10^{-15} J. **3.33** Infrared photons have insufficient energy to cause the chemical changes. **3.35** $v = 3.23 \times 10^{20}$ s^{-1}, $\lambda = 9.29 \times 10^{-13}$ m. **3.37** 7.40×10^{-19} J. **3.43** Analyze the emitted light by passing it through a prism. **3.45** Excited atoms of the chemical elements emit the same characteristic frequencies or lines in a terrestrial laboratory, in the sun, or in a star many light-years distant from earth. **3.47** 3.027×10^{-19} J. **3.49** $v = 1.60 \times 10^{14}$ Hz, $\lambda = 1.88 \times 10^3$ nm. **3.51** 5. **3.55** 0.565 nm. **3.57** 2.79×10^{-30} cm. **3.59** 377 m/s. **3.67** $\Delta u \geq 4.38 \times 10^{-26}$ m/s. This uncertainty is far smaller than can be measured. **3.71** $\ell = 1$, $m_\ell = -1, 0$, and 1; $\ell = 0$, $m_\ell = 0$. **3.73** 4s, 4p, 4d, and 4f subshells; 1, 3, 5, and 7 orbitals, respectively. **3.79** (a) $n = 2$, $\ell = 1$; $m_\ell = 1, 0$, or −1. (b) $n = 3$, $\ell = 0$; $m_\ell = 0$. (c) $n = 5$, $\ell = 2$; $m_\ell = 2, 1, 0, -1$, or −2. **3.81** A 2s orbital is larger than a 1s orbital and exhibits a node. Both have the same spherical shape. The 1s orbital is lower in energy than the 2s. **3.83** In H, energy depends only on n, but for all other atoms, energy depends on n and ℓ. **3.85** (a) 2s. (b) 3p. (c) Equal. (d) Equal. (e) 5s. **3.93** (a) 2. (b) 8. (c) 18. (d) 32. **3.95** (a) 3. (b) 6. (c) 0. **3.97** Al: two 2p electrons missing, $1s^2 2s^2 2p^6 3s^2 3p^1$; B: too many 2p electrons, $1s^2 2s^2 2p^1$; F: too many 2p electrons, $1s^2 2s^2 2p^5$. **3.99** B = F < C = O < N. **3.101** (a) One;

paramagnetic. (b) Three; paramagnetic. (c) One; paramagnetic. (d) Six; paramagnetic. (e) Zero; diamagnetic. **3.111** $[Xe]6s^24f^{14}5d^7$. **3.113** Ge: $[Ar]4s^23d^{10}4p^2$; Fe: $[Ar]4s^23d^6$; Zn: $[Ar]4s^23d^{10}$; Ni: $[Ar]4s^23d^8$; W: $[Xe]6s^24f^{14}5d^4$; Tl: $[Xe]6s^24f^{14}5d^{10}6p^1$. **3.117** Part (b) is correct in the view of contemporary quantum theory. Bohr's explanation of emission and absorption line spectra appears to have universal validity. Parts (a) and (c) are artifacts of Bohr's early planetary model of the hydrogen atom and are *not* considered to be valid today. **3.119** (a) 4; 2s and 2p. (b) 6; 4p, 4d, and 4f. (c) 10; 3d. (d) 1; 2s. (e) 2; 4f. **3.121** The frequency of the red light must be below the threshold frequency. The blue light must meet or exceed the threshold frequency. (a) No change. (b) The reading on the ammeter would be higher than it is for the lower intensity blue light. (c) The ammeter will indicate that current is flowing through the circuit. **3.123** (a) 1.20×10^{18} photons. (b) 3.76×10^8 W. **3.125** Krypton. **3.127** 3.0×10^{19} photons/s. **3.129** He$^+$: $n = 3 \longrightarrow 2$: $\lambda = 164$ nm; $n = 4 \longrightarrow 2$: $\lambda = 121$ nm; $n = 5 \longrightarrow 2$: $\lambda = 108$ nm; $n = 6 \longrightarrow 2$: $\lambda = 103$ nm. H: $n = 3 \longrightarrow 2$: $\lambda = 656$ nm; $n = 4 \longrightarrow 2$: $\lambda = 486$ nm; $n = 5 \longrightarrow 2$: $\lambda = 434$ nm; $n = 6 \longrightarrow 2$: $\lambda = 410$ nm. All the Balmer transitions for He$^+$ are in the ultraviolet region; whereas, the transitions for H are all in the visible region. **3.131** $\frac{1}{\lambda_1} = \frac{1}{\lambda_2} + \frac{1}{\lambda_3}$. **3.133** (a) He; $1s^2$. (b) N, $1s^22s^22p^3$. (c) Na, $1s^22s^22p^63s^1$. (d) As, $[Ar]4s^23d^{10}4p^3$. (e) Cl, $[Ne]3s^23p^5$.

3.135 (a) $\underset{1s^2}{\underline{\uparrow\downarrow}}$ $\underset{2s^2}{\underline{\uparrow\downarrow}}$ $\underset{2p^5}{\underline{\uparrow\downarrow}\;\underline{\uparrow\downarrow}\;\underline{\uparrow}}$.

(b) [Ne] $\underset{3s^2}{\underline{\uparrow\downarrow}}$ $\underset{3p^3}{\underline{\uparrow}\;\underline{\uparrow}\;\underline{\uparrow}}$.

(c) [Ar] $\underset{4s^2}{\underline{\uparrow\downarrow}}$ $\underset{3d^7}{\underline{\uparrow\downarrow}\;\underline{\uparrow\downarrow}\;\underline{\uparrow}\;\underline{\uparrow}\;\underline{\uparrow}}$.

3.137 $\lambda = 0.596$ m; microwave/radio region. **3.139** (a) False. (b) False. (c) True. (d) False. (e) True. **3.141** Blue light: 42 photons; green light: 53 photons; red light: 56 photons. **3.143** 2.2×10^5 J. **3.145** (b) and (d) are allowed transitions. Any of the transitions in Figure 3.11 is possible as long as ℓ for the final state differs from ℓ of the initial state by 1. **3.147** 17.4 pm. **3.149** $\lambda = 0.382$ pm, $\nu = 7.86 \times 10^{20}$ s^{-1}. **3.151** 3.9×10^5 m/s. **3.153** (a) We note that the maximum solar radiation centers around 500 nm. Thus, over billions of years, organisms have adjusted their development to capture energy at or near this wavelength. The two most notable cases are photosynthesis and vision. (b) Astronomers record blackbody radiation curves from stars and compare them with those obtained from objects at different temperatures in the laboratory. Because the shape of the curve and the wavelength corresponding to the maximum depend on the temperature of an object, astronomers can reliably determine the temperature at the surface of a star from the closest matching curve and wavelength.

Chapter 4

4.15 Sulfur; $[Ne]3s^23p^4$. **4.17** (a) and (d); (b) and (e); (c) and (f). **4.19** (a) Group 1A or 1. (b) Group 5A or 15. (c) Group 5A or 15. (d) Group 8B or 10. **4.21** (a) Sn. (b) V. (c) Cl. (d) Ba. **4.25** (a) $\sigma = 2$ and $Z_{eff} = +4$. (b) 2s: $Z_{eff} = +3.22$; 2p: $Z_{eff} = +3.14$; These values are lower than those in part (a) because the 2s and 2p electrons actually do shield each other somewhat. **4.39** (a) The force will be four times greater. (b) The force will be six times greater. (c) The force will be reduced by one-half. (d) The force will be eight times greater. (e) No change. **4.41** ii < iii < iv < i. **4.43** Cl < P < Si < Al < Mg. **4.45** Oxygen. **4.47** Left to right: S, Se, Ca, K. **4.49** K < Ca < P < F < Ne. **4.51** The Group 3A elements (such as Al) all have a single electron in the outermost p subshell, which is well shielded from the nuclear charge by the inner electrons and the ns^2 electrons. Therefore, less energy is needed to remove a single p electron than to remove a paired s electron from the same principal energy level

(such as for Mg). **4.53** 496 kJ/mol is paired with $1s^22s^22p^63s^1$. 2080 kJ/mol is paired with $1s^22s^22p^6$, a very stable noble gas configuration. **4.55** A: Group 3A or 3; B: Group 2A or 2; C: Group 1A or 1. **4.57** 8.40×10^6 kJ/mol. **4.59** Cl. **4.61** Alkali metals have a valence electron configuration of ns^1 so they can accept another electron in the ns orbital. On the other hand, alkaline earth metals have a valence electron configuration of ns^2. Alkaline earth metals have little tendency to accept another electron, as it would have to go into a higher energy p orbital. **4.63** The calculated number for magnesium is about 78 percent larger than that for sodium. **4.69** (a) [Kr]. (b) [Kr]. (c) $[Kr]5s^24d^{10}$. (d) $[Kr]5s^24d^{10}5p^6$. (e) [Xe]. (f) $[Kr]5d^{10}$. (g) $[Xe]6s^24f^{14}5d^{10}$. (h) $[Xe]4f^{14}5d^{10}$. **4.71** (a) $[Ar]3d^6$. (b) $[Ar]3d^9$. (c) $[Ar]3d^7$. (d) $[Ar]3d^5$. **4.73** (a) $[Ar]3d^8$. (b) $[Ar]3d^{10}$. (c) $[Kr]4d^{10}$. (d) $[Xe]4f^{14}5d^{10}$. (e) $[Xe]4f^{14}5d^8$. **4.75** (a) Cr^{3+}. (b) Sc^{3+}. (c) Rh^{3+}. (d) Ir^{3+}. **4.77** Be^{2+} and He; N^{3-} and F$^-$; Fe^{2+} and Co^{3+}; S^{2-} and Ar. **4.79** Cu$^+$ < Ti^{3+} < V^{3+} < Mn^{4+} < Fe^{2+}. **4.81** Se. **4.83** Fe. **4.85** (a) Fe^{2+} or Co^{3+}. (b) Ag$^+$ or Cd^{2+}. (c) Cu^{2+}. (d) Cu$^+$ or Zn^{2+}. (e) V^{2+} or Cr^{3+}. (f) Co^{2+} or Ni^{3+}. **4.89** (a) Cl. (b) Na$^+$. (c) O^{2-}. (d) Al^{3+}. (e) Au^{3+}. **4.91** The Cu$^+$ ion is larger than Cu^{2+} because it has one more electron. **4.93** (c). **4.95** In^{3+}. **4.97** (a) Br. (b) N. (c) Rb. (d) Mg. **4.99** O^{2-} < F$^-$ < Na$^+$ < Mg^{2+}. **4.101** O$^+$ and N; S^{2-} and Ar; N^{3-} and Ne; As^{3+} and Zn; Cs$^+$ and Xe. **4.103** (a) and (d). **4.105** The binding of a cation to an anion results from electrostatic attraction. As the $+2$ cation gets smaller (from Ba^{2+} to Mg^{2+}), the distance between the opposite charges decreases and the electrostatic attraction increases. **4.107** (a) B < D < A < C. (b) C < A < D < B. **4.109** This anomaly is a result of the lanthanide contraction. The lanthanide contraction is a term used to describe a decrease in atomic radius of the lanthanide elements. The lanthanide contraction also decreases the radius of the elements following the lanthanides in the periodic table, including Hf. The lanthanide contraction is caused by poor shielding of the nuclear charge from the partially-filled 4f electrons. **4.111** H$^-$; Since H$^-$ has only one proton compared to two protons for He, the nucleus of H$^-$ will attract the two electrons less strongly compared to He. **4.113** 0.66. **4.115** The effective nuclear charge changes less than the nuclear charge as we move down a column of the periodic table. Gallium has an additional ten *core* electrons in its 3d shell to shield valence electrons. Therefore, the effective nuclear charge is not as large as might be expected. **4.117** 77.5%. **4.119** 6.94×10^{-19} J/electron; If there are no other electrons with lower kinetic energy, then this is the electron from the valence shell. UV light of the *longest* wavelength (lowest energy) that can still eject electrons should be used. **4.121** A: Rb; B: F; C: Mg; D: Rb$^+$; E: F$^-$. **4.123** (a) $IE_1 = 3s^1$ electron; $IE_2 = 2p^6$ electron; $IE_3 = 2p^5$ electron; $IE_4 = 2p^4$ electron; $IE_5 = 2p^3$ electron; $IE_6 = 2p^2$ electron; $IE_7 = 2p^1$ electron; $IE_8 = 2s^2$ electron; $IE_9 = 2s^1$ electron; $IE_{10} = 1s^2$ electron; $IE_{11} = 1s^1$ electron. (b) Each break ($IE_1 \longrightarrow IE_2$ and $IE_9 \longrightarrow IE_{10}$) represents the transition to another shell ($n = 3 \longrightarrow 2$ and $n = 2 \longrightarrow 1$). **4.125** Considering electron configurations, Fe$^{2+}[Ar]3d^6 \longrightarrow$ Fe$^{3+}[Ar]3d^5$, Mn$^{2+}[Ar]3d^5 \longrightarrow$ Mn$^{3+}[Ar]3d^4$, a half-filled shell has extra stability. In oxidizing Fe^{2+}, the product is a d^5-half-filled shell. In oxidizing Mn^{2+}, a d^5-half-filled shell electron is being lost, which requires more energy. **4.127** Z_{eff} increases from left to right across the table, so electrons are held more tightly. (This explains the electron affinity values of C and O.) Nitrogen has a zero value of electron affinity because of the stability of the half-filled 2p subshell (that is, N has little tendency to accept another electron). **4.129** Once an atom gains an electron forming a negative ion, adding additional electrons is typically an unfavorable process due to electron-electron repulsions. Second and third electron affinities do not occur spontaneously and are therefore difficult to measure. **4.131** (a) It was determined that the periodic table was based on atomic number, not atomic mass. (b) Argon: 39.95 amu; potassium: 39.10 amu. **4.133** Element 119; $[Rn]7s^25f^{14}6d^{10}7p^68s^1$. **4.135** Group 2A; There is a large jump from the second to the third ionization energy, indicating a change in the principal quantum number n. **4.137** Group 2A or 2. **4.139** Sn^{4+}.

Chapter 5

5.7 (a) :Br̈: (b) ·N̈· (c) :Ï: (d) ·Äs· (e) :F̈· (f) [:P̈:]³⁻ (g) Na⁺. (h) Mg²⁺.
(i) [·Äs·]³⁺ (j) [·Pb·]²⁺ **5.9** (a) Group 4A or 14. (b) Group 6A or 16.
(c) Group 7A or 17. **5.15** (a) Decreases the ionic bond energy.
(b) Triples the ionic bond energy. (c) Increases the bond energy
by a factor of 4. (d) Increases the bond energy by a factor of 2.

5.17 (a) Ba + ·Ö· ⟶ Ba²⁺[:Ö:]²⁻ (b) Äl + ·N̈· ⟶ Al³⁺[:N̈:]³⁻

5.23 (a) KF; potassium fluoride. (b) Rb₂O; rubidium oxide. (c) Ba₃P₂;
barium phosphide. (d) Ga₂Se₃; gallium selenide. **5.25** (a) Na₂O. (b) FeS.
(c) Co₂Te₃. (d) BaF₂. **5.27** (a) Sodium hydride. (b) Lithium nitride.
(c) Sodium oxide. (d) Sodium peroxide. **5.29** (a) ⬤⬤ (b) ⬤⬤
(c) ⬤⬤⬤ (d) ⬤⬤ **5.41** (a) Element. (b) Compound. (c) Compound.
5.43 Elements: N₂, S₈, H₂; compounds: NH₃, NO, CO, CO₂, SO₂. **5.45** 2:3.
5.47 (a) CN. (b) CH. (c) C₉H₂₀. (d) P₂O₅. (e) BH₃. **5.49** C₃H₇NO₂. **5.55**
(a) Nitrogen trichloride. (b) Iodine heptafluoride. (c) Tetraphosphorus
hexoxide. (d) Disulfur dichloride. **5.57** (a) NF₃; nitrogen trifluoride.
(b) PBr₅; phosphorus pentabromide. (c) SCl₂; sulfur dichloride. **5.59**
Alcohol and aldehyde. **5.61** (a) Potassium hypochlorite. (b) Silver
carbonate. (c) Hydrogen nitrite. (d) Potassium permanganate. (e) Cesium
chlorate. (f) Potassium ammonium sulfate. (g) Iron(II) perbromate.
(h) Potassium hydrogen phosphate. **5.63** (a) CuCN. (b) Sr(ClO₂)₂.
(c) HBrO₄. (d) HI. (e) Na₂NH₄PO₄. (f) PbCO₃. (g) SnSO₃. (h) Cd(SCN)₂.
5.67 (a) 50.48 amu. (b) 92.02 amu. (c) 64.07 amu. (d) 84.16 amu.
(e) 34.02 amu. (f) 342.3 amu. (g) 17.03 amu. **5.69** (a) 16.04 amu.
(b) 46.01 amu. (c) 80.07 amu. (d) 78.11 amu. (e) 149.9 amu.
(f) 174.27 amu. (g) 310.2 amu. **5.71** (a) 120.9 amu. (b) 216.3 amu.
(c) 128.4 amu. **5.75** 78.77% Sn; 21.23% O. **5.77** 39.89% Ca; 18.50%
P; 41.41% O; 0.20% H. **5.79** Ammonia, NH₃. **5.83** 409 g/mol. **5.85**
3.01 × 10²² C atoms; 6.02 × 10²² H atoms; 3.01 × 10²² O atoms.
5.87 2.1 × 10⁹ molecules. **5.89** (a) 80.56% C; 7.51% H; 11.93% O.
(b) 4.614 × 10²¹ molecules C₉H₁₀O. **5.91** 1.72 g F. 5.93 5.28 × 10²¹
molecules. **5.95** 493 g. **5.97** C₁₈H₂₀O₂. **5.99** Na₂O and SrO. **5.101** NaCl is
an ionic compound; it doesn't consist of molecules. **5.103** (a) Molecule
and compound. (b) Element and molecule. (c) Element. (d) Molecule
and compound. (e) Element. (f) Element and molecule. (g) Element and
molecule. (h) Molecule and compound. (i) Compound, not molecule.
(j) Element. (k) Element and molecule. (l) Compound, not molecule.
5.105 (a) Yes; This is consistent with the Law of Multiple Proportions
which states that if two elements combine to form more than one
compound, the masses of one element that combine with a fixed mass of
the other element are in ratios of small whole numbers. In this case, the
ratio of the masses of hydrogen in the two compounds is 3:1. (b) Ethane:
any formula with C:H = 1:3 (CH₃, C₂H₆, etc.); Acetylene: any formula
with C:H = 1:1 (CH, C₂H₂, etc). **5.107** Ionic: LiF, BaCl₂, KCl; Molecular:
SiCl₄, B₂H₆, C₂H₄. **5.109** Ionic: NaF, MgF₂ AlF₃; covalent: SiF₄, PF₅,
SF₆, ClF₃. **5.111** Cation: Mg²⁺, Sr²⁺, Fe³⁺, Mn²⁺, Sn⁴⁺; Anion: HCO₃⁻,
Cl⁻, NO₂⁻, ClO₃⁻, Br⁻; Formula: Mg(HCO₃)₂, SrCl₂, Fe(NO₂)₃, Mn(ClO₃)₂,
SnBr₄; Name: magnesium bicarbonate, strontium chloride, iron(III)
nitrate, manganese(II) chlorate, tin(IV) bromide. **5.113** C₂H₆ < C₃H₈ <
C₂H₂ = C₆H₆. **5.115** (a) Covalent; BF₃; boron trifluoride. (b) Ionic; KBr;
potassium bromide. **5.117** C₃H₂OF₅Cl; 184.5 g/mol; 0.021 mol. **5.119**
(a) 0.212 mol O. (b) 0.424 mol O. **5.121** Ionic: RbCl and KO₂; covalent:
PF₅, BrF₃, and CI₄. **5.123** MgMoO₄. **5.125** 0.0011 mol chlorophyll.
5.127 HClO₄. **5.129** 30.20% C; 5.069% H; 44.57% Cl; 20.16% S. **5.131**
(a) 6.532 × 10⁴ g. (b) 7.6 × 10⁻² g HG. **5.133** (a) 4.24 × 10²² K⁺ ions and
4.24 × 10²² Br⁻ ions. (b) 4.58 × 10²² Na⁺ ions and 2.29 × 10²² SO₄²⁻ ions.
(c) 4.34 × 10²² Ca²⁺ ions and 2.89 × 10²² PO₄³⁻ ions. **5.135** (e) 0.50 mol
Cl₂. **5.137** 28.97 g/mol.

Chapter 6

6.9 (a) Covalent; BF₃; boron trifluoride. (b) Ionic; KBr; potassium bromide.
6.13 C—H (ΔEN = 0.4) < Br—H (ΔEN = 0.7) < F—H (ΔEN = 1.9) <
Li—Cl (ΔEN = 2.0) < Na—Cl (ΔEN = 2.1) < K—F (ΔEN = 3.2). **6.15**
Cl—Cl < Br—Cl < Si—C < Cs—F. **6.17** (a) Covalent; The two silicon
atoms are the same. (b) Polar covalent; The electronegativity difference is
1.2. (c) Ionic; The electronegativity difference is 3.0. (d) Polar covalent;
The electronegativity difference is 0.9. **6.19** 0.151 D. **6.21** 15.9 D.
6.23

(a) :F̈—Ö—F̈: (b) :F̈—N̈=N̈—F̈: (c) H—Si—Si—H (with H's above and below each Si)

(d) ⁻:Ö—H (e) H—C—C—Ö:⁻ with H and :O: and :Cl: groups (f) H—C—N⁺—H (with H's)

6.25

(a) :F̈—Cl̈—F̈: with :F̈: below (b) H—Së—H (c) H—N̈—H with :O—H below

(d) :Cl̈—P—Cl̈: with :O: above and :Cl̈: below (e) H—C—C—Br̈: with H's (f) :Cl̈—N̈—Cl̈: with :Cl̈: below

(g) H—C—N̈: with H's

6.29 (a) Ö=N⁺=Ö (b) ⁻:S̈—C≡N: (c) ⁻:S̈—S̈:⁻ (d) :F̈—Cl̈⁺—F̈:

6.31 (a) Neither oxygen atom has a complete octet, and the left-most
hydrogen atom shows two bonds (4 electrons). Hydrogen can hold only
two electrons in its valence shell.

(b) H—C—C—Ö—H with H's and :O: above

6.35 (a) H—C with :Ö:⁻ and :O: ↔ H—C with :O: and :Ö:⁻

(b) H₂C=N⁺ with :Ö:⁻ and :O:⁻ resonance structures

6.37 H—N̈=N⁺=N̈:⁻ ↔ H—N̈⁻—N⁺≡N: ↔ H—N≡N⁺—N̈:²⁻

6.39 Ö=C=N̈:⁻ ↔ ⁻:Ö—C≡N: ↔ :O≡C—N̈:²⁻

6.41 (b) and (e). **6.43** (guanine resonance structures)

6.49 No. :Cl̈—Be—Cl̈: To make an octet on Be is not plausible:

⁺Cl̈=Be=Cl̈⁺ with 2− on Be **6.51** :Cl̈—Al—Cl̈: + :Cl̈:⁻ ⟶ :Cl̈—Al—Cl̈: ; with :Cl̈: groups

coordinate covalent bond. **6.53** :Cl̈—Sb—Cl̈: with Cl groups; no. **6.55** H—Ö—Ö: ; :Cl̈—Ö:

6.57 Completed octet on S: $\left[:\ddot{O}-\ddot{S}-\ddot{O}:\right]^{2-}$;

$\qquad$ $:\ddot{O}:$

zero formal charge on S: $\left[:\ddot{O}-\ddot{S}-\ddot{O}:\right]^{2-}$

$\qquad\qquad$ $\underset{\|}{:\ddot{O}:}$

6.59 $^{-}\ddot{N}=\overset{+}{N}=\ddot{N}^{-} \longleftrightarrow :N\equiv\overset{+}{N}-\ddot{N}:^{2-} \longleftrightarrow {}^{2-}\ddot{N}-\overset{+}{N}\equiv N:$

6.61 (a) $AlCl_4^{-}$. (b) AlF_6^{3-}. (c) $AlCl_3$. **6.63** CF_2 would be very unstable because carbon does not have an octet; LiO_2 would not be stable because the lattice energy between Li^+ and superoxide O_2^- would be too low to stabilize the solid; $CsCl_2$ requires a Cs^{2+} cation. The second ionization energy is too large to be compensated by the increase in lattice energy. PI_5 appears to be a reasonable species. However, the iodine atoms are too large to have five of them "fit" around a single P atom. **6.65** (a) False. (b) False. (c) False. **6.69** N_2; since it has a triple bond. **6.69** CH_4 and NH_4^+; N_2 and CO; C_6H_6 and $B_3N_3H_6$.

6.71

6.73 $\left[:\ddot{O}-\ddot{S}=\ddot{O}:\right]^{-}$ $\left[:\ddot{O}-\ddot{S}=\ddot{O}:\right]^{-}$

$\qquad\qquad\qquad\qquad\qquad\qquad\qquad$ $\underset{\|}{:\ddot{O}:}$

6.75 The central iodine atom in I_3^- has *ten* electrons surrounding it: two bonding pairs and three lone pairs. The central iodine has an expanded octet. Elements in the second period such as fluorine cannot have an expanded octet as would be required for F_3^-.

6.77 $H-\underset{H}{\overset{H}{C}}-\ddot{N}=C=\ddot{O} \longleftrightarrow H-\underset{H}{\overset{H}{C}}-\overset{+}{N}\equiv C-\ddot{O}:^{-}$

6.79 Form (a) is the most important resonance structure with no formal charges and all satisfied octets. (b) is likely not as important as (a) because of the positive formal charge on O. Forms (c) and (d) do not satisfy the octet rule for all atoms and are likely not important.

6.81 (a) $:\ddot{F}-\underset{:\ddot{Cl}:}{\overset{:\ddot{Cl}:}{C}}-\ddot{Cl}:$ (b) $:\ddot{F}-\underset{:\ddot{Cl}:}{\overset{:\ddot{F}:}{C}}-\ddot{Cl}:$ (c) $H-\underset{:\ddot{F}:}{\overset{:\ddot{F}:}{C}}-\ddot{Cl}:$ (d) $:\ddot{F}-\underset{:\ddot{F}:}{\overset{:\ddot{F}:}{C}}-\underset{:\ddot{F}:}{\overset{:\ddot{F}:}{C}}-H$

6.83 (a) $^{-}:C\equiv O:^{+}$ (b) $:N\equiv O:^{+}$ (c) $^{-}:C\equiv N:$ (d) $:N\equiv N:$

6.85 The noble gases violate the octet rule. This is because each noble gas atom already has completely filled ns and np subshells.

6.87 (a) $:\ddot{N}=\ddot{O} \longleftrightarrow {}^{-}:\ddot{N}=\ddot{O}:^{+}$. The first structure is the most important.

(b) No. **6.89** The arrows indicate coordinate covalent bonds. This dimer does not possess a dipole moment.

6.91 RbF: 62.5%; RbI: 64.3%; We would expect the percent ionic character to be higher for RbF than it is for RbI, given the fact that fluorine is more electronegative. **6.93** Compound: B, C, A; Dipole moment: 1.9 D, 0.524 D, 10 D.

6.95

The C−N bond length with be shorter than that of a single bond (143 pm) and longer than that of a double bond (138 pm), approximately 141 pm.

6.97

$:N\equiv\overset{+}{N}-\ddot{N}=\overset{+}{N}=\ddot{N}^{-} \longleftrightarrow {}^{-}\ddot{N}=\overset{+}{N}=\ddot{N}-\overset{+}{N}\equiv N: \longleftrightarrow :N\equiv\overset{+}{N}-\ddot{N}^{-}-\overset{+}{N}\equiv N:$

6.99 EN(O) = 3.2 (Pauling 3.5); EN(F) = 4.4 (Pauling 4.0); EN(Cl) = 3.5 (Pauling 3.0).

Chapter 7

7.7 (a) Tetrahedral. (b) Trigonal planar. (c) Trigonal pyramidal. (d) Bent. (e) Bent. **7.9** (a) Trigonal pyramidal. (b) Tetrahedral. (c) Tetrahedral. (d) See-saw. **7.11** (a) Linear. (b) Linear. (c) Linear. **7.13** Carbon at the center of H_3C-: electron-domain geometry = tetrahedral, molecular geometry = tetrahedral; carbon at center of $-CO-OH$: electron-domain geometry = trigonal planar, molecular geometry = trigonal planar; oxygen in $-O-H$: electron-domain geometry = tetrahedral, molecular geometry = bent. **7.15** (ii) and (iv): The lone pair of electrons on the central atoms in each of these molecules repels the other bonds more strongly than the bonds repel one another. For this reason, the bonds will be squeezed closer together than the ideal angle. These bonds angles must get smaller than the ideal angle, rather than larger. **7.19** (a) Polar. (b) Polar. (c) Nonpolar. **7.21** Only (c) is polar. **7.23** PH_3 will condense to a liquid at a higher temperature because it is polar and has stronger intermolecular forces. **7.29** BF_3; The central atom in these molecules does not have enough unpaired electrons in its ground state to form the observed number of bonds. **7.35** SiH_4: sp^3; $H_3Si-SiH_3$: sp^3. **7.37** sp^3d. **7.39** In BF_3, B is sp^2 hybridized. In NH_3, N is sp^3 hybridized. In F_3B-NH_3, B and N are both sp^3 hybridized. **7.43** (a) sp. (b) sp. (c) sp. **7.45** sp. **7.47** Nine σ bonds and nine π bonds. **7.49** 36 σ bonds and 10 π bonds. **7.55** In order for the two hydrogen atoms to combine to form a H_2 molecule, the electrons must have opposite spins. If two H atoms collide and their electron spins are parallel, no bond will form. **7.57** $Li_2^- = Li_2^+ < Li_2$; Both Li_2^+ and Li_2^- have bond order of $\frac{1}{2}$. Li_2 has a bond order of 1. **7.59** B_2^+, with a bond order of $\frac{1}{2}$. (B_2 has a bond order of 1.) **7.61** The Lewis diagram has all electrons paired (incorrect) and a double bond (correct). The MO diagram has two unpaired electrons (correct), and a bond order of 2 (correct). **7.63** O_2: bond order = 2, paramagnetic; O_2^+: bond order = 2.5, paramagnetic; O_2^-: bond order = 1.5, paramagnetic; O_2^{2-}: bond order = 1, diamagnetic. **7.65** The two shared electrons that make up the single bond in B_2 both lie in pi molecular orbitals and constitute a pi bond. The four shared electrons that make up the double bond in C_2 all lie in pi molecular orbitals and constitute two pi bonds. **7.67** Be_2. **7.71** The left symbol shows three delocalized double bonds (correct). The right symbol shows three localized double bonds and three single bonds (incorrect). **7.73** (a) $\ddot{O}=N-\ddot{O}:^{-} \longleftrightarrow {}^{-}:\ddot{O}=N-\ddot{O}$

(b) sp^2. (c) Sigma bonds join the nitrogen atom to the fluorine and oxygen atoms. There is a pi molecular orbital delocalized over the N and O atoms. **7.75** The central oxygen atom is sp^2 hybridized. The unhybridized $2p_z$ orbital on the central oxygen overlaps with the $2p_z$ orbitals on the two terminal atoms. **7.77** $:\ddot{Br}-Hg-\ddot{Br}:$ Linear. You could establish the geometry of $HgBr_2$ by measuring its dipole moment. **7.79** Bent; sp^3. **7.81** (a) $C_6H_8O_6$. (b) Five central O atoms sp^3; hybridization of the sixth (double bonded) peripheral O atom is sp^2. Three C atoms sp^2; three C atoms sp^3. (c) The five central O atoms bent. The three sp^2 C atoms are trigonal planar. The three sp^3 C atoms are tetrahedral. **7.83** (a) 180°. (b) 120°. (c) 109.5°. (d) 109.5°. (e) 180°. (f) 120°. (g) 109.5°. (h) 109.5°.

7.85 (a) ; planar. (b) $\left[:\ddot{O}-\underset{\|}{\overset{}{Cl}}-\ddot{O}:\right]^{-}$; nonplanar. $\qquad$ $:O:$

(c) $H-C\equiv N:$; polar. (d) $:\ddot{F}\overset{\ddot{O}}{\diagdown}\ddot{F}:$; polar. (e) $\ddot{O}\diagdown\overset{\dot{N}}{}\diagup\ddot{O}:$; greater than 120°. Experimental value is around 135°. **7.87** The S−S bond is a normal 2-electron shared pair covalent bond. Each S is sp^3 hybridized, so the X−S−S angle is about 109°. **7.89** Only ICl_2^- and $CdBr_2$ are linear. **7.91** (a) sp^2. (b) The molecule on the right is polar. **7.93** Rotation about the sigma bond in 1,2-dichloroethane does not destroy the bond, so the bond is free to rotate. Thus, the molecule is polar because the C—Cl bond moments cancel each other because of the averaging effect brought about by rotation. The π bond between the C atoms in *cis*-dichloroethylene prevents rotation (in order to rotate, the π bond must be broken). Therefore, the molecule is polar. **7.95** All except homonuclear diatomic molecules N_2 and O_2.

7.97

The carbon atoms and nitrogen atoms marked with an asterisk (C* and N*) are sp^2 hybridized; unmarked carbon atoms and nitrogen atoms are sp^3 hybridized; and the nitrogen atom marked with (#) is sp hybridized. **7.99** (a) = sp: 0; (b) = sp^2: 2; (c) = sp^3: 5; (d) = sp^3d: 0. **7.101** The carbons are all sp^2 hybridized. The nitrogen double bonded to carbon in the ring is sp^2 hybridized. The other nitrogens are sp^3 hybridized. **7.103** (a) O_2. (b) 2. (c) 2. **7.105** Figure (c). **7.107** The second ("asymmetric stretching mode") and third ("bending mode").

7.109

The four carbons marked with an asterisk are sp^2 hybridized. The remaining carbons are sp^3 hybridized. **7.111** (a) $[Ne_2](\sigma_{3s})^2(\sigma_{3s}^*)^2(\pi_{3p_y})^2(\pi_{3p_z})^2(\sigma_{3p_x})^2$. (b) 3. (c) Diamagnetic. **7.113** In the Lewis structure, all the electrons are paired. From molecular orbital theory, the electrons would be arranged as follows: $[He_2](\sigma_{2s})^2(\sigma_{2s}^*)^2(\sigma_{2p_x})^2(\pi_{2p_y})^2(\pi_{2p_z})^2(\pi_{2p_y}^*)^1(\pi_{2p_z}^*)^1$. This shows two unpaired electrons. To pair these electrons, energy is required to flip the spin of one, thus making the Lewis structure and excited state. **7.115** (a) Although the O atoms are sp^3 hybridized, they are locked in a planar structure by the benzene rings. The molecule is symmetrical and therefore is not polar. (b) 20 σ bonds and 6 π bonds. **7.117** (a) $:C\equiv\overset{+}{\underset{-}{O}}:$ The electronegativity difference between O and C suggests that electron density should concentrate on the O atom, but assigning formal charges places a negative charge on the C atom. Therefore, we expect CO to have a small dipole moment. (b) CO is isoelectronic with N_2, bond order 3. This agrees with the triple bond in the Lewis structure. (c) Since C has a negative formal charge, it is more likely to form bonds with Fe^{2+}. (OC—Fe^{2+} rather than CO—Fe^{2+}). **7.119** Tetrahedral. **7.121** In losing an electron, the bond order of CF increases as a result of fewer electrons in antibonding orbitals. This results the formation of CF^+ which is more stable and has a shorter bond length.

Chapter 8

8.5 (a) $KOH + H_3PO_4 \longrightarrow K_3PO_4 + H_2O$. (b) $Zn + AgCl \longrightarrow ZnCl_2 + Ag$. (c) $NaHCO_3 \longrightarrow Na_2CO_3 + H_2O + CO_2$. (d) $NH_4NO_2 \longrightarrow N_2 + H_2O$. (e) $CO_2 + KOH \longrightarrow K_2CO_3 + H_2O$. **8.7** (a) Potassium and water react to form potassium hydroxide and hydrogen. (b) Barium hydroxide and hydrochloric acid react to form barium chloride and water. (c) Copper and nitric acid react to form copper nitrate, nitrogen monoxide and water. (d) Aluminum and sulfuric acid react to form aluminum sulfate and hydrogen. (e) Hydrogen iodide reacts to form hydrogen and iodine. **8.9** (a) $2N_2O_5 \longrightarrow 2N_2O_4 + O_2$. (b) $2KNO_3 \longrightarrow 2KNO_2 + O_2$. (c) $NH_4NO_3 \longrightarrow N_2O + 2H_2O$. (d) $NH_4NO_2 \longrightarrow N_2 + 2H_2O$. (e) $2NaHCO_3 \longrightarrow Na_2CO_3 + H_2O + CO_2$. (f) $P_4O_{10} + 6H_2O \longrightarrow 4H_3PO_4$. (g) $2HCl + CaCO_3 \longrightarrow CaCl_2 + H_2O + CO_2$. (h) $2Al + 3H_2SO_4 \longrightarrow Al_2(SO_4)_3 + 3H_2$. (i) $CO_2 + 2KOH \longrightarrow K_2CO_3 + H_2O$. (j) $CH_4 + 2O_2 \longrightarrow CO_2 + 2H_2O$. (k) $Be_2C + 4H_2O \longrightarrow 2Be(OH)_2 + CH_4$. (l) $3Cu + 8HNO_3 \longrightarrow 3Cu(NO_3)_2 + 2NO + 4H_2O$. (m) $S + 6HNO_3 \longrightarrow H_2SO_4 + 6NO_2 + 2H_2O$. (n) $2NH_3 + 3CuO \longrightarrow 3Cu + N_2 + 3H_2O$. **8.13** (a) Combustion. (b) Combination. (c) Decomposition. **8.17** $C_{10}H_{20}O$. **8.19** CH_2O. **8.21** Empirical formula: C_3H_2Cl; molecular formula: $C_6H_4Cl_2$. **8.25** 1.01 mol Cl_2. **8.27** 2.0×10^1 mol CO_2. **8.29** (a) $2NaHCO_3 \longrightarrow Na_2CO_3 + CO_2 + H_2O$. (b) 78.3 g $NaHCO_3$. **8.31** 255.9 g C_2H_5OH; 0.324 L. **8.33** 19.1 g KCN. **8.35** $NH_4NO_3(s) \longrightarrow N_2O(g) + 2H_2O(g)$. (b) 2.0×10^1 g N_2O. **8.37** 18.0 g O_2. **8.43** 6 mol NH_3 produced; 1 mol H_2 left. **8.45** $4NO_2 + O_2 \longrightarrow 2N_2O_5$. The limiting reagent is NO_2. **8.47** 0.709 g NO_2 produced; O_3 is the limiting reactant; 0.0069 mol NO remaining. **8.47** HCl is the limiting reactant; 23.4 g Cl_2. **8.51** (a) 7.05 g O_2. (b) 92.9%. **8.53** 3.48 $\times 10^3$ g C_6H_{14}. **8.55** 8.55 g S_2Cl_2; 76.6%. **8.57** 100%. **8.61** The electron configuration of helium is $1s^2$ and that of the other noble gases is ns^2np^6. The completely filled subshell represents great stability. Consequently, these elements are chemically unreactive. **8.63** Diagram (b). **8.65** Cl_2O_7. **8.67** (a) 0.212 mol O. (b) 0.424 mol O. **8.69** 39.6% NO. **8.71** 700 g. **8.73** (a) $Zn(s) + H_2SO_4(aq) \longrightarrow ZnSO_4(aq) + H_2(g)$. (b) 64.2%. (c) We assume that the impurities are inert and do not react with the sulfuric acid to produce hydrogen. **8.75** (a) 0.307 g salicylic acid. (b) 0.410 g salicylic acid. (c) 12.08 g aspirin; 90.2%. **8.77** 65.4 amu; Zn. **8.79** Mg_3N_2, magnesium nitride. **8.81** PbC_8H_{20}. **8.83** (a) $C_3H_8(g) + 3H_2O(g) \longrightarrow 3CO(g) + 7H_2(g)$. (b) 909 kg H_2. **8.85** (a) \$0.47/kg. (b) 0.631 kg K_2O. **8.87** (a) NH_4NO_2 is the *only* reactant. When a reaction involves only a single reactant, we usually do not describe that reactant as the "limiting reactant" because it is understood that this is the case. (b) In principle, two or more reactants can be limiting reactants if they are exhausted simultaneously. In practice, it is virtually impossible to measure the reactants so precisely that two or more run out at the same time. **8.89** 2.60 g H_2O. **8.91** $2NO(g) + SO_2(g) \longrightarrow SO_3(g) + N_2O(g)$. **8.93** 0.56 mol $NH_4V_3O_8$. **8.95** The atom economy for the recent synthesis, 73.36%, is nearly three times higher than it is for the traditional preparation, 25.46%. **8.97** (a) Compound X: MnO_2. (b) Compound Y: Mn_3O_4.

Chapter 9

9.9 $A_2F < A_2G < A_2E$. **9.11** Diagram (c). **9.13** (a) Strong electrolyte. (b) Nonelectrolyte. (c) Weak electrolyte. (d) Strong electrolyte. (e) Weak electrolyte. **9.17** Diagram (c). **9.19** Reaction (d). **9.21** (a) Insoluble. (b) Insoluble. (c) Soluble. (d) Soluble. (e) Insoluble. **9.23** (a) Ionic: $2Ag^+(aq) + 2NO_3^-(aq) + 2Na^+(aq) + SO_4^{2-}(aq) \longrightarrow Ag_2SO_4(s) + 2Na^+(aq) + 2NO_3^-(aq)$; net ionic: $2Ag^+(aq) + SO_4^{2-}(aq) \longrightarrow Ag_2SO_4(s)$. (b) Ionic: $Ba^{2+}(aq) + 2Cl^-(aq) + Zn^{2+}(aq) + SO_4^{2-}(aq) \longrightarrow BaSO_4(s) + Zn^{2+}(aq) + 2Cl^-(aq)$; net ionic: $Ba^{2+}(aq) + SO_4^{2-}(aq) \longrightarrow BaSO_4(s)$. (c) Ionic: $2NH_4^+(aq) + CO_3^{2-}(aq) + Ca^{2+}(aq) + 2Cl^-(aq) \longrightarrow CaCO_3(s) + 2NH_4^+(aq) + 2Cl^-(aq)$; net ionic: $Ca^{2+}(aq) + CO_3^{2-}(aq) \longrightarrow CaCO_3(s)$.

9.25 $Ba^{2+}(aq) + SO_4^{2-}(aq) \longrightarrow BaSO_4(s)$. **9.33** (a) Brønsted base.
(b) Brønsted base. (c) Brønsted acid. (d) Brønsted acid and Brønsted base.
9.35 (a) $HC_2H_3O_2(aq) + KOH(aq) \longrightarrow HC_2H_3O_2(aq) + H_2O(l)$; ionic:
$HC_2H_3O_2(aq) + K^+(aq) + OH^-(aq) \longrightarrow C_2H_3O_2^-(aq) + K^+(aq) +$
$H_2O(l)$; net ionic: $HC_2H_3O_2(aq) + OH^-(aq) \longrightarrow C_2H_3O_2^-(aq) + H_2O(l)$.
(b) $H_2CO_3(aq) + 2NaOH(aq) \longrightarrow Na_2CO_3(aq) + 2H_2O(l)$, ionic:
$H_2CO_3(aq) + 2Na^+(aq) + 2OH^-(aq) \longrightarrow 2Na^+(aq) + CO_3^{2-}(aq) +$
$2H_2O(l)$; net ionic: $H_2CO_3(aq) + 2OH^-(aq) \longrightarrow CO_3^{2-}(aq) + 2H_2O(l)$.
(c) $2HNO_3(aq) + Ba(OH)_2(aq) \longrightarrow Ba(NO_3)_2(aq) + 2H_2O(l)$, ionic:
$2H^+(aq) + 2NO_3^-(aq) + Ba^{2+}(aq) + 2OH^-(aq) \longrightarrow Ba^{2+}(aq) + 2NO_3^-$
$(aq) + 2H_2O(l)$; net ionic: $2H^+(aq) + 2OH^-(aq) \longrightarrow 2H_2O(l)$ or $H^+(aq)$
$+ OH^-(aq) \longrightarrow H_2O(l)$. **9.43** (a) $2Sr \longrightarrow 2Sr^{2+} + 4e^-$, Sr is the
reducing agent; $O_2 + 4e^- \longrightarrow 2O^{2-}$, O_2 is the oxidizing agent. (b) $2Li$
$\longrightarrow 2Li^+ + 2e^-$, Li is the reducing agent; $H_2 + 2e^- \longrightarrow 2H^-$, H_2 is
the oxidizing agent. (c) $2Cs \longrightarrow 2Cs^+ + 2e^-$, Cs is the reducing agent;
$Br_2 + 2e^- \longrightarrow 2Br^-$, Br_2 is the oxidizing agent. (d) $3Mg \longrightarrow 3Mg^{2+}$
$+ 6e^-$, Mg is the reducing agent; $N_2 + 6e^- \longrightarrow 2N^{3-}$, N_2 is the oxidizing
agent. **9.45** H_2S (-2), S^{2-} (-2), HS^- (-2) $< S_8$ (0) $< SO_2$ ($+4$) $< SO_3$ ($+6$),
H_2SO_4 ($+6$). **9.47** (a) $+1$. (b) $+7$. (c) -4. (d) -1. (e) -2. (f) $+6$. (g) $+6$.
(h) $+7$. (i) $+4$. (j) 0. (k) $+5$. (l) $-1/2$. (m) $+5$. (n) $+3$. **9.49** (a) $+1$. (b) -1.
(c) $+3$. (d) $+3$. (e) $+4$. (f) $+6$. (g) $+2$. (h) $+4$. (i) $+2$. (j) $+3$. (k) $+5$.
9.51 If nitric acid is a strong oxidizing agent and zinc is a strong reducing
agent, then zinc metal will probably reduce nitric acid when the two react;
that is, N will gain electrons and the oxidation number of N must decrease.
Since the oxidation number of nitrogen in nitric acid is $+5$, then the
nitrogen-containing product must have a smaller oxidation number for
nitrogen. The only compound in the list that doesn't have a nitrogen
oxidation number less than $+5$ is N_2O_5. This is never a product of the
reduction of nitric acid. **9.53** Molecular oxygen is a powerful oxidizing
agent. In SO_3, the oxidation number of the element bound to oxygen (S) is
at its maximum value ($+6$); the sulfur cannot be oxidized further. The
other elements bound to oxygen in this problem have less than their
maximum oxidation number and can undergo further oxidation. Only SO_3
does not react with molecular oxygen. **9.55** (a) Decomposition/
disproportionation. (b) Displacement. (c) Decomposition. (d)
Combination. **9.61** 232 g KI. **9.63** 6.00×10^{-3} mol $MgCl_2$. **9.65** (a) 1.16
M. (b) 0.608 M. (c) 1.78 M. **9.67** (a) 136 mL. (b) 62.2 mL. (c) 47 mL. **9.69**
Diagram (e). **9.71** Dilute 323 mL of the 2.00 M HCl solution to a final
volume of 1.00 L. **9.73** Dilute 3.00 mL of the 4.00 M HNO_3 solution to a
final volume of 60.0 mL. **9.75** 1.41 M $KMnO_4$. **9.149** 0.00699 M $C_6H_{12}O_6$.
9.79 (a) $BaCl_2$: 0.300 M Cl^-; NaCl: 0.566 M Cl^-; $AlCl_3$: 3.606 M Cl^-. (b)
1.28 M $Sr(NO_3)_2$. **9.81** 2.325 M. **9.83** (a) 0.26; 0.40; 0.53; 0.73. (b) 0.659
L/mol · cm. **9.91** Diagram (c). **9.93** 0.215 g AgCl. **9.95** NaOH: diagram
(d); $Ba(OH)_2$: diagram (c). **9.97** $Ag^+(aq) + Cl^-(aq) \longrightarrow AgCl(s)$;
0.165 g NaCl. **9.99** 0.1108 M. **9.101** (a) 42.78 mL. (b) 158.5 mL. (c) 79.23
mL. **9.103** (d) 0.20 M $Mg(NO_3)_2$ (greatest concentration of ions). **9.105** 773
mL. **9.107** (a) Weak electrolyte. (b) Strong electrolyte. (c) Strong electrolyte.
(d) Nonelectrolyte. **9.109** (a) $C_2H_5ONH_2$ molecules. (b) K^+ and F^- ions. (c)
NH_4^+ and NO_3^- ions. (d) C_3H_7OH molecules. **9.111** 1146 g/mol. **9.113** 1.28 M.
9.115 43.4 g $BaSO_4$. **9.117** (a) Redox. (b) Precipitation. (c) Acid-base. (d)
Combination. (e) Redox. (f) Redox. (g) Precipitation. (h) Redox. (i) Redox.
(j) Redox. **9.119** (a) Mix a solution containing Mg^{2+} ions such as
$MgCl_2(aq)$ or $Mg(NO_3)_2(aq)$ with a solution containing hydroxide ions
such as $NaOH(aq)$. $Mg(OH)_2$ will precipitate and can be collected by
filtration.
(b) 0.78 L. **9.121** 1.72 M. **9.123** Electrolysis to ascertain if hydrogen and
oxygen were produced; The reaction with an alkali metal to see if a base
and hydrogen gas were produced; The dissolution of a metal oxide to see
if a base was produced (or a nonmetal oxide to see if an acid was
produced). **9.125** Diagram (a) showing Ag^+ and NO_3^- ions; $AgOH(aq) +$
$HNO_3(aq) \longrightarrow H_2O(l) + AgNO_3(aq)$. **9.127** (a) Check with litmus
paper, combine with carbonate or bicarbonate to see if CO_2 gas is
produced, combine with a base and check for neutralization with an
indicator. (b) Titrate a known quantity of acid with a standard NaOH
solution. (c) Visually compare the conductivity of the acid with a standard

NaCl solution of the same molar concentration. **9.129** (a) $Pb(NO_3)_2(aq) +$
$Na_2SO_4(aq) \longrightarrow PbSO_4(s) + 2NaNO_3(aq)$; net ionic: $Pb^{2+}(aq) +$
$SO_4^{2-}(aq) \longrightarrow PbSO_4(s)$. (b) 6.34×10^{-5} M. **9.131** (a) $HI(aq) +$
$KOH(aq) \longrightarrow KI(aq) + H_2O(l)$; evaporate to dryness. (b) $2HI(aq) +$
$K_2CO_3(aq) \longrightarrow 2KI(aq) + CO_2(g) + H_2O(l)$; evaporate to dryness.
9.133 (a) Combine any soluble magnesium salt with a soluble hydroxide,
filter the precipitate. (b) Combine any soluble silver salt with any soluble
iodide salt, filter the precipitate. (c) Combine any soluble barium salt with
any soluble phosphate salt, filter the precipitate. **9.135** (a) Add Na_2SO_4.
(b) Add KOH. (c) Add $AgNO_3$. (d) Add $Ca(NO_3)_2$. (e) Add $Mg(NO_3)_2$.
9.137 Reaction 1: $SO_3^{2-}(aq) + H_2O_2(aq) \longrightarrow SO_4^{2-}(aq) + H_2O(l)$;
Reaction 2: $SO_4^{2-}(aq) + Ba^{2+}(aq) \longrightarrow BaSO_4(s)$. **9.139** Cl_2O ($+1$),
Cl_2O_3 ($+3$), ClO_2 ($+4$), Cl_2O_6 ($+6$), Cl_2O_7 ($+7$). **9.141** 4.99 grains.
9.143 (a) $CaF_2(s) + H_2SO_4(aq) \longrightarrow CaSO_4(s) + 2HF(g)$; $2NaCl(s) +$
$H_2SO_4(aq) \longrightarrow Na_2SO_4(aq) + 2HCl(g)$. (b) The sulfuric acid would
oxidize the Br^- and I^- ions to Br_2 and I_2. (c) $PBr_3(l) + 3H_2O(l) \longrightarrow$
$3HBr(g) + H_3PO_3(aq)$. **9.145** Electric furnace method: $P_4(s) + 5O_2(g)$
$\longrightarrow P_4O_{10}(s)$ (redox), $P_4O_{10}(s) + 6H_2O(l) \longrightarrow 4H_3PO_4(aq)$ (acid-
base); wet process: $Ca_5(PO_4)_3F(s) + 5H_2SO_4(aq) \longrightarrow HF(aq) +$
$3H_3PO_4(aq) + 5CaSO_4(s)$ (acid-base and precipitation). **9.147** (a) $4KO_2(s)$
$+ 2CO_2(g) \longrightarrow 2K_2CO_3(s) + 3O_2(g)$. (b) $-1/2$. (c) 34.4 L air.
9.149 No; the oxidation number of all oxygen atoms is zero.
9.151 (a) Acid: H_3O^+, base: OH^-.

$$OH^- \qquad H_3O^+ \qquad\qquad H_2O \qquad H_2O$$

(b) Acid NH_4^+; base NH_2^-.

$$NH_4^+ \qquad NH_2^- \qquad\qquad NH_3 \qquad NH_3$$

9.153 When a solid dissolves in solution, the volume of the solution
usually changes. **9.155** (a) The precipitate $CaSO_4$ formed over Ca
preventing the Ca from reacting with the sulfuric acid. (b) Aluminum is
protected by a tenacious oxide layer with the composition Al_2O_3. (c) These
metals react more readily with water: $2Na(s) + 2H_2O(l) \longrightarrow$
$2NaOH(aq) + H_2(g)$. (d) The metal should be placed below Fe and above
H. (e) Any metal above Al in the activity series will react with Al^{3+}. Metals
from Mg to Li will work. **9.157** (a) $Cu(s) + 4HNO_3(aq) \longrightarrow$
$Cu(NO_3)_2(aq) + 2NO_2(g) + 2H_2O(l)$ (redox); $Cu(NO_3)_2(aq) +$
$2NaOH(aq) \longrightarrow Cu(OH)_2(s) + 2NaNO_3(aq)$ (precipitation);
$Cu(OH)_2(s) \longrightarrow CuO(s) + H_2O(g)$ (decomposition); $CuO(s) +$
$H_2SO_4(aq) \longrightarrow CuSO_4(aq) + H_2O(l)$ (acid-base); $CuSO_4(aq) + Zn(s)$
$\longrightarrow Cu(s) + ZnSO_4(aq)$ (redox); $Zn(s) + 2HCl(aq) \longrightarrow ZnCl_2(aq)$
$+ H_2(g)$ (redox). (b) 194 g $Cu(NO_3)_2$; 101 g $Cu(OH)_2$; 82.1 g CuO; 165 g
$CuSO_4$; 65.6 g Cu. (c) All of the reaction steps are clean and almost
quantitative; therefore, the recovery yield should be high. **9.159** [Na^+]:
0.5295 M; [NO_3^-]: 0.4298 M; [OH^-]: 0.09968 M; [Mg^{2+}]: 0 M.

Chapter 10

10.11 48 J. **10.13** 577 J; work done *on* the system. **10.19** (a) 0 J. (b) -9.5 J.
(c) -18 J. **10.21** 4.51 kJ/g. **10.23** 4.80×10^2 kJ. **10.25** For processes
occurring in solution (cellular fluids), there is usually almost no volume
change, so $P\Delta V \approx 0$ and $\Delta U + P\Delta V \approx \Delta U$ (see Equation 10.8). **10.31**
728 kJ. **10.33** 50.7°C. **10.35** 26.3°C. **10.37** 47.8°C/day; 4.1 kg water/day.
10.39 2.36 J/g · °C. **10.43** 0.30 kJ/mol. **10.45** -238.7 kJ/mol. **10.51** $CH_4(g)$
and H(g). **10.53** $\Delta H_f^\circ[H_2O(l)]$. **10.55** $\Delta H_f^\circ[H_2O(l)]$ is more negative than
$\Delta H_f^\circ[H_2O_2(l)]$. **10.57** 177.8 kJ/mol. **10.59** (a) -571.6 kJ/mol.
(b) -2599 kJ/mol. **10.61** (a) -724 kJ/mol. (b) -1.37×10^3 kJ/mol.
(c) -2.01×10^3 kJ/mol. **10.63** -3924 kJ/mol. **10.65** -3.43×10^4 kJ.
10.69 303.0 kJ/mol. **10.71** (a) -2759 kJ/mol. (b) -2855.4 kJ/mol.
10.73 -651 kJ/mol. **10.77** 2255 kJ/mol. **10.79** -112.7 kJ/mol.
10.81 -44.35 kJ/mol. **10.83** -175.3 kJ. **10.85** -67 kJ/mol.

10.87 (a) −9.2 kJ/mol. (b) −9.2 kJ/mol. **10.89** −350.7 kJ/mol. **10.91** 0.492 J/g · °C. **10.93** The first reaction, which is exothermic, can be used to promote the second reaction, which is endothermic. Thus, the two gases are produced alternately. **10.95** 446 mol H_2. **10.97** 0.167 mol ethane. **10.99** 5.60 kJ/mol. **10.101** (a). **10.103** (a) 0 J. (b) −9.1 J. **10.105** −8.68 × 10^4 kJ. **10.107** −1.84 × 10^3 kJ. **10.109** 3.0 × 10^9 atomic bombs. **10.111** (a) $2LiOH(aq) + CO_2(g) \longrightarrow Li_2CO_3(aq) + H_2O(l)$. (b) 1.1 kg CO_2; 1.2 kg LiOH. **10.113** −5.2 × 10^6 kJ. **10.115** −3.60 × 10^2 kJ/mol Zn or −3.60 × 10^2 kJ/2 mol Ag^+. **10.117** (c) and (e); ΔH°_{rxn} is not the ΔH°_f value for (a) and (b) because more than 1 mole of a substance is formed; ΔH°_{rxn} is not the ΔH°_f value for (d) because $Cu^{2+}(aq)$ is not copper's standard state and SO_4^{2-} is not an element. **10.119** Water has a larger specific heat than air. Thus cold, damp air can extract more heat from the body than cold, dry air. By the same token, hot, humid air can deliver more heat to the body. **10.121** 5.8 × 10^2 m. **10.123** This law does not hold for Hg because it is a liquid. **10.125** $\Delta H^\circ_f(C_2H_2)$ = 226.6 kJ/mol; $\Delta H^\circ_f(C_6H_6)$ = 49.0 kJ/mol; ΔH_{rxn} = −630.8 kJ/mol. **10.127** (a) −46 kJ/mol. (b) 260 nm. **10.129** (a) 114 kJ/mol. (b) The bond in F_2^- is weaker. **10.131** (a) Glucose: 31 kJ; sucrose: 33 kJ. (b) Glucose: 15 m; sucrose: 16 m. **10.133** 347 kJ/mol. **10.135** −564.2 kJ/mol. **10.137** 96.21%. **10.139** (a) Although we cannot measure ΔH°_{rxn} for this reaction, the reverse process is the combustion of glucose. We could easily measure ΔH°_{rxn} for this combustion by burning a mole of glucose in a bomb calorimeter. (b) 1.1 × 10^{19} kJ. **10.141** (a) $CaC_2(s) + 2H_2O(l) \longrightarrow Ca(OH)_2(s) + C_2H_2(g)$. (b) 1.51 × 10^6 J. **10.143** We assume that when the car is stopped, its kinetic energy is completely converted into heat (friction of the brakes and friction between the tires and the road). Thus, $q = (\frac{1}{2})mu^2$, and the amount of heat generated must be proportional to the braking distance, d: $d \propto q$ or $d \propto u^2$. Therefore, as u increases to $2u$, d increases to $(2u)^2 = 4u^2$ which is proportional to 4d. **10.145** −413 kJ/mol. **10.147** w = 0 J; ΔU = −5153 kJ/mol. **10.149** 4.1 cents. **10.151** C—C: 347 kJ/mol; N—N: 193 kJ/mol; O—O: 142 kJ/mol; Lone pairs appear to weaken the bond.

Chapter 11

11.9 $u_{rms}(N_2)$: 472 m/s; $u_{rms}(O_2)$: 441 m/s; $u_{rms}(O_3)$: 360 m/s. **11.11** rms: 2.8 m/s; average speed: 2.7 m/s; The root-mean-square value is always greater than the average value, because squaring favors the larger values compared to just taking the average value. **11.13** 43.8 g/mol; CO_2. **11.23** 0.493 atm, 0.500 bar, 375 torr, 5.00 × 10^4 Pa. **11.25** 13.1 m. **11.27** 7.3 atm; 7.4 bar. **11.31** (a) Diagram (d). (b) Diagram (b). **11.33** 45.9 mL. **11.35** 587 mmHg. **11.37** 31.8 L. **11.39** 1 volume of NO. **11.43** 6.6 atm. **11.45** 1590°C. **11.47** 1.8 atm. **11.49** 0.70 L. **11.51** 63.31 L. **11.53** 6.1 × 10^{-3} atm. **11.55** 35.1 g/mol. **11.57** 2.1 × 10^{22} N_2 molecules; 5.6 × 10^{22} O_2 molecules. **11.59** 2.97 g/L. **11.61** SF_4. **11.67** 18.0 atm; ideal: 18.5 atm. **11.71** (a) 0.89 atm. (b) 1.4 L. **11.73** P_{Ne} = 349 mmHg. **11.75** P_{N_2}: 217 mm Hg, P_{H_2}: 650 mm Hg. **11.77** (a) Box 2. (b) Box 2. **11.79** 13 atm. **11.81** 3.70 × 10^2 L. **11.83** 88.9%. **11.85** $M(s) + 3HCl(aq) \longrightarrow$ 1.5$H_2(g) + MCl_3(aq)$, M_2O_3; $M_2(SO_4)_3$. **11.87** 94.7%. Assuming the impurity (or impurities) do not produce CO_2. **11.89** $C_2H_5OH(l) + 3O_2(g) \longrightarrow 2CO_2(g) + 3H_2O(l)$; 1.44 × 10^3 L air. **11.91** 19.8 g Zn. **11.93** 1.7 × 10^2 L. P_{CO_2}: 0.49 atm; P_{H_2O}: 0.41 atm; P_{N_2}: 0.25 atm; P_{O_2}: 0.041 atm. **11.95** (a) $NH_4NO_2(s) \longrightarrow N_2(g) + 2H_2O(l)$. (b) 0.273 g. **11.97** (a) P_{ii}: 4.0 atm; P_{iii}: 2.67 atm. (b) 2.67 atm, P_A: 1.33 atm; P_B: 1.33 atm. **11.99** (a) 9.54 atm. (b) If the tetracarbonylnickel gas starts to decompose significantly above 43°C, then for every mole of tetracarbonylnickel gas decomposed, four moles of carbon monoxide would be produced. **11.101** 1.3 × 10^{22} molecules; CO_2, O_2, N_2 and H_2O. **11.103** (a) $2KClO_3(s) \longrightarrow 2KCl(s) + 3O_2(g)$. (b) 6.21 L. **11.105** 0.0701 M. **11.107** P_{He}: 0.16 atm, P_{Ne}: 2.0 atm. **11.109** When the water enters the flask from the dropper, some hydrogen chloride dissolves, creating a partial vacuum. Pressure from the atmosphere forces more water up the vertical tube. **11.111** 7. **11.113** (a) 61.2 m/s. (b) 4.58 × 10^{-4} s. (c) 328 m/s; u_{rms}: 366 m/s; The magnitudes of the speeds are comparable, but not identical. The rms speed is derived for 3-dimensional motion and is not applicable to the speed distributions in directed molecular beams. Also, the experiment is measuring a most-probable speed, not an rms speed. **11.115** 20.9 kg O_2; 1.58 × 10^4 L O_2. **11.117** The fruit ripens more rapidly because the quantity (partial pressure) of ethylene gas inside the bag increases. **11.119** As the pen is used the amount of ink decreases, increasing the volume inside the pen. As the volume increases, the pressure inside the pen decreases. The hole is needed to equalize the pressure as the volume inside the pen increases. **11.121** (a) $NH_4NO_3(s) \longrightarrow N_2O(g) + 2H_2O(l)$. (b) 0.0821 L · atm/mol · K. **11.123** C_6H_6. **11.125** The gases inside the mine were a mixture of carbon dioxide, carbon monoxide, methane, and other harmful compounds. The low atmospheric pressure caused the gases to flow out of the mine (the gases in the mine were at a higher pressure), and the man suffocated. **11.127** (a) 4.90 L. (b) 6.0 atm. (c) 1 atm. **11.129** (a) 4 × 10^{-22} atm. (b) 6 × 10^{20} L/g of H. **11.131** 91%. **11.133** 1.7 × 10^{12} O_2 molecules. **11.135** NO_2. **11.137** 1.4 g LiH. **11.139** P_{CO_2}: 8.7 × 10^6 Pa; P_{N_2}: 3.2 × 10^5 Pa; P_{SO_2}: 1.4 × 10^3 Pa. **11.141** (a) (i): He atoms in both flasks have the same rms speed. (ii): The atoms in the larger volume strike the walls of their container with the same average force as those in the smaller volume, but pressure in the larger volume will be less. (b) (i): u_2 is greater than u_1 by a factor of $\sqrt{T_2/T_1}$; (ii): Both the frequency of collision and the average force of collision of the atoms at T_2 will be greater than those at T_1. (c) (i): False. The rms speed of He is greater than that of Ne because He is less massive; (ii): True. The average kinetic energies of the two gases are equal; (iii) The rms speed of the whole collection of atoms is 1.47 × 10^3 m/s, but the speeds of the individual atoms are random and constantly changing. **11.143** Vapor: 3.7 nm; liquid: 0.31 nm; Water molecules are packed very closely together in the liquid, but much farther apart in steam. **11.145** 9.98 atm. **11.147** 1.41 atm. **11.149** χ_{CH_4}: 0.789, $\chi_{C_2H_6}$: 0.211. **11.151** (a) 8$(\frac{4}{3}\pi r^3)$. (b) $4N_A(\frac{4}{3}\pi r^3)$/1 mole; The excluded volume per mole is four times the volume actually occupied by a mole of molecules. **11.153** NO. **11.155** Reaction (b). **11.157** 1.80 × 10^{-4} g/mL. **11.159** The kinetic energy of a particle depends on its mass and its speed (KE = $\frac{1}{2}mv^2$). At a given temperature, the more massive SF_6 molecules move more slowly than do the Ne molecules. **11.161** Intermolecular attractions tend to lower Z at low pressures and excluded volume tends to increase Z at high pressures.

Chapter 12

12.9 Butane would be a liquid in winter (boiling point −44.5°C), and on the coldest days even propane would become a liquid (boiling point −0.5°C). Only methane would remain gaseous (boiling point −161.6°C). **12.11** (a) Dispersion. (b) Dispersion and dipole-dipole. (c) Dispersion and dipole-dipole. (d) Dispersion and ionic. (e) Dispersion. **12.13** (e) CH_3COOH. **12.15** 1-butanol has greater intermolecular forces because it can form hydrogen bonds. **12.17** (a) Xe; it is larger and therefore stronger dispersion forces.(b) CS_2; it is larger (both molecules nonpolar) and therefore stronger dispersion forces.(c) Cl_2; it is larger (both molecules nonpolar) and therefore stronger dispersion forces.(d) LiF; it is an ionic compound, and the ion-ion attractions are much stronger than the dispersion forces between F_2 molecules.(e) NH_3; it can form hydrogen bonds and PH_3 cannot. **12.19** (a) Dispersion and dipole-dipole, including hydrogen bonding. (b) Dispersion only. (c) Dispersion only. (d) Covalent bonds. **12.21** The compound with $-NO_2$ and $-OH$ groups on adjacent carbons can form hydrogen bonds with itself (*intra*molecular hydrogen bonds). Such bonds do not contribute to *inter*molecular attraction and do not help raise the melting point of the compound. The other compound, with the $-NO_2$ and $-OH$ groups on opposite sides of the ring, can form only *inter*molecular hydrogen bonds; therefore, it will take a higher temperature to escape into the gas phase. **12.33** Ethylene glycol has two $-OH$ groups, allowing it to exert strong intermolecular forces through hydrogen bonding. Its viscosity should fall between ethanol (1 OH group) and glycerol (3 OH groups). **12.35** 331 mm Hg. **12.37** 29.9 kJ/mol. **12.45** Simple cubic: one sphere; body-centered cubic: two spheres; face-centered cubic: four spheres. **12.47** 6.20 × 10^{23} atoms/mol. **12.49** 458 pm. **12.51** XY_3. **12.53** 0.220 nm. **12.55** ZnO. **12.59** Molecular solid. **12.61** Molecular: Se_8, HBr, CO_2, P_4O_6, and SiH_4; covalent: Si and C. **12.63** Diamond: each carbon atom is covalently bonded to four other carbon atoms. Because these bonds are strong and uniform, diamond is a very hard substance. Graphite: the carbon atoms in each layer are linked by strong bonds, but the layers are bound by weak dispersion forces. As a result, graphite may be cleaved easily between layers and is not hard. In graphite, all atoms are sp^2 hybridized; each atom is covalently bonded to three other atoms. The remaining unhybridized $2p$ orbital is used in pi bonding, forming a delocalized molecular orbital. The electrons are free to move around in this extensively delocalized molecular orbital, making graphite a good conductor of electricity in directions along the planes of carbon atoms. **12.85** 2.72×10^3 kJ. **12.87** 47.03 kJ/mol. **12.89** Two phase changes occur in this process. First, the liquid is turned to solid (freezing), then the solid ice is turned to gas (sublimation). **12.91** When steam condenses to liquid water at 100°C, it releases a large amount of heat equal to the enthalpy of vaporization. Thus steam at 100°C exposes one to more heat than an equal amount of water at 100°C. **12.95** Initially, the ice melts because of the increase in pressure. As the wire sinks into the ice, the water above the wire refreezes. Eventually the wire actually moves completely through the ice block without cutting it in half. **12.97** (a) Ice would melt. (If heating continues, the liquid water would eventually boil and become a vapor.) (b) Liquid water would vaporize. (c) Water vapor would solidify without becoming a liquid. **12.99** (d). **12.101** Covalent. **12.103** CCl_4. **12.105** 0.26 cm; 7.69×10^6 base pairs. **12.107** 760 mmHg. **12.109** It has reached the critical point; the point of critical temperature (T_c) and critical pressure (P_c). **12.111** Crystalline SiO_2. Its regular structure results in a more efficient packing. **12.113** (a) and (b). **12.115** 8.3×10^{-3} atm. **12.117** (a) K_2S; Ionic forces are much stronger than the dipole-dipole forces in $(CH_3)_3N$. (b) Br_2; Both molecules are nonpolar; but Br_2 has a larger mass. **12.119** SO_2 will behave less ideally because it is polar and has greater intermolecular forces. **12.121** 62.4 kJ/mol. **12.123** Smaller ions can approach water molecules more closely, resulting in larger ion-dipole interactions. The greater the ion-dipole interaction, the larger is the heat of hydration. **12.125** (a) 30.7 kJ/mol. (b) 192.5 kJ/mol; It requires more energy to break the bond than to vaporize the molecule. **12.127** (a) Decreases. (b) No change. (c) No change. **12.129** $CaCO_3(s) \longrightarrow$ $CaO(s) + CO_2(g)$; Initial state: one solid phase, final state: two solid phase components and one gas phase component. **12.131** The molecules are all polar. The F atoms can form H-bonds with water and other −OH and −NH groups in the membrane, so water solubility plus easy attachment to the membrane would allow these molecules to pass the blood-brain barrier. **12.133** The time required to cook food depends on the boiling point of the water in which it is cooked. The boiling point of water increases when the pressure inside the cooker increases. **12.135** (a) Extra heat produced when steam condenses at 100°C. (b) Avoids extraction of ingredients by boiling in water. **12.137** (a) ~2.3 K. (b) ~10 atm. (c) ~5 K. (d) No. **12.139** (a) Pumping allows Ar atoms to escape, thus removing heat from the liquid phase. Eventually the liquid freezes. (b) The slope of the solid-liquid line of cyclohexane is positive. Therefore, its melting point increases with pressure. (c) These droplets are super-cooled liquids. (d) When the dry ice is added to water, it sublimes. The cold CO_2 gas generated causes nearby water vapor to condense, hence the appearance of fog. **12.141** (a) Two triple points: Diamond/graphite/liquid and graphite/liquid/vapor. (b) Diamond. (c) Apply high pressure at high temperature. **12.143** Ethanol mixes well with water. The mixture has a lower surface tension and readily flows out of the ear channel. **12.145** When water freezes it releases heat, helping keep the fruit warm enough not to freeze. Also, a layer of ice is a thermal insulator. **12.147** The fuel source for the Bunsen burner is most likely methane gas. When methane burns in air, carbon dioxide and water are produced. The water vapor produced during the combustion condenses to liquid water when it comes in contact with the outside of the cold beaker. **12.149** 6.019×10^{23} **12.151** 127 mmHg. **12.153** 55°C. **12.155** 0.833 g/L; The hydrogen-bonding interactions in HF are relatively strong, and since the ideal gas equation ignores intermolecular forces, it underestimates significantly the density of HF gas near its boiling point. **12.157** Fluoromethane; Of the three compounds, only fluoromethane has a permanent dipole moment. **12.159** 3.2×10^2 kJ; 1.1×10^3 kJ.

Chapter 13

13.9 "Like dissolves like." Naphthalene and benzene are nonpolar, whereas CsF is ionic. **13.11** $O_2 < Br_2 < LiCl < CH_3OH$. **13.17** (a) 0.0610 m. (b) 2.04 m. **13.19** (a) 1.7 m. (b) 0.87 m. (c) 7.0 m. **13.21** 3.0×10^2 g. **13.23** 18.3 M; 27.4 m. **13.25** $\chi(N_2)$: 0.677, $\chi(O_2)$: 0.323; Due to the greater solubility of oxygen, it has a larger mole fraction in solution than it does in the air. **13.33** 45.9 g KNO_3. **13.35** (a) Water soluble. (b) Fat soluble. **13.37** 1.0×10^{-5} mol/L. **13.39** 3.3 atm; This pressure is only an estimate since we ignored the amount of CO_2 that was present in the unopened container in the gas phase. **13.57** 1.3×10^3 g. **13.59** $P_{ethanol}$: 30 mmHg; $P_{1\text{-propanol}}$: 26.3 mmHg. **13.61** 187 g. **13.63** 0.59 m. **13.65** −5.4°C. **13.67** (a) $CaCl_2$. (b) Urea. (c) $CaCl_2$. $CaCl_2$ is an ionic compound and is therefore an electrolyte in water. Assuming that $CaCl_2$ is a strong electrolyte and completely dissociates (no ion pairs, van't Hoff factor $i = 3$), the total ion concentration will be $3 \times 0.35 = 1.05$ m, which is larger than the urea (nonelectrolyte) concentration of 0.90 m. **13.69** 0.15 m $C_6H_{12}O_6 > 0.15$ m $CH_3COOH > 0.10$ m $Na_3PO_4 > 0.20$ m $MgCl_2 > 0.35$ m NaCl. **13.71** Boiling point: 102.8°C; freezing point: −10.0°C. (b) Boiling point: 102.0°C; freezing point: −7.14°C. **13.73** Both NaCl and $CaCl_2$ are strong electrolytes. Urea and sucrose are nonelectrolytes. The NaCl or $CaCl_2$ will yield more particles per mole of the solid dissolved, resulting in greater freezing point depression. Also, sucrose and urea would make a mess when the ice melts. **13.75** 2.47. **13.77** 9.16 atm. **13.83** 4.3×10^2 g/mol; $C_{24}H_{20}P_4$. **13.85** 1.75×10^4 g/mol. **13.87** 342 g/mol. **13.89** 15.7%. **13.95** Before: 7.77×10^{-6} mol glucose/mL blood, 3.89×10^{-3} mol glucose, 7.00 g glucose; after: 1.33×10^{-5} mol glucose/mL blood, 6.66×10^{-2} mol glucose, 12.0 g glucose. **13.97** Water migrates through the semipermeable cell walls of the cucumber into the concentrated salt solution. **13.99** 3.5. **13.101** X: water; Y: NaCl; Z: urea. **13.103** The pill is in a hypotonic solution. Consequently, by osmosis, water moves across the semipermeable membrane into the pill. The increase in pressure pushes the elastic membrane to the right, causing the drug to exit through the small holes at a constant rate. **13.105** Reverse osmosis involves no phase changes and is usually cheaper than distillation or freezing; 34 atm. **13.107** 0.295 M; −0.55°C. **13.109** (a) 2.14×10^3 g/mol. (b) 4.50×10^4 g/mol. **13.111** (a) 0.099 L. (b) 9.9. **13.113** (a) At reduced pressure, the solution is supersaturated with CO_2. (b) As the escaping CO_2 expands it cools, condensing water vapor in the air to form fog. **13.115** (a) Runoff of the salt solution into the soil increases the salinity of the soil. If the soil becomes hypertonic relative to the tree cells, osmosis would reverse, and the tree would lose water to the soil and eventually die of dehydration. (b) Assuming the collecting duct acts as a semipermeable membrane, water would flow from the urine into the hypertonic fluid, thus returning water to the body. **13.117** 33 mL; 67 mL. **13.119** 12.3 M. **13.121** 14.2%. **13.123** (a) Solubility decreases with increasing lattice energy. (b) Ionic compounds are more soluble in a polar solvent. (c) Solubility increases with enthalpy of hydration of the cation and anion. **13.125** 1.43 g/mL; 37.0 m. **13.127** NH_3 can form hydrogen bonds with water; NCl_3 cannot. (Like dissolves like.) **13.129** 3%. **13.131** Egg yolk contains lecithins that solubilize oil in water (See Figure 13.18 of the text). The nonpolar oil becomes soluble in water because the nonpolar tails of lecithin dissolve in the oil, and the polar heads of the lecithin molecules dissolve in polar water (like dissolves like). **13.133** Yes. **13.135** As the water freezes, dissolved minerals in the water precipitate from solution. The minerals refract light and create an opaque appearance. **13.137** 1.8×10^2 g/mol. **13.139** 1.9 m. **13.141** P_B°: 4.0×10^2 mmHg; P_A°: 1.9×10^2 mmHg. **13.143** −0.737°C. **13.145** About 0.4 molal. **13.147** 1.0×10^{-4}% F⁻; 5.3×10^{-5} m NaF. **13.149** (a) χ_A: 0.52; χ_B: 0.48. (b) P_A: 51 mm Hg; P_B: 20 mm Hg. (c) χ_A: 0.72; χ_B: 0.28. (d) P_A: 71 mm Hg; P_B: 12 mm Hg.

Chapter 14

14.9 (a) Rate $= -\dfrac{\Delta[H_2]}{\Delta t} = -\dfrac{\Delta[I_2]}{\Delta t} = \dfrac{1}{2}\dfrac{\Delta[HI]}{\Delta t}$.

(b) Rate $= -\dfrac{1}{5}\dfrac{\Delta[Br^-]}{\Delta t} = -\dfrac{\Delta[BrO_3^-]}{\Delta t} = -\dfrac{1}{6}\dfrac{\Delta[H^+]}{\Delta t} = \dfrac{1}{3}\dfrac{\Delta[Br_2]}{\Delta t}$.

14.11 (a) 0.066 M/s. (b) 0.033 M/s. **14.19** 8.1×10^{-6} M/s. **14.21** The reaction is first order in A and first order overall; $k = 0.213$ s^{-1}. **14.23** (a) 2. (b) 0. (c) 2.5. (d) 3. **14.25** First order; $k = 1.19 \times 10^{-4}$ s^{-1}. **14.31** 30 min. **14.33** (a) 0.034 M. (b) 17 s; 23 s. **14.35** (a) 4:3:6. (b) The relative rates would be unaffected, each absolute rate would decrease by 50%. (c) 1:1:1. **14.37** (a) First-order. (b) Second-order. (c) Zeroth-order. **14.43** 103 kJ/mol. **14.45** 3.0×10^{3} s^{-1}. **14.47** 51.8 kJ/mol. **14.49** 1.3×10^{2} kJ/mol. **14.51** In order of increasing time required for the effervescence to stop: e < d < b < a < c. **14.61** (a) Second-order. (b) The first step is the slower (rate-determining) step. **14.63** Mechanism I can be discarded. Mechanisms II and III are possible. **14.73** At higher temperatures the enzyme loses its activity due to a change in the overall structure. **14.75** Temperature must be specified. **14.77** 0.035 s^{-1}. **14.79** Most transition metals have several stable oxidation states. This allows the metal atoms to act as either a source or a receptor of electrons in a broad range of reactions. **14.81** Since the methanol contains no oxygen-18, the oxygen atom must come from the phosphate group and not the water. The mechanism must involve a bond-breaking process like:

$$CH_3-O \overset{?}{-} \overset{\overset{\displaystyle O}{\|}}{\underset{\underset{\displaystyle O-H}{|}}{P}} -O-H$$

14.83 Temperature, energy of activation, concentration of reactants, and a catalyst. **14.85** (a) Rate = $k[CH_3COCH_3][H^+]$. (b) 3.8×10^{-3} M^{-1}s^{-1}. (c) $k = k_1k_2/k_{-1}$. **14.87** (I) Fe^{3+} oxidizes I$^-$: $2Fe^{3+} + 2I^- \longrightarrow 2Fe^{2+} + I_2$; (II) Fe^{2+} reduces S$_2O_8^{2-}$: $2Fe^{2+} + S_2O_8^{2-} \longrightarrow 2Fe^{3+} + SO_4^{2-}$; Overall Reaction: $2I^- + S_2O_8^{2-} \longrightarrow I_2 + SO_4^{2-}$ (Fe^{3+} undergoes a redox cycle: Fe$^{3+} \longrightarrow$ Fe$^{2+} \longrightarrow$ Fe^{3+}); The uncatalyzed reaction is slow because both I$^-$ and S$_2$O$_8^{2-}$ are negatively charged which makes their mutual approach unfavorable. **14.89** (a) (i) rate = $k[A]^0 = k$,

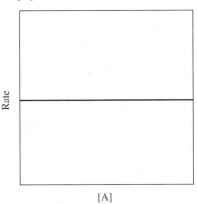

(ii) $[A] = -kt + [A]_0$,

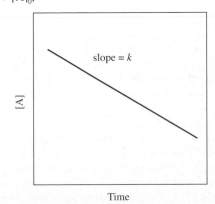

slope = k

(b) $t_{1/2} = \dfrac{[A]_0}{2k}$. (c) $t = 2t_{1/2}$. **14.91** There are three gases present and we can measure only the total pressure of the gases. To measure the partial pressure of azomethane at a particular time, we must withdraw a sample of

the mixture, analyze and determine the mole fractions. Then, $P_{azomethane} = P_T\chi_{azomethane}$.

14.93

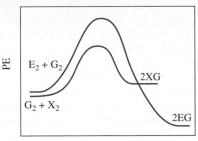

Reaction progress

14.95 (a) A catalyst works by changing the reaction mechanism, thus lowering the activation energy. (b) A catalyst changes the reaction mechanism. (c) A catalyst does not change the enthalpy of reaction. (d) A catalyst increases the forward rate of reaction. (e) A catalyst increases the reverse rate of reaction.

14.97 At very high [H$_2$]: $k_2[H_2] \gg 1$, rate $= \dfrac{k_1[NO]^2[H_2]}{k_2[H_2]} = \dfrac{k_1}{k_2}[NO]^2$;

At very low [H$_2$]: $k_2[H_2] \ll 1$, rate $= \dfrac{k_1[NO]^2[H_2]}{1} = k_1[NO]^2[H_2]$;

The result from Problem 14.80 agrees with the rate law determined for low [H$_2$]. **14.99** Rate = $k[N_2O_5]$; $k = 1.0 \times 10^{-5}$ s^{-1}. **14.101** The red bromine vapor absorbs photons of blue light and dissociates to form bromine atoms: Br$_2 \longrightarrow$ 2Br·. The bromine atoms collide with methane molecules and abstract hydrogen atoms: Br· + CH$_4 \longrightarrow$ HBr + ·CH$_3$. The methyl radical then reacts with Br$_2$, giving the observed product and regenerating a bromine atom to start the process over again: ·CH$_3$ + Br$_2 \longrightarrow$ CH$_3$Br + Br·, Br· + CH$_4 \longrightarrow$ HBr + ·CH$_3$ and so on. **14.103** Lowering the temperature would slow all chemical reactions, which would be especially important for those that might damage the brain. **14.105** (a) Rate = $k[X][Y]^2$. (b) 0.019 M^{-2}s^{-1}. **14.107** Second-order; $k = 2.4 \times 10^7$ M^{-1}s^{-1}. **14.109** During the first five minutes or so the engine is relatively cold, so the exhaust gases will not fully react with the components of the catalytic converter. Remember, for almost all reactions, the rate of reaction increases with temperature. **14.111** (a) The activation energy must be high. (b) The molecules must have the appropriate orientation and the energy that the colliding particles possess must be greater than the activation energy. **14.113** 5.7×10^5 yr. **14.115** (a) Catalyst: Mn^{2+}; intermediates: Mn^{3+}, Mn^{4+}; first step is rate-determining. (b) Without the catalyst, the reaction would be a termolecular one involving 3 cations! (Tl$^+$ and two Ce^{4+}). The reaction would be slow. (c) The catalyst is a homogeneous catalyst because it has the same phase (aqueous) as the reactants. **14.117** 0.45 atm. **14.119** (a) $\Delta[B]/\Delta t = k_1[A] - k_2[B]$. (b) $[B] = (k_1/k_2)[A]$. **14.121** (a) $k = 0.0247$ yr^{-1}. (b) 9.8×10^{-4}. (c) 187 yr. **14.123** (a) Three. (b) Two. (c) The third step. (d) Exothermic. **14.125** 1.8×10^3 K. **14.127** (a) 2.5×10^{-5} M/s. (b) 2.5×10^{-5} M/s. (c) 8.3×10^{-6} M. **14.133** Second-order; $k = 0.42/M \cdot$ min. **14.135** 60% increase; The result shows the profound effect of an exponential dependence. **14.137** Form (b). **14.139** Diagram (a).

Chapter 15

15.9 (a) $\dfrac{[N_2][H_2O]^2}{[NO]^2[H_2O]^2}$. (b) 7.2×10^2. **15.11** 1.08×10^7.

15.21 (a) Diagram (a). (b) Diagram (d); Volume will cancel from the K_c expression. **15.23** 2.40×10^{33}. **15.25** 3.5×10^{-7}. **15.27** (a) 8.2×10^{-2}. (b) 0.55. **15.29** K_P: 0.105; K_c: 2.05×10^{-3}. **15.31** 7.09×10^{-3}. **15.33** K_P: 9.6×10^{-3}; K_c: 3.9×10^{-4}. **15.35** 4.0×10^{-6}. **15.37** 5.6×10^{23}. **15.39** Diagrams (a), (b), and (c). **15.41** 0.173 mol H$_2$. **15.43** [H$_2$] = [Br$_2$] = 1.80×10^{-4} M; [HBr] = 0.267 M. **15.45** P_{COCl_2}: 0.408 atm; P_{CO}: P_{Cl_2} = 0.352 atm. **15.47** P_{CO}: 1.96 atm; P_{CO_2}: 2.54 atm. **15.49** The forward reaction will not occur. **15.55** Reaction (b). **15.57** (b), (d), and (e).

15.59 (a) The equilibrium would shift to the right. (b) The equilibrium would be unaffected. (c) The equilibrium would be unaffected. **15.61** (a) No effect. (b) No effect. (c) Shift to the left. (d) No effect. (e) Shift to the left. **15.63** (a) Shifts to the right. (b) Shifts to the left. (c) Shifts to the right. (d) Shifts to the left. (e) A catalyst has no effect on equilibrium position. **15.65** No change. **15.67** (a) Shift to the right. (b) No effect. (c) No effect. (d) Shift to the left. (e) Shift to the right. (f) Shift to the left. (g) Shift to the right. **15.69** (a) $2O_3(g) \rightleftharpoons 3O_2(g)$, $\Delta H^\circ_{rxn} = -284.4$ kJ/mol. (b) Equilibrium would shift to the left. **15.71** The concentration of oxyhemoglobin will decrease as acidosis occurs. **15.73** (a) 8×10^{-44}. (b) A mixture of H_2 and O_2 can be kept at room temperature because of a very large activation energy. **15.75** (a) 1.7. (b) P_A: 0.69 atm; P_B: 0.81 atm. **15.77** 1.5×10^5. **15.79** P_{H_2}: 0.28 atm; P_{Cl_2}: 0.051 atm; P_{HCl}: 1.67 atm. **15.81** 5.0×10^1 atm. **15.83** 0.038. **15.85** 3.3×10^2 atm. **15.87** 6.28×10^{-4}. **15.89** P_{N_2}: 0.860 atm, P_{H_2}: 0.366 atm, P_{NH_3}: 4.40×10^{-3} atm. **15.91** (a) 1.16. (b) 53.7%. **15.93** (a) 0.49 atm. (b) 23%. (c) 3.7%. (d) Greater than 0.037 mol. **15.95** [H_2]: 0.07 M, [I_2]: 0.18 M, [HI]: 0.83 M. **15.97** (c). N_2O_4(colorless) $\longrightarrow$ 2NO$_2$(brown) is consistent with the observations. The reaction is endothermic so heating darkens the color. Above 150°C, the NO$_2$ breaks up into colorless NO and O$_2$: $2NO_2(g) \longrightarrow 2NO(g) + O_2(g)$. An increase in pressure shifts the equilibrium back to the left, restoring the color by producing NO$_2$. **15.99** (a) 4.2×10^{-4}. (b) 0.83. (c) 1.1. (d) K_P (b): 2.3×10^3; K_P (c): 2.1×10^{-2}. **15.101** (a) Color deepens. (b) Increases. (c) Decreases. (d) Increases. (e) Unchanged. **15.103** Potassium is more volatile than sodium. Therefore, its removal shifts the equilibrium from left to right. **15.105** 3.5×10^{-2}. **15.107** (a) Shifts to the right. (b) Shifts to the right. (c) No change. (d) No change. (e) No change. (f) Shifts to the left. **15.109** (a) 1.8×10^{-16}. (b) [H$^+$][OH$^-$]: 1.0×10^{-14}; [H$^+$] = [OH$^-$]: 1.0×10^{-7} M. **15.111** $P_{N_2O_4}$: 0.09 atm; P_{NO_2}: 0.10 atm. **15.113** (a) 1.03 atm. (b) 0.39 atm. (c) 1.67 atm. (d) 62%. **15.115** (a) K_P: 2.6×10^{-6}; K_c: 1.1×10^{-7}. (b) 2.2 g; 22 mg/m^3; yes. **15.117** There is a temporary dynamic equilibrium between the melting of ice cubes and the freezing of water between the ice cubes. **15.119** [NH_3]: 0.042 M; [N_2]: 0.086 M; [H_2]: 0.26 M.

15.121 (a) $K_P = \dfrac{\left(\dfrac{4x^2}{1+x}\right)P}{1-x} = \dfrac{4x^2}{1-x^2}P$. (b) If P increases, the fraction $\dfrac{4x^2}{1-x^2}$ (and therefore x) must decrease. Equilibrium shifts to the left to produce less NO$_2$ and more N$_2$O$_4$ as predicted. **15.123** $P_{SO_2Cl_2}$: 3.58 atm, $P_{SO_2} = P_{Cl_2}$: 2.71 atm. **15.125** 4.0. **15.127** −3. **15.129** $K_P = K_c$: (d), (g); cannot write a K_P: (c), (f).

Chapter 16

16.3 (a) Both. (b) Base. (c) Acid. (d) Base. (e) Acid. (f) Base. (g) Base. (h) Base. (i) Acid. (j) Acid. **16.5** (a) NO$_2^-$. (b) HSO$_4^-$. (c) HS$^-$. (d) CN$^-$. (e) HCOO$^-$. **16.7** (a) CH$_2$ClCOO$^-$. (b) IO$_4^-$. (c) H$_2$PO$_4^-$. (d) HPO$_4^{2-}$. (e) PO$_4^{3-}$. (f) HSO$_4^-$. (g) SO$_4^{2-}$. (h) IO$_3^-$. (i) SO$_3^{2-}$. (j) NH$_3$. (k) HS$^-$. (l) S^{2-}. (m) OCl$^-$. **16.11** (a) H$_2$SO$_4$ > H$_2$SeO$_4$. (b) H$_3$PO$_4$ > H$_3$AsO$_4$. **16.13** The conjugate bases are C$_6$H$_5$O$^-$ from phenol and CH$_3$O$^-$ from methanol. The C$_6$H$_5$O$^-$ is stabilized by resonance:

The CH$_3$O$^-$ ion has no such resonance stabilization. A more stable conjugate base means an increase in the strength of the acid. **16.19** (a) 4.0×10^{-13} M. (b) 6.0×10^{-10} M. (c) 1.2×10^{-12} M. (d) 5.7×10^{-3} M. **16.21** (a) 2.05×10^{-11} M. (b) 3.07×10^{-8} M. (c) 5.95×10^{-11} M. (d) 2.93×10^{-1} M. **16.25** 7.1×10^{-12} M. **16.27** (a) 3.00. (b) 13.89. **16.29**

(a) 3.8×10^{-3} M. (b) 6.2×10^{-12} M. (c) 1.1×10^{-7} M. (d) 1.0×10^{-15} M. **16.31** pH < 7, [H$^+$] > 1.0×10^{-7} M, solution is acid; pH > 7, [H$^+$] < 1.0×10^{-7} M, solution is basic; pH = 7, [H$^+$] = 1.0×10^{-7} M, solution is neutral. **16.33** 2.5×10^{-5} M. **16.35** 2.2×10^{-3} g. **16.39** (a) −0.009. (b) 1.46. (c) 5.82. **16.41** (a) 6.2×10^{-5} M. (b) 2.8×10^{-4} M. (c) 0.10 M. **16.43** (a) pOH = −0.093; pH = 14.09. (b) pOH = 0.36; pH = 13.64. (c) pOH = 1.07; pH = 12.93. **16.45** (a) 1.1×10^{-3} M. (b) 5.5×10^{-4} M. **16.47** 2.24×10^{-5} M. **16.55** (a) Strong base. (b) Weak base. (c) Weak base. (d) Weak base. (e) Strong base. **16.57** 2.59. **16.59** 5.17. **16.61** (a) 10%. (b) 84%. (c) 0.97%. **16.63** 1.3×10^{-6}. **16.65** 4.8×10^{-9}. **16.67** 2.3×10^{-3} M. **16.69** 6.80. **16.73** 6.97×10^{-7}. **16.75** 11.98. **16.77** (a) A$^-$. (b) B$^-$. **16.81** K_b(CN$^-$) = 2.0×10^{-5}; K_b(F$^-$) = 1.4×10^{-11}; K_b(CH$_3$COO$^-$) = 5.6×10^{-10}; K_b(HCO$_3^-$) = 2.4×10^{-8}. **16.85** pH (0.040 M HCl) = 1.40; pH (0.040 M H$_2$SO$_4$) = 1.31. **16.87** [H$^+$] = [HCO$_3^-$] = 1.0×10^{-4} M, [CO$_3^{2-}$] = 4.8×10^{-11} M. **16.89** 1.00. **16.95** (a) Neutral. (b) Basic. (c) Acidic. (d) Acidic. **16.97** HZ < HY < HX. **16.99** pH > 7. **16.101** 4.82. **16.103** 5.39. **16.107** (a) Al$_2$O$_3$ < BaO < K$_2$O. (b) CrO$_3$ < Cr$_2$O$_3$ < CrO. **16.109** Al(OH)$_3$(s) + OH$^-$(aq) $\longrightarrow$ Al(OH)$_4^-$(aq); This is a Lewis acid-base reaction. **16.111** (a) Li$_2$O(s) + H$_2$O(l) $\longrightarrow$ 2LiOH(aq). (b) CaO(s) + H$_2$O(l) $\longrightarrow$ Ca(OH)$_2$(aq). (c) SO$_3$(g) + H$_2$O(l) $\longrightarrow$ H$_2$SO$_4$(aq). **16.115** AlCl$_3$ is a Lewis acid with an incomplete octet of electrons and Cl$^-$ is the Lewis base donating a pair of electrons. **16.117** CO$_2$, SO$_2$, and BCl$_3$. **16.119** (a) AlBr$_3$ is the Lewis acid; Br$^-$ is the Lewis base. (b) Cr is the Lewis acid; CO is the Lewis base. (c) Cu^{2+} is the Lewis acid; CN$^-$ is the Lewis base. **16.121** A strong acid: diagram (b); a weak acid: diagram (c); a very weak acid: diagram (d). **16.123** CH$_3$COO$^-$(aq) and HCl(aq); This reaction will *not* occur to any measurable extent. **16.125** pH = 1.70; percent ionizations = 2.3%. **16.127** (c). **16.129** (a) For the forward reaction NH$_4^+$ and NH$_3$ are the conjugate acid and base pair, respectively. For the reverse reaction NH$_3$ and NH$_2^-$ are the conjugate acid and base pair, respectively. (b) H$^+$ corresponds to NH$_4^+$; OH$^-$ corresponds to NH$_2^-$. For the neutral solution,

[NH$_4^+$] = [NH$_2^-$]. **16.131** $K_a = \dfrac{[H^+][A^-]}{[HA]}$; [HA] ≈ 0.1 M, [A$^-$] ≈ 0.1 M.

Therefore, $K_a = [H^+] = \dfrac{K_w}{[OH^-]}$ and $[OH^-] = \dfrac{K_w}{K_a}$. **16.133** 1.7×10^{10}.

16.135 (a) H$^-$ (base$_1$) + H$_2$O (acid$_2$) $\longrightarrow$ OH$^-$ (base$_2$) + H$_2$ (acid$_1$). (b) H$^-$ is the reducing agent and H$_2$O is the oxidizing agent. **16.137** 2.8×10^{-2}. **16.139** PH$_3$ is a weaker base than NH$_3$. **16.141** (a) HNO$_2$. (b) HF. (c) BF$_3$. (d) NH$_3$. (e) H$_2$SO$_3$. (f) HCO$_3^-$ and CO$_3^{2-}$. **16.143** (a) Trigonal pyramidal. (b) H$_4$O^{2+} does *not* exist because the positively charged H$_3$O$^+$ has no affinity to accept the positive H$^+$ ion. **16.145** Cl$_2$(g) + H$_2$O(l) $\rightleftharpoons$ HCl(aq) + HClO(aq); HCl(aq) + AgNO$_3$(aq) $\rightleftharpoons$ AgCl(s) + HNO$_3$(aq). In the presence of OH$^-$ ions, the first equation is shifted to the right: H$^+$ (from HCl) + OH$^-$ $\longrightarrow$ H$_2$O. Therefore, the concentration of HClO increases. (The 'bleaching action' is due to ClO$^-$ ions.) **16.147** 11.80. **16.149** (a) 0.181 or 18.1%. (b) 4.63×10^{-3}. **16.151** 4.26. **16.153** 7.2×10^{-3} g. **16.155** 1.000. **16.157** (a) The pH of the solution of HA would be lower. (b) The electrical conductance of the HA solution would be greater. (c) The rate of hydrogen evolution from the HA solution would be greater. **16.159** 1.4×10^{-4}. **16.161** 2.7×10^{-3} g. **16.163** (a) NH$_2^-$ (base) + H$_2$O (acid) $\longrightarrow$ NH$_3$ + OH$^-$; N^{3-} (base) + 3H$_2$O (acid) $\longrightarrow$ NH$_3$ + 3OH$^-$. (b) N^{3-}. **16.165** When smelling salt is inhaled, some of the powder dissolves in the basic solution. The ammonium ions react with the base as follows: NH$_4^+$(aq) + OH$^-$(aq) $\longrightarrow$ NH$_3$(aq) + H$_2$O. It is the pungent odor of ammonia that prevents a person from fainting. **16.167** (c). **16.169** 21 mL. **16.171** Magnesium. **16.173** The F$^-$ ions replace OH$^-$ ions during the remineralization process: 5Ca^{2+} + 3PO$_4^{3-}$ + F$^-$ $\longrightarrow$ Ca$_5$(PO$_4$)$_3$F (fluorapatite). Because F$^-$ is a weaker base than OH$^-$, fluorapatite is more resistant to attacks by acids compared to hydroxyapatite. **16.175** Li$_2$O, lithium oxide, basic; BeO, beryllium oxide, amphoteric; B$_2$O$_3$, diboron trioxide, acidic; CO$_2$, carbon dioxide, acidic; N$_2$O$_5$, dinitrogen pentoxide, acidic. **16.177** [H$_2$SO$_4$] = [HSO$_4^-$] = 0 M; [SO$_4^{2-}$] = 4.0×10^{-5} M; [H$^+$] 8.0×10^{-5} M.

Chapter 17

17.5 (a) 2.57. (b) 4.44. **17.9** (c) and (d). **17.11** 8.89. **17.13** 0.024. **17.15** 0.58. **17.17** 9.25; 9.18. **17.19** $Na_2A/NaHA$. **17.21** (a) Solutions (a), (b), and (c); (b) Solution (a). **17.27** 202 g/mol. **17.29** 0.25 M. **17.31** (a) 1.10 $\times$ 10^2 g/mol. (b) 1.6 $\times$ 10^{-6}. **17.33** 5.82. **17.35** (a) 2.87. (b) 4.56. (c) 5.34. (d) 8.78. (e) 12.10. **17.37** (a) Cresol red or phenolphthalein. (b) Most of the indicators in Table 17.3, except thymol blue and, to a lesser extent, bromophenol blue and methyl orange. (c) Bromophenol blue, methyl orange, methyl red, or chlorophenol blue. **17.39** Red. **17.41** (a) Diagram (c), (b) Diagram (b), (c) Diagram (d), (d) Diagram (a). The pH at the equivalence point is below 7 (acidic). **17.49** (a) $[I^-] = 9.1 \times 10^{-9}$ M. (b) $[Al^{3+}] = 7.4 \times 10^{-8}$ M. **17.51** 1.8 $\times$ 10^{-11}. **17.53** 3.3 $\times$ 10^{-93}. **17.55** 9.52. **17.57** Yes. **17.59** (c) AlA_3. **17.65** (a) 0.013 M or 1.3 $\times$ 10^{-2} M. (b) 2.2 $\times$ 10^{-4} M. (c) 3.3 $\times$ 10^{-3} M. **17.67** (a) 1.0 $\times$ 10^{-5} M. (b) 1.1 $\times$ 10^{-10} M. **17.69** (b), (c), (d), and (e). **17.71** (a) 0.016 M or 1.6 $\times$ 10^{-2} M. (b) 1.6 $\times$ 10^{-6} M. **17.73** A precipitate of $Fe(OH)_2$ will form. **17.75** $[Cd^{2+}] = 1.1 \times 10^{-18}$ M, $[Cd(CN)_4^{2-}] = 4.2 \times 10^{-3}$ M; $[CN^-] = 0.48$ M. **17.77** 3.5 $\times$ 10^{-5} M. **17.79** 3 $\times$ 10^{-60}. **17.83** Greater than 2.68 but less than 8.11. **17.85** 0.011 M. **17.87** 2.51 to 4.41. **17.89** 1.3 M. **17.91** $[H^+] = 3.0 \times 10^{-13}$ M; $[HCOOH] = 8.8 \times 10^{-11}$ M; $[HCOO^-] = 0.0500$ M; $[OH^-] = 0.0335$ M; $[Na^+] = 0.0835$ M. **17.93** $Cd(OH)_2(s) + 2OH^-(aq) \rightleftharpoons Cd(OH)_4^{2-}(aq)$; This is a Lewis acid-base reaction. **17.95** (d). **17.97** $[Ag^+] = 2.0 \times 10^{-9}$ M; $[Cl^-] = 0.080$ M; $[Zn^{2+}] = 0.070$ M; $[NO_3^-] = 0.060$ M. **17.99** 0.035 g/L. **17.101** 2.4 $\times$ 10^{-13}. **17.103** $[Ba^{2+}] = 1.0 \times 10^{-5}$ M. $Ba(NO_3)_2$ is too soluble to be used for this purpose. **17.105** (a) AgBr. (b) 1.8 $\times$ 10^{-7} M. (c) 0.0018%. **17.107** 3.0 $\times$ 10^{-8}. **17.109** (a) 1.0 $\times$ 10^{14}. (b) 1.8 $\times$ 10^9. (c) 1.8 $\times$ 10^9. (d) 3.2 $\times$ 10^4. **17.111** (a) Mix 500 mL of 0.40 M CH_3COOH with 500 mL of 0.40 M CH_3COONa. (b) Mix 500 mL of 0.80 M CH_3COOH with 500 mL of 0.40 M NaOH. (c) Mix 500 mL of 0.80 M CH_3COONa with 500 mL of 0.40 M HCl. **17.113** (a) Figure (b). (b) Figure (a). **17.115** (a) Add sulfate. (b) Add sulfate. (c) Add iodide. **17.117** They are insoluble in water. **17.119** The ionized polyphenols have a dark color. In the presence of citric acid from lemon juice, the anions are converted to the lighter-colored acids. **17.121** Yes. **17.123** (c). **17.125** Decreasing the pH would increase the solubility of calcium oxalate and should help minimize the formation of calcium oxalate kidney stones. **17.127** At pH = 1.0: $^+NH_3-CH_2-COOH$; at pH = 7.0: $^+NH_3-CH_2-COO^-$; at pH = 12.0: $NH_2-CH_2-COO^-$. **17.129** (a) Before dilution: pH = 4.74; after a 10-fold dilution: pH = 4.74. (b) Before dilution: pH = 2.52; after dilution, pH = 3.02. **17.131** AgBr(s) will precipitate first. $Ag_2SO_4(s)$ will precipitate last. **17.133** (c). **17.135** 8.8 $\times$ 10^{-12}. **17.137** 4.75. **17.139** (a) Diagram (b). (b) Diagram (e). (c) Diagram (d). (d) Diagram (a).

Chapter 18

18.7 (a) With barrier: 16; without barrier: 64. (b) 16; 16; 32; both particles on one side: $S = 3.83 \times 10^{-23}$ J/K; particles on opposite sides: $S = 4.78 \times 10^{-23}$. The most probable state is the one with the larger entropy; that is, the state in which the particles are on opposite sides. **18.13** (a) -0.031 J/K. (b) -0.29 J/K. (c) 1.5 $\times$ 10^2 J/K. **18.15** (c) $<$ (d) $<$ (e) $<$ (a) $<$ (b). (a) Ne(g): a monatomic gas of higher molar mass than H_2. (For gas phase molecules, increasing molar mass tends to increase the molar entropy. While Ne(g) is less complex structurally than H_2(g), its much larger molar mass more than offsets the complexity difference.) (b) SO_2(g): a polyatomic gas of higher complexity and higher molar mass than Ne(g). (c) Na(s): highly ordered, crystalline material. (d) NaCl(s): highly ordered crystalline material, but with more particles per mole than Na(s). (e) H_2: a diatomic gas, hence of higher entropy than a solid. **18.17** (a) 47.5 J/mol · K. (b) -12.5 J/mol · K. (c) -242.8 J/mol · K. **18.21** (a) 291 J/mol · K; spontaneous. (b) 2.10 $\times$ 10^3 J/mol · K; spontaneous. (c) 2.99 $\times$ 10^3 J/mol · K; spontaneous. **18.23** (a) $\Delta S_{sys} = -75.6$ J/mol · K; $\Delta S_{surr} = 185$ J/mol · K; spontaneous. (b) $\Delta S_{sys} = 215.8$ J/mol · K; $\Delta S_{surr} = -304$ J/mol · K; not spontaneous. (c) $\Delta S_{sys} = 98.2$ J/mol · K; $\Delta S_{surr} = -1.46 \times 10^3$ J/mol · K; not spontaneous. (d) $\Delta S_{sys} = -282$ J/mol · K; $\Delta S_{surr} = 7.20 \times 10^3$ J/mol · K; spontaneous. **18.29** 64 kJ/mol. **18.31**

(a) -1139 kJ/mol. (b) -140.0 kJ/mol. (c) -2935 kJ/mol. **18.33** (a) All temperatures. (b) Below 111 K. **18.35** $\Delta S_{fus} = 99.9$ J/K · mol; $\Delta S_{vap} = 93.6$ J/K · mol. **18.37** 75.9 kJ. **18.41** 0.35. **18.43** 79 kJ/mol. **18.45** (a) $\Delta G_{rxn}^\circ = 35.4$ kJ/mol; $K_P = 6.2 \times 10^{-7}$. (b) 44.6 kJ/mol. **18.47** (a) 1.6 $\times$ 10^{-23} atm. (b) 0.535 atm. **18.49** 3.1 $\times$ 10^{-2} atm or 23.6 mmHg. **18.53** 93 ATP molecules. **18.55** $\Delta H_{fus} > 0$. $\Delta S_{fus} > 0$. (a) $\Delta G_{fus} < 0$. (b) $\Delta G_{fus} = 0$. (c) $\Delta G_{fus} > 0$. **18.57** U and H. **18.59** 42°C. **18.61** ΔS must be positive ($\Delta S > 0$). **18.63** (a) Benzene: $\Delta S_{vap} = 87.8$ J/K · mol; hexane: $\Delta S_{vap} = 90.1$ J/K · mol; mercury: $\Delta S_{vap} = 93.7$ J/K · mol; toluene: $\Delta S_{vap} = 91.8$ J/K · mol; Trouton's rule is a statement about ΔS_{vap}°. In most substances, the molecules are in constant and random motion in both the liquid and gas phases, so $\Delta S_{vap}^\circ \approx 90$ J/K · mol. (b) Ethanol: $\Delta S_{vap} = 111.9$ J/K · mol; water: $\Delta S_{vap} = 109.4$ J/K · mol; In ethanol and water, there are fewer possible arrangements of the molecules due to the network of H-bonds, so ΔS_{vap}° is greater. **18.65** (a) $2CO + 2NO \longrightarrow 2CO_2 + N_2$. (b) The oxidizing agent is NO; the reducing agent is CO. (c) $K_P = 3 \times 10^{120}$. (d) $Q_P = 1.2 \times 10^{14}$; to the right. (e) No. **18.67** 2.6 $\times$ 10^{-9}. **18.69** 976 K = 703°C. **18.71** 38 kJ. **18.73** 174 kJ/mol. **18.75** (a) Positive. (b) Negative. (c) Positive. (d) Positive. **18.77** 625 K. **18.79** No; A negative $\Delta G°$ tells us that a reaction has the potential to happen, but gives no indication of the rate. **18.81** (a) $\Delta G° = -106.4$ kJ/mol; $K_P = 4 \times 10^{18}$. (b) $\Delta G° = -53.2$ kJ/mol; $K_P = 2 \times 10^9$. **18.83** ΔH and ΔS are both positive, indicating this is an endothermic process with high entropy; 320 K = 47°C. **18.85** (a) 86.7 kJ/mol. (b) 4 $\times$ 10^{-31}. (c) 3 $\times$ 10^{-6}. (d) Lightning supplies the energy necessary to drive this reaction, converting the two most abundant gases in the atmosphere into NO(g). The NO gas dissolves in the rain, which carries it into the soil where it is converted into nitrate and nitrite by bacterial action. This "fixed" nitrogen is a necessary nutrient for plants. **18.87** $T > 673.2$ K. **18.89** (a) 7.6 $\times$ 10^{14}. (b) 4.1 $\times$ 10^{-12}. The activity series is correct. The very large value of K for reaction (a) indicates that *products* are highly favored; whereas, the very small value of K for reaction (b) indicates that *reactants* are highly favored. **18.91** (a) Disproportionation redox reaction. (b) 8.2 $\times$ 10^{15}; this method is feasible for removing SO_2. (c) Less effective. **18.93** 1.8 $\times$ 10^{70}. Due to the large magnitude of K, you would expect this reaction to be spontaneous in the forward direction. However, this reaction has a large activation energy, so the rate of reaction is extremely slow. **18.95** $\Delta S_{sys} = 91.1$ J/K; $\Delta S_{surr} = -91.1$ J/K; $\Delta S_{univ} = 0$; the system is at equilibrium. **18.97** 8.5 kJ/mol. **18.99** (a) CH_3COOH: 27 kJ/mol; $CH_2ClCOOH$: 16 kJ/mol. (b) The *system's* entropy change dominates. (c) The breaking and making of specific O—H bonds. Other contributions include solvent separation and ion solvation. (d) The CH_3COO^- ion, which is smaller than CH_2ClCOO^-, can participate in hydration to a greater extent, leading to solutions with fewer possible arrangements. **18.101** $\chi_{CO} = 0.45$; $\chi_{CO_2} = 0.55$. We assumed that $\Delta G°$ calculated from ΔG_f° values was temperature independent. **18.103** 249 J/K. **18.105** $\Delta S_{sys} = -327$ J/K · mol; $\Delta S_{surr} = 1918$ J/K · mol; $\Delta S_{univ} = 1591$ J/K · mol. **18.107** q, and w are *not* state functions. **18.109** ΔG must be negative; ΔS must be negative; ΔH must be negative. **18.111** (a) 5.76 J/K · mol. (b) The fact that the actual residual entropy is 4.2 J/K · mol means that the orientation is not totally random. **18.113** $\Delta H° = 33.89$ kJ/mol; $\Delta S° = 96.4$ J/K · mol; $\Delta G° = 5.2$ kJ/mol. **18.115** 0.97.

Chapter 19

19.1 (a) $2H^+ + H_2O_2 + 2Fe^{2+} \longrightarrow 2Fe^{3+} + 2H_2O$. (b) $6H^+ + 2HNO_3 + 3Cu \longrightarrow 3Cu^{2+} + 2NO + 4H_2O$. (c) $3CN^- + 2MnO_4^- + H_2O \longrightarrow 3CNO^- + 2MnO_2 + 2OH^-$. (d) $6OH^- + 3Br_2 \longrightarrow BrO_3^- + 3H_2O + 5Br^-$. (e) $2S_2O_3^{2-} + I_2 \longrightarrow S_4O_6^{2-} + 2I^-$. **19.11** $Al(s) + 3Ag^+(1.0\ M) \longrightarrow Al^{3+}(1.0\ M) + 3Ag(s)$; $E_{cell}° = 2.46$ V. **19.13** $Cl_2(g)$ and $MnO_4^-(aq)$. **19.15** (a) Spontaneous. (b) Not spontaneous. (c) Not spontaneous. (d) Spontaneous. **19.17** (a) Li. (b) H_2. (c) Fe^{2+}. (d) Br^-. **19.21** 3 $\times$ 10^{54}. **19.23** (a) 2 $\times$ 10^{18}. (b) 3 $\times$ 10^8. (c) 3 $\times$ 10^{62}. **19.25** $Ce^{4+}(aq) + Fe^{2+}(aq) \longrightarrow Ce^{3+}(aq) + Fe^{3+}(aq)$; $\Delta G° = -81$ kJ/mol; $K = 2 \times 10^{14}$. **19.27** $2Sn + 4H^+ + O_2 \longrightarrow 2Sn^{2+} + 2H_2O$; 1.37 V.

19.31 1.09 V. **19.33** $E_{cell}^{\circ} = 0.76$ V; $E = 0.78$ V. **19.35** 6.0×10^{-38}. **19.41** 1.09 V. **19.45** 12.2 g. **19.47** Sodium. **19.49** 0.012 F. **19.51** 5.33 g Cu; 13.4 g Br_2. **19.53** 7.70×10^3 C. **19.55** 1.84 kg Cl_2/h. **19.57** 63.3 g/mol. **19.59** 27.0 g/mol. **19.65** (a) Half-reactions: $H_2(g) \longrightarrow 2H^+(aq) + 2e^-$, $Ni^{2+}(aq) + 2e^- \longrightarrow Ni(s)$; balanced equation: $H_2(g) + Ni^{2+}(aq) \longrightarrow 2H^+(aq) + Ni(s)$; the reaction will proceed to the left. (b) Half-reactions: $5e^- + 8H^+(aq) + MnO_4^-(aq) \longrightarrow Mn^{2+}(aq) + 4H_2O$; $2Cl^-(aq) \longrightarrow Cl_2(g) + 2e^-$; balanced equation: $16H^+(aq) + 2MnO_4^-(aq) + 10Cl^-(aq) \longrightarrow 2Mn^{2+}(aq) + 8H_2O(l) + 5Cl_2(g)$; the reaction will proceed to the left. (c) Half-reactions: $Cr(s) \longrightarrow Cr^{3+}(aq) + 3e^-$, $Zn^{2+}(aq) + 2e^- \longrightarrow Zn(s)$; balanced equation: $2Cr(s) + 3Zn^{2+}(aq) \longrightarrow 2Cr^{3+}(aq) + 3Zn(s)$. The reaction will proceed to the left. **19.67** 0.00944 g SO_2. **19.69** (a) $2MnO_4^- + 6H^+ + 5H_2O_2 \longrightarrow 2Mn^{2+} + 8H_2O + 5O_2$. (b) 0.0602 M. **19.71** 0.232 mg Ca^{2+}/mL blood. **19.73** 5×10^{-13}. **19.75** (a) 3.14 V. (b) 3.13 V. **19.77** 0.035 V. **19.79** Mercury(I) is Hg_2^{2+}. **19.81** 1.44 g Mg; $[Ag^+] = 7 \times 10^{-55}$ M; $[Mg^{2+}] = 0.0500$ M. **19.83** (a) H_2; 0.206 L. (b) 6.09×10^{23} e^-/mol e^-. **19.85** (a) −1356.8 kJ/mol. (b) 1.17 V. **19.87** +3. **19.89** $\Delta G^{\circ} = 6.8$ kJ/mol; $K = 0.064$. **19.91** 1.4 A. **19.93** +4. **19.95** 1.60×10^{-19} C/e^-. **19.97** Cells of higher voltage require very reactive oxidizing and reducing agents, which are difficult to handle. (From Table 19.1 of the text, we see that 5.92 V is the theoretical limit of a cell made up of Li^+/Li and F_2/F^- electrodes under standard-state conditions.) Batteries made up of several cells in series are easier to use. **19.99** 2×10^{20}. **19.101** (a) E_{red}° for X is negative. E_{red}° for Y is positive. (b) 0.59 V. **19.103** (a) Gold does not tarnish in air because the reduction potential for oxygen is not sufficiently positive to result in the oxidation of gold. (b) Yes. (c) $2Au + 3F_2 \longrightarrow 2AuF_3$. **19.105** $[Fe^{2+}] = 0.0920$ M; $[Fe^{3+}] = 0.0680$ M. **19.107** $H_2O_2(aq) + 2H^+(aq) + 2e^- \longrightarrow 2H_2O(l)$, $E_{cathode}^{\circ} = 1.77$ V; $H_2O_2(aq) \longrightarrow O_2(g) + 2H^+(aq) + 2e^-$, $E_{anode}^{\circ} = 0.68$ V. $E_{cell}^{\circ} = E_{cathode}^{\circ} - E_{anode}^{\circ} = 1.09$ V; The decomposition is spontaneous. **19.109** (a) Unchanged. (b) Unchanged. (c) Squared. (d) Doubled. (e) Doubled. **19.111** As $[H^+]$ increases, F_2 does become a stronger oxidizing agent. **19.113** 4.4×10^2 atm. **19.115** (a) 1.65 V. (b) 1.63 V. (c) 4.86×10^3 kJ/kg Zn. (d) 64 L of air. **19.117** −3.05 V. **19.119** 1×10^{-14}. **19.121** (a) 1A·h = 1A × 3600s = 3600 C. (b) 105 A·h. This ampere·hour cannot be fully realized because the concentration of H_2SO_4 keeps decreasing. (c) $E_{cell}^{\circ} = 2.01$ V; $\Delta G^{\circ} = $ −388 kJ/mol. **19.123** $217. **19.125** −0.037 V. **19.127** 2×10^{37}. **19.129** 5 mol ATP/mol NO_2^-. **19.131** Non-zero emf will appear if the temperatures of the two half-cells are different.

Chapter 20

20.5 (a) $_{11}^{23}Na$. (b) $_{1}^{1}p$ or $_{1}^{1}H$. (c) $_{0}^{1}n$. (d) $_{26}^{56}Fe$. (e) $_{-1}^{0}\beta$. **20.13** 2.72×10^{14} g/cm³. **20.15** (a) Ni. (b) Se. (c) Cd. **20.17** -4.85×10^{-12} kg/mol H_2. **20.19** (a) 6.30×10^{-12} J; 9.00×10^{-13} J/nucleon. (b) 4.78×10^{-11} J; 1.37×10^{-12} J/nucleon. **20.21** 7.963×10^{-26} kg.

20.25 (a) $_{90}^{232}Th \xrightarrow{\alpha} _{88}^{228}Ra \xrightarrow{\beta} _{89}^{228}Ac \xrightarrow{\beta} _{90}^{228}Th$.

(b) $_{92}^{235}U \xrightarrow{\alpha} _{90}^{231}Th \xrightarrow{\beta} _{91}^{231}Pa \xrightarrow{\alpha} _{89}^{227}Ac$.

(c) $_{93}^{237}Np \xrightarrow{\alpha} _{91}^{233}Pa \xrightarrow{\beta} _{92}^{233}U \xrightarrow{\alpha} _{90}^{229}Th$.

20.27 4.88×10^{19} atoms. **20.29** 3.09×10^3 yr. **20.31** No A remains; 0.25 mole of B; no C is left; 0.75 mole of D. **20.33** 5.5 dpm. **20.35** 43:1. **20.39** (a) $^{14}N(\alpha,p)^{17}O$. (b) $^9Be(\alpha,n)^{12}C$. (c) $^{238}U(d,2n)^{238}Np$. **20.41** (a) $^{40}Ca(d,p)^{41}Ca$. (b) $^{32}S(n,p)^{32}P$. (c) $^{239}Pu(\alpha,n)^{242}Cm$.

20.43 $_{80}^{198}Hg + _{0}^{1}n \longrightarrow _{80}^{199}Hg \longrightarrow _{79}^{198}Au + _{1}^{1}p$. **20.55** The fact that the radioisotope appears only in the I_2 shows that the IO_3^- is formed only from the IO_4^-. **20.57** Add iron-59 to the person's diet, and allow a few days for the iron-59 isotope to be incorporated into the person's body. Isolate red blood cells from a blood sample and monitor radioactivity from the hemoglobin molecules present in the red blood cells. **20.59** 257 days. **20.65** 65.3 yr. **20.67** (a) $_{1}^{3}H \longrightarrow _{2}^{3}He + _{-1}^{0}\beta$ (b) 70.5 dpm. **20.69** (a) $_{36}^{93}Kr$. (b) $_{0}^{1}n$. (c) $_{57}^{146}La$. (d) $_{0}^{1}n$. **20.71** (a) $_{1}^{3}H \longrightarrow _{2}^{3}He + _{-1}^{0}\beta$. (b) $_{94}^{242}Pu \longrightarrow _{2}^{4}\alpha + _{92}^{238}U$. (c) $_{53}^{131}I \longrightarrow _{54}^{131}Xe + _{-1}^{0}\beta$. (d) $_{98}^{251}Cf \longrightarrow _{96}^{247}Cm + _{2}^{4}\alpha$. **20.73** Because both Ca and Sr belong to Group 2A, radioactive strontium that

has been ingested into the human body becomes concentrated in bones (replacing Ca) and can damage blood cell production; 2.12×10^3 mCi. **20.75** Normally the human body concentrates iodine in the thyroid gland. The purpose of the large doses of KI is to displace radioactive iodine from the thyroid and allow its excretion from the body. **20.77** (a) $_{83}^{209}Bi + _{2}^{4}\alpha \longrightarrow _{85}^{211}At + 2_{0}^{1}n$. (b) $_{83}^{209}Bi(\alpha, 2n)_{85}^{211}At$. **20.79** 2.77×10^3 yr. **20.81** 0.070%. **20.83** (a) 5.59×10^{-15} J; 2.84×10^{-13} J. (b) 0.024 mol. (c) 4.26×10^6 kJ. **20.85** 6.1×10^{23} atoms/mol. **20.87** (a) 1.83×10^{-12} J. (b) The α particle will move away faster because it is smaller. **20.89** U-238, $t_{1/2} = 4.5 \times 10^9$ yr and Th-232, $t_{1/2} = 1.4 \times 10^{10}$ yr; They are still present because of their long half-lives. **20.91** 8.3×10^{-4} nm. **20.93** Only ^3H has a suitable half-life. The other half-lives are either too long or too short to determine the time span of 6 years accurately. **20.95** A small-scale chain reaction (fission of ^{235}U) took place. Copper played the crucial role of reflecting neutrons from the splitting uranium-235 atoms back into the uranium sphere to trigger the chain reaction. Note that a sphere has the most appropriate geometry for such a chain reaction. In fact, during the implosion process prior to an atomic explosion, fragments of uranium-235 are pressed roughly into a sphere for the chain reaction to occur (see Section 20.5 of the text). **20.97** 2.1×10^2 g/mol. **20.99** (a) $r = r_0 A^{1/3}$, where r_0 is a proportionality constant. (b) 1.7×10^{-42} m³. **20.101** Diagram (b). **20.103** 3.4 mL. **20.105** (a) X = $_{77}^{191}Ir$; $_{77}^{191}Ir + _{0}^{1}n \longrightarrow _{77}^{192}Ir + \gamma$. (b) 1.69×10^{-10} J; 1.35×10^{-12} J/nucleon.

Chapter 21

21.3 (a) $CaCO_3$. (b) $CaCO_3 \cdot MgCO_3$. (c) CaF_2. (d) NaCl. (e) Al_2O_3. (f) Fe_3O_4. (g) $Be_3Al_2Si_6O_{18}$. (h) PbS. (i) $MgSO_4 \cdot 7H_2O$. (j) $CaSO_4$. **21.13** $K_P = 4.5 \times 10^5$. **21.15** Ag, Pt, and Au will not be oxidized, but the other metals will. **21.17** (a) 8.9×10^{12} cm³. (b) 4.0×10^8 kg. **21.19** Al, Na, and Ca. **21.33** (a) $2Na(s) + 2H_2O(l) \longrightarrow 2NaOH(aq) + H_2(g)$. (b) $2NaOH(aq) + CO_2(g) \longrightarrow Na_2CO_3(aq) + H_2O(l)$. (c) $Na_2CO_3(s) + 2HCl(aq) \longrightarrow 2NaCl(aq) + CO_2(g) + H_2O(l)$. (d) $NaHCO_3(aq) + HCl(aq) \longrightarrow NaCl(aq) + CO_2(g) + H_2O(l)$. (e) $2NaHCO_3(s) \longrightarrow Na_2CO_3(s) + CO_2(g) + H_2O(g)$. (f) No reaction. **21.35** 5.59 L. **21.39** $3Mg(s) + 8HNO_3(aq) \longrightarrow 3Mg(NO_3)_2(aq) + 4H_2O(l) + 2NO(g)$. The magnesium nitrate is recovered from solution by evaporation, dried, and heated in air to obtain magnesium oxide: $2Mg(NO_3)_2(s) \longrightarrow 2MgO(s) + 4NO_2(g) + O_2(g)$. **21.41** The electron configuration of magnesium is [Ne]$3s^2$. The $3s$ electrons are outside the neon core (shielded), so they have relatively low ionization energies. Removing the third electron means separating an electron from the neon (closed shell) core, which requires a great deal more energy. **21.43** Even though helium and the Group 2A metals have ns^2 outer electron configurations, helium has a closed shell noble gas configuration and the Group 2A metals do not. The electrons in He are much closer to and more strongly attracted by the nucleus. Hence, the electrons in He are not easily removed. Helium is inert. **21.45** (a) CaO(s). (b) $Ca(OH)_2(s)$. **21.49** 60.7 h. **21.51** (a) 1.03 V. (b) 3.32×10^4 kJ/mol. **21.53** $4Al(NO_3)_3(s) \longrightarrow 2Al_2O_3(s) + 12NO_2(g) + 3O_2(g)$. **21.55** The "bridge" bonds in Al_2Cl_6 break at high temperature: $Al_2Cl_6(g) \rightleftharpoons 2AlCl_3(g)$. This increases the number of molecules in the gas phase and causes the pressure to be higher than expected for pure Al_2Cl_6. **21.57** In Al_2Cl_6, each aluminum atom is surrounded by 4 bonding pairs of electrons (AB_4-type molecule), and therefore each aluminum atom is sp^3 hybridized. VSEPR analysis shows $AlCl_3$ to be an AB_3-type molecule (no lone pairs on the central atom). The geometry should be trigonal planar, and the aluminum atom should therefore be sp^2 hybridized. **21.59** 65.4 g/mol. **21.61** Copper(II) ion is more easily reduced than either water or hydrogen ion. Copper metal is more easily oxidized than water. Water should not be affected by the copper purification process under standard conditions. **21.63** (a) 1482 kJ/mol. (b) 3152.8 kJ/mol. **21.65** Mg(s) reacts with $N_2(g)$ at high temperatures to produce $Mg_3N_2(s)$. Ti(s) also reacts with $N_2(g)$ at high temperatures to produce TiN(s). **21.67** (a) In water the aluminum(III) ion causes an increase in the concentration of hydrogen ion (lower pH). This results from the effect of the small diameter and high charge (3+) of the aluminum ion on surrounding water molecules. The aluminum ion draws electrons in the O—H bonds to itself, thus allowing easy formation of H^+ ions. (b) $Al(OH)_3$ is an amphoteric hydroxide. It will dissolve in strong base with the formation of a complex ion. $Al(OH)_3(s) + OH^-(aq) \longrightarrow Al(OH)_4^-(aq)$. The concentration of OH^- in aqueous ammonia is too low for this reaction to occur. **21.69** $CaO(s) + 2HCl(aq) \longrightarrow CaCl_2(aq) + H_2O(l)$. **21.71** Metals have closely spaced energy levels and (referring to Figure 23.10 of the text) a very small energy gap between filled and empty levels. Consequently, many electronic transitions can take place with absorption and subsequent emission of light continually occurring. Some of these transitions fall in the visible region of the spectrum and give rise to the flickering appearance. **21.73** NaF: cavity prevention; Li_2CO_3: antidepressant; $Mg(OH)_2$: laxative; $CaCO_3$: calcium supplement, antacid; $BaSO_4$: radiocontrast agent. **21.75** Both Li and Mg form oxides (Li_2O and MgO). Other Group 1A metals (Na, K, etc.) also form peroxides and superoxides. In Group 1A, only Li forms nitride (Li_3N), like Mg (Mg_3N_2). Li resembles Mg in that its carbonate, fluoride, and phosphate have low solubilities. **21.77** Zn. **21.79** 87.66% Na_2O; 12.34% Na_2O_2. **21.81** 727 atm.

Chapter 22

22.11 (a) +3. (b) 6. (c) Oxalate ion ($C_2O_4^{2-}$). **22.13** (a) Na: +1; Mo: +6. (b) Mg: +2; W: +6. (c) Fe: 0. **22.15** (a) *cis*-dichlorobis(ethylenediamine)cobalt(III). (b) Pentamminechloroplatinum(IV) chloride. (c) Pentamminechlorocobalt(III) chloride. **22.17** Six. **22.23** (a) Two. (b) Two.

22.25 (a)

trans   *cis*   (b)

22.31 Cyanide ion is a very strong field ligand. It causes a larger crystal field splitting than water, resulting in the absorption of higher energy (shorter wavelength) radiation when a *d* electron is excited to a higher energy *d* orbital. **22.33** (a) Orange. (b) 255 kJ/mol. **22.35** Two moles; $[Co(NH_3)_4Cl_2]Cl$; refer to Problem 22.25 (a) for a diagram of the structure. **22.37** Δ would be greater for the higher oxidation state. **22.41** Use a radioactive label such as $^{14}CN^-$ (in NaCN). Add NaCN to a solution of $K_3Fe(CN)_6$. Isolate some of the $K_3Fe(CN)_6$ and check its radioactivity. If the complex shows radioactivity, then it must mean that the CN^- ion has participated in the exchange reaction. **22.43** $Cu(CN)_2$ is the white precipitate. It is soluble in KCN(aq), due to formation of $[Cu(CN)_4]^{2-}$, so the concentration of Cu^{2+} is too small for Cu^{2+} ions to precipitate with sulfide. **22.45** 1.4×10^2. **22.47** The purple color is caused by the build-up of deoxyhemoglobin. When either oxyhemoglobin or deoxyhemoglobin takes up CO, the carbonylhemoglobin takes on a red color, the same as oxyhemoglobin. **22.49** Mn^{3+} is $3d^4$ and Cr^{3+} is $3d^3$. Therefore, Mn^{3+} has a greater tendency to accept an electron and is a stronger oxidizing agent. The $3d^5$ electron configuration of Cr^{3+} is a stable configuration. **22.51** Ti^{3+}; Fe^{3+}. **22.53** 1.6×10^4 g hemoglobin/mol Fe. The discrepancy between our minimum value and the actual value can be explained by realizing that there are four iron atoms per mole of hemoglobin. **22.55** (a) $[Cr(H_2O)_6]Cl_3$, number of ions: 4. (b) $[Cr(H_2O)_5Cl]Cl_2 \cdot H_2O$, number of ions: 3. (c) $[Cr(H_2O)_4Cl_2]Cl \cdot 2H_2O$, number of ions: 2. Compare the compounds with equal molar amounts of NaCl, $MgCl_2$, and $FeCl_3$ in an electrical conductance experiment. The solution that has similar conductance to the NaCl solution contains (c); the solution with the conductance similar to $MgCl_2$ contains (b); and the solution with conductance similar to $FeCl_3$ contains (a). **22.57** $\Delta G° = -1.8 \times 10^2$ kJ/mol; $K = 6 \times 10^{30}$. **22.59** Iron is much more abundant than cobalt. **22.61** Oxyhemoglobin absorbs higher energy light than deoxyhemoglobin. Oxyhemoglobin is diamagnetic (low spin), while deoxyhemoglobin is paramagnetic (high spin). These differences occur because oxygen (O_2) is a strong-field ligand. **22.63** Complexes are expected to be colored when the highest occupied orbitals

have between one and nine *d* electrons. Such complexes can therefore have *d* $\longrightarrow$ *d* transitions (that are usually in the visible part of the electromagnetic radiation spectrum). Zn^{2+}, Cu^+, and Pb^{2+} are d^{10} ions. V^{5+}, Ca^{2+}, and Sc^{3+} are d^0 ions. **22.65** Dipole moment measurement. Only the *cis* isomer has a dipole moment. **22.67** EDTA sequesters metal ions (like Ca^{2+} and Mg^{2+}) which are essential for the growth and function of bacteria. **22.69** 3. **22.71** 2.2×10^{-20} *M*. **22.73** (a) 2.7×10^6. (b) Free Cu^+ ions are unstable in solution. Therefore, the only stable compounds containing Cu^+ ions are insoluble. **22.75** Y. **22.77** 0.0 *M*. **22.79** $[Mn(CN)_6]^{5-}$: Mn is +1, one unpaired *d* electron; $[Mn(CN)_6]^{4-}$: Mn is +2, one unpaired *d* electron; $[Mn(CN)_6]^{3-}$: Mn is +3, two unpaired *d* electrons.

Chapter 23

23.11 HCl; CaH_2. A water solution of HCl is called hydrochloric acid. Calcium hydride will react according to the equation $CaH_2(s) + 2H_2O(l) \longrightarrow Ca(OH)_2(aq) + 2H_2(g)$. **23.13** NaH: ionic compound, reacts with water as follows: $NaH(s) + H_2O(l) \longrightarrow NaOH(aq) + H_2(g)$; CaH_2: ionic compound, reacts with water as follows: $CaH_2(s) + 2H_2O(l) \longrightarrow Ca(OH)_2(aq) + 2H_2(g)$; CH_4: covalent compound, unreactive, burns in air or oxygen: $CH_4(g) + 2O_2(g) \longrightarrow CO_2(g) + 2H_2O(l)$; NH_3: covalent compound, weak base in water: $NH_3(aq) + H_2O(l) \rightleftharpoons NH_4^+(aq) + OH^-(aq)$; H_2O: covalent compound, forms strong intermolecular hydrogen bonds, good solvent for both ionic compounds and substances capable of forming hydrogen bonds; HCl: covalent compound (polar), acts as a strong acid in water: $HCl(g) + H_2O(l) \longrightarrow H_3O^+(aq) + Cl^-(aq)$. **23.15** $CaH_2(s) + 2H_2O(l) \longrightarrow Ca(OH)_2(aq) + 2H_2(g)$; 22.7 g. **23.17** (a) $CuO(s) + H_2(g) \longrightarrow Cu(s) + H_2O(l)$. (b) No reaction. **23.25** $[:C \equiv C:]^{2-}$. **23.27** (a) $2NaHCO_3(s) \longrightarrow Na_2CO_3(s) + H_2O(g) + CO_2(g)$. (b) $Ca(OH)_2(aq) + CO_2(g) \longrightarrow CaCO_3(s) + H_2O(l)$. **23.29** Heat causes bicarbonates to decompose according to the reaction: $2HCO_3^- \longrightarrow CO_3^{2-} + H_2O + CO_2$. Generation of carbonate ion causes precipitation of the insoluble $MgCO_3$. **23.31** $NaHCO_3$ plus some Na_2CO_3. **23.33** Yes. **23.39** (a) $2NaNO_3(s) \longrightarrow 2NaNO_2(s) + O_2(g)$. (b) $NaNO_3(s) + C(s) \longrightarrow NaNO_2(s) + CO(g)$. **23.41** $2NH_3(g) + CO_2(g) \longrightarrow (NH_2)_2CO(s) + H_2O(l)$; the reaction should be run at high pressure. **23.43** The oxidation state of N in nitric acid is +5, the highest oxidation state for N. N can be reduced to an oxidation state −3. **23.45** (a) $NH_4NO_3(s) \longrightarrow N_2O(g) + 2H_2O(l)$. (b) $2KNO_3(s) \longrightarrow 2KNO_2(s) + O_2(g)$. (c) $Pb(NO_3)_2(s) \longrightarrow PbO(s) + 2NO_2(g) + O_2(g)$. **23.47** $KNO_3(s) + C(s) \longrightarrow KNO_2(s) + CO(g)$; 48.0 g. **23.49** (a) 86.7 kJ/mol. (b) 4×10^{-31}. (c) 4×10^{-31}. **23.51** 125 g/mol; P_4. **23.53** $4HNO_3(aq) + P_4O_{10}(s) \longrightarrow 2N_2O_5(g) + 4HPO_3(l)$; 60.4 g. **23.55** sp^3. **23.63** $\Delta G° = -198.3$ kJ/mol; $K_p = K_c = 6 \times 10^{34}$. **23.65** (a) To exclude light. (b) 0.371 L. **23.67** F: −1; O: 0. **23.69** (a) $HCOOH(l) \rightleftharpoons CO(g) + H_2O(l)$. (b) $4H_3PO_4(l) \rightleftharpoons P_4O_{10}(s) + 6H_2O(l)$. (c) $2HNO_3(l) \rightleftharpoons N_2O_5(g) + H_2O(l)$. (d) $2HClO_3(l) \rightleftharpoons Cl_2O_5(l) + H_2O(l)$. **23.71** To form OF_6 there would have to be six bonds (twelve electrons) around the oxygen atom. This would violate the octet rule. Since oxygen does not have accessible *d* orbitals, it cannot have an expanded octet. **23.73** 35 g. **23.75** $9H_2SO_4(aq) + 8NaI(aq) \longrightarrow 4I_2(s) + H_2S(g) + 4H_2O(l) + 8NaHSO_4(aq)$. **23.79** (a) $H-\ddot{F}:\cdots H-\ddot{F}:$ (b) $[:\ddot{F}:\cdots H\cdots:\ddot{F}:]^-$ **23.81** (a) Linear. (b) Tetrahedral. (c) Trigonal bipyramidal. (d) See-saw. **23.83** 25.3 L. **23.85** 2.81 L. **23.87** $I_2O_5(s) + 5CO(g) \longrightarrow 5CO_2(g) + I_2(s)$; iodine is reduced; carbon is oxidized. **23.89** (a) $2H_3PO_3(aq) \longrightarrow H_3PO_4(aq) + PH_3(g) + O_2(g)$. (b) $Li_4C(s) + 4HCl(aq) \longrightarrow 4LiCl(aq) + CH_4(g)$. (c) $2HI(g) + 2HNO_2(aq) \longrightarrow I_2(s) + 2NO(g) + 2H_2O(l)$. (d) $H_2S(g) + 2Cl_2(g) \longrightarrow 2HCl(g) + SCl_2(l)$. **23.91** (a) $SiCl_4$. (b) F^-. (c) F. (d) CO_2. **23.93** There is no change in oxidation number; it is zero for both compounds.

23.95 PCl_4^+: $\begin{bmatrix} & Cl & \\ & | & \\ Cl-&P&-Cl \\ & | & \\ & Cl & \end{bmatrix}^+$, sp^3; PCl_6^-: $\begin{bmatrix} Cl & Cl & Cl \\ & \diagdown | \diagup & \\ & P & \\ & \diagup | \diagdown & \\ Cl & Cl & Cl \end{bmatrix}^-$, sp^3d^2.

23.97 25°C: $K = 9.61 \times 10^{-22}$; 100°C: $K = 1.2 \times 10^{-15}$. **23.99** The glass is etched by the reaction: $6HF(aq) + SiO_2(s) \longrightarrow H_2SiF_6(aq) + 2H_2O(l)$. This process gives the glass a frosted appearance. **23.101** 1.18. **23.103** 0.833 g/L. The molar mass derived from the observed density is 74.41, which suggests that the molecules are associated to some extent in the gas phase. This makes sense due to strong hydrogen bonding in HF.

Chapter 24

24.7 (a) Amine. (b) Aldehyde. (c) Ketone. (d) Carboxylic acid. (e) Alcohol. **24.9** (a) 3-ethyl-2,4,4-trimethylhexane. (b) 6,6-dimethyl-2-heptanol. (c) 4-chlorohexanal. **24.11** 3,5-dimethyloctane.
24.13 (a) $(CH_3)_3CCH_2CH(CH_3)_2$. (b) $HO(CH_2)_2CH(CH_3)_2$. (c) $CH_3(CH_2)_4C(O)NH_2$. (d) Cl_3CCHO.

24.15
A = Carbonyl (Ketone)
B = Carboxy (Caroboxylic acid)
C = Hydroxy (Alcohol)

24.17
Primary amino
Carboxy

24.19 (a) $CH_3CH_2CHCH_2CH_2CH_3$
(b) $CH_3CHCHCH_2CH_3$
(c) $CH_3CHCH_2CHCH_3$
(d) $CH_3CH_2CHCHCHCH_2CH_2CH_3$

24.21 (a) Kekule:

skeletal (line):

(b) Condensed: $(C_2H_5)_2CHCH_2CO_2C(CH_3)_3$;

skeletal line:

(c) Condensed: $(CH_3)_2CHCH_2NHCH(CH_3)_2$;

Kekule:

24.23 (a) Condensed structural: $(CH_3)_2NCHO$;

Kekule:
Line:

(b) Condensed structural: $(CH_2COOH)_2C(OH)COOH$;

Kekule:
Line:

(c) Condensed structural: $(CH_3)_2CH(CH_2)_2OC(O)CH_3$;

Kekule:

Line:

24.25 (a)
(b) $(CH_3)_3CCH_2CHCH_2CH$

(c)

24.27 (a)
(b)
(c)

24.29 (a)
(b)
(c)

24.37

24.39

24.41

24.43 (a) (b)

24.45

24.47 (a) (b)

(c) (d)

24.55

24.57 (a)

(b)

24.59

elimination reaction.

24.61 This is not an oxidation-reduction reaction. There are no changes in oxidation states for any of the atoms.

24.63 (a) Sulfuric acid is a catalyst;

(b) n-propanol: (c) No. **24.65** Thalidomide: $C_{13}H_{10}N_2O_4$; lenalidomide: $C_{13}H_{13}N_3O_3$; CC-4047: $C_{13}H_{11}N_3O_4$.

24.73

24.75 (a) $CH_2{=}CHCH{=}CH_2$

(b)

24.77

GlyLys   LysGly

24.79

Butyl   sec-Butyl   Isobutyl   tert-Butyl

24.81

Leucine   Isoleucine

24.83 (a)

(b)

24.85 (a) *Cis/trans* stereoisomers. (b) Constitutional isomers. (c) Resonance structures. (d) Different representations of the same structure.

24.87   **24.89** (b).

24.91 $CH_3CH_2C{\equiv}CH$ $CH_3C{\equiv}CCH_3$ $H_2C{=}CHCH{=}CH_2$
             sp sp sp sp all sp^2

24.93 Since N is less electronegative than O, electron donation in the amide would be more pronounced. **24.95** (a) The more negative ΔH implies stronger alkane bonds; branching decreases the total bond enthalpy (and overall stability) of the alkane. (b) The least highly branched isomer (*n*-octane). **24.97** (a) 15.81 mg C; 1.32 mg H; 3.49 mg O. (b) C_6H_6O.

(c) HO—

24.99

24.101

24.103 8 different tripeptides: Lys—Lys—Lys, Lys—Lys—Ala, Lys—Ala—Lys, Ala—Lys—Lys, Lys—Ala—Ala, Ala—Lys—Ala, Ala—Ala—Lys, Ala—Ala—Ala.

24.105

Chapter 25

25.3 The monomer must have a triple bond.

25.5

25.9 (1) Produce the alkoxide: $Sc(s) + 2C_2H_5OH(l) \longrightarrow Sc(OC_2H_5)(alc) + 2H^+(alc)$ ("alc" indicates a solution in alcohol); (2) hydrolyze to produce hydroxide pellets: $Sc(OC_2H_5)(alc) + 2H_2O(l) \longrightarrow Sc(OH)_2(s) + 2C_2H_5OH(alc)$; (3) sinter pellets to produce ceramic: $Sc(OH)_2(s) \longrightarrow ScO(s) + 2H_2O(g)$. **25.11** Bakelite is best described as a thermosetting composite polymer. **25.15** No; These polymers are too flexible, and liquid crystals require long, relatively rigid molecules. **25.19** As shown, it is an alternating condensation copolymer of the polyester class. **25.21** Metal amalgams expand with age; composite fillings tend to shrink. **25.25** sp^2. **25.27** Dispersion forces; dispersion forces. **25.31** (a) n-type. (b) p-type. **25.35** $Bi_2Sr_2CuO_6$. **25.37** Two are $+2$ ($[Ar]3d^9$), one is $+3$ ($[Ar]3d^8$). The $+3$ oxidation state is unusual for copper.

25.39 $H_2N-(CH_2)_8-NH_2$

25.41 Plastic polymer: covalent bonds, disulfide (covalent) bonds, H-bonds and dispersion forces; ceramics: ionic and network covalent bonds. **25.43** Fluoroapatite is less soluble than hydroxyapatite, particularly in acidic solutions. Dental fillings must also be insoluble. **25.45** The molecule is long, flat and rigid, so it should form a liquid crystal. **25.47** $-CH=C(CH_2CH_3)-CH=C(CH_2CH_3)-CH=C(CH_2CH_3)-$; $-CH_2-CH(CH_2CH_3)-CH_2-CH(CH_2CH_3)-CH_2-CH(CH_2CH_3)-$; The two structures are similar in that they both have ethyl groups on alternating carbons. They are different in that poly(1-butyne) is a conjugated system and poly(1-butene) is not. The first structure is more likely to be an electrically conducting polymer.

Credits

Chapter 1

Opener: AP Photo/Nathan Denettek,CP; **1.1a:** © fStop/PunchStock RF; **1.1b:** © Brand X Pictures/PunchStock RF; **1.1c:** © Image Source/Corbis RF; **1.1d:** © Getty RF; p.5 (vaccination scar): © Chris Livingston/Getty Images; p. 5 (extinguisher): © Ingram Publishing/Fototsearch RF; p. 5 (oxygen sign): © Alamy RF; **1.4, 1.5a-b:** © The McGraw-Hill Companies, Inc./Charles D. Winters, photographer; **1.6a:** © Bloomimage/Corbis RF; **1.6b-c:** © Richard Megna/Fundamental Photographs.

Chapter 2

Opener: © Alamy RF; **2.1a:** © David A. Tietz/Editorial Image, LLC; **2.3a (both):** © Richard Megna/Fundamental Photographs; **2.4a-c, 2.10:** © The McGraw-Hill Companies, Inc./Charles D. Winters, photographer; **2.11:** © Ryan McVay/Getty Images..

Chapter 3

Opener: Vourtesy of Dr. Robert Wolkow, iCORE Chair, University of Alberta; **3.1 (x-ray):** © Getty RF; **p. 65:** © SPL/Photo Researchers; **3.6a:** © Getty RF; **3.6b:** © The McGraw-Hill Companies, Inc./Charles D. Winters, photographer; **3.8:** Courtesy of Sargent-Welch; **3.13a-b:** © Dr. Stanley Flegler/Visuals Unlimited.

Chapter 4

Opener: © fzd.it/Shutterstock RF; **p. 126:** © 3D4Medical.com/Getty Images.

Chapter 5

Opener: © Macmillan Publishers Ltd: Nature, Vol. 429 Issue 7078 "Chemistry: Volatile times for ionic liquids," by Peter Wasserscheid, 2006.; **p. 141:** © Studio 101/Alamy; **5.7:** © The McGraw-Hill Companies, Inc./Charles D. Winters, photographer.

Chapter 6

Opener: © Brand X Pictures/PunchStock RF; **p. 200:** © Eliot J Schechter/Stringer/AFP/Getty Images; **p. 201:** © Wesley Bocxe/Photo Researchers.

Chapter 7

Opener: © The Science Picture Company/Science Faction; **7.1a-e:** © The McGraw-Hill Companies, Inc./Stephen Frisch, photographer; **p. 245 (both):** © The McGraw-Hill Companies, Inc./Charles D. Winters, photographer.

Chapter 8

Opener: © Bill Bachman/Photo Researchers; **p. 272:** © The McGraw-Hill Companies, Inc./John Flournoy, photographer; **8.6:** © Richard Megna/Fundamental Photographs; **8.7 (all), 8.8, 8.9a:** © The McGraw-Hill Companies, Inc./Charles D. Winters, photographer; **8.9b:** © The McGraw-Hill Companies, Inc./Ken Cavanagh, photographer; **8.10 (all):** © Richard Megna/Fundamental Photographs; **8.11:** © Will & Deni McIntyre/Corbis; **8.12 (all):** © David A. Tietz/Editorial Image, LLC; **8.13:** Courtesy Argonne National Laboratory.

Chapter 9

Opener: © Dirk Wiersma/Photo Researchers; **9.1a-c:** © The McGraw-Hill Companies, Inc./Stephen Frisch, photographer; **9.3 (all):** © The McGraw-Hill Companies, Inc./Charles D. Winters, photographer; **9.5:** © David A. Tietz/Editorial Image, LLC; **p. 320 (all), 9.6 (both):** © The McGraw-Hill Companies, Inc./Charles D. Winters, photographer; **9.11 (both):** © David A. Tietz/Editorial Image, LLC; **9.12a-b, 9.13a-c:** © The McGraw-Hill Companies, Inc./Charles D. Winters, photographer.

Chapter 10

Opener: © Syracuse Newspapers/J. Berry/The Image Works; **10.1:** © Bettmann/Corbis; **10.13 (all):** © Richard Megna/Fundamental Photographs.

Chapter 11

Opener: © Medicimage/Phototake; **p. 418:** © David A. Tietz/Editorial Image, LLC; **11.7 (both), 11.13 (both):** © The McGraw-Hill Companies, Inc./Charles D. Winters, photographer; **p. 441:** © Kike Calvo/VW/The Image Works.

Chapter 12

Opener: © US Department of Energy/Photo Researchers; **p. 470:** © Yoav Levy/PhotoTake; **12.7a:** © Purestock/PunchStock RF; **12.7b:** © Ingram Publishing/SuperStock RF; **12.25a-b, 12.26:** © The McGraw-Hill Companies, Inc./Charles D. Winters, photographer; **p. 492:** © The McGraw-Hill Companies, Inc./Ken Karp, photographer; **p. 503:** © Simon Murrell/OJO Images/Getty Images.

Chapter 13

Opener: © Shawn Knol/Getty Images; **13.1 (all), 13.2 (all):** © The McGraw-Hill Companies, Inc./Charles D. Winters, photographer; **p. 530 (all):** © David M. Phillips/Photo Researchers; **13.12:** © The McGraw-Hill Companies, Inc./Charles D. Winters, photographer; **13.13:** © Photodisc/Getty RF; **p. 544 (both):** © David A. Tietz/Editorial Image, LLC; **p. 546:** © Bill Curtsinger/National Geographic/Getty Images.

Chapter 14

Opener: AP Photo/Duluth News Tribune, Justin Hayworth; **14.7, 14.11a:** © The McGraw-Hill Companies, Inc./Ken Karp, photographer; **p. 580 (effervescence series):** © David A. Tietz/Editorial Image, LLC; **p. 580 (sugar refinery):** AP Photo/Stephen Morton; **14.15 (both):** © The McGraw-Hill Companies, Inc./Charles D. Winters, photographer; **p. 605 (all):** © David A. Tietz/Editorial Image, LLC.

Chapter 15

Opener: © Comstock Images/Alamy RF; **15.1 (all), 15.2 (all):** © Richard Megna/Fundamental Photographs; **15.8 (both), 15.9 (all):** © The McGraw-Hill Companies, Inc./Charles D. Winters, photographer.

Chapter 16

Opener: © SuperStock/Alamy RF; **16.3:** © The McGraw-Hill Companies, Inc./Charles D. Winters, photographer.

Chapter 17

Opener: © PhotoDisc/Getty RF; **17.2, 17.7, 17.9 (both):** © The McGraw-Hill Companies, Inc./Ken Karp, photographer; **p. 743:** © The McGraw-Hill Companies, Inc.; **17.10:** © The McGraw-Hill Companies, Inc./Ken Karp, photographer; **17.11:** © The McGraw-Hill Companies, Inc./Stephen Frisch, photographer.

Chapter 18

Opener: © PhotoAlto RF.

Chapter 19

Opener: © Friedrich Saurer/Alamy; **19.2:** © The McGraw-Hill Companies, Inc./Ken Karp, photographer; **19.11:** © The McGraw-Hill Companies, Inc./Stephen Frisch, photographer; **p. 843:** © David A. Tietz/Editorial Image, LLC; **p. 845:** © The McGraw-Hill Companies, Inc./Ken Karp, photographer.

Chapter 20

Opener: © Pallava Bagla/Corbis; **20.6:** © Nick Wall/Photo Researchers; **20.12:** © Vanderlei Almeida/AFP/Getty; **20.13:** © E.R. Degginger/Color-pic Inc.; **20.14:** © Peter Essick/Aurora; **20.16:** © Lawrence Livermore National Labs; **20.17:** © Corbis; **p. 874 (top):** © David A. Tietz/Editorial Image, LLC; **20.18:** © Mediscan/Corbis.

Chapter 21

Opener: AP Photo/Eastman Kodak Company; **21.2:** © Peter Ryan/Photo Researchers; **21.5:** © Corbis RF; **21.7:** © Maximilian Stock Ltd/Photo Researchers; **21.13:** © David A. Tietz/Editorial Image, LLC; **21.14:** © Corbis RF; **21.15, 21.16, 21.17:** © The McGraw-Hill Companies, Inc./Charles D. Winters, photographer; **21.19:** © Phil Degginger/Color-Pic, Inc.

Chapter 22

Opener: Imaginechina via AP Images; **p. 913:** The Advertising Archives; **22.11:** © David A. Tietz/Editorial Image, LLC; **22.16:** © The McGraw-Hill Companies, Inc./Charles D. Winters, photographer; **p. 923:** © David A. Tietz/Editorial Image, LLC.

Chapter 23

Opener: AP Photo/Craig Ruttle; **23.5:** © David A. Tietz/Editorial Image, LLC; **23.6:** © David R. Frazier Photolibrary, Inc./Alamy; **23.7:** © The McGraw-Hill Companies, Inc./Charles D. Winters, photographer; **23.8, 23.14:** © David A. Tietz/Editorial Image, LLC; **23.18:** © Dynamic Graphics Group/Creatas/Alamy RF; **23.20:** © Inga Spence/Visuals Unlimited.

Chapter 24

Opener: © Digital Vision/Getty RF; **p. 965 (left):** © David A. Tietz/Editorial Image, LLC; **p. 965 (middle):** © Getty RF; **p. 965 (right):** © David A. Tietz/Editorial Image, LLC; **24.5a-b:** © The McGraw-Hill Companies, Inc./Charles D. Winters, photographer.

Chapter 25

Opener: © Delft University of Technology/Photo Researchers; **p. 1013:** © PhotoLink/Getty RF; **25.2 (left):** © David A. Tietz/Editorial Image, LLC; **25.2 (right):** © Richard Megna/Fundamental Photographs; **p. 1015 (top):** AP Photo/Robert E. Klein; **p. 1015 (bottom):** © Comstock Images/Alamy RF; **25.9:** NASA; **25.12:** © Stockbyte/Getty RF; **p. 1028:** © Photodisc/Getty RF; **25.13a:** © Tek Image/Photo Researchers; **25.13b:** © Dr. Ben Oostra/Visuals Unlimited; **25.13c:** Reprint Courtesy of International Business Machines Corporation copyright 1993 © International Business Machines Corporation; **p. 1029 (left):** © Phil Degginger/Color-Pic, Inc.; **p. 1029 (right):** © Getty RF; **25.17:** © David A. Tietz/Editorial Image, LLC; **25.18:** © IBM Research/Peter Arnold, Inc.

Index

A

absolute entropies, 778–779
absolute temperature scale, 10, 425
absolute zero, 10, 425
absorbance (A), 338
absorbed, 531–532
absorption spectrum, 338
acceptor impurities, 893
accuracy, 17–18
acetic acid, 308, 317, 713
achiral, 915
acid-base indicators, 729–731
acid-base reactions, 317–321
    acid-base neutralization, 319–321
    Brønsted acids and bases, 317–319
    strong acids and bases, 317
acid-base titrations, 343–346, 721
    acid-base indicators, 729–731
    strong acid–strong base titrations, 721–723
    strong acid–weak base titrations, 727–729
    weak acid–strong base titrations, 723–727
acid ionization constant, 672–673
acid rain, 678
acidic salt solutions, 692–694
acids
    in molecular compounds, 157
    oxoacids, 162–163, 659–660
    strong, 317, 668–669
acids and bases, 656
    acid-base properties of oxides and hydroxides, 696–697
    acid-base properties of salt solutions, 690–695
    acid-base properties of water, 661–663
    Brønsted, 657–659
    conjugate acid-base pairs, 684–687
    diprotic and polyprotic acids, 688–690
    Lewis acids and bases, 697–699
    molecular structure and acid strength, 659–661
    pH scale, 663–667
    strong, 668–672
    weak acids and acid ionization constants, 672–681
    weak bases and base ionization constants, 681–684
actinide series, 91, 110, 111
activated complex, 552
activation energy, 551
active metals, 289–290, 326
activity series, 326, 327

actual yield, 285
addition polymerization, 1013
addition polymers, 995, 1013–1018
addition reactions, 985–987
adhesion, 470, 471
alcohols, 963, 964, 965, 970–971
aldehydes, 963, 965, 971
aliphatic compounds, 962
alkali metals, 44, 894–897
alkaline batteries, 827–828
alkaline earth metals, 44, 290, 897–898
alkanes, 158, 963, 967, 968
alkenes, 1013
alkyl group, 963, 964, 967
alkynes, 1013, 1021
allotropes, 152, 935
alloys, 886
alpha (α) particles, 36, 875
alpha (α) rays, 36
altitude sickness, 640
aluminum, 106, 107, 898–901
amalgam
    defined, 886
    dental, 822, 1026
amide group, 963, 964, 965
amide ions, 936
amides, 963, 965, 972
amines, 963, 965, 972
amino acids, 966, 997, 998–999, 1019
amino group, 963, 964, 965
ammonia, 938
ammonium chloride, 10
amorphous solids, 475, 487–488
amount-volume relationship, 426–427, 429–430
amphoteric, 662, 697
amplitude, 60, 61
angstrom, 10
angular momentum quantum number, 79, 116
anhydrous, 163
anions, 118, 122, 141, 143, 147–148, 310, 695
anisotropic, 1023
anode, 34, 35, 809, 813
anthrax, 200
antibonding molecular orbitals, 245, 246, 247, 248, 249, 251
antimony, 948
antioxidants, 182
aqueous solutions, 511
    acid-base reactions, 729–731
    aqueous defined, 268
    aqueous reactions and chemical analysis, 341–346
    concentration of solutions, 331–341
    electrolytes in, 307–310

    general properties of, 307–311
    oxidation of metals in, 325–326
    oxidation-reduction reactions, 325–326
    precipitation reactions, 312–316
argon, 108
aromatic compounds, 962
Arrhenius acid, 318
Arrhenius base, 318
Arrhenius equation, 576–579
Arrhenius, Svante, 317
arsenic, 948
artificial hearts and valves, 1027
artificial joints, 1028
ascorbic acid, 961
astatine, 949
Aston, F. W., 42
atatic, 1018
atmospheres (atm), 419
atmospheric pressure, 418–419, 445, 488
atom economy, 287
atomic bomb, 868
atomic clocks, 859
atomic force microscopy, 56, 1028, 1029
atomic ions, 141
atomic line spectra, 67–68
atomic mass, 11–12
atomic mass unit (amu), 10, 46
atomic number (Z), 39, 108, 115
atomic orbitals, 78, 82–85
    d orbitals and other higher–energy orbitals, 84
    energies of orbitals, 84–85
    f orbitals, 84
    hybridization of, 230–237
    in many-electron systems, 85–86
    p orbitals, 82
    s orbitals, 82
atomic radius, 38, 113–115, 125, 127
atomic structure, 37–39
atomic theory, 33–34, 267
atoms, 3, 33–34
    atomic number, mass number, and isotopes, 39–40
    atomic theory, 33–34, 267
    average atomic mass, 41–43
    conversions among mass, moles, and number of atoms, 47–48
    defined, 33
    hydrogen atom, 38, 68–74, 78
    properties of, 184–185
    structure of, 37–39
    subatomic particles, 38–39
attractive forces, 35, 121, 469
Aufbau principle, 87
autoionization of water, 662
average atomic mass, 41–43

average reaction rates, 553, 556–557
Avogadro, Amedeo, 45, 426
Avogadro's constant, 45, 47
Avogadro's law, 426–427, 429
Avogadro's number, 45
axial, 217

B

balance (to measure mass), 8, 17
ball-and-stick models (molecular art), 151
Balmer, Johann, 68, 72, 73
band theory, 892
band theory of conductivity, 892
        conductors, 892
        semiconductors, 892–893
bar (unit of pressure), 419
Bardeen, John, 1034
barometer, 420, 421
base
        Brønsted acids and bases, 318–319,
            657–659
        defined, 307
        strong acids and bases, 317, 668–671
base ionization constant, 682
basic oxygen process, 888–889
basic salt solutions, 691–692
batteries
        defined, 827
        dry cells and alkaline, 827–828
        fuel cells, 829–830
        lead storage, 828
        lithium-ion, 828–829
Becquerel, Antoine, 36
Beer-Lambert law, 338
belt of stability, 854
bends, the, 441
bent (molecular geometry), 218, 221
benzene, 523–524
beryllium, 87, 199
beta-particle emission, 854–855
beta (β) particles, 36, 875
beta (β) rays, 36
bile salts, 537
bimolecular, 581
binary hydrides, 933–934
binary ionic compounds, 148
binary molecular compounds, 156
biodiesel, 362
biofuels, 362
biological catalysts, 591–592
biological equilibria, 640
biological polymers, 997–1000
biomagnification, 608
biomedical materials, 1026–1028
bioterrorism agents, 200
blackbody radiation, 63
blast furnace, 887, 888
blood doping, 640
blood, human, 530
blood lead level (BLL), 913
body-centered cubic cell, 477, 478
Bohr, Niels, 68–74, 78
Bohr's theory of the hydrogen atom, 67
        atomic line spectra, 67–68
        line spectrum of hydrogen, 68–73

boiling point, 11, 425, 488–489
boiling-point elevation, 524–525
Boltzmann constant, 764
Boltzmann, Ludwig, 415, 764
bond angles, 216–217, 230
        deviation from, 219, 221
bond dipoles, 224, 226
bond energy, 187, 238
bond enthalpy, 388–391
bond length, 186
bond order, 247, 251
bonding molecular orbitals, 245, 246, 247, 248,
            249, 251
bonding theories, 252–255
Born-Haber cycle, 392–393, 394–395
boron neutron capture therapy (BNCT), 874
Boyle, Robert, 422
Boyle's law, 422–424, 428
breeder reactors, 870
bromine, 952, 953–954
Brønsted acids and bases, 318–319, 657–659
Brønsted base, 318
Brønsted, Johannes, 318
buckyballs, 1029
buffer, 715
buffer solutions, 712, 715, 718–719
        with a specific pH, 720–721
        calculating the pH of a buffer,
            715–717, 720
burette, 8
burst lung, 441

C

calcium, 126, 898
calories, content of food, 364
calorimeter, 373, 378–379
calorimetry
        constant-pressure, 374–378
        constant-volume, 378–382
        defined, 373
        specific heat and heat capacity, 374
cancer
        drugs, 923
        radiation and, 876
capillary action, 470
carbocation, 985, 988, 989
carbon, 935–937, 961–962
        atomic mass of, 41
        carbon-12, 41, 45, 46
        carbon-13, 41
        carbon-14, 859–860
        electron configuration of, 88
carbon dioxide, 937
carbon disulfide, 947
carbon monoxide, 936–937
carbon nanotubes, 1030
carbonyl group, 963, 964, 965, 971
carborundum, 936
carboxy group, 963, 964, 971
carboxylic acids, 661, 963, 965, 971
Carothers, Wallace, 996
catalysis, 589–592, 635
catalyst, 589
Category A agents, 200
catenation, 936

cathode, 34, 809, 813
cathode ray tube, 34, 36
cathode rays, 34, 35, 36
cathodic protection, 837
cations, 116, 122, 141, 143, 147–148, 310, 695
cell potential, 809
Celsius, Ander, 10
Celsius scale, 10, 11, 425
cementite, 889
central science, 3
ceramic matrix composites, 1023
ceramics, 1021–1022
Chadwick, James, 38
chalcogens, 44
charge-to-mass ratio, 35, 42
Charles' and Gay-Lussac's law, 424–426
Charles, Jacques, 425
Charles' law, 425, 428
chelating agents, 910
chelation therapy, 913, 923
chemical analysis, 873, 923
chemical bonding
        bond enthalpy, 388–391
        Born-Haber cycle, 392–393, 394–395
        comparison of ionic and covalent
            compounds, 393–396
        covalent bonding, 149–155, 160–164
        drawing Lewis structures, 193–194
        electronegativity and polarity, 187–189
        exceptions to the octet rule, 199–204
        ionic bonding, 140, 143
        lattice energy, 144, 145, 392–393, 395
        Lewis dot symbols, 141–142
        Lewis structures and formal charge,
            194–197
        multiple bonds, 186–187
        resonance, 197–199
chemical bonds, 114, 141, 149, 228
chemical change, 7, 267
chemical energy, 57
chemical equations, 267
        balancing, 269–272
        calculations with balanced, 277–280
        interpreting and writing, 267–268
chemical equilibrium, 608
        concept of, 609–611
        equilibrium constant, 611–616
        equilibrium expressions, 616–623
        equilibrium expressions in problem
            solving, 623–629
        factors that affect, 630–639
        free energy and, 786–790
chemical formulas, 3, 143, 146, 151, 268
chemical kinetics, 550
        catalysis, 589–592
        collision theory of chemical reactions,
            551–553, 554–555
        dependence of reactant concentration
            on time, 568–575
        dependence of reaction rate on reactant
            concentration, 562–567
        dependence of reaction rate on
            temperature, 576–579
        reaction mechanisms, 581–588
        reaction rates, 551, 553, 556–562
chemical process, 7, 117
chemical properties, 7, 117

chemical reactions, 3, 4, 267
 collision theory, 551–553, 554–555
 comparison of nuclear reactions and, 851
 energy changes in, 363–364
 patterns of chemical reactivity, 273–274
chemical reduction, 886–887
chemical statement, 267
chemistry
 defined, 3
 study of, 3–5
chemotherapy, 923
chiral, 915, 981
chiral switching, 983
chlor-alkali process, 949–950, 951
chlorine, 949–951, 953
chlorine dioxide, 200
chlorous acid, 952
cholesteric, 1024
chromatography, paper, 7
cis isomers, 915, 980, 981
Clausius-Clapeyron equation, 473, 474
Clean Air Act, 678
closed system, 365
closest packing, 478–479
coefficients, 269
cohesion, 470, 471
coinage metals, 293
colligative properties, 521
collision theory, 551–553, 554–555
colloids, 534–537
color, 918–919
combination reactions, 273–274, 329
combined gas law, 429–430
combustion analysis of compounds, 275
 determination of empirical formula,
  275–276
 determination of molecular formula, 276
combustion reactions, 273, 330
comjugated linoleic acid, 272
common ion effect, 713–715, 737–740
complex ion, 742
complex ion formation, 742–746
composite materials, 1023
 compounds. *See also* inorganic
  compounds; ionic compounds;
  organic compounds
 defined, 141, 149
 insoluble, 313, 315
 molecular, 155–160, 310, 414
 percent composition of, 166–167
 soluble, 313, 315
compressibility, gas, 415, 437
concentration cells, 824–826
concentration of solutions, 331
 concentration defined, 331
 concentration units, 516–519
 dilution, 333, 336
 molarity, 331–333
 preparing a solution from a solid,
  334–335
 serial dilution, 337, 339
 solution stoichiometry, 339–341
concentrations, equilibrium, 625–629
condensation, 5, 6, 472, 473
condensation polymers, 995–996, 1018–1020
condensation reactions, 995
condensed structural formulas, 974

condensed structures, 974
conduction band, 892, 1031
conductors, 892
conjugate acid, 657
conjugate acid-base pairs, 684–687
conjugate base, 657
conjugate pair, 657
constant-pressure calorimetry, 374–378
constant-volume calorimetry, 378–382
constitutional isomerism, 980
constructive interference, 62, 247
contact process, 947
control rods, 870
conversion factors, 20, 21
Cooper, Leon Neil, 1034
coordinate covalent bonds, 200
coordination chemistry, 906
 applications of coordination compounds,
  922–923
 coordination compounds, 907–914
 coordination compounds, defined, 907
 crystal field theory, 916–922
 naming coordination compounds,
  911–912
 reactions of coordination
  compounds, 922
 structure of coordination
  compounds, 914–916
coordination numbers, 476–477, 910
copolymers, 995–996, 1017, 1019
copper, 762, 891
core electrons, 113, 117
corrosion, 7, 835–837
Coulomb's law, 35, 117, 121, 853
covalent bond, 149
covalent bonding, 140
 in ionic species, 160–164
 and molecules, 149–155
covalent compounds, 393, 396, 951
covalent crystals, 485, 486
covalent hydrides, 933–934
covalent molecules, stability of, 388–391
covalent radius, 114
cowpox, 3, 5
crenation, 530
critical mass, 868
critical temperature, 489, 490
cross-links, 1015
crystal field splitting, 917, 919, 921
crystal field theory, 916–917
 color, 918–919
 crystal field splitting in octahedral
  complexes, 917
 magnetic properties, 919–921
 tetrahedral and square-planar
  complexes, 921
crystal structure, 475
 closest packing, 478–479
 packing spheres, 476–478
 structures of crystals, 475–478
 types of crystals, 482–487
 unit cells, 475–476
crystalline solid, 475
cubic cells, 476–478
cubic centimeter, 11
cubic close-packed (ccp) structure, 478–479
cubic decimeter, 11

Cunningham, Orville, 441
curie (Ci), 875
cyanides, 936

D

d-block elements, ions of, 124
d orbitals, 84, 233–236, 917, 919–920, 921
Dalton, John, 34, 39, 43, 149, 150, 267
Dalton's law of partial pressures, 439–440
Daniell cell, 809
dative bonds, 200
daughter, in uranium decay series, 858
Davisson, Clinton, 76
de Broglie hypothesis, 74–75
de Broglie, Louis, 74
de Broglie wavelength, 75
Debye, Peter, 190
debye units, 190
decimeter, 11
decomposition reactions, 273, 329–330
decompression injury, 441
decompression sickness (DCS), 441
deflection, 35, 37, 42
degenerate, 87
delocalized bonding, 253
delocalized bonds, 253
demineralization, 743
Democritus, 34
denominator, 20
density, 7, 8, 11–13
dental implants, 1026–1027
dental pain, amalgam fillings and, 822
deoxyribonucleic acid (DNA), 997, 1000,
 1019–1020
deposition, 491
derived units, 11–13
destructive interference, 62, 74, 75, 247
detergents, 923
deuterium, 39
dextrorotatory isomer, 915, 982
diacids, 1019
diagonal relationships, 122, 288
dialysis, 531, 532
diamagnetic, 88
diamond, 485
diatomic molecules, 150, 190, 191, 226, 413
dibasic bases, 319
diffraction, electron, 76
diffusion, 417–418
digits, 14
dilution, 333, 336–337, 339
dimensional analysis, 20–21
diodes, 1033
dipole-dipole attraction, 226
dipole-dipole interactions, 466
dipole moment, 189–190, 225
dipoles, bond, 224, 226
diprotic acids, 319, 688–690
directionality, chemical bonds and, 228
dispersion forces, 467–468
displacement reactions, 325
disproportionation reaction, 330, 943
dissociation, 307, 527, 533
distillation, 890
diving, 441

donor atoms, 909
donor impurities, 893
doping, 893, 1032
double bonds, 186, 187, 238, 240, 241
double replacement reactions, 315
double-slit experiment, nature of light and, 61–62
doubling time, 870
drugs
    chiral switching in, 983
    organic chemistry and, 960
    single-isomer versions, 983
dry cells, 827–828
dynamic chemical equilibrium, 308
dynamic equilibrium, 472, 490

E

Earth
    alkaline earth metals, 44, 290, 897–898
    oceans, 960
effective collision, 551, 552
effective nuclear charge, 112–113
effusion, 417–418
Einstein, Albert, 64, 66, 855, 865
eka-aluminum, 106, 107
elastomers, 1015
electric fields, 35, 36, 38, 61
electrically conducting polymers, 1021
electrochemistry, 804
    balancing redox reactions, 805–808
    batteries, 827–830
    corrosion, 835–837
    electrolysis, 830–835
    galvanic cells, 809–811
    spontaneity of redox reactions under conditions other than standard state, 822–827
    spontaneity of redox reactions under standard-state conditions, 819–822
    standard reduction potentials, 812–818
electrodes, 809, 813
electrolysis
    of an aqueous sodium chloride solution, 832–833
    defined, 830
    in metals purification, 890
    of molten sodium chloride solution, 830–831
    quantitative applications of, 833–834
    of water, 831–832
electrolyte solutions, 527–529
electrolytes
    in aqueous solutions, 307–310
    compounds as, 310–311
    defined, 307
electrolytic cells, 830
electrolytic reduction, 887
electromagnet, 88
electromagnetic radiation, 60, 62, 63
electromagnetic spectrum, 60, 61, 64
electromagnetic theory, 81
electromagnetic wave, 61
electron affinity (EA), 118–120, 187, 189

electron capture, 855
electron configuration
    Aufbau principle, 87
    defined, 85
    energies of atomic orbitals in many-electron systems, 85–86
    general rules for writing, 89
    Hund's rule, 87–88
    of ions, 122–125
    Pauli exclusion principle, 86–87
    and the periodic table, 90–92, 108, 111
electron density, 78, 79, 245, 246
electron-domain geometry, 216–219, 220
    defined, 216
electron domains, 216
electron spin quantum number, 81
electronegativity, 187–189
electrons, 34–35, 36, 38, 39
    diffraction of, 76
    discovery of, 34–35
    free, 69
    odd number of, 200–201
    in orbitals, 85–86
electrophiles, 984
electrophilic addition, 986–987
electrophilic substitution reaction, 987–988
electrospinning, 1027–1028
electrostatic energy, 57
element 117, 106
elementary reactions, 581–582
elements. See also periodic table
    defined, 33
elimination reactions, 993
embolism, 441
emission spectra, 67, 68, 69
emission spectrum of hydrogen, 68, 70–71
empirical formula mass, 166–167
empirical formulas, 152–153
    determination of, 170, 275–276
    from percent composition, 166–167
emulsification, 537
emulsifier/emulsifying agent, 537
enantiomers, 915, 981, 982, 989
endothermic process, 364
    in bond enthalpies, 389
    entropy changes, 775
    in solution formation, 513
    in thermochemical equations, 371–372
endpoints, 344, 729
energy
    bond, 187, 238
    defined, 57, 363, 367
    energies of orbitals, 84–85
    energy changes in chemical reactions, 363–364
    forms of, 57, 363–368
    ionization energy, 115–117, 187
    nuclear binding energy, 855–857
    quantization of, 63–64
    in solution formation, 513–514
    units of, 58, 364
English units, 8
enthalpy
    bond, 388–391
    defined, 370
    and enthalpy changes, 370–371

reactions carried out at constant volume or at constant pressure, 368–370
    thermochemical equations, 371–372
enthalpy of reactions, 371
entropy, 513, 764–765
    defined, 764
    entropy changes in a system, 766–774
    entropy changes in the universe, 774–779
    living systems in, 778
    second law of thermodynamics, 775–777
    in solution formation, 513–514
    standard, 767–769, 779
    third law of thermodynamics, 778–779
Environmental Protection Agency (EPA), 200
enzymes, biological catalysts, 591–592
equatorial, 216–217, 218
equilibrium. See also chemical equilibrium
    concept of, 609–611
    defined, 610
    and tooth decay, 743
equilibrium constants, 611–612
    calculating, 612–615
    defined, 612
    magnitude of the, 615
equilibrium expressions, 612, 616
    calculating equilibrium concentrations, 625–629
    containing gases, 621–623
    heterogeneous equilibria, 616–617
    manipulating, 617–620
    predicting the direction of a reaction, 624–625
    in problem solving, 623–629
equilibrium mixture, 636
equilibrium process, 776
equilibrium vapor pressure, 472
equivalence points, 344
erythrocytes, 530
esters, 963, 965, 971, 1019
ethyl group, 964, 965
evaporation, 472
exact numbers, 13
excess reactants, 280
excited state, 69, 85
excluded volume, 437
exothermic process, 363, 364
    in bond enthalpies, 389
    entropy changes, 775
    in nuclear binding energy, 855
    in solution formation, 513
    in thermochemical equations, 372
expanded octets, 201–204
extensive properties, 7–8

F

f-block transition elements, 110
f orbitals, 84
face-centered cubic cell, 477, 478
factor-label method, 20
Fahrenheit, Daniel Gabriel, 10
Fahrenheit temperature scale, 10–11
fat-soluble vitamins, 537
ferromagnetic metals, 886

filtration, 7
first law of thermodynamics, 366–367
first-order reactions, 568–572
Fischer, Emil, 591
flotation, 886
fluoresce, 36
fluoride, 953
fluoride poisoning, 531–532
fluorine, 39, 948, 949, 950
fluoroapatite, 743
Food and Drug Administration (FDA), U.S., 984
formal charge, 194–197
formation constant, 743
formic acid, 146
formula mass, 165–166
formula weight, 165
formulas, 3, 143
fossil fuels, 362, 829, 930
fractional distillation, 890
fractional precipitation, 747–748
Frasch process, 945
free electron, 69
free elements, 268
free energy
    and chemical equilibrium, 786–790
    defined, 780
    Gibbs free energy, 780–781
free radicals, 201, 876
freezing, 526
freezing point, 11, 425, 490
freezing-point depression, 525–526
frequency, 60, 61, 62
fuel cells, 829–830
Fuller, R. Buckminster, 1029
fullerenes, 1030
functional groups, 159, 963–964, 970–971
fusion, 490, 491

G

gallium, 106, 107
galvanic cells, 809–811, 812
galvanization, 837
gamma rays, 36, 60, 62, 875
gangue, 886
gas, 5, 6
gas constant (*R*), 416
gas laws, 422–430
    defined, 422
gases
    characteristics of, 414
    deviation from ideal behavior, 435
    diving and property of, 441
    equilibrium expressions containing,
        621–623
    gas laws, 422–430
    gas mixtures, 438–442
    gas pressure, 418–421
    ideal gas equation, 431–434
    kinetic molecular theory of, 415–418
    molar volume of, 446–447
    properties of, 413–414
    reactions with gaseous reactants and
        products, 443–449
    real, 434–438

Gay-Lussac, Joseph, 424–426
Geiger counter, 874, 875
Geiger, Hans, 37
gel, 1022
General Conference on Weights and
        Measurements, 8
genetic damage, 876
geodesic dome, 1029
geometrical isomers, 914, 980–981
Gerlach, Walther, 81
Germer, Lester Halbert, 76
Gibbs free energy, 780–781
glass, 487–488
Goodyear, Charles, 1014–1015
Goyal, Arun, 550
graduated cylinder, 8
Graham's law, 418
grams, 46
graphene, 1030
graphite, 485, 1029–1030
gravimetric analysis, 341–342
Greek prefixes, 155, 157, 160
green chemistry, 287
ground state, 69, 85, 87, 874
Group 1A elements, 44, 289–290, 293
Group 1B elements, 44, 293
Group 2A elements, 44, 290
Group 3A elements, 290
Group 3B–8B elements, 44
Group 4A elements, 290–291
Group 5A elements, 291
Group 6A elements, 44, 291
Group 7A elements, 44, 292
Group 8A elements, 44, 293
groups, in periodic table, 44
Guldberg, Cato, 612, 613

H

half-cell potentials, 812
half-cells, 809
half-life, 571–572, 859–861, 873
half-reaction method, 327
half-reactions, 321–322, 805–808, 814–816
halides, 951
Hall process, 899
halogens, 44, 292, 932, 948–949, 968
    compounds of, 951–953
    properties of, 949–951
    uses of, 953–954
halous acid, 952
heat
    specific heat and heat capacity, 374
    thermal energy and, 363
    and work, 367–368
heat capacity, 374
heat flow, 363
heavy metal poisoning, 913
heavy water, 870
Heisenberg uncertainty principle, 77
Heisenberg, Werner, 77
helium, 32, 33, 293
helium atom, 43
    emission spectra of, 85
    in ground state, 87

mass of, 38
    removal of electrons from, 113
hemodialysis, 531
hemoglobin, 640
hemolysis, 530
Henderson-Hasselbalch equation, 717, 719, 724
Henry's law, 520–521
Henry's law constant, 520
Hess's law, 383–385
heteroatoms, 975
heterogeneous catalysis, 590
heterogeneous equilibria, 616–617
heterogeneous mixtures, 5–7
heteronuclear diatomic molecules, 150,
        191, 251
hexagonal close-packed (hcp) structure,
        478–479
high-temperature superconductor, 1033
Hindenburg airship, 363
homogeneous catalysis, 590–591
homogeneous mixtures, 5
homonuclear diatomic molecules, 150, 245
Hund's rule, 87–88, 122
hybrid orbitals, 231, 235, 238, 244
hybridization
    defined, 230
    in molecules containing multiple bonds,
        238–245
hybridization of atomic orbitals, 230–231, 252
    s and *p* orbitals, 231–233
    s, *p*, and *d* orbitals, 233–236
hydrates, 163–164
hydration, 312, 313, 514, 990
hydrazine, 938
hydride ions, 289
hydrocarbons, 158
hydrocyanic acid, 936
hydrofluoric acid, 948
hydrogen, 932–933
    binary hydrides, 933–934
    compounds containing, 157
    emission spectrum of, 68, 70–71
    hydrogen economy, 930, 935
    hydrogenation, 934–935
    isotopes of, 39, 40, 934
    in the periodic table, 44, 288–289
hydrogen atom
    Bohr's theory of the, 68–74
    mass of, 38
    quantum mechanical description
        of the, 78
hydrogen bomb, 872
hydrogen bonding, 465, 466–467
hydrogen bromide, 952
hydrogen chloride, 952
hydrogen displacement, 329
hydrogen fluoride, 948, 952
hydrogen halides, 951–952
hydrogen iodide, 952
hydrogen ion, 318
hydrogen peroxide, 943–944
hydrogen sulfide, 945–946
hydrogenation, 934–935
hydrohalic acids, 659
hydronium ion, 318
hydrophilic, 535, 536

hydrophobic, 535, 536
hydroxides, acid-base properties of oxides and, 696–697
hydroxy group, 963, 964, 965
hyperbaric chambers, 441
hyperbaric oxygen therapy (HBOT), 441
hypercalcemia, 913
hypertonic, 530
hypothesis, 3
hypotonic, 530

I

ibuprofen, 287
ideal behavior (gas), 434
    factors that cause deviation from, 435
    van der Waals equation, 435–437
ideal gas, 431
ideal gas equation, 431–434
ideal solution, 524
immunity, 5
implosion, 872
in phase, 62
incomplete octets, 199–200
indicators, 344
inert complex, 922
inexact numbers, 13, 14
influenza, 441
infrared radiation, 60, 62, 65
initial rate, 563
inorganic compounds, 158, 164
    defined, 961
insoluble compounds, 313, 315
instantaneous dipole, 467
instantaneous rates, 557–559
insulators, 892
integrated rate law, 568
intensive properties, 7, 8
interference, 61, 62
interference pattern, 61, 62
intermediates, 581
intermolecular bonding, 393
intermolecular forces, 226
    defined, 465
    dipole-dipole interactions, 466
    dispersion forces, 467–468
    hydrogen bonding, 465, 466–467
    ion-dipole interactions, 469
    solutions and, 512–513
International System of Units, 9
interstitial hydrides, 934
intramolecular bonding, 393
intravenous fluids, 530
iodine, 954
ion-dipole interactions, 469
ion pair, 528
ion-product constant, 662
ionic bonding, 140, 143
ionic bonds, 187, 189
ionic compounds, 143–146, 951
    comparison of covalent and, 393, 396
    defined, 143
    electrolytes and, 310
    formulas of, 147
    halides as, 951

lattice energy of, 144, 145, 393, 396
    naming, 146–149
    solubility products of, 732–735
    in water, solubility guidelines, 312–314
ionic crystals, 482–485, 486
ionic equations, 315
    net, 315–316
ionic hydrides, 933–934
ionic liquids, 140
ionic radius, 125–128
ionic solids, 392
ionizable hydrogen atoms, 157
ionization, electrolytes and, 307, 308, 309
ionization constants
    acid, 672–681
    base, 681–684
    of weak acids and bases, A13–A14
ionization energy (IE), 115–117, 187
ionizing radiation, 876
ions, 115
    atomic, 42, 141
    common ion effect, 713–715, 737–740
    complex ion formation, 742–746
    of d-block elements, 124
    defined, 143
    electron configuration of, 122–125
    formulas of ionic compounds, 147
    ionic and covalent compounds, 393, 396
    ionic bonding, 140, 143
    ionic compounds, 143–146, 310, 312–314
    of main group elements, 122–124
    naming ionic compounds, 146–149
    polyatomic, 123, 160–162, 193
    solubility and separation of, 747–749
iron, 7, 887–888
isoelectronic, 123, 141
isolated system, 365, 378
isolectronic series, 126–127
isomerism, 980–983
isomerization reactions, 993–994
isopropyl group, 964, 965
isotatic, 1018
isotonic, 530
isotopes, 39–40
    atomic masses of, 41, 42
    chemical analysis, 873
    hydrogen, 39, 40, 934
    in medicine, 873–884
    parent and daughter, 858
isotropic, 1023

J

Jenner, Edward, 3, 5
joule (J), 58, 364
Joule, James, 58

K

Kamerlingh-Onnes, H., 1033
Kekulé structures, 974
Kelvin temperature scale, 9, 10, 425
Kelvin, William Thomson, Lord, 425

ketones, 963, 965, 972
kilocalories, 364
kilojoule (jK), 58
kinetic energy, 57, 58, 366
kinetic isotope effect, 934
kinetic lability, 922
kinetic molecular theory, 415, 553
    gas laws and, 428–429
kinetic molecular theory of gases, 415–418

L

lanthanide (rare earth) series, 91, 110, 111
lattice, 143
lattice energy, 144, 145, 392–393, 395
lattice point, 475
lattice structure, 475
laughing gas, 146
law of conservation of energy, 57
law of conservation of mass, 269
law of definite proportions, 149–150
law of mass action, 612–613
law of multiple proportions, 150
law of octaves, 107
law, scientific, 3
Lawrence, Wendy, 1022
Le Châtelier's principle, 630, 640, 729, 895
lead compound, 960
lead poisoning, 913
lead storage batteries, 828
levorotatory isomer, 915, 982
Lewis acids and bases, 697–699, 907, 909
Lewis dot symbols, 141–142
Lewis, Gilbert, 141, 149
Lewis structures, 183, 189, 221
    drawing, 193–194, 218
    and formal charge, 194–197
    multiple bonds in, 239
    of oxoacids, 659–660
Lewis theory of bonding, 149, 227, 228, 252
ligand exchange, 922
ligands, 909–910, 919
light, nature of, 60, 63
    double-slit experiment, 61–62
    electromagnetic spectrum, 60, 61
    properties of waves, 60–61
light water reactors, 869, 870
limiting reactant, 280, 282–283
    determining the, 281, 284
    reaction yield, 285–286
line spectra, 67–68
liquid crystals, 1023–1026
liquids, 5, 6, 140
    liquid-vapor phase transition, 488–490
    properties of, 470–475
    solid-liquid phase transition, 490–491
    surface tension, 470
    vapor pressure, 471–475
    viscosity, 470–471
liter, 11, 12
lithium, 87
lithium-ion batteries, 828–829
living systems
    entropy in, 778
    thermodynamics in, 790–791

localized bonds, 253
lock-and-key theory, 591
London dispersion forces, 468
lone pairs, 183, 186, 218, 219, 220

M

macroscopic level, 3
magic numbers, 853
magnesium, 897–898
magnetic confinement, 872
magnetic fields, 35, 36, 38, 62, 81, 88
magnetic levitation transportation (maglev), 906
magnetic quantum number, 79–80
main group elements, 109
    ions of, 122–124
    reactivity of, 286–294
manometer, 420
many-electron systems, energies of atomic
    orbitals in, 85–86
Marsden, Ernest, 37
mass, 7–8
    atomic, 41–42
    of electrons, 35
    law of conservation mass, 269
    molecular and formula, 165–166
    percent composition by mass,
      166–167, 170
    of reactants and products, 279–280
    SI base units of, 9–10
mass defect, 855
mass-energy equivalence relationship,
    Einstein's, 855
mass number (A), 39
mass spectrometer, 42
mathematical operations, A1–A5
matter
    classification of, 5–7
    defined, 3
    properties of, 7–8
    states of, 5, 6
    wave properties of, 74–76
Maxwell, James Clerk, 61, 415, 416
measured numbers, 13, 15
measurement
    of pressure, 420–421
    uncertainty in, 13–19
medicine, nuclear, 873–874
Meissner effect, 1033
melting, 7, 490
melting point, 7, 490, 491
Mendeleev, Dimitri, 106, 107
mercury, 886, 950
metal matrix composites, 1023
metallic character, 120–122
metallic crystals, 486
metallic radius, 114
metalloids, 44, 111, 121, 268, 290, 931
metallurgy
    alkali metals, 894–897
    alkaline earth metals, 897–898
    aluminum, 898–901
    band theory of conductivity, 892–893
    coordination compounds and, 922
    defined, 886

    of iron, 887–888
    metallurgical processes, 886–891
    occurrence of metals, 885–886
    periodic trends in metallic properties, 894
    preparation of the ore, 886
    production of metals, 886–887
    purification of metals, 890–891
    semiconducting materials, 884
    steelmaking, 888–889
metals, 44
    in chemical equations, 268
    electron configuration of, 111
    oxidation in aqueous solutions, 325–326
    oxides of, 696–697
    qualitative analysis of metal ions in
      solution, 748–749
metathesis reactions, 315
meter, 11
meterstick, 8, 17
methyl group, 963, 964, 965
metric system, 8, 11
Meyer, Lothar, 106, 107
microwave radiation, 60, 62
milk of magnesia, 320, 898
millicurie (mCi), 875
Millikan, R. A., 35
Millikan's oil-drop experiment, 35, 36
milliliter (mL), 11, 12
millimeters mercury (mmHg), 419
millimoles (mmol), 336
minerals, 885
miscible, 514
mixtures, 5–7
    gas, 438–442
moderators, 869
modern materials, 1012
    biomedical materials, 1026–1028
    ceramics and composite materials,
      1021–1023
    liquid crystals, 1023–1026
    nanotechnology, 1028–1030
    polymers, 1013–1021
    semiconductors, 1030–1033
    superconductors, 1033–1034
molality, 516, 517, 532
molar absorptivity, 338
molar concentration, 331
molar enthalpy of sublimation, 492
molar heat of fusion, 491
molar heat of vaporization, 489
molar mass, 45–47, 168–171
molar solubility, 732
molar volume of gas, 446–447
molarity, 331–333, 516, 532
mole and molar masses, 44–48
    determining molar mass, 45–47
    empirical formula and molecular
      formula from percent
      composition, 170
    interconverting mass, moles, and
      numbers of atoms, 47–48
    interconverting mass, moles, and
      numbers of particles, 168
    the mole, 45
    mole defined, 44
    moles of reactants and products, 277–278

mole fractions, 440, 442, 517, 522
molecular art, 151
molecular compounds, 155–160, 310, 414
molecular crystals, 486
molecular equations, 314–315
molecular formulas, 151–152, 153
    determination of, 170, 276
    from percent composition, 166–167
molecular geometry, 215
    defined, 216
    deviation from ideal bond angles,
      219, 221
    electron-domain geometry and, 216–219
    geometry of molecules with more than
      one central atom, 221–222
    and polarity, 223–226
    VSEPR model, 216
molecular level, 3
molecular mass, 165–166
molecular orbital theory, 245, 253–254
    bond order, 247
    bonding and antibonding molecular
      orbitals, 245–246
    defined, 245
    molecular orbital diagrams, 250–251
molecular orbitals, 245, 246, 248–249
molecular polarity, 223
molecular speed, 416–417
molecular weight, 165
molecularity, 581
molecules, 3
    covalent bonding and, 149–155
    defined, 149
    with delocalized bonding, 253
    empirical formulas, 152–153
    hybridization and multiple bonds,
      238–245
    molecular formulas, 151
    naming molecular compounds,
      155–160
    representation of organic molecules,
      973–979
    stability of covalent, 388–391
molybdenum sulfide nanotubes, 1030
monatomic anions, 122, 146, 147
monatomic cations, 122, 146
monatomic ions, 146, 160
Mond process, 890
monobasic bases, 319
monomers, 994, 995, 1013, 1020
monoprotic acids, 162, 319
Moseley, Henry, 108
motional energy, 764
multiple bonds, 186–187
    hybridization and, 238–245

N

n-type semiconductors, 893, 1032
nanotechnology, 2, 1012, 1028–1030
NASCAR, 1015
native proteins, 778
natural rubber, 1014–1015
Nelson, Neil, 550
nematic, 1024

neon
        mass spectrum of, 42
        neon-20, 42
        neon-21, 42
        neon-22, 42
Nernst equation, 823–824
net ionic equations, 315–316
neutral salt solutions, 694–695
neutralization reactions, 319–321
neutron-to-proton ratio (n/p), 853
neutrons, 38, 39
Newlands, John, 107
Newton, Sir Isaac, 67, 69
newtons (N), 58, 419
night vision, 65
nitric acid, 939
nitric oxide, 939
nitrogen, 88, 937–939
nitrogen dioxide, 939
nitrogen fixation, 938
nitrous oxide, 938–939
Nobel Prize, 1033, 1034
noble gas core, 90
noble gases, 44, 110, 111, 141, 268, 293
noble metals, 326
nodes, 74
nomenclature, chemical, 146, 157
nonconductors, 1031
nonelectrolytes, 307–310
nonmetals, 44, 111
        carbon, 935–937
        in chemical equations, 268
        general properties of, 931
        halogens, 948–954
        hydrogen, 932–935
        nitrogen, 937–939
        oxides of, 696–697
        oxygen, 942–944
        in periodic table, 291
        phosphorus, 939–942
        sulfur, 944–947
nonpolar, 223
nonpolar covalent bonds, 189
nonpolar molecules, 467–468
nonspontaneous processes, 763
nonvolatile, 522
normal boiling point, 488
nuclear binding energy, 855–857
nuclear chain reaction, 865, 868
nuclear charge, 112–113
nuclear chemistry, 850
        biological effects of radiation, 875–876
        natural radioactivity, 858–862
        nuclear fission, 865–871
        nuclear fusion, 871–873
        nuclear stability, 853–858
        nuclear transmutation, 862–865
        nuclei and nuclear reactions, 851–883
        uses of isotopes, 873–874
nuclear fission, 865–871
nuclear fusion, 866–867, 871–873
nuclear medicine, 874
nuclear reactors, 850, 868–870
nuclear transmutation, 851, 862–865
nucleic acids, 997, 1000
nucleons, 39, 855

nucleophiles, 984
nucleophilic addition, 986–987
nucleophilic substitution reaction, 988–989
nucleotides, 997, 1000
nucleus, 37, 38
numerator, 20
nylon, 996, 1019

O

octahedral complexes, 917
octet rule, 183, 186
        exceptions to, 199–204
old quantum theory, 78
open system, 365
optical isomers, 914–915, 981
orbitals
        electrons in, 85–86
        hybridization of atomic, 230–237
        molecular orbital theory, 245–252
ore, 885, 886
organic chemistry
        carbon, 961–962
        classes of organic compounds, 963–973
        and drugs, 960
        isomerism, 980–983
        organic polymers, 994–1000
        organic reactions, 984–994
        representation of organic molecules,
                973–979
organic compounds, 158
        classes of, 963–973
        defined, 961
        naming, 967–970
osmosis, 527, 530, 531
osmotic pressure, 527, 530
out of phase, 62
overvoltage, 832
oxidation, 7, 322, 836
oxidation number, 323–325
oxidation-reduction reactions, 321–322, 993
        balancing simple redox equations,
                327–329
        oxidation numbers, 323–325
        oxidation of metals in aqueous
                solutions, 325–326
oxidation state, 323
oxides
        acid-base properties of hydroxides and,
                696–697
        basic and amphoteric hydroxides, 697
        of metals, 696–697
oxidizing agent, 322
oxoacids, 162–163, 659–660, 953
oxoanions, 162
oxygen, 942–944
ozone, 944

P

p-block elements, 91
p orbitals, 82, 83, 231–236, 248
p-type semiconductors, 893, 1032
packing spheres, 476–478

paired electrons, 116
paper chromatography, 7
paramagnetic, 88
parent, in uranium decay series, 858
parital charges, 189–190
partial pressure, 439–440, 445, 448
particle accelerator, 864–865
pascal (Pa), 419
passivation, 836
patina, 836
patterns, in scientific method, 3
Pauli exclusion principle, 86–87, 122
Pauling, Linus, 188
peptide bonds, 997
per mole of the reaction, 372
percent by mass, 516
percent composition by mass, 166–167, 170
percent dissociation, 533
percent ionic character, 189, 191–192
percent ionization, 533, 677, 678–680
percent yield, 285
periodic table, 43–44
        atomic radius, 38, 113–115
        classification of elements, 109–111
        comparing ionic radius with atomic
                radius, 125, 127
        comparison of Group 1A and Group 1B
                elements, 293
        development of, 107–109
        effective nuclear charge, 112–113
        electron affinity (*EA*), 118–120
        electron configuration and the, 90–92
        electron configuration of ions, 122–125
        general trends in reactivity, 288–289
        Group 1A elements, 44, 289–290, 293
        Group 1B elements, 44, 293
        Group 2A elements, 44, 290
        Group 3A elements, 290
        Group 3B–8B elements, 44
        Group 4A elements, 290–291
        Group 5A elements, 291
        Group 6A elements, 44, 291
        Group 7A elements, 44, 292
        Group 8A elements, 44, 293
        ionic radius, 125–128
        ionization energy (*IE*), 115–117
        ions of *d*-block elements, 124
        ions of main group elements, 122–124
        isoelectronic series, 126–127
        main group elements, 286–294
        metallic character, 120–122
        modern, 109–112
        periodic trends in metallic
                properties, 894
        periodic trends in properties, 113–122
        periodic trends in reactivity, 286–294
        properties of the active metals, 289–290
        properties of the other main group
                elements, 290–293
        properties of transition metals, 907–908
        representing free elements in chemical
                equations, 268
periodicity, 106, 107
periods, in periodic table, 44
peroxide, 289, 943–944
pesticides, 608

pH, 663
    of acid-base titrations, 721, 722
    acid ionization constants and,
        673–677, 680
    base ionization constants and, 682–684
    buffer solutions and, 715–717, 720–721
    of salt solutions, 694–695
    and solubility, 740–742
pH scale, 663–667
phase changes, 488
    dangers of, 492–493
    liquid-vapor phase transition, 488–490
    solid-liquid phase transition, 490–491
    solid-vapor phase transition, 491–492
phase diagrams, 494–496
phases, of atomic orbitals, 247
phenyl group, 1015
phosphine, 940
phosphorus, 939–942
photoelectric effect, 64–66
photons, 64, 66, 72
physical change, 7
physical processes, 6, 7
physical properties, 7
pi bonds, 238, 240, 241, 242–244
picometer, 38
pig iron, 888
pipette, 8
Planck, Max, 63–64
Planck's constant, 64
plum-pudding model, Thomson's, 37, 38
pOH scale, 666
polar, 187, 223
polar covalent bonds, 187, 189
polar molecules, 466, 468
polarimeter, 915, 916, 982
polarity, molecular geometry and, 223–226
polarized light, 915, 916, 982–983, 1025
polarized molecules, 468
polyalkenes, 1021
polyamides, 1019
polyatomic ions, 123, 160–162, 193
polyatomic molecules, 150, 389
polyesters, 1019
polyethylene, 1013–1014, 1021
polyisoprene, 1014–1015
polymer matrix composites, 1023
polymers
    addition, 995, 1013–1018
    biological, 997–1000
    condensation, 995–996, 1018–1020
    defined, 994, 1013
    electrically conducting, 1021
    organic, 994–1000
polypeptides, 997, 1019
polyprotic acids, 162, 319, 688–690
polysaccharides, 997
polystyrene, 1015, 1016, 1018
polyvinyl chloride (PVC), 953, 1015, 1016
porphyria, 948
positron, 852
potassium, 108
potassium hydroxide, 896
potassium nitrate, 896–897
potential energy, 57, 366

precipitate, 312
precipitation, fractional, 747–748
precipitation reactions
    in aqueous solutions, 312–316
    defined, 312
    solubility and, 735–736
precision, 17–18
prefixes, Greek, 155, 157, 160
pressure, 418
    calculation of, 419–420
    Dalton's law of partial pressures,
        439–440
    defined, 419
    equilibrium and, 633–634
    gaseous reactant and change in,
        444–445
    measurement of, 420–421
    pressure-temperature-amount-volume
        relationship, 429–430
    pressure-volume relationship, 422–424
    solubility and, 520–521
    units of, 419
    using partial pressure to solve problems,
        445, 448
pressure-volume, 369
primary amides, 972
primary amines, 972
primary carbon, 962
primary valence, 907
principal quantum number, 79, 116
probability density, 82, 83
problem solving
    equilibrium expressions in, 623–629
    pH of weak acid and, 674–675
    using entropy to solve problems,
        783–785
    using partial pressure to solve problems,
        445, 448
    using units and solving problems, 20–22
products, in chemical reactions, 267
propyl group, 964
proteins, 778, 997, 998–999, 1019
protium, 39
proton acceptor, 318
proton donor, 318
protons, 38, 39
Proust, Joseph, 149
psi (per square inch), 418
pyrometallurgy, 886

Q

qualitative analysis, 748–749
qualitative properties, 7
quantitative properties, 7, 8
quantum dots, 2
quantum mechanics, 56, 76–79
    beginning of, 78
    quantum mechanical description of the
        hydrogen atom, 78
    Schrödinger equation, 78
    uncertainty principle, 77–78
quantum numbers, 78, 79–81
    electron spin quantum number, 81

quantum theory, 63–67
    old, 78
    photons and the photoelectric effect,
        64–66
    quantization of energy, 63–64
    quantum defined, 63
quatenary carbon, 962

R

racemic mixture, 915, 982, 983
racemization, 989
radial probability distribution, 82, 83
radiation, 34, 36
    biological effects of, 875–876
    blackbody, 63
    infrared, 60, 62, 65
    microwave, 60, 62
    ultraviolet (UV), 60, 62
radiation absorbed dose (rad), 875
radicals, 182, 200, 876
radio waves, 60, 62
radioactive decay
    dating based on, 859–861
    defined, 851
    kinetics of, 858–859
radioactive decay series, 858
radioactivity, 36, 851
radiocarbon dating, 859–861
Raoult's law, 522
rare earth series, 91
rate-determining step, 582–587
rate law, 563
rate of reaction, 560
reactants
    in chemical equations, 267
    gaseous, 443–449
    limiting, 280–286
    mass of reactants and products, 279–280
    moles of reactants and products,
        277–278
    reversible, 610
reaction mechanism, 581
reaction order, 563
reaction quotient, 612
reaction rates, 551
    Arrhenius equation, 576–579
    average, 553, 556–557
    catalysis, 589–592
    collision theory, 551–553, 554–555
    elementary reactions, 581–582
    experimental determination of the rate
        law, 563–567
    first-order reactions, 568–572
    instantaneous rate, 557–559
    rate-determining step, 582–587
    rate law, 563
    reaction mechanisms, 581–588
    second-order reactions, 573–575
    stoichiometry and, 560–562
reaction yield, 285–286
reactions, organic, 984–994
real gases, 431, 434–438
reb blood cells, 530, 640

reciprocal, 20
red tides, 266
redox reactions
        balancing, 805–808
        balancing simple redox reactions,
                327–329
        defined, 321
        spontaneity of redox reactions under
                conditions other than standard
                state, 822–827
        spontaneity of redox reactions under
                standard–state conditions,
                819–822
        types of, 329–330
reducing agent, 322
reduction, 322
reinforced carbon-carbon composite (RCC),
        1023
Reinitzer, Frederick, 1023
relative biological effectiveness (RBE), 875
remineralization, 743
representative elements, 109
repulsive forces, 35, 121
resonance, 197–199, 976–977
resonance stabilized, 976
resonance structures, 197, 976
reversible process, 610
revised metric system (SI) units, 9
rhombic sulfur, 945
ribonucleic acid (RNA), 997, 1000, 1020
roentgen equivalent for man (rem), 875
Roman numerals, cations with, 147
Röntgen, Wilhelm, 36
root-mean-square (rms) speed, 416
rubber, 1014–1015
rust formation, 836
Rutherford, Ernest, 37, 38, 862
Rydberg constant, 68
Rydberg equation, 68
Rydberg, Johannes, 68

S

s orbitals, 82, 231–236
salt, in acid-base reactions, 319
salt bridge, 809, 812, 813
salt hydrolysis, 691
salt solutions
        acid-base properties of, 690–695
        acidic, 692–694
        basic, 691–692
        cations and anions, 695
        neutral, 694–695
saturated solutions, 511, 512
scanning electron microscopy, 56
scanning tunneling microscope (STM), 1029
Schrieffer, John Robert, 1034
Schrödinger equation, 78
Schrödinger, Erwin, 78
scientific measurement, 8–13
scientific method, 3–5
scientific notation, A1–A2
seawater, 885–886, 897
second electron affinity, 118
second law of thermodynamics, 775–777
second-order reactions, 573–575

secondary carbon, 962
secondary emission, 65
secondary valence, 907
semiconducting materials, 884
semiconductors, 892–893, 1030–1033
semipermeable membrane, 527, 530
sequestrants, 923
serial dilution, 337, 339
shielding, 112–113
SI base units, 9–10, 11
sigma bonds, 238, 240, 241
significant figures, 14–17
silver fluoride, 948
silver iodide, 954
simple cubic cell, 477, 478
single bonds, 186, 187, 241
single–isomer drugs, 983
sintering, 1022
skeletal structures, 974–975
slit, 61
smallpox, 3, 5
smectic, 1024
smelting, 762
Smith, Robert Angus, 678
sodium carbonate, 896
sodium chloride
        electrolysis of an aqueous sodium
                chloride solution, 832–833
        electrolysis of molten, 830–831
sodium hydroxide, 896, 951
sodium nitrate, 896–897
soft tissue materials, 1027–1028
sol-gel process, 1022
solids, 5, 6. See also crystal structure
        amorphous, 475, 487–488
        preparing a solution from, 334–335
        solid-liquid phase transition, 490–491
        solid-vapor phase transition, 491–492
solubility
        defined, 313, 511, 732
        factors that affect, 519–521, 737–746
        guidelines for ionic compounds,
                312–314
        product constants, A15–A16
        separation of ions in, 747–749
        vitamin, 537
solubility equilibria, 731–737
solubility product constant, 732
soluble compounds, 313, 315
solutes, 307, 511
solution stoichiometry, 339–341
solutions, 307. See also concentration of
                solutions
        colligative properties, 521–529, 532–534
        colloids, 534–537
        concentration units, 516–519
        energy and entropy in solution
                formation, 513–514
        factors that affect solubility, 519–521
        intermolecular forces, 512–513
        types of, 511–512
solvation, 512
solvents, 307
solving problems. See problem solving
somatic injuries, 876
space-filling models (molecular art), 151
space shuttle, ceramic tiles on, 1022, 1023

Spanish flu epidemic, 441
specific heat, 374
spectator ions, 315
spectrochemical series, 919
spherical distribution of electron density, 82, 83
splitting, of energy levels, 85
spontaneous pneumothorax, 441
spontaneous processes, 763–764
square-planar complexes, 921
stability, nuclear, 853–858
standard atmospheric pressure, 420
standard enthalpies of formation, 385–388
standard enthalpy of formation, 385
standard enthalpy of reaction, 385
standard entropy, 767–769, 779
standard free energy of formation, 782
standard free energy of reaction, 782
standard hydrogen electrode (SHE), 813
standard reduction potential, 813
standard solution, 343
standard temperature and pressure (STP), 431
standing/stationary waves, 74, 75
state functions, 365–366
state of a system, 365
Staudinger, Hermann, 994
steelmaking, 888–889
stereoisomerism, 980–983
stereoisomers, 914, 980
Stern, Otto, 81
Stock system, 147
stoichiometric amount, 278
stoichiometric coefficients, 269, 582
stoichiometry
        and reaction rates, 560–562
        solution, 339–341
stoichiometry, ratios of combination
        calculations with balanced chemical
                equations, 277–280
        chemical equations, 267–274
        combustion analysis, 275–276
        limiting reactants, 280–286
        mole and molar masses, 44–48
        molecular and formula masses, 165–166
        percent composition of compounds,
                166–167
strong acid-strong base titrations, 721–723
strong acid-weak base titrations, 727–729
strong acids, 317, 668–669
strong bases, 317, 669–671
strong conjugate acid, 685
strong conjugate base, 685
strong electrolytes
        in aqueous solutions, 308–310, 315
        defined, 308
strong-field ligands, 919
strontium, 126
structural formulas, 152
structural isomers, 225, 980
subatomic particles, 34, 38–39
subcritical mass, 868
sublimation, 491
submicroscopic level, 3
substances
        defined, 5
        equilibrium and addition/removal of,
                630–632
substituents, 968, 970

substitution reactions, 987–992
sugar, 580
sulfur, 944–947
sulfur dioxide, 946–947
sulfur hexafluoride, 947
sulfur trioxide, 946, 947
sulfuric acid, 947
superacids, 656
superconducting transition temperature, 1033
superconductors, 1033–1034
supercooling, 491
supercritical fluids, 489–490
superoxide radicals, 200
superoxides, 289
supersaturated solutions, 511, 512
surface area, 580
surface tension, 470
surroundings, 363, 364
suspension, 320
sutures, 1027
syndiotactic, 1018
systems, 363

T

tacticity, 1018
Tamiflu, 214
Teflon, 953, 1015, 1021
temperature, 8, 10–11
    critical, 489, 490
    dependence of reaction rate on, 576–579
    equilibrium and, 634, 637
    solubility and, 519–520
    temperature–volume relationship,
        424–426, 429–430
tempering, 889
termolecular, 581
tertiary carbon, 962
tetrahedral complexes, 921
thalidomide, 983, 984
theoretical yield, 285
theory, scientific, 3
thermal energy, 57, 363
thermal pollution, 520
thermite reaction, 900
thermochemical equations, 371–372
thermochemistry
    calorimetry, 373–383
    defined, 363
    energy and energy changes, 363–364
    enthalpy, 368–373
    Hess's law, 383–385
    standard enthalpies of formation,
        385–388
    thermodynamics, 365–368
thermodynamics
    data, A6–A12
    defined, 365
    first law of thermodynamics, 366–367
    in living systems, 778, 790–791
    second law of thermodynamics, 775–777
    states and state functions, 365–366
    third law of thermodynamics, 778–779
    work and heat, 367–368
thermonuclear bomb, 872
thermonuclear reactions, 871–872

thermoplastic, 1013
thermosetting, 1013
third law of thermodynamics, 778–779
Thomson, G. P., 76
Thomson, J. J., 35, 37, 38
threshold frequency, 64
thrombocytes, 530
titrations, 343, 344. See also acid-base titrations
tooth decay, 743
Torricelli, Evangelista, 420
tracers, 873
trans isomers, 225–226, 915, 980, 981
transition elements, 44
transition metals, 44, 91, 110, 111, 146, 742,
        906, 907–908
transition state, 552
transmittance, 338
transmutation, nuclear, 851, 862–865
transuranium elements, 863
trends, in scientific method, 3
trigonal planar (molecular geometry), 221
triple bonds, 186, 187, 240
triple point, 494, 495
triprotic acids, 319
tritium, 39
Tyndall effect, 534–535

U

ultraviolet (UV) radiation, 60, 62
uncertain digits, 14
uncertainty in measurement, 13–19
uncertainty principle, 77–78
unimolecular, 581
unit cells, 475–476
units, 8, 20–22
unsaturated solutions, 511
uranium, 36
    isotopes of, 39–40
uranium decay series, 858

V

vaccination, 5
valence band, 892, 1031
valence bond theory, 227–230, 252
valence electrons, 110, 111, 113, 141
valence-shell electron-pair repulsion (VSEPR)
        model, 215, 216, 252
van der Waals constants, 436, 437–438
van der Waals equation, 435–437
van der Waals forces, 465
van der Waals, J. D., 435
vanadium oxide, 947
van't Hoff factor, 528
vapor
    liquid-vapor phase transition, 488–490
    solid-vapor phase transition, 491–492
vapor pressure, 445, 471–475
vapor-pressure lowering, 522–524
vaporization, 5, 6, 7, 472, 473
    molar heat of vaporization, 489
vinyl chloride, 1015
viscosity, 470–471
visible light, 60, 62, 65

visible spectrophotometry, 338
vision, night, 65
vitamin solubility, 537
volatile, 523
volume, 11–13
    amount-volume relationship, 426–427
    calculating volume of gaseous reactant,
        443–444
    constant-volume calorimetry, 378–382
    equilibrium and, 633–634, 638–639
    pressure-volume relationship, 422–424,
        429–430
    temperature-volume relationship,
        424–426
volumetric flask, 8, 337
VSEPR model, 216
vulcanization, 1014–1015

W

Waage, Peter, 612, 613
water
    acid-base properties of, 661–663
    electrolysis of, 831–832
    ionic compounds in water, solubility
        guidelines, 312–314
    physical states of, 5, 6
water gas, 932
water-soluble, 307
    water-insoluble compounds, 313
    water-soluble compounds, 310, 313
wave function, 78
wave mechanics, 78
wave properties of matter, 74–76
    de Broglie hypothesis, 74–75
    diffraction of electrons, 76
wavelength, 60, 61, 62
waves, properties of, 60–61
weak acid-strong base titrations, 723–727
weak acids, 672
weak bases, 681
weak conjugate acid, 685
weak conjugate base, 685
weak electrolytes
    in aqueous solutions, 308–310
    defined, 308
weak-field ligands, 919
Werner, Alfred, 907
Werner's coordination theory, 907
white light, 67
Wilson's disease, 891
Wöhler, Friedrich, 961
work, and heat, 367–368
World Health Organization (WHO), 5

X

X-ray diffraction, 76, 480–481
X-rays, 36, 60, 62, 108

Z

zeroth-order reaction, 575
zone refining, 890–891